DISCARD

Hoover's Handbook of

Private Companies

2020

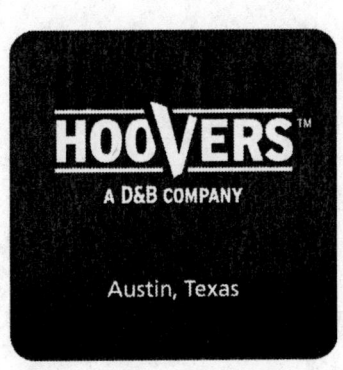

HOOVERS™

A D&B COMPANY

Austin, Texas

Hoover's Handbook of Private Companies 2020 is intended to provide readers with accurate and authoritative information about the enterprises covered in it. Hoover's researched all companies and organizations profiled, and in many cases contacted them directly so that companies represented could provide information. The information contained herein is as accurate as we could reasonably make it. In many cases we have relied on third-party material that we believe to be trustworthy, but were unable to independently verify. We do not warrant that the book is absolutely accurate or without error. Readers should not rely on any information contained herein in instances where such reliance might cause financial loss. The publisher, the editors, and their data suppliers specifically disclaim all warranties, including the implied warranties of merchantability and fitness for a specific purpose. This book is sold with the understanding that neither the publisher, the editors, nor any content contributors are engaged in providing investment, financial, accounting, legal, or other professional advice.

The financial data (Historical Financials sections) in this book are from a variety of sources. Mergent Inc., provided selected data for the Historical Financials sections of publicly traded companies. For private companies and for historical information on public companies prior to their becoming public, we obtained information directly from the companies or from trade sources deemed to be reliable. Hoover's, Inc., is solely responsible for the presentation of all data.

Many of the names of products and services mentioned in this book are the trademarks or service marks of the companies manufacturing or selling them and are subject to protection under US law. Space has not permitted us to indicate which names are subject to such protection, and readers are advised to consult with the owners of such marks regarding their use. Hoover's is a trademark of Hoover's, Inc.

10 9 8 7 6 5 4 3 2 1

Publishers Cataloging-in-Publication Data
Hoover's Handbook of Private Companies 2020
    Includes indexes.
    ISBN: 978-1-64141-562-0
    ISSN 1073-6433
    1. Business enterprises — Directories. 2. Corporations — Directories.
HF3010 338.7

U.S. AND WORLD BOOK SALES
Mergent Inc.
580 Kingsley Park Drive
Fort Mill, SC
29715
Phone: 800-342-5647
e-mail: orders@mergent.com
Web: www.mergentbusinesspress.com

Mergent Inc.

Executive Managing Director: John Pedernales

Publisher/Managing Director of Print Products: Thomas Wecera

Director of Print Products: Charlot Volny

Quality Assurance Editor: Wayne Arnold

Production Research Assistant: Davie Christna

Data Manager: Jason Horvat

MERGENT CUSTOMER SERVICE-PRINT
Support & Fulfillment: Thomas Wecera 212-413-7726

ABOUT MERGENT INC.

For over 100 years, Mergent, Inc. has been a leading provider of business and financial information on public and private companies globally. Mergent is known to be a trusted partner to corporate and financial institutions, as well as to academic and public libraries. Today we continue to build on a century of experience by transforming data into knowledge and combining our expertise with the latest technology to create new global data and analytical solutions for our clients. With advanced data collection services, cloud-based applications, desktop analytics and print products, Mergent and its subsidiaries provide solutions from top down economic and demographic information, to detailed equity and debt fundamental analysis. We incorporate value added tools such as quantitative Smart Beta equity research and tools for portfolio building and measurement. Based in the U.S., Mergent maintains a strong global presence, with offices in New York, Charlotte, San Diego, London, Tokyo, Kuching and Melbourne. Mergent, Inc. is a member of the London Stock Exchange plc group of companies. The Mergent business forms part of LSEG's Information Services Division, which includes FTSE Russell, a global leader in indexes.

Abbreviations

AFL-CIO – American Federation of Labor and Congress of Industrial Organizations
AMA – American Medical Association
AMEX – American Stock Exchange
ARM – adjustable-rate mortgage
ASP – application services provider
ATM – asynchronous transfer mode
ATM – automated teller machine
CAD/CAM – computer-aided design/ computer-aided manufacturing
CD-ROM – compact disc – read-only memory
CD-R – CD-recordable
CEO – chief executive officer
CFO – chief financial officer
CMOS – complementary metal oxide silicon
COO – chief operating officer
DAT – digital audiotape
DOD – Department of Defense
DOE – Department of Energy
DOS – disk operating system
DOT – Department of Transportation
DRAM – dynamic random-access memory
DSL – digital subscriber line
DVD – digital versatile disc/digital video disc
DVD-R – DVD-recordable
EPA – Environmental Protection Agency
EPS – earnings per share
ESOP – employee stock ownership plan
EU – European Union
EVP – executive vice president
FCC – Federal Communications Commission
FDA – Food and Drug Administration
FDIC – Federal Deposit Insurance Corporation
FTC – Federal Trade Commission

GATT – General Agreement on Tariffs and Trade
GDP – gross domestic product
HMO – health maintenance organization
HR – human resources
HTML – hypertext markup language
ICC – Interstate Commerce Commission
IPO – initial public offering
IRS – Internal Revenue Service
ISP – Internet service provider
kWh – kilowatt-hour
LAN – local-area network
LBO – leveraged buyout
LCD – liquid crystal display
LNG – liquefied natural gas
LP – limited partnership
Ltd. – limited
mips – millions of instructions per second
MW – megawatt
NAFTA – North American Free Trade Agreement
NASA – National Aeronautics and Space Administration
NASDAQ – National Association of Securities Dealers Automated Quotations
NATO – North Atlantic Treaty Organization
NYSE – New York Stock Exchange
OCR – optical character recognition
OECD – Organization for Economic Cooperation and Development
OEM – original equipment manufacturer
OPEC – Organization of Petroleum Exporting Countries
OS – operating system
OSHA – Occupational Safety and Health Administration
OTC – over-the-counter

PBX – private branch exchange
PCMCIA – Personal Computer Memory Card International Association
P/E – price to earnings ratio
RAID – redundant array of independent disks
RAM – random-access memory
R&D – research and development
RBOC – regional Bell operating company
RISC – reduced instruction set computer
REIT – real estate investment trust
ROA – return on assets
ROE – return on equity
ROI – return on investment
ROM – read-only memory
S&L – savings and loan
SEC – Securities and Exchange Commission
SEVP – senior executive vice president
SIC – Standard Industrial Classification
SOC – system on a chip
SVP – senior vice president
USB – universal serial bus
VAR – value-added reseller
VAT – value-added tax
VC – venture capitalist
VoIP – Voice over Internet Protocol
VP – vice president
WAN – wide-area network

Contents

Companies Profiled

Companies Profiled (continued)

Companies Profiled (continued)

Companies Profiled (continued)

Companies Profiled (continued)

Companies Profiled (continued)

Companies Profiled (continued)

Companies Profiled (continued)

Companies Profiled (continued)

Companies Profiled (continued)

Companies Profiled (continued)

Companies Profiled (continued)

About Hoover's Handbook of Private Companies 2020

Finding current relevant information about non-public companies can be a challenge, as many of these organizations see secrecy as a competitive strategy. In this edition of *Hoover's Handbook of Private Companies*, we have done for you the tough work of compiling these hard-to-find facts.

We consider this volume to be one of the premier sources of business information on privately held enterprises in the US. It features the facts on 900 of the largest and most influential of those enterprises. Entries feature overviews of company operations, up to five years of financial information, product information, and lists of company executives as found in Hoover's huge database of company information. Some larger and more visable companies will feature an additional History section.

HOOVER'S ARCHIVES FOR BUSINESS NEEDS

In addition to the 2,550 companies featured in our handbooks, comprehensive coverage of more than 6 years of Hoovers Books are published in the Hoovers Archives.. Our goal is to provide one site that offers authoritative, updated intelligence on US and global companies, industries, and the people who shape them. Stay with the Hoovers famaily of products and History and package the books with the archives products.

We welcome the recognition we have received as a provider of high-quality company information — online, electronically, and in print — and continue to look for ways to make our products more available and more useful to you.

Hoover's Handbook of Private Companies is one of our four-title series of handbooks that covers, literally, the world of business. The series is available as an indexed set, and also includes *Hoover's Handbook of American Business, Hoover's Handbook of World Business,* and *Hoover's Handbook of Emerging Companies.* This series brings you information on the biggest, fast-growing, and most influential enterprises in the world.

We believe that anyone who buys from, sells to, invests in, lends to, competes with, interviews with, or works for a company should know all there is to know about that enterprise. Taken together, this book and the other Hoover's products and resources represent the most complete source of basic corporate information readily available to the general public.

HOW TO USE THIS BOOK

This book has four sections:

1. "Using Hoover's Handbooks" describes the contents of our profiles and explains the ways in which we gather and compile our data.

2. "A List-Lover's Compendium" contains lists of the largest and fastest-growing private companies. The lists are based on the information in our profiles, or compiled from well-known sources.

3. The company profiles section makes up the largest and most important part of the book — 900 profiles of major private enterprises, arranged alphabetically.

4. Three indexes complete the book. The first sorts companies by industry groups, the second by headquarters location. The third index is a list of all the executives found in the Executives section of each company profile.

Using Hoover's Handbooks

SELECTION OF THE COMPANIES PROFILED

The 1000 enterprises profiled in this book include the largest and most influential companies in America. Among them are:

- private companies, from the giants (Cargill and Koch) to the colorful and prominent (Bad Boy Entertainment and L.L. Bean)
- mutuals and cooperative organizations owned by their customers (State Farm Insurance, Ace Hardware, Ocean Spray Cranberries)
- not-for-profits (Red Cross, Kaiser Permanente, Smithsonian Institution)
- joint ventures (Motiva Enterprises, Dow Corning)
- partnerships (PricewaterhouseCoopers, Baker & McKenzie)
- universities (Columbia, Harvard, University of California)
- government-owned corporations (US Postal Service and New York City's Metropolitan Transportation Authority)
- and a selection of other enterprises (National Basketball Association, AFL-CIO, Texas Lottery Commission).

ORGANIZATION

The profiles are presented in alphabetical order. You will find the commonly used name of the enterprise at the beginning of the profile; the full, legal name is found in the Locations section. If a company name is also a person's name, such as Henry Ford Health System or Mary Kay, it will be alphabetized under the first name; if the company name starts with initials, for example, L.L. Bean or S.C. Johnson, look for it under the combined initials (in the above examples, LL and SC, respectively).

Basic financial data are listed under the heading Historical Financials. The annual financial information contained in the profiles is current through fiscal year-ends occuring as late as October 2014. We have included certain nonfinancial developments , such as officer changes, through December 2014.

OVERVIEW

In the first section of the profile, we have tried to give a thumbnail description of the company and what it does. The description will usually include information on the company's strategy, reputation, and ownership. We recommend that you read this section first.

HISTORY

This extended section, which is available for some of the larger and more well-known companies, reflects our belief that every enterprise is the sum of its history and that you have to know where you came from in order to know where you are going. While some companies have limited historical awareness, we think the vast majority of the enterprises in this book have colorful backgrounds. We have tried to focus on the people who made the enterprises what they are today. We have found these histories to be full of twists and ironies; they make fascinating reading.

EXECUTIVES

Here we list the names of the people who run the company, insofar as space allows. In the few cases where available, we have shown the ages and pay of key officers. In some instances the published data is for the previous year, although the company has announced promotions or retirements since year-end. The pay represents cash compensation, including bonuses, but excludes stock option programs.

Although companies are free to structure their management titles any way they please, most modern corporations follow standard practices. The ultimate power in any corporation lies with the shareholders, who elect a board of directors, usually including officers or "insiders" as well as individuals from outside the company. The chief officer, the person on whose desk the buck stops, is usually called the chief executive officer (CEO). Often, he or she is also the chairman of the board.

As corporate management has become more complex, it is common for the CEO to have a "right-hand person" who oversees the day-to-day operations of the company, allowing the CEO plenty of time to focus on strategy and long-term issues. This right-hand person is usually designated the chief operating officer (COO) and is often the president of the company. In other cases one person is both chairman and president.

A multitude of other titles exists, including chief financial officer (CFO), chief administrative officer, and vice chairman. We have always tried to include the CFO, the chief legal officer, and the chief human resources or personnel officer.

The people named in the Executives section are indexed at the back of the book.

The Executives section also includes the name of the company's auditing (accounting) firm, where available.

LOCATIONS

Here we include the company's full legal name and its headquarters, street address, telephone and fax numbers, and Web site, as available. The back of the book includes an index of companies by headquarters locations.

In some cases we have also included information on the geographic distribution of the company's business, including sales and profit data. Note that these profit numbers, like those in the Products/Operations section below, are usually operating or pretax profits rather than net profits. Operating profits are generally those before financing costs (interest income and payments) and before taxes, which are considered costs attributable to the whole company rather than to one division or part of the world. For this reason the net income figures (in the Historical Financials section) are usually much lower, since they are after interest and taxes. Pretax profits are after interest but before taxes.

Headquarters for companies that are incorporated in Bermuda, but whose operational headquarters are in the US, are listed under their US address.

PRODUCTS/OPERATIONS

This section contains selected lists of products, services, brand names, divisions, subsidiaries, and joint ventures. We have tried to include a company's major lines and most familiar brand names.

The nature of this section varies by company and the amount of information contained in Hoover's storehouse of business information. If the company publishes sales and profit information by type of business, we have included it.

COMPETITORS

In this section we have listed companies that compete with the profiled company. This feature is included as a quick way to locate similar companies and compare them. The universe of competitors includes all public companies and all private companies with sales in excess of $500 million. In a few instances we have identified smaller private companies as key competitors.

HISTORICAL FINANCIALS

Here we have tried to present as much data about each enterprise's financial performance as we could compile in the allocated space. The information varies somewhat from industry to industry and is less complete in the case of private companies that do not release data. (We have always tried to provide annual sales and employment, although in some instances those numbers are simply not available). There are a few industries, venture capital and investment banking, for example, for which revenue numbers are not reported as a rule. In the case of private companies that do not publicly disclose financial information, we have statistics when reliable sources are available.

The following information is generally present.

A five-year table, with relevant annualized compound growth rates, covers:

- Sales — fiscal year sales (year-end assets for most financial companies)
- Net income — fiscal year net income (before accounting changes)
- Net profit margin — fiscal year net income as a percent of sales (as a percent of assets for most financial firms)
- Employees — fiscal year-end or average number of employees

The information on the number of employees is intended to aid the reader interested in knowing whether a company has a long-term trend of increasing or decreasing employment. As far as we know, we are the only company that publishes this information in print format.

The numbers on the left in each row of the Historical Financials section give the month and the year in which the company's fiscal year actually ends. Thus, a company with a March 31, 2020, year-end is shown as 3/19. The last item in the Financials section is a graph, which for private companies shows net income, or, if that is unavailable, sales.

Key year-end statistics are included in this section for insurance companies and companies required to file reports with the SEC. They generally show the financial strength of the enterprise, including:

- Debt ratio (long-term debt as a percent of shareholders' equity)
- Return on equity (net income divided by the average of beginning and ending common shareholders' equity)
- Cash and cash equivalents
- Current ratio (ratio of current assets to current liabilities)
- Total long-term debt (including capital lease obligations)
- Fiscal year sales for financial institutions

Hoover's Handbook of

Private Companies

A List-Lover's Compendium

The 300 Largest Private Companies by Sales 2020

Rank	Company	Sales ($ mil.)	Rank	Company	Sales ($ mil.)	Rank	Company	Sales ($ mil.)
1	STATE OF CALIFORNIA	$255,725	61	CHEVRON PHILLIPS CHEMICAL COMPANY LP	$7,919	121	BATTELLE MEMORIAL INSTITUTE	$4,775
2	STATE OF TEXAS	$115,336	62	INTERMOUNTAIN HEALTH CARE INC	$7,724	122	LUKOIL PAN AMERICAS, LLC	$4,746
3	ALBERTSONS COMPANIES, INC.	$60,535	63	CFJ PROPERTIES LLC	$7,672	123	BALFOUR BEATTY, LLC	$4,690
4	NOVARTIS PHARMACEUTICALS CORPORATION	$49,436	64	R. DIRECTIONAL DRILLING & UNDERGROUND	$7,668	124	TEXAS HEALTH RESOURCES	$4,689
5	MCLANE COMPANY, INC.	$48,016	65	COMPUTER SCIENCES CORPORATION	$7,607	125	BEAUMONT HEALTH	$4,660
6	DHPC TECHNOLOGIES, INC.	$38,584	66	REGENTS OF THE UNIVERSITY OF MICHIGAN	$7,467	126	SANFORD	$4,639
7	JOHNSON CONTROLS, INC.	$37,179	67	FEDERAL-MOGUL HOLDINGS LLC	$7,434	127	BIOURJA TRADING, LLC	$4,622
8	FINCANTIERI MARINE SYSTEMS NORTH AMER.	$35,834	68	ARMY & AIR FORCE EXCHANGE SERVICE	$7,211	128	DUKE UNIVERSITY	$4,612
9	PUBLIX SUPER MARKETS, INC.	$34,274	69	HEALTHPARTNERS, INC.	$7,062	129	HOBBY LOBBY STORES, INC.	$4,544
10	CITGO PETROLEUM CORPORATION	$24,100	70	STATE OF RHODE ISLAND AND PROVIDENCE PLA	$7,013	130	NYPRES HOS WEILL COR UNIV MEDICAL CENTER	$4,506
11	ASCENSION HEALTH ALLIANCE	$22,633	71	PRECISION CASTPARTS CORP.	$7,002	131	MEMORIAL SLOAN-KETTERING CANCER CENTER	$4,499
12	CANDID COLOR SYSTEMS, INC.	$21,742	72	ZEN-NOH GRAIN CORPORATION	$6,971	132	THE SCOULAR COMPANY	$4,486
13	BNSF RAILWAY COMPANY	$20,747	73	EATON CORPORATION	$6,925	133	THE PRESIDENT AND FELLOWS OF HARVARD	$4,409
14	TRINITY HEALTH CORPORATION	$18,345	74	WORLD WIDE TECHNOLOGY HOLDING CO., LLC	$6,702	134	MARYLAND DEPARTMENT OF TRANSPORTATION	$4,408
15	STATE OF OKLAHOMA	$17,806	75	GEISINGER HEALTH	$6,537	135	TEKSYSTEMS, INC.	$4,351
16	WHOLE FOODS MARKET, INC.	$16,030	76	SSM HEALTH CARE CORPORATION	$6,497	136	UNIVERSITY OF COLORADO HEALTH	$4,341
17	COMMONSPIRIT HEALTH	$14,982	77	CONSOLIDATED GRAIN & BARGE COMPANY	$6,431	137	UAW RETIREE MEDICAL BENEFITS TRUST	$4,292
18	KAISER FOUNDATION HOSPITALS INC	$14,795	78	ALLY BANK	$6,427	138	ALLINA HEALTH SYSTEM	$4,279
19	PROVIDENCE HEALTH & SERVICES	$14,434	79	THE PENNSYLVANIA STATE UNIVERSITY	$6,364	139	CHRISTUS HEALTH INTERNATIONAL	$4,212
20	GENERAL ELECTRIC INTERNATIONAL, INC.	$14,100	80	MERCY HEALTH	$6,254	140	COUNTY OF MONTGOMERY	$4,203
21	DAIRY FARMERS OF AMERICA, INC.	$13,803	81	THE CHARLOTTE-MECKLENBURG HOSPITAL	$6,228	141	IOWA HEALTH SYSTEM	$4,157
22	SUTTER HEALTH	$12,697	82	NIELSEN HOLDINGS PLC	$6,172	142	BRIGHTSTAR US, INC.	$4,138
23	ALLEGIS GROUP, INC.	$12,297	83	AEROTEK, INC.	$6,070	143	ADVENTIST HEALTH SYSTEM/WEST	$4,115
24	MAYO CLINIC HOSPITAL-ROCHESTER	$11,993	84	IHC HEALTH SERVICES, INC.	$6,037	144	WINCO HOLDINGS, INC.	$4,104
25	WAKEFERN FOOD CORP.	$11,871	85	JOHNS HOPKINS UNIVERSITY	$6,021	145	VANDERBILT UNIVERSITY MEDICAL CENTER	$4,086
26	KIEWIT CORPORATION	$11,826	86	SPECTRUM HEALTH SYSTEM	$6,004	146	CHS MCPHERSON REFINERY INC.	$4,081
27	PARTNERS HEALTHCARE SYSTEM, INC.	$11,666	87	HENRY FORD HEALTH SYSTEM	$5,977	147	AVAYA HOLDINGS CORP.	$4,081
28	LELAND STANFORD JUNIOR UNIVERSITY	$11,311	88	STATE UNIVERSITY OF NEW YORK	$5,961	148	THE INCOME FUND OF AMERICA INC	$4,051
29	PETER KIEWIT SONS', INC.	$11,220	89	WORLD WIDE TECHNOLOGY, LLC	$5,928	149	OHIOHEALTH CORPORATION	$4,046
30	ADVENTIST HEALTH SYSTEM SUNBELT HEALTHC	$10,974	90	FAIRVIEW HEALTH SERVICES	$5,709	150	NEW YORK UNIVERSITY	$4,017
31	THE TURNER CORPORATION	$10,524	91	ALASKA PERMANENT FUND CORPORATION	$5,671	151	CORNELL UNIVERSITY	$4,014
32	TURNER CONSTRUCTION COMPANY INC	$10,516	92	HILL/AHERN FIRE PROTECTION, LLC	$5,669	152	HMH HOSPITALS CORPORATION	$4,000
33	ROBERT BOSCH LLC	$10,474	93	CHALMETTE REFINING, L.L.C.	$5,648	153	THOMAS JEFFERSON UNIVERSITY	$3,952
34	CAMERON INTERNATIONAL CORPORATION	$10,381	94	MEDSTAR HEALTH, INC.	$5,604	154	MCCARTHY HOLDINGS, INC.	$3,926
35	TENASKA MARKETING VENTURES	$10,310	95	LEVI STRAUSS & CO.	$5,575	155	SHAMROCK FOODS COMPANY	$3,901
36	HY-VEE, INC.	$10,291	96	THE WHITING-TURNER CONTRACTING COMPANY	$5,522	156	HOUSTON METHODIST HOSPITAL	$3,887
37	UNIVERSITY OF PENNSYLVANIA	$10,094	97	GILBANE BUILDING COMPANY	$5,453	157	THE SCHOOL BOARD OF MIAMI-DADE COUNTY	$3,868
38	LIMETREE BAY TERMINALS LLC	$10,048	98	ADVOCATE HEALTH CARE NETWORK	$5,393	158	WHITEWAVE FOODS COMPANY	$3,866
39	EQUINOR MARKETING & TRADING (US) INC.	$9,874	99	ACE HARDWARE CORPORATION	$5,388	159	BALFOUR BEATTY CONSTRUCTION GROUP, INC.	$3,853
40	SHI INTERNATIONAL CORP.	$9,767	100	TEXAS PERMANENT SCHOOL FUND MA COMPAN	$5,375	160	MCCARTHY BUILDING COMPANIES, INC.	$3,852
41	ASSOCIATED WHOLESALE GROCERS, INC.	$9,704	101	AURORA HEALTH CARE, INC.	$5,334	161	YALE UNIVERSITY	$3,848
42	NEW YORK CITY HEALTH AND HOSPITALS CORP	$9,551	102	ADVOCATE HEALTH AND HOSPITALS CORPN	$5,310	162	AMERICAN TIRE DISTRIBUTORS HOLDINGS, INC.	$3,839
43	BAYLOR SCOTT & WHITE HOLDINGS	$9,477	103	AIRGAS, INC.	$5,305	163	THE REGENTS OF THE UNIVERSITY OF COLO	$3,834
44	DIGNITY HEALTH	$8,958	104	NEW YORK STATE CATHOLIC HEALTH PLAN, INC.	$5,305	164	BALFOUR BEATTY CONSTRUCTION, LLC	$3,809
45	THE CLEVELAND CLINIC FOUNDATION	$8,928	105	SENTARA HEALTHCARE	$5,298	165	MONTEFIORE MEDICAL CENTER	$3,763
46	ONEOK PARTNERS, L.P.	$8,918	106	BOARD OF EDUCATION OF CITY OF CHICAGO	$5,273	166	SANFORD HEALTH	$3,741
47	THE HERTZ CORPORATION	$8,803	107	MEMORIAL HERMANN HEALTH SYSTEM	$5,258	167	API GROUP INC.	$3,730
48	THE PRIDDY FOUNDATION	$8,792	108	BOARD OF REGENTS OF THE UNIV OF GEORGIA	$5,210	168	KWIK TRIP, INC.	$3,640
49	ALTICOR INC.	$8,783	109	UNIVERSITY OF WASHINGTON INC	$5,172	169	SWINERTON INCORPORATED	$3,632
50	METROPOLITAN TRANSPORTATION AUTHORITY	$8,736	110	NOVANT HEALTH, INC.	$4,986	170	MASSACHUSETTS INSTITUTE OF TECHNOLOGY	$3,627
51	JARDEN LLC	$8,604	111	ST. JOSEPH HEALTH SYSTEM	$4,956	171	UNIVERSITY OF WISCONSIN SYSTEM	$3,614
52	GROWMARK, INC.	$8,522	112	PLACID REFINING COMPANY LLC	$4,929	172	UNIVERSITY SYSTEM OF MARYLAND	$3,602
53	BANNER HEALTH	$8,520	113	PLACID HOLDING COMPANY	$4,929	173	DUKE UNIVERSITY HEALTH SYSTEM, INC.	$3,598
54	NEW YORK UNIVERSITY	$8,500	114	SPECTRA ENERGY CORP	$4,916	174	TRINITY HEALTH-MICHIGAN	$3,596
55	THE NEW YORK AND PRESBYTERIAN HOSPITAL	$8,484	115	STANFORD HEALTH CARE	$4,911	175	LONG ISLAND POWER AUTHORITY	$3,576
56	OCHSNER CLINIC FOUNDATION	$8,405	116	NEW YORK CITY TRANSIT AUTHORITY	$4,893	176	COUNTY OF RIVERSIDE	$3,572
57	SOLSTICE HOLDINGS INC.	$8,235	117	MERCY HEALTH	$4,860	177	UTI, (U.S.) HOLDINGS, INC.	$3,568
58	TATA AMERICA INTERNATIONAL CORPORATION	$8,197	118	TAUBER OIL COMPANY	$4,831	178	SCRIPPS NETWORKS INTERACTIVE, INC.	$3,562
59	U.S. VENTURE, INC.	$8,076	119	SANFORD HEALTH	$4,819	179	THE PARSONS CORPORATION	$3,561
60	UPMC PRESBYTERIAN SHADYSIDE	$8,046	120	FAIRFAX COUNTY VIRGINIA	$4,806	180	HCL AMERICA INC.	$3,559

SOURCE: MERGENT, INC., DATABASE, FEBRUARY 2020

The 300 Largest Private Companies by Sales 2020(continued)

Rank	Company	Sales ($ mil.)	Rank	Company	Sales ($ mil.)	Rank	Company	Sales ($ mil.)
181	THE WASHINGTON UNIVERSITY	$3,543	221	UNIVERSITY OF CHICAGO	$3,092	261	HOUCHENS INDUSTRIES, INC.	$2,614
182	CITY OF BOSTON	$3,542	222	BON SECOURS MERCY HEALTH, INC.	$3,085	262	ST. LUKE'S HEALTH SYSTEM, LTD.	$2,603
183	SWINERTON BUILDERS	$3,542	223	SALT RIVER PROJECT AGRICULTURAL IMPROVE	$3,085	263	LEXA INTERNATIONAL CORPORATION	$2,598
184	BLACK & VEATCH HOLDING COMPANY	$3,480	224	BIG WEST OIL, LLC	$3,053	264	BOARD OF TRUSTEES OF STATE INST OF HLL	$2,588
185	PROVIDENCE HEALTH & SERVICES - OREGON	$3,479	225	OREGON HEALTH & SCIENCE UNIVERSITY	$3,050	265	NEW YORK POWER AUTHORITY	$2,573
186	KIEWIT INDUSTRIAL GROUP INC	$3,474	226	TEXAS COUNTY AND DISTRICT RETIREMENT	$3,030	266	J M SMITH CORPORATION	$2,566
187	THE SCHOOL DISTRICT OF PHILADELPHIA	$3,474	227	COUNTY OF CLARK	$3,022	267	CLARK EQUIPMENT COMPANY	$2,544
188	CEDARS-SINAI MEDICAL CENTER	$3,470	228	AXEL JOHNSON INC.	$2,982	268	MAINEHEALTH	$2,524
189	SCHWAB CHARITABLE FUND	$3,466	229	J.E. DUNN CONSTRUCTION GROUP, INC.	$2,947	269	PRATT CORRUGATED HOLDINGS, INC.	$2,518
190	THE WALSH GROUP LTD	$3,462	230	AMC ENTERTAINMENT INC.	$2,947	270	GGP, INC.	$2,512
191	BEARINGPOINT, INC.	$3,456	231	J.E. DUNN CONSTRUCTION COMPANY	$2,946	271	KFHP OF THE MID-ATLANTIC STATES INC.	$2,512
192	THE GOLUB CORPORATION	$3,427	232	SCRIPPS HEALTH	$2,944	272	STANFORD HEALTH SERVICES	$2,511
193	AG PROCESSING INC A COOPERATIVE	$3,411	233	DO IT BEST CORP.	$2,926	273	THE ORANGE COUNTY PUBLIC SCHOOL DISTRICT	$2,506
194	VCU HEALTH SYSTEM AUTHORITY	$3,400	234	MULTICARE HEALTH SYSTEM	$2,923	274	BARTON MALOW ENTERPRISES, INC.	$2,503
195	SHARP HEALTHCARE	$3,397	235	THE UNIVERSITY OF UTAH	$2,908	275	BARTON MALOW COMPANY	$2,502
196	CAPITAL INCOME BUILDER, INC.	$3,385	236	THE UNIVERSITY OF IOWA	$2,860	276	SUFFOLK CONSTRUCTION COMPANY, INC.	$2,500
197	MONSTER BEVERAGE 1990 CORPORATION	$3,369	237	RICH PRODUCTS CORPORATION	$2,859	277	UMASS MEMORIAL HEALTH CARE, INC.	$2,496
198	BVH, INC.	$3,364	238	UNIVERSITY OF MISSOURI SYSTEM	$2,851	278	MARTIN RESOURCE MANAGEMENT CORPOR	$2,494
199	HENSEL PHELPS CONSTRUCTION CO.	$3,360	239	ICAHN SCHOOL OF MEDICINE AT MOUNT SINAI	$2,843	279	UNIVERSITY OF MASSACHUSETTS	$2,469
200	NOBLE HOLDING (U.S.) CORPORATION	$3,352	240	MEMORIAL HERMANN HEALTHCARE SYSTEM	$2,841	280	NORTHWESTERN UNIVERSITY	$2,464
201	CLARK COUNTY SCHOOL DISTRICT	$3,313	241	OSF HEALTHCARE SYSTEM	$2,826	281	THE MASSACHUSETTS GENERAL HOSPITAL	$2,452
202	CALIFORNIA INSTITUTE OF TECHNOLOGY	$3,303	242	OCHSNER HEALTH SYSTEM	$2,812	282	PAREXEL INTERNATIONAL CORPORATION	$2,442
203	PRODUCTION TECHNOLOGIES, INC.	$3,289	243	WILBUR-ELLIS HOLDINGS II, INC.	$2,812	283	SWEDISH HEALTH SERVICES	$2,439
204	DRIVETIME AUTOMOTIVE GROUP, INC.	$3,267	244	SCHOOL BOARD OF BROWARD COUNTY, (INC)	$2,806	284	BASIN ELECTRIC POWER COOPERATIVE	$2,437
205	RAYMOND JAMES & ASSOCIATES INC	$3,256	245	METALDYNE PERFORMANCE GROUP INC.	$2,791	285	MARSHFIELD CLINIC HEALTH SYSTEM, INC.	$2,431
206	VIRGINIA DEPARTMENT OF TRANSPORTATION	$3,240	246	AHS HOSPITAL CORP.	$2,776	286	JOHNS HOPKINS HOSPITAL	$2,423
207	PHILADELPHIA CONSOLIDATED HOLDING CORP.	$3,234	247	UNIVERSITY OF COLORADO	$2,775	287	NORTHERN INDIANA PUBLIC SERVICE COMPANY	$2,418
208	TRAMMO, INC.	$3,212	248	LEHIGH VALLEY HEALTH NETWORK, INC.	$2,740	288	UNIVERSITY OF ARKANSAS SYSTEM	$2,402
209	KAISER FDN HEALTH PLAN OF COLORADO	$3,197	249	BAPTIST HEALTHCARE SYSTEM, INC.	$2,725	289	YALE-NEW HAVEN HOSPITAL, INC.	$2,389
210	PROVIDENCE HEALTH & SERVICES-WASHINGTON	$3,178	250	EXPRESS SERVICES INC	$2,722	290	COBANK, ACB	$2,380
211	THE UNIVERSITY OF IOWA	$3,177	251	TALEN ENERGY SUPPLY, LLC	$2,714	291	WGL HOLDINGS, INC.	$2,342
212	COUNTY OF SUFFOLK	$3,175	252	AMERICAN BALANCED FUND, INC.	$2,698	292	GEISINGER HEALTH PLAN	$2,338
213	TRUMAN ARNOLD COMPANIES	$3,174	253	UNIVERSITY OF CALIFORNIA, DAVIS	$2,697	293	NATIONWIDE CHILDREN'S HOSPITAL	$2,317
214	REGAL ENTERTAINMENT GROUP	$3,163	254	HOUSTON INDEPENDENT SCHOOL DISTRICT	$2,696	294	THE SCHOOL DISTRICT OF WEST PALM	$2,308
215	RALEY'S	$3,162	255	HEARTLAND PAYMENT SYSTEMS, LLC	$2,682	295	ARCTIC SLOPE REGIONAL CORPORATION	$2,297
216	ESTES EXPRESS LINES, INC.	$3,160	256	HARTFORD HEALTHCARE CORPORATION	$2,678	296	UNIVERSITY OF PITTSBURGH	$2,276
217	FRANCISCAN ALLIANCE, INC.	$3,145	257	TEMPLE UNIVERSITY-OF THE COMMONWEALTH	$2,635	297	RUSH UNIVERSITY MEDICAL CENTER	$2,268
218	SKF USA INC.	$3,139	258	BROWARD COUNTY PUBLIC SCHOOLS	$2,630	298	CPS ENERGY	$2,258
219	THE OHIO STATE UNIVY WEXNER MEDICA	$3,106	259	NAVY EXCHANGE SERVICE COMMAND	$2,617	299	TRUSTEES OF INDIANA UNIVERSITY	$2,256
220	DYNCORP INTERNATIONAL LLC	$3,101	260	UMASS MEMORIAL HEALTH CARE INC AND	$2,614	300	PEACEHEALTH	$2,250

The 300 Largest Private Companies by Employees 2020

Rank	Company	Employees	Rank	Company	Employees	Rank	Company	Employees
1	EXPRESS SERVICES INC	373869	61	NPC RESTAURANT HOLDINGS, LLC	29000	121	AIRGAS, INC.	17070
2	ALBERTSONS COMPANIES, INC.	275000	62	SENTARA HEALTHCARE	28000	122	JARDEN LLC	17000
3	STATE OF CALIFORNIA	208580	63	UNIVERSITY SYSTEM OF MARYLAND	28000	123	THE UNIVERSITY OF IOWA	17000
4	PUBLIX SUPER MARKETS, INC.	193000	64	UNIVERSITY OF WASHINGTON INC	27228	124	SCOTTSDALE HEALTHCARE CORP.	17000
5	KAISER FOUNDATION HOSPITALS INC	175668	65	ALLINA HEALTH SYSTEM	26400	125	WAKE COUNTY PUBLIC SCHOOL SYSTEM	17000
6	STATE OF TEXAS	144175	66	OREGON UNIVERSITY SYSTEM	26000	126	SPECTRUM HEALTH SYSTEM	16996
7	JOHNSON CONTROLS, INC.	139000	67	ROBINSON HEALTH SYSTEM, INC.	26000	127	COBB COUNTY PUBLIC SCHOOLS	16336
8	ASCENSION HEALTH ALLIANCE	111719	68	REGAL ENTERTAINMENT GROUP	25359	128	THE RESEARCH FOUNDATION NEW YO	16330
9	ASCENSION HEALTH	109000	69	ADVOCATE HEALTH CARE NETWORK	25000	129	THE SALVATION ARMY	16168
10	WHOLE FOODS MARKET, INC.	89000	70	CHRISTUS HEALTH INTERNATIONAL	25000	130	UNIVERSITY OF SOUTH FLORIDA	16165
11	STATE UNIVERSITY OF NEW YORK	88024	71	HILLSBOROUGH COUNTY SCHOOL DIS	25000	131	HOUCHENS INDUSTRIES, INC.	16000
12	ALLEGIS GROUP, INC.	85000	72	SCHOOL BOARD OF ORANGE FLORIDA	25000	132	TRUSTEES OF INDIANA UNIVERSITY	16000
13	HY-VEE, INC.	83000	73	BARNABAS HEALTH, INC.	24600	133	ALSCO INC.	16000
14	UPMC	80000	74	SSM HEALTH CARE CORPORATION	24230	134	INOVA HEALTH SYSTEM FOUNDATION	16000
15	ADVENTIST HEALTH SYSTEM SUNBEL	78000	75	MEMORIAL HERMANN HEALTH SYSTEM	24000	135	UNIVERSITY SYSTEM OF NEW HAMP	16000
16	COMMONSPIRIT HEALTH	72500	76	THE EVANGELICAL LUTHERAN GOOD SA	24000	136	BAPTIST HEALTH SOUTH FLORIDA, INC.	16000
17	METROPOLITAN TRANSPORTATION	67457	77	THE NEW YORK AND PRESBY HOSPITAL	23709	137	MINNETONKA INDEPENDENT SCH D 276	16000
18	PARTNERS HEALTHCARE SYSTEM, INC.	67000	78	CAMERON INTERNATIONAL CORP	23000	138	DST SYSTEMS, INC.	15700
19	COMPUTER SCIENCES CORPORATION	66000	79	HENRY FORD HEALTH SYSTEM	23000	139	THE PARSONS CORPORATION	15633
20	THE CHARLOTTE-MECKLENBURG HOS	62000	80	ORLANDO HEALTH, INC.	23000	140	BEARINGPOINT, INC.	15200
21	MAYO FOUNDATION FOR MEDICAL ED	60000	81	ACCENTCARE, INC.	23000	141	BOARD OF REGENTS OF UN NEBRASKA	15200
22	ST MARY'S MEDICAL CENTER	56605	82	YALE NEW HAVEN HEALTH SERVICES C	22490	142	LELAND STANFORD JUNIOR UNIVERSITY	15000
23	DIGNITY HEALTH	55494	83	HOUSTON INDEPENDENT SCHOOL DIST	22440	143	OHIOHEALTH CORPORATION	15000
24	THE UNIVERSITY OF NORTH CAROLINA	55000	84	HEALTHPARTNERS, INC.	22000	144	PITT COUNTY MEMORIAL HOSPITAL,	15000
25	ALLIED SECURITY HOLDINGS LLC	53760	85	YALE-NEW HAVEN HOSPITAL, INC.	22000	145	AKAL SECURITY, INC.	15000
26	FEDERAL-MOGUL HOLDINGS LLC	53700	86	PRINCE GEORGE'S COUNTY PUBLIC SC	22000	146	BUHLER INC.	15000
27	PILOT CORPORATION	51337	87	TEXAS HEALTH RESOURCES	21277	147	PETER KIEWIT SONS', INC.	14700
28	TRINITY HEALTH CORPORATION	51100	88	THE SCHOOL DISTRICT OF PHILA	21065	148	HOSPITAL SISTERS HEALTH SYSTEM	14676
29	SANFORD	50000	89	NEW YORK UNIVERSITY	21000	149	UNIVERSITY OF CINCINNATI	14600
30	SUTTER HEALTH	48000	90	SCHOOL BOARD OF PALM BEACH CTY	21000	150	LEVI STRAUSS & CO.	14400
31	NEW YORK CITY TRANSIT AUTHORITY	47956	91	THE VANDERBILT UNIVERSITY	21000	151	WORLDWIDE MEDIA SERVICES GR	14375
32	THE CLEVELAND CLINIC FOUNDATION	44000	92	MCLANE COMPANY, INC.	20128	152	ALMOST FAMILY, INC.	14200
33	THE PENNSYLVANIA STATE UNIVERSITY	44000	93	BATTELLE MEMORIAL INSTITUTE	20000	153	ADVANCE SERVICES, INC.	14200
34	NIELSEN HOLDINGS PLC	43061	94	COUNTY OF RIVERSIDE	20000	154	MILWAUKEE PUBLIC SCHOOLS (INC)	14154
35	BNSF RAILWAY COMPANY	41000	95	LARSEN & TOUBRO INFOTECH LIMITED	20000	155	UNIVERSITY OF ARKANSAS SYSTEM	14025
36	BOARD OF REGENTS UNIVERSITY GEOR	40000	96	BAYCARE HEALTH SYSTEM, INC.	20000	156	ALTICOR INC.	14000
37	STATE OF OKLAHOMA	37613	97	NORTHWESTERN MEMORIAL HEALTH	20000	157	SOLSTICE HOLDINGS INC.	14000
38	JOHNS HOPKINS UNIVERSITY	37600	98	STAFF FORCE, INC.	20000	158	MEMORIAL HERMANN HEALTH SYSTEM	14000
39	CLARK COUNTY SCHOOL DISTRICT	37361	99	AMC ENTERTAINMENT INC.	19700	159	WINCO HOLDINGS, INC.	14000
40	THE HERTZ CORPORATION	37000	100	ADVENTIST HEALTH SYSTEM/WEST	19512	160	SHARP HEALTHCARE	14000
41	STEWARD HEALTH CARE SYSTEM LLC	37000	101	THE GOLUB CORPORATION	19500	161	RALEY'S	14000
42	NEW YORK CITY HEALTH AND HOSP	35700	102	OREGON HEALTH & SCIENCE UNIVY	19500	162	ESTES EXPRESS LINES, INC.	14000
43	BANNER HEALTH	35000	103	VANDERBILT UNIVERSITY MED CENTER	19000	163	NAVY EXCHANGE SERVICE COMMAND	14000
44	INTERMOUNTAIN HEALTH CARE INC	35000	104	FRANCISCAN ALLIANCE, INC.	19000	164	SCOTTSDALE HEALTHCARE HOSPITALS	14000
45	ARMY & AIR FORCE EXCHANGE SERVICE	35000	105	BON SECOURS MERCY HEALTH, INC.	19000	165	JEFFERSON COUNTY BOARD OF ED	14000
46	MERCY HEALTH	35000	106	OCHSNER HEALTH SYSTEM	19000	166	MORTON HOSPITAL AND MEDICAL CEN	14000
47	BEAUMONT HEALTH	35000	107	IOWA HEALTH SYSTEM	18923	167	NOVANT HEALTH, INC.	13800
48	THE OHIO STATE UNIVERSITY MEDCEN	35000	108	PAREXEL INTERNATIONAL CORPORAT	18900	168	NORTHSIDE INDEPENDENT SCH DIS	13698
49	MAXIM HEALTHCARE SERVICES, INC.	35000	109	CITY OF BOSTON	18760	169	STATE OF RHODE ISLAND AND PROV	13535
50	REGENTS OF THE UNIVERSITY OF MICH	34624	110	UNIVERSITY OF NEW MEXICO	18362	170	FLORIDA STATE UNIVERSITY	13497
51	MEDSTAR HEALTH, INC.	33000	111	WILLIAM BEAUMONT HOSPITAL	18050	171	SCRIPPS HEALTH	13445
52	MAYO CLINIC HOSPITAL-ROCHESTER	32271	112	FAIRVIEW HEALTH SERVICES	18000	172	RECTOR & VISITORS OF THE UNIV VIR	13300
53	HEARTLAND HEALTH	32000	113	THE UNIVERSITY OF UTAH	18000	173	DELTA TUCKER HOLDINGS, INC.	13200
54	BROWARD COUNTY PUBLIC SCHOOLS	31174	114	WHEATON FRANCISCAN SERVICES, INC.	18000	174	UNIVERSITY OF MASSACHUSETTS	13196
55	UNIVERSITY OF MISSOURI SYSTEM	30282	115	CHILDREN'S HOSPITAL MEDICAL CENTER	18000	175	GEISINGER HEALTH	13030
56	HOBBY LOBBY STORES, INC.	30218	116	ST. JOHN PROVIDENCE	17806	176	INOVA HEALTH CARE SERVICES	13000
57	PRECISION CASTPARTS CORP.	30100	117	UNIVERSITY OF GEORGIA	17800	177	CYPRESS-FAIRBANKS IND SCHOOL DIS	13000
58	UNIVERSITY HOSPITALS HEALTH SYS	30099	118	UNIVERSITY OF CALIFORNIA, DAVIS	17741	178	DUVAL COUNTY PUBLIC SCHOOLS	13000
59	AURORA HEALTH CARE, INC.	30000	119	MAIN LINE HEALTH SYSTEM	17485	179	TRIHEALTH, INC.	13000
60	THE SCHOOL DISTRICT OF WEST PALM	29656	120	INDIANA UNIVERSITY HEALTH, INC.	17242	180	WILLOW VALLEY COMMUNITIES	13000

SOURCE: MERGENT, INC., DATABASE, FEBRUARY 2020

The 300 Largest Private Companies by Employees 2020 (continued)

Rank	Company	Employees	Rank	Company	Employees	Rank	Company	Employees
181	ROBERT BOSCH LLC	12986	221	MONTEFIORE MEDICAL CENTER	11000	261	BAPTIST MEMORIAL HEALTH CARE SYS	9877
182	THE REGENTS OF THE UNIV OF COL	12980	222	SPECTRUM HEALTH HOSPITALS	11000	262	ONEAMERICA FINANCIAL PARTNERS, .	9875
183	COUNTY OF SUFFOLK	12814	223	DALLAS COUNTY HOSPITAL DISTRICT	11000	263	LOUDOUN COUNTY PUBLIC SCH	9822
184	THE FINISH LINE INC	12700	224	BAYSTATE HEALTH INC.	11000	264	KENTUCKYONE HEALTH, INC.	9801
185	UNIVERSITY OF HOUSTON SYSTEM	12608	225	PUBLIC HEALTH TRUST OF MIAMI DADE	11000	265	PROVIDENCE HEALTH & SERVICES	9700
186	BAPTIST HEALTHCARE SYSTEM, INC.	12601	226	LESTER E. COX MEDICAL CENTERS	11000	266	PROVIDENCE HEALTH & SERVICES-WAS	9700
187	THE FRESH MARKET INC	12600	227	VIRGINIA COMMONWEALTH UNIVERSITY	11000	267	SWEDISH HEALTH SERVICES	9700
188	NORTH CAROLINA BAPTIST HOSPITAL	12563	228	ST. MARYS DEAN VENTURES, INCORPOR	11000	268	BEALL'S, INC.	9700
189	MOUNT SINAI HOSPITALS GROUP, INC.	12559	229	BEAUMONT UNIFIED SCHOOL DISTR	11000	269	THE GEORGETOWN UNIVERSITY	9700
190	CORNELL UNIVERSITY	12207	230	BALTIMORE CITY PUBLIC SCHOOLS	10800	270	MESA UNIFIED SCHOOL DISTRICT 4	9621
191	UNIVERSITY OF NC AT CHAPEL HILL	12204	231	CALIFORNIA INSTITUTE OF TECHNO	10794	271	UNIVERSITY OF PITTSBURGH	9607
192	BOARD OF EDUCATION-MEMPHIS SCH	12015	232	VIRGINIA DEPARTMENT OF TRANSPORT	10737	272	SAINT LUKE'S HOSPITAL OF BETH, PENN	9604
193	FAIRFAX COUNTY VIRGINIA	12000	233	MED AMERICA HEALTH SYSTEMS CORP	10700	273	CATHOLIC BISHOP OF CHICAGO	9604
194	MASSACHUSETTS INSOF TECHNOLOGY	12000	234	LEGACY HEALTH	10675	274	THE WASHINGTON UNIVERSITY	9600
195	METALDYNE PERFORMANCE GROUP INC.	12000	235	THOMAS JEFFERSON UNIVERSITY	10625	275	SOUTHERN ILLINOIS UNIVERSITY INC	9576
196	LEHIGH VALLEY HEALTH NETWORK, INC.	12000	236	RICH PRODUCTS CORPORATION	10536	276	JOHNSON CONTROLS FIRE PROTLP	9500
197	JOHNS HOPKINS HOSPITAL	12000	237	OCHSNER CLINIC FOUNDATION	10500	277	INTEGRIS HEALTH, INC.	9500
198	NATIONWIDE CHILDREN'S HOSPITAL	12000	238	KWIK TRIP, INC.	10500	278	LOS ANGELES DEPART OF WATER POW	9500
199	THE MOSES H CONE MEMORIAL HOS	12000	239	LOYOLA UNIVERSITY OF CHICAGO INC	10500	279	CLEVELAND MUNICIPAL SCHOOL DIST	9500
200	MISSION HEALTH SYSTEM, INC.	12000	240	THE SALVATION ARMY	10447	280	MANAGEMENT & TRAINING CORPOR	9500
201	WESTCHESTER COUNTY HEALTH CARE	12000	241	KIEWIT CORPORATION	10441	281	MEMORIAL SLOAN-KETTERING CANCER	9325
202	UNIVERSITY OF MARYLAND MED SYS	12000	242	FORT WORTH INDEPENDENT SCH DIST	10360	282	ALEX LEE, INC.	9200
203	UNIVERSITY OF TENNESSEE	12000	243	THE MASSACHGENERAL HOSPITAL	10156	283	SOUTH BROWARD HOSPITAL DISTRICT	9200
204	THE GEISINGER CLINIC	12000	244	BOSCOV'S, INC.	10003	284	AUSTIN INDEPENDENT SCHOOL DIS	9200
205	JEFFERSON COUNTY SCH DIST NO. R-1	12000	245	MCLAREN HEALTH CARE CORPORATION	10003	285	PULSE ELECTRONICS, INC.	9200
206	UNIVERSITY OF HAWAII SYSTEMS	12000	246	RAYMOND JAMES & ASSOCIATES INC	10000	286	TEMPLE UNIVERSITY-OF THE COMMON	9061
207	TESLA ENERGY OPERATIONS, INC.	12000	247	UMASS MEMORIAL HEALTH CARE, INC.	10000	287	SCHOOL BOARD OF BREVARD COUNTY	9031
208	CHICAGO TRANSIT AUTHORITY	12000	248	HDR, INC.	10000	288	NORTHSHORE UNIVERSITY HEALTHSY	9000
209	BODDIE-NOELL ENTERPRISES, INC.	12000	249	COUNTY OF HILLSBOROUGH	10000	289	PLY GEM HOLDINGS, INC.	9000
210	PORTLAND ADVENTIST MEDICAL CEN	12000	250	UC HEALTH, LLC.	10000	290	FRANCISCAN MISSION	9000
211	FACTORY CONNECTION, LLC	12000	251	FULTON COUNTY BOARD OF EDUCATION	10000	291	KALEIDA HEALTH	9000
212	THE ROMAN CATHOLIC ARCHBISHOP LA	12000	252	FARM CREDIT SERVICES OF AMERICA	10000	292	KIEWIT INFRASTRUCTURE CO.	9000
213	HCL AMERICA INC.	11993	253	COLUMBUS CITY SCHOOL DISTRICT	10000	293	MINNEAPOLIS PUBLIC SCHOOL DIST	9000
214	VIA CHRISTI HEALTH, INC.	11970	254	MERCY HOSPITALS EAST COMMUNITIES	10000	294	EL PASO INDEPENDENT SCHOOL DIS	9000
215	VISITING NURSE SERVICE OF NY	11780	255	MISSION HOSPITAL, INC.	10000	295	SOUTHEASTERN PENNSYLVANIA TRAN	9000
216	AVAYA HOLDINGS CORP.	11701	256	NORTH EAST INDEPENDENT SCHOO	10000	296	TUCSON UNIFIED SCHOOL DISTRICT	9000
217	THE PRESIDENT AND FELLOWS OF HAR	11500	257	GUILFORD COUNTY SCHOOL SYSTEM	10000	297	KENTUCKY COMMUNITY AND TECHNI	9000
218	METHODIST LE BONHEUR HEALTHCARE	11459	258	COOPERATIVE FOR ASSISTANCE AND RE	10000	298	PRINCE WILLIAM COUNTY PUBSCHO	8907
219	MICHIGAN STATE UNIVERSITY	11100	259	UMASS MEMORIAL COMMUNITY HOS	10000	299	OKLAHOMA STATE UNIVERSITY	8882
220	YALE UNIVERSITY	11000	260	DIVERSIFIED MAINTENANCE SYSTEMS	10000	300	MERCY HEALTH	8800

The 100 Largest Private Companies by Net Income 2020

Rank	Company Headquarters	Net Income ($bil)	Rank	Company Headquarters	Net Income ($bil)
1	AMERICAN BALANCED FUND, INC.	$23,932	51	PROVIDENCE HEALTH & SERVICES - OREGON	$781
2	BNSF RAILWAY COMPANY	$12,119	52	BAYLOR SCOTT & WHITE HOLDINGS	$755
3	AMCAP FUND INC	$9,995	53	AMERICAN HONDA FINANCE CORPORATION	$753
4	NOVARTIS PHARMACEUTICALS CORPORATION	$6,698	54	UNIVERSITY OF COLORADO HEALTH	$747
5	FINCANTIERI MARINE SYSTEMS NORTH AMERICA, INC.	$6,671	55	DARTMOUTH COLLEGE	$740
6	ALASKA PERMANENT FUND CORPORATION	$5,109	56	THE BLOOMBERG FAMILY FOUNDATION INC	$737
7	STATE OF CALIFORNIA	$4,799	57	EQUINOR NATURAL GAS LLC	$722
8	THE PRESIDENT AND FELLOWS OF HARVARD COLLEGE	$4,608	58	INOVA HEALTH SYSTEM FOUNDATION	$717
9	TEXAS PERMANENT SCHOOL FUND MANAGEMENT COMP	$4,155	59	CITGO PETROLEUM CORPORATION	$715
10	YALE UNIVERSITY	$3,271	60	JOHNS HOPKINS UNIVERSITY	$705
11	LELAND STANFORD JUNIOR UNIVERSITY	$2,653	61	THOMAS JEFFERSON UNIVERSITY	$700
12	THE TRUSTEES OF PRINCETON UNIVERSITY	$2,583	62	TRUSTEES OF DARTMOUTH COLLEGE	$691
13	CANDID COLOR SYSTEMS, INC.	$2,535	63	DUKE UNIVERSITY HEALTH SYSTEM, INC.	$688
14	MASSACHUSETTS INSTITUTE OF TECHNOLOGY	$2,392	64	CHS MCPHERSON REFINERY INC.	$687
15	THE INCOME FUND OF AMERICA INC	$2,344	65	EDUCATIONAL TESTING SERVICE INC	$686
16	UNIVERSITY OF PENNSYLVANIA	2,327	66	GENERAL ELECTRIC INTERNATIONAL, INC.	$686
17	ST. JOSEPH HEALTH SYSTEM	$2,083	67	HOUSTON METHODIST HOSPITAL	$682
18	PUBLIX SUPER MARKETS, INC.	$2,026	68	AMERICAN LEBANESE SYRIAN ASSOCIATED CHARITIES, INC.	$658
19	PERMANENT UNIVERSITY FUND	$1,964	69	SADDLE BUTTE PIPELINE LLC	$656
20	STATE OF TEXAS	$1,883	70	NATIONWIDE CHILDREN'S HOSPITAL	$647
21	TEXAS COUNTY AND DISTRICT RETIREMENT SYSTEM	$1,761	71	ADVENTIST HEALTH SYSTEM SUNBELT HEALTHCARE CORP	$635
22	GROUP HEALTH COMMUNITY FOUNDATION	$1,730	72	VANGUARD CHARITABLE ENDOWMENT PROGRAM	$608
23	CENTRAL PUGET SOUND REGIONAL TRANSIT AUTHORITY	$1,684	73	NOBLE HOLDING (U.S.) CORPORATION	$607
24	JOHNSON CONTROLS, INC.	$1,679	74	STATE OF OKLAHOMA	$602
25	ASCENSION HEALTH ALLIANCE	$1,639	75	FIDELITY INV CHARITABLE GIFT FUND	$599
26	SCHWAB CHARITABLE FUND	$1,549	76	THE UNIVERSITY OF IOWA	$588
27	SUNOCO PIPELINE L.P.	$1,420	77	PRODUCTION TECHNOLOGIES, INC.	$580
28	TRINITY HEALTH CORPORATION	1,359	78	SENTARA HEALTHCARE	$580
29	DHPC TECHNOLOGIES, INC.	$1,320	79	AMERICAN HIGH INCOME TRUST	$578
30	AMERICAN FUNDS MORTGAGE FUND	$1,278	80	NIELSEN HOLDINGS PLC	$575
31	ALLY BANK	$1,273	81	NORTHWESTERN UNIVERSITY	$561
32	THE PENNSYLVANIA STATE UNIVERSITY	$1,082	82	SAINT MARYS HOSPITAL	$557
33	ONEOK PARTNERS, L.P.	$1,072	83	THE NEW YORK AND PRESBYTERIAN HOSPITAL	$527
34	SPECTRA ENERGY CORP	$1,020	84	OHIOHEALTH CORPORATION	$519
35	THE WASHINGTON UNIVERSITY	$1,012	85	BOSTON UNIVERSITY	$517
36	NEW YORK CITY TRANSIT AUTHORITY	$986	86	PETER KIEWIT SONS', INC.	$515
37	CORNELL UNIVERSITY	$986	87	FARM CREDIT SERVICES OF AMERICA	$514
38	COBANK, ACB	$937	88	THE VANDERBILT UNIVERSITY	$511
39	REGENTS OF THE UNIVERSITY OF MICHIGAN	$920	89	UNIVERSITY OF WASHINGTON INC	$490
40	RECTOR & VISITORS OF THE UNIVERSITY OF VIRGINIA	$909	90	ROCKIES EXPRESS PIPELINE LLC	$488
41	TEXAS HEALTH RESOURCES	$870	91	HARVARD MANAGEMENT PRIVATE EQUITY CORPORATION	$478
42	MAYO CLINIC HOSPITAL-ROCHESTER	$856	92	VIRGINIA DEPARTMENT OF TRANSPORTATION	$473
43	CAMERON INTERNATIONAL CORPORATION	$848	93	STANFORD HEALTH CARE	$457
44	CHEVRON PHILLIPS CHEMICAL COMPANY LP	$841	94	TRIBOROUGH BRIDGE & TUNNEL AUTHORITY	$454
45	EATON CORPORATION	$821	95	DST SYSTEMS, INC.	$452
46	MONSTER BEVERAGE 1990 CORPORATION	$821	96	HARTFORD HEALTHCARE CORPORATION	$440
47	PRECISION CASTPARTS CORP.	$817	97	AURORA HEALTH CARE, INC.	$438
48	SCRIPPS NETWORKS INTERACTIVE, INC.	$814	98	KAISER FOUNDATION HOSPITALS INC	$429
49	KIEWIT CORPORATION	$796	99	INTERMOUNTAIN HEALTH CARE INC	$421
50	PLAINS PIPELINE, L.P.	$783	100	CEDARS-SINAI MEDICAL CENTER	$418

SOURCE: MERGENT DATA FEBRUARY 2020

The 100 Largest Private Companies by Total Assets 2020

Rank	Company Headquarters	Net Income ($bil)	Rank	Company Headquarters	Net Income ($bil)
1	STATE OF CALIFORNIA	$333,689	51	CITGO PETROLEUM CORPORATION	$8,209
2	STATE OF TEXAS	$323,008	52	UPMC PRESBYTERIAN SHADYSIDE	$7,918
3	NOVARTIS PHARMACEUTICALS CORPORATION	$130,124	53	GEISINGER HEALTH	$7,703
4	ALLY BANK	$123,548	54	MERCY HEALTH	$7,507
5	METROPOLITAN TRANSPORTATION AUTHORITY	$84,702	55	SSM HEALTH CARE CORPORATION	$7,377
6	BNSF RAILWAY COMPANY	$83,098	56	FEDERAL-MOGUL HOLDINGS LLC	$7,076
7	ALASKA PERMANENT FUND CORPORATION	$67,671	57	NEW YORK CITY HEALTH AND HOSPITALS CORPORATION	$6,859
8	LELAND STANFORD JUNIOR UNIVERSITY	$54,746	58	PETER KIEWIT SONS', INC.	$6,793
9	TEXAS PERMANENT SCHOOL FUND MANAGEMENT COMP.	$44,517	59	ROBERT BOSCH LLC	$6,779
10	STATE OF OKLAHOMA	$44,500	60	WHOLE FOODS MARKET, INC.	$6,676
11	FINCANTIERI MARINE SYSTEMS NORTH AMERICA, INC.	$44,240	61	MCLANE COMPANY, INC.	$6,656
12	ASCENSION HEALTH ALLIANCE	$34,320	62	KIEWIT CORPORATION	$6,636
13	JOHNSON CONTROLS, INC.	$29,673	63	ARMY & AIR FORCE EXCHANGE SERVICE	$6,434
14	EATON CORPORATION	$27,466	64	SPECTRUM HEALTH SYSTEM	$5,801
15	UNIVERSITY OF PENNSYLVANIA	$26,415	65	MEDSTAR HEALTH, INC.	$5,690
16	TRINITY HEALTH CORPORATION	$26,196	66	ALTICOR INC.	$5,352
17	KAISER FOUNDATION HOSPITALS INC	$22,753	67	SOLSTICE HOLDINGS INC.	$5,091
18	REGENTS OF THE UNIVERSITY OF MICHIGAN	$22,063	68	HEALTHPARTNERS, INC.	$5,037
19	ALBERTSONS COMPANIES, INC.	$20,777	69	FAIRVIEW HEALTH SERVICES	$5,024
20	COMMONSPIRIT HEALTH	$20,595	70	HENRY FORD HEALTH SYSTEM	$4,459
21	PRECISION CASTPARTS CORP.	$20,497	71	R. DIRECTIONAL DRILLING & UNDERGROUND TECHN	$4,266
22	THE HERTZ CORPORATION	$20,058	72	THE TURNER CORPORATION	$3,736
23	GENERAL ELECTRIC INTERNATIONAL, INC.	$19,615	73	LEVI STRAUSS & CO.	$3,543
24	PUBLIX SUPER MARKETS, INC.	$17,464	74	TURNER CONSTRUCTION COMPANY INC	$3,440
25	SUTTER HEALTH	$17,303	75	DAIRY FARMERS OF AMERICA, INC.	$3,402
26	NEW YORK UNIVERSITY	$16,876	76	ALLEGIS GROUP, INC.	$3,250
27	MAYO CLINIC HOSPITAL-ROCHESTER	$16,307	77	HY-VEE, INC.	$3,006
28	THE CLEVELAND CLINIC FOUNDATION	$16,207	78	LIMETREE BAY TERMINALS LLC	$2,770
29	ADVENTIST HEALTH SYSTEM SUNBELT HEALTHCARE CORP	$15,977	79	OCHSNER CLINIC FOUNDATION	$2,651
30	PROVIDENCE HEALTH & SERVICES	$15,740	80	GROWMARK, INC.	$2,629
31	ONEOK PARTNERS, L.P.	$15,469	81	HILL/AHERN FIRE PROTECTION, LLC	$2,528
32	NIELSEN HOLDINGS PLC	$15,303	82	THE WHITING-TURNER CONTRACTING COMPANY	$2,498
33	PARTNERS HEALTHCARE SYSTEM, INC.	$15,070	83	ZEN-NOH GRAIN CORPORATION	$2,336
34	THE PENNSYLVANIA STATE UNIVERSITY	$15,017	84	SHI INTERNATIONAL CORP.	$2,240
35	STATE OF RHODE ISLAND AND PROVIDENCE PLANTATIONS	$14,901	85	EQUINOR MARKETING & TRADING (US) INC.	$2,031
36	STATE UNIVERSITY OF NEW YORK	$14,780	86	GILBANE BUILDING COMPANY	$1,899
37	JARDEN LLC	$14,293	87	ACE HARDWARE CORPORATION	$1,858
38	THE NEW YORK AND PRESBYTERIAN HOSPITAL	$14,204	88	TATA AMERICA INTERNATIONAL CORPORATION	$1,788
39	CHEVRON PHILLIPS CHEMICAL COMPANY LP	$12,987	89	TENASKA MARKETING VENTURES	$1,736
40	CAMERON INTERNATIONAL CORPORATION	$12,892	90	WORLD WIDE TECHNOLOGY, LLC	$1,659
41	INTERMOUNTAIN HEALTH CARE INC	$12,694	91	WAKEFERN FOOD CORP.	$1,646
42	BAYLOR SCOTT & WHITE HOLDINGS	$12,138	92	ASSOCIATED WHOLESALE GROCERS, INC.	$1,624
43	IHC HEALTH SERVICES, INC.	$11,568	93	CHALMETTE REFINING, L.L.C.	$1,519
44	BANNER HEALTH	$11,387	94	CONSOLIDATED GRAIN & BARGE COMPANY	$1,426
45	DIGNITY HEALTH	$11,076	95	WORLD WIDE TECHNOLOGY HOLDING CO., LLC	$1,377
46	JOHNS HOPKINS UNIVERSITY	$10,648	96	AEROTEK, INC.	$1,103
47	ADVOCATE HEALTH CARE NETWORK	$9,634	97	U.S. VENTURE, INC.	$1,025
48	THE CHARLOTTE-MECKLENBURG HOSPITAL AUTHORITY	$9,363	98	CFJ PROPERTIES LLC	$845
49	DHPC TECHNOLOGIES, INC.	$9,119	99	THE PRIDDY FOUNDATION	$121
50	COMPUTER SCIENCES CORPORATION	$8,663	100	CANDID COLOR SYSTEMS, INC.	$9

SOURCE: MERGENT DATA FEBRUARY 2020

Hoover's Handbook of

Private Companies

The Companies

1199 SEIU NATIONAL BENEFIT FUND FOR HEALTH AND HUMAN SERVICE EMPLOYEES

Auditors: KPMG LLP NEW YORK NY

LOCATIONS

HQ: 1199 SEIU NATIONAL BENEFIT FUND FOR HEALTH AND HUMAN SERVICE EMPLOYEES , NEW YORK, NY 10108
Phone: 646 473-6020

HISTORICAL FINANCIALS
Company Type: Private

Income Statement · FYE: December 31

	REVENUE ($ mil.)	NET INCOME ($ mil.)	NET PROFIT MARGIN	EMPLOYEES
12/17	1,642	45	2.8%	2
12/09	1,167	(19)	—	—
Annual Growth	4.4%			

2017 Year-End Financials
Return on assets: 5.3% Cash ($ mil.): 47
Return on equity: 8.2%
Current ratio: 8.70

21ST CENTURY ONCOLOGY HOLDINGS, INC.

EXECUTIVES

Ceo, Kimberly Commins-Tzoumakas
Chb, Robert L Rosner
Pres-Ceo, William R Spalding
Cfo, Leanne M Stewart
Cmo, Constantine A Mantz
Sr V Pres-Cao-Contrl-asst Trea, Joseph Biscardi
Sr V Pres US Oprs, Gary Delanois
Coo, Charlie Powell
Manager, Kasha Holt
Auditors: DELOITTE & TOUCHE LLP MIAMI

LOCATIONS

HQ: 21ST CENTURY ONCOLOGY HOLDINGS, INC. 2270 COLONIAL BLVD, FORT MYERS, FL 339071412
Phone: 239 931-7254
Web: WWW.21CO.COM

HISTORICAL FINANCIALS
Company Type: Private

Income Statement · FYE: December 31

	REVENUE ($ mil.)	NET INCOME ($ mil.)	NET PROFIT MARGIN	EMPLOYEES
12/14	1,026	(343)	—	3,930
12/13	736	(78)	—	—
12/12	693	(151)	—	—
Annual Growth	21.6%	—	—	—

2014 Year-End Financials
Return on assets: (-29.9%) Cash ($ mil.): 99
Return on equity: —
Current ratio: 1.40

A-1 SPECIALIZED SERVICES & SUPPLIES, INC.

EXECUTIVES

Pres, Suresh Khosla
V Pres*, Om Perkash
SEC*, Ashok Kumar
SEC*, Ashok K Khosla
Treas*, Leena Khosla
Auditors: MEENA JERATH CPA MED MBA

LOCATIONS

HQ: A-1 SPECIALIZED SERVICES & SUPPLIES, INC. 347 MOUNT PLEASANT AVE # 200, WEST ORANGE, NJ 070522744
Phone: 215 788-9200
Web: WWW.NORTHAM.CO.ZA

HISTORICAL FINANCIALS
Company Type: Private

Income Statement · FYE: December 31

	REVENUE ($ mil.)	NET INCOME ($ mil.)	NET PROFIT MARGIN	EMPLOYEES
12/10	1,359	7	0.6%	66
12/09	1,205	2	0.2%	—
12/08	2,637	15	0.6%	—
Annual Growth	(28.2%)	(28.9%)	—	—

2010 Year-End Financials
Return on assets: 1.5% Cash ($ mil.): 8
Return on equity: 12.5%
Current ratio: 1.10

AAA COOPER TRANSPORTATION

AAA Cooper Transportation (ACT) is a trucking company offering freight hauling services primarily in the Southwest Southeast and Midwest. ACT offers less-than-truckload (LTL) hauling in 21 states (LTL carriers combine freight from multiple shippers into a single truckload). The company also offers freight brokerage services dedicated contract carriage and fleet maintenance services through 40 locations. The company's International Services division offers cross-border services to Canada and Mexico. ACT can also facilitate transportation in Puerto Rico and the US Virgin Islands. The company's fleet includes 3000 tractors and 6500 trailers.

Operations
The company's five primary service offerings are LTL Services dedicated services international services (including port services) managed services and fleet maintenance services.

Geographic Reach
Through more than 70 locations ACT offers less-than-truckload (LTL) hauling in 21 states. The company also facilitates transportation in Puerto Rico and the US Virgin Islands.

Strategy
As part of its growth strategy ACT seeks to offer new services. In 2019 the company debuted its Action Trac system that allows shippers to track their shipments via GPS. With Action Trac customers have increased visibility into shipments by receiving texts and emails alerting them of shipment pick-up transit status and estimated time of delivery.

Company Background
ACT was founded in 1955.

EXECUTIVES

President And Coo, Reid Dove
Cfo, Steve Roy
Director Dedicated Services, Charles (Charlie) Prickett
Vp Strategic Services, Lee McMillan
Vp Information Services, Dan Christian
Senior Vice President Finance, Mark Griffis
National Account Manager, Teresa Riggs
Vice President Enterprise Development, John Hammons
National Account Manager, Bob Mazzeffi
National Account Manager, Christopher Holden

LOCATIONS

HQ: AAA COOPER TRANSPORTATION 1751 KINSEY RD, DOTHAN, AL 363035877
Phone: 334 793-2284
Web: WWW.AAACOOPER.COM

PRODUCTS/OPERATIONS

Selected Services

Dedicated
 Company branding
 Specialized equipment
International LTL
LTL
Port
 Consolidation
 Drayage
 Transloading

COMPETITORS

ArcBest	Saia
Averitt Express	Southeastern Freight
Estes Express	Lines
FedEx Freight	UPS Freight
Old Dominion Freight	YRC Worldwide
R+L Carriers	

HISTORICAL FINANCIALS
Company Type: Private

Income Statement · FYE: December 31

	REVENUE ($ mil.)	NET INCOME ($ mil.)	NET PROFIT MARGIN	EMPLOYEES
12/17*	664	31	4.8%	4,933
01/17	592	17	3.0%	—
01/16	595	14	2.4%	—
12/14	576	20	3.5%	—
Annual Growth	4.8%	16.5%	—	—
*Fiscal year change				

2017 Year-End Financials
Return on assets: 8.0% Cash ($ mil.): —
Return on equity: 15.4%
Current ratio: 1.50

AARP

Turn 50 and the doors of the AARP will open for you as they have for nearly 38 million current members. On behalf of its members the not-for-profit AARP acts as an advocate on public policy issues such as health care and financial security publishes information (the monthly AARP Bulletin and the bimonthly AARP The Magazine and through Spanish language media) promotes community service and works with business partners to offer products and services (including discounts on insurance and travel). The group is organized into some 1300 local chapters throughout the US. Royalties from businesses eager to reach AARP members account for about half of the group's revenue.

Operations

It may not be the most exclusive club around but AARP is one of the most powerful. As the largest advocacy group in the US the organization has a loud voice on Capitol Hill in part because older Americans tend to vote in greater relative numbers than many other segments of the population. AARP through its Foundation organization is focused on the national budget Medicare elder abuse and Social Security. To this end the organization operates Government Watch an interactive website designed to allow older Americans to hold Congress and the President's administration accountable on key issues that affect them.

AARP oversees volunteer services as well. The AARP Experience Corps is for volunteers aged 50+ who want to tutor and mentor youth in their communities primarily literacy for children in kindergarten through third grade. It operates in nearly 20 cities across the country.

Geographic Reach

The organization boasts staffed offices in all 50 US states the District of Columbia Puerto Rico and the US Virgin Islands.

Financial Performance

AARP generates revenue from several sources including royalties from businesses that partner with it membership dues advertising and investment income. For the year 2016 AARP generated $1.6 billion in operating revenue up 4% from the previous year. Royalties (mainly from United Healthcare Corp.) totaled $880 million membership dues amounted to $300 million and advertising sales were $150 million.

As a non-profit AARP does not report net income or earnings but instead records a change in its net assets. For the year 2016 the change in net assets due to operating activities was $3.9 million well below the $47 million of the prior year. Despite higher operating revenues the agency spent enough additional monies on program services (community outreach publications & communications membership engagement) that it eroded the upward movement in sales.

Strategy

AARP in 2016 achieved notable marks for its constituents. Its policy arm helped pass caregiver legislation in 14 US states; it entered the national conversation about updating the US Social Security program with its Take a Stand campaign and helped 2.7 million taxpayers file tax returns free of charge through the AARP Foundation Tax-Aide.

The group has worked to attract baby boomers with its 50+ campaign in anticipation of the aging generation. AARP continues to advance its legislative agendas at the state and federal government levels championing policies that aid its older membership base. Such policies include safe & affordable housing senior hunger issues reconnecting families & communities and helping seniors attain a stable source of income.

It's programs and services through which it directly interacts with its members and communities includes: Back to Work 50+ Drive to End Hunger Experience Corps and Work for Yourself@50+.

Employers who engage in age discrimination are likely to hear from the AARP which joins several age discrimination cases each year. It is watching with interest cases against Google and Spirit AeroSystems. It recently helped resolve a lawsuit pertaining to Northrup Grumman's 401k plan.

AARP offers insurance through partnerships with Aetna and UnitedHealth Group. The AARP-branded products includes policies designed to supplement Medicare coverage and policies intended to cover people ages 50 to 64. Other insurance partners include New York Life Insurance and The Hartford Financial Services Group.

EXECUTIVES

Evp And Cfo, Robert R. Hagans
Ceo, Jo Ann C. Jenkins
Evp And President Life Reimagined, Emilio Pardo
Evp And Chief Of Staff, Kevin Donnellan
Evp State And National Group, Nancy A. LeaMond
President And Ceo Aarp Services Inc., John J. Wider
Evp Membership And Integrated Value, Steve Cone
Evp Multicultural Markets And Engagement, Lorraine Cortés-V zquez
Evp States And Communities, Harroll (Hop) Backus
Evp And Cio, Hollis (Terry) Bradwell
Evp Policy Strategy And International Affairs, Debra Whitman
President Aarp Foundation, Lisa M. Ryerson
Executive Vice President Of Media, Beth Ellard
Chief Operating Officer, Scott Frisch
Executive Vice President Chief Human Resources Officer, Richard Randazzo
Senior Vice President Editorial Director, Myrna Blyth
Senior Vice President Data Analytics And Performance Management, Jason Mugg
Vice President And National Director, Julie Lee
Vice President Quality And Compliance, Michael Lewis
Vice President, Sanjay Khurana
Vice President Distribution, John Minniti
Executive Vice President And General Counsel, Cindy Lewin
Senior Vice President And Senior Associate General Counsel, David Morales
Vice President Distribution Ne Region, James Bayer
Vice President Grants And External Initiatives, Marc Mcdonald
Senior Vice President Campaigns, John Hishta
Experience Corps. Rsvp Project Manager, Ellen Acevedo
Vice President, Mary Signorille
Vice President, Steve Delvecchio
Vice President Enterprise Performance Management, Walter Harris
Vice President, Daphne Kwok
Regional Vice President Central Region, Sarah Jennings
Vice President Financial Planning And Analysis, Chuck Ullan
Senior Vice President For Public, Susan Reinhard
Vice President Of Operations, Kathryn Tefft-Keller
Vice President My Home And Family Portfolio, Robert Stephen
Vice President Hispanic Latino Audience Strategy, Yvette Pena
Vice President, Margaret Mannix
2nd Vice President, Callie Herd
Vice President Talent Development, Donna Gupton
Vice President Associate General Counsel, Laurel Gillis
Vice President Secretary Treasurer, Lee W Hammond
Senior Vice President Aarp Experience, Jim Pendergast
Senior Vice President And Treasurer, Karen Mercer
Vice President Corporate And Foundation Relations, Stephen Venute
Senior Vice President Litigation, William Rivera
Senior Vice President Strategy And Innovation Aarp Serv, Kimberly Moorehead
Vice President Strategic Partnership Development And Relations, Shani Hosten
Senior Vice President, Jon Dauphine
Vice President Marketing, Stephen Driscoll
Vp Distribution Midwest Region, Bernie Buonanno
Chairman, Carol Raphael
Vice Chairman, Ronald E. Daly
Board Member Treasurer Administration Executive, Joan Ruff
Assistant Treasurer, Bill Hermann
Board Member, Jewell Hoover
Auditors: GRANT THORNTON LLP WASHINGTON

LOCATIONS

HQ: AARP
601 E ST NW, WASHINGTON, DC 200490003
Phone: 202 434-2277
Web: WWW.AARP.ORG

PRODUCTS/OPERATIONS

2016 sales

	$ mil.	% of total
Royalties	880	55
Membership dues	299	19
Publications advertising	150	9
Contributions	96	6
Grant	97	6
Program income	73	5
Other	5	-
Total	**1,603**	**100**

Selected Operations & Programs

AARP Bulletin (monthly news update)
AARP Driver Safety (classroom refresher)
AARP Foundation Experience Corps
AARP Legal Services Network
AARP Services (taxable product management marketing and e-commerce subsidiary)
AARP The Magazine (bimonthly magazine)
Back to Work 50+
Financial Planning
Public Policy Institute
Research Information Center
Senior Community Service Employment Program (SCSEP)
Tax-Aide

HISTORICAL FINANCIALS

Company Type: Private

Income Statement				FYE: December 31
	REVENUE ($ mil.)	NET INCOME ($ mil.)	NET PROFIT MARGIN	EMPLOYEES
12/17	1,643	279	17.0%	1,800
12/16	1,604	141	8.8%	—
12/14	1,399	84	6.0%	—
12/13	1,438	408	28.4%	—
Annual Growth	3.4%	(9.1%)	—	—

2017 Year-End Financials

Return on assets: 6.5% Cash ($ mil.): 460
Return on equity: 16.2%
Current ratio: —

ABINGTON MEMORIAL HOSPITAL INC

Abington Memorial Hospital brings health care to residents of southeastern Pennsylvania. The not-for-profit community hospital has some 670 beds. In addition to general medical and surgical care the hospital offers specialized care centers for cancer and cardiovascular conditions operates high-tech orthopedic and neurological surgery units and serves as a regional trauma care facility. It also runs an inpatient pediatric unit in affiliation with The Children's Hospital of Philadelphia. Abington Memorial also known as Abington Health operates the neighboring 125-bed Lansdale Hospital and several area outpatient facilities.

Operations

The not-for-profit community hospital has some 670 beds and employs about 1400 physicians. Its specialty units include the Pilla Heart Center the Rosenfeld Cancer Center the Diamond Stroke Center as well as a level II trauma center and institutes for senior health and bariatric surgeries. Abington Memorial is affiliated with several medical schools including the Temple University School of Medicine and offers residency programs and postgraduate medical education.

In addition to its hospitals Abington Memorial operates an extensive outpatient care facility named Abington Health Center-Warminster. The Warminster facility is located in Bucks County and features an inpatient hospice center. Other outpatient facilities include Abington Health Center-Schilling (in Willow Grove) Abington Health Center-Blue Bell and Abington Physicians at Montgomeryville.

Altogether the organization's facilities handle 677000 outpatient visits and 33000 inpatient admissions each year.

Additionally Abington Memorial operates a nursing school and a clinical research center.

Geographic Reach

Abington Memorial provides care to residents of southeastern Pennsylvania. The hospital serves Montgomery Bucks and Philadelphia counties.

Strategy

Abington Memorial began using the Abington Health moniker to reflect its larger network of facilities after it acquired Lansdale Hospital which was previously known as Central Montgomery Medical Center from Universal Health Services in 2008. Abington Memorial has since invested in a number of improvements at the acquired hospital. The main Abington Memorial facility has also been enhanced including a new hybrid operating room for cardiac procedures in 2013.

Mergers and Acquisitions

In 2013 Abington Memorial acquired a home health agency the North Penn Visiting Nurse Association (NPVNA). The purchase expanded the geographic reach of Abington Memorial's home health operations.

Company Background

Abington Memorial first opened its doors in 1914.

EXECUTIVES

President Abington Hospitals, Margaret M. (Meg) McGoldrick
Chief Medical Officer, John J. Kelly

LOCATIONS

HQ: ABINGTON MEMORIAL HOSPITAL INC
1200 OLD YORK RD, ABINGTON, PA 190013788
Phone: 215 481-2000

PRODUCTS/OPERATIONS

Selected Facilities

Abington Health Center — Blue Bell Campus (Blue Bell PA)
Abington Health Center — Schilling Campus (Willow Grove PA)
Abington Health Center — Warminster Campus (Warminster PA)
Abington Memorial Hospital (Abington PA)
Abington Physicians at Montgomeryville (North Wales PA)
Lansdale Hospital (Lansdale PA)

COMPETITORS

Albert Einstein Healthcare Network
Aria Health
Crozer-Keystone Health System
Doylestown Hospital
Grand View
Main Line Health System
Memorial Hospital (PA)
Mercy Health System
Moses Taylor Hospital
North Philadelphia Health System
TUHS
Tenet Healthcare
University of Pennsylvania Health System
Virtua Memorial

HISTORICAL FINANCIALS

Company Type: Private

Income Statement   FYE: June 30

	REVENUE ($ mil.)	NET INCOME ($ mil.)	NET PROFIT MARGIN	EMPLOYEES
06/16	740	35	4.8%	4,018
06/15	697	28	4.1%	—
06/14	697	0	0.1%	—
06/13	708	20	2.9%	—
Annual Growth	1.5%	19.2%	—	—

2016 Year-End Financials

Return on assets: 4.5%   Cash ($ mil.): 176
Return on equity: 87.7%
Current ratio: 2.00

ACCESS BUSINESS GROUP LLC

Somehow all those Amway products have to get from factories to the sales floor and that's where Access Business Group (ABG) comes in. The company manufactures and distributes cosmetics nutritional supplements home care and personal care products for its sister company Amway. (Both companies are units of Alticor.) It also offers contract manufacturing services for third-party consumer goods companies but to a lesser extent. Other offerings include product packaging services as well as catalog and direct mail printing services. In addition the company operates R&D labs that develop and test products for Amway.

Operations

A major function of ABG is the manufacturing and distribution of some 200 products in Amway's NUTRILITE line which includes nutritional food supplements in liquid powder food bar tablet and capsule form. Other key operations include manufacturing and distributing products in the ARTISTRY cosmetics and skin care line.

Geographic Reach

ABG owns and operates 10 manufacturing plants that comprise more than 1 million sq. ft. of space.

Sales and Marketing

The company offers its products through distributors and retailers both in North America and Internationally.

Strategy

Amway announced in 2012 it was investing nearly $180 million to expand manufacturing and processing capacity to meet growing global demand for its NUTRILITE brand of vitamin mineral and dietary supplements. The investment includes a new $81 million nutrition plant at the company's Spaulding Avenue site in Ada Michigan near Amway's headquarters. In support of this initiative the Michigan government has approved a $1.6 million incentive from a fund to support construction of this nutrition products manufacturing facility for ABG.

EXECUTIVES

Vice President Brand Management, Jackie Nickel
Vice President Contract Sales, Ed VanEssendelft

LOCATIONS

HQ: ACCESS BUSINESS GROUP LLC
7575 FULTON ST E, ADA, MI 493550001
Phone: 616 787-6000
Web: WWW.ACCESSBUSINESSGROUP.COM

PRODUCTS/OPERATIONS

Selected Services and Products

Beauty
Blushes
Eye shadows
Lipsticks
Mascara
Skin care
Fulfillment
A-Frame
B2B & B2C
Customized order picking at the store level
High volume pick pack & ship
Pick-to-light
Tilt tray sorter
Home Care
Household cleaners
Plastic bottles
Powder and liquid dish washing detergents
Powder and liquid laundry detergents
Nutrition
Antioxidants/supplements/herbals
Food bars
Granulation
Multiminerals/multivitamins
OTC tableting
Powdered drinks
Personal Care
Bar soaps
Bath oils
Body mist
Conditioners
Lotions
Plastic bottles
Shampoos
Shower gels
Styling products
Print
Catalogs
Corrugated cases
Fine printing
Labels
L-Boards
Paperboard packaging

COMPETITORS

AppTech	Pfizer
Berry Global	Procter & Gamble
Botanical Laboratories	Strathmore
Essential Nutrition	UPS Supply Chain
Johnson & Johnson	Solutions

Income Statement				FYE: December 31
	REVENUE ($ mil.)	NET INCOME ($ mil.)	NET PROFIT MARGIN	EMPLOYEES
12/15	1,009	0	—	3,000
12/14	1,068	0	—	—
12/13	1,135	0	—	—
Annual Growth	(5.7%)	—	—	—

ACE HARDWARE CORPORATION

In an age of big-box home improvement centers (Home Depot Lowes) wholesaler Ace makes the case for the local hardware store. By sales it is the leading hardware cooperative in the US. Ace dealer-owners operate more than 95% of the 5200 Ace Hardware-branded stores home centers and lumber and building materials locations selling more than 115000 products across the US and about 70 other countries. Ace also provides value-added services such as advertising market research merchandising assistance site location store format design retail training insurance and technology assistance. From about 25 warehouses Ace distributes such products as electrical and plumbing supplies garden equipment hand tools housewares and power tools. Ace was founded in 1924 by a group of Chicago hardware store owners.

HISTORY

A group of Chicago-area hardware dealers — William Stauber Richard Hesse Gern Lindquist and Oscar Fisher — decided in 1924 to pool their hardware buying and promotional costs. In 1928 the group incorporated as Ace Stores named in honor of the superior WWI fliers dubbed aces. Hesse became president the following year retaining that position for the next 44 years. The company also opened its first warehouse in 1929 and by 1933 it had 38 dealers.

The organization had 133 dealers in seven states by 1949. In 1953 Ace began to allow dealers to buy stock in the company through the Ace Perpetuation Plan. During the 1960s Ace expanded into the South and West and by 1969 it had opened distribution centers in Georgia and California — its first such facilities outside Chicago. In 1968 it opened its first international store in Guam.

By the early 1970s the do-it-yourself market began to surge as inflation pushed up plumber and electrician fees. As the market grew large home center chains gobbled up market share from independent dealers such as those franchised through Ace. In response Ace and its dealers became a part of a growing trend in the hardware industry — cooperatives.

Hesse sold the company to its dealers in 1973 for $6 million (less than half its book value) and the following year Ace began operating as a cooperative. Hesse stepped down in 1973. In 1976 the dealers took full control when the company's first Board of Dealer-Directors was elected.

After signing up a number of dealers in the eastern US Ace had dealers in all 50 states by 1979. The co-op opened a plant to make paint in Matteson Illinois in 1984. By 1985 Ace had reached $1 billion in sales and had initiated its Store of the Future Program allowing dealers to borrow up to $200000 to upgrade their stores and conduct market analyses. Former head coach John Madden of the National Football League's Oakland Raiders signed on as Ace's mouthpiece in 1988.

A year later the co-op began to test ACENET a computer network that allowed Ace dealers to check inventory send and receive e-mail make special purchase requests and keep up with prices on commodity items such as lumber. In 1990 Ace established an International Division to handle its overseas stores. (It had been exporting products since 1975.) EVP and COO David Hodnik became president in 1995. That year the co-op added a net of 67 stores including a three-store chain in Russia. Expanding further internationally Ace signed a five-year joint-supply agreement in 1996 with Canadian lumber and hardware retailer Beaver Lumber. Hodnik added CEO to his title in 1996.

Ace fell further behind its old rival True Value in 1997 when ServiStar Coast to Coast and True Value merged to form TruServ (renamed True Value in 2005) a hardware giant that operated more than 10000 outlets at the completion of the merger.

Late in 1997 Ace launched an expansion program in Canada. (The co-op already operated distribution centers in Ontario and Calgary.) In 1999 Ace merged its lumber and building materials division with Builder Marts of America to form a dealer-owned buying group to supply about 2700 retailers. Ace gained 208 member outlet stores in 2000 but saw 279 member outlets terminated. The next year it gained 220 but lost 255.

Sodisco-Howden bought all the shares of Ace Hardware Canada in February 2003. To better serve international members Ace opened its first international buying office in Hong Kong in April 2004.

In all the company added 131 new stores in 2005. That year after 33 years with the company David F. Hodnik retired as president and CEO of Ace Hardware. He was succeeded by COO Ray A. Griffith.

In 2007 Griffith sent a letter to Ace's retailers saying the company was considering changing from a cooperative to a traditional corporation to become more competitive and to better fuel growth. Shortly after the company announced an accounting shortfall of about $150 million or nearly half of its equity which was uncovered while Ace prepared to convert formats. The error turned out to be an accident by a mid-level employee.

In 2009 Ace launched Aisle411 a free product-location service that can be accessed via phone similar to dialing for information. The company launched the service after learning that shoppers who were unable to find a product either left (about 20% of the time) or asked store associates for assistance (about 60%) which created a high demand for staff attention. Dedicated to pleasing its shoppers Ace was ranked "Highest in Customer Satisfaction among Home Improvement Stores" by J.D. Power and Associates in 2007 2008 and 2009.

In mid-2010 the hardware store chain became the first retailer — outside of Sears and Kmart stores — to sell Craftsman brand tools.

In January 2011 the company reorganized its international division into a stand-alone entity: Ace Hardware International Holdings. Ace Hardware owns about 78% of the newly-created entity.

In December 2012 Ace exited the paint manufacturing business with the sale of its paint manufacturing division including two paint manufacturing plants near Chicago to Valspar Corp. for about $45 million. Under the terms of the sale Valspar will continue to make and supply Ace-branded paint under a long-term supply agreement. Also it will supply a comprehensive line of Valspar-branded paints to Ace retail stores.

EXECUTIVES

President And Ceo, John S. Venhuizen, age 49
Vp Information Technology And Cio, Karen Fedyszyn
Evp Cfo And Chief Risk Officer, Bill Guzik
Vice President Merchandising, Frank Carroll
Associate Vice President, James Mallaney
Svp Of Marketing, Brian Wyborg
Vice President Of Marketing, Brian Wiborg
Vice President Of Merchandising And Vice President Of Finance, Lori Bossmann
Vice President Of Information Technology, Alan Sommer
Vice President, Dale Ganz
Vp Retail Operations And New Business, John Tovar
Svp And Chief Marketing Officer, Kim Lefko
Vice President Of Merchandising, John Sommers
Vice President Secretary, Tim Novac
Vice President, Ken Nicholas
Chairman, Jim Ackroyd
Auditors: ERNST & YOUNG LLP CHICAGO IL

LOCATIONS

HQ: ACE HARDWARE CORPORATION
2200 KENSINGTON CT, OAK BROOK, IL 605232100
Phone: 630 368-3393

PRODUCTS/OPERATIONS

2014 Sales

	$ mil.	% of total
Wholesale Revenues	4,466	95
Retail Revenues	233	5
Total	**4,700**	**100**

Selected Services

AssemblyAutomotive chip key cutting
Blade sharpening
Glass & Acrylic sheet cutting
Glass Repair
Hunting/Fishing license
In-store lock servicing
Selected Brands
ACCO BRANDS
ACE
ACME
ADANAC
BIG BEN
BILCO
EUREKA
EVEREADY

COMPETITORS

84 Lumber	McCoy Corp.
Akzo Nobel	Menard
BMC Stock	Northern Tool
Costco Wholesale	Orgill
Do it Best	Sears
Fastenal	Sutherland Lumber
Grossman's	True Value
Home Depot	United Hardware
Kmart	Distributing
Lowe's	Wal-Mart

HISTORICAL FINANCIALS
Company Type: Private

Income Statement				FYE: December 30
	REVENUE ($ mil.)	NET INCOME ($ mil.)	NET PROFIT MARGIN	EMPLOYEES
12/17	5,388	147	2.7%	4,500
12/16*	5,125	161	3.1%	—
01/16	5,045	156	3.1%	—
01/15	4,700	141	3.0%	—
Annual Growth	4.7%	1.4%	—	—
*Fiscal year change				

2017 Year-End Financials

Return on assets: 7.9%   Cash ($ mil.): 23
Return on equity: 26.3%
Current ratio: 1.30

ACTION CAPITAL CORPORATION

EXECUTIVES

Ceo, Becky J Cronister
V Pres, Patrick Thom
Cfo, John J Canning
Stckhldr, Cicero Garner
Stckhldr, Hugh Inman Jr
Executive Vice President, Brendan Dete
Chief Financial Officer, John Canning
Senior Vice President, Blake Kennedy
Account Specialist, Bridgett Kelley
Administrator Executive, Michael Montgomery
Auditors: MCGREGOR & COMPANY LLP COLUMB

LOCATIONS

HQ: ACTION CAPITAL CORPORATION
  230 PEACHTREE ST NW # 810, ATLANTA, GA
  303031568
Phone: 404 524-3181
Web: WWW.ACTIONCAPITAL.COM

HISTORICAL FINANCIALS

Company Type: Private

Income Statement

FYE: December 31

	ASSETS ($ mil.)	NET INCOME ($ mil.)	INCOME AS % OF ASSETS	EMPLOYEES
12/17	170	6	3.8%	17
12/16	146	4	3.0%	—
12/15	140	6	4.3%	—
12/14	128	5	4.6%	—
Annual Growth	9.8%	3.5%	—	—

2017 Year-End Financials

Return on assets: 3.8%   Sales ($ mil): 1,539
Return on equity: 23.6%

ADENA HEALTH SYSTEM

Adena Health System serves the residents of about a dozen counties in south and south-central Ohio centered on the city of Chillicothe. Its main facility is the 261-bed Adena Regional Medical Center which provides general medical and surgical care as well as specialty care in a number of areas including cardiology women's health oncology and rehabilitation. The not-for-profit health system also features two smaller hospitals six regional clinics surgery centers and a counseling center among other facilities. The history of the Adena Health System goes back to 1895 when a group of local women established an emergency hospital in the wake of a fatal train wreck.

Operations

Adena Health System facilities include three hospitals (located in Chillicothe Waverly and Greenfield) and six regional clinics with a total of 311 beds. Other facilities include Adena Cancer Center Adena Home Care and Hospice and Adena Rehabilitation and Wellness Center. The system also has a number of primary care physician offices in its service area.

Adena has partnered with Ohio University — Chillicothe to provide medical training. The program hosts physicians serving their internships and residencies and in 2016 it graduated its first class of Bachelors-prepared nurses.

Each year Adena serves roughly 105000 patients at its three hospitals.

Geographic Reach

Adena Health serves patients in southern and south-central Ohio. Its focus lies in improving community health in the counties of Ross Highland Pike Jackson Fayette Pickaway and Vinton.

Financial Performance

Adena Health's revenue increased 10% to $1.3 billion in fiscal 2016. This was primarily due to a 10% increase in billed patient services but the company's investment income (just 2% of total revenue) also doubled that year. Funds available after deductions such as charity care federal program discounts and bad debt totaled $448 million a 1% increase from the prior year.

Strategy

To stay competitive and remain independent Adena Health is always looking to expand its offerings improve existing sites and add new locations. For example it has committed $36 million to renovate and expand its flagship hospital's emergency department. The project which is expected to be complete in 2019 will triple the facility's size. Recent developments include the opening of a family medicine clinic in Wellston the opening of a health center in Hillsboro and the expansion of its Circleville Health Center (which also gained a new after-hours and walk-in clinic).

Much in line with the health care industry's move to a value-based methodology Adena has begun training its leaders to operate under a patient-centric model. The initiative's first areas of focus are Progression of Care (the patient's care journey from entry through discharge) and Patient safety.

The health system has done well financially with multiple years of stable performance and liquidity. It does run some risk due to its heavy reliance on government payers and some volatility in patient volumes.

EXECUTIVES

Division Chair Womenâ's And Childrenâ's, Sathish Jetty
Vp Adena Regional Medical Center, Nick Alexander
Coo, Eric Cecava
Interim Cfo, Lisa Carlson
Interim Cio, Ryan Mountjoy
Chief Nursing Officer, Kathleen Dye
Medical Director Adena Cancer Center, Alex Wilson
President And Ceo, Jeffrey J. Graham
Nursing Director, Bev Tolle
Director Of Radiology Services, Dave Zanni
Vice President Of Revenue Cycle, Michael Rhodes
Nursing Director Critical Care Services, Cammy Gilbert
Senior Vice President Information Technology Services, Saldana Tina
Chairman, Steve Burkhardt
Vice Chairman, Virginia Wettersten
Secretary Assistant, Ralph Metzger
Pca Unit Secretary, Kelli Fultz
Auditors: PLANTE & MORAN PLLC COLUMBUS

LOCATIONS

HQ: ADENA HEALTH SYSTEM
  272 HOSPITAL RD STE 4, CHILLICOTHE, OH
  456019031
Phone: 740 779-7500
Web: WWW.ADENA.ORG

PRODUCTS/OPERATIONS

Selected Services

Behavioral Health
Colon and Rectal Services
Endocrinology and Diabetes
Endoscopy Home Care
Hospitalist Laboratory
Occupational Health
Pain Management
Radiology
Rehabilitation Services
Sleep Urology
Surgery and Procedures
Wound Care

Selected Facilities

Adena Counseling Center (Chillicothe)
Adena Health Center - Jackson
Adena Health Center - Oak Hill
Adena Health Center - Waverly
Adena Health Center - Western Avenue (Chillicothe)
Adena Health Pavilion (Chillicothe)
Adena Home Care Services (Chillicothe)
Adena Pike Medical Center (Waverly)
Adena Medical Office Building (Chillicothe)
Adena Regional Medical Center (Chillicothe)
Adena Rehabilitation & Wellness Center (Chillicothe)
Adena Urgent Care Centers (Chillicothe and Waverly)
Greenfield Area Medical Center

COMPETITORS

Catholic Health Initiatives
Fairfield Medical Center
Licking Memorial Health Systems
Mount Carmel Health
Nationwide Children's Hospital
OhioHealth

HISTORICAL FINANCIALS

Company Type: Private

Income Statement

FYE: December 31

	REVENUE ($ mil.)	NET INCOME ($ mil.)	NET PROFIT MARGIN	EMPLOYEES
12/17*	470	29	6.3%	3,000
03/17	111	10	9.7%	—
12/15	393	11	3.0%	—
12/14	394	14	3.7%	—
Annual Growth	6.0%	26.6%	—	—

*Fiscal year change

2017 Year-End Financials

Return on assets: 4.9%   Cash ($ mil.): 28
Return on equity: 9.1%
Current ratio: 1.60

ADVANCED TECHNOLOGY INTERNATIONAL

EXECUTIVES

Pres, Chris Van Metre
Treas*, Julia Martin
Administrative Assistant, Amanda Ballou

Scientist, Gerry Graves
Program Manager, Mike Atkinson
Purchasing Administrator, Dee Green
Senior Project Manager, Jenny Swygert
Vlc Chief Administrative Offic, Morgan Odonnell
Technical Director Advanced Te, Nick Melillo
Senior Program Manager, Dick Tiano
Senior Program Manager, Jim Welborn
Auditors: BDO USA LLP RALEIGH NC

LOCATIONS

HQ: ADVANCED TECHNOLOGY INTERNATIONAL
315 SIGMA DR, SUMMERVILLE, SC 294867790
Phone: 843 760-4500
Web: WWW.ATI.ORG

HISTORICAL FINANCIALS

Company Type: Private

Income Statement				FYE: September 30
	REVENUE ($ mil.)	NET INCOME ($ mil.)	NET PROFIT MARGIN	EMPLOYEES
09/18	1,190	0	0.1%	117
09/17*	718	(11)	—	—
06/16	423	(2)	—	—
06/15	385	1	0.4%	—
Annual Growth	45.7%	(14.6%)	—	—

*Fiscal year change

2018 Year-End Financials

Return on assets: 0.1%   Cash ($ mil.): 464
Return on equity: 12.6%
Current ratio: 1.00

ADVENTIST HEALTH SYSTEM SUNBELT HEALTHCARE CORPORATION

EXECUTIVES

Pres, Donald Jernigan
V Pres, Robert Henderschedt
Coordinator, Pennie Moore
Administration Assisant, Almeda Tyren
Regional Laboratory Administra, Dhobie Wong
Information Security, Teresa Majors
Physician, Wasim Ahmar
Physician, Wynn Sullivan
Vice President, Barbara Flynn
Admin Director Strategic Plann, Belinda Grant
Prin, Daniel Nassar

LOCATIONS

HQ: ADVENTIST HEALTH SYSTEM SUNBELT
HEALTHCARE CORPORATION
900 HOPE WAY, ALTAMONTE SPRINGS, FL
327141502
Phone: 407 357-1000
Web: WWW.ADVENTHEALTH.COM

HISTORICAL FINANCIALS

Company Type: Private

Income Statement				FYE: December 31
	REVENUE ($ mil.)	NET INCOME ($ mil.)	NET PROFIT MARGIN	EMPLOYEES
12/18	10,974	635	5.8%	78,000
12/17	10,083	1,167	11.6%	—
12/16	9,651	806	8.4%	—
12/14	519	26	5.1%	—
Annual Growth	114.4%	121.7%		

2018 Year-End Financials

Return on assets: 4.0%   Cash ($ mil.): 576
Return on equity: 6.2%
Current ratio: 3.60

ADVENTIST HEALTH SYSTEM/WEST

Not content to wait around for the advent of good health Adventist Health System/West operates about 20 hospitals in the western US. Its health care facilities sprinkled throughout California Hawaii Oregon and Washington also include more than 260 physicians' clinics. Additionally the not-for-profit organization runs more than a dozen home health care agencies and a handful of retirement centers. The system has more than 5000 physicians on staff. Adventist Health maintains strong ties to the Seventh-day Adventist Church but is independently owned. A sister organization Adventist Health System operates in the central and southern parts of the country.

Operations

Adventist Health System/West works with its own churches and those of other denominations to offer such preventive health services as medical screenings immunizations and health education. The majority of Adventist Health's acute care hospitals are concentrated in California with the rest scattered throughout Hawaii Oregon and Washington. The system's nearly 300 clinics vary from small one or two provider offices to large facilities with primary care specialty medical services dental behavioral health perinatal and other services. Other facilities include home care agencies and four retirement centers.

Annually Adventist Health System/West has more than 150000 admissions 685000 emergency department visits and 2.9 million outpatient visits.

Geographic Reach

Adventist Health System/West serve patients throughout California Hawaii and Oregon. It also has a retirement center in Washington.

Financial Performance

In fiscal 2016 Adventist Health System/west received $3.95 billion in net revenue including patient care income and other sources of income. Its operating expenses totaled $3.77 billion that year.

Strategy

Adventist Health System/West often partners with others including organizations related to the Seventh-day Adventist church to enhance and grow its health care offerings. In early 2018 for example it joined forces with another not-for-profit health system Rideout Health (which operates acute care hospital Rideout Regional Medical Center). The partners aim to improve the wellness of California's Yuba City/Marysville community by providing expanded health care services.

EXECUTIVES

Vice President Clinical Effectiveness, Keith R Doram
Svp And Cfo, Jack W. Wagner
President And Ceo Southern California Region, Beth D. Zachary
President And Ceo, Scott Reiner
President And Ceo Central California Region, Wayne Ferch
President And Ceo Northern California Region, Jeff Eller
President And Ceo Northwest Region, Joyce Newmyer
Evp And Coo, Bill Wing
Vice President Cno, Gloria Bancarz
Vice President Finance, Dale Northorp
Vice President, John G Raffoul
Senior Vice President, Kirby McKague
Vice President Of Finance, Carlton Jacobson
Vice President And General Counsel, Meredith Jobe
Regional Vice President Of Marketing St Helena Adventist Health, Joshua Cowan
Vice President Information Technology, Harry Janke
Assistant Vice President Corporate Compliance Officer, Kevin Longo
Vice President, Janae Bowles
Senior Vice President, James Brewster
Assistant Vice President Marketing And Communications, Maureen Wisener
Vice President Plan Operations And Market Development, Dan Rhodes
Vp Mission Integration, Dustin Aho
Vice President Of Advocacy And Public Policy, Michael Griffin
Vice President Human Resources, Don Jones
Vice President Of Treasury, Jeffrey Graff
Secretary, Kirk Iverson

LOCATIONS

HQ: ADVENTIST HEALTH SYSTEM/WEST
1 ADVENTIST HEALTH WAY, ROSEVILLE, CA
956613898
Phone: 844 574-5686

COMPETITORS

Community Health Systems	Providence St. Joseph Health
Dignity Health	Queen's Medical Center
HCA	Shasta Regional Medical Center
Hawai'i Pacific Health	
John Muir Health	Sisters of Charity of Leavenworth
Kuakini Health System	
Legacy Health System	Stanford Health Care
LifePoint Health	Sutter Health
Memorial Health Services	Tenet Healthcare
	UCSF Medical

HISTORICAL FINANCIALS

Company Type: Private

Income Statement				FYE: December 31
	REVENUE ($ mil.)	NET INCOME ($ mil.)	NET PROFIT MARGIN	EMPLOYEES
12/17	4,114	199	4.9%	19,512
12/16	3,945	185	4.7%	—
12/15	251	10	4.3%	—
12/14	3,262	133	4.1%	—
Annual Growth	8.0%	14.3%	—	—

2017 Year-End Financials

Return on assets: 4.0%   Cash ($ mil.): 728
Return on equity: 8.6%
Current ratio: 2.90

ADVENTIST HEALTHCARE, INC.

From the newest newborn to the most senior senior Adventist HealthCare takes care of residents in the Washington DC region. The not-for-profit system with more than 1700 physicians and medical providers is home to two acute care hospitals two specialty hospitals and dozens of specialty clinics urgent care clinics and medical offices. Its acute care hospitals are Adventist HealthCare Shady Grove Medical Center and Adventist HealthCare Washington Adventist Hospital. Adventist Health-Care which is affiliated with the Seventh-day Adventist Church has been in operation since 1907.

Operations

Adventist HealthCare's Lourie Center for Children's Social & Emotional Wellness promotes the emotional health of parent-child relations through education training research early prevention and intervention. Its offerings include an early head start program to benefit low-income families parent-child programs a therapeutic nursery and the state-approved Lourie Center School a non-public elementary school for children with emotional and multiple disabilities. Another system school The Ridge School of the Eastern Shore provides general and special education to adolescents with emotional learning or behavioral health problems.

Additionally Adventist provides employee assistance programs and behavioral health and wellness services through its LifeWork Strategies subsidiaries.

The system has about 110000 emergency visits 424000 outpatient visits and delivers some 7000 babies a year.

Geographic Reach

Adventist HealthCare operates facilities in Maryland northwestern New Jersey and Washington DC. Its home health agencies operate throughout much of Maryland and parts of Washington DC.

Strategy

Adventist HealthCare is focused on physician integration and providing greater access to health care based on needs at the community level. Collaboration is part of a larger consolidation trend among the industry in order to strengthen all health care organizations financially and geographically.

The system is moving its Washington Adventist Hospital to an integrated campus currently under construction in White Oak Maryland. The new campus expected to open in 2019 will feature 170 beds in a seven-story building. It will be renamed Adventist HealthCare White Oak Medical Center.

The network is also taking measures to operate more efficiently and effectively by eliminating processes that are unnecessary and adopting green practices to lower energy costs.

EXECUTIVES

President Adventist Healthcare Behavioral Health And Wellness Services, Kevin Young
President And Ceo, Terry Forde
Evp And Coo; President Adventist Healthcare Shady Grove Medical Center, John Sackett
Evp And Cfo, James G. Lee
Vp Public Relations And Marketing, Thomas Grant
Vp And Cio, Christopher Ghion
President Adventist Healthcare Washington Adventist Hospital, Erik Wangsness
Svp Physician Integration Strategy; President Adventist Medical Group, Patrick Garrett
Senior Vice President And Chief Human Resources Officer, Marta Perez
Vice President, Kristen Pulio
Radiology Director, Mike Calhoun
Vice President Of Operations, David Smith
Vice President And Chief Medical Officer, Kevin Smothers
Vice President Mission And Spiritual Care, Ann Roda
Director Of Clinical Services, Jason Martin
Associate Vice President Managed Care, Kelli Forbes
Senior Vp, Marta Brito Perez
Vice President Chief Nursing Officer (cno), Mary Murphy
Trustee, David E. Weigley
Vice Chairman, Robert T. Vandeman
Secretary Ii, Diane Snider
Unit Secretary, Etta Coates
Unit Secretary, Swazenne Drew
Secretary Facilities Management, Malissa Clements
Auditors: BAKER TILLY VIRCHOW KRAUSE L

LOCATIONS

HQ: ADVENTIST HEALTHCARE, INC.
820 W DIAMOND AVE STE 600, GAITHERSBURG, MD 208781469
Phone: 301 315-3030

PRODUCTS/OPERATIONS

Selected Home Health Services
Nursing and Home Health
 Adult nursing
 Diabetes management
 Maternal/child care
 Nutrition management
 Pediatric nursing
 Personal care
 Pre- and post-op care
 Rehabilitation
 Wound care
Home Assistance
 Laundry and linens
 Light housekeeping
 Meal preparation
 Medication reminders
 Personal care

COMPETITORS

Bon Secours Health	Johns Hopkins Health
Calvert Memorial	System
Hospital	MedStar Health
Dimensions Healthcare	Trinity Health (Novi)
Frederick Memorial	University of Maryland
GBMC	Medical System

HISTORICAL FINANCIALS
Company Type: Private

Income Statement				FYE: December 31
	REVENUE ($ mil.)	NET INCOME ($ mil.)	NET PROFIT MARGIN	EMPLOYEES
12/18	820	21	2.6%	5,236
12/17	723	31	4.4%	—
12/16	779	0	0.1%	—
12/14	695	11	1.6%	—
Annual Growth	4.2%	17.7%	—	—

2018 Year-End Financials
Return on assets: 1.7%   Cash ($ mil.): 41
Return on equity: 4.8%
Current ratio: 2.20

ADVOCATE HEALTH AND HOSPITALS CORPORATION

EXECUTIVES

Pres, James H Skogsbergh
Vp, Patricia Smith-Calascibetta
Manager Clinical Engineering T, Steven Vanderzee
Director of Professional Devel, Linda Plewniak
Site Compliance Officer, Shelly Carling
Social Worker, Alberto Godinez
Data Design, Aleksandar Aleksic
Manager Tax Accounting, Amanda Kabat
Manager, Amy Cerny
Supervisor, Damir Radisic
Rn, Elizabeth Wilson
Auditors: ERNST & YOUNG US LLP CHICAGO

LOCATIONS

HQ: ADVOCATE HEALTH AND HOSPITALS CORPORATION
3075 HIGHLAND PKWY, DOWNERS GROVE, IL 605151288
Phone: 630 572-9393
Web: WWW.ADVOCATEGIVING.ORG

HISTORICAL FINANCIALS
Company Type: Private

Income Statement				FYE: December 31
	REVENUE ($ mil.)	NET INCOME ($ mil.)	NET PROFIT MARGIN	EMPLOYEES
12/17	5,310	243	4.6%	4,110
12/13	4,072	392	9.6%	—
12/12	3,645	419	11.5%	—
12/01	2,014	114	5.7%	—
Annual Growth	6.2%	4.8%	—	—

2017 Year-End Financials
Return on assets: 2.9%   Cash ($ mil.): 229
Return on equity: 4.8%
Current ratio: 0.50

ADVOCATE HEALTH AND HOSPITALS CORPORATION

Advocate Lutheran General Hospital also known simply as Lutheran General provides acute and long-term medical and surgical care to the residents of Park Ridge Illinois and the surrounding northern suburban Chicago area. As one of the largest hospitals in the region Lutheran General boasts nearly 640 beds and a Level I trauma center. Its operations also include a complete children's hospital and pediatric critical care center. Lutheran General serves as a teaching hospital and its specialized programs include oncology cardiology women's health emergency medicine and hospice care. Lutheran General is part of the Advocate Health Care network.

Operations

Lutheran General the sixth largest hospital in the Chicago area is a not-for-profit faith-based organization related to the Evangelical Lutheran Church in America and the United Church of Christ. With some 1150 physicians representing more than 50 specialties and subspecialties Advocate Lutheran General saw 62500 patients in its emergency department in 2012.

That year the company reported more than 29000 admissions 19000 surgeries and more than 4000 births.

Geographic Reach
The hospital system is the primary academic referral hospital for northwest Chicago and north Greater Chicago.

Strategy
Increase its services to meet specific demographics in 2012 Lutheran General opened a new South Asian Cardiovascular Center in the Midwest; it also launched Expressions a program aimed at helping seniors in the early stages of Alzheimer's disease.

That year thee hospital introduced a new Pet Therapy program to the Adult Oncology unit. It also launched of its neuroendovascular program to expand Lutheran General's acute stroke care to provide advanced acute stroke care to patients throughout the northern Chicago area.

Company Background
Lutheran General serves those who live in the northern suburban Chicago area specifically Park Ridge Illinois.

The hospital was founded in 1897.

EXECUTIVES

Secretary, Howard Baitcher
Secretary, Silvia De La Roca

LOCATIONS

HQ: ADVOCATE HEALTH AND HOSPITALS CORPORATION
1775 DEMPSTER ST, PARK RIDGE, IL 600681143
Phone: 847 723-6610
Web: WWW.ADVOCATEHEALTH.COM

Selected Hospitals
Advocate BroMenn Medical Center
Advocate Children's Hospital - Oak Lawn
Advocate Children's Hospital - Park Ridge
Advocate Christ Center for Breast Care
Advocate Christ Medical Center
Advocate Christ Medical Center - Physical Rehabilitation Center Center for Hearing and Sleep Center
Advocate Christ Outpatient Center
Advocate C
Advocate Condell Medical Center
Advocate Eureka Hospital
Advocate Good Samaritan Hospital
Advocate Good Shepherd Hospital
Advocate Illinois Masonic Medical Center
Advocate Lutheran General Hospital
Advocate South Suburban Hospital
Advocate Trinity Hospital

PRODUCTS/OPERATIONS

Selected Services
Adult Day Hospital
Adult Down Syndrome Center
Anticoagulation Center
Behavioral Health
Caldwell Breast Center
Cancer Care
Center for Fetal Care
Children's Services
The Comprehensive Continence Center
Emergency Services
Heart and Vascular
Hyperbaric Treatment
Interventional Radiology
Joint Reconstruction & Replacement
Nutrition Services Opthamology
Outpatient Testing Prep Instructions
Pain Management Center
Rehabilitation
Senior Services
Sleep Disorders
Surgical Services

The Center for Robotic Surgery
Women's Services
Wound Care

COMPETITORS

Children's Hopsital of Chicago
Gottleib Memorial Hospital
NorthShore University HealthSystem
Northwest Community Healthcare
Northwestern Lake Forest Hospital
Northwestern Memorial HealthCare
Rush System for Health
University of Chicago Medical Center

HISTORICAL FINANCIALS
Company Type: Private

Income Statement

	REVENUE ($ mil.)	NET INCOME ($ mil.)	NET PROFIT MARGIN	EMPLOYEES
			FYE: December 31	
12/15	5,392	60	1.1%	25,000
12/06	3,268	286	8.8%	—
12/05	2,973	140	4.7%	—
12/04	2,779	143	5.2%	—
Annual Growth	6.2%	(7.6%)	—	—

2015 Year-End Financials
Return on assets: 0.6%
Return on equity: 1.1%
Current ratio: 0.90
Cash ($ mil.): 203

ADVOCATE HEALTH CARE NETWORK

EXECUTIVES

Ceo-Pres, James H Skogsbergh
Director of Practice Acquisiti, Brian Rust
Administrative Assistant, Gail Michalski
Human Resources Consultant, Irma Martinez
Finance Manager Payroll and, Lynn Bicknase
Analyst 1 AMG Information Syst, Merilee Nielsen
Director of Claims Risk Manage, Sue Bujold-Lee
Physician, Alma Buckner
Director Hospitalist, Ana Nowell
Director of Practice Managemen, Angela Luridas
Business Office Associate II C, Brandi Archer
Auditors: ERNST & YOUNG LLP CHICAGO IL

LOCATIONS

HQ: ADVOCATE HEALTH CARE NETWORK
3075 HIGHLAND PKWY FL 6, DOWNERS GROVE, IL 605155563
Phone: 630 572-9393
Web: WWW.ADVOCATEHEALTH.COM

HISTORICAL FINANCIALS
Company Type: Private

Income Statement

	REVENUE ($ mil.)	NET INCOME ($ mil.)	NET PROFIT MARGIN	EMPLOYEES
			FYE: December 31	
12/17	790	79	10.0%	4,818
12/16	785	118	15.1%	—
12/15	752	104	13.9%	—
12/14	741	107	14.5%	—
Annual Growth	2.1%	(9.6%)	—	—

2017 Year-End Financials
Return on assets: 0.9%
Return on equity: 1.6%
Current ratio: 1.00
Cash ($ mil.): 229

AEROTEK, INC.

Aerotek a unit of staffing powerhouse Allegis Group offers commercial and technical staffing services throughout North America Europe and Asia Pacific. Through several divisions Aerotek staffs workers such as engineers mechanics scientists and technical professionals as well as administrative staff members general laborers and tradespeople. The company also provides training and support services. Along with aerospace auto and engineering companies Aerotek's clients include companies from the construction energy manufacturing health care and finance industries.

Operations
Aerotek solutions include staffing services workforce management engineering support and government services. Its staffing services provide short-term seasonal high-volume and niche contract support. It also offers contract-to-hire talent for project-based positions with the option to hire contractors as permanent employees.

Workforce management services comprise customized support for complex projects and business lines with specific timelines. Sciences support includes clinical and lab services across a range of industries through various delivery models. Aerotek also provides support and services to the government and government subcontractors with capabilities focused on contracts security compliance business development program management and finance.

Geographic Reach
Aerotek is headquartered in Hanover MD. The company has office locations in Asia Pacific (Australia Hong Kong China and Japan) Europe (Belgium France Germany Netherlands Sweden and UK) and North America (Canada and the US). Aerotek also operates a network of more than 250 non-franchised offices.

Sales and Marketing
Aerotek serves a wide variety of industries more than 18000 clients and 300000 contract employees every year.

Strategy
Aerotek has expanded its operations over the years through organic growth and acquisitions especially in niche markets such as the biotechnology health care clinical research chemical and plastics sectors. Despite economic ups and downs demand within these industries has been consistent along with engineering. Aerotek has also widened its client focus to include minority and woman-owned companies.

Company Background
Aerotek was founded in 1983 in Baltimore MD by entrepreneurs Steve Bisciotti and Jim Davis. It got its start by providing engineering staffing for the aerospace and defense industries and later for automotive manufacturers and suppliers. In 1990 the company formed Telecommunications Services now known as TEKsystems which has been recognized as the top information technology staffing firm in the US by the IT Services Business Report.

In 1993 Aerotek acquired Onsite Engineering & Management focused on environmental and energy services staffing. It later branched out to include staffing for other industries including biotechnology pharmaceuticals healthcare light industrial and light technical. It opened its first European office in 1993 and two years later expanded into Canada with an office in Mississauga Ontario.

In 1998 Allegis Group was formed as the parent entity of several operating companies including Aerotek TEKsystems and Onsite. In 2001 Aerotek and Onsite merged to become Onsite Companies and in 2004 Onsite Companies changed its name to Aerotek Inc. to leverage the reputation of the Aerotek name.

EXECUTIVES

Vp Technical And Professional Services, Mark Cooper
President, Todd M. Mohr
Cfo, Thomas B. (Tom) Kelly
Svp Operations, John Flanigan
Regional Vp Northeast, John Rudy
Regional Vp Midwest, Marty Schager
Regional Vp Central, Mike Hansen
Regional Vp West, Tony Bartolucci
Regional Vp Northwest, Brooks Wells
Vp Canada, Bryan Toffey
Regional Vp Southwest, Brad Kennedy
Regional Vp Mid-atlantic, Jeff Colvin
Regional Vp Southeast, Greg Jones
Vice President Client Delivery, Vinayak Nayak
Vice President Of Finance, James Mann
Regional Vice President, Anthony Bartolucci
Auditors: PRICEWATERHOUSECOOPERS LLP B

LOCATIONS

HQ: AEROTEK, INC.
7301 PARKWAY DR, HANOVER, MD 210761159
Phone: 410 694-5100
Web: WWW.AEROTEK.COM

PRODUCTS/OPERATIONS

INDUSTRIES SERVED

Accounting
Administrative & Support Services
Aerospace Aviation & Defense
Architecture & Design
Automotive
Construction
Customer Service
Energy & Utilities
Engineering
Environmental
Financial Services
Government & Public Administration
Healthcare
Manufacturing
Pharmaceutical
Sciences
Warehouse & Distribution

COMPETITORS

AMN Healthcare	Kforce
Adecco	MSX International
Bryant Bureau	ManpowerGroup
CDI	On Assignment
COMFORCE	Pinnacle Staffing
Insight Global	Randstad Holding
Integrity Staffing	Robert Half
Kelly Services	Roth Staffing

HISTORICAL FINANCIALS
Company Type: Private

Income Statement				FYE: December 31
	REVENUE ($ mil.)	NET INCOME ($ mil.)	NET PROFIT MARGIN	EMPLOYEES
12/17	6,070	0	—	4,200
12/16	5,565	0	—	—
12/15	5,492	0	—	—
12/14	5,353	0	—	—
Annual Growth	4.3%	—	—	—

2017 Year-End Financials
Return on assets: —   Cash ($ mil.): 8
Return on equity: —
Current ratio: 3.50

AFFILIATED FOODS MIDWEST COOPERATIVE, INC.

Affiliated Foods Midwest Cooperative is a wholesale food distribution cooperative that supplies more than 800 independent grocers in some 15 states in the Midwest. From its handful of distribution centers in Kansas Nebraska and Wisconsin the co-op distributes fresh produce meats deli items baked goods dairy products and frozen foods as well as general merchandise and equipment. It distributes goods under the Shurfine brand (from Topco Associates) and IGA labels. Additionally Affiliated Foods Midwest provides marketing merchandising and warehousing support services for its members. The cooperative was formed in 1931 to make wholesale purchases for a group of retailers in Nebraska.

Geographic Reach
Norfolk Nebraska-based Affiliated Foods Midwest Cooperative has distribution centers in Norfolk Elwood Kansas and Kenosha Wisconsin. It serves customers in 15 states across the Midwest.

Financial Performance
Affiliated Foods Midwest rang up an estimated $1.6 billion in sales in fiscal 2013 (ended June).

Auditors: BKD LLP LINCOLN NEBRASKA

LOCATIONS

HQ: AFFILIATED FOODS MIDWEST COOPERATIVE, INC.
1301 W OMAHA AVE, NORFOLK, NE 687015872
Phone: 402 371-0555
Web: WWW.AFMIDWEST.COM

PRODUCTS/OPERATIONS

Selected Private-Label Brands

CharKing
ChuckWagon (pet food)
Clear Value
Cow Belle Creamery (ice cream)
Domestix (household products)
Full Circle (organic natural products)
IGA
PAWS Premium (pet products)
Shurfine
TopCare (OTC drugs health and beauty)
Valu Time
Wide Awake Coffee Co. (coffee)
World Classics Trading Company

COMPETITORS

Associated Wholesale Grocers	Kroger
C&S Wholesale	McLane
Central Grocers	SUPERVALU
Certco	Wal-Mart
Dearborn Wholesale Grocers	

HISTORICAL FINANCIALS
Company Type: Private

Income Statement				FYE: June 26
	REVENUE ($ mil.)	NET INCOME ($ mil.)	NET PROFIT MARGIN	EMPLOYEES
06/15	1,527	1	0.1%	850
06/14	1,477	2	0.2%	—
06/13	1,391	2	0.2%	—
06/12	1,486	2	0.2%	—
Annual Growth	0.9%	(19.5%)	—	—

AFFILIATED FOODS, INC.

This company helps keep pantries stocked in the Texas Panhandle and elsewhere. Affiliated Foods is a leading wholesale distribution cooperative that supplies grocery stores and restaurants in about a half a dozen states including Texas New Mexico and Oklahoma. It distributes fresh produce meat and non-food products as well as dairy products and beverages through its Plains Dairy unit. Its Tri State Baking Company supplies bread and other baked goods. In addition Affiliated Foods owns a stake in private-label products supplier Western Family Foods. The company was founded in 1946 as Panhandle Associated Grocers which merged with South Plains Associated Grocers to form Affiliated Foods in 1968.

Geographic Reach
Based in Amarillo Texas Affiliated Foods supplies grocery stores and restaurants in Texas Oklahoma Kansas New Mexico Colorado Arizona and Arkansas.

Financial Performance
While privately-owned Affiliated Foods doesn't report its financial results the cooperative reported an estimated $1.5 billion in sales in fiscal 2012 (ends October).

EXECUTIVES

National Account Manager, Yolanda Davis
Vice President Of Food Service Sales, Doug Street

LOCATIONS

HQ: AFFILIATED FOODS, INC.
1401 W FARMERS AVE, AMARILLO, TX 791186134
Phone: 806 372-3851
Web: WWW.AFIAMA.COM

PRODUCTS/OPERATIONS

Selected Subsidiaries
Affiliated Food Service (restaurant supply)
Plains Dairy (Amarillo Texas)
Tri-State Baking Co. (Amarillo Texas)

COMPETITORS

Affiliated Foods Midwest	GSC Enterprises
Associated Wholesale Grocers	IGA
C&S Wholesale	McLane
	SUPERVALU

HISTORICAL FINANCIALS
Company Type: Private

Income Statement				FYE: September 30
	REVENUE ($ mil.)	NET INCOME ($ mil.)	NET PROFIT MARGIN	EMPLOYEES
09/17*	1,421	1	0.1%	1,200
10/16	1,440	0	0.1%	—
09/06	1,137	0	0.0%	—
10/05	1,133	1	0.1%	—
Annual Growth	1.9%	0.7%	—	—
*Fiscal year change				

2017 Year-End Financials
Return on assets: 0.5%   Cash ($ mil.): 10
Return on equity: 1.7%
Current ratio: 1.10

AFJ, LLC

EXECUTIVES

Chairman, J Phillip Adams
Committee Member*, James A Baker
Committee Member*, Richard D Peterson
Commitee Member*, Andre Lortz
Contl, Robert Inkley

LOCATIONS

HQ: AFJ, LLC
 1104 COUNTRY HILLS DR, OGDEN, UT 844032400
Phone: 801 624-1000

HISTORICAL FINANCIALS

Company Type: Private

Income Statement				FYE: January 31
	REVENUE ($ mil.)	NET INCOME ($ mil.)	NET PROFIT MARGIN	EMPLOYEES
01/07	661	(0)	—	735
01/06	574	(2)	—	—
01/05	401	3	0.8%	—
Annual Growth 28.4%		—	—	—

2007 Year-End Financials

Return on assets: (-0.3%)   Cash ($ mil.): —
Return on equity: (-0.6%)
Current ratio: 0.40

AG PROCESSING INC A COOPERATIVE

Soy far soy good for Ag Processing (AGP) the largest farmer-owned soybean processor in the world and roughly the fourth-largest soybean processor in the US based on capacity. It purchases and processes more than 5.5 million acres of members' soybeans per year. The farmer-owned cooperative is also a leading supplier of refined vegetable oil in the US. It procures processes markets and transports grains and grain products ranging from human food ingredients to livestock feed to renewable fuels. AGP is owned by about 180 local and regional cooperatives and represents more than 250000 farmers in 15 states throughout the US.

Operations

In addition to its soybean processing and vegetable oil refining facilities AGP operates a merchandising and trading group called Ag Products subdivided into three areas of focus: Grain Protein and Export. Ag Products Grain focuses on marketing grain for members seeking to better compete in the global grain industry. Ag Products Protein markets soybean meal and soy hulls; it also manufactures AMINOPLUS a protein that improves milk production. Ag Products Export offers international marketing of soybean meal oilseeds grains and other bulk agricultural commodities. Its main gateway to the fast growing Pacific Rim market is through a West Coast export shipping terminal in Washington state.

AGP also holds investment stakes in Masterfeeds a Canadian feed manufacturing business and in Protinal/Proagro Venezuela's largest poultry processor and one of country's largest animal feed producers.

Geographic Reach

AGP operates nine soybean processing plants including six located in Iowa. Other soybean processing plants are located in Minnesota Missouri and Nebraska. The company operates a growing ethanol plant in Nebraska to serve the renewable fuels market and soybean methyl ester plants in Iowa and Missouri. (Soy methyl ester an alternative to petroleum-based products is a byproduct that is used in everything from biodiesel to solvents.)

Financial Performance

AGP recorded its fourth best earnings year in the company's history in fiscal 2011. Its earnings from continuing operations (before income taxes) nearly doubled from 2010. Soybean processing rebounded from the previous year partly due to more aggressive export efforts. The company's vegetable oil business had its most profitable year yet as a result of improved demand from the soy biodiesel market improved oil quality and improved plant efficiency. Its renewable fuels business (ethanol and biodiesel) started slowly but finished 2011 strong posting improved earnings over 2010.

Strategy

With evolving EPA mandates the potential is still strong for integrated biodiesel producers like AGP which led it to acquire a 60-million gallon biodiesel plant in Algona Iowa in 2011. The acquisition doubled AGP's biodiesel production capacity now totaling about 120 million gallons.

Another major component of AGP's strategy is investing in expanding upgrading and modernizing various facilities for improved capacity and efficiency. In 2011 the company initiated major upgrade and modernization projects at soy processing plants in Sergeant Bluff Iowa and Dawson Minnesota. It also undertook a multi-million dollar expansion project at its Aberdeen Washington-based export terminal as overseas shipments to Pacific Rim countries increases.

In 2012 Ag Processing merged its Masterfeeds subsidiary with the Canadian commercial feed business (Feed-Rite) of Ridley to form the second-largest feed provider in Canada Masterfeeds LP. The new entity operates 22 manufacturing plants across the Quebec Ontario and Prairie provinces. Ridley and Ag Processing each own relative shares in Masterfeeds LP.

EXECUTIVES

Group Vice President, Scott Simmelink
Senior Vice President And General Counsel, Dave Wilwerding
Senior Vice President Transportation, Greg Twist
Vice President Management Information Systems, Ramanathan Narayanan
Senior Vice President Of Operations, Ernie Kiley
Group Vice President And Chief Operating Officer, Cal Meyer
Senior Vice President, Chris Schaffer
Vice President Human Resources, Matt Bendler
Senior Vice President, Mark Sandeen

LOCATIONS

HQ: AG PROCESSING INC A COOPERATIVE
 12700 W DODGE RD, OMAHA, NE 681546102
Phone: 402 496-7809
Web: WWW.AGP.COM

PRODUCTS/OPERATIONS

Selected Brands

Masterfeeds
 AMINOPLUS (dairy cattle feed additive)
 DIRECTOR (dairy cattle feed additive)
 FUSION (horse feed additive)
Proagro/Protinal
 Corral (Prepared chicken products Venezuela only)
SOYGOLD (bio-diesel fuel additives herbicides solvents surfacants fuel additives)

Selected Exported Products

Barley
Corn
Distillers dried grains (DDGS)
Feeding peas
High-protein soybean meal
Lecithin
Low-protein soybean meal
Oats
Soybean hulls
Soybean oil
Soybeans
Sunflowers
Wheat

Selected Operations and Products

Animal feed
Corn processing
Corn-based ethanol
Grain processing merchandising and sales
Industrial products (ethanol and methyl esters)
Soybean processing
Soybean oil
Soybean biodiesel
Prepared chicken products (Venezuela only)

COMPETITORS

ACH Food Companies	Liberty Vegetable Oil
ADM	Luckey Farmers
Bunge Limited	Marfrig
CGB	POET
CGC	Smucker
CHS	South Dakota Soybean
Cargill	Processors
ConAgra	Spectrum Foods
J-OIL MILLS	West Central Co-op
Land O'Lakes Purina	Zeeland Farm
Feed	

HISTORICAL FINANCIALS

Company Type: Private

Income Statement				FYE: August 31
	REVENUE ($ mil.)	NET INCOME ($ mil.)	NET PROFIT MARGIN	EMPLOYEES
08/16*	3,410	134	3.9%	1,456
12/10	3	0	1.3%	—
08/06	2,360	62	2.7%	—
Annual Growth	3.7%	7.9%	—	—

*Fiscal year change

2016 Year-End Financials

Return on assets: 9.9%   Cash ($ mil.): 210
Return on equity: 15.3%
Current ratio: 2.80

AGFIRST FARM CREDIT BANK

The expenses involved in equipping and operating a farm add up quickly which is where AgFirst Farm Credit Bank comes in. AgFirst is one of a half-dozen members of the Farm Credit System a federally chartered network of agricultural and rural lending cooperatives. Boasting $30 billion in assets the bank provides financing to 19 farmer-owned agricultural credit associations. The associations in turn offer mortgages and loans to some 80000 farmers agribusinesses and rural home-owners through 280 branches in 15 eastern states and Puerto Rico. They also offer crop insurance credit-related life insurance and financial planning services. Instead of accepting deposits AgFirst raises money by selling bonds and notes on the capital markets.

Operations

AgFirst's capital markets arm arranges participates in and sells loan syndications for agribusinesses. Its correspondent lending unit buys sells and services agricultural and rural home loans throughout the US. About 68% of the bank's loan portfolio consisted of direct notes in 2014 while purchased participations/syndications made up another 19% of loan assets. The rest of the portfolio consisted of correspondent lending (12%) and loans to OFIs (less than 1%).

The bank makes almost all of its money from interest income. About 79% of its total revenue came from loan interest in 2014 with another 18% of revenue coming from interest on investment securities and other assets. The remainder of its revenue mostly came from loan fees.

Geographic Reach

Columbia South Carolina-based AgFirst serves 15 eastern US states and Puerto Rico. Its largest markets are in Florida North Carolina Georgia Virginia and Pennsylvania. The bank is also active in Alabama Delaware the District of Columbia Kentucky Louisiana Maryland Mississippi Ohio South Carolina Tennessee West Virginia and Puerto Rico.

Financial Performance

AgFirst Farm Credit Bank has struggled to grow its annual revenues and profits over the past several years as its loan assets have not increased and as interest margins continue to be squeezed in the low-interest environment.

The bank's revenue fell 7% to $703.8 million during 2014 as its loan assets barely grew to $20.9 billion or about the same levels as they've been since 2010.

Revenue declines in 2014 coupled with a rise in insurance fund premiums and salaries caused AgFirst's net income to shrink 17% to $380.3 million for the year. The bank's operating cash levels fell sharply to $370.9 million on lower cash earnings and unfavorable working capital changes mostly related to changes in accounts receivables balances.

Strategy

AgFirst has focused on maintaining strong personal relationships with its local customer base. It's also been investing more in security-based IT investments to protect its customers from security breaches. In 2015 it built a modern Data Center to accommodate the bank's growth with 1 Petabyte of data.

Company Background

The Farm Credit System was established by Congress in 1916 to provide a reliable source of credit for US farmers and ranchers.

EXECUTIVES

Ceo, Leon T. (Timmy) Amerson
Svp And Cfo, Charl L. Butler
Svp And Cio, Benjamin F. Blakewood
Senior Vice President, David Bridges
Vice President Executive Account Manager, Michael Mancini
Vice President Capital Markets, Neda Beal
Vice President Technology Information Technology, Tony Stone
Vice President Chief Audit Officer, William Beckham
Executive Vice President, Larry Doyle
Vice President Corporate Services, Maribeth Corbett
Vice President Operations, James Camp
Vice President, Steven Oshea
Vice President Of Investments And Funding, Richard Wilkins
Vice Chairman, Dale R. Hershey
Chairman, Robert H. Spiers
Board Member, Robert Holden
Auditors: PRICEWATERHOUSECOOPERS LLP MI

LOCATIONS

HQ: AGFIRST FARM CREDIT BANK
 1901 MAIN ST, COLUMBIA, SC 292012443
Phone: 803 799-5000
Web: WWW.AGFIRST.COM

PRODUCTS/OPERATIONS

2014 Sales

	$ mil.	% of total
Interest		
Loans	566	79
Investment securities & other	127	18
Non-interest		
Loan fees	8	2
Building lease income	3	-
Net other-than-temporary impairment losses	(1.4)	-
Gains (losses) on called debt	(7.7)	-
Gains (losses) on investments net	0	-
Gains (losses) on other transactions	0	-
Other	7	1
Total	**703**	**100**

COMPETITORS

AgriBank	Farm Family Holdings
Bank of America	First National of
COUNTRY Financial	Nebraska
Cat Financial	Rabo AgriFinance

HISTORICAL FINANCIALS

Company Type: Private

Income Statement				FYE: December 31
	ASSETS ($ mil.)	NET INCOME ($ mil.)	INCOME AS % OF ASSETS	EMPLOYEES
12/17	32,487	344	1.1%	530
12/15	30,620	336	1.1%	—
Annual Growth	3.0%	1.2%	—	—

2017 Year-End Financials

Return on assets: 1.1%   Sales ($ mil): 883
Return on equity: 15.4%

AGNESIAN HEALTHCARE, INC.

EXECUTIVES

Pres, John St Peter
Pres, Mr Robert Fale
Administrator, Bonnie R Schmitz
Coordinator, Matthew White
Public Relations Director, Shelley Haberman
Vice-President, Susan Edminster
Coordinator, Tara Schmitz
Vice President, John McCullough
Vice President of Finance, Steve Little
Community Health Program Coord, Terri Lawrence
Staff, Zachary Parker
Auditors: WIPFLI LLP GREEN BAY WI

LOCATIONS

HQ: AGNESIAN HEALTHCARE, INC.
 430 E DIVISION ST, FOND DU LAC, WI 549354560
Phone: 920 929-2300
Web: WWW.AGNESIAN.COM

HISTORICAL FINANCIALS

Company Type: Private

Income Statement				FYE: June 30
	REVENUE ($ mil.)	NET INCOME ($ mil.)	NET PROFIT MARGIN	EMPLOYEES
06/17	479	11	2.3%	2,012
06/10	281	11	4.0%	—
06/09	276	0	—	—
06/08	220	0	—	—
Annual Growth	9.0%	—	—	—

2017 Year-End Financials

Return on assets: 1.7%   Cash ($ mil.): 15
Return on equity: 2.8%
Current ratio: 1.90

AGTEGRA COOPERATIVE

Who loves you a bushel and a peck? South Dakota Wheat Growers may; it is an agricultural co-op comprising some 6800 member-farmers. It provides a grain warehouse along with grain marketing services intended to compete with big food and ag companies. In addition to storage and drying Wheat Growers offers agronomy spreading and spraying and transportation. It supplies feed fertilizer chemicals and other farm-related provisions for members in and around counties in North and South Dakota. Wheat Growers generates more than half of its revenues through marketing some 160 million bushels of grain (corn wheat and soybeans) each year. Remaining revenues are made through agronomy and retail sales and services.

EXECUTIVES

Vp Human Resources And Organizational Development, Judy Stulken
First Vice President, Rick Osterday
Auditors: GARDINER THOMSEN PC DES MOIN

LOCATIONS

HQ: AGTEGRA COOPERATIVE
 908 LAMONT ST S, ABERDEEN, SD 574015515
Phone: 605 225-5500
Web: WWW.AGTEGRA.COM

Selected Counties of Operation

North Dakota
 Dickey
 LaMoure
 Stutsman
South Dakota
 Aurora
 Beadle
 Brown
 Brule
 Clark
 Corson
 Day
 Edmunds
 Faulk
 Hand
 Hyde
 Jerauld
 Lyman
 Marshall
 Sanborn
 Spink

COMPETITORS

ADM	North Central Farmers
CHS	Elevator
Cargill	Northern Growers

HISTORICAL FINANCIALS

Company Type: Private

Income Statement				FYE: July 31
	REVENUE ($ mil.)	NET INCOME ($ mil.)	NET PROFIT MARGIN	EMPLOYEES
07/18	1,544	32	2.1%	638
07/17	1,275	22	1.8%	—
07/16	1,209	6	0.6%	—
07/15	1,283	40	3.1%	—
Annual Growth	6.3%	(6.8%)	—	—

2018 Year-End Financials

Return on assets: 3.5%   Cash ($ mil.): —
Return on equity: 9.0%
Current ratio: 1.40

AHS HILLCREST MEDICAL CENTER, LLC

Hillcrest Medical Center as part of the Hillcrest HealthCare System provides a helping hand to health care patients in northeastern Oklahoma. The medical center operates health care facilities in Tulsa and surrounding areas. The main hospital facility has about 730 beds and offers emergency cancer cardiology neurology rehabilitation and other acute and specialty care services. Hillcrest Medical Center also operates outpatient and extended care facilities including general health and specialty clinics and provides home health foster care and hospice services. The health care organization is part of Ardent Health Services.

Operations

Hillcrest HealthCare System operates six hospitals and Utica Park Clinic. Operating under the Hillcrest Hospital name to better reflect their affiliation they include Hillcrest Hospital Claremore Hillcrest Hospital Cushing Hillcrest Hospital Henryetta and Hillcrest Hospital South.

As part of its services the medical center also provides patients with The Alexander Burn Center The Peggy V. Helmerich Women's Health Center The Spine & Orthopedic Center Kaiser Rehabilitation Center The Hillcrest Center for Diabetes Management Oklahoma CyberKnife and the Oklahoma Heart Institute.

Operation of the Oklahoma State University Medical Center was transferred from Ardent Health Services to a public trust in 2009. St. John Health System now manages the facility.

Geographic Reach

Located in Tulsa Oklahoma's midtown area Hillcrest Medical Center consists of half a dozen hospitals and several other facilities for specialty care.

EXECUTIVES

Ceo, Kevin Gross
Cfo, Joseph Mendoza
Coordinator, Delecia Foster
Coordinator, Jennifer Kelley
Coordinator, Cristie Gould
Chief of Cardiology, Gail Kelly

LOCATIONS

HQ: AHS HILLCREST MEDICAL CENTER, LLC
1120 S UTICA AVE, TULSA, OK 741044012
Phone: 918 579-1000
Web: WWW.HILLCRESTMEDICALCENTER.COM

PRODUCTS/OPERATIONS

Selected Services

Alexander Burn Center
Behavioral Health Services
Cancer Care
Diabetes
Emergency Care
Exercise & Lifestyle Program
Home Care
Hospice
Medical & Neurological Rehab
Medicare Incentive Payment
Oklahoma Heart Institute
Palliative Care
Pastoral Care Department
Pregnancy
Silver Elite
Spine & Orthopedics
Women's Health Center

COMPETITORS

Deaconess Health Care	North Memorial Health
Fairview Health	Care
HealthEast Care System	Saint Francis Health
INTEGRIS Health	System
Marian Health System	St. John Health System

HISTORICAL FINANCIALS

Company Type: Private

Income Statement				FYE: June 30
	REVENUE ($ mil.)	NET INCOME ($ mil.)	NET PROFIT MARGIN	EMPLOYEES
06/16	507	14	2.9%	2,126
06/15	472	7	1.6%	
Annual Growth	7.5%	89.4%	—	—

2016 Year-End Financials

Return on assets: 11.3%   Cash ($ mil.): 17
Return on equity: 106.3%
Current ratio: 2.90

AHS HOSPITAL CORP.

EXECUTIVES

Pres-Ceo, Joseph A Trunfio
V Pres*, Andrew L Kovach
V Pres*, Joseph A Dipaolo
Cfo*, Kevin Lenahan
Coordinator, Robert Swander
Executive Officer, Rubell Michael
Human Resources Manager, Andrea Holm
Clinical Oncology Professional, Paul Heller

LOCATIONS

HQ: AHS HOSPITAL CORP.
465 SOUTH ST, MORRISTOWN, NJ 079606442
Phone: 973 660-3100
Web: WWW.ATLANTICHEALTH.ORG

HISTORICAL FINANCIALS

Company Type: Private

Income Statement				FYE: December 31
	REVENUE ($ mil.)	NET INCOME ($ mil.)	NET PROFIT MARGIN	EMPLOYEES
12/18	2,776	30	1.1%	7,300
12/17	2,600	291	11.2%	—
12/16	2,466	134	5.5%	—
12/12	1,498	140	9.4%	—
Annual Growth	10.8%	(22.3%)		

2018 Year-End Financials

Return on assets: 0.9%   Cash ($ mil.): 287
Return on equity: 1.7%
Current ratio: 2.10

AIDS HEALTHCARE FOUNDATION

EXECUTIVES

Ceo, Michael Arthur Weinstein
M.D., Chairman*, Rodney L Wright
Cfo*, Lyle Honig
Sr V Pres*, Peter Reis
Prin*, Scott Carruthers
Coordinator, Santiago Leal
Benefits Specialist, Jesus Lopez
Director Global Accounting, Margareta Marro
HCC Operations Consultant, Barbara Chinn
Director of Contracts Administ, Charity MPA
Supply Chain Manager, David Fitzpatrick
Auditors: VASQUEZ & COMPANY LLP LOS ANG

LOCATIONS

HQ: AIDS HEALTHCARE FOUNDATION
6255 W SUNSET BLVD FL 21, LOS ANGELES, CA
900287422
Phone: 323 860-5200
Web: WWW.AIDSHEALTH.ORG

HISTORICAL FINANCIALS

Company Type: Private

Income Statement				FYE: December 31
	REVENUE ($ mil.)	NET INCOME ($ mil.)	NET PROFIT MARGIN	EMPLOYEES
12/16	1,163	40	3.5%	2,331
12/15	1,039	56	5.4%	—
12/14	879	30	3.5%	—
12/13	772	16	2.1%	—
Annual Growth	14.6%	35.2%	—	—

2016 Year-End Financials

Return on assets: 10.0%   Cash ($ mil.): 63
Return on equity: 15.1%
Current ratio: 1.90

AIR METHODS CORPORATION

It's a bird it's a plane ... it's an ambulance! With a fleet of more than 400 medically equipped aircraft mainly helicopters Air Methods is the largest provider of emergency medical air-transportation services in the US. The company operates through three divisions. A community-based operating segment which represents roughly 85% of revenues offers transportation and in-flight medical care from hubs in some two dozen states. It also provides tourism operations around the Grand Canyon and Hawaiian Islands. The smallest division United Rotorcraft designs manufactures and installs aircraft medical-transport products.In 2017 Air Methods was acquired by a private equity firm.

Operations

The company mainly provides air medical transportation services throughout the US and designs manufactures and installs medical aircraft interiors and other aerospace and medical transport products. It also provides tourism operations in and around the Grand Canyon and Hawaiian Islands.

Geographic Reach

The company has more than 300 bases of operations that serve 48 states in the US. It operates eight maintenance centers throughout the country and a national communications center.

Financial Performance

Air Methods has achieved extraordinary growth over the years with 2014 revenues peaking at the $1 billion mark for the first time in its history. Profits also climbed 52% from $62 million in 2013 to to a record-setting $95 million in 2014.

The historic growth was fueled by an explosion in tourism segment revenue — this segment more than doubled its revenue from 2013 to 2014. Air Methods also generated additional sales from new revenue generated from the addition of 41 new bases throughout the year.

Strategy

Business acquisitions are part of the company's strategy to gain market share. It in 2013 acquired Helicopter Consultants of Maui LLC (doing business as Blue Hawaiian Helicopters) for a cash purchase price of $67 million. The deal enhanced Air Methods' tourism segment and helped it to post milestone revenues during 2014.

EXECUTIVES

Ceo And Director, Aaron D. Todd, $765,000 total compensation
President Sundance Helicopters, James (Jim) Greiner
President Domestic Air Medical Services, Michael D. Allen, $459,000 total compensation
Vp Information Technology, Doni Perry
Director Operations, Dennis McCall
Evp Business Development, David M. Doerr, $408,000 total compensation
Cfo And Treasurer, Peter P. Csapo
President Tourism Division, David Doerr
Senior Vice President Patient Business Services, Mark Keene
Senior Vice President General Counsel And Secretary, Crystal L Gordon
Senior Vice President Process Improvement, Kevin Campbell
Svp, Tina Giangrasso
V Pres Internal Audit, Beth Womersley
Vice President, David Poulsen
Vp Safety, Mark Rambis
Medical Director, Janelle Martin
Chairman, C. David Kikumoto
Auditors: KPMG LLP DENVER COLORADO

LOCATIONS

HQ: AIR METHODS CORPORATION
5500 S QUEBEC ST STE 300, GREENWOOD VILLAGE, CO 801111926
Phone: 303 792-7400
Web: WWW.AIRMETHODS.COM

PRODUCTS/OPERATIONS

2014 Sales

	$ mil.	% of total
AMS	863	85
Tourism	116	11
United Rotorcraft	36	4
Corporate Activities	86	0
Adjustments	(11.4)	-
Total	**1,004**	**100**

Fleets

AS 350
EC 135
EC 130
Bell 407
EC 145
Bell 429
BK 117
A-109
SA 365
Bell 222
Bell 430
Bell 206
MD 902
King Air
PC 12
Agusta 119Kx

Services

AirCom
Complete Billing Solutions
DirectCall
TAMMA
United Rotorcraft
LifeShield Alliance

COMPETITORS

Acadian Ambulance Service Inc.	CHC Group
Bristow Group Inc	Evergreen Holdings
	PHI Inc.

HISTORICAL FINANCIALS

Company Type: Private

Income Statement

FYE: December 31

	REVENUE ($ mil.)	NET INCOME ($ mil.)	NET PROFIT MARGIN	EMPLOYEES
12/15	1,085	109	10.1%	5,133
12/14	1,004	95	9.5%	—
12/13	881	62	7.0%	—
Annual Growth	11.0%	32.7%	—	—

2015 Year-End Financials

Return on assets: 7.0%   Cash ($ mil.): 5
Return on equity: 19.0%
Current ratio: 3.20

AIRGAS, INC.

Airgas hopes its industrial customers walk on its air. The US industrial gas distributor's North American network of more than 1100 locations includes retail stores gas fill plants specialty gas labs production facilities (17 air separation plants) and distribution centers. Airgas distributes argon carbon dioxide hydrogen nitrogen oxygen and a variety of medical and specialty gases as well as dry ice and protective equipment (hard hats goggles). Its gases production unit operates air-separation plants that produce oxygen nitrogen and argon. The company also sells welding machines. The company is owned by Air Liquide SA.

Operations

The industrial manufacturing and repair and maintenance industries account for about a quarter each of the Airgas's sales; customers primarily make fabricated metal products industrial transportation and equipment chemical products and primary metal products. Other industries served include medical and health services agriculture mining repair and maintenance and wholesale trade.

Airgas' distribution business accounts for 88% of the company's 2016 sales. Almost all of its sales come from distributing bulk gases (nitrogen oxygen argon helium) gas cylinders and welding equipment. Airgas also produces gases to supply its regional distribution companies. Its other operations consist of six business units that manufacture and/or distribute carbon dioxide dry ice nitrous oxide ammonia and refrigerant gases. Gas and rent represented 61% of the distribution business segment's sales in fiscal 2016; hard goods 39%.

The distribution business operates a network of multiple use facilities consisting of 900 branches 300 cylinder fill plants 70 regional specialty gas laboratories 11 national specialty gas laboratories one research and development center two specialty gas equipment centers 11 acetylene plants and 16 air separation units as well as six national hard-goods distribution centers and various customer call centers buying centers and administrative offices.

Airgas' All Other Operations business segment consists of six operating segments all of which primarily manufacture and/or distribute single gas product lines (carbon dioxide dry ice nitrous oxide ammonia and refrigerant gases along with a nitrogen services business). It has 90 branch/distribution locations eight liquid carbon dioxide and 14 dry ice production facilities and three nitrous oxide production facilities.

Geographic Reach

Operating in all 50 states Airgas is the largest distributor of packaged gases in the US with a 25% market share. Outside the US it conducts operations mostly in Canada but also operates in the UAE Mexico Russia and in parts of Europe. It got less than 2% of its fiscal 2016 (ending in March) revenues from outside the US.

Sales and Marketing

The company serves customers in a range of industries including Manufacturing and Metal Fabrication Non-Residential (Energy and Infrastructure) Construction Life Sciences and Healthcare Food Beverage and Retail Energy and Chemical Production and Distribution Basic Materials and Services. It also has government clients.

Airgas markets its products and services through multiple sales channels including branch-based representatives retail stores telesales strategic customer account programs catalogs e-Business and other distributors.

Manufacturing & Metal Fabrication customers account for 30% of sales while Non-Residential (Energy & Infrastructure) Construction accounts for 15% and Food Beverage & Retail for 13%. Each bringing in more than 10% of sales are its Energy & Chemical Production & Distribution and Basic Materials & Services customers. Government & Other Life and Sciences & Healthcare customers account for the rest.

Strategy

Prior to its 2016 acquisition by global rival Air Liquide Airgas had grown its operations through acquisitions in its core businesses. It has bought more than 500 companies since its founding in 1986 and focuses on high-growth products with strong cross-selling opportunities. In fiscal 2016 it purchased 18 businesses (22 in fiscal 2015) with historical annual sales of $85 million. Airgas also grew through organic expansion.

HISTORY

In the early 1980s Peter McCausland was a corporate attorney involved in mergers and acquisitions for Messer Griesheim a large German industrial gas producer. When the German firm declined McCausland's recommendation in 1982 to buy Connecticut Oxygen he raised money from private sources and bought it himself. He acquired other distributors and then left Messer Griesheim in 1987 to run Airgas full-time.

Airgas began buying mostly small local and regional gas distributors in the US. By 1994 strategy shifted to purchasing larger "superregional" distributors such as Jimmie Jones Co. and Post Welding Supply of Alabama which added about $70 million combined to the company's revenues.

Airgas then began "rolling up" additional similar businesses. In 1995 it bought more than 25 companies and two years later it added more than 20 gas distributors. Also in 1997 Airgas expanded its manufacturing capabilities by building five plants that could fast-fill whole pallets of gas cylinders (the old manual system rolls cylinders two at a time). By 2000 the company had about 100 cylinder fill plants.

Struggling to integrate acquisitions while dealing with softening markets Airgas began a companywide realignment in 1998. To that end it sold its calcium carbide and carbon products operations to former partner Elkem ASA later that year; the company also consolidated 34 hubs into 16 regional companies and sold its operations in Poland and Thailand to Germany-based Linde in 1999.

In 2000 Airgas acquired distributor Mallinckrodt's Puritan-Bennett division (gas products for medical uses) with 36 locations in the US and Canada. The company also acquired the majority of Air Products' US packaged gas business excluding its electronic gases and magnetic resonance imaging-related helium operations in 2002.

In 2004 and 2005 it bought units from giants like Air Products and Chemicals BOC and LaRoche Industries. In 2006 Airgas continued to build with the purchase of 10 businesses including Union Industrial Gas which supplies Texas and much of the Southwest and then Linde's US bulk gas business for $495 million the next year. Linde in the process of integrating its 2006 acquisition of BOC then sold to Airgas a portion of its US packaged gas business for $310 million.

Rival Air Products had made a major bid to buy Airgas in 2010 but was rebuffed. Air Products extended its tender offer to Airgas stockholders several times and made a "best and final offer" of $70 a share (almost $6 billion) in December 2010. Airgas said it was holding out for $78 a share and rejected that offer too. In early 2011 a Delaware judge ruled for Airgas in a suit brought by Air Products to set aside a "poison pill" defense used by the Airgas board to fend off the takeover try. Following the verdict Air Products dropped its bid.

Airgas acquired six businesses in 2010 including Tri-Tech an independent distributor with 16 locations throughout Florida Georgia and South Carolina and annual sales of $31 million.

In 2011 Airgas reorganized its 12 regional segments into four new business support divisions — North South Central and West — to leverage a new SAP information systems platform in 2011. Each of the units is headed by a division president. The new company structure is designed to accelerate sales growth and pricing management and create operating efficiencies.

In fiscal 2012 the company added eight businesses with total annual sales of about $106 million. The largest of the businesses acquired were ABCO Gases Welding and Industrial Supply Company (ABCO); Pain Enterprises; and Industrial Welding Supplies of Hattiesburg (doing business as Nordan Smith). Connecticut-based ABCO has 12 industrial and gas welding supply locations throughout New England. Indiana-based Pain operates 20 dry ice and liquid carbon dioxide production and distribution sites. Mississippi-based Nordan Smith has 17 locations that distribute industrial medical and specialty gases and supplies throughout Alabama Arkansas and Mississippi.

In 2013 Airgas retained Chicago-based Acquity Group as a key partner in helping the company continue to provide new online digital customer platforms. As one of the leading digital marketing companies the Acquity Group will provide its e-channel expertise in leading the design and implementation of Airgas' new content-rich website.

In 2013 Airgas acquired two US-based industrial gas and welding supply distributors that complement the Airgas portfolio of products and services. Combined annual revenues for the two acquired businesses are more than $30 million.

In fiscal 2013 the company also acquired Illinois-based The Encompass Gas Group (one of the largest privately-owned suppliers of industrial medical and specialty gases and related hardgoods in the US) with about $55 million in annual revenues in 2012.

EXECUTIVES

Coo, Andrew R. (Andy) Cichocki, $296,936 total compensation
President Airgas North Division, Pamela J. (Pam) Claypool
Vice President Construction, John Appolonia
Svp Sales And Marketing, Ronald J. (Ron) Stark
Svp And Cio, Robert A. Dougherty, $263,779 total compensation
President Airgas South, John F. Sheehan
Svp And Cfo, Robert M. (Bob) McLaughlin, $470,453 total compensation
Division President Gases Production, Thomas S. Thoman
Division President West, Douglas L. (Doug) Jones
Svp And General Counsel, Robert H. Young, $397,272 total compensation
Division President Central, Terry L. Lodge
President East Region, Jack Appolonia
Ceo, Pascal Vinet
Vice President Area Sales, Ross Jones
Vice President Of Information Technology Airgas Mid South, George Turner
Vice President Central Division, Don Berndsen
Vice President Safety And Compliance, Jim McCarthy
Vice President Business Development, Bruce Woerner
Regional Vice President Healthcare, Linda Wissink
Vice President, James Cook
Regional Vice President Of Finance, Jana Bittinger
National Sales Manager, Jerry Anderskow
Vice President Finance, Monica Garza
Vice President Of Plant Operations, Roger Weber
Vice President Of Bulk Operations, Steve Scheuring
Vice President, Ted Schulte
Vice President Construction Markets, Jason Vetterick
Vice President Of Finance, Jennifer Mihaljcic
Vice President Of Finance, Michael Maley
Vice President Strategic Accounts, Otto Gaus
Area Vice President, Jeff Mann
Assistant Vice President, Brian Blackwood
Vice President Operations, Tom Mulqueen
Assistant Vice President Corporate Development, Brian Shammo
Vice President Hardgoods, David Levin
Regional Vice President Usa East, Adam Needles
Vice President, Chris Brazell
Division Vice President Of Sales, Mark Johnston
Vice President, Wayne Wilson
National Account Manager, Don Wallenfelsz
Area Vice President, Gene Klein
Area Vice President, Ron Weber
Vice President Internal Audit, E Coyne
National Account Manager, Earl Dyck
Vice President Of Sales, Marcelo Feistauer
Vice President Gulf Coast Region, Scott Koonce
Vice President Area, Luke Aass
Vice President Bulk Sales And Operations, Thomas Archie
Vice President Credit And Collections, Ed Burke
National Account Manager, Thomas White
Area Vice President, Beth Medford
National Account Manager, Daniel Christenson
Vice President Total Access, Kerrie Sodano
Vice President Bulk Sales And Operations, Richard Cassano
Vp Manufacturing, Jill Barth
Area Vice President, Brad Kahn
Vice President Of Food And Beverage, Bill Baker
Vice President Of Safety And Compliance, Chris Herbert
Division Vice President Human Resources, Stamy Paul
Vp Safety And Compliance, Curtis Henson
Chairman, Pierre Dufour
Vice Chairman, Michael J. (Mike) Graff
Auditors: KPMG LLP PHILADELPHIA PENNSY

LOCATIONS

HQ: AIRGAS, INC.
259 N RADNOR CHESTER RD # 100, RADNOR, PA 190875240
Phone: 610 687-5253
Web: WWW.AIRGAS.COM

PRODUCTS/OPERATIONS

2016 sales

	% of total
Manufacturing & Metal Fabrication	29
Non Residential (Energy & Infrastructure) construction	15
Life Science & Healthcare	14
Food Beverage & Retail	13
Energy & Chemical Production & Distribution	12
Basic Material & Services	11
Government & Others	6
Total	**100**

2016 sales

	$ mil.	% of total
Distribution	4,716	88
Other Operations	635	12
Adjustments	(38.2)	-
Total	**5,313**	**100**

Selected Products and Services

Products
Carbon dioxide
Dry ice
Industrial gases
Argon
Helium
Hydrogen
Liquid oxygen
Nitrogen
Nitrous oxide
Oxygen
Safety equipment
Specialty gases

Services
Container rental
Welding equipment rental

Selected Subsidiaries
Airgas Canada
Airgas Carbonic
Airgas East
Airgas Great Lakes
Airgas Intermountain
Airgas Medical Services
Airgas Mid America
Airgas Mid South
Airgas Nitrous Oxide
Airgas Nor Pac
Airgas North Central
Airgas Northern California & Nevada
Airgas Refrigerant
Airgas Safety
Airgas South
Airgas Southwest
Airgas Specialty Gases
Airgas Specialty Products
Airgas West
National Welders Supply Company dba Airgas National Welders
Nitrous Oxide Corp.
Red-D-Arc
WorldWide Welding LLC

COMPETITORS

Air Products
Lincoln Electric
Matheson Tri-Gas
Praxair Distribution
Valley National Gases
W.W. Grainger

HISTORICAL FINANCIALS
Company Type: Private

Income Statement				FYE: March 31
	REVENUE ($ mil.)	NET INCOME ($ mil.)	NET PROFIT MARGIN	EMPLOYEES
03/15	5,304	368	6.9%	17,070
03/13	4,957	340	6.9%	—
Annual Growth	3.4%	3.9%	—	—

2015 Year-End Financials
Return on assets: 6.2%   Cash ($ mil.): 50
Return on equity: 17.1%
Current ratio: 1.30

AKAL SECURITY, INC.

Unarmed?Â Akal Security provides contract security guard services for customersÂ in the US and abroad.Â Akal's Judicial Security divisionÂ specializes in security services forÂ protecting federal courthouses in 40 states. It also transports prisoners and illegal aliens for homeland security efforts. In addition Akal supplies security officers for detention facilities and military installations and offers electronic security surveillance and access control system design installation and integration. The companyÂ serves federal agencies as well as commercial clients and state and local government facilities. Clients have included the US Army the Department of Homeland Security the US Marshals Service and NASA.

EXECUTIVES

Pres, Sukhwinder Singh
Exec V Pres*, Mehtab Khalsa
Executive Assistant, Katie Burback
Security, Akal Global
Auditors: PULASKOS CPAS PC ALBUQUERQUE

LOCATIONS

HQ: AKAL SECURITY, INC.
  7 INFINITY LOOP, ESPANOLA, NM 875326737
Phone: 505 692-6600
Web: WWW.AKALGLOBAL.COM

PRODUCTS/OPERATIONS

Selected Services
Aviation security services (airport programs)
Investigations (US and international corporate clients)
Personal protection (US corporate executives)
Security officer services (guarding programs)
Security systems integration (design installation and
  integration of electronic security surveillance and
  access control systems)
Security training programs (Akal Training Academy)
Third country national personnel (trained former
  military personnel from Asia and Africa)

COMPETITORS

AlliedBarton Security
Command Security
D&D Security Training
Guardsmark
Securitas Security Services North America
Tyco Fire & Security
Walden Security

HISTORICAL FINANCIALS
Company Type: Private

Income Statement				FYE: December 31
	REVENUE ($ mil.)	NET INCOME ($ mil.)	NET PROFIT MARGIN	EMPLOYEES
12/11	461	3	0.8%	15,000
12/10	466	2	0.5%	—
12/09	479	2	0.6%	—
Annual Growth	(1.9%)	11.2%	—	—

2011 Year-End Financials
Return on assets: 3.4%   Cash ($ mil.): —
Return on equity: 10.3%
Current ratio: 1.40

AKRON GENERAL MEDICAL CENTER INC

Akron General Medical Center the flagship hospital of Akron General Health System is a not-for-profit teaching hospital that boasts more than 530 acute care beds. The hospital serves the residents of Northeast Ohio as a regional referral center in a number of medical specialties including cardiovascular disease heart surgery cancer care women's health orthopedics sports medicine and trauma care. Akron General Medical also operates Edwin Shaw Rehab the area's only rehabilitation hospital. Edwin Shaw has 35 beds and treats patients who have experienced stroke head trauma and other critical injuries. Akron General Medical was founded in 1914 as Peoples Hospital.

Operations
Akron General is a level I trauma center and holds the county's first certified chest pain and primary stroke centers. It also offers a level III obstetric unit and it operates a freestanding outpatient surgery center. As a major teaching hospital with more than 1000 physicians as well as 3400 professional and support staff members Akron General Medical offers medical students about a dozen residency programs. It does so through its affiliations with Northeastern Ohio Medical University which serves as the medical college for University of Akron Youngstown State University and Kent State University. Residencies include those in family medicine OB-GYN psychiatry and breast cancer.

Geographic Reach
Akron General Medical Center serves communities across the counties of Summit Medina Portage Stark and Wayne located in Northeast Ohio. In addition to facilities in Akron the hospital has satellite locations in Green Stow and Tallmadge. Edwin Shaw Rehab is located in the nearby town of Cuyahoga Falls. The center serves an area with a population of some 1.2 million people.

Strategy
The hospital conducts facility and equipment upgrades to meet the needs of a growing population in Northeast Ohio. Akron General enhanced its neurosurgical capabilities in 2012 as part of the establishment of its Neurosciences Institute. The center includes new Brainlab CT and MRI imaging systems for use during minimally invasive surgical procedures. The hospital is also upgrading its heart and vascular center which was certified as a heart failure clinic in 2013. In addition Akron General is working to upgrade IT systems to improve physician and patient resources.

EXECUTIVES

Chb, F William Steere
Director, Mary Beth Carroll
Director of Nursing, Phillip G Moser
Scientist, Barbara Klimonek
Scientist, Tookie Dunnie
Executive of Information Techn, Richard J Streck
Security Staff, Chris J Voller
Audiologist, Sharon Cargill
Information Specialist, Paul Hayslip
Coordinator, Karen Orndorf
Executive Vice President, Cathy Ceccio
Auditors: LB BLUE & CO LLC COLUMBUS OH

LOCATIONS

HQ: AKRON GENERAL MEDICAL CENTER INC
  1 AKRON GENERAL AVE, AKRON, OH 443072432
Phone: 330 344-6000
Web: WWW.CLEVELANDCLINIC.ORG

Selected Locations and Affiliates
Akron General Medical Center
Akron Health Center
Edwin Shaw Rehabilitation Institute
Green Health Center
Health and Wellness Centers (West North and Green)
Hospice Center
Lodi Community Hospital
Tallmadge Health Center

PRODUCTS/OPERATIONS

Selected Centers and Services

Anesthesiology

Audiology
Bariatric Surgery
Breast Health Center
Cancer Center
Community Health
Corporate Wellness
Critical Care Center
Diabetes Center
Diagnostic Services
Emergency Medicine/Level 1 Trauma Center
Endocrinology
Endoscopy
Executive Health Program
Family Medicine
Food and Nutrition Services
Gastroenterology
Health and Wellness
Heart and Vascular Center
Heartburn Center
Hyperbaric Medicine
Infectious Disease
Internal Medicine
Lab Services
Maternity Services
Nephrology
Neuroscience Institute
Nuclear Medicine
Occupational Therapy
Orthopedic Center
Osteoporosis Prevention
Pain Management
Physical Therapy
Primary Care
Psychiatry and Behavioral Sciences
Pulmonary Medicine
Radiology
Rehabilitation
Senior Services
Sleep Center
Speech and Language Pathology
Sports Medicine
Surgery
Urology
Women's Center
Wound Center

COMPETITORS

Akron Children's Hospital

Community Health Systems

OhioHealth

Regency Hospital

Sharon Regional Health System

Summa Health System

Trinity Health System

University Hospitals Health System

HISTORICAL FINANCIALS

Company Type: Private

Income Statement				FYE: December 31
	REVENUE ($ mil.)	NET INCOME ($ mil.)	NET PROFIT MARGIN	EMPLOYEES
12/14	544	47	8.7%	875
12/13	507	22	4.4%	—
12/12	486	10	2.2%	—
12/04	0	0		—
Annual Growth	—	—	—	—

2014 Year-End Financials

Return on assets: 10.3%

Return on equity: 35.3%

Current ratio: 0.40

Cash ($ mil.): 20

ALASKA NATIVE TRIBAL HEALTH CONSORTIUM

The Alaska Native Tribal Health Consortium (ANTHC) brings good health to Alaska Natives. The company is a not-for-profit statewide health care organization managed by regional tribal governments and their respective regional health organizations. The organization connects disparate medical providers by providing a range of health programs and services including community health care public health advocacy and education initiatives health research (including water and sanitation) and medical supply distribution. The 150-bed Alaska Native Medical Center (ANMC) a native-owned hospital is jointly managed by ANTHC and Southcentral Foundation a regional health corporation based in the Cook Inlet region.

Operations

ANMC's services are reserved primarily for Alaska Native Tribal groups with the exception of its Urgent Care centers and Emergency Room. (Emergency rooms are compelled to take patients of all types under US fair care guidelines.) The hospital handles about 8000 patient admissions each year as well as 300000 outpatient and 57000 emergency room visits. It also conducts some 11000 surgeries and 1600 births. ANMC has about 100 physicians.

The organization's primary mission is to improve the health of Alaska natives through health sanitation technology and advocacy services. It conducts a number of community outreach programs and it works to create a continuum of care for its members so they can move smoothly through the health care process (including initial specialist and follow-up care visits). The hospital is the regional hub of that health care continuum offering general and specialist care in a range of fields. ANTHC also operates outpatient care centers and it operates an extensive telemedicine network (allow providers to care for and consult with patients in outlying areas).

ANTHC provides administrative support to Alaska's Tribal health groups and it supports state legislative efforts such as the reauthorization of the Indian Health Care Improvement Act. The consortium formed in 1997 also works to improve the Alaskan health system by participating in strategic summit meetings and sponsoring electronic health record initiatives.

Geographic Reach

ANTHC and ANMC are located in Anchorage Alaska. The organization provides services throughout the state.

Financial Performance

The company's 2014 revenues stood at $643 million about 33% of which came from patient revenues. Other major operating segments include compact revenue (25% of sales) and grant and project income (17%).

Strategy

Infrastructure and service expansions are a key means of growth for ANTHC.

In 2015 ANTHC awarded Neeser Construction Inc. a contract to build the new ANMC patient housing facility on the Alaska Native Health Campus in Anchorage. The building will house patients and their families travelling to ANMC for medical care. The a new patient housing facility is expected to open in fall 2016. It will have 202 private rooms and six floors with a dedicated floor for new families.

In 2015 Alaska Governor Walker introduced legislation declaring his plan for Medicaid reform and expansion. ANTHC supports the Governor's efforts to expand Medicaid coverage to more than 41000 Alaskans.

Company Background

In 2012 ANMC expanded its maternal child health and neurosurgery departments due to increasing patient populations in the Anchorage area. In 2010 the medical center opened the only Level II trauma center in Alaska making it a referral hospital for major trauma cases.

The organization has also improved its health care technology resources; it expanded the use of electronic health records at ANMC in 2012 and it is expanding its telemedicine operations (as telemedicine is becoming an increasingly popular way for specialists to see patients without the expense of a personal visit). It has increased other community outreach efforts as well such as smoking cessation and behavioral health programs.

EXECUTIVES

Vp Professional And Support Services Alaska Native Medical Center Hospital, Vivian Echavarria

Cfo, Garvin Federenko

Ceo And Administrator, Roald Helgesen

Cio, Stewart Ferguson

Chief Medical Officer, Paul Franke

Chief Nursing Executive Alaska Native Medical Center Hospital, Richard Hall

Chairman And President, Andy Teuber

Vice Chairman, Lincoln A. Bean

Auditors: BDO USA LP ANCHORAGE AK

LOCATIONS

HQ: ALASKA NATIVE TRIBAL HEALTH CONSORTIUM
4000 AMBASSADOR DR, ANCHORAGE, AK 995085909

Phone: 907 729-1900

Web: WWW.ANTHC.ORG

PRODUCTS/OPERATIONS

2014 Sales

	$ mil.	% of total
Patient revenue	213	33
Compact revenue	161	25
Grant & project revenue	109	17
Warehouse revenue	22	3
Investment income	4	1
Other	133	21
Total	**643**	**100**

Selected Services

Ear Nose Throat

Emergency and Trauma

Family Medicine

Imaging and Laboratory Services

Internal Medicine Clinic

Maternal Fetal Medicine

OB/GYN Services

Oncology

Orthopedics Clinic

Pediatric ICU

Pediatrics

Pharmacy Services

Pregnancy and Childbirth

Primary Care Services

Respiratory Care

COMPETITORS

HCA

Immediate Care

PeaceHealth

Providence St. Joseph Health

South Peninsula Hospital

Tenet Healthcare

HISTORICAL FINANCIALS

Company Type: Private

Income Statement				FYE: September 30
	REVENUE ($ mil.)	NET INCOME ($ mil.)	NET PROFIT MARGIN	EMPLOYEES
09/16	587	72	12.4%	1,850
09/15	511	3	0.7%	—
09/14	618	154	24.9%	—
09/13	459	21	4.6%	—
Annual Growth	8.5%	50.5%	—	—

2016 Year-End Financials

Return on assets: 10.8%

Return on equity: 13.8%

Current ratio: 1.60

Cash ($ mil.): 121

ALASKA PERMANENT FUND CORPORATION

EXECUTIVES

Ceo, Angela Rodell

Coo*, Marcus Frampton

Chief Financial Officer*, Valerie Mertz

Information Specialist, Andrew Loney

Principal, Chris Poag

Communications Manager, Paulyn Swanson

Portfolio Manager, Timothy Andreyka

Controller, John Seagren

Human Resources Director, Chad Brown

Investment Officer Real Estate, Christi Grussendorf

Senior Associate Private Marke, Jared Brimberry

Auditors: KPMG LLP ANCHORAGE AK

LOCATIONS

HQ: ALASKA PERMANENT FUND CORPORATION
801 W 10TH ST STE 302, JUNEAU, AK 998011878

Phone: 907 796-1500

Web: WWW.APFC.ORG

HISTORICAL FINANCIALS

Company Type: Private

Income Statement				FYE: June 30
	ASSETS ($ mil.)	NET INCOME ($ mil.)	INCOME AS % OF ASSETS	EMPLOYEES
06/18	67,671	5,109	7.6%	50
06/17	61,824	6,675	10.8%	—
06/16	55,346	(30)	—	—
06/15	55,900	1,586	2.8%	—
Annual Growth	6.6%	47.7%	—	—

ALBANY MEDICAL CENTER

Albany Medical Center (AMC) provides medical care in upstate New York. Serving residents of northeastern New York and western New England the health system has at its heart the 730-bed Albany Medical Center Hospital. The general medical-surgical facility also provides specialty care in such areas as oncology rehabilitation and organ transplantation. AMC also features a children's hospital an outpatient surgery center and a group medical practice. It employs some 400 full-time physicians. Its Albany Medical College is one of the nation's first private medical schools. It offers undergraduate and graduate medical degrees and residency programs as well as fellowships and continuing medical education.

Operations

AMC's assets includes a biomedical research enterprise and one of the region's largest physicians practices with more than 400 doctors. Its physicians have extensive training and experience in 34 subspecialties of pediatric medicine. The system's subsidiaries include the Albany Medical Center Kidskeller Corporation a not-for-profit day care facility and Madison Avenue Services Corporation a taxable corporation.

AMC is affiliated with several community physician groups including Albany Vascular Group Capital Cardiology Associates and Capital Region Orthopaedic Group.

In 2013 the system reported some 33000 admissions 581000 outpatient visits 28000 surgical cases and 68000 emergency department visits.

Geographic Reach

AMC offers services in 25 counties in northeastern New York and western New England. In addition to treating patients at the main site in Albany providers also treat patients at community-based locations throughout the region including Clifton Park Latham Malta North Greenbush Delmar and others.

Sales and Marketing

HMOs account for around a third of net patient revenue while Medicare and Medicaid represent about 20% and 15% respectively.

Financial Performance

The company's revenues grew by 3% to $752 million in 2013 (versus $728 million in 2012) due to an increase in net patient revenue; this was partially offset by declines in interest income dividends and other revenue. Net income grew 21% to $63 million in 2013 as net realized gains on sales of securities and impairment charges rose. Other gains were made in pension-related changes and net unrealized gains and losses in investments.

Cash flow from operations fell 55% that year to $37 million as more was used in receivables and other liabilities.

Strategy

AMC grows through organic expansion partnerships and product initiatives. The company is in the midst of a $360 million expansion including a new patient tower with more than 100 beds and increased intensive care resources. The project — expected to last several years — will also increase Albany Medical Center Hospital's bed count to more than 700.

In 2014 The Neurology Group and The Endocrine Group joined AMC's Albany Med Faculty Physician Group.

AMC and Union Graduate College joined forces in 2013 to offer a new joint degree combining medical school with an MBA.

That year AMC and Saratoga Hospital formed a joint venture and opened the $17.5 million Malta Med Emergent Care to provide area residents an alternative to hospital emergency rooms for all but the most serious medical circumstances.

On the product innovation side in 2013 AMC introduced advanced imaging technologies in a pair of its new Patient Pavilion operating rooms that provide for greater precision and patient safety during brain and spinal surgeries.

Also that year the company opened a Chronic Kidney Disease Clinic as the sole source for comprehensive care for 6000 people in its service area suffering from the slow loss of kidney function.

AMC also engages in research and development of new pharmaceuticals through partnerships with companies like Aegis Therapeutics with which it is developing an anti-obesity peptide to benefit patients with type 2 diabetes. The college's research department is also studying brain mapping techniques as well as Alzheimer's disease vascular disease and cancer and multiple sclerosis treatments.

Company Background

AMC which produced Nobel prize winners in both 2009 and 2011 annually awards its own $500000 prize the largest monetary award in medicine and biomedical research in the US. In 2010 combined federal-state entities awarded the center $10 million the center's largest grant since its founding which will be used to expand research labs at Albany Medical College.

AMC's status as the Capital Region's reigning health care giant was toppled by the 2011 merger of four locals hospitals to form St. Peter's Health Partners with nearly 12000 employees vs. 6000 at AMC. Post merger the newly-merged group has nearly 50% of the Capital Region market while AMC has 25%. While AMC is no longer the area's largest hospital as the region's trauma center and only medical school it continues to draw many patients from outside the four-county area.

Albany Medical College was formed in 1839; the hospital's predecessor was formed in 1849. The two combined under the AMC umbrella in 1982.

EXECUTIVES

President And Ceo, James J. Barba
Evp And Coo, Gary J. Kochem
Evp And Cfo, William C. Hasselbarth
Svp And Cio, George T. Hickman
Evp Ids And Hospital Systems General Director, Steven M. Frisch
Evp Policy Planning And Communications, Kim Fine
Svp Hospital Business Services And Coo Hospital, Bernadette Pedlow
Dean And Evp Healthâ Affairs, Vincent Verdile
Svp And Chief Nursing Officer, Mary Ellen Plass
Senior Vice President And Chief Compliance Officer, Noel Hogan

Vice President Information Systems, Arthur Gross
Vice President Finance, Cooper Matthew
Physical Therapy Director, Louann Kuntz
Vice President For Communications, Jeffrey Gordon
Assistant Vice President Development, James Kellerhouse
Vice President Of Facility Operations, Don Stichter
Vice President, Anjali Singla
Vice President, Michael Gruenthal
Senior Vice President Of Integrated Delivery Systems And Hospital Director, Stephen Frisch
Vice President Community Development, Pamela Brown
Chairman, Robert Cushing
Auditors: KPMG LLP ALBANY NEW YORK

LOCATIONS

HQ: ALBANY MEDICAL CENTER
43 NEW SCOTLAND AVE, ALBANY, NY 122083478
Phone: 518 262-3125
Web: WWW.AMC.EDU

PRODUCTS/OPERATIONS

2013 Sales

	$ mil.	% of total
Net patient service	720	96
Inter-institutional	8	1
Interest & dividends	2	-
Other	17	2
Net assets released from restrictions	3	1
Total	**752**	**100**

2013 Net Patient Service Revenue

	% of total
Health maintenance organizations	32
Medicare	19
Medicaid	15
Blue Cross and Blue Shield	14
Commercial carriers	9
No fault & worker's compensation	5
Private pay	2
Other third-party payors	4
Total	**100**

Selected Services

Cancer center
Children's Hospital
Center for Donation and Transplant
Diabetes service
Emergency medical services
Hearing center
HIV medicine
Pain management
Perinatal
Physical therapy
Radiology
Rheumatology
Surgical
Trauma center
Women's wellness center

COMPETITORS

Berkshire Health Systems
Ellis Hospital
SUNY Upstate Medical University
Southwestern Vermont Health Care

St. Joseph's Hospital Health Center
St. Peter's Health Partners
United Health Services Hospitals

HISTORICAL FINANCIALS

Company Type: Private

Income Statement

FYE: December 31

	REVENUE ($ mil.)	NET INCOME ($ mil.)	NET PROFIT MARGIN	EMPLOYEES
12/17	664	267	40.2%	7,000
12/16	317	77	24.5%	—
12/15	1,167	5	0.5%	—
12/13	980	115	11.7%	—
Annual Growth	(9.3%)	23.4%	—	—

2017 Year-End Financials

Return on assets: 36.5%
Return on equity: 84.3%
Current ratio: 2.20
Cash ($ mil.): 113

ALBANY MEDICAL CENTER HOSPITAL

EXECUTIVES

Pres, James J Barba
Coo*, Gary J Kochem
SEC*, Sabine Needham
Doctor, Frederick Eames
Education, Roslyn Dahl
Information Analyst, John Lemperle
Auditors: KPMG LLP ALBANY NY

LOCATIONS

HQ: ALBANY MEDICAL CENTER HOSPITAL
43 NEW SCOTLAND AVE, ALBANY, NY 122083478
Phone: 518 262-3125
Web: WWW.AMC.EDU

HISTORICAL FINANCIALS

Company Type: Private

Income Statement

FYE: December 31

	REVENUE ($ mil.)	NET INCOME ($ mil.)	NET PROFIT MARGIN	EMPLOYEES
12/17	1,017	38	3.8%	1,568
12/16	960	46	4.8%	—
12/15	893	16	1.9%	—
12/14	812	51	6.3%	—
Annual Growth	7.8%	(9.5%)	—	—

2017 Year-End Financials

Return on assets: 3.5%
Return on equity: 8.4%
Current ratio: 2.20
Cash ($ mil.): 95

ALBERICI CONSTRUCTORS, INC.

EXECUTIVES

Pres, Gregory J Kozicz
V Pres, John S Alberici
V Pres, Leroy Stromberg
Cfo, Gregory T Hesser
Sr Acct, Sherry Morrow

Chief Information Officer, Frank C Kropiunik
Coordinator, Katie Schaper
Project Manager, Katy Beckerle
Assistant Project Manager, Audrey Leamy
Superintendent, Jim McGuirk
Project Manager, Ken Debrecht

LOCATIONS

HQ: ALBERICI CONSTRUCTORS, INC.
8800 PAGE AVE, SAINT LOUIS, MO 631146106
Phone: 314 733-2000
Web: WWW.ALBERICI.COM

HISTORICAL FINANCIALS

Company Type: Private

Income Statement

FYE: December 31

	REVENUE ($ mil.)	NET INCOME ($ mil.)	NET PROFIT MARGIN	EMPLOYEES
12/17	782	0	—	2,000
12/16	960	0	—	—
12/15	1,028	0	—	—
12/14	729	0	—	—
Annual Growth	2.4%	—	—	—

2017 Year-End Financials

Return on assets: —
Return on equity: —
Current ratio: 1.20
Cash ($ mil.): 76

ALBERICI CORPORATION

Alberici helped shape the St. Louis skyline; it now sets its sights — or its construction sites — across North America. As the parent company of Alberici Constructors the company encompasses a group of enterprises with a presence in North America Central America South America and Europe. Operations include construction services building materials and steel fabrication and erection units. Alberici offers general contracting design/build construction management demolition and specialty contracting services while also offering facilities management. Founded in 1918 the Alberici family still holds the largest share of the employee-owned firm.

Operations

The company boasts more than a dozen operating companies in the US Canada and Mexico that serve the automotive energy health care industrial manufacturing and wastewater treatment markets. Its Gunther-Nash subsidiary provides construction services to the mining industry. Another division Vertegy specializes in construction consulting for green and sustainable projects.

Geographic Reach

Alberici is active throughout North America and has offices in St. Louis Missouri; Detroit Michigan; Atlanta Georgia; Topeka Kansas; Burlington and Cambridge Ontario; Saskatoon Saskatchewan; and Léon Mexico.

Sales and Marketing

Alberici serves a range of different companies including those that are automotive building energy healthcare heavy industrial industrial process mining infrastructure or water-related.

Some of Alberici's completed projects include casinos for Ameristar modernization and new facilities for Anheuser-Busch and factories for Boeing. Nearly 80% of its revenue comes from repeat clients.

Financial Performance

While full financial information was not available for the privately held company Alberici reports that its annual revenue typically exceeds $1 billion. In 2013 the company took home $1.9 billion and was ranked the 46th largest contractor in the US by the Engineering News-Record .

In 2012 the company reported more than $530 million in industrial-related revenue thanks to a recovering economy supporting demand for major industrial projects in the US and Canada.

Strategy

In recent years the heavy construction firm has pursued acquisitions to better diversify its business both geographically and by entering new specialty markets. In 2013 for example Alberici purchased contractor Flintco LLC to broaden its reach into new markets in the southern and southwestern regions of the US. In early 2012 Alberici acquired a water treatment facility specialist to expand its service offerings in the water plant construction market.

Alberici has also become a recognized contractor in recent years which could help give the company a higher profile and thus more exposure to new potential clients. In 2013 the Associated General Contractors of St. Louis awarded Alberici with top prizes at its 16th Annual Keystone Awards for the company's work on the Seabrook Gates Complex and the Knights of Columbus Child Development Center. To date Alberici has won 14 Keystone Awards more than any other general contractor.

So far its high standing hasn't hurt business. In July 2014 Alberici was chosen to lead in the engineering procurement and construction of a major air quality improvement project — with the goal of installing environmental controls and reducing sulfur dioxide emissions by 90% — at one of the generating stations owned and operated by Alliant Energy's Wisconsin utility Wisconsin Power and Light Company.

Mergers and Acquisitions

Expanding it range of capabilities in January 2012 Alberici acquired water treatment facility specialist CAS Construction. The addition of CAS which has built facilities throughout the central and western US strengthens Alberici's capabilities in the water market. The company was renamed CAS Constructors.

In early 2013 Alberici closed on its acquisition of Flintco LLC a century-old Native American-owned contractor based in Tulsa Oklahoma. With offices in Oklahoma New Mexico Texas Arkansas and California Flintco presented an attractive geographic diversification opportunity for Alberici.

EXECUTIVES

Executive Vice President, Chris Hermann
Vice President Estimating, Matt Schumacher
Executive Vice President, Kevin Williams

LOCATIONS

HQ: ALBERICI CORPORATION
8800 PAGE AVE, SAINT LOUIS, MO 631146106
Phone: 314 733-2000
Web: WWW.ALBERICI.COM

PRODUCTS/OPERATIONS

Selected Markets

Automotive

Building

Energy
Green building
Health care
Industrial
Manufacturing/Food and Beverage
Mining infrastructure
Steel fabrication
Water and Wastewater Treatment

Selected Subsidiaries and Brands

Alberici Global Group GmbH
  Alberici Constructors Ltd. (Canada)
  Alberici Construcciones S.A. de C.V. (Mexico)
Alberici Group Inc.
  Alberici Constructors Inc.
  Alberici Global Automotive Constructors (automotive construction)
  Alberici Healthcare Constructors
  Alberici Industrial LLC
  CAS Construction LLC (water wastewater)
  Flintco LLC (Native American-owned contractor)
  Gunther-Nash Inc. (shaft slope and tunnel construction for mining industry)
  Hillsdale Fabricators (steel fabrication)
  Kienlen Constructors (structural concrete structural steel)
  Vertegy (green building consulting)

COMPETITORS

Barton Malow	Jacobs Engineering
Bechtel	McCarthy Building
Black & Veatch	Parsons Corporation
DPR Construction	Peter Kiewit Sons'
Fluor	TIC Holdings
Hensel Phelps Construction	Tutor Perini
Hoffman Corporation	Walbridge Aldinger
Hunt Construction	Walsh Group
	Zachry Inc.

HISTORICAL FINANCIALS

Company Type: Private

Income Statement   FYE: December 31

	REVENUE ($ mil.)	NET INCOME ($ mil.)	NET PROFIT MARGIN	EMPLOYEES
12/17	1,531	0	—	2,080
12/16	1,742	0	—	—
12/15	1,885	0	—	—
12/14	1,532	0	—	—
Annual Growth	(0.0%)	—	—	—

2017 Year-End Financials

Return on assets: —
Return on equity: —   Cash ($ mil.): 182
Current ratio: 1.40

ALBERICI GROUP, INC.

EXECUTIVES

Ceo, Gregory J Kozicz
Chb*, John S Alberici
Coo*, Leroy J Stromberg Jr
Exe V Pres*, Michael W Burke
Coordinator, Keeley Vickers
Safety Project Coordinator, Matt Walters
Director of Preconstruction, Frederick Biermann

LOCATIONS

HQ: ALBERICI GROUP, INC.
  8800 PAGE AVE, SAINT LOUIS, MO 631146106
Phone: 314 733-2000
Web: WWW.ALBERICI.COM

HISTORICAL FINANCIALS

Company Type: Private

Income Statement   FYE: December 31

	REVENUE ($ mil.)	NET INCOME ($ mil.)	NET PROFIT MARGIN	EMPLOYEES
12/17	838	0	—	2,000
12/16	1,036	0	—	—
12/15	1,124	0	—	—
12/14	729	0	—	—
Annual Growth	4.8%	—	—	—

2017 Year-End Financials

Return on assets: —
Return on equity: —   Cash ($ mil.): 105
Current ratio: 1.20

ALBERT EINSTEIN MEDICAL ASSOCIATES, INC.

EXECUTIVES

Pres, Barry Freedman
V Pres, Penny Rezet
Treas, Gerard McKee
Cfo, Brian Derrick
Pres, Herbert S Waxman
Treas, John Murino
Rabbi, Leah Wald
Coordinator, Nicole Amrik
Director, Len Matty
Coordinator, Monica Rollerson
Information Technology Manager, Anne Grugan

LOCATIONS

HQ: ALBERT EINSTEIN MEDICAL ASSOCIATES, INC.
  5501 OLD YORK RD STE 1, PHILADELPHIA, PA 191413018
Phone: 215 456-7890
Web: WWW.EINSTEIN.EDU

HISTORICAL FINANCIALS

Company Type: Private

Income Statement   FYE: June 30

	REVENUE ($ mil.)	NET INCOME ($ mil.)	NET PROFIT MARGIN	EMPLOYEES
06/09	670	0	—	5,251
06/08	693	33	4.9%	—
06/07	785	63	8.0%	—
06/06	718	29	4.1%	—
Annual Growth	(2.3%)	—	—	—

2009 Year-End Financials

Return on assets: —
Return on equity: —   Cash ($ mil.): 82
Current ratio: 0.40

ALBERT EINSTEIN MEDICAL CENTER

EXECUTIVES

Pres, Richard Greenberg
Placement Coordinator, Ardenia Dublin
Section Chief, Aman Amanullah
Administrator, Christine Wambold
Telehealth Project Manager, Gaesenee Kongsubto
Managing Director Hospitalist, Anita Govil
Administrator, Donna Brown
Msw, Paula Glazier
Osteopathy, Sandra S Jones
Doctor Internal Medici, Ken Hoellein

LOCATIONS

HQ: ALBERT EINSTEIN MEDICAL CENTER
  5501 OLD YORK RD STE 1, PHILADELPHIA, PA 191413098
Phone: 215 456-7890
Web: WWW.EINSTEIN.EDU

HISTORICAL FINANCIALS

Company Type: Private

Income Statement   FYE: June 30

	REVENUE ($ mil.)	NET INCOME ($ mil.)	NET PROFIT MARGIN	EMPLOYEES
06/18	820	7	1.0%	50
06/16	746	9	1.3%	—
06/15	679	38	5.7%	—
06/11	744	52	7.1%	—
Annual Growth	1.4%	(23.7%)	—	—

2018 Year-End Financials

Return on assets: 0.9%
Return on equity: 2.3%   Cash ($ mil.): 15
Current ratio: 1.60

ALBERTSONS COMPANIES, INC.

Albertsons Companies is one of the biggest supermarket retailers in the US with nearly 2300 stores in some 35 states and the District of Columbia. In addition to traditional grocery items many of the stores offer pharmacies and coffee shops and nearly 400 include adjacent gas stations. The company operates under some 20 banners including Albertsons Vons Jewel-Osco Shaw's/Star Market Safeway Acme and United. It also owns meal kit company Plated. Albertsons Companies which traces its roots to 1939 is owned by Cerberus Capital Management which has been looking to take the company public for quite some time. In 2018 the retailer called off its pending acquisition of the Rite Aid pharmacy chain amid investor pushback.

HISTORY

J. A. "Joe" Albertson Leonard Skaggs (whose family ran Safeway) and Tom Cuthbert founded Albertson's Food Center in Boise Idaho in 1939. Albertson who left his position as district manager for Safeway to run the store thought big from the start. The 10000-sq.-ft. store was not only eight times the size of the average competitor it also offered an in-store butcher shop and bakery one of the country's first magazine racks and homemade "Big Joe" ice-cream cones. The men ended their partnership in 1945 the year Albertson's was incorporated and by 1947 it operated six stores in Idaho.

The company opened its first combination food store and drugstore a 60000-sq.-ft. superstore in 1951 and began locating stores in growing suburban areas. Albertson's went public to raise expansion capital in 1959 and by 1960 had 62 stores in Idaho Oregon Utah and Washington. The food retailer acquired Greater All American Markets (1964) a grocery chain based in Downey California and Semrau & Sons (1965) of Oakland which aided the company's thrust into the California market.

Albertson's and the Skaggs chain (by this time run by L. S. Skaggs Jr.) reunited temporarily in 1969 financing six Skaggs-Albertson's food-and-drug-combination stores. (The partnership dissolved in 1977 with each side taking half of the units.) By 1986 the company had reached $5 billion in sales a fivefold increase over 1975.

The company purchased 74 Jewel Osco combination food stores and drugstores (mostly in Arkansas Florida Oklahoma and Texas) from American Stores in 1992. Co-founder Albertson died in 1993 at age 86.

In 1997 the United Food and Commercial Workers union which represents supermarket employees sued Albertson's alleging the company forced employees to work overtime without pay. (It was settled in 1999 resulting in a $22 million charge.) Also in 1997 Albertson's began selling gasoline at a few stores. Acquisitions the next year (including Buttrey Food and Drug Stores) added stores and states. That year the company began serving online customers in the Dallas-Fort Worth area.

In 1999 the grocer revisited its roots when it acquired American Stores (Skaggs' successor) which operated more than 1550 stores in 26 states. To obtain regulatory approval for the $12 billion deal Albertson's sold 145 stores in overlapping markets in three states (most were in California).

In 2001 Larry Johnston former CEO of GE Appliances took over as chairman and CEO of Albertson's. Facing increasing competition (especially from Wal-Mart) Johnston announced in March 2002 aggressive restructuring plans that included job cuts and closing 95 stores in under-performing markets specifically Memphis and Nashville Tennessee and Houston and San Antonio Texas.

Already allowing customers to order drugs online (from its online drugstore Savon.com) and groceries in Seattle Albertson's expanded its online operations to San Diego in 2001 and in early 2002 to Los Angeles San Francisco and parts of Oregon and Washington. Albertson's exited the New England drugstore market in 2002 when it sold 80 New England Osco stores to Brooks Pharmacy.

In February 2004 Albertson's launched its "Blue Ribbon" brand of beef a private-label line of roasts and steaks. Also in February the company consolidated its Southwest Intermountain Northwest and Rocky Mountain divisions to form a new Intermountain West Division and combined the Acme and Florida divisions into a new Eastern Division.

A four-and-a-half month strike by grocery workers in Southern California ended in March 2004. The dispute pitted workers' demands for continued generous health care coverage vs. management's call for cost cuts to remain profitable in the face of Wal-Mart's entry into the Southern California grocery market. In April Albertson's completed the acquisition of JS USA Holdings which runs Shaw's and Star Markets stores in New England from UK grocer J Sainsbury. The deal to buy Shaw's was worth about $2.4 billion (cash and leases). In September Albertson's gained a toehold in the gourmet-food market with the purchase of Bristol

Farms the operator of about a dozen upscale food markets in Southern California. In October Albertson's combined its Northern and Southern California food divisions into a single business unit the newly formed California Food Division. In an effort to improve efficiency Albertson's reorganized its supply chain food operations and Six Sigma Quality functions in May 2005.

In June 2006 Albertson's was sold to a consortium that included SUPERVALU CVS Cerberus Capital Management and Kimco for about $9.7 billion. Following the acquisition and the divvying up of Albertson's assets the surviving company went private and changed its name to Albertsons LLC. Concurrently Johnston left Albertsons and was succeeded by Robert Miller chairman of drugstore chain Rite Aid and the former head of Fred Meyer for eight years in the 1990s. Of the company's 27 price-impact Super Saver stores 25 closed their doors in mid-2006. Also in June the company put about 45 stores on the auction block. (It was announced in late 2006 that discount apparel retailer Ross Stores would acquire these stores.) In July the company shut down its online shopping service Albertsons.com.

In February 2007 Albertsons sold 132 grocery stores and two distribution centers in Northern California and Nevada to Save Mart Supermarkets for an undisclosed amount. Other recent closings include stores in Texas in the Dallas-Fort Worth Austin and Longview markets; Colorado; and Oklahoma.

Albertsons also sold eight of its stores in Wyoming to SUPERVALU in January 2008. The divestments continued in September with the sale of 49 supermarkets in Florida to Publix Super Markets for about $500 million. Also in 2008 Albertsons sold about 100 of its Express fuel centers in Arizona Colorado Florida Louisiana and Texas to Valero Energy and Reb Oil.

EXECUTIVES

Evp And General Counsel, Robert A. (Bob) Gordon
Evp Operations, Wayne A. Denningham
Chief Marketing & Merchandising Officer, Shane Sampson
President Jewel Osco, Mike Withers
President Seattle Division, Karl Schroeder
President Houston Division, Sidney Hopper
Chairman And Ceo, Robert G. (Bob) Miller
Chief Administrative Officer, Justin Dye
President Southwest Division, Shane Dorcheus
President United, Robert Taylor
Evp And Cio, Anuj Dhanda
President Portland Division, Greg McNiff
President Southern Division, Dennis Bassler
Evp East Operations, Susan Morris
President Shaws, Paul Gossett
President Southern California Division, Lori Raya
President Acme Markets Division, Dan Croce
Evp And Cfo, Bob Dimond
Evp West Region Operations, Jim Perkins
Evp Human Resources Labor Relations Public Affairs And Government Relations, Andrew (Andy) Scoggin
Evp Corporate Development And Real Estate, Justin Ewing
President Eastern Division, Dan Valenzuela
President Northern California Division, Tom Schwilke
President Denver Division, Todd Broderick
President Intermountain Division, Brad Street
Svp Merchandising, Dennis Clark
Vp Food Safety And Quality Assurance, Jerry Norland
Evp And Chief Data And Analytics Officer, Gautam Kotwal
Vice President Merchandising Strategy, Merritt Mccoy
Auditors: DELOITTE & TOUCHE LLP BOISE

LOCATIONS

HQ: ALBERTSONS COMPANIES, INC.
250 E PARKCENTER BLVD, BOISE, ID 837063999
Phone: 208 395-6200
Web: WWW.ALBERTSONS.COM

PRODUCTS/OPERATIONS

2018 Sales

	$ mil.	% of total
Non-perishables	26,372	44
Perishables	24,921	41
Pharmacy	4,987	8
Fuel	3,456	6
Other	799	1
Total	**60,535**	**100**

COMPETITORS

ALDI	Quality Food
Amazon.com	Roundy's
Costco Wholesale	Stater Bros.
Fry's Food	Target Corporation
H-E-B	Wal-Mart
Kroger	Wegmans
Lidl	Winn-Dixie
Publix	

HISTORICAL FINANCIALS

Company Type: Private

Income Statement   FYE: February 23

	REVENUE ($ mil.)	NET INCOME ($ mil.)	NET PROFIT MARGIN	EMPLOYEES
02/19	60,534	131	0.2%	275,000
02/18	59,924	46	0.1%	—
Annual Growth	1.0%	183.2%	—	—

2019 Year-End Financials

Return on assets: 0.6%   Cash ($ mil.): 926
Return on equity: 9.0%
Current ratio: 1.20

ALBUQUERQUE MUNICIPAL SCHOOL DISTRICT NUMBER 12

EXECUTIVES

Supt, Jason Martinez
Superintendent, Raquel Martinez Reedy
Substitute Teacher, Alysa Louton
Technology Manager, Amanda Stavig
Teacher, Amy Borchers
Middle School Math Teacher, Ann Maes
Voip Telecommunications Manage, Brian Thompson
Teacher, Cara Chavez
It Administrator, Chris Montano
Teacher, Cicely Ryan
Human Resources Operations Spe, Connie Rangel
Auditors: MOSS ADAMS LLP ALBUQUERQUE N

LOCATIONS

HQ: ALBUQUERQUE MUNICIPAL SCHOOL DISTRICT NUMBER 12
6400 UPTOWN BLVD NE, ALBUQUERQUE, NM 871104202
Phone: 505 880-3700
Web: WWW.APS.EDU

HISTORICAL FINANCIALS

Company Type: Private

Income Statement				FYE: June 30
	REVENUE ($ mil.)	NET INCOME ($ mil.)	NET PROFIT MARGIN	EMPLOYEES
06/18	954	50	5.3%	9
06/17	946	57	6.0%	—
06/16	998	11	1.2%	—
06/11	924	114	12.4%	—
Annual Growth	0.5%	(11.1%)	—	—

2018 Year-End Financials

Return on assets: 1.8%   Cash ($ mil.): 70
Return on equity: —
Current ratio: 2.80

ALDINE INDEPENDENT SCHOOL DISTRICT

EXECUTIVES

Supt, Dr Latonya Goffney
Principal, Ruth Dimmick
Principal, Jeannette Ross
Social Worker, Desiree Baham
Information Technology/Interne, Jamila
 Ashmeade-Brown
Assistant, Sonia Pace
Assistant, Akua Twumasi
Teacher, David Barfield
Manager, Pat Wade
Payroll Staff, Virginia Perez
Teacher, Abby Martinez
Auditors: WHITLEY PENN LLP HOUSTON TEX

LOCATIONS

HQ: ALDINE INDEPENDENT SCHOOL DISTRICT
 2520 WW THORNE BLVD, HOUSTON, TX 770733406
Phone: 281 449-1011
Web: WWW.ALDINEISD.ORG

HISTORICAL FINANCIALS

Company Type: Private

Income Statement				FYE: June 30
	REVENUE ($ mil.)	NET INCOME ($ mil.)	NET PROFIT MARGIN	EMPLOYEES
06/18	757	33	4.5%	7,000
06/17	743	(276)	—	—
06/16	766	104	13.7%	—
06/13	625	26	4.2%	—
Annual Growth	3.9%	5.0%	—	—

2018 Year-End Financials

Return on assets: 2.0%   Cash ($ mil.): 66
Return on equity: —
Current ratio: 2.90

ALEGENT HEALTH-BERGAN MERCY HEALTH SYSTEM

EXECUTIVES

Ceo, Cliff Robertson
Pres, Lawrence Beckman
Sr V Pres, Bonnie Burnett
Cfo, Jeanette Wojtalewicz
V Pres, Leigh Bertholf
Coo, Joan Neuhaus
Nursing Director, Kevin Schwedhelm

LOCATIONS

HQ: ALEGENT HEALTH- BERGAN MERCY HEALTH
SYSTEM
 7500 MERCY RD, OMAHA, NE 681242319
Phone: 402 398-6060

HISTORICAL FINANCIALS

Company Type: Private

Income Statement				FYE: June 30
	REVENUE ($ mil.)	NET INCOME ($ mil.)	NET PROFIT MARGIN	EMPLOYEES
06/17	727	23	3.2%	1
06/14	543	88	16.3%	—
Annual Growth	10.2%	(35.7%)	—	—

2017 Year-End Financials

Return on assets: 2.2%   Cash ($ mil.): 20
Return on equity: 3.1%
Current ratio: 1.80

ALEX LEE, INC.

The business of wholesaling groceries is only part of the bigger picture for Alex Lee. The company is a leading distributor of food and other products to retailers and food service operators. Its Merchants Distributors Inc. (MDI) subsidiary supplies food and general merchandise to more than 600 retailers in nearly a dozen mostly southeastern states. MDI's own Consolidation Services business provides warehousing and logistics services. As part of its business Alex Lee also operates Lowe's Food Stores a chain of about 100 grocery stores located in the Carolinas and Virginia. Alex and Lee George started the company in 1931. The George family continues to control Alex Lee.

Operations

Alex Lee named after Lebanese immigrant founder Moses George's two sons Alex and Lee boasts two operating companies: Merchants Distributors Inc. and Lowe's Food Stores Inc. Run as a division of MDI Consolidation Services operates under the Alex Lee and MDI umbrellas.

Geographic Reach

The company's reach extends to about a dozen US states. Alex Lee operates its Merchants Distributors Inc. (MDI) retail distribution unit across the Carolinas Georgia Tennessee Virginia Alabama West Virginia Ohio Florida Pennsylvania and Kentucky. Regional supermarket chain Lowe's Food Stores serves customers in Virginia South Carolina and North Carolina.

Strategy

The company's retail arm has grown to account for half of its total sales increasing Alex Lee's exposure to the competitive low-margin retail grocery business. Alex Lee is keeping its Lowe's stores network lean to maintain its focus on key markets. In 2012 it sold 10 stores to rival Harris Teeter in exchange for half a dozen Harris Tweeter stores. The deal which gave Lowe's $26.5 million allows Lowe's to focus on core areas such as the Triad the Triangle and Hickory. However the chain closed two stores in the Triangle region in September 2013 ahead of Publix Supermarkets entry and as grocery giant Kroger prepares to take of Harris Teeter Supermarkets. With these two grocery giants encroaching on Lowe's Food's turf the chain can look forward to more intense competition.

EXECUTIVES

Ceo, Boyd L. George, age 77
President Lowe's Food Stores, Steve Hall
President, Brian George
Svp And Cfo, Joyce Reto
Vice President, Roger Henderson
Auditors: RSM US LLP CHARLOTTE NORTH C

LOCATIONS

HQ: ALEX LEE, INC.
 120 4TH ST SW, HICKORY, NC 286022947
Phone: 828 725-4424
Web: WWW.ALEXLEE.COM

PRODUCTS/OPERATIONS

Selected Operations
Lowe's Food Stores Inc.
Merchants Distributors Inc.
 Consolidation Services Inc.

COMPETITORS

ALDI	Kroger
Associated Wholesale	MAINES
Grocers	McLane
Ben E. Keith	Meadowbrook Meat
C&S Wholesale	Company
Food Lion	SUPERVALU
H. T. Hackney	Southeastern Grocers
Harris Teeter	Sysco
Supermarkets	US Foods
Ingles Markets	Wal-Mart
K-VA-T Food Stores	Winn-Dixie

HISTORICAL FINANCIALS

Company Type: Private

Income Statement				FYE: September 29
	REVENUE ($ mil.)	NET INCOME ($ mil.)	NET PROFIT MARGIN	EMPLOYEES
09/18	2,238	14	0.7%	9,200
09/17*	2,261	4	0.2%	—
10/16	2,229	8	0.4%	—
10/15	2,287	25	1.1%	—
Annual Growth	(0.7%)	(17.3%)	—	—

*Fiscal year change

2018 Year-End Financials

Return on assets: 1.7%   Cash ($ mil.): 5
Return on equity: 2.8%
Current ratio: 1.00

ALEXIAN BROTHERS MEDICAL CENTER INC

EXECUTIVES

Ceo-Pres, John Werrbach
Treas*, James Sances
Cfo*, Sherri Vincent
Director of Operating Room, Ann Harie Herlehy
Nursing Staff Secy, Deb Pelka
Director, Lynwood A Jones
Administrative Assistant, Joan Matthys
Cardiac Physician, Mark Wernick
Facilities Manager, Jennifer Brennan
Icu Ccu Director, Amanda Kunash
Chief of Pediatrics, Renu Jain

LOCATIONS

HQ: ALEXIAN BROTHERS MEDICAL CENTER INC
   800 BIESTERFIELD RD FL 1, ELK GROVE VILLAGE,
   IL 600073310
Phone: 847 437-5500
Web: WWW.ALEXIANBROTHERSHEALTH.ORG

HISTORICAL FINANCIALS

Company Type: Private

Income Statement				FYE: June 30
	REVENUE ($ mil.)	NET INCOME ($ mil.)	NET PROFIT MARGIN	EMPLOYEES
06/16	457	58	12.8%	3,500
06/15	449	47	10.6%	—
06/14	450	29	6.6%	—
06/13	439	28	6.6%	—
Annual Growth	1.3%	26.7%	—	—

2016 Year-End Financials

Return on assets: 21.0%   Cash ($ mil.): —
Return on equity: 36.4%
Current ratio: 0.70

ALFRED I.DUPONT HOSPITAL FOR CHILDREN

EXECUTIVES

Ceo, Thomas Ferry
V Pres*, Stephen T Lawless
Cfo*, William Britton
Editor, Dustin Samples
Coordinator, Carol Eade-Viele
Coordinator, Julia Morrison
Director of Laboratory, Sonia Fair
Administrative Coordinator, Julia Mayne
Anesthesiologist, Phoebe Fisher
Doctor, Stephen Shaffer

LOCATIONS

HQ: ALFRED I.DUPONT HOSPITAL FOR CHILDREN
   1600 ROCKLAND RD, WILMINGTON, DE 198033607
Phone: 302 651-4000
Web: WWW.NEMOURS.ORG

HISTORICAL FINANCIALS

Company Type: Private

Income Statement				FYE: December 31
	REVENUE ($ mil.)	NET INCOME ($ mil.)	NET PROFIT MARGIN	EMPLOYEES
12/17	525	34	6.6%	3,068
12/16	516	(31)	—	—
12/15	450	28	6.4%	—
12/09	706	150	21.4%	—
Annual Growth	(3.6%)	(16.9%)		

2017 Year-End Financials

Return on assets: 5.4%   Cash ($ mil.): —
Return on equity: 5.7%
Current ratio: 2.80

ALGONQUIN GAS TRANSMISSION, LLC

EXECUTIVES

Pres, William T Yardley
V Pres, Frederick S Steve Bush
V Pres, Patricia M Rice
V Pres, John V Adams
V Pres, Allen C Capps
Vice-President Marketing, Bill Yardley
Senior Vice-President, Richard Kruse Jr
Auditors: DELOITTE & TOUCHE LLP HOUSTO

LOCATIONS

HQ: ALGONQUIN GAS TRANSMISSION, LLC
   5400 WESTHEIMER CT, HOUSTON, TX 770565353
Phone: 713 627-5400
Web: WWW.SPECTRAENERGY.COM

HISTORICAL FINANCIALS

Company Type: Private

Income Statement				FYE: December 31
	REVENUE ($ mil.)	NET INCOME ($ mil.)	NET PROFIT MARGIN	EMPLOYEES
12/17	504	166	32.9%	151
12/16	324	131	40.4%	—
Annual Growth	55.8%	26.9%	—	—

ALIEF INDEPENDENT SCHOOL DISTRICT

EXECUTIVES

Superintendent, H D Chambers
Cfo*, Deanna Wentz
Administrative Assistant, Brian Pilgreen
Management Info Dir, Doug Brown
Director of Teacher Personnel, Theresa Adame
Coordinator, Daniel Scudder
Administration Manager, Jonell Keller
Coordinator, Karen Flavin
Teacher, Kasonya Hardeman
Coordinator, Kelly Dolan

Coordinator, Laura Klubert
Auditors: NULL-LAIRSON PC HOUSTON TX

LOCATIONS

HQ: ALIEF INDEPENDENT SCHOOL DISTRICT
   4250 COOK RD, HOUSTON, TX 770721115
Phone: 281 498-8110
Web: WWW.ALIEFISD.NET

HISTORICAL FINANCIALS

Company Type: Private

Income Statement				FYE: August 31
	REVENUE ($ mil.)	NET INCOME ($ mil.)	NET PROFIT MARGIN	EMPLOYEES
08/18	535	(25)	—	6,000
08/17	519	(5)	—	—
08/16	514	38	7.5%	—
08/07	400	2	0.6%	—
Annual Growth	2.7%	—	—	—

2018 Year-End Financials

Return on assets: (-3.3%)   Cash ($ mil.): 151
Return on equity: (-34.6%)
Current ratio: —

ALLAN MYERS, INC.

American Infrastructure provides heavy civil construction services for projects in the Mid-Atlantic. Operating as Allan A. Myers in Pennsylvania and Delaware and as American Infrastructure in Maryland and Virginia the family-run business builds and reconstructs highways water treatment plants medical facilities and shopping centers and offers site development for homebuilders. Its quarries and asphalt plants operate under the Independence Construction Materials (ICM) subsidiary which supplies aggregates asphalt and ready-mixed concrete to its construction companies. The company is ranked by Engineering News-Record as 25th on the country's Top 50 list of heavy civil contractors.

Operations

American Infrastructure builds projects ranging from $100000 to more than $100 million per project.

As a land developer interested in conservation American Infrastructure offers a unique all-terrain tree spade vehicle that is designed to carry large mature trees harvested from heavily wooded sites intended to be replanted on developed sites. The process allows mature trees to be saved and relocated on a developed site.

Geographic Reach

American Infrastructure and its subsidiaries operate in the Mid-Atlantic region through about 20 locations (including quarries and plants) in Pennsylvania Maryland Virginia Delaware and Washington DC as well as four satellite offices in the region. The company also has 15 materials mining and/or asphalt production facilities in four states.

Sales and Marketing

American Infrastructure serves private developers general contractors departments of transportation utilities local and state governments and federal military customers throughout the Mid-Atlantic region.

Customers include CRB Military Housing Frederick Winchester Service Authority O'Brien & Gere Delaware Department of Transportation The Goldenberg Group Morgan-Keller Construction Forest Park Water Uniwest Construction Divinity Trucking Nardi Construction Hunt Building Company the City of Wilmington and Maryland State Highway Administration.

Strategy

American Infrastructure's financial capacity is strengthened by a bonding capacity of $800 million which allows it to tackle major projects. Selected projects includes Richmond Airport Connector Route 715/40 Interchange Virginia SR 29 Bridge Jersey Shore Pump Station Aberdeen Test Track Argonne Drive Bridge MARC Wedge Railyard Nicodemus Bridge Route 52 Ballenger McKinney wastewater treatment plant and Mount Holly wastewater treatment plant.

Company Background

Some past projects include Eagle Heights at Dover Air Force Base ($13.3 million) Cool Springs Reservoir ($18.6 million) and MD 43 ($46.7 million) in Baltimore County Maryland.

The company was established in 1939 as Allan A. Myers and Son a local hauling company in the suburbs of Philadelphia.

EXECUTIVES

Vice President And Corporate General Counsel, Nunzio Ruggeri
Vice President General Manager, Brock Myers
Vp Business Dev, Joe Prego
Vice President General Manager, Mark Carroll
Vice President Human Resources, Heather Peters
District Vice President, Jamie Kirby
Auditors: PRICEWATERHOUSECOPPERS LLP PH

LOCATIONS

HQ: ALLAN MYERS, INC.
1805 BERKS RD, WORCESTER, PA 19490
Phone: 610 222-8800
Web: WWW.ALLANMYERS.COM

PRODUCTS/OPERATIONS

Selected Services
Site Development
  Concrete flatwork
  Excavation and grading
  Hauling
  Large-diameter tree relocation
  Milling and paving
  Rock drilling and blasting
  Soft dig capabilities
  Stone and curb
  Stormwater management
  Survey and stakeout
  Underground utilities
Transportation
  Asphalt paving
  Box culverts
  Bridges and structures
  Concrete paving
  Maintenance of traffic
Water Resources
  New water/wastewater treatment plants
  Reservoirs and dams
  Underground reservoirs
  Water and sewer transmission lines
  Wetland mitigation and reconstruction

Selected Subsidiaries
Allan A. Myers Inc.
American Infrastructure-Maryland
American Infrastructure-Virginia
Independence Construction Materials

COMPETITORS

Angelo Iafrate
Balfour Beatty
  Infrastructure
Barnhill Contracting
Branch Group
Cherry Hill
  Construction
English Construction
  Company
Lane Construction
Peter Kiewit Sons'
Skanska USA Civil
Traylor Bros.
Vecellio & Grogan

ALLEGHENY GENERAL HOSPITAL INC

If there is a critical trauma anywhere near Pittsburgh Allegheny General Hospital (AGH) is ready to take it on. The roughly 630-bed hospital is the Level I Shock Trauma Center for the five-state region surrounding Steel City. AGH offers traditional medical and surgical services as well as cardiology care and organ transplants. The hospital also is engaged in research in areas such as neuroscience oncology trauma and genetics. AGH which treats nearly 22000 patients each year has about 800 physicians on its staff. The hospital which is affiliated with Philadelphia's Drexel University College of Medicine is a subsidiary of Allegheny Health System which itself is owned by Highmark Inc.

Operations

AGH receives more than 50000 emergency visits each year as well as had 300000 outpatient visits and more than 21000 surgical procedures. In order to receive those emergencies in an expedient manner the hospital also operates a LifeFlight aero medical service.

The hospital's cancer center provides programs for a wide range of diseases such as lung breast colon prostate brain and liver cancer.

AGH also operates a smaller satellite facility in the northern Pittsburgh suburb of McCandless as well as an outpatient facility in suburban Pittsburgh.

Strategy

In 2014 AGH proposed investing part of $175 million from Highmark Inc. in renovations and technology upgrades at its AGH and West Penn hospitals anticipating that they will accommodate more patients when Highmark insurance subscribers lose in-network access to the University of Pittsburgh Medical Center in 2015.

Company Background

AGH first opened in 1885.

EXECUTIVES

Chair Department Of Pathology, Jan Silverman
Interim President Chief Executive Officer, Michael Harlovic
Vice President Of Finance, Rick Fries
Chief Operating Officer, Ronald Andro
Vice President Of Research And Development, Stephanie Kladakis

LOCATIONS

HQ: ALLEGHENY GENERAL HOSPITAL INC
320 E NORTH AVE, PITTSBURGH, PA 152124772
Phone: 412 359-3131
Web: WWW.AHN.ORG

COMPETITORS

Butler Health System
Excela Health
Heritage Valley Health
Jefferson Regional Medical Center of Pennsylvania
Ohio Valley General
St. Clair Health
The Western Pennsylvania Hospital
UPMC
UPMC Mercy
Weirton Medical Center

HISTORICAL FINANCIALS

Company Type: Private

Income Statement — FYE: June 30

	REVENUE ($ mil.)	NET INCOME ($ mil.)	NET PROFIT MARGIN	EMPLOYEES
06/16	720	73	10.2%	5,064
06/15	700	107	15.4%	—
Annual Growth	2.8%	(31.7%)	—	—

2016 Year-End Financials

Return on assets: 19.5%   Cash ($ mil.): 1
Return on equity: —
Current ratio: 1.20

ALLEGIS GROUP, INC.

Allegis Group is one of the world's largest staffing and recruitment firms. Among its group of staffing companies are Aerotek (engineering automotive and scientific professionals) Aston Carter (recruitment for accounting finance and professional skills) and TEKsystems (information technology staffing and consulting). Other Allegis Group units include sales support outsourcer MarketSource. Allegis Group operates through more than 500 locations worldwide. Chairman Jim Davis helped found the company (originally known as Aerotek) in 1983 to provide contract engineering personnel to two clients in the aerospace industry.

Operations

Operating through a group of 10 companies Allegis Group serves businesses and organizations from the engineering automotive finance IT life sciences and other industries. The company also serves government agencies and subcontractors. Aerotek and TEKsystems are among the group's largest and most established companies; other Allegis companies provide niche services including disability recruitment through its Getting Hired unit and legal recruitment though Major Lindsey & Africa.

Allegis Group's core services include staffing and recruitment (screening onboarding and retention) executive search (CEO and board member services) sales force outsourcing and workforce management.

Geographic Reach

Hanover Maryland-based Allegis Group operates more than 500 locations around the globe including offices throughout the US Canada the UK and Europe as well as in the Middle East Asia and Asia Pacific region.

Financial Performance

Privately held Allegis Group doesn't publish consolidated financials; however the firm reports

HISTORICAL FINANCIALS

Company Type: Private

Income Statement — FYE: December 31

	REVENUE ($ mil.)	NET INCOME ($ mil.)	NET PROFIT MARGIN	EMPLOYEES
12/18	879	31	3.5%	2,000
12/17	751	21	2.8%	—
12/16	756	15	2.0%	—
12/15	745	14	1.9%	—
Annual Growth	5.7%	30.0%	—	—

2018 Year-End Financials

Return on assets: 5.5%   Cash ($ mil.): 162
Return on equity: 25.5%
Current ratio: 1.10

bringing in more than $12 billion in revenue each year.

Company Background

In 1983 Stephen Bisciotti and Jim Davis founded the company (originally known as Aerotek) in Maryland. At the time their firm matched job seekers with aeronautics engineering and light industrial positions. In the late 1980s the company expanded into the IT application markets.

Aerotek extended its reach into commercial environmental and energy industries through its 2001 acquisition of Onsite Companies. The company later changed its name to Allegis Group while the other divisions remained separate companies until eventually consolidating under the Allegis Group banner.

EXECUTIVES

It Vice President Of Finance, Celeste Slifer
Cfo, Paul J. Bowie
President, Andy Hilger
Senior Vice President, Mary Pat Smith
Vice President Organizational Development, Andrew Hilger
Vice President Human Resources, Tanya Axenson
Chairman, James C. (Jim) Davis
Auditors: PRICEWATERHOUSECOOPERS LLP BA

LOCATIONS

HQ: ALLEGIS GROUP, INC.
7301 PARKWAY DR, HANOVER, MD 210761159
Phone: 410 579-3000
Web: WWW.ALLEGISGROUP.COM

PRODUCTS/OPERATIONS

Selected Subsidiaries

Aerotek
Aerotek Aviation LLC
Aerotek Canada
Aerotek Scientific LLC
Allegis Group Canada
Allegis Group India
Major Lindsey & Africa
MarketSource Inc
Stephen James Associates
TEKsystems
TEKsystems Canada
TEKsystems Netherlands
TEKsystems United Kingdom

COMPETITORS

ASG Renaissance	Kelly Services
Adecco	Korn/Ferry
CDI	ManpowerGroup
Curran Partners	RDL Corporation
ExecuNet	Randstad Holding
Heidrick & Struggles	Robert Half
Horton International	Snelling Staffing
Innovative Management Solutions Group	Volt Information

HISTORICAL FINANCIALS

Company Type: Private

Income Statement				FYE: December 31
	REVENUE ($ mil.)	NET INCOME ($ mil.)	NET PROFIT MARGIN	EMPLOYEES
12/17	12,296	0	—	85,000
12/16	11,502	0	—	—
12/15	11,222	0	—	—
12/14	10,827	0	—	—
Annual Growth	4.3%	—	—	—

2017 Year-End Financials
Return on assets: —
Return on equity: —
Current ratio: 3.00
Cash ($ mil.): 414

ALLEGRO MICROSYSTEMS, LLC

Allegro MicroSystems' chips don't need touch to make contact. The company is one of the world's top makers of Hall-effect sensors which reduce mechanical wear by using magnets to produce contactless sensors. Automakers use these specialized components — named after an electromagnetic phenomenon called "the Hall effect" — in braking steering suspension and other systems. Allegro also makes power integrated circuits (ICs) used in printers and portable electronics along with driver controller and power interface ICs used in a variety of applications. The company is a subsidiary of Sanken Electric.

Operations

Allegro collaborates with parent Sanken which specializes in power semiconductors and Polar Semiconductor (another Sanken subsidiary) to speed development of chips used in power management energy efficiency and motion control applications.

Allegro Sanken and Polar collaborate on production as well. Production is handled by the Polar facility located in Minnesota. Testing and some assembly is done at a wholly owned subsidiary in the Philippines. Allegro also uses Taiwan-based United Microelectronics as a contract manufacturer.

Geographic Reach

Outside of Massachusetts Allegro has offices in Michigan and New Hampshire. It has global sales and design offices in Argentina France Scotland and the UK. As part of an initiative to increase business in China Allegro is building a second back-end assembly plant in Asia.

Sales and Marketing

Sales are about evenly split across North and South America Europe and Asia. Its products are sold primarily to OEMs through a sales channel that includes a direct sales force manufacturers representatives and distributors such as Digi-Key.

Strategy

Allegro has targeted the growing automotive sensors market and in 2016 it released what it called the industry's first automotive LED buck driver. The A6214 and A6216 devices are aimed at automotive lighting applications in which reliability is desired.

EXECUTIVES

Ceo, Ravi Vig
Cfo*, Mark A Feragne
V Pres*, Andre G Labrecque
Exec V Pres*, Yoshihiro Suzuki
V Pres*, Steven Miles
Treas*, Diane Macaluso
Marketing Manager, Walter Sullivan Jr
Assistant Engineer, Nathan B Baribeau
Layout, Peter Van Hoesen
Assistant Engineer, Patricia Borglund
Tech, Edward Beaudoin

LOCATIONS

HQ: ALLEGRO MICROSYSTEMS, LLC
955 PERIMETER RD, MANCHESTER, NH 031033353
Phone: 603 626-2300
Web: WWW.ALLEGROMICRO.COM

PRODUCTS/OPERATIONS

Selected Products

Current sensor integrated circuits (ICs)
Conductor sensor chips
High-side hot-swap Hall-effect current monitor chips

Magnetic digital position sensor chips
Bipolar switches
Dual-element switches
Hall-effect latches and bipolar switches
Hall-effect unipolar switches
Micropower switches and latches
Magnetic linear and angular position sensor chips
Angular position sensor chips
Linear position sensor chips
Magnetic speed sensor ICs (camshaft crankshaft transmission and wheel-speed sensor ICs)
Motor driver and interface ICs
Bipolar stepper motor drivers
Brushless DC motor drivers
Photo and ion smoke detector ICs
Regulators and lighting
LED drivers for backlighting and lighting
Regulators (single-output multiple output low-noise block)
Xenon photoflash drivers

COMPETITORS

Fairchild Semiconductor	NXP Semiconductors
Honeywell International	ON Semiconductor
Infineon Technologies	Optek Technology
Maxim Integrated Products	Power Integrations
Micronas Semiconductor	STMicroelectronics
Micropac Industries	Sypris Solutions
NVE	Texas Instruments
	Toshiba Semiconductor & Storage Products
	Vishay Intertechnology

HISTORICAL FINANCIALS

Company Type: Private

Income Statement				FYE: March 30
	REVENUE ($ mil.)	NET INCOME ($ mil.)	NET PROFIT MARGIN	EMPLOYEES
03/18	654	72	11.1%	3,500
03/17	600	65	10.9%	—
03/16	526	43	8.3%	—
03/13	489	45	9.3%	—
Annual Growth	6.0%	9.7%	—	—

2018 Year-End Financials
Return on assets: 12.1%
Return on equity: 14.8%
Current ratio: 3.40
Cash ($ mil.): 114

ALLEN LUND COMPANY, LLC

The Allen Lund Company (ALC) knows loads; it matches shippers' loads with a network of truckload and less-than-truckload (LTL) carriers. (LTL carriers collect consolidate and haul freight from multiple shippers.) The brokerage firm arranges the transport of dry refrigerated (predominantly produce) and flatbed cargo. It operates from 30 offices throughout more than 20 US states. ALC Logistics ALC Perishable Logistics and ALC International (an international division) assist shippers in managing transportation costs tracking and tracing shipments managing appointments and executing freight forward management services overseas. The company was founded in 1976 by Allen Lund and his wife Kathie Lund.

Operations

ALC has a Logistics & Software division ALC Logistics.

Geographic Reach

The company's international division provides transportation services worldwide along with transportation to and from the US including Puerto Rico Hawaii Alaska and ground transportation for Canada and Mexico.

Strategy

In an effort to expand its operation in 2012 the company opened a new office in Joplin Missouri and another in McAllen Texas which mainly focuses on handling heavy haul flatbed particularly in and out of Mexico. In addition the company opened four additional offices in 2012.

Mergers and Acquisitions

In an effort to grow its business in early 2014 ALC acquired Wisconsin based Northern Freight Service Inc. a company provides truckload LTL and intermodal services to the customers ranging from small shippers to FORTUNE 500 shippers.

EXECUTIVES

Vice President Sales And Branch Operations, Ed Lund

LOCATIONS

HQ: ALLEN LUND COMPANY, LLC
4529 ANGELES CREST HWY # 300, LA CANADA FLINTRIDGE, CA 910113247
Phone: 818 790-8412
Web: WWW.ALLENLUND.COM

PRODUCTS/OPERATIONS

Selected Services

Software and Logistics
  LTL Freight
  Scheduling
  Spot Pricing and Bid Management
  Truck Load
Transportation Services
  Dry Van
  Flatbed Trucking
  International Freight Shipping
  LTL Freight
  Refrigerated Transportation

COMPETITORS

C.H. Robinson	Ryder System
Worldwide	Universal Logistics
CEVA Logistics	

HISTORICAL FINANCIALS

Company Type: Private

Income Statement				FYE: December 31
	REVENUE ($ mil.)	NET INCOME ($ mil.)	NET PROFIT MARGIN	EMPLOYEES
12/17	515	10	2.0%	310
12/16	426	12	2.9%	—
12/15	457	13	2.9%	—
12/14	476	8	1.9%	—
Annual Growth	2.7%	5.1%	—	—

2017 Year-End Financials

Return on assets: 14.7%   Cash ($ mil.): 6
Return on equity: 28.3%
Current ratio: 1.90

ALLIANCE LAUNDRY HOLDINGS LLC

Laundry day can't come often enough for Alliance Laundry Holdings (ALH). Through its wholly owned subsidiary Alliance Laundry Systems the company designs makes and markets commercial laundry equipment used in Laundro-

mats multi-housing laundry facilities (such as apartments dormitories and military bases) and on-premise laundries (hotels hospitals and prisons). Its washers and dryers are sold under the brands Speed Queen UniMac Huebsch IPSO and Cissell. They're sold primarily in the US and Canada but also overseas. Investment firm BDT Capital Partners controls the company which was founded in 1908.

Operations

Commercial laundry equipment service and parts account for 98% of the firm's revenue. It also operates an equipment financing business which accounts for the rest.

Geographic Reach

North America is Wisconsin-based ALH's largest market accounting for about 70% of sales. Europe and Asia each represent about 10% of sales. The remainder comes from markets in Latin America the Middle East and Africa. The company's manufacturing facilities are located in Wisconsin and Wevelgem Belgium.

Sales and Marketing

ALH relies on an expansive distribution network to bring its goods to market. The company's more than 550 distributors in North America and 150-plus international distributors serve its Laundromat and on-premise laundry customers. Its multi-family housing laundry customers are served by ALH's roster of more than 100 route operators.

Financial Performance

The company's sales topped $505 million in 2012 a 10% increase compared with 2011. Net income fell 30% over the same period to $16.4 million as a result of a loss from early retirement of debt and higher expenses. The company attributed the gain in sales (its third in as many years) to increases across all of its markets with the exception of Europe. Increased sales volumes and price increases primarily in the US and Canada drove results. The strong performance over the past three years pushed sales to an all-time high following a drop-off during the recession.

Strategy

Despite difficult economic conditions globally ALH has seen its business strengthen driven by resilience in North America and international expansion. (The company is fortunate that consumers view clean clothes as an necessity with economic conditions historically having limited effect on frequency of use of commercial laundry equipment.) In the US and Canada the equipment financing business is posting higher earnings and demand for commercial laundry equipment is rising. Markets in Latin America including Colombia Peru and Venezuela are driving double-digit sales growth in the region. Expansion in Asia in such markets as Australia China the Philippines and Thailand is another growth driver.

In pursuit of future growth in 2013 the company completed a $23 million investment to increase production capacity for current and new products and to purchase tooling and equipment for its plant in Wisconsin. The expansion added more than 20000 square feet to the plant's existing assembly metal stampingand press shop facilities. The project increased ALH's production capacity for small chassis washers and dryers by more than 40% enabling the company to meet increasing consumer demand for its products.

EXECUTIVES

MBR, Thomas F Lesperance
MBR, Bruce Rounds
MBR, William Przybysz
MBR, Scott Gaster
MBR, Robert T Wallace
Manager, Matt Amend
Procurement Coordinator, Caitlyn Smith

Customer Support Representativ, Dan Miracle
Desktop Administrator, Elvis Rosario
Sales Assistant, Jennifer Dych
Associate Payables Clerk, Jill Jahn
Auditors: PRICEWATERHOUSECOOPERS MILWAU

LOCATIONS

HQ: ALLIANCE LAUNDRY HOLDINGS LLC
221 SHEPARD ST, RIPON, WI 549711390
Phone: 920 748-3121

COMPETITORS

BSH Bosch und Siemens	Haier Group
Hausger ᵒte	Miele
Electrolux	Whirlpool
GE Appliances & Lighting	

HISTORICAL FINANCIALS

Company Type: Private

Income Statement				FYE: December 31
	REVENUE ($ mil.)	NET INCOME ($ mil.)	NET PROFIT MARGIN	EMPLOYEES
12/14	726	29	4.1%	2,100
12/12	505	16	3.2%	—
12/09	393	16	4.2%	—
Annual Growth	13.1%	12.3%	—	—

2014 Year-End Financials

Return on assets: 2.4%   Cash ($ mil.): 48
Return on equity: 31.0%
Current ratio: 1.40

ALLIED BUILDING STORES, INC.

EXECUTIVES

Pres, Dale Mercer
Cfo*, Gary McManus
V Pres*, Kevin Cockrell
V Pres*, Tommy Ormond
V Pres*, Mike Cunningham
V Pres*, Larry Whitmire
Human Resources Director, Sherry Lewis
Senior Analyst, Mike Lindsay
Accounting Staff, Shirley Hinton
Merchandise Manager, Bill Harris
Buyer Apprentice, Cody Garlington
Auditors: HEARD MCELROY & VESTAL LLC

LOCATIONS

HQ: ALLIED BUILDING STORES, INC.
850 KANSAS LN, MONROE, LA 712034776
Phone: 318 699-9100

HISTORICAL FINANCIALS

Company Type: Private

Income Statement				FYE: August 31
	REVENUE ($ mil.)	NET INCOME ($ mil.)	NET PROFIT MARGIN	EMPLOYEES
08/18	570	0	0.0%	125
08/17	529	0	0.0%	—
08/16	497	0	0.0%	—
08/15	485	0	0.0%	—
Annual Growth	5.6%	3.0%	—	—

Return on assets: 0.1%   Cash ($ mil.): 3
Return on equity: 0.3%
Current ratio: 1.10

ALLIED SECURITY HOLDINGS LLC

Better than a blanket Allied Security Holdings gives customers a sense of security. One of the largest private contract security firms in the US it does business as AlliedBarton Security Services. It recruits and employs trained security guards to serve thousands of customers (some of which are large FORTUNE 500 companies) and their facilities. They include government facilities hospitals offices ports residential communities shopping centers and universities. The firm also provides employment and background screening services through its HR Plus subsidiary. In mid-2016 AlliedBarton merged with Universal Services of America to create Allied Universal North America's largest security services group.

EXECUTIVES

Vice President Of Operations, John Russell
Vice President Information Technology, Betty Ritts
Vice President Training And Development, Brent O'Bryan
Vice President Of Leasing, David Dunkelman
Regional Vice President, Jason Stapleton
Regional Vice President, Rafael Sorto

LOCATIONS

HQ: ALLIED SECURITY HOLDINGS LLC
161 WASHINGTON ST STE 600, CONSHOHOCKEN, PA 194282083
Phone: 484 351-1300
Web: WWW.AUS.COM

COMPETITORS

AFI International	Kroll
Asset Protection & Security Services	Securitas
Command Security	TransNational Security
G4S Secure Solutions	Walden Security
Guardsmark	Whelan Security

HISTORICAL FINANCIALS

Company Type: Private

Income Statement   FYE: December 31

	REVENUE ($ mil.)	NET INCOME ($ mil.)	NET PROFIT MARGIN	EMPLOYEES
12/14	2,149	24	1.1%	53,760
12/13	2,042	51	2.5%	—
12/12	1,923	43	2.3%	—
Annual Growth	5.7%	(25.0%)	—	—

2014 Year-End Financials

Return on assets: 2.6%   Cash ($ mil.): 51
Return on equity: —
Current ratio: 1.80

ALLINA HEALTH SYSTEM

Allina Health System is a not-for-profit health care system that works to protect people's #1 asset — their good health. The system owns and operates a dozen hospitals a network of nearly 100 clinics and specialty centers and a whole bunch of pharmacies. It has licensed bed capacity of 2451 acute care beds. Its vast system of provider locations serve residents throughout Minnesota and western Wisconsin providing disease prevention programs along with specialized inpatient and outpatient services. Allina's Aspen Medical Group division also operates a range of outpatient clinics providing primary and specialty care.

Operations

Allina has 12 hospitals (about 1800 beds) more than 90 clinics and 15 pharmacies. The largest hospital in the group is Abbott Northwestern Hospital (600 beds) followed by United Hospital which has about 570 beds. Five of Allina's hospitals are in the Minneapolis/St. Paul metropolitan area (where the system has more than a 30% share of the health care market) five are scattered throughout the rest of Minnesota and one is in western Wisconsin. The health system reported more than 103000 inpatient admissions in 2016; it also had some 1.4 million outpatient admissions. Each year it has around 360000 emergency care visits about 16000 births and more than 7 million clinic visits.

Regina Hospital has a 57-bed acute care hospital a 61-bed skilled care nursing home and a 134-bed assisted living facility. It also operates three outpatient multi-specialty clinics. Located in Minneapolis/St. Paul District One Hospital provides a broad range of health care services to Faribault and the surrounding communities.

Geographic Reach

The health care system's hospitals are located in Burnsville Champlin Coon Rapids Edina Inver Grove Heights Maplewood Plymouth St. Paul Shakopee and Woodbury in Minnesota and in River Falls in Wisconsin.

Financial Performance

In 2016 Allina Health had $3.9 billion in revenue a 4% increase over the prior year thanks to a 3% gain on hospital net patient revenue. A nurse's strike cut into operating income and the system reported a $27.4 million operating loss in 2016 (versus operating income of $155.3 million in 2015). Among the striking nurses' complaints was the Minnesota Nurses Association's allegations that estimate Allina Health has lost $80 million investing in interest-rate swaps — $80 million that could have been used to improve pay benefits and patient care.

Strategy

Despite Allina's already hefty size the system has a partnership with retail clinic provider MinuteClinic which offers basic health care at CVS Health stores. The hospital also has a multi-year collaboration with HealthPartners designed to reduce total medical costs at both hospitals.

In early 2017 Allina Health and insurance giant Aetna created a health plan joint venture — Allina Health and Aetna Insurance Company — to serve employers and individuals in the Minneapolis/St. Paul area. The venture is designed to streamline the patient experience by coordinating health care services with insurance benefits and administrative services.

The system's wide-ranging locations combined with its huge number of facilities have prompted Allina to embark on a multi-year initiative to install electronic medical records (EMR) at all of its hospitals and clinics. The installation gives medical providers the ability to track a patient's progress through any of the myriad health care settings operated by Allina. The EMR also gives patients access to coordinated care between the different providers as well as the ability to see portions of their medical records and lab results online. Patients can also schedule appointments and make use of a number of health and wellness tools all via the internet.

Allina was the first Minnesota health care organization to earn the Davies Award the industry's preeminent award for health information technology.

EXECUTIVES

System Vp; President Mercy Hospital, Sara Criger
Hospitalist And Lead Physician Abbott Northwestern; District Medical Director Allina Medical Clinic, Robert A. Wieland
Ceo, Penny Ann Wheeler
System Vp; President Abbott Northwestern Hospital, Ben Bache-Wiig
System Vp; President United Hospital, Thomas (Tom) O'Connor
Evp Administration And Cfo, Duncan P. Gallagher
Evp Hospital And Specialty Services, Daniel McGinty
Medical Director For Quality, Steven Bergeson
Pharmacy Manager, Matthew Wolf
Director Of Pharmacy, Jill Strykowski
Director Of Pharmacy Ambulatory, Lee Mork
Vice President Of Marketing, Cathy Runck
Director Of Nursing, Karen Tennis
Senior Vice President And Chief Information Office, Jonathan Shoemaker
Medical Director, John Mageli
Vice President Of Patient Care Services, Maribeth Olson
Senior Vice President Finance And Treasury, Richard Magnuson
Vice President Payor Contract Reimb, Margaret Hasbrouck
Senior Vice President, Lisa Smith
River Falls Area Hospital Pharmacy Manager, Scott Erickson
Vice President Patient Care Services, Sue Miller
Vice President Of Medical Affairs, Ryan Else
Vice President Of Cardiovascular Services, Mike Rasmussen
Vice President Medical Affairs, Dennis O'hare
Chairman, Mark S. Jordahl
Treasurer, Anne Uttermark
Auditors: KPMG LLP MINNEAPOLIS MINNESO

LOCATIONS

HQ: ALLINA HEALTH SYSTEM
2925 CHICAGO AVE, MINNEAPOLIS, MN 554071321
Phone: 612 262-5000

PRODUCTS/OPERATIONS

Selected Services

Care at home
Chronic and advanced illness
Clinics
Home oxygen and medical equipment
Hospitals
Lab services
Medical Services
Medical transportation
Pharmacies
Providers
Specialty services
Urgent care

Selected Hospitals

Abbott Northwestern Hospital (Minneapolis MN)
Buffalo Hospital (Buffalo MN)
Cambridge Medical Center (Cambridge MN)
District One Hospital (Faribault MN)
Mercy Hospital (Coon Rapids MN)
New Ulm Medical Center (New Ulm MN)
Owatonna Hospital (Owatonna MN)
Phillips Eye Institute (Minneapolis MN)
Regina Hospital (Hastings MN)

River Falls Area Hospital (River Falls WI)
St. Francis Regional Medical Center (Shakopee MN)
United Hospital (St. Paul MN)
Unity Hospital (Fridley MN)

COMPETITORS

Bethesda Hospital
Catholic Health Initiatives
CentraCare Health
Children's Hospitals and Clinics of Minnesota
Fairview Health
Hazelden Betty Ford
HealthEast Care System
Mayo Clinic
Methodist Hospital (MN)
North Memorial Health Care
Park Nicollet Health Services
Regions Hospital
St. John's Hospital (Minnesota)
University of Minnesota Medical Center

HISTORICAL FINANCIALS
Company Type: Private

Income Statement   FYE: December 31

	REVENUE ($ mil.)	NET INCOME ($ mil.)	NET PROFIT MARGIN	EMPLOYEES
12/17	4,279	173	4.0%	26,400
12/16	3,947	74	1.9%	—
Annual Growth	8.4%	131.3%	—	—

2017 Year-End Financials
Return on assets: 3.8%   Cash ($ mil.): 36
Return on equity: 6.4%
Current ratio: 0.60

ALLWAYS HEALTH PARTNERS, INC.

Neighborhood Health Plan (NHP) is a not-for-profit health plan provider that offers health insurance products and related services to more than 300000 members in Massachusetts. The organization is a leading provider of managed health care for members of MassHealth the state's Medicaid program for low-income and disabled residents. But it also provides commercial health plans for small businesses as well as low-cost and no-cost family and individual plans for people who qualify for subsidized health coverage under Massachusetts' 2006 health care reform law. NHP maintains a provider network of more than 4300 primary care physicians 13000 specialists and dozens of hospitals. The company was founded in 1986.

Sales and Marketing
NHP markets its products to individuals families and employers.

Its care network includes primary care providers specialists and hospitals such as Massachusetts General Hospital and Boston Children's Hospital. It also includes community health centers across the state.

In 2015 NHP hired Mechanica to manage its marketing branding and advertising efforts.

Strategy
The company's Partnership for Community Health initiative with Partners HealthCare with the Massachusetts League of Community Health Centers announced $6 million in grants for community health centers throughout Massachusetts.

In 2013 NHP was granted approval to expand coverage into Greater Plymouth County.

EXECUTIVES

President And Ceo, David Segal
Chief Medical Officer, Paul Mendis
Vp Operations And Cio, Marilyn Daly
Vp Operations, Katie Catlender
Interim Cfo, Doug Thompson
Vice President Of Clinical Operations, Deb Bonin
Vice President, Patty Rich
Chairman, Matthew E. Fishman

LOCATIONS

HQ: ALLWAYS HEALTH PARTNERS, INC.
399 REVOLUTION DR, SOMERVILLE, MA 021451444
Phone: 617 772-5500
Web: WWW.ALLWAYSHEALTHPARTNERS.ORG

COMPETITORS

Aetna
Blue Cross and Blue Shield of Massachusetts
CIGNA
ConnectiCare
Fallon Community Health Plan
Harvard Pilgrim
Health New England
MVP Health Plan
Tufts Health Plan
UnitedHealth Group

HISTORICAL FINANCIALS
Company Type: Private

Income Statement   FYE: December 31

	REVENUE ($ mil.)	NET INCOME ($ mil.)	NET PROFIT MARGIN	EMPLOYEES
12/15	2,178	(22)	—	340
12/14	1,743	(108)	—	—
12/13	1,380	(68)	—	—
Annual Growth	25.6%		—	—

2015 Year-End Financials
Return on assets: (-4.9%)   Cash ($ mil.): 120
Return on equity: (-11.6%)
Current ratio: 0.90

ALLY BANK

Ally Bank is on your side when it comes to banking. Formerly known as GMAC Bank Ally Bank (which is a subsidiary of government-backed Ally Financial) offers savings and money market accounts as well as traditional and no-penalty CDs. The online bank also offers interest checking accounts. The bank offers its services online and over the phone; it operates no physical branch locations. Clients also can use any ATM in the US and Ally will reimburse any fees charged by other banks. Ally Bank was revamped and renamed in 2009 in the midst of GM's (very public) financial difficulties. Predecessor GMAC Bank had been in operation since 2001.

EXECUTIVES

Chb-Pres-Ceo, Diane E Morais
Exec V Pres, Jeffrey J Brown
Cfo, James N Young
Secretary, Cathy L Quenneville
Director of Remarketing Sales, Mark Juday
Operations Manager, Michael Snel
Area Sales Manager, Anthony Stoothoff
CRA Officer, Jan Bergeson
Senior Credit Manager, Anthony Zimmer

LOCATIONS

HQ: ALLY BANK
6985 S UNION PARK CTR # 435, MIDVALE, UT
840474177
Phone: 801 790-5005
Web: WWW.ALLY.COM

COMPETITORS

Bank of America	Citibank
BofI	E*TRADE Bank
Charles Schwab	State Farm

HISTORICAL FINANCIALS
Company Type: Private

Income Statement   FYE: December 31

	ASSETS ($ mil.)	NET INCOME ($ mil.)	INCOME AS % OF ASSETS	EMPLOYEES
12/16	123,547	1,273	1.0%	42
12/07*	28,472	291	1.0%	—
06/06	3,586	0	0.0%	—
Annual Growth	38.0%	114.3%	—	—

*Fiscal year change

2016 Year-End Financials
Return on assets: 1.0%   Sales ($ mil): 6,427
Return on equity: 7.2%

ALMOST FAMILY, INC.

EXECUTIVES

Pres, Steven Guenthner
Branch Director, Debra Love
Graphic Designer, Lisa Landers
Vice President of Business Dev, Brent Piepenbring
Senior Living Coordinator, Jackie Alexander
Board Member, Jonathan Goldberg
Auditors: ERNST & YOUNG LLP LOUISVILLE

LOCATIONS

HQ: ALMOST FAMILY, INC.
9510 ORMSBY STATION RD # 300, LOUISVILLE, KY
402235016
Phone: 502 891-1000
Web: WWW.LHCGROUP.COM

COMPETITORS

Amedisys	HCR ManorCare
Apria Healthcare	Home Instead
Capital Senior Living	Hooper Holmes
Chemed	LHC Group
Continucare	NHC
Diversicare Healthcare Services	National Home Health
	Odyssey HealthCare
Gentiva	Providence Service
Girling Health Care	U.S. Physical Therapy

HISTORICAL FINANCIALS
Company Type: Private

Income Statement   FYE: December 29

	REVENUE ($ mil.)	NET INCOME ($ mil.)	NET PROFIT MARGIN	EMPLOYEES
12/17	796	20	2.6%	14,200
12/16*	623	18	2.9%	—
01/16	532	19	3.7%	—
12/14	495	13	2.7%	—
Annual Growth	17.1%	14.7%	—	—

*Fiscal year change

2017 Year-End Financials
Return on assets: 2.8%   Cash ($ mil.): 11
Return on equity: 4.0%
Current ratio: 2.00

ALPINE SCHOOL DISTRICT

EXECUTIVES

Supt, Vern Henshaw
Supt*, Samuel Y Jarman
Coordinator, Alex Goold
Accounting Staff, Steven Reese
Public Information Director, David Stephenson
Coordinator, Barbara Langford
Director, Adam Dajany
Research/Development Director, David Mower
Director of Teacher Personnel, John Spencer
Administrative Vice President, Jim Melville
Transportation Director, DOT Dean
Auditors: SQUIRE & COMPANY PC OREM UT

LOCATIONS

HQ: ALPINE SCHOOL DISTRICT
575 N 100 E, AMERICAN FORK, UT 840031758
Phone: 801 610-8400
Web: WWW.ALPINESCHOOLS.ORG

HISTORICAL FINANCIALS

Company Type: Private

Income Statement				FYE: June 30
	REVENUE ($ mil.)	**NET INCOME** ($ mil.)	**NET PROFIT MARGIN**	**EMPLOYEES**
06/18	680	77	11.4%	8,000
06/17	638	129	20.3%	—
Annual Growth	6.7%	(40.3%)	—	—

ALSCO INC.

Alsco has built a big business outfitting its customers in uniforms linens and related products. Operating from more than150 branches in about 10 countries worldwide the company (whose name stands for American linen supply company) rents and sells uniforms linens towels and clean room garments to more than 300000 customers in North America. It also manages janitorial services provides washroom supplies and launders and sterilizes garments. Alsco serves the automotive food processing restaurant medical and IT industries as well as the federal government. Founded in 1889 by George Steiner the company is owned and operated by the Steiner family.

Geographic Reach
Utah-based Alsco has locations in Australia Brazil Canada China Germany Italy New Zealand Singapore Switzerland Thailand and the US.

Strategy
Alsco heavily promotes its green cleaning solutions and the company has focused on international expansion in recent years. In 2014 the company expanded its uniform and linen services in Texas with a branch in San Antonio and service centers in Austin Houston and Waco.

In addition to uniforms and linens Alsco supplies promotional products for trade shows conventions golf outings sales meetings and other special events and occasions.

EXECUTIVES

Vice President, Steve Larson
Vice President Finance And Chief Financial Officer, Jim Kearns

LOCATIONS

HQ: ALSCO INC.
505 E 200 S STE 101, SALT LAKE CITY, UT 841022053
Phone: 801 328-8831
Web: WWW.ALSCO.COM

PRODUCTS/OPERATIONS

Selected Products and Services
Clean room garments
Gown room management
Hospitality/restaurant apparel
Laundry services
Linens
Mats
Mops
Napkins
Restroom service
Towels
Uniform rental and sales
Vacuum filters
Washroom supplies

COMPETITORS

ARAMARK	ISS A/S
Angelica Corporation	Rentokil Initial
Berendsen	ServiceMaster
Cintas	Sodexo USA
Crothall Healthcare	Superior Uniform Group
Diversey	Swisher Hygiene
Ecolab	Tranzonic
G&K Services	UniFirst
Healthcare Services	

HISTORICAL FINANCIALS

Company Type: Private

Income Statement				FYE: December 31
	REVENUE ($ mil.)	**NET INCOME** ($ mil.)	**NET PROFIT MARGIN**	**EMPLOYEES**
12/18	922	25	2.7%	16,000
12/17	892	64	7.2%	—
12/16	704	38	5.5%	—
12/15	683	30	4.5%	—
Annual Growth	10.5%	(6.5%)	—	—

2018 Year-End Financials
Return on assets: 2.2%   Cash ($ mil.): 34
Return on equity: 3.8%
Current ratio: 1.70

ALSTON CONSTRUCTION COMPANY, INC.

Panattoni Construction Inc. (PCI)Â is in theÂ business of building businesses. The design/build general contractor specializes in commercial and industrial construction projects which include manufacturing and distribution facilities master-planned business parks and office and retail buildings. The company provides construction management services for such clients as Clorox Amazon.com PetSmart and Whirlpool.The company's project portfolio ranges from smaller 2500 sq. ftÂ offices to large warehouses spanning more than one million sq. ft.Â PCI operates from 20 offices in Arizona California ColoradoÂ Florida Georgia Illinois Indiana MissouriÂ Nevada New JerseyÂ OregonÂ Tennessee Texas and Washington.

EXECUTIVES

Vice President, Jim Wegman
Senior Vp And Regional Manager Of, Chad Bouck
Vice President General Manager, William Hancock
Auditors: CAMPBELL TAYLOR & COMPANY AC

LOCATIONS

HQ: ALSTON CONSTRUCTION COMPANY, INC.
8775 FOLSOM BLVD STE 201, SACRAMENTO, CA 958263725
Phone: 916 340-2400
Web: WWW.ALSTONCO.COM

COMPETITORS

Alter Group	H and M Construction
Balfour Beatty Construction	KPRS Construction
Bechtel	Skanska USA Building
Fluor	Turner Corporation

HISTORICAL FINANCIALS

Company Type: Private

Income Statement				FYE: December 31
	REVENUE ($ mil.)	**NET INCOME** ($ mil.)	**NET PROFIT MARGIN**	**EMPLOYEES**
12/17	865	13	1.6%	200
12/15	642	6	1.1%	—
12/14	470	3	0.8%	—
12/13	332	4	1.3%	—
Annual Growth	27.0%	33.6%	—	—

2017 Year-End Financials
Return on assets: 6.3%   Cash ($ mil.): 43
Return on equity: 57.6%
Current ratio: 1.10

ALTICOR INC.

Where there's a will (and an army of independent sales representatives) there's Amway. Operated through holding company Alticor Amway is the world's top direct-selling company with millions of individual ABOs (Amway Business Owners) pitching everything from air filters to vitamins. The company makes some 450 unique products across the categories of nutrition (which generates about half of sales) beauty and personal care and home. It is active in more than 100 countries across the globe with Asia (led by China) its largest market. Alticor is controlled by the families of Rich DeVos and Jay Van Andel who founded Amway in 1959.

Operations
Nutrition products (supplements skin care products weight management programs) account for about 50% of total Amway sales. Beauty and personal care items (makeup shampoo toothpaste) generate about a quarter of sales and home products (water and air filters cookware cleaners) contribute about 20%. The company's top products include Nutrilite supplements Artistry color cosmetics eSpring water treatment systems and XS energy drinks.

Geographic Reach
Based in Ada Michigan Amway operates in more than 100 countries. Its top markets by sales are China the US and South Korea; other leading markets include India Japan Malaysia Russia Taiwan and Thailand.

The company has manufacturing facilities farms and warehouses in Brazil China Hungary India Japan Mexico the Netherlands Poland Russia

South Korea Taiwan Thailand Vietnam and the US.

Sales and Marketing

Amway's 450-plus products are marketing worldwide by more than 3 million independent distributors who purchase the products and resell them. The company provides a host of support services including personal mentors brand centers online learning tools and call centers.

Financial Performance

While privately-owned Alticor doesn't report full results Amway reported global sales of $8.6 billion in 2017 down from $8.8 billion in 2016. The company points to a challenging Chinese market for its revenue decline over the past few years

Strategy

Amway's strategy is pretty straight-forward: continue to enhance and expand its line of products to serve more markets and appeal to more customers and create tools that make selling those products easier for the 3+ million ABOs (Amway Business Owners).

In 2017 Amway introduced a new formula for its Nutrilife Double X product one of the best-selling supplements in the world that includes a phytonutrient blend designed to help the body fight free radicals. Other additions to the company's product portfolio that year include a reformulated Essentials by Artistry skincare line and its first in-car air filtration system Atmosphere Drive. Amway also pushed its XS brand of energy drinks into new countries in 2017 including China and India with more launches planned for 2018. The company has more than 800 patents worldwide and another 250 pending applications.

Direct selling of course looks a lot different in the age of Amazon than it did some 60 years ago when Amway was founded. The company has been making significant investment in tools and technologies in recent years to enable its ABOs to better compete. It has spent some $70 million in mobile apps for ABOs including the flagship Amway MyBiz app which provides back office data and analytics. In addition Amway has boosted its own customer service capabilities with instant messaging bots and other technologies to help it handle the more than 12 million annual customer requests. Other recent initiatives include a content sharing app for ABOs in the Philippines a beauty app for customers in South Korea and a one-stop product education and purchase portal in for ABOs in China.

EXECUTIVES

President And Director; President Amway; And President Quixtar, Doug DeVos
Executive Vice President Of Sales Amway Regions, Jim Payne
General Vice President Attorney, Scott Balfour
Vice President Regulatory Affairs And Quality Assurance, John Coyle
Vice President Internal Audit, Nick Thole
Vp Human Resources, Kelly Savage
Chairman, Steve Van Andel
Tres, Jeffery C Tuori

LOCATIONS

HQ: ALTICOR INC.
7575 FULTON ST E, ADA, MI 493550001
Phone: 616 787-1000
Web: WWW.AMWAY.COM

PRODUCTS/OPERATIONS

2017 Sales

	% of total
Nutrition	50
Beauty & personal care	26
Home	21
Other	3
Total	**100**

Selected Brands

Nutrition
  Nutrilite
Beauty & personal care
  Artistry
  G&H
  Glister
  Satinique
Home
  Amway Home
  Atmosphere Sky
  eSpring
  iCook
Other
  XS

COMPETITORS

Avon	Melaleuca
Bath & Body Works	New Avon
Bluestem Brands	Newell Brands
Colgate-Palmolive	Nikken
Estée Lauder	Nu Skin
Forever Living	Procter & Gamble
GNC	Revlon
Herbalife Ltd.	Shaklee
Johnson & Johnson	Tupperware Brands
L'Oréal	Unilever PLC
Mary Kay	

HISTORICAL FINANCIALS

Company Type: Private

Income Statement				FYE: December 31
	REVENUE ($ mil.)	NET INCOME ($ mil.)	NET PROFIT MARGIN	EMPLOYEES
12/16	8,783	0	—	14,000
12/15	9,459	0	—	—
12/14	10,804	0	—	—
12/13	11,754	0	—	—
Annual Growth	(9.3%)	—	—	—

2016 Year-End Financials

Return on assets: —
Return on equity: —
Current ratio: 1.10
Cash ($ mil.): 1,457

ALTISOURCE SOLUTIONS, INC.

EXECUTIVES

Ceo, William B Shepro
Cfo, Michelle Esterman
Coo, Marcello Mastioni
Auditors: DELOITTE & TOUCHE LLP ATLANT

LOCATIONS

HQ: ALTISOURCE SOLUTIONS, INC.
1000 ABERNATHY RD STE 200, ATLANTA, GA 303285604
Phone: 770 612-7007

HISTORICAL FINANCIALS

Company Type: Private

Income Statement				FYE: December 31
	ASSETS ($ mil.)	NET INCOME ($ mil.)	INCOME AS % OF ASSETS	EMPLOYEES
12/13	724	133	18.5%	700
12/12	429	115	27.0%	—
Annual Growth	68.9%	15.4%	—	—

2013 Year-End Financials

Return on assets: 18.5%
Return on equity: 84.8%
Sales ($ mil): 768

ALTRU HEALTH SYSTEM

Altru Health System provides medical care throughout northeastern North Dakota and northwestern Minnesota. The integrated health care network administers everything from primary care to inpatient medical and surgical care through its Altru Hospital (with roughly 265 beds) and about a dozen primary care clinics. It also operates a cancer center a rehabilitation center dialysis facilities and home health providers. For area seniors Altru Health operates Parkwood Place a senior living facility that provides several levels of care to residents depending on need. The not-for-profit center was formed in 1997 by the integration of Grand Forks Clinic and United Health Services.

Operations

The system employs more than 200 physicians and serves over 200000 residents. Altru Hospital with a Level II Trauma designation has a 16-bed critical care unit a 10-bed surgical critical care unit pulmonary and sleep labs and cardio and pulmonary rehabilitation facilities.

In 2013 Altru Health System had 12603 inpatient discharges 275000 outpatient discharges 1600 births and some 29000 emergency visits.

Sales and Marketing

Medicare and Medicaid payments accounted for more than 50% of net patient revenue in 2013; Blue Cross accounted for more than 30%. Self-pay and other third-party accounts represented the rest of patient revenue.

In 2013 the system paid $901799 for advertising up from $892641 in 2012.

Financial Performance

Altru Health System's net revenue increased 1% to $457 million in 2013 due to increased patient services charges. Net income also rose 5% to $26 million due to gains on investments. Cash flow also held steady rising 3% to $40 million due to a decline in cash used in receivables plus an increase in cash generated from accounts payable and accrued expenses.

Strategy

The system looks for opportunities to expand both its locations and its services. To that end it is building a new hospital in Grand Forks to replace Altru. The replacement will be built in three stages and is expected to be complete by 2020. The replacement for its main clinic is expected to be operational by 2022.

Altru opened its newest hospital the 45-bed Altru Specialty Center in Grand Forks North Dakota in 2014. The center has four operating rooms and offers such services as elective orthopedic and podiatry surgeries joint replacement and inpatient rehabilitation.

In 2013 Altru opened clinics in Thief River Falls Minnesota and East Grand Fork; it also expanded a clinic in Devils Lake North Dakota.

Company Background

The system was created in 1997 when United Hospital merged with the Grand Forks Clinic.

EXECUTIVES

Ceo, David Molmen
Cfo, Dwight Thompson
Chief Medical Executive, Eric Lunn
Administrative Director Primary Care, Renee Axtman
Chief Nurse Executive, Margaret Reed
Administrative Director Information Services, Mark Waind
Administrative Director Medical Specialty Care, Kerry Carlson
Coo, Brad Wehe

Executive Director Altru Health Foundation, Jon Green
Medical Director Primary Care, Colleen Swank
Medical Director Surgical Services, Scott Charette
Administrative Director Cardiology And Musculoskeletal Services, Kelly Hagen
Administrative Director Surgical Services, Joseph Myers
Vice President For Finance Operations University Of North Dakota, Liz Brekke
Chairman, John Snustad
Vice Chairman, Kris Compton
Department Secretary, Michelle Cummings

LOCATIONS

HQ: ALTRU HEALTH SYSTEM
1200 S COLUMBIA RD, GRAND FORKS, ND 582014044
Phone: 701 780-5000
Web: WWW.ALTRU.ORG

PRODUCTS/OPERATIONS

2013 Sales

	$ mil.	% of total
Net patient service	426	93
Other operating revenue	31	7
Total	**457**	**100**

2013 Net Patient Revenue

	% of total
Medicare	41
Blue Cross	31
Medicaid	11
Other third party	14
Patients	3
Total	**100**

Selected Centers

Bariatric Center
Breast Center
Cancer Center
Diabetes Center
Family Birthing Center
Grief Center
Hand Therapy Center
Hearing Center
Heart and Vascular Center
Joint Replacement Center
Medical Fitness Center
Outpatient Procedure Center
Pre-Admission Center
Psychiatry Center
Truyu Aesthetic Center

COMPETITORS

Avera Health
Catholic Health Initiatives
First Care
Sanford Health-MeritCare
St. Alexius Medical Center
St. Mary's Innovis Health

HISTORICAL FINANCIALS

Company Type: Private

Income Statement

FYE: December 31

	REVENUE ($ mil.)	NET INCOME ($ mil.)	NET PROFIT MARGIN	EMPLOYEES
12/18	566	(13)	—	3,800
12/17	549	20	3.7%	—
12/16	549	10	1.9%	—
12/15	488	16	3.3%	—
Annual Growth	**5.1%**	**—**	**—**	**—**

2018 Year-End Financials

Return on assets: (-2.5%)
Return on equity: (-5.2%)
Current ratio: 4.10
Cash ($ mil.): 34

AMC ENTERTAINMENT INC.

EXECUTIVES

Manager, Beth Olson
Vice President Investor Relations, John Merriwether
Vice President And Chief Audit Executive, Kathy Weekley
Vice President Guest Engagement, Julius Lai
Vice President Social Media And Content, Pamela Sandler
Vice President Benefits And Employment Practices, Rosalind Reeves
Vice President Government Affairs, Robert Bruchman
Vice President Leasing (legal), Ron Herman
Auditors: KPMG LLP KANSAS CITY MISSOUR

LOCATIONS

HQ: AMC ENTERTAINMENT INC.
11500 ASH ST, LEAWOOD, KS 662117804
Phone: 913 213-2000
Web: WWW.AMCTHEATRES.COM

HISTORICAL FINANCIALS

Company Type: Private

Income Statement

FYE: December 31

	REVENUE ($ mil.)	NET INCOME ($ mil.)	NET PROFIT MARGIN	EMPLOYEES
12/15	2,946	103	3.5%	19,700
12/14	2,695	64	2.4%	—
12/13	2,749	364	13.3%	—
12/12	811	(37)	—	—
Annual Growth	**53.7%**	**—**	**—**	**—**

2015 Year-End Financials

Return on assets: 2.0%
Return on equity: 6.7%
Current ratio: 0.60
Cash ($ mil.): 209

AMCAP FUND INC

EXECUTIVES

President, Marry Clemeson
Treas, Mary C Hall
Sr V Pres, Gordon Crawford
Sr V Pres, Paul G Haaga Jr
SEC, Julie Williams
Principal, Walter Stern

LOCATIONS

HQ: AMCAP FUND INC
333 S HOPE ST STE LEVB, LOS ANGELES, CA 900713003
Phone: 213 486-9200

HISTORICAL FINANCIALS

Company Type: Private

Income Statement

FYE: February 28

	ASSETS ($ mil.)	NET INCOME ($ mil.)	INCOME AS % OF ASSETS	EMPLOYEES
02/18	64,019	9,994	15.6%	300
02/16	44,148	(2)	—	—
Annual Growth	**20.4%**	**—**	**—**	**—**

2018 Year-End Financials

Return on assets: 15.6%
Return on equity: 15.7%
Sales ($ mil): 723

AMERICA CHUNG NAM (GROUP) HOLDINGS LLC

Ever wondered where all that paper and plastic to be recycled goes? If this company is any indication a lot of it — some 10 million tons — goes to China through America Chung Nam. The company sells recovered fiber sources to Chinese paper mills where they can be converted into fiberboard cardboard and packaging. It also collects and exports a number of grades of post-consumer plastics. The company sources its materials through exclusive relationships with recycling facilities waste management companies and distribution centers. Founder Yan Cheung owns the company.

Operations

America Chung Nam makes and supplies recovered paper recyclable plastics (including PET HDPE LDPE) ferrous and non-ferrous metals and livestock feed ingredients (including canola meal and fish meal).

It annually exports more 10 million tons of recovered paper from North America Europe and Asia.

The company's main customer for fiber is Nine Dragons a paper mill company founded by American Chung Nam's founders.

Geographic Reach

The company has operations in North America Asia and Europe. It has offices in the US (Jersey City Los Angeles and Wilmington North Carolina) Europe (the Netherlands and the UK) and Asia (China and Japan).

Strategy

America Chung Nam supplies fiber materials to Nine Dragons Paper China's largest packaging manufacturer. Nine Dragons (also owned by the owner of American Chung Nam) converts these products into the packaging material that is used to ship various Chinese products to consumers across the world. Once delivered the packaging is ready for recycling and export back to China. In 2013 Nine Dragons operated 35 production lines and had an annual capacity of 14 million metric tons.

The strong relationships with Nine Dragons other paper mills suppliers and transportation partners help the company to adapt to a changing marketplace. In addition to expanding into the recycled plastics market the company is looking for new opportunities in other segments of the recoverable materials market including ferrous and non-ferrous metals.

Company Background

America Chung Nam was founded in 1990 by Yan Cheung and Ming Chung Liu. Recognizing the demand for packaging materials driven by China's product exports and having a ready source for fiber materials through America Chung Nam Cheung established Nine Dragons Paper in 1996.

EXECUTIVES

Chief Executive Officer Worldwide Marketing, Peter Wang
Deputy Ceo Asia Pacific Region, Teresa Cheung
President And Ceo, Yan Cheung

LOCATIONS

HQ: AMERICA CHUNG NAM (GROUP) HOLDINGS LLC
1163 FAIRWAY DR, CITY OF INDUSTRY, CA
917892846
Phone: 909 839-8383
Web: WWW.ACNI.NET

COMPETITORS

Caraustar Recovered Fiber Group	International Paper Weyerhaeuser
Guanwei Recycling	

HISTORICAL FINANCIALS

Company Type: Private

Income Statement				FYE: December 31
	REVENUE ($ mil.)	NET INCOME ($ mil.)	NET PROFIT MARGIN	EMPLOYEES
12/09	1,125	16	1.5%	250
12/08	1,363	7	0.6%	—
12/07	1,088	9	0.9%	—
Annual Growth	1.7%	31.1%	—	—

2009 Year-End Financials

Return on assets: 9.3% Cash ($ mil.): 18
Return on equity: 32.9%
Current ratio: 1.40

AMERICAN ASSOCIATED PHARMACIES

EXECUTIVES

Pres-Ceo, Jon Copeland
SEC-Treas, Kevin Foshee
Territory Manager, Jim Kilborn
Territory Manager, Richard Nastasi
Personnel Director, Brandy Hooper
Director of Sales Central Regi, Mark Wegelin
Territory Manager, Brian Weglarz
Vice President of Preferred PA, Tracie Heyrman
Pog Analyst, Tim Bland
Auditors: GANT CROFT ASSOCIATES PC SC

LOCATIONS

HQ: AMERICAN ASSOCIATED PHARMACIES
201 LNNIE E CRAWFORD BLVD, SCOTTSBORO, AL
357697408
Phone: 256 574-7521

HISTORICAL FINANCIALS

Company Type: Private

Income Statement				FYE: December 31
	REVENUE ($ mil.)	NET INCOME ($ mil.)	NET PROFIT MARGIN	EMPLOYEES
12/15	642	(0)	—	220
12/14	513	0	0.0%	—
12/13	498	0	0.0%	—
12/12	476	0	0.1%	—
Annual Growth	10.5%	—	—	—

2015 Year-End Financials

Return on assets: (-0.1%) Cash ($ mil.): 34
Return on equity: (-1.1%)
Current ratio: 1.00

AMERICAN BALANCED FUND, INC.

EXECUTIVES

Chb-Ceo, Robert G O'Donnell
Pres, Paul G Haaga Jr
V Pres, Hilda L Applbaum
Sr V Pres, Abner Goldstine
Sr V Pres, John H Smet
V Pres, J Dale Harvey
V Pres, Jeffrey T Lager
Asst Treas, R Marcia Gould
SEC, Patrick F Quan
Auditors: DELOITTE & TOUCHE LLP COSTA M

LOCATIONS

HQ: AMERICAN BALANCED FUND, INC.
1 MARKET, SAN FRANCISCO, CA 941051596
Phone: 707 864-3945
Web: WWW.CAPITALGROUP.COM

HISTORICAL FINANCIALS

Company Type: Private

Income Statement				FYE: December 31
	ASSETS ($ mil.)	NET INCOME ($ mil.)	INCOME AS % OF ASSETS	EMPLOYEES
12/17	128,462	23,932	18.6%	9
12/15	87,394	4,903	5.6%	—
12/00	6,203	832	13.4%	—
12/99	5,996	218	3.6%	—
Annual Growth	18.6%	29.8%	—	—

2017 Year-End Financials

Return on assets: 18.6% Sales ($ mil): 2,698
Return on equity: 19.1%

AMERICAN BUREAU OF SHIPPING

One of the world's largest ship classification societies American Bureau of Shipping (ABS) offers inspection and analysis services to verify that vessels are mechanically and structurally fit. The not-for-profit company's surveyors examine ships in major ports throughout the world assessing whether the vessels comply with ABS rules for design construction and maintenance. Additionally its engineers consult with shipbuilders on proposed designs and repairs. The not-for-profit company operates from more than 150 offices in about 70 countries. For-profit subsidiaries ABS Group offers risk management consulting services while ABS Nautical Systems provides fleet management software. ABS was founded in 1862.

Geographic Reach

Houston-based ABS operates through a network of 150 offices in 70 countries. Its main divisional offices reside in China Singapore the UK and the US. The organization's technology headquarters is in Houston and it has research centers in Singapore China Korea Canada and Brazil.

Strategy

ABS's strategy for growth includes building upon its core capabilities in inspection integrity management and project quality management services. These services have also been the foundation for growth in the fast-growing regions of the Middle East and the Asia-Pacific. Recent initia-

tives include the formation of ABS Global Gas Solutions Team to leverage the organization's liquid natural gas and liquified petroleum gas capabilities in 2013. Also in 2013 ABS made significant investments in Singapore to strengthen its engineering and survey capabilities and lay the foundation for strategic global initiatives in the region.

ABS's efforts are meeting with some success: its classed fleet surpassed the 200 million gross tons in 2013. In June of 2013 the organization classed the world's largest container ship the Maersk Mc-Kinney M ller.

Additionally ABS Group invested in building its presence in Europe with added business development resources in London and the acquisition of Safetec Nordic AS in Trondheim Norway. The investment positioned ABS Group to capitalize on projects in the North Sea from both Norway and Aberdeen.

In 2012 ABS opened a new energy technology center in Korea and extended its services in Singapore an important region for catering to the deepwater sector.

EXECUTIVES

Vice President Engineering, Matthew Tremblay
Vice President Human Resources, John Ryder
Vice President Treasurer, James Clutterbuck
Vice President, Darren Leskoski
Senior Vice President Service Delivery, Robert Giuffra
Administrative Professional Vice President Of Offshore Technology, Lucille Farley
Regional Vice President Mexico And Equatorial America, Homero Guerra
Vice President And Chief Compliance Officer, Marta Johnson
Vice President, John Mcdonald
Vp Strategic Projects, Kash Mahmood
Auditors: ERNST & YOUNG LLP HOUSTON TX

LOCATIONS

HQ: AMERICAN BUREAU OF SHIPPING
1701 CITY PLAZA DR, SPRING, TX 773891831
Phone: 281 673-2878
Web: WWW.EAGLE.ORG

PRODUCTS/OPERATIONS

Selected Services
Casualty Response
Certification (Marine and Container)
Classification
Environmental
Statutory
Training
Type Approval

COMPETITORS

Accenture	Cotecna Inspection
BSI Group	Lloyd's Register
Booz Allen	Norske Veritas
Bureau Veritas	SGS
ClassNK	

HISTORICAL FINANCIALS

Company Type: Private

Income Statement				FYE: December 31
	REVENUE ($ mil.)	NET INCOME ($ mil.)	NET PROFIT MARGIN	EMPLOYEES
12/17	484	62	12.8%	3,000
12/12	1,134	155	13.7%	—
12/11	726	143	19.8%	—
12/09	648	180	27.9%	—
Annual Growth	(3.6%)	(12.5%)	—	—

2017 Year-End Financials

Return on assets: 3.6% Cash ($ mil.): 109
Return on equity: 4.5%
Current ratio: 0.90

AMERICAN CHEMICAL SOCIETY

This group has a lot of chemistry. With nearly 157000 members the American Chemical Society (ACS) is the world's largest scientific society. The not-for-profit organization provides information career development and educational resources to member chemists chemical engineers and technicians. ACS also publishes dozens of magazines journals and books and its Chemical Abstracts Service provides access to an online database o more than 70 million literature and research summaries from around the world. ACS also serves as an advocate for its members on public policy issues. The ACS Member Insurance Program provides insurance plans to members.

Operations
ACS has 47 Journals more than 44 million Chemical Abstracts records; more than 125 million CAS REGISTRY organic and inorganic substances; 83 million ACS journal article downloads; and $25.1 million Petroleum Research Grants. It has 185 local sections. The society offers members the opportunity to participate in 33 specialty divisions ranging from food and agriculture to industrial and engineering chemistry.

Geographic Reach
Based in Washington DC the ACS' international membership exceeds 24000 and represents more than 140 countries. The More than 60% of the content and articles published in ACS journals and abstracts originates from outside the US. The society hosts an annual International Chemistry Olympiad.

Financial Performance
DELELTE!

Strategy
ACS is in partnership with six other chemical societies from around the Pacific Basin. ACS Publications implemented a strategic partnership with Figshare an open repository that promotes broad access to scientific research data.

Company Background
ACS was founded in 1876 and chartered by the US Congress in 1937.

EXECUTIVES

Executive Director And Ceo, Thomas M. (Tom) Connelly
Cfo And Treasurer, Brian Bernstein
President Acs Publications Division, Brian Crawford
Director Member And Scientific Advancement Division, Denise Creech
President Chemical Abstracts Service (cas), Manuel Guzman
Director Education Division, Mary Kirchhoff
Cio Washington It Operations, John Sullivan
President, Diane Grob Schmidt
Vice President Sales And Marketing, Brandon Nordin
Vice President Of Sales, Sean Evans
Vice President Information Technology, John Gustafson
Vice President, Celia Henry
Chair, Pat N. Confalone
Secretary, Flint Lewis
Assistant Treasurer And Director Of Investments, Jordan Levine
Assistant Treasurer Pubs Bus Sup, Robert Beard
Auditors: LB KPMG LLP MC LEAN VA

LOCATIONS

HQ: AMERICAN CHEMICAL SOCIETY
1155 16TH ST NW, WASHINGTON, DC 200364892
Phone: 202 872-4600
Web: WWW.ACS.ORG

HISTORICAL FINANCIALS
Company Type: Private

Income Statement   FYE: December 31

	REVENUE ($ mil.)	NET INCOME ($ mil.)	NET PROFIT MARGIN	EMPLOYEES
12/13	568	62	11.0%	2,000
12/08	451	(38)	—	—
12/05	411	26	6.4%	—
Annual Growth	4.1%	11.3%		

2013 Year-End Financials
Return on assets: 4.8%   Cash ($ mil.): 37
Return on equity: 7.0%
Current ratio: 0.60

AMERICAN ELECTRIC POWER SERVICE CORPORATION

EXECUTIVES

Chb, Nicholas K Akins
Ex Vp Policy-Fin-Strat Plannin, Susan Tomasky
Deputy Gen Counsel, Jeffrey D Cross
Sr Vp Reg Svcs, J Craig Baker
Vp Corp Comm, Dale E Heydlauff
Exec V Pres- Cfo, Holly Koeppel
Svp Gen Counsel & SEC, John B Keane
Executive Vice President, Donald M Clements Jr
Dir Federal Agency Relations, Sabrina V Campbell
Vice-President, Van Der Walde
Information Specialist, Carole Root

LOCATIONS

HQ: AMERICAN ELECTRIC POWER SERVICE CORPORATION
1 RIVERSIDE PLZ FL 1 # 1, COLUMBUS, OH 432152373
Phone: 614 716-1000
Web: WWW.AEP.COM

HISTORICAL FINANCIALS
Company Type: Private

Income Statement   FYE: December 31

	REVENUE ($ mil.)	NET INCOME ($ mil.)	NET PROFIT MARGIN	EMPLOYEES
12/16	1,348	0	—	2,152
12/05	12,111	1,037	8.6%	—
12/02	1,391	0	—	—
Annual Growth	(0.2%)	—	—	—

2016 Year-End Financials
Return on assets: —   Cash ($ mil.): 16
Return on equity: —
Current ratio: 0.40

AMERICAN FURNITURE WAREHOUSE CO INC

Tony the Tiger hawking home furnishings might give some marketers pause but the combination seems to work for American Furniture Warehouse. American Furniture's television commercials often spotlight white-haired president and CEO Jake Jabs (who has become a well-known personality in the state as well as in the home furnishings industry) accompanied by baby exotic animals mostly tigers. The company sells furniture electronics and decor at discounted prices. It boasts about a dozen retail locations in Colorado and Arizona and sells through its website which also features bridal and gift registries. The company has built a reputation as a home-spun local furniture retailer. Jabs bought the company in 1975.

Geographic Reach
American Furniture has locations in the Colorado cities of Aurora Englewood Centennial Lakewood Thornton Westminster Colorado Springs Firestone/Longmont Fort Collins Glenwood Springs Pueblo and Grand Junction. In Arizona it has locations in Phoenix Gilbert and Glendale. It serves customers in the neighboring states of Wyoming Utah Kansas Nevada and New Mexico.

Financial Performance
American Furniture's 2013 sales reached more than $390 million.

Strategy
In 2013 the company made its first move outside Colorado when it opened a 630000-sq.-ft. store in Gilbert Arizona (near Phoenix). It opens another store — in Glendale Arizona — in late 2014. American Furniture hopes to net $3.4 million in direct revenue from the Glendale store during its first year in operation. The furniture retailer also has an eye on expanding into north Scottsdale.

EXECUTIVES

Pres-Ceo, Jacob Jabs
SEC-Treas*, Lori Tielke
General Manager, Kevin Michalek
Director, Rob Naish
Director of Communications, Charlie Shaulis
Sales Manager, Anna Campbell
Buyer, Tony Mitchell
Warehouse Manager, Jeff Harris
Customer Manager, Adriane Johnston
Information Technology/Interne, Daniel Jackson
Auditors: WIPFLI LLP DENVER CO

LOCATIONS

HQ: AMERICAN FURNITURE WAREHOUSE CO INC
8820 AMERICAN WAY, ENGLEWOOD, CO 801127056
Phone: 303 799-9044
Web: WWW.AFWONLINE.COM

PRODUCTS/OPERATIONS

Selected Products
Decorative accessories
Electronics
Furniture
  Bedroom
  Chairs
  Dining room
  Home office
  Indoor/outdoor
  Living room
  Occasional tables
  Sectionals
  Sofas
  Youth bedroom
Lighting
Mattresses
Rugs

COMPETITORS

Ashley Furniture	Rooms To Go
Big Lots	Sears
Costco Wholesale	Target Corporation
Kmart	Wal-Mart
Pier 1 Imports	

HISTORICAL FINANCIALS

Company Type: Private

Income Statement				FYE: March 31
	REVENUE ($ mil.)	NET INCOME ($ mil.)	NET PROFIT MARGIN	EMPLOYEES
03/18	673	28	4.2%	1,900
03/17	652	25	3.9%	—
03/16	615	23	3.7%	—
03/15	530	20	3.8%	—
Annual Growth	8.3%	11.5%	—	—

2018 Year-End Financials

Return on assets: 7.6% Cash ($ mil.): 79
Return on equity: 9.1%
Current ratio: 2.70

AMERICAN HIGH INCOME TRUST

EXECUTIVES

President, Larry Clemmenson
V Pres-Treas, Mary C Cremin
V Pres, Michael J Downer
SEC, Julie F Williams
Auditors: DELOITTE & TOUCHE LLP COSTA M

LOCATIONS

HQ: AMERICAN HIGH INCOME TRUST
333 S HOPE ST STE 5200, LOS ANGELES, CA
900713061
Phone: 949 766-6305

HISTORICAL FINANCIALS

Company Type: Private

Income Statement				FYE: September 30
	ASSETS ($ mil.)	NET INCOME ($ mil.)	INCOME AS % OF ASSETS	EMPLOYEES
09/18	16,817	577	3.4%	1
09/16	17,336	1,555	9.0%	—
Annual Growth	(1.5%)	(39.1%)		

2018 Year-End Financials

Return on assets: 3.4% Sales ($ mil): 1,093
Return on equity: 3.5%

AMERICAN HONDA FINANCE CORPORATION

If you're fonda the idea of driving a Honda you might want to call on American Honda Finance. Operating as Honda Financial Services the company provides retail financing in the US for Honda and Acura automobiles motorcycles all-terrain ve-hicles power equipment and outboard motors. Its American Honda Service division administers service contracts while Honda Lease Trust offers leases on new and used vehicles. Honda Financial Services also offers dealer financing and related dealer services. Ancillary services include servicing loans and securitizing and selling loans into the secondary market. A subsidiary of American Honda Motor the company began as a wholesale motorcycle finance provider in 1980.

Operations

American Honda Finance (AHF) acquires retail installment contracts and closed-end vehicle lease contracts from purchasers and lessees and authorized Honda and Acura dealers. It also provides these authorized dealers with wholesale flooring and commercial loans.

AHF also acquires used auto loans of non-Honda and non-Acura vehicles and provides these third-party dealers iwth wholesale loans. Additionally the company offers vehicle service contracts services underwriting and pricing of consumer financing services and incentive financing programs for Honda and Acura products.

Geographic Reach

The company is headquartered in Torrance California and operates nine regional offices that support all authorized Honda and Acura dealers across North America.

Financial Performance

While full financials of the subsidiary were not available American Honda Finance's (AHF) revenue has been on the uptrend as auto sales continue to strengthen along with the US economy. Revenue in fiscal 2014 (ended March 31 2014) grew by 22% to Å 5.97 trillion ($58.1 billion) thanks to larger revenues from its parent company's auto business and positive foreign currency exchange rates.

Despite higher selling general and administrative expenses and R&D expenses AHF's operating income also increased 39% to Å 290.9 billion ($2.83 billion) in 2014 after the company continued its cost reduction measures.

Strategy

American Honda Finance Corp. (AHFC) exists to provide stability to support sales of new and used Honda and Acura vehicles throughout North America Honda Motor's largest market. To that end AHFC seeks to preserve funding diversity balanced liquidity and maintain a prudent maturity profile. To spur growth of its US business in 2012 the company opened its ninth regional office a 25000-square-foot facility in Charlotte North Carolina to serve Honda buyers in the Carolinas Maryland Tennessee Virginia and West Virginia.

EXECUTIVES

Ceo, Hideo Tamaka
Sr V Pres*, Stephan Smith
V Pres-Cfo*, John Weisickle
Information Specialist, Hung Le
Information Technology Directo, David Newallis
Information Technology Directo, John Thompson
Corporate Recruiter, Breanna Robinson
Assistant Manager ABS Accounti, Jean Yamatsuka
Admin Asst, Debbie Lemire
Marine OEM Sales Manager, Dennis Ashley
Dealer Relations Manager, Jessica Havalotti
Auditors: KPMG LLP LOS ANGELES CALIFOR

LOCATIONS

HQ: AMERICAN HONDA FINANCE CORPORATION
20800 MADRONA AVE, TORRANCE, CA 905034915
Phone: 310 972-2239
Web: WWW.HONDAFINANCIALSERVICES.COM

Selected Offices

Alpharetta GA
Charlotte NC
Cypress CA
Elgin IL
Holyoke MA
Irving TX
San Ramon CA
Torrance CA
Wilmington DE

COMPETITORS

Ally Financial
Automotive Finance Corporation
Bank of America
Credit Acceptance
Ford Motor Credit
Mercedes-Benz Financial Services USA
Mitsubishi Motors Credit of America
Toyota Motor Credit

HISTORICAL FINANCIALS

Company Type: Private

Income Statement				FYE: March 31
	ASSETS ($ mil.)	NET INCOME ($ mil.)	INCOME AS % OF ASSETS	EMPLOYEES
03/17	69,854	753	1.1%	1,000
03/16	66,653	910	1.4%	—
03/08	50,526	(45)	—	—
03/07	41,431	394	1.0%	—
Annual Growth	5.4%	6.7%		

2017 Year-End Financials

Return on assets: 1.1% Sales ($ mil): 2,066
Return on equity: 5.9%

AMERICAN INSTITUTES FOR RESEARCH IN THE BEHAVIORAL SCIENCES

The American Institutes for Research (AIR) lives and breathes to enhance human performance. The not-for-profit organization conducts behavioral and social science research on topics related to education and educational assessment health international development and work and training. Clients including several federal agencies use AIR's research in developing policies. As a major ongoing initiative the organization provides tools to improve education both in the US and internationally particularly in disadvantaged areas. John C. Flanagan who developed the Critical Incident Technique personnel-selection tool to identify human success indicators in the workplace founded the organization in 1946.

Operations

AIR has organized its group into six program areas: Analysis of Longitudinal Data in Education Research Assessment Education Healthand Social Development Workforce and International Development Evaluation and Research.

AIR's assessment program focuses on score reports and online reporting tools to translate large-scale testing data on student achievement into a benchmark for school performance. International human and social development programs aim to improve the quality of life and education in developing areas. It works to achieve this through teacher and school administrator training curriculum development and teaching materials coupled with mobilizing health communications HIV/AIDS education and raising awareness about such issues as child labor exploitation. Working with governments private health care providers and the general public AIR's health programs design implement and evaluate the impact of health care policies.

Geographic Reach

Begun as a small research group affiliated with the University of Pittsburgh AIR's corporate headquarters and business offices are located in Washington DC. The group maintains about a dozen offices in the US. Domestic offices are located in San Mateo and Sacramento California; Atlanta Georgia; Honolulu Hawaii; Chicago and Naperville Illinois; Indianapolis Indiana; Baltimore Frederick and Silver Spring Maryland; Portland Oregon; Columbus Ohio; Chapel Hill North Carolina; New York New York; and Waltham Massachusetts. AIR also operates nearly 10 international offices located in Egypt Honduras Kyrgyzstan Liberia Tajikistan Cote d'Ivoire and Zambia.

Strategy

The National Center for Education Statistics a key source for statistical data about education and AIR team up to develop large-scale databases for policymaking. Among various efforts AIR designs surveys and assessments develops questionnaires and tests items as well as informational materials. It also helps in producing The Condition of Education the agency's chief report. The organization's successes include campaigns that address public health emergencies such as the flu and H1N1 and the prevention of HIV/AIDS heart disease and birth defects.

Adding to its educational research capabilities AIR has pursued a number of strategic alliances and acquisitions. In 2015 SEDL joined forced with AIR. The combined organizations will have new and enhanced capabilities around for example disability research as well as an increased capacity to conduct large-scale randomized control trials and provide technical assistance to diverse populations across a broader geographic area.

In 2015 AIR awarded a $500000 grant to Impact Network a nonprofit seeking to make high-quality education in Zambia sustainable.

In 2014 AIR launched the Education Policy Center.

Company Background

In 2011 the National Center for Analysis of Longitudinal Data in Educational Research (CALDER) began operating as a joint project of AIR. CALDER examines how public policies and community conditions impact teacher-student results. A year earlier AIR acquired Learning Point Associates a Chicago-based firm that delivers research in the educational sector. Its clients include state education agencies single-school districts private foundations and for-profit organizations.

EXECUTIVES

Chm, Patricia B Gurin
Pres-Ceo*, David Myers
Cfo-Sr V Pres*, Marijo Ahlgrimm
SEC*, Dona Kilpatrick
Facilities Specialist, Derrick Lewis
Scientist, San Keller
Project Director, Susan Heil
Researcher, Audrey Peek
Senior Research Analyst, Cheryl Graczewski
Researcher, Jason Katz
Researcher, Leah Brown
Auditors: RUBINO & COMPANY BETHESDA MA

LOCATIONS

HQ: AMERICAN INSTITUTES FOR RESEARCH IN THE BEHAVIORAL SCIENCES
1000 THMAS JFFERSON ST NW, WASHINGTON, DC 200073835
Phone: 202 403-5000
Web: WWW.AIR.ORG

PRODUCTS/OPERATIONS

Selected Program Areas

Education
Education assessment
Health
Human development
International development
Work & training

HISTORICAL FINANCIALS
Company Type: Private

Income Statement   FYE: December 31

	REVENUE ($ mil.)	NET INCOME ($ mil.)	NET PROFIT MARGIN	EMPLOYEES
12/17	497	55	11.1%	1,700
12/16	474	43	9.2%	—
12/15	488	45	9.2%	—
12/14	396	24	6.2%	—
Annual Growth	7.9%	30.6%	—	—

2017 Year-End Financials

Return on assets: 12.4%   Cash ($ mil.): 33
Return on equity: 16.5%
Current ratio: 1.70

AMERICAN LEBANESE SYRIAN ASSOCIATED CHARITIES, INC.

EXECUTIVES

Pres-Ceo, Rick Shadyac Jr
Cmo, Emily Callahan
Chief Admin Ofcr, Emily S Greer
CIO, Robert Machen
Cfo, Jeffrey T Pearson
Svp-Ceo Ops, Betty Macdougall
Executive Director of Fin, Sherri Tagg
Auditors: DELOITTE & TOUCHE LLP MEMPHIS

LOCATIONS

HQ: AMERICAN LEBANESE SYRIAN ASSOCIATED CHARITIES, INC.
501 SAINT JUDE PL, MEMPHIS, TN 381051905
Phone: 901 578-2000
Web: WWW.STJUDE.ORG

HISTORICAL FINANCIALS
Company Type: Private

Income Statement   FYE: June 30

	REVENUE ($ mil.)	NET INCOME ($ mil.)	NET PROFIT MARGIN	EMPLOYEES
06/17	1,741	658	37.8%	1,300
06/16	1,161	(27)	—	—
06/15	1,182	251	21.2%	—
06/13	976	210	21.5%	—
Annual Growth	15.6%	33.0%	—	—

2017 Year-End Financials

Return on assets: 15.8%   Cash ($ mil.): 178
Return on equity: 16.1%
Current ratio: —

AMERICAN MITSUBA CORPORATION

EXECUTIVES

Pres-Ceo-Coo, Masayoshi Shirato
V Pres*, Hideaki Fujii
V Pres*, Takashi Ichinokawa
V Pres*, Hiroshi Naito
Sr V Pres*, David Stevens
Sr V Pres*, Mishel Ashtary
Acctng Mgr, Ken Garber
Auditors: PLANTE & MORAN PLLC AUBURN

LOCATIONS

HQ: AMERICAN MITSUBA CORPORATION
2945 THREE LEAVES DR, MOUNT PLEASANT, MI 488584596
Phone: 989 779-4962
Web: WWW.AMERICANMITSUBA.COM

HISTORICAL FINANCIALS
Company Type: Private

Income Statement   FYE: December 31

	REVENUE ($ mil.)	NET INCOME ($ mil.)	NET PROFIT MARGIN	EMPLOYEES
12/16	697	(2)	—	765
12/15	687	9	1.4%	—
12/14	558	5	0.9%	—
12/13	557	17	3.1%	—
Annual Growth	7.7%	—	—	—

2016 Year-End Financials

Return on assets: (-0.9%)   Cash ($ mil.): 24
Return on equity: (-2.0%)
Current ratio: 1.70

AMERICAN MUNICIPAL POWER, INC.

Power to the Public is the motto of American Municipal Power (AMP). The non-profit membership organization supplies wholesale power to more than 80 community-owned distribution utilities in Ohio 30 in Pennsylvania 6 in Michigan 5 in Virginia 3 in Kentucky 2 in West Virginia 1 in Indiana and 1 in Delaware (a joint action agency). AMP and its members own and operate plants that generate more than 1500 MW of power. The company also handles projects on behalf of the Ohio Municipal Electric Generating Agency (OMEGA) Joint Ventures program (jointly owned generation and transmission projects). The power generation company is owned by its member municipalities. AMP member utilities serve some 635000 customers.

Operations

The company provides electric capacity and energy and furnishes other services to its members on a cooperative basis. As part of its joint venture responsibilities American Municipal Power also operates the Belleville Hydroelectric Plant a 42 MW plant located in Belleville West Virginia. AMP's wholly-owned subsidiary AMPO provides assistance in establishing electric and gas aggregation programs to benefit local consumers.

Geographic Reach
Ohio-based American Municipal Power serves 130 members - 129 member municipal electric communities in the states of Ohio Pennsylvania Michigan Indiana Virginia Kentucky and West Virginia as well as the Delaware Municipal Electric Corporation a joint action agency headquartered in Smyrna Delaware.

Financial Performance
American Municipal Power (AMP) reported $982.5 million in revenue in 2013 representing a 19% increase over 2012. Rising electric revenues and service fees up 19% and 44% respectively drove growth in 2013. AMP's net margin expanded to $5.3 million from $1.9 million over the same period.

Strategy
Expanding into Indiana in 2014 AMP gained its newest member the city of Cannelton.

Implementing a strategy to reduce carbon emissions the company is building six hydroelectric projects on the Ohio River. The Meldahl plant (with 105 MW of capacity) will be the largest hydroelectric plant on the Ohio River. American Municipal Power also has a deal to develop up to 300 MW of solar power with solar panel company Standard Energy. It also has wind power and landfill gas operations. Indeed AMP members' projected energy resource mix will be approximately 21% renewable by 2015.

In 2013 American Municipal Power and the Vermont Energy Investment Corporation agreed to extend the operation of Efficiency Smart beyond the end of the year. The program provides a broad range of energy efficiency services for the power coop's member utilities. Some 49 member communities in Ohio Pennsylvania and Michigan participated in Efficiency Smart in 2013.

Company Background
To replace lost capacity in 2011 it acquired the Fremont Energy Center in Fremont Ohio from FirstEnergy for $500 million. The 707-MW natural gas combined-cycle facility commenced commercial operation in early 2012. In 2010 American Municipal Power also secured a 368-MW ownership stake in the Prairie State Energy Campus in Illinois.

Expanding geographically American Municipal Power moved into a seventh state in 2011 when it made Delaware Municipal Electric its 129th member.

American Municipal Power was founded in 1971.

EXECUTIVES

Senior Vice President Generation Operations, Scott Kiesewetter

Assistant Vice President Energy Policy, Randell Corbin

Vice President Of Power Supply Planning, Mike Migliore

Auditors: PRICEWATERHOUSECOOPERS LLP CO

LOCATIONS

HQ: AMERICAN MUNICIPAL POWER, INC.
1111 SCHROCK RD STE 100, COLUMBUS, OH 432291155
Phone: 614 540-1111
Web: WWW.AMPPARTNERS.ORG

PRODUCTS/OPERATIONS

2013 Sales

	% of total
Electric revenues	97
Service fees	1
Programs & other	2
Total	**100**

Selected Services
Aggregation
Business Development
Clean Energy & Conservation
Community Outreach
Financial
Legislative Regulatory & Legal
Power Supply / AMP Energy Control Center
Safety Programs
Scholarship Programs
Technical Services

COMPETITORS

Dominion Energy	Ohio Valley Electric
Duke Energy Ohio	

HISTORICAL FINANCIALS
Company Type: Private

Income Statement				FYE: December 31
	REVENUE ($ mil.)	NET INCOME ($ mil.)	NET PROFIT MARGIN	EMPLOYEES
12/15	1,127	5	0.5%	229
12/14	1,039	2	0.2%	—
12/13	982	5	0.5%	—
12/12	823	1	0.2%	—
Annual Growth	11.0%	45.0%	—	—

2015 Year-End Financials
Return on assets: 0.1%
Return on equity: 8.6%
Current ratio: 1.80
Cash ($ mil.): 107

AMERICAN TIRE DISTRIBUTORS HOLDINGS, INC.

Business for American Tire Distributors starts where the rubber meets the road. The company is the largest independent tire wholesaler in North America. Its offerings include flagship brands Bridgestone Continental Pirelli and Michelin as well as budget brands and private-label tires. ATD also markets custom wheels and tire service equipment. Its network of 140-plus distribution centers serves independent tire dealers retail chains and auto service centers across the US and Canada. The company is owned by private equity firm TPG Capital.

Operations
Passenger and light truck tires contribute most of American Tire Distributors' sales; the company also supplies tires for medium trucks farm vehicles and specialty vehicles.

Beyond tires ATD distributes wheels and other automotive products. Its brands include Cruiser Alloy Drifz O.E. Performance and ICW Racing.

Geographic Reach
North Carolina-based American Tire Distributors has a strong position in North America. It rings up most of its sales in the US where it has some 115 distribution centers. The company has nearly 25 distribution centers across Canada.

Sales and Marketing
American Tire Distributors sells tires to local regional and national independent tire retailers as well as mass merchandisers warehouse clubs tire-manufacturer-owned stores automotive dealerships and web-based markets.

Financial Performance
As a privately held entity American Tire Distributions does not publicly release financials. Estimates place annual revenue at $5 billion-plus.

Strategy
As with many industries the auto parts industry is being disrupted by online and mobile retailing and other technologies. In addition manufacturers are looking to sell directly to end-users thereby removing distributors from the supply chain. American Tire Distributors is grappling with both trends as it sees online behemoth Amazon strengthen its position in the tire replacement market and it loses distribution rights to one of the world's largest tire brands.

In 2018 Amazon announced a partnership with Sears through which customers who purchase replacement tires from Amazon can have them installed for a fee at Sears Auto Centers. Also that year Goodyear one of the largest tire manufacturers in the world announced ATD would no longer distribute its tires as it is forming its own tire distribution joint venture with a subsidiary of Bridgestone. That follows an earlier tire distribution joint venture between Michelin North America and Sumitomo.

In the face of competition from Amazon ATD touts its nearly 10-year history of online sales. It also continues to invest in innovation including the recent transition of ATD Online to a new platform with enhanced tools and superior service. As more manufactures get in the distribution game themselves the company is emphasizing and working to improve its value-added services. ATD positions itself not just as a distributor but as a partner to tire dealers offering industry-leading technology sourcing training and insights and category management.

In addition ATD continues to strengthen its operations in Canada. In 2017 its Canadian subsidiary National Tire Distributors added three Quebec-based distribution centers via an acquisition.

EXECUTIVES

Senior Vice President Eastern Division Manager, Keith Calcagno

Evp General Counsel And Secretary, J. Michael (Mike) Gaither, $400,000 total compensation

Evp And Cfo, Jason T. Yaudes, $400,000 total compensation

President And Ceo, Stuart Schuette

Evp Product Strategy And Supply, Jason Shannon

Vice President Of Human Resources, Laurie Heavner

Senior Vice President Proprietary Brands, Joshua Simpson

Vice President Hercules Brand Marketing, Jedd Emans

Regional Vice President, John Reid

Vice President Business Development And Strategy, Donald Gualdoni

Senior Vice President Supply Chain, Mark Chandler

Chief People Officer, Rebecca Sinclair

Vice President Financial Planning And Analysis, Ryan Walsh

Regional Vice President, Mark Lindsey

Senior Vice President Of Transportation, Baltazar-huntersville Nelson

Vice President Operations, Larry Livingston

Vice President Of Operations, Chris Mckinley

Vice President Operations East Coast, Peter Holm
Senior Vp Applications And Technology, Murali Bandaru
Vice President Of Supply Chain, Randal Arthur
Auditors: PRICEWATERHOUSECOOPERS LLP CH

LOCATIONS

HQ: AMERICAN TIRE DISTRIBUTORS HOLDINGS, INC.
12200 HERBERT WAYNE CT # 150, HUNTERSVILLE, NC 280786335
Phone: 704 992-2000
Web: WWW.ATD-US.COM

PRODUCTS/OPERATIONS

Selected Brands

Tires
Alliance
BFGoodrich
Continental
Dunlop
Firestone
IronMan
Michelin
Toyo Tires
UniRoyal
Wheels
Center Line
ICW Racing
Konig
Motiv
Pacer
Ultra Motorsports
Supplies
Blaster
Chicago Pneumatic
Ingersoll-Rand
Ken-Tool
SuperSprings
Stoner
Western Pacific Storage Solutions

COMPETITORS

Amazon.com	TCI Tire Centers
Bridgestone	Tire Distribution
Dealer Tire	Systems
Goodyear Tire & Rubber	Tire Group
Sears Holdings	International Inc.
Sumitomo Corporation	Wal-Mart
of America	

HISTORICAL FINANCIALS

Company Type: Private

Income Statement				FYE: December 28
	REVENUE ($ mil.)	NET INCOME ($ mil.)	NET PROFIT MARGIN	EMPLOYEES
12/13	3,839	(6)	—	500
12/12	3,455	(14)	—	—
12/11	3,050	0	0.0%	—
Annual Growth	12.2%	—	—	—

2013 Year-End Financials
Return on assets: (-0.2%)   Cash ($ mil.): 35
Return on equity: (-0.9%)
Current ratio: 1.90

AMERICAN TRANSMISSION COMPANY, LLC

American Transmission Company is an entrepreneur in the US power grid business — a for-profit multi-state transmission-only utility. Connecting electricity producers to distributors American Transmission owns operates monitors and maintains 9480 miles of high-voltage electric transmission lines and 529 substations in portions of Illinois Michigan Minnesota and Wisconsin. The company a member of the Midwest Independent Transmission System Operator (MISO) regional transmission organization operates the former transmission assets of some of its shareholders. About 30 utilities municipalities electric companies and cooperatives in its service area have an ownership stake in American Transmission.

Operations

Unlike most other power utilities American Transmission is not engaged in the generation distribution or marketing of electricity. Its duties include reliable operation of the transmission system growing the system to meet current and future needs and upgrading and maintain the transmission equipment as needed.

American Transmission is a member of the MISO regional transmission organization and provides nondiscriminatory service to all customers supporting effective competition in energy markets without favoring any market participant.

Geographic Reach

American Transmission meets the power needs of about 5 million people in 72 counties in Illinois Michigan Minnesota and Wisconsin. It operates North central Wisconsin Michigan's Upper Peninsula and Northern Wisconsin South Central/Southwest Wisconsin and North Central Illinois Northeast Wisconsin and Southeast Wisconsin.

Sales and Marketing

The company's customers include local electric distribution companies municipal utilities and co-operative utilities (that procure primary network transmission service and are interconnected or plan on interconnecting to its transmission system) local and national marketers generators and utilities (that procure primarily point-to-point transmission service generators and other transmission systems that want to interconnect with American Transmission's system).

Financial Performance

American Transmission reported revenues of about $603 million in 2012 a 6% increase over 2011 revenues.

Strategy

The company is trying to use its single focus on power transmission to win more customers. American Transmission has invested more than $2.8 billion on infrastructure upgrades (since 2001) including 2305 miles of power line. It has also built more 560 miles of new lines during this time period. By 2021 the company plans to spend a further $3.9-$4.8 billion on infrastructure improvement with a focus on adding new renewable sources to its expanded grid.

In 2014 American Transmission filed applications with the Public Service Commission of Wisconsin to rebuild a 12.5 mile 138000-volt transmission line in western Kenosha County at a cost $12.2 million and a 69000-volt transmission line

between Dyckesville Wisconsin and Sturgeon Bay Wisconsin (for $23 million).

In 2013 American Transmission received authorizing to build two new 138-kilovolt transmission lines needed to improve electric system reliability in western Milwaukee County and began construction activities on a new 5.8-mile 345-kilovolt electric transmission line to strengthen the electric system in southeastern Wisconsin and northeastern Illinois. That year it energized the 32-mile 345-kilovolt Rockdale-West Middleton Transmission Line; and placed in service. In 2013 American Transmission

In 2012 it teamed up with ALLETE to study transmission options for transporting Midwestern wind energy as well as Canadian hydroelectric power into Minnesota Wisconsin and Michigan to help local utilities enhance reliability and meet renewable energy goals. To further enable movement of renewable energy that year the company and Minnesota Power agreed to develop a 50-mile double-circuit 345-kilovolt transmission line from the Mesabi Iron Range to the companies' jointly owned Arrowhead Substation in Duluth. The project is due to come into service in 2020.

Company Background

In 2010 it signed two agreements with the Department of Energy to access $12.7 million in investment grants for incorporating smart grid technologies into its transmission system.

In 2011 it announced a plan to build seven new transmission line projects (1800 miles of new line) aimed at filling gaps in the existing transmission grid improving grid reliability and enabling increased delivery of renewable power in Iowa Wisconsin Illinois Indiana and Ohio. The projects in total will cost about $4 billion. It also agreed to purchase of the Zephyr Power Transmission Project (950 miles of transmission line between Wyoming and southern Nevada) in another $4 billion deal.

Boosting its transmission assets in 2011 American Transmission formed a transmission utility joint venture with Duke Energy. Duke-American Transmission Co. builds owns and operates new power transmission infrastructure across North America.

American Transmission is one of the first for-profit transmission companies formed (in 2001) when the US market deregulated in the early 2000s. It is 88% owned by investor-owned utilities and 12% owned by municipalities municipal electric companies and electric cooperatives.

EXECUTIVES

Vice President Human Capital, Lori Lorenz
Auditors: DELOITTE & TOUCHE LLP MILWAU

LOCATIONS

HQ: AMERICAN TRANSMISSION COMPANY, LLC
W234N2000 RDGVIEW PKY CT, WAUKESHA, WI 531881022
Phone: 262 506-6700
Web: WWW.ATCLLC.COM

PRODUCTS/OPERATIONS

Contributing Owners
Adams-Columbia Electric Cooperative
Alger Delta Cooperative Electric Association
Badger Power Marketing Authority
Central Wisconsin Electric Cooperative
City of Algoma
City of Columbus
City of Kaukauna
City of Menasha
City of Oconto Falls
City of Plymouth
City of Reedsburg
City of Sheboygan Falls
City of Sturgeon Bay

City of Sun Prairie
City of Wisconsin Rapids
Cloverland Electric Cooperative
Edison Sault Electric Company
Madison Gas & Electric Company
Manitowoc Public Utilities
Marshfield Electric and Water Department
Ontonagon County Rural Electrification Association
Rainy River Energy
Rock Energy Cooperative
Stoughton Utilities
Upper Peninsula Public Power Agency
Wisconsin Electric Power Company
Wisconsin Power & Light Company
Wisconsin Public Service Corporation
WPPI Energy

COMPETITORS

AES   Exelon
Ameren   FirstEnergy
Duke Energy

HISTORICAL FINANCIALS
Company Type: Private

Income Statement   FYE: December 31

	REVENUE ($ mil.)	NET INCOME ($ mil.)	NET PROFIT MARGIN	EMPLOYEES
12/18	687	172	25.0%	547
12/17	714	172	24.2%	—
12/16	650	147	22.7%	—
12/15	615	200	32.5%	—
Annual Growth	3.7%	(5.0%)	—	—

2018 Year-End Financials
Return on assets: 3.5%   Cash ($ mil.): —
Return on equity: 14.2%
Current ratio: 0.20

AMERICAN TRANSMISSION SYSTEMS, INCORPORATED

EXECUTIVES

Pres, Richard R Grigg
Director, Richard A Ziegler

LOCATIONS

HQ: AMERICAN TRANSMISSION SYSTEMS, INCORPORATED
76 S MAIN ST, AKRON, OH 443081812
Phone: 330 761-4370
Web: WWW.FIRSTENERGYCORP.COM

HISTORICAL FINANCIALS
Company Type: Private

Income Statement   FYE: December 31

	REVENUE ($ mil.)	NET INCOME ($ mil.)	NET PROFIT MARGIN	EMPLOYEES
12/17	656	165	25.2%	1
12/16	540	133	24.7%	
Annual Growth	21.6%	23.8%	—	—

AMERICARES FOUNDATION, INC.

AmeriCares Foundation provides emergency medical aid around the world. The not-for-profit charitable organization helps victims of natural disasters and supports long-term humanitarian programs by collecting medical supplies in the US and overseas and delivering them to places where they are needed. AmeriCares has provided aid in more than 90 countries worldwide. In the US the organization offers medical assistance runs a camp for kids with HIV/AIDS and conducts HomeFront a program that renovates housing for the needy in parts of Connecticut and New York. Robert C. Macauley founded AmeriCares in 1982.

Geographic Reach
The company has presence in US Latin America Caribbean Asia and Eurasia Africa and Middle East.

Financial Performance
AmeriCares' revenue decreased 9% to $572 million in 2014 due to a decline in public support and loss on investments.

EXECUTIVES

Pres-Ceo, Michael Nyenhuis
Svp-Operations*, Richard K Trowbridge Jr
Vp-US Programs & Partnership, Lindsay O'Brien
Manager Special Events, Michelle Aquino
Auditors: GRANT THORNTON LLP NEW YORK

LOCATIONS

HQ: AMERICARES FOUNDATION, INC.
88 HAMILTON AVE STE 1, STAMFORD, CT 069023100
Phone: 203 658-9500
Web: WWW.AMERICARES.ORG

HISTORICAL FINANCIALS
Company Type: Private

Income Statement   FYE: June 30

	REVENUE ($ mil.)	NET INCOME ($ mil.)	NET PROFIT MARGIN	EMPLOYEES
06/15	742	101	13.7%	231
06/14	560	(4)	—	—
06/12	526	5	1.1%	—
06/11	671	(0)	—	—
Annual Growth	2.5%	—	—	—

2015 Year-End Financials
Return on assets: 45.9%   Cash ($ mil.): 10
Return on equity: 47.9%
Current ratio: —

AMES CONSTRUCTION, INC.

Ames Construction aims right for the heart of heavy construction. The company is a general contractor providing heavy civil and industrial construction services to the transportation mining and power industries mainly in the West and Midwest. The family-owned company works on highways airports bridges rail lines mining facilities power plants and other infrastructure projects. Ames also performs flood control environmental remediation reclamation and landfill work. Additionally the firm builds golf courses and undertakes commercial and residential site development projects. Ames typically partners with other companies to perform the engineering and design portion of construction jobs.

Operations
Some of Ames Construction's project include the Arlington Power Plant Dry Fork Station Unit 1 Site Work and Substructure Construction Rentech ClearFuels Cortez Hills Mine and Mills Site and Airport Extension Projects such as its MSP International Airport work.

Geographic Reach
Ames Construction has offices in the US in Minnesota Arizona California Colorado Nevada and Utah as well as in Canada.

Strategy
Through its subcontracting activities Ames Construction contributed to the construction of the Minnesota Twins ballpark and served as subcontractor and partner in a joint venture with Fluor and Balfour Beatty Rail that that undertook a $1 billion design/build portion of a rail line project for the Denver Regional Transit District.

EXECUTIVES

Vice President Of Management Services, Roger L Mcbride
Regional Vice President Of Engineering, Robert Gillis
Vice President Director Manager It Is, Tony W Meyers
Auditors: CLIFTONLARSONALLEN LLP MINNEA

LOCATIONS

HQ: AMES CONSTRUCTION, INC.
14420 COUNTY ROAD 5, BURNSVILLE, MN 553066997
Phone: 952 435-7106
Web: WWW.AMESCONSTRUCTION.COM

Selected Locations
Arizona
California
Canada
Colorado
Minnesota
Nevada
Utah

PRODUCTS/OPERATIONS

Selected Markets

Commercial
Commercial site development
Environmental remediation/ landfills
Residential site development
Mining
Contract mining
Leach pad construction
Mine development
Mine infrastructure
Mine reclamation/remediation
Mine tailings dam
Power
Coal fired
Combined-cycle/natural gas
Nuclear
Transmission
Wind
Transportation
Airports
Bridges
Highways
Railroads
Water resources
Dams reservoirs and flood control
Wastewater/water treatment
Water delivery
Water retention structures

COMPETITORS

American Civil Constructors Holdings
Balfour Beatty Construction
Clyde Companies
Granite Construction
Meadow Valley
Peter Kiewit Sons'
SEMA Construction
Skanska USA Civil
Sterling Construction
Tutor-Saliba

HISTORICAL FINANCIALS

Company Type: Private

Income Statement				FYE: November 30
	REVENUE ($ mil.)	NET INCOME ($ mil.)	NET PROFIT MARGIN	EMPLOYEES
11/16	845	2	0.3%	2,500
11/15	1,068	5	0.5%	—
11/14*	1,074	26	2.4%	—
12/12	582	5	1.0%	—
Annual Growth	9.8%	(19.4%)	—	—

*Fiscal year change

2016 Year-End Financials

Return on assets: 0.7%
Return on equity: 1.8%
Current ratio: 1.30

Cash ($ mil.): 40

ANCHORAGE SCHOOL DISTRICT

EXECUTIVES

Supt, Ed Graff
Supt*, Carol Comeau
SEC Accounting*, Lois Hartsfield
Exe SEC*, Vanessa Blake
Doctor*, Deena Bishop
Substitute Teacher, Carla Goldberg
Cafeteria Manager, Shani Pritchard
Teacher, Ardy Robertson
Administrative Assistant, Chekedia Rias
English Language Arts Teacher, Adam Mackie
Curriculum Chugiak H, Allison Susel
Auditors: BDO USA LLP ANCHORAGE ALASK

LOCATIONS

HQ: ANCHORAGE SCHOOL DISTRICT
5530 E NTHRN LIGHTS BLVD, ANCHORAGE, AK 99504
Phone: 907 742-4000
Web: WWW.ASDK12.ORG

HISTORICAL FINANCIALS

Company Type: Private

Income Statement				FYE: June 30
	REVENUE ($ mil.)	NET INCOME ($ mil.)	NET PROFIT MARGIN	EMPLOYEES
06/12	834	(8)	—	5,039
06/11	822	(2)	—	—
06/10	774	(19)	—	—
Annual Growth	3.8%	—	—	—

2012 Year-End Financials

Return on assets: (-0.6%)
Return on equity: (-1.3%)
Current ratio: —

Cash ($ mil.): 162

ANDERSON AND DUBOSE, INC.

You might say this company keeps the Big Mac big and the Happy Meals happy. Anderson-DuBose Pittsburgh is a leading wholesale distributor that supplies food and non-food items to McDonald's and Chipotle fast-food restaurants in Ohio Pennsylvania New YorkÂ and West Virginia. It serves about 500 Golden Arches locations with frozen meat and fish dairy products and paper goods and packaging as well as toys for Happy Meals. One of the largest black-owned companies in the US Anderson-DuBose was started in 1991 by Warren Anderson and Stephen DuBose who purchased control of a McDonald's distributorship from Martin-Brower. Anderson became sole owner in 1993 when he bought out his partner's stake in the business.

EXECUTIVES

Pres, Warren Anderson
Customer Staff, Nancy Wilson
Human Resource Manager, Linsey Gray

LOCATIONS

HQ: ANDERSON AND DUBOSE, INC.
5300 TOD AVE SW, WARREN, OH 444819767
Phone: 440 248-8800
Web: WWW.ANDERSON-DUBOSE.COM

COMPETITORS

Golden State Foods
Gordon Food Service
Keystone Foods
MAINES
Martin-Brower
Meadowbrook Meat Company
Reinhart FoodService
Sysco
US Foods

HISTORICAL FINANCIALS

Company Type: Private

Income Statement				FYE: December 30
	REVENUE ($ mil.)	NET INCOME ($ mil.)	NET PROFIT MARGIN	EMPLOYEES
12/16	518	2	0.4%	100
12/15	546	2	0.4%	—
12/14	550	2	0.5%	—
12/11	372	1	0.3%	—
Annual Growth	6.8%	11.0%	—	—

2016 Year-End Financials

Return on assets: 5.3%
Return on equity: 10.5%
Current ratio: 0.90

Cash ($ mil.): —

ANMED HEALTH

EXECUTIVES

Pres-Ceo, John A Miller Jr
Dir, Jimmy Kimbell
Compliance Staff, Chandra Snyder
Anesthesiologist, Amy Weaver
Family Practitioner, Jill Spencer
Data Coordinator, Donna Hamby
Auditors: DIXON HUGHES GOODMAN LLP GREE

LOCATIONS

HQ: ANMED HEALTH
800 N FANT ST, ANDERSON, SC 296215708
Phone: 864 512-1000
Web: WWW.ANMEDHEALTH.ORG

HISTORICAL FINANCIALS

Company Type: Private

Income Statement				FYE: December 31
	REVENUE ($ mil.)	NET INCOME ($ mil.)	NET PROFIT MARGIN	EMPLOYEES
12/18	543	(15)	—	2,600
12/17	513	41	8.0%	—
12/16	504	40	8.0%	—
12/16	590	(1)	—	—
Annual Growth	(2.7%)	—	—	—

2018 Year-End Financials

Return on assets: (-1.7%)
Return on equity: (-2.8%)
Current ratio: 1.90

Cash ($ mil.): 49

ANN & ROBERT H. LURIE CHILDREN'S HOSPITAL OF CHICAGO

When it comes to caring for kids Ann & Robert H. Lurie Children's Hospital of Chicago has the Windy City covered. Founded in 1882 the not-for-profit hospital provides a full range of pediatric services with acute and specialty care. Lurie Children's provides services through its main hospital campus with about 300 beds and outpatient centers in Chicago's Lincoln Park neighborhood and through more than a dozen suburban outpatient centers and outreach partner locations in the greater Chicago area. A leader in pediatric research the hospital operates the Children's Hospital of Chicago Research Center and is the pediatric teaching facility of Northwestern University's Feinberg School of Medicine.

Operations

Lurie Children's serves roughly 150000 patients each year and employs some 1350 pediatric specialists with expertise in 70 different specialties. The hospital is one of only about a dozen children's hospitals nationwide to perform more than 1000 liver transplants. The center performs on average 50 solid organ and 50 stem cell transplants annually.

A major research center Lurie Children's is one of nearly 30 interdisciplinary research centers and institutes belonging to the hospital's academic partner — Feinberg School of Medicine. Its research arm Stanley Manne Children's Research Institute employs some 200 physician-scientists and research investigators who in 2014 were awarded more than $40 million in external funding.

Geographic Reach

Based in Chicago Lurie Children's has cared for patients from throughout the US and about 50 countries around the globe.

Financial Performance

Lurie Children's saw revenues increase by 8% to $826 million in fiscal 2014 (ended August). That growth was attributed to a rise in patient care revenues and other earnings. Net income increased 198% to $128 million that year largely due to the higher revenue as well as strong investment returns.

Cash flow from operations rose 36% to $124.5 million in fiscal 2014.

Strategy

The hospital has all-private rooms even in the neonatal intensive care unit; private rooms are said to speed healing by reducing hospital-acquired infection and minimize noise. Lurie Children's is working to enhance its specialist services and has upgraded its information technology systems. In 2013 it implemented a Voalte system that allows nurses to communicate through rapid-response systems including text messages and high-definition voice calls. Also that year it opened the first pediatric gender identity clinic. In 2015 the hospital acquired the fourth-generation da Vinci Xi robotic system for use in minimally invasive surgery.

In 2014 Lurie Children's Health Partners (composed of Lurie Children's and two groups of pediatricians) launched the Clinically Integrated Network the first health care network in Chicago to focus exclusively on children and their families. Its areas of focus include care coordination obesity asthma immunizations and child development.

EXECUTIVES

Assistant Vice President Corporate Giving, Erin Coleman
Vice President Revenue Cycle, Susan Pfister
Vice President And Chief Of Staff, Wayne Magdziarz
Executive Vice President And Chief Development Officer, Grant Stirling
Vice President Human Resources Chro Chief Diversity Inclusion Officer, Winifred Williams
Medical Director, Gregory Gruener
Vice President Of Information Technology, Laura Bagus

LOCATIONS

HQ: ANN & ROBERT H. LURIE CHILDREN'S HOSPITAL OF CHICAGO
225 E CHICAGO AVE, CHICAGO, IL 606112991
Phone: 312 227-4000
Web: WWW.LURIECHILDRENS.ORG

Selected Illinois Locations
Lurie Children's at Cadence Health (Winfield)
Main Hospital (Chicago)
Outpatient Center in Arlington Heights (Arlington Heights)
Outpatient Center in Glenview (Glenview)
Outpatient Center in Lake Forest (Lake Forest)
Outpatient Center in Lincoln Park (Chicago)
Outpatient Center in New Lenox (New Lenox)
Outpatient Center in Westchester (Westchester)
Outpatient Services in Grayslake (Grayslake)
Outpatient Services in Gurnee (Gurnee)
Outpatient Services in Lincoln Square (Chicago)
Pediatrics - Uptown (Chicago)
Rehabilitation Services at Westbrook (Westchester)

PRODUCTS/OPERATIONS

2014 Sales

	$ mil.	% of total
Patient care revenues	706	85
Grants gifts & endowment income	62	8
Other revenues	57	7
Total	**825**	**100**

Selected Services
Adolescent Medicine
Allergy and Immunology
Anesthesiology
Audiology
Autonomic Medicine
Brain Tumor
Cancer and Blood Disorders
Cardiology (Heart Center)
Child Abuse Pediatrics
Child and Adolescent Psychiatry
Clinical Nutrition

Convenient Care
Critical Care
Cystic Fibrosis
Dentistry and Oral Surgery
Dermatology
Emergency Medicine
Endocrinology
Epilepsy
Fetal Health
Gastroenterology Hepatology and Nutrition (Digestive Disorders)
Gender and Sex Development
General Pediatric Surgery
General Pediatrics
Genetics Birth Defects and Metabolism
Heart Failure and Transplants
HIV/AIDS Prevention
Infectious Diseases
Intestinal Transplants
Kidney Diseases
Kidney Transplants
Liver Transplants
Medical Imaging (Radiology)
Neonatology
Neurology
Neurosurgery
Occupational Therapy
Ophthalmology
Orthopaedic Surgery
Orthotics/Prosthetics
Otolaryngology (ENT)
Palliative Care
Pathology and Laboratory Medicine
Physical Therapy
Plastic and Reconstructive Surgery
Pulmonary Medicine
Rehabilitative Services
Rheumatology
Speech-Language Pathology
Spina Bifida Center
Sports Medicine
Stem Cell Transplants
Transitioning to Adult Care
Transplantation
Urology

COMPETITORS

Advocate Health Care
Advocate Lutheran General Hospital
Alexian Brothers Health System
Covenant Ministries
HCA
Loyola University Health System
Mercy Hospital and Medical Center
NorthShore University HealthSystem
Northwestern Lake Forest Hospital
Northwestern Memorial HealthCare
Rush System for Health
SSM Health Care
Sinai Health System
University of Chicago Medical Center

HISTORICAL FINANCIALS
Company Type: Private

Income Statement				FYE: August 31
	REVENUE ($ mil.)	NET INCOME ($ mil.)	NET PROFIT MARGIN	EMPLOYEES
08/13	694	28	4.2%	2,800
08/10	599	52	8.8%	—
08/09	533	(5)	—	—
Annual Growth	6.8%	—	—	—

2013 Year-End Financials
Return on assets: 1.4%
Return on equity: 2.0%
Current ratio: 2.90
Cash ($ mil.): 92

ANNE ARUNDEL COUNTY BOARD OF EDUCATION

EXECUTIVES

Pres, Stacy Korbelak
Teacher, Matt Heist
Auditors: CLIFTONLARSONALLEN LLP BALTIM

LOCATIONS

HQ: ANNE ARUNDEL COUNTY BOARD OF EDUCATION
2644 RIVA RD, ANNAPOLIS, MD 214017427
Phone: 410 222-5000
Web: WWW.AACPS.ORG

HISTORICAL FINANCIALS
Company Type: Private

Income Statement				FYE: June 30
	REVENUE ($ mil.)	NET INCOME ($ mil.)	NET PROFIT MARGIN	EMPLOYEES
06/13	1,147	3	0.3%	130
06/04	712	0	0.1%	—
06/03	701	50	7.1%	—
Annual Growth	5.1%	(23.0%)	—	—

2013 Year-End Financials
Return on assets: 0.3%
Return on equity: 0.6%
Current ratio: —
Cash ($ mil.): 166

ANNE ARUNDEL MEDICAL CENTER, INC.

The ill and infirm get the royal treatment at Anne Arundel Medical Center. The full-service acute-care hospital serves the residents of Anne Arundel Calvert Prince George's and Queen Anne counties in Maryland. With about 425 beds the hospital administers care for women's health oncology pediatrics (it has a level III neonatal intensive care unit) neurology orthopedics and cardiovascular care. The medical center also has weight loss sleep disorder and rehabilitation centers. Anne Arundel which opened its doors in 1902 and is part of the Anne Arundel Health System has expanded its service offerings through various affiliations with regional specialty and primary care clinics. It also has a partnership with Johns Hopkins Medicine.

Operations

With more than 1000 staff members Anne Arundel handles some 26000 inpatient visits and 102000 outpatient visits per year. It also manages more than 5000 births and 93000 emergency room visits.

Johns Hopkins and the not-for-profit Anne Arundel share some services faculty and patients through their collaboration. They also operate a joint outpatient urgent-care facility. Additionally the two organizations work together to perform clinical research projects and conduct physician graduate medical education programs.

Geographic Reach

In addition to its 57-acre Annapolis campus Anne Arundel has outpatient centers in Bowie Kent Island Odenton Pasadena and Waugh Chapel.

Sales and Marketing

In 2014 Medicare payments accounted for about one-third of net patient revenues.

Financial Performance

In 2014 revenue grew 3% to $591 million as net patient services revenues increased. However net income fell 23% to $42 million due to a decline in non-operating income (investment earnings). Cash flow from operations spike 188% to $56 million as cash generated from patient receivables prepaid expenses and other sources rose.

Strategy

Anne Arundel has in recent years added new facilities to better keep up with a continued growth in demand for health care services throughout its service area. In 2015 it opened the second phase of its Pasadena Pavilion adding physical therapy orthopedics and sports medicine capabilities. It also opened a new FastCare walk-in clinic in a grocery store/pharmacy in Annapolis. In 2014 the system opened an outpatient mental health clinic in Annapolis which provides services for patients 13 years of age and older.

In 2013 Anne Arundel opened a training center — the James and Sylvia Earl Simulation to Advance Innovation and Learning (SAIL) Center — to enhance its medical education programs and improve the quality and safety of care in the region. It also opened the Hackerman-Patz House that year to provide an affordable and convenient housing option for families of patients.

Also in 2013 the organization was designated as a Medicare accountable care organization (ACO) by the US government. ACOs work to coordinate care for Medicare patients to improve quality and reduce expenses.

EXECUTIVES

Chb, Florence B Kurdle
V Chb*, James F McEncaney Jr
Pres*, Martin L Doordan
V Pres-Fin*, Bill Hughes
R V Pres, Joseph D Moser
Pres*, Stephen L Clarke
V Pres*, Shirley J Knelly
SEC*, Patricia Troy
Treas*, John M Suit II
Cso*, Paula Widerlite
Fo*, Bob Reilly
Auditors: SC&H TAX & ADVISORY SERVICES L

LOCATIONS

HQ: ANNE ARUNDEL MEDICAL CENTER, INC.
2001 MEDICAL PKWY, ANNAPOLIS, MD 214013773
Phone: 443 481-1000
Web: WWW.AAHS.ORG

PRODUCTS/OPERATIONS

Selected Centers and Services
Blood Donor Center
Breast Center
Cardiac Cath Lab
Chest Pain Center
DeCesaris Cancer Institute
Diabetes Wound and Hyperbaric Center
Diagnostic Imaging
Heart and Vascular Institute
Joint Center
Laboratory
Pediatrics
Rehabilitation
Research Institute
Sleep Disorder Center
Spine Center
Stroke Center
Surgery
Women's and Children's Center

COMPETITORS

Ascension Health
Bon Secours Health
Dimensions Healthcare
Franklin Square
 Hospital Center
GBMC
Harbor Hospital
Johns Hopkins Health
 System
Johns Hopkins Medicine
LifeBridge Health
MedStar Health
Sinai Hospital of
 Baltimore
St. Agnes HealthCare
University of Maryland
 Medical System

HISTORICAL FINANCIALS

Company Type: Private

Income Statement				FYE: June 30
	REVENUE ($ mil.)	NET INCOME ($ mil.)	NET PROFIT MARGIN	EMPLOYEES
06/15	526	39	7.6%	1,890
06/14	492	20	4.1%	—
06/13	493	16	3.4%	—
06/11	445	24	5.4%	—
Annual Growth	4.2%	13.4%	—	—

2015 Year-End Financials

Return on assets: 4.3%   Cash ($ mil.): 59
Return on equity: 10.3%
Current ratio: 0.30

ANNE ARUNDEL MEDICAL CENTER, INC.

EXECUTIVES

Ceo, Victoria W Bayless
V Pres*, Stephen L Clarke
Cfo*, Bob Reilly
General Practitioner, Mark D Phillips
Internal Medicine Practitioner, Anthony M Caputo
Health Professional, Adeeb Jaber
Coordinator, Barbara Peterson
Coordinator, Doreen Curry-Briggs
Health Professional, Eileen B Macdonald
Internal Medicine Practitioner, Elizabeth F Shade
Internal Medicine Practitioner, Katarzyna M Lechliter

LOCATIONS

HQ: ANNE ARUNDEL MEDICAL CENTER, INC.
2001 MEDICAL PKWY, ANNAPOLIS, MD 214013773
Phone: 443 481-1000
Web: WWW.AAHS.ORG

HISTORICAL FINANCIALS

Company Type: Private

Income Statement				FYE: June 30
	REVENUE ($ mil.)	NET INCOME ($ mil.)	NET PROFIT MARGIN	EMPLOYEES
06/16	515	(12)	—	4,000
06/15	498	(16)	—	—
06/14	1	0	23.5%	—
06/13	1	0	16.2%	—
Annual Growth	592.7%	—	—	—

2016 Year-End Financials

Return on assets: (-1.3%)   Cash ($ mil.): 34
Return on equity: (-3.7%)
Current ratio: 1.10

ANR PIPELINE COMPANY

ANR Pipeline keeps natural gas in line a pipeline that is. The company operates one of the largest interstate natural gas pipeline systems in the US. A subsidiary of TransCanada Corp. ANR controls about 10350 miles of pipeline and delivers more than 1 trillion cu. ft. of natural gas per year. The company primarily serves customers in the Midwest but through its network is capable of connecting to all major gas basins in North America. In tandem with its ANR Storage and Blue Lake Gas Storage subsidiaries ANR Pipeline also provides natural gas storage services and has ownership interests in more than 250 billion cu. ft. of underground natural gas storage capacity.

Operations

The ANR System is part of TransCanada's network 37000 miles of wholly owned and 4900 miles of partially owned pipelines connecting major supply basins with major markets all across North America.

Geographic Reach

ANR transports natural gas from producing fields in Texas and Oklahoma from offshore and onshore regions of the Gulf of Mexico and from the US midcontinent for delivery mainly to Illinois Indiana Michigan Ohio and Wisconsin.

Strategy

To create greater operating efficiency in 2012 ANR Pipeline Company sold assets and certain related onshore facilities to its wholly owned subsidiary TC Offshore LLC.

To support the growing natural gas production in the Haynesville Shale play in Texas and Louisiana the company is developing the ANR Haynesville Lateral Project to transport up to 1.8 billion cu. ft. of natural gas a day. The Haynesville Lateral pipeline enables producers to transport shale gas to markets in the Southeast Midwest and Northeast.

Company Background

ANR Pipeline was founded as Michigan-Wisconsin Pipe Line Company in 1945 and adopted its current name in 1984.

El Paso Corp. sold ANR Pipeline to TransCanada in 2007. The deal gave TransCanada a regulated natural gas pipeline and storage assets that complemented its other North American gas transmission operations.

EXECUTIVES

Pres-Ceo, Lee Hobbs
Pres-Ceo*, Lee G Hobbs
V Pres-Commercial Oprs*, Gary C Charette
V Pres-Commercial Sls*, Dean Patry
Contrl, Thomas Janish
Information Technology Manager, Kay Dennison

LOCATIONS

HQ: ANR PIPELINE COMPANY
700 LOUISIANA ST STE 700 # 700, HOUSTON, TX 770022873
Phone: 832 320-2000

COMPETITORS

Alliance Pipeline
Buckeye Pipe Line
Columbia Gulf
 Transmission
Duke Energy
OGE Energy
ONEOK Partners
Panhandle Eastern Pipe
 Line
Transcontinental Gas
 Pipe Line
Vector Pipeline
Williams Companies
Williston Basin
 Interstate Pipeline

| Income Statement | | | | FYE: December 31 |
	REVENUE ($ mil.)	NET INCOME ($ mil.)	NET PROFIT MARGIN	EMPLOYEES
12/17	758	139	18.5%	1,000
12/16	686	54	8.0%	—
12/06	540	152	28.1%	—
12/05	548	147	26.8%	—
Annual Growth	2.7%	(0.4%)	—	—

2017 Year-End Financials

Return on assets: 4.6%
Return on equity: 10.4%
Current ratio: 1.30

Cash ($ mil.): —

API GROUP INC.

Holding company APi Group has a piece of the action in two main sectors: fire protection systems and industrial and specialty construction services. APi boasts about 40 subsidiaries which operate as independent companies across the US (nearly half of them in Minnesota) the UK and Canada. Services provided by the company's construction subsidiaries include HVAC and plumbing system installation; electrical industrial and mechanical contracting; industrial insulation; and garage door installation. Safety-focused units install a host of fire sprinkler detection security and alarm systems. The family-owned company was founded in 1926 by Reuben Anderson father of chairman Lee Anderson.

Operations
Through its various companies APi Group is involved in engineering designing constructing and installing LEED green-building certification program projects. Its divisions include Architectural Roofing and Mechanical Classic Industrial Services APi Construction APi Distribution and Industrial Fabricators among others.

Geographic Reach
Minnesota-based APi Group operates companies throughout North America and the UK.

Sales and Marketing
APi Group serves several sectors such as security and defense education commercial industrial medical oil and gas and residential.

Strategy
Although APi Group companies are independent they often pool resources and work together to service clients.

Mergers and Acquisitions
The highly acquisitive APi Group regularly acquires new companies to strengthen its growing group.

In 2013 the company's Western States Fire Protection (WSFP) acquired Advanced Fire an Oklahoma City-based fire-suppression company that specializes in military work. Buying Advanced Fire extends the company's reach in the fire protection industry and boosts its market share in Oklahoma City and the surrounding area. APi Group's Delta Fire Systems acquired Idaho's 3-D Fire which provides full-fire-system design fabrication installation testing and certification capabilities for commercial and private projects.

APi Group previous purchases include Dynamic Fire Protection LLC (DFP) Omlid & Swinney Fire Protection and Security Canada-based Fire Stop Enterprises Ohio-based 3S and Kansas-based mainline pipeline contractor Jomax Construction.

EXECUTIVES

Pres-Ceo, Russell Becker
Treas-Cfo, Gregory Keup
SEC, William M Beadie
Creative Director, Shelly Pagano
Senior Web Developer, Kevin Roth
Director Business Information, Chinh Huynh
Director Human Resources, Les Larson
Chief Helicopter Pilot, Nicholas Serre
Client Technologies Manager, Ahmed Abdel-Kerim
Project Manager, Kim Norberg
Procurement Manager, Matthew Holker
Auditors: KPMG

LOCATIONS

HQ: API GROUP INC.
1100 OLD HIGHWAY 8 NW, SAINT PAUL, MN 551126447
Phone: 651 636-4320
Web: WWW.APIGROUPINC.COM

PRODUCTS/OPERATIONS

Selected Subsidiaries
Fire Protection Systems
  Alliance Fire Protection Inc.
  APi National Service Group
  Davis-Ulmer Sprinkler Company
  Delta Fire Systems Inc.
  Grunau Company
  Halon Banking Systems
  International Fire Protection Inc.
  Island Fire Sprinkler Inc.
  Reliance Fire Protection
  Rich Fire Protection Co Inc.
  Security Fire Protection Company
  United States Fire Protection Company
  VFP Fire Systems Inc.
  Viking Automatic Sprinkler Company
  Vipond Fire Protection Inc. (Canada)
  Vipond Fire Protection Ltd. (UK)
  Western States Fire Protection Inc.
Industrial and Specialty Construction Services
  3S Incorporated
  Anco Products Inc.
  APi CAD Services
  APi Construction Company
  APi Distribution Inc.
  APi Electric
  APi Supply Inc.
  Classic Industrial Services Inc.
  Doody Mechanical Inc.
  Garage Door Store
  Grunau Company Inc.
  Industrial Contractors Inc.
  Industrial Fabricators Inc.
  Jamar Company
  Jomax Construction Co.
  LeJeune Steel Company
  NYCO Inc.
  Tessier's Inc.
  Twin City Garage Door Company
Low Voltage
  APi Systems Group Inc.
  APi Systems Integrators
  Vipond Systems Group

COMPETITORS

Comfort Systems USA	TDIndustries
EMCOR	Team
IES Holdings	Turner Industries
Irex	Tyco Fire & Security
John E. Green	

| Income Statement | | | | FYE: December 31 |
	REVENUE ($ mil.)	NET INCOME ($ mil.)	NET PROFIT MARGIN	EMPLOYEES
12/18	3,730	122	3.3%	4,237
12/17	3,046	112	3.7%	—
12/16	2,608	104	4.0%	—
12/15	2,448	106	4.3%	—
Annual Growth	15.1%	5.0%	—	—

2018 Year-End Financials

Return on assets: 6.2%
Return on equity: 21.3%
Current ratio: 1.10

Cash ($ mil.): 54

APPALACHIAN REGIONAL HEALTHCARE, INC.

Under-the-weather coal miners (and their daughters) can turn to Appalachian Regional Healthcare (ARH) for medical services. The not-for-profit health system serves residents of eastern Kentucky and southern West Virginia through a dozen hospitals with more than 1000 beds as well as dozens of clinics home health care agencies HomeCare Stores and retail pharmacies. Its largest hospital in Hazard Kentucky has 310 beds and features an inpatient psychiatric unit that serves as the state mental health facility. Several of the system's hospitals are Critical Access Hospitals a federal government designation for rural community hospitals that operate in medically underserved areas.

Operations
ARH's HomeCare Stores provide home medical equipment and oxygen delivery as well as 24-hour support through eight respiratory therapists. Its HomeCare Stores are supported by the ARH Home Health Agencies which provide access to nursing care occupational and physical therapy and social services.

Among the system's hospitals are Beckley ARH Hospital a not-for-profit 173-bed acute-care facility; Harlan ARH Hospital a state-licensed 150-bed acute-care facility; and Mary Breckinridge ARH Hospital a critical access facility.

ARH is the largest provider of care and single largest employer in southeastern Kentucky and the third-largest private employer in southern West Virginia. It employs almost 5000 people and has a network of more than 600 medical staff members. In 2013 the system had 153000 emergency department visits 482000 outpatient visits some 1500 births and about 12000 outpatient surgeries.

Geographic Reach
ARH serves residents of eastern Kentucky and southern West Virginia. It has hospitals in Harlan Hazard Hyden Martin McDowell Middlesboro Morgan County South Williamson and Whitesburg Kentucky; and in Beckley and Summers County West Virginia.

Strategy
As the primary provider of health care to medically underserved populations ARH doles out millions of dollars in uncompensated care each year

to un- or underinsured residents of the Appalachian region.

Along with a larger population of uninsured patients and the resulting unpaid medical bills that come along with them rural health care providers face a number of hardships not encountered by their urban brethren. For example physician recruitment is more difficult at rural hospitals especially for some higher-risk specialties such as obstetrics. In order to attract and retain doctors ARH and other rural health care providers have to offer more competitive compensation packages pay for relocation and invest in technology and facility upgrades.

Also patients in rural areas are more likely to suffer from chronic health problems such as diabetes and obesity which can become a significant drain on a health system's resources. ARH is one of many health care providers looking to benefit from changes to the health care system outlined in Affordable Care Act especially the requirement that all US citizens carry health insurance.

To keep up with patient demand ARH also focuses on building and acquiring new facilities as well as investing in new technology and medical capacities.

Beckley ARH Hospital is undergoing a nearly $7 million renovation project that will add 19 more private rooms decrease utility costs and improve patient flow processes. In 2014 ARH completed a $47 million expansion project at the Hazard ARH Regional Medical Center that added an additional 100000 sq. ft. to the medical center including a new patient tower a new 24-bed emergency department on the first floor a dedicated 16-bed cardiac critical care unit and 34 private rooms. Hazard ARH is now the largest hospital in southeastern Kentucky.

Mergers and Acquisitions

In 2018 Appalachian Regional Healthcare acquired its twelfth hospital — the 25-bed Saint Joseph Martin Hospital — and its clinics. That facility now operates as ARH Our Lady of the Way.

Company Background

Appalachian Regional Healthcare was formed in 1956 by the United Mine Workers of America but became an independent not-for-profit entity in the early 1960s.

EXECUTIVES

Vice President Sales And Marketing, Holly Harris
Director Of Nursing, Dolores Luke
Vice President Corporate Strategy, Hollie Harris
Director Of Radiology, Jeremy Willis
Medical Director, Jim Maynard
Auditors: MCM CPA'S & ADVISORS LLP LOU

LOCATIONS

HQ: APPALACHIAN REGIONAL HEALTHCARE, INC.
2260 EXECUTIVE DR, LEXINGTON, KY 405054808
Phone: 859 226-2440
Web: WWW.ARH.ORG

PRODUCTS/OPERATIONS

Selected Facilities
Beckley ARH Hospital (Beckley West Virginia)
Hazard ARH Regional Medical Center (Hazard Kentucky)
Harlan ARH Hospital (Harlan Kentucky)
McDowell ARH Hospital (McDowell Kentucky)
Middlesboro ARH Hospital (Middlesboro Kentucky)
Morgan County ARH Hospital (West Liberty Kentucky)
Summers County ARH Hospital (Hinton West Virginia)
Tug Valley ARH Regional Medical Center (South Williamson Kentucky)
Whitesburg ARH Hospital (Whitesburg Kentucky)

Selected Services
Bariatrics
Behavioral Health
Cancer Care
Clinics
Emergency
Heart Care
Home Health
HomeCare Stores
Imaging
Laboratory
Medical Spa
Nephrology
Obstetrics and Gynecology
Pediatrics
Pharmacy
Rehabilitation Therapy
Respiratory Therapy
Rheumatology
Senior Care
Skilled Nursing
Sleep Lab
Surgery
Swing Beds

COMPETITORS

Baptist Health	Mercy Medical Center (NY)
Bon Secours Health	Montgomery Regional Hospital
Carilion Clinic	Norton Healthcare
Catholic Health Initiatives	Pikeville Medical Center
Community Health Systems	University of Kentucky Chandler Hospital
Highlands Health	University of Virginia Health System
Jewish Hospital & St. Mary's HealthCare	
Kindred Healthcare	

HISTORICAL FINANCIALS

Company Type: Private

Income Statement

FYE: June 30

	REVENUE ($ mil.)	NET INCOME ($ mil.)	NET PROFIT MARGIN	EMPLOYEES
06/18	689	65	9.4%	4,520
06/17	657	43	6.6%	—
06/16	653	17	2.6%	—
06/15	620	48	7.8%	—
Annual Growth	3.5%	10.4%	—	—

2018 Year-End Financials

Return on assets: 8.4%
Return on equity: 23.7%
Current ratio: 0.70
Cash ($ mil.): 40

APPLE AMERICAN GROUP LLC

This company must really enjoy casual dining in its neighborhood. Apple American Group is the largest franchisee of Applebee's with about 450 Applebee's Neighborhood Grill & Bar locations in about two dozen states. The #1 casual dining chain in the US Applebee's restaurants offer a full-service menu of beef chicken and seafood entrees along with a wide selection of appetizers. Apple American's restaurants are found from coast to coast with large concentrations in the Midwest (Ohio Indiana Pennsylvania) and on the West Coast (California Washington). Founded in 1998 by CEO Greg Flynn Apple American is controlled by private equity firm Weston Presidio Service.

Strategy

As a franchise operator the company benefits from the fact that its eateries carry a well-known brand backed by by the national marketing muscle of Applebee's parent DineEquity. It pays for the privilege of operating Applebee's restaurants in the form of royalties and franchise fees. The company also agrees to abide by operating agreements designed to ensure consistency in food and service quality. Locally Apple American's restaurants compete for business against a wide range of independent operators as well as such national chains as Chili's (owned by Brinker International) and Outback Steakhouse (OSI Restaurant Partners).

Apple American has been rapidly building its base of casual dining eateries; it has more than doubled its locations since 2010. It operates via a decentralized business model where each geographic region is managed by a market president who has wide latitude in decision-making.

EXECUTIVES

Vice President Of Procurement, Kasey Mania
Auditors: PRICEWATERHOUSECOOPERS LLP CL

LOCATIONS

HQ: APPLE AMERICAN GROUP LLC
6200 OAK TREE BLVD # 250, INDEPENDENCE, OH 441316943
Phone: 216 525-2775

Selected Locations
Alabama
California
Colorado
Delaware
Georgia
Idaho
Indiana
Maine
Massachusetts
Minnesota
Nevada
New Hampshire
New Jersey
New Mexico
New York
Ohio
Oregon
Pennsylvania
Rhode Island
Vermont
Washington
West Virginia
Wisconsin

COMPETITORS

Acapulco/El Torito Restaurants	Eat'n Park
Black Angus Steakhouse	Lone Star Steakhouse
Brinker	Marie Callender
Carlson Restaurants	OSI Restaurant Partners
Cheesecake Factory	Red Robin
Cracker Barrel	Ruby Tuesday
Darden	Texas Roadhouse
Denny's	

HISTORICAL FINANCIALS

Company Type: Private

Income Statement

FYE: December 27

	REVENUE ($ mil.)	NET INCOME ($ mil.)	NET PROFIT MARGIN	EMPLOYEES
12/09	479	19	4.0%	5,500
12/08	431	9	2.3%	—
12/07	339	0	0.0%	—
Annual Growth	19.0%	13783.8%	—	—

2009 Year-End Financials

Return on assets: 6.1%
Return on equity: 22.5%
Current ratio: 0.30
Cash ($ mil.): 6

APPLE HOSPITALITY REIT, INC.

EXECUTIVES

Pres-Ceo, Justin G Knight
Exec Chb*, Glade M Knight
Exec V Pres-Coo, Kristian M Gathright
Evp-Cfo, Bryan Peery
Exec V Pres-Clo, David P Buckley
Exec V Pres-CIO, Nelson G Knight
Chief Operating Officer, Kristian Gathright
Board Member, Bruce Matson
Board Member, Daryl Nickel
Board Member, Glenn Bunting
Manager Director, Debra Quin
Auditors: ERNST & YOUNG LLP RICHMOND V

LOCATIONS

HQ: APPLE HOSPITALITY REIT, INC.
814 E MAIN ST, RICHMOND, VA 232193306
Phone: 804 344-8121
Web: WWW.APPLEHOSPITALITYREIT.COM

HISTORICAL FINANCIALS

Company Type: Private

Income Statement

	ASSETS ($ mil.)	NET INCOME ($ mil.)	INCOME AS % OF ASSETS	EMPLOYEES
12/14	3,779	6	0.2%	62
12/13	1,491	115	7.7%	—
12/12	1,526	75	4.9%	—
12/11	1,700	69	4.1%	—
Annual Growth	30.5%	(54.0%)	—	—

FYE: December 31

APRO, LLC

EXECUTIVES

Mng MBR, Jeff Appel
MBR, Steve Roth
MBR, Ron Appel
Controller, Daniela Anton
Auditors: HOLTHOUSE CARLIN & VAN TRIGT

LOCATIONS

HQ: APRO, LLC
4130 COVER ST, LONG BEACH, CA 908081885
Phone: 310 323-3992
Web: WWW.EXXON.COM

HISTORICAL FINANCIALS

Company Type: Private

Income Statement

	REVENUE ($ mil.)	NET INCOME ($ mil.)	NET PROFIT MARGIN	EMPLOYEES
12/11	488	8	1.7%	100
12/10	551	7	1.4%	—
12/09	296	4	1.4%	—
Annual Growth	28.3%	40.0%	—	—

FYE: December 31

2011 Year-End Financials

Return on assets: 11.7%   Cash ($ mil.): 9
Return on equity: 13.1%
Current ratio: 2.50

ARCTIC SLOPE REGIONAL CORPORATION

The Inupiat people have survived the rigors of the Arctic for centuries and now they're surviving in the business world. The Inupiat-owned Arctic Slope Regional Corporation (ASRC) is the largest locally owned and operated business in Alaska. It gets the bulk of its of sales from energy services (ASRC Energy Services) and petroleum refining and marketing unit (Petro Star). Other operations include construction (ASRC Construction Holding) governmental services (ASRC Federal Holding) economic development (Alaska Growth Capital BIDCO) local services (Eskimos Inc.) and tourism (Tundra Tours).

Operations

ASRC owns title to nearly 5 million acres of land on Alaska's North Slope which contain a high potential for oil gas coal and base metal sulfides. It also owns subsurface and surface rights to certain lands.

The company seeks to adhere to traditional Inupiat values of protecting the land the environment and the native culture while developing economic programs.

It operates in five diverse major business segments: petroleum refining and marketing government services energy services resource development and construction industries. Petro Star has two refineries (strategically positioned along the Trans-Alaska Pipeline) and serves Interior Alaska South Central Alaska Kodiak and Dutch Harbor. Its North Pole facility supplies the mining industry in the interior region of Alaska and provides home heating oil to several communities.

ASRC Federal Holding Company provides professional and technical services to the federal government (including aviation space and missile defense base operations resource and development engineering IT and financial management).

ASRC Energy Services offers oilfield engineering operations maintenance construction fabrication regulation and permitting and other services to oil and gas companies. The company provides services to the energy industry throughout Alaska Canada and the Gulf of Mexico as well as in Russia.

ASRC Construction Holding Company provides construction services to commercial and government clients in Alaska the lower-48 the Gulf of Mexico and in other countries.

Alaska Growth Capital BIDCO offers economic development finance including small business loans and investments in economically challenged areas of Alaska.

LRS Inc. provides help to increase well flow output as well as well work-over and well production support.

Geographic Reach

ASRC represents 12000 members/shareholders in eight villages on the North Slope of Alaska: Anaktuvuk Pass Atqasuk Barrow Kaktovik Nuiqsut Point Hope Point Lay and Wainwright. ASRC has its head office in Barrow with a major administrative office in Anchorage. It has other subsidiary offices in the Lower 48 states.

Strategy

ASRC is owned by Inupiat Eskimo shareholders. The company has distributed more than $825 million in dividends to its shareholders since 1972. About 40% of ARSC's annual earnings are distributed directly to shareholders through dividends and other benefits. The remainder is reinvested in the company.

Since 2005 ARSC has distributed $15 million each year in benefits to its shareholders in the form of educational scholarships and community support funding as well as for training and development activities.

The company's strategic plan for 2012 through 2017 calls for ASRC to diversify its holdings to reach $225 million in sustainable earnings before interest and taxes (including a sustainable $55 dividend) and to achieve this goal through minimal debt a favorable tax position and by making cash available to acquire new businesses inside and outside of Alaska. It is looking for a successful acquisition strategy to diversify revenue streams increase earnings and generate new job opportunities for ASRC's shareholders.

In 2014 Royal Dutch Shell and the ASRC formed a new company — Arctic Inupiat Offshore LLC which includes six village corporations on the North Slope. The agreement with the Shell subsidiary Shell Gulf of Mexico Inc. gave the Alaska Native company the option of acquiring an overriding royalty interest from Shell's drilling on leases in the Chukchi Sea. (However Shell shelved its Arctic drilling plans in 2016 after disappointing results).

Mergers and Acquisitions

Expanding its presence in the continental US in 2016 subsidiary ASRC Industrial Services acquired Tennessee-based Restoration Services Inc (RSI). RSI's environmental services include regulatory strategy comprehensive characterization long-term stewardship project controls and beneficial site reuse.

Growing its energy services portfolio in 2015 ASRC acquired Houston-based Arctic Pipe Inspection which provides non-destructive testing of oil country tubular goods.

Company Background

ASRC was set up to own and manage 5 million acres on Alaska's North Slope after the Alaska Native Claims Settlement Act in 1971 cleared the way for oil development in the area.

In 2010 ASRC protested the US Fish and Wildlife Service's designation of Alaskan North Slope oil-producing areas as a critical habitat for endangered polar bears claiming it would cost ASRC millions of dollars in lost oil revenues. In 2011 it led a coalition of Native groups to sue the Department of the Interior over this issue.

In 2012 ASRC Construction Holding expanded into southeast Alaska with the acquisition of native-Alaskan owned McGraw's Custom Construction.

EXECUTIVES

Evp Lands And Natural Resources, Richard K. Glenn
President And Ceo, Rex A. Rock
Chairman And Evp Shareholder Community Programs, Crawford Patkotak
Evp And General Counsel, Denali Kemppel
Evp And Coo, Butch Lincoln
Evp And Cfo, Charlie Kozak
Vice President Tax, Mark Hamilton
Executive Vice President Human Resources, Debbie Akpik
Vice Chairman, George Sielak

LOCATIONS

HQ: ARCTIC SLOPE REGIONAL CORPORATION
3900 C ST STE 801, ANCHORAGE, AK 995035963
Phone: 907 339-6000
Web: WWW.ASRC.COM

PRODUCTS/OPERATIONS

Selected Businesses

Energy Services
  ASRC Energy Services Inc.
  Arctic Inupiat Offshore LLC.
Petroleum Refining and Marketing
  Petro Star Inc.
Government Services
  ASRC Federal Holding Company
Construction
  ASRC Construction Holding Company LLC
Resource Development
  Little Red Services
  Petrochem

COMPETITORS

Alaska Communications	Noble
Systems	Schlumberger
Baker Hughes	T-Mobile USA
Halliburton	Tesoro
Nabors Industries	

HISTORICAL FINANCIALS

Company Type: Private

Income Statement				FYE: December 31
	REVENUE ($ mil.)	NET INCOME ($ mil.)	NET PROFIT MARGIN	EMPLOYEES
12/08	2,297	151	6.6%	6,700
12/07	1,777	207	11.7%	—
12/06	1,700	206	12.1%	—
12/05	1,566	127	8.1%	—
Annual Growth	13.6%	5.8%	—	—

2008 Year-End Financials

Return on assets: 11.7%   Cash ($ mil.): 302
Return on equity: 19.0%
Current ratio: 1.70

ARIZONA STATE UNIVERSITY

Sun lovers and knowledge seekers can turn to Arizona State University (ASU) for a well-rounded college education. The research university offers a wide variety of bachelor's master's and doctoral degree programs with more than 300 majors through some 18 schools teaching a range of disciplines including nursing journalism and engineering. It has an enrollment of more than 98100 undergraduate graduate and professional students on its six campuses in metropolitan Phoenix; most students attend the Tempe campus. The university has a student-teacher ratio of 23:1. ASU was founded in 1885 as a teachers college and has become widely known for its extensive research programs.

Operations

ASU offers more than 90 undergraduate and graduate degrees and certificates online through some of its colleges including the W. P. Carey School of Business Mary Lou Fulton Teachers College College of Nursing and Health Innovation and the Ira A. Fulton School of Engineering. ASU also partners with Pearson Digital Learning to administer online courses; Pearson also monitors and analyzes student performance trends.

The university's extensive research programs cover a variety of fields in life science medicine and physical science categories. In addition subsidiary Arizona Technology Enterprises (AzTE) manages technology ventures for ASU. AzTE man-

ages the university's intellectual property (much of which is the result of its research programs) and facilitates startup businesses which have led to the formation of 80 companies and attracted $500 million in funding between 2002 and 2016.

Geographic Reach

ASU has an enrollment of students from more than 130 countries.

Financial Performance

The university's revenues increased by 11% (or $162 million) to $1.6 billion in fiscal 2016 primarily due a 10% increase in enrollment including a 23% growth in nonresident enrollment. Research grants and contracts revenue primarily funded by federal agencies rose by 7%.

Operating expenses grew by $143 million (or 7%) that year largely related to the increase in enrollment. Instruction and academic support expenses experienced the largest rise of $81 million.

Strategy

The university is working to become a top research university in interdisciplinary fields of science and technology. As part of that goal ASU is seeking to expand its AzTE entrepreneur business through additional technology discoveries and startup formations. It also seeks to help stimulate the Arizona economy by reaching out to local businesses and encouraging startups that will maintain a presence in the state.

ASU is also working to improve graduation rates increase graduate enrollment and enhance individual learning programs. The university intends to increase the quality of its academic programs and its student facilities.

In 2015 and 2016 the US News & World Report named ASU as the most innovative school in the US.

In 2016 the school opened the $130 million Arizona Center for Law and Society at its downtown campus. The center provides law students with greater access to Arizona's judicial political and economic centers. Other planned facilities include new educational and research centers near Phoenix's Mayo Clinic Hospital; they will deepen ASU's partnership with the Mayo Clinic and provide learning opportunities for ASU students.

In 2014 the university launched a partnership with Starbucks to provide tuition reimbursement to employees nationwide attending ASU online.

EXECUTIVES

Evp Treasurer And Cfo, Morgan R. Olsen
President, Michael M. Crow, age 64
Cio And Professor Of Parctice, Lev S. Gonick, age 59
Svp And President Asu Alumni Association, Christine K. Wilkinson
Evp And University Provost, Mark Searle
Cio, Gordon Wishon
Evp Knowledge Enterprise Development And Chief Research & Innovation Officer, Sethuraman (Panch) Panchanathan
Svp And Chief Marketing Officer, Daniel Dillon
Dean Educational Initiatives And Ceo Edplus, Philip Regier
Ceo And Director General Thunderbird School Of Global Management And Professor Of Global Strategy And Leadership, Allen Morrison
Auditors: LINDSEY PERRY CPA CFE PHOEN

LOCATIONS

HQ: ARIZONA STATE UNIVERSITY
  300 E UNIVERSITY DR # 410, TEMPE, AZ 852812061
Phone: 480 965-2100
Web: WWW.ASU.EDU

PRODUCTS/OPERATIONS

2014 Sales

	$ mil.	% of total
Tuition & fees	896	67
Research grants and contracts	244	18
Auxiliary enterprises	140	10
Other operating revenues	66	5
Total	1,348	100

Selected Colleges and Schools

Barrett Honors College
College of Health Solutions
College of Liberal Arts and Sciences
College of Nursing and Health Innovation
College of Public Programs
College of Technology and Innovation
Graduate College
Herberger Institute for Design and the Arts
Ira A. Fulton Schools of Engineering
Mary Lou Fulton Teachers College
New College of Interdisciplinary Arts and Sciences
Sandra Day O'Connor College of Law
School of Letters and Sciences
School of Sustainability
Thunderbird School of Global Management
University College
Walter Cronkite School of Journalism and Mass Communication
W.P. Carey School of Business

HISTORICAL FINANCIALS

Company Type: Private

Income Statement				FYE: June 30
	REVENUE ($ mil.)	NET INCOME ($ mil.)	NET PROFIT MARGIN	EMPLOYEES
06/18	1,915	63	3.3%	8,000
06/17	1,782	99	5.6%	—
06/16	1,644	108	6.6%	—
06/13	1,227	85	6.9%	—
Annual Growth	9.3%	(5.8%)	—	—

2018 Year-End Financials

Return on assets: 1.5%   Cash ($ mil.): 78
Return on equity: 5.0%
Current ratio: 0.60

ARIZONA STATE UNIVERSITY

LOCATIONS

HQ: ARIZONA STATE UNIVERSITY
  951 S PALM WALK, TEMPE, AZ 852870001
Phone: 480 965-4385
Web: WWW.ASU.EDU

HISTORICAL FINANCIALS

Company Type: Private

Income Statement				FYE: June 30
	REVENUE ($ mil.)	NET INCOME ($ mil.)	NET PROFIT MARGIN	EMPLOYEES
06/15	1,482	92	6.2%	26
06/14	1,348	103	7.7%	—
Annual Growth	9.9%	(10.7%)	—	—

2015 Year-End Financials

Return on assets: 6.4%   Cash ($ mil.): 47
Return on equity: 6.2%
Current ratio: 0.60

ARKANSAS CHILDREN'S HOSPITAL

As the only pediatric medical center in the state Arkansas Children's Hospital (ACH) serves the youngest Razorbacks from birth to age 21. The not-for-profit hospital with its 370 beds specializes in childhood cancer pediatric orthopedics and neonatology. Besides acute care services it operates more than 80 specialty clinics and outpatient centers. One of the US's largest pediatric hospitals ACH is also engaged in teaching and medical research through its affiliation with the University of Arkansas for Medical Sciences. Its Arkansas Children's Hospital Research Institute focuses on biological mechanisms underlying birth defects diabetes-related complications and childhood diseases.

Operations
ACH each year performs more than 14500 operations and boasts 55000-plus emergency department visits nearly 330000 outpatient visits and about 14800 inpatient admissions.

ACH's Circle of Friends clinic treats more than 20000 patients annually. The clinic which opened in 2008 provides primary care as well as a broad range of specialty care services related to endocrinology dermatological conditions hemophilia and tuberculosis.

The hospital also offers community outreach services that include help for children of domestic abuse and wellness programs as well as a number of clinics to support those with eating disorders and diabetes.

As a prime destination for treatment ACH also runs Angel One Transport an intensive care medical transportation system that brings critically ill and injured infants children and adolescents as well as adult burn patients from throughout Arkansas and the surrounding states to ACH. It also boasts a high risk obstetric transport program in partnership with the University of Arkansas for Medical Sciences.

ACH has a staff of 500 physicians including 95 residents in pediatrics and pediatric specialties. Its mobile clinics annually serve more than 6000 patients and provide more than $3 million in dental treatment.

Geographic Reach
Based in Little Rock Arkansas on a campus that extends nearly 30 city blocks ACH serves children nationwide as one of the largest pediatric hospitals in the US. It has several locations across Arkansas in Little Rock Jonesboro and Lowell.

Financial Performance
The hospital gets about 82% of its net sales from net patient service revenues.

Strategy
In 2015 ACH announced plans to build a $184 million hospital in Springdale. The 24-bed hospital will be located on 37 acres of land near Arvest Ballpark. The hospital is targeted to be completed in 2018.

In 2013 ACH inked a contract with Aetna health insurance under which patients with Aetna health insurance will be able to seek in-network care at ACH. The contract allows the company to reach more families throughout the region.

Company Background
The hospital opened a new $121 million south wing in mid-2012 that added more than 50 inpatient beds to the hospital's capacity. The nearly 260000-sq.-ft. four-story building features telemedicine technology (for remote patient care) new trauma rooms a dedicated orthopedics suite and a decontamination unit.

To its benefit ACH became the state's only pediatric Level I trauma center in 2010 after receiving a four-year designation from the Arkansas Department of Health. The designation means that the hospital is equipped for and capable of taking care of children with the most severe of traumas. Level I trauma centers serve as referral locations for hospitals that are unable to provide the same level of care.

EXECUTIVES

Vice President Human Resources, Andree Trosclair
President Ceo And Director, Jonathan R. (Jon) Bates
Evp, Scott R. Gordon
President Arkansas Childrens Hospital Research Institute, Richard F. Jacobs
Svp And Cio, Darrell T. Leonhardt
Svp And Cfo, Gena G. Wingfield
Svp And Coo, David T. Berry
President Ach Foundation, Fred Scarborough
Senior Vice President Chief Quality Officer, Jayant K. Deshpande
Senior Vice President Medical Director, W. Robert Morrow
Nursing Director Pediatric In, Kim White
Vice President Operations, Jennifer Carlisle
Nursing Director, Terri Songer
Director Of Pharmacy, Marita Q Nazarian
Nursing Director, Stephanie Rockett
Vice President Of Ancillary Services, Cindy Holland
Vice President Finance, Cindy Hill
Director Of Nursing, Rebecca Kersten
Vice President Of Information Technology Applications, Michael Hart
Nursing Director, Amy Allen
Nursing Director Of The Special Staffing Team, Jenny Janisko
Senior Vice President Chief Strategy Officer, Robert Steele
Senior Vice President Of Human Resource, Kimberly Frisbee
Vice President Acute Care, Tammy Webb
Vice President, Curtis Summers
Medical Director, Stephen Schexnayder
Respiratory Therapy Director, Patty Burge
Nursing Director, Tammy Wells
Senior Vice President Chief Strategy Officer, Bob Steele
Government Relations Vice President, Rosi Smith
Vice President Ambulatory Care Services, Lee A Eddy
Nursing Director, Tammy R Diamond-wells
Secretary To Vice President Human Resources, Charlotte Johnson
Unit Secretary, Shirley Brasfield
Secretary Ii, Shari Fobbs
Auditors: KPMG LLP MEMPHIS TN

LOCATIONS

HQ: ARKANSAS CHILDREN'S HOSPITAL
1 CHILDRENS WAY, LITTLE ROCK, AR 722023500
Phone: 501 364-1100
Web: WWW.ARCHILDRENS.ORG

PRODUCTS/OPERATIONS

Selected Services
Ambulatory Surgery
Audiology
Center for Good Mourning
Cleft Clinic
Dennis Developmental Center
Dental Clinic
ECMO
Gastroenterology Clinic
Genetic and Metabolic Clinic
Infectious Diseases
Neuroscience Unit
Physical Medicine & Rehab Outreach Clinics
Sleep Disorders Center
Volunteer Services
WHAM (Wellness Health Action & Motivation) Clinic

COMPETITORS

Arkansas Heart Hospital
Baptist Health (Arkansas)
Children's Healthcare of Atlanta
Children's Medical Center of Dallas
Children's Mercy Hospital
Children's National Medical Center
Cook Children's Health Care System
Dell Children's Medical Center
East Tennessee Children's Hospital
Jefferson Regional Medical Center of Arkansas
Methodist Healthcare
Shriners Hospitals For Children
St. Joseph's Mercy Health Center
St. Jude Children's Research Hospital
St. Vincent Health System
Texas Children's Hospital
Universal Health Services
White County Medical Center

HISTORICAL FINANCIALS
Company Type: Private

Income Statement
FYE: June 30

	REVENUE ($ mil.)	NET INCOME ($ mil.)	NET PROFIT MARGIN	EMPLOYEES
06/18	660	57	8.7%	3,700
06/17	615	59	9.7%	—
06/16	585	70	12.1%	—
06/15	562	44	8.0%	—
Annual Growth	5.5%	8.5%	—	—

2018 Year-End Financials
Return on assets: 3.9%   Cash ($ mil.): 91
Return on equity: 4.8%
Current ratio: 7.90

ARKANSAS ELECTRIC COOPERATIVES, INC.

EXECUTIVES

Pres, Duane Highley
Vice-President, Doug White
Engineer, Pat Patterson
Auditors: BKD LLP LITTLE ROCK ARKANSA

LOCATIONS

HQ: ARKANSAS ELECTRIC COOPERATIVES, INC.
1 COOPERATIVE WAY, LITTLE ROCK, AR 722095493
Phone: 501 570-2200
Web: WWW.AECC.COM

HISTORICAL FINANCIALS
Company Type: Private

Income Statement
FYE: December 31

	REVENUE ($ mil.)	NET INCOME ($ mil.)	NET PROFIT MARGIN	EMPLOYEES
12/18	679	50	7.4%	840
12/17	564	44	7.8%	—
12/15	462	35	7.7%	—
12/13	416	32	7.7%	—
Annual Growth	10.3%	9.4%	—	—

2018 Year-End Financials

Return on assets: 13.8%   Cash ($ mil.): 101
Return on equity: 18.5%
Current ratio: 3.60

ARLINGTON INDEPENDENT SCHOOL DISTRICT (INC)

EXECUTIVES

Supt, Marcelo Bavazls
Principal, Webb Elementary, Michael Martin
Coordinator, Kathy Hitt
Tech Prep Coordinator, Craig Wright
Tech Prep Coordinator, Ed Cannady
Teacher, Alison Felton
Classroom Assistant Elementary, Debbie Modawell
Teacher, Esther Ghio
Teacher, Gala Jones
Elementary School Teacher, Joan Swann
Academic Dean, Julie Lange
Auditors: WHITLEY PENN LLP HOUSTON TEX

LOCATIONS

HQ: ARLINGTON INDEPENDENT SCHOOL DISTRICT (INC)
1203 W PIONEER PKWY, ARLINGTON, TX 760136246
Phone: 682 867-4611
Web: WWW.AISD.NET

HISTORICAL FINANCIALS

Company Type: Private

Income Statement				FYE: June 30
	REVENUE ($ mil.)	NET INCOME ($ mil.)	NET PROFIT MARGIN	EMPLOYEES
06/18	680	(28)	—	8,000
06/17	641	(35)	—	—
06/16	636	115	18.1%	—
06/15	613	143	23.4%	—
Annual Growth	3.5%	—	—	—

2018 Year-End Financials

Return on assets: (-2.3%)   Cash ($ mil.): 520
Return on equity: —
Current ratio: —

ARMY & AIR FORCE EXCHANGE SERVICE

Paraphrasing the Army's longtime recruiting slogan buy all that you can buy at the PX (Post Exchange). The Army and Air Force Exchange Service (AAFES) runs about 3100 facilities including PXs and BXs (Base Exchanges) at US Army and Air Force bases in 30-plus countries all 50 US states and five US territories. Its presence includes some 180 retail stores and more than 1000 fast-food outlets (brands like Burger King and Taco Bell) as well as convenience stores/gas stations movie theaters and beauty shops. AAFES — which serves active-duty military personnel reservists re-

tirees and their families — also sells goods online. Although it's a government agency under the DOD it receives less than 5% of its funding from the department.

Operations

While the AAFES receives little federal money it pays neither taxes nor rent to occupy US government property. Its retail prices average about 25% less than the competition.

AAFES is also a major employer of veterans and military families. About 85 percent of its associates are connected to the military.

Geographic Reach

AAFES operates facilities in 30-plus countries all 50 US states and Washington DC and five US territories (Guam Puerto Rico US Virgin Islands Northern Mariana Islands and American Samoa). It also has contingency locations in Afghanistan Kuwait Iraq Saudi Arabia Jordan Qatar United Arab Emirates Romania Poland Bulgaria Bosnia and Kosovo.

Sales and Marketing

Besides its primary brick-and-mortar business AAFES boasts an online presence at shopmyexchange.com.

About 55% of its 13 million customers are military family members with retirees accounting for about 20% and active duty military and guardsmen/reservists each making up about 10%.

Financial Performance

In 2016 AAFES reported revenue of $8.3 billion and earnings of $384 million. Revenue is down about 20% since 2011 amid a shrinking customer base (fewer military personnel) and increased competition from online and other retailers.

Some two-thirds of its earnings go into Army Installation Management Command and Air Force Services programs for amenities such as libraries and youth centers. During the past decade AAFES has contributed more than $2.4 billion to these programs.

Strategy

As with most retailers AAFES shops are facing increased competition from discounters such as Walmart and online sites such as Amazon. In addition the organization is grappling with a smaller armed forces.

To combat these issues in recent years AAFES has enhanced the stores' product portfolio with top brands such as Disney and Michael Kors. It has also invested in the online customer experience and added shipping centers within stores that will allow for quicker and cheaper shipping for online purchases.

In late 2017 AAFES significantly expanded its customer base with a new online benefit rolled out to honorably discharged veterans that allows them to shop at AAFES' online stores. As a result the organization saw online sales more than double during Veterans Day weekend that year.

EXECUTIVES

Director And Ceo, Thomas C. (Tom) Shull
Evp And Chief Logistics Officer, Karen Stack
President And Chief Merchandising Officer, Ana Middleton
Deputy Director, Mike Immler
Coo, David Nelson
Cfo, James Jordan
Evp And Cio, Philip Stevens
Vice President Planning Allocation Replenishment, Sean Shaw
Auditors: ERNST & YOUNG LLP DALLAS TX

LOCATIONS

HQ: ARMY & AIR FORCE EXCHANGE SERVICE
3911 S WALTON WALKER BLVD, DALLAS, TX 752361598
Phone: 214 312-2011

PRODUCTS/OPERATIONS

Selected Merchandise & Services

Barber & beauty shops
Books newspapers & magazines
Catalog services
Concessions
Food facilities
Gas stations & auto repair
Military clothing stores
Movie theaters
Retail stores
Vending centers

COMPETITORS

7-Eleven	Fred's
99 Cents Only	Kroger
Amazon.com	METRO AG
Best Buy	Sears Holdings
Big Lots	Sport Clips
Costco Wholesale	Supercuts
Dollar General	Target Corporation
Dollar Tree	Wal-Mart
Family Dollar Stores	

HISTORICAL FINANCIALS

Company Type: Private

Income Statement				FYE: February 3
	REVENUE ($ mil.)	NET INCOME ($ mil.)	NET PROFIT MARGIN	EMPLOYEES
02/18*	7,210	299	4.2%	35,000
01/17	6,952	292	4.2%	—
Annual Growth	3.7%	2.5%		—

*Fiscal year change

2018 Year-End Financials

Return on assets: 4.7%   Cash ($ mil.): 96
Return on equity: 8.9%
Current ratio: 3.10

ARROWHEAD REGIONAL MEDICAL CENTER

Find yourself dehydrated after searching the Inland Empire deserts for arrowheads? Arrowhead Regional Medical Center (ARMC) can fix you up. The San Bernardino County owned and operated hospital provides a range of health services from general medical and surgical care to emergency services rehabilitation inpatient psychiatric care pediatric and women's health services. It also serves as a Level II trauma center a regional burn center and medical training facility. ARMC with some 460 beds (370 inpatient and 90 behavioral) opened in 1999 to replace the aging San Bernardino County Hospital. The hospital also offers outpatient services on its main campus and at area clinics.

Operations

Along with a full range of health care services ARMC offers about 10 residency programs including emergency and family medicine general surgery geriatrics orthopedics neurosurgery and gynecology. The hospital trains about 170 residents each year and also provides training programs for nurses pharmacists clinical laboratory scientists and radiologic technologists.

The ARMC emergency room handles about 140000 visits each year. The hospital's inpatient capacity handles about 25000 patients annually while its outpatient centers see some 250000 patients.

The Medical Center's Internal Medicine Primary Care Clinic offers services for individuals ranging in age from 18 to 100. Its Outpatient Care facility offers more than 60 different specialty services including pediatrics geriatrics orthopedics surgery internal medicine women's health and rehabilitation services.

ARMC's two Breath Mobiles provide pediatric asthma care management at sites throughout San Bernardino County.

Geographic Reach
The company serves patients in San Bernardino Riverside Inyo and Mono counties in California. ARMC's main facility campus in Colton includes an outpatient services complex. It also runs three primary care Family Health Centers in the nearby towns of Fontana Rialto and San Bernadino as well as wound care and elder care clinics.

Financial Performance
ARMC's revenues dropped by 1% to $385 million in 2012 due to a decline in net patient service revenues.

However net income decreased by 63% to $12 million in 2012 due to higher operating expenses (salaries benefits and purchased services) partially offset by a rise in non-operating revenues due to an increase in state funding.

Strategy
To better serve the needs of patients in its service territory ARMC looks to expand services in high-demand areas.

To enable doctors and technologists to provide a vastly expanded number of procedures for cardiac patients neurology patients and those requiring interventional radiology in 2013 ARMC opened its new Dual Purpose Interventional Lab (medical suite).

That year it also opened a new and larger Westside Family Health Center which was expanded from 12 to 21 exam rooms in a new co-location facility in Rialto. It also expanded its Breath Mobile service to the High Desert with service to sites including Adelanto Apple Valley Barstow Hesperia Phelan Victorville and Trona.

Company Background
An increase in cases of asthma (particularly among children) in the Central Valley led ARMC to expand its Breathmobile program an asthma clinic on wheels that travels to schools throughout San Bernadino County in 2010.

The hospital is also enhancing stationary outpatient care clinics. It added the ARMC Medical Office Building to its main campus in 2011; the center includes physician practices and an internal medicine clinic.

EXECUTIVES

Director Of Pharmacy, Cliff Hiroshige

LOCATIONS

HQ: ARROWHEAD REGIONAL MEDICAL CENTER
400 N PEPPER AVE, COLTON, CA 923241819
Phone: 909 580-1000
Web: WWW.ARROWHEADMEDCENTER.ORG

PRODUCTS/OPERATIONS

Selected Services

Audiology
Breast Cancer Clinic
Cardiology
Child Health Disability Program
Dialysis Center
Emergency Medicine
Family and Elder Care
Internal Medicine
Level II Trauma Center
Oncology/Infusion Therapy
Ophthalmology
Orthopedics

Pediatric Clinic
Psychiatric Emergency Services
Radiation Oncology
Rehabilitation Clinic
Surgery
Women's Health

COMPETITORS

Anaheim Regional
  Medical Center
Cedars-Sinai Medical
  Center
Children's Hospital of
  Orange County
City of Hope
Community Hospital of
  San Bernardino
Dignity Health

HCA
Loma Linda University
  Medical Center
Memorial Health
  Services
St. Jude Medical
  Center
Tenet Healthcare
Trinity Health (Novi)

HISTORICAL FINANCIALS
Company Type: Private

Income Statement | | | | FYE: June 30
	REVENUE ($ mil.)	NET INCOME ($ mil.)	NET PROFIT MARGIN	EMPLOYEES
06/15	468	74	15.8%	2,500
06/09	225	25	11.3%	—
06/04	439	3	0.8%	—
06/03	313	(1)	—	—
Annual Growth	3.4%	—	—	—

2015 Year-End Financials
Return on assets: 11.4%   Cash ($ mil.): 72
Return on equity: 55.2%
Current ratio: 1.90

ASCENSION HEALTH ALLIANCE

EXECUTIVES

Ceo, Joseph Impicciche
Int Pres-Ceo, Joseph R Impicciche
Sr Exec Advsr, Sister Bernice Coreil DC
Evp, John D Doyle
Evp, Robert J Henkel
Evp, Susan Nestor Levy
Evp, Sister Maureen McGuire DC
Evp, David B Pryor
Executive Administrative Assis, Teresa Hatton
Regional Director, Andrew Gwin
Cco Clinical & Network Svs, Richard Fogel
Auditors: ERNST & YOUNG LLP ST LOUIS M

LOCATIONS

HQ: ASCENSION HEALTH ALLIANCE
101 S HANLEY RD STE 450, SAINT LOUIS, MO
631053463
Phone: 314 733-8000

HISTORICAL FINANCIALS
Company Type: Private

Income Statement | | | | FYE: June 30
	ASSETS ($ mil.)	NET INCOME ($ mil.)	INCOME AS % OF ASSETS	EMPLOYEES
06/17	34,320	1,638	4.8%	111,719
06/16	32,469	(339)	—	—
06/15	30,963	(42)	—	—
Annual Growth	5.3%	—	—	—

2017 Year-End Financials
Return on assets: 4.8%   Sales ($ mil): 22,633
Return on equity: 8.0%

ASCENSION PROVIDENCE HOSPITAL

Providence Hospital and Medical Centers provides health care in the Motor City and surrounding areas. The main Providence Hospital is a 408-bed teaching facility that has been recognized for its cardiology program and clinical expertise in behavioral medicine. It offers a variety of other services ranging from cancer treatment and neurosurgery to orthopedics and women's health. The network also includes dozens of affiliated general practice and specialty health clinics. The not-for-profit medical center founded in 1845 as St. Vincent's Hospital in Detroit by the Daughters of Charity is part of Catholic health ministry St. John Health (itself a subsidiary of Ascension Health).

Operations
As part of its health care system Providence Hospital and Medical Centers operates a host of hospitals and medical centers across the metropolitan Detroit area. They include Providence Southfield and four namesake Providence Medical Center locations in Farmington Hills Livonia Dearborn Heights and South Lyon. Across its system the medical facilities employ some 1500 physicians and enlist the help of about 300 active volunteers.

Carroll Manor is a skilled nursing center that provides short- and long-term medical care and rehabilitation services. The system's behavioral health division Seton House provides alcohol and addiction treatment in Washington DC.

Providence Hospital and Medical Centers had more than 41600 emergency department visits in 2013.

Strategy
In order to provide better services the hospital renovated and expanded its emergency department in 2014. Also that year its family medicine division opened a new office in the Glenn Dale/Bowie area.

EXECUTIVES

Prin, Louise De Marillac
Prin*, Diane Radloff
Internal Medicine Practitioner, Zaid Yaldo
Chief Operating Officer, Vijay Mittal
Internal Medicine Practitioner, Elias Zeine
Internal Medicine Practitioner, Michael J Di Loreto
Chief of Medicine, Ernest Yoder
Coordinator, Tiffany Tscherne
Internist, Gurbir Singh
Administrative Assistant, Leslie Tippett
Director, Lou Bischoff
Auditors: DELOITTE TAX LP CINCINNATI O

LOCATIONS

HQ: ASCENSION PROVIDENCE HOSPITAL
16001 W 9 MILE RD, SOUTHFIELD, MI 480754818
Phone: 248 849-3000
Web: WWW.PROVIDENCEOBGYNRESIDENCY.COM

Selected Hospitals and Medical Centers
Providence Southfield-Southfield
Providence Medical Center-Farmington Hills
Providence Medical Center-Livonia
Providence Medical Center-Dearborn Heights
Providence Medical Center-South Lyon

PRODUCTS/OPERATIONS

Selected Primary Services
Cancer clinical trials
Cardiac rehabilitation
Childbirth
Congenital heart disease clinic
Emergency
Oncology
Orthopedics
Senior services
Surgery
Women's health

COMPETITORS

Beaumont Health System	McLaren Health Care
Crittenton Hospital	Trinity Health (Novi)
Detroit Medical Center	University of Michigan
Henry Ford Health	Health System
System	

HISTORICAL FINANCIALS

Company Type: Private

Income Statement   FYE: June 30

	REVENUE ($ mil.)	NET INCOME ($ mil.)	NET PROFIT MARGIN	EMPLOYEES
06/16	703	21	3.1%	4,700
06/15	654	25	3.9%	—
06/14	659	53	8.1%	—
06/11	706	27	3.9%	—
Annual Growth	(0.1%)	(4.9%)	—	—

2016 Year-End Financials
Return on assets: 0.5%
Return on equity: 3.2%   Cash ($ mil.): 3
Current ratio: 1.20

ASCENSION VIA CHRISTI HOSPITALS WICHITA, INC.

EXECUTIVES

Ceo, Michael Mullis
V Pres*, Michael McCullough
Aprn, Jamie K Gilstrap
Aprn, Jennifer M Daney
Director of Nursing, Lori Campbell
MD, Nicholas Cahoj
Pharmacy Director, James Garrelts
Risk Manager, Keith Maurath

LOCATIONS

HQ: ASCENSION VIA CHRISTI HOSPITALS WICHITA, INC.
929 N ST FRANCIS ST, WICHITA, KS 672143821
Phone: 316 268-5880
Web: WWW.VIACHRISTI.ORG

HISTORICAL FINANCIALS

Company Type: Private

Income Statement   FYE: September 30

	REVENUE ($ mil.)	NET INCOME ($ mil.)	NET PROFIT MARGIN	EMPLOYEES
09/15	538	36	6.7%	4,100
09/14	534	68	12.9%	—
09/13	534	24	4.5%	—
09/12	529	108	20.4%	—
Annual Growth	0.6%	(30.7%)	—	—

2015 Year-End Financials
Return on assets: 4.9%
Return on equity: 6.3%   Cash ($ mil.): 22
Current ratio: 3.20

ASI COMPUTER TECHNOLOGIES INC

ASI Computer Technologies is a wholesale distributor of computer software hardware and accessories. It offers more than 15000 products including PCs modems monitors networking equipment and data storage devices. The company sells to resellers retailers systems integrators and equipment makers from offices and facilities in the US Canada and Mexico. Its vendor partners include companies the likes of AMD Intel Microsoft and Western Digital. ASI's services include custom systems integration and contract assembly. It also markets PCs and notebooks under its own brands: Pegatron IQ and Nspire. The company was established in 1987 by president and owner Cristine Liang.

Geographic Reach
Based in California ASI operates nationwide as well as in Mexico and Canada. To support its business the wholesaler operates regional offices in Atlanta Chicago Dallas Houston Los Angeles Miami Portland and in Kansas and New Jersey. Its Canadian offices are in Montreal Toronto and Vancouver. In Mexico ASI has offices in Monterrey Nuevo Laredo and Torreon.

Sales and Marketing
ASI's diverse portfolio of products and services allow it to service a broad customer base (it counts some 8000 customers) which includes VARs system integrators retailers DMRs and OEM accounts.

Financial Performance
ASI reported $1.8 billion in sales in 2014 up from about $1.4 billion in 2013.

Strategy
The wholesale distributor regularly adds to its products portfolio through distribution agreements with multiple partners.

In 2015 it reached a distribution agreement with QLogic supplier of high performance network infrastructure products. ASI also expanded its distribution deal with SanDisk to include SanDisk's solid state drives.

In 2014 ASI partnered with Huawei a manufacturer of telecommunications equipment in China to distribute Huawei's IP network infrastructure communications and storage products through its resellers in North America. Also in 2014 the company partnered with Belkin a maker of USB devices and other products to distribute its full line of products. Previously in 2013 it inked a deal with computer hardware maker Rosewill to carry the company's computer cases power supplies net-

working cables and computer accessories which range from entry-level lines to high-end items.

The company supports its comprehensive products menu with value-added services that range from ISO 9001-certified integration system design and process validation kitting private labeling and custom packaging.

To its benefit ASI is the largest privately-held woman-owned business in California and the third largest of its kind in the nation. It holds certificates as a minority supplier and woman-owned business.

EXECUTIVES

President Of Asi Computer Systems, Dave Wirth
Auditors: MARCUM LLP SAN FRANCISCO CA

LOCATIONS

HQ: ASI COMPUTER TECHNOLOGIES INC
48289 FREMONT BLVD, FREMONT, CA 945386510
Phone: 510 226-8000
Web: WWW.ASIPARTNER.COM

PRODUCTS/OPERATIONS

Selected Products

Accessories

Cables

Cameras

Cases
CD-ROM drives
Central processing units
Controller cards
DVD drives
Fans
Floppy drives
Hard drives
Keyboards
Memory
Mice
Modems
Monitors
Motherboards
MP3 players
Multimedia products
Network connectivity products
Notebooks
Optical drives
PCs
Power supplies
Printers
Projectors
Removable drives and media
Scanners
Software
Sound cards
Speakers
Storage devices
Tape back-up products
Video cards
Zip drives

COMPETITORS

ASCII Group	MTM Technologies
Agilysys	Merisel
Arrow Electronics	MicroAge
Avnet	New Age Electronics
Avnet Technology	SED International
CompuCom	SHI International
Continental Resources	SYNNEX
D & H Distributing	Softmart
En Pointe	Supercom
Flextronics	Tech Data
Ingram Micro	

HISTORICAL FINANCIALS

Company Type: Private

Income Statement				FYE: December 31
	REVENUE ($ mil.)	NET INCOME ($ mil.)	NET PROFIT MARGIN	EMPLOYEES
12/13	1,746	17	1.0%	700
12/04	1,057	12	1.2%	—
12/03	982	13	1.3%	—
12/02	865	10	1.2%	—
Annual Growth	6.6%	4.9%	—	—

2013 Year-End Financials

Return on assets: 5.4%
Return on equity: 1.0%
Current ratio: 1.10

Cash ($ mil.): 28

ASIAINFO-LINKAGE, INC.

EXECUTIVES

Ceo-V Chb, Steve Zhang
V Pres-Cfo*, Ying Han
V Pres-GM*, Lihua Yan
Exec V Pres-Cto*, Yadong Jin
Vice President, Jie LI
Prin, Tom Manning
Finance Manager, Paul Yin
Vice-President, WEI LI
Chief Financial Officer, Michael Wu
Executive Director, Tao Long

LOCATIONS

HQ: ASIAINFO-LINKAGE, INC.
5201 GREAT AMERICA PKWY # 356, SANTA CLARA, CA 950541122
Phone: 408 970-9788
Web: WWW.ASIAINFO.COM

HISTORICAL FINANCIALS

Company Type: Private

Income Statement				FYE: December 31
	REVENUE ($ mil.)	NET INCOME ($ mil.)	NET PROFIT MARGIN	EMPLOYEES
12/11	481	72	15.2%	1,500
12/09	76	14	18.8%	—
Annual Growth	151.2%	125.8%	—	—

2011 Year-End Financials

Return on assets: 5.7%
Return on equity: 7.5%
Current ratio: 2.40

Cash ($ mil.): 272

ASPIRUS WAUSAU HOSPITAL, INC.

EXECUTIVES

Ceo, Duane Erwin
Pres*, Darrell Lentz
Scientist, Cindy Geiss
Coordinator, Judy Smith
Director, Raymond Hartke
Information Specialist, Mark Chickering

Manager of Information, Deb Draxler
Chief of Medicine, Erik Anderson
Quality Assurance Director, Deb Zahrt
Nurse, Debra Knapp
Coordinator, Lynn Mercier
Auditors: WIPFLI LLP EAU CLAIRE WISCON

LOCATIONS

HQ: ASPIRUS WAUSAU HOSPITAL, INC.
425 PINE RIDGE BLVD # 1, WAUSAU, WI 544014122
Phone: 715 847-2019

HISTORICAL FINANCIALS

Company Type: Private

Income Statement				FYE: June 30
	REVENUE ($ mil.)	NET INCOME ($ mil.)	NET PROFIT MARGIN	EMPLOYEES
06/18	497	8	1.7%	3,500
06/16	456	51	11.4%	—
06/14	369	42	11.4%	—
06/10	319	33	10.4%	—
Annual Growth	5.7%	(15.8%)	—	—

2018 Year-End Financials

Return on assets: 1.6%
Return on equity: 2.5%
Current ratio: 2.00

Cash ($ mil.): 4

ASPIRUS, INC.

Aspirus aspires to provide care for Midwesterners in need. The health system provides a comprehensive range of health and medical services to residents in a 14-county region of central and northern Wisconsin as well as Michigan's Upper Peninsula. Aspirus operates the Aspirus Wausau Hospital a 325-bed multi-specialty regional health center and seven smaller community hospitals. Its hospitals and network of community clinics provide specialized primary and emergency care. Aspirus also operates imaging centers hospice services home health care long-term care facilities and an outpatient dialysis center.

Operations

Other facilities in Aspirus' network include the 25-bed Aspirus Medford Hospital the Catholic Aspirus Langlade Hospital specialist hospital Riverview Family Clinic and 25-bed critical care access hospitals Aspirus Ontonagon and NORTHSTAR. In all it operates four hospitals in Michigan and four in Wisconsin as well as 50 clinics home health and hospice care helicopter transport nursing homes and pharmacies.

Sales and Marketing

Aspirus takes payments from most health plans and payers in the region in which it operates. It also contracts directly with employers and community business coalitions.

Mergers and Acquisitions

Michigan-based NORTHSTAR Health System became an Aspira subsidiary in 2014. It added a 25-bed critical access hospital as well as clinics to Aspira's network.

EXECUTIVES

President And Ceo, Duane L. Erwin, age 68
Senior Vice President Of Finance And Cfo Aspirus Wausau Hospital Aspirus Inc., Sidney Sczygelski
Executive Director Aspirus Network Inc., Joel Rueber
Interim President/coo Aspirus Wausau Hospital, Marita Hattem

President Of Aspirus Clinics And Chief Clinical Integration Officer For Aspirus, Bud Chumbley
Vice President Of Patient Care/chief Nursing Officer, Kathy Drengler
Ceo Of Aspirus Grand View, Carol Goffnett
Vice President Marketing And Planning, Rick L. Nevers
Executive Director Of Aspirus Health Foundation, Kalynn Pempek
Vice President Of Information Technology/chief Information Officer, Todd Richardson
Senior Vice President Of Business Development, Eric Anderson
Physical Therapy, Nathan Weiler
Vice President Of Compliance, Lori Peck
Clinical Director, Rae Kaare
Nursing Director, Ann Line
Director Of Pharmacy, Jill Michaud
Auditors: WIPFLI LLP WAUSAU WISCONSIN

LOCATIONS

HQ: ASPIRUS, INC.
2200 WESTWOOD DR, WAUSAU, WI 544017806
Phone: 715 847-2121

Selected Facilities U.P. of Michigan Aspirus Grand View Aspirus Keweenaw Hospital Aspirus Ontonagon Hospital NORTHSTAR Health System Wisconsin Aspirus Wausau Hospital Aspirus Langlade Hospital Aspirus Medford Hospital Riverview Hospital

PRODUCTS/OPERATIONS

Selected Services
Alzheimer's & Memory Disorders
Anesthesia Services
Angioplasty
Anticoagulation Clinic
Cardiac Electrophysiology
Cardiac Rehab
Cardioversion
Dentistry
Oral & Maxillofacial Surgery
Prosthodontics
Psychiatry
Psychology
Pulmonary Medicine
Sleep Disorders

COMPETITORS

Dean Health Systems Inc.
Howard Young Health Care
Luther Midelfort
ThedaCare Inc.
University of Wisconsin Hospital and Clinics

HISTORICAL FINANCIALS

Company Type: Private

Income Statement				FYE: June 30
	REVENUE ($ mil.)	NET INCOME ($ mil.)	NET PROFIT MARGIN	EMPLOYEES
06/18	911	78	8.6%	7,100
06/13	536	47	8.9%	—
06/12	529	26	4.9%	—
06/11	1,781	0		—
Annual Growth	—	—	—	—

2018 Year-End Financials

Return on assets: 5.9%
Return on equity: 8.6%
Current ratio: 2.30

Cash ($ mil.): 104

ASSOCIATED FOOD STORES, INC.

This business makes sure there's plenty of grub for the Wild West. Associated Food Stores (AFS) is a leading regional cooperative wholesale distributor that supplies groceries and other products to some 500 independent supermarkets in about eight Western states. It also offers support services for its member-owners including market research real estate analysis store design technology procurement and training. In addition AFS owns a stake in Western Family Foods a grocery wholesalers' partnership that produces Western Family private-label goods. The co-op formed in 1940 also operates 40-plus corporate stores in Utah under five different banners including Fresh Market.

Operations

In addition to its wholesale business AFS's retail arm — Associated Retail Operations — owns and operates corporate stores in Utah under five different formats and banners: Macey's; Fresh Market; Dan's Fresh Market in Salt Lake City; Lin's Fresh Market; and Dick's Fresh Market. The retail business accounts for about 35% of AFS's annual revenue.

The grocery distributor supplies independent supermarkets with over 3600 products. Products comprise a wide array including baking breakfast cereals frozen foods household supplies and even pet food and supplies. In early 2013 Associated closed its distribution centers in Helena and Billings Montana and consolidated warehouse operations for its nearly 100 Montana and Wyoming customers at its facility in Farr West Utah.

Geographic Reach

Salt Lake City-based Associated Food Stores has operations in Arizona Colorado Idaho Montana Nevada Oregon Utah and Wyoming. The

Financial Performance

While privately-owned Associated Food Stores doesn't report its financial results the company logged an estimated $2.2 billion in sales in fiscal 2013 (ended March) versus $2.1 billion in sales the previous year.

EXECUTIVES

Director Of Pharmacy Operations, Shawna Hanson
Treasurer, Bob Obray
Auditors: DELOITTE & TOUCHE LLP SALT L

LOCATIONS

HQ: ASSOCIATED FOOD STORES, INC.
  1850 W 2100 S, SALT LAKE CITY, UT 841191304
Phone: 801 973-4400
Web: WWW.AFSTORES.COM

PRODUCTS/OPERATIONS

Selected Brands
Western Family
Full Circle
Shur Saving

Selected Retail Banners
Dan's Fresh Market
Dick's Fresh Market
Fresh Market
Lin's Fresh Market
Macey's

COMPETITORS

AMCON Distributing	SUPERVALU
C&S Wholesale	Safeway
GSC Enterprises	URM Stores
Kroger	Wal-Mart
McLane	

HISTORICAL FINANCIALS

Company Type: Private

Income Statement   FYE: March 31

	REVENUE ($ mil.)	NET INCOME ($ mil.)	NET PROFIT MARGIN	EMPLOYEES
03/12	2,011	5	0.3%	300
03/11	1,953	(6)	—	—
03/10	1,785	(2)	—	—
Annual Growth	6.1%	—	—	—

2012 Year-End Financials
Return on assets: 1.0%   Cash ($ mil.): 105
Return on equity: 5.4%
Current ratio: 0.90

ASSOCIATED WHOLESALE GROCERS, INC.

Associated Wholesale Grocers (AWG) knows its customers can't live on bread and milk alone. The second-largest retailer-owned distribution cooperative in the US (behind Wakefern Food Corporation) AWG supplies more than 3800 grocery retail outlets in more than half of the US states from 10 distribution centers which collectively have some 7 million square feet of space. In addition to its wholesale grocery operation AWG offers a variety of business services to its members including marketing and merchandising programs retail accounting supermarket development and access to low-cost merchandise through its Value Merchandisers subsidiary. AWG was founded by a group of independent grocers in 1924.

Geographic Reach

Kansas City-headquartered Associated Wholesale Grocers began in Missouri and its operations are generally centered on that state. It operates ten wholesale divisions in Missouri Nebraska Kansas Oklahoma Louisiana Alabama Tennessee and Wisconsin. Its distribution activities extend into another 25 states.

AWG's Valu Merchandisers subsidiary is gaining a foothold in non-US regions such as the Caribbean Central & South America and the Middle East.

Sales and Marketing

As a cooperative AWG serves the needs of its members who collectively determine how best to utilize the co-ops operations. Its board of directors is made up of nearly 20 people each a key executive at a grocer retail chain which receives products from AWG.

AWG serves up several private label brands to stores. They include Superior Selections Clearly Organic Best Choice Always Save and IGA.

Financial Performance

Associated Wholesale Grocers (AWG) has grown net sales in recent years from $7.8 billion in 2016 to more recent results exceeding $9.0 billion. Net income has trended positively over the

same period from $175 million in 2012 to a spiked of more than $225 million in 2014 to a current result near $190 million.

For the year 2016 net sales grew 3% to $9.2 billion. Product price deflation pushed sales lower as did the loss of Albertsons' membership in the distribution co-op. AWG gained 800 new member stores in conjunction with its unification with Affiliated Foods Midwest which increased sales sufficiently to overcome the negative influencers.

Net income for the year was $190 million 4% lower than the prior year due to a corresponding increase in the co-op's general and administrative expenses.

Strategy

As a supplier to primarily independent and non-national grocers the co-op must retain size in order to compete with larger corporate firms. Years 2016 and 2017 saw its size shrink in Texas particularly in the hotly contested Dallas-Fort Worth market. Associated Wholesale Grocers lost two key members Albertsons (owner of Tom Thumb's and Safeway) and WinCo. It countered this by uniting with Affiliated Foods Midwest a distribution co-op with some 800 retail stores but the loss of such notable members is expected influence AWG's posturing within the North Texas area.

AWG continues to build sales of its billion-dollar private-label products line which includes the Best Choice IGA and Always Save brands. In addition to marketing the products as lower-cost alternatives to brand-name products the co-op has been investing in efforts to make sure the quality of its private-label items matches competing national brands. The company also owns and operates the Value Merchandisers Company (VMC) which offers some 22000 nonfood items to its members including health and beauty care general merchandise and seasonal and promotional products.

Operating in a fragmented business AWG competes with a large number of local and regional suppliers as well as distributors of specialty items. The food wholesale business also has its share of national giants including C & S Wholesale Nash-Finch and wholesale grocery and retail company SUPERVALU.

EXECUTIVES

Svp And Division Manager Nashville, Mike Danes
Evp And Chief Marketing Officer, Steve Arnold
Svp And Division Manager Memphis, Gary Jennings
Svp Finance, David Carl
Svp Distribution, Richard Kearns
Svp And Cio, Jon Payne
Svp And Division Manager Fort Worth, Linda Lawson
Svp Springfield, Tim Bellanti
President And Ceo, David Smith
Svp And Division Manager Oklahoma City, Danny Lane
Svp Grocery Products, Dan Funk
Svp Perishables, Jerry Edney
Svp And Division Manager Gulf Coast, Bob Durand
President Valu Merchandisers Company (vmc), Dave Sutton
President Always Fresh, Michael Schumacher
Vp Sales And Merchandising Memphis Division, David Gates
Senior Vice President, Maurice Henry
Vice President Of Sales Great Lakes, Sonny Leon
Vice President Of Fresh Merchandising Bakery Deli And Food Service, Daniel Koch
Director, Bob Hufford
Vice Chairman, Don Woods

LOCATIONS

HQ: ASSOCIATED WHOLESALE GROCERS, INC.
 5000 KANSAS AVE, KANSAS CITY, KS 661061135
Phone: 913 288-1000
Web: WWW.AWGINC.COM

COMPETITORS

Affiliated Foods	GSC Enterprises
Affiliated Foods	H. T. Hackney
Midwest	McLane
Albertsons	SUPERVALU
Alex Lee	SpartanNash
C&S Wholesale	Wakefern Food
Central Grocers	Wal-Mart
Dearborn Wholesale	WinCo Foods
Grocers	

HISTORICAL FINANCIALS

Company Type: Private

Income Statement   FYE: December 31

	REVENUE ($ mil.)	NET INCOME ($ mil.)	NET PROFIT MARGIN	EMPLOYEES
12/17	9,703	199	2.1%	5,500
12/15	8,935	198	2.2%	—
12/14	8,934	226	2.5%	—
12/13	8,380	192	2.3%	—
Annual Growth	3.7%	0.8%	—	—

2017 Year-End Financials

Return on assets: 12.3%
Return on equity: 39.4%
Current ratio: 1.20

Cash ($ mil.): 166

ATHENE ANNUITY & LIFE ASSURANCE COMPANY

EXECUTIVES

Ceo, James R Belardi
Pres, Chip Smith
V Pres Fin, Cfo, David Attaway
Evp, Matthew Easley
Pres, Guy H Smith
Exec V Pres, Christopher Grady
Sr V Pres, Rod Mims
Delivery Project Executive, Judy Burington
Finance Manager, Kristian Pflieger

LOCATIONS

HQ: ATHENE ANNUITY & LIFE ASSURANCE COMPANY
 2000 WADE HAMPTON BLVD, GREENVILLE, SC
 296151037
Phone: 864 609-1000
Web: WWW.ATHENE.COM

HISTORICAL FINANCIALS

Company Type: Private

Income Statement   FYE: December 31

	ASSETS ($ mil.)	NET INCOME ($ mil.)	INCOME AS % OF ASSETS	EMPLOYEES
12/13	11,775	49	0.4%	120
12/12	10,481	11	0.1%	—
Annual Growth	12.3%	330.4%	—	—

Return on assets: —
Return on equity: 22.8%

Sales ($ mil): 217

ATLANTIC DIVING SUPPLY, INC.

Atlantic Diving Supply (doing business as ADS) is geared toward gearing up the military. Serving agencies in the Department of Defense the company specializes in helping customers procure tactical and operational military equipment. Like a retailer it sells 160000 products manufactured by some 3000 vendors including Camelbak FLIR L-3 Communications and Oakley but its niche offering is its supply management services. These services which are tailored to military customers include kitting (packaging related products in groups) assembly training custom sourcing product research and development and quality assurance. International customers include foreign militaries and governments.

Sales and Marketing

While most of ADS' customers are within the Department of Defense and the Department of Homeland Security other customers include federal agencies defense contractors law enforcement and public safety organizations including fire departments and EMS. The company claims to employ many retired US military and law enforcement personnel.

Strategy

ADS intends to continue driving growth through a handful of long-term strategic efforts including continuing the expansion of its sales force broadening its product offerings to keep pace with the evolving technological needs of the military and attracting new customers from other defense-oriented government agencies and private security services organizations. However with the DOD and Homeland Security making up most of its business the company is vulnerable to cuts in the defense budget.

Mergers and Acquisitions

ADS also expands through the use of acquisitions. In late 2015 it extended its global reach when it purchased Theodor Wille Intertrade (TWI) a global provider of integrated supply chain products and services to customers primarily operating in the United States European Command (EUCOM) and the United States Central Command (CENTCOM) regions. TWI also supplies construction materials equipment hardware food and food services and it will continue to operate its business as a division of ADS.

EXECUTIVES

Evp, Bruce Dressel
Chairman And Ceo, Luke Hillier
President, Daniel Clarkson
Cfo, Patricia Bohlen
Coo, Jason S. Wallace
Evp, Donald L. Sayre
Vice President Sales (verticals), Craig Doren
Vice Chairman, Dan Clarkson

LOCATIONS

HQ: ATLANTIC DIVING SUPPLY, INC.
 621 LYNNHVEN PKWY STE 160, VIRGINIA BEACH,
 VA 23452
Phone: 757 481-7758
Web: WWW.ADSINC.COM

PRODUCTS/OPERATIONS

Selected Products

Apparel
Bags packs and cases
Eyewear
Footwear
Hydration systems
Knives
Lighting
Medical
Tools
Training aids

COMPETITORS

Amazon.com	Navy Exchange
Army and Air Force	Sears
Exchange	Target Corporation
Kmart	Wal-Mart

HISTORICAL FINANCIALS

Company Type: Private

Income Statement   FYE: December 31

	REVENUE ($ mil.)	NET INCOME ($ mil.)	NET PROFIT MARGIN	EMPLOYEES
12/10	1,327	77	5.8%	360
12/09	938	54	5.8%	—
12/08	650	40	6.2%	—
Annual Growth	42.8%	38.7%	—	—

2010 Year-End Financials

Return on assets: 28.7%
Return on equity: 676.2%
Current ratio: 1.10

Cash ($ mil.): 1

ATLANTICARE REGIONAL MEDICAL CENTER

EXECUTIVES

Ceo, David Tilton
V Pres-Coo*, Lori Herndon
Purchasing Coordinator, Ginny Smith
Senior Buyer, Nicole Hagan
Registered Nurse, Eunice Creamer
Emergency Medicine, Orest Dombchewsky
Director, Debra Valentine
Anesthesiologist, Nicholas Incandela
Psychiatrist, Adela Ortega
Pathologist, Bruno Dantas
Gynecologist, Diane Timms

LOCATIONS

HQ: ATLANTICARE REGIONAL MEDICAL CENTER
 65 W JIMMIE LEEDS RD, POMONA, NJ 082409102
Phone: 609 652-1000

HISTORICAL FINANCIALS

Company Type: Private

Income Statement   FYE: December 31

	REVENUE ($ mil.)	NET INCOME ($ mil.)	NET PROFIT MARGIN	EMPLOYEES
12/14	718	64	9.0%	249
12/08	560	(58)	—	—
12/05	457	51	11.3%	—
Annual Growth	5.1%	2.5%	—	—

2014 Year-End Financials

Return on assets: 6.4%
Return on equity: 14.0%
Current ratio: 0.50

Cash ($ mil.): —

ATLAS OIL COMPANY

EXECUTIVES

Ceo, Sam Simon
Pres*, Robert Kenyon
Cfo*, Joseph Rivera
Coo*, Michael Devoe
Vp-Wholesale & Real Estate, Jacob Leatherman
Pres of Truck & Rig Fueling, Michael Meredith
Vp of Business Development, Jeremiah Whiddon
Vp of Supply and Logistics, Clinton Werth
V Pres For Crude Hauling, Samuel Carmicheal
Vp-Technology, Mark Kryska
Director of Human Resources, Dawn Thomson
Auditors: ERNST & YOUNG LLP DETROIT M

LOCATIONS

HQ: ATLAS OIL COMPANY
24501 ECORSE RD, TAYLOR, MI 481801641
Phone: 313 292-5500
Web: WWW.ATLASOIL.COM

HISTORICAL FINANCIALS

Company Type: Private

Income Statement

	REVENUE ($ mil.)	NET INCOME ($ mil.)	NET PROFIT MARGIN	EMPLOYEES
12/08	1,153	1	0.1%	432
12/07	717	1	0.1%	—
12/06	617	0	0.1%	—
Annual Growth	36.7%	99.7%	—	—

2008 Year-End Financials

Return on assets: 1.6%
Return on equity: 8.6%
Current ratio: 1.00

Cash ($ mil.): 3

ATLAS WORLD GROUP, INC.

Willing to carry the weight of a moving world agent-owned Atlas World Group is the holding company for Atlas Van Lines one of the largest moving companies in the US. Atlas Van Lines' more than 500 agents transport household goods domestically and between the US and Canada; it also offers specialized transportation of items such as trade show exhibits fine art and electronics. Atlas Van Lines International provides international corporate relocation and freight forwarding services. Its Atlas Canada unit moves household goods in that country while American Red Ball International specializes in military relocations and serves van lines outside Atlas' network.

Operations

Atlas World Group oversees a family of companies that deliver transportation and related services globally through a network agents and select service partners. Several of its key locations are concentrated in Evansville Indiana.

Strategy

The company continues to grow by adding offices and regional moving agents. In 2013 Atlantic Relocation Systems the second largest agency group within the Atlas Van Lines' US network expanded both its national footprint as well as its local service area in Colorado by opening a new office in Colorado Springs.

EXECUTIVES

Vice President Human Resources, Nancy Priebe
Auditors: ERNST & YOUNG LLP INDIANAPOLI

LOCATIONS

HQ: ATLAS WORLD GROUP, INC.
1212 SAINT GEORGE RD, EVANSVILLE, IN 477112364
Phone: 812 424-2222
Web: WWW.ATLASVANLINES.COM

PRODUCTS/OPERATIONS

Selected Companies

American Red Ball International (international freight forwarding)
American Vanpac Carriers (international freight forwarding)
Atlas Terminal Company (relocation-related supplies and equipment)
Atlas Van Lines (transportation services)
Atlas Van Lines (Canada) (transportation services)
Atlas Van Lines International (transportation services)
Atlas World Class Travel (travel agency)
Avail Move Management (management programs)
AWG Logistics (transportation warehousing and distribution)
Cornerstone Relocation Group (relocation services)
Smart Move Transportation (containerized shipping)
Titan Global Distribution (logistics)

COMPETITORS

A-Mrazek Moving	Graebel
ALTAIR Global Relocation	Penske Truck Leasing
AMERCO	SIRVA
Bekins	Starving Students
Budd Van Lines	UniGroup
Business Products Group	

HISTORICAL FINANCIALS

Company Type: Private

Income Statement

	REVENUE ($ mil.)	NET INCOME ($ mil.)	NET PROFIT MARGIN	EMPLOYEES
12/18	900	10	1.1%	726
12/17	842	4	0.6%	—
12/16	795	6	0.8%	—
12/15	845	8	1.0%	—
Annual Growth	2.1%	6.9%	—	—

2018 Year-End Financials

Return on assets: 4.3%
Return on equity: 7.4%
Current ratio: 2.50

Cash ($ mil.): 9

ATMEL CORPORATION

Atmel is a leading maker of microcontrollers which are used in a wide range of products from computers and mobile devices (smartphones tablets e-readers) to automobile motor control systems television remote controls and solid-state lighting. In addition the company offers touchscreen controllers and sensors nonvolatile memory devices and radio frequency (RF) and wireless components. Its chips are used worldwide in consumer communications industrial military and networking applications. Most of Atmel's sales come from customers outside the US. In mid-2016 the company was bought by Microchip a chip maker for $3.6 billion.

Operations

In 2014 Atmel realigned its business segments for allocation of resources and focus on core its markets. The company created the Multi-Market and Other segment while eliminating the former Application Specific Integrated Circuit (ASIC) segment.

But it's the Microcontroller segment that leads the way for Atmel accounting for 70% of the company's sales. The segment includes Atmel's general purpose microcontroller and microprocessor families AVR 8-bit and 32-bit products SMART ARM-based products Atmel's 8051 8-bit products and designated commercial wireless products including low power radio and SOC products.

The Nonvolatile Memory segment 12% of sales includes electrically erasable programmable read-only erasable programmable read-only memory ('EPROM') devices and secure cryptographic products. The Automotive segment 11% makes devices for automotive electronics including products using radio frequency technology. The new segment Multi-Market and Other is 7% of sales and includes application specific and standard products for aerospace applications and legacy products.

Geographic Reach

The company generates about 60% of its sales from Asia including about a third from China and Hong Kong. After China and Hong Kong the US is Atmel's largest market accounting for 15% of sales with sales in Germany at 14%.

Sales and Marketing

Atmel markets its products to original equipment manufacturers (OEMs) via a direct sales force as well as through distribution partners; each method accounts for about half of revenue. Arrow Electronics and Samsung Electronics each account for more than 10% of sales.

End-market customers include some of the leading names in the fields of communications (Alcatel Lucent Cisco Ericsson) computer and consumer electronics (Acer Dell Motorola Nokia) automotive (Delphi Visteon) and military and aerospace (BAE Systems Airbus Honeywell Lockheed Martin).

Financial Performance

Revenue rose 2% to $1.4 billion in 2014 from $1.39 billion in 2013 boosted by a 4% increase in microcontroller sales. The unit experienced demand from industrial automotive and communications markets. The addition of Newport Media acquired in mid-2014 also abetted microcontroller revenue. Sales in the nonvolatile memory segment were up 9% for the year.

On the bottom line Atmel went from a $22 million loss in 2013 to a $32 million profit in 2014. Profit was pushed by revenue growth as well as a lack of charges the company contended with in 2013. Cash flow from operations jumped 41% higher in 2014 to about $180 billion from $127 million in 203.

Strategy

Looking to pursue a "fab-lite" strategy of streamlining existing facilities and relying more on silicon foundries (contract manufacturers of semiconductors) Atmel has sold most of its manufacturing plants and now operates only one fab located in Colorado. Wafer fabs are highly expensive to build and maintain mostly due to the cost of semiconductor production equipment and pushing some of those costs off on the foundries many of which have state-of-the-art plants is attractive.

Atmel has increased the release of new products in the past three years aiming to provide customers with high performing microcontrollers than use little power. The company has found a place for its products within the Internet of Things the conglomeration of devices that communicate through the Internet.

The company also has pushed its line of maX-Touch products for touchscreens in smartphones and tables. The products have found acceptance in automotive consumer and industrial markets. While that line thrives Atmel sold its XSense line of touch sensors to UniPixel in 2015. Atmel maintained possession of the XSense patent portfolio which it licensed to UniPixel.

With its sale to Dialog Atmel gets access to a range of new customers within Atmel's portfolio. Dialog expects to benefit from Atmel's products primed for the Internet of Things. The combined company would have about $2.7 billion sales annually. The deal is expected to close in the 2016 first quarter.

Mergers and Acquisitions

In agreeing to be bought by Microchip Atmel ended a deal to be purchased by Dialog. Atmel management said company shareholders would get a better return from the Microchip deal. Atmel was on the hook for a $137 million termination fee to be paid to Dialog. The Dialog offer had been valued at $4.6 billion when it was made but the value of Atmel stock has declined since then. The Atmel-Microchip deal enables the companies to gather competitive strength with complementary technologies and products.

In 2014 Atmel acquired Newport Media Inc. a provider of advanced Wi-Fi and Bluetooth products. This acquisition expands Atmel's wireless portfolio with the addition of 802.11n Wi-Fi and Bluetooth. Those product should speed up Atmel's introduction of low-energy Bluetooth products.

HISTORY

George Perlegos — a former Intel design engineer and co-founder of chip maker SEEQ Technology (later acquired by LSI Logic now LSI Corp.) — founded Atmel in 1984. (The name was short for Advanced Technology for Memory and Logic.) The enterprise started with a $30000 investment and a $5.1 million design contract from General Instrument; it soon added military and corporate contracts. In 1991 the company went public and introduced the first three-volt flash memory.

Atmel built its business by developing fast power-efficient chips — perfect for portable electronics. It acquired Concurrent Logic a maker of field-programmable gate arrays (user-programmable chips) in 1993. One year later Atmel became the #1 producer of EEPROMs (electrically erasable programmable ROM chips) when it bought SEEQ's chip business.

To strengthen its product line in 1995 Atmel licensed SRAM (static random-access memory) technology in an alliance with Paradigm Technology (now part of IXYS) for use in creating multimedia chips. It purchased RISC chip technology (which uses shorter instruction sets for faster processing) from Norwegian chip maker Nordic VLSI in 1996.

EXECUTIVES

Svp And Cfo, Stephen A. (Steve) Skaggs, $444,462 total compensation

Evp Office Of The President, Tsung-Ching Wu, $509,200 total compensation

Vp And General Manager, Jalil Shaikh

Svp And General Manager Automotive Aerospace And Memory Business Units, Robert (Rob) Valiton, $393,000 total compensation

Svp And Chief Legal Officer, Scott M. Wornow, $397,538 total compensation

Vp And General Manager Touch Business Unit, Vegard Wollan

Svp Worldwide Operations, Shahin Sharifzadeh

Vp Corporate Marketing, Sander Arts

Svp And General Manager Microcontroller Business Unit, Reza Kazerounian, $453,365 total compensation

Svp And Cto; General Manager Touch Business Unit, Stanley A. (Stan) Swearingen

LOCATIONS

HQ: ATMEL CORPORATION
1600 TECHNOLOGY DR, SAN JOSE, CA 951101382
Phone: 408 735-9110
Web: WWW.MICROCHIP.COM

2014 Sales

	$ mil.	% of total
Asia/Pacific		
China (including Hong Kong)	435	31
South Korea	119	9
Taiwan	60	4
Singapore	55	4
Japan	37	3
Other countries	102	7
Europe		
Germany	204	14
France	15	1
Other countries	139	10
US	211	15
Other regions	30	2
Total	**1,413**	**100**

PRODUCTS/OPERATIONS

2014 Sales

	$ mil.	% of total
Microcontrollers	994	70
Nonvolatile memory	166	12
Automotive	153	11
Multi-Market and others	99	7
Total	**1,413**	**100**

Selected Products and Applications

Application-Specific Integrated Circuits (ASICs)
  Cell-based ASICs
  Complex ASIC cores
  Gate arrays/embedded arrays
Application-Specific Standard Products (ASSPs)
  Aerospace and military
  Communications
  Cellular corded and cordless phones
  Internet appliances and voice over Internet Protocol (VoIP)
  Wireless datacom
  Industrial
  Industrial controls
  Power metering
  Multimedia
  Audio
  Video
  Power management
  Security and smart card
  Biometrics
  PC security
  Radio-frequency identification (RFID)
  Secure memories
  Secure microcontrollers
  USB controllers
Logic
  Field-programmable gate arrays (FPGAs)
  Programmable logic devices (PLDs)
Microcontrollers (MCUs)
  4- 8- 16- and 32-bit microcontrollers
  ARM microprocessor architecture-based MCUs
  Flash MCUs
Nonvolatile Memory
  EPROMs (erasable programmable read-only memories)
  Flash memory chips
  Parallel EEPROMs (electrically erasable PROMs)
  Serial EEPROMs

COMPETITORS

Cypress Semiconductor	NXP Semiconductors
Fairchild Semiconductor	ON Semiconductor
Fujitsu Semiconductor	Renesas Electronics
Hitachi	STMicroelectronics
Infineon Technologies	Samsung Electronics
Intel	Silicon Labs
Microchip Technology	Synaptics
Micron Technology	Texas Instruments

HISTORICAL FINANCIALS

Company Type: Private

Income Statement   FYE: December 31

	REVENUE ($ mil.)	NET INCOME ($ mil.)	NET PROFIT MARGIN	EMPLOYEES
12/14	1,413	35	2.5%	5,200
12/13	1,386	(22)	—	—
12/12	1,432	30	2.1%	—
Annual Growth	(0.7%)	7.5%		

2014 Year-End Financials

Return on assets: 2.6%   Cash ($ mil.): 206
Return on equity: 4.0%
Current ratio: 2.70

ATRIUS HEALTH, INC.

Not-for-profit multi-specialty group Atrius Health provides health care services in Boston and surrounding regions. The 900-physician (and some 6000 other health care professionals) medical group operates more than 30 offices throughout eastern Massachusetts providing primary and specialty care to some 720000 adult and pediatric patients. For acute health care services Harvard Vanguard patients have access to more than a dozen hospitals including Beth Israel-Deaconess Hospital Boston Children's Hospital and Emerson Hospital.

Operations

Atrius Health's network of doctors represent more than 50 medical specialties including primary care oncology cardiology and neurology. In addition to providing health care services the group conducts research in health systems clinical trials and epidemiological studies.

Members of Atrius Health include Dedham Medical Associates Granite Medical Group Harvard Vanguard Medical Associates and PMG Physician Associates. Subsidiary VNA Care provides home health and hospice services.

Geographic Reach

Atrius Health has four locations in the City of Boston about 30 locations in Greater Boston and two administrative offices in Newton and Needham.

Sales and Marketing

Atrius Health accepts insurance from most major health plans including Aetna Blue Cross and Blue Shield of Massachusetts Harvard Pilgrim Health Care Neighborhood Health Plan and Tufts Health Plan.

Strategy

Atrius Health collaborates with universities hospitals and other organizations locally and nationally to improve clinical practices and outcomes evaluate the effectiveness of drug treatments and protocols and increase patient involvement in their care. It receives funding from government agencies foundations and other external sponsors.

The system has been working steadily from being a fee-for-service provider to one that relies on value-based payments. Part of this evolution has involved improving efficiency and minimizing waste but it has also launched new initiatives to make more wide-ranging changes. For example its Care in Place program allows nurses to provide care to elderly patients in their homes; this reduces the need for costly emergency department visits.

The group relies heavily on health data analytics to find high-risk populations and intervene to prevent serious illnesses and costly emergency room visits.

Mergers and Acquisitions

PMG Physician Associates joined Atrius Health in 2017; the move added seven new office locations to the group's network.

Company Background

The group practices of Atrius Health include Dedham Medical Associates Granite Medical Group Harvard Vanguard Medical Associates and PMG Physician Associates. The companies work together to coordinate care in a number of ways including sharing an electronic medical records system. In 2015 the groups merged to create one not-for-profit group named Atrius Health. Reliant Medical Group Southboro Medical Group and South Shore Medical Center were no longer affiliated with the group after the transformation.

EXECUTIVES

Cfo Atrius Health And Harvard Vanguard Medical Associates, Thomas M. Congoran
Coo, Mary Dawley
Vp Nursing, Deborah S. Morsi
Interim President And Interim Ceo, H. Eugene (Gene) Lindsey
Chief Information Officer, Daniel Moriarty
Evp And Interim Chief Medical Officer, Michael Pinnolis
Interim Chief Medical Officer, Steven Lampert
Vice President General Counsel, Kimberly Nelson
Vice President Network Services, Rick Weisblatt
Auditors: PKF PC QUINCY MA

LOCATIONS

HQ: ATRIUS HEALTH, INC.
  275 GROVE ST STE 3-300, AUBURNDALE, MA 024662274
Phone: 617 559-8444

PRODUCTS/OPERATIONS

Selected Specialty Affiliations
Massachusetts Eye and Ear Infirmary
New England Baptist Hospital

Selected OB/GYN Affiliations
Beth Israel Deaconess Medical Center
Beth Israel Deaconess Hospital - Milton
Emerson Hospital
Lowell General Hospital
Mount Auburn Hospital
Newton-Wellesley Hospital
South Shore Hospital

Selected Services
Allergy
Andrology
Audiology
Behavioral Health
Cardiology
Central Patient Registration
Complex Chronic Care Program
Cosmetic Dermatology
Dermatology
Developmental and Behavioral Pediatrics
Ear Nose & Throat
Endocrinology
Endoscopy
Eye Care
Family Medicine
Fertility & Reproductive Health

Gastroenterology
Genetics
Geriatrics
Hematology/Oncology
Imaging/Radiology
Infectious Disease
Internal Medicine
Interpreter Services
Laboratory
Medical Billing
Medical Records
Minimally-Invasive GYN Surgery
Nephrology
Neurology
Nutrition
Obstetrics/Gynecology
Occupational
Hand Therapy
Orthopedics & Sports Medicine
Pain Management
Palliative Care
Pediatrics
Pharmacy
Physical Therapy
Podiatry
Pulmonology
Rheumatology
Speech and Language Therapy
Surgery
Travel Medicine
Urgent Care
Urology
Weight Management/HMR®; Program

COMPETITORS

Boston Medical Center	St. Elizabeth's
Hallmark Health	Medical Center
Massachusetts General	Winchester Healthcare
Hospital	

HISTORICAL FINANCIALS
Company Type: Private

Income Statement — FYE: December 31

	REVENUE ($ mil.)	NET INCOME ($ mil.)	NET PROFIT MARGIN	EMPLOYEES
12/17	1,872	39	2.1%	3,906
12/15	1,577	(28)	—	—
12/14	28	(0)	—	—
12/01	0	0	—	—
Annual Growth	—	—	—	—

2017 Year-End Financials
Return on assets: 6.0%   Cash ($ mil.): 153
Return on equity: 17.0%
Current ratio: 0.90

ATTORNEY GENERAL, TEXAS

The Office of the Attorney General of Texas defends the state Constitution represents the state in litigation and approves public bond issues. The office is legal counsel to state government boards and agencies and issues legal opinions when requested by the Governor and agency heads. The Attorney General also sits as an ex-officio member of state committees and commissions and defends state laws and suits against agencies and state employees. Other roles include enforcing health safety and consumer regulations; protecting elderly and disabled residents' rights; collecting court-ordered child support; and administering the Crime Victims' Compensation Fund. Greg Abbott was elected Attorney General in 2002.

EXECUTIVES

Exec Dir, Ken Paxton
Cfo*, Greg Herbert
Sergeant, Ingrid Retzer
Sergeant, Lamont Smith
Coordinator, Meghan Rainwater
Administrator, Jarrod Walton
Information Security, Cynthia Campbell
Analyst, Dale Oliverio
Law Clerk, Ixchel Parr
Assistant General, Laura Messina
Assistant General, Matt Harriger

LOCATIONS

HQ: ATTORNEY GENERAL, TEXAS
  300 W 15TH ST, AUSTIN, TX 787011649
Phone: 512 475-4375
Web: WWW.TEXASATTORNEYGENERAL.GOV

HISTORICAL FINANCIALS
Company Type: Private

Income Statement — FYE: August 31

	REVENUE ($ mil.)	NET INCOME ($ mil.)	NET PROFIT MARGIN	EMPLOYEES
08/16	659	45	6.8%	4,202
08/15	561	8	1.5%	—
08/14	571	(6)	—	—
08/06	0	0	—	—
Annual Growth	—	—	—	—

2016 Year-End Financials
Return on assets: 13.1%   Cash ($ mil.): 87
Return on equity: 16.5%
Current ratio: 4.20

AUBURN UNIVERSITY

Most of us bleed red but studentsÂ and alumni ofÂ this university bleed auburn. One of the largest schools in the South Auburn University has an enrollment of more than 30000 students on two campuses andÂ offersÂ bachelors master's and doctoral degrees in more than 140 different fields of study through about a dozen colleges and schools. Fields of study include agriculture business education construction forestry and mathematics and science as well as medical fields includingÂ nursingÂ pharmacy and veterinary medicine.Â Auburn has 1200 faculty members and a student-to-teacher ratioÂ of 18:1.

Operations

Unique research institutes at Auburn include the Space Research Institute the National Center for Asphalt Technology the Alabama Agricultural Experiment Station and the Canine and Detection Research Institute.

Geographic Reach

Auburn's main campus is in Auburn Alabama.Â The universityÂ alsoÂ has a branch campus in Montgomery Alabama. More than 800 students participate in the university's study abroad programs each year.

Financial Performance

Auburn reported a 5%Â rise in revenues to some $602 millionÂ in 2012 due to increased income from tuition and fees state and local grants and contracts and sales and services from educational departments. Net income fell 12% to $87 millionÂ in 2012 however due to higher operating expenses from benefits and compensation as well as due to the absence of federal stimulus funds (streamed through the state during 2011).

Company Background

Auburn was founded by the Alabama Conference of the Methodist Episcopal Church in 1856 as the East Alabama Male College. It became a state land-grantÂ institution in 1872 (known as the Agricultural and Mechanical College of Alabama)Â and adopted its current name in 1960. The university is governed by a board of trustees appointed by the Alabama governor.

EXECUTIVES

Vice President For Recruitment, Becky Wilbanks
Associate Vice President For Development Operations, Karen McCauley
Executive Vice President Of Initiatives, Austin Chandler
Executive Vice President Of Programs, Patrick Starr
Auditors: PRICEWATERHOUSECOOPERS LLP BI

LOCATIONS

HQ: AUBURN UNIVERSITY
   107 SAMFORD HALL, AUBURN, AL 368490001
Phone: 334 844-4539
Web: WWW.AUBURN.EDU

PRODUCTS/OPERATIONS

Selected Colleges and Schools
College of Agriculture
College of Architecture Design and Construction
College of Business
College of Education
College of Human Sciences
College of Liberal Arts
College of Sciences and Mathematics
College of Veterinary Medicine
Graduate School
Harrison School of Pharmacy
Honors College
Samuel Ginn College of Engineering
School of Forestry and Wildlife Sciences
School of Nursing

HISTORICAL FINANCIALS
Company Type: Private

Income Statement				FYE: September 30
	REVENUE ($ mil.)	NET INCOME ($ mil.)	NET PROFIT MARGIN	EMPLOYEES
09/18	876	78	9.0%	6,000
09/17	805	79	9.9%	—
09/16	775	129	16.8%	—
09/11	574	99	17.3%	—
Annual Growth	6.2%	(3.3%)	—	—

2018 Year-End Financials
Return on assets: 2.1%   Cash ($ mil.): 296
Return on equity: 6.6%
Current ratio: 1.30

AUGUSTANA HEALTH CARE CENTER OF APPLE VALLEY

EXECUTIVES

Pres, Timothy H Tucker
Coordinator, Alice Svihel

LOCATIONS

HQ: AUGUSTANA HEALTH CARE CENTER OF APPLE VALLEY
   14650 GARRETT AVE, SAINT PAUL, MN 551247543
Phone: 952 431-7700

HISTORICAL FINANCIALS
Company Type: Private

Income Statement				FYE: September 30
	REVENUE ($ mil.)	NET INCOME ($ mil.)	NET PROFIT MARGIN	EMPLOYEES
09/09	1,505	30	2.0%	280
09/05	6	(0)	—	—
Annual Growth	287.7%	—	—	—

2009 Year-End Financials
Return on assets: 162.5%   Cash ($ mil.): 1
Return on equity: 784.9%
Current ratio: 3.10

AURORA HEALTH CARE METRO, INC

EXECUTIVES

President, Marie Golanowski
Project Sys Dev, Shafei Fahim
Specialist, John Halverson
Chief of Medicine, Scott Hardin
Manager, Mary Ehlers
Manager of Clinic Operations, Melinda Moe
Registered Nurse Quality Manag, Molly Wick
Project Manager S, Russell Legg
Administrative Assistant, Cheryl Warzinski
Family Practitioner, Cory Dubose
Med Staff Manager Aslm, Julie Byrne

LOCATIONS

HQ: AURORA HEALTH CARE METRO, INC
   2900 W OKLAHOMA AVE, MILWAUKEE, WI 532154330
Phone: 414 649-6000
Web: WWW.AURORASTLUKES.ORG

HISTORICAL FINANCIALS
Company Type: Private

Income Statement				FYE: December 31
	REVENUE ($ mil.)	NET INCOME ($ mil.)	NET PROFIT MARGIN	EMPLOYEES
12/17	1,428	141	9.9%	4,000
12/16	1,416	164	11.6%	—
Annual Growth	0.8%	(14.0%)	—	—

2017 Year-End Financials
Return on assets: 5.4%   Cash ($ mil.): 1,804
Return on equity: 6.2%
Current ratio: 19.70

AURORA HEALTH CARE, INC.

EXECUTIVES

Innovation Manager, Moiz Dawoodbhai
Executive Assistant Chief of S, Zoemy Soto
Staff, Andy Monfre
Internal Medicine, Charles Brummitt
Supervisor, David Krum
Purchasing Account Manager Sou, Dennis Monahan
Research Associate, Lynn Erickson
Strategic Project Manager, Marian Tate
Human Resources Generalist, Mary Miller
Internist, Amy M Wachowiak
Treasurer, Thomas Komula
Auditors: DELOITTE & TOUCHE LLP MILWAUK

LOCATIONS

HQ: AURORA HEALTH CARE, INC.
   750 W VIRGINIA ST, MILWAUKEE, WI 532041539
Phone: 800 326-2250
Web: WWW.AURORAHEALTHCARE.ORG

HISTORICAL FINANCIALS
Company Type: Private

Income Statement				FYE: December 31
	REVENUE ($ mil.)	NET INCOME ($ mil.)	NET PROFIT MARGIN	EMPLOYEES
12/17	5,334	437	8.2%	30,000
12/16	5,124	385	7.5%	—
12/15	4,930	428	8.7%	—
Annual Growth	4.0%	1.1%	—	—

2017 Year-End Financials
Return on assets: 7.7%   Cash ($ mil.): 192
Return on equity: 14.4%
Current ratio: 3.50

AURORA PUBLIC SCHOOLS

EXECUTIVES

Supt, Rico Munn
Contrl*, Gina Lanier
Chief Operating Officer, Anthony Sturges
Executive Officer, Matthew Eckert
Coordinator, Stephanie Gianneschi
Assistant, Christopher Capron
General Manager, Mary Temple
Internal Auditor, Peter Doan
Dean of Students Athletics Dir, Casey Powell
Registrar, Rori Jimerson
Legal Counsel, Brandon Eyre
Auditors: BKD LLP DENVER COLORADO

LOCATIONS

HQ: AURORA PUBLIC SCHOOLS
   15701 E 1ST AVE STE 106, AURORA, CO 800119037
Phone: 303 344-8060
Web: WWW.AURORAK12.ORG

HISTORICAL FINANCIALS
Company Type: Private

Income Statement				FYE: June 30
	REVENUE ($ mil.)	NET INCOME ($ mil.)	NET PROFIT MARGIN	EMPLOYEES
06/18	492	(8)	—	6,000
06/17	466	193	41.5%	—
06/16	451	(8)	—	—
06/15	420	(25)	—	—
Annual Growth	5.4%	—	—	—

2018 Year-End Financials
Return on assets: (-0.7%)   Cash ($ mil.): 102
Return on equity: —
Current ratio: 1.60

AUSTIN INDEPENDENT SCHOOL DISTRICT (INC)

EXECUTIVES

Supt, Paul Cruz
Cfo*, Nicole Conley Johnson
Prin*, Teri Garcia
Coordinator, Artra Luckett
Executive Officer, Debbie Coco
Accounting Staff, Brenda Niles
Accounting Staff, Nancy Zuraitis
Occupational Specia, Gemma Cercone
Occupational Specia, Mary Coneway
Assistant, Emily Bush
Assistant Superintendent, Gilbert Hicks
Auditors: LISA SHACKELFORD CPA AUSTIN

LOCATIONS

HQ: AUSTIN INDEPENDENT SCHOOL DISTRICT (INC)
1111 W 6TH ST, AUSTIN, TX 787035399
Phone: 512 414-1700
Web: WWW.AUSTINISD.ORG

HISTORICAL FINANCIALS
Company Type: Private

Income Statement				FYE: June 30
	REVENUE ($ mil.)	NET INCOME ($ mil.)	NET PROFIT MARGIN	EMPLOYEES
06/18	1,534	(117)	—	9,200
06/16	1,231	110	9.0%	—
/*	0	0	—	—
Annual Growth	—	—	—	—

*Fiscal year change

2018 Year-End Financials
Return on assets: (-6.2%)   Cash ($ mil.): 24
Return on equity: —
Current ratio: —

AVAYA HOLDINGS CORP.

Avaya Holdings Corp. is the holding company that owns enterprise communications equipment and services provider Avaya Inc.. Spun off from Lucent Technologies in 2000 Avaya was a publicly traded company until 2007 when it was taken pri-

vate by Silver Lake Partners and TPG Capital for more than $8 billion. After four years of unprofitable private ownership its investors are looking for an exit and Avaya Holdings Corp. was created to make a second bid for listing on a US stock exchange filing for an initial public offering in 2011. The IPO is on hold however and Avaya has been expanding its business and product line through acquisitions.

EXECUTIVES

Vp Partnerships And Alliances, Eric Rossman
Vice President Of Sales, Thomas Henkel
National Account Manager, Tom Hicks
Worldwide Vice President Of Marketing, Achille Venturi

LOCATIONS

HQ: AVAYA HOLDINGS CORP.
4655 GREAT AMERICA PKWY, SANTA CLARA, CA 950541236
Phone: 908 953-6000
Web: WWW.AVAYA.COM

COMPETITORS

Alcatel-Lucent	Mitel Networks
Aspect Software	NEC
Cisco Systems	NSN
Fujitsu	ShoreTel
Hitachi	Tellabs
Huawei Technologies	ZTE
Logitech	

HISTORICAL FINANCIALS
Company Type: Private

Income Statement				FYE: September 30
	REVENUE ($ mil.)	NET INCOME ($ mil.)	NET PROFIT MARGIN	EMPLOYEES
09/15	4,081	(168)	—	11,701
09/14	4,371	(253)	—	—
09/13	4,708	(376)	—	—
09/11	5,547	(863)	—	—
Annual Growth	(7.4%)	—	—	—

2015 Year-End Financials
Return on assets: (-2.5%)   Cash ($ mil.): 323
Return on equity: —
Current ratio: 0.80

AVERITT EXPRESS INCORPORATED

EXECUTIVES

Pres, Gary D Sasser
Exec V Pres, Phil Pierce
Exec V Pres, George Johnson
Corporate Os and D Reliance Ne, Ashley Ferrell
Flatbed Area Manager, Bryan Aldridge
Associate Open Line, Connie Glover
Admin and Osd, Dora Allman
Inside Sales Representative, Hannah Fox
Cash Management Leader, Jodi Smith
Project Manager, John Sevier
Corporate Accounts Bid Coordin, Kellie Sorrell
Auditors: DUNCAN WHEELER & WILKERSON P

LOCATIONS

HQ: AVERITT EXPRESS INCORPORATED
1415 NEAL ST, COOKEVILLE, TN 385014328
Phone: 931 526-3306
Web: WWW.AVERITTEXPRESS.COM

HISTORICAL FINANCIALS
Company Type: Private

Income Statement				FYE: December 31
	REVENUE ($ mil.)	NET INCOME ($ mil.)	NET PROFIT MARGIN	EMPLOYEES
12/17	1,157	93	8.1%	8,210
12/16	1,097	52	4.8%	—
12/15	1,104	52	4.8%	—
12/14	1,088	55	5.1%	—
Annual Growth	2.1%	18.8%	—	—

2017 Year-End Financials
Return on assets: 9.2%   Cash ($ mil.): 132
Return on equity: 11.8%
Current ratio: 3.50

AVERITT EXPRESS, INC.

Small loads add up at Averitt Express. The company provides less-than-truckload (LTL) freight transportation service. (LTL carriers combine freight from multiple shippers into a single trailer.) It operates a fleet of about 4100 tractors and 12250 trailers from a network of 80 terminals. Averitt Express directly serves the southern US and Mexico and it provides service elsewhere in North America through partnerships with other carriers such as Lakeville Motor Express and DATS. The company also offers truckload and expedited freight transportation along with logistics warehousing and international freight forwarding. Customers have included Home Depot Shoe Carnival and V.F. Corporation.

Geographic Reach
Averitt Express has a total of roughly 140 facilities that serve thousands of points throughout the Southern US (in about 20 states) Canada Mexico and the Caribbean.

Strategy
The company aims to grow from solely a LTL carrier based in the Southeast to an international transportation and logistics company. To this end it continues to strategically broaden its geographic reach and range of services. Averitt Express over the years has launched a new business unit zeroing in on retailers in need of distribution services. The new unit Averitt Retail Distribution Services offers customized delivery services catering to the unique requirements of retailers and is targeting retailers needing delivery in large Southern markets.

EXECUTIVES

President And Ceo, Gary D. Sasser
Evp And Coo, Wayne Spain
Evp Sales And Marketing, Phil Pierce
Evp And Cfo, George Johnson
Auditors: DUNCAN WHEELER & WILKERSON P

LOCATIONS

HQ: AVERITT EXPRESS, INC.
1415 NEAL ST, COOKEVILLE, TN 385014328
Phone: 931 526-3306
Web: WWW.AVERITTEXPRESS.COM

PRODUCTS/OPERATIONS

Selected Services

Cross-border/domestic offshore (Canada Mexico Puerto Rico/Virgin Islands)
Dedicated
Expedited
Intermodal
International ocean/air (ocean/air Asia-Memphis Express)
LTL (regional nationwide distribution/consolidation)
Portside
Retail specialized services
Transportation management
Truckload (dry van flatbed brokerage)
Warehousing

COMPETITORS

AAA Cooper Transportation	Old Dominion Freight R+L Carriers
ArcBest	Schneider National
C.H. Robinson Worldwide	Southeastern Freight Lines
Estes Express	Swift Transportation
FedEx Freight	UPS Freight
J.B. Hunt	YRC Worldwide

HISTORICAL FINANCIALS

Company Type: Private

Income Statement · FYE: December 31

	REVENUE ($ mil.)	NET INCOME ($ mil.)	NET PROFIT MARGIN	EMPLOYEES
12/17	1,142	98	8.7%	8,208
12/16	1,088	45	4.1%	—
12/15	1,091	44	4.1%	—
12/14	1,075	46	4.3%	—
Annual Growth	2.1%	28.9%	—	—

2017 Year-End Financials

Return on assets: 10.7% Cash ($ mil.): 232
Return on equity: 13.4%
Current ratio: 5.10

AVI-SPL HOLDINGS, INC.

EXECUTIVES

Ceo, John Zettel
Coo, John Murphy
Cfo, Steve Palmer
Treas, Jean Constant
Treasury Mgr, Ed Bewley
Corporate Controller, Bill McGann
Training & Manager, Jennifer Schwartzberg
Controller, Mary Schaffel
Director Logistics, Rob Scott
Vp Strategic Accounts, Randy Bonham
Auditors: ERNST & YOUNG LLP TAMPA FL

LOCATIONS

HQ: AVI-SPL HOLDINGS, INC.
6301 BENJAMIN RD STE 101, TAMPA, FL 336345115
Phone: 866 708-5034
Web: WWW.AVISPL.COM

HISTORICAL FINANCIALS

Company Type: Private

Income Statement · FYE: December 31

	REVENUE ($ mil.)	NET INCOME ($ mil.)	NET PROFIT MARGIN	EMPLOYEES
12/11	555	5	1.1%	2,000
12/10	505	(0)	—	—
12/09	421	3	0.7%	—
Annual Growth	14.8%	38.5%		

2011 Year-End Financials

Return on assets: 1.8% Cash ($ mil.): 2
Return on equity: 4.2%
Current ratio: 1.50

AVIO INC.

LOCATIONS

HQ: AVIO INC.
270 SYLVAN AVE STE 130, ENGLEWOOD CLIFFS, NJ 076322545
Phone: 201 816-2720
Web: WWW.AVIOUSA.COM

HISTORICAL FINANCIALS

Company Type: Private

Income Statement · FYE: December 31

	REVENUE ($ mil.)	NET INCOME ($ mil.)	NET PROFIT MARGIN	EMPLOYEES
12/12	1,310	7	0.6%	34
12/05	293	0	0.2%	—
12/04	387	8	2.1%	—
12/03	1,817	0	—	—
Annual Growth	—	—	—	—

2012 Year-End Financials

Return on assets: 12.3% Cash ($ mil.): 42
Return on equity: 0.6%
Current ratio: 0.60

AXEL JOHNSON INC.

The Johnson family of Stockholm Sweden has an investment arm that stretches across the ocean. Axel Johnson owns and operates North American businesses on behalf of the Johnson dynasty. The investment firm focuses on several industries such as energy medical device manufacturing and water treatment. Its portfolio includes Sprague Energy Parkson Corp. and Kinetico Incorporated. Axel Johnson's companies boast about $4 billion in annual revenues. Axel Johnson along with Axel Johnson AB and AXFast are all affiliated with Sweden-based Axel Johnson Group but are independent. Established in 1873 the Johnson family of companies is in its fourth generation of family ownership.

Operations

Axel Johnson which was formed in 1920 is a long-term investor that typically holds on to its companies for about 20 years. Some companies have been a part of Axel Johnson's portfolio for more than 40 years. Two of its holdings Parkson and Kinetico are part of Axel Johnson's AxWater Group which was formed in 2000.

Financial Performance

Following the economic downturn the company has seen sales increase for several years. Axel Johnson's revenue rose by 6% in 2012 to $4.2 billion as compared to 2011. Energy product sales generated the largest portion of the company's revenue. The results were powered by higher commodity prices and growth at Kinetico Cadence and Mountain Lumber; the first two along with ConforMis and Walk2Campus reported record sales in 2012.

Strategy

Through NewtrAX Axel Johnson makes minority investments in smaller businesses. NewtrAX has stakes in Cadence a manufacturer of cutting and piercing instruments used for the medical and industrial applications. It also owns portions of wood reclamation company Mountain Lumber Co. and Walk2Campus a real estate management and acquisition company. The company in late 2011 invested some $15 million in ConforMIS which develops and markets customized medical devices for the treatment of osteoarthritis and joint damage.

EXECUTIVES

Pres-Chb, Michael D Milligan
Chb, Antonia Axson Johnson
Exec V Pres, Ben J Hennelly
Exec V Pres, John Pascale
Vice President, Sally Sarsfield
V Pres, Clare Peeters
Chief Information Security Off, Janie Wintermyer
Administrative Assistant, Stephanie Moots
Senior Accountant, Vicky Dong
Director Benefits, Lawrence Haynes
Accounting Manager, Sylwia Majewski
Auditors: ERNST & YOUNG LLP NEW YORK N

LOCATIONS

HQ: AXEL JOHNSON INC.
155 SPRING ST FL 6, NEW YORK, NY 100125254
Phone: 646 291-2445
Web: WWW.AXELJOHNSON.COM

PRODUCTS/OPERATIONS

Selected Portfolio Companies

Cadence Incorporated
ConforMIS Inc.
Decisyon Inc.
Kinetico Incorporated
Mountain Lumber Company
Parkson Corporation
Sprague Energy Corp.
Walk2Campus Holdings LLC

COMPETITORS

CCMP Capital	KKR
Court Square Capital Partners	Menlo Ventures
Enterprise Partners	Sevin Rosen

HISTORICAL FINANCIALS

Company Type: Private

Income Statement · FYE: December 31

	REVENUE ($ mil.)	NET INCOME ($ mil.)	NET PROFIT MARGIN	EMPLOYEES
12/10	2,982	15	0.5%	1,200
12/09	2,598	11	0.5%	—
12/08	4,312	8	0.2%	—
Annual Growth	(16.8%)	35.5%	—	—

2010 Year-End Financials

Return on assets: 1.4% Cash ($ mil.): 9
Return on equity: 5.2%
Current ratio: 1.70

AXOS BANK

EXECUTIVES

Ceo, Greg Garrabants
Sr V Pres-Cfo, Andrew Micheletti
Evp-Chief Credit Offr-Chief RE, Tom Constantine
Gen Counsel, Eshel Bar-Adon
Exec V Pres, Brian Swanson
Executive Vice-President, Adriaan Van Zyl
Vice-President, James Shoop
Assistant Vice-President, Joel Kodish
Facilities Manager, Dan Hager
Human Resources Manager, Maria Dews
Assistant Vice-President, Danielle Austin

LOCATIONS

HQ: AXOS BANK
4350 LA JOLLA VILLAGE DR, SAN DIEGO, CA
921221243
Phone: 858 350-6200
Web: WWW.AXOSBANK.COM

HISTORICAL FINANCIALS

Company Type: Private

Income Statement — FYE: December 31

	ASSETS ($ mil.)	NET INCOME ($ mil.)	INCOME AS % OF ASSETS	EMPLOYEES
12/17	8,908	150	1.7%	102
12/16	8,162	137	1.7%	—
12/15	6,656	104	1.6%	—
12/14	5,190	71	1.4%	—
Annual Growth	19.7%	28.1%	—	—

2017 Year-End Financials

Return on assets: 1.7%   Sales ($ mil): 483
Return on equity: 17.3%

B.L. HARBERT HOLDINGS, L.L.C.

EXECUTIVES

Ceo-Chm, Billy Harbert
Exe V Pres-Cfo-Sec, R Alan Hall
V Pres-Cao, James Stewart
V Pres-Risk MGT-Cco, William Lalor
Contrl-Treas-Asst SEC, John Rives
Senior Project Manager, Justin Allred
Auditors: CROWE HORWATH LLP ATLANTA GE

LOCATIONS

HQ: B.L. HARBERT HOLDINGS, L.L.C.
820 SHADES CREEK PKWY # 3000, BIRMINGHAM,
AL 352094564
Phone: 205 802-2800
Web: WWW.BLHARBERT.COM

HISTORICAL FINANCIALS

Company Type: Private

Income Statement — FYE: December 31

	REVENUE ($ mil.)	NET INCOME ($ mil.)	NET PROFIT MARGIN	EMPLOYEES
12/14	807	53	6.7%	2,000
12/05	361	0	—	—
12/04	203	0	—	—
Annual Growth	14.8%	—	—	—

2014 Year-End Financials

Return on assets: 6.8%   Cash ($ mil.): 191
Return on equity: 6.7%
Current ratio: 0.60

B.L. HARBERT INTERNATIONAL, L.L.C.

EXECUTIVES

Ceo-Chm, Billy Harbert
Exe V Pres-Cfo-Sec*, R Alan Hall
V Pres-Risk MGT-Cco*, William Lalor
V Pres-Cao*, James Stewart
Contrl-Treas-Asst SEC*, John Rives
Quality Control Manager, Benny Wilkins
Assistant Project Manager, Amanda Miller
Assistant Concrete Superintend, Bengaly Kouyate
Project Manager, Jeff Jernigan
Administrative Assistant, Stephanie Walker
Information Technology Applica, James Cowan
Auditors: CROWE HORWATH LLP ATLANTA GE

LOCATIONS

HQ: B.L. HARBERT INTERNATIONAL, L.L.C.
820 SHADES CREEK PKWY # 3000, BIRMINGHAM,
AL 352094564
Phone: 205 802-2800
Web: WWW.BLHARBERT.COM

HISTORICAL FINANCIALS

Company Type: Private

Income Statement — FYE: December 31

	REVENUE ($ mil.)	NET INCOME ($ mil.)	NET PROFIT MARGIN	EMPLOYEES
12/14	807	57	7.2%	1,400
12/08	554	33	6.0%	—
Annual Growth	6.5%	9.7%	—	—

2014 Year-End Financials

Return on assets: 6.8%   Cash ($ mil.): 182
Return on equity: 7.2%
Current ratio: 0.90

BABCOCK POWER INC.

EXECUTIVES

Pres-Ceo, Michael D Leclair
Evp-Cfo-Treas, Anthony Brandano
Dir, Nathan Hevrony
Dir, Dale Miller
Dir, Timothy Statton
Dir, William Sigmon
Dir, John H Heffernan
Evp-Admin-Gen Counsel-Sec, William J Ferguson Jr
Vp-Strategic Ops, Douglas J Harding
1st V Pres, James Dougherty
1st V Pres, Edward Dean

LOCATIONS

HQ: BABCOCK POWER INC.
6 KIMBALL LN STE 210, LYNNFIELD, MA 019402684
Phone: 978 646-3300
Web: WWW.BABCOCKPOWER.COM

HISTORICAL FINANCIALS

Company Type: Private

Income Statement — FYE: September 30

	REVENUE ($ mil.)	NET INCOME ($ mil.)	NET PROFIT MARGIN	EMPLOYEES
09/17	509	10	2.0%	935
09/16	678	14	2.1%	—
09/15	627	15	2.5%	—
09/14	746	16	2.2%	—
Annual Growth	(12.0%)	(14.3%)	—	—

2017 Year-End Financials

Return on assets: 3.4%   Cash ($ mil.): 43
Return on equity: 6.3%
Current ratio: 2.00

BALFOUR BEATTY CONSTRUCTION GROUP, INC.

Balfour Beatty Construction is deep in the heart of Texas — and beyond. The company provides start-to-finish project management pre-construction and related services for commercial construction projects. Offerings include site evaluation and analysis general contracting cost consulting process equipment installation turnkey medical facility development capital equipment planning and closeout services. The company works on a range of facilities including hotels office buildings civic centers airports hospitals schools public buildings and retail locations. UK firm Balfour Beatty plc acquired the company then named Centex Construction from Centex Corp. in 2007.

Operations

Balfour Beatty Construction ranks as the fifth largest general builder in the US. The firm is also active in the construction services infrastructure investment and professionals and support services markets.

Geographic Reach

Dallas-based Balfour Beatty Construction has locations in the West Mid-Atlantic and Southeast.

Strategy

The US arm of the international infrastructure group Balfour Beatty Construction is poised to profit from the recovery of the US economy. Indeed the US market has seen a quicker return to growth that its UK counterpart with more private and complex construction projects coming to the market. To that end the construction service firm is expanding its Houston Division to capitalize on growing demand from the energy and multifamily housing markets in the Houston area. To build its Campus Solutions business which specializes in the construction of education facilities Balfour Beatty Construction absorbed Charter Builders a specialist in educational facilities in 2012. Recent student housing projects include a 1274-bed student housing project at Texas A&M University. Construction of the $104 million project began in mid-2014 with completion and occupancy set for August 2015.

Some of the company's more notable projects include NASA Mission Control (Houston) Texas Stadium (home of the Dallas Cowboys) the Mayo Clinic The James Madison Library of Congress One America Plaza Miami International Airport and Cinderella's Castle at Walt Disney World.

EXECUTIVES

Exec V Pres, John Woodcock
Exec V Pres, Doug Jones
Auditors: KPMG LLP DALLAS TX

LOCATIONS

HQ: BALFOUR BEATTY CONSTRUCTION GROUP, INC.
 3100 MCKINNON ST FL 10, DALLAS, TX 752017007
Phone: 214 451-1000
Web: WWW.BALFOURBEATTYUS.COM

PRODUCTS/OPERATIONS

Selected Key Markets

Airports
Defense housing
Education
Health care
Judicial & institutional
Rail
Roads

Selected Projects
Air Force Memorial (Arlington VA)
Army/Air Force Exchange Shopping Center (Fort
 Jackson SC)
Bank of America (Charlotte NC)
Broward County Convention Center (Fort Lauderdale
 FL)
Burger King corporate headquarters (Miami)
Cape Coral Parkway Expansion (Cape Coral FL)
Carnival Cruise Lines corporate headquarters (Miami)
Children's Hospital & Health Center (San Diego CA)
Cisco Systems corporate headquarters (Research
 Triangle Park NC)
Disney's Wilderness Lodge Resort (Lake Buena Vista FL)
Duke University Levine Science Research Center
 (Durham NC)
Harrah's Casino (New Orleans)
Harris Methodist Hospital (Fort Worth TX)
James Madison Memorial Building Library of Congress
 (Washington DC)
J.P. Morgan International Plaza (Dallas)
Lucayan Beach Resort (Grand Bahama Island Bahamas)
Mescalero Apache K-12 (Mescalero NM)
Music City Central MTA Bus Facility (Nashville TN)
NASA Space Station Control Center (Houston)
Osceoloa County Courthouse (Kissimmee FL)
Port of Miami (Miami)
Southwest Airlines corporate headquarters (Dallas)
United Spirit Arena (Lubbock TX)
Vanderbilt University Medical Center (Nashville TN)
Walter Reed Army Medical Center military housing
 (Silver Spring MD)
White Sands Missile Range military housing (White
 Sands NM)

COMPETITORS

American Constructors	Hardaway Construction
Ames Construction	LeChase Construction
Axis Construction	M & H Enterprises
Bechtel	MW Builders
Cutler Associates	McGough Construction
Engelberth	Panattoni Construction
Construction	Rayco Construction
Falkenberg	Satterfield & Pontikes
Construction	Skanska USA Building
Fluor	Turner Construction
G. A. Johnson & Son	

HISTORICAL FINANCIALS

Company Type: Private

Income Statement   FYE: December 31

	REVENUE ($ mil.)	NET INCOME ($ mil.)	NET PROFIT MARGIN	EMPLOYEES
12/15	3,852	(14)	—	2,200
12/14	3,932	17	0.4%	—
12/13	3,816	24	0.6%	—
12/12	3,459	19	0.6%	—
Annual Growth	3.7%	—	—	—

2015 Year-End Financials

Return on assets: (-0.9%)   Cash ($ mil.): 69
Return on equity: (-3.0%)
Current ratio: 1.20

BALFOUR BEATTY CONSTRUCTION, LLC

EXECUTIVES

MBR, Mark Layman
MBR, John Woodcock
MBR, Eric Stenman
MBR, Richard Jaggers
MBR, Glenn Burns
MBR, John Parolisi
MBR, John Tarpey
Performance Awareness Cnsltnt, Patricia Laprade
Project Coordinator, Leonicio Alonzo
Assistant Controller, Colleen Anderson
Vice President, Jim Gough
Auditors: KPMG LLP DALLAS TX

LOCATIONS

HQ: BALFOUR BEATTY CONSTRUCTION, LLC
 3100 MCKINNON ST FL 10, DALLAS, TX 752017007
Phone: 214 451-1000
Web: WWW.BALFOURBEATTYUS.COM

HISTORICAL FINANCIALS

Company Type: Private

Income Statement   FYE: December 31

	REVENUE ($ mil.)	NET INCOME ($ mil.)	NET PROFIT MARGIN	EMPLOYEES
12/16	3,809	13	0.3%	2,190
12/13	3,816	23	0.6%	—
12/12	3,365	8	0.3%	—
12/10	0	0	—	—
Annual Growth	—	—	—	—

2016 Year-End Financials

Return on assets: 0.8%   Cash ($ mil.): 53
Return on equity: 2.8%
Current ratio: 1.20

BALFOUR BEATTY INFRASTRUCTURE, INC.

Balfour Beatty Infrastructure is the North American heavy construction and civil engineering arm of UK-based Balfour Beatty plc. The contractor has expertise in transportation and water infrastructure projects ranging in size from about $3 million to $400 million and specializes in constructing bridges highways tunnels rail lines and water treatment plants. The firm's primary clients are public agencies including municipalities and state departments of transportation. Beyond stand-alone projects it is involved in multiple joint ventures and works on some of the nation's largest public works projects including the design and construction of the $1.5 billion Texas State Highway 130 toll road.

Operations

The company acquired rail infrastructure contractor Balfour Beatty Rail and Fru-Con Construction in 2014 to operate as divisions under its company brand. Fru-Con is an expert in the construction of water and wastewater treatment plants and serves Virginia Maryland and Washington DC.

Balfour Beatty Infrastructure and its sister companies ranked 11th in the Engineering New Record's Top 400 Contractors in the United States in 2014. That year it also ranked 12th in the Top 50 Domestic Heavy Contractors list 14th among the Top 20 Transportation Contractors 10th among the Top 100 Contractors by New Contracts and third among the Top 50 in Domestic Building/Manufacturing Revenue.

Geographic Reach

Atlanta-based Balfour Beatty Infrastructure has a regional office in Wilmington North Carolina. Parent-company Balfour Beatty plc operates in more than 80 countries. Its rail services office is in Fleming Island Florida its rail transit office is in Denver and its Fru-Con Construction office is in Woodbridge Virginia.

Strategy

The infrastructure arm of Balfour Beatty has performed more than 100 major heavy civil construction projects since its founding. The company is focused on expanding its regional presence in existing markets. Roadway contracts with the North Carolina Department of Transportation for instance are helping it grow in the Southeast. In the Pacific Northwest region the company completed retrofitting work on the Seattle Transit Tunnel light rail system. Some of its recent infrastructure projects (around 2015) include the Harry S. Truman Parkway in Savannah Georgia; work on the Golden Gate Bridge; the Sikorsky Bridge in New Bern North Carolina; and Bridgeport I-95 in Bridgeport Connecticut.

Its recently acquired Balfour Beatty Rail group in 2015 continued working on rail projects (including the South Sacramento Corridor Phase II and the Burlington Station projects in San Francisco) in California Denver Philadelphia and Boston. Its Fru-Con Construction projects that year included work in Virginia on the Arlington Water Pollution Control Facility the Broad Run Water Reclamation Facility and the Flat Branc Pump Station & Force Main project; as well as work on water treatment plants in Galveston in Texas and Frederick and Baltimore in Maryland.

Since the global financial crisis Balfour Beatty Infrastructure has relied more heavily on government projects. More than half of the company's work comes from the government which had implemented stimulus programs to kickstart the economy and update outdated infrastructure. The company also has benefited from the realignment of the Department of Defense and several military housing projects.

EXECUTIVES

Vp Fru-con, Michael R. (Mike) Fischer
President And Ceo, Ray Bond
Cfo, Mark Birch
Vp And General Manager Southeast Region, Mark Johnnie
Vp And General Manager Southwest Region, John Rempe
Vp And General Manager Western Region,
 Crandall Bates
Vice President Eh And S, Darren Utecht
Vice President Of Finance, Drew Leist
Auditors: KPMG LLP DALLAS TX

LOCATIONS

HQ: BALFOUR BEATTY INFRASTRUCTURE, INC.
600 GALLERIA PKWY SE, ATLANTA, GA 303395994
Phone: 707 427-8900
Web: WWW.BALFOURBEATTYUS.COM

Selected Services

Architectural detailing
Concrete
Earthworks
Foundations
Mechanical systems installation
Paving
Structural steel erection
Surface finishing

Selected Project Types

Bridges
Highways
Pumping stations
Roadways
Rail systems
Water and wastewater infrastructure

PRODUCTS/OPERATIONS

Selected Mergers and Acquisitions

FY2011
Fru-Con Construction
FY2009
RT Dooley Construction ($40 million)

COMPETITORS

American Civil Constructors Holdings
American Infrastructure
Flatiron Construction
Granite Construction
Lane Construction
Peter Kiewit Sons'
Skanska USA Civil
Traylor Bros.
Walsh Group

HISTORICAL FINANCIALS

Company Type: Private

Income Statement				FYE: December 31
	REVENUE ($ mil.)	NET INCOME ($ mil.)	NET PROFIT MARGIN	EMPLOYEES
12/15	517	(3)	—	1,100
12/14	555	9	1.8%	—
12/13	509	9	1.9%	—
Annual Growth	0.8%	—	—	—

2015 Year-End Financials

Return on assets: (-1.1%)
Return on equity: (-2.7%)
Current ratio: 1.50
Cash ($ mil.): 50

BALFOUR BEATTY, LLC

EXECUTIVES

Mng MBR-Pres, Mark Crouser
V Pres, Peter Zinkin
V Pres, Leslie Cohn
V Pres-Asst SEC, Joanne Bonfiglio
Treas, Barry Crozier
SEC, Christine Schiltz
Asst Treas, Vicki Sizemore
Vp and Business Unit Leader Fo, Ed Prendergast
Chief Estimator, Bill Reinhart
Information Specialist, John Olaes
Auditors: DELOITTE & TOUCHE LLP DALLAS

LOCATIONS

HQ: BALFOUR BEATTY, LLC
1011 CENTRE RD STE 322, WILMINGTON, DE
198051266
Phone: 302 573-3873
Web: WWW.BALFOURBEATTYUS.COM

HISTORICAL FINANCIALS

Company Type: Private

Income Statement				FYE: December 31
	REVENUE ($ mil.)	NET INCOME ($ mil.)	NET PROFIT MARGIN	EMPLOYEES
12/15	4,690	(18)	—	2,200
12/12	4,378	43	1.0%	—
12/11	4,078	58	1.4%	—
Annual Growth	3.6%	—	—	—

2015 Year-End Financials

Return on assets: (-0.5%)
Return on equity: (-1.0%)
Current ratio: 1.70
Cash ($ mil.): 391

BALTIMORE CITY PUBLIC SCHOOLS

EXECUTIVES

Ceo, Sonja B Santelises
Ceo, Bonnie S Copeland
Chief School Supports Officer, Karl E Perry
Chief Achievement and Accounta, Theresa Jones
Accounting Staff, Michele Hayes
Chief Special Divisio, Alan Robinson
Deputy Program Manager, Carlos Espinosa
Officer, Dawn Wood
Environmental Health Superviso, Geraldine Woodson
Project Superviso, Joseph Belardo
Information Technology Special, Lisa White
Auditors: CLIFTONLARSONALLEN LLP BALTIM

LOCATIONS

HQ: BALTIMORE CITY PUBLIC SCHOOLS
200 E NORTH AVE, BALTIMORE, MD 212025984
Phone: 443 984-2000
Web: WWW.BALTIMORECITYSCHOOLS.ORG

HISTORICAL FINANCIALS

Company Type: Private

Income Statement				FYE: June 30
	REVENUE ($ mil.)	NET INCOME ($ mil.)	NET PROFIT MARGIN	EMPLOYEES
06/12	1,480	(18)	—	10,800
06/02	988	(23)	—	—
Annual Growth	4.1%	—	—	—

2012 Year-End Financials

Return on assets: (-2.0%)
Return on equity: (-3.6%)
Current ratio: —
Cash ($ mil.): 183

BANNER HEALTH

Banner Health is one of the largest secular not-for-profit health systems in the US. The organization operates about 30 acute-care hospitals (with roughly 4000 beds). It also operates clinics nursing homes clinical laboratories ambulatory surgery centers home health agencies and other health care-related organizations including physician practices and a captive insurance company. Banner Health participates in medical research in areas such as Alzheimer's disease and spinal cord injuries through its Banner Sun Health Research division. The company which has more than 400000 members provides services in seven states in the western US; its largest concentration of facilities is in Arizona.

Operations

Banner Health is one of the first not-for-profit hospital operators to reinsure its employees through its captive insurance company Samaritan Insurance Funding. By offering this service Banner Health is able to diversify its risk improve cash flow and lower life insurance costs by about half a million dollars a year.

The multi-specialty system also operates a health plan in Arizona for Medicare-eligible patients. Its MediSunONE plan includes Medicare and Medicare Part D. The company has joined forces with Aetna in what is called an accountable care collaboration (ACO). An ACO uses technology and a team-based approach to care for the hospital's patients. Doctors and hospitals assume accountability for patient outcomes and are rewarded financially for achieving higher quality greater efficiency and overall better patient outcomes. The partnership also includes a new product called Aetna Whole Health that allows Banner's patients access to a line of Aetna services including their own electronic patient record.

The system's specialty centers include Banner Alzheimer's Institute Banner Concussion Center Banner Heart Hospital and the Western States Burn Center. In addition Banner Health trains 270 doctors per year at Banner Good Samaritan and Northern Colorado Medical Center.

Banner Health also partners with M.D. Anderson Cancer Center to operate a comprehensive cancer center in Phoenix. Services include medical oncology radiation oncology surgical oncology pathology laboratory diagnostic imaging as well as other supportive clinical services. M.D. Anderson has clinical oversight for all aspects of care delivery.

Education looms large on Banner Health's list of priorities — the hospital operates one of the country's largest simulation education centers at its Banner Corporate Center-Mesa. Simulation education is an expanding field in which medical students use computerized mannequins to improve their surgical and medical skills. The school's research has paid off and with Scottsdale Healthcare Osborn Medical Center Banner Health invented the Sapien Transcatheter Heart Valve an artificial heart valve that can replace a diseased aortic heart valve without the open heart surgery that previously was required.

Geographic Reach

Banner Health operates in Alaska Arizona California Colorado Nebraska Nevada and Wyoming.

The system's Banner Health Network is a group of health care providers located in Arizona's Maricopa and Pinal counties.

Financial Performance

Banner Health's income is generally derived through three channels: third-party payers such as commercial insurance managed care agreements Medicare and Medicaid and a small portion of self-pay patients as well as by borrowing funds and receiving philanthropic donations.

Its revenues grew by 29% in 2015 from $5.4 billion to $7 billion; higher net patient service medical insurance premium and other revenues drove that increase. However rising expenses and a $49.3 million loss for ACO Banner Health Network led to a drop in net income which fell 65% to $83.7 million.

Strategy

The health system has grown through construction. Banner Health is nearly always engaged in some sort of construction renovation or upgrading at its numerous facilities. The organization has more than $1 billion in construction projects in progress or completed in recent years. The system has expanded its facilities at Banner Baywood Medical Center Banner Del E. Webb Medical Center Banner Desert Medical Center Banner Thunderbird Medical Center Cardon Children's Medical Center and McKee Medical Center.

In 2015 Banner Health opened a Fort Collins facility on a 28-acre campus with a two-story hospital featuring an emergency department a 24-bed inpatient unit labor and delivery rooms medical imaging women's services surgical services and lab services.

Also that year the system merged with the University of Arizona Health Network (now named Banner - University Medicine) as well as establishing a 30-year affiliation with the University of Arizona. The moves align with its strategy of combining health care provision with medical schools and academic training as well as expanding operations into new markets (in this case the Tuscon region). Banner Health hopes to both improve access to health care through a consumer-focused system and to provide opportunities for medical professionals to remain in Arizona. As part of the merger the company plans to build a new hospital and renovate an existing ambulatory campus.

In 2017 Banner Health restructured operations including cutting some 500 employees' positions. The move was part of its efforts to become more consumer-focused and included changes to its leadership lineup. Later that year after the restructuring was completed the company began recruiting to fill 1000 positions including spots for specialty nurses and physical and occupational therapists.

Mergers and Acquisitions

Banner Health does occasionally pick up a new hospital through acquisition. For instance in 2015 the company acquired The University of Arizona Health Network (now Banner - University Medicine). As a result University Medicine is the new academic medicine division of Banner Health which includes three academic medical centers: Banner - University Medical Center Tucson Banner - University Medical Center Phoenix and Banner - University Medical Center South.

In mid-2016 the company acquired more than 30 Arizona urgent-care centers from Urgent Care Extra. The centers to be rebranded under the Banner banner are among the expected 50 the company plans to have in Arizona by 2018.

In 2017 Banner Health acquired Medicare-certified home health agency SunLife Home Health which is based in Tucson Arizona. That deal allowed the system to expand its home care operations into southern Arizona.

Company Background

Banner Good Samaritan Medical Center first opened its doors as a 20-bed hospital in 1911. The medical center which is four months older than the state of Arizona marked its 100th anniversary in October 2011.

EXECUTIVES

Evp And Chief Administrative Officer, Ronald R. (Ron) Bunnell
President Ceo And Director, Peter S. Fine, age 67
Evp And Chief Clinical Officer, John Hensing
Evp University Medicine, Kathy Bollinger
Coo, Rebecca (Becky) Kuhn
Ceo Banner Estrella Medical Center, Tom Dickson
Cfo, Dennis L. Laraway
President Western Region, Jim Ferando
Ceo East Morgan County Hospital And Sterling Regional Medcenter, Linda Thorpe
President Arizona East Division, Todd S. Werner, age 51
Ceo Banner Baywood Medical Center And Banner Heart Hospital, Laura Robertson
Ceo Platte County Memorial Hospital And Community Hospital, Shelby Nelson
Ceo Banner Thunderbird Medical Center, Deb Krmpotic
Ceo Banner Research, Eric (Bill) Reiman
President Banner Health Network, Chuck Lehn
Ceo Banner Del E. Webb Medical Center And Banner Boswell Medical Center, Debbie Flores
Ceo University Medical Center Phoenix, Steve Narang
Ceo Banner Ironwood Medical Center And Banner Goldfield Medical Center, Sharon Lind
President And Ceo Banner Health Foundation And Banner Alzheimer's Foundation, Andy Kramer Petersen
Cio, Ryan Smith
Ceo Banner Casa Grande Medical Center, Rona Curphy
Ceo Banner Estrella Medical Center, Courtney Ophaug
Ceo Banner Gateway Medical Center Banner Md Anderson Cancer Center Banner Baywood Medical Center And Banner Heart Hospital, Lamont Yoder
Vp Post Acute Services And Ceo Banner Home Care/hospice, Lynn Rosenbach
Ceo Banner Lassen Medical Center, Catherine Harshbarger
Ceo Banner Churchill Community Hospital, Hoyt Skabelund
Ceo Washakie Medical Center, Jay Stallings
Ceo Ogallala Community Hospital, Drew Dostal
Ceo Banner Behavioral Health Hospital, Brian Beutin
Ceo Page Hospital, Brian Kellar
Interim Ceo Northern Colorado Service Area Including: Banner Fort Collins Medical Center Mckee Medical Center North Colorado Medical Center, Scott Baker
Vice President Materials Managerment, Doug Bowen
Vice President Of Information Technology, Frank Wallace
Vice President, Tony Blake
System Vice President Information Technology Business Services, Bryce Carder
Medical Director, Sathya Jyothinagaram
Medical Director, Carol Williams
Vice President Of Business Development, Christen Castellano
Cota L, Justin Ellis
Vice President, Robert Stern
Vice President Of Administration, Jason Armstrong
Director Of Pharmacy, Tina Peterson
Vice President, A Smith
Medical Director, Goodin Director
Director Of Nursing, Nancy Adamson
Vice Chair, Christopher H. (Chris) Volk
Chairman, Larry S. Lazarus
Secretary, Jennifer Manning
Secretary, Kathryn Mcswain
Auditors: ERNST & YOUNG LLP PHOENIX AZ

LOCATIONS

HQ: BANNER HEALTH
2901 N CENTRAL AVE # 160, PHOENIX, AZ 850122702
Phone: 602 747-4000
Web: WWW.BANNERHEALTH.COM

FEATURED SERVICES

Academic Medicine
Alzheimer's
Cancer
Heart
Insurance (Networks)
Maternity
Orthopedics
Pediatrics
Pharmacy
Physicians & Specialists
Research
Women's Health

COMPETITORS

Community Health Systems
Dignity Health
HCA
Inova
John C. Lincoln Health Network
Memorial Health System of East Texas
Northern Arizona Healthcare
Phoenix Children's Hospital

Poudre Valley Health System
Providence St. Joseph Health
Scottsdale Healthcare
Tenet Healthcare
Texas Health Resources
Wyoming Medical Center
Yuma Regional Medical Center

HISTORICAL FINANCIALS

Company Type: Private

Income Statement				FYE: December 31
	REVENUE ($ mil.)	NET INCOME ($ mil.)	NET PROFIT MARGIN	EMPLOYEES
12/18	8,519	64	0.8%	35,000
12/17	7,835	728	9.3%	—
12/16	7,633	309	4.1%	—
12/15	6,971	119	1.7%	—
Annual Growth	6.9%	(18.6%)	—	—

2018 Year-End Financials

Return on assets: 0.6% Cash ($ mil.): 383
Return on equity: 1.1%
Current ratio: 1.50

BANNER-UNIVERSITY MEDICAL CENTER TUCSON CAMPUS LLC

Banner - University Medicine (formerly The University of Arizona Health Network) heals Arizonans and trains Wildcats. It operates three academic medical centers in Phoenix and Tucson serving as the primary teaching hospital for the University of Arizona (UA) and offering medical treatment research and education services. The not-for-profit center provides cancer cardiology geriatric respiratory transplant and dialysis care as well as general practice and home health services. Specialty services include burn care behavioral health integrative medicine sports medicine and level I trauma care. The network merged with Banner Healthcare in 2015.

Operations

The University of Arizona Health Network merged with Banner Health to create Banner - University Medicine. The division includes three hospitals: Banner - University Medical Center Tucson Banner - University Medical Center South and Banner - University Medical Center Phoenix. The network also includes Banner - University Medical Group (formerly named University of Arizona Physicians) a group of Tucson-based physicians.

Geographic Reach

Banner - University Medicine serves patients in and around Phoenix and Tucson Arizona.

Strategy

In 2015 Banner - University Medical Center Phoenix broke ground on a new $160 million emergency department that will have the capacity to serve an additional 20000 patients each year. Expected to open in mid-2017 the new facility will include 60 private exam rooms a new trauma unit and 40 observation beds.

Company Background

The University of Arizona Health Network was formed in 2010 when University Physicians Hospital merged with University Medical Center.

LOCATIONS

HQ: BANNER-UNIVERSITY MEDICAL CENTER TUCSON CAMPUS LLC
1501 N CAMPBELL AVE, TUCSON, AZ 857240001
Phone:
Web: WWW.UAHEALTH.IXT.COM

COMPETITORS

John C. Lincoln Health Network	Scottsdale Healthcare Sun Health
Northern Arizona Healthcare	Yuma Regional Medical Center
Phoenix Children's Hospital	

HISTORICAL FINANCIALS

Company Type: Private

Income Statement				FYE: June 30
	REVENUE ($ mil.)	NET INCOME ($ mil.)	NET PROFIT MARGIN	EMPLOYEES
06/09	541	0	—	3,000
06/08	512	27	5.3%	—
06/05	708	0	0.0%	—
Annual Growth	(6.5%)	—	—	—

2009 Year-End Financials

Return on assets: 16.3%   Cash ($ mil.): 3
Return on equity: —
Current ratio: —

BAPTIST HEALTH

For those seeking medical salvation Baptist Health may be the answer to their prayers. The organization provides health services through about 175 points of care scattered throughout in Arkansas. Its facilities include seven hospitals and a number of rehabilitation facilities family clinics and therapy and wellness centers. Arkansas Health Group a division of Baptist Health runs more than 20 physician clinics across the state. Specialized services include cardiology women's health orthopedics rehabilitation and home and hospice care. Baptist Health's Parkway Village is a 90-acre retirement community for active seniors located close to Baptist Health Medical Center - Little Rock.

Operations

In addition to its hospitals the company has 47 physician clinics 20 therapy centers and 53 other centers and service locations. Its Baptist Health Mobile Health Unit travels the state to provide a temporary facility for health screenings health education and first-aid (emergent care) services.

Along with the standard roster of health care services Baptist Health also offers Little Rock residents nine programs of health care study through its Baptist Health Schools Little Rock division. The school coordinates with Arkansas Tech University to offer Baptist Health RN graduates an online option to complete their Bachelor of Science in Nursing degree. Its average enrollment is about 900 students each semester.

Geographic Reach

Baptist Health serves patients across Arkansas. Baptist Health's hospitals include Baptist Health Extended Care Hospital Baptist Health Medical Center - Arkadelphia Baptist Health Medical Center - Heber Springs Baptist Health Medical Center - Little Rock Baptist Health Medical Center - North Little Rock Baptist Health Medical Center - Stuttgart and Baptist Health Medical Center - Hot Spring County.

Sales and Marketing

Baptist Health works with a number of insurance policies and organizations including Aetna AMCO PPO Arkansas Blue Cross and Blue Shield Arkansas Municipal League Care Improvement Plus CIGNA Coventry/First Health PPO and GEHA.

Strategy

The hospital system has been growing to meet the needs of its customers. In 2013 it began leasing Hot Spring County Medical Center in Malvern. The 72-bed acute care hospital was renamed Baptist Health Medical Center Hot Spring County. Baptist Health also bought nearly 40 acres in Conway and began construction on a medical center to serve Faulkner county.

To improve operating efficiency in 2013 Baptist Health formed a new organization — Baptist Health Physician Partners a clinical integration program with more than 200 physician partners.

EXECUTIVES

Medical Director, Nancy Rector
Vice President Of It, Chris Parker
Nursing Director, Christopher Cox
Respiratory Therapy Director, Shelly Summersbrown
Auditors: BKD LLP LITTLE ROCK ARKANSA

LOCATIONS

HQ: BAPTIST HEALTH
9601 BAPTIST HEALTH DR # 109, LITTLE ROCK, AR 722056323
Phone: 501 202-2000

Selected Locations in Arkansas

Arkansas Health Group (statewide)
BH Extended Care (Little Rock)
BHMC Arkadelphia
BHMC Heber Springs
BHMC Hot Spring County
BHMC Little Rock
BHMC North Little Rock
BHMC Stuttgart
Baptist Health Rehabilitation Institute (Little Rock)
Parkway Village (Little Rock)

PRODUCTS/OPERATIONS

Selected Services

Behavioral Health
Cardiac Rehab
Diabetes Treatment & Management
Eye Center
Hospice & Home Health
Home Infusion Services

Imaging Services
Laboratory
MedFlight
Men's Health
Pastoral Care
Sleep Disorder
Transplant
Weight Loss Program
Wound Care Center

COMPETITORS

Arkansas Children's Hospital
Arkansas Heart Hospital
Baxter Regional Medical Center
Conway Regional Health System
Jefferson Regional Medical Center of Arkansas
Saline Memorial
Sparks Health System
St. Joseph's Mercy Health Center
St. Vincent Health System
White County Medical Center

HISTORICAL FINANCIALS

Company Type: Private

Income Statement				FYE: December 31
	REVENUE ($ mil.)	NET INCOME ($ mil.)	NET PROFIT MARGIN	EMPLOYEES
12/18	1,215	(45)	—	7,000
12/17	875	49	5.6%	—
12/09	924	64	7.0%	—
Annual Growth	3.1%	—	—	—

2018 Year-End Financials

Return on assets: (-2.9%)   Cash ($ mil.): 58
Return on equity: (-5.5%)
Current ratio: 1.70

BAPTIST HEALTH SOUTH FLORIDA, INC.

Baptist Health South Florida (BHSF) is a faith-based not-for-profit enterprise operating about a dozen acute-care hospitals in the Miami area. Its flagship facility Baptist Hospital has about 730 beds and provides a comprehensive range of medical and surgical services. The system also includes Bethesda Hospital (480 beds) South Miami Hospital (440 beds) a children's hospital and other community hospitals in surrounding areas. In all BHSF hospitals contain about 2650 beds. In addition to inpatient services the organization provides ambulatory surgery primary and urgent care diagnostic imaging rehabilitation and home health services from more than 100 outpatient centers and physician practices.

Strategy

BHSF's strategic goals focus on expansion through new construction and additions acquisitions and select partnerships. Additionally the health system works to improve patient care through medical equipment and information technology upgrades.

The company looks to attract patients seeking specialty care by maintaining specialist centers with state-of-the-art medical technologies and skilled physicians. For instance the organization opened a new multidisciplinary skin cancer clinic featuring a 3D whole-body imaging system at its Miami Cancer Institute facility in 2019. Other specialist centers include the Miami Cardiac and Vascular Institute the Miami Cancer Institute the Baptist Health

Neuroscience Center and the Miami Orthopedic and Sports Medicine Institute.

BHSF is also expanding its global alliances through its Baptist Health International unit. In 2019 Baptist Health International formed a partnership with ProHealth Urgent Care to open an urgent care center in St. Croix US Virgin Islands.

Mergers and Acquisitions

As part of an ongoing wave of consolidation among hospital operators BHSF acquired another South Florida-based health care organization the not-for-profit Boca Raton Regional Hospital in 2019. The acquired entity operates a 400-bed hospital and related outpatient facilities in the Boca Raton area.

Company Background

Baptist Hospital opened in 1960 and the Baptist Health organization was formed in 1990.

The company added a number of hospitals through acquisitions and construction efforts over the years. It opened the West Kendall Baptist Hospital in 2011. In 2017 the system merged with the not-for-profit Bethesda Health adding two hospitals (Bethesda East and Bethesda West) in Boynton Beach. It also added the Fishermen's Community Hospital that year.

EXECUTIVES

Evp And Cfo, Ralph E. Lawson
President And Ceo, Brian E. Keeley
Ceo And Executive Medical Director Miami Cancer Institute, Michael J. Zinner
Evp And Coo, D. Wayne Brackin
Evp And Chief Physician Executive, Jack A. Ziffer
Evp And Chief Administrative Officer, Joe Natoli
Corporate Vice President Real Estate, Kathy Moorman
Executive Vice President And Chief Administrative Officer, Joseph Natoli
Chairman, Rev. William W. White
Auditors: DELOITTE & TOUCHE LLP

LOCATIONS

HQ: BAPTIST HEALTH SOUTH FLORIDA, INC.
6855 S RED RD, SOUTH MIAMI, FL 331433647
Phone: 305 596-1960

PRODUCTS/OPERATIONS

2013 Sales

	$ mil.	% of total
Managed Care	1,655	69
Medicare	278	12
Medicaid	122	5
Other	331	14
Total		100

Selected Florida Facilities

Baptist Hospital of Miami (Kendall)
  Baptist Cardiac & Vascular Institute
  Baptist Children's Hospital
Doctors Hospital (Coral Gables)
Homestead Hospital (Homestead)
Mariners Hospital (Tavernier)
South Miami Hospital (South Miami)
West Kendall Baptist Hospital (Kendall)

Selected Services

Addiction treatment
Behavorial medicine
Blood conservation program
Cancer services
Cardiovascular services
Care and counseling services
Children's health
Community wellness
Critical care center
Diabetes
eICU LifeGuard
Emergency
Endoscopy
Executive health
Gamma knife center
Heart surgery

Home care
Hyperbaric services
Imaging
Intensive care unit
International services
Interventional/surgical Services
Laboratory
Maritime medical services
Neonatal
Neuroscience
Nutrition counseling services
Occupational health
Online appointments
Orthopedics
Outpatient/diagnostic services
Pain center
Pastoral care
Pediatric
Pelvic health
Physical and speech therapy
Pregnancy and childbirth
Progressive care unit
Prostate cancer
Pulmonary services
Radiation oncology
Rehabilitation services
Robotic surgery
Senior services
Sleep diagnostic center
Sports medicine and orthopedic programs
Stroke services
Surgery
Weight-loss surgery
Wellness Center
Women's health
Wound care

COMPETITORS

Adventist Health System Sunbelt Healthcare
Boca Raton Regional Hospital
Broward Health
HCA
Holy Cross Hospital Fort Lauderdale
Jackson Health System
Lakeland Regional Medical Center
Miami Children's Hospital
Mount Sinai Medical Center of Florida
South Broward Hospital District
Tenet Healthcare
The Cleveland Clinic
University of Miami Hospital

HISTORICAL FINANCIALS

Company Type: Private

Income Statement

FYE: September 30

	REVENUE ($ mil.)	NET INCOME ($ mil.)	NET PROFIT MARGIN	EMPLOYEES
09/17	608	244	40.2%	16,000
09/15	846	137	16.2%	—
09/09*	616	121	19.7%	—
12/08	2	(1)	—	—
Annual Growth 83.2%	—	—	—	—

*Fiscal year change

2017 Year-End Financials

Return on assets: 5.1%   Cash ($ mil.): 106
Return on equity: 7.1%
Current ratio: 1.50

BAPTIST HEALTH SYSTEM, INC.

Even if you don't root for the Jacksonville Jaguars you can still seek care from Baptist Health System. Baptist Health serves the Jacksonville

Florida area through four acute care hospitals and a children's hospital with a combined total of more than 1000 beds. Baptist Medical Center its flagship facility is a full-service hospital that also houses Baptist Heart Hospital. Across the street Wolfson Children's Hospital also cares for the city's youngest residents. The system's satellite acute-care facilities include Baptist Medical Center Beaches Baptist Medical Center Nassau and Baptist Medical Center South.

Operations

Baptist Health's flagship tertiary care hospital Baptist Medical Center is centrally located in Jacksonville and is a full-service medical center representing nearly all major health care specialties. Its Baptist Heart Hospital offers comprehensive cardiovascular care.

In addition to its hospitals Baptist Health System operates a network of about 200 outpatient centers including primary and specialty care physician practices and clinics (including cardiology and cancer care centers) as well as urgent care rehabilitation pharmacy and occupational health locations. In total Baptist Health System has 1200 physicians and handles some 51000 inpatient stays nearly 250000 emergency visits 44000 surgeries and 7000 births each year.

Financial Performance

In 2014 Baptist Health's net revenues increased by 3% due to higher net patient service revenues less provision for bad debts. Net patient service revenue by major payor source was: Medicare 40%; Blue Cross 23%; Medicaid 7%; other third-party payors 25%; and self pay 5%.

The hospital incurred a net loss of $8.9 million in 2014 (a 190% drop compared to 2013) despite the increase in net revenues.

Cash outflow decreased by 102% compared to 2013.

Strategy

Baptist Health is expanding certain programs to cater to targeted population segments in the Jacksonville area. For instance it is expanding its Baptist AgeWell Institute program at the Jacksonville hospital as well as the pastoral care program in Nassau. It is also enhancing its emergency room at the Beaches hospital and is conducting community outreach programs for low-income families.

In 2015 Baptist Health and The University of Texas MD Anderson Cancer Center moved forward with multidisciplinary cancer care for adult patients throughout their region by opening the Baptist MD Anderson Cancer Center.

Company Background

A major construction project was completed in late 2012 with the opening of a new 11-story patient tower at Baptist Jacksonville. The new $200 million tower features all private patient rooms and high-tech surgical suites.

Baptist Health was founded in 1955.

EXECUTIVES

Evp And Coo, John F. Wilbanks
Hospital President Baptist Medical Center South, Ron Robinson
Hospital President Wolfson Childrens Hospital, Michael D. Aubin
President And Ceo, A. Hugh Greene
Administrator Baptist Medical Center Beaches, Joseph M. (Joe) Mitrick
Svp Medical Affairs And Clinical Effectiveness; Chief Medical Officer, Keith L. Stein
Svp And Cfo, Scott Wooten
Hospital President Baptist Medical Center Jacksonville, Michael A. Mayo
Svp And Chief Nursing Officer, Diane S. Raines
President Physician Integration, Edward Sim
Svp And Cio, Roland Garcia

Chief Medical Officer Wolfson Children's Hospital, Jerry A. Bridgham
Hospital President Baptist Medical Center Nassau, Stephen Lee
Medical Director, Mark Stich
Medical Director, David Ross
Vice President Of Operations, Keon Falkner
Pharmacy Manager, Michael Brooks
Vice President Of Community Investment And Impact, Melanie Patz
Medical Director, Ted Glasser
Auditors: ERNST & YOUNG LLP JACKSONVIL

LOCATIONS

HQ: BAPTIST HEALTH SYSTEM, INC.
800 PRUDENTIAL DR, JACKSONVILLE, FL 322078202
Phone: 904 202-2000
Web: WWW.BAPTISTJAX.COM

PRODUCTS/OPERATIONS

Selected facilities

Baptist Medical Center Beaches (Jacksonville Beach Florida)
Baptist Medical Center Jacksonville (Jacksonville Florida)
Baptist Heart Hospital
Baptist Medical Center Nassau (Fernandina Beach Florida)
Baptist Medical Center South (Jacksonville Florida)
Wolfson Children's Hospital (Jacksonville Florida)

COMPETITORS

Bay Medical Center	Munroe Regional Health
Brooks Rehabilitation	System
Florida Hospital Tampa	Nemours Foundation
Bay Division	Orlando Health
Florida Hospital	St. Vincent's Health
Waterman	System
HCA	UF Health Jacksonville
Mayo Clinic	
Jacksonville	

HISTORICAL FINANCIALS
Company Type: Private

Income Statement				FYE: September 30
	REVENUE ($ mil.)	NET INCOME ($ mil.)	NET PROFIT MARGIN	EMPLOYEES
09/18	1,736	252	14.5%	7,000
09/17	1,630	304	18.7%	—
Annual Growth	6.5%	(17.1%)	—	—

2018 Year-End Financials
Return on assets: 7.1%   Cash ($ mil.): 120
Return on equity: 10.5%
Current ratio: 1.30

BAPTIST HEALTH SYSTEM, INC.

EXECUTIVES

Ceo, Keith Parrott
Cfo*, Greg Johnston
CIO*, Scott Fenn
Chro*, Beth Francis
Cmo*, Elizabeth Ennis
CIO*, Chris Davis
Health Professional, Syed A Ali
Chief of Medicine, Lynn Crawford
Vice-President Human Resources, Le Roy Walker
General, Steve Brooks
Nursing Director, Tiffany Garza
Auditors: WARREN AVERETT LLC BIRMINGHAM

LOCATIONS

HQ: BAPTIST HEALTH SYSTEM, INC.
1130 22ND ST S STE 3200, BIRMINGHAM, AL 352052867
Phone: 205 715-5000
Web: WWW.BROOKWOODBAPTISTHEALTH.COM

HISTORICAL FINANCIALS
Company Type: Private

Income Statement				FYE: December 31
	REVENUE ($ mil.)	NET INCOME ($ mil.)	NET PROFIT MARGIN	EMPLOYEES
12/14	565	(35)	—	4,300
12/12	528	(15)	—	—
12/11*	587	(34)	—	—
06/10	1,220	0	—	—
Annual Growth	—	—	—	—

*Fiscal year change

2014 Year-End Financials
Return on assets: (-4.5%)   Cash ($ mil.): 1
Return on equity: (-17.0%)
Current ratio: 0.90

BAPTIST HEALTHCARE SYSTEM, INC.

Baptist Healthcare System which goes by Baptist Health wants to keep all its followers healthy. The system owns eight acute-care hospitals one a long-term facility in Kentucky with a total capacity of more than 2100 beds. The not-for-profit health system's largest facility is Baptist Hospital East a 520-bed hospital in Louisville that provides a wide range of health services with special expertise in cardiology rehabilitation and women's health. In addition to its owned facilities Baptist Health manages Hardin Memorial a 300-bed hospital located in Elizabethtown and Russell County Hospital with 25 beds. The growing Baptist Health was founded as a single hospital in Louisville in 1924.

Operations
Along with inpatient acute care services Baptist Health offers home health care services runs two outpatient surgery centers provides urgent care through a handful of clinics and operates a regional physicians' practice group. It also runs a community-based not-for-profit health care plan Baptist Health Plan which operates across the state and into parts of Indiana and Tennessee. Baptist Health plans to shut the struggling health plan down in 2018.

Strategy
Baptist Health faced major losses during 2017 and laid off more than 500 employees that year. It announced plans to realign its structure and shut down its not-for-profit Baptist Health Plan.

Mergers and Acquisitions
In mid-2017 Baptist Health agreed to buy Hardin Memorial for an undisclosed amount. Hardin Memorial (which Baptist Health already manages) operates some 50 outpatient facilities as well as its 300-bed hospital.

EXECUTIVES

President And Ceo Bluegrass Family Health, James S. Fritz
President Baptist Hospital East, David L. Gray
President Central Baptist Hospital, William G. Sisson
President Baptist Hospital Northeast, Christopher M. (Chris) Roty
President Baptist Regional Medical Center, Larry W. Gray
President Hardin Memorial Hopsital, Dennis Johnson
Vice President And General Counsel, Janet Norton
Ceo, Stephen C. Hanson
Chief Clinical Officer, Timothy Jahn
Cio, David J. Bensema
Cfo, Carl G. Herde
Chief Health Integration Officer; President Baptist Health Medical Group, Isaac J. Myers
President Baptist Health Richmond, C. Todd Jones
Regional Executive And President Baptist Health Paducah, William A. Brown
President Baptist Health Madisonville, Michael A. Baumgartner
Vice President Marketing, Carla Conklin
Clinic Manager, Sean Sullivan
Vice President Human Resources And Development, Sue Christopher
Director Of Pharmacy, Michael Anderson
Vice President Human Resources Baptist Health Lexi, Lynette Walker
Auditors: DELOITTE & TOUCHE LLP LOUISVI

LOCATIONS

HQ: BAPTIST HEALTHCARE SYSTEM, INC.
2701 EASTPOINT PKWY, LOUISVILLE, KY 402234166
Phone: 502 896-5000
Web: WWW.BAPTISTHEALTH.COM

PRODUCTS/OPERATIONS

Selected Facilities and Operations (Kentucky)
Hospitals
Managed
Baptist Health Corbin
Baptist Health La Grange
Baptist Health Lexington
Baptist Health Louisville
Baptist Health Richmond
Baptist Health Madisonville
Baptist Health Paducah
ContinueCARE Hospital (Corbin)
Owned
Hardin Memorial Hospital (Elizabethtown)
Russell County Hospital (Russell Springs)
Other operations
Baptist East Milestone Wellness Center (Louisville)
Baptist Express Care (various Walmarts in state)
Baptist Medical Associates (medical practice group Louisville area)
Baptist Urgent Care (Louisville)
Bluegrass Family Health (provider-sponsored insurance)

COMPETITORS

Appalachian Regional	Norton Healthcare
Healthcare	Pikeville Medical
Catholic Health	Center
Initiatives	University Health Care
Jewish Hospital & St.	University of Kentucky
Mary's HealthCare	Chandler Hospital
Kindred Healthcare	

HISTORICAL FINANCIALS
Company Type: Private

Income Statement				FYE: August 31
	REVENUE ($ mil.)	NET INCOME ($ mil.)	NET PROFIT MARGIN	EMPLOYEES
08/18	2,725	149	5.5%	12,601
08/17	2,688	5	0.2%	—
08/16	2,331	1	0.0%	—
08/15	2,136	17	0.8%	—
Annual Growth	8.5%	105.4%	—	—

2018 Year-End Financials
Return on assets: 4.5%   Cash ($ mil.): 167
Return on equity: 8.1%
Current ratio: 2.60

BAPTIST HOSPITAL OF MIAMI, INC.

Baptist Hospital of Miami can treat many vices for Miami residents. The flagship facility of the Baptist Health South Florida health system provides residents of the city with a full range of health care services including pediatric cancer home health rehabilitation neurology and cardiovascular care. The hospital has more than 680 beds and includes the Baptist Children's Hospital which offers a pediatric emergency room and a neonatal intensive care unit. Baptist Hospital of Miami also includes the Baptist Cardiac & Vascular Institute a regional cancer program and a diabetes care center. Baptist Hospital of Miami was founded in 1960.

Operations

Baptist Children's Hospital offers 24-hour emergency care as well as two intensive care units and specialist services including pediatric cancer care. Baptist Hospital of Miami also contains the Baptist Cardiac and Vascular Institute which conducts treatment and research programs. The hospital's international care unit provides services to patients from the Caribbean Latin America and other regions. Other specialist divisions include a sleep diagnostic center and a spine care facility as well as a maternity ward. Baptist Hospital of Miami also operates several wellness centers.

As part of Baptist Health South Florida the Baptist Hospital of Miami is part of a network of six hospitals including South Miami Hospital Doctors Hospital and the West Kendall Baptist Hospital. In addition the health system includes outpatient care clinics including emergency surgery imaging and primary care centers.

Strategy

Controlling expenses through data management quality and wellness initiatives and other measures becomes increasingly important for the hospital and its affiliates as the cost of medical care in the US market continues to skyrocket. Maintaining an efficient organization is also imperative as the level of charity care provided by the system's facilities continues to rise in the face of economic difficulties.

As the largest hospital in the Baptist Health system Baptist Hospital of Miami takes a leading role in technology programs such as medical equipment and data management system upgrades. The Baptist Health network is in the process of installing an electronic health record (EHR) system to connect patient records across its facilities.

In 2012 Baptist Hospital of Miami launched a $90 million construction effort to expand the Cardiac and Vascular Institute. The new expanded institute facility will open in 2016 and will include centers for aneurysm treatment structural heart therapy and endovascular therapy. The project also includes expansion efforts on the hospital's surgery center which will have enhanced capabilities for neurological cardiac and robotic surgery procedures.

EXECUTIVES

Prin, William W White
Chm*, Calvin Babcock
Cfo*, Ralph Lawson
Treas*, Manuel Lasaga
Coordinator, Suzanne Balbosa
Pulmonary Disease Specialist, Mark J Hauser
Internal Medicine Practitioner, Ivette Acosta-Trant
Nuclear Medicine Specialist, Jason Samii
Information Specialist, Jorge Perez
Er Inventory Control Coordinat, Thomas Rotondi

LOCATIONS

HQ: BAPTIST HOSPITAL OF MIAMI, INC.
  8900 N KENDALL DR, MIAMI, FL 331762197
Phone: 786 596-1960

PRODUCTS/OPERATIONS

Selected Centers and Services
Baptist Cardiac & Vascular Institute (Heart Care)
Baptist Children's Hospital (Pediatrics)
Breast Care
Cancer Services
Center for Spine Care
Children's Cancer Services
Children's Emergency Center
Clinical Research Trials
Community Wellness
Critical Care/eICU LifeGuard
Diabetes Care
Diagnostic Imaging
Emergency Services
Endoscopy
Gynecology
Home Care
Intensive Care
International Services
Interventional
Maternity
Neonatal Intensive Care Unit
Neuroscience Center
Neurosurgery
Orthopedic Services
Pain Management
Physical & Speech Therapy
Pulmonary Services
Rehabilitation Services
Robotic Surgery
Senior Services
Sleep Diagnostic Center
Spine Care
Stroke Services
Surgery
Women's Services

COMPETITORS

Broward Health
H. Lee Moffitt Cancer Center & Research Institute
HCA
Jackson Health System
Larkin Community Hospital
Miami Children's Hospital
Mount Sinai Medical Center of Florida
South Broward Hospital District
University of Miami Hospital

HISTORICAL FINANCIALS

Company Type: Private

Income Statement				FYE: December 31
	REVENUE ($ mil.)	NET INCOME ($ mil.)	NET PROFIT MARGIN	EMPLOYEES
12/17*	1,004	73	7.3%	4,200
09/16	867	39	4.6%	—
09/15	889	108	12.2%	—
09/14	913	140	15.4%	—
Annual Growth	3.2%	(19.6%)	—	—

*Fiscal year change

2017 Year-End Financials
Return on assets: 7.7%   Cash ($ mil.): —
Return on equity: 30.3%
Current ratio: 0.70

BAPTIST MEMORIAL HOSPITAL

When most of us think of Memphis we think of Elvis Presley. When doctors think of Memphis they think of Elvis and Baptist Memorial Hospital-Memphis. As the flagship facility of Baptist Memorial Health Care the 710-bed hospital often simply called Baptist Memphis offers patients the full spectrum of health care services including cancer treatment orthopedics surgical services and neurology. The campus also features the Baptist Heart Institute for cardiovascular care and research a pediatric emergency room a skilled nursing facility and the Plaza Diagnostic Pavilion for outpatient health care. Baptist Memphis established in 1979 is one of the state's highest volume hospitals.

Operations

Doctors at the hospital see more than 27000 admissions 54000 emergency department visits and nearly 116000 outpatient visits each year. The emergency department houses more than 30 treatment bays. In addition Baptist Memphis' skilled nursing center includes 30 beds. The hospital also operates a 30-bed rehabilitation hospital and a 165000 sq. ft. heart institute for diagnostic and surgical cardiac care. The facility boasts advanced surgical systems including the CyberKnife radiation system for cancerous and non-cancerous tumor removal.

EXECUTIVES

Health Care Director, Janet Chapman

LOCATIONS

HQ: BAPTIST MEMORIAL HOSPITAL
  6019 WALNUT GROVE RD, MEMPHIS, TN 381202113
Phone: 901 226-5000
Web: WWW.BAPTISTONLINE.ORG

COMPETITORS

Methodist Healthcare	St. Jude Children's
Parkwest Medical	Research Hospital
Center	Tenet Healthcare
Shelby County Health	
Care	

HISTORICAL FINANCIALS

Company Type: Private

Income Statement				FYE: September 30
	REVENUE ($ mil.)	NET INCOME ($ mil.)	NET PROFIT MARGIN	EMPLOYEES
09/15	691	(1)	—	6,000
09/14	663	(47)	—	—
09/13	504	17	3.4%	—
09/12	697	15	2.2%	—
Annual Growth	(0.3%)	—	—	—

2015 Year-End Financials
Return on assets: (-0.2%)   Cash ($ mil.): 28
Return on equity: (-0.5%)
Current ratio: 1.40

BAPTIST ST. ANTHONY'S HOSPITAL CORPORATION

EXECUTIVES

Pres-Ceo, John D Hicks
V Pres-Fin-Cfo*, Elizebeth Pulliam
V Pres, Kenneth Johnston
V Pres*, Robert D Williams
Vpres*, Michael Cruz
V Pres*, Belinda Gibson
SEC*, Emily Kohn
Information Technology Supersv, Christine Castillo
Director, Brant Capps
Registered Nurse, Glenda Harris
Auditors: ERNST & YOUNG LLP DALLAS TEX

LOCATIONS

HQ: BAPTIST ST. ANTHONY'S HOSPITAL CORPORATION
1600 WALLACE BLVD, AMARILLO, TX 791061799
Phone: 806 212-2000
Web: WWW.BSAHS.ORG

HISTORICAL FINANCIALS

Company Type: Private

Income Statement			FYE: December 31
	REVENUE ($ mil.)	NET INCOME ($ mil.)	NET PROFIT MARGIN	EMPLOYEES
12/16	477	60	12.8%	2,500
12/15	424	77	18.3%	—
12/08*	285	3	1.3%	—
06/05	0	0	—	—
Annual Growth	—	—	—	—

*Fiscal year change

2016 Year-End Financials

Return on assets: 51.2%   Cash ($ mil.): 1
Return on equity: 67.1%
Current ratio: 2.80

BARCLAYS BANK DELAWARE

Spending money is a rewarding experience for holders of Barclays Bank Delaware cards. With co-branded credit cards from Barclays Bank Delaware (aka Barclaycard US) customers accumulate points that can be redeemed for air travel hotel stays and other perks. The company a division of Barclays issues Visa and MasterCard credit cards in addition to co-branded credit cards through partnerships with some 60 companies and institutions including Priceline Best Western L.L. Bean and BJ's Wholesale. Barclay's cards are accepted in more than 200 countries through some 600000 ATMs and banks worldwide. Founded as Juniper Financial in 2000; it became a part of Barclays in 2004.

Operations

The company creates customized co-branded credit card programs for some of the country's most successful travel entertainment retail and financial institutions.

Geographic Reach

Barclaycard US is part of a larger Barclaycard organization which operates internationally in 22 countries. In the Nordic region Barclaycard offers credit cards through Entercard a joint venture with Swedbank. In South Africa Barclaycard is offered through Absa. In total Barclaycard serves more than 21 million customers. Barclaycard US operates customer call centers in Delaware and Maine.

Sales and Marketing

Barclaycard US uses partnerships to expand its business. Some of its major partners include Barnes & Noble Frontier Airlines L.L. Bean Priceline.com Sallie Mae US Airways and Google.

Strategy

Barclaycard has been growing in recent years as the global economy improves. In 2014 the bank gained 3.6 million new customers and enjoyed Å 18.5 billion ($28.7 billion) worth of new and renewed lending to households in all regions.

Barclaycard continues to focus on next-generation payment technology in the UK South Africa and in the US with the goal of helping its customers adopt new digital platforms to pay using "tap and go" cards contactless stickers and smart phones. In 2012 the company started to promote mobile and online commerce by encouraging its cardholders in the US to save their card to Google Wallet which enables consumers to securely and easily shop online where they see the 'Google Wallet Buy' button or in-person using the Google Wallet mobile app.

Mergers and Acquisitions

In 2012 the company also signed an agreement Sallie Mae to acquire the $1.3 billion Upromise by Sallie Mae credit card portfolio from FIA Card Services.

EXECUTIVES

Managing Director Corporate Communications, Kevin M. Sullivan
Ceo, Amer Sajed
Cfo, Gerald (Jerry) Pavelich
Chief Credit Officer, Michael Mayer
Assistant Vp Strategic Cost Management, Glenn Watson
Vp Data Science And Advanced Analytics, Vishal Morde

LOCATIONS

HQ: BARCLAYS BANK DELAWARE
100 S WEST ST, WILMINGTON, DE 198015015
Phone: 302 255-8000
Web: WWW.BARCLAYCARDUS.COM

PRODUCTS/OPERATIONS

Selected Card Partnerships
Ameriprise
Bank Atlantic
Barnes & Noble
BJ's
Frontier
L.L. Bean
US Airways
Best Western
Priceline.com
Payless
Travelocity
Virgin America

COMPETITORS

Alliance Data Systems   Citibank
American Express   Discover
Bank of America   JPMorgan Chase
Capital One

HISTORICAL FINANCIALS

Company Type: Private

Income Statement				FYE: December 31
	ASSETS ($ mil.)	NET INCOME ($ mil.)	INCOME AS % OF ASSETS	EMPLOYEES
12/14	25,012	239	1.0%	349
12/13	19,055	331	1.7%	—
12/08	12,418	20	0.2%	—
12/07	7,470	0	—	—
Annual Growth	18.8%	—	—	—

2014 Year-End Financials

Return on assets: 1.0%   Sales ($ mil.): 2,245
Return on equity: 7.5%

BARNABAS HEALTH, INC.

EXECUTIVES

Ceo-Pres, Barry Ostrowsky
Cao, Stephen Jones
Program Director, Anthony Carlino
Director of Operations, Julie Owen
Vice-President Human Resources, Zachary Lipner
Associate, Kathryn Liguori
Doctor, Lara Morse
Information Specialist, Louis Graham
Coordinator, Sindhu Syamaprasad
Senior Information Technology, Anthony Centrone
Vice President Human Resources, Arnie Manzo

LOCATIONS

HQ: BARNABAS HEALTH, INC.
95 OLD SHORT HILLS RD, WEST ORANGE, NJ 070521008
Phone: 973 322-5000
Web: WWW.RWJBH.ORG

HISTORICAL FINANCIALS

Company Type: Private

Income Statement				FYE: December 31
	REVENUE ($ mil.)	NET INCOME ($ mil.)	NET PROFIT MARGIN	EMPLOYEES
12/18	730	(131)	—	24,600
12/17	624	293	47.0%	—
12/02	2,159	(92)	—	—
Annual Growth	(6.6%)	—	—	—

2018 Year-End Financials

Return on assets: (-3.0%)   Cash ($ mil.): 626
Return on equity: —
Current ratio: 0.20

BARNES-JEWISH HOSPITAL

LOCATIONS

HQ: BARNES-JEWISH HOSPITAL
  1 B J HOSPITAL PLAZA DR, SAINT LOUIS, MO 63110
Phone: 314 747-3000
Web: WWW.BARNESJEWISH.COM

HISTORICAL FINANCIALS

Company Type: Private

Income Statement				FYE: December 31
	REVENUE ($ mil.)	NET INCOME ($ mil.)	NET PROFIT MARGIN	EMPLOYEES
12/15	1,726	68	4.0%	30
12/14	1,664	83	5.0%	—
Annual Growth	3.7%	(18.2%)	—	—

2015 Year-End Financials

Return on assets: 5.1%   Cash ($ mil.): —
Return on equity: 5.7%
Current ratio: 3.00

BARRICK ENTERPRISES, INC.

EXECUTIVES

President, Robert L Barrick
Auditors: CROSKEY LANNI PC ROCHESTER

LOCATIONS

HQ: BARRICK ENTERPRISES, INC.
  4338 DELEMERE BLVD, ROYAL OAK, MI 480731876
Phone: 248 549-3737
Web: WWW.BARRICKENT.COM

HISTORICAL FINANCIALS

Company Type: Private

Income Statement				FYE: December 31
	REVENUE ($ mil.)	NET INCOME ($ mil.)	NET PROFIT MARGIN	EMPLOYEES
12/18	573	2	0.5%	35
12/17	534	0	0.1%	—
12/16	491	3	0.6%	—
12/15	552	3	0.7%	—
Annual Growth	1.2%	(8.8%)	—	—

2018 Year-End Financials

Return on assets: 8.5%   Cash ($ mil.): 10
Return on equity: 11.4%
Current ratio: 2.00

BARRY-WEHMILLER GROUP, INC.

With Barry-Wehmiller you get the whole package. The company manufactures and supplies packaging corrugating paper converting filling and labeling automation equipment for a broad range of industries. It conducts business around the world through a group of 60 companies including Accraply (labeling machinery) Barry-Wehmiller Company (bottle washers and pasteurizers); HayssenSandiacre and Thiele Technologies (packaging systems); PneumaticScaleAngelus (bottle fillers and cappers); and FleetwoodGoldcoWyard (conveyor systems). Other divisions manufacture paper converting machinery and offer engineering/design consulting services.

Operations

The company operates through three segments and ten divisions: Packaging Automation Equipment (Accraply BW Container Systems Hayssen Flexible Systems Pneumatic Scale Angelus Synerlink and Thiele Technologies); Engineering & IT Consulting (Barry-Wehmiller International and Design Group); and Paper Systems Equipment (BW Papersystems and Paper Converting Machine Company).

Geographic Reach

Barry-Wehmiller has operations in about 30 countries in some 100 locations spanning Asia Australia Europe and the Americas.

Sales and Marketing

Barry-Wehmiller's manufacturing technology and services serve a wide range of industries including packaging paper converting sheeting corrugating engineering and IT consulting.

Financial Performance

Through its aggressive acquisition strategy and the opening of new locations Barry-Wehmiller generated revenues of about $2 billion in 2014. The company has seen 18% compound revenue growth since 1987.

Strategy

Barry-Wehmiller's mantra is expansion through organic growth and acquisitions. The company has purchased more than 65 companies over approximately 25 years creating a mosaic of time and money-saving products and services in locations around the globe. In the same vein its businesses' operations are built upon lean manufacturing practices whereby employees are empowered and resources optimized to contribute to the end product's value.

Mergers and Acquisitions

In 2014 Barry-Wehmiller acquired K ¶rber AG's Papersystems companies (E.C.H. Will GmbH Pemco Inc. and Kugler-Womako GmbH) making BW Papersystems the world's leading supplier of sheeting and sheet packaging machinery with the widest range of applications for the paper converting manufacturing and packaging industries.

In 2013 this unit acquired the PTC software business of ENSER Corporation allowing it to more effectively service ENSER's existing PTC customers. Several months later Barry-Wehmiller entered the French market for the first time when it acquired Arcil SA a Paris-based supplier of packaging technology for the fresh dairy and food industry. The acquisition opened up the firm's packaging platform to six separate operating companies and escalated its reach within the growing global yogurt industry.

Company Background

In 2012 the company expanded its engineering IT consulting platform by buying Kansas-based Customer Driven Technology (CDT) a reseller of advanced IT and enterprise products for engineering and manufacturing companies. CDT provides products and services to address the rapidly changing landscape of product development product lifecycle management and global project collaboration.

Originally a provider of conveying equipment to St. Louis malt houses Barry-Wehmiller was founded by Thomas Barry and Alfred Wehmiller in 1885. Ownership passed from the Wehmiller family to the Chapman family in 1963 and the Chapmans continue as the majority owners.

EXECUTIVES

Chairman And Ceo, Robert H. (Bob) Chapman
Vp And Cfo, James W. (Jim) Lawson
Cio, Craig Hergenroether
President, Tim Sullivan
Vice President Senior Partner _ Product Development Solutions, James Webb
Vice President And Senior Partner, Jim Webb
Chief People Officer, Rhonda Spencer
Vp Of Finance, William Kuhn
Senior Vice President, Richard George
Auditors: ERNST & YOUNG LLP

LOCATIONS

HQ: BARRY-WEHMILLER GROUP, INC.
  8020 FORSYTH BLVD, SAINT LOUIS, MO 631051707
Phone: 314 862-8000
Web: WWW.BARRYWEHMILLER.COM

PRODUCTS/OPERATIONS

Selected Operations

Engineering/Consulting
  Barry-Wehmiller Design Group Inc. (high-speed complex automated manufacturing and packaging system design)
  Barry-Wehmiller International Resources (IT consulting and engineering services)
Converting equipment
  Paper Converting Machine Company (PCMC)
  Coaters
  Narrow web in-line printing systems
  Nonwovens converting equipment
  Tissue converting equipment
  Wide web flexo printing coating and laminating
Corrugating equipment
  MarquipWardUnited Inc. (corrugating sheeting and finishing equipment)
Packaging equipment
  Accraply Inc. (packaging label machinery)
  Arcil SA (supplier of packaging technology)
  FleetwoodGoldcoWyard (conveyer systems)
  HayssenSandiacre (form/fill/seal packaging machinery)
  PneumaticScaleAngelus (fillers cappers seamers and labelers)
  Thiele Technologies Inc. (packaging systems)

Selected Markets

Corrugated paperboard and folded carton
Dairy
Food and beverage
Household
Medical and biotech
Packaging
Personal care
Pharmaceutical
Tissue and nonwovens

COMPETITORS

Bradman Lake	STT Enviro
Gilbreth	Sencorp Inc
Industria Macchine	Tetra Laval
Automatiche	Traco Manufacturing
Kl ¶ckner-Werke	

HISTORICAL FINANCIALS

Company Type: Private

Income Statement				FYE: September 30
	REVENUE ($ mil.)	NET INCOME ($ mil.)	NET PROFIT MARGIN	EMPLOYEES
09/11	1,240	0	—	4,500
09/10	1,097	0	—	—
09/09	976	0	—	—
Annual Growth	12.7%	—	—	—

2011 Year-End Financials

Return on assets: —   Cash ($ mil.): 222
Return on equity: —
Current ratio: 1.80

BARTON MALOW COMPANY

Barton Malow scores by building end zones and home plates. The construction management and general contracting firm which has built its share of sporting facilities also focuses on projects such as schools hospitals offices and plants. Across the eastern US and Mexico the company offers design/build and program management services ranging from the pre-planning stage to completion. Projects have included the Detroit Institute of Arts and Cultural Center and the Baltimore Orioles stadium. Affiliate Barton Malow Design provides architecture and engineering services while Barton Malow Rigging installs process equipment and machinery. Carl Osborn Barton founded the employee-owned firm as C.O. Barton Company in 1924.

Operations
Barton Malow is a general contractor and construction manager. It provides a variety of building services including building information modeling (BIM) planning & scheduling service conceptual and hard dollar estimating services. It specializes in several areas such as routine boiler installation & service foundation & architectural concrete forming machinery moving & equipment installation and procurement & erection of steel building framework.

The company addresses niche markets in its geography focusing on energy health industrial and sports industries along with K-12 education and government institutions.

Geographic Reach
Michigan-based Barton Malow operates about a dozen offices in the eastern third of the US. It also has an office in San Luis Potosi Mexico.

Financial Performance
A private company Barton Malow provides little financial information. However Forbes Magazine estimates its revenue to be $2.4 billion in 2016.

Strategy
Headquartered in a Detroit suburb Barton Malow has historically maintained a healthy relationship with the steel and auto industries. It is somewhat atypical in that it maintains a staff of workers to perform its trade-based services as with boiler servicing and steel erection; other firms commonly hire out such work.

In 2017 the company received a Best Projects award from trade magazine Engineering News-Record (ENR) for its work on a MATS (Mercury and Air Toxics Standards) compliance project with energy client DTE Energy. In that same year the company completed a complete redesign of Bloomfield Hills (Michigan) High School which involved a partial demolition and partial renovation of existing structures and the design and buildout of a new open-plan educational campus.

EXECUTIVES

Evp And Corporate Secretary, Doug Maibach
Chairman And Ceo, Ben C. Maibach
Vp Central Region, Michael (Mike) Stobak
Vp Central Region, Todd Ketola
Vp Charlottesville Operations, Phil Kirby
Vp Eastern Region And Virginia, Carrie Shaeffer
Vp Florida, David Price
Vp National Sports, Len Moser
President, Ryan Maibach
Vp Central Region, Chuck Binkowski
Vp Project Financial Control, Michael Dishaw
Svp Southeast Region, Rod Creach
Vp Central Region, Dan Kovoch

Vice President, Jennifer Brown
Vice President, Joe Benvenuto
Vice President, Matt Lentini
Senior Vice President, Bob Grottenthaler
Vice President, Sheryl Maibach
Auditors: PRICEWATERHOUSECOOPERS LLP DE

LOCATIONS

HQ: BARTON MALOW COMPANY
26500 AMERICAN DR, SOUTHFIELD, MI 480342252
Phone: 248 436-5000
Web: WWW.BARTONMALOW.COM

Selected Locations
Atlanta
Baltimore
Charlottesville
Chicago
Columbus
Fairfax
Jacksonville
Oak Park
Orlando
Richmond
Southfield

PRODUCTS/OPERATIONS

Selcted Services
Architecture and planning
Building Information Management (BIM)
Concrete trade services
Construction management
Design/build
Facility audits
Facility services
     Administration
     Engineering
     Maintenance repair and operations
General contracting
Interior design
Interior trade services
Preconstruction
Program management
Rigging
Special projects
Technology consulting

COMPETITORS

Alberici	M. A. Mortenson
Clark Enterprises	McCarthy Building
Gilbane	Miron Construction
H.J. Russell	Skanska USA Building
Hensel Phelps Construction	Turner Corporation
	Walbridge Aldinger
Hunt Construction	Walsh Group
KBR Building Group	Whiting-Turner

HISTORICAL FINANCIALS
Company Type: Private

Income Statement
FYE: March 31

	REVENUE ($ mil.)	NET INCOME ($ mil.)	NET PROFIT MARGIN	EMPLOYEES
03/18	2,502	11	0.4%	1,600
03/17	2,361	0	0.0%	—
03/16	1,777	(2)	—	—
03/15	1,454	4	0.3%	—
Annual Growth	19.8%	36.5%	—	—

2018 Year-End Financials
Return on assets: 1.6%   Cash ($ mil.): 55
Return on equity: 19.3%
Current ratio: 1.00

BARTON MALOW ENTERPRISES, INC.

EXECUTIVES

Pres, Benjamin C Maibach III
SEC-Exec V Pres, Douglas L Maibach
Treas-Cfo, Michael F Dishaw
V Pres, Ronald J Torbert
Dir, Sheryl B Maibach
Project Director Central Regio, Alan Blanchette
Safety Manager, Anthony Allam
Project Manager, Chris Hofe
Senior Vice President Sports F, Harvey Oliva
Project Accountant, Jim Morse
Vice President, Lars Luedeman
Auditors: PRICEWATERHOUSECOOPERS LLP DE

LOCATIONS

HQ: BARTON MALOW ENTERPRISES, INC.
26500 AMERICAN DR, SOUTHFIELD, MI 480342252
Phone: 248 436-5000
Web: WWW.BARTONMALOW.COM

HISTORICAL FINANCIALS
Company Type: Private

Income Statement
FYE: March 31

	REVENUE ($ mil.)	NET INCOME ($ mil.)	NET PROFIT MARGIN	EMPLOYEES
03/18	2,502	18	0.7%	1,815
03/17	2,361	14	0.6%	—
03/16	1,777	9	0.6%	—
03/15	1,454	8	0.6%	—
Annual Growth	19.8%	27.8%	—	—

2018 Year-End Financials
Return on assets: 2.4%   Cash ($ mil.): 80
Return on equity: 18.6%
Current ratio: 1.10

BASIN ELECTRIC POWER COOPERATIVE

Ranges at home on the range depend on Basin Electric Power Cooperative as do other electric-powered items in nine states from Montana to Iowa to New Mexico. The consumer-owned power generation and transmission co-op provides power to 138 rural electric member systems which serve about 2.8 million people. It had generating capacity of 5478 MW (mostly coal-fired) in 2014. Basin Electric's subsidiaries include Dakota Gasification (which produces natural gas from coal) Dakota Coal (markets lignite and limestone) Basin Telecommunications (Internet access) Basin Cooperative Services (property management) PrairieWinds (wind power) and Souris Valley Pipeline (CO2 pipeline).

Operations
The company maintains about 2250 miles of high-voltage transmission 70 switchyards and about 150 telecommunication locations. It generates about 990 MW for participants in the Missouri Basin Power Project (a group of six regional consumer-owned energy entities that built the Laramie River Station in Wyoming). Its generation portfolio includes 4913 MW of wholesale electric generating capacity.

Geographic Reach

Basin Electric serves customers in Colorado Iowa Minnesota Montana Nebraska New Mexico North Dakota South Dakota and Wyoming. The enterprise's generation facilities are located in Iowa Minnesota Montana North Dakota South Dakota and Wyoming.

Financial Performance

In 2013 Basin Electric's revenues grew by 12% due to higher members sales as a result of an increase in higher electricity resales.

The coop's net income decreased by 62% that year as the result of to higher operating expenses caused by an increase in depreciation and amortizations.

The company's operating cash inflow decreased to $306.56 million in 2013 (from $354.18 million in 2012) due to lower net income and a change in working capital as a result of higher customer account receivables and inventories.

Strategy

Basin Electric like all power utilities is under regulatory pressure to lower the carbon emissions from its power production. As part of its commitment to cleaner energy production the company has established two wind power subsidiaries to build wind farms in the Dakotas.

In 2013 Basin Electric signed two power purchase agreements with California-based Infinity Wind Power associated with the development of two new wind projects in North Dakota with a combined capacity is 278 MW.

Company Background

The company generated 437 MW of its total capacity of 482 MW of renewable energy in 2012 from wind power sources. That year about 16% of Basin Electric's generating capacity came from renewable sources.

In 2011 Basin Electric opened the Crow Lake Wind Project (Nebraska) its largest renewable project to date with 162 MW of power generating capacity. Basin Electric's operations are overseen by a 10-member board of directors elected by and representing individual membership districts. Dakota Gasification and Dakota Coal have separate boards.

The not-for-profit generation and transmission cooperative was formed in 1961.

EXECUTIVES

Coo And Svp Dakota Coal Company And Montana Limestone Company, Robert J. Bartosh
Ceo And General Manager, Paul Sukut
Svp Transmission, Michael Risan
Coo And Svp Dakota Gasification Company, Dave Sauer
Svp Generation, Matt Greek
Vp Marketing And Trading, Kenneth S. Rutter
Vice President Basin Electric Board, Kermit Pearson
President Basin Electric Board, Wayne Peltier
Auditors: DELOITTE & TOUCHE LLP MINNEAP

LOCATIONS

HQ: BASIN ELECTRIC POWER COOPERATIVE
1717 E INTERSTATE AVE, BISMARCK, ND 585030564
Phone: 701 223-0441
Web: WWW.BASINELECTRIC.COM

PRODUCTS/OPERATIONS

2013 Power Generation Fuel Mix

	% of total
Coal	60
Renewables	15
Natural gas	14
Hydro	6
Oil	4
Nuclear	1
Total	**100**

2012 Sales

	% of total
Utility	62
Synthetic gas	13
Lignite coal	7
Byproducts co-products & other	18
Total	**100**

Regional Member Cooperatives

Regional Member Cooperatives
Central Montana Electric Power Cooperative (District 6)
  Beartooth Electric Cooperative (Red Lodge MT)
  Big Flat Electric Cooperative (Malta MT)
  Fergus Electric Cooperative (Lewistown MT)
  Hill County Electric Cooperative (Havre MT)
  Marias River Electric Cooperative (Shelby MT)
  Mid-Yellowstone Valley Electric Cooperative (Hysham MT)
  Northern Electric Cooperative (Opheim MT)
  Park Electric Cooperative (Livingston MT)
  Sun River Electric Cooperative (Fairfield MT)
  Tongue River Electric Cooperative (Ashland MT)
  Valley Electric Cooperative (Glasgow MT)
  Vigilante Electric Cooperative (Dillon MT)
  Yellowstone Valley Electric Cooperative (Huntley MT)
Central Power Electric Cooperative (District 3)
  Capital Electric Cooperative (Bismarck ND)
  Dakota Valley Electric Cooperative (Milnor ND)
  McLean Electric Cooperative (Garrison ND)
  North Central Electric Cooperative (Bottineau ND)
  Northern Plains Electric Cooperative (Carrington ND)
  Verendrye Electric Cooperative (Velva ND)
Corn Belt Power Cooperative (Humboldt IA)
District 9
  Grand Electric Cooperative (Bison SD)
  KEM Electric Cooperative (Linton ND)
  Minnesota Valley Cooperative Light & Power Association (Montevideo MN)
  Mor-Gran-Sou Electric Cooperative (Flasher ND)
  Oliver-Mercer Electric Cooperative (Hazen ND)
  Rosebud Electric Cooperative (Gregory ND)
  Wright-Hennepin Cooperative Electric Association (Rockford MN)
  Wyoming Municipal Power Agency (Lusk WY)
East River Electric Power Cooperative (District 1)
  Bon Homme-Yankton Electric Association (Tabor SD)
  Central Electric Cooperative
  Charles Mix Electric Association (Lake Andes SD)
  Clay-Union Electric Corp. (Vermillion SD)
  Codington-Clark Electric Cooperative (Watertown SD)
  Dakota Energy Cooperative (Huron SD)
  Douglas Electric Cooperative (Armour SD)
  FEM Electric Association (Ipswich SD)
  H-D Electric Cooperative (Clear Lake SD)
  Kingsbury Electric Cooperative (De Smet SD)
  Lake Region Electric Association (Webster SD)
  Lyon-Lincoln Electric Cooperative (Tyler MN)
  McCook Electric Cooperative (Salem SD)
  Northern Electric Cooperative (Bath SD)
  Oahe Electric Cooperative (Blunt SD)
  Renville-Sibley Cooperative Power Association (Danube MN)
  Sioux Valley-Southwestern Cooperative (Colman SD)
  Southeastern Electric Cooperative (Marion SD)
  Traverse Electric Cooperative (Wheaton MN)
  Union County Electric Cooperative (Elk Point SD)
  Whetstone Valley Electric Cooperative (Milbank SD)
Flathead Electric Cooperative (Kalispell MT)
L & O Power Cooperative (District 2)
  Lyon Rural Electric Cooperative (Rock Rapids IA)
  Osceola Electric Cooperative (Sibley IA)
Northwest Iowa Power Cooperative (NIPCO) (District 4)
  Harrison County Electric Cooperative (Woodbine)
  Iowa Lakes Electric Cooperative (Estherville)
  Nishnabotna Valley Rural Electric Cooperative (Harlan)
  North West Rural Electric Cooperative (Orange City)
  Western Iowa Municipal Electric Association (Manning)
  Western Iowa Power Cooperative
  Woodbury County Rural Electric Cooperative (Moville)
Powder River Energy Corp. (District 10 Sundance WY)
Rushmore Electric Power Cooperative (District 7)
  Black Hills Electric Cooperative (Custer SD)
  Butte Electric Cooperative (Newell SD)
  Cam Wal Electric Cooperative (Selby SD)
  Cherry-Todd Electric Cooperative (Mission SD)
  Lacreek Electric Association (Martin SD)
  Moreau-Grand Electric Cooperative (Timber Lake SD)
  West Central Electric Cooperative (Murdo SD)
  West River Electric Association (Wall SD)
Tri-State Generation and Transmission Association (District 5)
  Big Horn Rural Electric Co. (Basin WY)
  Carbon Power & Light (Saratoga WY)
  Central New Mexico Electric Cooperative (Mountainair NM)
  Chimney Rock Public Power District (Bayard NE)
  Columbus Electric Cooperative (Deming NM)
  Delta-Montrose Electric Association (Delta CO)
  Empire Electric Association (Cortez CO)
  Garland Light & Power Co. (Powell WY)
  Gunnison County Electric Association (Gunnison CO)
  Highline Electric Association (Holyoke CO)
  High Plains Power Inc. (Thermopolis and Riverton WY)
  High West Energy (Pine Bluffs WY)
  Jemez Mountains Electric Cooperative (Hernandez NM)
  K. C. Electric Association (Hugo CO)
  Kit Carson Electric Cooperative (Taos NM)
  La Plata Electric Association (Durango CO)
  Midwest Electric Cooperative Corp. (Grant NE)
  Morgan County Rural Electric Association (Fort Morgan CO)
  Mountain Parks Electric (Granby CO)
  Mountain View Electric Association (Limon CO)
  Niobrara Electric Association (Lusk WY)
  Northern Rio Arriba Electric Cooperative (Chama NM)
  Northwest Rural Public Power District (Hay Springs NE)
  Panhandle Rural Electric Membership Association (Alliance NE)
  Poudre Valley Rural Electric Association (Fort Collins CO)
  Roosevelt Public Power District (Mitchell NE)
  San Isabel Electric Association (Pueblo CO)
  San Luis Valley Rural Electric Cooperative (Monte Vista CO)
  San Miguel Power Association (Nucla CO)
  Sangre De Cristo Electric Association (Buena Vista CO)
  Sierra Electric Cooperative Inc. (Elephant Butte NM)
  Southeast Colorado Power Association (La Junta)
  Springer Electric Cooperative (Springer MN)
  United Power (Brighton CO)
  Wheat Belt Public Power District (Sidney NE)
  Wheatland Rural Electric Association (Wheatland WY)
  White River Electric Association (Meeker SD)
  Wyrulec Co. (Lingle WY)
  Y-W Electric Association (Akron CO)
Upper Missouri Generation and Transmission Electric Cooperative (District 8)
  Burke-Divide Electric Cooperative (Columbus ND)
  Goldenwest Electric Cooperative (Wibaux MT)
  Lower Yellowstone Rural Electric Cooperative (Sidney MT)
  McCone Electric Cooperative (Circle MT)
  McKenzie Electric Cooperative (Watford City ND)
  Mountrail-Williams Electric Cooperative (Williston ND)
  Sheridan Electric Cooperative (Medicine Lake MT)
  Slope Electric Cooperative (New England ND)
  Southeast Electric Cooperative (Ekalaka MT)
  West Plains Electric Cooperative (Dickinson ND)
????

COMPETITORS

Alliant Energy	Nebraska Public Power
Berkshire Hathaway Energy	NorthWestern
	Omaha Public Power
Black Hills	Otter Tail
MDU Resources	Xcel Energy

HISTORICAL FINANCIALS

Company Type: Private

Income Statement

FYE: December 31

	REVENUE ($ mil.)	NET INCOME ($ mil.)	NET PROFIT MARGIN	EMPLOYEES
12/18	2,436	64	2.6%	1,579
12/17	2,112	72	3.4%	—
12/16	1,561	54	3.5%	—
12/15	1,445	8	0.6%	—
Annual Growth	19.0%	99.9%	—	—

2018 Year-End Financials
Return on assets: 0.9% Cash ($ mil.): 168
Return on equity: 4.4%
Current ratio: 0.90

BATTELLE MEMORIAL INSTITUTE

EXECUTIVES

BR Mgr, Jeffrey Wadsworth
Information Technology Manager, Dana Murry
Senior Research Scientist, Aaron Frank
Senior Research Scientist, Amit Gupta
Program Manager, Jane Oloughlin
Geologist, Joel Main
Senior Research Scientist, Lindy Dejarme
Program Manager, Susan Houser
Auditors: DELOITTE & TOUCHE LLP COLUMBU

LOCATIONS

HQ: BATTELLE MEMORIAL INSTITUTE
2555 INTERNATIONAL ST, COLUMBUS, OH
432284604
Phone: 800 201-2011
Web: WWW.BATTELLE.ORG

HISTORICAL FINANCIALS
Company Type: Private

Income Statement				FYE: September 30
	REVENUE ($ mil.)	NET INCOME ($ mil.)	NET PROFIT MARGIN	EMPLOYEES
09/14	4,775	(95)	—	20,000
09/13	4,795	(7)	—	—
09/12	5,228	(20)	—	—
Annual Growth	(4.4%)	—	—	—

2014 Year-End Financials
Return on assets: 2.7% Cash ($ mil.): 117
Return on equity: (-2.0%)
Current ratio: 0.70

BAYCARE HEALTH SYSTEM, INC.

BayCare Health System takes care of folks lounging (or limping) at the bay in the Sunshine State. Established in 1997 the health system operates14 not-for-profit hospitals and about 300 additional outpatient facilities that serve the residents of Florida's Tampa Bay and surrounding areas. The system's member hospitals boast about 3500 beds; the facilities offer a variety of specialty services ranging from orthopedics to cancer care to women's services. BayCare has some 5400 physicians on staff. CHE Trinity owns a 50.4% stake in BayCare Health System.

Operations

BayCare's family of hospitals includes Morton Plant (687 beds) St. Joseph's (486 beds) Winter Haven (468 beds) St. Anthony's (393 beds) Mease Countryside (311 beds) St. Joseph's Children's (186 beds) St. Joseph's Women's (108 beds) Winter Haven Women's Hospital (61 beds) Morton

Plant North Bay (150 beds) South Florida Baptist (147 beds) Mease Dunedin (120 beds) St. Joseph's Hospital-North (108 beds) St. Joseph's Hospital-South (114 beds) and Bartow Regional Medical Center (72 beds).

Winter Haven Hospital serves as the major medical center for east Polk County.

In 2016 the system had 5400 physicians and reported about 59700 outpatient surgeries and 592000 emergency room visits.

Geographic Reach

BayCare serves the residents of Florida's greater Tampa Bay area consisting of the Citrus Hillsborough Pasco and Pinellas counties.

Strategy

In recent years BayCare has invested heavily in expanding and updating its hospitals both organically and through acquisitions. The system is also working with telemedicine vendor American Well to expand its telehealth services making health care services more convenient and accessible. In 2017 BayCare established a partnership with supermarket chain Publix; the partners will open 25 walk-in telehealth centers within Publix stores within two years.

EXECUTIVES

Evp And Coo, Glenn Waters
Evp And Chief Medical Officer, Bruce Flareau
President And Ceo, Tommy Inzina
President St. Joseph's Children's Hospital And St. Joseph's Women's Hospital, Kate Reed
Evp And Cfo, Janice Polo
Director Of Pharmacy, Mike McGee
Auditors: ERNST & YOUNG US LLP ATLANTA

LOCATIONS

HQ: BAYCARE HEALTH SYSTEM, INC.
2985 DREW ST, CLEARWATER, FL 337593012
Phone: 727 519-1200
Web: WWW.BAYCARE.ORG

Selected Locations
Baycare Alliant Hospital (Dunedin Florida)
Mease Countryside Hospital (Safety Harbor Florida)
Mease Dunedin Hospital (Mease Dunedin Florida)
Morton Plant Hospital (Clearwater Florida)
Morton Plant North Bay Hospital (New Port Richey Florida)
St. Anthony's Hospital (St. Petersburg Florida)
St. Joseph's Children's Hospital (Tampa Florida)
St. Joseph's Hospital (Tampa Florida)
St. Joseph's Hospital-North (Lutz Florida)
St. Joseph's Women's Hospital (Tampa Florida)
South Florida Baptist Hospital (Plant City Florida)
Winter Haven Hospital (Plok Florida)

PRODUCTS/OPERATIONS

Selected Services
Advance Care Planning
BayCare Behavioral Health
BayCare HomeCare
BayCare Outpatient Imaging
Breast Health
Behavioral Health Services
Patient Secure Identity
Pediatric Specialty Centers
Physician Office EMR
Robotic Surgery
Wellness Centers

COMPETITORS

Adventist Health System Sunbelt Healthcare
All Children's Hospital
Ascension Health
Bayfront Health
DeSoto Memorial
Florida Hospital Tampa Bay Division
HCA
Lakeland Regional Medical Center
Lee Memorial
Manatee Memorial Hospital
Sarasota Memorial Health Care
Tampa General Hospital

HISTORICAL FINANCIALS
Company Type: Private

Income Statement				FYE: December 31
	REVENUE ($ mil.)	NET INCOME ($ mil.)	NET PROFIT MARGIN	EMPLOYEES
12/14*	463	163	35.3%	20,000
09/06	1,733	128	7.4%	—
12/05	1,733	128	7.4%	—
Annual Growth	(13.6%)	2.7%	—	—
*Fiscal year change				

2014 Year-End Financials
Return on assets: 5.1% Cash ($ mil.): 149
Return on equity: 54.4%
Current ratio: 0.20

BAYHEALTH MEDICAL CENTER, INC.

EXECUTIVES

Pres, Terry Murphy
Information Department, Bob Mucha
Director, Craig Hochstein
Doctor, Cathy Diven
Warehouse Manager, David Webb
Board of Directors, Harjinder Grewal
Web Developer, Jim Welch
Manager, Susan Litchford
Director, John Demarie
Health Care Director, Nadine Pieniaszek
Physician, James Everette
Auditors: GRANT THORNTON LLP PHILADELPH

LOCATIONS

HQ: BAYHEALTH MEDICAL CENTER, INC.
640 S STATE ST, DOVER, DE 199013530
Phone: 302 422-3311
Web: WWW.BAYHEALTH.ORG

HISTORICAL FINANCIALS
Company Type: Private

Income Statement				FYE: June 30
	REVENUE ($ mil.)	NET INCOME ($ mil.)	NET PROFIT MARGIN	EMPLOYEES
06/18	615	87	14.2%	2,790
06/17	583	86	14.9%	—
06/16	570	19	3.4%	—
06/15	551	39	7.1%	—
Annual Growth	3.8%	30.8%	—	—

2018 Year-End Financials
Return on assets: 7.2% Cash ($ mil.): 29
Return on equity: 10.3%
Current ratio: 1.10

BAYLOR SCOTT & WHITE HOLDINGS

EXECUTIVES

Exec Dir, Paul E Madeley
Auditors: PRICEWATERHOUSECOOPERS LLP DA

LOCATIONS

HQ: BAYLOR SCOTT & WHITE HOLDINGS
  350 N SAINT PAUL ST # 2900, DALLAS, TX
  752014234
Phone: 214 820-3151

HISTORICAL FINANCIALS

Company Type: Private

Income Statement   FYE: June 30

	REVENUE ($ mil.)	NET INCOME ($ mil.)	NET PROFIT MARGIN	EMPLOYEES
06/18	9,476	754	8.0%	1
06/17	9,084	630	6.9%	—
06/15	7,535	356	4.7%	—
Annual Growth	7.9%	28.4%	—	—

2018 Year-End Financials

Return on assets: 6.2%
Return on equity: 12.2%
Current ratio: 1.70
Cash ($ mil.): 1,263

BAYLOR UNIVERSITY

Don't mess with Texas and don't mess around at Baylor University. The world's largest Baptist institution of higher learning requires its more than 15000 students to follow a strict code of conduct. The universityÂ hasÂ approximately 150 undergraduate degree programs as well asÂ about 75 masters and more than 30 doctoral programs. With a student-to-faculty ratio of 15:1 the private co-educational university also offers degrees from its law school (juris doctor) and theological seminary (master of divinity and doctor of ministry) as well as extensive research programs. Founded in 1845 the college is affiliated with the Baptist General Convention of Texas.

EXECUTIVES

Treasurer, Carolyn Kronenberger
Auditors: GRANT THORNTON LLP DALLAS TX

LOCATIONS

HQ: BAYLOR UNIVERSITY
  700 S UNIVERSITY PARKS DR, WACO, TX 767061003
Phone: 254 710-1561
Web: WWW.BAYLOR.EDU

PRODUCTS/OPERATIONS

Selected Colleges and Schools
College of Arts and Sciences
George W. Truett Theological Seminary
Graduate School
Hankamer School of Business
Honors College
Law School
Louise Herrington School of Nursing
School of Education
School of Engineering and Computer Science
School of Music
School of Social Work

Selected Institutes
Allbritton Art Institute
Institute for Air Science
Institute for Faith and Learning
Institute for Oral History
Institute of Biblical and Related Languages
Institute of Biomedical Studies
J. M. Dawson Institute of Church-State Studies

HISTORICAL FINANCIALS

Company Type: Private

Income Statement   FYE: May 31

	REVENUE ($ mil.)	NET INCOME ($ mil.)	NET PROFIT MARGIN	EMPLOYEES
05/18	674	96	14.3%	2,500
05/16	656	(20)	—	—
Annual Growth	1.4%	—	—	—

2018 Year-End Financials

Return on assets: 3.4%
Return on equity: 4.9%
Current ratio: —
Cash ($ mil.): 75

BAYLOR UNIVERSITY MEDICAL CENTER

Baylor University Medical Center at Dallas is the flagship institution of the Baylor Health Care System. The medical center (known as Baylor Dallas) serves more than 300000 patients annually with more than 1000 inpatient beds and some 1200 physicians. It offers general medical and surgical services to specialty care in a wide range of fields including oncology cardiovascular disease and neuroscience. The hospital also features a Level I trauma center neonatal ICU and organ transplantation center. Founded in 1903 the Baylor Dallas campus includes the Charles A. Sammons Cancer Center and the Baylor Research Institute which conducts basic and clinical research across numerous medical specialties.

Operations
The Baylor University Medical Center campus consists of 20 specialty centers for treating a range of medical conditions. Primary facilities include the Charles A. Sammons Cancer Center Neuroscience Center Annette C. and Harold C. Simmons Transplant Institute James M. and Dorothy D. Collins Womens and Children's Center and the George Truett James Orthopaedic Institute as well as a top trauma center digestive care program and heart and vascular unit. The Heart and Vascular Institute conducts more than 50 research studies a year.

Strategy
The hospital received a boost in 2011 when Texas A&M's Health Science Center struck an affiliation with Baylor Health Care System. The two parties agreed to make Baylor Dallas a primary teaching hospital for A&M's third and fourth-year medical students. No hospital in the Baylor Health Care System held such a designation after it became independent from Baylor University in 1997.

As one of only two adult Level 1 trauma centers in the region Baylor Dallas has worked to bolster its emergency services to keep up with increasing demand. To this end it has broadened its Level 1 trauma capabilities increased the size of its minor emergency care area and added more patient care areas. The Riggs Emergency Department treats some 67000 patients each year.

Baylor Dallas' transplant program is considered a national leader in solid organ transplantation and in partnership with the program at Baylor All Saints Medical Center is one of only three programs worldwide to have performed more than 3000 adult liver transplants. The program is also known for its kidney pancreas heart and lung small bowel and blood and marrow transplants.

EXECUTIVES

Vice President Engineering, Bobby Wallace
Vice President Finance Decision Support Services, Lavone Neal

LOCATIONS

HQ: BAYLOR UNIVERSITY MEDICAL CENTER
  2001 BRYAN ST STE 2200, DALLAS, TX 752013024
Phone: 214 820-3151
Web: WWW.BSWHEALTH.COM

Selected Locations
A. Webb Roberts Hospital
Baylor Charles A. Sammons Cancer Center
Baylor Jack and Jane Hamilton Heart and Vascular Hospital
Carr P. Collins Hospital
Erik and Margaret Jonsson Medical and Surgical Hospital
George W. Truett Memorial Hospital
Karl and Esther Hoblitzelle Memorial Hospital
Baylor Specialty Hospital
Our Children's House at Baylor

PRODUCTS/OPERATIONS

Selected Speciality Centers
Baylor Cancer Hospital
Baylor Center for Pain Management
Baylor Diagnostic Imaging Centers
Baylor George Truett James Orthopaedic Institute
Baylor Geriatric and Senior Center
Baylor Heart and Vascular Institute
Baylor Heart Failure Program
Baylor Motion and Sports Performance Center
Baylor Neuroscience Center
Baylor Radiosurgery Center
Baylor Ruth Collins Diabetes Center
Baylor Sammons Bone Tumor Center
Baylor Sammons Lung Cancer Center
Baylor Spine Center
Baylor SportsCare
Comprehensive Wound Center
Darlene G. Cass Women's Imaging Center
Digestive Care Services
Ernie's Appearance Center
Gastrointestinal and Endoscopy Laboratory
Hereditary Cancer Risk Program
Infectious Disease Center
James M. and Dorothy D. Collins Women and Children's Center
Kimberly H. Courtwright and Joseph W. Summers Institute of Metabolic Disease
Louise Gartner Center for Hyperbaric Medicine
Martha Foster Lung Care Center
Non-invasive Heart and Vascular Laboratory
Reuben H. Adams Family Health Center
Simply Mom's Mother and Baby Boutique
Sleep Center
TINY TOTS Clinic
Virginia R. Cvetko Cancer Patient Education Center
Visual Function Testing Center
W.H. and Peggy Smith Baylor Sammons Breast Center
Weight Loss Surgery Program

COMPETITORS

CHRISTUS Health	Presbyterian Hospital
Children's Medical Center of Dallas	of Dallas
	Southwestern Medical
Dynacq Healthcare	Center
Harris Methodist Fort Worth Hospital	Texas Health Denton
	Texas Health Resources
Parkland Health & Hospital System	The Methodist Health System

HISTORICAL FINANCIALS

Company Type: Private

Income Statement — FYE: June 30

	REVENUE ($ mil.)	NET INCOME ($ mil.)	NET PROFIT MARGIN	EMPLOYEES
06/15	1,394	378	27.2%	5,003
06/09	1,072	0	—	—
06/08	155	16	10.3%	—
06/06	937	114	12.2%	—
Annual Growth	4.5%	14.3%	—	—

2015 Year-End Financials

Return on assets: 18.8%
Return on equity: 19.5%
Current ratio: 3.10

Cash ($ mil.): —

BAYSTATE HEALTH INC.

Baystate Medical Center is the flagship facility of the not-for-profit Baystate Health System. It is a tertiary care facility and Level I trauma center that provides comprehensive acute care services to residents of Springfield Massachusetts and the surrounding region. The more than 700-bed medical center is also a teaching hospital serving as a secondary campus for Tufts University School of Medicine. The Baystate Medical Center campus includes Baystate Children's Hospital a 110-bed/57-bassinette unit that boasts neonatal and pediatric ICUs. Other Baystate Medical Center operations include specialty programs in radiology cardiac care cancer and neurology.

Operations

As the only Level I trauma center in western Massachusetts Baystate Medical Center is responsible for treating the most critical and urgent cases in the region. The hospital is also home to the second-busiest emergency department in the state. Along with performing its own research activities Baystate Medical Center collaborates with the University of Massachusetts Amherst on biomedical technology research projects through the Pioneer Valley Life Sciences Institute. The center is home to one of only about 40 American College of Surgeons-accredited Level I Comprehensive Education Institutes in the world.

Other Baystate Health System facilities include Baystate Franklin Medical Center and Baystate Mary Lane Hospital.

Strategy

In partnership with nine other area not-for-profit hospitals Baystate Medical Center is working to improve its region's access to health care services and overall well-being. Social and economic factors impeding access to care include the community's poverty levels poor housing conditions and lack of transportation. Health conditions include high rates of obesity diabetes asthma and cardiovascular disease as well as the growing incidence of opioid overdoses. The coalition of hospitals aims to improve matters by working together combining resources to increase care capabilities.

EXECUTIVES

President And Ceo, Mark A. Keroack
Svp Coo And Chief Nursing Officer, Nancy Shendell-Falik
Medical Director Emergency Department, Rakesh Talati
Vice President Sales And Marketing, Lisa Hill
Vice President, Chris Shirtcliff
Vice President Sales, Holly Dinnie

Medical Director Inpatient Informatics, Thomas Higgins
Vice President, Neil Kudler
Director Of Pharmacy, Aaron J Michelucci
Vice President Marketing, Walter Hollihan
Senior Vice President Human Resources, Paula Squires
Vice President Of Information Technology, Philip Lacombe
Human Resource Vice President, William Mclean
Vice President, Stephen Wittenberg
Director Of Nursing, Townsend Vernette
Vp Human Resources Operations Total Rewards, Michele Talka
Senior Vice President Division Academic Affairs, Paul Friedmann
Medical Director, Boos Stephen
Vice President Clinical Informatics And Re Engineering, Joan Sullivan
Vice President Strategic Accounts, Odonnell Marleen
Vice President Strategic Planning And Business Development, Jean Ahn
Vice President Marketing And Communications, Suzanne Hendery
Medical Director, Orlando Torres
Medical Director, Dan Engelman
Vice President Regulatory Affair, Fabrizio Pluchino
Vice President, Stephen Wittenburg
Treasurer, Kieth Mclean-shinaman
Secretary, Nancy Melanson
Auditors: DELOITTE & TOUCHE LLP BOSTON

LOCATIONS

HQ: BAYSTATE HEALTH INC.
 759 CHESTNUT ST, SPRINGFIELD, MA 011991001
Phone: 413 794-0000
Web: WWW.BAYSTATEHEALTH.ORG

PRODUCTS/OPERATIONS

Selected Programs and Services
Baystate Children's Hospital
Baystate Heart & Vascular Program
Baystate Regional Cancer Program
Department of Surgery
Regional Sleep Program
Women's Health

COMPETITORS

Berkshire Health Systems
Boston Medical Center
CareGroup
Children's Hospital Boston
Connecticut Children's Medical Center
Harrington Memorial Hospital
Hartford Health Care
Hospital of Central Connecticut
Partners HealthCare
Saint Francis Hospital and Medical Center
St. Elizabeth's Medical Center
University of Connecticut Health Center
Yale New Haven Health System

HISTORICAL FINANCIALS

Company Type: Private

Income Statement — FYE: September 30

	REVENUE ($ mil.)	NET INCOME ($ mil.)	NET PROFIT MARGIN	EMPLOYEES
09/18	1,284	62	4.9%	11,000
09/17	1,217	107	8.8%	—
09/16	1,095	108	9.9%	—
09/15	1,048	76	7.3%	—
Annual Growth	7.0%	(6.4%)	—	—

2018 Year-End Financials

Return on assets: 4.6%
Return on equity: 7.6%
Current ratio: 3.50

Cash ($ mil.): 79

BAYSTATE HEALTH SYSTEM HEALTH SERVICES, INC.

Patients in need of medical care can dock at this bay. Not-for-profit Baystate Health is the largest health care services provider in western Massachusetts. The system operates five acute-care and specialty hospitals with a total of approximately 1000 beds including the flagship Baystate Medical Center which operates a Level 1 Trauma Center and a specialized children's hospital. Baystate Health also offers ancillary medical services such as cancer care respiratory care infusion therapy visiting nurse and hospice services through its regional clinics and agencies. The system controls for-profit health plan provider Health New England as well as clinical pathology firm Baystate Reference Laboratories.

Operations

Baystate Medical Center accounts for more than 700 of the system's beds. Its other four acute care hospitals are Baystate Franklin Medical Center (89 beds) Baystate Wing Hospital (74 beds) Baystate Noble Hospital (97 beds) and Baystate Mary Lane Hospital (25 beds). The system also runs a physicians group Baystate Medical Practices which operates more than two dozen physician practices in several surrounding counties and towns. Other outpatient centers include surgery centers imaging and radiology clinics and neighborhood health centers. Altogether its facilities serve a population of 750000 western New England residents and admit more than 45000 inpatients perform some 34000 surgeries handle about 4500 births and conduct 1.4 million outpatient visits each year.

Baystate Health provides academic and community educational programs as well as conducting basic clinical and biomedical research. For instance the Baystate Medical Center is a teaching hospital that serves as the western campus of the Tufts University School of Medicine. Baystate Health also partners with a number of regional colleges to offer nursing programs.

In the research realm Tufts and Baystate Health work on biomedical studies through the Tufts Clinical and Translational Science Institute. Baystate Medical Center also has a partnership with the University of Massachusetts that forms the Pioneer Valley Life Sciences Institute. Areas of research include clinical care quality of care and diabetes and metabolism. The Baystate Health system receives about $10 million per year in research funding from the National Institutes of Health and other agencies.

Geographic Reach

Baystate Health has some 60 locations serving western Massachusetts including Berkshire Franklin Hampden Hampshire and Worcester counties.

Sales and Marketing

Patient service revenue accounts for a majority (about 60%) of the hospital system's sales; Medicare and Medicaid reimbursements make up 57% of patient service payments. Other sources include commercial insurers and private-pay customers.

Financial Performance

In fiscal 2015 (ended September) Baystate Health revenues grew 17% to $1.2 billion; this was driven by a growth in premiums as well as net patient service revenue. However that year the system reported a net loss of $78 million due to higher medical claims and capitation as well as losses on investments and pension adjustments.

Following net income's suit cash flow from operations dropped 38% to $51 million in fiscal 2015.

Strategy

Baystate Health has been conducting expansion and renovation efforts at its facilities in recent years including medical technology and information system upgrades. The system's largest effort was the construction of a $300 million clinical building on the Baystate Medical Center Campus.

Other facilities and divisions are undergoing expansion as well: The system is adding new space to house a pharmacy and nearly 100 modern inpatient rooms at its flagship campus while a new surgical center is being added to Baystate Franklin Medical Center in Greenfield. Baystate Medical Practices continues to grow by adding new practices on a regular basis. Baystate Health is also upgrading its medical equipment and its information technology systems.

Mergers and Acquisitions

Baystate Health acquired Noble Hospital (now Baystate Noble Hospital) a 97-bed not-for-profit community hospital in 2015. The year before that it added another acute care facility when it bought the 74-bed Wind Memorial Hospital (now Baystate Wing Hospital) from UMass Memorial Healthcare.

EXECUTIVES

Svp Community Hospitals Cfo And Treasurer, Dennis W. Chalke

Interim President And Chief Administrative Officer Baystate Health Eastern Region, Michael F. Moran

President And Ceo Health New England Inc., Maura C. McCaffrey

Ceo Baycare Health Partners, Stephen J. Sweet

Vp And Chief Information Officer, Joel L. Vengco

Evp And Coo, Mark A. Keroack

Svp Coo And Chief Nursing Office Baystate Medical Center, Nancy Shendell-Falik

President Baystate Medical Practices And Chief Physician Executive, John R. Schreiber

President Eastern Region, Charles E. Cavagnaro

Auditors: ERNST & YOUNG LLP BOSTON MAS

LOCATIONS

HQ: BAYSTATE HEALTH SYSTEM HEALTH SERVICES, INC.

280 CHESTNUT ST, SPRINGFIELD, MA 011991000

Phone: 413 794-9939

Selected Locations

Baystate Medical Center (Springfield)
  Baystate Children's Hospital (Springfield)
Baystate Franklin Medical Center (Greenfield)
Baystate Mary Lane Hospital (Ware)
Baystate Noble Hospital (Westfield)
Baystate Wing Hospital (Palmer)
Outpatient Centers
  Baystate Home Infusion & Respiratory Services
  Baystate Medical Practices
  Baystate Radiology and Imaging (BRI)
  Baystate Reference Laboratories (BRL)
  Baystate Visiting Nurse Association & Hospice
  Brightwood Health Center
  Chestnut Surgery Center
  D'Amour Center for Cancer Care
  High Street Center (adult and pediatrics)
  Mason Square Neighborhood Health Center
  Neurodiagnostics & Sleep Center
  Orthopedic Surgery Center
  Wesson Women & Infants Health Center

PRODUCTS/OPERATIONS

2015 Sales

	$ mil.	% of total
Net patient service revenue	1,222	57
Premiums	822	39
Other	94	4
Total	**2,138**	**100**

Selected Services

Ambulance
Anesthesiology
Behavioral health services
Birthing services
Cancer
Cardiovascular
Emergency medicine
Endoscopy
Home care and home medical supplies
Hospital medicine
Neurosciences
Obstetrics and gynecology
Pain management center
Pathology
Pediatrics
Radiology
Rehabilitation care
Reproductive medicine
Sleep program
Surgery
Weight management
Women's health

COMPETITORS

Berkshire Health
  Systems
Cambridge Health
  Alliance
Cape Cod Healthcare
CareGroup
Harrington Memorial
  Hospital

Partners HealthCare
Shriners Hospitals For
  Children
Southcoast Hospitals
  Group
Steward Health Care
Universal Health
  Services

HISTORICAL FINANCIALS

Company Type: Private

Income Statement   FYE: September 30

	REVENUE ($ mil.)	NET INCOME ($ mil.)	NET PROFIT MARGIN	EMPLOYEES
09/07	1,286	125	9.7%	5,000
09/06	1,209	83	6.9%	
09/05	0	0	—	—
09/04	0	0	—	—
Annual Growth	—	—	—	—

2007 Year-End Financials

Return on assets: 5.4%   Cash ($ mil.): 61
Return on equity: 9.7%
Current ratio: 0.70

BEALL'S, INC.

Residents of the Sun Belt have been known to leave their homes with Beall's on. The retail holding company operates through subsidiaries Beall's Department Stores Beall's Outlet and Burke's Outlet Stores in a dozen states. The multi-brand retailer has more than 530 department and outlet stores (about 200 are in Florida) located throughout states in the southern and western US including Arizona California Georgia Louisiana and Texas. Products range from off-price clothing and footwear for men and women to cosmetics gifts and housewares. Each chain has its own online shopping destination. The family-owned company was founded in 1915 by the grandfather of chairman Robert Beall (pronounced "bell").

Operations

Beall's Inc. oversees operations of its three operating companies. Beall's Florida operates some 190 stores in the Sunshine State. Beall's Outlet operates about 300 stores in Arizona Florida Texas and Georgia while Burke's Outlet operates more than 190 stores in 16 states.

Geographic Reach

Beall's trio of chain's operate stores in Alabama Arkansas Arizona California Florida Georgia Kentucky Louisiana Mississippi Nevada New Mexico North Carolina South Carolina Tennessee Texas Virginia and West Virginia.

Financial Performance

Privately-owned Beall's rings ups more than $1 billion in sales annually.

Strategy

The company has aspirations to transform itself into a major discount retailer much like its larger rivals TJX and Ross Stores. To that end the company plans to add new stores outside its traditional markets with an eye on establishing a national retail presence. Targets include adding 30 to 50 stores a year for the next several years and raising brand awareness beyond Florida.

With many of its stores in Arizona Florida and California (three of the states hit hardest by the housing crisis and deep recession) Beall's Inc. should have been in a heap of retail trouble. However its largest chain — Beall's Outlet —proved to be quite popular during this recession. Indeed the budget-priced outlet chain outperformed its two sister chains as well as more moderately priced department stores. The retailer has also benefited from the demise of other retailers including Goody's Linens 'n Things and Mervyn's.

The three operating companies share resources provided by Beall's Inc. such as distribution finance loss prevention and information systems. Conversely each chain is responsible for its purchasing product development real estate and advertising activities.

Company Background

Stores operating under the Bealls name in Alabama New Mexico and Texas are owned by Stage Stores and are not affiliated with Beall's Inc.

EXECUTIVES

Dvp Merchandise Support, Pam Meyer
Vice President Of Real Estate, Wade Laufenberg
Divisional Vice President Gmm, Eric Kozlowski
Auditors: CHRISTOPHER SMITH LEONARD B

LOCATIONS

HQ: BEALL'S, INC.
1806 38TH AVE E, BRADENTON, FL 342084700
Phone: 941 747-2355
Web: WWW.BEALLSINC.COM

PRODUCTS/OPERATIONS

Selected Retail Operations

Bealls Department Stores (Florida)
Bealls Outlet (deep-discount outlet stores in Arizona Florida Georgia)
Burke's Outlet (11 southern states)

COMPETITORS

Bed Bath & Beyond
Costco Wholesale
Dillard's
J. C. Penney Company
Kohl's
Macy's
Nordstrom

Ross Stores
Sears
Stage Stores
TJX Companies
Target Corporation
The Gap
Wal-Mart

HISTORICAL FINANCIALS

Company Type: Private

Income Statement   FYE: August 1

	REVENUE ($ mil.)	NET INCOME ($ mil.)	NET PROFIT MARGIN	EMPLOYEES
08/15*	1,321	25	1.9%	9,700
07/12	1,232	14	1.1%	—
07/11	1,166	15	1.3%	—
Annual Growth	3.2%	12.8%	—	—
*Fiscal year change				

2015 Year-End Financials
Return on assets: 4.5%   Cash ($ mil.): 107
Return on equity: 8.7%
Current ratio: 1.60

BEARING DISTRIBUTORS, INC.

Bearing Distributors Inc. (BDI) began as a regional Midwestern distributor of replacement parts to OEMs. Among the world's largest industrial suppliers today the company also provides maintenance and repair services as well as training and inventory management. Its offerings include bearings electrical power products material handling systems and motion control products hydraulic and pneumatic systems and fluid power components. BDI serves customers in automotive to power generation industries and from mining to food and beverage paper processing and package handling operations. Founded in 1935 the company a unit of Forge Industries has locations dotting North America Europe and Asia.

Geographic Reach

BDI operates more than 200 global branches spanning 12 countries including the US Canada Mexico Europe and Asia. Its distribution centers reside in Cleveland Ohio; Montreal and Mississauga Canada; Budapest Hungary; Tianjin China; Suzhou China; and Bangalore India.

Strategy

BDI grows its business through acquisitions and organic growth. As part of this strategy in early 2015 it purchased Munnell & Sherrill an industrial distribution company based in the Pacific Northwest with locations in Oregon Washington and Northern California.

In 2013 BDI opened a new branch in Flint Michigan to serve customers in central and southeastern Michigan. That year it also relocated a branch in Maine and a branch in Detroit to better serve its expanding customer base.

EXECUTIVES

Pres, Carl G James
Coo, John Ruth
V Pres, Bud Thayer
V Pres, Steve Kieffer
Cfo, Dan Maisonville
Salesman, Andy Svymbersky
Data Processing Manager, Mike Fryz
Inside Sales, Rikki Barnard
Inside Sales, Sean Baldwin
Operations Manager, Thomas Sedmak
Inside Sales, Bob Milliken

LOCATIONS

HQ: BEARING DISTRIBUTORS, INC.
   8000 HUB PKWY, CLEVELAND, OH 441255788
Phone: 216 642-9100

PRODUCTS/OPERATIONS

Selected Products
Adhesive sealant and lubricant products
   Adhesives
   Cleaners
   Epoxies
   Hand cleaners
   Lube systems
   Lubricants
   Micro poly
   Paints
   Sealants
   Silicones
   Solvents
   Thread lockers
   Thread repair
Bearings
   Ball and roller bearings
   Lubricated bearings
   Mounted bearing units
   Specialty bearings
Bulk chemicals
   Adhesives
   Metalworking fluids
   Surface treatment
Electrical Products
   Clutches and brakes
   DC SCR drives
   Electric motors
   Tachometers
Fluid power components
   Components
   Hydraulic cylinders and actuators
   Hydraulic and pumps
   Pressure gauges
   PVC fittings
   Temperature gauges
   Valves (ball butterfly hydraulic and pneumatic)
Industrial hose and fittings
   High pressure hose
   Hydraulic fittings
   PVC fittings
   Quick disconnect fittings
   Tube fittings
Linear motion control
   Electromechanical actuators
   Linear accelerators
   Linear actuators
Material handling products and systems
   Belt fasteners idlers and lacers
   Conveyors
   Conveyor components
   Drive components
Mechanical power transmission
   Belts
   Chain attachments
   Couplings
   Drive systems
   Gears
   Speed reducers

COMPETITORS

Applied Industrial Technologies
DXP Enterprises
HD Supply Industrial Distribution Group
Lewis-Goetz
MRC Global
Milk Specialties Company
THG Corporation
W.W. Grainger
WESCO International

HISTORICAL FINANCIALS

Company Type: Private

Income Statement				FYE: December 31
	REVENUE ($ mil.)	NET INCOME ($ mil.)	NET PROFIT MARGIN	EMPLOYEES
12/08	528	5	1.1%	896
12/07	502	13	2.6%	—
12/06	0	0	—	—
Annual Growth	—	—	—	—

2008 Year-End Financials
Return on assets: 3.0%   Cash ($ mil.): 5
Return on equity: 5.9%
Current ratio: 1.90

BEARINGPOINT, INC.

EXECUTIVES

Ceo, F Edwin Harbach
Chb, Roderick C McGeary
Cfo, Kenneth A Hiltz
Coo, David Hunter
Svp Comm & Media Practice, Michael Reuschel
Director, Gov't Relations, Charles Cantus
Vp-Mgr Dir/Bus Dev, Jose Garcia
National Mgr Dir, Mark Gembicki
Sr. Administrative Assistant,, Alicia Flakes-Cuffee
Managing Director, Andrew Smith
Vice President, Business Devel, Bettina Smilo
Auditors: ERNST & YOUNG LLP MCLEAN VI

LOCATIONS

HQ: BEARINGPOINT, INC.
   100 CRESCENT CT STE 700, DALLAS, TX 752012112
Phone: 214 459-2770
Web: WWW.BEARINGPOINT.COM

HISTORICAL FINANCIALS

Company Type: Private

Income Statement				FYE: December 31
	REVENUE ($ mil.)	NET INCOME ($ mil.)	NET PROFIT MARGIN	EMPLOYEES
12/07	3,455	(362)	—	15,200
12/06	3,444	(177)	—	—
Annual Growth	0.3%	—	—	—

2007 Year-End Financials
Return on assets: (-18.3%)   Cash ($ mil.): 468
Return on equity: —
Current ratio: 1.40

BEAUMONT HEALTH

Beaumont Health is an eight-hospital regional health system in southeastern Michigan. The health system boasts about 3400 hospital beds 150 outpatient sites and 5000 affiliated physicians. Outpatient facilities include community medical centers nursing homes a home health agency a research institute and primary and specialty care clinics as well as rehabilitation cardiology and cancer centers. Beaumont is the exclusive clinical teaching site for the Oakland University William Beaumont School of Medicine; it also has affiliations with Michigan State University College of Osteopathic Medicine and Wayne State University School of Medicine. In 2019 it agreed to acquire Ohio hospital operator Summa Health.

EXECUTIVES

Vice President System Compliance, Edward Grima
Executive Vice President Business Development, Jack Devaney
Senior Vice President And Chief Development Officer, Margaret Casey
Senior Vice President Chief Medical Officer Beaumont Hospital Troy, James Lynch
Senior Vice President, Leslie Rocher
Vice President Information Technology, Karie Lyon
Director Of Patient Care Nursing, Randy Whitney
Senior Vice President And Associate Chief Medical Officer Acute Care, Malcolm Henoch
Senior Vice President And Executive Director Beaumont Medical Group, Michael Herbert
Vice President Finance, Mark Leonard
Vice President Finance, Steve Collard
Executive Vice President Quality Safety Clinical Effectiveness, Sam Flanders
Vice President Information Technology Service Delivery And Crm, Neha Yale
Senior Vice President Chief Marketing And Communications Officer, Mark Bohen
Vp Revenue Integrity, Lynn Flynn

Vice President Development Services, Jennifer Post

Vice President Human Resources, Ronald Lilek

Vice President Outpatient Services Beaumont Physician Partners, Theresa Peters

Senior Vice President And Chief Compliance Officer, Dawn Geisert

Executive Vice President And Chief Nursing Officer, Susan Grant

Vice President Financial Operations And Corporate Accounting, Donna Zuk

Executive Vice President Chief Operating Officer, Carolyn Wilson

Executive Vice President Chief Financial Officer, John Kerndl

Vp Perioperative Services Beaumont Royal Oak And Oncology Services Beaumont Health, Angela Beck

Senior Vice President Chief Human Resources Officer, Aaron Gillingham

Svp Government Relations And Community Affairs, Mary Zatina

Senior Vice President, David Walters

Vice President, Margaret Lightner

Vice President Of Clinical Outcomes, Linda Fitzgerald-mays

Vp, Debbie Hernandez

LOCATIONS

HQ: BEAUMONT HEALTH
3601 W 13 MILE RD, ROYAL OAK, MI 480736712
Phone: 248 898-5000
Web: WWW.BEAUMONT.ORG

Selected Michigan Locations
Lake Orion
Macomb
Rochester Hills
Royal Oak
St. Clair Shores
Sterling Heights
Warren
West Bloomfield

PRODUCTS/OPERATIONS

Selected Michigan Facilities
Health Wellness and Outpatient Care
  Beaumont Bon Brae Center (fitness; St. Clair Shores)
  Beaumont Health and Wellness Center (Rochester Hills)
  Beaumont Health Center (outpatient services; Royal Oak)
  Beaumont Medical Centers
Hospitals
  Beaumont Hospital Grosse Pointe
  Beaumont Hospital Royal Oak
  Beaumont Hospital Troy
Nursing and Rehabilitation
  Evergreen Health and Living Center (Southfield)
  Shelby Nursing Center (Shelby Township)
  ShorePointe Nursing Care (St. Clair Shores)
  ShorePointe Village Assisted Living (St. Clair Shores)
  West Bloomfield Nursing Center
  Woodward Hills Nursing Center (Bloomfield Hills)
Research and Education
  Oakland University William Beaumont School of Medicine (Royal Oak)

Selected Centers of Excellence
Cancer
Children's Hospital
Digestive health
Heart and vascular
Neuroscience
Orthopedics
Women's health

COMPETITORS

Children's Hospital of Michigan
Crittenton Hospital
Detroit Medical Center
Garden City Hospital
Henry Ford Health System
Kindred Healthcare
Mayo Clinic
McLaren Health Care
Mount Clemens Regional Medical Center
Providence Hospital and Medical Centers
Sinai-Grace Hospital
St. John Health
St. John Hospital & Medical Center
Trinity Health (Novi)
University of Michigan Health System

HISTORICAL FINANCIALS
Company Type: Private

Income Statement				FYE: December 31
	REVENUE ($ mil.)	NET INCOME ($ mil.)	NET PROFIT MARGIN	EMPLOYEES
12/18	4,659	142	3.0%	35,000
12/17	4,438	392	8.8%	—
12/16	4,373	286	6.6%	—
Annual Growth	3.2%	(29.6%)	—	—

2018 Year-End Financials
Return on assets: 2.6%   Cash ($ mil.): 324
Return on equity: 5.5%
Current ratio: 2.00

BEAVER STREET FISHERIES, INC.

After more than 60 years of fishing Beaver Street Fisheries can tell a tale or two of the one that got away. It's a top supplier of fish and other seafood products to wholesalers retailers and food service operators. Sourcing its products from more than 50 countries family-owned Beaver Street Fisheries offers one of the largest selections of seafood in the US. It boasts a variety of fresh and frozen seafood — including octopus shrimp and turtle — sold under its flagship Sea Best brand as well as the HF's and Island Queen names. Beaver Street Fisheries also imports lamb from New Zealand and sells Silver Fern-brand pork and beef via its Florida-New Zealand Lamb & Meat unit.

Operations

Beaver Street Fisheries has expanded its products portfolio in recent years through the efforts of its sister companies Bahamas Food Service and Tropic Seafood. Based in Nassau Bahamas the company's food service operation specializes in food distribution as one of the largest full-line food service distributors in the Bahamas. The company's Tropic Seafood business concentrates on lobster tail and seafood processing in the Bahamas. Specifically it processes lobster tails conch and other seafood items under the Island Queen and Island Prince brand names for sale worldwide.

The company maintains 8 million cubic feet of freezer space in Jacksonville Florida and offers 27 loading bays to facilitate a speedy dock turn-around process. It also has a network of cold storage facilities works with carriers to ensure national and international delivery within 48 hours.

Strategy

The food service operation specializes in food distribution as one of the largest full-line food service distributors in the Bahamas. In 2012 it working

to double the size of its warehouse in Nassau while also fine-tuning the company's automation labor and transportation processes. Beaver Street Fisheries hopes to automate the workforce management processes in Nassau so that it can boost order volume without greatly expanding its employee count there.

Company Background

Alfred and Hans Frisch started the business as a retail fish shop in 1950. It established the Sea Best brand in 1979.

EXECUTIVES

Chb-V Pres, Hans Frisch
Pres-Sec-Treas*, Benjamin Frisch
V Pres*, Mark Frisch
Payroll Staff, Chris Wiles
Human Resources Assistant, Andrea Favarelli
Human Resource, Dianna Sowder
Executive Administrative Assis, Tammy Pate
Human Resources, Terri Carrigg
Marketing Assistant, Veka Jovanovic

LOCATIONS

HQ: BEAVER STREET FISHERIES, INC.
1741 W BEAVER ST, JACKSONVILLE, FL 322097570
Phone: 904 354-5661
Web: WWW.BEAVERFISH.COM

PRODUCTS/OPERATIONS

Selected Products
Fish and other seafood
  Albacore tuna
  Black cod
  Bluefish
  Calamari
  Catfish
  Clams
  Cod
  Conch
  Crab
  Crawfish
  Flounder
  Grouper
  Haddock
  Halibut
  Lake perch
  Langostinos
  Lobster
  Mackerel
  Mahi mahi
  Marlin
  Mullet
  Mussels
  Ocean catfish
  Ocean perch
  Orange roughy
  Oysters
  Pollock
  Salmon
  Scallops
  Sea bass
  Sea trout
  Shark
  Shrimp
  Snails/escargot
  Snapper
  Sole
  Squid
  Surimi
  Swordfish
  Tilapia
  Whiting
  Yellowfin tuna
  Value-added
  Breaded seafood
  Crab cakes
  Crab patties
  Crabmeat stuffing
  Deviled crab
  Lobster tails
  Paella mix
  Salted fish
  Smoked fish
Other
  Alligator

Beef
Frog legs
Lamb
Octopus
Pork
Turtle

COMPETITORS

American Seafoods	Maid-Rite Steak
Brown Packing Company	Company
Colorado Boxed Beef	Niman Ranch
Del Monte Capitol Meat	North Pacific Seafoods
Fishhawk Fisheries	Ocean Beauty Seafoods
Florida Fresh Seafood	Pacific Seafood Group
Corp.	Pioneer Wholesale Meat
Fossil Farms	Red Chamber Co.
Freedman Meats	Ronald A. Chisholm
Gorton's	Limited
Harvest Meat Company	SYSCO Newport Meat
High Liner Foods	Company
Icelandic Group	Smithfield Foods
JBS USA	Trident Seafoods
Jim Pattison Group	Wolverine Packing

HISTORICAL FINANCIALS

Company Type: Private

Income Statement

FYE: May 28

	REVENUE ($ mil.)	NET INCOME ($ mil.)	NET PROFIT MARGIN	EMPLOYEES
05/11	450	13	3.0%	350
05/10	442	19	4.4%	—
05/09	468	17	3.7%	—
Annual Growth	(1.9%)	(11.8%)	—	—

2011 Year-End Financials

Return on assets: 7.7%
Return on equity: 10.3%
Current ratio: 4.20
Cash ($ mil.): 19

BEAVERTON SCHOOL DISTRICT

EXECUTIVES

Supt, Jerome Colonna
Asst Supt*, Sarah Boly
Asst Supt*, Bud Moore
Cfo*, Janice Essenberg
CIO*, Stephen Langford
Coordinator, Jill Bogle
Project Coordinator, Jay Dwyer
Coordinator, Kara Yunck
Project Coordinator, Krista Hawkins
Supervisor, Laurette Byrns
Information Technology/Interne, Sheila Bell
Auditors: GROVE MUELLER & SWANK PC

LOCATIONS

HQ: BEAVERTON SCHOOL DISTRICT
    16550 SW MERLO RD, BEAVERTON, OR 970035179
Phone: 503 591-8000
Web: WWW.BEAVERTON.K12.OR.US

HISTORICAL FINANCIALS

Company Type: Private

Income Statement

FYE: June 30

	REVENUE ($ mil.)	NET INCOME ($ mil.)	NET PROFIT MARGIN	EMPLOYEES
06/18	584	(97)	—	4,000
06/17	529	119	22.5%	—
06/16	513	(137)	—	—
06/15	495	431	87.0%	—
Annual Growth	5.7%	—	—	—

BELLIN HEALTH SYSTEMS, INC.

EXECUTIVES

Pres, George Kerwin
Cfo*, Jim Dietsche
Controller, Kevin Mc Gurk
Director, Jason Perry
Coordinator, Diane Koepke
Vice-President Business Develo, Randy Vanstraten
Executive Officer, John Rocheleau
Information Specialist, Teresa Krause
Account Executive, Amanda Verhagen
Staff, Brian Knapp
Health Professional, Linda Falk
Auditors: WIPFLI LLP GREEN BAY WISCONS

LOCATIONS

HQ: BELLIN HEALTH SYSTEMS, INC.
    744 S WEBSTER AVE, GREEN BAY, WI 543013505
Phone: 920 433-3500
Web: WWW.BELLIN.ORG

HISTORICAL FINANCIALS

Company Type: Private

Income Statement

FYE: September 30

	REVENUE ($ mil.)	NET INCOME ($ mil.)	NET PROFIT MARGIN	EMPLOYEES
09/18	608	24	4.0%	2,300
09/17	571	43	7.6%	—
09/16	533	31	6.0%	—
09/15	502	27	5.5%	—
Annual Growth	6.6%	(4.5%)	—	—

2018 Year-End Financials

Return on assets: 3.7%
Return on equity: 5.2%
Current ratio: 2.50
Cash ($ mil.): 71

BELLIN MEMORIAL HOSPITAL, INC.

EXECUTIVES

Pres, George Kerwin
Cfo*, Jim Dietsche
Director of Information Techno, Troy Schiesl
Licensed Practical Nurse, Ann Conley

Nurse Practitioner, Patti Marquardt
Internal Medicine Practitioner, Andrea Akpoguma
Administrator, Kevin J McGurk
Security Staff, Tom Brault
Accounting Staff, Ann Tedrick
Manager, Kathy Vandehei
Registered Nurse, Luann Woodland
Auditors: WIPFLI LLP GREEN BAY WISCONS

LOCATIONS

HQ: BELLIN MEMORIAL HOSPITAL, INC.
    744 S WEBSTER AVE, GREEN BAY, WI 543013581
Phone: 920 433-3500
Web: WWW.BELLINHEALTHPHARMACY.COM

HISTORICAL FINANCIALS

Company Type: Private

Income Statement

FYE: September 30

	REVENUE ($ mil.)	NET INCOME ($ mil.)	NET PROFIT MARGIN	EMPLOYEES
09/18	561	26	4.7%	1,725
09/17	571	42	7.5%	—
09/16	488	32	6.7%	—
09/15	462	27	6.0%	—
Annual Growth	6.7%	(1.7%)	—	—

2018 Year-End Financials

Return on assets: 4.4%
Return on equity: 6.3%
Current ratio: 2.70
Cash ($ mil.): 65

BENCO DENTAL SUPPLY CO.

Benco Dental Supply is a one-stop shop for the tooth doc. Through regional showrooms and distribution centers Benco provides dental and dentistry supplies to more than 30000 dental professionals throughout the US. Its offerings include dental hand pieces furniture and disposable supplies. Its BencoNET division develops and distributes custom computers and proprietary programming and networking systems for dentists. Other services include dental office design practice consulting financing and real estate planning wealth management and equipment repairs.

Operations

Benco offerings range from large equipment to small supplies made by a broad range of manufacturers. The company supplies more than 80000 products including dental cement impression supplies and curing lights made by manufacturers such as 3M Dentsply Sirona Sybron (Kerr) Hu-Friedy and more. It also sells products under its own Benco Dental brand.

Support services include offers inventory management services and hand piece equipment and upholstery repair.

Benco Dental's practice management services include staff recruitment assistance product training programs for dentists peer-to-peer networking solutions and continuing medical education programs.

Geographic Reach

Benco Dental's main headquarters and showroom is located in Pittston Pennsylvania. It also operates another CenterPoint Experience (large-scale) showroom in Costa Mesa California and it has a network of about 50 smaller regional showrooms and five distribution centers (in Pittston; Dallas; Fort Wayne Indiana; Jacksonville Florida;

and Reno Nevada) across the US that serve customers in all 50 US states.

Although most of its operations are in the US the company also ships products to overseas customers.

Sales and Marketing

Benco markets its products and services directly to dental practices. It also increasing the number of orders placed through its online ordering system (Painless) and it promotes services to dentists through affiliations with dental organizations and associations (including the American Academy of Dental Group Practice and the American Association of Orthodontists). The company has more than 400 sales representatives. To support sales it also has about 300 factory-trained service technicians.

Financial Performance

Benco increased net sales by 9% in 2012 due to new product sales launches and increased sales of existing products in fields including 3D imaging equipment and digital sensors.

Strategy

Benco tends to expand its operations through organic growth initiatives including offering new products and services to a wider customer base. In addition the company grows through acquisitions in key growth regions. The company launched 14 Benco branded products during 2012 as well as 3800 new products made by its vendor partners. It also added about 50 new sales reps that year to meet rising customer demands. The company estimated that it grew market share to some 11% of the US market that year (placing itself among the top three dental supply distributors).

Benco increased sales to community health centers that year through its partnership with PSS. To expand its educational programs in 2012 the company also formed a partnership with the Kois Center which offers a nine-course program on topics including aesthetic and restorative dentistry.

To reach additional customers and expand its capacity the company opened its fifth distribution center — a 120000-sq. ft. facility in Reno Nevada — in 2011. It also opened a new sales branch office in Los Angeles to serve the Southern California market in 2012.

Benco Dental moved into its CenterPoint headquarters and showroom in Pittston Pennsylvania in early 2010. The facility is one of the largest dental equipment showrooms in the US with exhibits including more than two dozen dental rooms 14 digital X-ray units three sterilization centers and other oral surgery and orthodontic units as well as an office design concept suite and a training and education center. Following the success of that location the company opened a second CenterPoint Experience showroom in Costa Mesa California in 2012.

EXECUTIVES

V Pres, George Rable
V Pres, Paul Jackson
Vice President Operations, Lou Mangino
Vice President Business Innovation, Julie Radzyminski
Vp Operations, Louis Mangino
Vice President Of Sales And Branch Operations, Kari Taylor
Vice President Sales And Branch Operations, Mike McElaney
Managing Director Executive Assistant Charles Cohen, Jamie Semanek
Auditors: COHEN AND CO CLEVELAND OHIO

LOCATIONS

HQ: BENCO DENTAL SUPPLY CO.
295 CENTERPOINT BLVD, PITTSTON, PA 186406136
Phone: 570 602-7781
Web: WWW.BENCO.COM

Selected Distribution Center Locations
Dallas Texas
Fort Wayne Indiana
Jacksonville Florida
Pittston Pennsylvania
Reno Nevada

PRODUCTS/OPERATIONS

Selected Brands
Large Equipment
  A-dec
  Belmont
  BIOLASE
  Cadent
  Gendex
  Instrumentarium
  Marus
  Midmark
  Pelton & Crane
  Sirona
  Soredex
  Vatech
Small Equipment
  Accutron
  Aceton
  Air Techniques
  Cadent
  KaVo
  Midmark
  Midwest
  Tuttnauer
  W&H
Supplies and technology (Benco brands)
  BencoNET
  BluChip rewards
  BluPrint (dental impression material)
  fas-TRACT
  HD
  Iris (dental pit and fissure sealant)
  Natural Extensions (nitrile gloves)
  Painless
  ValuGrip (latex gloves)
  Vision XR (oral x-ray film)
  XLR8 (dental equipment)
  Z3

COMPETITORS

Burkhart Dental	Henry Schein
Cardinal Health	McKesson
Darby Dental	Owens & Minor
Dentsply Sirona	Patterson Companies
Discus Dental	Sybron Dental

HISTORICAL FINANCIALS

Company Type: Private

Income Statement				FYE: January 4
	REVENUE ($ mil.)	NET INCOME ($ mil.)	NET PROFIT MARGIN	EMPLOYEES
01/14*	620	8	1.4%	1,600
12/12	600	7	1.2%	—
12/07	389	5	1.3%	—
Annual Growth	8.1%	10.0%	—	—

*Fiscal year change

2014 Year-End Financials

Return on assets: 4.9%   Cash ($ mil.): —
Return on equity: —
Current ratio: 1.60

BENEFIS HOSPITALS, INC

EXECUTIVES

Ceo-Cfo, John Goodnow
Pres*, Laura Goldhahn
V Pres*, Steven Ballock
Dentist, Will Daniels DDS
Vice-President Information Ser, Alexander N Chung
Vice-President Information Ser, Mary Davis
General Practitioner, Justin Madill
Coordinator, Stacy McKittrick
Director, Patty Harris
Marketing Director, Bill Preston
Clinical Engineering Manager, Bryan McCulloch

LOCATIONS

HQ: BENEFIS HOSPITALS, INC
1101 26TH ST S, GREAT FALLS, MT 594055161
Phone: 406 455-5000
Web: WWW.BENEFIS.ORG

HISTORICAL FINANCIALS

Company Type: Private

Income Statement				FYE: December 31
	REVENUE ($ mil.)	NET INCOME ($ mil.)	NET PROFIT MARGIN	EMPLOYEES
12/16	865	26	3.0%	2,419
12/15	860	20	2.4%	—
12/14*	363	14	4.0%	—
05/06	86	9	10.5%	—
Annual Growth	23.3%	10.1%	—	—

*Fiscal year change

BERGELECTRIC CORP.

One of the nation's top electrical contractors Bergelectric provides design/build and design/assist services on projects that include office buildings public-sector facilities bioscience labs entertainment complexes hotels data centers and hospitals. Its projects also consist of parking garages water treatment plants residential towers and correctional facilities. The company boasts expertise in building information modeling fire alarms and security and telecommunications and data infrastructure. Bergelectric operates mainly in the western and southeastern US from about a dozen offices.

Operations

The electrical company keeps a lengthy list of projects past and current. More recent projects have included the San Ysidro Land Port of Entry Lackland Ambulatory Care Center Northwest Water Reclamation Facility Naval Hospital Camp Pendleton Fort Riley Community Replacement Hospital Wilshire Boulevard Temple California Health Care Facility Visitors Center at King Gillette Ranch Variety Special Education School Greenlaw Partners and Sandy High School.

The company has more than $550 million in backlog.

Geographic Reach

From its headquarters in Los Angeles Bergelectric maintains a presence in California through a handful of offices in San Diego Los Angeles Orange County Sacramento and Ventura. It also serves as an electrical contractor in half a dozen cities including Austin Texas; Denver Colorado; Las Vegas Nevada; Orlando Florida; Phoenix Arizona; Portland Oregon; and Raleigh North Carolina.

Strategy

The company is also focused on green initiatives completing Leadership in Energy and Environmental Design (LEED) construction projects for the likes of Sony the FBI the EPA and the University of Oregon. To this end the company formed the Fire-Alarm/Security Division which provides projects and clients with comprehensive electrical services for such fire alarm projects as the Morongo Casino & Hotel Pechanga Hotel & Casino and San Manuel Indian Bingo & Casino.

Bergelectric has extended the reach of its traditional electrical contracting operations by expanding into new markets including sustainable building structures and renewable energy systems such as wind farms. Through a partnership with telecommunications firm Teo Bergelectric provides communications services to wind energy producers. As part of the agreement Bergelectric designs and installs fiber connections and equipment while Teo supplies phones switches and other hardware.

To simplify the integration of complex systems Bergelectric established a national Technology Systems group which serves to consolidate all of the company's existing low-voltage divisions under one management umbrella. The move aims to differentiate Bergelectric from the traditionally fragmented industry of electrical and systems components.

Company Background

Bergelectric was founded in 1946.

EXECUTIVES

Chb, Thomas R Anderson
Ceo*, William Wingrning
Pres*, Alan Mashburn
V Pres*, Steve Buhr
Exec V Pres*, William M Wingerning
Sr V Pres*, Edward P Billig
Sr V Pres*, Ronald Wood
V Pres*, William Sorber
Systems/Programming Manager, Brock Knowles
Project Manager, Don Kuhn
Coordinator, Justin Bratton
Auditors: MOSS LEVY & HARTZHEIM LLP B

LOCATIONS

HQ: BERGELECTRIC CORP.
  3182 LIONSHEAD AVE, CARLSBAD, CA 920104701
Phone: 760 638-2374
Web: WWW.BERGELECTRIC.COM

Selected Locations

Agoura Hills CA
Austin TX
Costa Mesa CA
Denver
Durham NC
Escondido CA
Los Angeles
North Las Vegas NV
Orlando FL
Portland OR
Rancho Cordova CA
Tempe AZ

COMPETITORS

Cupertino Electric
EMCOR
Fisk Electric
Henkels & McCoy
IES Holdings

MYR Group
Morrow-Meadows
Rosendin Electric
Sachs Electric

HISTORICAL FINANCIALS

Company Type: Private

Income Statement   FYE: January 31

	REVENUE ($ mil.)	NET INCOME ($ mil.)	NET PROFIT MARGIN	EMPLOYEES
01/17	483	4	0.9%	2,100
01/16	507	2	0.4%	—
01/15	494	1	0.2%	—
01/14	525	4	0.9%	—
Annual Growth	(2.7%)	(5.0%)	—	—

2017 Year-End Financials

Return on assets: 2.5%
Return on equity: 10.7%
Current ratio: 1.60

Cash ($ mil.): 16

BERRY GLOBAL FILMS, LLC

Making plastic cling is this company's thing. AEP Industries manufactures plastic packaging films — more than 15000 types — including stretch wrap for industrial pallets packaging for foods and beverages and films for agricultural uses such as wrap for hay bales. AEP also makes dispenser-boxed plastic wraps which are sold to consumers as well as institutions ranging from schools to hospitals. Other industries courted by AEP are packaging transportation food autos chemicals textiles and electronics. The company operates in the US and in Canada. In the summer of 2016 AEP agreed to be acquired by rival Berry Plastics Group.

Change in Company Type

AEP agreed to be acquired by Berry Plastics Group in mid-2016 in a deal valued at $765 million a price that includes AEP's debt load. AEP will be combined with Berry's Engineered Materials Division.

Geographic Reach

AEP conducts about 95% of its business in the US market. Remaining sales take place in Canada. It has about 15 manufacturing facilities in the US (about 11 states) and Canada. The company also exports its products to Latin America through its office in Waxahachie Texas.

Sales and Marketing

About two-thirds of AEP's sales are made to distributors and the remainder directly to end-users of its products. It serves about 3000 customers. The company works to maintain customer relationships and it provides technical training to its sales personal so that they are able to provide customer support and communicate customer needs to the company's product development team. Distribution functions are mostly contracted to third parties.

Financial Performance

AEP's revenues have fluctuated over the years. After peaking at $1.19 billion in 2014 revenues fell by 4% to $1.14 billion in 2015. The revenue decrease for 2015 was fueled by a 3% dip in average selling prices primarily due to the pass-through of lower resin costs negatively affecting net sales by $31 million.

The company in 2015 also experienced a 1% decrease in sales volumes attributed to volatility in the resin markets. This resulted in soft customer demand in certain stock product lines customer bankruptcies and the impact of exiting certain low-margin businesses during fiscal 2014.

After experiencing a net loss of $6 million in 2014 AEP posted positive net income of $29 million in 2015. This was the result of a decline in costs coupled with a larger amount of income tax benefits.

Strategy

With little product differentiation among plastic film producers AEP positions itself as the low-cost source with technological expertise to customize value-added flexible films to satisfy myriad manufacturing and processing applications. The company aims to provide long-term value to shareholders by becoming the preferred provider of flexible packaging products in the North American market.

To strengthen its finances and increase manufacturing output and productivity AEP is investing heavily in capital improvements. During the last decade it has purchased or leased new equipment and made equipment upgrades intended to optimize its manufacturing footprint in high-growth product categories.

The company looks for success in its sales and distribution model by establishing long-term relationships with its customers. To mitigate the volatility of raw material prices the company pursues volume raw material rebates by making most of its purchases from three primary suppliers.

Company Background

Brendan Barba a former salesman for polyethylene film maker PPD formed Flexible Plastics in 1967 in Lodi New Jersey. In 1970 his partner bought him out. That year Barba founded AEP Industries briefly called Automatically Extruded Products. In 1982 the company moved into the specialty and premium films market. It established a plant in Waxahachie Texas in 1985 and went public a year later.

EXECUTIVES

Vp Manufacturing Polyvinyl Chloride Products, Richard Boyette
Evp Operations, Paul C. Vegliante, $317,300 total compensation
President And Coo, John J. Powers, $349,300 total compensation
Evp Finance Cfo And Director, Paul M. Feeney, $463,800 total compensation
Chairman President And Ceo, J. Brendan Barba, $958,700 total compensation
Evp National Accounts, Robert Cron
Vp Custom Films Division, Robert Covella
Division Manager Resinite Products, Steve Firmery
Vp Stretch Film Division, Brian Ochsner
Vp Proformance Films Products, Gary Bobko
Vp Ipd Division, Philip A. Hernberg
Vice President Engineering, Carl Opperman
Vice President Of Information Technology, Ken Ribe

LOCATIONS

HQ: BERRY GLOBAL FILMS, LLC
  95 CHESTNUT RIDGE RD, MONTVALE, NJ 076451801
Phone: 201 641-6600
Web: WWW.AEPINC.COM

2015 Sales

	$ mil.	% of total
US	1,073	94
Canada	68	6
Total	**1,141**	**100**

PRODUCTS/OPERATIONS

2015 Sales

	$ mil.	% of total
Custom films	357	31
Stretch (pallet) wrap	332	29
Food contact	165	14
Canliners	144	13

PROformance films	63	6
Printed & converted films specialty films & other	77	7
Total	**1,141**	**100**

Selected Products

Canliners
Kitchen and standard garbage bags
Custom films (polyethylene co-extruded and monolayer custom designed film)
  Drum box carton pail liners
  Films to cover high value products
  Furniture and mattress bags
  Magazine overwrap
PROformance films (co-extruded and monolayer polyolefin films)
  Cereal box liners
  Fresh cut produce packaging
  Frozen foods
  Medical
Polyvinyl chloride wrap
  Food and freezer wrap
Printed and converted films (polyethylene)
  Printed laminated converted films for flexible packaging to consumer markets
  Printed shrink films
Stretch (pallet) wrap (polyethylene)
  Pallet wrap
Other products and specialty films (unplasticized polyvinyl chloride polyethylene)
  Agricultural films
  Battery labels
  Canliners
  Credit card laminate
  Retail and institutional films and products
  Table covers aprons bibs and gloves
  Twist wrap

COMPETITORS

Acme Packaging	Pactiv
Ampac	Plastic Suppliers
Bemis	Primex Plastics
Berry Global	Printpack
Dow Chemical	S.C. Johnson
FlexSol Packaging	Sealed Air Corp.
Griffon	Sigma Plastics
Inteplast	Tredegar
Intertape Polymer	

HISTORICAL FINANCIALS

Company Type: Private

Income Statement				FYE: October 31
	REVENUE ($ mil.)	NET INCOME ($ mil.)	NET PROFIT MARGIN	EMPLOYEES
10/15	1,141	28	2.5%	2,600
10/14	1,192	(5)	—	—
10/13	1,143	10	0.9%	—
Annual Growth	(0.1%)	63.8%	—	—

2015 Year-End Financials

Return on assets: 6.6%
Return on equity: 32.2%
Current ratio: 2.10

Cash ($ mil.): 20

BEST PETROLEUM CORPORATION

EXECUTIVES

Pres, Antonio De Jesus Nieves
Head of Business Development, Manuel F Rojas
Auditors: JESUS OYOLA CUADRADO BAYAMON

LOCATIONS

HQ: BEST PETROLEUM CORPORATION
KM 20 HM 5 RR 2, TOA BAJA, PR 00951
Phone: 787 251-6218
Web: WWW.BESTPETROLEUMCORP.COM

HISTORICAL FINANCIALS

Company Type: Private

Income Statement				FYE: December 31
	REVENUE ($ mil.)	NET INCOME ($ mil.)	NET PROFIT MARGIN	EMPLOYEES
12/17	547	26	4.8%	130
12/16	439	16	3.7%	—
12/15	479	11	2.4%	—
12/98	0	0		
Annual Growth	—	—	—	—

2017 Year-End Financials

Return on assets: 20.6%
Return on equity: 22.0%
Current ratio: 14.20

Cash ($ mil.): 75

BETH ISRAEL DEACONESS MEDICAL CENTER, INC.

Beth Israel Lahey Health (formerly Beth Israel Deaconess Medical Center or BIDMC) is a Boston-based health system with 13 hospitals across Massachusetts. Its flagship location is the hospital for Major League Baseball's Red Sox but it's perhaps best known for being a teaching hospital of Harvard Medical School. The facility has about 675 beds and provides general medical and surgical care as well as outpatient services at its facilities. The health system traces its roots to Deaconess Hospital founded in 1896 and Beth Israel Hospital established in 1916. In 2019 BIDMC merged with Lahey Health to create a stronger rival to Massachusetts' largest system Partners HealthCare.

Operations

Beth Israel Lahey Health's operations include the hospitals previously owned by BIDMC and Lahey Health as well as Anna Jaques Hospital Mount Auburn Hospital Baptist Hospital and several medical offices.

Many of the system's physicians hold faculty appointments at Harvard Medical School. Along with helping students become doctors Beth Israel Lahey Health provides clinical education to students in social work radiology and pharmacy.

The Carl J. Shapiro Institute for Education and Research provides medical students and physicians in training with an on-site centralized educational facility.

Financial Performance

Beth Israel Lahey Health is very active in medical research and consistently ranks among the top recipients of biomedical research funding from the National Institutes of Health totaling nearly $200 million annually. The health system is also home to the Harvard-Thorndike Laboratory the nation's oldest clinical research laboratory.

Strategy

Being on the forefront of medical education goes hand-in-hand with using cutting-edge technology and Beth Israel Lahey Health does just that with its Carl J. Shapiro Institute for Education and Re-search administers training for learners at all levels and from all disciplines using progressive teaching methods to replicate real-life patient care situations from routine procedures to acute management crises. The institute features a range of technologically advanced educational resources including realistic models simulators virtual reality experiences computer-based materials ultrasound technology and filmed operations.

In late 2017 the hospital announced plans to build a 10-story patient tower its largest such project in more than 20 years. The facility will have private patient rooms operating rooms imaging suites and a landing pad for helicopters.

Mergers and Acquisitions

In early 2017 BIDMC agreed to merge with Lahey Health to become Massachusetts' second-largest health system (after Partners HealthCare). The merger was official in March 2019. Other hospitals joined the combined system including Anna Jaques Hospital of Newburyport New England Baptist Hospital and Mount Auburn Hospital. Now named Beth Israel Lahey Health the system has 13 hospitals.

EXECUTIVES

Svp Information Systems And Cio, John D. Halamka, age 56
Svp Finance And Cfo, Steven Fischer
President And Ceo Beth Israel Deaconess Hospital Plymouth, Peter J. Holden
Coo, Nancy Formella
President And Ceo Affiliated Physicians Group, John Christoforo
Chief Department Of Medicine, Mark L. Zeidel
President Ceo And Director, Kevin Tabb
Chief Nursing Officer And Svp Patient Care Services, Marsha Maurer
President And Ceo Beth Israel Deaconess Hospital - Needham, John Fogarty
President And Ceo Beth Israel Deaconess Hospital Milton, Peter Healy
Svp Communications And Marketing, Paul Donovan
Interim President And Ceo Beth Israel Deaconess Care Organization, Jeff Hulburt
President And Ceo Harvard Medical Faculty Physicians, Stuart Rosenberg
Deputy Cio/cto, Manu Tandon
Medical Director Of Cytogenetics, Christine Bryke
Director, Ronald P. (Ron) O'Hanley, age 62
Vice Chair, Margaret A. McKenna, age 74
Vice Chair, Edward H. (Ted) Ladd
Director, Daniel Jick
Treasurer, Allan S Bufferd

LOCATIONS

HQ: BETH ISRAEL DEACONESS MEDICAL CENTER, INC.
330 BROOKLINE AVE, BOSTON, MA 022155400
Phone: 617 667-7000
Web: WWW.BIDMC.ORG

PRODUCTS/OPERATIONS

Centers and Departments
Cancer Center
CardioVascular Institute
Digestive Disease Center
Spine Center
Transplant Institute
Clinical Departments
Anesthesia Critical Care and Pain Medicine
Dermatology
Emergency Medicine
Medicine
Neonatology
Neurology
Obstetrics and Gynecology
Orthopedic Surgery
Pathology
Psychiatry

Radiation Oncology
Radiology
Rehabilitation Services
Surgery

Selected Facilities

Beth Israel Deaconess HealthCare-Chelsea
Beth Israel Deaconess HealthCare-Chestnut Hill
Beth Israel Deaconess HealthCare-Lexington
Beth Israel Deaconess Hospital-Milton
Beth Israel Deaconess Hospital-Needham
Beth Israel Deaconess Hospital-Plymouth

COMPETITORS

Boston Medical Center
Brigham and Women's Hospital
Cambridge Health Alliance
Care New England
Children's Hospital Boston
Dana-Farber
Massachusetts General Hospital
Newton-Wellesley Hospital
Northeast Health System
Partners HealthCare
Southcoast Hospitals Group
Spaulding Rehabilitation Hospital
Steward Health Care

HISTORICAL FINANCIALS

Company Type: Private

Income Statement				FYE: September 30
	REVENUE ($ mil.)	NET INCOME ($ mil.)	NET PROFIT MARGIN	EMPLOYEES
09/17	1,335	37	2.8%	6,500
09/16	1,279	28	2.3%	—
09/15	1,198	44	3.7%	—
09/14	1,113	37	3.4%	—
Annual Growth	6.3%	(0.1%)	—	—

2017 Year-End Financials

Return on assets: 2.3%   Cash ($ mil.): 17
Return on equity: 3.9%
Current ratio: 3.10

BETH ISRAEL MEDICAL CENTER

Residents of New York City's Lower East Side look to Beth Israel Medical Center to keep them healthy. A member of Continuum Health Partners the tertiary care medical facility has more than 1100 inpatient beds at two facilities in the New York area — its main location in Manhattan and another in Brooklyn. It also operates outpatient care centers and physician offices. Along with its patient care operations Beth Israel Medical Center maintains medical residency programs through its affiliation with Yeshiva University's Albert Einstein College of Medicine. The hospital also conducts institutional medical research with Rockefeller University and offers a nursing degree through its Phillips Beth Israel School of Nursing.

Operations

The main campus in Petrie has about 900 beds and hosts several major specialist units while the Brooklyn location has more than 210 beds and provides general medicine surgery radiology and intensive care services. Outpatient centers include the Phillips Ambulatory Care Center in Manhattan and the Beth Israel Ambulatory Surgi-Center in Brooklyn which provide diagnostic and ambulatory surgery services. Another affiliated clinic the Continuum Center for Health and Healing provides

primary and specialty care as well as alternative services including acupuncture. The Beth Israel Medical Group operates several primary and specialty care physician clinics in Manhattan.

Altogether the Beth Israel Medical Center facilities handle about 59000 inpatient encounters annually. It also manages about 107000 emergency room visits 3500 births 11000 inpatient surgeries and 21000 outpatient surgeries. The center employs about 2300 medical and dental staff members.

Geographic Reach

The hospital's main campus in Manhattan is known as the Beth Israel Medical Center-Petrie Campus. The Brooklyn location is known as Beth Israel Brooklyn; prior to 2012 the campus was known as the Beth Israel Medical Center-Kings Highway Division.

Strategy

Continuum Health is investing in upgrades to Beth Israel Medical Center's facilities. For instance it added a new endoscopy suite at the Brooklyn campus in 2012. The main Petrie campus is renovating its emergency room and various inpatient units are increasing quality programs.

In 2012 a major expansion project was launched at the Continuum Center for Health and Healing to expand access to outpatient care for area residents; the program will add services including dermatology cardiology and podiatry. In addition the hospital opened a new cancer center in Manhattan in 2010 and a deluxe unit for high-income patients having orthopedic and other surgeries in 2008. Continuum Health is also upgrading some of Beth Israel Medical Center's IT functions including its radiology data management systems.

EXECUTIVES

President, Harris M. Nagler
The Alfred And Gail Engelberg Department Of Family Medicine, Robert M. Schiller
Chairman Medicine, Henry C. Bodenheimer
Clinical Director Continuum Heart Institute, Steven R. Bergmann
Co-director Institue For Head And Neck Cancer, Roy B. Sessions
Senior Vice President Business Development, Marc Hall
Medical Director, Bernard Brahm
Vice President Administration, Timothy Day
Vice President Administration, Joanne Coffin
Occupational Medicine, Sabrina Perry
Vice President, Kenneth R Holden
Chairman, Steven Hochberg
Vice Chairman, Sorrell Mathes
Treasurer Vice President, Stacey Resk
Auditors: PRICEWATERHOUSECOOPERS LLP NE

LOCATIONS

HQ: BETH ISRAEL MEDICAL CENTER
281 1ST AVE, NEW YORK, NY 100032925
Phone: 212 420-2000
Web: WWW.MOUNTSINAI.ORG

PRODUCTS/OPERATIONS

Selected Centers and Services

AIDS Services
Allergy and Immunology
Anesthesiology
Appel-Venet Comprehensive Breast Service
Asian Services
Beth Israel ALS Center
Beth Israel Hernia Center
Beth Israel Medical Group
Betty & Morton Yarmon Stroke Center
Brief Psychotherapy Research Program
Cancer Center (Oncology)
Center for Blood Management and Bloodless Medicine and Surgery
Center for Endovascular Surgery
Center for Health and Healing

Craniofacial and Cleft Palate Center
Cystic Fibrosis Center
Dermatology
Endocrinology and Metabolism
Epilepsy
Friedman Diabetes Institute
Genetics
Geriatrics
Heart Institute (Cardiology)
Hematology
Hospice
Hyman Newman Institute for Neurology and Neurosugery (INN)
The Chris and Morton P. Hyman Patient Care Unit
Hyperhidrosis Program
Incontinence
Integrative Medicine
Interventional Neuroradiology
Israeli Health Program
Karpas Health Information Center
Latino Health Institute
Live Well New York
Louis Armstrong Center for Music and Medicine:
Lung Nodule Center
Maternity Services
Methadone Maintenance Treatment Program
Midwifery
Nephrology
Neurology
Orthopedics
Ostomy Program
Pain Medicine and Palliative Care
Pediatrics
Phillips Beth Israel School of Nursing
Primary Care
Psychiatry
Pulmonary and Critical Care Medicine
Radiation Oncology
Radiology
Rheumatology
Senior Health
Sleep Health
Speech-Language and Learning Center
Spine Institute
Sports Medicine
Stroke Centers
Styuvesant Square Chemical Dependency Services
Surgery
Urology
Vascular and Birthmarks Institute of New York
Women's Health
Women's Heart NY
Wound Healing Center

COMPETITORS

Bronx-Lebanon Hospital
Catholic Healthcare System
Kingsbrook Jewish Medical Center
Lutheran HealthCare
Maimonides Medical Center
MediSys Health Network
Memorial Sloan-Kettering
Montefiore Medical
NYU Hospital for Joint Diseases
New York City Health and Hospitals
NewYork-Presbyterian Healthcare
Northwell Health
SUNY Downstate

HISTORICAL FINANCIALS

Company Type: Private

Income Statement				FYE: December 31
	REVENUE ($ mil.)	NET INCOME ($ mil.)	NET PROFIT MARGIN	EMPLOYEES
12/09	1,256	15	1.2%	8,100
12/08	932	(59)	—	—
Annual Growth	34.8%	—	—	—

2009 Year-End Financials

Return on assets: 1.6%   Cash ($ mil.): 98
Return on equity: 5.6%
Current ratio: 0.50

BETHESDA HOSPITAL, INC.

From modest beginnings as a informal cottage hospital Bethesda North Hospital has grown into the fourth largest medical center in Cincinnati Ohio. Bethesda North is a full-service acute care hospital with some 360 beds for adults and 60 for children. It provides comprehensive medical and surgical care including maternity and fertility services emergency care and diagnostic imaging. The hospital joined with fellow Cincinnati health care provider Good Samaritan Hospital in 1995 to form TriHealth. Together the two hospitals offer care at some 80 locations including primary care offices fitness centers and occupational health facilities.

Operations
The full-service 420-bed acute care hospital handles some 24000 inpatient admissions each year as well as 260000 outpatient visits 77000 emergency room visits and 4000 births. It employs 165 full-time doctors and dentists and provides more than $30 million in community outreach efforts (including charity care programs) each year.

Specialty units at Bethesda North Hospital include institutes for cancer heart surgical and digestive care as well as centers for outpatient imaging breast stroke obstetrics-gynecology orthopedics and emergency trauma care. As a regional teaching center the hospital offers residency programs in a number of specialties including family medicine internal medicine OB-GYN and surgery.

Geographic Reach
Bethesda North is located in northern Cincinnati Ohio and serves as a regional trauma center as well as a major teaching hospital in the area.

Strategy
Parent organization TriHealth has aligned skilled physicians specialists surgeons and its staff to create specialty institutes offering best-of-class medical assistance in fields including heart and cancer care. To further enhance its facilities in 2013 the organization renovated the labor and delivery wing at Bethesda North Hospital. Other recent projects include the addition of a seven-story patient tower and a new outpatient imaging center.

Additionally the company has invested in TriHealth Connect the electronic medical records system that will help access accurate patient information.

Company Background
In early 2012 TriHealth unveiled a new logo.

Bethesda North traces it roots to 1896 and a cottage occupied by seven German Methodist deaconesses ministering to the poor and sick.

EXECUTIVES
Pres, John Prout
Cfo*, Craig Rucker
Senior Buyer, Chris Hein
Auditors: LB BKD LLP CINCINNATI OH

LOCATIONS
HQ: BETHESDA HOSPITAL, INC.
4750 WESLEY AVE, CINCINNATI, OH 452122244
Phone: 513 569-6100
Web: WWW.TRIHEALTH.COM

PRODUCTS/OPERATIONS

List of Selected Services
Breast health
Cancer care
Digestive diseases
Heart and vascular care
Maternity (OB-GYN childbirth)
Orthopedics
Outpatient imaging
Pallative Care
Pharmacy
Robotic-assisted surgery
Stroke care
Trauma/Emergency services

COMPETITORS

Cincinnati Children's Hospital	St. Elizabeth Healthcare
Deaconess Associations	The Christ Hospital Corporation
Kettering Health Network	UC Health
Miami Valley Hospital	
Premier Health Partners	

HISTORICAL FINANCIALS
Company Type: Private

Income Statement				FYE: June 30
	REVENUE ($ mil.)	NET INCOME ($ mil.)	NET PROFIT MARGIN	EMPLOYEES
06/18	639	52	8.2%	3,000
06/15	551	71	13.0%	—
06/14	552	76	13.8%	—
06/13	534	57	10.8%	—
Annual Growth	**3.7%**	**(1.9%)**	**—**	**—**

2018 Year-End Financials
Return on assets: 4.4%   Cash ($ mil.): —
Return on equity: 8.1%
Current ratio: 1.40

BETHESDA, INC.

EXECUTIVES

Pres, J James Pearce Jr
V Pres, Chip Crowther
SEC, Ellen Katz
Treas, William A Tsacalis
V Chm, Michael F Haverkamp
Officer, Lynn Meyer
Associate Director Divi, Steven Kleeman
MD, Craig Eisentrout
Family Medicine, Emily E Dixon
Director, Jennifer Zimmerman
Vice Chair Treasurer, Ralph Mike
Auditors: BKD LLP CINCINNATI OH

LOCATIONS
HQ: BETHESDA, INC.
619 OAK ST 7N, CINCINNATI, OH 452061613
Phone: 513 569-6400
Web: WWW.TRIHEALTH.COM

HISTORICAL FINANCIALS
Company Type: Private

Income Statement				FYE: June 30
	REVENUE ($ mil.)	NET INCOME ($ mil.)	NET PROFIT MARGIN	EMPLOYEES
06/18	679	78	11.6%	5,543
06/17	615	91	14.8%	—
06/15	53	7	14.7%	—
06/13	9	5	61.1%	—
Annual Growth	**134.4%**	**68.1%**	**—**	**—**

2018 Year-End Financials
Return on assets: 5.3%   Cash ($ mil.): —
Return on equity: 8.4%
Current ratio: 1.40

BEXAR COUNTY HOSPITAL DISTRICT

As the hospital system of the Bexar County Hospital District University Health System serves residents of San Antonio and the surrounding region. Its flagship facility University Hospital boasts about 720 beds and is the primary teaching facility for The University of Texas Health Science Center at San Antonio. In addition to general medical and surgical care the hospital is a designated Level I trauma center and a Level II pediatric trauma and burn center. The system provides health care for families near its clinic locations including the Robert B. Green Campus Texas Diabetes Institute more than a dozen neighborhood clinics five ExpressMed urgent-care clinics and four outpatient renal dialysis centers.

Operations
The system which has about 800 physicians also operates preventive care centers including the Texas Diabetes Institute which provides treatment research and education for diabetes patients and health care professionals. The University Transplant Center performs a range of procedures such as kidney liver and lung transplants. The Harlandale Independent School District school-based Health Center is a collaboration with Harlandale ISD that helps keep students healthy and learning.

University Health System's emergency department is the busiest in the area taking in nearly 70000 visits annually. In 2013 it had about 22000 inpatient discharges 3000 births and 139000 outpatient visits.

As part of its operations University Health System is joint owner of San Antonio AirLIFE which provides emergency air medical transport services aboard its fleet of Bell 430 helicopters.

University Health System provides health insurance through its Community First Health Plans a not-for-profit HMO with thousands of members in Bexar and surrounding counties.

Geographic Reach
The system's University Hospital is the lead trauma hospital for a 22-county area of Texas serving patients from Bexar County to South Texas and beyond.

Financial Performance
University Health System's revenue rose 11% to $564 million in 2013 thanks to net patient revenue growth. Net income decreased 24% to $75 million that year as operating expenses including salaries and benefits purchased services and supplies rose.

Strategy
To its benefit University Hospital is the only pediatric trauma center that serves San Antonio and the greater South Texas area. Its emergency center remains the busiest in the region averaging nearly 70000 visits annually.

The organization is in the midst of a system-wide capital improvement program aimed at "right-sizing" its facilities to meet growing demand. To this end the system in 2014 completed construction on a $778 million 10-story Sky Tower at University Hospital that features an expanded emergency department 35 new surgical suites and 420 new private patient rooms. It also opened a six-story Clinical Pavilion at its Robert B. Green Campus in 2013. In 2015 the system was granted approval to renovate and expand its emergency department which will convert most semi-private rooms to fully private rooms and provide additional observance and recovery space. The new facilities are part of University Health System's $900 million Capital Improvement Program to expand and renovate facilities at University Hospital and its downtown Robert B. Green Campus.

Additionally University Health System's downtown health center has added services that include acute and crisis care diagnostic imaging and pharmacy.

In 2014 the system launched its healthyUexpress2 mobile health vehicle which extends its new school-based health care initiative throughout Bexar County.

Company Background

University Health System was founded in 1968.

EXECUTIVES

Evp And Cfo, Peggy Deming
Vice President Chief Information Officer, Bill Phillips
Executive Vice President Chief Operating Officer, Christann Vasquez
Vp Managed Care; President Community First Health Plans, Greg Gieseman
Senior Vice President Chief Nursing Officer, Nancy Ray
Evp Chief Medical Officer, Bryan Alsip
President And Ceo Community Medicine Associates, Priti Mody-Baily
President And Ceo, George B. Hernandez
Executive Vice President Chief Operating Officer, Ed Banos
Svp Chief Revenue Officer, Awoala Banigo
Chairman, James R. Adams
Auditors: BKD LLP DALLAS TEXAS

LOCATIONS

HQ: BEXAR COUNTY HOSPITAL DISTRICT
4502 MEDICAL DR STOP 65-1, SAN ANTONIO, TX 782294402
Phone: 210 358-4000
Web: WWW.UNIVERSITYHEALTHSYSTEM.COM

PRODUCTS/OPERATIONS

2013 Sales

	$ mil.	% of total
Net patient services revenue	462	60
Premium revenue	261	34
Other revenue	49	6
Total	**773**	**100**

2013 Net Patient Revenue

	% of total
Medicare	22
Medicaid	21
Self-Pay including CareLink	37
Commercial insurance	19
Other	1
Total	**100**

Selected Locations
University Hospital
University Health Care
Texas Diabetes Institute
University Family Health Centers

Selected Medical Services
Audiology
Blood Bank
Breast Health
Cancer
Cardiology
Craniosynostosis
Diabetes
ExpressMed
Emergency Center
Endoscopy
Epilepsy
Gynecology
Health Education
Hepatology
HIV/AIDS
Mammography
Maternal-fetal Medicine
Men's Health
Neurosciences
Newborn Services
NICU
Obstetrics
Outpatient Surgery
Pharmacy Services
Pediatrics
Primary Care
Rehabilitation
Respiratory Care
Robot Assisted Surgery
Stroke
Texas Diabetes Institute
Transcatheter Aortic Valve Replacement
Transplant Center
Trauma Center
Vascular
Women's Health

COMPETITORS

CHRISTUS Health	Tenet Healthcare
Methodist Healthcare System	Valley Baptist Health System (Texas)

HISTORICAL FINANCIALS
Company Type: Private

Income Statement				FYE: December 31
	REVENUE ($ mil.)	NET INCOME ($ mil.)	NET PROFIT MARGIN	EMPLOYEES
12/17	1,349	54	4.1%	3,998
12/16	1,253	82	6.6%	—
Annual Growth	**7.6%**	**(33.1%)**	**—**	**—**

2017 Year-End Financials
Return on assets: 2.0%
Return on equity: 4.9%
Current ratio: 3.00
Cash ($ mil.): 91

BI-MART ACQUISITION CORP.

EXECUTIVES

Pres-Coo, Richard Truett
SEC, David B Zientara
Cfo, Dan Chen
Exec Admin, Jodie Murchy
Auditors: DELOITTE & TOUCHE LLP PORTLAN

LOCATIONS

HQ: BI-MART ACQUISITION CORP.
220 SENECA RD, EUGENE, OR 974022725
Phone: 541 344-0681
Web: WWW.BIMART.COM

HISTORICAL FINANCIALS
Company Type: Private

Income Statement				FYE: February 23
	REVENUE ($ mil.)	NET INCOME ($ mil.)	NET PROFIT MARGIN	EMPLOYEES
02/08	721	10	1.4%	3,300
02/07	694	11	1.7%	—
02/06	665	6	1.0%	—
02/05	648	7	1.1%	—
Annual Growth	**3.6%**	**12.8%**		**—**

2008 Year-End Financials
Return on assets: 5.6%
Return on equity: 105.3%
Current ratio: 1.90
Cash ($ mil.): 3

BIG RIVER RESOURCES, LLC.

EXECUTIVES

Ceo-Pres, Raymond E Defenbaugh
Coo, Jim Leiting
Cfo, Jim Hall
MBR-Treas, Les Allen
MBR-V Pres, Andy Brader
Secretary, Gene Youngquist
Scientist, Jeannette Peterson
Information Technology Special, Michael High
Cmms Administrator, Brent Kosowski
Water Treatment Coordinator, Jim Dutton
Operations Manager, Jim Gunter
Auditors: CHRISTIANSON PLLP WILLMAR MI

LOCATIONS

HQ: BIG RIVER RESOURCES, LLC.
211 N GEAR AVE STE 200, WEST BURLINGTON, IA 526551027
Phone: 319 753-1100
Web: WWW.BIGRIVERRESOURCES.COM

HISTORICAL FINANCIALS
Company Type: Private

Income Statement				FYE: December 31
	REVENUE ($ mil.)	NET INCOME ($ mil.)	NET PROFIT MARGIN	EMPLOYEES
12/17	817	33	4.2%	250
12/16	851	74	8.8%	—
12/15	863	74	8.7%	—
12/14	1,184	224	18.9%	—
Annual Growth	**(11.6%)**	**(46.7%)**	**—**	**—**

2017 Year-End Financials
Return on assets: 8.3%
Return on equity: 9.7%
Current ratio: 3.00
Cash ($ mil.): 54

BIG RIVERS ELECTRIC CORPORATION

EXECUTIVES

Ceo, Robert Berry
Chm*, Wayne Elliott
V Chm*, Larry Elder
SEC/Treas*, Paul Edd Butler
Dir*, James Sills
Dir/Acctg/Fin*, Donna Windhaus
Director, Mark McAdams
Supervisor, Nancy Utley
Manager, Tim Tapp
Director, Tom Shaw
Network Technician, Greg Hight

LOCATIONS

HQ: BIG RIVERS ELECTRIC CORPORATION
201 3RD ST, HENDERSON, KY 424202979
Phone: 270 827-2561
Web: WWW.BIGRIVERS.COM

HISTORICAL FINANCIALS

Company Type: Private

Income Statement				FYE: December 31
	REVENUE ($ mil.)	NET INCOME ($ mil.)	NET PROFIT MARGIN	EMPLOYEES
12/12	568	11	2.0%	599
12/11	561	5	1.0%	—
12/10	527	6	1.3%	—
Annual Growth	3.8%	27.0%	—	—

2012 Year-End Financials

Return on assets: 0.7%   Cash ($ mil.): —
Return on equity: 2.8%
Current ratio: 1.70

BIG WEST OF CALIFORNIA, LLC

EXECUTIVES

Member, Fred Greener
Member, Eugene Cotten
Member, Robert Payne
Manager, Eric Byers

LOCATIONS

HQ: BIG WEST OF CALIFORNIA, LLC
1104 COUNTRY HILLS DR, OGDEN, UT 844032400
Phone: 801 296-7890
Web: WWW.BIGWESTOIL.COM

HISTORICAL FINANCIALS

Company Type: Private

Income Statement				FYE: January 31
	REVENUE ($ mil.)	NET INCOME ($ mil.)	NET PROFIT MARGIN	EMPLOYEES
01/07	1,438	(32)	—	260
01/06	1,109	23	2.1%	—
Annual Growth	29.6%	—	—	—

BIG WEST OIL, LLC

Big West Oil keeps the wagon trains rolling across the big West — at least the station wagons. The company is in the oil processing and products business centered around its 35000 barrels-a-day refinery in North Salt Lake Utah to its fleet of tanker trucks that gather crude oil from the refinery and other purchases and deliver to wholesale customers and gas station/convenience stores in seven Western states including Colorado Idaho Nevada Utah and Wyoming. The company's refinery processes crude oil produced in Utah Wyoming and Canada. Big West Oil is a subsidiary of FJ Management.

EXECUTIVES

Pres, Fred L Greener
Mgr of Env Health, Dusty Ott
Manager of Crude Oil Supply, Ed Hatch
Executive Assistant, Kris Barkdull
Process Safety Management Coor, Laura Plummer
It Technical Manager, Orson Thornton
Compliance Manager, Stuart Smith
Pricing, Tawna Cruz

LOCATIONS

HQ: BIG WEST OIL, LLC
333 W CENTER ST, NORTH SALT LAKE, UT 840542805
Phone: 801 624-1000
Web: WWW.BIGWESTOIL.COM

COMPETITORS

HollyFrontier   Sinclair Oil
Marathon Petroleum   Tesoro

HISTORICAL FINANCIALS

Company Type: Private

Income Statement				FYE: January 31
	REVENUE ($ mil.)	NET INCOME ($ mil.)	NET PROFIT MARGIN	EMPLOYEES
01/08	3,053	191	6.3%	460
01/07	2,399	89	3.7%	—
01/06	2,014	102	5.1%	—
01/05	735	50	6.9%	—
Annual Growth	60.7%	55.6%	—	—

2008 Year-End Financials

Return on assets: 19.9%   Cash ($ mil.): 6
Return on equity: 50.4%
Current ratio: 1.20

BIG-D CONSTRUCTION CORP.

Big-D builds big things. Founded in 1967 by Dee Livingood (who carried the nickname "Big-Dee") the family-run construction firm offers design/build services to customers in about 20 states from offices in Utah Arizona California and Wyoming. Known for its work on projects in the food and beverage sector Big-D also works on light commercial office and retail properties manufacturing health care and hospitality projects among others. Its clients have included SYSCO and Marriott. Big-D's Signature Group division builds high-end luxury homes as well as condominiums spas and other special projects in resort communities. Its Self-Performed Services unit works on parking garage architectural and structural projects.

Operations

Big-D reported in mid-2016 that it generates around $1 billion in revenues per year and staffs roughly 800 employees on average.

The contractor operates four main divisions. The Commercial division serves commercial and industrial customers with projects exceeding $5 million in scope while the Light Commercial division offers more streamlined construction services for tenant improvement commercial and light industrial clients with smaller projects (less than $5 million in scope).

The Self-Performed Services division works on concrete (like parking garages) carpentry and specialty construction projects. The Signature division mostly works on higher-end housing and resort-related projects for private estate and resort property owners.

Geographic Reach

The Salt Lake City-based contractor serves clients in 20 states. Its other offices are in Ogden Lindon and Park City in Utah; Pleasanton California; Tempe Arizona; Jackson Wyoming; and Minneapolis Minnesota.

Sales and Marketing

Some of Big-D's clients (as of mid-2016) have included Cabela's SJ Quinney College of Law Epidemiology Utah Department of Health GBR Capital Intermountain Healthcare Salt Lake Community College Monogram Food Solutions and People's Intermountain Bank among others.

Strategy

Big-D Construction continues to steadily open new offices to move closer to target markets. One of its most recent office openings was in Park City Utah in January 2016 which would be used to support its Signature Group. The company has been building in Park City for the past three decades and is known for its work on the Park City Medical Center expansion (still in progress in early 2016) the Swaner Eco Center the Newpark Hotel & Condominiums and the Newpark Town Center.

Company Background

Big-D courted more government projects as a way to weather the economic downturn which has put a halt on many commercial jobs. Among those public projects was the Utah Museum of Natural History at The University of Utah and the Wallace F. Bennett Federal Building in Salt Lake City. Big-D also is focusing on developing its eco-friendly construction business.

EXECUTIVES

Cfo, Larry Worrell
President Mountain West Group, Forrest McNabb
President Big-d Construction, Rob Moore
President Big-d Pacific, Ken Mitchell
Evp And National Managing Director Of Regional Offices, Cory Moore
Vp And Managing Director Southwest, Jeff Arnold
Vp And Managing Director Signature, Michael Kerby
Evp, Troy Thompson
Vice President, Will Hopkins
Chairman, Jack Livingood
Auditors: GRANT THORNTON LLP SALT LAKE

LOCATIONS

HQ: BIG-D CONSTRUCTION CORP.
404 W 400 S, SALT LAKE CITY, UT 841011108
Phone: 801 415-6000
Web: WWW.BIG-D.COM

Selected Markets
Arizona
Arkansas
California
Colorado
Georgia
Hawaii
Idaho
Montana
Nevada
New Mexico
North Carolina
North Dakota
Oklahoma
Oregon
South Dakota
Tennessee
Texas
Utah
Washington

PRODUCTS/OPERATIONS

Selected Services
Construction management
Design/build
Field services
   Architectural concrete
   Finish carpentry
   Rough framing
   Structural concrete
General contracting
Green and Leadership in Energy and Environmental
   Design

Selected Industry Specializations
Commercial/public spaces (governmental educational
   and office complexes; mixed-use projects)
Food processing and distribution
Health care
Hospitality and resort
Manufacturing
Retail

COMPETITORS

Bechtel	Jaynes Companies
Hensel Phelps	Layton
Construction	Okland Construction
J.F. Shea	Swinerton
Jacobsen Construction	

HISTORICAL FINANCIALS
Company Type: Private

Income Statement   FYE: December 31

	REVENUE ($ mil.)	NET INCOME ($ mil.)	NET PROFIT MARGIN	EMPLOYEES
12/12	541	0	—	574
12/11	554	0	—	
12/10	259	0	—	
Annual Growth	44.4%	—	—	

2012 Year-End Financials
Return on assets: —   Cash ($ mil.): 38
Return on equity: —
Current ratio: 1.40

BILLINGS CLINIC

Billings Clinic is an integrated health care system that serves the residents of Big Sky Country. Through a group of more than 320 doctors and other providers the clinic caters to some 570000 people in Billings Montana and in surrounding communities. It offers 50-plus specialties such as emergency and trauma cancer orthopedics birthing cardiovascular neurosciences dialysis and pediatrics. Its operations include a more than 285-bed hospital and the organization's main clinic. Additionally Billings Clinic operates the 90-bed Aspen Meadows Retirement Community and provides support services to several regional community hospitals. The not-for-profit health care system is owned by the community.

Operations
With its vast service area the health care system provides a MedFlight advanced life support fixed-wing aircraft service that transports critically ill or injured patients from rural communities. The service averages 700 flights per year.

As part of its operations Billings Clinic runs a Level II emergency and trauma center 14-suite family birthing center Level III neonatal intensive care unit inpatient cancer care unit and a 15-bed transitional care unit. The health care system's cancer center provides both inpatient and outpatient care in Billings and the surrounding four-state region.

Billings Clinic is governed by a 12-member board consisting of mostly community members but also a pair of doctors and a physician CEO.

In 2014 Billings Clinic's Community Benefit totaled $37.6 million including $14.8 million in financial assistance (charity care) provided to 5744 patients.

Geographic Reach
As the largest health care organization in the area Billings Clinic's service area comprises 40 counties and extends more than 120000 miles in Montana Wyoming and the western Dakotas.

Strategy
Billings Clinic works with pharmaceutical sponsors on a variety of clinical research trials in various phases and indications. To this end it operates a research center with more than 20 years of experience in the areas of basic and clinical research. The center has participated in more than 200 clinical research studies with the help of some 5000 volunteer subjects since 1988.

The health care system has been growing. In 2014 it completed construction of a 24-bed Intensive Care Unit located on the second floor of the hospital directly above the Emergency and Trauma Center. That year Billings Clinic also opened a second ExpressCare retail clinic in the Albertsons store and opened two new major cardiac facilities.

In 2014 Billings Clinic began offering a new non-invasive surgery for the brain using Gamma Knife Perfexion an advanced technology for stereotactic radiosurgery.

Company Background
It expanded its capacity for infusions in 2012 when its Billings Clinic Cody location opened an infusion center. In late 2012 the organization also opened a new Stillwater Billings Clinic medical facility which combines Stillwater Community Hospital and Billings Clinic Columbus and integrates the billing process for the two health care facilities.

The Billings Clinic evolved from the general practice of Dr. Arthur J. Movius who founded his Billings practice in 1911.

EXECUTIVES

Vp And Cio, Chris Stevens
Physician In Chief, Mark C. Rumans
President Billings Clinic Foundation, Jim Duncan
Vp Hospital Operations, Lu Byrd
Cfo, Connie F. Prewitt
Ceo, Randall Gibb
Director Of Radiology, Douglas Bell
Director Of Nursing, Irene Lohkamp
Director Of Medical Records, Lorraine Jelle
Vice President, Erik Wood
Chairman, J. Scott Millikan
Vice Chairman, David Brown
Board Certified Member, Stacy Shomento

LOCATIONS
HQ: BILLINGS CLINIC
  2800 10TH AVE N, BILLINGS, MT 591010703
Phone: 406 657-4000
Web: WWW.BILLINGSCLINIC.COM

PRODUCTS/OPERATIONS

Selected Services
Advance Medical Directives
Allergy Asthma Immunology
Aspen Meadows - Skilled Nursing and Assisted Living
Anticoagulation Clinic
Breast Center
Cancer Center
Cardiovascular Services
Cardiovascular Surgery
Children's Services
Continence Center
Community Training Center
Cosmetic Surgery
da Vinci Surgical System
Dermatology Center
Diabetes Management Center
Diagnostic Imaging
Diabetes
Dialysis Center
Eldercare Solutions
Emergency & Trauma Center
Emmi Educational Videos
Employer Services - Occupational Health
Endocrinology
Eye Center
Facial Plastic Surgery
Family Medicine
Family Birth Center
Gastroenterology
General Surgery
Genetic Counseling
Geriatric Assessment Program
Gynecologic Cancer
Heart Services
Heart Surgery
Home Oxygen & Medical Equipment
Hospitalist Program
Infectious Diseases
Insurance Finder
Internal Medicine
Laboratory Services
LifeFit
Maternal-Fetal Medicine
MedFlight Air Ambulance
Mental Health Services
Metabolism Center
Mohs Surgery
Nutrition Services
Neurosciences
Obstetrics & Gynecology
Occupational Health - Employer Services
Ophthalmology
Orthopedics & Sports Medicine
Palliative Care
Pediatrics
   Pediatric Center
   Pediatric Cancer
   Pediatric Diabetes
   Pediatric Gastroenterology
   Pediatric Pulmonology
   Rehabilitation (Therapy)
Pharmacy
Physical Medicine & Rehabilitation
Plastic Surgery
Primary Care for Adults
Pulmonary Rehabilitation Program
Radiology Services
Reproductive Medicine and Fertility Care
Robotic Surgery
SameDay Care
Senior Services
Sleep Disorders Center
Sports Medicine
Sports Specific Camps
Stroke Care
Surgery Center
Transitional Care Unit
Urology Services
Vascular Surgery
Vein Clinic
Women's Free Screenings
Women's and Children's Services

Selected Affiliate Hospitals and Clinics
Beartooth Billings Clinic - Red Lodge
Colstrip Medical Center - Colstrip
Daniels Memorial Healthcare - Scobey
Livingston HealthCare - Livingston
North Big Horn Hospital - Lovell
Pioneer Medical Center - Big Timber
Roundup Memorial Healthcare - Roundup
Sheridan Memorial Hospital Association
Stillwater Billings Clinic

COMPETITORS

Glendive Medical Center	St. James Healthcare
St. Alexius Medical Center	St. Patrick Hospital
	Wyoming Medical Center

HISTORICAL FINANCIALS

Company Type: Private

Income Statement   FYE: June 30

	REVENUE ($ mil.)	NET INCOME ($ mil.)	NET PROFIT MARGIN	EMPLOYEES
06/16	586	(2)	—	3,300
06/15	565	30	5.4%	—
06/14	593	38	6.6%	—
06/13	560	14	2.6%	—
Annual Growth	1.6%	—	—	—

2016 Year-End Financials
Return on assets: (-0.3%)   Cash ($ mil.): 13
Return on equity: (-0.6%)
Current ratio: 1.80

BIOMEDICAL RESEARCH FOUNDATION OF NORTHWEST LOUISIANA

EXECUTIVES

Chb, Stephen F Skrivanos
V Pres*, James D Dean
V Pres*, Dennis Lower
Prin*, John F George Jr
SEC*, Johnette Magner
Treas*, Arthur Thompson
Director, Joseph Sarpy Jr
Director, John F Sharp
Director, Virginia K Shehee
Director, Elaine Joyce Simpkins PHD
Director, W Juan Watkins
Auditors: POSTLETHWAITE & NETTERVILLE B

LOCATIONS

HQ: BIOMEDICAL RESEARCH FOUNDATION OF NORTHWEST LOUISIANA
2031 KINGS HWY, SHREVEPORT, LA 711033600
Phone: 318 716-4190
Web: WWW.BRFLA.ORG

HISTORICAL FINANCIALS

Company Type: Private

Income Statement   FYE: September 30

	REVENUE ($ mil.)	NET INCOME ($ mil.)	NET PROFIT MARGIN	EMPLOYEES
09/15	564	14	2.6%	50
09/14	502	(1)	—	—
09/13*	10	(5)	—	—
12/09	15	0	2.1%	—
Annual Growth	81.9%	88.0%	—	—

*Fiscal year change

2015 Year-End Financials
Return on assets: 3.8%   Cash ($ mil.): 8
Return on equity: 24.4%
Current ratio: 1.10

BIOURJA TRADING, LLC

EXECUTIVES

Ceo, Amit Bhandari
President, Dan Gordon
MBR, Nathalie De Vos Burchart
MBR, Arpita Bhandari
MBR, Abhi Shek Jain
MBR, Dushyant Kansara
Law Specialist, Varinder Gill
Head of Human Resources, Steve Sfamenos
Auditors: CARR RIGGS & INGRAM LLC HOUST

LOCATIONS

HQ: BIOURJA TRADING, LLC
1080 ELDRIDGE PKWY # 1175, HOUSTON, TX 770772582
Phone: 832 775-9000
Web: WWW.BIOURJA.COM

HISTORICAL FINANCIALS

Company Type: Private

Income Statement   FYE: December 31

	REVENUE ($ mil.)	NET INCOME ($ mil.)	NET PROFIT MARGIN	EMPLOYEES
12/13	4,622	26	0.6%	72
12/12	2,992	11	0.4%	—
12/11	3,842	13	0.4%	—
Annual Growth	9.7%	38.6%	—	—

2013 Year-End Financials
Return on assets: 16.9%   Cash ($ mil.): 15
Return on equity: 57.0%
Current ratio: 1.40

BLACK & VEATCH CORPORATION

Black & Veatch (BV) is one of the world's top global engineering procurement consulting and construction firms specializing in infrastructure development for the energy oil and gas water environmental and telecommunications industries and governments. BV offers environmental consulting operations and maintenance security design and consulting management consulting and IT services. Boasting roughly $3.5 billion in annual revenue the employee-owned contractor has completed projects in more than 100 countries including coal nuclear and combustion turbine plants; drinking water and coastal water operations; and wireless and broadband installations. The company was founded by engineers E. B. Black and Tom Veatch in 1917.

Financial Performance
A privately-owned company Black & Veatch (BV) reported $3.5 billion in revenue in 2018.

Strategy
Black & Veatch (BV) frequently seeks partnerships to expand its business reach. In 2019 the company announced a collaboration with Inflowmatix to develop resilient water networks in England and Wales where water companies have been tasked with reducing water leakage by 15% by 2025. That same year the company partnered with tech startup grants competition Launch KC (a joint venture between the Downtown Council and the Economic Development Corporation of Kansas City) to launch its IgniteX Cleantech Accelerator. Part of its Growth Accelerator segment the initiative will look to fund startups in renewable and distributed energy mobility agritech and machine learning.

The company is also unafraid to expand its internal operations to better address its end markets. In 2019 BV reorganized its global power business to focus on its renewables operations and introduce a new unit that will concentrate solely on emerging fuel sources and power distribution. The division will focus on regions with high population growth and reliance on power grids including North America and Southeast Asia and flexibly address energy types from zero-carbon to conventional. It also created a Smart Maintenance business to provide asset health analysis preventative maintenance and AI-based maintenance interventions to UK utilities.

EXECUTIVES

Ceo Energy Business, O. H. (Dean) Oskvig
Cfo, Karen L. Daniel
President Federal Services Division, William R. (Bill) Van Dyke
President Telecommunications, Martin G. Travers
President Water Business, Cindy Wallis-Lage
Chief Administrative Officer; President Administrative Division, James R. (Jim) Lewis
Svp B&v Energy Asia Middle East India Europe And B&v Water Asia Pacific, Hoe Wai Cheong
President Management Consulting, John Chevrette
Chairman President & Ceo, Steven L. Edwards
President Construction & Procurement, John E. Murphy
Vice President, Lisa Terry
Associate Vice President, Adrienne Mickells
Vice President Finance, Angela Hoffman
Vice President Tax Counsel, Jeffrey Stamm
Vice President Senior Project Director, Jim Doull
Vice President Of Service, Emily Vijayakirthi
Associate Vice President Mechanical Department Manager Energy, Joel Lundquist
Operations Manager Of Oil And Gas China Associate Vice President Energy Division, Michael Gai
Vice President Of Enterprise Systems, Bob Brnilovich
Associate Vice President, Scott Roesle
Senior Vice President Assistant General Counsel And Chief Compliance Manager, Peter Loftspring
Vice President Projects Service Area, Doug Anderson
Associate Vice President Project Manager, David Lefebvre
Vice President Marketing, Peter Sheckleford-lister

Vice President And Project Director Power
  Business, Jeffrey Kurtz
Associate Vice President, Norman Song
Associate Vice President Construction Group
  Leader, Mike Baker
Vice President, Scott Kinner
Associate Vice President, Christopher Mueller
Associate Vice President And Division Counsel,
  Curtis J Martin
Associate Vice President Asset Management
  Services, David Brill
Associate Vice President And Project Manager For
  Global Energy Business, Mark Mcdermott
Vice President Public Safety, Chris Krafft
Vice President, Dave Abrams
Associate Vice President, Matt Bond
Associate Vice President, Donnie Griffin
Associate Vice President Director Wastewater
  Treatment Technology President Mark Steichen
  Process Engineer. J Associate Vice, Mark
  Steichen
Department Head, Dan Nelson
Vice President, Richard Jacober
Associate Vice President, Derek Cambridge
Associate Vice President Asset Management,
  David Price
Associate Vice President Asset Management,
  David C Price
Vice President And Project Director, Charles
  Mitchell
Associate Vice President, John H Johnson
Associate Vice President Director Of Finance And
  Administration B And V Water Americas, Mike
  Goff
Senior Vice President Mining, James Spenceley
Vice President Client Director, Peter Cohlmia
Senior Vice President And Managing Direc, James
  Schnieders
Associate Vice President Project Director, Jim
  Morley
Vice President Business Development, Julie
  Cronin
Secretary, Cheryl Toske

LOCATIONS

HQ: BLACK & VEATCH CORPORATION
  11401 LAMAR AVE, OVERLAND PARK, KS 662111598
Phone: 913 458-2000
Web: WWW.BV.COM

PRODUCTS/OPERATIONS

Market Sectors

Energy
  Air quality control
  Coal
  Combustion turbine
  Gas oil and chemicals
  Hydropower
  IGCC
  Nuclear
  Power delivery
  Renewables
Environmental
  Air quality
  Compliance management
  Due diligence
  Field studies/investigations
  Permitting
  Prevention plans
  Remediation
  Watershed analysis and restoration
  Water/wastewater
Federal
  Civil works
  Disaster support
  Facilities
  Federal design-build
  Management programs
  Security
Management consulting
  Integrated strategy development
  Process improvement
  Technology application services

Services
  Asset management
  Climate change solutions
  Construction
  Design/build
  Engineering and design
  Engineering consulting
  Infrastructure planning
  Management consulting
  Procurement
  Program management
  SAP services
  Smart utility
  Water spares
Telecommunications
  Broadband wireline
  Cyber and physical security
  Site acquisition services
  Telecom for smart utilities
  Utility automation
  Utility telecommunications
  Wireless
Water
  Conveyance systems and tunneling services
  Drinking water
  Hydropower
  River and coastal management
  Wastewater
  Water resources

COMPETITORS

AECOM	Louis Berger
ARCADIS	MWH Global
Amec Foster Wheeler	McDermott
Balfour Beatty	Michael Baker
Infrastructure	Mott MacDonald
Bechtel	Parsons Brinckerhoff
Burns & McDonnell	Parsons Corporation
Burns and Roe	SNC-Lavalin
Costain	TIC Holdings
EA Engineering	Tetra Tech
Fluor	Zachry Inc.
HNTB Companies	

HISTORICAL FINANCIALS
Company Type: Private

Income Statement				FYE: December 31
	REVENUE ($ mil.)	NET INCOME ($ mil.)	NET PROFIT MARGIN	EMPLOYEES
12/09	1,163	58	5.0%	4,065
12/08	1,267	16	1.3%	—
12/07	1,287	33	2.6%	—
Annual Growth	(4.9%)	31.7%	—	—

2009 Year-End Financials
Return on assets: 6.9%   Cash ($ mil.): 16
Return on equity: 21.8%
Current ratio: 1.30

BLACK & VEATCH HOLDING COMPANY

EXECUTIVES

Chb-Pres-Ceo, Steven L Edwards
Evp-Cfo, Kenneth L Williams
Svp-Treasurer, Michael Williams
Exec V Pres-SEC*, Timothy W Triplett
Asst SEC, Andrea C Bernica
Coordinator, Arnaldo Jusino
Mre Engineer, Brigitta Wade
Employee, Derrick Draper
Bim Coordinator, Jason Seck
Librarian, Jennifer Langlois

Project Controls Manager, Kevin Bogner
Auditors: KPMG LLP KANSAS CITY MISSOUR

LOCATIONS

HQ: BLACK & VEATCH HOLDING COMPANY
  11401 LAMAR AVE, OVERLAND PARK, KS 662111598
Phone: 913 458-2000
Web: WWW.BV.COM

HISTORICAL FINANCIALS
Company Type: Private

Income Statement				FYE: December 28
	REVENUE ($ mil.)	NET INCOME ($ mil.)	NET PROFIT MARGIN	EMPLOYEES
12/18	3,479	80	2.3%	8,495
12/17	3,364	87	2.6%	—
12/16*	3,207	75	2.3%	—
01/16	2,955	109	3.7%	—
Annual Growth	5.6%	(9.7%)	—	—
*Fiscal year change

2018 Year-End Financials
Return on assets: 4.9%   Cash ($ mil.): 383
Return on equity: 54.7%
Current ratio: 1.10

BLACK & VEATCH INTERNATIONAL COMPANY

EXECUTIVES

Chb, Steve Edwards
President, Mario Azar
Evp-SEC, Timothy W Triplett
Evp-Cfo, Kenneth L Williams
Svp-Treasurer, Michael Williams
Svp-Assst SEC, Peter D Loftspring
Asst Secretary, Andrea C Bernica
Associate Vice President, Donnie Ginn
Engineer, Jeff Coggins
Auditors: KPMG LLP KANSAS CITY MO

LOCATIONS

HQ: BLACK & VEATCH INTERNATIONAL COMPANY
  11401 LAMAR AVE, OVERLAND PARK, KS 662111598
Phone: 913 458-2000
Web: WWW.BV.COM

HISTORICAL FINANCIALS
Company Type: Private

Income Statement				FYE: December 31
	REVENUE ($ mil.)	NET INCOME ($ mil.)	NET PROFIT MARGIN	EMPLOYEES
12/09	711	43	6.1%	283
12/08	711	43	6.1%	—
12/07	1	(0)	—	—
12/06	1	(0)	—	—
Annual Growth	754.9%	—	—	—

2009 Year-End Financials
Return on assets: 8.5%   Cash ($ mil.): 39
Return on equity: 37.5%
Current ratio: 1.10

BLARNEY CASTLE OIL CO.

While kissing the Blarney stone has a reputation for reliably making people loquacious Blarney Castle Oil and Propane has a reputation for reliably supplying its customers with fuels. The family-owned company transports petroleum products to customers throughÂ about 10Â office locations in Michigan. Its products include agricultural and commercial fuels (diesel and gasoline) commercial and industrial lubricants and coolants home heating oil fuel oil and propane. Blarney Castle Oil and Propane also operates 90 convenience stores under the EZ Mart brand name.

EXECUTIVES

Pres-Treas, Dennis E McCarthy
V Pres*, William J McCarthy
SEC*, Helen McCarthy
Project Manager, Tim McKay
Senior Accountant, Jen Roach
Chief Financial Officer, Joe Taraskavage
Branch Manager Alpena, Scott Datema
Auditors: HUNGERFORD NICHOLS GRAND RAPI

LOCATIONS

HQ: BLARNEY CASTLE OIL CO.
12218 WEST ST, BEAR LAKE, MI 496149453
Phone: 231 864-3111
Web: WWW.BLARNEYCASTLEOIL.COM

COMPETITORS

Crystal Flash Energy   Vesco Oil

HISTORICAL FINANCIALS

Company Type: Private

Income Statement				FYE: March 31
	REVENUE ($ mil.)	NET INCOME ($ mil.)	NET PROFIT MARGIN	EMPLOYEES
03/13	513	6	1.2%	700
03/12	501	4	0.8%	—
03/11	415	2	0.7%	—
Annual Growth	11.2%	42.7%	—	—

2013 Year-End Financials

Return on assets: 10.9%
Return on equity: 15.5%   Cash ($ mil.): 7
Current ratio: 2.60

BLOUNT INTERNATIONAL, INC.

Folks at Blount International have their work cut out for them. The manufacturer produces cutting chain guide bars sprockets and accessories for chainsaws concrete-cutting equipment and lawnmower blades. Blount's lineup is sold under brands Oregon Carlton Tiger and Windsor to outdoor equipment OEMs including Husqvarna and the replacement and retail markets. Other subsidiaries supply log splitters post-hole diggers and other agriculture add-ons. End users are professionals and consumers engaged in forestry lawn and garden farming and construction activities. The company's manufacturing facilities dot Brazil Canada China and the US. About two-thirds of Blount's sales are made outside the US. In early 2016 it was acquired by private-equity firms American Securities and P2 Capital Partners.

Operations

Blount sells its products across two segments: forestry lawn and garden (FLAG) and farm ranch and agriculture (FRAG). The former segment represents about 70% of its total sales each year while the latter accounts for the remainder.

The company also operates a concrete cutting and finishing (CCF) equipment business that is reported within the "corporate and other" category. This business manufactures and markets diamond-cutting chains assembles and markets concrete cutting chain saws and purchases other concrete cutting products that are marketed to the construction and utility industries.

Sales and Marketing

The company sells its products through a global sales and distribution network of over 300 distributors 30000 dealers direct sales companies and mass merchants which sell to the global forestry lawn and garden; farm ranch and agriculture; and construction products end markets. The company also sells through nearly 100 original equipment manufacturers.

Financial Performance

After posting a decline in 2013 Blount saw its revenues rebound for 2014 increasing 5% to peak at a record-setting $945 million. Profits also skyrocketed over 650% from $5 million in 2013 to $37 million in 2014. Its operating cash flow has fluctuated over the years rising sharply in 2013 but declining by 15% during 2014.

The historic growth for 2014 was driven by a 5% increase from its FLAG segment due to a rise in demand across most geographic regions especially South America (increased by 8%) and North America (7%). Its FRAG operations experienced a 3% increase in 2014 due to higher unit sales volumes (led by increased sales of log splitters and tractor attachments) and higher average selling prices across North America.

Blount's surge in profits for 2014 was attributed to the improved revenue coupled with lower expenses related to the impairment of acquired intangible assets along with charges related to restructuring activities.

Strategy

Blount has also fueled its momentum by strategically expanding its product portfolio and customer base through acquisitions. In 2014 the company acquired Arizona-based Pentruder. As part of the transaction the company became the exclusive distributor of Pentruder high-performance concrete cutting systems in North and South America. Pentruder now operates under Blount's concrete cutting and finishing (CCF) equipment business.

EXECUTIVES

Vp Treasurer And Controller, Calvin E. Jenness, age 63, $385,000 total compensation
Ceo And Chairman, Joshua L. (Josh) Collins, age 54, $565,000 total compensation
President Frag Division, Gerald D. (Jerry) Johnson, $350,000 total compensation
Vp Flag Manufacturing Operations, William C. Alford
President And Coo, David A. Willmott, age 49, $500,000 total compensation
Svp Global Supply Chain, David K. Parrish
Vp And Cio, Kevin M. Trepa
Svp Global Sales And Marketing Flag Division, Dave P. Gillrie
Vice President Marketing, Alan Lofurno
Vice President, Valdir R Viana
Auditors: KPMG LLP PORTLAND OREGON

LOCATIONS

HQ: BLOUNT INTERNATIONAL, INC.
4909 SE INTERNATIONAL WAY, PORTLAND, OR 972224679
Phone: 503 653-8881
Web: WWW.BLOUNT.COM

PRODUCTS/OPERATIONS

Selected Products

Chain drive sprockets
Chainsaw guide bars
Concrete-cutting chainsaws and circular saws (gasoline and hydraulic powered)
Cutting chain (for chainsaws)
Diamond-segmented chain (for cutting concrete)
Farm accessories
Lawn and garden cutting attachments
Lawnmower and edger cutting blades
Log splitters
Maintenance tools (for chainsaws and mechanical timber harvesting equipment)
Tractor driven post-hole diggers
Tractor three-point linkage parts

COMPETITORS

Alamo Group	Great Plains
Ariens	Manufacturing
Briggs & Stratton	Husqvarna
Caterpillar	Kubota
Champion Cutting Tool	MTD Products
Deere	Metso
Dover Corp.	STIHL Incorporated
Emak Group	Terex

HISTORICAL FINANCIALS

Company Type: Private

Income Statement				FYE: December 31
	REVENUE ($ mil.)	NET INCOME ($ mil.)	NET PROFIT MARGIN	EMPLOYEES
12/15	828	(49)		4,000
12/14	944	36	3.9%	—
12/13	900	4	0.5%	—
12/12	927	39	4.3%	—
Annual Growth	(3.7%)	—	—	—

2015 Year-End Financials

Return on assets: (-7.2%)   Cash ($ mil.): 25
Return on equity: (-45.1%)
Current ratio: 2.60

BLUE BUFFALO PET PRODUCTS, INC.

Blue Buffalo Pet Products is converting pet parents into what it refers to as "True Blue Believers" with its wholesome pet food offerings. The company makes natural dog and cat food using whole meats fruits and vegetables with no by-products or artificial ingredients; some products are also grain-free. By riding the wave of people forking over big bucks for natural and wholesome food for themselves and their families Blue Bufallo has positioned dogs and cats as members of the family and has risen to be the #1 brand in the Wholesome Natural pet food market segment. The company sells its products internationally but the majority of net sales remains in the US. Bill Bishop started the company when his dog Blue developed cancer but recovered after eating food he formulated. Cereal giant General Mills bought Blue Buffalo in 2018.

Change in Company Type

In mid-2018 consumer packaged goods company General Mills paid some $8 billion for Blue Buffalo in its quest to reshape its portfolio with more natural and organic brands. Blue Buffalo will operate as an independent subsidiary while taking advantage of the supply chain distribution and sales capabilities of its new parent.

Operations

Blue Buffalo operates its business in one reportable segment. It makes five main lines of pet food covering different product types diet types breed sizes for dogs and life stages.

The company has traditionally sold its products through specialty channels such as pet stores in the past but has recently expanded its distribution into the food drug and mass (FDM) markets (such as grocery stores) in the US where it now generates more than half its revenues.

The company produces 55% of its dry food in its own food production facility in Joplin MO and plans to open a new facility in Richmond IN by the end of 2018. Blue Buffalo hopes to handle 85% of its dry food production at these two sites over the next several years. The remainder of food production is through third-party contract manufacturers.

Geographic Reach

Blue Bufallo's BLUE brand products are sold in the US Canada Japan and Mexico. The US accounts for more than 95% of net sales.

Sales and Marketing

Blue Buffalo BLUE products are sold through multiple distributors who also provide logistics services and some in-field sales support. Products appear in specialty channels such as national and regional pet stores farm and feed stores e-commerce retailers and select grocery stores. The company has minimal sales through veterinary clinics and hospitals. Its sales teams are organized by type of retail accounts they sell to — National Accounts Regional Accounts eCommerce and Food-Drug-Mass (FDM).

The company promotes and markets its products through television internet and print advertisements produced by an in-house agency. Blue Buffalo has increased its advertising spend about 60% in the past three years ($132.3 million in 2016 $101.2 million in 2016 and $83.6 million in 2015).

In 2017 almost 60% of Blue Buffalo's sales were generated from its two largest customers PetSmart and Petco. Other customers include Tractor Supply Company Pet Supermarket Target Kroger Meijer and Publix.

Financial Performance

Blue Buffalo has enjoyed double digit growth over the past several years with sales in 2017 amounting to $1.3 billion (an 11% increase over 2016). Net sales were driven by a favorable product mix growth in sales in national pet superstores and expansion in farm and feed stores and e-commerce retailers.

Net income increased 49% to $193.5 million in 2017 compared with $130.2 million in 2016 mainly due to increased volume supply chain efficiencies and lower tax rates.

Cash at the end of fiscal 2017 was $282.2 million a decrease of $10.3 million from the prior year. Cash from operations contributed $193.9 billion to the coffers while investing activities used $171.0 million mainly for capital expenditures for a three-year program to expand its internal manufacturing capabilities. Financing activities used another $33.5 million for repurchases of common stock.

Strategy

Blue Buffalo touts its extensive product line and continuous innovation as differentiators for the company. It also includes educating "pet parents" as part of the company's strategy for attracting new customers; it uses part-time employees it calls Pet Detectives to interact with and market directly to customers shopping for pet food in stores in the US and Canada. The company has also significantly increased spending on advertising over the past three years. Some of Blue Buffalo's key initiatives going forward include expanding distribution in the US growing its FDM business expanding the wet food and pet treat lines and increasing its focus on e-commerce sales.

The company is leveraging General Mills' resources and expertise to expand its FDM distribution in the US and refine its supply chain and category management operations. It will also capitalize on General Mills' customer relationship management (CRM) capabilities to to increase communication with customers.

In the pet specialty channel Blue Buffalo is investing in media advertising to support sales as well as new packaging and products in the wet food and treats categories an area it feels is currently underdeveloped.

The company aims to continue manufacturing operations at both company-owned as well as co-manufacturing facilities. It will open a new facility in Richmond IN in 2018 and a new treat facility at its existing location in Joplin MO.

EXECUTIVES

Evp Cfo And Treasurer, Michael (Mike) Nathenson, $318,270 total compensation
Ceo, William (Billy) Bishop, $269,088 total compensation
Auditors: KPMG LLP STAMFORD CONNECTICU

LOCATIONS

HQ: BLUE BUFFALO PET PRODUCTS, INC.
11 RIVER RD STE 103, WILTON, CT 068976011
Phone: 203 762-9751
Web: WWW.BLUEBUFFALO.COM

PRODUCTS/OPERATIONS

2017 Sales

	$ mil.	% of total
Dry foods	1,013	80
Wet foods treats and other	261	20
Total	**1,274**	**100**

Selected Product Lines

BLUE Life Protection Formula
BLUE Wilderness
BLUE Basics
BLUE Freedom
BLUE Natural Veterinary Diet

COMPETITORS

Big Heart Pet Brands	OurPet's Co.
Breeder's Choice	Pet Supermarket
Hill's Pet Nutrition	Pet Valu
Iams	Procter & Gamble
Mars Incorporated	Royal Canin
Nestlé Purina PetCare	Simmons Foods
Nutro Products	WellPet

HISTORICAL FINANCIALS

Company Type: Private

Income Statement

FYE: December 31

	REVENUE ($ mil.)	NET INCOME ($ mil.)	NET PROFIT MARGIN	EMPLOYEES
12/17	1,274	193	15.2%	1,800
12/16	1,149	130	11.3%	—
12/15	1,027	89	8.7%	—
Annual Growth	11.4%	47.1%	—	—

2017 Year-End Financials

Return on assets: 22.8%
Return on equity: 64.7%
Current ratio: 3.70

Cash ($ mil.): 282

BLUE CROSS & BLUE SHIELD ASSOCIATION

Blue insurers prefer to sing a happy healthy tune. Health plan providers affiliated with the Blue Cross and Blue Shield Association (BCBSA) — known as "the Blues" — serve some 106 million members nationwide. The association is a federation of about 40 independent health insurance companies who license the Blue Cross and Blue Shield brand names. Member companies own the rights to sell Blue-branded health plans within defined regions. BCBSA coordinates some national programs such as BlueCard which allows members of one franchisee to have coverage in other service areas and the Federal Employee Program (FEP) which covers more than half of federal government employees retirees and their families. The company traces its roots back to 1929.

HISTORY

Blue Cross was born in 1929 when Baylor University official Justin Kimball offered schoolteachers 21 days of hospital care for $6 a year. A major plan feature was a community rating system that based premiums on the community claims experience rather than members' conditions.

The Blue Cross symbol was devised in 1933 by Minnesota plan executive E. A. van Steenwyck. By 1935 many of the 15 plans in 11 states used the symbol. Many states gave the plans not-for-profit status and in 1936 the American Hospital Association formed the Committee on Hospital Service (renamed the Blue Cross Association in 1948) to coordinate them.

As Blue Cross grew state medical societies sponsored prepaid plans to cover doctors' fees. In 1946 they united under the aegis of the American Medical Association (AMA) as the Associated Medical Care Plans (later the Association of Blue Shield Plans).

In 1948 the AMA thwarted a Blue Cross attempt to merge with Blue Shield. But the Blues increasingly cooperated on public policy matters while competing for members and each Blue formed a not-for-profit corporation to coordinate its plan's activities.

Blue Cross insured about a third of the US by 1960. Over the next decade the Blues started administering Medicare and other government health plans and by 1970 half of Blue Cross' premiums came from government entities.

In the 1970s the Blues adopted such cost-control measures as review of hospital admissions; many plans even abandoned the community rating system. Most began emphasizing preventive care in HMOs or PPOs. The two Blues finally merged in 1982 to form the Blue Cross and Blue Shield Association (BCBSA) but this had little effect on the associations' bottom lines as losses grew.

By the 1990s the Blues were big business. Some of the state associations offered officers high salaries and perks but still insisted on special regulatory treatment.

But as lower-cost plans attracted the hale and hearty the Blues' customers became older sicker and more expensive. With their quasi-charitable status and outdated rate structures many Blues plans lost market share.

The Blues fought back by updating their technology and rate structures merging among themselves creating for-profit subsidiaries forming alliances with for-profit enterprises or (in some cases) dropping their not-for-profit status and going public — while still using the Blue Cross Blue Shield name.

Blue Cross of California became the first chapter to give up its tax-free status when it was bought by WellPoint Health Networks a managed care subsidiary it had founded in 1992. In a 1996 deal WellPoint became the chapter's parent and converted it to for-profit status assigning all of the stock to a public charitable foundation which received the proceeds of its subsequent IPO. WellPoint also bought the group life and health division of Massachusetts Mutual Life Insurance.

The for-profit switches picked up in 1997. Blue Cross of Connecticut merged with insurance provider Anthem and other mergers followed. Half the nation's Blues formed an alliance called BluesCONNECT (now BlueCard) competing with national health plans by offering employers one nationwide benefits organization. BCBSA also pursued overseas licensing agreements in Europe South America and Asia assembling a network of Blue Cross-friendly caregivers aiming for worldwide coverage.

In 1998 Blues in more than 35 states sued the nation's big cigarette companies to recoup costs of treating smoking-related illnesses. In a separate lawsuit Blue Cross and Blue Shield of Minnesota received nearly $300 million from the tobacco industry. In 1999 Anthem moved to acquire or affiliate with Blues in Colorado Maine Nevada and New Hampshire.

After years of discussions in 2000 the New York attorney general permitted Empire Blue Cross and Blue Shield to convert to for-profit status. The pace of for-profit conversions slowed down in following years however as state regulators became increasingly wary of signing off on the procedure. The improved financial situation of most of the not-for-profit Blues also took away a key incentive for for-profit conversion — access to capital markets.

In 2004 Anthem and WellPoint Health Networks merged and Anthem's name changed to Wellpoint (though it continued to use the Anthem brand name in certain markets) becoming the largest for-profit health insurer in the nation. WellPoint acquired Empire Blue Cross and its parent WellChoice as well as non-Blue consumer-driven plan provider Lumenos in 2005. In addition to snapping up Blues providers the for-profit WellPoint acquired a number of non-Blue subsidiaries such as American Imaging Management while meeting the requirement that it get two-thirds of its insurance revenue from Blue products to keep its BCBSA license. (Wellpoint changed its name back to Anthem in 2012.)

Consolidation among Blues plans continued when Health Care Service Corporation added its fourth not-for-profit Blues plan (Blue Cross and Blue Shield of Oklahoma) in 2005.

In 2007 BCBSA was approved under a Federal Savings Bank charter to provide health-related banking services through its Blue Healthcare Bank.

Two licensees Highmark and Independence Blue Cross had agreed to merge in 2008 but the deal was terminated in early 2009 after long delays and heavy regulatory concern that the merger would create an unfair advantage in the Pennsylvania market. Some consolidation continued however as Triple-S which operates under the Blue Shield brand in Puerto Rico acquired and absorbed Blue Cross licensee La Cruz Azul from Independence Blue Cross in 2009.

Highmark reached a formal affiliation agreement (including shared administrative and IT resources) with Blue Cross Blue Shield of Delaware in 2011.

Another regional Blues provider Cambia Health Solutions (formerly Regence Group) changed its name in 2011 to signify its diversification efforts though its BCBS subsidiaries continue to operate under the Regence name.

Three Blues companies — Anthem Health Care Service Corp. (HCSC) and BCBS of Michigan— joined together in 2011 to invest in a commercial insurance exchange (Bloom Health) designed to allow businesses to contribute to employees' selected health coverage. The venture was part of the Blues' efforts to meet the changing US insurance needs under health reform laws.

BCBSA launched a new wellness rewards program for FEP participants in 2012.

EXECUTIVES

President And Ceo, Scott P. Serota, $1,307,804 total compensation
Evp And Cfo, Robert J. (Bob) Kolodgy
Svp Operations And Cio, Doug Porter
Evp And Chief Of Staff, Jennifer Vachon
Chief Medical Officer, Trent Haywood
Svp Commercial Markets, Kari Hedges
Vp And Cto, Nasir Khan
Vice President, Cynthia Rolfe
Vice President Congressional Relations, Kathy Didawick
Executive Vice President Of He, Andrew Dreyfus
Vice President Of Marketing, Joan Davis
Vp Enterprise Data Solutions, Ngan Macdonald
Vice President Operations, Gerri Grove
Vice President Information Technology Process Excellence, Chris Privoznik
Vice President Information Security, Brenda Callaway
Chairman, Daniel J. Hilferty

LOCATIONS

HQ: BLUE CROSS & BLUE SHIELD ASSOCIATION
225 N MICHIGAN AVE FL 5, CHICAGO, IL 606017658
Phone: 312 297-6000
Web: WWW.BCBS.COM

PRODUCTS/OPERATIONS

Selected Blue Cross and Blue Shield Licensees
Arkansas Blue Cross and Blue Shield
Blue Cross and Blue Shield of Alabama
Blue Cross and Blue Shield of Arizona
Blue Cross and Blue Shield of Delaware
Blue Cross and Blue Shield of Florida
Blue Cross and Blue Shield of Kansas
Blue Cross and Blue Shield of Kansas City
Blue Cross and Blue Shield of Louisiana
Blue Cross and Blue Shield of Massachusetts
Blue Cross and Blue Shield of Michigan
Blue Cross and Blue Shield of Minnesota
Blue Cross and Blue Shield of Mississippi
Blue Cross and Blue Shield of Montana
Blue Cross and Blue Shield of Nebraska
Blue Cross and Blue Shield of North Carolina
Blue Cross and Blue Shield of North Dakota
Blue Cross and Blue Shield of Rhode Island
Blue Cross and Blue Shield of South Carolina
Blue Cross and Blue Shield of Tennessee
Blue Cross and Blue Shield of Vermont
Blue Cross and Blue Shield of Wyoming
Blue Cross of Idaho Health Service
Blue Cross of Northeastern Pennsylvania
California Physicians' Service (dba Blue Shield of California)
Cambia Health Solutions Inc. (formerly The Regence Group)
  Regence BlueCross and BlueShield of Oregon
  Regence BlueCross BlueShield of Utah
  Regence BlueShield of Idaho
  Regence BlueShield (Washington)
Capital BlueCross (Pennsylvania)
CareFirst
  CareFirst Blue Cross and Blue Shield (District of Columbia)
  CareFirst Blue Cross and Blue Shield of Maryland
Excellus BlueCross BlueShield of New York
Hawaii Medical Service Association
Health Care Service Corporation
  Blue Cross and Blue Shield of Illinois
  Blue Cross and Blue Shield of New Mexico

  Blue Cross and Blue Shield of Oklahoma
  Blue Cross and Blue Shield of Texas
HealthNow New York
  BlueCross and BlueShield of Western New York
  BlueShield of Northeastern New York
Highmark Blue Cross Blue Shield (Pennsylvania)
  Mountain State Blue Cross and Blue Shield (West Virginia)
Horizon Healthcare Services (dba Horizon Blue Cross and Blue Shield of New Jersey)
Independence Blue Cross (Pennsylvania)
Premera Blue Cross (Alaska and Washington)
Triple-S (Puerto Rico)
Wellmark
  Wellmark Blue Cross and Blue Shield of Iowa
  Wellmark Blue Cross and Blue Shield of South Dakota
WellPoint
  Anthem Blue Cross and Blue Shield of Colorado
  Anthem Blue Cross and Blue Shield of Connecticut
  Anthem Blue Cross and Blue Shield of Indiana
  Anthem Blue Cross and Blue Shield of Kentucky
  Anthem Blue Cross and Blue Shield of Maine
  Anthem Blue Cross and Blue Shield of Nevada
  Anthem Blue Cross and Blue Shield of New Hampshire
  Anthem Blue Cross and Blue Shield of Ohio
  Anthem Blue Cross and Blue Shield of Virginia
  Blue Cross and Blue Shield of Georgia
  Blue Cross and Blue Shield of Missouri (dba Anthem Blue Cross and Blue Shield)
  BlueCross BlueShield of Wisconsin (dba Anthem Blue Cross and Blue Shield)
  California Blue Cross (Anthem Blue Cross)
  Empire Blue Cross and Blue Shield of New York
International plans
  Blue Cross & Blue Shield de Uruguay
  BlueCross BlueShield of Panama

COMPETITORS

AMERIGROUP	Kaiser Foundation
Aetna	Health Plan
CIGNA	Molina Healthcare
Centene	Principal Financial
Health Net	UnitedHealth Group
Humana	WellCare Health Plans

HISTORICAL FINANCIALS

Company Type: Private

Income Statement				FYE: December 31
	REVENUE ($ mil.)	NET INCOME ($ mil.)	NET PROFIT MARGIN	EMPLOYEES
12/17	591	(1)	—	1,880
12/06	320	14	4.5%	—
12/05	275	8	3.0%	—
12/04	270	11	4.3%	—
Annual Growth	6.2%	—	—	—

2017 Year-End Financials

Return on assets: (-0.2%) Cash ($ mil.): 486
Return on equity: (-1.5%)
Current ratio: 1.00

BLUE CROSS AND BLUE SHIELD OF ARIZONA, INC.

Blue Cross Blue Shield of Arizona (BCBSAZ) provides health insurance products and services to nearly 1.5 million Arizonans. The not-for-profit company offers a variety of managed care plans to small and large employer groups individuals and families including PPO HMO and high-deductible health plans. It also provides dental vision and prescription drug coverage as well as supplemental health plans for Medicare beneficiaries. Additionally BCBSAZ's HealthyBlue wellness and disease management programs give members information and services that encourage healthy lifestyles. Founded in 1939 the company is an independent licensee of the Blue Cross and Blue Shield Association.

Geographic Reach
BCBSAZ serves customers throughout the state of Arizona from its offices in Chandler Flagstaff Phoenix and Tucson. It has a contracted network of physicians and dentists located across the state.

Sales and Marketing
BCBSAZ offers insurance services to individuals and families seniors employers brokers and consultants and health care professionals through agents.

Its Alliance Network includes contracted hospitals and doctors that are part of Banner Health John C. Lincoln Health Network and Scottsdale Healthcare. Its Select Network comprises contracted hospitals and doctors that are part of Phoenix Children's Hospital Dignity Health IASIS Healthcare and Abrazo Health.

Strategy
BCBSAZ has been revamping many of its health plan offerings revising coverage terms and lowering premiums in an effort to attract more customers. To help reduce skyrocketing costs plaguing the health care industry the company has also been enhancing its HealthyBlue wellness program offering which promotes preventative care and fitness and allows for personalized online health assessment and coaching services.

EXECUTIVES

President And Ceo, Richard L. (Rich) Boals
Evp External Operations, Susan H. Navran
Evp Internal Operations, Sandra Lee Gibson
Cio, Elizabeth A. Messina
Svp And Cfo, Karen Abraham
Svp Health Services And Chief Medical Officer, Vishu Jhaveri
Svp Strategy Sales And Marketing, Jeff Stelnik
Ceo Blue Cross Blue Shield Of Arizona Advantage, Dave Firdaus
Chairman, Harry A. Papp
Vice Chairman, Alton J. Washington

LOCATIONS

HQ: BLUE CROSS AND BLUE SHIELD OF ARIZONA, INC.
2444 W LAS PALMARITAS DR, PHOENIX, AZ 850214860
Phone: 602 864-4100
Web: WWW.AZBLUE.COM

PRODUCTS/OPERATIONS

Selected Plans
Family and Individual Medical Plans
  BlueBasic Plus PPO
  BlueEssential Plus PPO
  BlueOptimum Plus PPO
  BluePortfolio Plus (high deductible PPO with HSA)
  BlueValue Plus PPO
  Medicare Part D
  Medicare Supplement
Group Medical Plans
  BlueAlliance benefit
  BluePreferred PPO
  BluePreferred HSA Plus (high deductible PPO with HSA)
  BlueSelect HMO
  Dental plans
  Eyewear plans
  GeoBlue Expat

COMPETITORS

Aetna
CIGNA HealthCare of Arizona
First Dental Health
Health Net
Humana
Southwest Catholic Health Network
UnitedHealth Group
Western Dental Services

HISTORICAL FINANCIALS
Company Type: Private

Income Statement   FYE: December 31

	ASSETS ($ mil.)	NET INCOME ($ mil.)	INCOME AS % OF ASSETS	EMPLOYEES
12/09	1,059	64	6.1%	1,278
12/08	975	71	7.4%	—
Annual Growth	**8.6%**	**(9.9%)**	**—**	**—**

BLUE TEE CORP.

Handling a variety of steel products and scrap materials suits Blue Tee to a tee. The holding company which operates through two primary subsidiaries distributes steel building materials and scrap metal. Blue Tee's Brown-Strauss Steel subsidiary is one of the largest distributors of wide flange beam and structural steel products (beams pipe and tubing) in North America. The metal distributor's other primary business is Azcon a leading scrap processor broker and mill services management company which handles scrap metal sales rail cars and other steel parts.

Operations
Azcon is a major scrap processor broker and mill services management company. Brown-Strauss Steel distributes steel products.

Azcon buys collects warehouses and distributes a wide variety of rail and track accessories for the railroad industry across North America. Its core businesses include Processing Yard Mill Scrap Management and Brokerage. Other product lines include Relaying and Re-rolling Rail Railroad Equipment and Railroad Parts.

Brown-Strauss Steel's focus is on the distribution of new steel (wide flange beam and structural steel tubing) across the US.

Geographic Reach
The company has major offices in Denver Kansas City Longview (Washington) New York City Phoenix Salt Lake City and Stockton and Fontana (California). It has additional locations in Alton Chicago and Sterling (Illinois); Austin Texas; Duluth Minnesota; and Sharpsburg Pennsylvania.

In Canada Blue Tee has offices in Edmonton Calgary Grande Prairie Grimshaw Kamloops Prince George and Red Deer.

Sales and Marketing
Blue Tee serves a range of industries including construction forestry road building mining farming power oil and gas solid waste water waste management highway transportation environmental and groundwater monitoring.

Strategy
The company is focusing its resources developing Azcon and Brown-Strauss Steel. Brown-Strauss is looking to grow its product offerings to include structural tubing; it also plans to expand its facilities. In this regard in 2012 Blue Tee Corp (through Brown-Strauss) purchased a 69190 sq. ft. industrial building in Aurora Colorado from The Lowenberg Corp. for $6 million.

Company Background
Blue Tee is owned by its employees through an employee stock ownership plan.

In 2011 Blue Tee divested subsidiaries GEFCO (an OEM of portable drilling rigs and other industrial equipment) and STECO (transfer and dump-truck trailers) to Astec Industries for about $30.8 million.

The move to axe its GEFCO and STECO subsidiaries followed another sale. Blue Tee sold its pump parts subsidiary Texas-based Standard Alloys to German pump manufacturer KSB in mid-2010.

The Blue Tee holding company was founded in 1986. Azcon was formed in 1863 and Brown-Strauss Steel was established in 1905.

EXECUTIVES

Pres-Ceo, William M Kelly
Sr V Pres-Cfo-Chb, David P Alldian
Exec Dir, Annette Marino D'Arienzo
Real Estate Conultant, Cristina Hungria
Auditors: DELOITTE & TOUCHE LLP NEW YO

LOCATIONS

HQ: BLUE TEE CORP.
387 PARK AVE S FL 5, NEW YORK, NY 100161495
Phone: 212 598-0880
Web: WWW.BROWN-STRAUSS.COM

PRODUCTS/OPERATIONS

Selected Subsidiaries
Azcon Corporation (ferrous and nonferrous scrap; rail cars locomotives and parts; relay and reroll rail)
Brown-Strauss Steel (steel distribution including angles beams channels pipe and tubing)

Selected Azcon Services
Barge Services
Brokerage Services
Demolition Services
Foundries - Scrap Management
Industrial Plants - Scrap Management
Mill Service
Mine Services
Railroad Industry Services
Steel Mills - Scrap Management

Selected Brown-Strauss Steel Products and Services
Products:
Structural Angle
Structural Channels
Structural Pipe
Structural Tubing
Wide Flange Beams

Services:
Cambering
Inventory Stocking program
Length/cutting optimization program
Mill Brokerage
Saw Cutting
Track Torch Cutting

COMPETITORS

A. M. Castle
APi Group
Dover Corp.
Metals USA
OmniSource
Pacesetter Steel
Reliance Steel
Russel Metals
Ryerson
TTX
Wescast Industries

HISTORICAL FINANCIALS
Company Type: Private

Income Statement				FYE: December 31
	REVENUE ($ mil.)	NET INCOME ($ mil.)	NET PROFIT MARGIN	EMPLOYEES
12/10	809	14	1.8%	900
12/09	564	(10)	—	—
12/08	1,549	33	2.1%	—
Annual Growth	(27.7%)	(34.4%)	—	—

2010 Year-End Financials
Return on assets: 3.7% Cash ($ mil.): 8
Return on equity: 8.2%
Current ratio: 2.10

BMW CONSTRUCTORS, INC.

EXECUTIVES
Pres-Ceo, Bryan Acton
V Pres*, David Clements
SEC*, Kevin Cohart
Accounting Staff, Nicole Lippard

LOCATIONS
HQ: BMW CONSTRUCTORS, INC.
 1740 W MICHIGAN ST, INDIANAPOLIS, IN 462223855
Phone: 219 922-5000
Web: WWW.BMWC.COM

HISTORICAL FINANCIALS
Company Type: Private

Income Statement				FYE: December 31
	REVENUE ($ mil.)	NET INCOME ($ mil.)	NET PROFIT MARGIN	EMPLOYEES
12/12	481	0	—	700
12/11	269	9	3.4%	—
12/10	211	0	—	—
Annual Growth	50.9%	—	—	—

2012 Year-End Financials
Return on assets: — Cash ($ mil.): —
Return on equity: —
Current ratio: 1.00

BNSF RAILWAY COMPANY

BNSF Railway operates one of the largest railroad networks in North America. A wholly-owned subsidiary of Burlington Northern Santa Fe itself a unit of Berkshire Hathaway the company provides freight transportation over a network of about 32500 route miles of track across some 30 US states and three provinces in Canada. BNSF Railway owns or leases a fleet of about 8000 locomotives. It also has some 25 intermodal facilities that help to transport agricultural consumer and industrial products as well as coal. In addition to major cities and ports BNSF Railway serves smaller markets in alliance with short-line partners.

Operations
BNSF Railway transports a wide range of products and commodities through its four main product segments.

The Consumer Products segment generates about 35% of revenue and consists of the Domestic Intermodal International Intermodal and Automotive business units. The Industrial Products segment provides about 25% of revenue and comprises five business units: Construction Products Petroleum Products Building Products Chemicals and Plastics Products and Food and Beverages.

Agricultural Products represents 20% of revenue and includes the transportation of commodities like corn wheat ethanol soybeans fertilizer oil seeds flour and other grains. The Coal business (less than 20%) is primarily BNSF's operations that originate from the Powder River Basin of Wyoming and Montana.

The company also generates about 5% of revenue from its wholly-owned non-rail logistics subsidiary BSNF Logistics LLC through logistics and transportation services such as storage as well as demurrage (detention fees for delays in loading and unloading of freight).

Geographic Reach
Headquartered in Fort Worth TX BNSF Railway's network spreads across about 30 US states and three Canadian provinces.

Sales and Marketing
BNSF Railway serves smaller markets by working closely with 200 shortline partners. It also forms marketing agreements with other rail carriers expanding the marketing reach for each railroad and its customers.

Financial Performance
BNSF has seen steady growth in recent years with revenue reaching $23.9 billion in 2018 a 12% increase compared with $21.4 billion in 2017. The increase in 2018 was mainly due to increased volume and increased rates per car as well as tight truck capacity in the transportation sector which converted some business from highway to rail.

Net income however plummeted to $5.2 billion less than half that of the previous year. This was primarily due to an increased tax liability as a result of the Tax Cuts and Jobs Act.

Cash at the end of fiscal 2018 was $2.0 billion about the same as the prior year. Cash from operations contributed $7.9 billion to the coffers while investing activities used $3.2 billion mainly for capital expenditures related to equipment purchases. Financing activities used another $4.7 billion primarily for cash distributions to its parent company.

Strategy
BNSF plans capital spending of about $3.5 billion in 2019 for network maintenance and replacement of assets to ensure safe and reliable operations. These include expansion and efficiency projects focused on key growth areas along its Southern and Northern Trancon routes. The company faces challenges in its supply chain environment with competition from improving productivity in the trucking industry. Another hurdle is consumers' expectations for quicker and quicker delivery as online shopping continues to grow. In response BSNF is focusing on providing consistent reliable and efficient transportation services to its customers.

Company Background
BNSF's traces its roots to 1849 when the Aurora Branch Railroad was founded in Illinois with 12 miles of track. Over the years additional rail lines were built including Atchison Topeka & Santa Fe;Burlington Northern; Chicago Burlington & Quincy; Frisco; Great Northern; Northern Pacific; and Spokane Portland & Seattle.

BNSF was created in 1995 when Burlington Northern Inc. (the parent company of Burlington Northern Railroad) merged with Santa Fe Pacific Corporation (parent company of the Atchison Topeka & Santa Fe Railway). The company was acquired by Berkshire Hathaway in 2010 and BNSF now operates as a subsidiary of that company.

EXECUTIVES
Evp And Coo, Carl R. Ice, age 62
Evp Law And Corporate Affairs, Roger Nober, age 54
Evp And Cfo, Julie A. Piggott
Evp And Chief Marketing Officer, Stevan B. Bobb
Evp Operations, Gregory C. Fox
Vice President Federal Government Affairs, Amy Hawkins
Executive Vice President Law And Government Affairs And Secretary, Jeffrey Moreland
Vice President Network Strategy, Dean Wise
Vice President Controller, Dannis Johnson
Chairman President And Ceo, Matthew K. (Matt) Rose, age 60
Auditors: DELOITTE & TOUCHE LLP FORT WO

LOCATIONS
HQ: BNSF RAILWAY COMPANY
 2650 LOU MENK DR, FORT WORTH, TX 761312830
Phone: 800 795-2673
Web: WWW.BNSF.COM

PRODUCTS/OPERATIONS

2018 Sales
	$ mil.	% of total
Consumer Products	7,902	33
Industrial Products	5,967	25
Agricultural Products	4,697	20
Coal	4,012	17
Other revenues	1,277	5
Total	23,855	100

COMPETITORS
CSX	Kansas City Southern Railway
Canadian National Railway	Norfolk Southern
Canadian Pacific Railway	Union Pacific Railroad

HISTORICAL FINANCIALS
Company Type: Private

Income Statement				FYE: December 31
	REVENUE ($ mil.)	NET INCOME ($ mil.)	NET PROFIT MARGIN	EMPLOYEES
12/17	20,747	12,119	58.4%	41,000
12/16	19,278	4,260	22.1%	—
12/14	22,714	4,397	19.4%	—
12/13	21,552	4,271	19.8%	—
Annual Growth	(0.9%)	29.8%	—	—

2017 Year-End Financials
Return on assets: 14.6% Cash ($ mil.): 516
Return on equity: 19.3%
Current ratio: 1.00

BOARD OF EDUCATION FOR THE CITY OF SAVANNAH AND THE COUNTY OF CHATHAM (INC)

EXECUTIVES

Pres, Jolene Byrne
Contrl, Beth Stanford
Auditors: KRT CPAS PC SAVANNAH GEORG

LOCATIONS

HQ: BOARD OF EDUCATION FOR THE CITY OF
SAVANNAH AND THE COUNTY OF CHATHAM (INC)
208 BULL ST, SAVANNAH, GA 314013997
Phone: 912 395-1000
Web: WWW.SAVANNAH.COM

HISTORICAL FINANCIALS

Company Type: Private

Income Statement				FYE: June 30
	REVENUE ($ mil.)	NET INCOME ($ mil.)	NET PROFIT MARGIN	EMPLOYEES
06/18	525	41	7.8%	4,781
06/17	500	(30)	—	—
06/16	493	21	4.3%	—
06/15	478	(11)	—	—
Annual Growth	3.2%	—	—	—

BOARD OF EDUCATION OF CITY OF CHICAGO

EXECUTIVES

Pres, Frank Clark
Technology, James V Dispensa
Coordinator, Samantha Treworgy
Technology Manager, Denise Sangster
Auditors: MCGLADREY LLP CHICAGO ILLINO

LOCATIONS

HQ: BOARD OF EDUCATION OF CITY OF CHICAGO
42 W MADISON ST FL 2, CHICAGO, IL 606024309
Phone: 773 553-1600
Web: WWW.CPSBOE.ORG

HISTORICAL FINANCIALS

Company Type: Private

Income Statement				FYE: June 30
	REVENUE ($ mil.)	NET INCOME ($ mil.)	NET PROFIT MARGIN	EMPLOYEES
06/16	5,272	(381)	—	5,151
06/12	5,760	324	5.6%	—
06/11	5,660	238	4.2%	—
06/08	17	(0)	—	—
Annual Growth	103.8%	—	—	—

BOARD OF EDUCATION-MEMPHIS CITY SCHOOLS

LOCATIONS

HQ: BOARD OF EDUCATION-MEMPHIS CITY
SCHOOLS
160 S HOLLYWOOD ST, MEMPHIS, TN 381124801
Phone: 901 416-5300

HISTORICAL FINANCIALS

Company Type: Private

Income Statement				FYE: June 30
	REVENUE ($ mil.)	NET INCOME ($ mil.)	NET PROFIT MARGIN	EMPLOYEES
06/13	1,157	(12)	—	12,015
06/12	1,169	(2)	—	—
06/11*	1,173	(5)	—	—
12/09	449	(64)	—	—
Annual Growth	37.1%	—	—	—

*Fiscal year change

2013 Year-End Financials
Return on assets: —
Return on equity: (-1.1%)
Current ratio: —
Cash ($ mil.): 177

BOARD OF PUBLIC EDUCATION SCHOOL DISTRICT OF PITTSBURGH (INC)

EXECUTIVES

Pres, Thomas Sumpter
SEC*, Cindy Polis
Coordinator, Susan Chersky
Auditors: MAHER DUESSEL PITTSBURGH PEN

LOCATIONS

HQ: BOARD OF PUBLIC EDUCATION SCHOOL
DISTRICT OF PITTSBURGH (INC)
341 S BELLEFIELD AVE, PITTSBURGH, PA
152133516
Phone: 412 622-3500
Web: WWW.PGHSCHOOLS.ORG

HISTORICAL FINANCIALS

Company Type: Private

Income Statement				FYE: December 31
	REVENUE ($ mil.)	NET INCOME ($ mil.)	NET PROFIT MARGIN	EMPLOYEES
12/14	631	13	2.1%	5,016
12/13	624	19	3.1%	—
12/12	613	3	0.6%	—
12/11	631	(14)	—	—
Annual Growth	(0.0%)	—	—	—

2014 Year-End Financials
Return on assets: 1.8%
Return on equity: 4.9%
Current ratio: 2.70
Cash ($ mil.): 89

BOARD OF REGENTS OF THE UNIVERSITY OF NEBRASKA

The University of Nebraska has sprouted four campuses out in the fields of the Cornhusker State. Founded in 1869 the university confers bachelor's master's and doctoral degrees in more than 170 majors including agriculture business education and engineering at its campuses in Kearney Lincoln and Omaha. The university's Medical Center in Omaha trains doctors performs research and is affiliated with a roughly 700-bed teaching hospital. The school also operates research and extension services across the state. Nearly 50000 students attend classes in the system that has a student-teacher ratio of about 16:1. It was founded as a land-grant university just two years after the Nebraska became a state.

EXECUTIVES

Svp Business And Finance, David E. Lechner
Chancellor University Of Nebraska Lincoln,
Harvey S. Perlman
Chancellor University Of Nebraska Kearney,
Douglas A. (Doug) Kristensen
Chancellor University Of Nebraska Omaha, John Christensen
Evp And Provost, Susan M. Fritz
Interim President, James Linder
Chancellor University Of Nebraska Medical Center, Jeffrey P. Gold
Cio, Walter Weir
President, Hank M. Bounds
Assistant Vice President And Director Human Resources, Ed Wimes
Assistant Vp And Director Federal Relations, Matt Hammons
Vice President, Elbert Dickey
Vice Chancellor And Vice President, Ronnie Green
Vice President, Joel Pedersen
Assistant Vp Global Strategy And International Initiatives, Steven Duke
Vice President And General Counsel, James P Pottorff
Department Head, Martha Mamo
Chairman, Howard L. Hawks
Vice Chairman, Bob Phares
Auditors: MARK AVERY CPA LINCOLN NEBR

LOCATIONS

HQ: BOARD OF REGENTS OF THE UNIVERSITY OF
NEBRASKA
3835 HOLDREGE ST, LINCOLN, NE 685031435
Phone: 402 472-3906
Web: WWW.UNMC.EDU

PRODUCTS/OPERATIONS

University Campuses
The University of Nebraska at Kearney
The University of Nebraska-Lincoln
The University of Nebraska Medical Center
The University of Nebraska at Omaha

HISTORICAL FINANCIALS

Company Type: Private

Income Statement				FYE: June 30
	REVENUE ($ mil.)	NET INCOME ($ mil.)	NET PROFIT MARGIN	EMPLOYEES
06/16	1,490	215	14.5%	15,200
06/15	1,405	221	15.8%	—
06/14	1,333	222	16.7%	—
06/13	1,313	254	19.4%	—
Annual Growth	4.3%	(5.4%)	—	—

2016 Year-End Financials

Return on assets: 4.3%   Cash ($ mil.): 613
Return on equity: 6.0%
Current ratio: 2.80

BOARD OF REGENTS OF THE UNIVERSITY SYSTEM OF GEORGIA

EXECUTIVES

Chancellor, Hank Huckaby
Director For Grants Accounting*, Jennifer Shaw
Procurement Staff, Michael Haun
Coordinator, Taylor Smith
Coordinator, Charlotte Stauffer
Customer Representativ, Justina Washington
Administrative Coordinator, Blair Witte
Director, Cherry Zhang
Ecampus Director, Christy Talley-Smith
Office Manager, Juanita D Ervin
Archival Manager, Kayla Barrett
Auditors: GREG S GRIFFIN ATLANTA GEORG

LOCATIONS

HQ: BOARD OF REGENTS OF THE UNIVERSITY SYSTEM OF GEORGIA
270 WASHINGTON ST SW FL 7, ATLANTA, GA 303349009
Phone: 404 962-3050
Web: WWW.USG.EDU

HISTORICAL FINANCIALS

Company Type: Private

Income Statement				FYE: June 30
	REVENUE ($ mil.)	NET INCOME ($ mil.)	NET PROFIT MARGIN	EMPLOYEES
06/18	5,210	221	4.3%	40,000
06/17	5,100	57	1.1%	—
06/15	4,704	124	2.6%	—
06/11	0	0	—	—
Annual Growth	—	—	—	—

2018 Year-End Financials

Return on assets: 1.6%   Cash ($ mil.): 1,345
Return on equity: 13.8%
Current ratio: 2.50

BOARD OF TRUSTEES OF STATE INSTITUTIONS OF HIGHER LEARNING

EXECUTIVES

Comm'r, Hank Bounds
Director, Casey Turnage
Coordinator, Tonya Neely
Security Staff, Ivy Babb
Director, Marsha Watson
Director, Pete Walley
Director of Accreditation, Menia Dykes
Director, Jim Steil
Director of Administrative Ser, Karana Carroll
Associate Commissioner For EXT, Paul Sumrall
Director, Darrell McCaffrey
Auditors: KPMG LLP JACKSON MISSISSIPP

LOCATIONS

HQ: BOARD OF TRUSTEES OF STATE INSTITUTIONS OF HIGHER LEARNING
3825 RIDGEWOOD RD, JACKSON, MS 392116453
Phone: 601 432-6198
Web: WWW.MISSISSIPPI.EDU

HISTORICAL FINANCIALS

Company Type: Private

Income Statement				FYE: June 30
	REVENUE ($ mil.)	NET INCOME ($ mil.)	NET PROFIT MARGIN	EMPLOYEES
06/18	2,588	(5)	—	65
06/17	2	0	1.1%	—
06/16	2,539	173	6.8%	—
06/15	2,383	257	10.8%	—
Annual Growth	2.8%	—	—	—

2018 Year-End Financials

Return on assets: (-0.1%)   Cash ($ mil.): 601
Return on equity: (-0.3%)
Current ratio: 2.70

BOARDRIDERS, INC.

Boardriders rides the wave of youth appeal. Formerly Quiksilver the company caters to the young and athletic with surfwear snowboardwear sportswear and swimwear sold under the Quiksilver Billabong Element VonZipper and Roxy names among others. It also owns the DC Shoes brand of footwear and apparel for young men and juniors. It sells its apparel footwear and accessories in specialty and department stores worldwide as well as through its own network of about 630 retail stores. It emerged from Chapter 11 bankruptcy protection in 2016 and is now owned by Oaktree Capital Management; in 2018 it bought rival Billabong.

Geographic Reach

Boardriders serves customers in more than 110 countries; it has e-commerce capabilities in about 35 countries and company-owned retail stores in nearly 30. More than 60% of revenue comes from outside North America.

Strategy

To grow sales and return to profitability after emerging from bankruptcy Boardriders is focused on strengthening its brands; expanding its business in emerging markets; and driving operational efficiencies. The company has also invested in improving its e-commerce platform and growing its store network.

It owns a portfolio of the leading brands in surf and sportswear including Quiksilver DC Shoes Element and Billabong. The company is dedicated to preserving and promoting each of these distinctive historic brands.

In addition Boardriders is pushing its brands into new product areas including personal care (Roxy and Quiksilver sun care and other products through an agreement with Inter Parfums) and hotels (Quiksilver and Roxy have partnered with Accor's Jo&Joe a new hotel chain targeting millennials).

To help it focus the company has divested noncore business to focus on its most iconic brands. Jettisoned brands include Surfdome (sold to Surf-Stitch) Mervin Manufacturing (sold to Extreme Holdings) and skateboarder Tony Hawk's Hawk Designs (sold to Cherokee).

Mergers and Acquisitions

In April 2018 Boardriders completed the acquisition of Australian rival Billabong which owns Element VonZipper Billabong and other brands that make surf and action sports apparel and accessories. The deal valued around $155 million creates one of the world's largest action sports companies.

EXECUTIVES

Evp Global Human Resources, Carol E. Scherman
Evp And Cio, Michael B. Tasooji
Ceo, Pierre Agnes, $617,500 total compensation
President Americas, Nate Smith
Evp New Business Development; President Quiksilver Americas, Robert (Rob) Colby, $400,000 total compensation
Cfo, Richard Shields, $522,900 total compensation
President Asia Pacific (apac), Greg Healy
Senior Vice President Of Global Sourcing, Christopher Dubes
Vice President Worldwide Controller, Michael Henry
Vice President Of Merchandising And Design, Guy Stagman
Senior Vice President Of Marketing, Ryan Scanlon
Chairman, Bob McKnight
Auditors: DELOITTE & TOUCHE LLP COSTA M

LOCATIONS

HQ: BOARDRIDERS, INC.
5600 ARGOSY AVE STE 100, HUNTINGTON BEACH, CA 926491063
Phone: 714 889-2200
Web: WWW.QUIKSILVER.COM

PRODUCTS/OPERATIONS

Selected Brands
Billabong
DC Shoes
Element
Kustom
Palmers
Quiksilver
Roxy
RVCA
VonZipper
Xcel

COMPETITORS

Abercrombie & Fitch	Oakley
Bleach Group	Skullcandy
Body Glove	Sole Technology
Burton	St ssy
Calvin Klein	Tecnica
Columbia Sportswear	Tommy Hilfiger
Fat Face	Under Armour
Foot Locker	VF Corporation
Head N.V.	Volcom
Levi Strauss	Warnaco Swimwear
NIKE	adidas
Nautica Apparel	

HISTORICAL FINANCIALS

Company Type: Private

Income Statement   FYE: October 31

	REVENUE ($ mil.)	NET INCOME ($ mil.)	NET PROFIT MARGIN	EMPLOYEES
10/14	1,570	(320)	—	700
10/13	1,810	(233)	—	—
10/12	2,013	(9)	—	—
Annual Growth	(11.7%)	—	—	—

2014 Year-End Financials

Return on assets: (-25.5%) Cash ($ mil.): 46
Return on equity: (-556.7%)
Current ratio: 2.10

BON SECOURS MERCY HEALTH, INC.

Bon Secours Mercy Health (formerly Bon Secours Health System) is a Roman Catholic health care organization. Sponsored by the Bon Secours Ministries it is home to 43 hospitals with more than 2100 physicians. First founded in 1919 its facilities are in seven states in the eastern US from New York to Florida. In addition to its acute care hospitals the not-for-profit system operates a psychiatric hospital numerous nursing homes and assisted-living facilities as well as hospices and home health care agencies. Bon Secours merged with Cincinnati-based Mercy Health to create Bon Secours Mercy Health in 2018. The combined entity expanded into Ireland in 2019.

Geographic Reach

Bon Secours Mercy Health has hospitals in Florida Kentucky Maryland New York Ohio South Carolina and Virginia.

Sales and Marketing

Medicare and Medicaid payments account for around 35% of Bon Secours Mercy Health's total net patient revenue.

Strategy

Bon Secours Mercy Health plans to continue to grow its operations in existing and new communities targeting expansion in ambulatory care elderly services and home health and hospice. The health system has opened several new ambulatory care centers in existing service territories and it is conducting renovation and expansion efforts at some of its hospital facilities.

The system has also initiated information technology restructuring efforts; it has developed a new clinical information management system (electronic medical records) ConnectCare which is being implemented at its facilities in gradual stages.

The company branched out internationally through the purchase of Irish hospital operator Bon Secours Health System in 2019. Additionally its Global Ministry Initiative provides outreach for health care and social services in developing countries particularly Haiti Peru and South Africa.

Mergers and Acquisitions

In 2018 Bon Secours and Cincinnati-based Mercy Health joined forces to create a system with 43 hospitals in seven states. The combined entity has more than 2100 physicians and clinicians working in more than 1000 locations.

The following year Bon Secours Mercy Health acquired Ireland-based Bon Secours Health System which operates five hospitals and other health facilities.

EXECUTIVES

President Ceo And Director, Richard J. (Rich) Statuto
Svp And Cio, Skip Hubbard
Evp, Mark S. Nantz
Evp, Janice Burnett
Ceo Bon Secours Baltimore Health System, Samuel L. Ross
Ceo Bon Secours St. Francis Health System, R. Craig McCoy
Ceo Bon Secours Charity, Mary Leahy
Senior Vice President Of Mission, Pam Phillips
Vice President Revenue Cycle Services, Vickie Kleski
Vice President, Jennifer Scholtz
Vice President Financial Planning And Analysis, James Siegel
Senior Vice President Human Resources, Fernando Fleites
Clinical Director, Deborah A Pope
Vice President Ancillary Amb Services, Johnna S Reed
Vice President Revenue Cycle, Sheila Kuenzle
Vice President Treasury Services, Pamela Schmidt
Director Of Nursing Resources, Candace Porter
Senior Vice President Of Services, Robert Rosenthal
Medical Director And Residency Director, John Unkel
Medical Director And Physician, Mark Miranda
Cota L, Heather Miller
Pharmacy Manager, Ryan Cann
Director Of Pharmacy, Terri Spearman
Medical Director, Janet Eddy
Director Of Radiology, William Long
Medical Director Emergency Services, Adrienne Wasserman
Vice President Service Line Strategy, Leigh Sewell
Vice President Corporate Communications, Terri Mcnorton
Senior Vice President Provider Networks, Wael Haidar
Medical Director, Joseph Scarpa
Vice President Patient Care Services, Leana Fox
Director Of Pharmacy, Kerri Musselman
Medical Director Clinical Ethics, Kelly Stuart
Vice President Bon Secours Hampton Roads Foundations, Judy Bilicki
Senior Vice President Sponsorship And Theology, Thomas Morris
Senior Vice President, Archuleta Bob
Vice President Patient Care Cne, Sophie Crawford
Assistant Vice President Quality And Patient Safety, Kathleen Geisinger
Director, Charles H. Brown
Secretary, Maria Sorice
Unit Secretary, Corie Miller
Unit Secretary, Noel Townes
Secretary Admin, Huff Brenda
Unit Secretary, Tamara Pearson
Auditors: KPMG LLP BALTIMORE MD

LOCATIONS

HQ: BON SECOURS MERCY HEALTH, INC.
1505 MARRIOTTSVILLE RD, MARRIOTTSVILLE, MD 211041301
Phone: 410 442-5511
Web: WWW.BONSECOURS.COM

Selected Facilities

Florida
Bon Secours St. Petersburg Health System
Bon Secours - Maria Manor Nursing Care and Rehabilitation Center
Bon Secours Place at St. Petersburg
Bon Secours St. Petersburg Home Care Services
Kentucky
Bon Secours Kentucky Health System
Our Lady of Bellefonte Hospital (Ashland)
Maryland
Bon Secours Baltimore Health System
Bon Secours Hospital
Bon Secours Washington Village
Community Institute of Behavioral Sciences
Hollins Terrace/Benet House
New York
Bon Secours Charity Health System
Bon Secours Community Hospital (Port Jervis)
Good Samaritan Hospital (Suffern)
St. Anthony Community Hospital (Warwick)
Bon Secours New York Health System
Schervier Nursing Care Center (Riverdale)
Pennsylvania
Altoona Regional Health System (joint venture)
South Carolina
Bon Secours St. Francis Health System Inc.
St. Francis Hospital (Downtown and Eastside Campuses Greenville)
Roper St. Francis Healthcare (Charleston joint venture)
Virginia
Bon Secours Hampton Roads Health System
Bon Secours Maryview Nursing Care Center (Suffolk)
DePaul Medical Center (Norfolk)
Mary Immaculate Hospital (Newport News)
Maryview Medical Center (Portsmouth)
Province Place (Norfolk and Portsmouth)
St. Francis Nursing Care Center (Newport News)
Bon Secours Richmond Health System (joint venture)
Memorial Regional Medical Center (Mechanicsville)
Richmond Community Hospital
St. Francis Medical Center (Midlothian)
St. Mary's Hospital (Richmond)

Selected Affiliations

Cosponsoring Congregational Relationships
Bernardine Sisters of the Third Order of St. Francis (Newport News Virginia)
Sisters of Charity of Saint Elizabeth of Convent Station (New Jersey and New York)
Affiliated Organizations
Health Corporation of Virginia (Richmond)
Medical Society of South Carolina and Carolinas Health Care System (Charleston)
Life Care Services (Florida and Virginia)

PRODUCTS/OPERATIONS

2014 Sales

	$ mil.	% of total
Net Patient Service Revenue	3,328	96
Other revenue	133	4
Total	**3,461**	**100**

COMPETITORS

Adventist HealthCare	Highlands Health
Albany Medical Center	Inova
Albert Einstein	Johns Hopkins Medicine
Healthcare Network	MedStar Health
Appalachian Regional	MediSys Health Network
Healthcare	New York City Health
Carilion Clinic	and Hospitals
Catholic Health	Novant Health
Initiatives	Riverside Health
Centra Health Inc.	System (Virginia)
Christiana Care	Sentara Healthcare
Community Health	St. Agnes HealthCare
Systems	University of Maryland
Conemaugh Health	Medical System
System	University of Miami
Franklin Square	Hospital
Hospital Center	Upstate Affiliate
GBMC	Virginia Hospital
HCA	Center

HISTORICAL FINANCIALS

Company Type: Private

Income Statement
FYE: August 31

	REVENUE ($ mil.)	NET INCOME ($ mil.)	NET PROFIT MARGIN	EMPLOYEES
08/10	3,084	(41)	—	19,000
08/09	2,895	(291)	—	—
08/08	187	51	27.6%	—
Annual Growth	305.4%	—	—	—

2010 Year-End Financials

Return on assets: (-1.5%)
Return on equity: (-7.6%)
Current ratio: 1.50

Cash ($ mil.): 180

BOSCOV'S, INC.

EXECUTIVES

Ceo, Albert Boscov
Pres*, Kenneth S Lakin
Treas*, Russell C Diehm
Exec V Pres*, Toni Miller
V Pres*, Peter D Lakin
Prin*, Edwin A Lakin
Consultant, Patricia Creque
Staff, Ronnie Eddinger
Sales Staff, Chantal Van Bauwel
Sales and Marketing Staff, Emile De Cordier
Director, Seppe De Roeck
Auditors: KPMG LLP PHILADELPHIA PA

LOCATIONS

HQ: BOSCOV'S, INC.
 4500 PERKIOMEN AVE, READING, PA 196063946
Phone: 610 779-2000
Web: WWW.BOSCOVS.COM

HISTORICAL FINANCIALS

Company Type: Private

Income Statement
FYE: February 2

	REVENUE ($ mil.)	NET INCOME ($ mil.)	NET PROFIT MARGIN	EMPLOYEES
02/19	1,215	47	3.9%	10,003
02/18*	1,192	37	3.2%	—
01/17	1,139	32	2.8%	—
01/16	1,101	27	2.5%	—
Annual Growth	3.3%	20.6%	—	—

*Fiscal year change

2019 Year-End Financials

Return on assets: 9.3%
Return on equity: 16.3%
Current ratio: 2.80

Cash ($ mil.): 89

BOSTON MEDICAL CENTER CORPORATION

Located in Boston's South End neighborhood Boston Medical Center (BMC) offers a full spectrum of health care services from prenatal care and obstetrics to surgery and rehabilitation. BMC is also the city's largest provider of indigent care spending millions of dollars annually on care for uninsured patients and offering free screenings and other community outreach programs. The not-for-profit hospital boasts nearly 500 licensed beds more than 700 physicians and includes a Level 1 trauma center acute rehabilitation facilities and neonatal and pediatric intensive care units. The center is the primary teaching hospital of Boston University's School of Medicine.

Operations

BMC also operates Boston HealthNet a network affiliation of the medical center Boston University School of Medicine and more than a dozen community health centers. Boston HealthNet provides outreach prevention primary care and specialty care and dental services at sites located throughout the community.

Hand-in-hand with being a major teaching hospital is engaging in extensive medical research. BMC oversees more than 590 research and service projects and conducts both biomedical and clinical research programs exploring infectious disease cardiology vascular biology Parkinson's disease geriatrics and endocrinology among other areas. With Boston University BMC also operates a 16-acre research and business park called BioSquare that serves as a collaborative center for the development and commercialization of new biomedical technologies.

In 2015 BMC had more than 712 000 outpatient clinic visits 204000 outpatient ancillary visits 125000 emergency department visits and 24000 admissions.

Sales and Marketing

In addition to its medical and research services BMC provides health insurance through its BMC HealthNet Plan a managed care plan that has more than 240000 Medicaid and low-cost health plan members. The center markets its services through social media.

Financial Performance

BMC received more than $119 million in sponsored research funding in fiscal 2015; it oversees 594 research and service projects separate from research activities at Boston University School of Medicine.

Strategy

In late 2014 BMC's Center for Regenerative Medicine and Boston University were awarded a $2.7 million grant from the National Heart Lung and Blood Institute to establish a stem cell repository that researchers across the US can access for free. The first-of-its-kind repository will help promote stem cell research particularly in the area of lung disease.

EXECUTIVES

Svp Finance And Cfo, Richard Silveria
President And Ceo, Kate E. Walsh
Svp And Chief Nursing Officer, Nancy Gaden
Svp And Chief Medical Officer, Ravin Davidoff
Coo, Alastair Bell
President And Ceo Faculty Practice Foundation, William Creevy
Svp Quality Safety And Technology; Chief Quality Officer, Stanley Hochberg
Senior Vice President, David Beck
Associate Vice President For Human Resources, Manuel Monteiro
Chairman, James S. Phalen, age 68
Auditors: BMC HEALTH SYSTEM INC BOSTO

LOCATIONS

HQ: BOSTON MEDICAL CENTER CORPORATION
 1 BOSTON MEDICAL CTR PL # 1, BOSTON, MA 021182999
Phone: 617 414-5000
Web: WWW.BMC.ORG

PRODUCTS/OPERATIONS

Selected Services and Programs
Alzheimer's Disease Center
Anesthesiology
Boston HealthNet
Boston University Affiliated Physicians
Boston University Cosmetic and Laser Center
Cardiovascular Center
Care Management
Dermatology
Diabetes
Elders Living at Home Program
Emergency Medicine
Facial Plastic and Reconstructive Surgery
General Internal Medicne / Primary Care
Geriatrics
Head and Neck Cancer Center of Excellence
Hematology & Medical Oncology
Immigrant & Refugee Health Program
Integrative Medicine
LocoMotor Training
Mattapan Community Health Center
Melanoma Program
Neurosurgery
Nursing
Ophthalmology
Oral and Maxillofacial Surgery
Pediatrics - bWell Center

Pediatrics

Rehabilitation Therapies
Renal Medicine
South End Community Health Center
Special Kids Special Help
Thoracic Surgery
Transplant Surgery
Uphams Corner Health Center
Urology
Vascular Center
Vascular and Endovascular Surgery
Weight Loss Surgery (Bariatric Surgery)
Whittier Street Health Center

COMPETITORS

Beth Israel Deaconess Medical Center
 Brigham and Women's Hospital
 Cambridge Health Alliance
 Care New England
 CareGroup
 Children's Hospital Boston
 Dana-Farber
 Massachusetts General Hospital
 Newton-Wellesley Hospital
 Northeast Health System
 Partners HealthCare
 Shriners Hospitals For Children
 Spaulding Rehabilitation Hospital
 St. Elizabeth's Medical Center
 Steward Health Care

HISTORICAL FINANCIALS
Company Type: Private

Income Statement				FYE: September 30
	REVENUE ($ mil.)	NET INCOME ($ mil.)	NET PROFIT MARGIN	EMPLOYEES
09/18	1,481	78	5.3%	4,200
09/17	1,089	12	1.2%	—
09/15	1,004	7	0.8%	—
09/12	886	2	0.3%	—
Annual Growth	8.9%	76.9%	—	—

2018 Year-End Financials
Return on assets: 3.2%   Cash ($ mil.): 306
Return on equity: 5.8%
Current ratio: 1.70

BOSTON UNIVERSITY

EXECUTIVES
Pres, Robert Brown
Cfo*, Martin Howard
V Pres*, Todd Klipp
Co-Director, Ellen Shell
Scientist, Jeffrey Baumgardner
Scientist, Karen Hirsch
Associate Professor, Ellen Devoe
Associate Professor, Aaron Garrett
Coordinator, Lisa Murphy
Assistant Professor, Francois Gourio
Teacher, Archie Burnett

LOCATIONS
HQ: BOSTON UNIVERSITY
590 COMMONWEALTH AVE # 255, BOSTON, MA
022152521
Phone: 617 353-2600
Web: WWW.BU.EDU

HISTORICAL FINANCIALS
Company Type: Private

Income Statement				FYE: June 30
	REVENUE ($ mil.)	NET INCOME ($ mil.)	NET PROFIT MARGIN	EMPLOYEES
06/18	2,018	517	25.6%	70
06/17	1,895	507	26.8%	—
Annual Growth	6.5%	2.0%	—	—

2018 Year-End Financials
Return on assets: 8.1%   Cash ($ mil.): 148
Return on equity: 13.2%
Current ratio: —

BOZZUTO'S, INC.

Bozzuto's is a leading wholesale grocery distribution company that supplies food and non-food products to independent supermarkets belonging to the IGA network in New Jersey New York Pennsylvania and in New England. The company distributes a full line of grocery items including meat products produce and frozen food as well as household goods and other general merchandise. It carries goods sold under both the IGA and Hy-Top labels in addition to national brands. Bozzuto's also owns five supermarkets in Connecticut and Massachusetts operating under the Adams Super Food Stores banner.

Geographic Reach
Cheshire Connecticut-based Bozzuto's operates a pair of distribution centers in Cheshire as well as facilities in North Haven Connecticut and Allentown Pennsylvania.

Company Background
The company founded in 1945 is owned and operated by the Bozzuto family including chairman and CEO Michael Bozzuto.

EXECUTIVES
Vice President Human Resources, Bonnie Sirois
Svp Business Technology Systems And Services, John Keeley
Evp Retail Development, George Motel
Chairman President And Ceo, Michael A. Bozzuto
Vice President Finance, Jim Beaudreault
Vice President Ecommerce Retail Technology, Stephen Methvin
Vice President Information Technology, John Martin
Vice President Customer Service, Gail Handley
Vice President Wholesale Business Information Systems, Samar Saha
Senior Vice President Of Warehouse Transportation And Risk Management, Rick Clark
Vice President Of Center Store, Jeff King
Vice President Informationtechnologies, Jhon Kelly
Vice President And General Counsel, Kevin Daly
Vice President Of Transportation, Steven Schwartz
Vice President Human Resources, Scott Grove
Vice President Business Performance Coated And Specialties And Pulp And Lumber Operations, Craig B Stevens
Auditors: FEDERMAN LALLY & REMIS LLC F

LOCATIONS
HQ: BOZZUTO'S, INC.
275 SCHOOLHOUSE RD, CHESHIRE, CT 064101257
Phone: 203 272-3511
Web: WWW.BOZZUTOS.COM

PRODUCTS/OPERATIONS

Selected Services
New store site and demographic analysis
Retail merchandising specialists and sales support
Retail financial services accounting and payroll
Operational analysis
Shelf management programs
Market/pricing strategies
Employee training seminars and workshops
Profit building ideas
Retail technology

COMPETITORS

Associated Grocers of New England	Pine State Trading
C&S Wholesale	SUPERVALU
Krasdale Foods	Shaw's
McLane	Stop & Shop
	Wakefern Food

HISTORICAL FINANCIALS
Company Type: Private

Income Statement				FYE: September 27
	REVENUE ($ mil.)	NET INCOME ($ mil.)	NET PROFIT MARGIN	EMPLOYEES
09/08	1,243	(5)	—	3,100
09/07	1,180	(0)	—	—
09/06	955,449	0	0.0%	—
Annual Growth	(96.4%)	—	—	—

2008 Year-End Financials
Return on assets: 7.0%   Cash ($ mil.): 1
Return on equity: (-0.5%)
Current ratio: 0.60

BRANDSMART USA OF HENRY COUNTY, LLC

EXECUTIVES
Pres, Michael Pearlman
Exec V Pres, Larry Sinewgz
Cfo, Eric Beazley
Chief Operating Officer, Bobby Johnson
Vice President of Loss Prevent, Paul Garcia
Auditors: KAUFMAN ROSSIN AND CO

LOCATIONS
HQ: BRANDSMART USA OF HENRY COUNTY, LLC
3200 SW 42ND ST, FORT LAUDERDALE, FL
333126808
Phone: 954 797-4000
Web: WWW.BRANDSMARTUSA.COM

HISTORICAL FINANCIALS
Company Type: Private

Income Statement				FYE: September 25
	REVENUE ($ mil.)	NET INCOME ($ mil.)	NET PROFIT MARGIN	EMPLOYEES
09/10	800	7	0.9%	2,100
09/09	826	8	1.0%	—
Annual Growth	(3.2%)	(12.4%)	—	—

2010 Year-End Financials
Return on assets: 2.4%   Cash ($ mil.): 2
Return on equity: 4.4%
Current ratio: 1.00

BRAZOS ELECTRIC POWER COOPERATIVE, INC.

Brazos means "arms" in Spanish and the generation and transmission arms of Brazos Electric Power Cooperative reach across 68 Texas counties. It serves 16 member/owner distribution cooperatives andÂ oneÂ municipality in Northern and Central Texas. Brazos Electric Power annually generates (throughÂ its four power stations)Â and/or accesses from other power marketers some 3655 MW of electric power. The cooperative's members include Comanche Electric Cooperative Association Heart of Texas Electric Co-op (McGregor) Mid-South Synergy (Navasota) United Coop Services (Cleburne) and Wise Electric (Decatur).

EXECUTIVES
Vice President, Johnny York
Vice President Technology, Lynn Gustafson
Vp Supply Chain, Josh Clevenger

Secretary, Lois Anderson
Auditors: PRICEWATERHOUSECOOPERS LLP KA

LOCATIONS

HQ: BRAZOS ELECTRIC POWER COOPERATIVE, INC.
7616 BAGBY AVE, WACO, TX 767126924
Phone: 254 750-6500
Web: WWW.BRAZOSELECTRIC.COM
Brazos Electric Power Cooperative has operations in 68 counties in northern and Central Texas.

PRODUCTS/OPERATIONS

Member/Owners
Barlett Electric Cooperative
BEPC
Comanche Electric Cooperative
Cooke County Electric Cooperative
CoServ Electric
Fort Belknap Electric Cooperative
Hamilton County Electric Cooperative
Heart of Texas Electric Cooperative
HILCO Electric Cooperative
J-A-C Electric Cooperative
Mid-South Synergy
Navarro County Electric Cooperative
Navasota Valley Electric Cooperative
South Plains Electric Cooperative
Tri-County Electric Cooperative
United Cooperative Services
Wise Electric Cooperative

COMPETITORS

AEP	Entergy
CenterPoint Energy	LCRA
El Paso Electric	

HISTORICAL FINANCIALS

Company Type: Private

Income Statement				FYE: December 31
	REVENUE ($ mil.)	NET INCOME ($ mil.)	NET PROFIT MARGIN	EMPLOYEES
12/17	905	58	6.5%	366
12/09	963	56	5.9%	
12/99	307	6	2.3%	—
Annual Growth	6.2%	12.6%	—	—

2017 Year-End Financials
Return on assets: 1.9%   Cash ($ mil.): 353
Return on equity: 7.4%
Current ratio: 15.30

BRG SPORTS, INC.

BRG Sports is helmet and shoulder pads above the field. The company's Riddell brand is one of the main providers of helmets and shoulder pads worn by players of American football at all levels from junior leagues to the NFL. Riddell is the official helmet and protective gear provider of USA Football and American Youth Football which together have more than 3 million youth participants.As concerns about football and brain injuries have risen Riddell has responded with research to development new helmet models. The company also makes sports apparel and accessories. In 2016 the company parted with its action sport division selling it to Vista Outdoor Inc.

Change in Company Type

BRG Sports is still BRG even after it lost the Bell and Giro products that with Riddell made up the moniker acronym. The company sold those product lines and others in its action sports unit to Vista Outdoor Inc. for some $400 million in 2016.

Operations
BRG's helmets and pads are worn by athletes in other sports where protection is desired such as ice hockey baseball and softball.

Geographic Reach
BRG Sports is based in Rosemont Illinois and has 14 offices in the US and internationally.

Strategy
BRG Sports is betting on football. With the sale of its action sports division the company focuses on making safer helmets for all levels of football players. The company has invested in research to develop helmets that better absorb the shock of the constant head strikes that occur on the football field. One area is precision-fit helmets. The helmets are made for each player through a process in which each players head is measured and the helmet is custom built for each head. The company is involved with the NFL medical groups and competitors in helmet research.

The $400 million the company received from Vista Outdoor Inc. for the action sports unit has provided flexibility for its football bet. The proceeds have been used to pay down debt strengthen the balance sheet and to pursue growth initiatives for Riddell.

EXECUTIVES

Cfo, Mark A. Tripp, $316,875 total compensation
President Easton Sports, Christopher (Chris) Zimmerman
President And Chief Operating Officer, Timothy P. (Tim) Mayhew
President Ceo And Director, Paul E. Harrington, $715,385 total compensation
Executive Chairman And Chief Executive Officer, Terry G. Lee
President Riddell, Daniel J. (Dan) Arment, $337,038 total compensation
Chief Operations Officer President Of Giro Easton Cycling, Donna L. Flood, $339,692 total compensation
Evp And General Manager Mass Division And Action Sports Sales, Steven T. Bigelow
Evp And General Manager Of Giro/easton Cycling, Greg Shapleigh
Evp And General Manager Of Bell/blackburn, Jessica Klodnicki
President Easton, Mike Zlaket
Auditors: ERNST & YOUNG LLP LOS ANGELE

LOCATIONS

HQ: BRG SPORTS, INC.
1700 E HIGGINS RD STE 500, DES PLAINES, IL 600183800
Phone: 224 585-5200

2013 Sales

	$ mil.	% of total
North America	667	85
Europe	84	11
Other	28	4
Total	**780**	**100**

PRODUCTS/OPERATIONS

Selected Products
Riddell helmets
Riddell shoulder pads
Riddell padded shirts
Riddell game pants
Riddell compression shirts and pants

COMPETITORS

Amer Sports	Reebok-CCM Hockey
Bauer Hockey	Russell Brands
Merrithew	Under Armour
NIKE	Wilson Sporting Goods
Rawlings Sporting Goods	adidas

HISTORICAL FINANCIALS

Company Type: Private

Income Statement				FYE: December 29
	REVENUE ($ mil.)	NET INCOME ($ mil.)	NET PROFIT MARGIN	EMPLOYEES
12/12	827	(3)	—	2,370
12/11*	834	10	1.2%	
01/11	772	8	1.1%	—
Annual Growth	3.5%	—	—	—

*Fiscal year change

2012 Year-End Financials
Return on assets: (-0.3%)   Cash ($ mil.): 40
Return on equity: (-0.9%)
Current ratio: 2.50

BRIDGEPORT HOSPITAL

EXECUTIVES

Pres-Ceo, William M Jennings
Sr V Pres-Med Staff, Bruce Mc Donald
V Pres-Hr*, Joseph E Janell
SEC*, Norman Roth
Dir, David Bindelglass
Human Resources Coordinator, Maria Alicea
Pediatrician, Mary Gaeta
Radiology Manager, Michael D Angelico
Engineer, Peter Romano
Director, Susan French
Doctor, Armand J Wolff

LOCATIONS

HQ: BRIDGEPORT HOSPITAL
267 GRANT ST, BRIDGEPORT, CT 066102870
Phone: 203 384-3000
Web: WWW.BRIDGEPORTHOSPITAL.ORG

HISTORICAL FINANCIALS

Company Type: Private

Income Statement				FYE: September 30
	REVENUE ($ mil.)	NET INCOME ($ mil.)	NET PROFIT MARGIN	EMPLOYEES
09/17	482	25	5.4%	200
09/16	470	46	9.9%	—
09/15	466	55	11.9%	—
09/14	439	42	9.8%	—
Annual Growth	3.1%	(15.5%)	—	—

2017 Year-End Financials
Return on assets: 4.9%   Cash ($ mil.): 26
Return on equity: 15.0%
Current ratio: 1.70

BRIGHTSTAR US, INC.

EXECUTIVES

Mng MBR, Joe Kalinoski
MBR, Catherine Smith
MBR, Jack Negro
MBR, Chad Meadinger

HQ: BRIGHTSTAR US, INC.
600 N US HIGHWAY 45 100W, LIBERTYVILLE, IL
600481286
Phone: 847 573-2600

HISTORICAL FINANCIALS
Company Type: Private

Income Statement				FYE: December 31
	REVENUE ($ mil.)	NET INCOME ($ mil.)	NET PROFIT MARGIN	EMPLOYEES
12/16	4,137	52	1.3%	225
12/15	4,418	50	1.1%	
Annual Growth	(6.4%)	2.8%	—	—

BRIXMOR LLC

EXECUTIVES

MBR, Michael Carroll
Chief Financial Officer*, Tiffanie Fisher
MBR*, Steven F Siegel
MBR*, Leonard Brumberg
MBR*, Steve Splain
Pres*, Michael Pappagallo
Exec V Pres*, Dean Bernstein
Exec V Pres*, Timothy Bruce
Exec V Pres*, Steven Siegel
Director, Chris Reed
Project Manager, Stephen Herget
Auditors: ERNST & YOUNG LLP

LOCATIONS

HQ: BRIXMOR LLC
450 LEXINGTON AVE FL 13, NEW YORK, NY
100173956
Phone: 212 869-3000
Web: WWW.BRIXMOR.COM

HISTORICAL FINANCIALS
Company Type: Private

Income Statement				FYE: December 31
	ASSETS ($ mil.)	NET INCOME ($ mil.)	INCOME AS % OF ASSETS	EMPLOYEES
12/08	4,157	(550)	—	442
12/07	5,702	(486)	—	
Annual Growth	(27.1%)	—	—	—

2008 Year-End Financials

Return on assets: —   Sales ($ mil): 418
Return on equity: (-131.6%)

BRODER BROS., CO.

Selling clothes had been in the genes of sportswear distributor Broder Bros. for years. Begun as a haberdashery in 1919 the company evolved from making hats and gloves into a leading distributor of imprintable sportswear distributing 40000-plus SKUs across more than 40 retail brands including adidas Golf Champion Russell Athletic alternative Dickies and private labels. It operates under the Broder Alpha and NES divisions. Private labels include Devon & Jones Chestnut Hill and Harriton. Customers mostly small US retailers order merchandise through seasonal catalogs or online. Private investment firm Bain Capital has held a majority interest in the company since 2000 when the Broder family sold the company.

Operations

Broder Bros.' business comprises eight distribution facilities nationwide as well as 10 Express locations that offer pickup services to customers. Express facilities ship through ground parcel service to more than 80% of the continental US population within one business day and to more than 98% of the continental US population within two business days.

Its two primary markets are imprintable sportswear and accessories. Typically undecorated or blank items such as sweatshirts polo shirts fleece outerwear caps bags and other imprintable accessories are bought from Broder Bros. and decorated for the purposes of advertising and promotion. Decorator customers are offered value-added merchandising marketing and promotional support to help them grow their businesses.

Geographic Reach

Based in Pennsylvania Broder Bros. boasts the industry's largest distribution network. It provides its products to customers across the continental US.

Sales and Marketing

The company which caters to more than 70000 customers relies on a handful of suppliers such as Gildan Hanes and Fruit of the Loom.

In general Broder Bros. clients include advertising specialty companies screen printers embroiderers and specialty retailers that purchase Broder Bros. products (blank T-shirts sweatshirts polo shirts outerwear caps bags and more) to embellish for their own clients. Broder Bros. distributes popular brands such as Anvil Jerzees Hanes Fruit of the Loom and Gildan.

Strategy

Broder Bros. has seen its business pick up on the heels of a tough selling environment. One way it has turned its business around is by ensuring that it had in stock the most popular products while it rebuilt its inventory of proprietary brands. It also strengthened its commitment not to be undersold by rivals. To ensure that its dozen distribution centers were bustling with business Broder Bros. also recruited a senior sales and marketing executive to review and fine-tune how the company sells its products help to decide which product assortment is ideal going forward and figure out how to attract a wider customer base from the imprintable sportswear market.

Mergers and Acquisitions

Looking to post more than $900 million in sales and $50 million in pro forma EBITDA in 2013 Broder Bros. bought Denver-based Imprints Wholesale one of the top wholesale clothing distributors in the Rocky Mountain region. The deal is Broder Bros.' first acquisition since 2006 and first since private investment firm Littlejohn & Co. took over control of the board of directors in mid-2012.

EXECUTIVES

Regional Vice President, Jason Buchanan
Vice President Of Customer Service, Dave Null Hance
Vice President Of Information Technology, Andrew Pomerleau
Regional Vice President, Joe Bunsness
Vice President Operations, Ron Wittebort
Executive Vice President Sales, Lindstrom Hays

LOCATIONS

HQ: BRODER BROS., CO.
6 NESHAMINY INTERPLEX DR, TREVOSE, PA
190536964
Phone: 215 291-0300
Web: WWW.ALPHABRODER.COM

PRODUCTS/OPERATIONS

Selected Products

Accessories

Bags
Decoration supplies
Fleece
Headwear
Pants
Shorts
Sport shirts
T-shirts
Woven shirts

Selected Brands
Trade
　Adams Cap
　American Apparel
　Anvil
　Bella
　Canvas
　Cross Creek
　Fruit of the Loom
　Gildan
　Hanes
　Izod
　Outer Banks
　Van Heusen
　Weatherproof
　Yupoong
Retail
　adidas Golf
　Champion
　Dickies Chef
　Dickies Workwear
　Rossignol Pure Mountain Company
Private-label
　Chestnut Hill
　Harriton
　Devon & Jones
　HYP
　Harvard Square

COMPETITORS

Anvil Holdings	Hanesbrands
Concept One Accessories	M. J. Soffe
	PremiumWear
Delta Apparel	Russell Brands
Fruit of the Loom	VF Corporation
Gildan Activewear	

HISTORICAL FINANCIALS
Company Type: Private

Income Statement				FYE: December 26
	REVENUE ($ mil.)	NET INCOME ($ mil.)	NET PROFIT MARGIN	EMPLOYEES
12/09	705	(13)	—	1,826
12/08	926	(68)	—	—
12/07	929	(124)	—	—
Annual Growth	(12.9%)	—	—	—

2009 Year-End Financials

Return on assets: (-4.5%)   Cash ($ mil.): 3
Return on equity: —
Current ratio: 2.10

BRONSON HEALTH CARE GROUP, INC.

Bronson Health Care Group has a strong presence as a provider of a wide range of medical services in southern Michigan and northern Indiana. The company operates several regional hospitals and health clinics including Bronson Methodist Hospital (some 400 beds) Bronson Battle Creek (220 beds) and Bronson Lakeview Hospital (35 beds). The not-for-profit health care system's facilities provide general and specialty services including trauma stroke burn cancer and cardiac care as well as emergency medicine pediatrics obstetrics rehabilitation and home health care.

Operations

Bronson Health Care Group serves about 24000 patients each year at more than 60 locations. The medical system offers a full range of services from primary care to critical care; it has more than 1000 medical staff members and 812 licensed beds.

The hospital group provides $94 million in community benefits a year including charity care for under-insured or uninsured patients.

Geographic Reach

Bronson Health Care Group operates hospitals clinics and physician practice facilities in Kalamazoo Calhoun and Van Buren counties in southwestern and south central Michigan; its locations also serve patients from areas of northern Indiana.

Strategy

Expanded its infrastructure to meet demand in 2013 the company opened Bronson Commons a rehabilitation and skilled nursing community in Mattawan. The all-private room healthcare facility has the capacity to serve 100 patients.

That year 2013 Bronson Battle Creek opened a new outpatient center on Beckley Road.

Mergers and Acquisitions

In 2013 HealthCare Midwest a multidisciplinary physician group (with 80 doctors) serving southwest Michigan joined the Bronson family of companies and became Bronson HealthCare Midwest. That year Associated Internal Medicine Specialists a medical practice focused on internal medicine and rheumatology joined Bronson Battle Creek and was renamed Bronson Internal Medicine & Rheumatology.

In 2012 Colon and Rectal Surgery Center PC joined the Bronson network and became Bronson Center for Colon & Rectal Diseases.

Company Background

To expand its services and geographic reach in 2011 Bronson Health Care System acquired the Battle Creek Health System (now named Bronson Battle Creek located in south central Michigan. The purchase added acute care inpatient mental health cancer care occupational health and other specialized services in the region.

The not-for-profit health care system was founded in 1900.

EXECUTIVES

Vp Cno, Denise Neely
Senior Vice President Strategy And Communication, Sue Birch
Vice President Contracting And Clinically Integrated Network, Nancy Vannest
Medical Secretary, Nicole Blain
Auditors: PLANTE & MORAN PLLC GRAND RA

LOCATIONS

HQ: BRONSON HEALTH CARE GROUP, INC.
301 JOHN ST, KALAMAZOO, MI 490075295
Phone: 269 341-6000

PRODUCTS/OPERATIONS

Selected Facilities
Bronson Athletic Club
Bronson Battle Creek
Bronson Commons
Bronson Health Foundation
Bronson HealthCare Midwest
Bronson Home Health Care
Bronson LakeView Hospital
Bronson LakeView Outpatient Center
Bronson Lifestyle Improvement & Research Center
Bronson Medical Group
Bronson Methodist Hospital
Bronson Vicksburg Outpatient Center
Van Buren Emergency Medical Services

COMPETITORS

Ascension Health	Mercy Health Hackley
Gerber Memorial	Sheridan Community
Hayes Green Beach	Hospital
Memorial Hospital	Spectrum Health

HISTORICAL FINANCIALS

Company Type: Private

Income Statement
FYE: December 31

	REVENUE ($ mil.)	NET INCOME ($ mil.)	NET PROFIT MARGIN	EMPLOYEES
12/17	1,233	63	5.1%	4,180
12/16	1,136	28	2.5%	—
12/09	119	16	13.8%	—
12/08	588	(62)	—	—
Annual Growth	8.6%	—	—	—

2017 Year-End Financials
Return on assets: 4.5%
Return on equity: 9.4%
Current ratio: 5.60
Cash ($ mil.): 103

BRONSON METHODIST HOSPITAL INC

From your leg bone to your knee bone; your neck bone to your head bone Bronson Methodist Hospital has the specialists to cure what ails you. The 435-bed hospital is the flagship facility of the Bronson Healthcare Group a not-for-profit health care system. Bronson Methodist provides care in just about every specialty including orthopedics surgery and oncology. The hospital also contains specialist units for critical care (level I trauma center) neurology (primary stroke center) cardiology (Chest pain emergency center) women's health (BirthPlace) and pediatrics (children's hospital).

EXECUTIVES

Vice President Of Finance And Human Resources, Erica Nagra
Auditors: PLANTE & MORAN PLLC CHICAGO

LOCATIONS

HQ: BRONSON METHODIST HOSPITAL INC
601 JOHN ST STE E-012, KALAMAZOO, MI 490075346
Phone: 269 341-7654

PRODUCTS/OPERATIONS

Selected Services
Anticoagulation
Bereavement
Breast Health
Burn
Cancer Care
Critical Care
Diabetes
Flu
Heart and Vascular
Home Health
Hyperbaric Oxygen Therapy
Infusion
Laboratory
Medical and Surgical Weight Management
Neurosciences
Nutrition
Occupational Health
Orthopedics
Palliative Care
Pediatrics
Pharmacy
Pregnancy and Childbirth
Rehabilitation
Respiratory Care
Sleep
Surgery
Stomal Therapy
Testing and Imaging
Trauma and Emergency
Women's Health
Wound

COMPETITORS

Ascension Health	Holland Hospital
Borgess Health	Spectrum Health
Bronson Battle Creek	Trinity Health (Novi)
Community Hospital	Zeeland Community
Elkhart General	Hospital
Healthcare System	
Hayes Green Beach	
Memorial Hospital	

HISTORICAL FINANCIALS

Company Type: Private

Income Statement
FYE: December 31

	REVENUE ($ mil.)	NET INCOME ($ mil.)	NET PROFIT MARGIN	EMPLOYEES
12/18	864	26	3.1%	2,861
12/17	864	85	9.8%	—
12/15	726	69	9.5%	—
12/13	647	(8)	—	—
Annual Growth	6.0%	—	—	—

2018 Year-End Financials
Return on assets: 2.8%
Return on equity: 4.2%
Current ratio: 9.40
Cash ($ mil.): 109

BRONXCARE HEALTH SYSTEM

Bronx-Lebanon Hospital Center cares for patients in the central and south Bronx no doubt while rooting for the Yankees a few blocks away. The health care provider maintains more than 970 beds across its two campuses as well as psychiatric and nursing home facilities. Hospital specialty units include chest pain orthopedic cancer and women's health centers. Bronx-Lebanon also manages a network of about 70 owned and affiliated medical practices (under the BronxCare brand). This network includes primary care doctors and specialty clinics as well as rehabilitation facilities. The hospital is also a primary teaching hospital for the Albert Einstein College of Medicine.

Operations

Aside from its two major hospitals Bronx-Lebanon operates a psychiatric facility a pair of specialized long-term care facilities and the BronxCare network of medical practices that include Dr. Martin Luther King Jr. Health Center and a 51-unit facility to house seniors and low-income residents. Bronx-Lebanon cares for those with mental or substance abuse problems through the Family Wellness Center. It also operates a 240-bed Special Care Center and the 90-bed Highbridge Woodycrest Center to provide long term health care to geriatric AIDS and disabled residents. Its ER Department responds to about 141000 patient visits a year.

Geographic Reach

The hospital system's 37 locations serve residents of central and south Bronx in New York.

Sales and Marketing

In 2013 the company spent about $144000 on advertising.

Financial Performance

The Hospital Center is supported primarily by patient service fees paid by Medicaid Medicare and commercial insurance carriers. In 2013 the Medicaid contributed 63% of the revenue whereas Medicare contributed 28% and the rest 9% was contributed other third-party insurance carriers.

In 2013 Bronx-Lebanon's net revenues increased by about 5% due to a rise in patient service revenues and grants partially offset by a decrease in auxiliary services.

The company's net income increased by more than 790% in 2013 as the result of an increase in revenues.

Bronx-Lebanon's operating cash flows increased by 53% thanks to higher income.

Strategy

Bronx-Lebanon emphasizes its role as a community health care provider not only through its BronxCare network but through a number of community outreach and service efforts including school-based programs mobile health units free health screening and even a weekly live television show that discusses health issues.

To accommodate the growing population in and around the Bronx the hospital system has expanded in recent years with a new children's wing for inpatient and outpatient services; a nine-story ambulatory care facility; and an extensive emergency room modernization. Bronx-Lebanon also maintains a short stay observation unit in the emergency room area to monitor and evaluate patients in cardiac distress prior to admission or discharge.

Bronx-Lebanon is one of many hospital organizations to have joined a regional health information organization (RHIO) to allow medical professionals to access a patient's medical records at any number of health care locations. Other members of the Bronx RHIO include Montefiore Medical Center Jacobi Medical Center St. Barnabas Hospital and Hebrew Home at Riverdale.

Bronx-Lebanon is also one of the few hospitals in New York that is fully computerized with a complete inpatient and outpatient electronic medical record.

The hospital center's expansion plans include a $42 million 60000 sq. ft ambulatory care facility and a $34 million 56000 sq. ft. life recovery center for chemical dependency services.

In 2014 the company completed the construction of its Health and Wellness Center a new state-of-the-art outpatient facility with general and specialty services and new treatment rooms and diagnostic equipment. It also completed the construction of its Life Recovery Center to combine inpatient outpatient and residential services for individuals suffering from chemical dependency.

The company also expanded its Emergency room adding a new 11-bay treatment area.

In the same year it also relocated and expanded its main Dentistry Practice adding 39 dental chairs (a 50% increase).

EXECUTIVES

Medical Director, Soni Mathew
Vice President, Milton A Gumbs
Vice Chairman Department Of Otolaryngology Head And Neck Surgery, Srinivasan Krishna

LOCATIONS

HQ: BRONXCARE HEALTH SYSTEM
1276 FULTON AVE, BRONX, NY 104563402
Phone: 718 590-1800
Web: WWW.BRONXCARE.ORG

PRODUCTS/OPERATIONS

Selected Services

Anesthesiology

Asthma
  Adult
  Pediatric
Cardiology
Dentistry
Diabetes
  Adult
  Pediatric
Ear Nose & Throat
Gastroenterology
Hematology & Oncology
Neonatology
Neurology
Ophthalmology
Orthopaedics
Pediatrics
Physical Medicine
Psychiatry
Radiology
Special Care Center
Urology & Men's Health

Selected Academic Affiliations
Albert Einstein College of Medicine
Bronx Community College
Hostos Community College
Lehman College City University of New York
State University of New York at Stony Brook

COMPETITORS

Beth Israel Medical Center	Montefiore Medical New York City Health
Catholic Healthcare System	and Hospitals NewYork-Presbyterian
Continuum Health Partners	Healthcare Northwell Health
Lenox Hill Hospital	Winthrop-University
Maimonides Medical Center	Hospital
Memorial Sloan-Kettering	

HISTORICAL FINANCIALS

Company Type: Private

Income Statement   FYE: December 31

	REVENUE ($ mil.)	NET INCOME ($ mil.)	NET PROFIT MARGIN	EMPLOYEES
12/17	750	12	1.6%	4,000
12/16	641	6	1.0%	—
12/15	631	18	3.0%	—
12/14	598	(34)	—	—
Annual Growth	7.9%	—	—	—

Return on assets: 2.4%   Cash ($ mil.): 117
Return on equity: 19.6%
Current ratio: 0.70

BROTHER INTERNATIONAL CORPORATION

Brother International is part of one big global family. A subsidiary of Japan-based Brother Industries Brother International sells a host of products — including inkjet and laser printers fax machines scanners typewriters sewing machines gear motors and machine tools — manufactured by its parent company. Its products are marketed to consumers and businesses in North America and across Latin America. Through its subsidiaries Brother International operates production and sales facilities in some 30 countries worldwide; it serves customers in about 100 countries. The business was formed in 1954.

Strategy

Although it provides a range of products for office and home use including home appliances such as sewing machines Brother International is increasingly focused on office equipment technology and document management. In 2019 it partnered with software firm Accusoft by integrating Accusoft's OnTask SaaS workflow platform into select Brother devices allowing for remote collaboration improved visibility and tracking of documents and shortened turnaround times.

EXECUTIVES

Chairman Brother International Corporation, Tadashi Ishiguro
Vice President, Bill Henderson
Senior Vp, Henry Sacco

LOCATIONS

HQ: BROTHER INTERNATIONAL CORPORATION
200 CROSSING BLVD FL 1, BRIDGEWATER, NJ 088072861
Phone: 908 704-1700
Web: WWW.BROTHER-USA.COM

PRODUCTS/OPERATIONS

Selected Services
Brother Business Solutions
Brother Cloud

Selected Products
Fax machines
Garment printers
Gear motors
Home sewing & embroidery
Industrial printing & sewing
Labeling systems
Machine tools
Mobile products (portable scanners printers industrial labelers)
Printers
Scanners
Sewing and embroidery machines
Stamp-making systems
Typewriters
Web conferencing

COMPETITORS

Canon USA	OKI Data Americas
Epson	Oracle
HP	RISO Inc.
IBM	Retail Holdings
Kyocera Document	Ricoh Americas
Solutions America	Xerox
Microsoft	

HISTORICAL FINANCIALS

Company Type: Private

Income Statement — FYE: March 31

	REVENUE ($ mil.)	NET INCOME ($ mil.)	NET PROFIT MARGIN	EMPLOYEES
03/18	1,751	33	1.9%	2,000
03/15	1,852	3	0.2%	—
03/14	1,826	26	1.5%	—
Annual Growth	(1.0%)	6.1%	—	—

2018 Year-End Financials

Return on assets: 4.2%
Return on equity: 6.0%
Current ratio: 3.30
Cash ($ mil.): 29

BROWARD COUNTY PUBLIC SCHOOLS

EXECUTIVES

Supt, Robert W Runcie
Acct*, Paul Purrier
Executive of Information Techn, Sharon Simmons
Customer Staff, Kendra Demme
Director, Angela St Hubert
Teacher, Joann Hoy
Director, Judy Zinn
Office Manager, Kathryn McArthur
Administrative Assistant, Nicoletta Williams
Information Technology Manager, Becky Schmaus
Teacher Th, Karen Tobias

LOCATIONS

HQ: BROWARD COUNTY PUBLIC SCHOOLS
600 SE 3RD AVE, FORT LAUDERDALE, FL 333013125
Phone: 754 321-0000
Web: WWW.BROWARDSCHOOLS.COM

HISTORICAL FINANCIALS

Company Type: Private

Income Statement — FYE: June 30

	REVENUE ($ mil.)	NET INCOME ($ mil.)	NET PROFIT MARGIN	EMPLOYEES
06/16	2,630	(37)	—	31,174
06/15	2,536	186	7.3%	—
06/11	2,515	(37)	—	—
Annual Growth	0.9%	—	—	—

2016 Year-End Financials

Return on assets: (-0.9%)
Return on equity: (-6.4%)
Current ratio: 1.50
Cash ($ mil.): 671

BROWARD GENERAL MEDICAL CENTER

EXECUTIVES

Ceo, James Thaw
SEC*, Beverly Virago
Admin*, Maxine James Francis
Pathologist, Julian Garcia
Compliance Director, Natassia Orr
Chief of Pathology, Peter S Johnson
Doctor, Erol Yoldas
Scientist, Maryluz Osorio
Acting Director, Melanie Hatcher
Doctor, Leonard Erdman
Ceo, Broward Health Coral Spri, Jared M Smith

LOCATIONS

HQ: BROWARD GENERAL MEDICAL CENTER
1600 S ANDREWS AVE, FORT LAUDERDALE, FL
333162510
Phone: 954 355-4400
Web: WWW.BROWARDHEALTH.ORG

HISTORICAL FINANCIALS

Company Type: Private

Income Statement — FYE: June 30

	REVENUE ($ mil.)	NET INCOME ($ mil.)	NET PROFIT MARGIN	EMPLOYEES
06/16	455	26	5.9%	86
06/15	458	58	12.8%	—
Annual Growth	(0.7%)	(54.2%)	—	—

2016 Year-End Financials

Return on assets: 3.0%
Return on equity: 4.3%
Current ratio: 1.50
Cash ($ mil.): —

BROWN UNIVERSITY IN PROVIDENCE IN THE STATE OF RHODE ISLAND AND PROVIDENCE PLANTATIONS

Ivy isn't always green — particularly when it's Brown. Founded in 1764 Brown University is both an Ivy League college and one of the oldest universities in the US. About 8700 undergraduate graduate and medical students have about 70 undergraduate and 70 graduate programs of study at their disposal in areas ranging from acting to pharmacology and from history to business administration. The university's specialty programs include the Warren Alpert Medical School and the Brown School of Engineering; it also has continuing education and online learning programs. Brown has some 700 faculty members giving it a student-teacher ratio of about 8:1. It has an endowment of more than $3 billion.

Operations

Nearly all applicants to Brown have graduated in the top 10% of their high school class. Undergraduate tuition and fees at Brown run at more than $62000 per year and as such nearly half of its students receive needs-based scholarships.

Brown's medical school partners with a number of area medical facilities to provide specialized medical training as well as specialized health care services to the public in addition to research in a variety of disease and treatment areas.

In fiscal 2015 Brown spent $152 million on research expenditures funded by both government and private sources.

Geographic Reach

Brown's students come from all 50 US states as well as from more than 115 other countries. The university campus is located in Providence Rhode Island and consists of 235 buildings on nearly 140 acres. It also has study abroad partnerships with schools in countries including Scotland and China.

Financial Performance

Brown University's endowment was up to nearly $3 billion until 2009 when the troubled economy caused it to lose more than a quarter of its value leading Brown to cut its operating budget in subsequent year. The university has recovered some of the lost funds through rebounding markets and a diverse investment strategy (including traditional stocks and fixed-income securities as well as alternative investment funds) with the endowment rising to just over $2.5 billion in 2012. By fiscal 2015 the endowment reached a new peak at $3.3 billion.

Also that year revenue increased 5% to $808 million on an equal amount of growth in net tuition and fees as well as growth in contributions and grants and auxiliary enterprises. However net income declined steeply falling $334 million to $67 million in 2015. This was a result of lower investment earnings and higher operating expenses (salaries supplies etc.). Operating cash outflow increased 8% to $73 million due to changes in accounts payable and accrued liabilities.

Strategy

To enhance its students' educational experience Brown is looking to expand its campus facilities and grow its portfolio of programs. Of its three professional schools (public health medical and engineering) two were established within the past five years. In 2015 Brown introduced a new master's program in social analysis and research.

In terms of physical facilities the university is also making additions and changes. It recently completed projects updating the mathematics (2015) and sports (2014) departments and it is expanding the engineering school complex.

Company Background

Founded in 1764 as the College of Rhode Island the university was renamed Brown University in 1804 for benefactor Nicholas Brown. Brown was the the first Ivy League school to appoint an African-American to the position president; Ruth Simmons was president of the university from 2001-2012. Simmons was also the university's first female president.

EXECUTIVES

Evp Finance And Administration, Elizabeth C. Huidekoper
Svp Corporation Affairs And Governance, Russell C. Carey
Dean Of Admission, James Miller
Dean Medicine And Biological Sciences, Jack A. Elias
Provost, Mark S. Schlissel

LOCATIONS

HQ: BROWN UNIVERSITY IN PROVIDENCE IN THE
 STATE OF RHODE ISLAND AND PROVIDENCE
 PLANTATIONS
 1 PROSPECT ST, PROVIDENCE, RI 029129127
Phone: 401 863-1000
Web: WWW.BROWN.EDU

PRODUCTS/OPERATIONS

2015 Revenues

	$ mil.	% of total
Net tuition & fees	289	36
Grants & contracts	151	18
Endowment income	142	18
Contributions	98	12
Auxiliary enterprises	90	11
Other	36	5
Total	**808**	**100**

Selected Programs

Africana Studies Department of
American Studies Department of
Anthropology Department of
Applied Mathematics Division of
Archaeology and the Ancient World Joukowsky Institute
 for
Behavioral and Social Sciences Department of
Biology & Medicine Division of
Biomedical Engineering Center for
Biostatistics Department of
Biotechnology Graduate Program
Brown-Pfizer MA Program in Biology
Chemistry Department of
Classics Department of
Cognitive Linguistic and Psychological Sciences
 Department of
Commerce Organizations & Entrepreneurship C.V. Starr
 Program in
Comparative Literature Department of
Computational Biology Center for
Computer Science Department of
Development Studies Program in

HISTORICAL FINANCIALS

Company Type: Private

Income Statement				FYE: June 30
	REVENUE ($ mil.)	NET INCOME ($ mil.)	NET PROFIT MARGIN	EMPLOYEES
06/13	732	289	39.6%	5,100
06/12	704	(69)	—	—
06/11	666	359	53.9%	—
Annual Growth	4.8%	(10.2%)	—	—

2013 Year-End Financials

Return on assets: 6.6%   Cash ($ mil.): 14
Return on equity: 8.4%
Current ratio: —

BROWNSVILLE INDEPENDENT SCHOOL DISTRICT

EXECUTIVES

Supt, Esperanza Zendejas
Cfo*, Lucio Mendoza
SEC*, Yvonne F
Federal Program Director, Mary Lou L Esparza
Tech Prep Coordinator, Robby Fisher
Payroll Staff, Mary Flores
Sergeant, Lorena Bermudez
Coordinator, Paul Johnson
Human Resources Officer, Monica De
Network Administrator, Sergio Garcia
Secretary, Terry Lamas
Auditors: PATTILLO BROWN & HILL LLP B

LOCATIONS

HQ: BROWNSVILLE INDEPENDENT SCHOOL
 DISTRICT
 1900 PRICE RD, BROWNSVILLE, TX 785212495
Phone: 956 548-8000
Web: WWW.BISD.US

HISTORICAL FINANCIALS

Company Type: Private

Income Statement				FYE: June 30
	REVENUE ($ mil.)	NET INCOME ($ mil.)	NET PROFIT MARGIN	EMPLOYEES
06/11*	504	(17)	—	7,500
12/05	415	0	—	—
06/05	0	0	—	—
08/03	0	0	—	—
Annual Growth	—	—	—	—

*Fiscal year change

2011 Year-End Financials

Return on assets: (-2.5%)   Cash ($ mil.): 4
Return on equity: (-4.7%)
Current ratio: —

BRUCE OAKLEY, INC.

From little acorns mighty Oakleys grow. Bruce
Oakley provides road and river (barge)Â transportation of dry bulk commodities as well as grain
storage and bulk fertilizer sales. The company's
trucking division which uses both end-dump and
pneumatic tank trailers serves the continental US
and Canada. OverallÂ Bruce OakleyÂ operates
some 450 trailers.Â It maintains about half a dozen
ports in Arkansas Louisiana and Missouri on the
Arkansas Mississippi and Red rivers and the company's river barge transportation unit operates on
those and other inland and intracoastal waterways.
Grain storage services are available inÂ fiveÂ ports
in Arkansas. Bruce Oakley was founded in 1968.

EXECUTIVES

Vice President, Edward Bubba Vance
Vice President, Shane Smith
Vice President, David Choate
Vice President, Josh Childress
Vice President Sales Division, Russell Vallance
Vice President, Autumn Whiting
Vice President Fuel, Tim Lloyd

LOCATIONS

HQ: BRUCE OAKLEY, INC.
 3700 LINCOLN AVE, NORTH LITTLE ROCK, AR
 721146448
Phone: 501 945-0875
Web: WWW.BRUCEOAKLEY.COM

PRODUCTS/OPERATIONS

Selected Products and Services
Bagging
Barges
Bulk fertilizer
Grain and grain storage
Oakley vessel freight
River ports and stevedoring
Trucking

COMPETITORS

American Commercial Lines	Groendyke Transport
Bulkmatic	Kansas City Southern
Comcar	Superior Bulk
GrainCorp	Logistics

HISTORICAL FINANCIALS

Company Type: Private

Income Statement				FYE: September 25
	REVENUE ($ mil.)	NET INCOME ($ mil.)	NET PROFIT MARGIN	EMPLOYEES
09/08	1,160	31	2.8%	720
09/07	526	11	2.2%	—
09/06	419	13	3.2%	—
Annual Growth	66.3%	53.6%	—	—

2008 Year-End Financials

Return on assets: 21.7%   Cash ($ mil.): 3
Return on equity: 34.6%
Current ratio: 2.50

BRUCKNER TRUCK SALES, INC.

EXECUTIVES

Pres, Brian M Bruckner
Exec V Pres*, Chris B Bruckner
Sec-Treas-Cfo*, Wesley L Lawhorn
V Pres*, Keith Martin
V Pres*, Brian Murphy
Parts Sales, Tyler Ferrell
Manager, Lois Bieker
Auditors: CLIFTON LARSON ALLEN LLP DALL

LOCATIONS

HQ: BRUCKNER TRUCK SALES, INC.
 9471 E INTERSTATE 40, AMARILLO, TX 791186960
Phone: 806 376-6273
Web: WWW.BRUCKNERTRUCK.COM

HISTORICAL FINANCIALS

Company Type: Private

Income Statement				FYE: June 30
	REVENUE ($ mil.)	NET INCOME ($ mil.)	NET PROFIT MARGIN	EMPLOYEES
06/15	580	10	1.8%	900
06/14	490	10	2.1%	—
06/10	200	2	1.1%	—
Annual Growth	23.8%	37.9%	—	—

Return on assets: 3.5%   Cash ($ mil.): 31
Return on equity: 12.9%
Current ratio: 1.20

BRYAN HEALTH

EXECUTIVES

President, Kimberly Russel
Chairperson*, Gene Brake
Vice Chairman*, Steven Erwin
Trustee*, Andrew Hove Jr
Trustee*, William Lester
Trustee*, Donde Plowman PHD
Trustee, David Dyke
Trustee, Jon Hinrichs
Trustee*, Prem Paul Dvm
Trustee*, Jack Huck
Trustee*, Renee Sjulin

LOCATIONS

HQ: BRYAN HEALTH
 1600 S 48TH ST, LINCOLN, NE 685061299
Phone: 402 481-1111
Web: WWW.BRYANHEALTH.COM

HISTORICAL FINANCIALS
Company Type: Private

Income Statement   FYE: December 31

	REVENUE ($ mil.)	NET INCOME ($ mil.)	NET PROFIT MARGIN	EMPLOYEES
12/17	682	87	12.8%	4,344
12/16	650	70	10.9%	—
12/15	6	50	769.7%	—
12/14	3	30	796.7%	—
Annual Growth	465.5%	42.8%	—	—

2017 Year-End Financials

Return on assets: 7.9%   Cash ($ mil.): 218
Return on equity: 10.4%
Current ratio: 3.20

BRYAN MEDICAL CENTER

Bryan Medical Center is the centerpiece of a not-for-profit health care system serving residents of Lincoln Nebraska and surrounding communities. The medical center which operates as part of Bryan Health features two acute-care hospitals (Bryan East and Bryan West) housing a combined 670 beds. In addition to providing general medical and surgical care it serves as a regional trauma center and provides specialty care in areas such as cancer orthopedics and cardiology. The Bryan Health organization also includes a rural hospital and several outpatient clinics and it provides medical training home health care services and wellness programs.

Operations

In addition to Bryan Medical Center the Bryan Health organization operates the Crete Area Medical Center a 25-bed community hospital. Outpatient facilities include the Bryan Heart Institute (cardiology and cardiothoracic surgery) the Bryan

Physician Network (family practice urgent care and specialist locations) and Bryan LifePointe (wellness and fitness programs). In addition the network includes the Bryan College of Health Sciences which provides bachelor's and master's degrees in nursing and health professional fields and the Bryan Foundation. It also conducts community education activities.

In the latest year for which data is available the hospital had 5912 inpatient visits; 6650 outpatient surgeries; and 68352 emergency department visits.

Geographic ReachBryan Medical Center serves patients throughout Nebraska as well as portions of neighboring states including Kansas Iowa and Missouri with clinics in more than 30 communities including Lincoln Columbus and Hastings.

Sales and Marketing

Bryan Medical Center advertises through magazines and through the Internet.

Strategy

In 2015 the hospital became the first in Nebraska to utilize the CardioMEMS HF System a miniaturized and wireless monitoring device to manage heart failure and reduce hospital admissions. That year it also began using the Kiva VCF Treatment System for the treatment of patients with vertebral compression fractures.

Company Background

The BryanLGH system was formed through the 1997 combination of Bryan Memorial Hospital (named after populist firebrand William Jennings Bryan) and Lincoln General Hospital. Bryan Health is part of the Heartland Health Alliance a group of about 40 Nebraska hospitals that work together to improve rural health care services through shared services and best practices.

In 2012 the health organization rebranded itself to reflect its expanded position in the region's health care market. BryanLGH Medical Center was renamed Bryan Medical Center and the broader health organization changed its name from the BryanLGH Health System to simply Bryan Health.

EXECUTIVES

Pharmacy Manager, Jeff Weber
Auditors: CROWE HORWATH LLP SIMSBURY C

LOCATIONS

HQ: BRYAN MEDICAL CENTER
 1600 S 48TH ST, LINCOLN, NE 685061283
Phone: 402 481-1111
Web: WWW.BRYANHEALTH.COM

PRODUCTS/OPERATIONS

Selected Services
Bariatrics
Cardiac Services
Cancer
Cardiothoracic Surgery
Childbirth/Family Birthplace
Corporate & Community Wellness
Diabetes Center
Early Detection
Emergency Department
Heart Valve Center of Excellence
Hospitalists
Independence Center
Inpatient Rehabilitation
Neuroscience
Mental Health
Orthopedics
Outpatient Specialty Clinic
Radiation Oncology
Radiology
Rehabilitation/Therapy
Robotic Surgery
Sleep Medicine
StarCare Air Ambulance
Substance Abuse
Trauma Center
Urgent Care

Vascular Services
Women's & Children's

COMPETITORS

Catholic Health
 Initiatives
Children's Hospital &
 Medical Center
Madonna Rehabilitation
 Hospital

Methodist Health
 System
Nebraska Medical
 Center

HISTORICAL FINANCIALS
Company Type: Private

Income Statement   FYE: December 31

	REVENUE ($ mil.)	NET INCOME ($ mil.)	NET PROFIT MARGIN	EMPLOYEES
12/17	606	74	12.3%	3,970
12/16	586	60	10.3%	—
12/15	558	43	7.8%	—
12/14	507	34	6.8%	—
Annual Growth	6.1%	29.4%	—	—

2017 Year-End Financials

Return on assets: 7.3%   Cash ($ mil.): 190
Return on equity: 9.6%
Current ratio: 3.30

BUFFALO CITY SCHOOL DISTRICT

EXECUTIVES

Supt, Kriner Cash
Coordinator, Shannon Standing
Coordinator, Jeanine Groll
Assistant Superintendent, Mary Jo Conrad
Teacher, Patrcia Walker
Associate Superintendent For T, Anne Botticelli
Teacher Assistant, Aubrey Agugliaro
Director of School Plant Opera, Barry Kirker
Assistant, Catherine Dulak
Central Cse Coordinator, Dawn Haring
Coordinator Parent Co, Heather Paluch
Auditors: FREEDMAXICK CPAS PC BUFFALO

LOCATIONS

HQ: BUFFALO CITY SCHOOL DISTRICT
 712 CITY HALL, BUFFALO, NY 142027537
Phone: 716 816-3575
Web: WWW.BUFFALOSCHOOLS.ORG

HISTORICAL FINANCIALS
Company Type: Private

Income Statement   FYE: June 30

	REVENUE ($ mil.)	NET INCOME ($ mil.)	NET PROFIT MARGIN	EMPLOYEES
06/12	868	(194)	—	3,700
06/05	0	0	1.4%	—
Annual Growth	215.8%	—	—	—

2012 Year-End Financials

Return on assets: (-11.2%)   Cash ($ mil.): 348
Return on equity: —
Current ratio: —

BVH, INC.

EXECUTIVES

Ceo-Chb-Pres, Steve L Edwards
Evp-SEC, Timothy W Triplett
Evp-Cfo, Kenneth L Williams
Svp-Treasurer, Michael Williams
Electrical Engineer, Anders Fornberg
Chemical Engineering, Andrea Lorton
Water Project Manager, Andrew Mally
Business Process Manager, Angela Cain
Gasification Consultant, Anthony Black
Marketing Coordinator, Belinda Walk
Mechanical Engineer, Ben Connell
Auditors: KPMG LLP KANSAS CITY MO

LOCATIONS

HQ: BVH, INC.
11401 LAMAR AVE, OVERLAND PARK, KS 662111508
Phone: 913 458-2000
Web: WWW.BV.COM

HISTORICAL FINANCIALS

Company Type: Private

Income Statement   FYE: December 29

	REVENUE ($ mil.)	NET INCOME ($ mil.)	NET PROFIT MARGIN	EMPLOYEES
12/17	3,363	87	2.6%	8,495
12/16*	3,207	75	2.4%	—
01/16	2,955	108	3.7%	—
01/15	3,029	113	3.7%	—
Annual Growth	3.6%	(8.3%)	—	—

*Fiscal year change

2017 Year-End Financials

Return on assets: 5.6%   Cash ($ mil.): 344
Return on equity: 73.5%
Current ratio: 1.10

C & K MARKET, INC.

Family-owned C&K Market operates more than 40 supermarkets in southern Oregon and northern California mostly under the name Ray's Food Place but also under Shop Smart and C&K banners. The Shop Smart warehouse-style stores focus on value-priced groceries and household goods. Most of C&K's stores are situated in small rural communities. C&K Market was founded in 1957 by Raymond "Ray" Nidiffer. Stung by competition from large national discounters including Wal-Mart and Costco the regional chain filed for bankruptcy in late 2013 and closed 15 supermarkets and sold 15 pharmacies. It emerged from bankruptcy in 2014.

Bankruptcy

C&K Market filed a voluntary petition for Chapter 11 bankruptcy protection in November 2013 blaming competition from larger chains legacy costs underperforming stores and debt issues. C&K expects to emerge from bankruptcy in May 2014.

Geographic Reach

The Oregon-based grocer operates about 45 stores in Oregon and northern California.

Financial Performance

C&K's stores rang up an estimated $480 million in sales in 2012.

Strategy

Traditionally C&K has focused on serving small rural communities. However as more rural shoppers travel to buy groceries at larger grocery chains and mega-stores its sales have declined. Indeed in its bankruptcy filing C&K said most of its stores are within 40 miles of "a large discount grocery operation such as Wal-Mart of Costco." By closing about a third of its grocery stores and selling its freestanding pharmacies the chain hopes to remain viable. The store closings resulted in a workforce reduction of about 20%. The company sold its 15 Pharmacy Express stores in late 2013 to focus on its core grocery business.

Prior to its Chapter 11 filing C&K was experimenting with new store formats. In late 2012 it launched a new everyday low price grocery banner called Lo Buck$. The 40000-square-foot store features a "wall of values" and has a large Hispanic foods section. It also serves up natural and organic items fresh meat and produce.

EXECUTIVES

Ceo, Karl Wissmann
Ceo*, Douglas Nidiffer
V Pres*, Rocky Campbell
V Pres*, Jon Wissmann
Cfo*, David D Doty
Coordinator, Jackie Knudsen
Chief Financial Officer, David Doty

LOCATIONS

HQ: C & K MARKET, INC.
850 OHARE PKWY STE 100, MEDFORD, OR 975047720
Phone: 541 469-3113
Web: WWW.GORAYS.COM

PRODUCTS/OPERATIONS

2013 Stores

	No.
Ray's Food Place	37
Shop Smart Food Warehouse	7
C&K Market	1
Total	45

COMPETITORS

7-Eleven	Safeway
Albertsons	Target Corporation
Costco Wholesale	Wal-Mart
Fred Meyer Stores	

HISTORICAL FINANCIALS

Company Type: Private

Income Statement   FYE: December 31

	REVENUE ($ mil.)	NET INCOME ($ mil.)	NET PROFIT MARGIN	EMPLOYEES
12/10	457	3	0.8%	2,000
12/09	467	5	1.1%	—
12/07	479	0	0.0%	—
Annual Growth	(1.6%)	245.6%	—	—

2010 Year-End Financials

Return on assets: 1.9%   Cash ($ mil.): 6
Return on equity: 8.2%
Current ratio: 0.90

C.R. ENGLAND, INC.

The world's top refrigerated trucking company and one of North America's largest transportation firms C.R. England hauls refrigerated and dry cargo throughout the US. The family-owned company also serves parts of Canada and through alliances points in Mexico. C.R. England's fleet includes more than 3500 Freightliner Peterbilt Volvo and International tractors and 8000 trailers. Besides for-hire freight hauling C.R. England offers dedicated contract carriage in which drivers and equipment are assigned to a customer long-term; logistics services including freight brokerage; and intermodal railroad service.

Operations

The company's operations include national US US regional and Mexican truckload service as well as dedicated (customized) truck contracts and intermodal service.

In addition to freight brokerage C.R. England's England Logistics unit offers intermodal service for refrigerated cargo in which customers' containerized freight is shuttled between truck and railroad facility. The logistics unit also arranges the transportation of less-than-truckload quantities of freight and provides ground transportation of ocean containers for shipping lines.

This unit also provides global logistics - international shipping and freight forwarding solutions); supply chain management (freight management) and carrier services (factoring solutions fuel discounts tire discounts and other services).

C.R. England's business also benefits from operating five truck driving schools in the US and a course on becoming a freight broker. The school helps improve driver safety as well as provides a pool of qualified truck drivers for hire.

Geographic Reach

The company operates primarily in California Illinois Texas and Utah.

Strategy

Greening its fleet C. R. England has announced a multi-year liquefied natural gas (LNG) bulk fueling agreement with Shell. C.R. England will replace existing diesel trucks with LNG-powered trucks servicing southern California the most mature US market for fueling LNG-powered trucks.

The company is focusing on innovation in its intermodal and dedicated operations. The intermodal division has more than 1000 TempStack 53 ft. temperature-controlled containers which can be double-stacked on the flatcars of its partner railroad reducing customer costs increasing shipping capacity and efficiency and lowering fuel costs.

C.R. England is also beefing up its trucking operations working to deliver faster more secure shipments for its customers in its national and regional divisions.

Company Background

C.R. England was founded in 1920 by Chester Rodney England and is run by his descendants.

EXECUTIVES

President Mexico Division, David (Dave) Akers
Evp Maintenance, Todd D. England
Evp Operations Support, Corey D. England
Ceo, Chad England
President, Josh England
Coo, Brandon Harrison
Evp Corporate Sales And Marketing, David A. Kramer
Coo; President England Logistics, Zach England
Corporate Vp Compliance And Safety, Dustin England
President National And Regional, Sam Scott
President Intermodal, Coby Bullard
President Dedicated, Tracy Brown
Cfo, TJ McGeean
Vice President Of Recruiting, Wayne Cederholm
Vice President Of Technology, Rich Farr
Chairman And President, Daniel E. (Dan) England
Co-chairman, Dean D. England
Auditors: TANNER LLC SALT LAKE CITY UT

LOCATIONS

HQ: C.R. ENGLAND, INC.
4701 W 2100 S, SALT LAKE CITY, UT 841201223
Phone: 800 421-9004
Web: WWW.CRENGLAND.COM

PRODUCTS/OPERATIONS

Selected Operations

Trucking
National - Long haul truckload service
Mexico - Shipments in and out of Mexico
Regional - Short haul truckload service positioned in
the West Midwest and Texas and surrounding areas
(AR LA OK)
Dedicated - Tailor-made services dedicating trucks and
drivers to specific customer needs
Intermodal - Expedited priority rail service using
TempStack 53' refrigerated containers
England Logistics

COMPETITORS

C.H. Robinson	KLLM Transport
Worldwide	Services
Central Refrigerated	Landstar System
Service	Marten Transport
Covenant	Navajo Shippers
Transportation	Prime Inc.
Crete Carrier	Stevens Transport
Frozen Food Express	Swift Transportation
J.B. Hunt	Willis Shaw Express

HISTORICAL FINANCIALS

Company Type: Private

Income Statement   FYE: December 31

	REVENUE ($ mil.)	NET INCOME ($ mil.)	NET PROFIT MARGIN	EMPLOYEES
12/12	1,579	56	3.6%	6,500
12/11	1,315	55	4.3%	—
12/07	829	41	5.0%	—
Annual Growth	13.7%	6.2%	—	—

2012 Year-End Financials
Return on assets: 7.4%   Cash ($ mil.): 15
Return on equity: 24.7%
Current ratio: 1.40

CABELL HUNTINGTON HOSPITAL INC

EXECUTIVES

Pres-Ceo, Brent A Marsteller
V Pres*, David Graley
SEC*, Steven L Burton
Treas*, Floyd Eharlow Jr
Dir*, Carolyn L Bagby
Executive Officer, Judith Riley
Chief of Medicine, Ross Patton
Coordinator, Amy Bullington
Manager, April Phr
Accounting Staff, Bert Millman
Coordinator, Bridgett Cunningham
Auditors: BAKER TILLY VIRCHOW KRAUSE LL

LOCATIONS

HQ: CABELL HUNTINGTON HOSPITAL INC
1340 HAL GREER BLVD, HUNTINGTON, WV
257010195
Phone: 304 526-2000
Web: WWW.CABELLHUNTINGTON.ORG

HISTORICAL FINANCIALS

Company Type: Private

Income Statement   FYE: September 30

	REVENUE ($ mil.)	NET INCOME ($ mil.)	NET PROFIT MARGIN	EMPLOYEES
09/17	587	76	13.0%	2,300
09/16	559	18	3.2%	—
09/15	473	17	3.8%	—
09/14	417	8	2.0%	—
Annual Growth	12.0%	109.3%	—	—

2017 Year-End Financials
Return on assets: 12.2%   Cash ($ mil.): 70
Return on equity: 26.1%
Current ratio: 2.20

CADDO PARISH SCHOOL BOARD

EXECUTIVES

II Coo, James W Woolfolk
Supt, Ollie Tyler
Supt, Dr T Lamar Goree
Principal, Mary D Rounds
Director of Child Nutrition PR, Kaye Lynch
Secretary, Lakeisha Jones
Auditors: ALLEN GREEN & WILLIAMSON LLP

LOCATIONS

HQ: CADDO PARISH SCHOOL BOARD
1961 MIDWAY ST, SHREVEPORT, LA 711082200
Phone: 318 603-6300
Web: WWW.CADDOSCHOOLS.ORG

HISTORICAL FINANCIALS

Company Type: Private

Income Statement   FYE: June 30

	REVENUE ($ mil.)	NET INCOME ($ mil.)	NET PROFIT MARGIN	EMPLOYEES
06/18	461	(13)	—	5,680
06/17	457	(7)	—	—
06/16	468	0	0.0%	—
06/08	448	15	3.4%	—
Annual Growth	0.3%	—	—	—

2018 Year-End Financials
Return on assets: (-2.8%)   Cash ($ mil.): 135
Return on equity: —
Current ratio: —

CAJUN INDUSTRIES, LLC

Offering a mixed gumbo of services Cajun Industries builds oil refineries power plants process plants water-treatment plants and other industrial and infrastructure projects primarily in Louisiana and Texas. Subsidiary Cajun Constructors provides a full range of services from design/build to maintenance; Cajun Deep Foundations offers drilling piles installation and related services. Cajun Maritime focuses on marine coastal and oilfield services including construction repair and power distribution. Cajun Equipment Services manages aÂ fleet of trucks and trailers that transport heavy and specialized loads. Chairman and owner Lane Grigsby founded the company as Cajun Contractors and Engineers in 1973.

EXECUTIVES

Ceo, Todd Grigsby
MBR, Lane Grigsby
Exec V Pres, Milton Graugnard
V Pres, Donnie McDowell
Cfo, Shane Recile
Pipe Foreman, Buford Sonnier
Vice President Texas Operation, Carlton Janise
Network Administrator, Chris Foster
Qc Supervisor, Jackie Kennamore
Network Administrator, Jason Davis
Personnel Director, Ken Jacob
Auditors: HANNIS T BOURGEOIS LLP BATO

LOCATIONS

HQ: CAJUN INDUSTRIES, LLC
15635 AIRLINE HWY, BATON ROUGE, LA 708177318
Phone: 225 753-5857
Web: WWW.CAJUNUSA.COM

PRODUCTS/OPERATIONS

Selected Divisions
Cajun Constructors Inc.
Cajun Deep Foundations LLC
Cajun Equipment Services LLC
Cajun Maritime LLC

Selected Services
ASME code work
Bridge construction and repair
Building construction
Coastal restoration
Dock facility construction and repair
Deep foundation work
  Drill shafts
  Driven piles
  Earth retention
  Marine piles
Design/build
Emergency response
Hauling
Maintenance
Marsh and marine power transmission and distribution
Oilfield construction
Paving
Pipeline installation and repair
Plant dismantling and relocation
Procurement
Project management
Retrofits
Stevedoring
Structural steel erection
Turnarounds
Water quality

COMPETITORS

Bechtel	Jacobs Engineering
Boh Bros Construction	KBR
Eby	Performance
Fluor	Contractors

HISTORICAL FINANCIALS

Company Type: Private

Income Statement   FYE: September 30

	REVENUE ($ mil.)	NET INCOME ($ mil.)	NET PROFIT MARGIN	EMPLOYEES
09/18	515	19	3.8%	1,500
09/17	616	56	9.2%	—
09/16	721	56	7.9%	—
09/15	559	28	5.2%	—
Annual Growth	(2.7%)	(11.9%)	—	—

2018 Year-End Financials
Return on assets: 6.8%   Cash ($ mil.): 5
Return on equity: 20.6%
Current ratio: 1.30

CAJUN INDUSTRIES, LLC

EXECUTIVES

Ceo, Todd Grigsby
Chm of The Board, L Lane Grigsby
Exec V Pres, Milton Graugnard
Cfo, Shane Recile
Senior Vice-President, Euclid Michel
Vice-President, Mike Barber
Recruiter, Wayne Litton
Manager, Clint Burroughs
Project Manager Detailer, Chad Duplessis
Project Manager Estimator, Chris Usry
Project Manager Estimator, James Wischer
Auditors: HANNIS T BOURGEOIS LLP BATO

LOCATIONS

HQ: CAJUN INDUSTRIES, LLC
15635 AIRLINE HWY, BATON ROUGE, LA 708177318
Phone: 225 753-5857
Web: WWW.CAJUNUSA.COM

HISTORICAL FINANCIALS
Company Type: Private

Income Statement				FYE: September 30
	REVENUE ($ mil.)	NET INCOME ($ mil.)	NET PROFIT MARGIN	EMPLOYEES
09/18	455	16	3.5%	1,000
09/17	573	47	8.2%	—
09/16	658	41	6.3%	—
09/15	521	25	4.9%	—
Annual Growth	(4.3%)	(14.4%)		

2018 Year-End Financials
Return on assets: 9.2%   Cash ($ mil.): 2
Return on equity: 18.5%
Current ratio: 1.80

CALGON CARBON CORPORATION

Calgon wants impurities in water and air gone. A global leader in activated carbons and purification systems it offers purification separation and concentration services to industrial process and environmental markets. Services include ballast water treatment ultraviolet light disinfection and advanced ion-exchange technologies used in the treatment of drinking water wastewater ballast water air emissions and manufacturing processes. Its products find usage more than 700 discrete market applications including air drinking water foods and pharmaceuticals purification and the removal of mercury emissions from coal-powered electrical plants. More than half of the Calgon's sales comes from the US. In 2017 Calgon was acquired by Kuraray and became its subsidiary.

Change in Company Type
In 2017 the company entered into a definitive merger agreement with Kuraray Co under which Calgon became a wholly owned subsidiary of the latter for a transaction value of $1.3 billion.

Operations
Calgon has three segments?Activated Carbon Alternative materials and Advanced Water Purification.

Activated Carbon makes granular and powdered activated carbon to remove organic compounds from liquids and gases bringing in roughly 90% of total sales.

The Alternative Materials unit (some 10%) offers diatomaceous earth and perlite filtration media which are primarily used as filter aids in beverage food and industrial applications. Products also includes carbon cloth which is activated carbon in cloth form.

Its Advance Water Purification (less than 5%) unit makes and sells a broad line of UV light disinfection.

Geographic Reach
Calgon Carbon operates in a geographically diverse array of markets. It operates about 20 production plants in Belgium China France Italy Japan the UK and the US. It has about 40 warehouses service centers and sales office facilities in various locations in US Europe and Asia-Pacific region.

Financial Performance
Calgon Carbon's revenues increased by 4% in 2012 due to 43% jump in Equipment revenues driven by ultraviolet light systems principally ballast water treatment which rose by 71%. Consumer revenues went up by 20% thanks to higher demand for activated carbon cloths. The increases were partially offset by 0.15% decrease in the Activated Carbon and Service sales due to the negative impact of foreign currency translation.

The company posted a net income of $23.2 million in 2012 (41% down on 2011) due to higher interest expenses and restructuring charges.

Mergers and Acquisitions
In 2016 Calgon Carbon completed the acquisition of CECA's wood-based activated carbon reactivation and mineral-based filtration media business for $153 million. The business joined Calgon Carbon's European operations under the name Chemviron.

EXECUTIVES

Evp And Coo, Robert P. (Bob) O'Brien, age 69, $378,325 total compensation
Evp Advanced Materials Manufacturing And Equipment Division, Stevan R. Schott, age 56, $322,500 total compensation
Chairman President And Ceo, Randall S. (Randy) Dearth, age 56, $560,000 total compensation
Evp Core Carbon And Services Division, James A. Coccagno, age 48
Svp And Cfo, Robert Fortwangler
National Accounts Manager, Michael Prevade
Senior Vice President Global Procurement And Strategic Initiatives, Jim Coccagno
Senior Vice President General Counsel Secretary, Chad Whalen
Auditors: DELOITTE & TOUCHE LLP PITTSBU

LOCATIONS

HQ: CALGON CARBON CORPORATION
3000 GSK DR, MOON TOWNSHIP, PA 151081381
Phone: 412 787-6700
Web: WWW.CALGONCARBON.COM

2015 sales

	$ mil.	% of total
United States	288	53
United Kingdom	43	8
Japan	35	7
France	20	4
China	17	3
Germany	17	3
Canada	17	3
South Korea	12	2
Belgium	10	2
Singapore	9	2
Netherlands	5	1
Denmark	4	1
Switzerland	3	1
Spain	3	1
Thailand	3	1
Other	41	8
Total	535	100

PRODUCTS/OPERATIONS

2015 Sales

	$ mil.	% of total
Activated Carbon & Service	486	91
Equipment	39	7
Consumer	9	2
Total	535	100

Selected Products
Ballast Water Treatment
Energy Storage
Environmental Air Treatment
Environmental Water Treatment
Food and Beverage
Industrial Processes
Medical
Mercury Removal
Metals Recovery
Municipal Water Treatment
Personal Protection Equipment
Residential Point of Use/Entry

COMPETITORS

3M Purification
ITT Water & Wastewater
  Herford
Met-Pro

Norit
Siemens Water
  Technologies
Trojan Technologies

HISTORICAL FINANCIALS
Company Type: Private

Income Statement				FYE: December 31
	REVENUE ($ mil.)	NET INCOME ($ mil.)	NET PROFIT MARGIN	EMPLOYEES
12/17	619	21	3.4%	1,334
12/16	514	13	2.7%	—
12/15	535	43	8.1%	—
12/14	555	49	8.9%	—
Annual Growth	3.7%	(24.7%)	—	—

2017 Year-End Financials
Return on assets: 2.5%   Cash ($ mil.): 42
Return on equity: 5.0%
Current ratio: 2.60

CALIFORNIA INSTITUTE OF TECHNOLOGY

The California Institute of Technology (Caltech) has an enlightened perspective on science. The institute enrolls about 2250 students and offers about two dozen majors across six academic divisions focused on biology chemistry engineering geology humanities and physics. Caltech has a very low student-teacher ratio of 3:1. The school receives about half of its operating revenue through research grants primarily from government agencies. Caltech operates the Jet Propulsion Laboratory (JPL) which supervises robotic Mars exploration programs and other interplanetary missions under contract to NASA. The school was founded in 1891.

Operations
CalTech's most popular majors are chemical engineering computer science electrical engineering mechanical engineering and physics. The school's primary research focus areas include energy medical science information science the universe the environment and nanoscience.

The JPL lab is responsible for about two dozen spacecraft missions in a given year.

Geographic Reach

Caltech has a student population that comes from more than 30 US states and 11 countries; international students account for more than 20% of enrollment. In addition to its facilities in California the institute has a network of about a dozen astronomy observatories across the US and in Antarctica and Chile.

Financial Performance

Caltech has a budget of about $2.3 billion and an endowment of about $2.1 billion. It gets some 54% of its revenue from contracts and grants and 19% from its endowment. Tuition and fees only account for about 6% of revenue.

Strategy

The institute has established new divisions of biology and biological engineering in recent years.

Company Background

Caltech's professors and graduates have snared more than 30 Nobel Prizes. Other alumni include filmmaker Frank Capra and Apollo 17 astronaut Harrison Schmitt.

EXECUTIVES

Provost, Edward M. Stolper
Vp Business And Finance, Dean W. Currie
Cio, Richard E. (Rich) Fagen
Vp; Director Jet Propulsion Laboratory, Charles Elachi, age 72
Chair Biology And Biological Engineering Division, Stephen L. Mayo
President, Thomas F. Rosenbaum
Chief Investment Officer, Scott Richland
Chair Chemistry And Chemical Engineering Division, Jacqueline K. Barton
Chair Physics Mathematics And Astronomy Division, B. Thomas Soifer
Chair Engineering And Applied Science Division, Guruswami Ravichandran
Chair Geological And Planetary Sciences Division, John P. Grotzinger
Chair Humanities And Social Sciences Division, Jean-Laurent Rosenthal
Vice President Of Operations, Luisa Avila
Senior Vice President Financial Investigations Unit, Bob Binnie
Vice President, Kevin Vu
Chairman, David L. Lee, age 63
Vice Chairman, Ronald K. Linde
Secretary, Zachary Erickson
Auditors: PRICEWATERHOUSECOOPERS LLP LO

LOCATIONS

HQ: CALIFORNIA INSTITUTE OF TECHNOLOGY
1200 E CALIFORNIA BLVD, PASADENA, CA
911250001
Phone: 626 395-6811
Web: WWW.CALTECH.EDU

PRODUCTS/OPERATIONS

Selected Academic Divisions

Academics
 Biology
 Chemistry and Chemical Engineering
 Engineering and Applied Science
 Geological and Planetary Sciences
 Humanities and Social Sciences
 Physics Mathematics and Astronomy
Jet Propulsion Laboratory (NASA partnership)
 Galaxy Evolution Explorer Science Center
 Infrared Processing and Analysis Center
 NASA Exoplanet Science Institute
 NASA Herschel Science Center
 Spitzer Space Telescope Science Center

HISTORICAL FINANCIALS

Company Type: Private

Income Statement   FYE: September 30

	REVENUE ($ mil.)	NET INCOME ($ mil.)	NET PROFIT MARGIN	EMPLOYEES
09/18	3,303	165	5.0%	10,794
09/17	2,894	412	14.3%	—
09/16	2,561	203	7.9%	—
09/14	2,153	154	7.2%	—
Annual Growth	11.3%	1.7%		

2018 Year-End Financials

Return on assets: 3.0%   Cash ($ mil.): 6
Return on equity: 5.2%
Current ratio: —

CALIFORNIA STEEL INDUSTRIES, INC.

California Steel Industries (CSI) doesn't use forensic evidence but its work does involve a steel slab. The company uses steel slab produced by third parties to manufacture steel products such as hot-rolled and cold-rolled steel galvanized coils and sheets and electric resistance weld (ERW) pipe. Its customers include aftermarket automotive manufacturers oil and gas producers roofing makers tubing manufacturers and building suppliers. CSI serves the western region of the US. The company operates slitting shearing coating and single-billing services for third parties. Japan's JFE Holdings and Brazilian iron ore miner Vale SA each own 50% of CSI.

Operations

CSI has an annual production capacity of 2.8 million metric tons of flat rolled steel and pipe. It is the leading producer of flat rolled steel in the Western US and the only West Coast steel supplier capable of producing more than 2 million tons of steel in five different product lines: hot rolled pickled and oiled galvanized and cold rolled sheet and electric resistance welded pipe.

Geographic Reach

At its California plant the company processes steel slab purchased from suppliers around the world including Brazil Mexico Australia Japan Europe and the US.

CSI buys more than two-thirds of its steel slab from ArcelorMittal subsidiary Lazaro Cardenas in Mexico; ArcelorMittal Tubar o in Brazil; and Australia's Bluescope Steel. The purchased slab is transported to the Port of Los Angeles and then sent by train to CSI's facilities.

Sales and Marketing

Most of CSI's product lines are also sold to service distribution centers throughout the Western and Midwestern US with some product also sold worldwide through the export market. Its steel framing studs roofing decking and metal lath products are used in the home and commercial building industries. Other uses include water gas and oil pipelines automotive pans tubing (used by construction and furniture makers) and heating and cooling parts.

Strategy

In 2014 CSI built a new pipe mill on its site near Fontana California. The mill produces high-strength electrical resistance welded pipe up to 24 inches in diameter and up to 80 feet in length. Its existing pipe mill was limited to 16-inch diameter and 60-foot lengths.

Since 1992 CSI has invested more than $1 billion on its facilities to maintain modernize and expand operations.

Company Background

The company was formed in 1983.

EXECUTIVES

Vice President, Brett Guge
Secretary, Beverly Sprinkle
Auditors: ERNST & YOUNG LLP LOS ANGELES

LOCATIONS

HQ: CALIFORNIA STEEL INDUSTRIES, INC.
14000 SAN BERNARDINO AVE, FONTANA, CA
923355259
Phone: 909 350-6300
Web: WWW.CALIFORNIASTEEL.COM

PRODUCTS/OPERATIONS

Selected Steel Products
Cold Rolled
ERW Pipe
Galvanized
Hot Rolled
Pickled and Oiled

COMPETITORS

AK Steel Holding Corporation	Steel Dynamics Steelscape
Evraz Inc. NA	Ternium Mexico
Nucor	USS-POSCO Industries
O'Neal Steel	

HISTORICAL FINANCIALS

Company Type: Private

Income Statement   FYE: December 31

	REVENUE ($ mil.)	NET INCOME ($ mil.)	NET PROFIT MARGIN	EMPLOYEES
12/09	551	(13)	—	1,000
12/08	1,510	13	0.9%	—
Annual Growth	(63.5%)	—	—	—

2009 Year-End Financials

Return on assets: (-2.2%)   Cash ($ mil.): 61
Return on equity: (-4.4%)
Current ratio: 4.30

CALIFORNIA'S VALUED TRUST

EXECUTIVES

Exec Dir, Valerie Cornuelle
Exec Dir, David Vaughn
Receptionist, Lois Casey
Member, Ashley Aguilar
Accountant, MAI Thao

LOCATIONS

HQ: CALIFORNIA'S VALUED TRUST
520 E HERNDON AVE, FRESNO, CA 937202907
Phone: 559 437-2960
Web: WWW.CVTRUST.ORG

CAMERON INTERNATIONAL CORPORATION

Cameron is a leading manufacturer provider and servicer of oil and gas industry equipment. The company makes products that control pressure at oil and gas wells including blowout preventers chokes controls wellheads measurement tools and valves. The company's products are used for offshore onshore and subsea applications. Cameron is a wholly owned subsidiary of oilfield product and services giant Schlumberger (a major provider of technology for reservoir characterization drilling production and processing services to the oil and gas industry).

Financial Performance

Cameron generates about 15% of Schlumberger's sales. The subsidiary's revenue declined 4% to $6.5 billion on lower sales for its OneSubsea and Valves & Measurements product segments. OneSubsea offers products and services for subsea oil and gas companies including wellheads subsea trees control systems and production system optimization. The company's Valves & Measurements products span valves and measurement systems for oil and gas flow for the upstream midstream and downstream sectors.

Strategy

To keep pace with rivals increasingly adopting automation technology Schlumbeger formed a joint venture in 2019 with Rockwell Automation to form Sensia. Sensia combines Cameron's sensor and measurement products with Rockwell's industrial automation technology and analytics capabilities. The new company's offerings will facilitate automated oilfield operations and connect equipment with software to gather data from sensors and devices. About two-fifths of the JV's revenue is expected to derive from North America.

EXECUTIVES

President Cameron Group, Olivier Le Peuch
Auditors: ERNST & YOUNG LLP HOUSTON TE

LOCATIONS

HQ: CAMERON INTERNATIONAL CORPORATION
4646 W SAM HOUSTON PKWY N, HOUSTON, TX 770418214
Phone: 713 939-2282
Web: WWW.SLB.COM

PRODUCTS/OPERATIONS

COMPETITORS

ABB Inc.
Aker Solutions
Atlas Copco
CIRCOR International
Dresser-Rand
Dril-Quip
Ebara
FMC
Flotek
GE Oil
Ingersoll-Rand Industrial Technologies
McDermott
National Oilwell Varco
Weatherford International

HISTORICAL FINANCIALS

Company Type: Private

Income Statement   FYE: December 31

	REVENUE ($ mil.)	NET INCOME ($ mil.)	NET PROFIT MARGIN	EMPLOYEES
12/14	10,381	848	8.2%	23,000
12/13	9,838	724	7.4%	—
12/12	8,502	750	8.8%	—
Annual Growth	10.5%	6.3%		

2014 Year-End Financials

Return on assets: 6.6%   Cash ($ mil.): 1,513
Return on equity: 15.6%
Current ratio: 1.80

CAMPUS CRUSADE FOR CHRIST INC

EXECUTIVES

Ceo-Pres, Stephen B Douglass
Dir*, Vonette Z Bright
Recruiter, Ada Morgan
Human Resources Administrator, Barbara Beecher
Director, Dave Dickens
Engineer, David Wilkins
Senior Manager, Joanna Bailey
Leader, John Emmans
Analyst, Patricia Smith
Director of Risk Management, Pete Johnson
Senior Manager, Shawn Durnell

LOCATIONS

HQ: CAMPUS CRUSADE FOR CHRIST INC
100 LAKE HART DR, ORLANDO, FL 328320100
Phone: 407 826-2000
Web: WWW.JOSH.ORG

HISTORICAL FINANCIALS

Company Type: Private

Income Statement   FYE: August 31

	REVENUE ($ mil.)	NET INCOME ($ mil.)	NET PROFIT MARGIN	EMPLOYEES
08/17	598	26	4.4%	7,688
08/08	7	1	25.1%	—
08/05	0	0	—	—
08/04	423	414	97.7%	—
Annual Growth	2.7%	(19.0%)		

2017 Year-End Financials

Return on assets: 7.4%   Cash ($ mil.): 45
Return on equity: 10.8%
Current ratio: 0.70

CANDID COLOR SYSTEMS, INC.

EXECUTIVES

Pres-Ceo, Jack E Counts Jr
SEC-Treas, Beverly Ellis
Designer, David J Wall
Coo, Dan Hays

LOCATIONS

HQ: CANDID COLOR SYSTEMS, INC.
1300 METROPOLITAN AVE, OKLAHOMA CITY, OK 731082042
Phone: 405 947-8747
Web: WWW.CANDID.COM

HISTORICAL FINANCIALS

Company Type: Private

Income Statement   FYE: July 31

	REVENUE ($ mil.)	NET INCOME ($ mil.)	NET PROFIT MARGIN	EMPLOYEES
07/07	21,742	2,534	11.7%	300
07/05	22	1	8.3%	—
07/04	21	2	10.9%	—
07/03	21	1	9.4%	—
Annual Growth	467.2%	498.3%	—	—

2007 Year-End Financials

Return on assets: 999.9%   Cash ($ mil.): 2
Return on equity: 999.9%
Current ratio: 2.30

CANNERY CASINO RESORTS, LLC

EXECUTIVES

Mng MBR, William Wortman
MBR, William J Paulos
MBR, Tom Lettero
Coordinator, Martin Giovi
Corporate Director of Purchasi, Danny Campbell
Information Technology Securit, Joshua Terry
Transportation Options, Shoe Whisperer
Database Marketing Manager, Tina Aronov

LOCATIONS

HQ: CANNERY CASINO RESORTS, LLC
9107 W RUSSELL RD, LAS VEGAS, NV 891481243
Phone: 702 507-5700

HISTORICAL FINANCIALS

Company Type: Private

Income Statement				FYE: December 31
	REVENUE ($ mil.)	NET INCOME ($ mil.)	NET PROFIT MARGIN	EMPLOYEES
12/10	513	(15)	—	1,860
12/09	509	(23)	—	—
12/08	1,235	0	0.0%	—
Annual Growth	(35.5%)			

2010 Year-End Financials

Return on assets: 1.6%
Return on equity: (-2.9%)
Current ratio: 1.20

Cash ($ mil.): 55

CAPE COD HEALTHCARE, INC.

Cape Cod Healthcare (CCHC) is a not-for-profit healthcare organization that operates two acute care hospitals (Cape Cod Hospital and Falmouth Hospital) with a total of more than 350 beds. Specializations include heart and vascular women's health bones and muscles cancer care and brain spine and nerves. CCHC also operates a home health services agency (Visiting Nurse Association of Cape Cod) primary and specialized care clinics a 130-bed skilled nursing and rehabilitation facility (JML Care Center) and a 60-unit assisted living facility (Heritage at Falmouth). The health care system has an affiliation with UMass Medical School whereby students can receive hands-on training at Cape Cod Hospital.

Operations

CCHC is the Cape's largest private employer with nearly 5000 staff members including more than 450 physicians. The system has about 120000 emergency department visits each year and facilitates about 1200 births and performs more than 14000 surgical procedures annually.

Financial Performance

CCHC's net patient revenue numbers have been increasing over the past five years. In fiscal 2016 it increased 8% to $817 million. Like most hospitals net patient revenue represents the bulk of CCHC's total revenue.

Strategy

While CCHC enjoys a strong market share in the Cape Cod region it also struggles with seasonal fluctuations and high Medicare and Medicaid numbers within its patient load. As such the company could be impacted by reform measures that could decrease Medicare reimbursement levels. CCHC plans to continue its efforts to control costs and increase efficiencies to keep its operations nimble and keep pace with the changing health care environment.

Faced with rising operating costs and lower reimbursement rates the system in 2017 agreed to sell its outreach lab services operations to Quest Diagnostics. As a focused lab services provider Quest is able to provide testing at a lower cost than the typical hospital-based laboratory. The two companies will partner to provide an expanded array of diagnostics to the Cape Cod community.

EXECUTIVES

Svp Chief Legal Officer, Michael Jones
President And Ceo, Michael K. (Mike) Lauf, age 48
Coo, Michael Bundy

Svp Communications And Business Development, Patrick Kane
Svp Finance And Cfo, Michael L. Connors
Chief Medical Officer, Donald A. Guadagnoli
Svp And Cio, Jeanne M. Fallon
President And Ceo Vna Of Cape Cod, Dianne C. Kolb
Senior Vice President Of Managed Care, Jack Lipomi
Vice President Patient Financial Services, Victor Oliveira
Senior Vice President Human Resources, Emily Schorer
Senior Vice President And Chief Quality Officer, Kevin Mulroy
Medical Director, Vladimir Koren
Vice Chairman, William Zammer
Vice Chairman, DeWitt Davenport
Auditors: PRICEWATERHOUSECOOPERS LLP BO

LOCATIONS

HQ: CAPE COD HEALTHCARE, INC.
27 PARK ST, HYANNIS, MA 026015230
Phone: 508 862-5030
Web: WWW.CAPECODHEALTH.ORG

PRODUCTS/OPERATIONS

Selected Massachusetts Facilities
Bourne Health Center
Cape Cod Hospital (Hyannis)
Davenport Mugar Cancer Center (Hyannis)
Falmouth Hospital
  Clark Cancer Center
Fontaine Medical Center (Harwich)
Heritage at Falmouth
JLM Care Center (Falmouth)
Mashpee Health Center
Sandwich Health Center
Wilkins Outpatient Medical Complex (Hyannis)

COMPETITORS

Baystate Health
Boston Medical Center
Cambridge Health Alliance
Care New England
CareGroup
Milford Regional Medical Center
Northeast Health System
Partners HealthCare
Southcoast Hospitals Group
Steward Health Care
Universal Health Services
Winchester Healthcare

HISTORICAL FINANCIALS

Company Type: Private

Income Statement				FYE: September 30
	REVENUE ($ mil.)	NET INCOME ($ mil.)	NET PROFIT MARGIN	EMPLOYEES
09/18	921	80	8.7%	1,850
09/17	872	74	8.5%	—
09/16	837	74	8.9%	—
09/12	680	80	11.9%	—
Annual Growth	5.2%	(0.1%)	—	—

2018 Year-End Financials

Return on assets: 7.1%
Return on equity: 10.2%
Current ratio: 1.70

Cash ($ mil.): 43

CAPE COD HOSPITAL

Get too much sun or eat too much lobster while visiting Cape Cod? Never fear Cape Cod Hospital can treat whatever ails you. Cape Cod Hospital a subsidiary of Cape Cod Healthcare is a 260-bed acute care hospital that serves the Cape Cod Massachusetts area. Its specialty services include pediatrics maternity care cancer treatment and infectious disease therapeutics. The not-for-profit Cape Cod Hospital also includes a specialty cardiovascular center a psychiatry unit a surgical pavilion and a diagnostic imaging facility as well as outpatient medical offices.

Operations

Cape Cod Hospital's emergency department treats about 85000 patients each year. The medical center also performs more than 12500 surgeries and 1000 birth procedures each year as well as about 2 million laboratory tests. Its 20-bed Cape Psych Center provides inpatient and outpatient mental and behavioral services. The campus also includes more than a dozen medical offices buildings and a community health center. Cape Cod Hospital's staff includes about 300 physicians.

Geographic Reach

Cape Cod Hospital is located on a 40-acre campus on the shoreline of Hyannis Massachusetts.

Strategy

To keep its facilities modern and efficient in 2015 the company opened a new emergency center located adjacent to the existing emergency center. The 18-month $22 million project added 25000 sq. ft. of space and 72 patient treatment rooms.

In 2013 Cape Cod Hospital reopened the renovated and expanded Intensive Care Unit. That project cost $4.9 million and doubled the size of the original area.

To control the cost of providing hospital care parent Cape Cod Healthcare has also been expanding its outpatient and ambulatory care services. It is adding new urgent care centers and surgery centers both near the hospital and in surrounding communities.

Company Background

Cape Cod Hospital was established in Hyannis in 1920.

EXECUTIVES

Medical Director, Kelsey Rezendes
Medical Records Director, Tim Greene
Vice President Ofperioperative Andsurgical Services, Cynthia Marlin-mha

LOCATIONS

HQ: CAPE COD HOSPITAL
27 PARK ST, HYANNIS, MA 026015203
Phone: 508 862-7575
Web: WWW.CAPECODHEALTH.ORG

PRODUCTS/OPERATIONS

Selected Services
Allergy and Immunology
Behavioral Health
Blood Center
Dermatology
Foot Care & Surgery
Hand Surgery
Orthopedics
Pregnancy & Birth
Sports Medicine
Women's Health

COMPETITORS

Baystate Health
Boston Medical Center
Cambridge Health Alliance
Care New England
CareGroup
Children's Hospital Boston
Milford Regional Medical Center
Northeast Health System
Partners HealthCare
Southcoast Hospitals Group
Steward Health Care
Sturdy Memorial
Universal Health Services
Winchester Healthcare

HISTORICAL FINANCIALS
Company Type: Private

Income Statement   FYE: September 30

	REVENUE ($ mil.)	NET INCOME ($ mil.)	NET PROFIT MARGIN	EMPLOYEES
09/18	564	46	8.3%	1,700
09/17	526	47	9.0%	—
09/16	515	43	8.4%	—
09/15	462	33	7.2%	—
Annual Growth	6.9%	11.9%	—	—

2018 Year-End Financials
Return on assets: 7.3%   Cash ($ mil.): 9
Return on equity: 10.3%
Current ratio: 2.20

CAPE FEAR VALLEY MEDICAL CENTER

LOCATIONS
HQ: CAPE FEAR VALLEY MEDICAL CENTER
1638 OWEN DR, FAYETTEVILLE, NC 283043424
Phone: 910 615-4000
Web: WWW.CAPEFEARVALLEY.COM

HISTORICAL FINANCIALS
Company Type: Private

Income Statement   FYE: September 30

	REVENUE ($ mil.)	NET INCOME ($ mil.)	NET PROFIT MARGIN	EMPLOYEES
09/15	630	23	3.8%	2,711
09/14	590	40	6.8%	—
09/13	823	398	48.4%	—
Annual Growth	(12.5%)	(75.5%)	—	—

2015 Year-End Financials
Return on assets: 2.6%   Cash ($ mil.): 38
Return on equity: 5.1%
Current ratio: 2.80

CAPISTRANO UNIFIED SCHOOL DISTRICT

EXECUTIVES
Ceo, John M Alpay
SEC Brd*, Jane Boss
Supt*, Joseph M Farley
Dir of Fin*, Philippa Geiger
Mng MBR*, Joel Drew
Interm Dep Superintendent, Robyn Phillips
Superintendent, Lois Anderson
Information Technology Manager, Barbara Scholl
Director, Kristin Nelson
Administrative Manager, T K Frantz
Transportation Director, Carlos Chicas
Auditors: VAVRINEK TRINE DAY & CO LL

LOCATIONS
HQ: CAPISTRANO UNIFIED SCHOOL DISTRICT
33122 VALLE RD, SAN JUAN CAPISTRANO, CA
926754859
Phone: 949 234-9200
Web: WWW.CAPOUSD-CA.SCHOOLLOOP.COM

HISTORICAL FINANCIALS
Company Type: Private

Income Statement   FYE: June 30

	REVENUE ($ mil.)	NET INCOME ($ mil.)	NET PROFIT MARGIN	EMPLOYEES
06/18	539	1	0.2%	4,500
06/17	521	(3)	—	—
06/16	528	29	5.6%	—
06/05	3	0	—	—
Annual Growth	48.3%	—	—	—

2018 Year-End Financials
Return on assets: 0.1%   Cash ($ mil.): 144
Return on equity: 0.3%
Current ratio: —

CAPITAL DISTRICT PHYSICIANS' HEALTH PLAN, INC.

Capital District Physicians' Health Plan (CDPHP) is an independent not-for-profit health plan serving some 448000 members in two dozen New York counties. It offers employer-sponsored and individual managed care plans (including HMO PPO and consumer-directed plans) as well as a Medicare Advantage plan for seniors. The company's coverage include full coverage for some preventative medical services as well as options for covering prescription drugs dental work and vision services. CDPHP also provides wellness programs that help members with weight loss smoking cessation and chronic disease management.

Operations
In addition to its commercial and Medicare offerings CDPHP provides health plans under several state-subsidized insurance programs including Family Health Plus and Child Health Plus (intended for residents who don't qualify for Medicaid) and Healthy NY (intended for small businesses and sole proprietors). Altogether the CDPHP provider network includes more than 10000 physicians and facilities.

The company's classifies its products in three lines of business: Health Maintenance Organization (HMO) products (which includes Healthy New York Medicare Choices Medicaid Child Health Plus and Family Health Plus) provided by CDPHP; Preferred Provider Organization (PPO) products (which include PPO High Deductible PPO Medicare Choices Exclusive Provider Organization -EPO- and High Deductible EPO products) provided by CDPHP Universal Benefits Inc.; and the Administrative Services Organization (ASO) plans (which includes ASO and self-insured plans) provided by Capital District Physicians' Healthcare Network Inc.

In 2013 CDPHP's membership increased by about 38000.

Geographic Reach
CDPHP serves customers in 24 New York counties: Albany Broome Chenango Columbia Delaware Dutchess Essex Fulton Greene Hamilton Herkimer Madison Montgomery Oneida Orange Otsego Rensselaer Saratoga Schenectady Schoharie Tioga Ulster Warren and Washington.

Financial Performance
CDPHP reported a 13% increase in revenues in 2013 due to an increase in membership and in earned premiums.

The company suffered a loss of $43 million in 2013 (a decrease of more than 375%) due to an increase in claims and general expenses.

Strategy
CDPHP's self-proclaimed strategy is to use the majority of its premium income to pay out medical claims while maintaining necessary reserve levels to keep its solid financial performance and to comply with federal medical loss-ratio guidelines. It earmarks a small amount of income for operational expenses as well as to fund growth and wellness initiatives.

In mid-2014 the company teamed upewith Independent Health to build innovative products tools and services for providers employers and individuals across New York State. The partnership will focus on developing new tools technology and products along with recruiting new physicians.

In the early 2013 the company opened a new CDPHP Service Center location at Latham New York and a health and fitness center inside an Albany supermarket.

CDPHP also works to lower medical expenses by partnering with other regional care and plan providers.

Company Background
In 2011 CDPHP partnered with Trendshift in 2011 to provide a new group funding management system for employers.

An association of local Albany physicians founded CDPHP in 1984.

EXECUTIVES
Vice President Of State Programs, Sheila Nelson
Vice President Of Medical Affairs Operations, Tracy Langlais
Vice President Strategy Implementation And Vendor Management, Laura Kabay
Vice President Application Management, Sigrid Cerio
Senior Vice President Government And External Relations, Robert Hinckley
Medical Director Behavioral Health, Kelly J Clark
Senior Vice President Chief Information Officer, Linda Navarra
Vice President Medical Affairs And Senior Medical Director, Richard Dal Col
Vice President Information Technology Infrastructure Management, George Waghorn

LOCATIONS
HQ: CAPITAL DISTRICT PHYSICIANS' HEALTH PLAN, INC.
500 PATROON CREEK BLVD, ALBANY, NY 122065006
Phone: 518 641-3700
Web: WWW.CDPHP.COM

PRODUCTS/OPERATIONS

Selected Products
Dental and Vision Health Plans
   CVS ExtraCare Health Card
   Delta Dental
Government Plans
   Child Health Plus
   Family Health Plus
   Medicaid Select Plan
   Medicare Choices (HMO)
Group Health Plans
   Embrace Health

Exclusive Provider Organization (EPO)
Group Medicare
High Deductible Health Plans (HDHP)
Health Maintenance Organization (HMO)
Healthy Direction
Lifestyle Riders
Preferred Provider Organization (PPO)
Transitional Health Plans
Health Funding Arrangements
Flexible Spending Accounts
Health Reimbursement Arrangement
Health Savings Account
Individual Health Plans
Healthy New York
Non-Group Health Plans

COMPETITORS

Aetna
Anthem
CIGNA
EmblemHealth
Fidelis Care New York
Humana
Independent Health
MVP Health Plan
UnitedHealth Group
excellus bluecross blueshield rochester region
healthnow new york inc

HISTORICAL FINANCIALS
Company Type: Private

Income Statement				FYE: December 31
	REVENUE ($ mil.)	NET INCOME ($ mil.)	NET PROFIT MARGIN	EMPLOYEES
12/13	1,314	22	1.7%	700
12/09	1,037	33	3.2%	—
12/03	818	(1)	—	—
Annual Growth	4.9%	—	—	—

2013 Year-End Financials
Return on assets: 4.4%   Cash ($ mil.): 61
Return on equity: 7.0%
Current ratio: 0.80

CAPITAL INCOME BUILDER, INC.

EXECUTIVES

Pres, James B Lovelace

LOCATIONS

HQ: CAPITAL INCOME BUILDER, INC.
333 S HOPE ST FL 52, LOS ANGELES, CA 900713061
Phone: 213 486-9200
Web: WWW.CAPITALGROUP.COM

HISTORICAL FINANCIALS
Company Type: Private

Income Statement				FYE: October 31
	ASSETS ($ mil.)	NET INCOME ($ mil.)	INCOME AS % OF ASSETS	EMPLOYEES
10/18	102,648	(7,919)	—	2
10/16	100,286	2,628	2.6%	—
Annual Growth	1.2%	—	—	—

2018 Year-End Financials
Return on assets: (-7.7%)   Sales ($ mil): 3,385
Return on equity: (-7.9%)

CARE NEW ENGLAND HEALTH SYSTEM INC

Care New England Health System take pains to ease its patients' pain. The system operates four hospitals: Kent Hospital a general acute care facility with about 360 beds; the 290-bed Memorial Hospital of Rhode Island; psychiatric facility Butler Hospital; and Women & Infants Hospital of Rhode Island which specializes in obstetrics gynecology and newborn pediatrics. All told the system has more than 963 licensed beds. Care New England formed in 1996 by three member hospitals also operates a home health agency and outpatient care facilities. In late 2016 the system dropped its plans to merge with Southcoast Health. The following year it agreed to be acquired by Partners Health-Care which is expanding outside of Massachusetts.

EXECUTIVES

Ceo, John Hynes
Pres, James Fanale
SEC, Paula Phelan
Chief of Medicine, Alfred Arcand
Scientist, Linda Lupo-Adams
Coordinator, Greg Spaziano
Program Director, Kenneth Chen
Database Administrator II, Stone Deb
Revenue Cycle Supervisor, Amy Randall
Associate Application Analyst, Edward Robert
Family Practice, Jennifer Kilduff
Auditors: PRICEWATERHOUSECOOPERS LLP BO

LOCATIONS

HQ: CARE NEW ENGLAND HEALTH SYSTEM INC
45 WILLARD AVE, PROVIDENCE, RI 029053218
Phone: 401 453-7900

COMPETITORS

Baystate Health
Community Health Systems
Lifespan Corporation
Partners HealthCare
Roger Williams Medical Center
Southcoast Hospitals Group
Tenet Healthcare
Universal Health Services
Yale New Haven Health System

HISTORICAL FINANCIALS
Company Type: Private

Income Statement				FYE: September 30
	REVENUE ($ mil.)	NET INCOME ($ mil.)	NET PROFIT MARGIN	EMPLOYEES
09/17	1,132	21	1.9%	6,500
09/16	1,154	(63)	—	—
09/15	126	(8)	—	—
09/13	94	1	2.1%	—
Annual Growth	86.0%	82.7%	—	—

2017 Year-End Financials
Return on assets: 2.5%   Cash ($ mil.): 54
Return on equity: 8.1%
Current ratio: 1.20

CAREALLIANCE HEALTH SERVICES

CareAlliance Health Services (doing business as Roper St. Francis Healthcare) operates four hospitals — the 370-bed Roper Hospital the 200-bed Bon Secours St. Francis Hospital the 85-bed Mount Pleasant Hospital and the Roper Rehabilitation Hospital. Besides providing home health services it also operates outpatient emergency primary care and diagnostic facilities. Roper St. Francis Healthcare serves Charleston South Carolina and surrounding communities. Its Roper St. Francis Physician Partners is one of the region's largest physician practices.

Operations
The health system comprises Roper Hospital Bon Secours St. Francis Hospital Roper St. Francis Mount Pleasant Hospital Roper St. Francis Foundation and Roper St. Francis Physicians Network. Altogether it boasts three acute care hospitals with 655-plus beds one specialty hospital 15 centers for outpatient services three industrial medicine sites five emergency rooms and two urgent care centers.

Roper St. Francis Healthcare has a medical staff of some 800 physicians. The Roper St. Francis Physician Partners organization has more than 230 physicians who offer primary and specialty care including family practice internal medicine and pediatrics.

Geographic Reach
Altogether Roper St. Francis Healthcare operates about 90 facilities in seven counties in the lowcountry region of South Carolina.

Strategy
The health system in 2014 signed an agreement with Trendlines Lab to collaborate on the development of new medical device inventions as well as low-cost solutions for clinical problems. The partnership will work to create devices that will address unmet needs identified by physicians and other health care providers.

Company Background
Roper St. Francis Healthcare was formed through the merger of Roper Hospital and Bon Secours St. Francis Hospital in 1998.

Roper St. Francis Physician Partners was formed through the 2009 combination of Roper St. Francis Physicians' Network and Lowcountry Medical Associates.

EXECUTIVES

President And Ceo, David L. Dunlap
Vp And Cio, Mike Taylor
President Medical Affairs And Chief Medical Officer, Steven Shapiro
Cfo, Bret Johnson
Ceo Roper Hospital And Svp Operations, Matthew Severance
Ceo Roper St. Francis Mount Pleasant Hospital And Vp Operations, John Sullivan
Ceo Bon Secours St. Francis Hospital And Svp Operations, Allen Carroll
Chairman Roper St. Francis Foundation, John B. Holloway
Vice Chairman Roper St. Francis Foundation, Charles T. Cole
Vice President Nursing & Senior Nurse Executive Bon Secours St. Francis, Pennie Peralta
Ceo Rsf Physician Partners & Rsfh Vice President & Chief Strategy Officer, Douglas Bowling
Pharmacy Manager, Thomas Baxley

Interim Chief Nursing Officer Vice President Nursing Roper Hospital, Susan Bennett
Vp Operations, Capers Limehouse
Vice President Quality And Training, Tanya Lott
Vice President Of Nursing, P Floyd
Director Of Pharmacy, Holly Balcer
Vice President Of Finance, Lynn Roberts
Vice President And Chief Diversity And Inclusion Officer, Toni Flowers
Chairman Of The Board, Pierre Manigault
Auditors: DELOITTE & TOUCHE LLP CHARLO

LOCATIONS

HQ: CAREALLIANCE HEALTH SERVICES
316 CALHOUN ST, CHARLESTON, SC 294011113
Phone: 843 724-2000
Web: WWW.RSFH.COM

Selected South Carolina Facilities

Hospitals
Mt. Pleasant Hospital Campus - Mount Pleasant
Roper Hosp
Roper Rehabilitation Hospital
St. Franci

Outpatient Centers
After Hours Care - James Island
Kiawah-Seabrook Medical & Urgent Care
Roper Hosp
Roper Hospital Ambulatory Surgery & Pain
Management - James Island
Roper Hosp
Roper Hosp
Roper Hosp
Roper Hosptial Diagnostics - Goose Creek
Roper Hosptial Diagnostics - James Island
Roper Hosp
Roper Hosptial Diagnostics - Moncks Corner
Roper Hospital Imaging - Wesley Drive
Roper Hospital Imaging - Wingo Way

COMPETITORS

Beaufort Memorial Hospital	HCA
Conway Medical Center	Medical University of South Carolina
Georgetown Hospital System	Tenet Healthcare
Grand Strand Regional Medical Center	

HISTORICAL FINANCIALS
Company Type: Private

Income Statement FYE: December 31

	REVENUE ($ mil.)	NET INCOME ($ mil.)	NET PROFIT MARGIN	EMPLOYEES
12/15	827	16	1.9%	5,000
12/14	793	(2)	—	—
12/09	682	56	8.3%	—
12/08	618	(51)	—	—
Annual Growth	4.3%	—	—	—

2015 Year-End Financials
Return on assets: 1.7%   Cash ($ mil.): 31
Return on equity: 4.3%
Current ratio: 1.20

CAREOREGON, INC.

EXECUTIVES

Pres, Chris Krenk
Exec Dir*, Mylia Christensen
Coordinator, Crystal Page
Customer Representativ, Brian M McManus
Personnel Assistant, Vicki Greenwald
Administrative Assistant, Kim Wiseman

Network Technician, Ross Ludeman
Claims Examiner Supervisor, Jeremy Brown
Human Resources Benefits Speci, Shannon Clesceri
Senior Administrative Assistan, Deborah Haren
Qnxt Administrator, Herb Kaaihue
Auditors: LB KPMG LLP SEATTLE WA

LOCATIONS

HQ: CAREOREGON, INC.
315 SW 5TH AVE STE 900, PORTLAND, OR 972041703
Phone: 503 416-4100
Web: WWW.CAREOREGON.ORG

HISTORICAL FINANCIALS
Company Type: Private

Income Statement FYE: December 31

	REVENUE ($ mil.)	NET INCOME ($ mil.)	NET PROFIT MARGIN	EMPLOYEES
12/16	886	(9)	—	140
12/14	851	87	10.3%	—
12/13	564	(0)	—	—
12/08	343	22	6.5%	—
Annual Growth	12.6%	—	—	—

2016 Year-End Financials
Return on assets: (-2.3%)   Cash ($ mil.): 49
Return on equity: (-3.3%)
Current ratio: 5.40

CARILION MEDICAL CENTER

EXECUTIVES

Ceo, Nancy Howell Agee
Pres*, Steve Arner
SEC*, Briggs Andrews
V Pres-Treas*, Rob Vaughan
Treas*, George Robert Vaughan Jr
Cfo*, Donald E Lorton
Prin*, Edward Murphy
Department SEC, Donna Webb
Chief of Surgery, Joseph T Moskal
Director, Cleo Williams
Coordinator, Mary Edwards
Auditors: DELOITTE & TOUCHE LLP CHARLOT

LOCATIONS

HQ: CARILION MEDICAL CENTER
1906 BELLEVIEW AVE SE, ROANOKE, VA 240141838
Phone: 540 981-7000
Web: WWW.CARILIONCLINIC.ORG

HISTORICAL FINANCIALS
Company Type: Private

Income Statement FYE: September 30

	REVENUE ($ mil.)	NET INCOME ($ mil.)	NET PROFIT MARGIN	EMPLOYEES
09/18	1,281	134	10.5%	6,390
09/17	1,232	134	10.9%	—
09/16	1,177	4	0.4%	—
09/15	1,064	(36)	—	—
Annual Growth	6.4%	—	—	—

2018 Year-End Financials
Return on assets: 9.1%   Cash ($ mil.): —
Return on equity: 20.3%
Current ratio: 1.00

CARILION NEW RIVER VALLEY MEDICAL CENTER

EXECUTIVES

Pres, Donald Halliwill
Ceo*, John Piatkowski
Bus Anylst, Mike Bunker
Coordinator, Becky Garnett

LOCATIONS

HQ: CARILION NEW RIVER VALLEY MEDICAL CENTER
2900 LAMB CIR STE 150, CHRISTIANSBURG, VA 240736341
Phone: 540 731-2000
Web: WWW.CARILIONCLINIC.ORG

HISTORICAL FINANCIALS
Company Type: Private

Income Statement FYE: September 30

	REVENUE ($ mil.)	NET INCOME ($ mil.)	NET PROFIT MARGIN	EMPLOYEES
09/13	896	116	12.9%	800
09/05	30	2	6.5%	—
09/04	115	18	16.0%	—
09/03	88	11	13.5%	—
Annual Growth	26.1%	25.5%	—	—

2013 Year-End Financials
Return on assets: 10.9%   Cash ($ mil.): —
Return on equity: 27.1%
Current ratio: 1.20

CARILION SERVICES, INC.

EXECUTIVES

Pres, Bill Flattery
SEC, Briggs Andrew
Prin, Carolyn Brown
Prin, Lawrence G Hincker
Prin, William J Flattery
Recruiter, Jill Lusher
Senior Vice President, Curtis Mills
Auditors: DELOITTE & TOUCHE LLP CHARLOT

LOCATIONS

HQ: CARILION SERVICES, INC.
213 S JEFFERSON ST # 633, ROANOKE, VA 240111700
Phone: 540 981-7000
Web: WWW.CARILION.COM

Income Statement				FYE: September 30
	REVENUE ($ mil.)	NET INCOME ($ mil.)	NET PROFIT MARGIN	EMPLOYEES
09/08	1,221	(147)	—	935
09/05	87	(2)	—	—
09/04	228	(23)	—	—
09/03	205	17	8.3%	—
Annual Growth	42.8%	—	—	—

2008 Year-End Financials

Return on assets: (-8.4%) Cash ($ mil.): 1
Return on equity: (-18.4%)
Current ratio: 0.90

CARLE FOUNDATION HOSPITAL

Carle Foundation Hospital is a 393-bed acute-care facility that serves the residents of east central Illinois. The hospital includes the region's only Level I trauma center as well as a Level III perinatal center a neonatal ICU and centers devoted to cardiac and cancer care. It also runs a handful of specialty centers in the region. Carle Foundation Hospital is the primary teaching hospital for the University of Illinois College of Medicine at Urbana-Champaign. It is controlled by the not-for-profit Carle Foundation; sister company Carle Physician Group which boasts more than 400 physicians representing 80 specialties is one of the nation's largest private physician groups.

Operations
The hospital averages more than 22000 annual patient admissions and treats 63000-plus emergency room patients. It offers services related to bariatrics stroke sports medicine women's health and heart and cancer care.

Geographic Reach
Carle Foundation Hospital's service area spans 14 communities across east-central Illinois.

Sales and Marketing
Revenue increased 12% to $2 billion in 2014 as patient service earnings and rental income grew. However due to an increase in medical benefits of insured and pension-related changes net income fell 65% to $112 million that year.

Despite the lower net income cash flow from operations rose 20% to $193 million on changes in medical claims payable as well as an increase in cash generated fro third-party payor settlements.

Strategy
Construction has been key to Carle Foundation Hospital's growth in recent years. The hospital built a $6 million center for children with hearing loss; the center houses the Expanding Children's Hearing Opportunities Center and the Carle Auditory Oral School. Carle Foundation Hospital Research Institute opened an $11-million Biomedical Research Center that houses hospital and University of Illinois staff conducting research in breast cancer gastrointestinal and cardiovascular disease and neuroscience.

The hospital in 2013 added a $200 million seven-story patient tower that houses the heart and vascular institute. The new patient capacity replaced patient beds in older parts of the hospital and provides for future growth opportunities. Carle Foundation Hospital now plans to build a new fa-cility to address the region's needs for increased orthopedic and sports medicine services.

In 2015 Crawford Memorial Hospital and Carle Foundation Hospital entered into an affiliation agreement. Crawford's 25-bed facility joined Carle's network of rural care centers to better provide care for patients in the area.

EXECUTIVES

President And Ceo, James C. Leonard
Vice President Of Facility, Scott Harding
Medical Director, Andy Arwari
Medical Director, Douglas Filipov
Associate Medical Director Emergency Department, Benjamin Davis
Vice President Medical Affairs, Napoleon Knight
Medical Records Director, Tricia Truscott
Vice President Corporate Counsel, Kurt Leifheit
Occupational Medicine, Laura Shanks
Vice President Of Human Resources, Lauren Schmid
Vice President Revenue Cycle Operations, Dawn Walden
Vice President Information Management And Analytics, Cheryl Gerow
Medical Director, Thomas Scaggs
Radiology Director, Tim Sapyta
Occupational Medicine, Martina Stika
Vice President And Medical Director, Kirk Moberg
Board Member, Sean Grambart

LOCATIONS

HQ: CARLE FOUNDATION HOSPITAL
611 W PARK ST, URBANA, IL 618012529
Phone: 217 326-2900
Web: WWW.CARLE.ORG

PRODUCTS/OPERATIONS

2014 Sales

	$ mil.	% of total
Net premium revenue-health insurance	1,296	63
Net patient service revenue	709	34
Rental income	15	1
Net assets released from restrictions	1	-
Other	34	2
Loss on the disposal of property & equipment	(2.8)	-
Total	**2,054**	**100**

Selected Medical Services
Bariatrics
Cancer
Cancer
Cardiology & Heart Surgery
Diabetes & Endocrinology
Ear Nose & Throat
Gastroenterology & GI Surgery
Geriatrics
Gynecology
Heart
Nephrology
Neurology & Neurosurgery
Sports Medicine
Stroke
Women's Health

COMPETITORS

Advocate BroMenn	Sarah Bush Lincoln Health Center
Decatur Memorial Hospital	Silver Cross Hospital
Hospital Sisters Health System	St. Elizabeth Regional Health
Iroquois Memorial Hospital	St. John's Hospital (Illinois)
Memorial Health System	Union Hospital (Indiana)
Morris Hospital	
OSF Healthcare System	

Income Statement				FYE: December 31
	REVENUE ($ mil.)	NET INCOME ($ mil.)	NET PROFIT MARGIN	EMPLOYEES
12/17	900	247	27.5%	2,500
12/16	812	185	22.8%	—
12/15	754	163	21.7%	—
12/13	616	180	29.2%	—
Annual Growth	9.9%	8.3%	—	—

CARNEGIE MELLON UNIVERSITY

If you can't act maybe Carnegie Mellon University can help. The university is known around the world for churning out award-winning actors from its highly regarded drama school. Drama isn't all Carnegie teaches though — the school has seven colleges and schools that offer academic programs in areas such as psychology computer science engineering biology and public policy. It has more than 13000 students and 5300 faculty and staff and it has a relatively small student-teacher ratio of 10:1. Carnegie Mellon was founded by philanthropist and industrialist Andrew Carnegie who established the Carnegie Technical Schools in 1900 for the sons and daughters of Pittsburgh's blue-collar workers.

Operations
Along with its undergraduate and graduate degree programs Carnegie offers working adults a chance to continue their learning through the Professional & Distance Learning arm of the school. Students there can hone their international business management skills and bone up on information technology health systems and human resources among other topics.

Carnegie prides itself on its innovation efforts and to support them operates more than 100 research institutes and centers across its campus. Carnegie's CyLab is one of the largest university-based cybersecurity education and research centers in the country. Cylab focuses on seven primary areas of research and development spanning a wide range of technologies and systems and users.

Tuition for residential undergraduates in the fiscal year ending 2017 totals more than $51000.

The school's alumni network includes about 20 Nobel Prize laureates some 100 Emmy Award winners and a half-dozen Academy Award winners.

Geographic Reach
The school's main campus nearly 150 acres with more than 100 buildings is located in Pittsburgh; Carnegie Mellon also has branch campuses in Qatar and Silicon Valley California. Additionally the university offers degrees in nearly 20 locations around the world including Australia Greece Japan Mexico Portugal and Singapore.

Financial Performance
The university's revenue increased 5% to $1.1 billion in 2015. This was driven by increases in tuition and fees and higher enrollments. Contributions revenue rose 15% that year and investment income rose nearly that much.

However net income dropped 36% to $161 million as investment returns declined. An increase in accounts payable and other factors led the school's operating cash to rise 14% to $75 million that year.

Strategy

In 2015 Carnegie Mellon focused on four major capital projects. Among those were the addition of a classroom and central hub in its Heinz College Hamburg Hall and the addition of fitness amenities to the Cohon University Center. The David A. Tepper Quadrangle which will include the Tepper School of Business and the Swartz Center for Entrepreneurship is scheduled to be completed in 2018.

Company Background

Carnegie Tech merged with the Mellon Institute of Research to become Carnegie Mellon University in 1967.

EXECUTIVES

Provost, Farnam Jahanian
Ceo Software Engineering Institute, Paul D. Nielsen, age 68
Dean Student Affairs, Gina Casalegno
Dean Qatar Campus, Ilker Baybars
President, Subra Suresh
Dean Heinz College, Ramayya Krishnan
Chief Investment Officer, Charles A. Kennedy
Vp Finance And Cfo, Amir Rahnamay-Azar
Dean College Of Engineering, James H. Garrett
Dean College Of Fine Arts, Dan Martin
Dean Mellon College Of Science, Fred Gilman
Dean Tepper School Of Business, Robert M. Dammon
Vp Marketing And Communications, Steve Kloehn
Interim Cio, David Baisley
Dean School Of Computer Science, Andrew Moore
Dean Dietrich College Of Humanities And Social Sciences, Richard Scheines
Dean Of Admission, Michael Steidel
Dean University Libraries, Keith Webster
Vice President President Elect, Martin Aurand
Department Head, Terry Hurlbert
Vice President Marketing, Peter Boatwright
Senior Management (senior Vice President General Manager Director), Gretchen Beck
Associate Vice President, Tim McNulty
Assistant Vice President For Marketing Communications, Marilyn Kail
Vice President Institutional Advancement And Assistant Secretary, Neel Kishan
Vice President Of Mentorship, Adrian Galarza
Department Head, Patsy McCarthy
Vice President, Chinmayi Bhavanishankar
Vice President Of Investment Banking, Samantha Speer
Vice President Of Communications, Ted Lee
Contracts Manager Associate Vice President For Re, Lynn Young
Assistant Vice President For Research Compliance, Ann Mathias
Department Head, Stephen Garoff
Vice President Of Treasury, Kaijie Hu
Vice President Of Education, Anjali Guatam
Vice President, Robert Sekerka
Deputy General Counsel And Associate Vice President, James Mercolini
Vice President Of Technology, Daniel Dallala
Vice President Of Finance, Peter Tran
Vice President Of Finance, Jorge Carvallo
Assistant Vice President Internationa, Carrie Nelson
Vice President Of Finance, Sam Phong
Vice President Of Technology Education, Silvio Tannert
Vice President Finance, Maneesh Lekkala
Co Vice President Of Finance, Sahil Jain
Vice President Of Education Technology, Georgia Tech
Vice President Of Finance, Kevin Gallagher
Vice President Of Finance And Technology, Daniel Robinson
Associate Vice President Development, Pamela Eager

Vice President, Egon Balas
Assistant Vice President For Planning, Keith Cook
Vice President For University Advancement, Scott Mory
Assistant Vice President Advancement Marketing And Communications, Brian Thornton
Associate Vice President For Academic Affairs And Dean Of Graduate Studies, Rodney Mcclendon
Chairman, James E. (Jim) Rohr, age 71
Vice Chairman, Tod S. Johnson
Vice Chairman, Edward H. (Ed) Frank, age 62
Treasurer, Jay Calhoun
Treasurer, Michelle Martin
Secretary, Alice Yochum
Assistant Secretary, Karen Khan
Department Secretary, Nancy Watson
Secretary, Ginger Placone
Auditors: PRICEWATERHOUSECOOPERS LLP PI

LOCATIONS

HQ: CARNEGIE MELLON UNIVERSITY
  5000 FORBES AVE, PITTSBURGH, PA 152133890
Phone: 412 268-2000
Web: WWW.CMU.EDU

Selected Locations
Adelaide Australia
Athens Greece
Aveiro and Coimbra Portugal
Doha Qatar
Kobe Japan
Lisbon Portugal
Los Angeles
Madeira Portugal
Minho and Porto Portugal
Mexico
Silicon Valley
Singapore

PRODUCTS/OPERATIONS

2015 Sales

	$ mil.	% of total
Tuition and other educational fees revenue net of financial aid	450	39
Sponsored projects revenue	376	32
Contributions revenue	136	12
Auxiliary services revenue	57	5
Investment income	37	3
Other sources	109	9
Total	**1,168**	**100**

Selected Departments

Chemical Engineering
Civil and Environmental Engineering
Energy Science Technology & Policy
Electrical and Computer Engineering
Engineering and Public Policy
Engineering & Technology Innovation Management
Information Networking Institute
Materials Science Engineering
Mechanical Engineering
Software Engineering and
Software Management
Architecture
Art
Design
Drama
Master of Arts Management
Master of Entertainment Industry Management
Music
English
History
Modern Languages
Philosophy
Psychology
Social and Decision Sciences
Statistics

Selected Schools

Carnegie Institute of Technology
School of Computer Science
College of Fine Arts
College of Humanities & Social Sciences
H. John Heinz III College
Mellon College of Science
Tepper School of Business

HISTORICAL FINANCIALS

Company Type: Private

Income Statement				FYE: June 30
	REVENUE ($ mil.)	NET INCOME ($ mil.)	NET PROFIT MARGIN	EMPLOYEES
06/18	1,313	296	22.6%	4,913
06/17	1,229	556	45.2%	—
06/13	1,106	182	16.5%	—
06/12	1,061	44	4.2%	—
Annual Growth	3.6%	37.1%	—	—

2018 Year-End Financials

Return on assets: 7.3%
Return on equity: 9.3%
Current ratio: —
Cash ($ mil.): 481

CAROLINA HEALTHCARE CENTER OF CUMBERLAND LP

Auditors: RSM MCGLADREY CHARLOTTE NC

LOCATIONS

HQ: CAROLINA HEALTHCARE CENTER OF CUMBERLAND LP
  4600 CUMBERLAND RD, FAYETTEVILLE, NC 283062412
Phone: 910 429-1690
Web: WWW.CAROLINA-HEALTH.COM

HISTORICAL FINANCIALS

Company Type: Private

Income Statement				FYE: September 30
	REVENUE ($ mil.)	NET INCOME ($ mil.)	NET PROFIT MARGIN	EMPLOYEES
09/09	1,019	62	6.2%	150
09/03	6	(0)	—	—
Annual Growth	132.0%	—	—	—

2009 Year-End Financials

Return on assets: 771.0%
Return on equity: 999.9%
Current ratio: 0.60
Cash ($ mil.): —

CAROLINAS MEDICAL CENTER NORTHEAST

LOCATIONS

HQ: CAROLINAS MEDICAL CENTER NORTHEAST
  920 CHURCH ST N, CONCORD, NC 280252927
Phone: 704 783-3000
Web: WWW.ATRIUMHEALTH.ORG

HISTORICAL FINANCIALS
Company Type: Private

Income Statement				FYE: December 31
	REVENUE ($ mil.)	NET INCOME ($ mil.)	NET PROFIT MARGIN	EMPLOYEES
12/17	576	158	27.4%	4,500
12/16	552	130	23.6%	—
12/15	557	117	21.0%	—
Annual Growth	1.7%	16.3%		

2017 Year-End Financials
Return on assets: 10.1% Cash ($ mil.): —
Return on equity: 10.3%
Current ratio: 23.20

CAROMONT HEALTH, INC.

CaroMont Health is an independent not-for-profit health care system serving residents of North Carolina's Piedmont region. Anchoring CaroMont Health is Gaston Memorial Hospital a 435-bed medical and surgical facility that features a birthing center an inpatient psychiatric ward and specialized facilities for heart disease cancer sleep disorders diabetes and wound care. Other operations include a nearly 100-bed nursing home outpatient surgery and urgent care centers and a network of primary and specialty medical practices. CaroMont Health also provides home health and hospice care services. CaroMont Health is governed by the North Carolina Medical Care Commission.

Operations
CaroMont Health employs a total of some 3900 health professionals including about 450 physicians. Its CaroMont Medical Group physician practice organization includes 140 doctors that serve patients from 45 outpatient locations including primary and specialty practices surgery centers and urgent and immediate care clinics.

Geographic Reach
CaroMont's primary facilities are located in Gastonia a community just west of Charlotte North Carolina. The health network also operates clinics and offices in Cleveland Mecklenburg Mountain Island Lake and Lincoln North Carolina as well as in York South Carolina.

Strategy
Like many medical networks CaroMont Health is establishing urgent care and walk-in immediate care centers to offset unnecessary use of hospital emergency rooms. Such facilities help to lower costs and increase efficient patient care management.

In other efforts to meet area population needs CaroMont has begun an expansion program to significantly increase the size of its Gaston Hospice facility. It is also expanding and renovating the emergency department of its main campus; the facility will gain 10000 sq. ft. of new space and a pediatric emergency area. In 2015 the system opened the CaroMont Regional Medical Center in Mount Holly which is designed to meet the emergency care needs of eastern Gaston southern Lincoln and western Mecklenburg counties.

Partnering with community groups is another way CaroMont works to improve general health and medical services. In 2014 it partnered with Gaston County Schools to begin providing athletic training services; the following year it initiated a two-year pilot program with North Carolina State Health Plan encouraging plan members' physicians to improve engagement and improve member experiences in general.

EXECUTIVES

Medical Director Cardiac Surgery, James Greelish
Managing Director Diplomate American Board Of Internal Medicine Caromont Internal Medicine, Jacqueline Folks
Nursing Director, Janet Hamrick
Director Of Radiology Cardiology, Deanna Roe
Vice President Operations, Ryan Campbell
Vice President Strategy, Del Murphy
Vice President, Danny Wharton
Secretary Housekeeping, Lori Sosebee
Auditors: DIXON HUGHES GOODMAN LLP ASHE

LOCATIONS

HQ: CAROMONT HEALTH, INC.
 2525 COURT DR, GASTONIA, NC 280542140
Phone: 704 834-2000
Web: WWW.CAROMONTHEALTH.ORG

PRODUCTS/OPERATIONS

Selected Service Areas
Cancer (oncology)
Diabetes
Emergency care
Heart and vascular
Hospice and palliative care
Immediate care
Long-term care
Mental health
Mobile screening
Neuroscience
Orthopedics
Pain management
Rehabilitation
Sleep medicine
Surgery
Trauma
Wellness programs
Women's health
Wound care

COMPETITORS

Blue Ridge HealthCare	Mission Hospitals
Carolinas HealthCare System	New Hanover Regional Medical Center
Community Health Systems	Novant Health
High Point Regional Health System	Tenet Healthcare

HISTORICAL FINANCIALS
Company Type: Private

Income Statement				FYE: June 30
	REVENUE ($ mil.)	NET INCOME ($ mil.)	NET PROFIT MARGIN	EMPLOYEES
06/18	602	63	10.5%	2,400
06/17	552	80	14.6%	—
06/15	38	36	95.3%	—
06/14	37	35	95.9%	—
Annual Growth	100.7%	15.4%	—	—

2018 Year-End Financials
Return on assets: 5.4% Cash ($ mil.): 25
Return on equity: 7.5%
Current ratio: 1.00

CARTER-JONES COMPANIES, INC.

EXECUTIVES

Pres-Ceo, Neil Sackett
Sr V Pres-Cfo*, Jeffrey Donley
SEC*, Judy Lee
Controller*, Brian Horning
Auditors: BDO USA LLP AKRON OHIO

LOCATIONS

HQ: CARTER-JONES COMPANIES, INC.
 601 TALLMADGE RD, KENT, OH 442407331
Phone: 330 673-6100

HISTORICAL FINANCIALS
Company Type: Private

Income Statement				FYE: December 31
	REVENUE ($ mil.)	NET INCOME ($ mil.)	NET PROFIT MARGIN	EMPLOYEES
12/18	1,482	39	2.7%	3,225
12/17	1,365	29	2.1%	—
12/16	1,241	15	1.2%	—
12/15	1,109	17	1.6%	—
Annual Growth	10.1%	30.0%	—	—

2018 Year-End Financials
Return on assets: 5.5% Cash ($ mil.): 14
Return on equity: 10.7%
Current ratio: 1.90

CARY OIL CO., INC.

EXECUTIVES

Pres-Ceo, Craig Stephenson
Chb*, Don Stephenson
V Pres*, Betty Phillips
V Pres*, Jim Bosworth
V Pres*, Mark Maddox
Asst SEC-Treas*, Rick Stephenson
V Pres-Chief Fin Officer*, Jason Holt
It Manager, Buster Clark
Vp Strategy & Innovation, Adam Stephenson
Sales Representative, Jim Pendergast
Wholesale Account Manager, Steven Goolsby
Auditors: BATCELOR TILLERY & ROBERTS L

LOCATIONS

HQ: CARY OIL CO., INC.
 110 MACKENAN DR STE 300, CARY, NC 275117901
Phone: 919 462-1100
Web: WWW.CARYOIL.COM

HISTORICAL FINANCIALS
Company Type: Private

Income Statement				FYE: December 31
	REVENUE ($ mil.)	NET INCOME ($ mil.)	NET PROFIT MARGIN	EMPLOYEES
12/12	1,647	2	0.2%	100
12/11	1,608	2	0.1%	—
12/10	1,177	1	0.1%	—
Annual Growth	18.3%	28.2%	—	—

2012 Year-End Financials
Return on assets: 4.8% Cash ($ mil.): 4
Return on equity: 25.1%
Current ratio: 1.00

CASE WESTERN RESERVE UNIVERSITY

Looking for a research-oriented university? Case Western Reserve University (CWRU) is a private research school with an enrollment of more than 11300 students from all US states and more than 90 countries more than half of whom are graduate and professional students. CWRU offers about 200 undergraduate and graduate degree programs from its eight colleges and schools — business engineering law arts and sciences dentistry social work nursing and medicine — as well as a graduate school at its campus in Cleveland. The university has 3360 faculty members and a student-to-teacher ratio of 8:1.

Operations

The school receives close to $400 million in external funding each year to pay for its various research enterprises. CWRU provides research opportunities to more than 5100 undergraduates and partners with corporations foundations and other universities to operate more than 100 research centers and institutes. Some of its priority research initiatives include energy and the environment culture creativity and design social justice and ethics. Medical studies are conducted in coordination with health care entities; its most predominant partner is the Cleveland Clinic.

Geographic Reach

CWRU is located on the a 178-acre campus in Cleveland Ohio; the campus is located within the 500-acre University Circle district; and houses more than 40 educational medical cultural social and religious institutions. CWRU's students come from all 50 US states and more than 90 countries.

Strategy

CWRU's core priorities include enhancing its education and research programs advancing institutional resources strengthening partnerships and building a diverse community.

In 2016 CWRU launched the Master of Arts in Military Ethics program the nation's first in a field of study that contends with questions of how advancing military technologies relate to the common humanity of both enemy and ally.

In 2014 the university reached its initial goal of raising $1 billion to increase financial support for students grow the number of endowed professorships and support capital projects. That year it launched a $64 million renovation and expansion of the Temple-Tifereth Israel complex as part of its 21-acre campus expansion; the project will turn the facility into a performing arts center that will house the school's dance theatre and music departments.

Company Background

The university's origins date back to 1826 in the Ohio region then known as the Western Reserve of Connecticut; its current structure was formed in 1967 with the combination of neighboring Case Institute of Technology and Western Reserve College.

EXECUTIVES

Vice President For Campus Services, Dick Jamieson
Vice President Of Technology Research, Mark Coticchia
Director Media Relations, Lisa Chiu
President, Barbara R. Snyder, age 63
Dean School Of Graduate Studies, Charles Rozek
Dean Undergraduate Studies, Jeffrey Wolcowitz
Chief Investment Officer, Sally J. Staley

Dean School Of Dental Medicine, Kenneth B. Chance
Dean Mandel School Of Applied Social Sciences, Grover C. (Cleve) Gilmore
Provost And Evp, William A. (Bud) Baeslack
Svp Finance And Cfo, John F. Sideras
Dean School Of Medicine, Pamela Bowles Davis
Dean College Of Arts And Sciences, Cyrus Taylor
Vp University Marketing And Communications, Chris Sheridan
Dean Case School Of Engineering, Jeffrey Duerk
Dean Weatherhead School Of Management, Robert E. Widing
Dean Bolton School Of Nursing, Mary E. Kerr
Vp Information Technology Services And Cio, Sue B. Workman
Dean School Of Law, Jessica Berg
Dean School Of Law, Michael P. Scharf
Medical Director Professor, Kingman Strohl
Director Of Admissions, David Dalsky
Vice President Information Services, Lev Gonick
Vice President Of Marketing, Marlene Gambatese
Associate Vice President, Julie Rehm
Vice President Emeritus, Kenneth Kutina
Associate Vice President For Operations And Planning, Dennis Rupert
Vice President Of Planning, Kenneth Basch
Department Chair, James McGuffin-Cawley
Director Of Nursing University Health Service, Timothy Eppich
Medical Director, ELIZABETH CLICK
Second Vice President, Clare Rimnac
Vice President, Meredith Sorenson
Medical Director Of Respiratory Therapy, Tony Dimarco
Vice President Of Membership Development, Akash K Menon
Vice President Finance Executive, Anthony D Kinslow
Vice President Finance, Kelsey Nurmi
Vice President University Relations, Lara Kalafatis
Vice President, Raymond Neff
Associate Vice President Information Technology, Michael Edwards
Vice President, Jacqueline Musacchia
Second Vice President, Katherine Lanese
Medical Director Clinical Microbiology, Michael Jacobs
Vice President Of Marketing, Jim Hammerstone
Vice President Its, Dean Bianchi
Vice President Technology, Karmar Clifton
Vice President Treasury, Bradley Bond
Vice President, Tom Mullen
Vice President For Development, Lawrence Gibson
Senior Vice President Secretary And General Counsel, Elizabeth Keefer
Vice President For Student Affairs, Nicholls Glenn
Vice President Of Marketing, Juanita Cutler
Associate Vice President For Student Affairs, Dean Patterson
Medical Director Family Practice Ambulatory Services, Wayne Forde
Vice President, Casandra Tice
Vice President Corporate Solutions, Ryan Terry
Vice President Operations, Victoria Saybe
Vice President Human Resources, Anthony Kislow
Vice President, Marissa Morgan
Vice President, Ranjith Ramachandran
Vice President, Ray Braun
Associate Vice President For University Planning And Administration, Victoria Wright
Associate Vice President Of University Relations And Development, Taylor Gladys
Vice President Finance Director Of Finance And Suppo, Sonia Salvino
Assistant Vice President And Director Of Equity, Christopher Jones
Assistant Vice President Of Human Resources, Stephanie Hathaway
Chairman, Charles D. (Chuck) Fowler

Board Member, Gerald Ferretti
Board Member, Fred Collopy
Secretary, Ellen Rothchild
Vice Chair Of Research And Professor, Irina Pikuleva
Secretary, Susan Grimm
Secretary, Kimberly Racut
Board Member, Deborah Frontczak
Department Secretary, Carol Samuels
Treasurer, Joseph Thomas
Treasurer, Robert Thompson
Advisory Board Member Tiime Program, Ronald Copfer
Secretary, Meghan Gallagher
Secretary, Krystle Elder
Treasurer, Paul Simmons
Auditors: PRICEWATERHOUSECOOPERS LLP CL

LOCATIONS

HQ: CASE WESTERN RESERVE UNIVERSITY
10900 EUCLID AVE, CLEVELAND, OH 441064901
Phone: 216 368-2000
Web: WWW.CASE.EDU

PRODUCTS/OPERATIONS

2014 Sales

	$ mil.	% of total
Grants and contracts	249	27
Student tuition and fees	218	24
Gifts and pledges	85	9
CCLCM grants and contracts	83	9
Facilities and administrative cost recovery	72	8
Others	217	23
Total	**926**	**100**

Selected Schools and Programs

Case School of Engineering
College of Arts and Sciences
Cleveland Clinic (part of the School of Medicine)
Frances Payne Bolton School of Nursing
Mandel Center for Nonprofit Organizations
Mandel School of Applied Social Sciences
School of Dental Medicine
School of Graduate Studies
School of Law
School of Medicine
Weatherhead School of Management

HISTORICAL FINANCIALS

Company Type: Private

Income Statement   FYE: June 30

	REVENUE ($ mil.)	NET INCOME ($ mil.)	NET PROFIT MARGIN	EMPLOYEES
06/18	1,016	111	10.9%	6,599
06/17	1,022	208	20.4%	—
06/15	1,093	48	4.4%	—
06/14	926	214	23.2%	—
Annual Growth	2.3%	(15.2%)	—	—

2018 Year-End Financials

Return on assets: 3.5%   Cash ($ mil.): 105
Return on equity: 4.6%
Current ratio: —

CATHOLIC HEALTH INITIATIVES - IOWA, CORP.

EXECUTIVES

Ceo, David Vellinga
Purchasing Coordinator, Matt Rouse
Coordinator, Kelli Cain
Coordinator, Valerie Diehl
Auditors: CATHOLIC HEALTH INITIATIVES E

LOCATIONS

HQ: CATHOLIC HEALTH INITIATIVES - IOWA, CORP.
1111 6TH AVE, DES MOINES, IA 503142613
Phone: 515 247-3121
Web: WWW.MERCYDESMOINES.ORG

HISTORICAL FINANCIALS

Company Type: Private

Income Statement				FYE: June 30
	REVENUE ($ mil.)	NET INCOME ($ mil.)	NET PROFIT MARGIN	EMPLOYEES
06/16	804	58	7.3%	6,100
06/14	733	(14)	—	—
06/10	691	39	5.8%	—
06/08	577	36	6.3%	—
Annual Growth	4.2%	6.2%	—	—

2016 Year-End Financials

Return on assets: 6.9%   Cash ($ mil.): 82
Return on equity: 9.5%
Current ratio: 3.60

CATHOLIC HEALTH INITIATIVES COLORADO

EXECUTIVES

Ceo, Kevin E Lofton
Pres*, Gregory H Burfitt
Corporate Revenue Integrity, Shelly Vendemo
Chief Officer, Terry Orourke
Orsos Reimbursement Coordinato, Terry Walb
Vice President of Operations, Geoffrey Lawton Pharmd
Chief Operating Officer, Jameson Smith Fache
Senior Network Engineer, Shawn Crockett
Security Risk Management Analy, Ada Scorsone
Office Manager, Angela Anspach
Meditech Ancillary, Chris Mierzwinski
Auditors: LB CATHOLIC HEALTH INITIATIVES

LOCATIONS

HQ: CATHOLIC HEALTH INITIATIVES COLORADO
198 INVERNESS DR W, ENGLEWOOD, CO 801123637
Phone: 303 290-6500
Web: WWW.CATHOLICHEALTHINITIATIVES.ORG

HISTORICAL FINANCIALS

Company Type: Private

Income Statement				FYE: June 30
	REVENUE ($ mil.)	NET INCOME ($ mil.)	NET PROFIT MARGIN	EMPLOYEES
06/15	1,735	101	5.8%	8,000
06/14	1,689	96	5.7%	—
06/10	1,307	50	3.9%	—
06/09	1,226	24	2.0%	—
Annual Growth	6.0%	26.4%		

2015 Year-End Financials

Return on assets: 5.4%   Cash ($ mil.): 45
Return on equity: 7.2%
Current ratio: 1.50

CATHOLIC MEDICAL MISSION BOARD INC

EXECUTIVES

Pres, John F Galbraith
Pres, Bruce Wilkinson
Senior Vice-President, Marivette Cannon
Director, Chris Foster
Vice-Chairman, F W Smullen
Government Affairs Manager, Jennifer Paulk
Director of Information Techno, Joshua Freeman
Financial Controller, Patrick Opembe
Director Finance, John Phiri
Manager, Leanne Deshong
Program Manager, Felix Chibesa
Auditors: MARKS PANETH & SHRON LLP NEW

LOCATIONS

HQ: CATHOLIC MEDICAL MISSION BOARD INC
100 WALL ST FL 9, NEW YORK, NY 100055765
Phone: 212 242-7757
Web: WWW.CMMB.ORG

HISTORICAL FINANCIALS

Company Type: Private

Income Statement				FYE: September 30
	REVENUE ($ mil.)	NET INCOME ($ mil.)	NET PROFIT MARGIN	EMPLOYEES
09/18	740	105	14.2%	38
09/17	603	19	3.2%	—
09/16	371	(12)	—	—
09/15	290	(3)	—	—
Annual Growth	36.7%	—	—	—

2018 Year-End Financials

Return on assets: 48.2%   Cash ($ mil.): 5
Return on equity: 49.6%
Current ratio: —

CATHOLIC RELIEF SERVICES - UNITED STATES CONFERENCE OF CATHOLIC BISHOPS

EXECUTIVES

Ceo, Sean Callahan
Exec V Pres, Schuyler Thorup
Exec V Pres, Joan Rosenhauer
Exec V Pres, Annemarie Reilly
Exec V Pres-Dir, Mark Melia
Exec V Pres-Dir, Shawn Mood
Cfo-Dir, James Bond
Relationship Manager, Jeffrey Wallace
Regional Project Monitoring, Adam Keough
Assistant II, Andrea Hamilton
Manager, Cheryl Neff
Auditors: RSM US LLP GAITHERSBURG MARY

LOCATIONS

HQ: CATHOLIC RELIEF SERVICES - UNITED STATES
CONFERENCE OF CATHOLIC BISHOPS
228 W LEXINGTON ST, BALTIMORE, MD 212013443
Phone: 410 625-2220
Web: WWW.CRS.ORG

HISTORICAL FINANCIALS

Company Type: Private

Income Statement				FYE: September 30
	REVENUE ($ mil.)	NET INCOME ($ mil.)	NET PROFIT MARGIN	EMPLOYEES
09/18	989	(3)	—	7,100
09/17	978	20	2.1%	—
09/16	917	(47)	—	—
09/15	738	(11)	—	—
Annual Growth	10.2%	—	—	—

2018 Year-End Financials

Return on assets: (-0.6%)   Cash ($ mil.): 58
Return on equity: (-1.6%)
Current ratio: 1.30

CEB INC.

EXECUTIVES

Ceo, Thomas L Monahan III
Cfo*, Richard S Lindahl
Cao*, J Barron Anschutz
Information Specialist, Gary Banks
Executive Officer, Christoffer Ellehuus
Executive Officer, Teresa Green
Head, Corporate Strategy and D, Jesse Levin
Chief Administrative Officer, Melody L Jones
Staff, Kevin Hoyle
Director, Christopher Cook
Senior Manager, Ailsa Thomas
Auditors: ERNST & YOUNG LLP MCLEAN VIR

LOCATIONS

HQ: CEB INC.
1201 WILSON BLVD STE 1800, ARLINGTON, VA
222092316
Phone: 571 303-3000

HISTORICAL FINANCIALS

Company Type: Private

Income Statement				FYE: December 31
	REVENUE ($ mil.)	NET INCOME ($ mil.)	NET PROFIT MARGIN	EMPLOYEES
12/16	949	(34)	—	4,600
12/15	928	92	10.0%	—
12/14	908	51	5.6%	—
12/13	820	31	3.9%	—
Annual Growth	5.0%	—	—	—

2016 Year-End Financials

Return on assets: (-2.5%)   Cash ($ mil.): 134
Return on equity: —
Current ratio: 0.80

CEDARS-SINAI MEDICAL CENTER

Many a star has been born literally at Cedars-Sinai Medical Center. The 886-bed teaching and research hospital is located right where Los Angeles meets Beverly Hills and West Hollywood and has tended to the medical needs of a number of celebrities since its founding in 1902. However the center is also a major teaching hospital for UCLA's David Geffen School of Medicine and is engaged in hundreds of research programs in areas such as cancer neuroscience and genetics. It also includes two multi-specialty physician associations Cedars-Sinai Medical Group and Ceders-Sinai Health Associates and operates a number of community health centers and outreach programs (such as mobile health clinics).

Operations

The not-for-profit hospital's more than 2100 physicians represent just about every clinical specialty out there. Cedars-Sinai is consistently listed as a top-ranked hospital by U.S. News & World Report in such specialties as cancer cardiology endocrinology gastrointestinal disorders gynecology heart surgery kidney disease neurology orthopaedics and respiratory disorders.

Cedars-Sinai is the only private hospital with a Level 1 trauma center in Los Angeles County; as such the hospital sees about 1600 trauma patients a year. The hospital also provides a number of outpatient services.

Federal funding from the National Institutes of Health and other sources have provided the hospital with some $40 million towards research. Cedars-Sinai currently has some 1300 research projects.

The hospital sees some 660000 outpatient visits and 85000 emergency department visits each year.

Geographic Reach

Cedars-Sinai's hospital is located in Los Angeles; it has an administrative office in Beverly Hills California.

Financial Performance

Revenues from patient care and other sources totaled nearly $2.77 billion in fiscal 2015 while net income amounted to $472.9 million.

Strategy

To meet increasing patient demand and expand its capacity for research projects Cedars-Sinai added nearly 7000 sq. ft. of space to house the Cedars-Sinai Biobank and Translational Research Core Facility in 2015. The previous year it opened a new clinic dedicated to the evaluation of heart and vascular disease patients for participation in stem cell medical studies.

EXECUTIVES

Senior Vice President Human Resources And Organization Development, Jeanne Flores
Senior Vice President Legal Affairs, Peter Braveman
President And Ceo, Thomas M. (Tom) Priselac
Evp Finance And Cfo, Edward M. Prunchunas
Evp Hospital Operations And Coo Medical Center, Mark R. Gavens
Evp Academic Affairs And Dean Of The Faculty, Shlomo Melmed
Svp Medical Affairs And Chief Medical Officer, Michael L. Langberg
Evp System Development And Chief Strategy Officer, Richard B. Jacobs
Svp Enterprise Information Systems And Cio, Darren Dworkin
Evp Medical Network, John Jenrette
Pharmacy Manager, Melsen Kwong
Vice President Legal Affairs, James Laur
Vice President Strategic Planning And Business Development, Lori Weise
Vice President Of Marketing And Public Relations, Richard Elbaum
Medical Director Liver Transplant, Tram Tran
Medical Director Genrisk Adult Genetic, Ora Gordon
Senior Vice President Medical Network, Thomas D Gordon
Medical Director, Spencer Koerner
Senior Vice President Community Relations, Arthur Ochoa
Director Of Radiology, Lynne Roy
Medical Director, Jaime Moriguchi
Medical Director, Syed Naqvi
Vice President Of Medical Affairs, Neil Romanoff
Medical Director Enterprise Information Systems, Lisa Masson
Medical Director Care Management, Joe Kim
Vice President Service Line Operations, Bryan Croft
Medical Director Partial Hospitalization Program, David Callander
Senior Vice President System Development, Rick Jacobs
Mph Chc Vice President Corporate Integrity Program, Ginny Kim
Medical Director, Edward Wolin
Senior Vice President And Chief Nursing Executive, David R Marshall
Vp Clinical Operations Medical Network, Prasanna Mohanty
Medical Director Information Systems, Victor Brodsky
Vice President For Development, Ken Massey
Medical Director, Howard Moss
Senior Vice President Legal Affairs, Terri Wagner Cammarano
Chairman, Marc H. Rapaport
Vice Chair, Steven Romick

LOCATIONS

HQ: CEDARS-SINAI MEDICAL CENTER
8700 BEVERLY BLVD, WEST HOLLYWOOD, CA
900481804
Phone: 310 423-3277
Web: WWW.CEDARS-SINAI.ORG

PRODUCTS/OPERATIONS

Selected Centers and Services
Ambulatory Care Center
Cedars-Sinai Center for Chest Disease
Cedars-Sinai Center for Digestive Diseases
Cedars-Sinai Heart Institute
Cedars-Sinai Institute Spine Center
Cedars-Sinai Health Associates (affiliated independent physician association)
Cedars-Sinai Medical Group (multi-specialty physicians group)
Cedars-Sinai Orthopedic Center
Diagnostic imaging center
Emergency department and trauma center
Hospice services
Kidney and pancreas transplant center
Neuroscience services
Pediatric services
Psychiatry and mental health services
Samuel Oschin Comprehensive Cancer Institute
Surgical services
Organ and bone marrow transplantation
Radiation therapy
Radiology
Stroke program
Pain management services
Women's health services

COMPETITORS

Adventist Health System West
Brotman Medical Center
Childrens Hospital Los Angeles
City of Hope
Community Health Systems
Dignity Health
Eisenhower Medical Center
Glendale Adventist Medical Center
Glendale Memorial Hospital
Golden State Health Centers
Good Samaritan Hospital (IN)
HCA
Hollywood Presbyterian Medical Center
Newhall Memorial Hospital
Pasadena Hospital Association
Providence Health System Southern California
Scripps Health
Tenet Healthcare
UCSF Medical
White Memorial Medical Center

HISTORICAL FINANCIALS

Company Type: Private

Income Statement				FYE: June 30
	REVENUE ($ mil.)	NET INCOME ($ mil.)	NET PROFIT MARGIN	EMPLOYEES
06/18	3,470	418	12.0%	8,000
06/17	3,788	380	10.0%	—
06/16	2,910	301	10.4%	—
06/15	2,760	366	13.3%	—
Annual Growth	7.9%	4.5%	—	—

2018 Year-End Financials

Return on assets: 6.5%   Cash ($ mil.): 320
Return on equity: 9.5%
Current ratio: 4.70

CENTERPOINT ENERGY SERVICES RETAIL LLC

EXECUTIVES

Pres-Ceo, David McClanahan
Auditors: GRANT THORNTON LLP TULSA OKL

LOCATIONS

HQ: CENTERPOINT ENERGY SERVICES RETAIL LLC
1111 LA ST FL 20 FLR 20, HOUSTON, TX 77002
Phone: 800 752-8036

HISTORICAL FINANCIALS

Company Type: Private

Income Statement				FYE: December 31
	REVENUE ($ mil.)	NET INCOME ($ mil.)	NET PROFIT MARGIN	EMPLOYEES
12/14	695	8	1.2%	35
12/13	549	9	1.7%	—
Annual Growth	26.6%	(11.9%)	—	—

CENTIMARK CORPORATION

Shout it from the rooftops Centimark is one of the largest commercial and industrial roofing contractors in North America. The company provides roof installation inspection repair and emergency leak service. Centimark typically works on flat roofs using EPDM rubber thermoplastic bitumen metal and coatings. Top customers have included NASA and the US Army Corps of Engineers. Its QuestMark division offers commercial industrial and retail flooring do-it-yourself (DIY) products and floor maintenance and cleaning products. The company which has about 80 offices throughout North America.

Operations

The company offers roof and floor services roof replacement roof repairs floor repairs emergency services preventative maintenance programs energy efficient solutions safety options and accessories online project management and DIY floor products. Centimark also provides systems such as thermoplastic solutions sprayed polyurethane foams roof coatings modified bitumen and built-up roofing metal products and steep slope products. In addition it engages in the online retail of flooring products such as patch and repair and maintenance/floor care products and coatings.

QuestMark a division of Centimark offers materials for commercial retail and industrial floors. It specializes in DiamondQuest polished concrete flooring epoxy flooring floor repair materials floor maintenance and floor cleaning products.

Centimark's Asset Management service provides extensive roof surveys roof life expectancy models return-on-investment analysis for roof repairs and evaluations for roof repair or roof replacement.

Geographic Reach

Pittsburgh Pennsylvania-based Centimark also does business in Canada through subsidiary Centimark Ltd. which has offices in Calgary Edmonton Toronto and Vancouver.

Sales and Marketing

The company serves customers in different segments including retail industrial general contractors and education.

Financial Performance

Centimark's 2014 sales totaled $485 million.

Strategy

In response to customer demand for more energy-efficient options Centimark has been increasing its use of spray polyurethane foam (which adds insulation and a waterproof barrier to roofs). The company also installs electricity-producing photovoltaic solar panels onto roofs. Other green options available from Centimark include skylights and garden roofs.

The company also tries to stay ahead of the pack with technological innovations such as its MyCentimark service. The online resource allows property owners to view invoices work authorizations before-and-after photos and recommendations for future roof maintenance. In 2014 the company launched a tablet and smartphone app that allows customers to request service and find the nearest Centimark office based on their current location.

Company Background

Chairman and CEO Edward Dunlap founded Centimark as an industrial cleaning business in 1967. Centimark is owned by its employees.

EXECUTIVES

Vice President Applications, Joe Filtz
Vice President, Thor Dicesare
Chairman And Ceo, Edward B. Dunlap
President And Coo, Timothy M. Dunlap
Evp And Northern Group Director, Robert J. Rudzik
Evp And Western Group Director, Steven M. Ferencz
Evp National And Regional Sales, John T. Godwin
Evp And Cfo, John L. Heisey
Evp And Southern Group Director, Sherman L. Gaskins
Evp And Questmark Flooring Group Director, John P. Scanlon
Evp And Eastern Group Director, Mark A. Cooper
Vp And Canada Group Director Centimark Ltd, Robert T. Penney
Svp And Southern Group Director, Keith Battenfield
Evp Service, Kenneth W. Zmich
National Accounts Manager, Cindy Molnar
Vice President Of Human Resources, Landon Connolly
National Account Manager, Robert Marinkoski
Vice President Marketing, Patrick Dunlap
Vice President Benefits And Compensation, Laura Kickbusch
National Account Manager, Eric Gorman
National Account Manager, Ryan Alyea
Executive Vice President, John Rudzik
National Account Manager, Tony Alderson
Vice President National Accounts Questmark Flooring, Jim Gasper
Vice President Of Litigation Department, John Liekar
National Account Manager, Shaun Bynum
National Accounts Manager, Chuck Blair
National Account Manager, Kevin Russell
National Account Manager, Tony Crawford
National Account Manager, Brian Short
National Account Manager, John Luck
National Accounts Manager, Bob Roche
Vice President National Accounts, Thomas Vehrs
National Account Manager, Eric Ii
National Account Manager, Dean Morrison
Auditors: SCHNEIDER DOWNS & CO INC P

LOCATIONS

HQ: CENTIMARK CORPORATION
12 GRANDVIEW CIR, CANONSBURG, PA 153178533
Phone: 724 514-8700
Web: WWW.CENTIMARK.COM

PRODUCTS/OPERATIONS

Selected Operations

CentiMark (roofing)
CentiMark ltd. (Canada roofing)
QuestMark (flooring)

Selected Systems

Roof Systems
EPDM
Green Roofing
Metal Roofs
Modified Bitumen and Built-Up Roofs
Roof Coatings
SPF
Steep Slope
TPO & PVC
Floor Systems
Chemical Resistant Systems
Decorative Broadcast
Decorative Concrete
Electric Static Dissipative
Heavy Duty Resurfacer
High Build Coating
Polished Concrete
Thin Mil

COMPETITORS

Armstrong World Industries	Duro-Last Roofing
Cabral Roofing & Waterproofing	Garcia Roofing
	Holland Roofing
D. C. Taylor	Pickens Roofing
	Tecta America

HISTORICAL FINANCIALS

Company Type: Private

Income Statement				FYE: April 30
	REVENUE ($ mil.)	NET INCOME ($ mil.)	NET PROFIT MARGIN	EMPLOYEES
04/18	670	54	8.1%	3,500
04/17	625	51	8.2%	—
04/15	540	46	8.7%	—
04/14	508	42	8.3%	—
Annual Growth	7.2%	6.4%	—	—

2018 Year-End Financials

Return on assets: 12.4%   Cash ($ mil.): 161
Return on equity: 16.6%
Current ratio: 4.40

CENTRA HEALTH, INC.

Centra Health is a constellation of hospitals and medical practices targeting the health care needs of residents in central and southern Virginia. At the not-for-profit entity's core are two acute care facilities in Lynchburg: the 358-bed Lynchburg General which is the region's main emergency center and specializes in orthopedic pediatric and cardiac care; and Virginia Baptist a 161-bed facility focused on surgery women's health infant care mental health and rehabilitation. Centra also operates a nearby community hospital and an array of primary care physician practices home health agencies retirement centers and other physical and behavioral health businesses.

Operations

In addition to Lynchburg General and Virginia Baptist Centra's acute care facilities include Southside Community Hospital (Farmville). Southside Community Hospital serves as a central acute care and birthing facility for an eight-county region. Centra also operates the Bedford Memorial Hospital through a partnership with Carilion Health System; it plans to buy out Carilion's shares in the partnership.

Outside of its acute care operations Centra Health administers senior care services through The Summit assisted living and independent living facilities. The Summit offers senior residents private apartments medical care and personal assistance. Centra also operates a network of treatment centers for patients of all ages with behavioral and psychiatric disorders. The network includes facilities that specialize in treating children and adolescents with emotional and behavioral disorders.

Altogether the network handles more than 300000 patient visits each year including more than 90000 emergency room visits and more than 5000 cardiac procedures. Its hospitals have a medical staff of about 500 doctors who perform more than 6300 inpatient and 9300 outpatient surgeries annually. Centra also operates the Centra Medical Group which includes about 140 primary care and specialist physicians.

Geographic Reach
Centra Health serves Lynchburg and surrounding communities in central Virginia including Farmville (located in Prince Edward County) Bedford Danville/Gretna and Moneta/Smith Mountain Lake Virginia.

Strategy
Centra Health is expanding its breadth of services as well as its network of facilities. Recent additions include new behavioral health facilities and an expansion of Bedford Memorial's orthopedic center. In 2015 it announced plans to buy out Carilion Clinic's shares of Bedford Memorial Hospital and the Oakwood Health and Rehabilitation Center for $11 million.

Company Background
Centra Health was founded in 1987 through the merger of Lynchburg General and Virginia Baptist. Southside Community Hospital joined the network in 2006.

EXECUTIVES

Chairman Centra Foundation, George A. Hurt
President And Ceo, E. W. Tibbs
Vp And Ceo Centra Southside Community Hospital, William L. Bass
Medical Director, Peter Betz
Vice President Of Nursing Operations, Carolyn Jacques
Medical Director, James Cure
Chairman, Walker P. Sydnor
Vice Chairman, Amy G. Ray
Secretary, Kelly Overstreet

LOCATIONS

HQ: CENTRA HEALTH, INC.
1920 ATHERHOLT RD, LYNCHBURG, VA 245011120
Phone: 434 200-3204
Web: WWW.CENTRAHEALTH.COM

PRODUCTS/OPERATIONS

Selected Facilities
Bedford Memorial Hospital (Bedford Virginia; partnership with Carilion Health System)
Lynchburg General Hospital (Lynchburg Virginia)
Virginia Baptist Hospital (Lynchburg Virginia)
Southside Community Hospital (Farmville Virginia)
Physician Practices
Altavista Medical Center (Altavista Virginia)
Big Island Medical Center (North Big Island Virginia)
Brookneal Family Medical Center (Brookneal Virginia)
Gretna Medical Center (Gretna Virginia)
Lynchburg Family Medicine Center (Lynchburg Virginia)

Other Facilities
Bridges Treatment Center (Lynchburg Virginia)
Fairmont Crossing Health and Rehabilitation Center (Amherst Virginia)
Guggenheimer Health and Rehabilitation Center (Lynchburg Virginia)
Piedmont Psychiatric Center (Lynchburg Virginia)
Rivermont Schools (regional)
The Summit (regional)

COMPETITORS

Alleghany Regional Hospital	Martha Jefferson Hospital
Bon Secours Health	Mary Washington Healthcare
Carilion Clinic	Montgomery Regional Hospital
Clinch Valley Medical Center	Sentara Healthcare
Danville Regional Medical Center	University of Virginia Health System
Encompass Health	

HISTORICAL FINANCIALS
Company Type: Private

Income Statement				FYE: December 31
	REVENUE ($ mil.)	NET INCOME ($ mil.)	NET PROFIT MARGIN	EMPLOYEES
12/15	742	25	3.4%	6,000
12/14	553	63	11.5%	—
12/09	534	16	3.1%	—
12/08	419	33	7.9%	—
Annual Growth	8.5%	(3.9%)	—	—

2015 Year-End Financials
Return on assets: 2.6% Cash ($ mil.): 25
Return on equity: 4.5%
Current ratio: 0.50

CENTRAL CRUDE, INC.

EXECUTIVES

Ceo, Steve Jordan
Pres, George Jordan
V Pres, Joe Milazzo
Health Professional, Lisa Gustas
Vice-President Business Develo, Kevin Hickey
Auditors: MCELROY QUIRK & BURCH

LOCATIONS

HQ: CENTRAL CRUDE, INC.
4187 HIGHWAY 3059, LAKE CHARLES, LA 706153310
Phone: 337 436-1000
Web: WWW.CENTRALCRUDE.COM

HISTORICAL FINANCIALS
Company Type: Private

Income Statement				FYE: March 31
	REVENUE ($ mil.)	NET INCOME ($ mil.)	NET PROFIT MARGIN	EMPLOYEES
03/09	637	1	0.2%	50
03/08	635	0	0.1%	—
03/06	280	0	0.1%	—
Annual Growth	31.5%	56.2%	—	—

2009 Year-End Financials
Return on assets: 2.4% Cash ($ mil.): —
Return on equity: 40.0%
Current ratio: 1.00

CENTRAL ELECTRIC POWER COOPERATIVE, INC.

EXECUTIVES

Ceo, Ronald J Calcaterra
Sr V Pres*, Art Fusco
Sr V Pres*, Jim Lamb
Dir*, David Logeman
Cfo*, John Brantley
Prin*, John Tiencken
Program Manager, Scott Hammond
Information Technology Manager, Mike Kelly
Pricing Manager, Cole Price
Director of Power Supply Opera, Gerald Fleming
Engineer, Kale Ford

LOCATIONS

HQ: CENTRAL ELECTRIC POWER COOPERATIVE, INC.
20 COOPERATIVE WAY, COLUMBIA, SC 292103112
Phone: 803 779-4975
Web: WWW.CEPCI.ORG

HISTORICAL FINANCIALS
Company Type: Private

Income Statement				FYE: December 31
	REVENUE ($ mil.)	NET INCOME ($ mil.)	NET PROFIT MARGIN	EMPLOYEES
12/15	1,220	0	0.0%	44
12/14	1,254	0	0.0%	—
12/13	1,198	0	0.0%	—
12/09	1,037	1	0.2%	—
Annual Growth	2.8%	(33.9%)	—	—

2015 Year-End Financials
Return on assets: — Cash ($ mil.): 8
Return on equity: 0.4%
Current ratio: —

CENTRAL FLORIDA EXPRESSWAY AUTHORITY

EXECUTIVES

Exec V Pres, Joseph Berenis
Exec V Pres*, Laura Kelley
Cfo*, Lisa Lumbard
Manager of Public Affairs, Emily Brown
Procurement Coordinator, Diane McClary
Director of Engineering, Glenn Pressimone
Chief of Staff Public Affiars, Michelle Maikisch
Office Coordinator, Ruth Valentin
Manager of Engineering, Will Hawthorne
Manager of Traffic Operations, Bryan Homayouni
It Support Specialist, Emmanuel Rivers
Auditors: MOORE STEPHENS LOVELACE PA O

LOCATIONS

HQ: CENTRAL FLORIDA EXPRESSWAY AUTHORITY
4974 ORL TOWER RD, ORLANDO, FL 328071684
Phone: 407 690-5000
Web: WWW.CFXWAY.COM

HISTORICAL FINANCIALS
Company Type: Private

Income Statement				FYE: June 30
	REVENUE ($ mil.)	NET INCOME ($ mil.)	NET PROFIT MARGIN	EMPLOYEES
06/18	452	212	47.0%	50
06/17	433	235	54.3%	—
06/16	400	203	50.8%	—
06/09	208	74	35.6%	—
Annual Growth	9.0%	12.4%	—	—

2018 Year-End Financials
Return on assets: 4.0% Cash ($ mil.): 59
Return on equity: 9.6%
Current ratio: 0.90

CENTRAL GROCERS, INC.

In a city of big stores Central Grocers helps keep neighborhood markets stocked. Founded in 1917 the cooperative wholesale food distributor is owned by some 225 members. It supplies 40000 food items and general merchandise to more than 400 independent grocery stores serving several states such as Illinois Indiana Iowa Michigan and Wisconsin. Central Grocers distributes products under both national brands and its own Centrella brand which is marketed exclusively to its member stores. The co-op also operates about 30 stores under a handful of banner names including Strack & Van Til Town & Country Key Market and the low-cost Ultra Foods chain.In 2017 the company filed for Chapter 11 bankruptcy protection.

Bankruptcy
In May 2017 Central Grocers filed for Chapter 11 bankruptcy protection. The company intends to sell its Strack & Van Tilstores and its Joliet Ill. distribution warehouse as its seeks to exit its wholesale distribution business.

Operations
As part of its business Central Grocers caters to its customers with the help of a fleet of 100 refrigerated trucks 300 dry trailers and about 70 Freightliner tractors.

Sales and Marketing
Central Grocers services a wide variety of store formats and ethnic groups including Hispanic Italian and African Americans. Besides older and smaller 5000-sq.-ft. stores its clients include large-scale warehouse discount stores that measure 75000 sq. ft. and large conventional stores that average 70000 sq. ft.

Financial Performance
While privately-owned Central Grocers doesn't report financial results. The co-op rings up an estimated $2 billion in sales and it returns (in the form of dividends) to its members about $243 million.

Strategy
Central Grocers the 7th largest grocery cooperative in the US boasts the second-largest market share in the Chicago area. It specializes in serving Chicago independent supermarkets. Central Grocers supplies them with a comprehensive menu of groceries produce fresh meat service deli items frozen foods ice cream and items from its own Centrella brand.

Central Grocers expanded its distribution center by 15000-sq.-ft. to 940000-sq.-ft. of storage capacity in 2011. The reason for expansion was due to demand for produce and fresh meats.

LOCATIONS
HQ: CENTRAL GROCERS, INC.
2600 HAVEN AVE, JOLIET, IL 604338467
Phone: 815 553-8800
Web: WWW.CENTRAL-GROCERS.COM

PRODUCTS/OPERATIONS

Selected Products
Fresh meat
Frozen foods
Groceries
Ice cream
Produce
Service deli items

COMPETITORS

ALDI	Kroger
Albertsons	Meijer
Alex Lee	SUPERVALU
Associated Wholesale Grocers	Safeway
C&S Wholesale	Schnuck Markets
Certco	Wal-Mart
Dearborn Wholesale Grocers	Winkler

HISTORICAL FINANCIALS
Company Type: Private

Income Statement				FYE: July 28
	REVENUE ($ mil.)	NET INCOME ($ mil.)	NET PROFIT MARGIN	EMPLOYEES
07/07	1,197	(10)	—	2,300
07/06	1,108	5	0.5%	—
07/05	1,103	4	0.4%	—
07/04	1,047	3	0.3%	—
Annual Growth	4.5%	—	—	—

2007 Year-End Financials
Return on assets: (-3.8%) Cash ($ mil.): —
Return on equity: (-35.2%)
Current ratio: 1.00

CENTRAL HUDSON GAS & ELECTRIC CORPORATION

EXECUTIVES

Chb-ceo, Stephen Lant
Executive Vice President, James Laurito
Vice President Human Resources And Safety, Sharon A Mcginnis

LOCATIONS
HQ: CENTRAL HUDSON GAS & ELECTRIC CORPORATION
284 SOUTH AVE DEPT 100, POUGHKEEPSIE, NY 126014839
Phone: 845 452-2700
Web: WWW.CENHUD.COM

HISTORICAL FINANCIALS
Company Type: Private

Income Statement				FYE: December 31
	REVENUE ($ mil.)	NET INCOME ($ mil.)	NET PROFIT MARGIN	EMPLOYEES
12/17	671	55	8.2%	869
12/16	640	52	8.2%	—
/	0	0	—	—
Annual Growth	—	—	—	—

2017 Year-End Financials
Return on assets: 2.5% Cash ($ mil.): 14
Return on equity: 8.8%
Current ratio: 1.80

CENTRAL IOWA HOSPITAL CORP

EXECUTIVES

Ceo, Eric Crowell
Executive Director-Finance*, Kara Dunham
Chief of Urology, Markham J J Anderson
Regional Vice-President, Jean Shelton

LOCATIONS
HQ: CENTRAL IOWA HOSPITAL CORP
1200 PLEASANT ST, DES MOINES, IA 503091406
Phone: 515 241-6212
Web: WWW.UNITYPOINT.ORG

HISTORICAL FINANCIALS
Company Type: Private

Income Statement				FYE: December 31
	REVENUE ($ mil.)	NET INCOME ($ mil.)	NET PROFIT MARGIN	EMPLOYEES
12/17	832	3	0.4%	3,495
12/16	573	153	26.8%	—
12/15	548	152	27.9%	—
12/14	534	145	27.2%	—
Annual Growth	15.9%	(71.6%)	—	—

2017 Year-End Financials
Return on assets: 0.3% Cash ($ mil.): 2
Return on equity: 0.4%
Current ratio: 3.20

CENTRAL STEEL AND WIRE COMPANY

When it comes to metal service center Central Steel & Wire Company (CS&W) can shape up and ship out. CS&W distributes ferrous and nonferrous metals in a variety of shapes and forms including bars coils plates sheets structurals tubing and wire. Among the company's processing services are annealing blanking computer numerical control (CNC) laser cutting galvanizing and structural fabrication. CS&W distributes its products throughout North America from five facilities that are located primarily in the Midwestern US. The company has metallurgical engineers on its staff to support customers with metal specifications and interpretation expertise.

Operations

The company distributes processed and unprocessed ferrous and nonferrous metals which are are generally obtained from rolling mills in many forms and distributed from CS&W's warehouses.

Geographic Reach

CS&W is based in Chicago. It has stocking facilities in Cincinnati Detroit Milwaukee Greensboro (North Carolina). Its Central Coil Processing unit is in Portage Indiana.

Financial Performance

In 2013 CS&W's revenues decreased by 10% due to lower prices caused by excess mill capacity and a 4% drop in tons shipped caused by lower net sales.

The company's net income decreased by 79% that year primarily due to a decline in revenues.

CS&W's operating cash inflow increased to $11 million (compared to $10 million in 2012) due to cash generated from inventories and receivables.

Strategy

In 2013 the company launched a new web based material test reporting feature increasing its ability to service customers more efficiently through an additional channel when material certifications are required.

Company Background

In 2011 CS&W added pre-painted steel and aluminum coil to its full-line inventory of metal products. The pre-paint program includes material stocked and processed to customer specific specifications for next day delivery. The main intent of this expansion is to develop inventory management programs to reduce total costs and support short-dated delivery requirements.

CS&W was founded in 1909. The company is majority-owned by a trust set up by a former chairman the late James Lowenstein.

EXECUTIVES

Ceo, Stephen E Fuhrman
Cfo*, Kevin G Powers
Foreman, Beau Valentine
Senior Buyer, Bryan Thompson
Assistant Manager Order Proces, Cindy Lambros
Assistant Manager Quotation PR, Cindy Witowski
Engineer, Darius Nausedas
Inside Sales Representative, Denise Downing
Inside Sales Representative, Elie Youssef
Inside Sales, Frank Polakowski
Customer Rep, Hilda Villalobos

LOCATIONS

HQ: CENTRAL STEEL AND WIRE COMPANY
3000 W 51ST ST, CHICAGO, IL 606322198
Phone: 773 471-3800

PRODUCTS/OPERATIONS

Selected Products

Alloy bars
Aluminum
Bar and structural shapes
Brass and copper
CF bars/flat wire
Grating/Morton products
HR bars
Steel plates
Steel sheets/strapping
Stainless steel
Steel tubing/pipe
Wire/drill rod/tool steel

Selected Processing Capabilities

Angle Rings
Annealing
Annodizing
Band Saw Cutting
Beam Splitting
Blanking
Burning - Oxyfuel
Centerless Grinding
Circle Shearing
CNC Laser Cutting
CNC Plasma Cutting
CNC Punching
CNC Waterjet Cutting
Coil Blanking
Coil Cut To Length
Cold Sawing Bar
Cold Sawing Plate
Contour Sawing
Deep Hole Drilling
Drilling & Tapping
F&D Heads
Facing & Centering
Forming
Galvanizing
Grinding
Heat Treating
Honing
Lathe Cut Tube/Pipe
Machining
Mech Descale and Oil
Miter Cutting
Normalizing
Painting
Perforating
Pickling & Oiling
Plate and Struct Rolling
Plating
Polishing
Precision Plasma
Precision Sawing
Protex Covering
Sand/Shot Blasting
SCS Finishing
Seam Planishing
Seam Welding
Shearing
Slitting
Straightening
Stress Relieving
Struct Fabrication
Threading
Tube/Pipe Fabrication
Tumble Deburring
Ultrasonic Testing
Welding
Wire Brush Deburr

COMPETITORS

Alro	Precision Steel
Macsteel Service	Reliance Steel
Centers USA	Ryerson
Metals USA	Worthington Industries
Olympic Steel	

HISTORICAL FINANCIALS

Company Type: Private

Income Statement				FYE: December 31
	REVENUE ($ mil.)	NET INCOME ($ mil.)	NET PROFIT MARGIN	EMPLOYEES
12/14	698	(2)	—	1,075
12/13	678	2	0.3%	—
12/12	750	10	1.4%	—
Annual Growth	(3.6%)	—	—	—

2014 Year-End Financials

Return on assets: (-1.3%)   Cash ($ mil.): 28
Return on equity: (-1.8%)
Current ratio: 7.10

CENTURY HEALTH ALLIANCE JOINT VENTURE

EXECUTIVES

Director, Emily Avery
Credentials Coordinator, Mitzi Carter
Benefits Manager, Wanda Nichols
Physical Therapist, Albert White
Information Technology Special, Amanda Marsh
Mm Pur, David Kendrick
Assistant Don, Janet Tidwell
Anesthesiologist, Melinda Banks
Administrative Supervisor, Michelle Fagin
Chief Financial Officer, Nina Dusang
Vice President, Sease Peggy

LOCATIONS

HQ: CENTURY HEALTH ALLIANCE JOINT VENTURE
809 UNIVERSITY BLVD E, TUSCALOOSA, AL 354012029
Phone: 205 759-7111
Web: WWW.DCHSYSTEM.COM

HISTORICAL FINANCIALS

Company Type: Private

Income Statement				FYE: September 30
	REVENUE ($ mil.)	NET INCOME ($ mil.)	NET PROFIT MARGIN	EMPLOYEES
09/17	469	13	2.8%	1
09/16	475	25	5.3%	—
09/15	450	34	7.6%	—
09/14	420	15	3.7%	—
Annual Growth	3.7%	(5.3%)	—	—

2017 Year-End Financials

Return on assets: 2.0%   Cash ($ mil.): 245
Return on equity: 3.2%
Current ratio: 2.20

CERTCO, INC.

Certco has built a business serving about 200 independent grocers in Minnesota Wisconsin Iowa and Illinois. The food distribution cooperative offers customers an inventory of more than 57000 items including bakery goods frozen foods meat products produce and general merchandise. It distributes products under the Shurfine Shurfresh and Top Care labels. Additionally Certco offers its member-operators such services as advertising accounting client data services warehousing merchandising store planning and design and other business support services. The cooperative was founded in 1930 as Central Wisconsin Cooperative Food Stores.

Operations

To support its business Certco operates a nearly 1 million-sq.-ft. distribution center. Its brands include Shurfine Shurfresh Value Time Full Circle Topco and Top Care.

Geographic Reach

Based in Madison Wisconsin Certco operates in Minnesota and Wisconsin with an extended reach into parts of Iowa and Illinois.

Sales and Marketing

Many of Certco's clients are Fortune 500 companies. It distributes the national brands of major companies such as Kraft General Mills Procter & Gamble and Johnson & Johnson. The company also distributes specialty items under the names Amy's Hodgson Mills Bob's Red Mill and Annie's that are only available through direct-store-delivery suppliers.

Company Background

Certco was established in 1930 when five Madison-area retailers formed an alliance to boost their combined purchasing muscle.

EXECUTIVES

Treasurer Vice President, David Ryman
Auditors: SATTELL JOHNSON APPEL & CO

LOCATIONS

HQ: CERTCO, INC.
   5321 VERONA RD, FITCHBURG, WI 537116050
Phone: 608 271-4500
Web: WWW.CERTCOINC.COM

PRODUCTS/OPERATIONS

Selected Brands
Full Circle
Shurfine
Shurfresh
Top Care
Topco
Value Time

Selected Services
Advertising
Client data services
Retail accounting
Retail meetings/seminars
Retail support
Retail technology
Store planning & design
Trade shows
Value added services
Warehouses
Web architecture

COMPETITORS

Affiliated Foods Midwest	Dearborn Wholesale Grocers
Associated Wholesale Grocers	Kroger Roundy's
C&S Wholesale	Winkler
Central Grocers	

HISTORICAL FINANCIALS

Company Type: Private

Income Statement				FYE: April 26
	REVENUE ($ mil.)	NET INCOME ($ mil.)	NET PROFIT MARGIN	EMPLOYEES
04/14	640	5	0.9%	325
04/13	607	5	0.9%	—
04/12	569	5	0.9%	—
Annual Growth	6.0%	5.6%	—	—

2014 Year-End Financials
Return on assets: 5.0%   Cash ($ mil.): 11
Return on equity: 8.4%
Current ratio: 2.00

CFJ PROPERTIES LLC

EXECUTIVES

Chb, Crystal Call Maggelet
Exec Committee MBR*, Andre Lortz
Exec Committee MBR*, Richard D Peterson
Manager, Dale Rushton
Executive Committee MBR, Richard Peterson
Auditors: KPMG LLP SALT LAKE CITY UTAH

LOCATIONS

HQ: CFJ PROPERTIES LLC
   5508 LONAS DR, KNOXVILLE, TN 379093221
Phone: 801 624-1000
Web: WWW.PEPPERONIGRILLNC.COM

HISTORICAL FINANCIALS

Company Type: Private

Income Statement				FYE: January 31
	REVENUE ($ mil.)	NET INCOME ($ mil.)	NET PROFIT MARGIN	EMPLOYEES
01/09	7,672	157	2.1%	6,250
01/07	6,769	50	0.7%	—
01/06	6,166	48	0.8%	—
Annual Growth	7.6%	47.7%	—	—

2009 Year-End Financials
Return on assets: 18.7%   Cash ($ mil.): 37
Return on equity: 47.1%
Current ratio: 0.60

CHALMETTE REFINING, L.L.C.

EXECUTIVES

Ceo, Thomas J Nimbley
Manager, Eric Beam

LOCATIONS

HQ: CHALMETTE REFINING, L.L.C.
   500 W SAINT BERNARD HWY, CHALMETTE, LA 700434821
Phone: 504 281-1212
Web: WWW.CHALMETTEREFINING.COM

HISTORICAL FINANCIALS

Company Type: Private

Income Statement				FYE: December 31
	REVENUE ($ mil.)	NET INCOME ($ mil.)	NET PROFIT MARGIN	EMPLOYEES
12/07	5,647	364	6.4%	600
12/06	5,020	423	8.4%	—
12/05	3,462	264	7.6%	—
12/04	3,130	221	7.1%	—
Annual Growth	21.7%	18.1%	—	—

2007 Year-End Financials
Return on assets: —   Cash ($ mil.): 302
Return on equity: 6.4%
Current ratio: 0.50

CHAPMAN UNIVERSITY

Chapman UniversityÂ enrollsÂ 7000 students at campuses throughout CaliforniaÂ as well as in Washington State. From its main campus in Orange California the university offers traditionalÂ undergraduate graduate and professional programs at seven colleges and schools. It also confers bachelor and master's degrees and teaching credentials to non-traditional students at its two-dozen satellite campuses. The universityÂ offersÂ someÂ 50 undergraduate majorsÂ and 40 graduate programs. It has 650 faculty members and a student-to-teacher ratio of 15:1.Â Chapman University includes Brandman University a distance learning program for some 10000 working adultsÂ that operatesÂ two dozenÂ locations andÂ offers online courses.

Financial Performance

Chapman University reported a 9% increase in revenues to $304 millionÂ in 2011 due to higher income from tuition fees gifts grants and bequests. Net income also increased 27% to $70 million due to increased endowment returns offset slightly by increased general educational and auxiliary expenses.

Strategy

Chapman University is expanding programs to widen opportunities for students. In 2011 theÂ School of LawÂ launched a new business law program and in 2013 the Argyros School of Business and Economics opened a new financial center for real-time student investor trading and portfolio management training. Facilities expansions include the construction of a new center for the arts and a new health sciences campus; both projects were launched in 2012.

Company Background

Chapman University was founded in 1861 as Hesperian College; it was re-named Chapman College in 1934 in honor of philanthropist Charles C. Chapman.

EXECUTIVES

Vice President Of Finance, Ernest Wang
Vice President For Public Relations, Jesse Richards
Vp Finance, Hannah Brown
Vice President, Ryan Huffman
Vice President, Katie Walsh
Vice President President Elect Faculty Senate Jimmy Blalock, Gordon Babst
Vice President, Lauren Flynn
Pharmd Phd Assistant Professor, Dan Tomaszewski
Vice President Strategic Marketing And Communications, Jamie Ceman
Assistant Vice President For Research Office Of Research, Dawn Underwood
Vp And Chro, Brian K Powell
Auditors: KPMG LLP IRVINE CA

LOCATIONS

HQ: CHAPMAN UNIVERSITY
   1 UNIVERSITY DR, ORANGE, CA 928661005
Phone: 714 997-6815
Web: WWW.CHAPMAN.EDU

PRODUCTS/OPERATIONS

Selected Colleges and Schools
College of Educational Studies
College of Performing Arts
George L. Argyros School of Business and Economics
Lawrence and Kristina Dodge College of Film and Media Arts
Schmid College of Science and Technology
School of Law
Wilkinson College of Humanities and Social Sciences

Company Type: Private

Income Statement				FYE: May 31
	REVENUE ($ mil.)	NET INCOME ($ mil.)	NET PROFIT MARGIN	EMPLOYEES
05/18	483	90	18.8%	3,300
05/17	437	76	17.6%	—
05/16	424	31	7.4%	—
05/15	400	50	12.7%	—
Annual Growth	6.5%	21.4%	—	—

2018 Year-End Financials

Return on assets: 5.9% Cash ($ mil.): 88
Return on equity: 8.6%
Current ratio: 1.10

CHARLESTON AREA MEDICAL CENTER, INC.

CAMC Health System is a catalyst for care in Charleston. The health network includes flagship facility Charleston Area Medical Center (CAMC) which is the largest hospital in West Virginia and consists of three campuses with some 840 beds total. The system also includes the CAMC Health Education and Research Institute which coordinates education programs for medical students from West Virginia University. In addition the health system operates smaller rural hospital CAMC Teays Valley and several urgent care and family practice clinics. CAMC Health System operates an online medical information system and physician services company Integrated Health Care Providers.

Operations

The three campuses of CAMC include CAMC General Hospital CAMC Memorial Hospital and CAMC Women and Children's Hospital all of which are located in Charleston. Specialty services at the hospitals include cardiology kidney transplants trauma and pediatrics. The CAMC Institute conducts graduate and continuing education courses; it also connects education and health care through clinical research projects in areas such as cancer and cardiovascular clinical science studies. The Teays Valley Hospital is a 70-bed facility located in nearby Hurricane West Virginia.

CAMC General Hospital is home to the highest level Trauma Center nationally-accredited Medical Rehabilitation and Stroke Centers The Center for Joint Replacement Neurosciences Center one of two Facial Surgery Centers Charleston's only accredited Sleep Center and West Virginia's only kidney transplant program affiliated with the Cleveland Clinic.

CAMC Memorial Hospital hosts one of highest volume heart programs in the US which performs 8000 procedures in the cardiac catheterization labs and more than 1600 open-heart bypass surgeries a year.

CAMC Women and Children's Hospital facilitates the birth of more than 3000 babies (including many high-risk births) per year.

Teays Valley Hospital is a not-for-profit 70-bed hospital. More than 100 doctors are authorized to practice at the hospital.

CAMC serves as a clinical training site for 700 additional learners per year through educational affiliations with regional colleges and universities.

Sales and Marketing

Commercial insurance providers and other third parties accounted for more than half of CAMC's net patient revenue in 2013; Medicare and Medicaid account for 30% and 13% respectively.

Financial Performance

The company's revenue grew by 4% to $969 million in 2013 due to higher net patient revenues and investment income. Net income fell 8% to $86 million though as expenses including salaries and employee benefits rose. Cash flow from operations dropped 48% to $33 million both as a result of the lower net income and an increase in cash used in short-term trading investments.

Strategy

In 2013 CAMC teamed up with The Ohio State University University of Michigan and West Virginia University to raise awareness and educate the community about cervical cancer. Community Awareness Resources and Education (CARE) is one of OSU Cancer Center's programs sponsored by the National Cancer Institute that focuses on an important health disparity among an underserved Appalachian population.

The following year CAMC teamed with Alliance Oncology a division of Alliance HealthCare Services to work on establishing a department of radiation therapy at CAMC Cancer Center.

Upgrading its infrastructure in 2013 Teays Valley Hospital completed a $3.7 million ICU expansion project.

EXECUTIVES

Vice President, Jeff Goode
Director Of Radiology, John J Anton
Director Of Pharmacy Operations, Tracy Hall
Director Of Radiology, Michael E Anton
Interim Vice President For Medical Affairs, Joan Phillips
Director Of Radiology, Jeffrey C Dameron
Vice President Chief Medical Officer, Pinckney Mcilwain
Board Member, Gail Pitchford
Secretary And Receptionist, Diana Gallik
Auditors: DELOITTE TAX LLP CHICAGO IL

LOCATIONS

HQ: CHARLESTON AREA MEDICAL CENTER, INC.
501 MORRIS ST, CHARLESTON, WV 253011326
Phone: 304 348-5432
Web: WWW.CAMC.ORG

PRODUCTS/OPERATIONS

2013 Net Patient Revenue

	% of total
Commercial insurance & other third-party payment programs	51
Medicare	30
Medicaid	13
Self-pay	1
PEIA	5
Total	100

2013 Sales

	$ mil.	% of total
Net patient revenue less provision for bad debts	876	91
Investment income	49	5
Other revenue	41	4
Net assets released from restrictions	1	.
Total	968	100

Selected Service Areas

Behavioral health
Cancer
Cardiac
Children's medicine
Craniofacial surgery
Endoscopy
Fertility
Gynecology
Hemophilia
Kidney transplant
Orthopedics
Palliative care
Perinatal
Plastic surgery
Stroke
Trauma
Urology
Vascular

COMPETITORS

Charleston Hospital
Ohio Valley Medical Center
Princeton Community Hospital
St. Mary's Medical Center
WVUHS
Weirton Medical Center
West Virginia University Hospitals

Company Type: Private

Income Statement				FYE: December 31
	REVENUE ($ mil.)	NET INCOME ($ mil.)	NET PROFIT MARGIN	EMPLOYEES
12/16	1,044	(17)	—	4,000
12/15	932	36	4.0%	—
12/14	877	42	4.9%	—
12/13	861	54	6.3%	—
Annual Growth	6.6%	—	—	—

2016 Year-End Financials

Return on assets: (-1.8%) Cash ($ mil.): 106
Return on equity: (-4.7%)
Current ratio: 0.80

CHARTER MANUFACTURING COMPANY, INC.

Charter Manufacturing's magna carta calls for it to make steel products. The family-owned company manufactures such steel products as special bar quality (SBQ) bar rod wire and stainless steel rod. The company also supplies precision cold-rolled custom profiles and engineered components including driveline engine and transmission parts for the automotive industry. It operates primarily in the US but also in Europe and Asia through subsidiaries Charter Steel (general steel products) Charter Wire (precision cold-rolled custom profiles flat wire and standard shapes) Charter Dura-Bar (cast iron bar and bronze alloys) and Charter Automotive (engineered components for automotive applications).

Operations

The company manufactures special bar quality bar rod and wire as well as precision cold-rolled custom profiles flat wire and standard shapes and engineered components for use in engines transmissions and drivelines. Charter Steel is an integrated producer of special bar quality bar rod and wire products has an annual coil-making capacity of 1.2 million tons; Charter Dura-Bar is a leading producer of continuous cast iron bar stock and a distributor (through Dura-Bar Metal Services) of Dura-Bar products and bronze alloys; Charter Wire supplies precision cold-rolled custom profiles flat wire and standard shapes; while Charter Automotive supplies of engineered components for engine driveline and transmission applications.

Geographic Reach

Charter Manufacturing serves customers around the world and has plants in the US (Illinois North Carolina Ohio Pennsylvania and Wisconsin) China (one plant) and the UK (two plants).

Sales and Marketing

Charter Manufacturing sells its products through its operating subsidiaries and sales representatives.

Strategy

The company is looking to expand both geographically and in terms of product offerings. Growing its global footprint in 2012 the company expanded its European operations with the purchase of a 57000 sq.-ft. manufacturing plant in Burntwood UK. The expansion strengthens Charter Automotive's position as a global supplier to OEM automotive and powertrain industries and helps it meet the growing demands of customers in Europe and elsewhere.

Mergers and Acquisitions

In 2012 the company acquired Wells Manufacturing Company (owner of Dura-Bar and DuraBar Metal Services). The acquired assets (which added a fourth division to Charter Manufacturing's family of companies — Charter Dura-Bar) focus on producing specialty iron bar and distributing bronze alloy products.

Company Background

Facing tough market conditions Charter Automotive closed part of its steelmaking operations in Milwaukee Wisconsin in 2010. The company ceased making steel dipsticks and tubes for cars and trucks as part of a wider response to global market trends. The company which kept its engine components operations elsewhere in Milwaukee active sold the Heather Avenue plant idled by this move.

Charter Manufacturing was established in 1936 and is owned by the family of founder Alfred Mellowes.

EXECUTIVES

Senior Business Intelligence Developer, Jason Odrzywolski
Vice President Of Human Resources Safety And Environmental Charter Steel, Bill Fiorelli
Vice President Information Technology, Sarah Urban
Auditors: DELOITTE & TOUCHE LLP MILWAU

LOCATIONS

HQ: CHARTER MANUFACTURING COMPANY, INC.
1212 W GLEN OAKS LN, MEQUON, WI 530923357
Phone: 262 243-4700
Web: WWW.CHARTERMFG.COM

PRODUCTS/OPERATIONS

Selected Operating Units
Charter Automotive
Charter Dura-Bar
Charter Steel
Charter Wire

Selected Mergers and Acquisitions

COMPETITORS

AK Steel Holding Corporation
Federal-Mogul
Gerdau Ameristeel
Nucor
Republic Steel
Timken
United States Steel

HISTORICAL FINANCIALS

Company Type: Private

Income Statement   FYE: December 31

	REVENUE ($ mil.)	NET INCOME ($ mil.)	NET PROFIT MARGIN	EMPLOYEES
12/10	903	74	8.3%	2,000
12/09	517	2	0.4%	—
12/08	996	26	2.7%	—
Annual Growth	(4.8%)	66.8%	—	—

2010 Year-End Financials

Return on assets: 14.4%   Cash ($ mil.): 85
Return on equity: 24.7%
Current ratio: 1.60

CHEMIUM INTERNATIONAL CORP.

EXECUTIVES

Pres, Ofer Levy
V-Pres, Thomas Holzmann
Software Developer, Nicolas Folgado
Vice-President, Sanjeev Vora
Accounting Team Member, Jimena Ferrufino
Financial Analyst, Daniela Weir
Head of Crude, Ed More
Director of Global Business De, Jack Nicholas
Human Resources, Zoyla Hernandez
Independent Representative, Cesar Calvo
Senior Account Manager, Karen Pons

LOCATIONS

HQ: CHEMIUM INTERNATIONAL CORP.
3773 RICHMOND AVE STE 600, HOUSTON, TX 770463725
Phone: 713 622-7766
Web: WWW.CHEMIUMCORP.COM

HISTORICAL FINANCIALS

Company Type: Private

Income Statement   FYE: December 31

	REVENUE ($ mil.)	NET INCOME ($ mil.)	NET PROFIT MARGIN	EMPLOYEES
12/15	2,015	3	0.2%	24
12/06	450	3	0.9%	—
12/03	103	0	—	—
Annual Growth	28.1%	—	—	—

2015 Year-End Financials

Return on assets: 2.9%   Cash ($ mil.): 5
Return on equity: 0.2%
Current ratio: 0.80

CHENEGA CORPORATION

An Alaska Native Corporation Chenega Corporation has gone from landowner to business titan. Representing the Chenega people residing in the central Alaskan Prince William Sound region it operates mostly through its subsidiaries. Chenega Integrated Systems and Chenega Technology Services offer information technology security training manufacturing research and development network engineering and military operation support services. Chenega Corporation's clients have included the Department of Defense Department of Homeland Security and EPA.

Geographic Reach

The company's headquarters are located in Anchorage Alaska. Chenega Corporation and its subsidiaries operate in 45 states and 11 countries.

Strategy

Government contracts are a source of revenue growth. Chenega Corporation began to participate in the Government Services marketplace in 1997. By 2012 it was performing on more than 158 prime contracts and 100 principal sub-contracts through a combination of competitive and negotiated best-value awards.

EXECUTIVES

Director Of Government Relations, Kristina Woolston
Senior Vice President Of Finance Chief Financial Officer, Robb A Milne
Executive Vice President Chief Operating Officer, Jeff Hueners
Vice President And Director, Lloyd Kompkoff
Vice President, Ronald Lee
Vice President, Kathy Ward
Vice President, Marty Reyes
Senior Vice President, Ken Bishop
Board Member, Amy Steele Arm

LOCATIONS

HQ: CHENEGA CORPORATION
3000 C ST STE 301, ANCHORAGE, AK 995033975
Phone: 907 277-5706
Web: WWW.CHENEGA.COM

PRODUCTS/OPERATIONS

Selected Services
Base operations and maintenance
Environmental management
Information technology
Intel and military operations
Light manufacturing
Logistics support
Telecommunications
Tourism and hospitality
Training services
Security services

COMPETITORS

Akal Security
Arctic Slope Regional Corporation
Computer Sciences Corp.
HP Enterprise Services
Halliburton
IBM Global Services
Parsons Corporation
TKC Communications
chugach alaska

HISTORICAL FINANCIALS

Company Type: Private

Income Statement   FYE: September 30

	REVENUE ($ mil.)	NET INCOME ($ mil.)	NET PROFIT MARGIN	EMPLOYEES
09/18	829	19	2.3%	4,500
09/17	875	12	1.4%	—
09/16	926	14	1.5%	—
09/15	881	12	1.4%	—
Annual Growth	(2.0%)	15.0%	—	—

2018 Year-End Financials

Return on assets: 4.9%   Cash ($ mil.): 33
Return on equity: 9.7%
Current ratio: 2.70

CHEROKEE NATION BUSINESSES LLC

EXECUTIVES

MBR-Ceo, Shawn Slaton
Chb*, Bill John Baker
MBR*, Gary Cooper
MBR-Cfo*, Doug Evans
MBR-Board MBR*, Bob Berry
Snr Dir Fin*, Kimberly Barnette
Information Specialist, Aaron Lowther
Information Specialist, Cody Hardy
Information Specialist, Curtis Starling
Information Specialist, Daniel Basden
Regional Vice-President, David Mullen
Auditors: BKD LLP TULSA OKLAHOMA

LOCATIONS

HQ: CHEROKEE NATION BUSINESSES LLC
  777 W CHEROKEE ST, CATOOSA, OK 740153235
Phone: 918 384-7474
Web: WWW.CHEROKEENATIONBUSINESSES.COM

HISTORICAL FINANCIALS
Company Type: Private

Income Statement — FYE: September 30

	REVENUE ($ mil.)	NET INCOME ($ mil.)	NET PROFIT MARGIN	EMPLOYEES
09/18	1,098	65	5.9%	3,117
09/17	1,018	40	4.0%	—
09/16	1,021	50	4.9%	—
09/15	925	32	3.5%	—
Annual Growth	5.9%	26.7%	—	—

2018 Year-End Financials
Return on assets: 6.3%
Return on equity: 7.4%
Current ratio: 2.60
Cash ($ mil.): 271

CHERRY CREEK SCHOOL DISTRICT 5

EXECUTIVES

Superintendent, Harry Bull
Coordinator, Jon Pierce
Assistant, Jonathan Hoerl
Information Specialist, Paul Bates
Senior Buyer, Teresa Shermer
Digital Communications Manager, Adam Goldstein
Director of Information, Javier Trujillo
Teacher, Kristen Olander
Terminal Manager, Marcy Phelps
Technology Coordinator, Ned Gilardino
Director of Accounting, Bradley Arnold
Auditors: CLIFTONLARSONALLEN GREENWOOD

LOCATIONS

HQ: CHERRY CREEK SCHOOL DISTRICT 5
  4700 S YOSEMITE ST # 223, GREENWOOD VILLAGE, CO 801111307
Phone: 303 773-1184
Web: WWW.CHERRYCREEKSCHOOLS.ORG

HISTORICAL FINANCIALS
Company Type: Private

Income Statement — FYE: June 30

	REVENUE ($ mil.)	NET INCOME ($ mil.)	NET PROFIT MARGIN	EMPLOYEES
06/13	531	116	21.9%	5,707
06/12	510	(24)	—	—
06/10	520	25	4.8%	—
Annual Growth	0.7%	66.6%		

2013 Year-End Financials
Return on assets: 12.2%
Return on equity: 41.5%
Current ratio: 3.30
Cash ($ mil.): 108

CHEVRON PHILLIPS CHEMICAL COMPANY LP

EXECUTIVES

Ceo, Peter L Cella
Exec V Pres, Mark E Lashier
Sr V Pres, Ron Corn
Sr V Pres, Tim Hill
V Pres, Mitch Eichelberger
Coordinator, Aprile Turner
It Security, Mohit Chanana
Staff, Aaron Evitts
Human Resources Consultant, Susan Allen
Coordinator, Tom Shomette
Safety Manager, Carolyn Rogers
Auditors: ERNST & YOUNG LLP HOUSTON T

LOCATIONS

HQ: CHEVRON PHILLIPS CHEMICAL COMPANY LP
  10001 SIX PINES DR, THE WOODLANDS, TX 773801498
Phone: 832 813-4100
Web: WWW.CPCHEM.COM

HISTORICAL FINANCIALS
Company Type: Private

Income Statement — FYE: December 31

	REVENUE ($ mil.)	NET INCOME ($ mil.)	NET PROFIT MARGIN	EMPLOYEES
12/17	7,919	841	10.6%	5,000
12/16	7,106	1,301	18.3%	—
12/15	7,990	2,020	25.3%	—
12/14	11,758	2,444	20.8%	—
Annual Growth	(12.3%)	(29.9%)		

2017 Year-End Financials
Return on assets: 6.5%
Return on equity: 7.5%
Current ratio: 1.80
Cash ($ mil.): 519

CHG FOUNDATION

EXECUTIVES

Director, Sheila Martz
High Risk Case Manager Supervi, Mark David
Auditors: MOSS ADAMS LLP SAN FRANCISCO

LOCATIONS

HQ: CHG FOUNDATION
  740 BAY BLVD, CHULA VISTA, CA 919105254
Phone: 619 422-0422
Web: WWW.CHGSD.COM

HISTORICAL FINANCIALS
Company Type: Private

Income Statement — FYE: December 31

	REVENUE ($ mil.)	NET INCOME ($ mil.)	NET PROFIT MARGIN	EMPLOYEES
12/16	1,098	206	18.8%	1
12/14	622	34	5.5%	—
12/13	323	(11)	—	—
12/09	133	1	1.0%	—
Annual Growth	35.1%	106.8%	—	—

2016 Year-End Financials
Return on assets: 28.0%
Return on equity: 53.6%
Current ratio: —
Cash ($ mil.): 659

CHICAGO TRANSIT AUTHORITY

The CTA is focused on making its ETA. The Chicago Transit Authority operates the second-largest public transportation system in the US behind the New York City Transit Authority. On a typical weekday CTA passengers take about 1.7 million rides on the agency's buses and trains which travel in and around Chicago and about 35 suburbs. The CTA operates a fleet of 1865 buses on almost 130 routes. Its rail system includes eight rail lines with some 1356 rail cars operating on 224 miles of track at more than 145 stations. The agency created by the Illinois legislature in 1947 is part of the state's Regional Transportation Authority which also oversees Metra (commuter rail system) and Pace (suburban bus system).

Financial Performance
The agency generates the majority of its revenue from fare and passes; the remainder comes from a reduced fare subsidy from the state of Illinois advertising and concessions investment income parking fees the sale of real estate and the sale of CTA merchandise.

The company's net revenue increased the last three years (2012-2014). In fiscal 2014 revenues jumped by 1% primarily due to increases in farebox revenue. CTA's net income has fluctuated the last three years; however it decreased by 81% in 2014 mainly due to a surge in provision for depreciation and labor and fringe benefits.

Strategy
CTA has raised prices several times to keep up with the cost of doing business.

EXECUTIVES

Cfo And Treasurer, Karen Walker, $180,000 total compensation
Inspector General, Paul Sidrys, $160,000 total compensation
Coo, Peter Ousley
President, Forrest Claypool
Chairman, Terry Peterson
Auditors: CROWE LLP CHICAGO ILLINOIS

LOCATIONS

HQ: CHICAGO TRANSIT AUTHORITY
567 W LAKE ST STE CTA, CHICAGO, IL 606611465
Phone: 312 664-7200
Web: WWW.TRANSITCHICAGO.COM

PRODUCTS/OPERATIONS

2014 Sales

	$ mil.	% of total
Farebox	364	57
Pass	219	35
Advertising & Concessions	27	4
Other Revenue	22	4
Total	**633**	**100**

HISTORICAL FINANCIALS

Company Type: Private

Income Statement				FYE: December 31
	REVENUE ($ mil.)	NET INCOME ($ mil.)	NET PROFIT MARGIN	EMPLOYEES
12/16	625	(79)	—	12,000
12/10	548	(323)	—	—
12/05	448	(153)	—	—
12/04	397	(9)	—	—
Annual Growth	**3.8%**	—	—	—

2016 Year-End Financials

Return on assets: (-1.2%)   Cash ($ mil.): 79
Return on equity: —
Current ratio: 1.10

CHILDREN'S HOSPITAL

EXECUTIVES

Pres, Kurt Newman
Director, Carole Helmandollar
Facilities Director, Robert Beckwith
Admissions Manager, Jennifer Cameron
Director, Jyoti Jaiswal
Executive Director of Performa, Lisbeth Fahey
Director of Diagnostic, Laurie Hogan
Auditors: GRANT THORNTON LLP MC LEAN V

LOCATIONS

HQ: CHILDREN'S HOSPITAL
111 MICHIGAN AVE NW, WASHINGTON, DC
200102916
Phone: 202 232-0521
Web: WWW.CHILDRENSNATIONAL.ORG

HISTORICAL FINANCIALS

Company Type: Private

Income Statement				FYE: June 30
	REVENUE ($ mil.)	NET INCOME ($ mil.)	NET PROFIT MARGIN	EMPLOYEES
06/15	1,076	118	11.0%	6,000
06/14	983	43	4.4%	—
Annual Growth	**9.4%**	**174.2%**	—	—

2015 Year-End Financials

Return on assets: 11.2%   Cash ($ mil.): 114
Return on equity: 20.9%
Current ratio: 0.60

CHILDREN'S HOSPITAL COLORADO

Rocky Mountain rugrats can count on Children's Hospital Colorado. The not-for-profit organization runs a network of health facilities in Colorado anchored by its nearly 50-acre main campus in Aurora. The campus includes a 260-bed inpatient hospital and numerous outpatient clinics. Children's Hospital Colorado also operates more than a dozen satellite locations in and around Denver that specialize in providing children with emergency and specialty care. Affiliated with the University of Colorado Denver School of Medicine the hospital provides medical training and performs a wide range of research into pediatric illnesses including cancer and HIV/AIDS.

Operations

The main hospital is located on the Anschutz Medical Campus with the medical school and the University of Colorado Hospital Authority's 620-bed acute care center. With help from its medical staff of 2330 Children's Hospital Colorado had 18500 inpatient admissions; 21000 surgeries 527000 outpatient visits and about 158000 emergency department visits in 2014.

The hospital boasts two additional emergency locations at Exempla Saint Joseph Hospital in Denver and Centura's Parker Adventist Hospital in Parker. Children's Hospital Colorado provides urgent care through three nearby community locations: Centura Littleton Adventist Hospital Children's Hospital North Campus at Broomfield and Exempla Lutheran Medical Center in Wheat Ridge. In addition it has about 10 specialty care clinics in the Denver area that provide cancer pulmonary and surgery services.

The health care facility's research initiatives are conducted at the Children's Hospital Colorado Research Institute. Along with its affiliation with the university the Children's Hospital works with the Pediatric Clinical Translational Research Center to conduct research and clinical trials in a number of fields including cardiology gastroenterology oncology orthopedics pulmonology and psychiatry.

Geographic Reach

Children's Hospital Colorado established in 1908 serves a seven-state region through its Level 1 trauma center. Its other facilities cater to residents of the Denver metropolitan area.

Sales and Marketing

Medicaid accounted for 47% of the hospital's net patient revenue in 2014; managed care accounted for 45%.

Financial Performance

Gross patient services revenue totaled $2.2 billion in 2014; other operating revenue totaled $60.7 million.

Strategy

Children's Hospital Colorado boasts the capacity to handle the most challenging emergencies as the only dedicated Level 1 trauma center in a seven-state region. Through its affiliation with the University of Colorado the hospital conducts physician assistant residency fellowship and internship programs in a variety of fields including anesthesiology orthopedics dentistry and neurology. It also provides continuing education programs for doctors and nurses.

The health care facility is expanding its footprint in the Colorado Springs area as the region experiences noteworthy growth. To this end it is building a new $110 million hospital on the University of Colorado Health Memorial North campus that will house 100 inpatient beds an emergency room neonatal and pediatric intensive care units and operating rooms. The complex is expected to open in 2018.

EXECUTIVES

President And Ceo Children's Hospital Colorado Foundation, Steve Winesett
President Ceo And Director, James E. Shmerling, age 65
Svp Patient Care Services And Chief Nursing Officer, Kelly M. Johnson
Surgeon-in-chief, Timothy M. Crombleholme
Pediatrician-in-chief, Stephen Daniels
Chief Medical Officer, Joan Bothner
President And Ceo, Jena Hausmann
Svp And Cio, Mary Anne Leach
Svp And Cfo, Jeff Harrington
Chief Research Officer, Frederick J. Suchy
Medical Director Pediatric Sports Medicine, Aaron Provance
Clinical Director, Sheila Kaseman
Nursing Director, Norine Hemphill
Ambulatory Operations Manager For Occupational And Physical Therapy, Felicia Latsko
Medical Director, Lalit Bajaj
Finance Vice President, Jeffrey Harrington
Medical Director, George Wang
Vice President Of Support Services, Dan Coxall
Senior Vice President, Cary Larger
Senior Vice President And Chief Information Officer, Dana Moore
Medical Director Of Clinical Chemistry And Point Of Care Testing Transfusion Medicine Physician, Melkon DomBourian
Chairman, Kevin Reidy

LOCATIONS

HQ: CHILDREN'S HOSPITAL COLORADO
13123 E 16TH AVE, AURORA, CO 800457106
Phone: 720 777-1234
Web: WWW.CHILDRENSCOLORADO.ORG

Selected Locations

Children's Hospital Colorado Main Campus
Children's Hospital Colorado at Saint Joseph Hospital
Children's Hospital Colorado KidStreet
Children's Hospital Colorado Orthopedic Care Centennial
Children's Hospital Colorado Outpatient Specialty Care Centennial
Children's Hospital Colorado Outpatient Specialty Care Colorado Springs
Children's Hospital Colorado Outpatient Specialty Care Parker
Children's Hospital Colorado Therapy Care Parker
Children's Hospital Colorado Therapy Care Pueblo
Children's Hospital Colorado Urgent and Outpatient Specialty Care Wheat Ridge

PRODUCTS/OPERATIONS

Selected Departments

Adolescent Medicine Program
Adult Congenital Heart Disease Program
Aerodigestive Program
Allergy Program
Arrhythmia Center
Asthma Program
Audiology Speech and Learning Program
Bill Daniels Center for Children's Hearing
Bone Marrow Transplant Program
Breathing Institute
Burn program
Cardiac Anesthesia
Cardiac Catheterization
Cardiology Clinic
Cardiology Outreach Programs
Cardiomyopathy Program
Center for Cancer and Blood Disorders
Center for Celiac Disease
Child Abuse Services
Child Development Unit
Child Health Clinic
Colorado Fetal Care Center
Colorado Institute for Maternal and Fetal Health

Colorectal and Complex Pelvic Floor Disorders Program
Complex Congenital Heart Disease and Development Clinic
Craniofacial Center
Critical Care
Cystic Fibrosis Research and Care Center
Dental
Dermatology
Digestive Health Institute
Ear Nose and Throat
Eating Disorder Program
Emergency Department
Endocrinology
Endoscopy Clinic (ATECh)
Experimental Therapeutics Program
Extracorporeal Membrane Oxygenation (ECMO) Program
Eye
Fetal Cardiology Program
Fiberoptic Endoscopic Evaluation of Swallowing (FEES) Clinic
Flight for Life
Gastroenterology
Gastrointestinal Eosinophilic Diseases
Genetics Program
Gynecology
Healthy Expectations Perinatal Mental Health Program
Heart Institute
Heart Surgery
Heart Transplant Program
HOPE Clinic for Cancer Survivors
Hospitalist Services

COMPETITORS

Banner Health
Catholic Health Initiatives
Centura Health
Denver Health and Hospital Authority
Exempla Healthcare
HealthONE
North Colorado Medical Center
Presbyterian/St. Luke's Medical Center
Rose Medical Center
Shriners Hospitals For Children
The Memorial Hospital

HISTORICAL FINANCIALS

Company Type: Private

Income Statement   FYE: December 31

	REVENUE ($ mil.)	NET INCOME ($ mil.)	NET PROFIT MARGIN	EMPLOYEES
12/17	960	76	8.0%	2,200
12/16	911	50	5.5%	—
12/15	908	25	2.8%	—
12/14	879	58	6.6%	—
Annual Growth	3.0%	9.8%	—	—

2017 Year-End Financials

Return on assets: 5.0%   Cash ($ mil.): 70
Return on equity: 12.4%
Current ratio: 1.70

CHILDREN'S HOSPITAL MEDICAL CENTER

Cincinnati Children's Hospital Medical Center has a special place in its heart for kids. The pediatric health care facility offers specialty treatments for children and adolescents suffering from just about any malady including ailments of the heart and liver as well as blood diseases and cancer. Cincinnati Children's Hospital has some 600 beds and operates about a dozen outpatient care centers. Founded in 1883 the not-for-profit hospital runs the only level I pediatric trauma center in the region and serves as a teaching and research facility for the University of Cincinnati College of Medicine. It is also ranked in the top 10 for all 10 pediatric specialties by U.S. News & World Report

Operations

With a staff of some 1500 physicians Cincinnati Children's Hospital serves more than 1 million patients each year including about 100000 emergency room visits and 32000 surgical procedures. Its outpatient centers include community urgent and emergency care facilities and general and specialty physician practices as well as laboratory radiology dentistry and physical therapy clinics. The Cincinnati Children's Research Foundation conducts research and clinical trials of pediatric medical innovations including new vaccines and surgical techniques. It has research partnerships with hospitals in Africa Asia Latin America and the Middle East. The hospital and research foundation's contributions to pediatric medicine include the rotavirus vaccine and Albert Sabin's discovery of the oral polio vaccine (first tested in 1960).

The hospital's educational programs are also renowned.

Geographic Reach

Reaching beyond Cincinnati Cincinnati Children's Hospital also provides services to communities in southeastern Indiana and northern Kentucky through its network of outpatient clinics. The hospital serves patients from all 50 US states as well as from about 60 international countries. It has international research collaborations with institutions in Bangladesh Brazil China Honduras Israel Malawi Mexico Nepal and the United Arab Emirates.

Financial Performance

In 2014 revenue grew 10% to $2.1 billion as the center saw rises in revenue from net patient services capitation professional services and other operations. Net income rose 13% to $172 million due to the higher revenue.

Strategy

Cincinnati Children's Hospital regularly expands its facilities to improve medical services and enhance research and education programs. In 2015 it opened a new 15-story clinical research building at its main campus in Avondale. In 2014 it opened a new urgent care center at its Liberty Campus.

In addition the institution forms collaborations to expand its operations. In 2015 it signed a three-year partnership with Shire to research rare diseases. The partners will work to discover and develop novel therapies to treat these diseases.

The hospital has remained on the forefront of the digital revolution that has swept the health care industry. In recent years the organization has linked its emergency inpatient radiology pharmacy and specialty department patient data together to create an electronic medical record (EHR). The EHR system helps to reduce patient errors (such as medication errors) and improves communication between departments.

To prepare for health reform measures Cincinnati Children's Hospital is also reducing costs through workflow purchasing and care delivery improvement programs.

EXECUTIVES

Vice President Family Relations, David Anderson
President And Ceo, Michael Fisher, age 60
Evp And Coo, Scott J. Hamlin
Svp Information Services And Cio, Marianne F. James
Cfo, Mark D. Mumford, age 57
Chief Medical Officer, Margaret Hostetter
Medical Director, Paul Edward Steele
Vice President Facilities Management, Thomas Kinman

Medical Director, Douglas Rose
Assistant Vice President, Carolyn Karageorges
Clinical Director, Victoria Decastro
Svp Strategy And Growth, Jennifer Dauer
Clinical Director, Natalie Elsbrock
Assistant Vice President, Melissa Saladonis
Assistant Vice President, Stephanie Ebken
Assistant Vice President Patient Service, Deborah Browning
Clinical Director, Anna Sheets
Pharmacy Manager, John Hingl
Vice President Clinical Affairs, Jana Bazzoli
Medical Director Cv Surgeon, Angela Lorts
Assistant Vice President, Jackie Hausfeld
Clinical Director, Thomas Cahill
Vice President Business Development, Jim Barter
Clinical Director, Dolores Puthoff
Assistant Vice President, Charlie Baverman
Assistant Vice President, Maria Britto
Clinical Director, Michael Sorter
Medical Director, Alessandro De alarcon
Clinical Director, Lois Curtwright
Clinical Director, Barbara Valerius
Assistant Vice President Business Intelligence, Mike Naber
Senior Vice President Human Resources, Chris Browning
Clinical Director, Travee Sanderson
Senior Business Intelligence Developer, Brad Blackmore
Medical Director Of Transfusion Services, Stephanie Kinney
Chair, Thomas G. Cody, age 77
Board Member, Karen Salchli
Assistant Treasurer, Alex Miller

LOCATIONS

HQ: CHILDREN'S HOSPITAL MEDICAL CENTER
3333 BURNET AVE, CINCINNATI, OH 452293039
Phone: 513 636-4200
Web: WWW.CINCINNATICHILDRENS.ORG

PRODUCTS/OPERATIONS

Selected Locations

Anderson

Batesville
Burnet Campus
                                          Children's
College Hill Campus
Drake
Eastgate
Fairfield
Harrison
Hopple Street Center
Kenwood
Liberty Campus
Lindner Center of Hope (Mason)
Mason Campus
Northern Kentucky
Oak Campus

Selected Treatment Areas
Abdomen and Digestive Tract
Allergy Asthma Immunology
Anesthesia
Arthritis and Rheumatology
Babies / Infants
Bones Joints and Muscles
Brain Spinal Cord and Nerves
Cancer
Cerebral Palsy
Chest and Lungs
Craniofacial Anomalies
Dental and Oral Health
Developmental Disabilities
Ear Nose Throat
Endocrine Metabolism and Diabetes
Eyes
Genetics
Growth and Development
Heart
Hemangiomas and Vascular Malformations
Hematology and Blood

Infectious Diseases
Injuries and Poisonings
Kidney Bladder and Genitals
Liver
Medications
Mental Health
Nutrition and Diet
Pain Management
Rehabilitation
Safety and Injury Prevention
Skin
Speech
Sports Medicine
Surgery
Teen Health
X-Ray / Radiology

COMPETITORS

Bethesda North	Shriners Hospitals For
Children's Hospital of	Children
Philadelphia	St. Elizabeth
Deaconess Associations	Healthcare
Kettering Health	St. Jude Children's
Network	Research Hospital
Nationwide Children's	The Christ Hospital
Hospital	Corporation
Nemours Foundation	TriHealth
Premier Health	UC Health
Partners	

HISTORICAL FINANCIALS

Company Type: Private

Income Statement				FYE: June 30
	REVENUE ($ mil.)	NET INCOME ($ mil.)	NET PROFIT MARGIN	EMPLOYEES
06/16	1,597	213	13.4%	18,000
06/15	1,527	209	13.7%	—
06/14	2,116	140	6.6%	—
06/11	1,693	53	3.2%	—
Annual Growth	(1.2%)	32.0%	—	—

2016 Year-End Financials

Return on assets: 8.3%   Cash ($ mil.): 148
Return on equity: 20.6%
Current ratio: 1.70

CHILDREN'S HOSPITAL OF ORANGE COUNTY

EXECUTIVES

Ceo-Pres, Kimberly Cripe
Chb*, L Kenneth Heuler DDS
Pediatric Hematology Oncology, David K Buchbinder
Vice-President Engineering, Sally Gallagher
Patient Safety Officer, Cathy Mc Donnell
Nurse Practitioner, Jill D Stites
Manager, Dorit Ben Ezer
Senior Vice President and Acco, Susan Feidner
Pediatrician, Alexandra Roche
Neonatologist, Anthony Liu
Pediatrician, Asha Dutt
Auditors: KPMG LLP LOS ANGELES CA

LOCATIONS

HQ: CHILDREN'S HOSPITAL OF ORANGE COUNTY
1201 W LA VETA AVE, ORANGE, CA 928684203
Phone: 714 997-3000
Web: WWW.CHOC.ORG

HISTORICAL FINANCIALS

Company Type: Private

Income Statement				FYE: June 30
	REVENUE ($ mil.)	NET INCOME ($ mil.)	NET PROFIT MARGIN	EMPLOYEES
06/16	523	10	2.0%	3,200
06/15	518	20	3.9%	—
06/14	517	(15)	—	—
06/13	548	29	5.3%	—
Annual Growth	(1.6%)	(28.7%)	—	—

2016 Year-End Financials

Return on assets: 1.1%   Cash ($ mil.): 93
Return on equity: 2.2%
Current ratio: 3.40

CHILDREN'S HOSPITAL OF WISCONSIN, INC

EXECUTIVES

Pres-Coo, Cindy Christensen
Treas*, Timothy L Birkenstock
V Pres-CIO*, Michael Jones
Corp V Pres of Hr*, Marge Nienen
Consultant, Lisa Makowski
Manager, Debbie Merkt
Health Professional, Marianne Burton
Manager, Barbara Salisbury
Administrative Secretary, Blanche McQuitty
General Counsel, Cynthia Christiansen
Database Administrator, INA Zinger

LOCATIONS

HQ: CHILDREN'S HOSPITAL OF WISCONSIN, INC
999 N 92ND ST STOP 1, MILWAUKEE, WI 532264876
Phone: 414 266-2000
Web: WWW.CHW.ORG

HISTORICAL FINANCIALS

Company Type: Private

Income Statement				FYE: December 31
	REVENUE ($ mil.)	NET INCOME ($ mil.)	NET PROFIT MARGIN	EMPLOYEES
12/13	600	57	9.6%	2,045
12/12	34	(0)	—	—
12/09	588	74	12.7%	—
Annual Growth	0.5%	(6.2%)	—	—

2013 Year-End Financials

Return on assets: 4.1%   Cash ($ mil.): 86
Return on equity: 5.8%
Current ratio: 3.20

CHILDREN'S MEDICAL CENTER OF DALLAS

Children's Medical Center of Dallas (operating as Children's Health) treats children with various medical needs from birth to age 18. Specialties include craniofacial deformities cystic fibrosis gas-troenterology cancer and heart disease. Children's is also a major pediatric center for heart kidney bone marrow and other transplant procedures. The not-for-profit hospital has about 600 beds and is the pediatric teaching facility for UT Southwestern Medical. Children's also operates a network of about 20 primary care and specialty clinics in and around Dallas in addition to its two full-service campuses.

Operations

The Children's system serves patients through two full-service hospitals a specialty care center in Southlake and a network of primary care offices called MyChildren's located throughout the Metroplex. As the primary pediatric teaching facility for UT Southwestern Children's supports a three-year residency program for physicians and academic fellowships in numerous subspecialties.

Children's Health's Dallas campus operates the city's only pediatric emergency room and the region's only pediatric-centered teaching hospital. It was also the first Level I trauma center for pediatrics in the state. Together the Dallas and Plano hospital campuses serve some 800000 patients annually and provide more than 50 sub-specialty programs. Additionally the organization provides primary health care services to the county's children living in under-served areas; some of these care services are provided through academic programs for doctors in training.

The system's research and development areas includes cancer cardiothoracic neonatology kidney disease infectious disease pharmacology sickle cell disease and psychiatry. It also provides Level IV Neonatal Intensive Care Unit.

In 2014 Children's logged some 173000 patient visits in its emergency departments in Dallas and Plano.

Geographic Reach

Children's main hospital campuses are in Dallas and Plano Texas. It has a handful of specialty centers and 16 primary care locations in the Dallas suburbs and area communities including Southlake.

Financial Performance

Children's receives revenues from a mix of third-party payers including HMOs and PPOs as well as Medicaid and Medicare and the state Children's Health Insurance Program (CHIP). It also relies heavily on private donations and fundraising efforts but provides a hefty amount of charity care each year for the region's uninsured children.

Strategy

Children's introduced its Children's Health brand in 2014. The new identity serves to reflect its operations as an integrated health system beyond the two primary campus locations.

At any given time it seems that Children's is building or opening one facility or another. In 2015 it opened the nation's second Pitt Hopkins Syndrome clinic treating a rare genetic condition that can cause development delays intellectual disabilities breathing issues and seizures.

Mergers and Acquisitions

In 2015 the system bought Our Children's House which provides rehabilitative and transitional care to children with special needs from Baylor Scott & White. Children's took over operations of Our Children's House's inpatient and outpatient facilities as well as eight outpatient clinics.

Company Background

In the four-year period between 2001 and 2005 the center spent more than $250 million on new construction and expansion projects. It opened a 72-bed Children's Legacy Hospital in nearby Plano in 2008 and in 2009 Children's completed construction of a new $150 million tower on its main Dallas campus to house its heart center cancer center and neonatal intensive care unit.

The company was founded in 1913.

EXECUTIVES

Evp And Chief Administrative Officer Corporate Services, Michele Chulick
Chief Clinical Officer And Evp, W. Robert (Bob) Morrow
Evp Population Health And Business Development, Peter W. Roberts
President Childrenâ's Medical Center Dallas Foundation And Evp Childrenâ's Health System Texas, Kern Wildenthal
President And Ceo, Christopher J. Share
President And Coo, Douglas G. Share

LOCATIONS

HQ: CHILDREN'S MEDICAL CENTER OF DALLAS
1935 MEDICAL DISTRICT DR, DALLAS, TX
752357701
Phone: 214 456-7000
Web: WWW.CHILDRENS.COM

Children's Medical Center Selected Locations
Chase Bank Building Specialty Center (Dallas)
Children's Medical Center and Ambulatory Care Pavilion at Legacy (Plano)
Children's Medical Center of Dallas Main Campus
Dallas Ambulatory Care Pavilion
Irving Specialty Center
Mesquite Specialty Center
MyChildren's Primary Care (about 16 locations)
Pediatric Urology Clinic at Rockwall
Southlake Specialty Care Center
Walnut Hill Urology Clinic

PRODUCTS/OPERATIONS

Children's Medical Center Selected Services

Allergy/Immunology/Asthma

Audiology
Cystic fibrosis
Day surgery
Dentistry
Dermatology
Diabetes
Ear/Nose/Throat
Endocrinology
Gastroenterology
General surgery
Genetics/Metabolism
International adoption medicine
Laboratory services
Neurology
Nutrition
Obesity program
Occupational therapy
Ophthalmology
Orthodontics
Orthopaedics
Physical therapy
Plastic Surgery
Pulmonary function lab
Pulmonology
Radiology
Rheumatology
Sickle cell treatment
Sleep disorders
Speech therapy
Trauma
Urology

COMPETITORS

Baylor University Medical Center	HCA
Cook Children's Health Care System	Parkland Health & Hospital System
Dell Children's Medical Center	Tenet Healthcare
	Texas Children's Hospital

HISTORICAL FINANCIALS
Company Type: Private

Income Statement
FYE: December 31

	REVENUE ($ mil.)	NET INCOME ($ mil.)	NET PROFIT MARGIN	EMPLOYEES
12/15	712	(185)	—	5,318
12/14	1,120	135	12.1%	—
12/13	1,111	166	15.0%	—
12/08	744	(4)	—	—
Annual Growth	(0.6%)	—	—	—

2015 Year-End Financials
Return on assets: (-7.7%)
Return on equity: (-6.6%)
Current ratio: 4.70
Cash ($ mil.): 9

CHILDREN'S NATIONAL MEDICAL CENTER

Along with the National Archives and the National Mall Children's National Medical Center is a US capital city gem. Its flagship Children's Hospital which was founded in 1870 is an acute care facility with some 310 beds. It serves as a regional referral center for pediatric trauma cancer and other kinds of complex pediatric cases. Additionally it operates eight outpatient centers in DC and the Delmarva peninsula that provide specialized medical services (such as chemotherapy and outpatient surgery) and community health clinics that offer primary care to children and adolescents. Children's National Health Network links more than 900 community-based pediatricians with the specialists and services of the center.

Operations
Children's National treats more than 300000 patients from around the world each year. It performs more than 17000 surgeries and provides more than 460000 outpatient visits annually. The company serves as the regional referral center for pediatric emergency trauma cancer cardiac critical care neonatology orthopedic surgery sports medicine neurology and neurosurgery. Every year it hosts 150 subspecialty fellows in 30 fellowship programs more than 100 pediatric residents 750 rotating residents and 300 medical students.

In the realm of research Children's National has more than 475 projects investigating diseases including brain and spinal cord injuries obesity and type 2 diabetes renal disease and autism. More than half of its funding for research comes from federal agencies including 40% from the National Institutes of Health.

Geographic Reach
Children's National operates in 30 locations in the District of Columbia and in Virginia Maryland Delaware and West Virginia.

Financial Performance
Revenue totaled $1 billion in 2014.

Strategy
The system continues to expand to provide improved access to health care in the region. Pediatric Specialists of Virginia is a private practice launched in 2013 to provide quality specialty care to families in northern Virginia. It was established by Children's National and INOVA Health Systems and operates eight locations throughout the region. Its specialties include endocrinology gasteroenterology/hepatology/nutrition genetics hematology and oncology infectious disease neurology nephrology orthopedics and rheumatology.

In 2015 the company opened the new Youth Pride Clinic within the Adolescent Health Center at the Sheikh Zayed Campus for Advanced Pediatric Medicine.

EXECUTIVES

Evp; Physician In Chief And Chief Academic Officer Director Childrenâ's Research Institute, Mark Batshaw
Evp; Chief Medical Officer Ambulatory And Community Health Services, Denice Cora-Bramble
Svp Center For Heart Lung And Kidney Disease; Co-director Children's National Heart Institute; Acting Svp Center For Cancer And Blood Disorders, Gerard R. Martin
President And Ceo, Kurt D. Newman
Svp Center For Neuroscience And Behavioral Health, Roger J. Packer
Evp And Chief Legal Officer, Raymond S. Sczudlo
Evp And Cfo, Douglas T. Myers
Evp; Chief Development Officer Children's Hospital Foundation, Pam King Sams
Evp And Chief People Officer, Darryl Varnado
Svp Child Health Advocacy Institute; Professor And Vice Chair Department Of Pediatrics, Joseph Wright
Evp; Chief Medical Officer Hospital And Specialty Services, David Wessel
Chief Research Officer Childrenâ's Research Institute, Mendel Tuchman
Vp Nursing; Chief Nursing Officer, Linda Talley
Evp; Coo Patient Care Services, Kathleen E. Chavanu Gorman
Evp And Chief Strategy Officer, Elizabeth Flury
Vp And Cio; Chief Medical Information Officer Bear Institute, Brian Jacobs
Vice Chairman Medical Education, Mary Ottolini
Svp Joseph E. Robert Jr. Center For Surgical Care; Chief Of Pediatric Surgery, Anthony Sandler
Executive Vice President Of Patient Care Services And Chief Operating Officer, Kathleen Chavanu Gorman
Medical Director, Lamia Soghier
Radiology Director, Laurie Hogan
Vice President Of Nursing, Debbie Freiburg
Medical Director, Karen Fratantoni
Senior Vice President, Kathleen Coppedge
Medical Director Anatomic Pathology, Christopher Rossi
Vice President, Mark Weissman
Director Of Nursing, Colleen Whitmore
Vice President Operations, Christine Heath
Medical Director, Deborah Hirtz
Medical Director, Tanya Hinds
Vice President, William Quirk
Vice President Human Resources, Nina Deshazo
Medical Director, James A Mutcherson
Associate Vice President Principal Gifts And Leadership Giving, Dennis Mcclellan
Vice President Global Services, H Whitehead
Vp Bear Institute, Matt Macvey
Board Member, Richard Jonas

LOCATIONS

HQ: CHILDREN'S NATIONAL MEDICAL CENTER
111 MICHIGAN AVE NW, WASHINGTON, DC
200102916
Phone: 202 476-5000
Web: WWW.CHILDRENSNATIONAL.ORG

PRODUCTS/OPERATIONS

Selected Departments and Programs
Back/spine surgery
Bone marrow transplant
Cancer
Cardiac surgery

Fetal medicine
Genetics and metabolism
Imaging/radiology
Neurosurgery
Obesity
Pediatric anesthesiology
Pediatric cardiology
Pediatric surgery
Weight loss surgery

COMPETITORS

Adventist HealthCare	Georgetown University
Ascension Health	Hospital
Children's Healthcare	HSC Pediatric Center
of Atlanta	IU Health
Children's Hospital	Inova
Boston	Johns Hopkins Medicine
Children's Hospital of	Kennedy Krieger
Philadelphia	Institute
Children's Hospital of	MedStar Health
Pittsburgh	Seattle Children's
Children's Hospital of	Hospital
Richmond	Shriners Hospitals For
Children's Hospital of	Children
The King's Daughters	St. Jude Children's
Children's Medical	Research Hospital
Center of Dallas	Washington Hospital
Cincinnati Children's	Center
Hospital	
Dell Children's	
Medical Center	

HISTORICAL FINANCIALS

Company Type: Private

Income Statement   FYE: June 30

	REVENUE ($ mil.)	NET INCOME ($ mil.)	NET PROFIT MARGIN	EMPLOYEES
06/09	516	16	3.2%	6,000
06/07	694	76	11.0%	—
06/06	573	85	15.0%	—
Annual Growth	(3.5%)	(42.4%)	—	—

2009 Year-End Financials

Return on assets: 1.6%   Cash ($ mil.): 65
Return on equity: 3.8%
Current ratio: 1.30

CHILDRENS HOSPITAL

EXECUTIVES

Prin, Kurt Newman
Doctor, Ashley D Hill
Dentist, Edwin Zechman DDS
Manager, David Thibodeau
Director of Mis/Is, Gary Manion
Quality Assurance Manager, Lorna Riach
Auditors: GRANT THORNTON LLP MC LEAN V

LOCATIONS

HQ: CHILDRENS HOSPITAL
 1917 C ST NE, WASHINGTON, DC 200026753
Phone: 202 476-5000
Web: WWW.CHILDRENSNATIONAL.ORG

HISTORICAL FINANCIALS

Company Type: Private

Income Statement   FYE: June 30

	REVENUE ($ mil.)	NET INCOME ($ mil.)	NET PROFIT MARGIN	EMPLOYEES
06/13	970	24	2.5%	41
06/10	806	66	8.2%	—
Annual Growth	6.4%	(28.3%)	—	—

2013 Year-End Financials

Return on assets: 2.5%   Cash ($ mil.): 59
Return on equity: 6.0%
Current ratio: 0.50

CHILDRENS HOSPITAL MEDICAL CENTER OF AKRON

Akron Children's Hospital is the largest pediatric health care system in northeast Ohio. The health system operates through more than 80 locations scattered around the state including its flagship 253-bed hospital in Akron. Among Children's specialized services are cardiology orthopedics rehabilitation and home care. It also has a second 50-bed inpatient hospital called the Akron Children's Beeghly Campus. The main hospital's emergency department treats nearly 70000 patients each year. Its regional burn center sees about 3700 visits per year. Akron Children's Hospital started as a nursery more than 100 years ago.

Operations
Each year Akron Children's Hospital sees some 800000 outpatients performs more than 15000 surgeries and admits more than 10000 inpatients.

Geographic Reach
Akron Children's Hospital is a major teaching facility affiliated with Northeastern Ohio Medical University and offering nearly a dozen subspecialty fellowship training programs. Children's also runs one of the state's largest pediatric primary care networks with 15 offices in seven counties including Cuyahoga Medina Wayne Tuscawaras and Portage.

Sales and Marketing
In 2014 Medicaid payments accounted for 52% of gross patient service revenue while commercial payments accounted for 44%.

Financial Performance
The hospital's net revenue was about $701000 in fiscal 2014 with about 90% of that coming from patient services revenues.

Strategy
The system has expanded its campuses and opened new facilities to broaden its care offerings. In 2014 it opened its first location in Columbiana County opened a pediatric specialty care office in Mansfield and expanded its sports rehabilitation hours and services at LifeCenter Plus in Hudson.

EXECUTIVES

President And Ceo, William H. (Bill) Considine
Vp Medical Services; Clinical Leader Ohio Children's Hospitals Solutions For Patient Safety, Michael Bird
Vp Managed Care, Karen Richter
Vp Operations And Coo, Grace Wakulchik
Evp, Shawn Lyden

Vp Akron Children's Hospital Foundation, John Zoilo
Noah Miller Chair Department Of Pediatrics, Norman C. Christopher
Vp Akron Children's Mahoning Valley, Sharon Hrina
Cfo, Michael Trainer
Vp Patient Services And Chief Nursing Officer, Lisa Aurilio
Cio, Tom Ogg
Vp Department Of Pediatrics, Cindy Dormo
Chief Medical Information Officer, Amy Maneker
Vp Surgical Subspecialty Practices, Craig McGhee
Chief Medical Officer, Robert McGregor
Director Of Health Information Management, Cindy Donelan
Vice President Marketing, Carolyn Davis
Medical Director, Ilka Warshawsky
Physical Therapy Director, Mary Marino
Medical Director Of The Locust Pediatric Care Group, Cooper White
Director Of Pharmacy, Todd Grisez
Nursing Director, Diane Sprankle
Vice President Administration, Sharin Hrina
Vice President Of Public Policy And Government Affairs, Rhonda Perkins
Medical Director, Julia Papouras
Secretary, Alice Smiley
Secretary For Clincal Administration, Sue Good
Department Secretary, Carolyn Carr
Auditors: ERNST & YOUNG LLP CLEVELAND

LOCATIONS

HQ: CHILDRENS HOSPITAL MEDICAL CENTER OF AKRON
 1 PERKINS SQ, AKRON, OH 443081063
Phone: 330 543-1000
Web: WWW.AKRONCHILDRENS.ORG

COMPETITORS

Akron General Medical	OhioHealth
Center	Parma Community
Aultman Health	General Hospital
Foundation	Robinson Memorial
Lake Health	Hospital
Mercy Medical Center	Summa Health System
(NY)	The Cleveland Clinic
MetroHealth System	University Hospitals
Nationwide Children's	Health System
Hospital	

HISTORICAL FINANCIALS

Company Type: Private

Income Statement   FYE: December 31

	REVENUE ($ mil.)	NET INCOME ($ mil.)	NET PROFIT MARGIN	EMPLOYEES
12/15	747	47	6.3%	4,763
12/14	701	93	13.3%	—
12/13	623	80	13.0%	—
12/12	579	46	8.1%	—
Annual Growth	8.8%	0.3%	—	—

2015 Year-End Financials

Return on assets: 3.9%   Cash ($ mil.): 52
Return on equity: 6.9%
Current ratio: 1.80

CHRISTIANA CARE HEALTH SERVICES, INC.

EXECUTIVES

Pres-Ceo, Robert Laskowski
Sr V Pres*, Sharon Anderson
Sr V Pres*, Rosa M Colon-Kolacko
Sr V Pres*, Thomas L Corrigan
Sr V Pres*, Alan S Greenglass
V Pres-Fin*, Richard Ellis
Exec V Pres*, Gary Ferguson
SEC-Treas*, Howard Cohen
Pres*, Janice Nevins
Director Manager Information T, Rich Butler
Nurse Practitioner II, Susan Stewart

LOCATIONS

HQ: CHRISTIANA CARE HEALTH SERVICES, INC.
4755 OGLETOWN STANTON RD, NEWARK, DE
197182200
Phone: 302 733-1000
Web: WWW.CHRISTIANACARE.ORG

HISTORICAL FINANCIALS

Company Type: Private

Income Statement   FYE: June 30

	REVENUE ($ mil.)	NET INCOME ($ mil.)	NET PROFIT MARGIN	EMPLOYEES
06/09	1,097	(55)	—	8,800
06/07	1,102	122	11.1%	—
06/05	0	0	—	—
06/04	847	33	4.0%	—
Annual Growth	5.3%	—	—	—

2009 Year-End Financials

Return on assets: (-3.6%)   Cash ($ mil.): 237
Return on equity: (-6.3%)
Current ratio: 1.70

CHRISTUS HEALTH INTERNATIONAL

In CHRISTUS there is no east or west but plenty of care nonetheless. The not-for-profit Catholic health care system operates about 350 medical facilities from its more than 60 hospitals including general hospitals and long-term acute care facilities to clinics and outpatient centers. It operates mostly in Louisiana and Texas where its hospitals are but also has facilities in Arkansas Georgia Iowa Missouri and New Mexico and in six states in Mexico and one in Chile. In addition to its acute care facilities CHRISTUS runs medical groups home health and hospice agencies and senior living facilities. Specialized services include oncology pediatrics rehabilitation and women's and children's health care.

Operations

In addition to its more than 30 hospitals CHRISTUS also operates about 20 long-term care facilities 175 clinics and outpatient centers and dozens of other "health ministries" including mobile clinics fitness centers and daycare centers for adults and children.

Geographic Reach

CHRISTUS has a dozen hospitals in Texas and Louisiana one in Puebla Mexico and one in Santi-

ago Chile. Its clinics outpatient centers long-term care facilities (under the Dubois and Advanced Care names) are found in Texas Louisiana Iowa Georgia Missouri and New Mexico in the US and in the Mexican states of Chihuahua Coahuila Nuevo Le n Puebla San Luis Potos and Tamaulipas.

Financial Performance

In 2013 CHRISTUS reported a 3% increase in revenue from $3.6 billion to $3.7 billion based on increased net patient and premium revenues. Net income was $261 million against net loss in 2012 due to an increase in investment returns.

Strategy

CHRISTUS has been expanding its Continuing Care division which includes non-acute care operations like home care hospice palliative care residential facilities and fitness centers.

Another goal of CHRISTUS Health is to reduce overcrowding and such misuses as patients being seen for routine illnesses in its emergency rooms. To that end and to make primary care a bit more accessible the company has opened immediate care clinics in a number of Texas Wal-Mart stores. CHRISTUS Health has plans to expand the clinics into Wal-Marts in Louisiana.

CHRISTUS Health has taken other steps to try to offset some costs of indigent care including pushing for the establishment of hospital districts to pay for charity care costs in some of its markets. It has also sold some of it facilities.

The organization has been focused on growing its operations in Mexico where it operates about a dozen clinics in six states. CHRISTUS Health's Mexico operations are a majority-owned partnership with Monterrey-based Muguerza. The organization's main Monterrey facility became the first Mexican hospital to win accreditation from the Joint Commission International a unit of the organization that certifies US hospitals.

Because Mexican citizens overwhelmingly rely on public hospitals run by the national health care system CHRISTUS Muguerza markets itself as a "medical tourism" destination where Americans can go for cheaper and lower-hassle medical care. Services include acute and primary care dental care urgent care and post-surgical rehabilitation.

Company Background

CHRISTUS Health was formed through the 1999 merger of Incarnate Word Health System and Sisters of Charity Health System. Both systems have their roots in the religious order Sisters of Charity of the Incarnate Word founded when three French nuns arrived in Texas in 1866 to care for the poor and sick.

EXECUTIVES

Evp And Chief Clinical Officer, John A. Gillean
President And Ceo, Ernie W. Sadau
Evp And Chief Administrative Officer, Linda McClung
Svp And Cio, George S. Conklin
Evp And Coo, Jeffrey M. (Jeff) Puckett
Evp And Cfo, Randolph W. Safady
Evp And Chief Strategy And Health Network Officer, Paul Generale
Evp Corporate Services And Chief Human Resources Officer, Marty Margetts
President And Ceo Good Shepherd Hospital Longview, Todd Hancock
Vp, Inez White
Chairman, Arthur M. Southam
Vice Chair, Maricela S. Moore
Auditors: ERNST & YOUNG LLP DALLAS TX

LOCATIONS

HQ: CHRISTUS HEALTH INTERNATIONAL
919 HIDDEN RDG, IRVING, TX 750383813
Phone: 469 282-2000
Web: WWW.CHRISTUSHEALTH.ORG

PRODUCTS/OPERATIONS

2015 Payor Mix

	% of total
Managed care organizations	47
Medicare	22
Self-pay	14
Medicaid	9
Commercial insurance	8
Total	**100**

2015 Revenues

	$ mil.	% of total
Patient services	3,233	90
Premium revenue	161	4
Other revenue	188	5
Equity in income of unconsolidated organizations	25	1
Total	**3,609**	**100**

Selected Facilities in Texas

CHRISTUS HomeCare - Corpus Christi
CHRISTUS HomeCare - Texarkana
CHRISTUS Hospital - St. Elizabeth
CHRISTUS Hospital - St. Mary
CHRISTUS Jasper Memorial Hospital
CHRISTUS Santa Rosa Alamo Heights Imaging Center
CHRISTUS Santa Rosa Ambulatory Surgery Center
CHRISTUS Santa Rosa Cancer Center
CHRISTUS Santa Rosa Children's Hospital
CHRISTUS Santa Rosa Hospital - City Centre
CHRISTUS Santa Rosa Hospital - Medical Center
CHRISTUS Santa Rosa Hospital - New Braunfels
CHRISTUS Santa Rosa Hospital - Westover Hills
CHRISTUS Santa Rosa Imaging Center
CHRISTUS Santa Rosa Outpatient Rehabilitation Center
CHRISTUS Santa Rosa Rehabilitation Hospital
CHRISTUS Santa Rosa Rehabilitation Services - Downtown
CHRISTUS Santa Rosa Rehabilitation Services - Medical Center
CHRISTUS Santa Rosa Wound Care and Hyperbaric Center - Downtown
CHRISTUS Santa Rosa Wound Care and Hyperbaric Center - Medical Center
CHRISTUS Spohn Family Center Northside
CHRISTUS Spohn Family Health Center
CHRISTUS Spohn Family Health Center Falfurrias
CHRISTUS Spohn Family Health Center Padre Island
CHRISTUS Spohn Family Health Center Robstown
CHRISTUS Spohn Family Health Center San Diego
CHRISTUS Spohn Family Health Center Westside
CHRISTUS Spohn Health System
CHRISTUS Spohn Hospital Alice
CHRISTUS Spohn Hospital Beeville
CHRISTUS Spohn Hospital Corpus Christi - Memorial
CHRISTUS Spohn Hospital Corpus Christi - Shoreline
CHRISTUS Spohn Hospital Corpus Christi - South
CHRISTUS Spohn Hospital Kleberg
CHRISTUS Spohn Medical Group - Obstetrics and Gynecology Associates
CHRISTUS St. Catherine Hospital
CHRISTUS St. John Hospital
CHRISTUS St. Michael Health System
CHRISTUS St. Michael Rehabilitation Hospital
CHRISTUS Transplant Institute
CHRISTUS Visiting Nurse Association - Houston
CHRISTUS Visiting Nurse Association - Nassau Bay
CHRISTUS Visiting Nurse Association - San Antonio
David Christopher Goldsbury Center for Children and Families
Dubuis Hospital of Beaumont
Dubuis Hospital of Bryan Texas
Dubuis Hospital of Corpus Christi
Dubuis Hospital of Houston Texas (long-term acute care)
Dubuis Hospital of Paris
Dubuis Hospital of Port Arthur Texas (long-term acute care)
Dubuis Hospital of Texarkana

Selected Other US Facilities

Advance Care Hospital of Fort Smith (Arkansas)
Advance Care Hospital of Hot Springs (Arkansas)
CHRISTUS Coushatta Health Care Center (Coushatta Louisiana)
CHRISTUS HomeCare - Jennings (Louisiana)
CHRISTUS HomeCare - Lake Charles (Louisiana)
CHRISTUS HomeCare - Shreveport (Louisiana)

CHRISTUS Hospice and Palliative Care - Alexandria
(Louisiana)
CHRISTUS Schumpert Health System (Shreveport
Louisiana)
CHRISTUS Schumpert Highland (Shreveport Louisiana)
CHRISTUS Schumpert St. Mary Place (Shreveport
Louisiana)
CHRISTUS St. Frances Cabrini Hospital (Alexandria
Louisiana)
CHRISTUS St. Patrick Hospital (Lake Charles Louisiana)
CHRISTUS St. Vincent (Santa Fe New Mexico)
Dubuis Hospital of Alexandria (Louisiana)
Dubuis Hospital of Lake Charles (Louisiana)
Dubuis Hospital of Shreveport (Louisiana)
Dubuis Hospital of St. Louis (Chesterfield Missouri)
Natchitoches Parish Hospital (Louisiana)
Southern Crescent Hospital for Specialty Care (Riverdale
Georgia)

Selected Facilities in Mexico

CHRISTUS MUGUERZA Hospital Alta Especialidad
(Monterrey Nuevo Leon)
CHRISTUS MUGUERZA Hospital Conchita (Monterrey
Nuevo Leon)
CHRISTUS MUGUERZA Hospital Del Parque
(Chihuahua)
CHRISTUS MUGUERZA Hospital Reynosa
(Tamaulipas¸ C.P.)
CHRISTUS MUGUERZA Hospital Saltillo (Coahuila)
CHRISTUS MUGUERZA Hospital Sur (Monterrey Nuevo
Leon)
CHRISTUS MUGUERZA Hospital UPAEP (Puebla)

COMPETITORS

Ascension Health	Mercy Health
Catholic Health	Methodist Hospital
Initiatives	System
Community Health	St. Luke's Episcopal
Systems	Hospital
HCA	Tenet Healthcare
Intermountain Health	Texas Children's
Care	Hospital
LifePoint Health	Universal Health
MD Anderson Cancer	Services
Center	University of Utah
Memorial Health	Hospitals & Clinics
Services	
Memorial Hermann	
Healthcare	

HISTORICAL FINANCIALS
Company Type: Private

Income Statement				FYE: June 30
	REVENUE ($ mil.)	NET INCOME ($ mil.)	NET PROFIT MARGIN	EMPLOYEES
06/16	4,212	149	3.6%	25,000
06/15	658	(44)	—	—
06/14	673	25	3.8%	—
06/13	646	124	19.3%	—
Annual Growth	86.7%	6.3%	—	—

2016 Year-End Financials
Return on assets: 2.9%
Return on equity: 5.1%
Current ratio: 2.50
Cash ($ mil.): 483

CHRISTUS SANTA ROSA HEALTH CARE CORPORATION

EXECUTIVES

Pres, Don Beeler

Pres, Patrick B Carrier
Dir, Melissa Krause
Coo, Renato Baciarelli
Cfo, Kenneth Kolb
Coordinator, Carl Zepeda
Coordinator, Amy Lopez
Chief of Emergency Room, Greg Roth
Chief of Medicine, Hugo Castaneda
Executive of Information Techn, Ron Love
Health Care Director, Natasha Marable
Auditors: ERNST & YOUNG US LLP INDIANAP

LOCATIONS

HQ: CHRISTUS SANTA ROSA HEALTH CARE
CORPORATION
333 N SANTA ROSA ST, SAN ANTONIO, TX 782073108
Phone: 210 704-2011
Web: WWW.CHRISTUSHEALTH.ORG

HISTORICAL FINANCIALS
Company Type: Private

Income Statement				FYE: June 30
	REVENUE ($ mil.)	NET INCOME ($ mil.)	NET PROFIT MARGIN	EMPLOYEES
06/15	656	(14)		3,700
06/14	635	6	1.1%	—
06/13	612	2	0.4%	—
06/10	577	(19)	—	—
Annual Growth	2.6%	—	—	—

2015 Year-End Financials
Return on assets: (-2.0%)
Return on equity: (-4.1%)
Current ratio: 2.70
Cash ($ mil.): 2

CHRISTUS TRINITY MOTHER FRANCES HEALTH SYSTEM

EXECUTIVES

Pres, Chris Glenney
Cmo, Steve Keuer
Coo, Jason Proctor
Cfo, Elizabeth Tulliam
It Manager, Gena King
Manager of CMR Program, Jennifer Hawkins
Director of Plant Oprs, Bobby Parker
Chief Nursing Officer, Shelly Welch
Exec Asst, Susan Wilson
Rn, Aliesha McCuller
Medipac Coordinator, Angie Matson
Auditors: ERNST & YOUNG LLP DALLAS TX

LOCATIONS

HQ: CHRISTUS TRINITY MOTHER FRANCES HEALTH
SYSTEM
800 E DAWSON ST, TYLER, TX 757012036
Phone: 903 593-8441
Web: WWW.TMFHC.ORG

HISTORICAL FINANCIALS
Company Type: Private

Income Statement				FYE: June 30
	REVENUE ($ mil.)	NET INCOME ($ mil.)	NET PROFIT MARGIN	EMPLOYEES
06/17	789	42	5.4%	4,000
06/15	752	48	6.4%	—
Annual Growth	2.5%	(5.6%)	—	—

CHS MCPHERSON REFINERY INC.

Cooperation is a refined art and refining a cooperative art for the National Cooperative Refinery
Association (NCRA) which provides its member
owners farm supply cooperatives CHS GROW-
MARK and MFA Oil with gasoline and diesel fuel
through its oil refinery in McPherson Kansas. The
refinery's production rate is 85000 barrels per day.
Fuel from the refinery is allocated to
member/owners on the basis of ownership per-
centages. In addition to the refinery NCRA owns
Jayhawk Pipeline stakes in two other pipeline companies and an underground oil storage facility.

Operations
NCRA's logistical system includes 76 trucks. (In
2012 almost 40000 barrels per day of crude was
gathered from more than 6000 oil wells mainly in
Kansas and transported to the McPherson refinery
by truck.)

The system also includes more than 1000 miles
of pipelines to move crude oil and finished products from its refinery to tanks and terminals. Its
Conway Texas underground storage facility has
1.5 million barrels of refined products capacity.
NCRA also has two refined products terminals (in
McPherson Kansas and Council Bluffs Iowa).

Strategy
The cooperative's primary strategy is to gather
oil and gas and make diesel and gasoline to serve
it members (and the farms of rural America) while
maintaining and upgrading its systems in order to
stay competitive with better resourced private sector refining rivals.

In 2011 NCRA announced a $555 million in-
vestment to build a new Delayed Coking Unit at
its McPherson refinery. The new facility will allow
the refiner to process a larger variety of crude oils.
It is scheduled to be completed in 2015 and will
replace a unit that was built in 1952.

In 2012 the company agreed to pay $700000 in
federal and state penalties to settle violations of
environmental laws at its McPherson petroleum
refinery and underground storage facility.

Company Background
The enterprise has its origins in 1943 when five
regional farm supply cooperatives tired of wartime
fuel shortages created the NCRA to buy the Globe
oil refinery in McPherson Kansas.

EXECUTIVES

Exec V Pres-, Shirley Cunningham
Exec V Pres-Coo*, Jay Debertin
Exec V Pres-Cfo*, Timothy Skidmore
Exec V Pres*, Lisa Zell
Coordinator, Maury Hoefer
Information Technology Manager, Jason Beckman
Auditors: PRICEWATERHOUSECOOPERS LLP MI

LOCATIONS

HQ: CHS MCPHERSON REFINERY INC.
2000 S MAIN ST, MCPHERSON, KS 674609402
Phone: 620 241-2340
Web: WWW.CHSINC.COM

COMPETITORS

BP
CVR Refining
Chevron
Exxon Mobil

HollyFrontier
Marathon Petroleum
Tesoro
Valero Energy

HISTORICAL FINANCIALS

Company Type: Private

Income Statement   FYE: August 31

	REVENUE ($ mil.)	NET INCOME ($ mil.)	NET PROFIT MARGIN	EMPLOYEES
08/13	4,081	686	16.8%	700
08/12	4,045	705	17.4%	—
08/11	3,405	378	11.1%	—
Annual Growth	9.5%	34.7%	—	—

2013 Year-End Financials

Return on assets: 32.8%   Cash ($ mil.): 386
Return on equity: 51.0%
Current ratio: 1.60

CHUGACH ALASKA CORPORATION

At the heart of Chugach Alaska Corporation is a vision of indigenous people running their own businesses on their own land. Chugach Alaska was formed following the activation of the Alaska Native Claims Settlement Act (which was passed by the US Congress in 1971) to provide land management services for the 928000-acre Chugach region of Alaska. The company derives the bulk of its sales from oil and gas production mining commercial timber and tourist activities that occur in the region and from its engagement in military base construction projects at more than 30 locations in Alaska the US Pacific Northwest and the Western Pacific. Chugach Alaska's shareholders consist of Aleut Eskimo and Indian natives.

Operations

In 2011 the company's Chugach World Services unit secured a $32 million contract (with the option for an additional $33 million) for housing and maintenance operations at Naval Base Guam and Andersen Air Force Base Guam.

In late 2010 the Chugach Alaska Services unit won a renewal of its existing oil spill prevention and response contract with Alyeska Pipeline Service Company. The new contract to service the Alaska Pipeline runs from 2011 to 2016.

Geographic Reach

With operations in Alaska the Pacific Northwest and the Western Pacific the company has major offices in Alabama Alaska Hawaii and Nevada.

Financial Performance

To raise cash in 2013 Chugach Alaska sold its three-story former headquarters building in downtown Anchorage.

Strategy

Developing and sustaining multiple revenues streams has been a key to the company's growth. Chugach Alaska is looking to continue to grow its Alaskan gas natural gas projects while diversifying into markets that are not traditional for the com-

pany such as the niche market of environmentally responsible guided tourism.

Expanding its global engineering footprint in 2012 the company acquired bankrupt Hawaii-based engineering firm Heide & Cook LLC.

Company Background

Chugach Alaska was founded in 1972 as an Alaska Native Claims Settlement Act Corporation. A nine-person board of directors elected from the corporation's more than 2300 shareholders oversees Chugach Alaska's management and operations. The company has gone from filing bankruptcy protection in 1990 (in the wake of the Exxon Valdez oil spill and a major cannery fire) to generating about $1 billion in annual revenues.

EXECUTIVES

Vice President Finance, Kathleen Shreiber
Senior Vice President Of Operations, Scott Davis
Vice President Business Development, Tim Hopper
Vice President Cultural, John Johnson

LOCATIONS

HQ: CHUGACH ALASKA CORPORATION
3800 CNTRPINT DR STE 1200, ANCHORAGE, AK 99503
Phone: 907 563-8866
Web: WWW.CHUGACH.COM

PRODUCTS/OPERATIONS

Selected Services
Base Operating Services
Construction Services
Educational Services
Engineering Services
IT/Telecommunications
Manufacturing Services
Oil and Gas Services

Selected Subsidiaries
Chugach Alaska Services Inc. (CASI)
Chugach Education Services Inc. (CESI)
Chugach Federal Solutions Inc. (CFSI)
Chugach Government Services Inc. (CGSI)
Chugach Industries Inc. (CII)
Chugach Information Technology Inc. (CITI)
Chugach Management Services Inc. (CMSI)
Chugach McKinley Inc. (CMI)
Chugach Support Services Inc. (CSSI)
Chugach Systems Integration Llc (CSI)
Chugach World Services Inc. (CWSI)
Heide & Cook LLC. (H&C)
Wolf Creek Federal Services Inc. (WCFS)

COMPETITORS

ConocoPhillips Alaska
Doyon
Fluor

Freegold Ventures
Jacobs Engineering
Sealaska

HISTORICAL FINANCIALS

Company Type: Private

Income Statement   FYE: December 31

	REVENUE ($ mil.)	NET INCOME ($ mil.)	NET PROFIT MARGIN	EMPLOYEES
12/17	919	20	2.3%	4,822
12/16	842	35	4.2%	—
12/15	758	22	3.0%	—
12/14	7	(12)	—	—
Annual Growth	387.6%	—	—	—

2017 Year-End Financials

Return on assets: 4.5%   Cash ($ mil.): 66
Return on equity: 6.5%
Current ratio: 2.60

CIC GROUP, INC.

CIC Group can see clearly that its future (like its present) is in heavy manufacturing and construction. Its group of commercial and industrial subsidiaries specialize in the manufacture maintenance and repair of equipment for the crude oil natural gas coal and other energy industries. Its largest subsidiary is Nooter/Eriksen which supplies heat recovery steam generators for combustion gas turbines worldwide. CIC's Nooter Construction is a construction contractor serving the refining petrochemical pulp and paper and power industries among others. The employee-owned holding company was formed in 2002.

Operations

CIC through its 20 subsidiaries is engaged in the heavy industrial construction of refineries and petrochemical and power plants. It also designs and builds heat recovery systems for power plants.

Sales and Marketing

Some of the company's largest customers include Ameren Calpine Chevron ConocoPhillips Exxon Mobil Florida Power & Light and Royal Dutch Shell.

Financial Performance

Although privately held the company reported 2012 revenue of $1.2 billion up 30% from 2011. CIC anticipates revenue of $2 billion by 2017 or 2018.

Strategy

The company is taking advantage of the low price and abundance of natural gas in the US which has encouraged companies to shift the manufacture of petrochemical plants to the US from the Middle East and Asia.

However CIC is also strengthening its position in the growth markets of Eastern Europe and Asia. In 2012 the company announced plans to work on photovoltaic projects for Chinese solar manufacturer LDK Solar and to act as a distributor for the company.

EXECUTIVES

Pres-Ceo, Donald H Lange
V Pres Finance-Treas, Derek J Falb
Chief Accountant, Jason Arnold
Sales Manager, Joe Schomber
Benefits Manager, Kayla Cabrera
Director Corporate Risk Manage, Michael Murphy
Corporate Controller, Thomas Lafloure
Office Manager, Jennifer Rossomanno

LOCATIONS

HQ: CIC GROUP, INC.
530 MARYVILLE CENTRE DR # 100, SAINT LOUIS, MO 631415838
Phone: 314 682-2900
Web: WWW.CICGROUP.COM

PRODUCTS/OPERATIONS

Selected Subsidiaries

ArcMelt
Delta Nooter
Megamet Sold Metals Co.
Nooter Construction
Nooter/Eriksen s.r.l.
Pressline Services
RMF Nooter
Schoeller Bleckmann Nooter GmbH
St. Louis Metallizing
Superior Corporate Travel
Wyatt Field Service Co.
Wyatt Virgin Islands

COMPETITORS

BWX Technologies	Mitsubishi Heavy
Clarkson Construction	Industries
Fluor	Phillips-Medisize
Fred Weber	U.S. Pipe
Jacobs Engineering	

HISTORICAL FINANCIALS
Company Type: Private

Income Statement				FYE: November 30
	REVENUE ($ mil.)	NET INCOME ($ mil.)	NET PROFIT MARGIN	EMPLOYEES
11/11	838	0	—	1,500
11/10	758	0	—	
11/08	1,120	0	—	
Annual Growth	(9.2%)	—	—	—

2011 Year-End Financials

Return on assets: —
Return on equity: —
Current ratio: 1.70

Cash ($ mil.): 136

CIMA ENERGY, LP

EXECUTIVES

Ceo, Charles M Oglesby
Pres, Thomas K Edwards
Cfo, Michael D Rupe
Accounting Staff, Audrey Blum
Director of Information Techno, Roger Heiniluoma
Auditors: DELOITTE & TOUCHE LLP HOUSTON

LOCATIONS

HQ: CIMA ENERGY, LP
  100 WAUGH DR STE 500, HOUSTON, TX 770074600
Phone: 713 209-1112
Web: WWW.CIMA-ENERGY.COM

HISTORICAL FINANCIALS
Company Type: Private

Income Statement				FYE: December 31
	REVENUE ($ mil.)	NET INCOME ($ mil.)	NET PROFIT MARGIN	EMPLOYEES
12/07	1,195	8	0.7%	65
12/06	902	11	1.3%	—
12/05	872	0	—	—
12/04	569	4	0.8%	—
Annual Growth	28.0%	19.1%	—	—

2007 Year-End Financials

Return on assets: 5.6%
Return on equity: 26.2%
Current ratio: 1.20

Cash ($ mil.): 16

CINCINNATI PUBLIC SCHOOLS

EXECUTIVES

Spdt, Laura Mitchell
SEC*, Denae Coco

Cfo-Treas*, Jonathan Boid
Facilities, Michael L Burson
Coordinator, Melvina Stokes
Information Technology/Interne, Christine Shields
Instructor, Gerald Powell
Instructor, John Breig
Executive Secretary, Kathleen Crable
Education Assistant, Leah Runyon
Teacher, Lisa Shelly
Auditors: CAUDILL & ASSOCIATES CPA POR

LOCATIONS

HQ: CINCINNATI PUBLIC SCHOOLS
  2651 BURNET AVE, CINCINNATI, OH 452192551
Phone: 513 363-0000
Web: WWW.CPS-K12.ORG

HISTORICAL FINANCIALS
Company Type: Private

Income Statement				FYE: June 30
	REVENUE ($ mil.)	NET INCOME ($ mil.)	NET PROFIT MARGIN	EMPLOYEES
06/17	703	17	2.5%	7,070
06/16	650	13	2.1%	—
06/15	654	(0)	—	—
06/05	402	0	—	—
Annual Growth	4.8%	—	—	—

CIRCLE HEALTH, INC.

EXECUTIVES

Ceo, Joseph White
Manager, Pam Gordon
Team Lead, Greg Green
Project Manager, Marie Voltaire
Emergency Medicine, Rugg Christopher
Director of Radiology, Judy Canal
Manager, Angel Santana

LOCATIONS

HQ: CIRCLE HEALTH, INC.
  295 VARNUM AVE, LOWELL, MA 018542134
Phone: 978 937-6000
Web: WWW.LOWELLGENERAL.ORG

HISTORICAL FINANCIALS
Company Type: Private

Income Statement				FYE: September 30
	REVENUE ($ mil.)	NET INCOME ($ mil.)	NET PROFIT MARGIN	EMPLOYEES
09/18	536	2	0.4%	3,000
09/17	509	7	1.6%	—
09/16	0	(0)	—	—
Annual Growth	55628.7%	—	—	—

2018 Year-End Financials

Return on assets: 0.4%
Return on equity: 1.3%
Current ratio: 1.20

Cash ($ mil.): 51

CITGO PETROLEUM CORPORATION

CITGO Petroleum is the fifth-largest independent refiner in the US. It refines and markets petroleum products including transportation fuels lubricants and petrochemicals. It markets CITGO branded gasoline through about 5300 independent retail outlets in about 30 US states mainly east of the Rockies. CITGO Petroleum owns oil refineries in Illinois Louisiana and Texas. The company has the refining capacity to process more than 749000 barrels of crude oil per day. It markets more than 600 types of lubricants and sells over 13 billion gallons of refined products annually. CITGO Petroleum is the operating subsidiary of PDV America itself a subsidiary of Venezuela's national oil company PDVSA.

Operations

CITGO has a total refining capacity of about 749000 barrels of crude oil per day. It operates through three US refineries in Texas Illinois and Louisiana.

The company's TriCLEAN TOP TIER gasoline is sold to independent marketers who sell motor fuels at CITGO branded retail outlets. CITGO Lubricants provides a line of agricultural automotive and industrial lubricants as well as oil and greases and private label lubricants. Lubricants are manufactured through blending and packaging plants located across the US with products marketed under the CITGO Mystik and Clarion brands. CITGO's petrochemicals and solvents business provides products such as adhesives paints and coatings.

CITGO also offers its loyalty program Club CITGO which offers special savings and rewards such as free coffee and snacks through its downloadable Club CITGO app.

Geographic Reach

Headquartered in Houston TX CITGO operates three refineries in Lemont IL; Corpus Christi TX; and Lake Charles LA and three lubricant blending plants in Cicero (IL) Oklahoma City and Atlanta. The company stores and distributes its petroleum products through several locations across the US. The CITGO Terminal Facilities & Pipeline network comprises three fully-owned pipelines six jointly-owned pipelines and approximately 50 petroleum product terminals.

Sales and Marketing

The company markets automotive fuels to independent marketers which sell to nearly 5300 CITGO branded retail outlets in the US and markets jet fuel directly to airlines. CITGO produces a variety of agricultural automotive industrial and private label lubricants which are sold to independent distributors mass marketers and industrial customers across the US and in 41 countries around the world.

Financial Performance

With a focus on safety and operational performance CITGO generated $851 million in net income in 2018 a significant increase compared with prior years. The company's oil refining processing capacity increased 8% from 2017 to 2018 allowing CITGO to increase exports to 206000 barrels per day in 2018 up 4 percent relative to 2017. The company was also able to increase volumes and capture higher margins in international markets with improvements to its logistics operations.

Strategy

The company is currently working to cut ties with its Venezuelan parent company Petroleos de Venezuela SA (PDVSA). CITGO Petroleum is being hampered by US sanctions imposed on PDVSA (still controlled by socialist President Nicolas Maduro) possibly preventing it from refinancing a revolving credit and term loan to generate cash. CITGO has stopped making payments to PDVSA ended subscriptions to corporate services and email communications and is avoiding mentioning PDVSA in any of its marketing materials. The company has also shut down PDVSA Services its procurement subsidiary that operated from CITGO's headquarters.

Company Background

CITGO was founded in 1910 by pioneer oilman Henry L. Doherty. First named Cities Service Company the company was one of the first to supply gas and electric utility services in the Midwest. It provided the electricity that lit the Statue of Liberty for the first time in 1916 and during World War II supplied much of the fuel used by US armed forces and its allies.

In 1928 the company was the first to discover the Oklahoma City Pool one of the most productive oil fields in the US. During the 1950s Cities Service began exploration in the Middle East. As part of a joint venture it also was the first company to discover oil in the Gulf of Mexico in 1952.

In 1965 Cities Service introduced its new name and marketing brand CITGO which used the first part of its former name ending with "GO" which represents energy and the company's forward-thinking culture. It added the CITGO Quik Mart convenience store platform to its gas stations in 1972.

In 1983 CITGO was acquired by 7-Eleven operator Southland Corporation. Three years later Petr leos de Venezuela S.S. (PDVSA) purchased a 50% stake in the company and in 1990 became wholly owned by PDVSA.

EXECUTIVES

Chairman, Alejandro Granado
Vp Finance And Treasurer, Maritza Villanueva
Vp Refining And General Manager Lake Charles Manufacturing Complex, Eduardo Assef
Vp Supply And Marketing, Gustavo Vel squez
Vp And General Manager Lemont Refinery, Jim Cristman
Vice President General Manager, Tomeu Vadell
Vice President And General Manager Corpus Christi Refinery, Randy Flowers
Vice President Manager Director, Bob Pennington
Vice President Supply Marketing, Fernando Valera
Vice President Finance, Jose Pereira
National Account Manager, Jason Williams
Auditors: KPMG LLP HOUSTON TEXAS

LOCATIONS

HQ: CITGO PETROLEUM CORPORATION
1293 ELDRIDGE PKWY, HOUSTON, TX 770771670
Phone: 832 486-4000
Web: WWW.CITGO.COM

PRODUCTS/OPERATIONS

Selected Products

Fuels
TriCLEAN Gasoline
Premium Diesel
Lubricants
CITGO
Mystik
Clarion
Petrochemicals and Solvents

COMPETITORS

Anadarko Petroleum	Exxon Mobil
Apache	Holly Energy Partners
BP	Shell Oil Products
CVR	Sunoco
Chevron	Valero Energy
ConocoPhillips	

HISTORICAL FINANCIALS
Company Type: Private

Income Statement
FYE: December 31

	REVENUE ($ mil.)	NET INCOME ($ mil.)	NET PROFIT MARGIN	EMPLOYEES
12/17	24,100	715	3.0%	4,000
12/16	19,914	234	1.2%	—
/ 0	0	0	—	—
Annual Growth	—	—	—	—

2017 Year-End Financials

Return on assets: 8.7%   Cash ($ mil.): 276
Return on equity: 37.0%
Current ratio: 1.30

CITIZENS ENERGY GROUP

Hoosiers are happy to have their homes provided with gas and water services by Public Utilities of the City of Indianapolis (dba Citizens Energy and CWA Authority public charitable trusts). Its Citizens Water unit provides water and wastewater services to 300000 customers in Indianapolis; Citizens Gas serves more than 266000 gas customers. Citizens Energy also provides steam heating and chilled water cooling services to about 250 customers through Citizens Thermal Energy. The regional utility also has a small oil production unit (Citizens Oil Division). Its Citizens Resources unit has joint venture stakes in some companies not regulated by the Indiana Utility Regulatory Commission such as ProLiance Energy.

EXECUTIVES

Vice President Information Technology, John Lucas
Vice President And Controller, Sabine Karner
Vice President Capital Programs And Engineering, Mark C Jacob

LOCATIONS

HQ: CITIZENS ENERGY GROUP
2020 N MERIDIAN ST, INDIANAPOLIS, IN 462021306
Phone: 317 924-3341
Web: WWW.CITIZENSENERGYGROUP.COM

PRODUCTS/OPERATIONS

2012 Sales

	$ mil.	% of total
Utility	650	93
Non-utility	45	7
Total	**696**	**100**

2012 Sales

	% of total
Citizens Gas	37
Water	24
Wastewater	22
Steam	9
Chilled Water	6
Oil	1
Resources	1

Total	100

COMPETITORS

American States Water	NIPSCO
Duke Energy	Vectren
Indiana Municipal Power Agency	Veolia Environnement

HISTORICAL FINANCIALS
Company Type: Private

Income Statement
FYE: September 30

	REVENUE ($ mil.)	NET INCOME ($ mil.)	NET PROFIT MARGIN	EMPLOYEES
09/12	696	(11)	—	1,100
09/11	463	32	7.0%	—
09/10	440	(1)	—	—
Annual Growth	25.7%	—	—	—

2012 Year-End Financials

Return on assets: (-0.3%)   Cash ($ mil.): 393
Return on equity: (-10.5%)
Current ratio: 1.50

CITRUS VALLEY HEALTH PARTNERS, INC.

Citrus Valley Health Partners is a 660-bed hospital system that serves the residents of California's San Gabriel Valley region located between Los Angeles and San Bernardino. It operates through four health care facilities: Citrus Valley Medical Center (CVMC) Queen of the Valley Campus CVMC Inter-Community Campus Foothill Presbyterian Hospital and Citrus Valley Hospice. Citrus Valley Health Partners also operates a home health care provider that offers nursing and rehabilitation care. The hospital system boasts several areas of specialty including diabetes care cancer treatment palliative care wound care and cardiac therapy.

Operations

Representing the largest slice of the Citrus Valley Health Partners system the CVMC Queen of the Valley Campus manages 325 beds and handles more than 54000 emergency room visits each year. The campus includes the Geleris Family Cancer Center; it is also known for birthing services that include a Level III Newborn Intensive Care Unit and it boasts robotic surgery systems and rehabilitation programs such as speech occupational and physical therapy for both children and adults.

With 220 beds the CVMC Inter-Community Campus specializes in cancer treatment electrophysiology cardiac care and wound care. The health system's Foothill Presbyterian Hospital boasts 105 beds and focuses on general acute care and such specialty services as an outpatient diabetes education program and rehabilitation. The Citrus Valley Hospice is a 10-bed inpatient facility that is the first freestanding hospice of its kind in California. Citrus Valley Home Health provides nursing and rehabilitation care.

Altogether the system employs some 1000 physicians at its facilities.

Geographic Reach

Citrus Valley Health Partners serves about 1 million residents from Covina Glendora and other California communities located in the San Gabriel Valley region.

Strategy

As part of a renovation and modernization program in 2013 the organization launched a construction program at its CVMC Inter-Community Campus to increase emergency operating and diagnostic capabilities. Once completed (in 2015) the new emergency department will nearly double the capacity of the campus' current 12-bed department. New patient treatment stations will enable medical nursing and support professionals to provide improved urgent care and other diagnostic care and treatment to more than 40000 patients each year.

In 2013 the Speech Pathology Outpatient Program expanded to include a Voice Clinic at Citrus Valley Medical Center — Queen of the Valley Campus in West Covina.

To reduce operational expenses that year Citrus Valley Health Partners signed a five-year $4.5 million managed print services agreement with Auxilio. Through the deal Auxilio will help the network improve process efficiencies supply chain management volume reduction and other initiatives.

Company Background

Inter-Community Campus began as a seven-bed hospital founded in 1922 by sisters Melisse and Mary Wittler a nurse and a schoolteacher.

EXECUTIVES

Ceo, Robert Curry
Pres, James Yoshioka
Exec V Pres Coo, Alvia Polk
Sr V Pres Cfo, Lois Conyers
Cmo/Cmio, Paveljit Bindra
Coordinator, Estela Bautista
Coordinator, Jaime Vasquez
Coordinator, Nadia Sanchez
Coordinator, Vladimir Zarian
Coordinator, Yvonne Hagerman
Application Analyst, Elias Picazo
Auditors: ERNST & YOUNG LLP LOS ANGELES

LOCATIONS

HQ: CITRUS VALLEY HEALTH PARTNERS, INC.
210 W SAN BERNARDINO RD, COVINA, CA 917231515
Phone: 626 331-7331
Web: WWW.CVHP.ORG

PRODUCTS/OPERATIONS

Selected Services
Cancer services
Diabetes care unit
Diabetes education program
Emergency room services
Home health
Hospice
Maternity services
Newborn intensive care
Palliative care
Pediatric services
Rehabilitation
Robotic surgery

COMPETITORS

Anaheim Regional Medical Center
City of Hope
Glendale Adventist Medical Center
Good Samaritan Hospital (Los Angeles)
Memorial Health Services
Methodist Hospital of Southern California
Newhall Memorial Hospital
Pasadena Hospital Association
St. Jude Medical Center
Western Medical Center - Santa Ana

HISTORICAL FINANCIALS
Company Type: Private

Income Statement
FYE: December 31

	REVENUE ($ mil.)	NET INCOME ($ mil.)	NET PROFIT MARGIN	EMPLOYEES
12/18	606	21	3.5%	2,800
12/17	64	2	3.8%	—
12/16	61	0	1.4%	—
12/15	58	(2)	—	—
Annual Growth	118.5%	—	—	—

2018 Year-End Financials
Return on assets: 2.9%
Return on equity: 4.3%
Current ratio: 1.90
Cash ($ mil.): 24

CITRUS VALLEY MEDICAL CENTER, INC.

EXECUTIVES

Pres-Ceo, Robert Curry
Coo*, Elvia Foulke
Cfo*, Roger Sharma
Patient Financial Dir, Angel Hovanessian
Marketing Director, Annette Macias
Director of Home Sr, Jean Hunn
Risk Management Director, Jill Jacobs
Chief Human Resources Officer, Ryan Burke
Auditors: ERNST & YOUNG LLP LOS ANGELE

LOCATIONS

HQ: CITRUS VALLEY MEDICAL CENTER, INC.
1115 S SUNSET AVE, WEST COVINA, CA 917903940
Phone: 626 962-4011
Web: WWW.CVHP.ORG

HISTORICAL FINANCIALS
Company Type: Private

Income Statement
FYE: December 31

	REVENUE ($ mil.)	NET INCOME ($ mil.)	NET PROFIT MARGIN	EMPLOYEES
12/17	502	90	18.0%	3,500
12/16	452	43	9.5%	—
12/14	397	31	7.9%	—
12/12	384	22	5.8%	—
Annual Growth	5.5%	32.3%	—	—

2017 Year-End Financials
Return on assets: 18.0%
Return on equity: 26.7%
Current ratio: 1.80
Cash ($ mil.): 14

CITY CENTER HOLDINGS, LLC

Auditors: DELOITTE & TOUCHE LLP LAS VE

LOCATIONS

HQ: CITY CENTER HOLDINGS, LLC
3950 LAS VEGAS BLVD S, LAS VEGAS, NV 891191005
Phone: 702 632-9800
Web: WWW.CITIZENSLASVEGAS.COM

HISTORICAL FINANCIALS
Company Type: Private

Income Statement
FYE: December 31

	REVENUE ($ mil.)	NET INCOME ($ mil.)	NET PROFIT MARGIN	EMPLOYEES
12/12	1,189	(510)	—	—
12/11	1,081	(502)	—	—
Annual Growth	10.0%	—	—	—

2012 Year-End Financials
Return on assets: (-5.6%)
Return on equity: (-8.3%)
Current ratio: 1.20
Cash ($ mil.): 252

CITY OF ALEXANDRIA

HistoricallyÂ a wartime victim of occupying forces modern Alexandria is home to many Defense Department contractors and employees. It uses a council-manager form of government wherein the mayor is part of theÂ six-memberÂ city council (all elected at large) which determines city policy. The city manager works to carry out the policy and run the day-to-day operations of Alexandria. In addition to the city manager the council also appoints the city attorney city clerk and members of various commissions and boards. Alexandria's more than 30 departments operate on anÂ annual budget of about $400 million and serve about 130000 citizens. The city was founded in 1749.

EXECUTIVES

Mayor, Allison Silberberg
City Mgr*, Mark Jinks
Deputy Cty Mgr*, Emily A Baker
U.S. Attorney, Tyler McGaughey
Supervisory Patent Examiner, Campbell Julie
Administrative Assistant, Brandi Galloway
Fiscal Officer, Brenda Dsylva
Counselor, Charles Johnson
Administration Technician, Lakisha Dennis
Police Sergeant, Nick Ruggiero
Real Estate Records Manager, Roxanne Vanderford
Auditors: CLIFTONLARSONALLEN LLP ARLING

LOCATIONS

HQ: CITY OF ALEXANDRIA
301 KING ST, ALEXANDRIA, VA 223143211
Phone: 703 746-4000
Web: WWW.ALEXANDRIACITYWEBSITE.COM

HISTORICAL FINANCIALS
Company Type: Private

Income Statement
FYE: June 30

	REVENUE ($ mil.)	NET INCOME ($ mil.)	NET PROFIT MARGIN	EMPLOYEES
06/18	842	108	12.9%	2,375
06/16	751	15	2.0%	—
06/15	730	3	0.5%	—
06/14	0	0	—	—
Annual Growth	—	—	—	—

2018 Year-End Financials
Return on assets: 6.0%   Cash ($ mil.): 336
Return on equity: 21.5%
Current ratio: —

CITY OF BOSTON

Boston's legacy includes a famous Tea Party Paul Revere's Ride and clam chowder. With about 625000 residents Boston has been called the economic and cultural hub of New England. The GreaterÂ Boston metro area is home to about 4.6 million people making it the 10th largest city in the US. Boston also boasts world classÂ educational institutions (Harvard Massachusetts Institute of Technology)Â championÂ sportsÂ teams (Red Sox Celtics Patriots) and a rich cultural and historical identity. Boston is also the capital of Massachusetts.

EXECUTIVES

Vice President, Peter Derosa
Auditors: KPMG LLP

LOCATIONS

HQ: CITY OF BOSTON
 1 CITY HALL STE 242, BOSTON, MA 022011020
Phone: 617 635-4545
Web: WWW.AFTMA.NET

HISTORICAL FINANCIALS
Company Type: Private

Income Statement				FYE: June 30
	REVENUE ($ mil.)	NET INCOME ($ mil.)	NET PROFIT MARGIN	EMPLOYEES
06/17	3,542	93	2.7%	18,760
06/16	3,393	138	4.1%	—
06/15*	3,278	79	2.4%	—
12/13	11	1	9.4%	—
Annual Growth	578.2%	344.2%	—	—

*Fiscal year change

CITY OF LONG BEACH

It's a city it's a port it's Long Beach. The City of Long Beach boasts the Port of Long Beach one of the busiest ports in the nation. With a population of more than 460000 Long Beach is part of the greater Los Angeles metropolitan area. The city uses a charter form of government with an elected mayor and city council as well as an appointed city manager. It's also known for its large oil reserves managed by the Long Beach Gas & Oil Department.

EXECUTIVES

Secretary, Jessica Rosa

LOCATIONS

HQ: CITY OF LONG BEACH
 333 W OCEAN BLVD, LONG BEACH, CA 908024664
Phone: 562 570-6450
Web: WWW.CITYAUDITORLAURADOUD.COM

HISTORICAL FINANCIALS
Company Type: Private

Income Statement				FYE: September 30
	REVENUE ($ mil.)	NET INCOME ($ mil.)	NET PROFIT MARGIN	EMPLOYEES
09/18	779	26	3.4%	5,028
09/17	716	9	1.3%	—
09/16	675	(1)	—	—
09/15	648	(119)	—	—
Annual Growth	6.3%	—	—	—

2018 Year-End Financials
Return on assets: 0.2%   Cash ($ mil.): 538
Return on equity: 0.5%
Current ratio: 2.20

CITY OF MESA

This city which literally covers a "mesa" or plateau stands roughly 100 feet higher than Phoenix and spreads across 130 square miles. With a population of more than 468000 the City of Mesa is the third-largest city in Arizona behind Phoenix and Tucson. Its city government consists of the mayor six city council members (elected to four-year terms) and a city manager. Mesa is also home to the Chicago Cubs baseball team during spring training. The city was founded in 1878 by Mormon (Latter-day Saint or LDS) pioneers who gave it its name; Mesa still has a large Mormon population. It was incorporated in 1883.

EXECUTIVES

Police Sergeant Vice President Mesa Assoc, Kurt Scanio
Treasurer, Dawn Forrest
Auditors: CLIFTONLARSONALLEN LLP PHOEN

LOCATIONS

HQ: CITY OF MESA
 20 E MAIN ST, MESA, AZ 852017425
Phone: 480 644-2011
Web: WWW.MESAAZ.GOV

HISTORICAL FINANCIALS
Company Type: Private

Income Statement				FYE: June 30
	REVENUE ($ mil.)	NET INCOME ($ mil.)	NET PROFIT MARGIN	EMPLOYEES
06/18	515	47	9.1%	4,068
06/17	476	38	8.1%	—
Annual Growth	8.3%	22.4%	—	—

CITY OF SANTA MONICA

EXECUTIVES

Mayor, Ed Winterer
Prin, Rod Gould
Coordinator, Melissa Lindley
Information Specialist, Ivy Weston
Staff, Brian Mondragon
Coordinator, Diane Cancino
Information Specialist, Michelle Dimas
Staff, Constance Babos
Auditors: MACIAS GINI & O'CONNELL LLP L

LOCATIONS

HQ: CITY OF SANTA MONICA
 1685 MAIN ST, SANTA MONICA, CA 904013248
Phone: 310 458-8281
Web: WWW.SANTA-MONICA.ORG

HISTORICAL FINANCIALS
Company Type: Private

Income Statement				FYE: June 30
	REVENUE ($ mil.)	NET INCOME ($ mil.)	NET PROFIT MARGIN	EMPLOYEES
06/18	475	115	24.3%	2,100
06/17	450	(4)	—	—
06/16	453	27	6.0%	—
06/15	419	11	2.6%	—
Annual Growth	4.3%	118.4%	—	—

CITY OF STAMFORD

EXECUTIVES

Mayor, David Martin
Sergeant, Diedrich Hohn
Project Coordinator, Laura Labosky
Coordinator, Sharon Wade
Chief of Staff, Michael Pollard
Risk Manager, Ann Mones
Director of Health, Jennifer Calder
Accounts Receivable, Audrey Brizan
Assistant Corporation Counsel, Chris Dellaselva
Captain, Elizabeth Erickson
Assistant Director of Special, Kathleen Quaglino
Auditors: BLUM SHAPIRO & COMPANY PC

LOCATIONS

HQ: CITY OF STAMFORD
 888 WASHINGTON BLVD, STAMFORD, CT 069012902
Phone: 203 977-4150
Web: WWW.CI.STAMFORD.CT.US

HISTORICAL FINANCIALS
Company Type: Private

Income Statement				FYE: June 30
	REVENUE ($ mil.)	NET INCOME ($ mil.)	NET PROFIT MARGIN	EMPLOYEES
06/18	709	(6)	—	2,878
06/17	678	5	0.8%	—
06/16	648	29	4.5%	—
06/15	627	19	3.0%	—
Annual Growth	4.2%	—	—	—

2018 Year-End Financials
Return on assets: (-0.5%)   Cash ($ mil.): 67
Return on equity: (-3.9%)
Current ratio: —

CITY UTILITIES OF SPRINGFIELD MO

City Utilities of Springfield Missouri springs to action with multiple services and products. The multi-utility supplies electricity natural gas and water for residents and businesses in the southwestern Missouri town. It has about 1870 miles of power lines and 1260 miles of natural gas mains serves about 110000 electric customers 82000 natural gas customers and 81000 water customers. It also operates the municipal bus system which has 25 regular street buses and five demand/response buses and serves about 790 broadband contracts through SpringNet Telecommunications. City Utilities of Springfield has a service region of 320 sq. ml. and serves a base population of 229000.

Geographic Reach
The multi-utility's service territory covers Springfield Missouri portions of Greene county and a part of northern Christian county.

Financial Performance
In 2012 City Utilities of Springfield's revenues declined by 4% primarily due to milder-than-usual weather crimping demand (heating degree days were 21% below normal). This drop was partially offset by an increase in revenues from its Transportation Telco/Broadband and Water segments. In 2012 revenues from electric retail sales increased 5% thanks to rate increases. However off-system sales volumes decreased 38%.

Natural gas sales decreased 15% as a direct result of lower volumes due to a mild winter and lower natural gas prices.

Water retail sales increased in 2012 to $36.4 million as compared to $32.8 million in 2011 thanks in part to lower-than-usual rainfall.

Telco/Broadband had 25 new SpringNet customers billed in 2012 and saw its revenues rise by 6%.

Strategy
With coal-fired plants accounting for 62% of its power generation capacity City Utilities of Springfield is looking to boost its green power options. The utility offers its customers the option of using renewable wind-generated electricity imported to Springfield from a Kansas wind farm (the 50 MW Smoky Hills Wind Farm in Salina).

In 2013 City Utilities of Springfield was working on a deal to buy solar power from Missouri's largest solar energy farm - a 5 MW plant on a 40 acre site in eastern Greene County near to the multi-utility's McCartney natural gas turbine between Springfield and Strafford.

Company Background
The utility traces its origins to the gas works of Springfield Gas Lighting Company which opened in 1874. In 1945 Springfield Gas and Electric was bought by the City of Springfield resulting in the creation of City Utilities of Springfield.

EXECUTIVES

Vice President Customer Sales And Service, Marsha McClanahan
Vice President Staff, Andrew Foster
Auditors: BKD LLP SPRINGFIELD MISSOUR

LOCATIONS

HQ: CITY UTILITIES OF SPRINGFIELD MO
301 E CENTRAL ST, SPRINGFIELD, MO 658023858
Phone: 417 863-9000
Web: WWW.CITYUTILITIES.NET

HISTORICAL FINANCIALS
Company Type: Private

Income Statement — FYE: September 30

	REVENUE ($ mil.)	NET INCOME ($ mil.)	NET PROFIT MARGIN	EMPLOYEES
09/18	459	60	13.3%	980
09/17	432	34	8.1%	—
09/16	417	41	9.9%	—
Annual Growth	4.9%	21.3%	—	—

2018 Year-End Financials
Return on assets: 3.2%
Return on equity: 5.4%
Current ratio: 1.30
Cash ($ mil.): 25

CITYSERVICEVALCON, LLC

You don't have to live in the city to get the services of CityServiceValcon which markets and distributes petroleum products throughoutÂ the Inland Northwest and Rocky Mountain regions of the US as well as in the adjacent Plains states. Its products include gasoline diesel aviation fuels lubricants propane and heating oil. The company has diesel gasoline and heating oils for delivery through its network of bulk plants. CityService-Valcon also operates cardlock fueling facilities under the Pacific Pride brand name. Regional independent petroleum marketers City Service and Valcon merged their operations in 2003 to form CityServiceValcon.

EXECUTIVES

Information Technology Director And Vice President Finance, Kurt Tonjum

LOCATIONS

HQ: CITYSERVICEVALCON, LLC
640 W MONTANA ST, KALISPELL, MT 599013834
Phone: 406 755-4321
Web: WWW.CITYSERVICEVALCON.COM

COMPETITORS

Farstad Oil	SPF Energy
Redwood Coast Petroleum	Wilson Oil

HISTORICAL FINANCIALS
Company Type: Private

Income Statement — FYE: September 30

	REVENUE ($ mil.)	NET INCOME ($ mil.)	NET PROFIT MARGIN	EMPLOYEES
09/08	625	4	0.6%	150
09/07	490	3	0.6%	—
09/06	459	4	1.0%	—
Annual Growth	16.6%	(8.0%)	—	—

2008 Year-End Financials
Return on assets: 9.3%
Return on equity: 19.2%
Current ratio: 1.30
Cash ($ mil.): 1

CLARCOR INC.

CLARCOR cleans up with filters. The company's industrial and environmental filtration unit makes air and antimicrobial filters for commercial industrial and residential buildings along with filters used in industrial processes. Brands include Airguard Facet ATI Transweb UAS Keddeg MKI TF-Sand Purolator. Companies in CLARCOR's engine and mobile filtration business make products under brands such as Baldwin Hastings Filters and Clark that filter the air oil fuel coolant and hydraulic fluids. In 2017 in order to expand its filtration portfolio Parker-Hannifin acquired CLARCOR for about $4.3 billion.

Operations
CLARCOR operates in two industry segments: Engine/Mobile Filtration and Industrial/Environmental Filtration.

The Engine/Mobile Filtration segment (about 60% of total revenue) makes and sells filtration products for engines used in stationary power generation and for engines in mobile equipment applications including trucks automobiles buses and locomotives and marine construction industrial mining and agricultural equipment. The company manufactures and sells both 'First-fit' filtration systems and replacement products such as oil air fuel coolant transmission and hydraulic filters.

The company's Industrial/Environmental Filtration segment (about 40%) centers around the manufacturing and marketing of filtration products used in industrial and commercial processes and in buildings and infrastructures of various types. Its liquid process filtration products include specialty industrial process liquid filters; filters for pharmaceutical processes and beverages; and filtration systems and filters for the oil and natural gas industry sewage treatment and water recycling and other industrial uses.

Its air filtration products represent air filters and systems including advanced medias and treatments and high efficiency first-fit systems used in gas turbine power generation systems heavy industrial manufacturing processes thermal power plants commercial buildings hospitals general factories residential buildings paint spray booths medical devices and facilities motor vehicle systems aircraft cabins clean rooms compressors and compressor stations.

Geographic Reach
CLARCOR makes and sells its products worldwide and more than 30% of the company's sales come from outside the US. The company has manufacturing distribution and service facilities in US Brazil China France Germany India Italy Malaysia Netherlands the UAE the UK Japan and Mexico.

Sales and Marketing
The company's filtration products are sold through independent distributors and dealers for OEMs as well as directly to end users.

The 10 largest customers of the Engine/Mobile Filtration segment accounted for 35% of 2016 fiscal year (November year end) segment sales.

The 10 largest customers of the Industrial/Environmental Filtration segment accounted for more than 15% of that segment's revenue.

Financial Performance
In fiscal 2016 CLARCOR's revenue declined by 6% ($91 million) due to a number of factors including the 2015 divestiture of J.L. Clark (the former Packaging Segment) which accounted for $40.9 million; decreased net sales volume (due to lower industrial demand) of $26.3 million in the Industrial/Environmental Filtration segment; and $25.1 from a negative currency exchange rate impact due to the strong dollar.

CLARCOR's net income grew by 3.4% to $139.3 million primarily due to Other net income of $20.7 million (flat in 2015) which primarily reflected $27.3 million from 3M to settle a patent litigation case.

Net cash provided by operating activities increased by $131.7 million in 2016 to $285.4 million. Some $18.1 million of this increase came from the 3M patent litigation award and the remainder primarily from cost cutting activities including lowering inventory levels by $36.4 million (resulting in a $58.5 million improvement in cash from operations). The company also reported a $26 million impact from lower cash taxes paid driven by the timing of tax payments in 2016 and 2015.

Strategy

Following the closing of its acquisition by Parker Hannifin in 2017 CLARCOR will be combined with Parker's Filtration Group to form a diverse global filtration business.

Restructuring to focus on two core business lines in 2015 CLARCOR sold its J.L. Clark business (the former Packaging Segment) to CC Industries.

Mergers and Acquisitions

In addition to organic growth CLARCOR has pursued a strategy of expanding its portfolio through acquisitions.

To support its global growth and innovation activities in 2016 the company acquired certain assets of US-based FibeRio Technology (a technology company focused on the research development and commercialization of performance fabric and filtration media) for $11.9 million. That year its CLARCOR Industrial Air division acquired TDC Filter Manufacturing a top US manufacturer and supplier of pleated filter bags dust collection cartridges and gas turbine air filters for $11 million.

In 2014 the company acquired Stanadyne's diesel fuel filtration business for $327.7 million and changed its name to CLARCOR Engine Mobile Solutions. That year it also bought Filter Resources Inc. Filtration Inc. and Fabrication Specialties Inc. for $21.9 million.

Company Background

In 2013 CLARCOR purchased the air filtration business of General Electric's power and water division for $260.3 million.

In 2013 CLARCOR announced plans to invest $40 million for subsidiary Baldwin Filters Inc. to build a new 400000 sq. ft. warehouse and distribution center adjacent to Baldwin's manufacturing facility in Kearney Nebraska.

In 2012 the company acquired Modular Engineering Pty Ltd. an Australian manufacturer of natural gas filtration products as well as a distributor of aftermarket elements. Modular a longtime supplier to CLARCOR's PECOFacet division became part of the division. PECOFacet is included in the company's Industrial/Environmental Filtration segment. Modular produces skid-mounted equipment for the natural gas industry in the Asia/Pacific region and expands CLARCOR's presence in that region in both manufacturing and aftermarket sales.

In 2011 the company purchased one of its suppliers of filtration media Transweb LLC. New Jersey-based Transweb manufactures and supplies media used in end-market applications including respirators and HVAC filters.

CLARCOR was founded in 1904 and reincorporated in 1969.

EXECUTIVES

Senior Business Development Officer, Sam Ferrise, $400,795 total compensation
Vp Finance And Cfo, David J. Fallon, $394,808 total compensation

Chairman President And Ceo, Christopher L. Conway, $689,615 total compensation
Group President Clarcor Industrial Air, Keith A. White
President Engine And Mobile Group, Jacob Thomas
Vice President Of Operations, John Reuss
Vice President Strategic Business Systems, Chris Schechter
Vice President Of Business Development, Naimesh Dave
Vice President Human Resources, Pam K Kile
Vice President Advanced Product And Process Engineering, Thomas B Green
Vice President Finance, Dennis M Haun
Vice President Innovation Product And Process Engineering, Monte A Crabtree
Vice President Strategic Accounts, David Amato
Auditors: PRICEWATERHOUSECOOPERS LLP NA

LOCATIONS

HQ: CLARCOR INC.
840 CRESCENT CENTRE DR # 600, FRANKLIN, TN 370674687
Phone: 615 771-3100
Web: WWW.CLCAIR.COM

Sales 2016

	$ mil.	% of total
United States	944	68
Europe	152	11
Asia	144	10
Other International	148	11
Total	**1,389**	**100**

PRODUCTS/OPERATIONS

sales 2016

	$ mil.	% of total
Industrial/Environmental Filtration	803	58
Engine/Mobile Filtration	586	42
Total	**1,389**	**100**

COMPETITORS

Crown Holdings	EMD Millipore
Cummins	ESCO Technologies
Dana	Pall Corporation
Delphi Automotive Systems	Parker-Hannifin
Donaldson Company	W rth Group

HISTORICAL FINANCIALS

Company Type: Private

Income Statement — FYE: November 30

	REVENUE ($ mil.)	NET INCOME ($ mil.)	NET PROFIT MARGIN	EMPLOYEES
11/16	1,389	139	10.0%	5,773
11/15	1,481	134	9.1%	—
11/14	1,512	144	9.5%	—
11/13	1,130	118	10.5%	—
Annual Growth	7.1%	5.6%	—	—

2016 Year-End Financials

Return on assets: 8.0% Cash ($ mil.): 134
Return on equity: 12.2%
Current ratio: 3.10

CLARK COUNTY SCHOOL DISTRICT

EXECUTIVES

Supt, Patrick Skorkowsky
Coordinator, Monica Robles
Executive of Information Techn, Alisha Bragg
Coordinator, Ransom Terrell
Project Coordinator, Steven Holyoak
Executive of Information Techn, Chris Ahrens
Executive Officer, Teresa Holden
Executive of Information Techn, Robin Thomas
Security Staff, Tashaan Swayne
Information Specialist, Jonathan Swaby
Teacher, April Holloway
Auditors: EIDE BAILLY LLP LAS VEGAS NE

LOCATIONS

HQ: CLARK COUNTY SCHOOL DISTRICT
5100 W SAHARA AVE, LAS VEGAS, NV 891463406
Phone: 702 799-5000
Web: WWW.CCSD.NET

HISTORICAL FINANCIALS

Company Type: Private

Income Statement — FYE: June 30

	REVENUE ($ mil.)	NET INCOME ($ mil.)	NET PROFIT MARGIN	EMPLOYEES
06/18	3,313	134	4.1%	37,361
06/17	3,178	(112)	—	—
06/16	3,048	328	10.8%	—
06/15	2,971	(52)	—	—
Annual Growth	3.7%	—	—	—

CLARK EQUIPMENT COMPANY

EXECUTIVES

Ceo, Scott Park
Design Engineer, Chris Gillund
Manager, Christopher Young
Executive of Sales, Dirk Pettit
Vice-President, Joel Honeyman
Administrator, Glenn Comegys
Manager, Paul White
Corporate Communications Staff, Brianne Hill
Manager, Beth Nelson
Design Engineer, Arnaud Guinee
Executive Administrative Assis, Deb Hanson
Auditors: DELOITTE & TOUCHE LLP

LOCATIONS

HQ: CLARK EQUIPMENT COMPANY
250 E BEATON DR, WEST FARGO, ND 580782656
Phone: 701 241-8700
Web: WWW.DOOSANMACHINETOOLS.US

HISTORICAL FINANCIALS

Company Type: Private

Income Statement				FYE: December 31
	REVENUE ($ mil.)	NET INCOME ($ mil.)	NET PROFIT MARGIN	EMPLOYEES
12/17	2,543	174	6.9%	5,000
12/16	2,415	166	6.9%	—
12/15	0	0	—	—
12/14	2,539	492	19.4%	—
Annual Growth	0.1%	(29.3%)	—	—

2017 Year-End Financials

Return on assets: 6.1%
Return on equity: 24.8%
Current ratio: 1.40

Cash ($ mil.): 127

CLEAR LAKE REGIONAL MEDICAL CENTER, INC.

EXECUTIVES

Ceo, Michael Roussos
Director of Mis/Is, Ley Sampson
Administrator, Sharon Holdorff
Diagnostic Radiologist, Larry Schock
Diagnostic Radiologist, Steven Gerguis
Board Member, Eduardo Ramirez
Director, Glenda Parish
Director of It and Is, Ley Samson
Anesthesiologist, Andrea Reidy
Chief of Surgery, Hoang Q Pham
Director, Richard Marietta

LOCATIONS

HQ: CLEAR LAKE REGIONAL MEDICAL CENTER, INC.
500 W MEDICAL CENTER BLVD, WEBSTER, TX
775984220
Phone: 713 371-5000
Web: WWW.CLEARLAKERMC.COM

HISTORICAL FINANCIALS

Company Type: Private

Income Statement				FYE: December 31
	REVENUE ($ mil.)	NET INCOME ($ mil.)	NET PROFIT MARGIN	EMPLOYEES
12/16	476	54	11.5%	720
12/15	469	56	12.0%	—
Annual Growth	1.5%	(2.6%)	—	—

2016 Year-End Financials

Return on assets: 21.4%
Return on equity: 4.7%
Current ratio: 0.80

Cash ($ mil.): —

CLEVELAND MUNICIPAL SCHOOL DISTRICT

EXECUTIVES

Ceo, Eric Gordon
Coo*, Patrick Zohn
Chb*, Denise W Link
Cfo*, John Scanlan
Exec Dir*, Megan Obryan
Teacher, Brenda Robinson
Manager Management Director, Brianne Otey
Purchasing Agent, Marilyn Landrum
Program Manager, Pamela Scott
Director of Special Education, Patricia Schulz
Secretary, Shanetta Harris
Auditors: DAVE YOST-AUDITOR OF STATE CL

LOCATIONS

HQ: CLEVELAND MUNICIPAL SCHOOL DISTRICT
1111 SUPERIOR AVE E # 1800, CLEVELAND, OH
441142500
Phone: 216 838-0000
Web: WWW.MC2STEMHIGHSCHOOL.ORG

HISTORICAL FINANCIALS

Company Type: Private

Income Statement				FYE: June 30
	REVENUE ($ mil.)	NET INCOME ($ mil.)	NET PROFIT MARGIN	EMPLOYEES
06/18	957	(49)	—	9,500
06/17	854	(71)	—	—
06/16	902	18	2.1%	—
06/11	888	38	4.3%	—
Annual Growth	1.1%	—	—	—

2018 Year-End Financials

Return on assets: (-2.6%)
Return on equity: (-22.4%)
Current ratio: —

Cash ($ mil.): 224

CLIFTONLARSONALLEN LLP

CliftonLarsonAllen (CLA) is all about the CPAs. Boasting more than $3 billion in client assets under management and 500 partners CLA is the US' 10th-largest accounting firm that serves privately owned firms and their principals along with not-for-profits and government agencies. Also serving as a financial advisory and business consultancy CLA is organized as a holding company with three main business segments: Public Accounting Wealth Management and Outsourcing Services. It mostly serves clients in the agribusiness financial employee benefit plan healthcare manufacturing and government sectors. With 1800 CPAs and nearly 3000 other professionals the firm's annual revenues exceed $750 million.

Operations

The company's service areas include audit accounting tax consulting outsourcing and wealth advisory. Its investment advisory services are conducted through CliftonLarsonAllen Wealth Advisors LLC. CLA serves clients outside the US through its affiliations with Nexia International.

Geographic Reach

Minnesota-based CLA boasts nearly 100 offices in about 20 states and the District of Columbia.

Sales and Marketing

CLA which counts more than 150000 clients serves privately-held businesses individuals not-for-profits and governmental entities. Its major client groups include agribusiness and cooperatives dealerships employee benefit plans federal government financial institutions healthcare manufacturing and distribution companies as well as state and local governments.

Financial Performance

CLA's revenue has risen more than 36% since the end of 2012. The company's revenue reached $750 million at the end of 2015.

Strategy

CLA has been acquiring local accounting and consulting firms around the US to expand into new geographic markets while bolstering its service offerings and client list.

Mergers and Acquisitions

In February 2016 CLA bought Bruner Cox LLP the 10th-largest accounting firm in Northeast Ohio (according to the Crain's 2016 Book of Lists). The deal was expected to take effect in June.

In November 2015 the firm purchased Pittsburgh-based KFMR Katz McMurtry PC the region's 19th-largest accounting firm.

In April 2014 the company acquired accounting and consulting firm Illinois Agricultural Auditing Association expanding its presence in Illinois to more than a dozen locations with the addition of IAAA's Bloomington/Normal and Springfield locations.

In January 2014 CLA purchased several companies to expand its consultancy including: Massachusetts consulting firm Bankers Advisory Inc.; Maryland-based OneSource Professional Services Group a consulting technology accounting and tax services firm; and Sullivan Rogers & Company a Massachusetts CPA and consulting firm dedicated to the state and local government market.

In 2013 in looking to take advantage of the implementation of healthcare reform in the US CLA acquired Idaho-based national healthcare consulting firm Beck Advisory Group. That year it also bought accounting firm Monaghan Group boosting its outsourcing practice and services in the Charlotte North Carolina area as well as Indiana-based Nonprofit Financial Solutions a firm focused on providing nonprofits with CFO consulting and outsourcing services.

Company Background

CLA was formed in 2011 by the merger of Clifton Gunderson and LarsonAllen. Prior to the pairing both companies had been active in expanding across the country by purchasing smaller firms and parts of other firms.

EXECUTIVES

Coo, David E. Bailey
Cfo, Sharon Ten Clay
Cio, Steve Noble
Ceo Cliftonlarsonallen Wealth Advisors Llc, Tony Hallada
Ceo And Chief Business Officer, Denny Schleper

LOCATIONS

HQ: CLIFTONLARSONALLEN LLP
220 S 6TH ST STE 300, MINNEAPOLIS, MN
554021418
Phone: 612 376-4500
Web: WWW.CLACONNECT.COM

Selected Locations

Arizona
California
Colorado
Florida
Idaho
Illinois
Indiana
Iowa
Maryland
Massachusetts
Michigan
Minnesota
Mississippi
Missouri
New Jersey
New Mexico
New York
North Carolina

Ohio
Pennsylvania
Texas
Virginia
Washington
Wisconsin

PRODUCTS/OPERATIONS

Selected Services
Audit and assurance
Consulting
CLA Intuition financial modeling
Employee benefit plans
Executive search
Forensic
Information security
Intacct software
Litigation support
Risk management
Technology
Transaction support
Valuation
International
Outsourci

COMPETITORS

BDO	Grant Thornton
BKD LLP	KPMG L.L.P.
Baker Tilly Virchow	Moore Stephens
Krause	International
Crowe Horwath	PricewaterhouseCoopers
Deloitte & Touche	UK
Eide Bailly	RSM US
Ernst & Young LLP	SVA

HISTORICAL FINANCIALS

Company Type: Private

Income Statement   FYE: December 31

	REVENUE ($ mil.)	NET INCOME ($ mil.)	NET PROFIT MARGIN	EMPLOYEES
12/16	755	226	30.1%	4,786
12/15	650	170	26.3%	—
12/14	598	163	27.3%	—
12/13	563	154	27.5%	—
Annual Growth	10.3%	13.6%	—	—

2016 Year-End Financials
Return on assets: 84.6%   Cash ($ mil.): 11
Return on equity: 120.4%
Current ratio: 3.50

CLOUD PEAK ENERGY RESOURCES LLC

EXECUTIVES

Ceo, Colin Marshall
Treas, Oscar Martinez
Exec V Pres, Michael Barrett
Exec V Pres, Gary Rivenes
Sr V Pres, Bruce Jones
Sr V Pres, Cary W Martin
Vice-President Business Develo, Todd Myers
Executive Assistant, Karen Nelson
Auditors: PRICEWATERHOUSECOOPERS LLP DE

LOCATIONS

HQ: CLOUD PEAK ENERGY RESOURCES LLC
   505 S GILLETTE AVE, GILLETTE, WY 827164203
Phone: 303 956-7596
Web: WWW.CLOUDPEAKENERGY.COM

HISTORICAL FINANCIALS

Company Type: Private

Income Statement   FYE: December 31

	REVENUE ($ mil.)	NET INCOME ($ mil.)	NET PROFIT MARGIN	EMPLOYEES
12/13	1,396	58	4.2%	1,200
12/12	1,516	155	10.3%	—
12/11	1,553	201	13.0%	—
12/10	1,370	170	12.4%	—
Annual Growth	0.6%	(29.8%)	—	—

2013 Year-End Financials
Return on assets: 2.5%   Cash ($ mil.): 231
Return on equity: 5.5%
Current ratio: 1.80

CMC HEALTHCARE SYSTEM

EXECUTIVES

Pres-Ceo, Joseph Pepe

LOCATIONS

HQ: CMC HEALTHCARE SYSTEM
   100 MCGREGOR ST, MANCHESTER, NH 031023770
Phone: 603 663-6888

HISTORICAL FINANCIALS

Company Type: Private

Income Statement   FYE: September 30

	REVENUE ($ mil.)	NET INCOME ($ mil.)	NET PROFIT MARGIN	EMPLOYEES
09/18	469	29	6.3%	61
09/17	546	61	11.3%	—
Annual Growth	(14.0%)	(51.6%)	—	—

2018 Year-End Financials
Return on assets: 6.0%   Cash ($ mil.): 61
Return on equity: 16.8%
Current ratio: 2.20

CMC-NORTHEAST, INC.

LOCATIONS

HQ: CMC-NORTHEAST, INC.
   920 CHURCH ST N, CONCORD, NC 280252927
Phone: 704 403-3000

HISTORICAL FINANCIALS

Company Type: Private

Income Statement   FYE: December 31

	REVENUE ($ mil.)	NET INCOME ($ mil.)	NET PROFIT MARGIN	EMPLOYEES
12/14	527	118	22.5%	1,143
12/08	457	(56)	—	—
Annual Growth	2.4%	—	—	—

2014 Year-End Financials
Return on assets: 1.3%   Cash ($ mil.): —
Return on equity: 22.5%
Current ratio: 2.20

COASTAL CHEMICAL CO., L.L.C.

EXECUTIVES

MBR-Pres, Randy King
Pres*, Jim Doyle
Information Technology/Interne, Bryant Angelle
Administrative Assistant, Lana Rogers
Controller, Bonnie Broussard

LOCATIONS

HQ: COASTAL CHEMICAL CO., L.L.C.
   3520 VETERANS MEMORIAL DR, ABBEVILLE, LA
   705105708
Phone: 337 898-0001
Web: WWW.FIELDDATAONLINE.COM

HISTORICAL FINANCIALS

Company Type: Private

Income Statement   FYE: December 31

	REVENUE ($ mil.)	NET INCOME ($ mil.)	NET PROFIT MARGIN	EMPLOYEES
12/14	736	33	4.6%	750
12/09	386	10	2.6%	—
12/08	635	16	2.6%	—
Annual Growth	2.5%	12.9%	—	—

2014 Year-End Financials
Return on assets: 10.3%   Cash ($ mil.): 3
Return on equity: 88.0%
Current ratio: 0.90

COASTAL PACIFIC FOOD DISTRIBUTORS, INC.

Coastal Pacific Food Distributors (CPF) fuels the military forces from facility to fork. The company is one of the top wholesale food distributors that primarily serves the US armed forces across the Western US and in the Far East. As part of its business CPF provides a full line of groceries to military bases run by the US Army Navy Air Force and Marines. It delivers a variety of products from distribution centers located in California Washington and Hawaii. CPF also offers information system programming services for its customers to track sales and shipping as well as procurement and logistics through partnerships in Iraq Kuwait and Saudi Arabia. The company was founded in 1986.

Operations

CPF has grown to become the second-largest worldwide military distributor of food and related products.

As part of its business CPF operates distribution centers in California Washington Hawaii and Canada. In California its largest Stockton facility spans more than 500000 sq. ft. while its Ontario center boasts 429000 sq. ft. Its distribution center in Fife Washington is 153000 sq. ft. A 45000-sq.-ft. facility in Hawaii delivers food to four military commissaries.

Geographic Reach
California-based CPF caters to the Western US as well as Alaska Hawaii Guam Japan Okinawa Korea Singapore Kwajalein Diego Garcia and the Philippines. Its business extends to the Middle East through partnerships for procurement and logistics with other companies. These additional areas include Iraq Kuwait and Saudi Arabia.

Sales and Marketing
Industry partners that keep CPF busy include the Defense Logistics Agency the Defense Commissary Agency Air Force NAF Purchasing Office Navy Exchange (NEXCOM) Army and Air Force Exchange Service (AAFES) and the American Logistics Association to name a few.

The company counts on food manufacturers to keep its customers happy. They include Kraft Foods Tyson Foods Procter & Gamble General Mills Nestle ConAgra Unilever Frito-Lay Campbell J.M. Smucker Global Military Marketing Mars S&K Sales Del Monte Corp. Georgia-Pacific Johnson & Johnson and Alder Foods.

Strategy
The company works to support its existing markets. In 2013 CPF opened a new prime vendor platform in Calamba Luguna Philippines as it looks to serve future growth there. The platform supports Naval ships with dry chill and frozen items.

EXECUTIVES

Vice President Prime Vendor, Brian Murdoch
Executive Vice President Finance And Administration, Monika Bertke
Auditors: DIXON HUGHES GOODMAN LLP NORF

LOCATIONS

HQ: COASTAL PACIFIC FOOD DISTRIBUTORS, INC.
1015 PERFORMANCE DR, STOCKTON, CA 952064925
Phone: 909 947-2066
Web: WWW.CPFD.COM

PRODUCTS/OPERATIONS

Selected Products

Bakery

Candy

Deli
Fresh & frozen meats
Frozen foods
Pet foods
Refrigerated items
Sushi

Selected Brokers
Acosta Sales & Marketing
Alder Foods Inc.
Bisek & Co. Inc.
Dixon Marketing Inc.
Dunham & Smith Agencies
Elite Brands
Finnegan International Sales
First Wave Sales
Gateway Military LLC
Global Office Building
HI-PAC Ltd
Mid Valley
Overseas Service Corporation
Otis McAllister
Parra Sales Inc
Reese Group
S&K
S. Schwartz Sales Inc.
Turnkey Management
WEBCO General Partnership

COMPETITORS

AdvancePierre
JTM Provisions
Richmond Wholesale Meat

HISTORICAL FINANCIALS
Company Type: Private

Income Statement				FYE: December 29
	REVENUE ($ mil.)	NET INCOME ($ mil.)	NET PROFIT MARGIN	EMPLOYEES
12/12	1,212	15	1.2%	459
12/11*	1,162	25	2.2%	—
01/11	1,113	17	1.6%	—
Annual Growth	4.4%	(7.6%)	—	—

*Fiscal year change

2012 Year-End Financials

Return on assets: 6.7%
Return on equity: 50.6%
Current ratio: 2.60

Cash ($ mil.): 5

COBANK, ACB

You could say CoBank is dependent on its rural customers and vice versa. A member of the Farm Credit System (which is regulated by the FCA) the $110 billion cooperative bank provides seasonal and wholesale loans to agribusinesses as well as to rural power water and communications cooperatives across the US. The bank also leases vehicles farming equipment and agricultural facilities through various Farm Credit System affiliates. Its core agribusiness customers range from local and regional farmers' cooperatives to multinational food companies. It has counted Land O' Lakes Blue Diamond Almonds and National Beef as among its larger customers. Formed in 1989 CoBank merged with US AgBank in early 2012.

Operations
CoBank operates three main business segments: Strategic Relationships Agribusiness and Rural Infrastructure. Its Strategic Relationships loans made up 50% of its $80 billion loan portfolio at the end of 2014 while Agribusiness and Rural Infrastructure made up another 30% and 20% respectively.

About 76% of CoBank's total revenue came from loan interest in 2014 while another 16% came from interest income on investment securities. The rest of its revenue came from fee income (5% of revenue) prepayment income (1%) and other miscellaneous sources.

Geographic Reach
Based in Colorado the bank operates 15 regional offices throughout the US including locations in Iowa Georgia Texas Connecticut Kansas Missouri and Kentucky. It also has an international office in Singapore.

Sales and Marketing
CoBank mainly serves clients in rural America in the agribusiness water communications and power sectors.

Financial Performance
CoBank's annual revenues and profits have been rising over the past several years thanks to steady loan asset growth across all three of its target loan types (Strategic Relationships Agribusiness and Rural Infrastructure).

The bank's revenue jumped 5% to $2.2 million during 2014 mostly thanks to higher average loan volume and increased earnings from a strengthened balance sheet. CoBank's lending business grew with food and agribusiness customers Farm Credit Association customers and rural energy and communications customers which all in turn contributed to its top-line growth.

Revenue growth in 2014 drove CoBank's net income up 6% to $904.3 million for the year. The bank's operating cash levels dipped 2% to $883.1 million during the year due to unfavorable working capital changes related to accrued interest balance changes.

EXECUTIVES

Cfo, David P. Burlage
Chief Risk Officer, Lori L. O'Flaherty
Coo, Ann Trakimas
Evp Banking Services Group, Antony M. Bahr
Svp And Cio, James R. Bernsten
Evp Regional Agribusiness Banking Group, Amy H. Gales
Central Region President Regional Agribusiness Banking Group, Mike Hechtner
Chief Credit Officer, Daniel Key
Evp Corporate Agribusiness Banking Group, Jonathan B. Logan
Southern Region President Regional Agribusiness Banking Group, Lynn Scherler
Svp And Manager Communications Division, Robert F. (Rob) West
Eastern Region President Regional Agribusiness Banking Group, David Sparks
Western Region President Regional Agribusiness Banking Group, Leili Ghazi
Ceo, Robert B. Engel, $880,000 total compensation
President, Mary E. McBride
Chief Banking Officer; Member Management Executive Committee, Thomas Halverson
Vp And Managing Counsel Legal And Loan Processing Division, Chris Clayton
President Farm Credit Leasing, Mike Romanowski
Svp Power Energy And Utilities Banking Division, Todd E. Telesz
Svp Electric Distribution Water And Community Facilities, Nivin Elgohary
Vice President And Managing Counsel, Christian Clayton
Vice President Lead Relationship Manager, David James
Vice President And Lead Relationship Manager, Natalya Rivkin
Vice President Energy Banking, Allison Dunn
Vice President, Kevin Oliver
Vice President, Marshall Essig
Vice President Policy And Public Affairs, Sarah Tyree
Regional Vice President, Catherine Roddick
Senior Vice President, Matt Cammer
Vice President And Executive D, Matthew Brill
Vice President, Richard Dill
Second Vice Chair, Kevin A. Still
First Vice Chair, Daniel T. (Dan) Kelley
Chairman, Everett M. Dobrinski
Auditors: PRICEWATERHOUSECOOPERS LLP DE

LOCATIONS

HQ: COBANK, ACB
6340 S FIDDLERS GREEN CIR, GREENWOOD VILLAGE, CO 801114951
Phone: 303 740-6527
Web: WWW.COBANK.COM

Selected Regional Offices
Ames IA
Atlanta GA
Austin TX
Enfield CT
Fargo ND
Louisville KY
Lubbock TX
Minneapolis MN
Omaha NE
Roseville CA
Spokane WA
St. Louis MO
Washington D.C.
Wichita KS

COMPETITORS

AgFirst	Northwest Farm Credit
AgStar	Rabo AgriFinance
AgriBank	Wells Fargo
Bank of America	
Farm Credit Services	
of Mid-America	

HISTORICAL FINANCIALS

Company Type: Private

Income Statement — FYE: December 31

	ASSETS ($ mil.)	NET INCOME ($ mil.)	INCOME AS % OF ASSETS	EMPLOYEES
12/15	117,470	936	0.8%	500
12/14	107,428	904	0.8%	—
12/10	67,700	818	1.2%	—
12/09	58,160	565	1.0%	—
Annual Growth	12.4%	8.8%	—	—

2015 Year-End Financials

Return on assets: 0.8% Sales ($ mil.): 2,379
Return on equity: 12.0%

COBB COUNTY BOARD OF EDUCATION

EXECUTIVES

Chair, Randy Scamihorn
Cfo*, Cathy Adams
Staff, Cherry Herron
Staff, Danielle Jesko
Auditors: MAULDIN & JENKINS LLC ATLANT

LOCATIONS

HQ: COBB COUNTY BOARD OF EDUCATION
514 GLOVER ST SE, MARIETTA, GA 300602750
Phone: 770 426-3300
Web: WWW.COBBK12.ORG

HISTORICAL FINANCIALS

Company Type: Private

Income Statement — FYE: June 30

	REVENUE ($ mil.)	NET INCOME ($ mil.)	NET PROFIT MARGIN	EMPLOYEES
06/17	1,299	(13)	—	115
06/16	1,238	(1)	—	—
06/15	1,166	(29)	—	—
06/14	532	67	12.6%	—
Annual Growth	34.7%	—	—	—

2017 Year-End Financials

Return on assets: (-0.6%) Cash ($ mil.): 247
Return on equity: (-1.6%)
Current ratio: —

COBB COUNTY PUBLIC SCHOOLS

EXECUTIVES

Principal, Dr Ashley Hosey
Asst, David Chiprany

Administrator, Joseph Sharp
Auditors: MAULDIN & JENKINS ATLANTA GE

LOCATIONS

HQ: COBB COUNTY PUBLIC SCHOOLS
4575 WADE GREEN RD NW, ACWORTH, GA
301023407
Phone: 678 594-8320
Web: WWW.COBBK12.ORG

HISTORICAL FINANCIALS

Company Type: Private

Income Statement — FYE: June 30

	REVENUE ($ mil.)	NET INCOME ($ mil.)	NET PROFIT MARGIN	EMPLOYEES
06/17	1,299	(13)	—	16,336
06/16	1,238	(1)	—	—
06/15	1,166	(29)	—	—
06/14	0	0	13.9%	—
Annual Growth	1017.7%	—	—	—

2017 Year-End Financials

Return on assets: (-0.6%) Cash ($ mil.): 247
Return on equity: (-1.6%)
Current ratio: —

COBB ELECTRIC MEMBERSHIP CORPORATION

Cobb Electric Membership Corporation (Cobb EMC) makes sure that Cobb County Georgia residents can cook corn on the cob (and anything else) using either electric power or natural gas. The utility distributes electricity to more than 200000 meters (more than 177000 residential commercial and industrial members) in Cobb County and four other north metro Atlanta counties. Cobb EMC operates about 10000 miles of power lines. The company's Gas South unit markets natural gas to customers who receive their service on Atlanta Gas & Light's natural gas distribution pipelines in Georgia.

Operations

Its Cobb Energy Management provides administrative and labor support to Cobb EMC and offers phone and Internet services to Cobb EMC's customers primarily through subsidiaries. Cobb Energy Management provides call center training tree trimming and billing software services and other ancillary support to EMC's core activities.

Geographic Reach

One of the largest of Georgia's 41 EMCs Cobb EMC's distribution system covers approximately 1434 square miles (Cobb Bartow Cherokee Fulton and Paulding counties in the north metro Atlanta area and Randolph Calhoun Quitman and Clay counties in Southwest Georgia).

Financial Performance

In 2012 the company reported a 46% increase in revenues thanks to a 10% rise in natural gas sales which outpaced a 2% decline in electric revenues. Net income grew by 194% in 2012 as a result of higher net sales and lower operating costs.

Strategy

Cobb EMC is a partner in Power4Georgians a consortium of six Georgia EMCs that collectively is developing a comprehensive strategy to provide reliable and affordable energy to the EMC members.

In 2013 as part of its ongoing transition out of non-energy businesses Cobb EMC announced today plans to cut its workforce by up to 20% percent through a company-wide offer of voluntary separation packages.

In 2012 Smart Energy Capital LLC and Jacoby Development Inc. signed a power purchase deal with Cobb EMC to provide power from the Azalea Solar Facility the largest solar power plant (10MW) in Georgia and one of the largest in the Southeast.

Company Background

The cooperative has been embroiled in litigation in recent years and in 2011 a Cobb County grand jury indicted Cobb EMC Dwight Brown on 31 counts of theft and racketeering. Brown was replaced as CEO by W.T. "Chip" Nelson.

The gas and support companies were merged into EMC as wholly owned units in 2009 as a way to streamline EMC's overall operations. The company has also sold a number of former assets to raise cash including Cooperative Business Ventures in 2009 for $2 million and the health and welfare brokerage business of Cooperative Benefits and Financial Services for a gain of $470000 in 2010.

Formed in 1938 Cobb EMC began life as an electric utility with 489 residential members and 14 commercial customers.

EXECUTIVES

Associate Vice President, Jim Gantt
Vice President Of Marketing And Corporate Communications, Kevan Espy
Vice President Member Care, Tim Sosebee
Vp Internal Audit, Kristi Knight
Vp, Tim Jarell
Board Of Directors, Ed Crowell
Auditors: MCNAIR MCLEMORE MIDDLEBROOKS &

LOCATIONS

HQ: COBB ELECTRIC MEMBERSHIP CORPORATION
1000 EMC PKWY NE, MARIETTA, GA 300607908
Phone: 770 429-2100
Web: WWW.COBBEMC.COM

HISTORICAL FINANCIALS

Company Type: Private

Income Statement — FYE: April 30

	REVENUE ($ mil.)	NET INCOME ($ mil.)	NET PROFIT MARGIN	EMPLOYEES
04/18*	849	25	3.0%	548
12/13	416	(8)	—	—
04/09	641	3	0.6%	—
12/08	2,104	0	—	—
Annual Growth	—	236.5%	—	—

*Fiscal year change

2018 Year-End Financials

Return on assets: 2.6% Cash ($ mil.): 20
Return on equity: 7.6%
Current ratio: 0.80

COBORN'S, INCORPORATED

Coborn's hopes you'll shop at your convenience. The company operates 52 stores across Minnesota North Dakota South Dakota Iowa Illinois and Wisconsin under the Coborn's Cash Wise Foods and Save-A-Lot banners. To support its more than 100 retail locations Coborn's operates its own central bakery dry cleaning facility and grocery distribution center. It supplies its stores with baked goods deli items and meat from its own central bakery and manufacturing plant. Along with its grocery stores the firm owns and operates pharmacies and convenience liquor and video stores.

Operations

As part of its business Coborn's operates under several banner names including Cash Wise Foods Save-A-Lot Economart Food Pride Mike's Super Value and namesake Coborn's. These supermarkets are supported by their own central bakery dry cleaning facility and grocery distribution center. The company also runs more than 65 stand-alone convenience liquor video and pharmacy locations.

Geographic Reach

Based in Minnesota Coborn's operates across the Upper Midwest in Minnesota the Dakotas Iowa Illinois and Wisconsin.

Strategy

Independently-owned Corborn's is building a sizable empire in the Upper Midwest through acquisitions and organic growth. In 2015 it purchased Marketplace Foods which owns four grocery/liquor stores in Western Wisconsin. The four Marketplace Foods stores are located in Hayward Menomonie Rice Lake and St. Croix Falls and will continue to operate as Marketplace Foods.

In fall 2013 it acquired four Captain Jack's liquor stores in Bismarck North Dakota as well as a single Bill's Liquor store in Mandan. (North Dakota's economy is growing rapidly thanks to the oil boom.)

Company Background

Founded in 1921 when Chester Coborn started a single produce market the company opened its first Cash Wise Foods store in 1979 and its first convenience store in 1986.

EXECUTIVES

Vp Information Technology, Dale D. Monson
Cfo, Tom Velin
President And Ceo, Chris Coborn
Evp, Greg Sandeno
Vp Operations, Dave Meyer
Vice President Of Organizational Development, Becky Estby
Auditors: RSM US LLP MINNEAPOLIS MINNE

LOCATIONS

HQ: COBORN'S, INCORPORATED
 1921 COBORN BLVD, SAINT CLOUD, MN 563012100
Phone: 320 252-4222
Web: WWW.COBORNSINC.COM

PRODUCTS/OPERATIONS

Selected Store Formats
Convenience stores (Little Dukes Holiday)
Hardware stores (Ace)
Liquor stores
Pharmacies
Restaurants (Subway)
Supermarkets (Coborn's Cash Wise Foods JK Markets Save-A-Lot)
Video stores

COMPETITORS

7-Eleven	Kroger
ALDI	Lunds
Couche-Tard	Target Corporation
Cub Foods	Wal-Mart
Kowalski's Markets	

HISTORICAL FINANCIALS

Company Type: Private

Income Statement   FYE: December 31

	REVENUE ($ mil.)	NET INCOME ($ mil.)	NET PROFIT MARGIN	EMPLOYEES
12/16	1,403	15	1.1%	7,200
12/13	1,246	30	2.5%	—
12/12	1,220	32	2.7%	—
Annual Growth	3.6%	(17.0%)	—	—

2016 Year-End Financials

Return on assets: 3.4%   Cash ($ mil.): 19
Return on equity: 7.1%
Current ratio: 1.30

COC PROPERTIES, INC.

EXECUTIVES

Chb, Harry D Stephenson
Pres, Don Stephenson
V Pres, Betty Phillips
V Pres, Mark Maddox
V Pres, Jim Bosworth
Vice President, Craig Stephenson
Territory Sales Manager, Don Richardson
Auditors: BATCHELOR TILLERY & ROBERTS

LOCATIONS

HQ: COC PROPERTIES, INC.
 110 MACKENAN DR STE 300, CARY, NC 275117901
Phone: 919 462-1100
Web: WWW.CARYOIL.COM

HISTORICAL FINANCIALS

Company Type: Private

Income Statement   FYE: December 31

	ASSETS ($ mil.)	NET INCOME ($ mil.)	INCOME AS % OF ASSETS	EMPLOYEES
12/18	102	8	8.8%	100
12/16	90	9	10.3%	—
12/15	77	4	6.1%	—
12/14	79	7	8.8%	—
Annual Growth	6.4%	6.3%	—	—

2018 Year-End Financials

Return on assets: 8.8%   Sales ($ mil): 1,728
Return on equity: 20.3%

COLONIAL PIPELINE COMPANY

With a reach that extends far beyond the original English colonies Colonial Pipeline delivers about 105 million gallons of gasoline diesel jet fuel home heating oil aviation and military fuels per day to cities and businesses across the eastern and southern US. The more than 5500-mile Colonial Pipeline system transports these fuels from Alabama Louisiana Mississippi and Texas to more than 265 marketing terminals near major urban centers in the Southeast and along the Eastern Seaboard. The company owns more than 3000 miles of right of way. Colonial Pipeline is owned by a consortium of companies including Koch a KKR affiliate Caisse de depot et placement du Quebec and Shell Pipeline.

Operations

The company operates an underground pipeline system that originates in the Houston Texas area and terminates at Linden New Jersey on the New York harbor.The Colonial Pipeline system connects refineries in the Gulf Coast and other locations to more than 260 marketing terminals. Colonial Pipeline delivers 100 million gallons of gasoline kerosene home heating oil diesel fuel and national defense fuels a day to shipper terminals in 13 states and Washington DC. The batches of oil shipments carried by the pipeline vary from 75000 barrels to 3.2 million barrels.

The Colonial Pipeline system services seven airports directly and provides fuel to multiple Department of Defense installations each day. It has 15 storage tanks strategically positioned along the pipeline to serve its customers' requirements.

Geographic Reach

Colonial Pipeline's network of customer-operated pipelines and terminals serves communities across the Southeast and Eastern US. It has shipper terminals in 13 states and the District of Columbia.

Strategy

The company is used to battling rough weather due to its pipeline being close to the hurricane-prone Gulf Coast. It has portable generators and emergency procedures it brings into action when confronted by power outages and other storm damage and is developing new infrastructure projects and additions to better serve its customers. In 2013 Colonial Pipeline outlined a strategy for expanding services. One project adds 100000 barrels of capacity to Colonial Pipeline's main gasoline pipeline which originates in Houston and terminates at Greensboro North Carolina; a second project adds 60000 barrels of daily capacity to the Greensboro-to-Linden New Jersey mainline which will be transported by Colonial Pipeline. Once completed Colonial Pipeline's capacity to carry gasoline diesel fuel jet fuel heating oil and other refined petroleum products through the pipeline would increase to 2.4 million barrels per day.

Other new projects include Clear Skies (a facilities modification program to support the delivery of ultra low sulfur diesel); Bengal Pipeline (a joint venture between Colonial Pipeline and Shell Pipeline serving refineries in Louisiana and Texas); and the Dulles Expansion Project (which links Colonial Pipeline's Line 3 mainline directly to Washington Dulles International Airport enabling the delivery of jet fuel to an onsite 579000-barrel tank farm).

Colonial Pipeline and Buckeye Pipe Line teamed up in 2013 to enable Gulf Coast refineries to supply eastern Pennsylvania and upstate New York markets. The deal allows Colonial Pipeline barrels to transfer to Buckeye's Paulsboro Pipeline and on to the Malvern and Macungie Pennsylvania terminals

The company also plans to further harden the Northeast infrastructure against another severe storm like Sandy. Modeled on its Gulf Coast contingency operations the improved system will add portable generators capable of replacing the loss of commercial power during a storm or other emergency.

Company Background

Responding to increased customer demand in 2011 Colonial Pipeline expanded the northern part of its Houston-to-New York system adding 100000 barrels per day of capacity (increasing its capacity in the New York Harbor market by 14%). In 2011 and 2012 it also conducted a series of system upgrades including adding 55000 barrels of daily capacity for diesel fuel home heating oil jet fuel and fuels and other petroleum products for the US military.

Taking advantage of the Yorktown Virginia refinery shut down and the conversion of its storage tanks to a delivery facility serving the Tidewater area in 2011 the company announced a capacity expansion to increase deliveries to the Tidewater region by 24000 barrels a day.

In 2010 Chevron sold its 23% stake in Colonial Pipeline to a KKR affiliate as part of its plan to sell non-core assets. In 2014 KKR-Keats Pipeline Investors L.P. owned 28% of Colonial Pipeline.

EXECUTIVES

Interim Ceo, John W. Somerhalder
Vp; General Manager Operations, Doug Belden
Director Technical Services, Rob Barbeauld
Vp And Cfo, Dave Doudna
Vice President Human Resources, Wayne Claire
Business Operations Vice President Director Manager, Denise Kirk
Vice President Of Human Resources, Eve Brooks
Vice President Human Resources, James America
Vice President And General Counsel, Helene Long
Treasurer, Reca Porter

LOCATIONS

HQ: COLONIAL PIPELINE COMPANY
1185 SANCTUARY PKWY # 100, ALPHARETTA, GA 300094765
Phone: 678 762-2200
Web: WWW.COLPIPE.COM
Colonial Pipeline operates a pipeline system that spans from Texas to New Jersey.

PRODUCTS/OPERATIONS

Selected Customers
American Airlines Inc
Apex Oil Company
Astra Oil Co. Inc.
Atlantic Trading & Marketing
BP Oil Company
Cargill Incorporated
Center Oil Company
Chalmette Refinery
Charter-Triad Terminals LLC
Chevron Corporation
CHS Inc
CITGO Petroleum Corp.
ConocoPhillips
Continental Airlines Fuel Mgmt.Inc
Cummins Terminal Inc.
Department Of Defense
Energy Merchant LLC
Epsilon Trading Inc.
Equiva Trading
ExxonMobil Oil Corporation
Flint Hills Resources
George E. Warren Corporation
Glencore Ltd
Global Companies LLC
Gulf Oil Limited Partnership
Hess Corporation
Hunt Refining Co.
J. Aron & Company
Kinder Morgan Energy
Koch Petroleum Group LP
Lion Oil Company
Louis Dreyfus Energy Services LP
Mabanaft
Maples Gas Company Inc.
Marathon Petroleum Co. LLC
Metroplex Energy Inc
Morgan Stanley Capital Group Inc.
Motiva
Murphy Oil USA Inc.
Musket Corporation
NIC Holding Corp
NWA Fuel Services Corp.
Petro Services
Petrocom Energy Group Ltd
Petroleum Traders Corporation
Phibro Inc.
Pilot Corporation

Placid Refining Company
Premcor Refining Group Inc
Quiktrip Corp.
Rwe Trading Americas Inc
Sheetz Inc
Shell Oil Products US
Shell Trading
Societe Generale Energie (USA) Corp
South Padre Energy LTD
Southwest Airlines
Sprague Energy Corporation
Sun Refining & Marketing
Tauber Oil Co.
Trafigura AG
Transmontaigne
Truman Arnold
United Parcel Service
US Airways Inc
Valero Marketing And Supply
Valley Oil Company LLC
Vitol S.A. Inc.
WAWA Incorporated
Williams Energy Marketing And Trading
World Fuel Services

COMPETITORS

Buckeye Partners
Enterprise Products
Gateway Energy
Kinder Morgan Energy Partners

Magellan Midstream
Sunoco Logistics
TransMontaigne

HISTORICAL FINANCIALS
Company Type: Private

Income Statement				FYE: December 31
	REVENUE ($ mil.)	NET INCOME ($ mil.)	NET PROFIT MARGIN	EMPLOYEES
12/18	1,340	407	30.4%	700
12/17	1,231	509	41.4%	—
12/16	1,214	233	19.2%	—
12/06	798	192	24.1%	—
Annual Growth	4.4%	6.4%		

2018 Year-End Financials

Return on assets: 13.7% Cash ($ mil.): 155
Return on equity: —
Current ratio: 1.20

COLORADO SEMINARY

Want a mile-high education? Colorado Seminary which does business as University of Denver (DU) offers graduate and undergraduate degrees in more than 100 fields of study including law government humanities education engineering and psychology. About 11600 undergraduate and graduate students from across the US and more than 80 countries are enrolled at the school. Founded in 1864 the university has a staff of 700 full-time faculty members; its student-to-faculty ratio is 11:1. DU is located on a 125-acre campus. Former Secretary of State Condoleezza Rice former Interior Secretary Gale Norton and former Coors Brewing CEO Peter Coors attended DU.

Strategy
DU has added about 20 buildings since 1997 to enhance its academic administrative athletic and residential capacities. Projects have included a soccer stadium and a center for international security and diplomacy within the School of International Studies. In 2016 it opened the Daniel Felix Ritchie School of Engineering and Computer Science.

Despite campus growth between 2006 and 2015 the University shrank its carbon footprint by 27% due the use of carbon offsets and vehicles fueled

by compressed natural gas (CNG). It operates the only CNG fueling station on a Colorado university campus.

EXECUTIVES

Provost, Robert D. (Bob) Coombe
Dean Josef Korbel School Of International Studies, Christopher R. Hill
Vice Chancellor Business And Financial Affairs, Craig W. Woody
Dean Women's College, Lynn Gangone
Provost, Gregg Kvistad
Dean Divisions Of Arts Humanities And Social Sciences, Anne E. McCall
Dean Sturm College Of Law, Martin J. (Marty) Katz
Dean Graduate School Of Professional Psychology, Shelly Smith-Acuna
Dean Natural Sciences And Mathematics, Andrei Kutateladze
Interim Dean Daniel Felix Ritchie School Of Engineering And Computer Science, Michael Keables
Vice Chancellor Division Of Marketing & Communications And Chief Marketing Officer, Kevin Carroll
Vice President Of Marketing, Katey Webber
Apalsa Vice President, Christiane Omoto
Auditors: CLIFTONLARSONALLEN LLP GREEN

LOCATIONS

HQ: COLORADO SEMINARY
2199 S UNIVERSITY BLVD, DENVER, CO 802104711
Phone: 303 871-2000
Web: WWW.DU.EDU

PRODUCTS/OPERATIONS

Selected Schools and Programs
Undergraduate Schools and Colleges
 Daniels College of Business
 Division of Natural Sciences & Mathematics
 Division of Arts Humanities and Social Sciences
 Josef Korbel School of International Studies
 Morgridge College of Education
 School of Engineering and Computer Science
 University College
 Women's College
Graduate and Professional Programs
Daniels College of Business
Divisions of Arts Humanities and Social Sciences
Divisions of Natural Sciences and Mathematics
Graduate School of Professional Psychology (GSPP)
Graduate School of Social Work (GSSW)
Graduate Tax Program
Interdisciplinary Degree Programs
Josef Korbel School of International Studies
Morgridge College of Education (MCE)
School of Engineering and Computer Science
The Sturm College of Law
University College

HISTORICAL FINANCIALS
Company Type: Private

Income Statement				FYE: June 30
	REVENUE ($ mil.)	NET INCOME ($ mil.)	NET PROFIT MARGIN	EMPLOYEES
06/17	467	86	18.6%	2,770
06/16	458	9	2.2%	—
06/15	431	69	16.0%	—
06/14	396	122	31.0%	—
Annual Growth	5.7%	(10.9%)	—	—

2017 Year-End Financials

Return on assets: 4.9% Cash ($ mil.): 52
Return on equity: 6.3%
Current ratio: —

COLORADO SPRINGS UTILITIES

Even one of the country's most scenic areas needs creature comforts and that's where utilities come in. Community-owned Colorado Springs Utilities is a multi-utility company that provides natural gas electric water and wastewater services in the Pikes Peak region. Colorado Springs Utilities' service territories include Colorado Springs Manitou Springs and several of the suburban residential areas surrounding the city. The City of Colorado Springs is the only customer of the streetlight system and is responsible for all streetlight service charges. The military installations of Fort Carson Peterson Air Force Base and the US Air Force Academy are also serviced by the multi-utility.

Operations

Colorado Springs Utilities operates an electric generation transmission and distribution system; a streetlight system; a natural gas distribution system; a water collection treatment and distribution system; and a wastewater collection and treatment system. The wastewater system provides services for 134007 active accounts in the city and for those areas approved by the Utilities Board on a long-term contractual basis including Peterson Air Force Base Manitou Springs and the Stratmoor Hills Water and Sanitation District. The water system serves 137619 active water meters including city residents and businesses and customers living in Ute Pass communities west of Colorado Springs military bases and other suburban areas outside the City limits. In 2013 the water system delivered 66413 acre feet (21.6 billion gallons).

Geographic Reach

The company's utilities serve the Colorado Springs Manitou Springs and many of the surrounding suburban residential areas as well as a number of military installations.

Financial Performance

The company's revenues declined by 3% in 2013 to $823.76 million primarily due to decreases in water and wastewater revenues of $30.2 million and $1.3 million respectively offset partially by increases in electric and natural gas revenues of $10.5 million and $1.1 million respectively. (Operating revenue changes are driven by base rate changes and unit sales that are primarily affected by weather).

Colorado Springs Utilities' net income dropped by 73% to $32.6 million in 2013 as the result of lower revenues and increased loss from derivatives.

In 2013 the company's operating cash inflow decreased to $256.3 million (from to $270.1 million in 2012) was primarily due to lower net income and higher interest rates and by capital spending that was deferred to future periods offset by unrestricted cash from higher utility rates.

Strategy

Colorado Springs Utilities' Strategic Plan is focused on fiscal responsibility planning for long term risks and identifying new business opportunities. In 2013 the company proposed a $3.38 monthly rate increase for electric and natural gas services for area residents. The utility's proposed 2014 budget of $1.154 billion (up about $95 million over the existing budget) is driven by an increase in capital investments needed to implement EPA-required air quality controls at the Martin Drake Power Plant and for the continued building of the Southern Delivery System.

In 2013 it began construction of a new $125 million water treatment plant in El Paso County as part of the Southern Delivery System water project. The water treatment plant will treat up to 50 million gallons of water per day when completed in 2016. Southern Delivery System is a $1 billion regional project that will deliver water to Colorado Springs Fountain Security and Pueblo West.

Company Background

Colorado Springs built its first municipal water system in 1878 and in 1888 a municipal wastewater system. Dissatisfied with the private utilities citizens of Colorado Springs approved a measure in 1924 to combine all of the city's utilities under the control of a municipally-owned company.

EXECUTIVES

Ceo, Phillip H Tollefson
Fin & Accting Mgr*, Edward Easterlin
Accountant*, Debra Hobson
Chief Plan/Fin Officer*, Dick Comerford
Senior Instructional Technolog, Ben Lucero
Chief Customer and Corporate S, Carl Cruz
and Database Specialis, Gary Crawford
Senior and Database, Patrick McGlynn
Procurement Staff, Beth Forrest
Accounting Tech, Ann Green
Senior Research Analyst, Beth Gaster

LOCATIONS

HQ: COLORADO SPRINGS UTILITIES
121 S TEJON ST STE 200, COLORADO SPRINGS, CO 809032187
Phone: 719 448-4800
Web: WWW.CSU.ORG

PRODUCTS/OPERATIONS

2013 Sales

	% of total
Electric	49
Gas	25
Water	17
Wastewater	8
Streetlight & other	1
Total	**100**

HISTORICAL FINANCIALS
Company Type: Private

Income Statement   FYE: December 31

	REVENUE ($ mil.)	NET INCOME ($ mil.)	NET PROFIT MARGIN	EMPLOYEES
12/18	890	109	12.3%	1,800
12/17	839	74	8.8%	—
12/16	793	130	16.4%	—
12/15	830	174	21.0%	—
Annual Growth	2.3%	(14.4%)	—	—

2018 Year-End Financials

Return on assets: 2.3%   Cash ($ mil.): 12
Return on equity: 5.9%
Current ratio: 2.20

COLORADO STATE UNIVERSITY

Colorado State University (CSU) got its start as an agricultural college in 1870 six years before Colorado was even a state. The school still has agricultural and forestry programs as well as a veterinary medicine school but it also offers degrees in liberal arts business engineering and the sciences. True to its roots as a land-grant college CSU engages the larger community in research and outreach through statewide Cooperative Extension programs and centers like the Colorado Agricultural Experiment Station. More than 30000 students are enrolled at CSU about 80% of whom are Colorado residents. It employs about 1500 faculty members and has aÂ student-to-teacher ratioÂ of 19:1.

Operations

The school's student body is largely composed of undergraduate students (more than 80%) but also includes some graduate and professional veterinary medicine students. CSU'sÂ most popularÂ undergraduate majors are business health and exercise science psychology biological science construction management and human development and family studies. Overall the university offers about 150 undergraduate graduate and professional degree programs through eight colleges.

CSU has extensive research programs in fields including atmospheric science clean energy the environment biomedicine and infectious diseases. The university's research programs attract some $300 million in external funding each year.

Geographic Reach

CSU's main campusÂ and itsÂ nearby foothills agricultural and mountain campusesÂ are located on about 5000 acres in Fort Collins Colorado.Â The universityÂ has more than 1200 international students and scholars from about 90 countries on its campus. Additionally about 900 CSU students travel abroad every year to participate in educational programs.

Financial Performance

CSU's revenues increased 8% in 2012 to $827 million from higher earnings on student tuition and fees grants and contracts auxiliary enterprises and other education activity sales and service income. Net income increased by 63% to $67 millionÂ that year as a result of theÂ university's revenue growth.

CSU has primarily experienced an increase in revenues over the last five years with the exception a slight dip during 2010 caused by decreased state capital contributions and grants and contracts.

Student tuition and feesÂ run at about $9000 per year for Colorado residents and $24000 for out-of-state students.

EXECUTIVES

Senior Advisor To The Executive Vice President, Bill Farland
Sr. Vice President, Mahoney Baja
Jr. Vice President, Colton Whitman
Vice President, James Heisel
Graduate Secretary, Kathleen Chynoweth

LOCATIONS

HQ: COLORADO STATE UNIVERSITY
6003 CAMPUS DELIVERY, FORT COLLINS, CO 805236003
Phone: 970 491-1372
Web: WWW.COLOSTATE.EDU

PRODUCTS/OPERATIONS

Selected Colleges Schools and Programs

Colleges
  College of Agricultural Sciences
  College of Applied Human Sciences
  College of Business
  College of Engineering
  College of Liberal Arts
  College of Natural Sciences
  College of Veterinary Medicine and Biomedical Sciences
  Warner College of Natural Resources
Schools and Programs
  Graduate School
  International Programs

Online Degrees and Courses (Online Plus)
School of the Arts
School of Biomedical Engineering
School of Education
School of Global Environmental Sustainability
School of Social Work

HISTORICAL FINANCIALS
Company Type: Private

Income Statement				FYE: June 30
	REVENUE ($ mil.)	NET INCOME ($ mil.)	NET PROFIT MARGIN	EMPLOYEES
06/08	740	(44)	—	6,701
06/06	562	26	4.7%	—
Annual Growth 14.7%		—	—	—

2008 Year-End Financials
Return on assets: (-3.6%)   Cash ($ mil.): 249
Return on equity: (-6.6%)
Current ratio: 4.20

COLORADO STATE UNIVERSITY SYSTEM

EXECUTIVES

Chancellor, Joe Blake
Chancellor, Michael Martin
Cfo, Henry Sobanet
Pres-Colorado State Univ.-Glob, Becky Takeda
Executive Assistant To Boa, Sharon Teufel
Deputy General Counsel, Johnna Doyle
Coordinator, Kathi Nietfeld
Doctor, Larue Johnson
Auditors: BKD LLP DENVER CO

LOCATIONS

HQ: COLORADO STATE UNIVERSITY SYSTEM
  475 17TH ST STE 1550, DENVER, CO 802024012
Phone: 303 534-6290
Web: WWW.CSUSYSTEM.EDU

HISTORICAL FINANCIALS
Company Type: Private

Income Statement				FYE: June 30
	REVENUE ($ mil.)	NET INCOME ($ mil.)	NET PROFIT MARGIN	EMPLOYEES
06/15	1,011	33	3.3%	6,701
06/14	938	(5)	—	—
06/13	884	22	2.6%	—
Annual Growth 6.9%		21.7%	—	—

2015 Year-End Financials
Return on assets: 1.5%   Cash ($ mil.): 352
Return on equity: 7.5%
Current ratio: 2.40

COLUMBIA GAS OF OHIO, INC.

Columbia Gas of Ohio takes pride in the fact that it can deliver gas first class en masse without impasse to the working class the middle class and the upper class. The utility is the largest natural gas utility in the state serving 1.4 million customers (including about 1.3 million residential 112000 commercial and 2600 industrial customers in more than 1030 communities in more than 60 of Ohio's 88 counties). The NiSource subsidiary offers a customer choice program which allows customers to choose their energy suppliers while Columbia Gas of Ohio continues to deliver the gas.

Operations
In addition to operating more than 19160 miles of distribution mains the company also provides other gas products services and programs across its 25400-sq.-mi. service area. Columbia Gas of Ohio is part of the NiSource's Gas Distribution segment which contributed about 54% of the total sales in fiscal 2013.

Geographic Reach
Columbia Gas of Ohio distributes natural gas to residential commercial and industrial customers in Columbus Mansfield Parma Springfield and Toledo. It is one of a handful of NiSource's distribution companies which collectively serve about 3.4 million gas and electric customers in seven states and operates about 58000 miles of pipeline.

Financial Performance
Columbia Gas of Ohio is part of the NiSource's Gas Distribution segment which reported an increase of 9% in 2013 due primarily to an increase for regulatory and service programs (including the impact from the rate cases at Columbia of Pennsylvania and Columbia of Massachusetts and the implementation of rates under Columbia of Ohio's approved infrastructure replacement program); the effects of colder weather which increased residential commercial and industrial usage; and an increase in the numbers of residential and commercial customers.

Strategy
The company's strategy includes spending about $2 billion over 25 years to improve its underground pipeline system.

In 2014 it asked state regulators for permission to replace a mile-long 12-inch diameter pipeline that crosses the Maumee River between Maumee and Perrysburg with a new 20-inch pipeline.

Upgrading its main offices in order to be more efficient in 2013 Columbia Gas of Ohio announced plans to relocated to the Arena District of Columbus taking about 208000 sq. ft. of a planned 288000-sq.-ft. office complex.

In 2012 Columbia Gas of Ohio has finished work on its $14 million Ackerman Road natural gas pipeline replacement project in Columbus.

That year it moved more than 722000 customers to independent suppliers as part of a decade-long deregulation plan by the state.

Company Background
In 2011 Columbia Gas of Ohio announced plans to secure permission from the Public Utilities Commission of Ohio for a five year extension of its energy efficiency programs (home energy audits weatherization and other initiatives) aimed at bringing down energy costs for individual customers.

In 2010 Columbia Gas of Ohio commenced a $1.3 million gas mains upgrade in two neighborhoods in Toledo.

EXECUTIVES

Vice President, Vince Parisi
Vice President And General Manager Operations, Lisa Carmean
Treasurer Area Director Central, Michael Loges

LOCATIONS

HQ: COLUMBIA GAS OF OHIO, INC.
  290 W NATIONWIDE BLVD # 114, COLUMBUS, OH 432151082
Phone: 614 460-6000
Web: WWW.COLUMBIAGASOHIO.COM

COMPETITORS

Dominion East Ohio	The Illuminating
Duke Energy Ohio	Company
Ohio Edison	Toledo Edison
Ohio Power	Vectren Energy
Stand Energy	Delivery of Ohio

HISTORICAL FINANCIALS
Company Type: Private

Income Statement				FYE: December 31
	REVENUE ($ mil.)	NET INCOME ($ mil.)	NET PROFIT MARGIN	EMPLOYEES
12/17	908	96	10.7%	2,500
12/16	854	114	13.4%	—
12/15	872	113	13.0%	—
12/14	993	102	10.3%	—
Annual Growth (3.0%)		(1.9%)	—	—

2017 Year-End Financials
Return on assets: 2.3%   Cash ($ mil.): 7
Return on equity: 7.9%
Current ratio: 0.40

COLUMBUS CITY SCHOOL DISTRICT

EXECUTIVES

Supt, Gene T Harris
Dpty Supt*, Marvenia Bosley
Treas*, Mike Kinneer
V Pres*, Terry Boyd
Executive Officer, Blain Waldron
Executive Officer, Carol Rood
Executive Officer, Craig Bickley
Executive Officer, David Nelson
Executive Officer, Lean Katterheinrich
Executive Officer, Roxanne Moses
Administrator, Chris Francia
Auditors: DAVE YOST COLUMBUS OHIO

LOCATIONS

HQ: COLUMBUS CITY SCHOOL DISTRICT
  270 E STATE ST FL 3, COLUMBUS, OH 432154312
Phone: 614 365-5000
Web: WWW.CCSOH.US

HISTORICAL FINANCIALS
Company Type: Private

Income Statement				FYE: June 30
	REVENUE ($ mil.)	NET INCOME ($ mil.)	NET PROFIT MARGIN	EMPLOYEES
06/18	1,087	66	6.2%	10,000
06/17	1,038	106	10.3%	—
06/16	972	(13)	—	—
06/06	667	(51)	—	—
Annual Growth 4.2%		—	—	—

2018 Year-End Financials
Return on assets: 3.3%   Cash ($ mil.): 450
Return on equity: —
Current ratio: —

COMENITY BANK

World Financial Network National Bank (WFNNB) will take credit for the credit it extends. The company is the private-label and co-branded credit card banking subsidiary of Alliance Data Systems. Along with affiliate World Financial Capital Bank the company underwrites cards on behalf of more than 85 businesses. The company's largest clients include apparel retailers L Brands and Redcats USA. WFNNB oversees about 120 million cardholder accounts and roughly $4 billion in receivables. Private equity giant Blackstone planned to acquire parent Alliance Data Systems for more than $6 billion but that deal was terminated in 2008.

EXECUTIVES

Pres, Timothy King
Computer Operations, Mike Schick
Project Manager, Connie Murphy
Information Technology, Paul Wroten
Client Sales Manager, Stacey Siak
Director Financial Planning, Don Borowy
Client Sales Manager, Jennifer Staten
Marketing Staff, Jeffrey Fasino
Administrative Assistant, Kurt Fraczkowski
Senior Vice President Chief Co, Michael F Swallow

LOCATIONS

HQ: COMENITY BANK
1 RIGHTER PKWY STE 100, WILMINGTON, DE 198031533
Phone: 614 729-4000

COMPETITORS

American Express	Citigroup
Bank of America	Target Receivables
Barclays Bank Delaware	

HISTORICAL FINANCIALS

Company Type: Private

Income Statement

	ASSETS ($ mil.)	NET INCOME ($ mil.)	INCOME AS % OF ASSETS	EMPLOYEES
12/14	9,149	389	4.3%	200
12/13	7,453	350	4.7%	—
12/05	332	10	3.2%	—
12/03	672	88	13.2%	—
Annual Growth	26.8%	14.4%	—	—

2014 Year-End Financials

Return on assets: 4.3%   Sales ($ mil): 1,976
Return on equity: 30.8%

COMFORT SYSTEMS USA (ARKANSAS), INC.

EXECUTIVES

Pres, Clyde A Jester
V Pres*, Trent McKenna
SEC*, Dawn McElyea
General Manager, Tad Hankins
Auditors: ERNST & YOUNG LLP HOUSTON TE

LOCATIONS

HQ: COMFORT SYSTEMS USA (ARKANSAS), INC.
4806 RIXIE RD, NORTH LITTLE ROCK, AR 721171537
Phone: 501 834-3320
Web: WWW.COMFORTAR.COM

HISTORICAL FINANCIALS

Company Type: Private

Income Statement   FYE: December 31

	REVENUE ($ mil.)	NET INCOME ($ mil.)	NET PROFIT MARGIN	EMPLOYEES
12/15	1,580	49	3.1%	102
12/14	1,410	28	2.0%	—
12/13	1,357	28	2.1%	—
Annual Growth	7.9%	31.5%	—	—

2015 Year-End Financials

Return on assets: 7.1%   Cash ($ mil.): 56
Return on equity: 13.5%
Current ratio: 1.40

COMMERCIAL CONTRACTING GROUP, INC.

EXECUTIVES

Ceo-Pres, Stephen Fragnoli
Cfo*, Steven Teper
Exec V Pres*, Bradford Kimmel
Exec V Pres*, Joel Lewandowski
Senior Project Manager, Doug Moody
Director of Business Developme, Karen Kelly

LOCATIONS

HQ: COMMERCIAL CONTRACTING GROUP, INC.
4260 N ATLANTIC BLVD, AUBURN HILLS, MI 483261578
Phone: 248 209-0500
Web: WWW.CCCNETWORK.COM

HISTORICAL FINANCIALS

Company Type: Private

Income Statement   FYE: December 31

	REVENUE ($ mil.)	NET INCOME ($ mil.)	NET PROFIT MARGIN	EMPLOYEES
12/17	480	0	—	300
12/16	284	0	—	—
12/15	281	0	—	—
12/14	289	0	—	—
Annual Growth	18.4%	—	—	—

2017 Year-End Financials

Return on assets: —   Cash ($ mil.): 12
Return on equity: —
Current ratio: 1.30

COMMONSPIRIT HEALTH

Formed in 2019 through the merger of Catholic hospital systems Catholic Health Initiatives and Dignity Health CommonSpirit Health is a $29 billion not-for-profit organization with more than 140 hospitals in 21 states. Its hospitals range from large urban medical centers (many with educational and research programs) to small hospitals in rural areas. The company also operates clinics long-term care assisted-living and senior residential facilities (totaling more than 700 health care facilities) and provides home-based care services. The system is sponsored by nearly 20 different congregations of nuns. CommonSpirit is the largest not-for-profit health system in the US.

Operations

CHI's network includes acute-care hospitals including academic and teaching facilities rural facilities with critical-care access nursing colleges home-health agencies community health services organizations long-term care facilities assisted-care and residential senior homes research and development programs and labs. The company has about 25000 physicians and advanced practice clinicians.

Geographic Reach

CHI operates in Arkansas California Colorado Indiana Iowa Kansas Kentucky Minnesota Nebraska Nevada New Jersey New Mexico North Dakota Ohio Oregon Pennsylvania South Dakota Tennessee Texas Washington and Wisconsin — 21 states in all.

Strategy

The 2019 merger of California-based Dignity Health and Colorado-based Catholic Health Initiatives that resulted in the creation of CommonSpirit Health was just one of several health system transactions in a time of rising M&A activity. The systems joined forces to strengthen their operations enabling them to provide better care for more people. The combined system's operating goals include expanding its clinical capabilities shifting to providing care outside of the hospital investing in technology addressing social determinants of health and maintaining an experienced workforce.

Mergers and Acquisitions

After years of discussions CHI and Dignity Health merged in early 2019. The combined health system CommonSpirit Health is the largest not-for-profit hospital system in the US. The size of the system allows for it to provide expanded care to patients through such methods as virtual appointments a broader range of clinical programs and advanced technologies. The new organization with 142 hospitals in 21 states is headquartered in Chicago. Individual hospitals continue to operate under their existing names.

HISTORY

In 1860 the Sisters of St. Francis established a hospital in Philadelphia laying the foundation for a larger health care organization. In 1981 Franciscan Health System was formally established to be a national holding company for Catholic hospitals and related organizations. By the mid-1990s the system consisted of 12 member and two affiliate hospitals and 11 long-term-care facilities located in the mid-Atlantic states and the Pacific Northwest.

Sisters of Charity of Cincinnati and the Sisters of St. Francis Perpetual Adoration of Colorado Springs co-sponsored The Sisters of Charity Health Care Systems incorporated in 1979 as a multi-institutional health care network. By the mid-1990s the system included 20 hospitals in Colorado Kentucky Nebraska New Mexico and Ohio.

Three congregations collaborated to form Catholic Health Corporation in 1980 one of the first such health care partnerships between religious communities within the Roman Catholic Church in the US. By 1996 this coalition operated 100 health care facilities in 12 states.

The development of modern managed care health care systems put pressure on the smaller Catholic hospital operations so the three systems established Catholic Health Initiatives (CHI) in 1996 as a national entity serving five geographic regions. Patricia Cahill a lay health care veteran who previously served the Archdiocese of New York was appointed president and CEO of CHI. The following year CHI absorbed the 10-hospital Sisters of Charity of Nazareth Health Care System based in Bardstown Kentucky (founded in a log cabin in 1812).

That year CHI continued to seek new partnerships to improve efficiency. With Alegent Health it formed provider network Midwest Select with nearly 200 hospitals marketing discounted rates to businesses. CHI allied with the Daughters of Charity to form for-profit joint venture Catholic Healthcare Audit Network to provide operational financial compliance and information systems audits as well as due diligence reviews. CHI also joined insurance joint venture NewCap Insurance with the Daughters of Charity and Catholic Health East; the firm allowed CHI to operate independently of commercial insurers.

CHI made a secular tie-in with the University of Pennsylvania Health System in 1998 whereby the university's system would offer care through five Catholic hospitals (CHI made plans to transfer these hospitals to Catholic Health East in 2001). The next year CHI announced its first loss due to lackluster performance in the Midwest. During 2000 the company responded by streamlining operations and changing management resulting in a positive bottom line. In 2001 it sold three hospitals in Pennsylvania one in Delaware and one in New Jersey to Catholic Health East.

EXECUTIVES

President And Chief Executive Officer, Kevin E. Lofton, age 64
President Enterprise Business Lines And Cfo, J. Dean Swindle
Svp Divisional Operations (texas), Michael H. Covert
Svp Marketing And Communications, Joyce M. Ross
Executive Vice President Mission, Thomas R. Kopfensteiner
Svp Divisional Operations And Ceo Chi Memorial (tennessee), Larry Schumacher, age 61
Svp Legal Services And General Counsel, Mitch H. Melfi
Interim Svp And Coo, Paul W. Edgett
Evp Chief Administrative Officer And Chief Human Resources Officer, Patricia G. (Pat) Webb
Svp Divisional Operations And Ceo Chi Health (nebraska And Southwest Iowa), Cliff A. Robertson
Senior Vice President And Division Executive Officer, Jeffrey S. Drop
Svp And Chief Nursing Officer, Kathleen D. Sanford
Svp Divisional Operations And Ceo Mercy Health Network (iowa), David H. Vellinga
Svp Divisional Operations And Ceo Chi Franciscan Health (tacoma), Ketul J. Patel
Svp And President And Ceo Kentuckyone Health, Ruth W. Brinkley
Ceo Chi St. Alexius Health, Matt Grimshaw, age 44
Interim Evp Operations, Anthony Jones
Svp And Chief Medical Officer, Robert J. Weil
Senior Vice President And Chief Medical Officer, Stephen L Moore
Divisional Assistant Vice President Information Technology Business Relationship, Debbie Mullins
Vp Governance And Administrative Services, Ellen Barton

Vice President Contracting Supply Chain, Susan Schrupp
Director Of Medical Records, Becki Thompson
Senior Vice President Divisional Operationsceo, Robert Ratzi
Vice President Human Resource Business Practices, Thomas Sams
Vice President Of Operations, Dan Bjerknes
Vice President Supply Chain Data Analytics, Kevin Kakuda
Vice President Corporate Responsibility, Susan Shiflett
Vice President Clinical Operations And Physician Leadership Development, Manoj Pawar
Vice President Of Patient Care, Deb Haagenson
Vice President Outreach, Ellen Lee
Director Of Pharmacy, Sandy Jacobson
Director Of Pharmacy, Nicki Bohl
Director Of Pharmacy, Marian Rhoads
Senior Vice President Performance Excellence, Robert Strickland
Vice President Of Nursing, Heike Duban
Vice President Corporate Responsibility, Betsy Wade
Senior Vice President Strategy Development, Meta Dooley
Vice President And Medical Director National Cardiovascular Service Line, Jerome Granato
Vice President Care Management, Chris Stanley
Svp Ciso, Sheryl Rose
Vice President Strategic Planning And Alignment, Tim Moran
Vice President Of Finance, Christy Spitser
Vice President, Deeanna Opstedahl
Vice President Operational Finance Mercy Medical Center, Joseph Ruark
Vice President Clinic, Marilyn Mcginley
Vp Business Intelligence, Deborah Odell
National Vp Supply Chain Operations Procurement, John Frye
Vp Finance, Brent Schmidt
Auditors: ERNST & YOUNG LLP DENVER CO

LOCATIONS

HQ: COMMONSPIRIT HEALTH
444 W LAKE ST STE 2500, CHICAGO, IL 606060097
Phone: 312 741-7000
Web: WWW.CATHOLICHEALTHINITIATIVES.ORG

COMPETITORS

Adventist Health System Sunbelt Healthcare
Allina Hospitals
Ascension Health
Baptist Health
Baptist Health (Arkansas)
BryanLGH Medical Center
Denver Health and Hospital Authority
Exempla Healthcare
HCA
Life Care Centers
Memorial Health System (Colorado)
Methodist Health System
OhioHealth
Tenet Healthcare
Universal Health Services

HISTORICAL FINANCIALS
Company Type: Private

Income Statement				FYE: June 30
	REVENUE ($ mil.)	NET INCOME ($ mil.)	NET PROFIT MARGIN	EMPLOYEES
06/18	14,982	222	1.5%	72,500
06/17	15,547	128	0.8%	—
06/16	15,942	(703)	—	—
06/07	7,731	902	11.7%	—
Annual Growth	6.2%	(12.0%)	—	—

2018 Year-End Financials
Return on assets: 1.1%   Cash ($ mil.): 510
Return on equity: 3.1%
Current ratio: 0.80

COMMUNITY BEHAVIORAL HEALTH

EXECUTIVES

Director, Arthur C Evans Jr
Director*, Estelle Richmond
Director*, Nancy Luckas
Human Resources Director, Peter Bezrucik
Auditors: MITCHELL & TITUS LLP PHILADEL

LOCATIONS

HQ: COMMUNITY BEHAVIORAL HEALTH
801 MARKET ST STE 7000, PHILADELPHIA, PA 191073158
Phone: 215 413-3100
Web: WWW.DBHIDS.ORG

HISTORICAL FINANCIALS
Company Type: Private

Income Statement				FYE: December 31
	REVENUE ($ mil.)	NET INCOME ($ mil.)	NET PROFIT MARGIN	EMPLOYEES
12/17	935	0	—	270
12/16	919	0	—	—
12/15	811	0	—	—
12/02	453	(0)	—	—
Annual Growth	4.9%	—	—	—

2017 Year-End Financials
Return on assets: —   Cash ($ mil.): 42
Return on equity: —
Current ratio: —

COMMUNITY FOUNDATION OF NORTHWEST INDIANA, INC.

EXECUTIVES

Pres, Frankie Fesko
SEC*, James J Richards
Treas*, David E Wickland
Administrative Assistant, Kathryn Johnson
Registered Nurse, Annette Haney
Registered Nurse, David Gasper
Security Staff, Derek Gilliam
Registered Nurse, Lynda Koppen
Rn, Betsy Lunsford
Phlebotomy Supervisor, Dorothy Grisham
Rn, Heather Helmuth

LOCATIONS

HQ: COMMUNITY FOUNDATION OF NORTHWEST INDIANA, INC.
905 RIDGE RD, MUNSTER, IN 463211773
Phone: 219 836-0130
Web: WWW.COMHS.ORG

HISTORICAL FINANCIALS

Company Type: Private

Income Statement   FYE: June 30

	REVENUE ($ mil.)	NET INCOME ($ mil.)	NET PROFIT MARGIN	EMPLOYEES
06/18	1,150	137	12.0%	2,000
06/17	1,084	122	11.2%	—
06/15	108	(4)	—	—
Annual Growth	119.5%	—	—	—

2018 Year-End Financials

Return on assets: 9.1%   Cash ($ mil.): 18
Return on equity: 15.4%
Current ratio: 1.50

COMMUNITY HEALTH CHOICE, INC.

EXECUTIVES

Coo, Karen Love
Cfo, Brian Maude
Associate Web Developer, Becky Cantu
Coordinator, Richard Hobbs
Director, John Coakley
Vice-President, John Petrosino
Sales Staff, Leticia Neri
Administrative Assistant, Delwin Beene
Administrative Assistant, Catherine Bowers
Vice President, Jeff Allen
Director of Claims, Mychelle Scott
Auditors: I KPMG LLP OKLAHOMA CITY OK

LOCATIONS

HQ: COMMUNITY HEALTH CHOICE, INC.
2636 S LOOP W STE 700, HOUSTON, TX 770545630
Phone: 713 295-2200
Web: WWW.COMMUNITYHEALTHCHOICE.ORG

HISTORICAL FINANCIALS

Company Type: Private

Income Statement   FYE: December 31

	ASSETS ($ mil.)	NET INCOME ($ mil.)	INCOME AS % OF ASSETS	EMPLOYEES
12/15	239	1	0.5%	700
12/14	192	16	8.6%	—
12/13	166	(3)	—	—
12/12	172	(17)	—	—
Annual Growth	11.6%	—	—	—

2015 Year-End Financials

Return on assets: 0.5%   Sales ($ mil): 851
Return on equity: 1.2%

COMMUNITY HEALTH NETWORK, INC.

Community Hospitals of Indiana (aka Community Health Network) has Indianapolis surrounded. The health care system includes 10 acute care hospitals nine surgery centers seven imaging centers seven immediate care centers 40 ambulatory care centers two endoscopy centers and four long term care facilities. One of its acute care facilities Community Hospital Anderson is located outside the state capital. It also runs the Community Heart and Vascular Hospital. Community Health Network whose origin reaches back to the 1950s has a total of about 1200 staffed beds and 2000 physicians. Other operations include physician practices occupational health facilities a rehab center and home health practices.

Operations

Community Health Network's physician practice Community Physician Network has more than 600 providers and working out of over 80 locations.

Together with its clinics health pavilions surgery centers and physician affiliations Community Health Network's service area covers an eight-county area in central Indiana. Various specialty centers treat digestive and joint ailments wounds spinal problems and gastrointestinal disease and also provide imaging services. Community's MedCheck clinics offer routine checkups and screenings in stand-alone locations while its MedCheck Express locations inside area Wal-Mart stores serve customers where they shop. Four Wellspring pharmacies all but one of which are located inside hospitals cover prescriptions patient education and wellness programs.

Among the system's notable features the Community Heart and Vascular Hospital which opened its doors in 2003 is an all-digital facility with digital equipment and wireless communications systems linking all its operations. Additionally the 42-bed neonatal intensive care room at Community Hospital North is one of the nation's largest labor delivery recovery and postpartum units and Westview Hospital is the state's only such facility offering osteopathic services.

In 2014 the system had more than a million outpatient visits. It also conducted some 96000 surgeries facilitated 7300 infant births and had more than 243000 emergency department visits.

Sales and Marketing

In 2014 Medicare patients accounted for about 41% of gross patient charges while Medicaid patients accounted for another 14%.

Financial Performance

Revenue grew 10% in 2014 to $1.9 billion thanks largely to growth in net patient service earnings and other revenue. This was partially offset by a decline in incentive payments related to electronic health records as well as the absence of gains on contributions to a joint venture.

Also that year the company reported a net loss of $0.9 million (versus a $179 million profit in 2013) as pension assets underperformed and gains on investments declined. However cash flow from operations rose 84% to $208 million due to changes in accrued pensions accounts payable and estimated third-party payor settlements.

Strategy

The health network is expanding in and around Indianapolis. It is investing nearly $250 million on two large building projects including a new hospital on the Community Hospital East campus and a new cancer center at the Community Hospital North campus.

In 2015 Community Health Network opened a new cardio-oncology clinic in Indianapolis. The facility is dedicated to understanding the impact that cancer-fighting treatments have on the heart.

EXECUTIVES

President And Ceo Community Health Network, William E. (Bill) Corley
President And Ceo Community Hospital Anderson, William C. (Bill) VanNess
Ceo Visionary Enterprises Inc., Bryan A. Mills
President Community Hospital North, Barbara (Barb) Summers
Ceo Community Physicians Of Indiana, Timothy L. Hobbs
Ceo The Indiana Heart Hospital, Thomas A. Malasto
Ceo Community Home Health Services, Jessie Westlund
President Community Hospital East, Robin Ledyard
President Community Hospital South, Anthony Lennen
President And Ceo, Beth Tharp
Chief Information Officer, Ron Strachan
Cfo, Joe Kessler
Coo, Tony Javorka
Senior Vice President And Head Human Resources, Jeffrey Purkey
Vice President Real Estate Services At Vei, Linda Pendleton
Vice President Of Innovation, Pete Turner
Svp Physician Executive And Interim President North Region, Dee Moonesinghe
Auditors: PRICEWATERHOUSECOOPERS LLP I

LOCATIONS

HQ: COMMUNITY HEALTH NETWORK, INC.
1500 N RITTER AVE, INDIANAPOLIS, IN 462193027
Phone: 317 355-1411
Web: WWW.ECOMMUNITY.COM

PRODUCTS/OPERATIONS

2014 Sales

	$ mil.	% of total
Net patient service revenue less provision for bad debts	1,815	94
Service fee revenue	25	1
Other revenue	100	5
Total	**1,942**	**100**

Selected Services

Advanced Wound Center
Assisted Fertility Services
Bariatric Services
Behavioral Health
Breast Care Services
Cancer Care Services
Children's Health
Clinical Research Trials
Community Home Health
Diet and Nutrition Services
Digestive Health Services
Emergency Services
Heart and Vascular
Inpatient Rehabilitation
Interventional Radiology
Maternity Services
Mid America Clinical Labs
Neuroscience Services
Orthopedic Services
Physical Therapy and Rehab
Radiology/Imaging Services
Sleep Wake Services
Sports Medicine
Surgical Services
Symptom Management Group
Weight Loss and Wellness
Women's Services

Selected Facilities and Affiliates

Community Health Pavilions
Community Heart and Vascular Hospital
Community Hospital Anderson

Community Hospital East
Community Hospital North
Community Hospital South
Community Imaging Centers
Community Physicians of Indiana network
Community Spine Center
Community Westview Hospital
Hook Rehabilitation Center
Indiana Surgery Centers
Indianapolis Endoscopy Center
MedCheck walk-in clinics
MedCheck Express clinics
Wellspring Pharmacy chain

COMPETITORS

Ball Memorial Hospital	Riverview Hospital
Henry County Memorial	St. Elizabeth Regional
Hospital	Health
IU Health	St. Vincent Health
IU Health Bloomington	Wabash County Hospital
Hospital	
Memorial Hospital	
(Logansport)	

HISTORICAL FINANCIALS
Company Type: Private

Income Statement				FYE: December 31
	REVENUE ($ mil.)	NET INCOME ($ mil.)	NET PROFIT MARGIN	EMPLOYEES
12/14	1,942	(0)	—	5,000
12/13	1,763	179	10.2%	—
12/12	384	44	11.7%	—
Annual Growth	124.7%	—	—	—

2014 Year-End Financials
Return on assets: —   Cash ($ mil.): 230
Return on equity: (-0.1%)
Current ratio: 2.10

COMMUNITY HOSPITAL OF THE MONTEREY PENINSULA

Community Hospital of the Monterey Peninsula has a sunny disposition when it comes to medical care. The not-for-profit health care facility provides general medical and surgical services to residents of Monterey California. It has about 235 acute care and skilled nursing beds and offers specialty services including cardiac and cancer care obstetrics orthopedics and rehabilitation. In addition to its main facility the hospital operates several ancillary centers including a mental health clinic an inpatient hospice medical laboratory branches and several outpatient centers offering diagnostic imaging diabetes care and other services.

Operations
Community Hospital offers a broad range of healthcare services at 15 locations including the main hospital outpatient facilities satellite laboratories a mental health clinic a short-term skilled nursing facility Hospice of the Central Coast and business offices.

In 2012 the hospital systems served 12130 inpatients in 2012. It also had 49565 emergency visits 283181 outpatient visits and assisted in 1193 births.

Geographic Reach
The company has facilities in Carmel Marina Monterey and Seaside counties in California.

Financial Performance
Medicare accounted for 53% of Community Hospital of the Monterey Peninsula's revenues in 2012; commercial insurance 23% and Medi-Cal 10%.

Strategy
To improve care in its service territory the hospital is working to increase best-practice sharing among physicians. It is also supporting information sharing by coordinating electronic health records (EHRs).

In 2014 the hospital received a $200000 contribution from the Auxiliary of Community Hospital of the Monterey Peninsula completing a five-year $1 million pledge by the service organization to support the hospital.

Company Background
As health care costs skyrocket in the US Community Hospital of the Monterey Peninsula has worked to lower its expenses. Between 2008 and 2011 the organization lowered annual costs by about $44 million.

Community Hospital of the Monterey Peninsula was founded in 1934.

EXECUTIVES
Pres-Ceo, Steven J Packer
V Pres*, Terrill Lowe
Cfo*, Laura Zehm
V Pres*, Cynthia Peck
V Pres*, Tim Nylen
SEC*, Shelley Post
Vp*, Steven X Cabrales
Chief of Medicine, Berry Gendelman
Health Professional, Christian Le
Security Staff, Garry Glaser
Vice President Nursing, Terril Lowe

LOCATIONS
HQ: COMMUNITY HOSPITAL OF THE MONTEREY PENINSULA
23625 HOLMAN HWY, MONTEREY, CA 939405902
Phone: 831 624-5311
Web: WWW.CHOMP.ORG

PRODUCTS/OPERATIONS

Selected Community Hospital Service Locations
Community Hospital of the Monterey Peninsula: Monterey
Carol Hatton Breast Care Center: Monterey
Development/Patient Business Services: Monterey
Hartnell Professional Center: Monterey Peninsula
Primary Care/Satellite Laboratory: Carmel
Peninsula Wellness Center: Marina
Ryan Ranch Outpatient Campus: Monterey
Seaside Satellite Laboratory: Seaside
Westland House: Monterey

Selected Services
Bariatric Surgery
Behavioral Health Services
Carol Hatton Breast Care Center
Comprehensive Cancer Center
Diabetes
Diagnostic and Interventional Radiology
Emergency
Family Birth Center
Hospice of the Central Coast
Intermediate Intensive Care Nursery
Laboratory Services
Nutrition Therapy Program
Orthopedics
Outpatient Immunology Services
Outpatient Surgery Center
Pulmonary Wellness Services
Radiation Oncology
Rehabilitation Services
Sleep disorders
Social Services
Stroke Program
Tyler Heart Institute (Cardiac Care)
Westland House Skilled Nursing Facility
Wound Care and Hyperbaric Healing

COMPETITORS

Dignity Health	Stanford Health Care
John Muir Health	Sutter Health
Queen of the Valley	The Palo Alto Medical
Medical Center	Foundation
Salinas Valley	UCSF Medical
Memorial	
Sequoia Healthcare	
District	

HISTORICAL FINANCIALS
Company Type: Private

Income Statement				FYE: December 31
	REVENUE ($ mil.)	NET INCOME ($ mil.)	NET PROFIT MARGIN	EMPLOYEES
12/16	526	71	13.7%	1,947
12/15	560	66	11.9%	—
12/12	442	81	18.4%	—
12/09	475	26	5.6%	—
Annual Growth	1.5%	15.2%	—	—

2016 Year-End Financials
Return on assets: 11.5%   Cash ($ mil.): 73
Return on equity: 36.3%
Current ratio: 3.60

COMMUNITY HOSPITALS OF CENTRAL CALIFORNIA

Community Medical Centers helps California's San Joaquin Valley stay healthy. The not-for-profit system operates four hospitals — along with nursing homes and freestanding outpatient facilities — in the greater Fresno area. Its Community Regional Medical Center is a roughly 600-bed academic hospital that provides advanced care in areas such as trauma cardiac care neuroscience and orthopedics. Clovis Community Medical Center (some 200 beds) provides general medical-surgical care with expertise in women's health and bariatric surgery. Specialty hospitals Fresno Heart & Surgical Hospital and Community Behavioral Health Center (the largest psychiatric care facility in the area) each have about 60 beds.

Operations
Community Medical Centers employs some 3000 nurses and has about 1200 affiliated physicians on its staff. Community Regional Medical Center serves about 35000 inpatient visitors and 111000 emergency room patients each year while Clovis Community Medical Center has some 13000 admissions and 51000 emergency encounters. Fresno Heart & Surgical Hospital which conducts cardiac vascular and bariatric procedures handles more than 3500 inpatient visits each year. Meanwhile Community Behavioral Health Center sees some 4000 admissions annually.

The network operates central California's only Level I trauma center and comprehensive regional burn center. It is also home to the region's only high-risk pregnancy unit as well as the Central California Neuroscience Institute and a Level III neonatal intensive care unit. The hospital system has a physician residency program it operates in conjunction with the University of California San Francisco.

Community Medical Centers serves as the area's essential "safety-net" provider conducting some $140 million in community benefits each year including care for uninsured and under-insured patients. Along with its acute care hospitals the organization operates outpatient centers clinics home care services community education programs and physician groups.

Geographic Reach

Community Medical Centers serves a 15000-mile territory including the California counties of Fresno Kings Madera Mariposa and Tulare. All four of the organization's main hospital facilities are located in the city of Fresno.

Sales and Marketing

Patient service revenues account for most of Community Medical Centers' earnings. Payer groups for patient services include Medicare and Medicaid plans which account for about 70% of sales as well as commercial insurance and self-paying clients.

Strategy

The system's Clovis campus in 2014 completed its largest-ever expansion through a $300 million project — expanding its bed count from 110 to 205 — and making the medical center the first full-service hospital in the region to have all private rooms. The renovations added a five-story bed tower a dedicated women's pavilion a special care nursery a physician practice office building and a new parking structure. The emergency department is also expanding to accommodate a projected 50000 patient visits annually.

EXECUTIVES

Ceo Clovis Community, Craig S. Castro
Svp Managed Care, Abdul Kassir
Ceo Fresno Heart And Surgical Hospital, Wanda Holderman
President And Ceo, Tim A. Joslin
Evp And Cfo, Stephen R. Walter
Evp And Coo, Patrick Rafferty
Svp And Cio, George Vasquez
Svp And Chief Nursing Officer, Mary Contreras
Ceo Community Regional, Jack Chubb
Vp Community Medical Foundation, Rob Saroyan
Vp And Chief Nursing Informatics Officer, David Boyd
Vice President Strategic Development, Charles Hensley
Director Of Nursing, Richard Brescione
Pharmacy Manager, Melissa Reger
Vice President Finance Administration, Debbie Moffett
Vice President Of Medical Records, Janet Perry
Vice President Pfs, Michele Earnhart
Director Of Radiology, Steven Bergthold
Vice President Legal Services, Brianne Marriott
Vice President Finance And Administration, Debbie Vega
Vice President Learning And Training, Sheldon Cohen
Vice President Cmio, Judi Binderman
Vice President Chief Information Security Officer, Eric Saff
Senior Vice President Human Resources, Margaret Breen
Vice President Of Information Technology, Joe Yzaguirre
Board Member, Mark Mathieson

LOCATIONS

HQ: COMMUNITY HOSPITALS OF CENTRAL CALIFORNIA
2823 FRESNO ST, FRESNO, CA 937211324
Phone: 559 459-6000
Web: WWW.COMMUNITYMEDICAL.ORG

PRODUCTS/OPERATIONS

Selected Locations

Hospitals
Clovis Community Medical Center (Fresno)
Community Regional Medical Center (Fresno)
Community behavioral Health Center (Fresno)
Fresno Heart & Surgical Care (Fresno)
Outpatient centers
Advanced Medical Imaging
California Cancer Center
Community Medical Center-SierraDeran Koligian
Ambulatory Care Center

COMPETITORS

Adventist Health System West
Catholic Health Initiatives
Dignity Health
Good Samaritan Hospital (San Jose)
HCA
Saint Agnes Medical Center
Sierra View District Hospital
Stanford Health Care
Sutter Health
Tenet Healthcare
UCSF Medical
ValleyCare Health System

HISTORICAL FINANCIALS
Company Type: Private

Income Statement				FYE: August 31
	REVENUE ($ mil.)	NET INCOME ($ mil.)	NET PROFIT MARGIN	EMPLOYEES
08/18*	1,667	108	6.5%	6,200
06/10	33	0	2.1%	—
/ 0	0	0	—	—
Annual Growth	—	—	—	—

*Fiscal year change

2018 Year-End Financials
Return on assets: 4.9%   Cash ($ mil.): 88
Return on equity: 8.9%
Current ratio: 1.20

COMMUNITY HOSPITALS OF CENTRAL CALIFORNIA

EXECUTIVES

Pres, Tim Joslin
Coordinator, Jennifer Trytten
Doctor, Dalpinder Sandhu
Manager, Denise Curry
Human Resources Director, Linda Jeffers
Doctor, Mohinder Poonia
Pharmacist, Staci Anderson
Rn, Bonnie Harkins
Manager, Jonathan Miller
Nurse Coordinator, Kathy Norkunas
Director of Lending, Caitlyn Meyer
Auditors: MOSS ADAMS LLP STOCKTON CA

LOCATIONS

HQ: COMMUNITY HOSPITALS OF CENTRAL CALIFORNIA
2823 FRESNO ST, FRESNO, CA 937211324
Phone: 559 459-6000
Web: WWW.COMMUNITYMEDICAL.ORG

HISTORICAL FINANCIALS
Company Type: Private

Income Statement				FYE: August 31
	REVENUE ($ mil.)	NET INCOME ($ mil.)	NET PROFIT MARGIN	EMPLOYEES
08/17	1,529	48	3.1%	1,000
08/14	127	0	0.5%	—
Annual Growth	128.9%	320.6%	—	—

2017 Year-End Financials
Return on assets: 2.4%   Cash ($ mil.): 64
Return on equity: 4.3%
Current ratio: 1.60

COMPASSION INTERNATIONAL INC

EXECUTIVES

Pres-Ceo, Santiago Mellado
Gen Dir*, Ronald Mathieu
V Chm*, Laurent Mbanda
Chm*, Karen Wesolowski
Gen Dir*, Jean-Franois Bussy
Svp-Gen Coun*, Robert Hawkins
Gen Dir*, Mike Jeffs
Gen Dir*, Francisco Batres
SEC*, Judy Briscoe Golz
Gen Mgr*, Kenneth Morgan
Gen Dir*, Chris Knepper
Auditors: CAPIN CROUSE LLP COLORADO SPR

LOCATIONS

HQ: COMPASSION INTERNATIONAL INC
12290 VOYAGER PKWY, COLORADO SPRINGS, CO 809213694
Phone: 719 487-7000
Web: WWW.COMPASSION.COM

HISTORICAL FINANCIALS
Company Type: Private

Income Statement				FYE: June 30
	REVENUE ($ mil.)	NET INCOME ($ mil.)	NET PROFIT MARGIN	EMPLOYEES
06/16	800	13	1.6%	2,002
06/15	768	(8)	—	—
06/14	719	8	1.2%	—
06/13	659	15	2.3%	—
Annual Growth	6.6%	(4.4%)	—	—

2016 Year-End Financials
Return on assets: 4.4%   Cash ($ mil.): 95
Return on equity: 6.2%
Current ratio: 1.30

COMPUTER SCIENCES CORPORATION

Computer Sciences Corporation (CSC) has been one of the world's leading providers of systems integration and other information technology services. It offers application development data center management communications and networking development IT systems management and business consulting. It also provides business process outsourcing (BPO) services in such areas as billing and payment processing customer relationship management (CRM) and human resources. CSC boasts 2500 clients in more than 70 countries. In 2017 CSC merged with the Enterprise Services segment of Hewlett-Packard Enterprise to form DXC Technology Co. This report is based on CSC's last year as an independent company.

Change in Company Type

DXC is the result of mixing and matching of downsizing and upsizing corporate units. Computer Sciences Corp. spun out its government service unit several years ago which reduced CSC's revenue. Hewlett Packard Enterprise Services was part of Hewlett Packard Enterprise one of two companies created with Hewlett-Packard split up. The combination of HP Enterprise Services and CSC began in 2016 and concluded in April 2017 when DXC formally began operations. The new company is expected to have annual revenue of about $26 billion. This report reflects the final year of CSC as an independent company.

Operations

Prior to the creation of DXC CSC conducted business in through Global Business Services (GBS) and Global Infrastructure Services (GIS). GBS (55% of revenue) addresses key business challenges such as consulting applications services and software. GIS (45% of revenue) provides IT infrastructure services such as managed and virtual desktop solutions unified communications and collaboration services data center management cyber security and cloud-based offerings.

Geographic Reach

CSC has major operations throughout North America Europe Asia and Australia. The company has clients in more than 70 countries. About 40% of sales are made in the US and about 20% are in the UK the second biggest market.

Sales and Marketing

CSC's clients have included AboveNet Communications Deutsche Telekom DirecTV Vodafone and Ryman Hospitality Properties (formerly Gaylord Entertainment).

Financial Performance

After seven straight years of revenue declines CSC's sales rebounded in 2017 (ended March) to $7.6 billion a 7% increase from 2016. The increase was driven by the Global Business Services unit's business processing services offerings and contributions from recent acquisitions in the Digital Applications business. The Global Infrastructure Services unit posted a small revenue increase from new business and sales from acquisitions.

CSC lost about $123 million in 2017 down from a $251 million profit in 2016 mainly due to large restructuring charges.

Cash flow from operating activities rose to $978 million in 2017 from $802 million in 2016. The increase flowed from an increase in trade payables and a decrease in net account receivables.

Strategy

After going through corporate breakups DXC Technology bets that bigger will be better and stronger in competing in the worldwide market for IT services. The companies have a wide footprint and with some $26 billion in annual revenue and will have some weight to throw around. A question will be if the company can effectively compete with companies that provide similar services such as Cognizant WiPro Accenture IBM Global Service and Dell Technologies.

DXC has bulked up to ride the wave of digital transformation that its customers and potential customers are going through. The company's range of services could lead customers from legacy systems to private or public or hybrid cloud systems.

Mergers and Acquisitions

In 2016 CSC acquired Xchanging plc provider of technology-enabled business services for $633 million. Xchanging brings its Xuber software which is used by commercial insurance companies around the world.

Also in 2016 CSC acquired Aspediens a European provider in the service-management sector and a preferred partner of ServiceNow. The deal extended CSC's reach in software-as-a-service in Europe.

EXECUTIVES

Vice President, Debbie Granberry
Vice President Finance Corporate Development And Corporate Treasurer, Charles Diao
Vice President Finance And Administration, Frank Sossi
Vice President Of Global Human Resources And Trans, Mike Darcy
Division Director Deputy Vice President General Manager, Richard Morrow
Managing Director India And Global Head Workforce Management, Sreehanth Krishnan Arimanithaya
Senior Vice President And General Manager Security, Art Wong
Vice President Sales, Robb Maltempo
Vice President And General Manager Global Insurance, Phil Ratcliff
Vice President Global Pricing, Mike Brocato
Vice President, Brad Canel
Senior Vice President Federal Government Solutions, John Kavanaugh
Vp Corporate Communications, Caryn Kboudi
Svp Of Leasing, Michelle Waak
Auditors: DELOITTE & TOUCHE LLP MCLEAN

LOCATIONS

HQ: COMPUTER SCIENCES CORPORATION
1775 TYSONS BLVD STE 1000, TYSONS, VA 221024284
Phone: 703 245-9675
Web: WWW.DXC.TECHNOLOGY

2017 Sales

	$ mil.	% of total
United States	2,986	40
United Kingdom	1,482	19
Australia	921	12
Other Europe	1,594	21
Other International	624	8
Total	**7,607**	**100**

PRODUCTS/OPERATIONS

2017 Sales

	$ mil.	% of total
Global Business Services	4,173	55
Global Infrastructure Services	3,434	45
Total	**7,607**	**100**

Selected Service Areas

Application outsourcing
Business process outsourcing
Customer relationship management
Data hosting
Enterprise application integration
Knowledge management
Management consulting
Risk management
Security
Supply chain management

Selected Solutions

Application Services
Big Data & Analytics
Business & Technology Consulting
Cloud Solutions & Services
Cybersecurity
Industry Software & Solutions
Infrastructure Services

Managed Services & Outsourcing
Mobility Solutions

COMPETITORS

ADP
Accenture
Atos
Booz Allen
CACI International
CIBER
Capgemini
Cognizant Tech Solutions
Computacenter
Convergys
Dell
Deloitte Consulting
Dimension Data
General Dynamics Information Technology
Getronics
HCL Technologies
Honeywell International
IBM Global Services
Infosys
Leidos
ManTech
NTT Data
Northrop Grumman
Siemens AG
Tata Consultancy
Tech Mahindra
Unisys
Wipro
Wipro Technologies

HISTORICAL FINANCIALS

Company Type: Private

Income Statement

FYE: March 31

	REVENUE ($ mil.)	NET INCOME ($ mil.)	NET PROFIT MARGIN	EMPLOYEES
03/17*	7,607	(100)	—	66,000
04/16	7,106	263	3.7%	—
04/15	12,173	7	0.1%	—
03/14	12,998	690	5.3%	—
Annual Growth	(16.4%)	—	—	—

*Fiscal year change

2017 Year-End Financials

Return on assets: (-1.2%)   Cash ($ mil.): 1,263
Return on equity: (-4.6%)
Current ratio: 1.10

CONCORD HOSPITAL, INC.

Concord Hospital is agreeably an acute care regional hospital serving central New Hampshire. The hospital has some 300 licensed beds and provides general inpatient and outpatient medical care as well as specialist centers for cardiology orthopedics cancer care urology and women's health. Concord Hospital operates other medical facilities either on its main campus or nearby including surgery imaging diagnostic hospice and rehabilitation facilities as well as physician practice locations. With roots reaching back to 1884 Concord Hospital is part of the Capital Region Health Care system which also offers mental health and home health care services.

Operations

With a staff of some 350 doctors Concord Hospital sees about 18000 patients (including some 9000 rehabilitation patients) performs more than 9600 surgeries and handles about 65000 emergency room visits and 1200 births each year. The hospital provides services in about 40 specialty medical fields.

As part of Capital Region Health Care Concord Hospital shares education purchasing and outpatient service functions (and expenses) with its network sister entities which include the Concord Regional Visiting Nurse Association and the Riverbend Community Mental Health center. Through Capital Regional Health Care Concord Hospital also has affiliations with area organizations including Dartmouth-Hitchcock Medical Center Concord Ambulatory Center and Concord Imaging Center.

Concord Hospital is also part of a collaborative network the Granite Healthcare Network with four regional New Hampshire health care providers: Elliot Health System (which operates the Elliot Hospital) LRGHealthcare (consisting of Lakes Region General Hospital and Franklin Regional Hospital) Southern New Hampshire Health System (operating the Southern New Hampshire Medical Center) and Wentworth-Douglass Hospital. Hospitals in the network remain independently managed and owned and have the option to participate or not participate in each of the group efforts.

Geographic Reach

Concord Hospital is located on a 110-acre campus in Concord New Hampshire. It provides services in area communities including Allenstown Andover Barnstead Boscawen Bow Bradford Canterbury Chichester Deering Dunbarton Epsom Henniker Hillsboro Hopkinton Loudon Northwood Pembroke Pittsfield Salsibury Warner Washington Weare Webster and Windsor.

Sales and Marketing

Medicare and Medicaid accounted for some 27% and 3% of net patient revenues respectively in 2014.

Financial Performance

Annual operating revenues increased 3% to some $440 million due to higher net patient revenues in 2014. However net income fell 72% to $18 million due to factors including loss from pension adjustments and declines in net unrealized gains. Cash flow from operations rose 14% to $32 million as less cash was used in accounts receivable and towards supplies and other assets.

Strategy

To help control the spiraling costs of medical care in the US as well as to meet health reform mandates Concord and its affiliated facilities are launching programs to share technology and administrative resources such as claims management software data storage linen service liability insurance pooling and Medicare patient management.

Concord Hospital has also launched independent initiatives to improve quality and patient safety programs including putting infection reduction protocols in place consolidating electronic health record (EHR) consolidation efforts and enacting medication management practices.

EXECUTIVES

Vice President Finance, Scott Sloane
Director Of Health Information Medical Records Director, Jodi Panzino
Vice President Information Technology, Kevin Call
Vice President Human Resources, Linda Flewelling
Vice President Of Medical Records, Mark Carwell
Vice President Of Information Technology, Brian Hutchins
Vice President Planning, Lisa Drouse
Vice President Provider Services, Bill Dooley
Vice President Of Information Technology, Matthew Wooldridge
Vice President Finance, Allyson Hicks
Senior Vice President Coo, Timothy P Jones

Vice President, Peter Evers
Vice President, Betsey Rynhart
Secretary, Ronald Yap

LOCATIONS

HQ: CONCORD HOSPITAL, INC.
250 PLEASANT ST, CONCORD, NH 033012598
Phone: 603 227-7000
Web: WWW.CONCORDHOSPITAL.ORG

PRODUCTS/OPERATIONS

2014 Sales

	$ mil.	% of total
Net patient service revenue	410	93
Other revenue	23	6
Disproportionate share revenue	5	1
Net assets released from restrictions for operations	1	-
Total	**440**	**100**

Selected Services

Ambulatory Care Center
Behavioral Health
Breast Care Center
Cancer
Cardiac
Center for Health Promotion
Child Life
Clinical Decision Unit
Day Surgery Center
Diabetes Self-Management Education
Concord Hospital Medical Group
Emergency Services
End Of Life
Family Health Centers
Infectious Disease
Intensive Care
Laboratory Services
Maternity
Neurology
Occupational Health
Orthopedics
Pediatrics
Primary Care
Radiology
Rehabilitation
Sleep Center
Surgery
Urology
Walk-in Urgent Care
Women's Health
Wound Care

COMPETITORS

Cambridge Health Alliance
Catholic Medical Center
Elliot Health System
Exeter Health Resources
Frisbie Memorial Hospital
HCA
Partners HealthCare
Southern New Hampshire Medical Center
Steward Health Care

HISTORICAL FINANCIALS

Company Type: Private

Income Statement   FYE: September 30

	REVENUE ($ mil.)	NET INCOME ($ mil.)	NET PROFIT MARGIN	EMPLOYEES
09/18	500	23	4.6%	2,000
09/17	481	35	7.3%	—
09/16	447	15	3.4%	—
09/15	396	24	6.3%	—
Annual Growth	8.1%	(2.6%)	—	—

2018 Year-End Financials

Return on assets: 3.3%   Cash ($ mil.): 4
Return on equity: 5.7%
Current ratio: 1.10

CONROE INDEPENDENT SCHOOL DISTRICT

EXECUTIVES

Supt, Don Stockton
Asst Supt For Elementary Schl, Cathy Gibson
Special Education Assistant, Marla Mong
Teacher Jhstudent Success Teac, Vonelle Clark
Teacher, Wendy Ward

LOCATIONS

HQ: CONROE INDEPENDENT SCHOOL DISTRICT
3205 W DAVIS ST, CONROE, TX 773042039
Phone: 936 709-7751
Web: WWW.CONROEISD.NET

HISTORICAL FINANCIALS

Company Type: Private

Income Statement   FYE: August 31

	REVENUE ($ mil.)	NET INCOME ($ mil.)	NET PROFIT MARGIN	EMPLOYEES
08/18	637	57	9.0%	6,223
08/17	609	7	1.2%	—
08/16	590	81	13.9%	—
08/15	552	24	4.4%	—
Annual Growth	4.9%	33.7%	—	—

2018 Year-End Financials

Return on assets: 3.2%   Cash ($ mil.): 5
Return on equity: —
Current ratio: 3.10

CONSIGLI CONSTRUCTION CO INC.

EXECUTIVES

Pres-Ceo, Anthony M Consigli
V Pres*, Matthew D Consigli
V Pres-Cfo*, J Scott Lerner
Internal Medicine Practitioner, Harrison Bond
Coordinator, Morgan Buckley
Accounting Staff, Patrick McNamara
Internal Medicine Practitioner, Zach Pearce
Assistant Project Manager, Patrick Gildea

LOCATIONS

HQ: CONSIGLI CONSTRUCTION CO INC.
72 SUMNER ST, MILFORD, MA 017571663
Phone: 508 473-2580
Web: WWW.CONSIGLI.COM

HISTORICAL FINANCIALS

Company Type: Private

Income Statement   FYE: December 31

	REVENUE ($ mil.)	NET INCOME ($ mil.)	NET PROFIT MARGIN	EMPLOYEES
12/12	616	34	5.6%	390
12/11	297	12	4.3%	—
12/10	0	0	—	—
12/09	297	12	4.3%	—
Annual Growth	27.5%	39.6%	—	—

Return on assets: 21.7%   Cash ($ mil.): 29
Return on equity: 120.7%
Current ratio: 1.20

CONSOLIDATED GRAIN & BARGE COMPANY

EXECUTIVES

Ceo, Kevin D Adams
V Pres*, Gregory Beck
Auditors: KPMG LLP NEW ORLEANS LA

LOCATIONS

HQ: CONSOLIDATED GRAIN & BARGE COMPANY
1127 HWY 190 E SERVICE RD, COVINGTON, LA
704334929
Phone: 985 867-3500

HISTORICAL FINANCIALS

Company Type: Private

Income Statement   FYE: May 31

	REVENUE ($ mil.)	NET INCOME ($ mil.)	NET PROFIT MARGIN	EMPLOYEES
05/17	6,430	16	0.3%	2,000
05/16	5,759	21	0.4%	—
05/14	7,093	44	0.6%	—
05/12	5,996	50	0.8%	—
Annual Growth	1.4%	(20.4%)	—	—

2017 Year-End Financials

Return on assets: 1.1%   Cash ($ mil.): —
Return on equity: 5.1%
Current ratio: 1.00

CONSOLIDATED PIPE & SUPPLY COMPANY, INC.

Consolidated Pipe and Supply lives up to its name: Its nine divisions supply pipe and pipeline materials to a swath of industries from energy to water and waste treatment chemical mining nuclear oil and gas and pulp and paper. Its industrial unit specializes in carbon and stainless alloy pipe valves and fittings. Vulcan makes all types of PVC. Corrosion resistant coatings are offered by a Line Pipe and Tubular unit and liquid applied coatings by Specialty Coatings. Its Consolidated Power Supply is the largest in the business of safety related metallic materials for commercial nuclear generation. Another unit caters to utilities. Consolidated also provides engineering services and inventory systems.

Operations

Consolidated Pipe and Supply is one of nearly 20 US Steel distributors authorized to sell seamless and electric resistance welded products in North America. Not limited to its branch and sales centers Consolidated Pipe and Supply's fitted semi-trailers complete with area row and bin and bar coded shelving serve as mobile warehouses for construc-

tion customers requiring on-site materials management.

The company operates through nine divisions: Industrial Line Pipe Structural Pipeline Coatings Utility Products Specialty Coatings Consolidated Power Vulcan Plastics and Consolidated Controls.

Geographic Reach

The company's reach extends to 19 US states including Alabama Arkansas Florida Georgia Illinois Indiana Kentucky Missouri Mississippi North Carolina Pennsylvania South Carolina Tennessee Texas and Virginia. It has nearly 50 sales offices in 15 states.

EXECUTIVES

Executive Vice President, Robert Kerr

LOCATIONS

HQ: CONSOLIDATED PIPE & SUPPLY COMPANY, INC.
1205 HILLTOP PKWY, BIRMINGHAM, AL 352045002
Phone: 205 323-7261
Web: WWW.CONSOLIDATEDPIPE.COM

PRODUCTS/OPERATIONS

Selected Industries Served

Chemical

Energy

Mining
Nuclear Generation
Oil and Gas
Petro-Chemical
Pulp and Paper
Water and Waste Treatment

Selected Divisions
Consolidated Controls (valves)
Consolidated Power (provides materials to energy industries)
Industrial (provides materials construction commercial energy pulp and paper chemical petro-chemical mining and fabrication industries)
Line Pipe (line pipe and tubular products)
Pipeline Coatings
Specialty Coatings (specialty linings for use in jet fuel and military applications)
Structural (1/8" through 48" structural and prime grades of carbon steel pipe)
Utility Products (provides utilities with products such as steel ductile iron PVC polyethylene and brass fittings and valves and steel PVC and polyethylene pipe)
Vulcan Plastics (water and sewer pipe)

COMPETITORS

American Cast Iron Pipe	Phoenix Tube
Bristol Metals	Seymour Tubing
Bull Moose Tube	Southland Tube
Chicago Tube & Iron	Steel Ventures
Kelly Pipe Co. LLC	U.S. Pipe

HISTORICAL FINANCIALS

Company Type: Private

Income Statement   FYE: December 31

	REVENUE ($ mil.)	NET INCOME ($ mil.)	NET PROFIT MARGIN	EMPLOYEES
12/16	550	17	3.3%	700
12/15	575	7	1.3%	—
12/14	667	23	3.5%	—
12/13	602	19	3.2%	—
Annual Growth	(3.0%)	(2.3%)	—	—

2016 Year-End Financials

Return on assets: 7.8%   Cash ($ mil.): 1
Return on equity: 10.8%
Current ratio: 3.70

CONSUMER PRODUCT DISTRIBUTORS, INC.

Consumer Product Distributors helps convenience stores provide convenient services to their customers. The company which operates as J. Polep Distribution Services is a leading wholesale supplier serving more than 4000 convenience retailers in New York PennsylvaniaÂ and the New England states. J. Polep distributes a variety of products including cigarettes and other tobacco items candy dairy products frozen foods snack items and general merchandise as well as alcohol and other beverages.Â As part of its businessÂ J. Polep provides merchandising sales and marketing and technology services. The family-owned company was founded as Polep Tobacco in 1898 by Charles Polep.

EXECUTIVES

Pres-Ceo, Jeff Polep
V Pres, Stephen J Martin
Exec V Pres, Kenneth Morris
V Pres-Data Proc, Lori Polep Saffer
Sr V Pres-Cfo, Bill Fitzsimmons
SEC, David A Shrair
Cfo, William Fitzsimmons
Transportation Director, Jonathan Lasko
Human Resources, Kim Hewes
Information Technology Manager, Daniel O'Connor
Whse Transportation Manager PR, Alan Ritchotte
Auditors: MEYERS BROTHERS KALICKA PC

LOCATIONS

HQ: CONSUMER PRODUCT DISTRIBUTORS, INC.
705 MEADOW ST, CHICOPEE, MA 010134820
Phone: 413 592-4141
Web: WWW.JPOLEP.COM

PRODUCTS/OPERATIONS

Selected Products

Alcohol
Spirits
Wine
Automotive
Branded Motor Oils
Mag 1
Additives
Cleaning Supplies
Bakery/Pastry
Rachael's Gourmet
Mrs. Freshley's
Dolly Madison
Bon Appetite
Bellow's House
Diana's
Table Talk
Beverages
Poland Springs (Nestle Waters)
Adirondack Soda
Arizona
Florida's Natural
Simply Juices
Sweet Leaf Tea
Trade Winds
Daily Juice

Selected Services
Credit & Return Policy
Management Information Systems
Merchandising Support
Sales and Marketing Support

COMPETITORS

Atlantic Dominion	Harold Levinson
C&S Wholesale	McLane
Core-Mark	SUPERVALU
Eby-Brown	Tripifoods
H. T. Hackney	

HISTORICAL FINANCIALS
Company Type: Private

Income Statement			FYE: September 29
	REVENUE ($ mil.)	NET INCOME ($ mil.)	NET PROFIT MARGIN	EMPLOYEES
09/18	1,248	1	0.1%	400
09/17*	1,101	5	0.5%	—
10/16	1,005	5	0.6%	—
10/15	968	2	0.3%	—
Annual Growth	8.8%	(14.4%)	—	—

*Fiscal year change

2018 Year-End Financials
Return on assets: 0.9% Cash ($ mil.): 6
Return on equity: 5.0%
Current ratio: 3.20

CONTINUUM ENERGY SERVICES, L.L.C.

EXECUTIVES

MBR-Exec V Pres-Cfo, Dan Hawk
MBR*, Robert Rosene Jr
MBR*, John Greene
Acct Mgr, Derek Chesbro
Member, Kent Dunbar
Human Resources Administrator, Linda Brewer
Program Director, Rick Pemberton
Account Executive, Tom Sumner
Financial Executive, T J McRuy
General Manager, John Pettus
Evp Midstream, Pat Giroir
Auditors: GRANT THORNTON LLP TULSA OKL

LOCATIONS

HQ: CONTINUUM ENERGY SERVICES, L.L.C.
  1323 E 71ST ST STE 300, TULSA, OK 741365068
Phone: 918 492-2840
Web: WWW.CONTINUUMES.COM

HISTORICAL FINANCIALS
Company Type: Private

Income Statement			FYE: December 31
	REVENUE ($ mil.)	NET INCOME ($ mil.)	NET PROFIT MARGIN	EMPLOYEES
12/13	2,092	5	0.2%	159
12/12	1,558	16	1.0%	—
12/11	2,021	26	1.3%	—
Annual Growth	1.7%	(56.3%)	—	—

2013 Year-End Financials
Return on assets: 1.0% Cash ($ mil.): 11
Return on equity: 3.3%
Current ratio: 1.10

CONTINUUM MIDSTREAM, L.L.C.

EXECUTIVES

Member, Kent Dunbar
Member*, Robert B Rosene Jr
Member*, Daniel Frey
Member*, John Greene
Member*, Bob Malapkowski
Vice-President Business Develo, Brian Cutter
Auditors: GRANT THORNTON LLP TULSA OKL

LOCATIONS

HQ: CONTINUUM MIDSTREAM, L.L.C.
  1323 E 71ST ST STE 300, TULSA, OK 741365068
Phone: 918 492-2840

HISTORICAL FINANCIALS
Company Type: Private

Income Statement			FYE: December 31
	REVENUE ($ mil.)	NET INCOME ($ mil.)	NET PROFIT MARGIN	EMPLOYEES
12/14	1,153	(2)	—	75
12/13	296	0	0.2%	—
12/02	17	0	5.3%	—
12/01	13	1	11.9%	—
Annual Growth	40.8%	—	—	—

2014 Year-End Financials
Return on assets: (-1.7%) Cash ($ mil.): 3
Return on equity: (-2.2%)
Current ratio: 0.70

COOK CHILDREN'S HEALTH PLAN

EXECUTIVES

Pres, Doris Hunt
Coordinator, Chase Robinson
Coordinator, Allyson Tate
Director Facilities Management, Nick Markham
Manager of Fleet Operations, Robert Hailey
Manager of Engineering, Robert Weber
Manager Mkt, Teresa Hebert
Procurement Coordinator, Willy Rensing
Deputy Chief Investment Office, Apurva Mehta
Librarian, Dena Hanson
Pn Manager, Christine Oehlert
Auditors: BKD LLP HOUSTON TX

LOCATIONS

HQ: COOK CHILDREN'S HEALTH PLAN
  801 7TH AVE, FORT WORTH, TX 761042733
Phone: 817 334-2247

HISTORICAL FINANCIALS
Company Type: Private

Income Statement			FYE: September 30
	REVENUE ($ mil.)	NET INCOME ($ mil.)	NET PROFIT MARGIN	EMPLOYEES
09/17	484	(8)	—	27
09/15	307	17	5.8%	—
09/14	284	11	3.9%	—
09/13	259	5	2.0%	—
Annual Growth	16.9%	—	—	—

2017 Year-End Financials
Return on assets: (-6.7%) Cash ($ mil.): 63
Return on equity: (-11.5%)
Current ratio: 5.00

COOK CHILDREN'S MEDICAL CENTER

EXECUTIVES

Pres-Ceo, Rick W Merrill
Director of Infection Control, Lisa La Rue
Credentaling Coordinator, Sandy Martin
Director of Human Resources, Beth Schmidt
Coordinator Audio Visual/Media, Terry Wilder
Trustee, Joann Sanders
Human Resources Information MA, Jill Wegman
Osteopathy, Orlando Chapa Do
Director, Gary B Strong
Director of Operations, Meri Cozart
Manager, Ross Jones

LOCATIONS

HQ: COOK CHILDREN'S MEDICAL CENTER
  801 7TH AVE, FORT WORTH, TX 761042796
Phone: 682 885-4000
Web: WWW.COOKCHILDRENS.ORG

HISTORICAL FINANCIALS
Company Type: Private

Income Statement			FYE: September 30
	REVENUE ($ mil.)	NET INCOME ($ mil.)	NET PROFIT MARGIN	EMPLOYEES
09/15	753	159	21.1%	2,000
09/14	753	107	14.2%	—
09/13	828	160	19.4%	—
09/09	563	99	17.7%	—
Annual Growth	5.0%	8.1%	—	—

2015 Year-End Financials
Return on assets: 14.5% Cash ($ mil.): 255
Return on equity: 27.5%
Current ratio: 0.90

COOPERATIVE ENERGY, A MISSISSIPPI ELECTRIC COOPERATIVE

EXECUTIVES

Pres-Ceo, Jeff Bowman
V Pres*, Harlan Rogers
V Pres*, Billy Harden
SEC*, W T Shows
Gen Mgr*, James M Compton
Director Mrktg, John Carley

LOCATIONS

HQ: COOPERATIVE ENERGY, A MISSISSIPPI
ELECTRIC COOPERATIVE
7037 U S HIGHWAY 49, HATTIESBURG, MS
394029128
Phone: 601 579-0215
Web: WWW.COOPERATIVEENERGY.COM

HISTORICAL FINANCIALS
Company Type: Private

Income Statement — FYE: December 31

	REVENUE ($ mil.)	NET INCOME ($ mil.)	NET PROFIT MARGIN	EMPLOYEES
12/16	822	0	—	238
12/13	811	0	—	—
12/12	771	0	—	—
12/11	766	0	—	—
Annual Growth	1.4%	—	—	—

2016 Year-End Financials
Return on assets: —
Return on equity: —
Current ratio: 1.50
Cash ($ mil.): 41

COOPERATIVE FOR ASSISTANCE AND RELIEF EVERYWHERE, INC. (CARE)

The Cooperative for Assistance and Relief Everywhere (CARE) strives to be the beginning of the end of poverty. The organization works to reduce poverty in about 85 countries by helping communities in areas such as health education economic development emergency relief and agriculture. CARE supports more than 1100 projects to combat poverty.Â It also operates a small economic activity development (SEAD) unit that supports moneymaking activities. Through SEAD CAREÂ provides technical training and savings and loans programs to help people — particularlyÂ women —Â open or expand small businesses. CARE was founded in 1945 to give aid to WWII survivors.

Operations

In addition to its home office in Georgia CARE maintains field offices in about 10 US cities including Boston Chicago Miami New York and Washington DC. The group'sÂ internationalÂ field offices are located inÂ more than 55 countries.

CARE's 1100 projects reach 122 million people more than half of which are women. About 90% of the funds that CARE receives go toward its aid efforts. The organization helps people in the poorest communities of developing nations. (It does not provide assistance in the US.)

Geographic Reach

From its headquarters in Atlanta CARE serves poor communities in nearly 85 countries. It does not provide assistance in the US.

Financial Performance

CARE's revenue increasedÂ a modest 1% to $590 million in fiscal 2011 as compared to 2010. While it logged a drop in revenues from the US government the organization saw a boost in private contributions — totaling $310 million — from CARE international members.

Strategy

CARE is supported by donations from thousands of individuals and dozens of corporations foundations and other charitable organizations in the US. Some of the participating organizations include World Wildlife Fund Covance Merck Meredith Corporation and the Wal-Mart Foundation. The group also receives funding and supplies from government agencies including the United Nations and European Union.Â As a result of the economicÂ downturn CARE hasÂ beenÂ working to raise contribution levels as governments businesses and individuals cut back their spending including charitable donations.

EXECUTIVES

**Vice President Finance And Information
Technology And Chief Financial Officer,** Peter Buijs
Vice President, Phil Mazzara
Auditors: ERNST & YOUNG LLP ATLANTA GA

LOCATIONS

HQ: COOPERATIVE FOR ASSISTANCE AND RELIEF
EVERYWHERE, INC. (CARE)
151 ELLIS ST NE, ATLANTA, GA 303032420
Phone: 404 681-2552
Web: WWW.CARE.ORG

PRODUCTS/OPERATIONS

Selected International Partner Organizations
Covance Inc.
Merck Foundation
Meredith Corporation
The Wal-mart Foundation
WWF

HISTORICAL FINANCIALS
Company Type: Private

Income Statement — FYE: June 30

	REVENUE ($ mil.)	NET INCOME ($ mil.)	NET PROFIT MARGIN	EMPLOYEES
06/18	604	15	2.6%	10,000
06/16	530	(21)	—	—
06/13	492	(18)	—	—
06/11	589	10	1.7%	—
Annual Growth	0.4%	6.3%	—	—

2018 Year-End Financials
Return on assets: 3.0%
Return on equity: 4.3%
Current ratio: —
Cash ($ mil.): 64

COOPERATIVE REGIONS OF ORGANIC PRODUCER POOLS

Cooperative Regions of Organic Producers Pool (CROPP) is the largest organic farming cooperative in North America. The group's 1840-plus farmer/members produce the co-op's Organic Valley Family of Farms and Organic Prairie brands of fluid and shelf-stable milk along with cheese butter and soy milk. Beyond the dairy barn the cooperative also offers organic citrus juices produce eggs meats and poultry. Its Organic Valley products are sold by food retailers and its ingredients are marketed to other organic food processors. Wisconsin-headquartered CROPP's farmer/members are located throughout North America and Australia. The co-op was founded in 1988.

Geographic Reach

The Wisconsin-based cooperative's farmer members are located in 35 US states including California and Florida and three Canadian provinces. It also has members in Australia.

Financial Performance

The co-op's sales grew 8% in 2013 versus 2012 to $928 million after increasing by 20% in the previous annual comparison. Sales have risen sharply along with increasing demand for organic milk and other dairy foods. CROPP added 10 new members in 2013. The co-op struggled in 2013 as a result of a fire that burned down part of its headquarters building. The blaze occurred about a year after the co-op completed a $6.7 million addition to the structure.

Strategy

CROPP seeks to quench consumers' growing thirst for organic milk with new products including the 2012 launch of Organic Valley Grassmilk an organic specialty milk produced from cows that are 100% grass fed. Organic Valley Grassmilk attained nationwide distribution in mid-2013.

The co-op operates under a regional business model by which milk is produced bottled and distributed in the region where it's farmed to ensure fewer miles from farm to table and to support local economies. About 75% of the co-ops 1800-plus farmers are located in the "Heartland" region of the US which includes Iowa Illinois Kansas Minnesota North Dakota Nebraska South Dakota Wisconsin Indiana Ohio and Michigan.

EXECUTIVES

Ceo, George Siemon
Coo, Louise Hemstead
Cfo, Mike Bedessem
Vice President Of Brand Marketing, Lewis Goldstein

LOCATIONS

HQ: COOPERATIVE REGIONS OF ORGANIC
PRODUCER POOLS
1 ORGANIC WAY, LA FARGE, WI 546396604
Phone: 608 625-2602
Web: WWW.ORGANICVALLEY.COOP

PRODUCTS/OPERATIONS

Selected Products
Butter
Cheese
Cottage cheese
Cream
Cream cheese
Eggs
Healthy snacks
Juice
Meat
Milk
Sour cream
Soy
Yogurt

COMPETITORS

Albert's Organics
Aurora Organic Dairy
Berkeley Farms
Chiquita Brands
Crowley Foods
Dairy Crest
Dairy Farmers of
 America
Dakota Beef
Dannon
Dean Foods
Dole Food
Egg Innovations
Foster Dairy Farms
Fresh Del Monte
 Produce
Friendship Dairies
Galaxy Nutritional
 Foods
Garelick Farms
Great Lakes Cheese
Jonathan Sprouts

Keller's Creamery
Land O'Lakes
Laura's Lean Beef Co.
Lifeway Foods
Niman Ranch
Oberweis Dairy
Odwalla
Organically Grown
 Company
Rachel's Organic Dairy
Rockview Dairies
Sargento
Springfield Creamery
Stonyfield Farm
Straus Family Creamery
Stremicks Heritage
 Foods
Tyson Foods
Tyson Fresh Meats
United Natural
Willow Wind Organic
 Farms

HISTORICAL FINANCIALS

Company Type: Private

Income Statement
FYE: December 31

	REVENUE ($ mil.)	NET INCOME ($ mil.)	NET PROFIT MARGIN	EMPLOYEES
12/10	619	12	2.0%	764
12/08	527	3	0.7%	—
12/07	432	6	1.4%	—
Annual Growth	12.7%	24.6%	—	—

2010 Year-End Financials
Return on assets: 7.5%   Cash ($ mil.): 29
Return on equity: 12.8%
Current ratio: 2.20

CORE CONSTRUCTION GROUP, LTD.

EXECUTIVES

Pres, Mark A Steffen
Exec V Pres*, Dennis Barber
Treas*, Michael J Thomas
Manager, Tim Hickey

LOCATIONS

HQ: CORE CONSTRUCTION GROUP, LTD.
 601 SW WATER ST, PEORIA, IL 616021531
Phone: 309 263-0808

HISTORICAL FINANCIALS

Company Type: Private

Income Statement
FYE: December 31

	REVENUE ($ mil.)	NET INCOME ($ mil.)	NET PROFIT MARGIN	EMPLOYEES
12/17	1,007	0	—	450
12/15	782	0	—	—
12/12	624	0	—	—
12/06	620	0	—	—
Annual Growth	4.5%	—	—	—

2017 Year-End Financials
Return on assets: —   Cash ($ mil.): 37
Return on equity: —
Current ratio: 1.20

CORNELL UNIVERSITY

To excel at Cornell you'll need every one of your brain cells. The Ivy League school's 22000 students can select undergraduate graduate and professional courses from 14 colleges and schools. In addition to its Ithaca New York campus the university has medical and professional programs in New York City and Doha Qatar. Cornell's faculty includes a handful of Nobel laureates and the university has a robust research component studying everything from animal health to space to waste management. It has a student-faculty ratio of about 9:1. Notable alumni include author E. B. White and US Supreme Court Justice Ruth Bader Ginsburg.

Operations
Cornell awarded the nation's first university degree in veterinary medicine and first doctorates in electrical engineering and industrial engineering. It awarded the world's first degree in journalism (and taught the first university course in that subject) and established the first four-year schools of hotel administration and industrial and labor relations.

Cornell is deeply involved in research with more than 100 interdisciplinary research organizations pursuing research teaching and outreach on broad topics like nanofabrication life sciences computing and information science environmental sustainability human development agriculture space research and international issues. Cornell has dozens of research centers such as the Cornell High Energy Synchrotron Source (CHESS) the Cornell Electroacoustic Music Center (CEMC) the Cornell Center for Wildlife Conservation (CCWC) the National Biomedical Center for Advanced ESR Technology (ACERT) and the Laboratory of Elementary-Particle Physics (LEPP).

Geographic Reach
Cornell's main campus in Ithaca NY is comprised of endowed colleges and contract colleges (operated on behalf of the state) spanning a 2300 acre campus in New York State's Finger Lakes region. Its location in New York City primarily consists of the Sanford I. Weill Medical College which has an extension campus in Doha Qatar and the Graduate School of Medical Sciences.

Financial Performance
University operating revenues grew by 25% between 2012 and 2017 from $3.2 billion to $4.0 billion. The largest area of growth was the Medical Physician Organization at the Weill Cornell Medicine which makes up more than 25% of Cornell's operating revenue.

In FY2017 (ended June 30 2017) operating revenue was $4.0 billion with tuition & fees and the Medical Physician Organization each contributing about $1.0 billion. Grants contracts and similar agreements accounted for another $600 million. It also garnered money through gifts & contributions of $535 million in FY2017. Because it operates contract colleges on behalf of the State University of New York (SUNY) it received appropriations of about $132 million for the year.

Non-operating revenue which includes contributions for its endowment change in value of its endowment investments and other items accounted for a $424 million rise in overall asset value leading to a FY2017 year-end amount exceeding $3.1 billion.

The university's endowment is more than $6.5 billion.

Company Background
The Ivy League university has been educating young minds since its founding in 1865.

EXECUTIVES

Evp And Cfo, Joanne M. DeStefano
Dean School Of Continuing Education And Summer Sessions, Glenn C. Altschuler
Provost, Michael I. Kotlikoff
Dean College Of Human Ecology, Alan D. Mathios
Dean And Provost Cornell Nyc Tech, Daniel P. Huttenlocher
President, Martha E. Pollack
Dean College Of Agriculture And Life Sciences, Kathryn J. Boor
Dean College Of Engineering, Lance R. Collins
Dean Of The Cornell Sc Johnson College Of Business, Soumitra Dutta
Dean College Of Architecture Art And Planning, Kent Kleinman
Dean Graduate School, Barbara A. Knuth
Dean Graduate School Of Medical Sciences And Senior Associate Dean For Research At Weill Cornell Medicine, Gary Koretzky
Dean College Of Arts And Sciences, Gretchen Ritter
Dean School Of Law, Eduardo M. Peñalver
Provost For Medical Affairs And Dean Of Weill Cornell Medicine, Augustine M.K. Choi
Vp Information Technology And Chief Information Office, David Lifka
Dean Of The School Of Industrial And Labor Relations (ilr), Kevin F. Hallock
Interim Dean School Of Applied Economics And Management, Edward W. McLaughlin
Dean Of The Faculty Of Computing And Information Science, J. Gregory Morrisett
Dean Of The Samuel Curtis Johnson Graduate School Of Management, Mark W. Nelson
Interim Dean Of The School Of Hotel Administration And E. M. Statler Professor Of Hotel Administration, Kate Walsh
Dean Of The College Of Veterinary Medicine, Lorin D. Warnick
Vice President University Relations, Joel Malina
Co Vice President, Kevin McGovern
Vice President, Jane Hammond
Vice President Of Business Development And Marketing, Arthur Brent
Assistant Vice President Finance Administration, Edna Dugan
Vice President Human Resources, Irene Hendricks
Vice President, Jeff Gurtman
Vice Chairman, David D. Croll
Chairman, Robert S. Harrison
Vice Chairman, Barton J. Winokur
Board Member, Andrea Schultz
Secretary, Charles Bucher
Auditors: PRICEWATERHOUSECOOPERS LLP RO

LOCATIONS

HQ: CORNELL UNIVERSITY
308 DUFFIELD HALL, ITHACA, NY 148532700
Phone: 607 254-4636
Web: WWW.CORNELL.EDU

HISTORICAL FINANCIALS

Company Type: Private

Income Statement				FYE: June 30
	REVENUE ($ mil.)	NET INCOME ($ mil.)	NET PROFIT MARGIN	EMPLOYEES
06/17	4,013	985	24.6%	12,207
06/16	3,809	(442)	—	—
06/12	2,956	(341)	—	—
06/11	2,955	814	27.5%	—
Annual Growth	5.2%	3.2%	—	—

2017 Year-End Financials

Return on assets: 7.5% Cash ($ mil.): 181
Return on equity: 9.8%
Current ratio: —

CORONA-NORCO UNIFIED SCHOOL DISTRICT

EXECUTIVES

Ceo, Cathy L Sciortino
Supt*, Kent Bechler
Prin*, Ted Rozzi
Pres*, John Z Zickefoose
V Pres*, Jose W Lalas
SEC*, Linda Hawkins
Teacher, Scott Foster
Supervisor, Amanda Ruiz
Vice-President, Tammy Baer
Data Integrity Supervisor, Patty Painter
Secretary, Sylvia Nunez
Auditors: VAVRINEK TRINE DAY & CO LL

LOCATIONS

HQ: CORONA-NORCO UNIFIED SCHOOL DISTRICT
2820 CLARK AVE, NORCO, CA 928601903
Phone: 951 736-5000
Web: WWW.CNUSD.K12.CA.US

HISTORICAL FINANCIALS

Company Type: Private

Income Statement				FYE: June 30
	REVENUE ($ mil.)	NET INCOME ($ mil.)	NET PROFIT MARGIN	EMPLOYEES
06/18	658	42	6.5%	614
06/17	637	(8)	—	—
06/16	635	113	17.8%	—
06/11	1	(20)	—	—
Annual Growth	146.1%	—	—	—

CORPORATION FOR PUBLIC BROADCASTING

This organization is made possible by a grant from the federal government and by support from viewers like you. The Corporation for Public Broadcasting (CPB) is a private not-for-profit corporation created by the federal government that receives appropriations from Congress to help fund programming for more than 1000 locally-owned public TV and radio stations. CPB-funded programs are distributed by the Public Broadcasting Service (PBS) National Public Radio (NPR) and Public Radio International (PRI). Funds are also used for research on media and education. CPB was created by Congress in 1967.

EXECUTIVES

Executive Vice President And Chief Operating Officer, Michael Levy
Senior Vice President Radio, Greg Schnirring
Senior Vice President, Debra Tica Sanchez
Vice President Human Resources, Cara Dalrymple
Vice President Of Education, Michael Fragale
Vice President Information Technology, Stephen Wolfe
Vice President Compliance, Jackie J Livesay
Senior Vice President For Corporate Communications, Letitia King
Vice President And Controller, Nicholas Stromann
Vice President Radio, Erika Pulley
Vice President Business Affairs, Jeff Breslow
Auditors: GRANT THORNTON LLP BALTIMORE

LOCATIONS

HQ: CORPORATION FOR PUBLIC BROADCASTING
401 9TH ST NW STE 200, WASHINGTON, DC 200042129
Phone: 202 879-9600
Web: WWW.CPB.ORG

HISTORICAL FINANCIALS

Company Type: Private

Income Statement				FYE: September 30
	REVENUE ($ mil.)	NET INCOME ($ mil.)	NET PROFIT MARGIN	EMPLOYEES
09/16	510	31	6.1%	99
09/15	461	(11)	—	—
09/14	463	1	0.4%	—
09/13	446	(18)	—	—
Annual Growth	4.6%	—	—	—

2016 Year-End Financials

Return on assets: 16.6% Cash ($ mil.): 78
Return on equity: 33.5%
Current ratio: 1.90

COUNTRYMARK COOPERATIVE HOLDING CORPORATION

EXECUTIVES

Ceo-Pres, Charles Smith
V Pres, John Deaton
Accounting Manager, Pamala Durham
Director of Engineering, David Sawyer
Internal Medicine Practitioner, Devon Sullivan
Scientist, Dustin Stolz
Accounting Staff, Georgette Bailey
Staff, Jeremy Bourne
Director, Kathy Lloyd
Internal Medicine Practitioner, Kendra Brandenstein
Coordinator, Larry Conyers

LOCATIONS

HQ: COUNTRYMARK COOPERATIVE HOLDING CORPORATION
225 S EAST ST STE 144, INDIANAPOLIS, IN 462024059
Phone: 800 808-3170
Web: WWW.COUNTRYMARK.COM

HISTORICAL FINANCIALS

Company Type: Private

Income Statement				FYE: December 31
	REVENUE ($ mil.)	NET INCOME ($ mil.)	NET PROFIT MARGIN	EMPLOYEES
12/08	1,325	26	2.0%	425
12/07	964	56	5.9%	—
12/05	774	40	5.2%	—
Annual Growth	19.6%	(12.7%)	—	—

2008 Year-End Financials

Return on assets: 7.7% Cash ($ mil.): 8
Return on equity: 13.5%
Current ratio: 1.60

COUNTY OF CLARK

EXECUTIVES

County Mgr, Don Burnette
County Manager*, Don Burnett
Cfo*, Yolanda King
Staff, Hanks Jeffrey
Information Specialist, Bill Bonner
Coordinator, Fernando Martinez
Family Supervisor, Angela Ranck
Family Supervisor, Bree-Annette Seaton
Family Supervisor, Elizabeth Stumpf
Manager, Jim Nance
Rec, Kelly Salyer
Auditors: KAFOURY ARMSTRONG & CO CPAS

LOCATIONS

HQ: COUNTY OF CLARK
500 S GRAND CENTRAL PKWY # 6, LAS VEGAS, NV 891554502
Phone: 702 455-3530

HISTORICAL FINANCIALS
Company Type: Private

Income Statement				FYE: June 30
	REVENUE ($ mil.)	NET INCOME ($ mil.)	NET PROFIT MARGIN	EMPLOYEES
06/18	3,021	89	3.0%	8,528
06/17	2,873	96	3.4%	—
06/16	2,768	74	2.7%	—
06/15	2,595	(26)	—	—
Annual Growth	5.2%	—	—	—

2018 Year-End Financials
Return on assets: 0.3%
Return on equity: 0.9%
Current ratio: —
Cash ($ mil.): 4,468

COUNTY OF DEKALB

EXECUTIVES

Ceo, Vernon Jones
Interim Ceo*, Lee May
Cpo*, Talisa R Clark
Attorney, Jonathan Weintraub
Gis Specialist, Tony Hall
Acting Sheriff, Ruth M Stringer
Director of Operations, Andria Daniels
Its Director, Angela Carter
Human Resources Recruiter, Lynnie Beauvoir
Auditors: KPMG LLP ATLANTA GA

LOCATIONS

HQ: COUNTY OF DEKALB
 1300 COMMERCE DR, DECATUR, GA 300303222
Phone: 404 371-2881
Web: WWW.CO.DEKALB.GA.US

HISTORICAL FINANCIALS
Company Type: Private

Income Statement				FYE: December 31
	REVENUE ($ mil.)	NET INCOME ($ mil.)	NET PROFIT MARGIN	EMPLOYEES
12/17	628	20	3.2%	7,300
12/16	577	15	2.7%	—
12/15	599	(3)	—	—
12/10	583	(39)	—	—
Annual Growth	1.1%	—	—	—

2017 Year-End Financials
Return on assets: 0.5%
Return on equity: 1.8%
Current ratio: —
Cash ($ mil.): 690

COUNTY OF HARFORD

EXECUTIVES

County Exec, David Craig
Council Pres*, William Boniface
Treas*, Kathryn Hewitt
Procurement Staff, James P Barker
Procurement Staff, Stacy R Appold
Procurement Staff, Peter D Wakefiel
Procurement Staff, Stephanie L Si
Procurement Staff, Walter Ballesteros

Information Specialist, Constance Hirsch
Deputy Treasurer, Rick Pernas
Senior Internal Auditor, Brad Delauder
Auditors: SB & COMPANY LLC HUNT VALLEY

LOCATIONS

HQ: COUNTY OF HARFORD
 220 S MAIN ST, BEL AIR, MD 210143820
Phone: 410 638-3000
Web: WWW.HARFORDCOUNTYMD.GOV

HISTORICAL FINANCIALS
Company Type: Private

Income Statement				FYE: June 30
	REVENUE ($ mil.)	NET INCOME ($ mil.)	NET PROFIT MARGIN	EMPLOYEES
06/18	630	22	3.5%	1,400
06/17	603	47	7.9%	—
06/13	553	(7)	—	—
06/09	1	0	—	—
Annual Growth	96.5%	—	—	—

COUNTY OF HILLSBOROUGH

EXECUTIVES

County Admin, Mike Merrill
Dep County Admin*, Gregory Horwedel
Chief Fin Admin*, Bonnie Wise
Chief Development Svs*, Lucia Garsys
Chief of Human Svs*, Carl Harness
Grants Admin*, Wayne Finley
Executive of Information Techn, Hammond R Powes
Program Inspector, Bobby Jackson
Program Inspector, Wayne New
Admin Splst, Catherine Achat
Information Specialist, Douglas Blythe
Auditors: CHERRY BEKAERT LLP TAMPA FL

LOCATIONS

HQ: COUNTY OF HILLSBOROUGH
 601 E KENNEDY BLVD, TAMPA, FL 336024156
Phone: 813 276-2720
Web: WWW.HILLSBOROUGHCOUNTY.ORG

HISTORICAL FINANCIALS
Company Type: Private

Income Statement				FYE: September 30
	REVENUE ($ mil.)	NET INCOME ($ mil.)	NET PROFIT MARGIN	EMPLOYEES
09/18	1,737	66	3.9%	10,000
09/17	1,613	83	5.2%	—
09/16	1,521	(9)	—	—
09/15	1,434	64	4.5%	—
Annual Growth	6.6%	1.5%	—	—

2018 Year-End Financials
Return on assets: 0.6%
Return on equity: 0.7%
Current ratio: 4.70
Cash ($ mil.): 207

COUNTY OF MONTGOMERY

EXECUTIVES

County Executive, Marc Elrich
Pres, Hans Riemer
Exec Dir, Linda Herman
Prin, Amy Moskowitz
Captain, Dan Ogren
Captain, Gary Rebsch
Captain, Mike Green
Program Inspector, Brian Keeler
Program Inspector, Kevin Embry
Coordinator, Michael Brown
Coordinator, Paulina Alvarado
Auditors: CLIFTONLARSONALLEN LLP BALTIM

LOCATIONS

HQ: COUNTY OF MONTGOMERY
 101 MONROE ST FL 15, ROCKVILLE, MD 208502503
Phone: 240 777-8220

HISTORICAL FINANCIALS
Company Type: Private

Income Statement				FYE: June 30
	REVENUE ($ mil.)	NET INCOME ($ mil.)	NET PROFIT MARGIN	EMPLOYEES
06/18	4,203	217	5.2%	7,400
06/17	4,191	52	1.3%	—
06/16	3,874	(89)	—	—
06/15	0	0	—	—
Annual Growth	—	—	—	—

2018 Year-End Financials
Return on assets: 1.6%
Return on equity: 20.7%
Current ratio: —
Cash ($ mil.): 337

COUNTY OF RIVERSIDE

EXECUTIVES

First Dist Sup, Bob Buster
2nd Dist Sup*, John Tavaglinoe
3rd Dist Sup*, Jeff Stone
Sup*, Cynthia R
Sup*, Marion Ashley
SEC*, Judy Green
Dir*, Jean Strey
Dir*, John Mooney
Dir*, Lucas Robert
Acct Mngr, Susan Porte
Prin, Diana Grant
Auditors: BROWN ARMSTRONG ACCOUNTANCY CO

LOCATIONS

HQ: COUNTY OF RIVERSIDE
 4080 LEMON ST FL 11, RIVERSIDE, CA 925013609
Phone: 951 955-1110
Web: WWW.COUNTYOFRIVERSIDE.US

HISTORICAL FINANCIALS
Company Type: Private

Income Statement
FYE: June 30

	REVENUE ($ mil.)	NET INCOME ($ mil.)	NET PROFIT MARGIN	EMPLOYEES
06/18	3,572	(24)	—	20,000
06/17	3,504	(132)	—	—
06/16	3,390	(124)	—	—
06/15	3,245	293	9.0%	—
Annual Growth	3.3%	—	—	—

2018 Year-End Financials
Return on assets: (-0.3%)
Return on equity: (-1.0%)
Current ratio: —
Cash ($ mil.): 1,287

COUNTY OF SUFFOLK

EXECUTIVES

County Exec, Steven Bellone
Comptroller*, John Kennedy Jr
Treasurer, Angie M Carpenter
Controller, Joseph Sawicki
Coordinator, David Rubin
Chief Deputy County Executive, Dennis Cohen
Operations, Robert Braun
Human Resources Compliance, Al McCoy
Technology Teacher, Barbara Rodriguez
Associate Public Health Sanita, Cynthia Campbell
Planning, Danielle Lingg
Auditors: CHERRY BEKAERT LLP RICHMOND

LOCATIONS

HQ: COUNTY OF SUFFOLK
100 VETERANS HWY, HAUPPAUGE, NY 117885402
Phone: 631 853-4000

HISTORICAL FINANCIALS
Company Type: Private

Income Statement
FYE: December 31

	REVENUE ($ mil.)	NET INCOME ($ mil.)	NET PROFIT MARGIN	EMPLOYEES
12/17	3,174	(9)	—	12,814
12/16	3,069	(83)	—	—
12/15	2,938	(71)	—	—
12/12	2,712	(138)	—	—
Annual Growth	3.2%	—	—	—

2017 Year-End Financials
Return on assets: (-0.2%)
Return on equity: —
Current ratio: 1.20
Cash ($ mil.): 834

COUNTY OF TARRANT

EXECUTIVES

Judge, B Glen Whitely
County Judge, B Glen Whiitely
Commissioner, Roy Brooks
Comissioner, Andy H Nguyen
Commissioner, J D Johnson
Information Specialist, Hannelore Baker
Coordinator, Velina Willis
Coordinator, Donna Zavala

Coordinator, Joyce Kirk
Coordinator, Linda Blair
Coordinator, Mary Chaisson
Auditors: KPMG LLP DALLAS TX

LOCATIONS

HQ: COUNTY OF TARRANT
100 E WEATHERFORD ST, FORT WORTH, TX
761960206
Phone: 817 884-1205
Web: WWW.TARRANTCOUNTY.COM

HISTORICAL FINANCIALS
Company Type: Private

Income Statement
FYE: September 30

	REVENUE ($ mil.)	NET INCOME ($ mil.)	NET PROFIT MARGIN	EMPLOYEES
09/16	597	5	1.0%	139
09/15	580	52	9.1%	—
09/14	0	0	—	—
09/13	537	20	3.8%	—
Annual Growth	3.6%	(33.8%)	—	—

COUNTY OF WAKE

EXECUTIVES

County Mgr, David Ellis
Commissioner*, Betty Lou Ward
Accountant*, William Phillips
Chairman*, Joe Bryan
Vice Chair*, Phil Matthews
Commissioner*, Tony Gurley
Commissioner*, Caroline Sullivan
Commissioner*, James West
Commissioner*, Paul Coble
Attorney, Stephen Sizemore
Customer Staff, Mike Bass
Auditors: ELLIOTT DAVIS PLLC RALEIGH

LOCATIONS

HQ: COUNTY OF WAKE
300 S SALISBURY ST # 4800, RALEIGH, NC
276011751
Phone: 919 856-6160
Web: WWW.WAKEGOV.COM

HISTORICAL FINANCIALS
Company Type: Private

Income Statement
FYE: June 30

	REVENUE ($ mil.)	NET INCOME ($ mil.)	NET PROFIT MARGIN	EMPLOYEES
06/18	1,377	67	4.9%	3,700
06/16	1,291	(297)	—	—
06/15	0	0	—	—
06/14	1,112	(107)	—	—
Annual Growth	5.5%	—	—	—

COUNTY SANITATION DISTRICT NO. 2 OF LOS ANGELES COUNTY

EXECUTIVES

Gen Mgr, Stephen Maguin
Acctg, Sherry Rachman
Acct Mgr, Kim Black
Human Resources Manager, Jennifer Allen
Director, Debra Bogdanoff
Director of Information Techno, Daniel Lee
Scientist, Jennipher CU
Scientist, James Jackson
Senior Analyst, Ron Viloria
Project Engineer, Ryan Hall
Department Chairman, Victoria Conway
Auditors: MOSS LEVY & HARTZHEIM LLP CU

LOCATIONS

HQ: COUNTY SANITATION DISTRICT NO. 2 OF LOS
ANGELES COUNTY
1955 WORKMAN MILL RD, WHITTIER, CA 906011415
Phone: 562 699-7411
Web: WWW.LACSD.ORG

HISTORICAL FINANCIALS
Company Type: Private

Income Statement
FYE: June 30

	REVENUE ($ mil.)	NET INCOME ($ mil.)	NET PROFIT MARGIN	EMPLOYEES
06/16	545	144	26.4%	1,700
06/15	555	92	16.7%	—
06/12	550	74	13.6%	—
06/11	575	115	20.0%	—
Annual Growth	(1.1%)	4.6%	—	—

2016 Year-End Financials
Return on assets: 2.6%
Return on equity: 3.6%
Current ratio: 13.70
Cash ($ mil.): 115

COVENANT HEALTH

Covenant Health has made a pact to provide good health to the good people of Tennessee. The not-for-profit health care system established in 1996 provides a variety of medical services through seven acute care hospitals a psychiatric hospital and a number of specialty outpatient centers offering geriatrics pediatric care cancer services weight management and diagnostics. Covenant Health also operates home health and hospice agencies and a physician practice management company. Covenant Health provides staffing and medical management services to its affiliated facilities and to make itself a really well-rounded health care provider it operates the Covenant Health Federal Credit Union.

EXECUTIVES

Senior Vice President, Mark Browne
Vice President Patient Accounting, Kevin Brown
Senior Vice President, Debra Honey
Nursing Director, Welch Bridgette

LOCATIONS

HQ: COVENANT HEALTH
100 FORT SANDERS W BLVD, KNOXVILLE, TN
379223353
Phone: 865 531-5555
Web: WWW.COVENANTHEALTH.COM

PRODUCTS/OPERATIONS

Selected Tennessee Facilities
Fort Loudon Medical Center (Lenoir City TN)
Fort Sanders Regional Medical Center (Knoxville TN)
LeConte Medical Center (formerly Fort Sanders Sevier
    Medical Center; Sevierville TN)
Methodist Medical Center of Oak Ridge (Oak Ridge TN)
Parkwest Medical Center (Knoxville TN)
    Peninsula Hospital (behavioral health care Louisville
    TN)
Roane Medical Center (Harriman TN)

COMPETITORS

Blount Memorial	Saint Thomas
Hospital	Rutherford Hospital
East Tennessee	Tennova Healthcare
Children's Hospital	University Health
Kindred Healthcare	System Inc.
LifePoint Health	Vanderbilt University
Parkridge Medical	Medical Center
Center	
Saint Thomas Midtown	
Hospital	

HISTORICAL FINANCIALS
Company Type: Private

Income Statement				FYE: December 31
	REVENUE ($ mil.)	NET INCOME ($ mil.)	NET PROFIT MARGIN	EMPLOYEES
12/18	1,296	(49)	—	2,469
12/17	1,268	144	11.4%	—
12/16	1,246	57	4.6%	—
12/05	1,056	32	3.1%	—
Annual Growth	1.6%	—	—	—

2018 Year-End Financials
Return on assets: (-2.1%)   Cash ($ mil.): 51
Return on equity: (-3.7%)
Current ratio: 1.00

COVENANT HEALTH SYSTEM

Covenant Health System ties West Texas and Eastern New Mexico together with quality health care. The health services provider offers some 1100 beds in its five primary acute-care and specialty hospitals; it also manages about a dozen affiliated community hospitals. Covenant Health System part of Providence St. Joseph Health also maintains a network of family health care and medical clinics. Covenant Health System's major facilities are Covenant Medical Center Covenant Specialty Hospital and Covenant Women's and Children's Hospital. The health system also includes some 20 clinics and 50 physician practices and its extensive outreach programs target isolated rural communities with mobile services.

EXECUTIVES

Vice President, Sharon Prather
Director Of Health Information, Beverly Houk
Director Of Radiology, David Donaldson
Medical Director, Jack Dubose

Auditors: ERNST & YOUNG US LLP IRVINE

LOCATIONS

HQ: COVENANT HEALTH SYSTEM
3615 19TH ST, LUBBOCK, TX 794101209
Phone: 806 725-1011
Web: WWW.COVENANTHEALTH.ORG

COMPETITORS

Baptist St. Anthony's	Tenet Healthcare
Health System	Texas Health Resources
Del Sol Medical Center	The Methodist Health
Encompass Health	System
Hunt Memorial	University Medical
NW Texas Healthcare	Center of El Paso
Parkland Health &	
Hospital System	

HISTORICAL FINANCIALS
Company Type: Private

Income Statement				FYE: June 30
	REVENUE ($ mil.)	NET INCOME ($ mil.)	NET PROFIT MARGIN	EMPLOYEES
06/15	703	76	10.9%	5,000
06/13	552	35	6.5%	—
06/09	1,185	(38)	—	—
Annual Growth	(8.3%)	—	—	—

2015 Year-End Financials
Return on assets: 10.5%   Cash ($ mil.): 39
Return on equity: 14.7%
Current ratio: 3.20

COVENANT HEALTH, INC.

EXECUTIVES

Pres-Ceo, David R Lincoln
SEC*, Patricia Karl
Treas*, Harold R Acres
Chm*, Dorothy Cooper
V Chb*, Richard J Hanley
Dir*, Margaret Mary Modde
Svp-Cfo*, Stephen Forney
Controller*, Donald Clark
Asst Cfo, Laural Haug
Assistant Controller, Becky Lehoux
Director of Information, Glenn Spargo
Auditors: WILLIAM STEELE & ASSOCIATES PC

LOCATIONS

HQ: COVENANT HEALTH, INC.
100 AMES POND DR STE 102, TEWKSBURY, MA
018761240
Phone: 978 654-6363
Web: WWW.COVENANTHEALTH.NET

HISTORICAL FINANCIALS
Company Type: Private

Income Statement				FYE: December 31
	REVENUE ($ mil.)	NET INCOME ($ mil.)	NET PROFIT MARGIN	EMPLOYEES
12/18	666	(74)	—	6,500
12/17	670	38	5.8%	—
12/16	645	18	2.9%	—
12/12	12	1	12.0%	—
Annual Growth	95.2%	—	—	—

2018 Year-End Financials
Return on assets: (-8.5%)   Cash ($ mil.): 49
Return on equity: (-16.0%)
Current ratio: 1.70

COVENANT MEDICAL CENTER, INC.

Covenant Medical Center (operating as Covenant HealthCare) has made a pact with Wolverine Staters to try to keep them in good health. The not-for-profit health care provider operates more than 20 inpatient and outpatient care facilities including its two main Covenant Medical Center campuses. It serves residents in a 20-county area of east-central Michigan with additional facilities in Bay City Frankenmuth and Midland. Specialized care services include cardiovascular health cancer treatment and obstetrics. The regional health care system has more about 650 beds.

Operations
Covenant HealthCare programs and services range from high-risk obstetrics and neonatal/pediatric intensive care to acute care. Its assets include cardiology oncology orthopedics robotic surgery and Level II Adult and Pediatric Trauma Center.

The health system has more than 20 inpatient and outpatient facilities and a trauma/emergency department that provides 85000 visits per year. The system employs more than 500 physicians from 52 medical specialties.

Sales and Marketing
Covenant HealthCare markets its services via social media.

Financial Performance
In 2014 the company's revenue increased 4% to $528 million as patient service revenue rose; this gain was partially offset by a decline in realized gain and other revenues. An increase in salaries and wages as well as higher supplies expenses led to a 12% decline in net income (to $57 million).

Cash flow from operations also fell slipping 20% to $48 million as accounts receivable increased.

Strategy
Expanding its infrastructure to keep up with demand in 2014 Covenant HealthCare added 11456 sq. ft. to its Emergency Department. The addition allows for more efficient triage enhanced patient waiting areas and additional space for current technology. It added 18 treatment bays to the existing 47 and also brought a dedicated CT scanner and mini-laboratory within the department.

Also that year it opened the assisted living community of Covenant Glen in Frankenmuth. The 35000 sq. ft. structure has 45 rooms (15 dedicated to memory care and 30 with assisted living beds).

Company Background
Covenant HealthCare was formed in 1998 through the merger of Saginaw General and St. Luke's Hospitals.

EXECUTIVES

Medical Director, Babu Nahata
Physical Therapy Director, Jeff Berger
Vice President Patient Services, Carol Stoll
Director Of Pharmacy, Terry Wernette
Dir Of Home Healthcare Srv, Diane Glasgow

LOCATIONS

HQ: COVENANT MEDICAL CENTER, INC.
1447 N HARRISON ST, SAGINAW, MI 486024727
Phone: 989 583-0000
Web: WWW.COVENANTHEALTHCARE.COM

PRODUCTS/OPERATIONS

2014 Revenues

	% of total
Net patient service revenues	95
Other revenues	5
Total	**100**

Selected services

Bariatrics
Birth Center
Cancer Care
Cardiology - Center for the Heart
Childbirth Classes
da Vinci Robotic Surgery
Diabetes Self-Management Program
Emergency Care Center
Imaging and Diagnostics
Neonatal Intensive Care
Neurology
Osteoporosis
Orthopaedics
Pediatrics
Physical Medicine and Rehab.
Pulmonary/Respiratory Care
Sleep Center
Surgical Services
Trauma
Urologic Surgery
Women's Health
Wound Healing Center

COMPETITORS

Genesys Health System
  Genesys Regional
  Medical Center
Hurley Medical Center
McLaren Bay

McLaren Health Care
Munson Healthcare
Sparrow Health System
University of Michigan
  Health System

HISTORICAL FINANCIALS
Company Type: Private

Income Statement				FYE: June 30
	REVENUE ($ mil.)	NET INCOME ($ mil.)	NET PROFIT MARGIN	EMPLOYEES
06/16	579	40	7.0%	4,000
06/15	535	31	5.8%	—
06/14	566	34	6.1%	—
06/10	508	28	5.5%	—
Annual Growth	2.2%	6.2%	—	—

2016 Year-End Financials
Return on assets: 6.4%
Return on equity: 12.9%
Current ratio: 1.80
Cash ($ mil.): 21

CPS ENERGY

CPS Energy (formerly City Public Service of San Antonio) serves more than 765000 electricity customers and 335000 natural gas customers in the greater San Antonio Texas area. The utility operates in a 1514-square-mile service territory and has a generating capacity of more than 6570 MW from its 16 fossil-fueled power plants. It also owns interests in the South Texas Project (STP) nuclear power plant and wind and solar power projects. As a municipally-owned utility CPS Energy is exempt from retail competition in Texas.

Operations
CPS Energy offers services such as new service installation service remodel all-night security lighting and street lighting (associated with new residential developments).

Geographic Reach
CPS Energy serves customers in the greater San Antonio texas area including Bexar County and portions of Atascosa Bandera Comal Guadalupe Kendall Medina and Wilson counties.

Sales and Marketing
Throughout its service territory CPS Energy provides electric and natural gas services for residential and commercial customers/developments

Strategy
Pushing renewables to reduce green house gas emissions to meet state and federal standards CPS Energy is now leading in wind-energy capacity among municipally owned utilities across the US with a goal of getting 20% of its power from renewable sources by 2020 including 100 MW from solar power. It also plans to cut its customers' demand for electricity by 771 MW by that year. In a major acceleration of its green energy/conservation commitments in fiscal year 2012 CPS Energy announced plans to deactivate its J.T. Deely Units 1 and 2 coal-fired power plants in fiscal year 2018 instead of the projected dates of fiscal year 2032 and fiscal year 2033.

Looking to reduce both power use and its carbon footprint CPS Energy is retrofitting more than 1 million electric and gas meters in order to bring them into a smart technology grid to help customers save money and conserve power. It is also encouraging customers to switch to compact fluorescent lights and has a goal of reducing power demand by 771 MW by 2020.

In 2015 Clean Energy Collective (CEC the world's leading community solar provider) signed a partnership agreement with CPS Energy bringing the first roofless community solar pilot project to San Antonio. CEC will develop a 1.2 MW solar PV facility providing CPS Energy customers the opportunity to own local clean energy generation through CEC's Roofless Solar program.

Company Background
A venerable company CPS Energy traces its roots to the 1860s when its predecessor opened a manufactured gas plant on Houston Street.

EXECUTIVES

Vice President Of Customer Service And Solutions, Maria Koudouris
Evp And General Counsel, Carolyn E. Shellman
President And Ceo, Doyle N. Beneby
Evp Cto And Chief Strategy Officer, Cris Eugster
Vp Finance, Justin Locke
Executive Vice President, Alfonso Lujan
Vice President Of People And Culture, Lisa Lewis
Vice President Of Energy Supply And Market Operations, Frank Almaraz
Senior Vice President Of Engineering Services, Joel — Jupe
Vice President Operations, Edward Escamilla
Vice President, Patsy Velez
Senior Vice President Power Generation, Tammy Preiss
Vice President Marketing, Donald Murray
Senior Vice President Marketing, Curt Powell
Vice President Community Engagement, Maria Garcia
Vice President Of Engineering, Ronald Schaefer
Vice President Of Accounting, Gary Gold
Senior Vice President Partner Solutions, Deborah Gunn
Vice President Of Information Technolo, Stan Torvick
Senior Vice President Power Generation, Tammy Priess
Executive Vice President And Chief Administrative Officer, Laura Jimenez
It Vice President, Dan Torvik
Vice President And Chief Administrative Officer, Jelynne LeBlanc-Burley
Vice President, Marisol Mari
Lead Secretary, Sabrina L Hearn
Senior Secretary, Grace Robledo
Auditors: GARZA PREIS & CO LLC/BAKER

LOCATIONS

HQ: CPS ENERGY
  145 NAVARRO ST, SAN ANTONIO, TX 782052934
Phone: 210 353-2222
Web: WWW.CPSENERGY.COM

PRODUCTS/OPERATIONS

2015 Sales

	$ mil.	% of total
Electric	2,320	92
Gas	175	7
Other	36	1
Total	2,531	100

COMPETITORS

AEP
AES
Duke Energy

NextEra Energy
ONEOK

HISTORICAL FINANCIALS
Company Type: Private

Income Statement				FYE: January 31
	REVENUE ($ mil.)	NET INCOME ($ mil.)	NET PROFIT MARGIN	EMPLOYEES
01/12	2,258	21	0.9%	3,743
01/11	2,068	78	3.8%	—
01/10	1,930	107	5.6%	—
Annual Growth	8.1%	(55.5%)	—	—

2012 Year-End Financials
Return on assets: 0.2%
Return on equity: 0.6%
Current ratio: 1.30
Cash ($ mil.): 148

CREATIVE MANAGEMENT INC

EXECUTIVES

Pres, Bikram Gil
SEC, Kashmir Gill
Vice President, Seif Abdraboh

LOCATIONS

HQ: CREATIVE MANAGEMENT INC
  935 SR 34 STE 3A, MATAWAN, NJ 07747
Phone: 732 696-2201
Web: WWW.GILLENERGY.COM

HISTORICAL FINANCIALS
Company Type: Private

Income Statement				FYE: December 31
	REVENUE ($ mil.)	NET INCOME ($ mil.)	NET PROFIT MARGIN	EMPLOYEES
12/11	532	1	0.3%	50
12/98	4	0	2.4%	—
Annual Growth	44.6%	23.4%	—	—

2011 Year-End Financials
Return on assets: 3.5%
Return on equity: 6.9%
Current ratio: 0.90
Cash ($ mil.): 3

CREIGHTON ALEGENT HEALTH

CHI Health (formerly Alegent Creighton Health) pledges allegiance to medical well-being in its corner of the Midwest. The not-for-profit health care system operates 15 hospitals with about 3000 beds in Omaha and surrounding communities in eastern Nebraska and southwestern Iowa including Bergan Mercy Medical Center and Immanuel Medical Center. Alegent Creighton Health's hospitals provide specialty services including cardiovascular orthopedic and cancer care; it also operates psychiatric long-term care home health and outpatient centers. The health system is sponsored by Catholic Health Initiatives and is affiliated with Creighton University.

Operations

CHI Health is the primary provider of teaching locations for the Creighton University School of Medicine with academic programs in a number of fields including psychiatry women's health nursing and pharmacy. Its hospitals have some 1500 physicians on staff and include 10 acute care facilities and one psychiatric hospital. Specialty units include an orthopedic hospital and skilled nursing centers.

In addition to its acute care facilities the organization provides primary and specialty outpatient care services through its CHI Health Alegent Creighton Clinic unit. The division has more than 20 specialties and operates about 100 physician practices and clinics in Omaha and surrounding areas. There are also two Express Care clinics that offer urgent care for non-life-threatening ailments and six Quick Care clinics in Omaha (located in Hy-Vee retail stores) that provide minor medical ailment treatment as well as sports physicals and vaccinations. The idea behind the clinics is to divert patients who might otherwise end up at ERs with non-emergency symptoms (thus lowering hospital expenses).

Geographic Reach

The network's hospitals are located in Omaha (five medical centers) Papillion Plainview and Schuyler Nebraska; as well as in Corning Council Bluffs and Missouri Valley Iowa.

Strategy

The company has been pursuing growth to signify its presence as a unified regional health network. The efforts are intended to allow it to better compete and thrive in the changing US health care landscape by expanding its facilities training programs and resources in the Omaha area. Growth efforts include the formation of an intensive care partnership with Good Samaritan Hospital in 2013. The network has also opened several new community care clinics in recent years.

In 2015 CHI Health partnered with Aetna to create Nebraska's first commercial product-based accountable care organization (ACO). The ACO offers employers a health care option that is designed to improve quality of care outcomes and patient experiences.

EXECUTIVES

Department Secretary, Mary Nastase
Auditors: LB CATHOLIC HEALTH INITIATIVES

LOCATIONS

HQ: CREIGHTON ALEGENT HEALTH
12809 W DODGE RD, OMAHA, NE 681542155
Phone: 402 343-4300
Web: WWW.CHIHEALTH.COM

PRODUCTS/OPERATIONS

Selected Facilities and Operations

Alegent Creighton Health Clinics (primary care multiple locations in Iowa and Nebraska)
Alegent Creighton Health Urgent Care clinics (urgent care three locations in Nebraska)
Alegent Creighton Health Quick Care (minor care clinics; seven locations in Omaha Nebraska in Hy-Vee stores)
Alegent Health at Home (home health care)

Bergan Mercy Medical Center (Omaha Nebraska; 300 beds)
Community Memorial Hospital (Missouri Valley Iowa; 20 beds)
Creighton University Medical Center (Omaha Nebraska; 400 beds)
Immanuel Communities (independent and assisted living in Omaha and Lincoln)
Immanuel Fontenelle (nursing home in Omaha)
Immanuel Medical Center (Omaha Nebraska; 280 beds)
Immanuel Rehabilitation Center (Omaha Nebraska)
Lakeside Hospital (Omaha Nebraska; 160 beds)
Lasting Hope Recovery Center (Omaha Nebraska; psychiatric hospital with 120 beds)
Memorial Hospital (Schuyler Nebraska; 25 beds)
Mercy Corning Hospital (Corning Iowa; 20 beds)
Mercy Hospital (Council Bluffs Iowa; 160 beds)
Midlands Hospital (Papillion Nebraska; 50 beds)
Plainview Hospital (Plainview Nebraska)

COMPETITORS

BryanLGH Medical Center
Children's Hospital & Medical Center
Fremont Area Medical Center
Heartland Health
Madonna Rehabilitation Hospital
Mercy Health Network
Methodist Health System
Nebraska Medical Center
Saint Elizabeth Regional Medical Center
UNMC Physicians
UnityPoint Health

HISTORICAL FINANCIALS

Company Type: Private

Income Statement				FYE: June 30
	REVENUE ($ mil.)	NET INCOME ($ mil.)	NET PROFIT MARGIN	EMPLOYEES
06/15	516	(147)	—	8,600
06/13	525	63	12.2%	—
Annual Growth	(0.9%)	—	—	—

2015 Year-End Financials

Return on assets: (-21.3%)   Cash ($ mil.): 20
Return on equity: (-55.8%)
Current ratio: 2.30

CRETE CARRIER CORPORATION

Holding company Crete Carrier Corporation's flagship business Crete Carrier provides dry van truckload freight transportation services in the 48 contiguous states. It operates from some two dozen terminals mainly in the midwestern and southeastern US. The company's Shaffer Trucking unit transports temperature-controlled cargo and Hunt Transportation (no relation to J.B. Hunt Transport Services) hauls heavy equipment and other cargo on flatbed trailers. Overall the companies operate more than 5400 tractors and 13000 trailers. Family-owned Crete Carrier was founded in 1966 by chairman Duane Acklie; president and CEO Tonn Ostergard is his son-in-law.

EXECUTIVES

Vice President National Accounts, Bill Boehler
Vice President, Janelle Sullivan
National Account Manager, Tim Stakolich
Vice President And Corporate General Counsel, Curtis Ruwe
Vice President Of Maintenance And Equipment, Winston Ostergard

LOCATIONS

HQ: CRETE CARRIER CORPORATION
400 NW 56TH ST, LINCOLN, NE 685288843
Phone: 800 998-4095
Web: WWW.CRETECARRIER.COM

COMPETITORS

Boyd Bros. Transportation
C.R. England
Celadon
Comcar
Covenant Transportation
Heartland Express
J.B. Hunt
Landstar System
Prime Inc.
Schneider National
Swift Transportation
U.S. Xpress
Werner Enterprises

HISTORICAL FINANCIALS

Company Type: Private

Income Statement				FYE: September 30
	REVENUE ($ mil.)	NET INCOME ($ mil.)	NET PROFIT MARGIN	EMPLOYEES
09/18	1,150	139	12.1%	6,000
09/16	984	95	9.7%	—
09/15	0	0	—	—
09/14	1,034	127	12.3%	—
Annual Growth	2.7%	2.3%		

2018 Year-End Financials

Return on assets: 13.3%   Cash ($ mil.): 128
Return on equity: 15.8%
Current ratio: 2.20

CROWE LLP

EXECUTIVES

Ceo, James Powers
Cfo-Ptnr, Todd Welu
Cro-Ptnr, Fred J Bauters
Cmo, Ann Lathrop
CIO, Yvonne Scott
Coo, Joseph P Santucci Jr
Chief Strategy & Innovation of, Derek Bang
Cdso, Justin Bass
Taxes Manager, Joohee Ohk
Senior Project Manager, Karen Messersmith
Staff, Ashley Dana
Auditors: CROWE HORWATH

LOCATIONS

HQ: CROWE LLP
225 W WACKER DR STE 2600, CHICAGO, IL 606061228
Phone: 312 899-7000
Web: WWW.CROWE.COM

HISTORICAL FINANCIALS

Company Type: Private

Income Statement				FYE: March 31
	REVENUE ($ mil.)	NET INCOME ($ mil.)	NET PROFIT MARGIN	EMPLOYEES
03/15	700	204	29.2%	3,130
03/14	670	163	24.4%	—
03/13	0	0	—	—
Annual Growth	—	—	—	—

2015 Year-End Financials

Return on assets: 71.1%   Cash ($ mil.): 6
Return on equity: 260.7%
Current ratio: 2.00

CROWLEY MARITIME CORPORATION

Crowley Maritime has pushed and pulled its way into prominence as a tug and barge operator. The company's Liner Services unit provides scheduled transportation of containers trailers and other cargo mainly among ports in Latin and North America Puerto Rico and the Caribbean Basin. Other units transport oil and chemical products and oil field equipment and provide ship assist/escort marine salvage and emergency towing logistics ship management and fuel distribution services. Overall the company's fleet includes more than 200 vessels. Members of the founding Crowley family own the company.

Operations

The company functions through its six operating lines of business which include Puerto Rico Liner Services Caribbean and Latin America Liner Services Logistics Services Marine Services and Technical Services. Its sixth business line which is Petroleum Services provides transportation distribution and sales of petroleum products for the fuel industry in Alaska through its Service Oil and Gas Group. Crowley Maritime operates fuel terminals and a barge and truck fleet to transport fuel throughout Alaska.

Crowley operates RO/RO (roll-on-roll-off) and LO/LO (lift-on-lift-off) vessels as well as tankers tugs and barges. In less than 10 years Crowley Maritime has invested almost one-quarter of a billion dollars in cargo equipment for its Liner Shipping Services segment. While Liner Shipping Services handles more traditional cargo such as automobiles trucks buses construction equipment refrigerated cargo apparel and even hazardous materials its TITAN Salvage subsidiary occasionally contends with more nontraditional cargo. It has a salvage base in Australia (strategically located to respond to marine emergencies in the Great Barrier Reef and in other South-West Pacific regions) and three other facilities in that country.

Geographic Reach

Crowley has operations in Africa the Asia/Pacific Canada the Caribbean (including Puerto Rico and Cuba) Central America the Middle East Europe Russia and the US.

Sales and Marketing

Crowley targets 20 industries such as oil and gas retail consumer services government and military manufacturing and apparel. The company's major customers have included such big names as Sears Toyota Bacardi Coca-Cola Hanes Procter & Gamble BP Exxon Mobil Parker Drilling Worley-Parsons and the US Government.

Strategy

One important growth market for Crowley is in Cuba. Although the company has been shipping cargo to Cuba since 2001 it made its first shipment from Cuba to the US in 2017 due to the Obama administration's easing of American/Cuban relations.

Mergers and Acquisitions

Crowley grows through acquisitions and joint ventures. In mid-2016 Crowley acquired the aviation fuels business of Ace Fuels LLC a fixed base operator (FBO) headquartered at Merrill Field Alaska in downtown Anchorage offering Jet A and AV 100LL fuels. The acquisition enhanced the company's footprint by adding additional aviation fuels service stations throughout Alaska and also gave Ace Fuels customers better access to high-quality fuels in the south central and western parts of the state.

In 2015 Crowley and Svitzer Salvage merged their salvage divisions and created a joint venture called Ardent to offer customers a broader range of capabilities and marine related services. Ardent is headquartered in Houston Texas with operational offices in the Netherlands the UK and Singapore along with supporting offices in Australia Brazil South Korea Greece South Africa and other regions.

Company Background

Crowley traces its historical roots back to 1892.

EXECUTIVES

Vice Chairman And Evp, William A. (Bill) Pennella
Chairman And Ceo, Thomas B. (Tom) Crowley
Svp And General Manager Puerto Rico And Caribbean Liner Services, John P. Hourihan
Director Sales And Marketing Ship Assist And Escort, Todd Busch
Svp And General Manager Logistics, Frank Larkin
Svp And General Manager Latin America Liner Services, Steven M. (Steve) Collar
Svp And General Manager Petroleum Distribution And Marine Services, Rockwell E. (Rocky) Smith
Svp And General Manager Petroleum Services, Robert B. (Rob) Grune
Svp Treasurer, Dan Warner
Vice President Of Labor Relations, Rudy Leming
Vice President Business Development, Ned Lagoy
Vice President Of Government Services, Jay Brickman
Vice President Of Information Technology, Herman Reich
Vice President Of Finance, Reynaldo Rojas
Vice President Marine Operations, Cole Cosgrove
Senior Vice President And General Manager Latin America Liner Services, Steve Collar
Executive Vice President Purchasing And Technology, Kelly Conaty
Vp Finance And Planning, David Nickless
Vice Presidents, Tony Otero
Vice President Of Organizational Development And C, Susan Michel
Vp Procurement Strategic Sourcing, Jean Matthews
Treasurer, Daniel Warner

LOCATIONS

HQ: CROWLEY MARITIME CORPORATION
9487 REGENCY SQUARE BLVD, JACKSONVILLE, FL 322258183
Phone: 904 727-2200
Web: WWW.CROWLEY.COM

PRODUCTS/OPERATIONS

Selected Services
Energy industry support services

Fuel sales and distribution
Liner services
Logistics
Ocean towing and transportation
Petroleum and chemical transportation
Project management
Salvage and emergency response
Ship assist and escort
Ship management
Vessel construction and naval architecture
Alaska fuel sales and distribution
Arctic all-terrain transportation
Harbor ship assist and tanker escort
Marine salvage wreck removal and emergency response
Ocean towing and barge transportation
OPA 90 compliance
Petroleum and chemical transportation
Ship management
Shipping And Logistics
Vessel design and construction management

COMPETITORS

A.P. M ller - M rsk	Sea Star Line
APL	Tidewater Inc.
Foss Maritime	Trailer Bridge
Horizon Lines	U.S. Shipping
Hornbeck Offshore	UPS Supply Chain
K-Sea Transportation	Solutions
Lynden Incorporated	Washington Companies
SEACOR	

HISTORICAL FINANCIALS

Company Type: Private

Income Statement
FYE: December 31

	REVENUE ($ mil.)	NET INCOME ($ mil.)	NET PROFIT MARGIN	EMPLOYEES
12/08	1,955	86	4.4%	4,329
12/07	1,622	122	7.5%	—
12/06	1,467	38	2.6%	—
12/05	1,190	38	3.3%	—
Annual Growth	18.0%	30.3%		

2008 Year-End Financials
Return on assets: 6.2%   Cash ($ mil.): 64
Return on equity: 18.2%
Current ratio: 1.40

CROWLEY PETROLEUM DIST INC

EXECUTIVES

Pres, Rockwell Smith
Treas, Daniel Warner
V Pres, Bob Cox
V Pres, Alex Sweeney
SEC, Bruce Love
Law Specialist, Billye Sepe
Director, Michael Moeller
Auditors: DELOITTE & TOUCHE LLP JACKSON

LOCATIONS

HQ: CROWLEY PETROLEUM DIST INC
201 ARCTIC SLOPE AVE, ANCHORAGE, AK 995183033
Phone: 907 822-3375
Web: WWW.CROWLEY.COM

HISTORICAL FINANCIALS

Company Type: Private

Income Statement
FYE: December 31

	REVENUE ($ mil.)	NET INCOME ($ mil.)	NET PROFIT MARGIN	EMPLOYEES
12/13	476	16	3.5%	100
12/12	449	19	4.3%	—
Annual Growth	6.1%	(14.2%)	—	—

2013 Year-End Financials
Return on assets: —   Cash ($ mil.): 10
Return on equity: 3.5%
Current ratio: 2.00

CRST INTERNATIONAL, INC.

CRST International promises f-a-s-t freight transportation through its operating units. CRST Expedited provides standard dry van truckload transportation primarily on long-haul routes along with dedicated and expedited transportation services. CRST Malone hauls steel and other freight requiring flatbed trailers or trailers with removable sides and CRST Logistics arranges freight transportation and provides other third-party logistics services. The family-owned business' other operations include CRST Dedicated Services and Specialized Transportation. Overall the companies operate a fleet of about 4500 tractors and 7300 van trailers.

Operations
CRST operates through seven distinct operations. CRST Expedited is a long-haul truckload carrier and CRST Malone is a flatbed carrier serving customers in North America. The company's CRST Dedicated Services unit offers tailor-made specialized transportation services while CRST Logistics helps customers reduce costs and optimize their performance.

CRST Specialized Transportation provides multi-modal logistics supported by distribution centers located throughout the US and Canada. Other operations include Temperature Controlled Team Service (TCTS) (expedited transcontinental transportation of perishable products) and BESL Transfer Company (provider of short haul flatbed services).

Geographic Reach
Based in Cedar Rapids Iowa CRST operates more than 50 distribution centers terminals and offices across North America.

Sales and Marketing
The company targets the business and retail industrial metals building products technology telecommunications automotive government tradeshows and events health care transportation and residential markets.

Strategy
In 2015 CRST broke ground on its new $37 million world headquarters in downtown Cedar Rapids Iowa.

In 2013 CRST Expedited opened a training and repair facility in Riverside California.

Mergers and Acquisitions
CRST also continues to grow through the use of acquisitions.

In 2015 the company bought privately-held Pegasus Transportation based in Louisville Kentucky. The acquisition allows CRST to expand its temperature controlled operations nationwide footprint through its expanded customer base.

In early 2014 CRST obtained a privately held short haul and flatbed services provider BESL Transfer Co. based in Cincinnati Ohio in a transaction that fortified its CRST Malone operations. The acquisition of BESL allowed CRST to expand its flatbed operations nationwide footprint through its short haul regional services and expanded agent base.

In 2013 it picked up the Allied Special Products Division of Allied Van Lines based in Fort Wayne Indiana. The deal enabled its Specialized Transportation operations to further develop its distribution center network and provide better service and faster transit to its customers. That year subsidiary CRST Logistics added Top Shelf Logistics LLC to its rapidly growing agency network.

Company Background
CRST was founded in 1955 by Herald Smith father of chairman John Smith.

EXECUTIVES
Regional Vice President Sales, Linda Mundie
Vice President Dedicated Services, Chad Humphrey
Auditors: DELOITTE & TOUCHE LLP CEDAR R

LOCATIONS
HQ: CRST INTERNATIONAL, INC.
201 1ST ST SE, CEDAR RAPIDS, IA 524011421
Phone: 319 396-4400

PRODUCTS/OPERATIONS

Selected Services
Expedited Team Service
Dry Van
Flatbed
Dedicated
High Value/White Glove
Temperature Controlled
Transportation Management
Brokerage
Home Delivery/First & Final Mile
Warehousing/Inventory Solutions
LTL
Intermodal
Equipment Sales

COMPETITORS

Anderson Trucking Service	J.B. Hunt
Boyd Bros. Transportation	Ruan Transportation Management Systems
C.H. Robinson Worldwide	Schneider National
Comcar	Swift Transportation
Crete Carrier	UPS Supply Chain Solutions
Forward Air	Werner Enterprises

HISTORICAL FINANCIALS
Company Type: Private

Income Statement				FYE: December 31
	REVENUE ($ mil.)	NET INCOME ($ mil.)	NET PROFIT MARGIN	EMPLOYEES
12/12	1,258	75	6.0%	5,960
12/11	1,143	81	7.1%	—
Annual Growth	10.1%	(7.8%)	—	—

2012 Year-End Financials
Return on assets: 13.7%   Cash ($ mil.): 71
Return on equity: 45.2%
Current ratio: 2.70

CSC SUGAR, LLC

EXECUTIVES
MBR-Pres, Paul J Farmer
Cfo-Treas, Francis X Claps
Customer Representativ, Rhea Kirkland
Auditors: GRANT THORNTON LLP MINNEAPOLI

LOCATIONS
HQ: CSC SUGAR, LLC
36 GROVE ST STE 2, NEW CANAAN, CT 068405329
Phone: 203 846-5610
Web: WWW.CSCSUGAR.COM

HISTORICAL FINANCIALS
Company Type: Private

Income Statement				FYE: December 31
	REVENUE ($ mil.)	NET INCOME ($ mil.)	NET PROFIT MARGIN	EMPLOYEES
12/09	574	18	3.2%	40
12/08	790	5	0.7%	—
12/07	515	6	1.2%	—
Annual Growth	5.6%	74.5%	—	—

2009 Year-End Financials
Return on assets: 24.8%   Cash ($ mil.): 4
Return on equity: 104.6%
Current ratio: 1.20

CUMBERLAND COUNTY HOSPITAL SYSTEM, INC.

Don't fear for a lack of medical services at Cumberland County Hospital System (doing business as Cape Fear Valley Health System). The medical provider comprises five acute-care and specialty hospitals with about 765 total beds and more than a dozen primary-care physician practices scattered throughout the region in North Carolina. The hospital system serves residents of coastal North Carolina providing general and specialized medical services such as cancer treatment open-heart surgery psychiatric care and rehabilitation. It also operates the HealthPlex fitness and wellness facility and provides home health and hospice services.

Operations
Cumberland County Hospital System is the ninth-largest health systems in North Carolina with more than 935000 patient visits annually. It is also Cumberland County's largest non-government employer.

The system's 490-bed county hospital Cape Fear Valley Medical Center specializes in heart care cancer treatment and surgical services. Cumberland's other health centers include: the 66-bed acute care Highsmith-Rainey Specialty Hospital; the 78-bed Cape Fear Valley Rehabilitation Center; Bladen County Hospital; and the 41-bed acute care Hoke Hospital.

Additionally the system's Cape Fear Valley Behavioral Health Care boasts a 32-bed psychiatric facility a full-service Risk Labor and Delivery department a Level-III Neonatal Intensive Care Unit (UNIT) for newborns and a pediatric Intensive Care Unit (PICU).

Geographic Reach
Cumberland County Hospital System's facilities are located throughout the six-county Cape Fear region near the city of Wilmington in the Southeastern part of North Carolina.

Financial Performance
Cumberland's revenue fell by 2% to $646 million in 2014 primarily due declines in patient revenue.

Despite declining revenue the system's excess of revenue over expenses grew by 13% to $36.5 million mostly thanks to lower salary expenses but also thanks to lower medical supply costs and fewer other expenses.

Cumberland's cash generated from operations rose by 15% to $51 million mostly because the system spent less cash on its employee and vendor payments.

EXECUTIVES

Ceo, Michael Nagowski
Cfo, Sandra Williams
Chief Nursing Officer, Jana Stonestreet
Chief Medical Officer, Christopher Aul
Vice President Clinical Services Development And Operations, Vanessa King
Respiratory Therapy Director, Christopher Meredith
Pharmd, Amy Jones
Pharmacist Manager, Clarence Minter
Medical Director Of Perioperative Services, Monson Shuh
Medical Records Director, Kandi Smalls
Chairman, Jerry Dean
Vice Chairman, Marion Gillis Olion
Unit Secretary, Cora Dixon
Unit Secretary, Casharol Robinson
Auditors: DELOITTE TAX LLP RALEIGH NC

LOCATIONS

HQ: CUMBERLAND COUNTY HOSPITAL SYSTEM, INC.
   1638 OWEN DR, FAYETTEVILLE, NC 283043424
Phone: 910 609-4000
Web: WWW.CAPEFEARVALLEY.COM

PRODUCTS/OPERATIONS

2014 Sales

	$ mil.	% of total
Net patient service revenue	621	96
Other revenue	25	4
Total	**646**	**100**

Selected Services

Birth center
Healthplex
Heart and vascular
Imaging/diagnostics
Minority health
Neuroscience
Orthopedics
Outpatient services
Pediatrics
Physician practice
Rehabilitation
Scancer treatment
Surgical services
Weight loss surgery

COMPETITORS

Alamance Regional Medical Center	Morehead Memorial Hospital
Carolinas HealthCare System	Rex Healthcare
Cone Health	Rowan Regional Medical Center
Danville Regional Medical Center	UNC Hospitals
Duke University Health System	Vidant Health
High Point Regional Health System	WakeMed

HISTORICAL FINANCIALS

Company Type: Private

Income Statement				FYE: September 30
	REVENUE ($ mil.)	NET INCOME ($ mil.)	NET PROFIT MARGIN	EMPLOYEES
09/07	504	23	4.6%	5,000
09/06	492	29	6.0%	—
09/05	446	16	3.8%	—
Annual Growth	6.4%	16.7%	—	—

2007 Year-End Financials

Return on assets: 3.2% Cash ($ mil.): 11
Return on equity: 7.4%
Current ratio: 1.70

CURATION FOODS, INC.

EXECUTIVES

Ceo, Bill Richardville
Controller, Jeff Kraetsch
Management Vice-President, Debra Vanhorsen
Management Vice-President, Tim Nykoluk
Safety Manager, Janice Van Ryn
Reedley Business S, Kent Huckabay
Coordinator, Jill Merritt
Director, Micah Fuson
Executive Officer, Arthur Degoede
Manager, Keri Morrelli
Human Resources Director, Raul Solis

LOCATIONS

HQ: CURATION FOODS, INC.
   4575 W MAIN ST, GUADALUPE, CA 93434
Phone: 800 454-1355
Web: WWW.APIOINC.COM

HISTORICAL FINANCIALS

Company Type: Private

Income Statement				FYE: May 28
	REVENUE ($ mil.)	NET INCOME ($ mil.)	NET PROFIT MARGIN	EMPLOYEES
05/17	470	3	0.8%	600
05/16	488	(31)	—	—
05/14	430	19	4.4%	—
Annual Growth	3.0%	(42.3%)	—	—

2017 Year-End Financials

Return on assets: 1.5% Cash ($ mil.): —
Return on equity: 2.6%
Current ratio: 1.40

CYPRESS-FAIRBANKS INDEPENDENT SCHOOL DISTRICT

EXECUTIVES

Supt, Mark Henry
Supt*, Richard E Berry
General, Mary Jadlowski
Assistant Director, Eric May
Rector, David Villareal
Bus/Finance/Purchasing Directo, Stuart Snow
Auditors: WEAVER & TIDWELL LLP CONR

LOCATIONS

HQ: CYPRESS-FAIRBANKS INDEPENDENT SCHOOL DISTRICT
   10300 JONES RD, HOUSTON, TX 770654208
Phone: 281 897-4000
Web: WWW.CFISD.NET

HISTORICAL FINANCIALS

Company Type: Private

Income Statement				FYE: June 30
	REVENUE ($ mil.)	NET INCOME ($ mil.)	NET PROFIT MARGIN	EMPLOYEES
06/18	1,259	20	1.6%	13,000
06/17	1,208	(58)	—	—
Annual Growth	4.3%	—	—	—

2018 Year-End Financials

Return on assets: 0.6% Cash ($ mil.): 15
Return on equity: —
Current ratio: —

D/L COOPERATIVE INC.

Yes the farmer takes a wife then hi-ho the dairy-o the farmer takes membership in milk-marketing organizations such as Dairylea Cooperative. Owned by some 2000 dairy farmers in the northeastern US Dairylea processes and markets 6.3 billion pounds of milk for its farmers annually to dairy-product customers including food manufacturers. Its Agri-Services holding company provides members with a full range of financial and farm-management services as well as insurance. Its Empire Livestock Marketing unit operates regional livestock auction locations. Dairylea which was established in 1907 by New York dairy farmers merged with the US's largest milk marketing coop Dairy Farmers of America in 2014.

Operations
Through its DMS partnership with Dairy Farmers of America Dairylea sells and distributes raw milk. DMS serves both organizations as well as independent producers and cooperatives that produce 16 billion pounds of milk each year.

Geographic Reach
Dairylea sells 6 billion pounds of raw milk annually through a milk-marketing network that stretches from Maine to Ohio to Maryland.

Services provided by holding company Agri-Services LLC include insurance coverage information management livestock marketing loan programs milk price risk management services business planning and consulting services purchasing programs and investment and retirement planning advice.

Financial Performance
Dairylea has annual sales of about $1 billion.

Auditors: HERBEIN COMPANY INC READING

LOCATIONS

HQ: D/L COOPERATIVE INC.
   5001 BRITTONFIELD PKWY, EAST SYRACUSE, NY 130579201
Phone: 315 233-1000
Web: WWW.DAIRYLEA.COM

PRODUCTS/OPERATIONS

Selected Affiliates & Subsidiaries

Agri-Edge Development
Agri-Max Financial Services
Agri-Services Agency
Dairy Risk Management Services
Eagle Dairy Direct
Empire Livestock Marketing Services

HISTORICAL FINANCIALS

Company Type: Private

Income Statement				FYE: March 31
	REVENUE ($ mil.)	NET INCOME ($ mil.)	NET PROFIT MARGIN	EMPLOYEES
03/11	1,333	1	0.1%	107
03/10	1,066	1	0.1%	
Annual Growth	25.1%	7.6%	—	—

2011 Year-End Financials

Return on assets: 9.2%
Return on equity: 0.1%
Current ratio: 0.60

Cash ($ mil.): 14

DAIRY FARMERS OF AMERICA, INC.

Dairy Farmers of America (DFA) is one of the world's largest dairy cooperatives with nearly 15000 member farmers across the US. Millions of cows belonging to member farmers produce 64 billion pounds of milk a year (roughly 30% of milk production in the US) which DFA markets. Along with fresh and shelf-stable fluid milk the co-op produces cheese butter dried milk powder and other dairy products for industrial wholesale and retail customers. It also offers contract manufacturing services. The co-op owns more than 40 manufacturing plants nationwide. DFA whose profits are shared based on member contribution is a major supplier to dairy giant Dean Foods as well as joint venture partners such as Hiland Dairy.

Operations

DFA owns more than 40 manufacturing plants nationwide. The facilities are focused on several functions and product categories including consumer cheese and butter consumer fluid ingredient cheese and protein and contract manufacturing.

The company's brands include Borden and Cache Valley for consumer cheese; Keller's Creamery Plugra Breakstone's Falfurrias and Hotel Bar for butter; and other dairy products under Sport Shake (sports beverage) La Vaquita (queso) Kemps Guida's Dairy and Dairy Maid Dairy.

Geographic Reach

DFA is based in Kansas City Missouri and divides the US into seven areas: Central (which shares the main headquarters) Mideast (Medina OH) Mountain (Salt Lake City UT) Northeast (East Syracuse NY) Southeast (Knoxville TN) Southwest (Grapevine TX) and Western (Corona CA).

Sales and Marketing

DFA's customers include big names in the dairy food and retail businesses including Hiland Dairy Borden supermarket giant Kroger Dean Foods Kraft Foods Nestle and many others.

Financial Performance

In 2017 DFA reported revenue of $14.7 billion up nearly 10% from the prior year due to unit sales growth as well as higher milk prices.

Net income that year was $127.4 million.

Strategy

In a statement that could be written about most companies across most industries DFA's strategic focus is on technology and innovation. In late 2018 it invested in SomaDetect a startup that promotes artificial intelligence as a way for dairy farmers to more closely monitor herd health and improve milk quality. Also that year it partnered with startup ripe.io to evaluate the usefulness of blockchain technology in the food supply chain.

As far as product innovation DFA introduced a new cheese brand (Craigs Creamery) in early 2019 and invested in a whey protein-infused yogurt (MOPRO) in 2018.

The cooperative also continues to invest in its facilities expanding existing plants and acquiring new ones.

Mergers and Acquisitions

In late 2018 DFA agreed to purchase a St. Paul Minnesota facility from Canada-based dairy cooperative Agropur which will expand DFA's extended shelf-life capabilities and introduce aseptic processing (sterilization techniques to produce items that don't need refrigeration) into its business portfolio.

Company Background

DFA was established in 1998 by leaders of four of the nation's leading milk cooperatives: Associated Milk Producers Mid-America Dairymen Milk Marketing and Western Dairymen Cooperative.

HISTORY

Mid-America Dairymen (Mid-Am) the largest of the cooperatives that merged to form Dairy Farmers of America (DFA) was born in 1968. At that time several Midwestern dairy co-ops banded together to attack common economic problems such as reduced government subsidies price drops resulting from a rising milk surplus dealer consolidation and improvements in production processing and packaging. The merging organizations — representing 15000 dairy farmers — were Producers Creamery Company (Springfield Missouri) Sanitary Milk Producers (St. Louis) Square Deal Milk Producers (Highland Illinois) Mid-Am (Kansas City Missouri) and Producers Creamery Company of Chillicothe (north central Missouri).

During the early 1970s Mid-Am struggled with internal restructuring. Most dairy farmers and co-ops were hit hard by the energy crisis and the government's decision to allow increased dairy imports in 1973 the same year the US Justice Department filed an antitrust suit against Mid-Am. (A judge cleared the co-op 12 years later.)

In 1974 Mid-Am lost almost $8 million on revenues of $625 million chalked up to record-high feed prices a weakened economy a milk surplus and a massive inventory loss. Co-op veteran Gary Hanman was named CEO that year. Over the next two years Mid-Am cut costs sold corporate frills downsized management and began marketing more of its own products under the Mid-America Farms label thus reducing dependency on commodity sales.

Mid-Am expanded its research and development efforts throughout the 1980s. The co-op opened its services to farmers in California and New Mexico in 1993 and a series of mergers in 1994 and 1995 nearly doubled its size. In 1997 it purchased some of Borden's dairy operations including rights to the valuable Elsie the Cow and Borden's trademarks.

Wary of falling milk prices Mid-Am merged with Western Dairymen Cooperative Milk Marketing and the Southern Region of Associated Milk Producers at the end of 1997 to form DFA. Hanman moved into the seat of CEO at the new co-op. DFA began a series of joint ventures with the #1 US dairy processor Suiza Foods (now Dean Foods).

DFA added California Gold (more than 330 farmers 1998) and Independent Cooperative Milk Producers Association (730 dairy farmer members in Michigan and parts of Ohio and Indiana 1999). In another joint venture with Suiza in early 2000 DFA sold its 50% stake in the US's #3 fluid milk processor Southern Foods in exchange for 34% of a new company named Suiza Dairy Group.

After mollifying the government's antitrust fears DFA acquired the butter operations of Sodiaal North America in 2000. It then molded all its butter businesses into a new entity Keller's Creamery. However another acquisition did not fare as well. The same year DFA acquired controlling interest in Southern Belle Dairy only to have the merger challenged three years later by the Department of Justice. Arguing that the merger formed a monopoly in school milk sales in several states the Department of Justice filed suit which a federal judge later dismissed.

During 2001 the cooperative went in with Land O'Lakes 50/50 to purchase a cheese plant from Kraft. Later in the year as Suiza Foods acquired Dean Foods (and took on its name) DFA sold back its stake in Suiza Dairy Group to the new Dean Foods. DFA then teamed up with a group of dairy investors to form a new 50/50 joint venture National Dairy Holdings which received 11 processing plants from Dean Foods as part of the exchange for Suiza Dairy.

EXECUTIVES

Senior Adviser; President Affiliate Division, Alan J. Bernon, age 64
Coo Northeast Area, Gregory I. (Greg) Wickham
President Ceo And Director, Richard P. (Rick) Smith
Evp; President Global Dairy Products Group, Mark Korsmeyer
Svp Finance, David Meyer
Executive Vice President Of Commercial Operations, Doug Glade
Vice President Sales And Marketing Global Ingredients, Lavonne Dietrich
Vice Chairman, Bill Siebenborn
Chairman, Randy Mooney
Vice Chairman, Wayne Palla
Vice Chairman, George Mertens
Auditors: KPMG LLP KANSAS CITY MO

LOCATIONS

HQ: DAIRY FARMERS OF AMERICA, INC.
1405 N 98TH ST, KANSAS CITY, KS 661111865
Phone: 816 801-6455
Web: WWW.DFAMILK.COM

PRODUCTS/OPERATIONS

Selected Products and Brands
Consumer brands
 Borden cheese
 Breakstone's butter
 Cache Valley cheese
 Keller's Creamery butter
 Plugrá butter
 Sport Shake energy milk shake
Contract manufacturing
 Cheese dips
 Cheese powders & flavors
 Coffee-based flavored drinks
 Instant formula
 Sour cream
 Sports drinks
Dairy ingredients
 Cheeses (American & Italian)
 Nonfat dry milk powder
 Skim milk powder
 Sweetened condensed milk

COMPETITORS

Arla Foods	Glanbia plc
Associated Milk	Great Lakes Cheese
Producers	HP Hood
Berkeley Farms	Humboldt Creamery
California Dairies	Lactalis
Inc.	Land O'Lakes
ConAgra	Marathon Cheese
Darigold Inc.	Mayfield Dairy Farms
Dean Foods	Northwest Dairy
Farmland Dairies	Prairie Farms Dairy
Foremost Farms	Quality Chekd
Friendship Dairies	Sargento
Garelick Farms	

HISTORICAL FINANCIALS

Company Type: Private

Income Statement				FYE: December 31
	REVENUE ($ mil.)	NET INCOME ($ mil.)	NET PROFIT MARGIN	EMPLOYEES
12/15	13,803	98	0.7%	7,000
12/14	17,856	48	0.3%	—
12/13	12,826	58	0.5%	—
12/12	12,082	(126)	—	—
Annual Growth	4.5%			

2015 Year-End Financials

Return on assets: 2.9%
Return on equity: 13.6%
Current ratio: 1.10
Cash ($ mil.): 228

DAIRYAMERICA, INC.

EXECUTIVES

Ceo, Hoyt Huffman
SEC, Bill Schreiber
Treas, Craig Alexander
Office Manager, Annette Smith
Director of Sales, Dan Block
Customer Rep, Diane Calaman
Commercial Director, Renee Leenen
Regional Sales Manager, Todd Wittlinger
Auditors: DELOITTE & TOUCHE LLP FRESNO

LOCATIONS

HQ: DAIRYAMERICA, INC.
7815 N PALM AVE STE 250, FRESNO, CA 937115528
Phone: 559 251-0992
Web: WWW.DAIRYAMERICA.COM

HISTORICAL FINANCIALS

Company Type: Private

Income Statement				FYE: December 31
	REVENUE ($ mil.)	NET INCOME ($ mil.)	NET PROFIT MARGIN	EMPLOYEES
12/12	1,222	21	1.8%	51
12/11	1,319	19	1.5%	—
12/10	1,514	19	1.3%	—
Annual Growth	(10.2%)	5.5%		

2012 Year-End Financials

Return on assets: 12.8%
Return on equity: 108.5%
Current ratio: 1.80
Cash ($ mil.): 1

DAIRYLAND POWER COOPERATIVE

Dairyland Power Cooperative provides its customers with lots of juice in the land of lactose. The firm provides electricity generation (1366 MW of generating capacity) and transmission services for 25 member distribution cooperatives and 16 municipal utilities in five states (including Wisconsin). The member cooperatives and municipal utilities in turn distribute electricity to almost 254460 consumers. Dairyland Power generates 1030 MW of capacity from its coal-fired power plants; it also operates more than 3180 miles of transmission lines and 228 substations. The power cooperative also markets electricity and offers energy management services.

Operations

In addition to its traditional fossil fuel-powered plants the company to meet green energy regulations also contracts renewable and alternative energy power plants including "cow power" animal waste to energy facilities (8 farms with manure digesters which collectively produce 3 MW of power). It also has 40 MW of contracted biomass energy 47 MW of wind and 14 MW of landfill gas. In 2012 it expanded its wind portfolio agreeing to buy 5 MW of electricity from a wind farm near Lewiston Minnesota. It also agreed that year to buy the excess energy output from a new 368 kW solar photovoltaic installation at the City of Galena wastewater treatment plant in Illinois.

Geographic Reach

Dairyland Power Cooperative has member coops in Illinois Iowa Minnesota North Dakota and Wisconsin.

Financial Performance

In 2012 Dairyland Power Cooperative's revenues grew by 2% thanks to an increase in margins. Net income grew by 11% as the result of an increase in net sales.

Strategy

While admitting no violations of law in 2012 the company settled litigation with the EPA and Sierra Club agreeing to install hundreds of millions of dollars of air emission controls at its fossil-fueled power plants.

Company Background

In 2010 the cooperative integrated fully into regional transmission operator Midwest ISO. The move gave Dairyland Power Cooperative access to the Midwest ISO's wholesale ancillary services and other markets helping to improve the coop's regional grid reliability by giving it access to more energy sources to help avoid power shortages.

Dairyland Power Cooperative was founded in 1941.

EXECUTIVES

Executive Vice President Human Resources, Mary Lund
Vice President Strategic Planning, Rob Palmberg
Vice President, Brian Rude
Auditors: DELOITTE & TOUCHE LLP MINNEAP

LOCATIONS

HQ: DAIRYLAND POWER COOPERATIVE
3200 EAST AVE S, LA CROSSE, WI 546017291
Phone: 608 788-4000
Web: WWW.DAIRYLANDPOWER.COM

COMPETITORS

ALLETE	DTE
Alliant Energy	MGE Energy
Berkshire Hathaway	WEC Energy
Energy	Xcel Energy

HISTORICAL FINANCIALS

Company Type: Private

Income Statement				FYE: December 31
	REVENUE ($ mil.)	NET INCOME ($ mil.)	NET PROFIT MARGIN	EMPLOYEES
12/18	472	16	3.5%	500
12/17	441	27	6.1%	—
12/16	414	23	5.6%	—
12/15	418	26	6.4%	—
Annual Growth	4.2%	(14.8%)	—	—

2018 Year-End Financials

Return on assets: 1.2%
Return on equity: 5.3%
Current ratio: 0.80
Cash ($ mil.): 25

DALLAS COUNTY HOSPITAL DISTRICT

Many people know Dallas County Hospital District doing business as Parkland Health and Hospital System or PHHS as Parkland Memorial Hospital the hospital where JFK died. Parkland Memorial sits at the heart of the health system and is Dallas' only public hospital. PHHS also manages a network of about 20 community clinics as well as Parkland Community Health Plan a regional HMO for Medicaid and CHIP (Children's Health Insurance Program) members. Additionally the system offers Parkland Financial Assistance a program to help residents of Dallas County pay for health care services. Parkland Memorial Hospital has more than 700 beds and is the primary teaching institution of The University of Texas Southwestern Medical Center.

Operations

PHHS is one of the largest public hospital systems in the US. In addition to its community-based clinics it offers a number of outreach and education programs to improve wellness in its service area.

Parkland Memorial Hospital has 870 single-patient rooms and is a Level I trauma center. Each year the hospital has some 39000 inpatient discharges and some 260000 emergency department visits. Specialty community and women's clinic outpatient visits total more than 1 million.

The system also manages the health system for Lew Sterrett — Dallas County Jail one of the nation's largest jails.

Sales and Marketing

Medicare and Medicaid payments account for about 15% and 30% of PHHS's net patient service revenues respectively.

Strategy

PHHS's original hospital location was established in 1954; more recently the system replaced the aging facility with a new hospital. The expansion included an 870-bed hospital an outpatient center an office center and parking. PHHS also invested in new and replacement information systems and medical equipment.

Additionally the system is working to open more primary care health clinics and launch new programs to reach further into its community. For example in 2016 it introduced the Acute Integrated Mental Health Services (AIMS) program to assist underserved patients with complex behavioral health issues and diabetes. It combines health care and social work services to connect patients with valuable resources and help them manage their health in an integrated manner.

Similarly the Parkland Information Exchange Portal (IEP) launched by PHHS health IT think tank Parkland Center for Clinical Innovation services to connect underserved individuals with social services including homeless shelters and food banks.

In early 2017 the system completed construction of a new five-story clinic with 171 exam rooms MRI's CT scanners radiology and ultrasound rooms laboratories and a pharmacy.

EXECUTIVES

Coo, David S. Lopez
President And Ceo, Frederick P. (Fred) Cerise, age 56
Evp And Chief Administrative Officer Population Health, Sharon Phillips
Evp And General Counsel, Paul Leslie
Evp And Chief Nursing Officer, Karen Watts
Evp And Chief Medical Officer, Roberto de la Cruz
Evp And Chief Talent Officer, Jim Dunn
Evp And Chief Strategy And Integration Officer, Esmaeil Porsa
Evp And Cfo, Richard Humphrey
Vice President Of Nursing Ambulatory Clinics, Michael Turturro
Medical Director Of Homeless Outreach Medical Services, Susan Spalding
Vice President And Chief Compliance Officer, Mary Findley
Medical Director, Waseem Ahmed
Medical Director, Barry Lachman
Senior Vice President, Miriam Sibley
Medical Director Of Pediatrics, Donna Persaud
Vice President Finance And Controller, Elizabeth Mcmullen
Senior Vice President Quality Safety And Performance Improvement, Jacqueline Sullivan
Vice President Of Government Relations, Katherine Yoder
Operating Room Dir, SUZANNE SIMS
Vice President Health Information Management, Deirdre Leblanc
Vice President, Christina Mintner
Vice President Of Transformational Initiatives, John Raish
Executive Vice President And Chief Talent Officer, Corey Jackson
Radiology Director, Terry Napper
Vice President Professional And Support Services, Saul Cordero
Vice President And Chief Workforce Officer, Sebastien Girard
Vice President Quality And Clinical Effectiveness, Beverly Hardy-decuir
Vice Chair, Michael D. (Mike) Williams
Chair Board Of Managers, Winfred Parnell
Auditors: GRANT THORNTHON LLP DALLAS T

LOCATIONS

HQ: DALLAS COUNTY HOSPITAL DISTRICT
5200 HARRY HINES BLVD, DALLAS, TX 752357709
Phone: 214 590-8000
Web: WWW.PARKLANDHOSPITAL.COM

PRODUCTS/OPERATIONS

Selected Facilities
Bluitt Flowers Health Center
de Haro-Saldivar Health Center
East Dallas Health Center
Garland Health Center
Oak West Health Center
Pediatric Primary Care Center

Simmons Ambulatory Surgery Center
Southeast Dallas Health Center
Vickery Health Center

COMPETITORS

Baylor University
  Medical Center
CHRISTUS Health
Children's Medical
  Center of Dallas
Community Health
  Systems
HCA
Harris Methodist Fort
  Worth Hospital

JPS Health Network
Presbyterian Hospital
  of Dallas
Tenet Healthcare
Texas Health Resources
The Methodist Health
  System

HISTORICAL FINANCIALS
Company Type: Private

Income Statement				FYE: September 30
	REVENUE ($ mil.)	NET INCOME ($ mil.)	NET PROFIT MARGIN	EMPLOYEES
09/18	1,456	17	1.2%	11,000
09/17	1,734	(17)	—	—
09/16	1,641	(71)	—	—
09/15	665	33	5.1%	—
Annual Growth	29.8%	(20.0%)	—	—

2018 Year-End Financials

Return on assets: 0.7%   Cash ($ mil.): 244
Return on equity: 1.9%
Current ratio: 1.60

DALLAS/FORT WORTH INTERNATIONAL AIRPORT

Many things are bigger in Texas and Dallas/Fort Worth International Airport (DFW) is no exception. Covering some 30 square miles DFW is one of the world's largest airports by land mass. The facility includes seven runways two active control towers five terminals and 165 gates. Some 65 million passengers pass through DFW annually to destinations domestic and international. Aside from airport fare DFW provides private warehouse and distribution centers to tenants and features Grand Hyatt and Hyatt Regency hotels. Opened in 1974 DFW is owned by the cities of Dallas and Fort Worth; it is situated halfway between them and within about a four-hour flight time of most US destinations.

Operations
DFW's primary operating goal is the facilitation of movement of people cargo and airplanes. Beyond that it leases land to travel-related businesses (car rental agencies) provide parking coordinates concessions and permits hotels to operate within its confines. About 45% of revenue comes from airlines (landing fees terminal usage fees) and 55% comes from non-airline activities.

With about 1800 flights per day serving 65 million customers a year DFW is the world's fourth busiest airport. Airlines flying out of DFW provide nonstop service to 163 domestic and 55 international non-stop destinations through about 25 passenger carriers and nearly 20 cargo carriers.

DFW is the home airport for the world's largest carrier American Airlines (AA) which operates 745 flights per day to nearly 200 domestic destinations

and some 50 international destinations. AA is constructing a new headquarters on a 300-acre campus on DFW property.

Financial Performance
In FY2016 (ended September 30 2016) Dallas Fort Worth International Airport generated revenue of $745 million a 10% increase from the prior year.

The airport's earnings in FY2016 had a hard landing losing almost $94 million. Although its operations incurred a relatively small $4.6 million loss the big contributor was massive interest expense on its revenue bonds. The interest is a recurring annual charge and the airport has recently been running at an annual loss.

Strategy
DFW is in the midst of a $2.34 billion terminal improvement project that's expected to be completed in late 2018. Improvements include new gates and a new concourse light rail connections to downtown Dallas and renovations to existing terminals. Improvements to Terminals A B and E completed in 2017 and work on Terminal C is on hold due to financing decisions. The physical airfield is also on tap to receive capital funding: runway 17C to get $250 million and end-around taxiways to get $430 million.

The airport has excellent connectivity to Latin & South America and to Asia and believes it is well positions to serve as a gateway between the two world regions. It is geographically situated in an advantageous place and already has an extensive network of destinations into Mexico and Latin & South America.

EXECUTIVES

Ceo, Sean P. Donohue
Evp Operations, James M. (Jim) Crites
Evp And Cfo, Christopher A. Poinsatte
Evp Administration, Linda Valdez Thompson
Vp Marketing, Sharon McCloskey
Evp Revenue Management, Kenneth (Ken) Buchanan
Evp Global Strategy And Development, John Ackerman
Evp Airport Development And Planning, Khaled Naja
Svp Information Technology Services, Stephen Shaffer
Vice President, Ollie Malone
Vice President Information Technology, Michael Youngs
Vp Airline Relations And Cargo Business Development, Milton De La Paz
Chairman, Sam Coats, age 78
Vice Chairman, William W. (Bill) Meadows

LOCATIONS

HQ: DALLAS/FORT WORTH INTERNATIONAL AIRPORT
2400 AVIATION DR, DFW AIRPORT, TX 75261
Phone: 972 973-5400
Web: WWW.DFWAIRPORT.COM

HISTORICAL FINANCIALS
Company Type: Private

Income Statement				FYE: September 30
	REVENUE ($ mil.)	NET INCOME ($ mil.)	NET PROFIT MARGIN	EMPLOYEES
09/16	745	(88)	—	1,700
09/07	567	28	5.0%	—
09/06	388	140	36.2%	—
09/05	388	140	36.2%	—
Annual Growth	6.1%			

2016 Year-End Financials

Return on assets: (-1.2%)   Cash ($ mil.): 164
Return on equity: (-31.0%)
Current ratio: 1.60

DANA-FARBER CANCER INSTITUTE, INC.

The Dana-Farber Cancer Institute fights cancer on two fronts: It provides treatment to cancer patients young and old and researches new cancer diagnostics treatments and preventions. The organization's scientists also research AIDS treatments and cures for a host of other deadly diseases. Patients receive treatment from Dana-Farber through its cancer centers operated in conjunction with Brigham and Women's Hospital Children's Hospital Boston and Massachusetts General Hospital. The institute is also a principal teaching affiliate of Harvard Medical School. Dana-Farber is funded by the National Cancer Institute the National Institute of Allergy and Infectious Diseases and private contributions.

Operations
Dana-Farber reports more than 38300 patient visits a year and is involved in some 700 clinical trials.

Dana-Farber provides care to children and adults with cancer while advancing the understanding diagnosis treatment cure and prevention of cancer and related diseases. As an affiliate of Harvard Medical School and a Comprehensive Cancer Center designated by the National Cancer Institute the Institute also provides training for new generations of physicians and scientists designs programs that promote public health particularly among high-risk and underserved populations and disseminates innovative patient therapies and scientific discoveries to target community across the US and around the world. In 2014 the hospital has a community benefit of $6.75 million.

Geographic Reach
The institute primarily serves patients in New England. Dana-Farber's main campus is in Boston's Longwood Medical Area and it also has facilities in Brighton Milford South Weymouth and Pittsfield (all in Massachussets); Londonderry New Hampshire; and Waterford Connecticut.

Dana-Farber Community Cancer Care physician practices are in seven communities throughout eastern Massachusetts.

Financial Performance
The institute reported a 7% rise in revenues in 2014 thanks to an increase in patient service revenues unrestricted contributions and bequests and other operating revenues. Revenues from the Medicare and Medicaid programs accounted for approximately 25% and 5% respectively of Dana-Farber's net patient service revenue in 2014

Net income decreased by 11% due to an increase in temporarily restricted net assets and contributions.

Strategy
When it comes to patient care Dana-Farber emphasizes the importance of forming research and treatment partnerships with other health care organizations. To that end the institute has opened a handful of treatment clinics on other medical campuses including one at Faulkner Hospital in southwest Boston and another at Milford Regional Medical Center in Massachusetts.

Along with expanding on other campuses Dana-Farber built a new cancer care center on its main campus in Boston.

Although Dana-Farber directs its research efforts toward saving lives from deadly diseases some of its discoveries also bring in a tidy income as the company and its research partners occasionally license out their drug discoveries to pharmaceutical companies.

In 2015 new research by Dana-Farber scientists raised the prospect of cancer therapy that works by converting a tumor's best friends in the immune system into its gravest enemies. In a study published in the journal Science an international collaboration of investigators from Dana-Farber Harvard Medical School Boston Children's Hospital and the University of Strasbourg uncovered a mechanism that allows key immune system cells to keep a steady rein on their more belligerent brother cells thereby protecting normal healthy tissue from assault. The discovery has powerful implications for cancer. By blocking the mechanism with a drug it may be possible to turn the attack-suppressing cells into tumor-attacking cells.

Company Background
In 2013 the institute and Lawrence + Memorial Cancer Center opened a $34.5 million 47000 sq.-ft. cancer facility in Waterford Connecticut.

The Yawkey Center for Cancer Care named in honor of long-time contributor The Yawkey Foundation opened in 2011 to serve a growing number of patients. The 275000-sq.-ft center's 14-stories house most of Dana-Farber's adult outpatient care. The building has more than 100 exam rooms about 140 infusion chairs and a number of consultation rooms for family and patients. It also connected Dana-Farber to other campus buildings and to its clinical partners Brigham and Women's Hospital and Children's Hospital Boston.

Dana-Farber Cancer Institute was founded as a children's cancer research foundation in 1947 by Dr. Sidney Farber. The institute later expanded its services to provide programs for adults as well as children.

EXECUTIVES

President And Ceo, Laurie H. Glimcher, age 67
Evp And Coo, Dorothy E. Puhy, age 67
Vp And Chief Marketing Officer, David A. Feinberg
Svp Patient Care Services And Chief Nursing Officer, Anne Gross
Chair Department Of Medical Oncology, James D. Griffin
Chief Scientific Officer, Barrett J. Rollins
Svp And Cfo, Michael L. Reney
Chief Department Of Imaging, Annick D. Van den Abbeele
Chief Surgical Officer, Scott J. Swanson
Chief Medical Officer, Craig A. Bunnell
Chief Clinical Research Officer, Bruce E. Johnson
Chair Department Of Pediatric Oncology, Scott A. Armstrong
Chief Medical Officer Dana-farber/boston Childrenâ's Cancer And Blood Disorders Center, Lisa R. Diller
Professor And Chair Department Of Radiation Oncology Dana-farber Cancer Institute/brigham And Womenâ's Hospital/boston Childrenâ's Hospital, Daphne Haas-Kogan
Chair Executive Committee For Research (ecr), William C. Hahn
Chair Executive Committee For Clinical Programs (eccp), Robert J. Soiffer
Chair Executive Committee For Clinical Research (eccr), Mary-Ellen Taplin
Chair Department Of Psychosocial Oncology And Palliative Care, James Tulsky
President Dana-farber/boston Childrenâ's Cancer And Blood Disorders Center, David A. Williams
Vice President, Melissa Shore
Senior Vice President, Barbara Bierer
Senior Vice President, Lesley Solomon
Vice President, Kelly Steve
Senior Vice President Chief Philanthropy Officer, Melany Duval
Senior Vice President, Maria Megdal
Board Treasurer, Sarah Solomon

LOCATIONS
HQ: DANA-FARBER CANCER INSTITUTE, INC.
450 BROOKLINE AVE, BOSTON, MA 022155450
Phone: 617 632-3000
Web: WWW.DANA-FARBER.ORG

PRODUCTS/OPERATIONS

2014 Sales

	% of total
Patients Services	62
Research	30
Unrestricted Contributions and Bequests	6
Other revenue	2
Total	**100**

Selected Clinical Affiliations
Dana-Farber/Brigham and Women's Cancer Center (outpatient services for adult cancer patients provided by Dana-Farber; and inpatient care provided by Brigham and Women's Hospital)
Dana-Farber/Children's Hospital Cancer Center (Dana-Farber Cancer Institute and Children's Hospital Boston outpatient care for children provided at Dana-Farber's Jimmy Fund Clinic)
Dana-Farber/Harvard Cancer Center (Beth Israel Deaconess Medical Center Brigham and Women's Hospital Children's Hospital Boston and Massachusetts General Hospital collaborate on research cancer prevention and treatments and therapies for cancer patients)
Dana-Farber/Lawrence + Memorial Cancer Center (cancer facility Waterford Connecticut).
Dana-Farber/Partners Cancer Care (consolidated adult oncology programs and clinical research of Dana-Farber Cancer Institute Brigham and Women's Hospital and Massachusetts General Hospital)

Selected Satellite Centers
Dana-Farber/Brigham and Women's Cancer Center at Faulkner Hospital in Jamaica Plain (southwest Boston area)
Dana-Farber/Brigham and Women's Cancer Center at Milford Regional Medical Center (Massachusetts)
Dana-Farber/Brigham and Women's Cancer Center in clinical affiliation with South Shore Hospital (South Weymouth Massachusetts)
Dana-Farber/New Hampshire Oncology-Hematology (Londonderry)
Adult Treatment Centers and Clinical Services
Blood Cancers
Breast Cancer
Cancer Genetics and Prevention
Cutaneous (Skin) Cancer
Gastrointestinal Cancer
Genitourinary Cancer
Gynecologic Cancer
Head and Neck Cancer
Hematology
Melanoma
Neuro-Oncology
Sarcoma
Thoracic (Lung) Cancer
Pediatric Treatment Centers and Clinical Services
Blood Disorders Center
Brain Tumor Center
Hematologic Malignancies Center
Solid Tumors Center
Stem Cell Transplant Center

COMPETITORS

Baystate Health	Johns Hopkins Medicine
Beth Israel Deaconess Medical Center	MD Anderson Cancer Center
Boston Medical Center	Mayo Clinic
Brigham and Women's Hospital	Memorial Sloan-Kettering
Care New England	Partners HealthCare
CareGroup	Roswell Park Cancer Institute
Children's National Medical Center	St. Elizabeth's Medical Center
Emory Healthcare	St. Jude Children's Research Hospital
Fox Chase Cancer Center	

HISTORICAL FINANCIALS
Company Type: Private

Income Statement				FYE: September 30
	REVENUE ($ mil.)	NET INCOME ($ mil.)	NET PROFIT MARGIN	EMPLOYEES
09/15	739	4	0.6%	3,000
09/14	672	34	5.1%	—
09/13	635	56	8.8%	—
09/10	894	16	1.9%	—
Annual Growth	(3.7%)	(22.7%)	—	—

2015 Year-End Financials
Return on assets: 0.4%
Return on equity: 0.8%
Current ratio: 0.90

Cash ($ mil.): 28

DANFOSS POWER SOLUTIONS INC.

EXECUTIVES

Pres-Ceo, Eric Alstrom
Exec V Pres-Cfo-Treas, Jesper V Christensen
V Pres-Cao-Sec, Kenneth D McCuskey
Exec V Pres-Cmo, Marc A Weston
Exec V Pres Hr, Anne Wilkinson
Chb*, Jorgen M Clausen
Vp-Pres Work Function Division, Helge Jorgensen
Coordinator, Lisa Williams
Customer Representativ, Kristen Behling
Procurement Staff, Richard Wang
Auditors: KPMG LLP DES MOINES IOWA

LOCATIONS

HQ: DANFOSS POWER SOLUTIONS INC.
  2800 E 13TH ST, AMES, IA 500108600
Phone: 515 239-6000
Web: WWW.DANFOSS.COM

HISTORICAL FINANCIALS
Company Type: Private

Income Statement				FYE: December 31
	REVENUE ($ mil.)	NET INCOME ($ mil.)	NET PROFIT MARGIN	EMPLOYEES
12/11	2,057	259	12.6%	6,400
12/10	1,640	246	15.0%	—
12/09	1,159	(332)		—
Annual Growth	33.2%	—	—	—

2011 Year-End Financials
Return on assets: 20.3%
Return on equity: 45.0%
Current ratio: 2.30

Cash ($ mil.): 251

DARTMOUTH COLLEGE

EXECUTIVES

Mgr, James Fries
Assistant Professor, Ethan M Berke
Assistant Professor, WEI Wang
Coordinator, Ben Myers
Grants Officer, Lisa Thompson

Bakala Professor of Strategy, Richard D'Aveni
Research Scientist, Scot Zens
Associate Professor, Sean Smith
Auditors: PRICEWATERHOUSECOOPERS LLP BO

LOCATIONS

HQ: DARTMOUTH COLLEGE
  6193 HINMAN, HANOVER, NH 037554007
Phone: 603 646-2191
Web: WWW.DARTMOUTHCOOP.COM

HISTORICAL FINANCIALS
Company Type: Private

Income Statement				FYE: June 30
	REVENUE ($ mil.)	NET INCOME ($ mil.)	NET PROFIT MARGIN	EMPLOYEES
06/18	893	739	82.8%	10
06/17	887	691	77.9%	—
06/16	859	(301)	—	—
06/15	876	236	27.0%	—
Annual Growth	0.7%	46.2%	—	—

2018 Year-End Financials
Return on assets: 8.9%
Return on equity: 11.5%
Current ratio: —

Cash ($ mil.): 203

DARTMOUTH-HITCHCOCK HEALTH

EXECUTIVES

Ceo, James Weinstein
Cfo, Daniel Jantzen
General Counsel, John Kacavas
Cao, Stephen Leblanc
Coo, Patrick Jordan III
Pediatrician, Marni Silverstein
Auditors: PRICEWATERHOUSECOOPERS LLP

LOCATIONS

HQ: DARTMOUTH-HITCHCOCK HEALTH
  1 MEDICAL CENTER DR, LEBANON, NH 037560001
Phone: 603 653-1118
Web: WWW.DARTMOUTH-HITCHCOCK.ORG

HISTORICAL FINANCIALS
Company Type: Private

Income Statement				FYE: June 30
	REVENUE ($ mil.)	NET INCOME ($ mil.)	NET PROFIT MARGIN	EMPLOYEES
06/18	2,069	87	4.2%	8,000
06/16	1,791	(44)	—	—
Annual Growth	7.5%	—	—	—

2018 Year-End Financials
Return on assets: 4.2%
Return on equity: 13.3%
Current ratio: 1.90

Cash ($ mil.): 200

DATS TRUCKING, INC.

DATS Trucking specializes in less-than-truck-load (LTL) freight transportation in the western US but that's not all there is to the company's operations. In addition to its LTL operations in which freight from multiple shippers is combined into a single trailer DATS Trucking provides truckload transportation. The company's tanker division Overland Petroleum transports gasoline diesel fuel and other petroleum products. Overall DATS Trucking operates a fleet of about 500 tractors and 2500 trailers. It offers LTL service outside its home territory via The Reliance Network a group of regional carriers that covers the US and Canada. President and CEO Don Ipson founded DATS Trucking in 1988.

LOCATIONS

HQ: DATS TRUCKING, INC.
  321 N OLD HIGHWAY 91, HURRICANE, UT 847373194
Phone: 435 673-1886
Web: WWW.DATSTRUCKING.COM

COMPETITORS

Bulkmatic	Schneider National
Central Freight Lines	Swift Transportation
FedEx Freight	UPS Freight
J.B. Hunt	Werner Enterprises
Kenan Advantage Group	YRC Worldwide
Penn Tank Lines	

HISTORICAL FINANCIALS
Company Type: Private

Income Statement				FYE: December 31
	REVENUE ($ mil.)	NET INCOME ($ mil.)	NET PROFIT MARGIN	EMPLOYEES
12/07	717	1	0.3%	475
12/06	658	7	1.2%	—
12/05	600	1	0.2%	—
12/04	391	1	0.4%	—
Annual Growth	22.3%	4.6%	—	—

DAVIS SCHOOL DISTRICT

EXECUTIVES

Pres, Tamara Lowe
V Pres*, Burke Larsen
Supt*, W Bryan Bowles
Asst Supt*, Lynn V Trenbeath
Asst Supt*, Nancy Fleming
MBR*, Barbara A Smith
MBR*, Larry Smith
MBR*, Peter Cannon
Facilities Director, John Swain
Before/After School Coordinato, Susy Jenson
Database Administrator, Casey Brown
Auditors: SQUIRE & COMPANY PC OREM UT

LOCATIONS

HQ: DAVIS SCHOOL DISTRICT
  45 E ST ST, FARMINGTON, UT 84025
Phone: 801 402-5261
Web: WWW.DAVIS.K12.UT.US

HISTORICAL FINANCIALS

Company Type: Private

Income Statement				FYE: June 30
	REVENUE ($ mil.)	NET INCOME ($ mil.)	NET PROFIT MARGIN	EMPLOYEES
06/18	645	(15)	—	6,310
06/14	509	12	2.5%	
06/13	500	(6)		
06/11	482	1	0.4%	
Annual Growth	4.2%	—	—	—

DB US HOLDING CORPORATION

EXECUTIVES

Pres-Ceo, Dr Josef Blank
Ex V Pres-Cfo, Joseph L Groneman
V Pres-SEC, Brian P Lynch
Manager, Laura Beckmeyer
Assistant General Counsel, Vicki Hassman
Assistant General Counsel, Dennis St George
Office Manager, Andrea Hollandt
Auditors: PRICEWATERHOUSECOOPERS LLP N

LOCATIONS

HQ: DB US HOLDING CORPORATION
  120 WHITE PLAINS RD, TARRYTOWN, NY 105915526
Phone: 914 366-7200
Web: WWW.DBUSHOLDING.COM

HISTORICAL FINANCIALS

Company Type: Private

Income Statement				FYE: December 31
	REVENUE ($ mil.)	NET INCOME ($ mil.)	NET PROFIT MARGIN	EMPLOYEES
12/16	914	(2)	—	6,300
12/15	1,766	(10)	—	
/	0	0	—	
Annual Growth	—	—	—	—

2016 Year-End Financials

Return on assets: (-2.2%)   Cash ($ mil.): 122
Return on equity: (-2.3%)
Current ratio: 102.70

DBSI INC

EXECUTIVES

Pres, Douglas Swenson
V Pres-Sec-Treas*, Charles Hassard
V Pres*, John Mayeron
Contrl, Paris Cole
Representative, Bonni L White
Administration Manager, Jeremy Evans
Human Resources Manager, Richard Stonhill

LOCATIONS

HQ: DBSI INC
  12426 W EXPLORER DR # 100, BOISE, ID 837131560
Phone: 208 955-9800
Web: WWW.DBSI.COM

HISTORICAL FINANCIALS

Company Type: Private

Income Statement				FYE: December 31
	ASSETS ($ mil.)	NET INCOME ($ mil.)	INCOME AS % OF ASSETS	EMPLOYEES
12/07	244	15	6.4%	70
12/06	168	2	1.6%	—
12/05	150	25	17.0%	—
12/04	70	49	69.9%	—
Annual Growth	51.2%	(31.7%)	—	—

2007 Year-End Financials

Return on assets: 6.4%   Sales ($ mil.): 625
Return on equity: 14.9%

DC WATER AND SEWER AUTHORITY

EXECUTIVES

Ceo-Gen Mngr, David L Gadis
Cfo, Olo Adebo
Treas, Robert Hunt
CIO, Omer Siddiqui
Acting Manager, Maxine Buchanan
Electrical Engineer, Dai Tran
Senior Financial Analyst, Stacey Johnson
Designer, Walter Burnett
Manager, Asa Chapman
Coordinator, Nicole Kaiser
Foreman/Supervisor, Bonnie Riggans
Auditors: KPMG LLP WASHINGTON DC

LOCATIONS

HQ: DC WATER AND SEWER AUTHORITY
  5000 OVERLOOK AVE SW, WASHINGTON, DC 200325212
Phone: 202 787-2000
Web: WWW.DCWATER.COM

HISTORICAL FINANCIALS

Company Type: Private

Income Statement				FYE: September 30
	REVENUE ($ mil.)	NET INCOME ($ mil.)	NET PROFIT MARGIN	EMPLOYEES
09/18	684	187	27.4%	1,000
09/06	0	0	18.4%	—
09/05	272	48	17.6%	
Annual Growth	7.3%	11.0%	—	—

2018 Year-End Financials

Return on assets: 2.4%   Cash ($ mil.): 123
Return on equity: 9.0%
Current ratio: 1.40

DCR WORKFORCE, INC.

EXECUTIVES

Prin, Naveen Dua
Pres*, Ammu Warrier
Cgo*, Daniel Weinfurter
Payroll Staff, Juliana Vasquez
Accountant, Elena Wilson
Program Manager, Shannon White
Human Resources Lead, Allen Alexander
Supervisor, Kathleen Belotto
Human Resources, Shayla Jackson
Director Business, Tracy White
Operations Analyst, Vishal Hotwani
Auditors: JOHN KAMMERER BOCA RATON FLO

LOCATIONS

HQ: DCR WORKFORCE, INC.
  7795 NW BEACON SQ 201, BOCA RATON, FL 334871394
Phone: 561 998-3737
Web: WWW.DCRWORKFORCE.COM

HISTORICAL FINANCIALS

Company Type: Private

Income Statement				FYE: December 31
	REVENUE ($ mil.)	NET INCOME ($ mil.)	NET PROFIT MARGIN	EMPLOYEES
12/12	548	2	0.5%	82
12/11	464	2	0.6%	—
12/01	12	0	6.3%	—
Annual Growth	41.0%	11.9%	—	—

2012 Year-End Financials

Return on assets: 16.9%   Cash ($ mil.): —
Return on equity: 21.1%
Current ratio: 3.80

DE PAUL UNIVERSITY

In the land of da Bulls and da Bears there's De-Paul. One of the largest private not-for-profit universities in the US DePaul has some 23000 students attending classes at its Chicago-area campuses and its increasing offerings of online learning courses. The university offers more than 300 undergraduate and graduate programs through 10 colleges and schools including the Kellstadt Graduate School of Business and the College of Communication. It has a student teacher ratio of 15 to 1. One of the country's largest Catholic institutions of higher learning DePaul was founded in 1898 by the Vincentian religious community and is named after 17th century French priest St. Vincent de Paul.

Geographic Reach

DePaul's five Chicago-area campuses are located in Lincoln Park the Loop and the O'Hare area. Although 67% of its students come from Illinois DePaul's student body hosts learners from the 50 US states and more than 100 countries.

Financial Performance

DePaul has an annual budget of about $550 million and its endowment is about $420 million. Undergraduate tuition for the 2017-2018 academic year was $39000.

EXECUTIVES

Vice President, Bonnie Frankel
Evp Financial Affairs, Robert L. (Bob) Kozoman
Vp Facilities, Robert (Bob) Janis

Dean Driehaus College Of Business And Kellstadt Graduate School Of Business, Ray Whittington
Dean School For New Learning, Marisa Alicea
Dean Theatre School, John Culbert
Dean College Of Computing And Digital Media, David Miller
President, A. Gabriel Esteban
Vp Information Services, Bob McCormick
Dean College Of Communication, Salma Ghanem
Provost, Marten denBoer
Vp Planning And Presidential Administration, Jay Braatz
Svp Enrollment Management, David Kalsbeek
Dean College Of Science And Health, Gerald P. Koocher
Athletic Director, Jean Lenti-Ponsetto
Interim Dean College Of Liberal Arts And Social Sciences, Lucy Rinehart
Dean College Of Law, Jennifer Rosato Perea
Dean School Of Education, Paul Zionts
Vice President Institutional Advancement, Alyssa Kupka
Vice President And General Counsel, Jose Padilla
Executive Vice President For Operations Loop, Susan Carolan
Clinical Director, Alexander Brown
Assistant Vice President, Lisa Cheers
Vice President Of Finance Operating Loop Campus, Rebecca Awells
Assistant Vice President Academic Affairs, Charles Strain
Director Of Admissions, Dennis Shea
Associate Vice President For Enrollment Management, Jon Boeckenstedt
Assistant Vice President Planned Giving, Joel Schaeffer
Assistant Vice President For Marketing Communications, Gwyn Friend
Assistant Vice President Of Development, Elizabeth Soete
Assistant Vice President, Peter Harris
Associate Vice President Of Financial, Paula Luff
Executive Vice President Academic Affairs, Richard Meister
Vice President Student Affairs, James Doyle
Assistant Vice President Gems Loop Campus, Suzanne Adepeder
Vice President Of Information Services, Vincent Kellen
Vice President Enrollment Management, Jessica Shisler
Vice President Student Affairs Lincoln Park Campus, Kathryn Ao'brien
Associate Vice President, Barbara Schaffer
Assistant Vice President Communication Strategies, Linda Blakley
Associate Vice President, Doris Brown
Executive Vice President For Academic Affairs, Michael Greene
Director Of Admissions, Jason Beck
Assistant Vice President For Academic Space, Ralph Erber
Vice President And Chief Human Resources Officer, Stephanie Smith
Vice President Enrollment Management, Maria Null Molina-frias
Vice President Public Relations, Donna Washington
Department Chair Social Work, Noam Ostrander
Assoc Vice President Career Services, Carol Montgomery
Executive Vice President, Marina Lozano-corona
Associate Vice President For Philanthropy, Ivan Adames
Vice President For Mission And Ministry, Rev Edward Udovic
Executive Vice President, Sophia Modzelewski
Treasurer, Bonnie Hirsch
Secretary, Edtra Flowers
Auditors: KPMG LLP CHICAGO ILLINOIS

LOCATIONS

HQ: DE PAUL UNIVERSITY
1 E JACKSON BLVD, CHICAGO, IL 606042287
Phone: 312 362-6714
Web: WWW.DEPAUL.EDU

HISTORICAL FINANCIALS

Company Type: Private

Income Statement   FYE: June 30

	REVENUE ($ mil.)	NET INCOME ($ mil.)	NET PROFIT MARGIN	EMPLOYEES
06/18	575	67	11.7%	3,895
06/17	575	67	11.7%	—
06/15	562	38	6.9%	—
06/14	564	59	10.5%	—
Annual Growth	0.5%	3.1%	—	—

2018 Year-End Financials

Return on assets: 4.0%   Cash ($ mil.): 59
Return on equity: 6.1%
Current ratio: —

DEACONESS HEALTH SYSTEM, INC.

While it primarily presides over numerous health care facilities in the southwestern corner of Indiana Deaconess Health System also serves residents in parts of southeastern Illinois and western Kentucky. The system consists of two general acute-care hospitals as well as specialty hospitals for women's health mental health and medical rehabilitation. Its flagship Deaconess Hospital boasts 365 beds and serves as a regional referral center. Deaconess Health also operates a standalone cancer treatment center medical group practice Deaconess Clinic and about 20 outpatient and urgent care clinics. Its Deaconess Health Plans unit is a PPO network that contracts with various health insurers.

Operations

As part of its operations the health system comprises half a dozen facilities including Deaconess Hospital (365 beds) Deaconness Gateway Hospital (120 beds) The Women's Hospital (50 beds) Deaconess Cross Pointe (60 beds) HealthSouth Deaconess Rehabilitation Hospital (80 beds) and The Heart Hospital of Deaconess Gateway (24 beds). It also operates primary care locations such as Deaconess Clinic Deaconess Primary Care for Seniors and Deaconess Urgent Care.

The hospital treats 18000 inpatients 350000 outpatients 65000 emergency patients and 7500 surgical patients each year.

Geographic Reach

Deaconess Health System primarily serves those who reside in 26 counties in Southern Indiana Southeast Illinois and West Kentucky.

Financial Performance

In 2014 net sales increased by 13% due to higher revenues from net patient service.

Deaconess Health System's net patient service revenue increased due to increased contractual adjustments. Medicare and Medicaid together accounted 57% of total net sales in 2014. Commercial and managed care and Self pay and other accounted for 36% and 7% respectively

In 2014 net income increased by 40% compared to 2013. The primary reason was due to increased

sales partially offset by decreased benefit related changes other than net periodic benefit cost.

Deaconess Health System's net cash provided by the operating activities increased by 28%.

Strategy

Deaconess Health System has been focused on improving information technology systems including the implementation of an electronic health record (EHR) system. It has increased efficiencies through IT initiatives by installing new automated medication dispensing and prescription management programs.

MyChart is available at Deaconess Hospital Main Deaconess Gateway Deaconess Riley Hospital for Children The Heart Hospital Cross Point all Deaconess Clinic locations Deaconess Critical Care Deaconess Family Practice and Residency and Deaconess Primary Care for Seniors physician offices. MyChart is a secure online health management tool that connects MyChart patients to their personalized health information. MyChart contains inpatient and outpatient test results and information.

In 2015 the company finalized a letter of intent to partner directly with Methodist Hospital on a not-for-profit joint venture to bring additional and enhanced healthcare services to Henderson. The joint venture will improve access to care providers and quality of care in Henderson. Deaconess Health System purchased 10-plus acres of land off Barret Boulevard near Walmart in Henderson in 2014.

Company Background

Founded in 1892 Deaconess Hospital is a teaching facility that offers residency and clinical education programs in addition to providing general and specialty inpatient care. It also conducts medical research programs.

EXECUTIVES

Pharmd, Meredith L Petty
Vice President Business Development, Jared Florence
Medical Director Clinical Research, Majed Koleilat
Director Of Radiology And Cardiology, Susan Brumley
Medical Director Deaconess Clinic, Amanda Bohleber
Senior Vice President And Chief Medical Officer, Mack Blanton
Auditors: BLUE & CO LLC INDIANAPOLIS I

LOCATIONS

HQ: DEACONESS HEALTH SYSTEM, INC.
600 MARY ST, EVANSVILLE, IN 477101658
Phone: 812 450-5000
Web: WWW.DEACONESS.COM

PRODUCTS/OPERATIONS

Selected Services
Back & Spine
Behavioral Health
Cancer
Children's Health
Clinical Research
Diabetes
Emergency Care
Joint Replacement
Orthopedic
Pain Management
Physical Medicine
Radiology
Respiratory
Senior Health
Weight Loss
Women's Health
Wound Care

COMPETITORS

Ball Memorial Hospital
Baptist Health
  Madisonville
Commonwealth Health
  Corporation
Community Health
  Network
Daviess Community
  Hospital
Good Samaritan
  Hospital (IN)

Henry County Memorial
  Hospital
Kosciusko Community
  Hospital
Memorial Hospital
  (Logansport)
St. Mary's Medical
  Center of Evansville

HISTORICAL FINANCIALS
Company Type: Private

Income Statement   FYE: September 30

	REVENUE ($ mil.)	NET INCOME ($ mil.)	NET PROFIT MARGIN	EMPLOYEES
09/18	1,058	170	16.1%	6,086
09/17	930	127	13.7%	—
09/16	2	(27)	—	—
09/15	2	(24)	—	—
Annual Growth	628.6%	—	—	—

2018 Year-End Financials
Return on assets: 10.3%   Cash ($ mil.): 83
Return on equity: 15.4%
Current ratio: 1.90

DEACONESS HOSPITAL INC

Deaconess Hospital provides benevolent medical assistance to residents of southern Indiana western Kentucky and southeastern Illinois. The not-for-profit hospital is a 365-bed acute care medical facility that is the flagship hospital of the Deaconess Health System. Specialized services include cardiovascular surgery cancer treatment orthopedics neurological and trauma care. The hospital also offers home health care hospice services and medical equipment rental and it operates outpatient family practice surgery wellness and community outreach centers. Founded in 1892 Deaconess Hospital is a teaching and research facility affiliated with the Indiana University School of Medicine.

Operations

Deaconess handles about 18000 inpatient visits per year. It also sees about 350000 outpatients and 65000 emergency room visitors and it handles about 7500 annual surgery procedures.

Geographic Reach

Deaconess Hospital is located in Evansville Indiana and provides services to about 26 surrounding counties.

Strategy

To improve services to area residents Deaconess Hospital is expanding its outpatient care facilities and enhancing its IT resources. For instance in 2013 it moved its urgent care center to a larger more efficient facility. The hospital is also pursuing recognition for specialist programs such as its stroke center which was certified as a level one facility in 2013.

EXECUTIVES

Pres & Ceo, Linda E White
Chb*, John Lipert
Cfo-Asst SEC*, Richard Stivers
Program Director, Kim Volz

Manager, Leighann Gamble
Pharmacist, Mark Bauer
Staff Pharmacist, Grace Voight
Project Manager, Linda Conway
Director Bariat, Todd Burry
Pharmacist, Tracy Herr
Administrative Director, Gregory Folz

LOCATIONS

HQ: DEACONESS HOSPITAL INC
  600 MARY ST, EVANSVILLE, IN 477101674
Phone: 812 450-5000
Web: WWW.DEACONESS.COM

Selected Services
24-hour Emergency Center
Cancer Services
Corporate Wellness
Family Medicine Clinic
Heart Services
Home Medical Equipment
Home-based Medical Care
Hospice Care
Inpatient and Outpatient Surgery
Mental Health Services
Neuro Services
Orthopedics
Pediatrics
Physician Referral Service
Radiology Services
Residency Program
Support Groups and Programs
Women's Hospital

COMPETITORS

Ball Memorial Hospital
Baptist Health
Baptist Health
  Madisonville
Commonwealth Health
  Corporation
Community Health
  Network
Daviess Community
  Hospital
Good Samaritan
  Hospital (IN)

Henry County Memorial
  Hospital
Jewish Hospital & St.
  Mary's HealthCare
Kosciusko Community
  Hospital
Memorial Hospital
  (Logansport)
Norton Healthcare
St. Mary's Medical
  Center of Evansville

HISTORICAL FINANCIALS
Company Type: Private

Income Statement   FYE: September 30

	REVENUE ($ mil.)	NET INCOME ($ mil.)	NET PROFIT MARGIN	EMPLOYEES
09/17	725	94	13.0%	5,300
09/16	698	108	15.5%	—
09/15	680	138	20.3%	—
09/14	623	113	18.1%	—
Annual Growth	5.2%	(5.9%)	—	—

2017 Year-End Financials
Return on assets: 6.5%   Cash ($ mil.): 66
Return on equity: 10.5%
Current ratio: 2.90

DEER PARK REFINING LIMITED PARTNERSHIP

EXECUTIVES

Prin, Bruce A Henderson
Auditors: ERNST & YOUNG LLP HOUSTON TX

LOCATIONS

HQ: DEER PARK REFINING LIMITED PARTNERSHIP
  5900 HIGHWAY 225, DEER PARK, TX 775362434
Phone: 713 246-7280
Web: WWW.DEERPARKTX.GOV

HISTORICAL FINANCIALS
Company Type: Private

Income Statement   FYE: December 31

	REVENUE ($ mil.)	NET INCOME ($ mil.)	NET PROFIT MARGIN	EMPLOYEES
12/17	867	97	11.2%	3
12/16	897	154	17.2%	—
Annual Growth	(3.3%)	(36.9%)	—	—

2017 Year-End Financials
Return on assets: 4.7%   Cash ($ mil.): 77
Return on equity: 6.7%
Current ratio: 1.90

DEKALB COUNTY BOARD OF EDUCATION

EXECUTIVES

Chm, Michael A Erwin
Vice Chm*, Marshall D Orson
Executive of Information Techn, Will Thomas
Auditors: RUSSELL W HINTON CPA CGFM

LOCATIONS

HQ: DEKALB COUNTY BOARD OF EDUCATION
  1701 MOUNTAIN INDUS BLVD, STONE MOUNTAIN,
  GA 300831027
Phone: 678 676-1200
Web: WWW.DEKALBSCHOOLSGA.ORG

HISTORICAL FINANCIALS
Company Type: Private

Income Statement   FYE: June 30

	REVENUE ($ mil.)	NET INCOME ($ mil.)	NET PROFIT MARGIN	EMPLOYEES
06/07	1,128	350	31.1%	168
06/06	1,055	10	0.9%	—
Annual Growth	7.0%	3405.8%	—	—

2007 Year-End Financials
Return on assets: 22.9%   Cash ($ mil.): 116
Return on equity: 33.3%
Current ratio: 3.60

DEKALB COUNTY PUBLIC LIBRARY

EXECUTIVES

Exec Dir, Darro Willey
Asst Dir*, Mag Dasossa
Supervisor, Myguail Chappel
Information Technology Manager, Chris Lee
Executive Director, Joe Davich

Manager, Susan Williams
Coordinator, Gina Jenkins
Director, Allison Weissinger
Assistant Director, Nancy Wright
Member Staff, Pao Ku
Senior Librarian Clarkston Lib, Effie Chisholm
Auditors: KPMG LLP ATLANTA GA

LOCATIONS

HQ: DEKALB COUNTY PUBLIC LIBRARY
    215 SYCAMORE ST FL 4, DECATUR, GA 300303413
Phone: 404 370-3070
Web: WWW.DEKALBLIBRARY.ORG

HISTORICAL FINANCIALS
Company Type: Private

Income Statement				FYE: December 31
	REVENUE ($ mil.)	NET INCOME ($ mil.)	NET PROFIT MARGIN	EMPLOYEES
12/07	622	(124)	—	228
12/06	622	186	30.0%	—
12/05	564	56	10.0%	—
Annual Growth	5.1%	—	—	—

2007 Year-End Financials

Return on assets: (-3.8%)   Cash ($ mil.): 536
Return on equity: (-6.5%)
Current ratio: —

DEKALB REGIONAL HEALTH SYSTEM, INC.

Auditors: DIXON HUGHES GOODMAN LLP ATLA

LOCATIONS

HQ: DEKALB REGIONAL HEALTH SYSTEM, INC.
    2701 N DECATUR RD, DECATUR, GA 300335918
Phone: 404 501-1000
Web: WWW.DEKALBMEDICAL.ORG

HISTORICAL FINANCIALS
Company Type: Private

Income Statement				FYE: June 30
	REVENUE ($ mil.)	NET INCOME ($ mil.)	NET PROFIT MARGIN	EMPLOYEES
06/17	487	(6)	—	2,827
06/15	4	(7)	—	—
06/14	5	(5)	—	—
06/13	4	(9)	—	—
Annual Growth	215.4%	—	—	—

2017 Year-End Financials

Return on assets: (-1.6%)   Cash ($ mil.): 3
Return on equity: (-5.3%)
Current ratio: 2.10

DELTA DENTAL OF TENNESSEE

EXECUTIVES

Ceo, Phillip Wenk DDS
V Pres*, Pam Dishman
Cfo*, J Thomas Perry
Sr Exec V Pres*, Kay Martin
Contrl, Frank Turbeville
Coordinator, Brenda Fare
Manager, Gwen Coyne
Manager, Jackie Moss
Manager, Mary Turner
Network Engineer, Eric James
Coordinator, Karen Wynn
Auditors: PLANTE & MORAN PLLC EAST LANS

LOCATIONS

HQ: DELTA DENTAL OF TENNESSEE
    240 VENTURE CIR, NASHVILLE, TN 372281604
Phone: 615 255-3175
Web: WWW.DELTADENTAL.COM

HISTORICAL FINANCIALS
Company Type: Private

Income Statement				FYE: December 31
	ASSETS ($ mil.)	NET INCOME ($ mil.)	INCOME AS % OF ASSETS	EMPLOYEES
12/12	70	6	9.8%	92
12/10	62	3	5.1%	—
12/09	46	1	4.1%	—
12/03	23	4	17.0%	—
Annual Growth	12.8%	6.1%	—	—

2012 Year-End Financials

Return on assets: 9.8%   Sales ($ mil): 456
Return on equity: 13.1%

DELTA TUCKER HOLDINGS, INC.

Through operating company DynCorp International (DI) Delta Tucker Holdings works behind the scenes to support military and diplomatic efforts on front lines. A US national security contractor the company supports the US Departments of State and Defense by providing linguist services and international police force training especially in Afghanistan and Iraq. It provides turnkey solutions for post-conflict countries to rebuild infrastructure install utilities and telecommunications provide security transport equipment and remove and dismantle weapons. About 40% the holding company's sales come from the US.

Operations

Delta Tucker Holdings' two reporting segments DynAviation and DynLogistics contribute about equally to the company's total revenue.

DynAviation's service offerings include aircraft operations and logistics. Through DynAviation Delta Tucker maintains modernizes and refurbishes planes and helicopters for governmental military and commercial clients. It provides operational support for managing bases and large fleets such as engineering and upkeep.

DynLogistics acts as an international development contractor for the US government and military by helping to build stable government infrastructures in foreign countries primarily in the Middle East. Furthermore it supports military bases' operations engineering supply logistics war reserve materiel facilities marine maintenance ground vehicle program management and contingency responses.

Cost-reimbursement contracts produce about 60% of the company's revenue; around 35% of revenue is from contracts with fixed prices. The rest is from contracts wherein the company invoices its clients for time and materials.

Geographic Reach

Headquartered in McLean Virginia with major administrative offices in Fort Worth Texas Delta Tucker Holdings has some 40 commercial facilities in more than 10 countries including India the United Arab Emirates and Oman. About 40% of its revenue is generated in the US around 30% in Afghanistan and roughly 20% in the Middle East. The rest comes from countries other than the US in the Americas Europe and the Asia-Pacific region.

Sales and Marketing

Delta Tucker Holdings receives about 85% of its revenue from the US Department of Defense some 10% from the Department of State and the remainder from other sources. The company is involved in national and international tradeshows in aviation logistics contingency support defense diplomacy and development markets.

Financial Performance

Delta Tucker Holdings' revenue decreased each year from 2014 to 2016 as the US military drawdown in Afghanistan impacted demand for services under some key contracts and programs. The holding company for DynCorp International (DI) bounced back in 2017 and 2018 as the scope of some of its major contracts?including LOGCAP IV and ALiSS?increased. The company is providing military support services to the US in the Middle East under LOGCAP IV and base life support services to the US military in Afghanistan including the US Embassy in Kabul under ALiSS. Delta Tucker has posted positive net income since 2017 after six straight years of losses.

The company's revenue increased 7% to $2.1 billion in 2018. Completion of two large aviation maintenance contracts with the US government and the Bureau for International Narcotics and Law Enforcement Affairs Office of Aviation partially offset increased revenue from contracts including LOGCAP IV and aviation contracts CLS Transport and Naval Test Wing Pacific. Net income skyrocketed by 176% to $84.5 million.

Delta Tucker added $35.5 million to its cash in 2018 to end the year with $203.8 million. Operations provided $146.6 million; $5.5 million was used on investments (primarily for property and equipment and contributions to equity investees) and financing activities depleted $105.5 million (almost entirely to pay down senior debt).

Strategy

That Delta Tucker Holdings is a US government contractor puts it at the mercy of defense budgets and policies set by the government's administration and Congress. Government contracts?some of which are referred to as IDIQ (indefinite quantity-type) contracts?may be canceled or modified for the convenience of the government. IDIQ contracts are subject to competitive bidding and the holding company for DynCorp International (DI) faces a host of strong competitors. The majority of the company's contracts are considered IDIQ.

For the same reasons the company may find itself at a disadvantage conducting business in contractual fashion it may also reap the benefits of such a process. Because the company provides more labor-related services than it does products DI practices flexible staffing which means it hires staff per contract. If the contract is canceled then the employees are let go or reassigned which keeps the company's costs and overhead down; there are no separation costs related to the terminations. Also the types of services DI provides do not generally require capital investment in fixed assets and its contract mix is such that if equipment is purchased it can be used on multiple projects.

Company Background

DynCorp International (DI) got its beginnings in 1946 from two companies: Land-Air and California Eastern Airways. In mid-2010 DI was acquired by Delta Tucker Holdings an affiliate of private investment firm Cerberus for about $1.5 billion.

EXECUTIVES

President, Chris Bernhardt
Cfo, Bill Kansky
Ceo, Lewis F. Von Thaer
Chairman, James E. Geisler
Auditors: DELOITTE & TOUCHE LLP FORT WO

LOCATIONS

HQ: DELTA TUCKER HOLDINGS, INC.
1700 OLD MEADOW RD, MC LEAN, VA 221024302
Phone: 571 722-0210
Web: WWW.DYN-INTL.COM

2018 Sales

	$ mil.	% of total
US	896	42
Afghanistan	693	32
Middle East	301	14
Other Americas	96	4
Europe	38	2
Asia-Pacific	101	5
Other	21	1
Total	**2,148**	**100**

PRODUCTS/OPERATIONS

2016 Sales

	$ mil.	% of total
DynAviation	1,114	52
DynLogistics	1,034	48
Headquarters/Other	(92)	-
Total	**2,148**	**100**

2018 Sales

	$ mil.	% of total
DOD	1,803	84
DOS	252	12
Other	92	4
Total	**2,148**	**100**

2018 Sales by contract type

	$ mil.	% of total
Fixed-Price	790	37
Time-and-Material	98	4
Cost Reimbursement	1,259	59
Total	**2,148**	**100**

Selected Services

Aviation
  Aircraft modifications
  Aircrew services
  Airfield management communications and navigation equipment
  Airlift
  Avionics upgrades
  Cockpit and fuselage redesign
  Construction
  Depot support
  Engineering design
  Fleet management
  IT installation
  Logistics support
  Maintenance
  Security
Contingency operations
  Disaster readiness and response (peacekeeping support recovery operations firefighting)

Infrastructure engineering and management (construction telecom electrical power hazardous waste management)
  Personnel equipment and materiel transport
  Transportation (aircraft heavy equipment air traffic control management vehicles and heavy equipment)
  Weapons removal
Infrastructure
  Aviation hangars and aprons
  Barracks
  Ranges
  Utilities
Intelligence
  Intelligence training (through joint venture with Phoenix Training Center)
  Training (law enforcement counterintelligence and special operations)
  Translation (Global Linguist Solutions a joint venture with McNeil Technologies)
International development
  Conflict management and recovery
  Health issues
  Post-conflict and transition programs
Land systems
  Armor replacement
  Fleet maintenance
  Ground vehicle maintenance
  HVAC installation
Logistics
  Large-scale military deployments
Training and mentoring
  Base security
  Convoy planning
  Emergency response support (operations centers response forces global monitoring continuity of operations)
  Explosives detection (using dogs)
  Global security systems (design installation/construction operation and training)
  Guard services
  International police training and support
  Personnel and perimeter security
  Threat assessment
  Workforce organization and deployment

COMPETITORS

AAR Corp.
AECOM
Academi
Albors & Associates
Bell Helicopter
Boeing
DRS Technologies
Elbit Systems
Fluor
General Dynamics
KBR
L3 Technologies
Lockheed Martin
ManTech
Mission Essential Personnel
Northrop Grumman
Raytheon Intelligence Information and Services

HISTORICAL FINANCIALS

Company Type: Private

Income Statement				FYE: December 31
	REVENUE ($ mil.)	NET INCOME ($ mil.)	NET PROFIT MARGIN	EMPLOYEES
12/18	2,148	85	4.0%	13,200
12/17	2,004	30	1.5%	—
12/16	1,836	0	—	—
12/15	1,923	(132)	—	—
Annual Growth	**3.8%**	—	—	—

2018 Year-End Financials

Return on assets: 11.9%   Cash ($ mil.): 203
Return on equity: —
Current ratio: 1.70

DENNIS K. BURKE INC.

EXECUTIVES

Ceo, Edmund F Burke
Cfo*, Joe Cote
Director of Operations, Dan Hill
Auditors: TONNESON & COMPANY INC WAKE

LOCATIONS

HQ: DENNIS K. BURKE INC.
555 CONSTITUTION DR, TAUNTON, MA 027807365
Phone: 617 884-7800
Web: WWW.BURKEOIL.COM

HISTORICAL FINANCIALS

Company Type: Private

Income Statement				FYE: April 30
	REVENUE ($ mil.)	NET INCOME ($ mil.)	NET PROFIT MARGIN	EMPLOYEES
04/12	929	3	0.3%	110
04/11	807	0	0.1%	—
04/10	2,050	0	—	—
Annual Growth	**—25724.5%**	—	—	—

2012 Year-End Financials

Return on assets: 5.3%   Cash ($ mil.): 1
Return on equity: 21.3%
Current ratio: 1.20

DENVER HEALTH AND HOSPITALS AUTHORITY INC

When you live a mile high you sometimes need a safety net; that's where Denver Health and Hospital Authority comes in. Though it serves all the people of Colorado's capital annually attending to a fourth of the city's population and a third of its children Denver Health is also the "safety net" care provider for the city's indigent uninsured mentally ill and other high-risk patients. The medical system's primary facility is the Denver Health Medical Center a 525-bed hospital offering care in more than 50 medical specialties that also houses a regional trauma center. It also includes a network of family health and dental clinics; a poison and drug center; and a 911 response system for Denver County.

Operations

Denver Health's principal facility Denver Health Medical Center is a teaching hospital affiliated with the University of Colorado at Denver and is one of the busiest medical centers in the state. The trauma center (known as Rocky Mountain Regional Trauma Center) has Level I status and is known for having one of the highest survival rates in the nation. In addition the hospital operates an ambulance service a pediatric emergency center and a terrorism and catastrophe response center. Denver Health operates Denver's 911 medical emergency response system. Annually Denver Health paramedics respond to about 90000 calls for emergency medical assistance and transport more than 61000 patients to 11 area hospitals.

The health system provides medical care at 16 K-12 school-based health centers as well as eight family health centers located throughout the city.

It also runs a number of public health clinics that offer immunizations infectious disease treatment detoxification and behavioral health consultation.

Denver Health cares for some 66000 children each year. In 2013 the system delivered 3175 babies and reported 55511 emergency department visits.

Financial Performance

Denver Health's revenue increased 7% to $793 million in 2013 due to an increase in net patient service revenue as well as safety net reimbursements and government grants. The number of uninsured patients has fallen dramatically under the Affordable Care Act which has helped the system improve its earnings. However the company reported a net loss of $15 million as non-operating revenue declined and fair value of investments fell.

Strategy

Denver Health integrates acute hospital and emergency care with public and community health offerings to deliver preventive primary and acute care services.

The health system's health plan covers 17000 city and hospital employees members of Medicaid's child plan and Medicare and another 53000 Medicaid patients. It expects to serve 40000 new Medicaid customers over the next few years as a result of the 2014 Affordable Care Act including about 15000 the hospital already sees without any payment.

In 2014 the company opened the Lowry Family Health Center adding new exam rooms to its operations. It also opened a new dental clinic and Women Infants and Children (WIC) office location.

Company Background

Denver Health traces its beginnings back to territorial days in 1860. As Denver General Hospital it operated as an agency of Denver's city and county governments until 1997 when it became a freestanding authority.

Denver Health's flagship medical center joined forces with Children's Hospital Colorado in late 2010 to share best practices and resources to expand and improve pediatric care throughout the region. Through the collaboration the two have increased access to pediatric mental health services; they also coordinate recruitment and sharing of highly specialized pediatric providers.

EXECUTIVES

Coo, Stephanie Thomas
Ceo, Arthur A. Gonzalez
Chief Nursing Officer, Kathy Boyle
Cfo, Peg Burnette
Director Rocky Mountain Poison And Drug Center, Richard C. Dart
Chief Medical Officer, Phillip S. Mehler
Executive Director Denver Health Foundation, Paula Herzmark
Director Of Nursing, Keith Moorhead
Nursing Director, Nicole Stafford
Medical Director, Jeanne Rozwadowski
Pharmacy Manager, Renee Toner
Pharmacy Manager, Bob Wilson
Second Vice Chairman, Hubert A. Farbes
Chair, Caz Matthews
Vice Chair, Rus Heise

LOCATIONS

HQ: DENVER HEALTH AND HOSPITALS AUTHORITY INC
777 BANNOCK ST, DENVER, CO 802044597
Phone: 720 956-2580
Web: WWW.DENVERHEALTHMEDICAID.ORG

PRODUCTS/OPERATIONS

2013 Sales

	$ mil.	% of total
Net patient service	368	46
Captation earned net of reinsurance expense	129	16
Medicaid disproportionate share & other safety net reimbursements	125	16
Federal state & other grants	71	9
Others	98	13
Total	**793**	**100**

Selected Medical Centers Clinics and Affiliates

Denver Emergency Center for Children
Denver Health Dental Care Clinics
Denver Health Medical Center
Denver Health Medical Plan (for Denver Health employees)
Denver Health Primary Care Clinics
Denver Paramedics
Denver Public Health
Rocky Mountain Center for Medical Response to Terrorism Mass Casualties and Epidemics
Rocky Mountain Poison & Drug Center
Rocky Mountain Regional Trauma Center

COMPETITORS

Banner Health
Catholic Health Initiatives
Centura Health
Children's Hospital Colorado
Exempla Healthcare

HealthONE
Porter Adventist Hospital
Rose Medical Center
University of Colorado Hospital

HISTORICAL FINANCIALS

Company Type: Private

Income Statement				FYE: December 31
	REVENUE ($ mil.)	NET INCOME ($ mil.)	NET PROFIT MARGIN	EMPLOYEES
12/18	1,119	62	5.6%	3,541
12/17	1,056	14	1.3%	—
12/16	505	(6)	—	—
12/14	449	45	10.2%	—
Annual Growth	25.6%	8.2%	—	—

2018 Year-End Financials

Return on assets: 5.5%
Return on equity: 14.9%
Current ratio: 1.10
Cash ($ mil.): 25

DESAROLLADORA DEL NORTE S E

EXECUTIVES

Pres, Gabriel Escarrer
V Pres of Devel, Edgar Motta
Buyer, Luis Molina

LOCATIONS

HQ: DESAROLLADORA DEL NORTE S E
200 COCO BCH BL HWY 955, RIO GRANDE, PR 00745
Phone: 787 657-1026

HISTORICAL FINANCIALS

Company Type: Private

Income Statement				FYE: December 31
	REVENUE ($ mil.)	NET INCOME ($ mil.)	NET PROFIT MARGIN	EMPLOYEES
12/16	1,801	102	5.7%	500
12/15	1,738	0	—	—
Annual Growth	3.7%			

2016 Year-End Financials

Return on assets: 3.1%
Return on equity: 6.6%
Current ratio: 0.90
Cash ($ mil.): 366

DETROIT WAYNE MENTAL HEALTH AUTHORITY

EXECUTIVES

Ceo, Thomas Watkins
Coordinator, Robert Spruce
Deputy Chief Financial Officer, Dhannetta Brown
Trainer, Marsha Adams
Department Manager Quality Man, April Siebert
Children's Initiatives Coordin, Monica Hampton

LOCATIONS

HQ: DETROIT WAYNE MENTAL HEALTH AUTHORITY
707 W MILWAUKEE ST, DETROIT, MI 482022943
Phone: 313 833-2500
Web: WWW.DWMHA.COM

HISTORICAL FINANCIALS

Company Type: Private

Income Statement				FYE: September 30
	REVENUE ($ mil.)	NET INCOME ($ mil.)	NET PROFIT MARGIN	EMPLOYEES
09/16	736	4	0.6%	99
09/15	701	19	2.8%	—
Annual Growth	5.0%	(77.0%)	—	—

2016 Year-End Financials

Return on assets: 2.1%
Return on equity: 4.7%
Current ratio: 1.70
Cash ($ mil.): 176

DEVCON CONSTRUCTION INCORPORATED

Devcon Construction has built a sturdy business from building in the Bay Area. One of the area's top general building contractors Devcon has constructed more than 30 million sq. ft. of office industrial and commercial space. Its focus is on Northern California mainly in the San Francisco Bay Area and Silicon Valley. The company provides engineering design/build and interior design services. It specializes in high-tech projects including data centers and industrial research and development facilities. In addition to building company facilities and offices Devcon works on such projects as hotels restaurants parking structures retail stores sports facilities and schools.

Geographic Reach

Based in Milpitas California Devcon maintains several satellite offices in California in Petaluma Stockton and Santa Cruz as well as an office in Reno Nevada.

Strategy

Although most of Devcon's work is in California the company also has completed projects in Nevada Oregon Idaho Texas Massachusetts and Florida. Recent projects in the San Francisco Forty Niners Stadium in Santa Clara San Jose Sharks Ice Center in Pleasanton and the Stanford Research Computing Facility.

The company partnered with US-based Central Concrete in 2012 to supply its high-performing low-CO2 concrete for the new San Francisco 49er Stadium. The move showcases Devcon's focus on sustainability as part of its projects.

EXECUTIVES

Vice President Of Construction, Jonathan Harvey
Auditors: JOHANSON & YAU ACCOUNTANCY COR

LOCATIONS

HQ: DEVCON CONSTRUCTION INCORPORATED
690 GIBRALTAR DR, MILPITAS, CA 950356317
Phone: 408 942-8200
Web: WWW.DEVCON-CONST.COM

PRODUCTS/OPERATIONS

Selected Projects

1880 Mission Street San Francisco

3333 Scott Blvd. Buildings A B & C Santa Clara
Anderson Collection At Stanford University Stanford
Barnes & Nobles Palo Alto
Cisco Parking Structure 1 San Jose
Cisco Parking Structure 2 San Jose
Downtown Sunnyvale Town Center Sunnyvale
El Camino Family Housing South San Francisco
Fresno Hyatt Place Hotel Fresno
Friedenrich Center For Translational Research At 800 Welch Road
Lawson Lane East - Buildings A & B Santa Clara
Oakland Air Traffic Control Tower (ATCT) Oakland
San Francisco 49ers Stadium Santa Clara
San Jose Earthquakes - MLS Soccer Stadium San Jose
SanDisk Milpitas
Santa Clara University Admissions & Enrollment Services Building Santa Clara
Sharks Ice Center Pleasanton
Stanford Research Computing Facility Stanford
The Plaza At Triton Park Foster City
University Plaza Palo Alto
Villa Siena Nursing Care Units Mountain View

COMPETITORS

Charles Pankow Builders
DPR Construction
Hathaway Dinwiddie Construction
Hensel Phelps Construction

KPRS Construction
Obayashi
Rudolph & Sletten
Structure Tone
Swinerton
Turner Corporation
Webcor Builders

HISTORICAL FINANCIALS

Company Type: Private

Income Statement

FYE: December 31

	REVENUE ($ mil.)	NET INCOME ($ mil.)	NET PROFIT MARGIN	EMPLOYEES
12/15	1,224	14	1.2%	350
12/14	1,181	20	1.7%	—
12/13	1,012	12	1.2%	—
12/12	779	3	0.5%	—
Annual Growth	16.3%	60.4%	—	—

2015 Year-End Financials

Return on assets: 4.7%   Cash ($ mil.): 7
Return on equity: 38.2%
Current ratio: 1.10

DHPC TECHNOLOGIES, INC.

EXECUTIVES

Pres, Joseph Aletta
V Pres-Ops & Program MGT*, John Antonino
V Pres Engr*, Richard Gifford
Controller*, Robert Jansen
Director, Robert Lake
Engineer, Tom Tokash
Senior Consultant, Dan Glasel
Engineer, Kevin Sullivan
Engineer, Daniel Vance
Associate, David Gandarillas
Chief Scientist, Frank Barone

LOCATIONS

HQ: DHPC TECHNOLOGIES, INC.
10 WOODBRIDGE CENTER DR, WOODBRIDGE, NJ 070951152
Phone: 732 791-5400
Web: WWW.DHPCTECH.COM

HISTORICAL FINANCIALS

Company Type: Private

Income Statement

FYE: May 11

	REVENUE ($ mil.)	NET INCOME ($ mil.)	NET PROFIT MARGIN	EMPLOYEES
05/17*	38,584	1,320	3.4%	150
12/09	11	1	9.0%	—
12/07	6	1	29.2%	—
06/06	1,726	0	0.0%	—
Annual Growth	32.6%	179.9%	—	—

*Fiscal year change

2017 Year-End Financials

Return on assets: 14.5%   Cash ($ mil.): 2,039
Return on equity: 21.9%
Current ratio: 2.80

DIALYSIS CLINIC, INC.

Dialysis Clinic Inc. or DCI is dedicated to caring for patients with end-stage renal disease (ESRD). The not-for-profit company which operates a network of more than 210 dialysis centers serving more than 14000 patients in 27 states also provides kidney transplant assistance services. Affiliate DCI Donor Services is an organ and tissue procurement agency. DCI also funds kidney-related research and educational programs and is affiliated with various universities and teaching hospitals throughout the US including Tufts University the University of Arizona and Tulane University.

Geographic Reach

The company has its locations in Alabama Arizona Arkansas California Colorado Connecticut Florida Georgia Indiana Iowa Kentucky Louisiana Maine Massachusetts Missouri Montana Nebraska Nevada New Jersey New Mexico New York North Carolina Ohio Pennsylvania South Carolina Tennessee and Texas.

Strategy

DCI grows its network of facilities by forming partnerships with health care providers and other organizations. The company provides funding for construction and operation of the facility and it provides clinic support services including supply procurement and central laboratory services (through its DCI Lab subsidiary).

In 2012 the company opened a dialysis clinic in Albuquerque its first dialysis clinic in the South Valley region of New Mexico.

Company Background

DCI was established in 1971 by nephrologist Keith Johnson.

EXECUTIVES

Chb, H Keith Johnson
Dir*, James Perry
Pres*, Ed Attrill
SEC-Treas*, William Wood
Attorney, Karin A Barrett
Nurse Manage, Debra Breault
Nurse Manage, Kimberly Kale
Administrative Assistant, Eric Lee
Director of Corporate, Hal Whetstone
Director, Allen Vessels
Coordinator, Jessica Emler
Auditors: DELOITTE & TOUCHE LLP NASHVIL

LOCATIONS

HQ: DIALYSIS CLINIC, INC.
1633 CHURCH ST STE 500, NASHVILLE, TN 372032948
Phone: 615 327-3061
Web: WWW.DCIINC.ORG

COMPETITORS

DaVita
FMCNA
Fresenius

Renal Advantage
U.S. Renal Care

HISTORICAL FINANCIALS

Company Type: Private

Income Statement

FYE: September 30

	REVENUE ($ mil.)	NET INCOME ($ mil.)	NET PROFIT MARGIN	EMPLOYEES
09/18	760	5	0.7%	5,000
09/17	736	23	3.3%	—
09/16	719	22	3.2%	—
09/15	712	29	4.1%	—
Annual Growth	2.2%	(42.5%)	—	—

2018 Year-End Financials

Return on assets: 0.7%   Cash ($ mil.): 135
Return on equity: 0.9%
Current ratio: 3.40

DIGNITY HEALTH

Dignity Health has steadily grown to become the hospital provider in the state of California and the fifth-largest health system in the US. The not-for-profit health care provider operates a network of 40 acute-care facilities located in the Golden State and to a lesser extent in Arizona and Nevada. Those facilities house 8300 acute care beds as well as 600 skilled nursing beds. Dignity Health provides home health and hospice services through agencies in California and Nevada. It also operates more than 670 emergency and specialty clinics imaging centers and medical labs as well as managed care and wellness programs. Dignity Health is the official health care provider of the San Francisco Giants. In 2019 Dignity merged with Denver-based hospital group Catholic Health Initiatives to create CommonSpirit Health the largest not-for-profit health system in the US.

Change in Company Type

In 2019 Dignity Health and Catholic Health Initiatives joined forces to become CommonSpirit Health which operates more than 700 care sites and some 40 hospitals. It also has research programs home health operations and living communities. After the combination Dignity Health operates as part of CommonSpirit.

Operations

Dignity Health offers inpatient outpatient sub-acute and home health care services as well as physician services through affiliates including Dignity Health Medical Foundation. Through another affiliate U.S. HealthWorks Dignity Health provides occupational health and urgent care services in about 20 additional states.

Geographic Reach

Dignity Health operates some 680 hospitals urgent care centers clinics emergency rooms and specialty care centers in California Nevada and Arizona. It has some 540 facilities in California 85 in Arizona and 60 in Nevada.

Strategy

Although Dignity Health combined with Catholic Health Initiatives in 2019 to become part of the larger CommonSpirit Health system it continues to pursue its own strategic goals. Those include improving quality of care in a just work environment implementing clinical and administrative changes to cut costs and expanding operations in existing markets and new markets. For example it broke ground on a $215 million campus expansion in downtown Los Angeles in early 2019. In another project it is embarking on a multi-million dollar expansion of a campus in Chandler Arizona.

The system is also working to establish more wellness programs and increasingly provide ambulatory and non-urgent care in order to improve the overall health of the communities it serves. In late 2018 it acquired six urgent care centers from San Francisco-based Golden Gate Urgent Care.

In 2018 Dignity Health joined forces with Concentra to operate urgent care centers. Concentra acquired Dignity subsidiary U.S. HealthWorks operator of about 250 urgent care centers and onsite clinics in 21 states. The combined urgent care operator which operated more than 550 urgent care centers is majority owned by Concentra; Dignity holds a 20% stake. The deal allowed the companies to standardize best practices while reaching more patients as rising demand for urgent care centers brings more business to their operators.

Mergers and Acquisitions

After years of discussions Dignity Health and Catholic Health Initiatives merged in early 2019. The combined health system named Common-Spirit Health and with 142 hospitals in 21 states is the largest not-for-profit hospital system in the US. The size of the new system allows for it to provide expanded care to patients through such methods as virtual appointments a broader range of clinical programs and advanced technologies. The new organization is headquartered in Chicago. The group's hospitals continue to operate under their existing names.

Company Background

Dignity Health traces its roots to 1857. The Sisters of Mercy Catholic order was established in Dublin in 1831. In the 1850s eight Sisters arrived in San Francisco and began caring for residents with cholera typhoid and influenza. They established St. Mary's Hospital now that city's oldest continuously operating hospital. The order merged operations with another community of Sisters of Mercy in 1986 to create Catholic Healthcare West. The combined system had one retirement home and 10 hospitals throughout California.

The system changed its name to Dignity Health in early 2012 as part of a governance restructuring program. While the firm remained a not-for-profit organization with Catholic roots and its Catholic hospitals continued to be sponsored by their founding congregations (and governed by the Catholic health care directives) the parent organization itself was no longer an official ministry of the Catholic church. In 2019 Dignity Health joined forces with Catholic Health Initiatives to create CommonSpirit Health the nation's largest not-for-profit health system.

HISTORY

Dignity Health formerly Catholic Healthcare West (CHW) traces its roots to 1857 when the Sisters of Mercy founded St. Mary's Hospital in San Francisco. The order expanded in that area and in 1986 two different communities of the Sisters of Mercy merged their hospitals into an organization with one retirement home and 10 hospitals from the Bay Area to San Diego. Declining membership in Roman Catholic religious orders combined with consolidation in the field led the orders to see merger as their only route to survival.

CHW continued to add facilities including AMI Community Hospital in Santa Cruz California in 1990. Since CHW already owned the area's only other acute care hospital Dominican Santa Cruz Hospital CHW in 1993 was ordered not to acquire any more acute care hospitals in Santa Cruz County without FTC approval.

As the trend to managed care became a stampede in the 1990s CHW moved more into preventive care and began reigning in costs through productivity improvement plans. It continued to add hospitals including tax-supported institutions trying to compete with national for-profit systems.

The network increased its medical clout in 1994 by allying with San Diego-based Scripps one of the state's largest HMO systems. In 1995 the Daughters of Charity Province of the West realigned its six-hospital operation with CHW. The next year the Dominican Sisters (California) the Dominican Sisters of St. Catherine of Siena (Wisconsin) and the Sisters of Charity of the Incarnate Word allied their California hospitals with CHW. New community hospitals included Bakersfield Memorial Sierra Nevada Memorial (Grass Valley) Sequoia Hospital (Redwood City) and Woodland Healthcare.

Charity and cost-consciousness clashed in 1996 when union members staged a walkout to protest nonunion outsourcing of vocational nursing housekeeping and kitchen jobs. This dispute was settled but CHW continued to be a target for union organizers with a bitter battle against the Service Employees International Union (SEIU) starting in 1998.

The year 2000 brought CHW more problems with labor relations: SEIU argued that the organization was resistant to unionization. Continued losses led the organization to implement major restructuring the following year as its 10 regional divisions were consolidated into four.

The company parted ways with one of its sponsoring organizations the Franciscan Sisters of the Sacred Heart of Frankfort Illinois in 2003. The sponsorship ended when CHW closed St. Francis Medical Center of Santa Barbara. However the hospital operator that fiscal year posted its first operating profit in seven years.

The company changed its name from Catholic Healthcare West (CHW) to Dignity Health in early 2012 as part of a governance restructuring program. While the firm remained a not-for-profit organization with Catholic roots and its Catholic hospitals continued to be sponsored by their founding congregations (and governed by the Catholic health care directives) the parent organization itself was no longer an official ministry of the Catholic church.

The company's rebranding and restructuring aimed to give it more flexibility to pursue its growth strategy of widening its presence into additional regions of the US while lowering the overall cost of care (a desire of most large hospital operators as the US government works to reform its ailing health system). At the time of the governance shift Dignity Health operated 25 Catholic hospitals and 15 non-Catholic hospitals.

EXECUTIVES

Evp Sponsorship Mission Integration And Philanthropy, Bernita McTernan
President And Ceo, Lloyd H. Dean
Evp And Chief Human Resources Officer, Darryl L. Robinson
Evp And Chief Administrative Officer, Elizabeth Shih
Sevp And Coo, Marvin O'Quinn
Sevp And Cfo, Daniel J. Morissette
Sevp And Chief Strategy Officer, Charles P. Francis
Evp And Cio, Deanna L. Wise
Evp And Chief Medical Officer, Robert L. Wiebe
Evp And General Counsel, Rick Grossman
Evp Sponsorship And Mission Integration, Elizabeth Keith
Vice President, Adam Berman
Vice President, Jeff Land
Senior Vice President And Chief Strategy Officer, Charlie Francis
Vice President Epmo And Performance Excellence, Joan Beach
Vice President Population Health, Julie Bietsch
Vice President Chief Strategy Officer, Joe Diefenderfer
Clinical Director, Pat Britt
Vice President Ambulatory Services, Margie Roper
Vp Strategic Market Development, Gary Spaugh
Senior Vice President Of Philanthropy, Fred Najjar
Director Of Radiology, Richard Siegel
Associate Medical Director, Albert Tejada
Medical Director Nicu And Pediatrics, Madhu Bhogal
Director Of Pharmacy, Jason Glick
Vice President, Kathleen Sullivan
Physical Therapy, Robert Zvada
Vice President Employee And Labor Relations, Scott Fuller
Medical Director, Christina Kwasnica
Director Of Pharmacy, Reed Howe
Senior Vice President Of Operations For Bay Area Service Area, Todd Strumwasser

Vice President Chief Strategy Office, Jordan Wright
Vice President Communications And Public Relations, Marie Kennedy
Vice President Mission Integration, Margaret McBride
Professor; Vice President Research, Ron Lukas
Medical Director, Javier Cardenas
Vice President Medical Affairs, Sahin Yanik
Director Of Pharmacy, Patty Womack
Vice President Employer Relationships, Duncan Ross
Vice President Patient Care Services Cne, Sherie Ambrose
Vice President Of Philanthropy, Jessa Brooks
Vp Of Strategy And Business Development, Isaac Lin
Vice President Marketing Communications, Jennifer Fagnani
Chairman, Caretha Coleman
Vice Chair, Judy Carle
Medical Secretary, Ann Vong
Auditors: DELOITTE & TOUCHE LLP SAN FRA

LOCATIONS

HQ: DIGNITY HEALTH
185 BERRY ST STE 300, SAN FRANCISCO, CA 941071773
Phone: 415 438-5500

Selected Facilities

Arizona
Barrow Neurological Institute (Phoenix)
Chandler Regional Medical Center
Mercy Gilbert Medical Center
St. Joseph's Hospital and Medical Center (Phoenix)
California
Arroyo Grande Community Hospital
Bakersfield Memorial Hospital
California Hospital Medical Center (Los Angeles)
Community Hospital of San Bernardino
Dominican Hospital (Santa Cruz)
French Hospital Medical Center (San Luis Obispo)
Glendale Memorial Hospital and Health Center
Marian Medical Center (Santa Maria)
Mark Twain St. Joseph's Hospital (San Andreas)
Mercy General Hospital (Sacramento)
Mercy Hospital of Bakersfield
Mercy Hospital of Folsom
Mercy Medical Center Merced Community Campus
Mercy Medical Center Merced Dominican Campus
Mercy Medical Center Mt. Shasta
Mercy Medical Center Redding
Mercy San Juan Medical Center (Carmichael)
Mercy Southwest Hospital (Bakersfield)
Methodist Hospital of Sacramento
Northridge Hospital Medical Center
Oak Valley Hospital (Oakdale)
Saint Francis Memorial Hospital (San Francisco)
Sequoia Hospital (Redwood City)
Sierra Nevada Memorial Hospital (Grass Valley)
St. Bernardine Medical Center (San Bernardino)
St. Elizabeth Community Hospital (Red Bluff)
St. John's Pleasant Valley Hospital (Camarillo)
St. John's Regional Medical Center (Oxnard)
St. Joseph's Behavioral Health Center (Stockton)
St. Joseph's Medical Center (Stockton)
St. Mary Medical Center (Long Beach)
St. Mary's Medical Center (San Francisco)
Woodland Healthcare
Nevada
St. Rose Dominican Hospital Rose de Lima Campus (Henderson)
St. Rose Dominican Hospital San Martín Campus (Las Vegas)
St. Rose Dominican Hospital Siena Campus (Henderson)

PRODUCTS/OPERATIONS

Sponsoring Organizations
Congregation of the Dominican Sisters of St. Catherine of Siena of Kenosha (Kenosha Wisconsin)
Congregation of the Sisters of Charity of the Incarnate Word (Houston Texas)

Sisters of Mercy of the Americas West Midwest Community (Omaha Nebraska; formerly Auburn Regional Community of the Sisters of Mercy and Burlingame Regional Community of the Sisters of Mercy in California)
Sisters of St. Dominic Congregation of the Most Holy Rosary (Adrian Michigan)
Sisters of St. Francis of Penance and Christian Charity St. Francis Province (Redwood City California)
Sisters of the Third Order of St. Dominic Congregation of the Most Holy Name (San Rafael California)

COMPETITORS

Adventist Health System West
Banner Health
Community Health Systems
Community Hospital of the Monterey Peninsula
Ensign Group
HCA
John C. Lincoln Health Network
John Muir Health
Loma Linda University Medical Center
Memorial Health Services
Prospect Medical
Providence St. Joseph Health
Salinas Valley Memorial
Shasta Regional Medical Center
Stanford Health Care
Sutter Health
Tenet Healthcare
UCSF Medical
Universal Health Services
VITAS Healthcare

HISTORICAL FINANCIALS

Company Type: Private

Income Statement				FYE: June 30
	REVENUE ($ mil.)	NET INCOME ($ mil.)	NET PROFIT MARGIN	EMPLOYEES
06/09	8,957	(799)	—	55,494
06/08	8,401	169	2.0%	—
Annual Growth	6.6%	—	—	—

2009 Year-End Financials
Return on assets: (-7.2%)   Cash ($ mil.): 868
Return on equity: (-22.6%)
Current ratio: 1.50

DIGNITY HEALTH MEDICAL FOUNDATION

EXECUTIVES

Pres, Laurie Schwarctz
Cfo*, Theresa Hylen
Coordinator, Leticia Mendoza
Clinic Manager, Isabel Reyes
Clinical Pharmacist Utilizatio, Jonathan Miano
Financial Analyst, Sonja Greene
Diagnostic Radiologist, Lindsey Satre
Diagnostic Radiologist, Mohammad Khorasani
Diagnostic Radiologist, Nataraj Shanmugam
Diagnostic Radiologist, Yauk Lee
Director, Steve Scharmann
Auditors: KPMG LLP SAN FRANCISCO CA

LOCATIONS

HQ: DIGNITY HEALTH MEDICAL FOUNDATION
3400 DATA DR, RANCHO CORDOVA, CA 956707956
Phone: 916 379-2840

HISTORICAL FINANCIALS

Company Type: Private

Income Statement				FYE: June 30
	REVENUE ($ mil.)	NET INCOME ($ mil.)	NET PROFIT MARGIN	EMPLOYEES
06/14	570	17	3.1%	1,000
06/09	297	0	0.1%	—
Annual Growth	13.9%	120.7%	—	—

2014 Year-End Financials
Return on assets: 9.4%   Cash ($ mil.): 31
Return on equity: 19.7%
Current ratio: 1.40

DO IT BEST CORP.

Do it Best Corp. is one of the industry's largest hardware cooperatives boasting some 3800 member-owned stores in 50-plus countries but primarily the US. Besides the usual tools and building materials merchandise includes automotive items bicycles camping gear housewares office supplies and small appliances. Customers also can have products specially shipped to their local stores through Do it Best's e-commerce site. The co-op's buying power enables member stores which do not have to use the Do it Best name to offer items at competitive prices.

Operations

Through its member locations and e-commerce site Do it Best offers a broad range of products (some 67000 items are available online) across such categories as automotive electrical hardware housewares outdoor living plumbing and storage and organization.

Geographic Reach

Based in Fort Wayne Indiana Do it Best has member-owned hardware stores across the US as well as in some 50 countries throughout Central and South America the Caribbean and numerous countries in Southeast Asia.

Its warehouses (called Retail Service Centers) are located in Dixon Illinois; Lexington South Carolina; Medina Ohio; Mesquite Nevada; Montgomery New York; Sikeston Missouri; Waco Texas; and Woodburn Oregon.

Financial Performance

As a non-public entity Do it Best does not publicly release full financials. It does report annual revenue of about $3 billion however.

Company Background

Formerly named Hardware Wholesalers Do it Best was founded in 1945 in Fort Wayne Indiana by Arnold Gerberding. The company launched its doitbest.com e-commerce site in 1996.

EXECUTIVES

Vp Finance And Cfo, Doug Roth
Vp Information Technology, Michael J. (Mike) Altendorf
Evp And Coo, Daniel B. (Dan) Starr
Vp Marketing, Timothy (Tim) Miller
Vp Merchandising, Steve Markley
Vp Lumber And Building Materials, Gary Nackers
Gm Vice President Business Unit Manager, Dori Meighan
Vice President Information Technology, John Mergy
National Sales Manager, Rob Schmiedel
Vice President Information Technology, Mike Altenborf
Vice Chairman, Brad McDaniel

Chairman, John Holmes
Treasurer, Zach Higgins
Auditors: CROWE HORWATH LLP FORT WAYNE

LOCATIONS

HQ: DO IT BEST CORP.
   6502 NELSON RD, FORT WAYNE, IN 468031947
Phone: 260 748-5300
Web: WWW.DOITBESTCORP.COM

COMPETITORS

84 Lumber	Orgill
Ace Hardware	Sears
Home Depot	Sutherland Lumber
Lowe's	True Value
Menard	Wal-Mart
Northern Tool	

HISTORICAL FINANCIALS

Company Type: Private

Income Statement   FYE: June 25

	REVENUE ($ mil.)	NET INCOME ($ mil.)	NET PROFIT MARGIN	EMPLOYEES
06/16	2,925	0	0.0%	1,519
06/11	2,328	0	0.0%	—
06/10	2,296	0	0.0%	—
Annual Growth	4.1%	(5.7%)	—	—

2016 Year-End Financials

Return on assets: 0.1%   Cash ($ mil.): 20
Return on equity: 0.2%
Current ratio: 1.40

DOCTOR'S ASSOCIATES INC.

Doctor's Associates owns the Subway chain of sandwich shops the world's largest quick-service restaurant chain by number of locations surpassing burger giant McDonald's. The company boasts more than 44000 restaurants in greater than 110 countries. Virtually all Subway restaurants are franchised and offer such fare as hot and cold sub sandwiches turkey wraps and salads. The widely recognized eateries are in freestanding buildings as well as in airports convenience stores sports facilities and other locations.

Strategy

The Subway chain has tapped into the health food and weight loss zeitgeist in the US prominently featuring in its advertising Jared Fogle a man who famously lost nearly 250 lbs. by switching to a Subway sandwich diet. The chain continues to tout the health benefits of its sandwiches over traditional burgers and fries by introducing new low-fat menu items.

Subway has been developing an upscale concept called Subway Café. The new format conceived for office buildings and other high-end locations is larger than the average Subway restaurant and features coffee espresso lattes and hot chocolate along with an expanded breakfast menu.

The company also seeks partnerships with other food brands to generate buzz around its products. In 2019 the company partnered with Halo Top Creamery to introduce Halo Top milkshakes at almost 1000 Subway restaurants. That year it also collaborated with Hubert's Lemonade to offer the company's drinks at its locations. The company also began testing a Kings Hawaiian-branded bread offering at three cities.

The company is investing in improving the look of its operations. It has remodeled nearly 1400 franchise locations and has around 900 remodels underway. In 2019 Subway announced a grant program that will cover 25% of remodeling costs for more than 10500 restaurants.

Company Background

Co-founders DeLuca and Buck opened the first Subway in 1965.

HISTORY

In 1965 17-year-old Fred DeLuca dreamed of becoming a doctor while working as a stock boy in a Bridgeport Connecticut hardware store to earn college tuition. It wasn't enough so he cornered family friend Peter Buck at a backyard barbecue and asked for advice. Buck a nuclear physicist suggested DeLuca open a submarine sandwich shop and put up $1000 to get him started.

As the summer of 1965 was coming to an end DeLuca rented a small location in a remote area of Bridgeport opened Pete's Super Submarines and there he sold foot-long sandwiches. On the first day the sandwiches were so popular that DeLuca hired his own customers to work behind the counter; by the end of the day he had sold out of all his supplies. The sandwiches continued to be popular for a while but within a few months the shop started losing money and DeLuca and Buck found that selling submarine sandwiches was a seasonal business. They decided they could create an illusion of success by opening a second location and then a third. The third store was finally successful partly because of its more visible location and increased marketing and partly because of a new name — Subway.

DeLuca and Buck had set a goal of 32 shops opened by 1975 but they had only 16 by 1974. They realized that the only way they could reach their goal in one year was to license the Subway name. The first franchise opened that year in Wallingford Connecticut and they opened 32 by the end of 1975. The partners hit 100 by 1978 then 200 by 1983 and DeLuca set a new goal: 5000 Subway shops by 1994. The first international Subway opened in Bahrain in 1984 and DeLuca achieved his goal of 5000 shops by 1990.

During the 1990s DeLuca experimented with several other franchise concepts including We Care Hair (budget styling salons) Cajun Joe's (spicy fried chicken) and Q Burgers. But none of these ventures fared as well as his sandwich empire. As Subway grew however controversy surrounding its treatment of franchisees began to surface. A Federal Trade Commission investigation of the company was dropped in 1993 but Subway continued to battle franchisees complaining about broken contracts market over-saturation (and therefore too much competition and self-cannibalization) and what the franchisees viewed as unreasonably high royalty fees.

In spite of its franchising troubles Subway kept growing. It expanded into Russia and China in the mid-1990s and opened its 11000th restaurant in 1995. In 1997 Subway inked deals with the Army Navy and Air Force exchange services to bring Subway units to military bases. Two years later the company opened its 14000th restaurant in Mount Gambier Australia an event that coincided with Subway's renewed push to expand internationally.

The company got some unexpected publicity in 1999 when 22-year-old Jared Fogle claimed that he dropped 245 pounds from his 425-pound frame by subsisting on a diet of Subway turkey sandwiches. Subway helped Fogle extend his 15 minutes of fame by featuring him and his oversized pants in a TV commercial. (The company has since built an entire campaign around Fogle that fea-

tures other weight watchers attributing their success to Jared and Subway.) Subway introduced its largest menu initiative ever in 2000 when it unveiled its Subway Selects Gourmet Sandwiches adding 13 items to the menu. In April 2001 the company opened its 15000th store.

Also that year Buck retired as chairman but stayed on as a member of the board of directors. Becoming one of the fastest-growing franchises in the world Subway expanded from 16000 locations in 2002 to more than 22000 stores by the end of 2004.

All US Subway outlets switched from Pepsi to Coke products in 2005. Two years later the chain surpassed 21000 locations in the US.

EXECUTIVES

Director Research And Development, Suzanne Greco
Executive Vice President, Cynthia M Eadie
Secretary, Haydee Buck
Secretary, Steven Phillips

LOCATIONS

HQ: DOCTOR'S ASSOCIATES INC.
   325 SUB WAY, MILFORD, CT 064613081
Phone: 203 877-4281
Web: WWW.SUBWAY.COM

COMPETITORS

Burger King	Panera Bread
CKE Restaurants	Papa John's
Chick-fil-A	Popeyes
Chipotle	Potbelly Sandwich Shop
Church's Chicken	Quiznos
Dairy Queen	Sonic Corp.
Domino's	Starbucks
Jack in the Box	Tim Hortons
McDonald's	Wendy's
Panda Restaurant Group	YUM!

HISTORICAL FINANCIALS

Company Type: Private

Income Statement   FYE: December 31

	REVENUE ($ mil.)	NET INCOME ($ mil.)	NET PROFIT MARGIN	EMPLOYEES
12/10	1,049	7	0.7%	650
12/08	926	6	0.7%	—
12/07	780	5	0.7%	—
Annual Growth	10.4%	9.8%	—	—

2010 Year-End Financials

Return on assets: 6.5%   Cash ($ mil.): 43
Return on equity: 49.4%
Current ratio: 1.00

DOCTORS HOSPITAL AT RENAISSANCE, LTD.

EXECUTIVES

Ceo, Lawrence Gelman
Pres*, Susan Turley
Accounting Staff, Joyce Lustgarten
Vice-President, Patrick Blackwell
Coordinator, Ricardo Maldonado
Manager, Rick Gomez
Program Director, Steve Butler
Internist, Constantine Ohabor
Sales Client Coordinat, Mari Alarcon
Benefit Coordinator, Noel Flores
MD, Ravindra Veeramachaneni

LOCATIONS

HQ: DOCTORS HOSPITAL AT RENAISSANCE, LTD.
5501 S MCCOLL RD, EDINBURG, TX 785395503
Phone: 956 362-8677
Web: WWW.DHR-RGV.COM

HISTORICAL FINANCIALS
Company Type: Private

Income Statement			FYE: December 31
	REVENUE ($ mil.)	NET INCOME ($ mil.)	NET PROFIT MARGIN	EMPLOYEES
12/16	580	80	13.9%	176
12/14	436	63	14.4%	—
Annual Growth	15.3%	13.1%	—	—

2016 Year-End Financials

Return on assets: 17.7%
Return on equity: 44.6%
Current ratio: 2.00

Cash ($ mil.): 49

DOCTORS MEDICAL CENTER OF MODESTO, INC.

EXECUTIVES

Ceo, Warren J Kirk
Cfo*, Greg Berry
Manager, Cindy Vingerhoets
Internist, Veronica Ortiz
Chief of Neurosurgery, Benjamin Remington
Clinical Operationws Manager P, Joseph Garcia
Nurse, Linda Hawkins
Hospitalist, Arun Manoharan
Staff Pharmacist, Berna Hilgers
MD, Edward W Verde
Pac, Nancy A Howard

LOCATIONS

HQ: DOCTORS MEDICAL CENTER OF MODESTO, INC.
1441 FLORIDA AVE, MODESTO, CA 953504404
Phone: 209 578-1211
Web: WWW.DMC-MODESTO.COM

HISTORICAL FINANCIALS
Company Type: Private

Income Statement			FYE: May 31
	REVENUE ($ mil.)	NET INCOME ($ mil.)	NET PROFIT MARGIN	EMPLOYEES
05/16	587	86	14.6%	2,000
05/09	306	4	1.4%	—
Annual Growth	9.8%	52.8%	—	—

2016 Year-End Financials

Return on assets: 28.1%
Return on equity: 41.1%
Current ratio: 2.30

Cash ($ mil.): —

DON FORD SANDERSON INC

EXECUTIVES

Pres, David Kimmerle
Chb*, La Verne Sanderson
SEC-Treas*, Stephen C Wendt
Prin*, Sandra Sue Kimmerle
Sales Associate, Brad Bailey
Parts Manager, Dave Beard
Sales Associate, Florin Nichitean
Graphic Designer, Jenny Kester
Sales Manager, John Pratt
Advertising Director, Max Sirstins
Consultant, Ron Wilson

LOCATIONS

HQ: DON FORD SANDERSON INC
6400 N 51ST AVE, GLENDALE, AZ 853014600
Phone: 623 842-8600
Web: WWW.SANDERSONFORD.COM

HISTORICAL FINANCIALS
Company Type: Private

Income Statement			FYE: December 31
	REVENUE ($ mil.)	NET INCOME ($ mil.)	NET PROFIT MARGIN	EMPLOYEES
12/15	679	3	0.5%	416
12/14	671	4	0.7%	—
12/13	692	5	0.8%	—
12/12	590	3	0.6%	—
Annual Growth	4.8%	(3.8%)	—	—

2015 Year-End Financials

Return on assets: 2.7%
Return on equity: 8.9%
Current ratio: 1.40

Cash ($ mil.): 1

DORMITORY AUTHORITY - STATE OF NEW YORK

EXECUTIVES

Exec Dir, Paul T Williams
Exec V Pres-Cheif ADM*, Maryanne Gridley
Gen Counsel*, Jeffery Pohl
Cfo*, John G Pasicznyk
Mng Dir Public Fin*, Cheryl Ishmael
Mng Dir Construction*, Douglas Vanvleck
Mng Dir Policy & Prog Dev*, Thomas E Guiley
Deputy Exec Dir*, Micheal Coorigan
Chief of Staff*, Caroline Griffin
Cfo-Treasurer*, Kim Nadeau
Personnel Assistant, Gail Beerle
Auditors: KPMG LLP ALBANY NY

LOCATIONS

HQ: DORMITORY AUTHORITY - STATE OF NEW YORK
515 BROADWAY STE 100, ALBANY, NY 122072964
Phone: 518 257-3000
Web: WWW.DASNY.ORG

HISTORICAL FINANCIALS
Company Type: Private

Income Statement			FYE: March 31
	REVENUE ($ mil.)	NET INCOME ($ mil.)	NET PROFIT MARGIN	EMPLOYEES
03/11	2,075	(115)	—	625
03/06	1,693	(40)	—	—
03/05	0	0	—	—
Annual Growth	—	—	—	—

2011 Year-End Financials

Return on assets: (-0.3%)
Return on equity: (-27.6%)
Current ratio: 1.10

Cash ($ mil.): 452

DOUGLAS COUNTY SCHOOL DISTRICT

EXECUTIVES

Pres, David Ray
Supt*, Thomas Tucker
Finance Manager, Alyson Plummer
Volunteer Coordinator Mountain, Joyce Paich
Teacher, Kristen Parsons
Lcsw, Tricia Anderson
Its Technician III Information, Curtis Gundersen
Teacher Rock Canyon High Schoo, Dayna Moore
Teacher, Jason Dunkle
Teacher, Jim Dollaghan
Teacher of Cougar Run Elementa, Julie Davidson

LOCATIONS

HQ: DOUGLAS COUNTY SCHOOL DISTRICT
620 WILCOX ST, CASTLE ROCK, CO 801041730
Phone: 303 387-0100
Web: WWW.DCSDK12.ORG

HISTORICAL FINANCIALS
Company Type: Private

Income Statement			FYE: June 30
	REVENUE ($ mil.)	NET INCOME ($ mil.)	NET PROFIT MARGIN	EMPLOYEES
06/13	562	(0)	—	8,000
06/10	551	(11)	—	—
06/08	480	(48)	—	—
06/07	0	0	—	—
Annual Growth	—	—	—	—

DPR CONSTRUCTION, INC.

From bio labs to wafer fabs DPR Construction runs the gamut for its high-tech and health care clients. The employee-owned firm provides general contracting and construction management services for the advanced technology/mission-critical life sciences health care higher education and corporate office markets. The construction firm specializes in developing retail stores hospitals data centers clean rooms laboratories manufacturing facilities and green buildings. Altogether DPR Construction boasts about 20 regional offices nationwide. Company head Doug Woods former CEO Peter Nosler and secretary/treasurer Ron Davidowski (the D P and R in DPR Construction) founded the firm in 1990.

Operations
Since its founding the company has completed some 8500 projects. DPR Construction has expertise in collaborative virtual building and Building Information Modeling (BIM) sustainability preconstruction and other niche areas.

Geographic Reach
To maintain a presence near customers DPR boasts nearly 20 regional offices. Its operations span 10 states including Arizona California Colorado North Carolina Florida Georgia Maryland Texas Virginia and Washington DC.

Sales and Marketing
DPR serves several core markets including advanced technology corporate offices healthcare higher education and life sciences. Customers have includes CHRISTUS Health Clif Bar & Company Intuit Facebook and Kaiser Permanente.

Strategy
The company is looking to leverage its expanded East Coast operations especially in the growing mid-Atlantic market. Its three offices in Maryland Virginia and the District of Columbia also serve customers in West Virginia Delaware Pennsylvania and New Jersey.

DPR has been focusing on eco-friendly construction. More than 40% of its projects incorporate green building techniques or products and approximately one in four of its employees are Leadership in Energy and Environmental Design (LEED) certified.

EXECUTIVES

Management Committee, Jim Dolen
Management Committee, Peter A. Salvati
President, Douglas E. (Doug) Woods
Management Committee, Eric Lamb
Regional Manager Raleigh-durham Nc Office, Mark Whitson
Regional Manager Tampa Fl Office, Page W. McKee
Regional Manager Redwood City, Jody Quinton
Regional Manager Baltimore And Washington Dc, Greg Haldeman
Management Committee, George Pfeffer
Management Committee, Mike Ford
Regional Manager West Palm Beach, Deborah Beetson
Regional Manager Austin And Houston Tx Offices, Gary Nauert
Regional Manager Phoenix, David Elrod
Regional Manager San Diego, Jay Leopold
Regional Manager Sacramento, Mark Cirksena
Regional Manager San Jose, Scott Greubel
Cfo, Michele Leiva
Regional Manager San Francisco, Mike Humphrey
Regional Manager Richmond Va, Lisa Lingerfelt
Regional Manager Atlanta, Russ Brockelbank
Regional Manager Denver Office, Michael Devens
Regional Manager Newport Beach And Pasadena Ca Offices, Dave Seastrom
Regional Manager Orlando Fl Office, Scott Lyons
Auditors: PRICEWATERHOUSECOOPERS LLP LO

LOCATIONS

HQ: DPR CONSTRUCTION, INC.
1450 VETERANS BLVD, REDWOOD CITY, CA
940632617
Phone: 650 474-1450
Web: WWW.DPR.COM

Selected Offices

Atlanta
Austin TX
Baltimore
Denver
Houston
Newport Beach CA
Orlando Florida
Pasadena CA
Phoenix
Raleigh-Durham NC
Redwood City CA
Richmond VA
Sacramento CA
San Diego CA
San Francisco CA
San Jose CA
Tampa Florida
Washington DC
West Palm Beach FL

COMPETITORS

Austin Industries	Jacobs Engineering
Bechtel	M. A. Mortenson
Devcon Construction	PC Construction
Fluor	Skanska USA Building
Hensel Phelps Construction	Swinerton
	Turner Corporation
Hoffman Corporation	Whiting-Turner

HISTORICAL FINANCIALS

Company Type: Private

Income Statement   FYE: December 31

	REVENUE ($ mil.)	NET INCOME ($ mil.)	NET PROFIT MARGIN	EMPLOYEES
12/08	1,836	68	3.7%	6,500
12/00	1,958	25	1.3%	—
Annual Growth	(0.8%)	13.0%	—	—

2008 Year-End Financials

Return on assets: 13.0%   Cash ($ mil.): 162
Return on equity: 37.9%
Current ratio: 1.50

DRIVETIME AUTOMOTIVE GROUP, INC.

In this story the ugly duckling changes into DriveTime Automotive Group. Formerly known as Ugly Duckling the company is a used-car dealership chain that primarily targets low-income customers and those with less-than-stellar credit. To cater to subprime clients it's a "buy here-pay here" dealer meaning it finances and services car loans rather than using outside lenders. DriveTime operates more than 125 dealerships in 50 US metropolitan areas in 24 mostly southern and western states. The company provides customers with a comprehensive end-to-end solution for their automotive needs including the sale financing and maintenance of their vehicle.

Change in Company Type
The company withdrew its SEC registration in 2014.

Operations
The company's activities includes vehicle acquisition vehicle reconditioning and distribution vehicle sales underwriting and finance loan servicing and after sale support. DriveTime has sold more than 750000 used cars to consumers of all credit types and services a $2 billion loan portfolio.

DriveTime's financing business operates under the name DT Acceptance Corporation. The unit generates about a quarter of the company's total revenues

The company also offers DriveCare a 36-month/36000 miled (5-Year/50000 miled in some states) vehicle protection plan and extended powertrain coverage.

Geographic Reach
Phoenix-based DriveTime operates dealerships in 47 US metro areas throughout 24 states. More than a third of the dealerships are located in Florida and Texas.

Sales and Marketing
DriveTime markets its automotive products and services through TV commercials.

Strategy
DriveTime's long-term strategic goal is to expand its network of dealerships throughout the US targeting metropolitan areas with populations of 500000 to 3 million residents. In 2015 the company opened its first New Jersey location in Williamstown. In 2014 it established its presence in the Chicago area with the opening of the Lombard location; it also opened first location in the Washington DC area.

The used car dealer is also expanding in Texas opening a dealership in Corpus Christi in late 2013 its 20th in the Lone Star State.

As part of its business model DriveTime acquires used vehicles at auction. In 2013 the company purchased more than 96000 vehicles nationwide primarily from used vehicle auctions.

That year DriveTime teamed up with fellow car dealer Manheim to form Go Auto Exchange a new separate and independent wholesale auction company focused on independent dealers and the low-end vehicle segment.

Company venture Carvana (launched in early 2013) allows customers to buy its used cars online. Carvana expands the company's customer base by targeting customers outside its traditional credit-impaired low-income cohort.

Company Background
Chairman Ernest Garcia III owns the company through his Verde Investments firm. In 2012 the company abandoned plans to split its finance and used vehicle retail operations by selling the financing arm to Santander Consumer USA and the used car dealerships to a group of third-party investors. Prior to that DriveTime in early 2010 filed to go public but withdrew the proposed offering seven months later. It with drew a second IPO attempt in 2014.

EXECUTIVES

Prin, Ernest C Garcia II
Exec V Pres*, Jon D Ehlinger
Cfo*, Kurt Wood
Cfo*, Matthew Peel
Dir*, Gregg Tryhuss
Director, William N Plamondon
Corp Liaison, Kimberly Moon
General Manager, Seth Taylor
Senior Network Engineer, Mark Donahoo
General Manager, Matthew Bergantzel
CIO Cto, Paul Kaplan

LOCATIONS

HQ: DRIVETIME AUTOMOTIVE GROUP, INC.
1720 W RIO SALADO PKWY, TEMPE, AZ 852816590
Phone: 602 852-6600
Web: WWW.DRRICHSCHUTTLER.COM

2014 Stores

	No.
Alabama	5
Arkansas	1
Arizona	6
California	5
Colorado	2
Delware	1
Florida	21
Georgia	9
Illinois	2
Indiana	2
Kentucky	2
Maryland	2
Missouri	4
Mississippi	1
North Carolina	9
New Jersey	1
New Mexico	3
Nevada	2
Ohio	7
Oklahoma	3
South Carolina	4
Tennessee	6
Texas	22
Virginia	7
Total	**127**

COMPETITORS

AutoNation	Gunn Automotive
CarMax	McCombs Enterprises
Gillman Auto	Sonic Automotive

HISTORICAL FINANCIALS

Company Type: Private

Income Statement   FYE: December 31

	REVENUE ($ mil.)	NET INCOME ($ mil.)	NET PROFIT MARGIN	EMPLOYEES
12/17	3,267	(16)	—	3,165
12/15	2,372	32	1.4%	
/ 0	0		—	
Annual Growth	—	—	—	—

2017 Year-End Financials

Return on assets: (-0.3%)   Cash ($ mil.): 32
Return on equity: (-3.0%)
Current ratio: 1.20

DST SYSTEMS, INC.

EXECUTIVES

Ceo, William C Stone
Pres-Coo, Normand A Boulanger
Sr V Pres-Cfo, Patrick J Pedonti
Sr V Pres-Gencounsel-Sec, Paul G Igoe
Director, Roger Stanley
Senior Executive Assistant, Scott Jones
Senior Vice President, Wayne Armstrong
Administrator Lan Administrato, Anthony Lombardo
Information Technology Manager, Debbie Brunk
Implementation Consultant, Jan Carter
Sys Manager, Jeffrey Greig
Auditors: PRICEWATERHOUSECOOPERS LLP K

LOCATIONS

HQ: DST SYSTEMS, INC.
333 W 11TH ST, KANSAS CITY, MO 641051773
Phone: 816 435-1000
Web: WWW.DSTSYSTEMS.COM

COMPETITORS

ADP	HP Enterprise Services
Advent Software	HealthPort
Algorithmics	IBM
Alliance Data Systems	Iron Mountain Inc
Assurant	McKesson
Bank of New York Mellon	Misys
	NCR
Broadridge	Paychex
CSG Systems International	Pegasystems
	Progress Software
CVS Caremark	R.R. Donnelley
Cerner	Recall Corporation
Convergys	SEI Investments
Emdeon	SS&C
Express Scripts	StatPro Group
Fidelity National Information Services	State Street
	SunGard
First Data	TIBCO Software
Fiserv	TMG Health
GE Healthcare	TeleTech
Greenway Medical Technologies	Total System Services
	TriZetto

HISTORICAL FINANCIALS

Company Type: Private

Income Statement   FYE: December 31

	REVENUE ($ mil.)	NET INCOME ($ mil.)	NET PROFIT MARGIN	EMPLOYEES
12/17	2,218	452	20.4%	15,700
12/16	1,556	426	27.4%	—
12/15	2,825	358	12.7%	—
12/14	2,749	593	21.6%	—
Annual Growth	(6.9%)	(8.7%)		—

2017 Year-End Financials

Return on assets: 15.4%   Cash ($ mil.): 80
Return on equity: 36.4%
Current ratio: 1.10

DUKE UNIVERSITY

Duke University is home to some 15000 Blue Devils who attend undergraduate- and graduate-level classes in 10 schools and colleges. Trinity College of Art and Sciences the Fuqua School of Business and the Pratt School of Engineering are among the most well known. Duke's law and medical schools are also highly regarded nationwide. The private institution boasts a student-teacher ratio of 8:1. Programs include arts and sciences engineering nursing allied health and public policy as well as schools in business divinity environment law medicine and nursing. Founded in 1838 as Trinity College Duke took its present name in 1924 after American Tobacco Co. magnate James Duke established the Duke Endowment.

Operations

Duke oversees several large scale programs including student academics (undergraduate and graduate) student athletics (27 NCAA Division I teams) Duke Medicine (education two hospitals and other medical operations) Duke Libraries (10 private research libraries) the Duke Marine Laboratory and Duke University Press (publishes about 120 new books annually).

Like most universities its it governed by a board of trustees which serves as the institution's fiduciary. The board manages and oversees long-term financial health strategic direction educational policy finances and operations.

Geographic Reach

Most of Duke University's academic operations occur in the heart of Durham North Carolina. It also operates research facilities and Duke University Health System (DUHS). DUHS consists of Duke University Hospital Durham Regional Hospital Duke Raleigh Hospital and related health care clinics.

The university cooperates with other US-based institutions to support student exchanges in New York Washington D.C. Los Angeles Chicago Alaska and Silicon Valley in California. It also boasts programs abroad such as in Berlin Paris Glasgow Madrid St. Petersburg Venice Kunshan and Bangalore.

Sales and Marketing

Notable alumni include Richard Nixon Melinda French Gates Elizabeth Dole and Charlie Rose.

Financial Performance

In FY2017 (ended June 30 2017) Duke University generated consolidated operating revenue of $5.7 billion with more than half of that amount due to the Duke University Health System Patient Services. Operating revenue for the academic portion of Duke increased 8% on the year rising to $2.83 billion.

The university's endowment was nearly $8.0 billion at the end of FY2017 up more than $1.0 billion from the prior year. FY2017 marked the end of the Duke Forward fundraising campaign which raised $3.85 billion over several years.

Strategy

Duke's academic strategy pursues investment in its faculty improving the educational experience for all students building its capacity to address global challenges and supporting research learning and academia.

It is investing in its East West and Central campuses as well by building new facilities and improving on existing ones. Projects ongoing in 2017 are a new residence hall (Keohane Quad K-4) and the conversion of its Indoor Practice Facility into a Multi-Purpose Field House which will be used for varsity football practice soccer lacrosse band practice and intramural sports.

Duke is working toward several goals as part of its current expansion strategy. It has set aside an additional $100 million to recruit retain and support an outstanding and diverse faculty. While it's focused on existing fields such as humanities and social sciences the university is extending its reach into genome sciences ethics and global health as it addresses important world issues. To deepen engagement across its undergraduate and graduate student bodies Duke is reaching beyond its Focus Program for first-year students and its joint degree programs for professional students by creating new opportunities for students to make connection with the world outside the confines of the classroom. It's working in the arts to create opportunities for Duke students to interact with distinguished practitioners and create their own works.

To ensure that Duke maintains its commitment to diversity it has developed collaborative partnerships across Durham North Carolina the region and the world. Duke boasts that during the past 10 years the percentage of African-American faculty members has doubled. Indeed a third of all graduate and professional students are admitted from other countries. To ensure it's able to attract and retain a diverse student population Duke rolled out a major financial aid initiative which aims to strengthen its needblind admissions policy to keep Duke on the list of qualified applicants regardless of their family incomes.

EXECUTIVES

Evp And Treasurer, Tallman Trask
President, Richard H. (Dick) Brodhead
Vp Information Technology, Tracy Futhey
Dean Fuqua School Of Business, William F. Boulding

Dean School Of Medicine, Nancy C. Andrews
Dean Law School, David F. Levi
Provost, Sally Kornbluth
Chancellor Health Affairs; President And Ceo Health System, A. Eugene Washington
President And Ceo Duke Management Company, Neal Triplett
Interim Dean Divinity School, Ellen F. Davis
Dean Graduate School, Paula D. McClain
Dean Nicholas School Of The Environment, Alan Townsend
Dean Pratt School Of Engineering, George Truskey
Dean Sanford School Of Public Policy, Kelly D. Brownell
Dean Trinity College Of Arts And Sciences, Valerie S. Ashby
Dean School Of Nursing, Marion E. Broome
Chancellor Duke Kunshan University, Liu Jingnan
Dean Duke-nus Graduate Medical School, Thomas Coffman
Vice President Of Finance, Tim Walsh
Vice President Manager Director, Karen Hicks
Vice President And Director Of Athletics, Kevin White
Assistant Vice President Office Of Information Technology, Angel Wingate
J. Lamar Callaway Professor And Chair Department Of Dermatology, Russell Hall
Medical Director, Joseph Moore
Associate Vice President, Kimberly Denty
Vice Chairman, Jack O. Bovender
Vice Chairman, Robin A. Ferracone
Chairman, David M. Rubenstein
Under Secretary General, Ian Jaffe
Board Member, Karin Shapiro
Chairman Emeritus Board Of Visitors, Ronald L Nicol
Board Member, Matthew Kanaan
Auditors: KPMG LLP GREENSBORO NC

LOCATIONS

HQ: DUKE UNIVERSITY
2200 W MAIN ST STE 710, DURHAM, NC 277054677
Phone: 919 684-8111
Web: WWW.DUKE.EDU

PRODUCTS/OPERATIONS

Selected Institutes
Center for the Study of Aging and Human Development
Duke Cancer Institute
Duke Global Health Institute
Duke Institute for Brain Sciences
Duke Science & Society Initiative
Duke University Energy Initiative
Institute for Genomic & Computational Biology
Interdisciplinary Studies
John Hope Franklin Humanities Institute
Kenan Institute for Ethics
Nicholas Institute for Environmental Policy Solutions
Trent Center for Bioethics Humanities and History of Medicine
Social Science Research Institute

Selected Schools and Colleges
Divinity School (Since 1926)
Duke Kunshan University (Since 2014; China)
Duke-NUS Medical School (Since 2005)
Fuqua School of Business (Since 1969)
Graduate School (Since 1926)
Nicholas School of the Environment (Since 1938)
Pratt School of Engineering (Since 1939)
Sanford School of Public Policy (Since 1971)
School of Law (Since 1904)
School of Medicine (Since 1930)
School of Nursing (Since 1931)
Trinity College of Arts & Sciences (Since 1859)

HISTORICAL FINANCIALS

Company Type: Private

Income Statement   FYE: June 30

	REVENUE ($ mil.)	NET INCOME ($ mil.)	NET PROFIT MARGIN	EMPLOYEES
06/12	4,611	(507)	—	3,400
06/05	1,832	246	13.5%	—
06/04	2,806	679	24.2%	—
Annual Growth	6.4%	—	—	—

2012 Year-End Financials

Return on assets: (-3.6%)   Cash ($ mil.): 526
Return on equity: (-5.2%)
Current ratio: —

DUKE UNIVERSITY HEALTH SYSTEM, INC.

More than a campus infirmary the Duke University Health System operates the Duke University Hospital and other medical educational and research facilities on the Duke University grounds. Duke University Hospital has about 960 acute pediatric and psychiatric patient beds and specializes in trauma care diagnostics and cardiac and endoscopic surgeries. The health system also operates two community hospitals — Duke Regional Hospital (370 beds) and Duke Raleigh Hospital (186 beds) — as well as other area health clinics. Duke University Health System's facilities provide primary and specialty care home and hospice care clinical research physician and nurse training and public education programs.

Operations
The system was formed in 1998 to expand the core Medical Center operations and has since added the Durham and Raleigh community hospitals. The Duke University Health System is closely affiliated with the Duke University Medical School as well as with the Duke University School of Nursing. The three entities are all located within the Duke University Medical Center complex (consisting of research educational and clinical care facilities on the Duke campus) also known as Duke Medical. The medical complex also includes the health system's Duke Clinic which provides outpatient and non-emergency specialist care.

Duke University Health System and the university's medical schools train health care professionals in cutting-edge technologies and infrastructures. The entities also work together to advance biomedical and general medical research with the goal of discovering and improving methods of care. Funding for medical research comes from the National Institutes of Health and other government organizations as well as from partnerships with pharmaceutical and medical device companies.

Geographic Reach
While Duke University Health System focuses on medical educational and research work in the US (in the states of North Carolina and Virginia) as part of its business the health system operates a joint venture in India.

Financial Performance
In 2014 revenues increased 2% to $4.9 billion mainly as a result of increases in patient service revenues tuition and fees and investment earnings. The system's net income rose 14% to $1.8 billion led by higher investment returns.

Cash flow from operations fell 90% to $12 million in 2014 due to an increase of cash used for accounts and contributions receivable and changes in inventories.

Strategy
Duke University Health System is working to expand further in existing and new territories and is looking to widen its service offerings in cancer vascular orthopedic musculoskeletal women and children's care and outpatient ambulatory care. To this end the health system is expanding by adding new medical locations and boosting its expertise in technology. For example in 2015 the Duke Eye Center opened a new four-story clinical pavilion. The system also aims to improve efficiencies across all locations and to help community members access needed services.

The company's DLP Healthcare joint venture with LifePoint Health provides management and cost-control services to community hospitals in North Carolina. Maria Parham Medical Center its first client is a small hospital looking for operational support in the face of health reform changes and rising competition in the marketplace. DLP Healthcare holds an 80% stake in the Maria Parham facility through the management agreement. An investment of $15 million in nearby Person Memorial Hospital will go to capital improvements help eliminate its debt and pave the way for DLP Healthcare to acquire the hospital.

Duke Medicine has a partnership with Medanta — The Medicity — through which the pair has established the Medanta Duke Research Institute (MDRI) in India to research medical treatments (drugs and devices). Medanta a 1500-bed institute will fund the creation and operation of the facility as part of the agreement with Duke providing scientific clinical research and operational expertise. Medanta and Duke share joint oversight over implementation and management of the unit.

EXECUTIVES

Cfo, Kenneth C. Morris
Evp, William J. Fulkerson
Vp Patient Care And System And Chief Nurse Executive, Mary Ann Fuchs
President Duke Regional Hospital, Katie Galbraith
President Private Diagnostic Clinic Pllc, Mark F. Newman
Chief Medical Officer, Thomas A. Owens
President Duke Raleigh Hospital, David Zaas
President And Ceo, A. Eugene Washington
Associate Vice President, Britt Crewse
Vice President, Philip Stern
Assistant Vice President Development And Alumni Affairs, Ellen Luken
Assistant Vice President Government Relations, Doug Heron
Vice President Business Development, Jennie Simpson
Chair, Thomas M. Gorrie
Vice Chair, Peter Van Etten
Auditors: KPMG LLP NORFOLK VA

LOCATIONS

HQ: DUKE UNIVERSITY HEALTH SYSTEM, INC.
2301 ERWIN RD, DURHAM, NC 277054699
Phone: 919 684-8111
Web: WWW.DUKE.EDU

Selected Facilities
Duke Clinic (Durham North Carolina)
Duke Raleigh Hospital (Raleigh North Carolina)
Duke University Hospital (Durham North Carolina)
  Duke Children's Hospital & Health Center
Durham Regional Hospital (Durham North Carolina)

PRODUCTS/OPERATIONS

2014 Sales

	$ mil.	% of total
Patient service	2,437	50
Grants & contracts	1,097	22
Tuition & fees	408	8
Investment return	384	8
Auxiliary enterprises	186	5
Contributions	92	4
Net assets released from restrictions	46	2
Other	228	1
Total	**4,882**	**100**

Selected Services

AIDS Research and Treatment Center (DART)
Anesthesiology
Aortic Disease
Asthma and Allergies
Attention Deficit Hyperactivity Disorder
Breast Cancer
Cardiac Rehabilitation
Children's Health
Coronary Artery Disease
Dermatology
Developmental and Behavioral Pediatrics
Diabetes
Diet & Fitness Center
Duke Heart Center
Duke Medicine
Ear Nose Throat Head & Neck Surgery
Eating Disorders
Endocrinology
Esophageal Cancer
Executive Health
Eye Center
Foot and Ankle
Gastroenterology
Gastrointestinal Cancer
General Orthopaedics
General and Consultative Heart Care
Geriatrics
Gynecologic Cancer
Gynecology
Health & Fitness Center
Health and Wellness
Healthy Lifestyles for Children
Heart Rhythm Services
Hematology
Hereditary Cancer
Hyperbaric Diving and Altitude Medicine
Infectious Diseases
Integrative Medicine
Knee Treatments
Leukemias Lymphomas and Myelomas
Lung Cancer
Men's Health
Neurological Disorders
Neuroscience
Obstetrics and Gynecology
Pain Disorders
Peripheral Vascular Disease
Prostate Cancer
Psychiatry
Pulmonology and Respiratory Medicine
Radiology
Research
Rheumatology and Immunology
Skin Cancer
Sleep Disorders
Smoking/Smoking Cessation
Speech and Audiology
Sports Medicine
Stroke Center
Transplants
Urologic Cancer
Valvular Heart Disease
Vascular Diseases
Women's Health
Women's Heart Care

COMPETITORS

Carolinas HealthCare System
Cone Health
Cumberland County Hospital System
Danville Regional Medical Center
FirstHealth of the Carolinas
Morehead Memorial Hospital
Novant Health
Rex Healthcare
Rowan Regional Medical Center
UNC Hospitals
Vidant Health
WakeMed
Wesley Long Community Hospital

HISTORICAL FINANCIALS

Company Type: Private

Income Statement

FYE: June 30

	REVENUE ($ mil.)	NET INCOME ($ mil.)	NET PROFIT MARGIN	EMPLOYEES
06/18	3,597	688	19.1%	2,400
06/16	3,160	(787)	—	—
06/13	2,539	516	20.4%	—
06/09	2,070	198	9.6%	—
Annual Growth	**6.3%**	**14.8%**		

2018 Year-End Financials

Return on assets: 11.1%
Return on equity: 19.0%
Current ratio: 2.80
Cash ($ mil.): 277

DUQUESNE LIGHT COMPANY

Duquesne Light is the first and last resort for light for many residential customers in the Keystone State. The utility company provides electricity to more than 588000 customers (90% of which are residential) in southwestern Pennsylvania via an extensive transmission and distribution system. The utility a subsidiary of Duquesne Light Holdings (formerly DQE) acts as a generation Provider of Last Resort (POLR) for customers who do not choose an alternative supplier. A consortium led by Macquarie Infrastructure Partners controls the company's parent.

Operations

The company has 212000 utility poles 103000 transformers and more than 45000 miles of overhead [pwer lines.

Geographic Reach

Duquesne Light provides electric service to customers in southwestern Pennsylvania including the city of Pittsburg in a service area that covers 817 square miles in Allegheny and Beaver counties.

Strategy

Duquesne Light which has been hurt by declining margins provided by its POLR service due to unrecovered payments to PJM Interconnection generators implemented a 2011-2013 POLR plan to yield more reliable returns taking advantage of favorable changes in Pennsylvania law regarding POLR costs and surcharges.

In an effort to improve reliability and public safety Duquesne Light has replaced 205 network transformers across its service region since 2002. In 2012 it replaced 29 of these network transformers and was working on replacing 42 more in 2013.

Company Background

The company was founded in 1880.

EXECUTIVES

Vice President Information Technology And Chief Information Officer, Mark S Miko
Vice President Communications And Corporate Citizenship, Jessica J Rock
Managing Director Engineering And Programs, John Hilderbrand

LOCATIONS

HQ: DUQUESNE LIGHT COMPANY
411 7TH AVE 6-1, PITTSBURGH, PA 152191942
Phone: 412 393-6000
Web: WWW.DUQUESNELIGHT.COM

COMPETITORS

Dominion Energy
Exelon
FirstEnergy
PPL Corporation

HISTORICAL FINANCIALS

Company Type: Private

Income Statement

FYE: December 31

	REVENUE ($ mil.)	NET INCOME ($ mil.)	NET PROFIT MARGIN	EMPLOYEES
12/18	938	152	16.2%	1,000
12/17	911	130	14.3%	—
12/16	903	118	13.1%	—
Annual Growth	**1.9%**	**13.2%**	**—**	**—**

2018 Year-End Financials

Return on assets: 4.3%
Return on equity: 11.8%
Current ratio: 0.90
Cash ($ mil.): 6

DUVAL COUNTY PUBLIC SCHOOLS

EXECUTIVES

Supt, John C Fryer Jr
Payroll Staff, Bobbie Johns
General Manager, Adora Davis
Technical Manager, Cathy S Maycott
Instructor, Amy Guth
Education Specialist, Darcey Gray
Buyer, Caleb Powell
Cashier, Anastasia Dixon
Supervisor, Beth Tramel
Teacher, Denisha Jordan
Maintenance Supervisor, Gus Coles

LOCATIONS

HQ: DUVAL COUNTY PUBLIC SCHOOLS
1701 PRUDENTIAL DR, JACKSONVILLE, FL 322078152
Phone: 904 390-2000
Web: WWW.DUVALSCHOOLS.ORG

HISTORICAL FINANCIALS

Company Type: Private

Income Statement

FYE: June 30

	REVENUE ($ mil.)	NET INCOME ($ mil.)	NET PROFIT MARGIN	EMPLOYEES
06/18	1,231	(7)	—	13,000
06/17	1,207	(25)	—	—
06/16	1,184	(63)	—	—
06/07	1,189	27	2.3%	—
Annual Growth	**0.3%**	**—**		

Return on assets: (-0.5%)   Cash ($ mil.): 75
Return on equity: (-1.9%)
Current ratio: —

DYNCORP INTERNATIONAL LLC

EXECUTIVES

Ceo, George Krivo
Coordinator, Jeff Angus
Director, Kathryn Van Vleck
Accounting Staff, Arthur Jordan
Management Vice-President, Richard Minor
Information Specialist, Jason Granger
Electrical Engineer, Erick McAfee
Administrator II, Marvin Lockhart
Senior Director, James Sagen
Human Resource Specialist, Nazeer Khan
Auditors: FRYE & COMPANY CPAS MANASSAS

LOCATIONS

HQ: DYNCORP INTERNATIONAL LLC
  1700 OLD MEADOW RD, MC LEAN, VA 221024302
Phone: 571 722-0210
Web: WWW.DYN-INTL.COM

HISTORICAL FINANCIALS

Company Type: Private

Income Statement				FYE: April 3
	REVENUE ($ mil.)	NET INCOME ($ mil.)	NET PROFIT MARGIN	EMPLOYEES
04/09*	3,101	69	2.2%	100
03/08	2,139	47	2.2%	—
Annual Growth	44.9%	45.5%	—	—

*Fiscal year change

2009 Year-End Financials

Return on assets: 4.5%   Cash ($ mil.): 200
Return on equity: 14.0%
Current ratio: 2.00

EAST TEXAS MEDICAL CENTER REGIONAL HEALTHCARE SYST

East Texas Medical Center (ETMC) Regional Healthcare System works to meet the health care needs of residents of the Piney Woods. The not-for-profit health system operates more than a dozen hospitals across eastern Texas along with behavioral rehabilitation and home health care businesses. Its flagship 450-bed Tyler location serves as the hub and referral center for satellite medical centers located in more rural locations. The system also runs numerous primary care and outpatient clinics throughout the region. Serving more than 300000 patients each year ETMC operates an emergency ambulance service subsidiary and a clinical laboratory which provide services to the ETMC Regional Healthcare System.

Operations

The flagship ETMC Tyler facility offers specialized care for cancer and cardiovascular and neurological conditions. It is a Level I regional trauma center and provides diagnostic and outpatient surgery services.

The system is organized so that primary care is provided in the rural health clinics. Secondary care is also provided locally in the ETMC affiliate hospitals. High-level secondary and tertiary care is provided at ETMC Tyler.

Geographic Reach

ETMC serves the more than 1 million people who reside in East Texas communities. It caters to nearly 20 Texas counties including Anderson Camp Cherokee Ellis Franklin Freestone Henderson Hopkins Houston Panola Red River Rusk Shelby Smith Trinity Upshur Van Zandt and Wood. These communities range in size from fewer than 500 residents to more than 50000.

Sales and Marketing

The Medicare program accounted for 50% of net patient revenues in 2012; Medicaid contributed 12% of the same. Some 16% of total net patient service revenue came from commercial insurance carriers and preferred provider organizations.

Financial Performance

Due to an increase in patient service revenue ETMC's revenue rose by 6% to $942 million in 2012 from $888 million in 2011. Net income for the same reporting period dropped some 92% to $1.1 million from $16 million due to rising salaries and wages and employee benefits expenses as well as from an increase in loss from defined benefit pension adjustment.

Strategy

To keep up with the needs of its residents the ETMC Regional Healthcare System works to expand its operations.

In 2013 ETMC Pittsburg broke ground on a 5000-sq.-ft. expansion of the hospital's surgery department. Its East Texas Medical Center Regional Healthcare System also added a pair of emergency transport helicopters valued at more than $9 million.

In 2012 the company completed $30-million expansion and renovation project at East Texas Medical Center Henderson including a new emergency department grand lobby and clinic space. It also wrapped up the second phase of an expansion project at ETMC Fairfield that involved adding a new entrance lobby clinic space cardiopulmonary rehabilitation facility and administrative suite.

Its 100-bed Henderson Memorial Hospital joined the network in 2009 as ETMC Henderson. Soon after becoming part of the network ETMC assisted its new affiliate with facility upgrades that included building new emergency department facilities renovating old rooms and installing new electrical and HVAC systems all completed in 2011. ETMC also expanded its Trinity facility with a 15-bed patient wing at the cost of $7.4 million and expanded its mammography services at ETMC Cedar Creek Lake. A $35 million ETMC Quitman facility is expected to be completed in 2013.

ETMC also concentrates on upgrading its information systems. The healthcare system's data exchange organization FirstNet Exchange received a grant from the state of Texas in 2011 to develop and operate a secure health information network to support hospitals and clinicians.

EXECUTIVES

Director Of Him, Christa Wyatt
Nursing Director, Maria Kulma
Medical Director, Richard Yates
Vice President Of Engineering, Robert Layton
Radiology Director, Bill Tobin

LOCATIONS

HQ: EAST TEXAS MEDICAL CENTER REGIONAL
  HEALTHCARE SYST
  1000 S BECKHAM AVE, TYLER, TX 757011908
Phone: 866 333-3862
Web: WWW.UTHEALTHEASTTEXAS.COM

PRODUCTS/OPERATIONS

Selected Health and Medical Services

Bariatric Surgery Center
Behavioral Health Center
Cancer Institute
Cardiovascular Institute
Digestive Disease Center
Emergency Services
Fitness Centers
Home Health
Neurological Institute
Orthopedic Institute
Plastic Surgery
Podiatry Care
Radiology and Imaging
Rehabilitation Center
Sleep Disorders Center
Specialty Hospital
Transplant Center
Urology Institute
Women's Health
Wound Healing Center

Selected East Texas Medical Center Hospitals

ETMC Athens
ETMC Carthage
ETMC Clarksville
ETMC Crockett
ETMC Fairfield
ETMC Gilmer
ETMC Henderson
ETMC Jacksonville
ETMC Lake Palestine
ETMC Mount Vernon
ETMC Pittsburg
ETMC Quitman
ETMC Rehabilitation Hospital (Tyler)
ETMC Specialty Hospital (Tyler)
ETMC Trinity
ETMC Tyler

COMPETITORS

Community Health
  Systems
Good Shepherd Health
  System
HCA
Hunt Memorial
  Memorial Health System
  of East Texas

Tenet Healthcare
Trinity Mother Frances
  Hospital and Clinics
Wadley Regional
  Medical Center
Woodland Heights
  Medical Center

HISTORICAL FINANCIALS

Company Type: Private

Income Statement				FYE: October 31
	REVENUE ($ mil.)	NET INCOME ($ mil.)	NET PROFIT MARGIN	EMPLOYEES
10/08	876	30	3.4%	7,600
10/07	827	40	4.8%	—
10/06	837	0	—	—
10/05	837	17	2.1%	—
Annual Growth	1.5%	20.4%	—	—

2008 Year-End Financials

Return on assets: 4.0%   Cash ($ mil.): 175
Return on equity: 11.1%
Current ratio: 3.20

EASTERN MAINE HEALTHCARE SYSTEMS

Eastern Maine Healthcare Systems (EMHS) keeps the folks in the Pine Tree State feeling fine. With more than a dozen member hospitals and multiple medical practices and clinics the organization offers patients emergency primary mental-health laboratory and other specialty services. It primarily serves eastern central and northern portions of rural Maine. Some hospitals include Eastern Maine Medical Center (410 beds) Acadia Hospital (100 beds) Aroostook Medical Center (75 beds) and Inland Hospital (50 beds). The system also operates long-term care hospice and home health facilities as well as emergency transportation and administrative services businesses.

Operations

Besides its Acadia Hospital Aroostook Medical Center Eastern Maine Medical Center and Inland Hospital EMHS operates three smaller community hospitals with 15 to 30 beds each: Blue Hill Memorial Hospital Charles A. Dean Memorial Hospital and Sebasticook Valley Hospital. The system has affiliations with the Houlton Regional Hospital and Millinocket Regional Hospital.

Subsidiaries of EMHS include Affiliated Healthcare Systems (medical communications and retirement ventures) Affiliated Laboratory (pathology services) Affiliated Material Services (medical supplies distribution and pharmacies) and Affiliated Healthcare Management (transcription and employee services).

As part of its operations EMHS also runs the Eastern Maine Medical Center Clinical Research Center which performs clinical studies in several medical disciplines and diseases including cancer hospital-acquired infections heart disease and physician best practices.

In fiscal 2014 EMHS had 105629 emergency room visits; 32964 inpatient and outpatient surgeries; 3017 births; and 388920 primary care visits.

The company's total Community Benefit that year was about $200 million and its philanthropy giving was nearly $3 million.

Geographic Reach

Despite its name Eastern Maine Healthcare System serves those in eastern central and northern portions of rural Maine.

Strategy

EMHS continues to work collaboratively at the national level looking at not only making a difference in healthcare in Maine but to be a change leader throughout the country. The Northern New England Accountable Care Collaborative is creating resources necessary to propel the reinvention of care model. In addition their work in the High Value Healthcare Collaborative (co-owned with Dartmouth MaineHealth and the University of Vermont Medical Center) this past year has been focused on sepsis care and prevention patient engagement and shared decision-making pilot projects.

In fiscal 2015 Maine's largest health insurer teamed up with Eastern Maine Healthcare Systems under a new venture aimed at keeping patients healthier while reducing costs. The deal involves Anthem Blue Cross and Blue Shield in Maine EMHS and an EMHS-led coalition of hospitals and physician practices across the state. EMHS and its partners have agreed to avoid any cost increase for services they deliver to 40000 Anthem policyholders.

In mid-2014 EMHS completed a community health needs assessment of the northern two-thirds of Maine including the counties of Aroostook Cumberland Hancock Kennebec Penobscot Piscataquis Somerset and Washington. This report was seen as foundational to the company achieving its mission of improving the health and well-being of the communities it serves.

Company Background

The system was established in 1982.

EXECUTIVES

Vice President Talent And Diversity Human Resources, Catherine Maclaren
Vice President Network Development And Aco Activity, Michael Donahue
Senior Vice President And Chief Transformation Officer, Richard Freeman
Vice President Of Organizational Effectiveness, Deborah Sanford
Vice President Of Finance Chief Finance, Elmer Doucette
Vice President, Scott Oxley
Medical Director, Jens Rueter
Department Head, Mikele Neal
Director Of Pharmacy, James Cattin
Medical Secretary, Chris Shaw
Board Member, Karen Marsters
Auditors: BERRY DUNN MCNEIL & PARKER LL

LOCATIONS

HQ: EASTERN MAINE HEALTHCARE SYSTEMS
43 WHITING HILL RD # 500, BREWER, ME 044121005
Phone: 207 973-7050
Web: WWW.NORTHERNLIGHTHEALTH.ORG

PRODUCTS/OPERATIONS

Selected Strategic Affiliates
Houlton Regional Hospital
Millinocket Regional Hospital
Member Hospitals
Acadia Hospital
Affiliated Healthcare Systems
Aroostook Medical Center
Beacon Health
Blue Hill Memorial Hospital
Charles A. Dean Memorial Hospital and Nursing Home
Dirigo Pines Retirement Community
Eastern Maine HomeCare
Eastern Maine Medical Center
Healthcare Charities
Inland Hospital
Rosscare
Sebasticook Valley Hospital

COMPETITORS

Franklin Community Health Network	Mercy Health System of Maine
Maine Coast Memorial Hospital	Miles Health Care
MaineGeneral Health	Millinocket Regional Hospital
MaineHealth	St. Joseph Healthcare

HISTORICAL FINANCIALS

Company Type: Private

Income Statement				FYE: September 30
	REVENUE ($ mil.)	NET INCOME ($ mil.)	NET PROFIT MARGIN	EMPLOYEES
09/18	1,672	8	0.5%	8,175
09/17	1,654	43	2.6%	—
09/16	1,523	21	1.4%	—
09/15	1,374	(1)	—	—
Annual Growth	6.7%	—	—	—

2018 Year-End Financials
Return on assets: 0.5%   Cash ($ mil.): 109
Return on equity: 1.1%
Current ratio: 1.90

EASTERN MAINE MEDICAL CENTER

EXECUTIVES

Ceo, Deborah C Johnson
V Pres-Cfo*, Elmer Doucette
V Pres*, John Doyle
Coor, Melissa Cadieux
Business Analyst, Karen Egan
Manager, Michelle Mayo
Information Technology/Interne, Darlene Bean
Health Professional, Resmi Rajan
Internal Medicine Practitioner, Chheki Sherpa
Internal Medicine Practitioner, Gayathri Thampatty
Surgeon, John Baxter
Auditors: BERRY DUNN MCNEIL & PARKER LL

LOCATIONS

HQ: EASTERN MAINE MEDICAL CENTER
489 STATE ST, BANGOR, ME 044016674
Phone: 207 973-7000
Web: WWW.NORTHERNLIGHTHEALTH.ORG

HISTORICAL FINANCIALS

Company Type: Private

Income Statement				FYE: September 24
	REVENUE ($ mil.)	NET INCOME ($ mil.)	NET PROFIT MARGIN	EMPLOYEES
09/16	776	23	3.0%	1,119
09/15	720	41	5.8%	—
09/13	646	56	8.8%	—
09/12	669	67	10.1%	—
Annual Growth	3.8%	(23.2%)	—	—

2016 Year-End Financials
Return on assets: 2.4%   Cash ($ mil.): 65
Return on equity: 5.6%
Current ratio: 2.20

EATON CORPORATION

EXECUTIVES

Chair-Ceo, Craig Arnold
Cfo, Richard Fearon
Exec V Pres, Mark McGuire
Sr V Pres-SEC, Thomas Moran
Sr V Pres-Contrl, Billie Rawot
Sr V Pres Corp Devt & Treas, David Foster
Senior Engineer, Fred James
Manager, Gordon Harmon
Sales Manager, Jim Lago
Executive Officer, Matt Greene
Coordinator, Sandy Benzin
Auditors: ERNST & YOUNG LLP CLEVELAND

LOCATIONS

HQ: EATON CORPORATION
1000 EATON BLVD, CLEVELAND, OH 441226058
Phone: 440 523-5000
Web: WWW.EATON.COM

Income Statement				FYE: December 31
	REVENUE ($ mil.)	NET INCOME ($ mil.)	NET PROFIT MARGIN	EMPLOYEES
12/15	6,925	821	11.9%	736
12/14	6,990	170	2.4%	
Annual Growth	(0.9%)	382.9%	—	—

EDUCATIONAL TESTING SERVICE INC

Please completely fill in each circle on the answer sheet as prepared by Educational Testing Service (ETS). ETS develops and administers the Graduate Record Examinations (GRE) and Test of English as a Foreign Language (TOEFL). The not-for-profit group develops and administers more than 50 million achievement admissions academic and professional tests a year at some 9000 locations in more than 180 countries. It also develops assessment programs for corporations professional associations and state entities. ETS' research unit conducts education-focused analysis and policy studies; test-development firm Prometric is a for-profit subsidiary.

Operations

ETS' K-12 products include Advanced Placement (AP) exams and tests to meet individual state standards. Teachers are not forgotten — the company also develops and administers the Praxis Series assessments for teacher licensing and certifications. For college-bound scholars ETS supports The College Board's Scholastic Assessment Test (SAT) and the College Level Examination Program (CLEP).

More than 3300 employees work at ETS's offices worldwide. Of these more than 2300 of its professional staff have training and expertise in education psychology statistics psychometrics computer sciences sociology and the humanities. Almost 1000 have advanced degrees and 390 hold doctorates. Some 1150 employees support ETS's wholly owned subsidiary Prometric.

Its Computerized Assessments and Learning subsidiary is a computerized assessment company based in Lawrence Kansas. Edusoft Ltd. a foreign subsidiary is a global leader in technology-based comprehensive English Language Learning solutions serving a range of educational government and corporate sectors worldwide.

Prometric a global leader in technology-enabled testing and assessment services provides test development test delivery and data management capabilities to 500 clients in the academic professional government corporate and information technology markets via the web or by utilizing a robust test center network in 135 countries.

ETS Global the international arm of ETS brings expertise to educational and business communities around the world such as companies language schools academic institutions and public service organizations.

Geographic Reach

ETS serves US customers from offices in California Florida New Jersey Pennsylvania Puerto Rico Washington State and Washington DC. In addition ETS has direct operating subsidiaries in Canada China Korea and other countries in Latin America Asia Europe the Middle East and Africa; these offices provide services to customers in about 80 countries.

Strategy

In addition to launching new graduate and college-preparation tests and online support programs of its own ETS teams with partners such as Pearson SchoolNet and the Kansas State Department of Education to develop new products such as online tutorials assessment tests for elementary and secondary-education students and teacher leadership assessments. ETS is also increasing security measures to ensure that test takers' identities are properly verified such as a voice recognition system.

ETS also works to increase the market share of its existing products. For instance ETS has been steadily nudging its way into the niche previously dominated by the Graduate Management Admission Council — which administers the GMAT for students heading to graduate business schools — by convincing a growing number of business schools that its GRE General Test is a valuable instrument and to accept the test for admissions.

In 2014 ETS launched the 2015 TOEFL Scholarship Program in India. ETS will award a total of US$70000 in TOEFL scholarships to exceptional students in India who have proven their academic excellence.

Mergers and Acquisitions

In early 2017 ETS agreed to buy K-12 testing services firm Questar Assessment for $127.5 million. Questar specializes in state tests for third to eighth grades; its Nextera assessment platform combines content management student-test interface and image-based hand-scoring abilities.

Company Background

In 2011 the company opened several new customer support centers to support international customers seeking to take the TOEFL test.

The company bulked up its testing technology in early 2011 with the acquisition of Computerized Assessments and Learning (CAL). Operating as a subsidiary of ETS CAL offers assessment products for K-12 education systems.

To move beyond assessment and into actual education ETS acquired Edusoft an English language learning firm in 2011. The 2011 acquisition brought in Edusoft's English Discoveries Online product used around the world. The online product is designed to accompany and support classroom instruction with courses for general and technical English language instruction. Edusoft operates as a for-profit subsidiary.

ETS was founded in 1947.

EXECUTIVES

Svp And President Institute For Student Achievement (isa), Gerry House
Svp And Chief Administrative Officer, Yvette Donado
Vp Higher Education, Walt MacDonald
Svp And Cfo, Jack Hayon
Svp Strategy Marketing And Growth And Chief Marketing Officer, Scott Nelson
Svp Global Education And Workforce, David Hunt
Vice President Of Education, William Seibert
Senior Vice President And General Manager, Nancy Segal
Associate Vice President Research And Technology Transfer, Marissa Farnum
Vice President, Ida Lawrence
Vice President Administration, Bruce Gilbertson
Vice President Of Training, Jane Borden
Vice President, Anne Rockey
Vice President Of Research, Joanna Gorin
Senior Strategic Advisor To The Vice President And Chief Operating Officer Of Global Education, Alberto Acereda
Manager Government Relations, Polina Levit
Vice President And Chief Learning Officer, Tj Elliott
Auditors: DELOITTE & TOUCHE LLP

LOCATIONS

HQ: EDUCATIONAL TESTING SERVICE INC
   660 ROSEDALE RD, PRINCETON, NJ 085402218
Phone: 609 921-9000
Web: WWW.ETS.ORG

PRODUCTS/OPERATIONS

Selected Testing Programs
Advanced Placement (AP)
Algebra end of course assessment (EOC)
California High School Exit Examination (CAHSEE)
California State University Placement Test (EPT/ELM)
College-Level Examination Program (CLEP)
ETS Literacy
ETS Proficiency Profile
EXADEP
Graduate Record Examinations (GRE)
High Schools That Work Assessment
iSkills Assessment
Major Field Tests (MFT)
Middle Grades Assessment (MGA)
National Assessment of Educational Progress (NAEP)
ParaPro Assessment
The Praxis Series: Professional Assessments for Beginning Teachers
Preliminary SAT/National Merit Scholarship Qualifying Test (PSAT/NMSQT)
Scholastic Aptitude Test (SAT)
School Leaders Licensure Assessment (SLLA)
School Leadership Series (SLS)
School Superintendent Assessment (SSA)
Secondary Level English Proficiency Test (SLEP)
Test Link Test Collection
TFI Test
Test of English as a Foreign Language (TOEFL)
Test of English for International Communication (TOEIC)

Selected Acquisitions

COMPETITORS

ACT Inc.	S&P Global
Houghton Mifflin	Scantron
Harcourt	The Princeton Review
Kaplan	University of Iowa
Questar Assessment	

HISTORICAL FINANCIALS
Company Type: Private

Income Statement				FYE: September 30
	REVENUE ($ mil.)	NET INCOME ($ mil.)	NET PROFIT MARGIN	EMPLOYEES
09/18	1,392	686	49.3%	2,756
09/17	1,398	53	3.8%	—
09/16	1,592	73	4.6%	—
Annual Growth	(6.5%)	204.6%	—	—

2018 Year-End Financials

Return on assets: 33.1%	Cash ($ mil.): 225
Return on equity: 45.1%	
Current ratio: 1.30	

EDWARD HOSPITAL

EXECUTIVES

System Ceo, Pamela Davis
System Evp-Cfo*, William Devoney
System Vp-Physician Ambulatory*, Bill Kottman
Vice Pres-Facilities*, Gary Mielak

System Evp-Gen Counsel*, Chris Mollet
Exec V Pres*, Vince Pryor
V Pres*, Barbara Byrne
V Pres*, Patti Ludwig-Beymer
System Evp-Hr*, Susan Mitchell
System Vp-CIO*, Bobbie Byrne
System Vp-Cmo*, Brian Davis

LOCATIONS

HQ: EDWARD HOSPITAL
  801 S WASHINGTON ST, NAPERVILLE, IL 605407499
Phone: 630 355-0450
Web: WWW.EEHEALTH.ORG

HISTORICAL FINANCIALS

Company Type: Private

Income Statement				FYE: June 30
	REVENUE ($ mil.)	**NET INCOME** ($ mil.)	**NET PROFIT MARGIN**	**EMPLOYEES**
06/16	592	2	0.5%	4,700
06/15	567	39	7.0%	—
06/14	615	106	17.2%	—
06/13	517	52	10.1%	—
Annual Growth	4.6%	(62.8%)	—	—

EDWARD-ELMHURST HEALTHCARE

EXECUTIVES

Pres*, Pamela Meyer-Davis
Exec V Pres*, Chris Mollet
Exec V Pres*, Susan Mitchell
V Pres*, Bobbie Byrne
Cfo*, Vince Pryor
Vice President-Facilities, Gary Mielak
Neurology, Henry C Echiverri
Information Technology Project, Laura Georges
Director, Glenn Nelson
Family Medicine, Debarati Bose
BSN, Donna Preisler
Auditors: CROWE HORWATH LLP CHICAGO IL

LOCATIONS

HQ: EDWARD-ELMHURST HEALTHCARE
  801 S WASHINGTON ST, NAPERVILLE, IL 605407430
Phone: 630 355-0450
Web: WWW.EEHEALTH.ORG

HISTORICAL FINANCIALS

Company Type: Private

Income Statement				FYE: June 30
	REVENUE ($ mil.)	**NET INCOME** ($ mil.)	**NET PROFIT MARGIN**	**EMPLOYEES**
06/18	1,474	119	8.1%	6,500
06/17	1,372	105	7.7%	—
06/15	75	5	7.3%	—
06/10	62	11	18.6%	—
Annual Growth	48.4%	33.8%	—	—

2018 Year-End Financials

Return on assets: 5.0%   Cash ($ mil.): 55
Return on equity: 10.7%
Current ratio: 0.60

EL PASO COUNTY HOSPITAL DISTRICT

University Medical Center is a community not-for-profit health care system serving West Texas and southern New Mexico. The networkÂ includes the 330-bed University Medical Center of El Paso (formerly also known asÂ Thomason General Hospital) several neighborhood primary care clinics and the El Paso First Health Plans HMO.Â The hospitalÂ is an acute-care teaching hospital affiliated with Texas Tech. It specializes in emergency/trauma care obstetrics pediatric medicine and orthopedics. The hospital district through its affiliates provides a range of outpatient services including physical rehabilitation speech therapy family planning dental care cancer treatment diagnostics and pharmacy services.

Company Background

University Medical Center of El Paso openedÂ in 1915. The hospital was rebranded under the University Medical Center name in 2009 when Texas Tech opened a full four-year medical school on the Thomason General campus.

EXECUTIVES

Medical Records Director, Monica Blancas
Secretary Of Medical Executive Committee, Pedro Serrato
Auditors: BKD LLP DALLAS TEXAS

LOCATIONS

HQ: EL PASO COUNTY HOSPITAL DISTRICT
  4815 ALAMEDA AVE, EL PASO, TX 799052705
Phone: 915 544-1200
Web: WWW.UMCELPASO.ORG

PRODUCTS/OPERATIONS

Selected Services
After Hours Pediatrics
Aquatic Therapy
Cardiac Cath
CAT Scan
Case Management
Dental Clinic
Diabetes Management
Diagnostic Radiology
Echocardiograms
Electrocardiograms
Emergency Department
Endoscopy/Special Procedures
Family Planning
Infusion Center
Interventional Radiology
Laboratory Services
Labor and Delivery
Laparoscopic Surgery
Lithotripsy
Mammography
Medical Unit
Mother/Baby Unit
MRI
Neonatal Intensive Care
Neonatal Intermediate Care
Neonatal Continuing Care
Newborn Nursery
Neurosurgery
Nuclear Medicine
Nutritional Care
Occupational Health
Occupational Therapy
Patient Financial Services
Pediatric Unit
Pediatric Rehabilitation
Pharmacy
Physical Therapy
Poison Control Center
Prenatal Services
Primary Care Clinics
Public Affairs
Rehabilitative Services
Respiratory Services
Special Care Nurseries
Speech Therapy
Surgical Services
Surgical Unit
Telemetry Unit
Trauma - Level 1
Ultrasound
West Texas Regional Poison Control Center
Wound Care

COMPETITORS

Covenant Health System   Tenet Healthcare
  Del Sol Medical Center   Texas Health Resources
  Encompass Health

HISTORICAL FINANCIALS

Company Type: Private

Income Statement				FYE: September 30
	REVENUE ($ mil.)	**NET INCOME** ($ mil.)	**NET PROFIT MARGIN**	**EMPLOYEES**
09/18	599	(31)	—	1,898
09/16	578	0	0.1%	—
09/15	177	(2)	—	—
09/14	361	(66)	—	—
Annual Growth	13.4%			

2018 Year-End Financials

Return on assets: (-4.9%)   Cash ($ mil.): 33
Return on equity: (-29.8%)
Current ratio: 0.90

EL PASO INDEPENDENT SCHOOL DISTRICT EDUCATION FOUNDATION

EXECUTIVES

Spdt, Juan Cabrera
Superintendent, Tippin Message
Auditors: GIBSON RUDDOCK PATTERSON LLC

LOCATIONS

HQ: EL PASO INDEPENDENT SCHOOL DISTRICT EDUCATION FOUNDATION
  6531 BOEING DR, EL PASO, TX 799251008
Phone: 915 230-2000
Web: WWW.EPISD.ORG

HISTORICAL FINANCIALS

Company Type: Private

Income Statement				FYE: June 30
	REVENUE ($ mil.)	**NET INCOME** ($ mil.)	**NET PROFIT MARGIN**	**EMPLOYEES**
06/18	625	(34)	—	9,000
06/17	621	188	30.3%	—
06/16	651	2	0.4%	—
06/15	620	(13)	—	—
Annual Growth	0.3%			

2018 Year-End Financials
Return on assets: (-3.1%)   Cash ($ mil.): 347
Return on equity: —
Current ratio: —

EL PASO NATURAL GAS COMPANY, L.L.C.

EXECUTIVES

Pres-Ceo, James J Cleary
Exec V Pres-Cfo, John R Sult
V Pres-Controller-Cao, Rosa P Jackson
Technician, Jesse Watkins
Engineer Senior, Sule Amadu

LOCATIONS

HQ: EL PASO NATURAL GAS COMPANY, L.L.C.
1001 LOUISIANA ST, HOUSTON, TX 770025089
Phone: 713 420-2600
Web: WWW.KINDERMORGAN.COM

HISTORICAL FINANCIALS

Company Type: Private

Income Statement				FYE: December 31
	REVENUE ($ mil.)	NET INCOME ($ mil.)	NET PROFIT MARGIN	EMPLOYEES
12/17	648	141	21.8%	525
12/16	627	128	20.5%	
/ 0	0	0	—	—
Annual Growth	—	—	—	—

ELECTRIC POWER BOARD OF CHATTANOOGA

Pardon me .... is that the Electric Power Board (EPB) of Chattanoogó EPB keeps on choo-chooin' along by providing electricity to more than 167410 residents and businesses. The utility (a non-profit agency of the City of Chattanooga) distributes energy in a 600 sq.-ml. area that includes greater Chattanooga as well as parts of surrounding counties in Georgia and Tennessee. It gets its wholesale power supply from the Tennessee Valley Authority. EPB also provides telecommunications (telephone and Internet) services to area homes and businesses through its EPB Fiber Optics unit.

Operations

In addition to its electric distribution business the company's all-fiber Internet product gives 50000 businesses and residences access to up to 500 Mbps of bandwidth a capacity 300 times faster than standard DSL cable or T1 connections. This service gives all EFB customers internet bandwidth capacity and service on a par with or superior to that offered in Atlanta Chicago and Los Angeles.

Geographic Reach

EPB serves greater Chattanooga and parts of surrounding counties (Bledsoe Bradley Marion Rhea and Sequatchie) and North Georgia (parts of Catoosa Dade and Walker counties).

Financial Performance

The company saw its operating revenues rise by 1% in 2013 thanks to an increase of $12.4 million in Fiber Optics residential services sales.

Strategy

EFB is pushing technological innovation and the modernization of its systems as a way to increase value and efficiency.

To help reduce power outages in 2013 the company added 200 smart switches to its 46 Kv system (in addition to its 1200 smart swtiches on the 12kV system already in place.

Company Background

During 2009 the company received a $111 million federal stimulus grant to build and operate a Smart Grid (an automated electric system with communication capabilities to help improve response time reduce outages cut down on theft and help clients take charge of their own power use). In 2012 EFB completed the installation of the 1170 IntelliRupterÂ® PulseCloser (smart switches) making EPB's Smart Grid the most automated system of its size in the US.

The utility was established in 1935 to provide electric power to the people of the greater Chattanooga area.

EXECUTIVES

Vice President Information Technology, David Johnson
Vice President Of Strategic Research, Jim Ingraham
Vice President Legal Services, Aaron Webb
Vice President Economic Developmentandgov.rel., Diana Bullock
Vice President Human Resources, Marie Webb
Vice President Marketing, Jed Marston
Vice President Finance And Controller, Michael Kaiser
Executive Board Member, Steve Dover
Board Of Directors, Jon Kinsey
Auditors: MAULDIN & JENKINS LLC CHATTA

LOCATIONS

HQ: ELECTRIC POWER BOARD OF CHATTANOOGA
10 W MARTIN LUTHER KING B, CHATTANOOGA, TN 374021813
Phone: 423 756-2706
Web: WWW.EPB.COM

PRODUCTS/OPERATIONS

2013 Sales

	% of total
Electric	86
Fiber Optics	12
Other	2
Total	**100**

COMPETITORS

AT&T	Southern Company Gas
Constellation Energy Group	

HISTORICAL FINANCIALS

Company Type: Private

Income Statement				FYE: June 30
	REVENUE ($ mil.)	NET INCOME ($ mil.)	NET PROFIT MARGIN	EMPLOYEES
06/18	729	43	6.0%	400
06/17	716	35	4.9%	
06/16	683	32	4.7%	
06/15	671	17	2.6%	
Annual Growth	2.8%	36.7%	—	—

2018 Year-End Financials
Return on assets: 4.9%   Cash ($ mil.): 105
Return on equity: 10.5%
Current ratio: 1.30

ELEMENT14 US HOLDINGS INC

EXECUTIVES

Pres, Ralf Buehler
Vp, Gen Counsel and Secretary, Joseph R Daprile
Treasurer and Assistant Secret, Paul M Barlak

LOCATIONS

HQ: ELEMENT14 US HOLDINGS INC
4180 HIGHLANDER PKWY, RICHFIELD, OH 442869352
Phone: 330 523-4280
Web: WWW.PREMIERFARNELL.COM

HISTORICAL FINANCIALS

Company Type: Private

Income Statement				FYE: February 1
	REVENUE ($ mil.)	NET INCOME ($ mil.)	NET PROFIT MARGIN	EMPLOYEES
02/16	598	9	1.6%	1,043
02/15	717	48	6.7%	—
02/14	698	35	5.1%	—
Annual Growth	(7.5%)	(48.4%)	—	—

2016 Year-End Financials

Return on assets: 3.0%   Cash ($ mil.): 70
Return on equity: 4.2%
Current ratio: 6.40

ELLIOT HEALTH SYSTEM

EXECUTIVES

Ceo, Doug Dean
Coo*, Joseph Tate Curti
Human Resources, Paul Carter
Physical Medicine Specialist, Jill Mack
Administrative Assistant, Joann Walsh
Analyst, Bob Blanchette
Benefits Administrator, Joanna Block
Assistant Business Manager, Mary Guarino
Information Technology, Benjamin Tasker
Benefits Administrator, Erica Raiche
Accounts Receivable Coordinato, Jenny Kane

LOCATIONS

HQ: ELLIOT HEALTH SYSTEM
1 ELLIOT WAY, MANCHESTER, NH 031033502
Phone: 603 663-1600
Web: WWW.ELLIOTHOSPITAL.ORG

HISTORICAL FINANCIALS

Company Type: Private

Income Statement				FYE: June 30
	REVENUE ($ mil.)	NET INCOME ($ mil.)	NET PROFIT MARGIN	EMPLOYEES
06/18	556	9	1.6%	3,400
06/17	544	20	3.7%	—
06/08	0	0	4.0%	—
Annual Growth	96.8%	79.8%	—	—

2018 Year-End Financials

Return on assets: 1.6%   Cash ($ mil.): 76
Return on equity: 4.3%
Current ratio: 1.1

EMJ CORPORATION

EMJ does it all for the mall. Founded in 1968 by namesake Edgar M. Jolley the company specializes in building and renovating retail outlets and shopping centers throughout the US. It is also known for other building projects such as offices warehouses churches hotels multifamily residences hospitals and wind farms. Working from five offices nationwide EMJ provides general construction and construction management. The company's pre-construction services include creating detailed budgets and construction schedules and coordinating permitting utility companies and municipal requirements. To track a project's progress and monitor costs EMJ offers quality control and safety and warranty management.

Operations

EMJ owns several operating divisions including Signal Energy which engineers and builds renewable energy projects such as wind farms and solar and biomass energy projects. Another division Accent Construction Management provides site selection budgeting scheduling and other services. Its RedStone Construction Services builds commercial retail hospitality healthcare government facilities and others. It is focused on fostering economic growth in Native American communities.

Geographic Reach

From its base in Chattanooga Tennessee EMJ serves clients through a handful of US offices in Massachusetts Tennessee Texas and California.

Sales and Marketing

EMJ has built more than 500 million sq. ft. of construction projects. Its client roster includes Academy Barnes & Noble Bed Bath & Beyond Blue Cross and Blue Shield Home Depot PetSmart and Winn-Dixie.

The company serves several sectors such as airports education entertainment government and civic grocery healthcare hospitality industrial and warehouse and Native American tribal communities office buildings parking lifestyle and mixed use development retail renewable energy renovations and worship centers.

Strategy

The company is working on projects for Whole Foods Market TownPlace Suites Silverdale Baptist student center and Dick's Sporting Goods. Inked in 2013 EMJ's $250-million deal with Native American Chris Samples operating under the name RedStone Construction Services is building a 500-room hotel and expanding a casino in Tulsa Oklahoma.

EXECUTIVES

Vice President, Christopher Hall

Executive Vice President, Ray Catlin
Senior Vice President Of Construction, Jack Bowen
Vice President, Lance Gopffarth
Senior Vice President Of Construction, Philip Augustino
Vice President Southwest Office, Drew Halsey
Senior Vice President, Chas Torrence
Vice President Of Construction, Howard Smith
Vice President Of Construction, George Heath

LOCATIONS

HQ: EMJ CORPORATION
2034 HAMILTON PLACE BLVD # 400,
CHATTANOOGA, TN 374216102
Phone: 423 855-1550
Web: WWW.EMJCORP.COM

PRODUCTS/OPERATIONS

Selected Projects

Airports

Education

Entertainment

Government/civic

Grocery

Healthcare

Hospitality

Industrial/warehouse
Lifestyle/mixed use development and retail
Native American tribal communities
Office buildings
Parking
Renewable energy
Renovations
Worship centers

Selected Services
Construction
Construction management
General contracting
Pre-construction services
Quality control
Safety consultation
Site evaluation
Warranty

COMPETITORS

Case Contracting	Hoar Construction
Embree Construction	JESCO
Fisher Development	Rodgers Builders
Graycor	S.D. Deacon
Hardaway Construction	Skanska USA Building
Hardin Construction	Weis Builders
Hayward Baker	Workman Commercial

HISTORICAL FINANCIALS

Company Type: Private

Income Statement				FYE: March 7
	REVENUE ($ mil.)	NET INCOME ($ mil.)	NET PROFIT MARGIN	EMPLOYEES
03/17*	960	4	0.5%	210
12/11	437	0	0.1%	—
12/08	821	7	1.0%	—
12/07	959	10	1.1%	—
Annual Growth	0.0%	(7.9%)	—	—
*Fiscal year change				

2017 Year-End Financials

Return on assets: 2.3%   Cash ($ mil.): 29
Return on equity: 18.5%
Current ratio: 1.10

EMORY UNIVERSITY HOSPITAL MIDTOWN

EXECUTIVES

Ceo, Robert J Bachman
Dir*, Rosalind K Lett
Pres*, John T Fox
Exec V Pres*, S Wright Caughman
Attorney, Lorraine Spencer
Chief of Medicine, Harold Ramos
Director, Jakob V Johansen
Assistant Professor, James Weisberg
Coordinator, Crystal Evans
Otolaryngologist, Sarah Wise
Cardiovascular Disease, Alexis G Cutchins

LOCATIONS

HQ: EMORY UNIVERSITY HOSPITAL MIDTOWN
550 PEACHTREE ST NE, ATLANTA, GA 303082212
Phone: 404 686-4411
Web: WWW.EMORYHEALTHCARE.ORG

HISTORICAL FINANCIALS

Company Type: Private

Income Statement				FYE: August 31
	REVENUE ($ mil.)	NET INCOME ($ mil.)	NET PROFIT MARGIN	EMPLOYEES
08/16	735	64	8.7%	2,500
08/15	641	(21)	—	—
Annual Growth	14.8%	—	—	—

2016 Year-End Financials

Return on assets: 9.9%   Cash ($ mil.): 269
Return on equity: 38.5%
Current ratio: 2.50

EMPIRE RESOURCES, INC.

When it comes to aluminum Empire Resources is especially resourceful. The company distributes semi-finished aluminum products including sheet foil wire plate and coil. Products are sold primarily to manufacturers of appliances automobiles packaging and housing materials. Empire Resources provides a variety of related services including sourcing of aluminum products storage and delivery and handling foreign exchange transactions. Company president and CEO Nathan Kahn and CFO Sandra Kahn who are husband and wife own some 40% of Empire Resources.

EXECUTIVES

Vice President, Ginette Raymond
Auditors: EISNERAMPER LLP NEW YORK NEW

LOCATIONS

HQ: EMPIRE RESOURCES, INC.
2115 LINWOOD AVE STE 200, FORT LEE, NJ 070245022
Phone: 201 944-2200
Web: WWW.EMPIRERESOURCES.COM

PRODUCTS/OPERATIONS

Selected Aluminum Products
Circles
Coil/sheet
Foil
Plate
Profiles/extruded products
Treadplate

COMPETITORS

Arconic	Ryerson
Commercial Metals	SASA
Rio Tinto Alcan	

HISTORICAL FINANCIALS

Company Type: Private

Income Statement				FYE: December 31
	REVENUE ($ mil.)	**NET INCOME** ($ mil.)	**NET PROFIT MARGIN**	**EMPLOYEES**
12/16	458	3	0.7%	60
12/15	521	2	0.5%	—
12/14	582	3	0.6%	—
12/13	482	2	0.5%	—
Annual Growth	(1.7%)	11.3%	—	—

2016 Year-End Financials
Return on assets: 1.6%   Cash ($ mil.): 4
Return on equity: 6.6%
Current ratio: 1.30

EMPIRE SOUTHWEST, LLC

With CAT-like tread Empire Southwest has created a heavy equipment sales rental and leasing empire in the US Southwest. One of the largest Caterpillar dealerships in the US Empire Southwest operates through five divisions: hydraulic service machinery power systems precision machining and transport. The company's equipment includes backhoes compactors dozers front shovels loaders pipelayers telehandlers and tractors. It also handles equipment used for mining and forestry projects. Empire Southwest also sells ARCO agricultural equipment carries batteries power generators engines and tools and has a service department.

Operations
Empire Southwest consists of five operating divisions. Empire Machinery sells rents and provides product support for Caterpillar equipment and other brands. Empire Power Systems sells rents and provides product support for the Caterpillar engines used to provide power for electricity generation water pumping and other industrial applications.

Empire Transport hauls heavy equipment and other oversize loads for customers and other Empire divisions while Empire Precision Machining is a large machining shop that can handle massive components. Empire Hydraulic Service specializes in repairing and refurbishing all brands of heavy equipment hydraulic systems.

Geographic Reach
Since moving to the Southwest Empire has carved out a territory that includes more than 30 communities in Arizona southeastern California and portions of northern Mexico.

Sales and Marketing
The company targets the agriculture mining demo and scrap oil and gas forestry on-highway truck general construction heavy construction railway power marine and waste management industries.

Company Background
The company was founded in 1950 when Jack Whiteman acquired Empire Machinery (which held the Caterpillar and John Deere dealerships in eastern Oregon). In 1959 he relocated to Arizona and took over a Caterpillar dealership there.

EXECUTIVES

President And Ceo, Jeffrey S. (Jeff) Whiteman
Executive Vice President, Chris Zaharis
Vice President, Jim Smith

LOCATIONS

HQ: EMPIRE SOUTHWEST, LLC
 1725 S COUNTRY CLUB DR, MESA, AZ 852106099
Phone: 480 633-4000

PRODUCTS/OPERATIONS

Selected Industries Served

Agriculture
Demo and Scrap
Forestry
General Construction
Governmental
Heavy Construction
Landscaping
Marine
Mining
Oil and Gas
On-Highway Truck
Paving
Pipeline
Quarry and Aggregates
Waste

COMPETITORS

Arnold Machinery	Multiquip
Cashman Equipment	NES Rentals
Cummins	Sunbelt Rentals
Komatsu	United Rentals
Komatsu America	

HISTORICAL FINANCIALS

Company Type: Private

Income Statement				FYE: October 31
	REVENUE ($ mil.)	**NET INCOME** ($ mil.)	**NET PROFIT MARGIN**	**EMPLOYEES**
10/11	683	38	5.6%	1,450
10/10	528	22	4.3%	—
10/09	448	7	1.6%	—
Annual Growth	23.5%	127.0%	—	—

EMPLOYERS RESOURCE MANAGEMENT COMPANY

EXECUTIVES

Chb-Ceo, George H Gersema
Pres*, Ray O'Leary
V Pres*, Douglas W Gersema

Exec V Pres*, Mary D Gersema
Sales Underwriting Manager, Bob Henbest
Information Technology Manager, David Collette
Corporate Administrative Assis, Michael Norris
Auditors: EIDE BAILLY LLP BOISE IDAHO

LOCATIONS

HQ: EMPLOYERS RESOURCE MANAGEMENT COMPANY
 1301 S VISTA AVE STE 200, BOISE, ID 837052576
Phone: 208 376-3000
Web: WWW.EMPLOYERSRESOURCE.COM

HISTORICAL FINANCIALS

Company Type: Private

Income Statement				FYE: June 30
	REVENUE ($ mil.)	**NET INCOME** ($ mil.)	**NET PROFIT MARGIN**	**EMPLOYEES**
06/17	515	0	0.1%	95
06/16	489	0	0.1%	—
06/14	456	0	0.1%	—
06/11	357	0	0.1%	—
Annual Growth	6.3%	19.3%	—	—

2017 Year-End Financials
Return on assets: 2.1%   Cash ($ mil.): 10
Return on equity: 12.9%
Current ratio: 1.10

ENABLE GAS TRANSMISSION, LLC

EXECUTIVES

MBR, David McClanahan
MBR*, Gregory Harper
MBR*, Peter Kirsch
MBR*, Marc Kilbride
Senior Manager, Don McMahon
Director, Amrish Patel
Director, Avik Sarkar
Senior Manager Change Manageme, Christy Cowden
Senior Manager, Dan Patino
Lead Oq Compliance Program Man, Jeffrey Avery
I, Alan Purvis

LOCATIONS

HQ: ENABLE GAS TRANSMISSION, LLC
 1111 LOUISIANA ST, HOUSTON, TX 770025230
Phone: 405 525-7788
Web: WWW.CENTERPOINTENERGY.COM

HISTORICAL FINANCIALS

Company Type: Private

Income Statement				FYE: December 31
	REVENUE ($ mil.)	**NET INCOME** ($ mil.)	**NET PROFIT MARGIN**	**EMPLOYEES**
12/16	483	100	20.9%	310
12/02	232	53	23.1%	—
/	0	0	—	—
Annual Growth	—	—	—	—

ENTERGY OPERATIONS, INC.

EXECUTIVES

Pres, Jeff S Forbes
V Pres, Wanda C Curry
V Pres, Clifford Eubanks
SEC, Daniel T Falstad
Supervisor, Deepak RAO
Senior Engineer, Eric Lewis
Senior Engineer, Samuel Hedgepeth
Controller, Beth Spivey
Information Technology Team ME, Garry Brown
Executive, Harold Keiser
Components Manager, Linda Patterson

LOCATIONS

HQ: ENTERGY OPERATIONS, INC.
 1340 ECHELON PKWY STE 100, JACKSON, MS
 392138210
Phone: 601 366-2727
Web: WWW.ENTERGY.COM

HISTORICAL FINANCIALS
Company Type: Private

Income Statement				FYE: December 31
	REVENUE ($ mil.)	NET INCOME ($ mil.)	NET PROFIT MARGIN	EMPLOYEES
12/16	473	0	—	3,600
12/02	20	0	—	—
12/01	19	0	—	—
12/00	701	159	22.8%	—
Annual Growth	(2.4%)	—	—	—

2016 Year-End Financials
Return on assets: —   Cash ($ mil.): 27
Return on equity: —
Current ratio: 0.70

ENTERGY SERVICES, INC.

EXECUTIVES

Ceo, Leo P Denault
Cfo*, Andrew Marsh
Coo*, Mark T Savoff
Pres*, Theo Bunting Jr
Exec Pres*, Marcus V Brown
V Pres*, Kimberly H Despeaux
V Pres*, Jere M Ahrens
V Pres*, Kay K Arnold
V Pres*, Michael A Balduzzi
V Pres*, Kelle J Barfield
Director, Cory Gruntz

LOCATIONS

HQ: ENTERGY SERVICES, INC.
 639 LOYOLA AVE STE 300, NEW ORLEANS, LA
 701137106
Phone: 504 576-4000
Web: WWW.ENTERGY.COM

HISTORICAL FINANCIALS
Company Type: Private

Income Statement				FYE: December 31
	REVENUE ($ mil.)	NET INCOME ($ mil.)	NET PROFIT MARGIN	EMPLOYEES
12/16	1,112	10	0.9%	1,325
12/04	10,123	933	9.2%	—
Annual Growth	(16.8%)	(31.2%)	—	—

2016 Year-End Financials
Return on assets: 0.8%   Cash ($ mil.): 51
Return on equity: —
Current ratio: 0.70

ENTERPRISE CRUDE PIPELINE LLC

EXECUTIVES

Pres, W Randall Fowler
Technician, Jacob Kahanek
Technician Mechanical, Willie Stubbs

LOCATIONS

HQ: ENTERPRISE CRUDE PIPELINE LLC
 1100 LOUISIANA ST # 1000, HOUSTON, TX
 770027499
Phone: 713 381-6500

HISTORICAL FINANCIALS
Company Type: Private

Income Statement				FYE: December 31
	REVENUE ($ mil.)	NET INCOME ($ mil.)	NET PROFIT MARGIN	EMPLOYEES
12/17	596	378	63.5%	300
12/16	472	284	60.2%	—
Annual Growth	26.2%	33.1%	—	—

ENTERPRISE TE PRODUCTS PIPELINE COMPANY LLC

EXECUTIVES

Ceo-MBR, Jerry E Thompson
Cfo-MBR, William G Manias
Coordinator Maintenance, Matthew Nolan
Technician, Brian Hall
Supervisor, Juan Contreras
Technician, Richard Ames
Technician Pipeline, Kenneston Hale
Technician, Destry Starkey
Technician Pipeline, Rusty Bengston
Supervisor, Tim Kistner

LOCATIONS

HQ: ENTERPRISE TE PRODUCTS PIPELINE COMPANY
 LLC
 1100 LOUISIANA ST # 1600, HOUSTON, TX
 770025227
Phone: 713 381-6500

HISTORICAL FINANCIALS
Company Type: Private

Income Statement				FYE: December 31
	REVENUE ($ mil.)	NET INCOME ($ mil.)	NET PROFIT MARGIN	EMPLOYEES
12/17	659	337	51.1%	3
12/16	628	275	43.9%	—
Annual Growth	5.0%	22.3%	—	—

EQUINOR MARKETING & TRADING (US) INC.

Check the stats. Oil. Hundreds of thousands of barrels of oil gasoline and more. Statoil Marketing & Trading is a wholesaler of oil and petroleum products. The company is the US trading arm of StatoilÂ the leading Scandinavian oil and gas enterprise. Statoil Marketing & Trading delivers about 600000 barrels a day in the form of crude oil gasoline liquefied petroleum gas (LPG) propane and butane to the North American market. In addition to supplying Norwegian crude the company trades crude oil from Africa South America and North America.Â Statoil Marketing & Trading sells itÂ oil products primarilyÂ to customers in Northeastern Canada the US East Coast and Gulf Coast.

EXECUTIVES

Senior Vice President, Thore Kristiansen
Vice President Human Resources, Shild Larsen
Vice President Human Resources Services, Siv
 Oftedal
Vice President Operations Subsea, Rune Aase
Vice President Legal, Paul Owen
Vice President Project Management, Erik Westad
Vice President Project Management, Johnny
 Wollberg
Vice President Quality, Magne Ottera
Vice President, Sverre Serck-hanssen
Vice President Operations, Atle Kjenes
Vice President Project Management, Kjell Eide
Vice President Operations, Lars Hier
Vice President Of Supply Chain, Mauro Andrade
Vice President Operations, Dag Johnsgaard
Vp Tax, Tom Geczik
**Executive Vice President Technology Projects And
 Drilling,** Anders Opedal
Vice President Communications, Nathaniel Teti
Vice President Drilling And Well Engineering,
 Erik Kirkemo
Auditors: KPMG LLP STAMFORD CONNECTICU

LOCATIONS

HQ: EQUINOR MARKETING & TRADING (US) INC.
 120 LONG RIDGE RD 3EO1, STAMFORD, CT
 069021839
Phone: 203 978-6900
Web: WWW.EQUINOR.COM

COMPETITORS

Global Partners   Irving Oil Limited
Gulf Oil   Shell Oil
Hess Corporation   Tauber Oil

HISTORICAL FINANCIALS

Company Type: Private

Income Statement				FYE: December 31
	REVENUE ($ mil.)	NET INCOME ($ mil.)	NET PROFIT MARGIN	EMPLOYEES
12/17	9,874	(28)	—	5
12/16	5,984	(259)	—	—
12/15	6,947	(132)	—	—
12/14	12,075	(140)	—	—
Annual Growth	(6.5%)	—	—	—

2017 Year-End Financials

Return on assets: (-1.4%)   Cash ($ mil.): 46
Return on equity: (-9.6%)
Current ratio: 1.30

EQUINOR NATURAL GAS LLC

EXECUTIVES

Pres, Jan Rune Schoepp
Sec-General Counsel, Charles T O'Brien
Vp-Tax & Asst SEC, Martin J Pastore
Controller, Neil Tarling
Chairman, Tor Martin Anfinnsen
Mgr-Ssu, Gary Aucoin
Mgr-Origination, Teddy Muhlfelder
Cfo, Gary A Turiano
Vice President Investor Relati, Geir Bjornstad
Originator, Hugh Gleason
Operator, Paula Ahern
Auditors: KPMG LLP STAMFORD CONNECTICU

LOCATIONS

HQ: EQUINOR NATURAL GAS LLC
  120 LONG RIDGE RD, STAMFORD, CT 069021839
Phone: 203 978-6900
Web: WWW.EQUINOR.COM

HISTORICAL FINANCIALS

Company Type: Private

Income Statement				FYE: December 31
	REVENUE ($ mil.)	NET INCOME ($ mil.)	NET PROFIT MARGIN	EMPLOYEES
12/15	1,967	722	36.7%	15
12/13	3,507	(127)	—	—
12/10	1,614	149	9.3%	—
12/08	1,640	168	10.3%	—
Annual Growth	2.6%	23.1%	—	—

2015 Year-End Financials

Return on assets: 46.0%   Cash ($ mil.): 20
Return on equity: 67.1%
Current ratio: 3.40

ERIE COUNTY MEDICAL CENTER CORP.

EXECUTIVES

Ceo, Jody L Lomeo
Cfo, Michael J Sammarco
Coo, Richard C Cleland
R V Pres, Ronald Krawiec
R V Pres, Karen Ziemianski
Cfo, Steven Gary
Chro-General Counsel, Joseph T Giglia II
Evp, Anthony J Colucci III
Asst Ceo, Kathleen Gellart
Infectious Diseases, Chiu Bin Hsiao
Internal Medicine Practitioner, Nelda Lawler
Auditors: RSM US LLP

LOCATIONS

HQ: ERIE COUNTY MEDICAL CENTER CORP.
  462 GRIDER ST, BUFFALO, NY 142153098
Phone: 716 898-3000
Web: WWW.SYNERGYBARIATRICS.COM

HISTORICAL FINANCIALS

Company Type: Private

Income Statement				FYE: December 31
	REVENUE ($ mil.)	NET INCOME ($ mil.)	NET PROFIT MARGIN	EMPLOYEES
12/16	616	1	0.3%	3,300
12/14	514	3	0.6%	—
12/13	467	9	2.0%	—
12/12	425	13	3.1%	—
Annual Growth	9.7%	(37.9%)	—	—

2016 Year-End Financials

Return on assets: 0.3%   Cash ($ mil.): 15
Return on equity: 1.7%
Current ratio: 1.90

ESTES EXPRESS LINES, INC.

Founded during the Depression with a Chevy truck Estes Express Lines has grown into a multiregional less-than-truckload (LTL) freight hauler. Its fleet of some 7100 tractors and 25700 trailers operates via a network of some 210 terminals dotting the US. Service in Canada is provided by TST Overland Express an ExpressLINK partner and in Mexico through affiliate Almex. Estes Express works with designated carriers to offer door-to-door delivery in the Caribbean and in Mexico. Subsidiary Estes Forwarding Worldwide services ocean/air freight forwarding. The company is owned and run by the family of founder W.W. Estes.

Operations

The company operates through several divisions and companies. Divisions include Estes Time-Critical (offering four levels of shipping) Level2 Logistics (business-to-business and business-to-consumer shipping) Estes Specialized Truckload and Delivery Services and Estes SureMove (customers load shipments themselves and Estes provides transportation). Companies include Estes Forwarding Worldwide Estes Brokerage Estes Leasing and Big E Transportation.

Geographic Reach

Estes Express offers regional service to all 50 US states. It also offers direct service to Canada Mexico and the Caribbean.

Strategy

Estes Express has continued to build out its LTL business by offering expedited delivery volume truckload transportation supply chain management nationwide brokerage services warehousing services and equipment leasing. The latter has provided such rental services as laundry trucks for the Department of Veterans Affairs. Its slate of services are supported by an upgraded wireless onboard pickup and delivery system featuring real-time data enabling terminals and drivers to process freight more efficiently. It has also formed a Mexico third-party logistics subsidiary Estes Logistica for managing freight consolidation and transportation to points south of the US border.

Estes Express over the years has opened new offices in San Francisco Los Angeles Dallas Chicago Miami and New York. To support the continuing market growth in the Midwest in 2015 it opened a new terminal in Oswego Illinois. The next year it opened an additional terminal in the Chicago area to replace a smaller facility. The new location is in Markham Illinois and is the seventh terminal the company owns in the state.

Company Background

The company was formed in 1931.

EXECUTIVES

President And Ceo, Rob W. Estes, age 67
President And Ceo Estes Forwarding Worldwide, Scott Fisher
Coo, Billy Hupp
Vp And Chief Information Officer, Bob Fowler
Vice President Customer Service, Mike Campese
Corporate Vice President Of Operations, Al Bucher
Vice President National Accounts, Morton Mustian
Vice President Information Technology, Hugh Canden
Vice President Fleet Services, Mike Palmer
Vice President Corporate Sales, Chuck Parker
Vice President Of Pricing And Traffic, Paul Dugent
Vice President Operations, Jt Johnson
Vice President Of Human Resources, Greg Richardson
Vp Integrated Solutions, Ken Niemaseck

LOCATIONS

HQ: ESTES EXPRESS LINES, INC.
  3901 W BROAD ST, RICHMOND, VA 232303962
Phone: 804 353-1900
Web: WWW.ESTES-EXPRESS.COM

PRODUCTS/OPERATIONS

Selected Services

Global (airfreight ocean international consolidation/deconsolidation customs brokerage international freight forwarding)
Less-than-truckload (regional national international/offshore)
Time critical (expedited guaranteed time/date definite)
Volume & truckload (LTL full loads backhaul services truckload brokerage dedicated truckload)

COMPETITORS

AAA Cooper Transportation   R+L Carriers
ArcBest   Ryder System
Averitt Express   Saia
FedEx Freight   UPS Freight
Old Dominion Freight   Vitran
Penske Truck Leasing   YRC Worldwide

HISTORICAL FINANCIALS

Company Type: Private

Income Statement   FYE: December 31

	REVENUE ($ mil.)	NET INCOME ($ mil.)	NET PROFIT MARGIN	EMPLOYEES
12/18	3,159	252	8.0%	14,000
12/17	2,731	231	8.5%	—
12/16	2,403	128	5.3%	—
12/15	2,367	135	5.7%	—
Annual Growth	10.1%	23.1%	—	—

2018 Year-End Financials

Return on assets: 13.7%   Cash ($ mil.): 169
Return on equity: 19.4%
Current ratio: 1.90

EVERSOURCE ENERGY SERVICE COMPANY

Northeast Utilities Service Company (NUSCO) provides support and reports for its cohorts. The company was created in 1966 to centralize corporate activities for Northeast Utilities (renamed Eversource Energy). NUSCO acts as an agent and offers centralized administrative services not only for its parent company Northeast Utilities but all of its subsidiaries (Connecticut Light and Power Public Service Company of New Hampshire Western Massachusetts Electric and Yankee Gas Services Company) as well. NUSCO duties include accounting financial legal operational information technology engineering planning and purchasing services.

EXECUTIVES

Vice President Finance Treasurer And Secretary Select Energy Services, Linda A Jensen
Vice President Governmental Affairs Northeast Utilities, Margaret Morton
Vice President Sales, Michael Ahern
Vice President Customer Operations, Jessica Cain
Vice President Of Electric Field Operations, Steven Gilkey
Vice President, Mary J Keating
Vice President Electric System Operations, Joseph Luchini
Vice President Network Support, Alan Landever
Vice President Customer Operations, Robert Coates
Vice President Rates And Regulatory Requirements, Christine Vaughan
Vice President Finance, Michael J Ausere
Vice President Engineering, Ken Bowes
Vice Chairman, Guy Carpenter

LOCATIONS

HQ: EVERSOURCE ENERGY SERVICE COMPANY
56 PROSPECT ST, HARTFORD, CT 061032818
Phone: 800 286-5000
Web: WWW.EVERSOURCE.COM

COMPETITORS

Connecticut Water   PSEG Fossil
Service

HISTORICAL FINANCIALS

Company Type: Private

Income Statement   FYE: December 31

	REVENUE ($ mil.)	NET INCOME ($ mil.)	NET PROFIT MARGIN	EMPLOYEES
12/16	831	11	1.4%	4,550
12/08	5,800	260	4.5%	—
12/07	5,822	246	4.2%	—
12/05	0	0	—	—
Annual Growth	—	—	—	—

2016 Year-End Financials

Return on assets: 0.8%   Cash ($ mil.): 11
Return on equity: 8.2%
Current ratio: 0.60

EXPRESS SERVICES INC

When you need a worker fast Express Services delivers. Operating as Express Employment Professionals the staffing company provides work for some 566000 employees each year. It operates on a franchise business model from a network of more than 800 employment agency offices across the US Canada and South Africa. It helps fill full-time temporary and part-time positions in a range of sectors that span Professional Light Industrial and Office Services. Professional employment includes accounting engineering IT sales and marketing HR and legal sector positions while Light Industrial covers assignments such as assembly maintenance and warehousing. Bob Funk and Bill Stoller founded the firm in 1983.

Financial Performance

Express Services' revenue reached a record high in 2018 with more than $3.56 billion in sales up from $3.4 billion in 2017. Contributing to growth was a hot job market and low unemployment levels spurring the company's expansion of franchise locations from 799 to 807 as well as an increase in the total number of workers it placed from 540000 to 566000.

Strategy

Through its franchising business model the company sells local Express Services office owners the right to use its methods and tools for staffing. Local offices can focus on the attributes and requirements of its specific community while having access to all the resources of the international company.

Since its founding Express Employment Professionals has put more than 7.7 million people to work. More than 1.6 million people found jobs through the company in the three-year period between January 1 2016 and December 31 2018. The company operates with a long-term goal of placing a million jobs each year.

Express Services was forced to respond to a years-long legal battle between its two founders. Bill Stoller alleged Bob Funk diverted company funds in the form of unauthorized loans that Funk claimed to use for his franchises but Stoller claimed were for personal use. The two settled the suit in mid-2018 resulting in Funk returning assets to the company paying $30 million in deferred compensation to Stoller and agreeing to Stoller taking over as CEO.

EXECUTIVES

Senior Vice President Information Systems, Terry Weldon
Chairman And Ceo, Robert A. Funk
Vice President International Headquarters, Harvey Homsey
Evp Sales And Director, Robert E. (Bob) Fellinger
Svp Sales And Marketing, Cory Benton
Cfo, Tony Bostwick
Vice President Central Zone, Dan Healy
Vice President, Sharon Patric
Vice President Of Franchising, David Lewis
Vice President, Jonathan Thom
Vice President Human Resources, Russ Moen
Vice President Sales And Marketing, Jane McHann
Vice President Of Finance, Ashley A Ruiz
Vp Operations, Lucy Kaji
Vice Chairman, William H. (Bill) Stoller
Auditors: RSM US LLP OKLAHOMA CITY OK

LOCATIONS

HQ: EXPRESS SERVICES INC
9701 BOARDWALK BLVD, OKLAHOMA CITY, OK 731626029
Phone: 405 840-5000
Web: WWW.EXPRESSPROS.COM

PRODUCTS/OPERATIONS

Selected Services
Evaluation and direct hire
Human resource services
Professional contract staffing
Temporary and flexible staffing

Selected Staffing Fields
Express Personnel
   General labor
   Government
   Health care
   Industrial
   Office and clerical
   Scientific
   Technical
Express Professional
   Accounting and financial
   Engineering and manufacturing
   Health care
   Human resources
   Information technology
   Sales and marketing
   Technical

COMPETITORS

ADP TotalSource	Kelly Services
Adecco	ManpowerGroup
Barrett Business Services	Randstad Holding
Butler America	Robert Half
Insperity	Volt Information

HISTORICAL FINANCIALS

Company Type: Private

Income Statement   FYE: December 31

	REVENUE ($ mil.)	NET INCOME ($ mil.)	NET PROFIT MARGIN	EMPLOYEES
12/16	2,722	89	3.3%	373,869
12/15	2,648	99	3.7%	—
12/14	0	55	—	—
12/13	0	58	—	—
Annual Growth	—	14.8%	—	—

2016 Year-End Financials

Return on assets: 12.0%   Cash ($ mil.): 21
Return on equity: 30.1%
Current ratio: 1.40

FAIRFAX COUNTY VIRGINIA

EXECUTIVES

City Exec, Anthony H Griffin
Staff, Mark Young
Business Dir, Angela Shaw
Telecommunications Staff, Alton Drew
Information, Tanya Quinonez
Captain, Roger Arnn
Captain, John Piper
Coordinator, Kelly Bachand
Law Specialist, Casey Sheehan
Facilities Specialist, Jonathan Murray
Programmer Analyst, Phubinh Nguyen
Auditors: KPMG LLP WASHINGTON DC

LOCATIONS

HQ: FAIRFAX COUNTY VIRGINIA
   12000 GOVERNMENT STE 214, FAIRFAX, VA 22035
Phone: 703 324-3126
Web: WWW.FAIRFAXCOUNTYEDA.ORG

HISTORICAL FINANCIALS

Company Type: Private

Income Statement — FYE: June 30

	REVENUE ($ mil.)	NET INCOME ($ mil.)	NET PROFIT MARGIN	EMPLOYEES
06/18	4,806	71	1.5%	12,000
06/17	4,695	171	3.6%	—
06/16	4,469	49	1.1%	—
06/15	0	60	—	—
Annual Growth	—	5.8%	—	—

2018 Year-End Financials

Return on assets: 0.4%   Cash ($ mil.): 1,364
Return on equity: 18.8%
Current ratio: —

FAIRVIEW HEALTH SERVICES

It's fair to say that when it comes to health care Fairview Health Services takes the long view. The not-for-profit system serves Minnesota's Twin Cities and nearby communities. Fairview Health is affiliated with the medical school of the University of Minnesota and counts among its 10 hospitals the University of Minnesota Medical Center. The hospitals house more than 2500 beds and provide comprehensive medical and surgical services. The system also operates primary and specialty care clinics that provide preventive and wellness care. Additionally it operates retail pharmacies and nursing homes and provides home health care and rehabilitation. Merger talks with University of Minnesota Physicians have stalled.

EXECUTIVES

Vice President Chief Information Security Officer, Barry Caplin
Nursing Director, Debbie Tharp
Vice President Business Development, Jerry Plourde
Vice President, John Swanholm
Vp It Systems And Ciso, Judy Hatchett
Auditors: ERNST & YOUNG LLP MINNEAPOLI

LOCATIONS

HQ: FAIRVIEW HEALTH SERVICES
   2450 RIVERSIDE AVE, MINNEAPOLIS, MN 554541450
Phone: 612 672-6300
Web: WWW.FAIRVIEW.ORG

COMPETITORS

Abbott Northwestern Hospital	Mayo Clinic
Allina Hospitals	North Memorial Health Care
Bethesda Hospital	Park Nicollet Health Services
Catholic Health Initiatives	Regions Hospital
CentraCare Health	St. John's Hospital (Minnesota)
HealthEast Care System	

HISTORICAL FINANCIALS

Company Type: Private

Income Statement — FYE: December 31

	REVENUE ($ mil.)	NET INCOME ($ mil.)	NET PROFIT MARGIN	EMPLOYEES
12/18	5,709	5	0.1%	18,000
12/17	5,275	511	9.7%	—
Annual Growth	8.2%	(98.9%)	—	—

2018 Year-End Financials

Return on assets: 0.1%   Cash ($ mil.): 74
Return on equity: 0.2%
Current ratio: 1.90

FAMILY HEALTH NETWORK, INC.

EXECUTIVES

Ceo, Keith Kudla
Pres*, Philip C Bradley
Cfo*, Tom Tennison
Information Specialist, Linda Merchant
Information Specialist, Shawn Cull
Vice President, James Kiamos
Senior Financial Analyst, Elisa Chiu
Senior Director Network Manage, Gail Vuckovich
Intake Coordinator, Karin Fields
Compliance Director, Camille Trunkett
Claims Supervisor, James Segatto

LOCATIONS

HQ: FAMILY HEALTH NETWORK, INC.
   222 MERCHANDISE MART PLZ # 960, CHICAGO, IL 606541236
Phone: 312 243-5235

HISTORICAL FINANCIALS

Company Type: Private

Income Statement — FYE: December 31

	REVENUE ($ mil.)	NET INCOME ($ mil.)	NET PROFIT MARGIN	EMPLOYEES
12/17	549	(23)	—	30
12/09	60	2	4.9%	—
12/08	56	0	—	—
Annual Growth	28.7%	—	—	—

2017 Year-End Financials

Return on assets: (-15.2%)   Cash ($ mil.): 59
Return on equity: (-341.2%)
Current ratio: —

FAMILYCARE, INC.

EXECUTIVES

Pres, Jeff Heatherington
Vice-President Finance, Kevin Clancy
Coordinator, Annmarie Rainford
Project Manager, Joanna Langberg
Controller, Anthony Jackson
Coordinator, Jon Chao
Director, Jack Coleman
Community Manager, Paige Jackson
Msw, Kevin Dickson
Manager, Darin Brink
Bilingual Member Navigator 1, Edith Lopez
Auditors: PERKINS & COMPANY PC PORTLAND

LOCATIONS

HQ: FAMILYCARE, INC.
   825 NE MULTNOMAH ST # 300, PORTLAND, OR 972322135
Phone: 503 222-2880
Web: WWW.FAMILYCAREINC.ORG

HISTORICAL FINANCIALS

Company Type: Private

Income Statement — FYE: December 31

	REVENUE ($ mil.)	NET INCOME ($ mil.)	NET PROFIT MARGIN	EMPLOYEES
12/16	497	(20)	—	61
12/14	410	73	17.9%	—
12/13	168	14	8.7%	—
Annual Growth	43.4%	—	—	—

2016 Year-End Financials

Return on assets: (-7.7%)   Cash ($ mil.): 128
Return on equity: (-15.4%)
Current ratio: —

FARM CREDIT BANK OF TEXAS

The largest member of the federal Farm Credit System the Farm Credit Bank of Texas provides loans and financial services to about 20 lending cooperatives and financial institutions in Alabama Louisiana Mississippi New Mexico and Texas. These include agricultural credit associations which provide agricultural production loans agribusiness financing and rural mortgage financing; and federal land credit associations which offer real estate loans on farms ranches and other rural property. Farm Credit Bank of Texas is owned by the lending cooperatives it serves.

EXECUTIVES

Senior Vice President, Rusty Lampman
Vice President, Steve Donnell
Vice President And Controller, Vicki Rodriguez
Vice President Business Development, Jeremy Lightfoot
Vice President, Paul Rudd
Vice President Business Systems Unit Manager, Ed Benson
Vice President, Darren Cannon
Senior Vice President And Cco, John Logsdon
Vice President Regional Manager, Chris Amend
Vice President Lending, Boyd J Chambers
Vice President Collateral Risk Management, Brad Swinney

Vice President, Amy Pala
Vice President, Ronnie Sellers
Vp Of Compliance, Thomas Ringler
Vice President, Jason Gandy
Vice President, Mike Tippit
Board Of Directors, Buddy Cortese
Board Member, Larry Fairchild
Auditors: PRICEWATERHOUSECOOPERS LLP AU

LOCATIONS

HQ: FARM CREDIT BANK OF TEXAS
4801 PLAZA ON THE LK # 1200, AUSTIN, TX
787461081
Phone: 512 465-0400
Web: WWW.FARMCREDITBANK.COM

HISTORICAL FINANCIALS

Company Type: Private

Income Statement   FYE: December 31

	ASSETS ($ mil.)	NET INCOME ($ mil.)	INCOME AS % OF ASSETS	EMPLOYEES
12/16	21,222	192	0.9%	200
12/13	16,212	179	1.1%	
/	0	0	—	—
Annual Growth	—	—	—	—

2016 Year-End Financials

Return on assets: 0.9%   Sales ($ mil): 530
Return on equity: 11.9%

FARM CREDIT SERVICES OF AMERICA

EXECUTIVES

Pres-Ceo, Doug Stark
Exec V Pres*, Neil Olsen
Sr V Pres-Cfo*, Eugene College
Sr V Pres*, Michelle Mapes
Sr V Pres*, David Martin
Turner Youth Initiative Direct, Twila Phillips
Engineer, Dave Cook
Senior Vice President Agribusi, Marshall Hansen
Auditors: PRICEWATERHOUSECOOPERS LLP M

LOCATIONS

HQ: FARM CREDIT SERVICES OF AMERICA
5015 S 118TH ST, OMAHA, NE 681372210
Phone: 800 884-3276
Web: WWW.FCSAMERICA.COM

HISTORICAL FINANCIALS

Company Type: Private

Income Statement   FYE: December 31

	ASSETS ($ mil.)	NET INCOME ($ mil.)	INCOME AS % OF ASSETS	EMPLOYEES
12/15	24,772	514	2.1%	10,000
12/04	8,475	294	3.5%	—
12/03	7,633	114	1.5%	—
12/02	0	132	—	—
Annual Growth	—	11.0%	—	—

2015 Year-End Financials

Return on assets: 2.1%   Sales ($ mil): 1,099
Return on equity: 11.9%

FARM CREDIT WEST

EXECUTIVES

Ceo-Pres, Mark D Littlefield
Sr V Pres, Chris N Brumfield
Exec V Pres, John C Boyes
Exe V Pres, William M Noland
Cfo, Chris Doherty
Exec V Pres-Fiscal ADM, Ernest M Hodges
Prin, K E Graff
Vice-President, Michael Moore
Loan Officer, Danielle Vietti
Information Technology Special, David Dynes
Senior Vice President Chief, Denise Warkomski
Auditors: PRICEWATERHOUSECOOPERS LLP SA

LOCATIONS

HQ: FARM CREDIT WEST
3755 ATHERTON RD, ROCKLIN, CA 957653701
Phone: 916 724-4800
Web: WWW.FARMCREDITWEST.COM

HISTORICAL FINANCIALS

Company Type: Private

Income Statement   FYE: December 31

	ASSETS ($ mil.)	NET INCOME ($ mil.)	INCOME AS % OF ASSETS	EMPLOYEES
12/12	6,668	151	2.3%	165
12/11	6,282	176	2.8%	—
12/10	6,129	0	—	—
Annual Growth	4.3%			

2012 Year-End Financials

Return on assets: 2.3%   Sales ($ mil): 295
Return on equity: 12.5%

FARMERS COOPERATIVE

EXECUTIVES

Pres, Ron Velver
SEC-Treas*, Glen Capek
Manager, Ronald Velder
Location Manager, Lane Kalkwarf
Location Manager, Steve Killeen
Location Manager, Matt Thompson
Auditors: GARDINER THOMSEN LINCOLN NE

LOCATIONS

HQ: FARMERS COOPERATIVE
208 W DEPOT ST, DORCHESTER, NE 683432375
Phone: 402 946-4631
Web: WWW.FARMERSCO-OPERATIVE.COM

HISTORICAL FINANCIALS

Company Type: Private

Income Statement   FYE: August 31

	REVENUE ($ mil.)	NET INCOME ($ mil.)	NET PROFIT MARGIN	EMPLOYEES
08/14	830	19	2.3%	470
08/12	918	22	2.5%	—
08/11	695	21	3.1%	—
08/10	636	0	0.0%	—
Annual Growth	6.9%	1803.9%	—	—

2014 Year-End Financials

Return on assets: 7.6%   Cash ($ mil.): 28
Return on equity: 11.5%
Current ratio: 1.80

FARMERS COOPERATIVE COMPANY

The importance of cooperation — it's one of life's most important lessons. Dating back to the early 1900s the Farmers Cooperative Company (FCC) learned that lesson early on. The 5500-member-plus co-op offers agronomy and grain marketing services to its members who oversee some 3 million acres of farmland in central and north central Iowa. The largest of its kind in Iowa FCC operates 40 grain elevators and provides soil testing and mapping services. It sells supplies including seed feed and fertilizer to its members. The coop merged with another Iowa coop West Central Cooperative in 2016 to form Landus Cooperative.

Operations

Farmers Cooperative (FCC) operates four departments: Agronomy Feed Grain and Seed. Agronomy serves customers at some 40 locations across central Iowa and is one of largest agronomy divisions in the state. The Feed department has six manufacturing locations across central north central and northwest Iowa. FCC's feed mills produce more than 900000 tons of complete feed annually. FCC has 40 grain elevators across its membership area. More than 118 million bushels of grain are handled annually. FCC also has grain storage capacity of 75 million bushels. The cooperative's Seed department works closely with the Agronomy division since both serve the same customers.

EXECUTIVES

Ceo, James Chism
Pres*, Rick Brand
V Pres*, Chuck Lindberg
Student Supervisor, Darren Struthers
Auditors: MERIWETHER WILSON & COMPANY

LOCATIONS

HQ: FARMERS COOPERATIVE COMPANY
105 GARFIELD AVE, FARNHAMVILLE, IA 505386712
Phone: 515 817-2100
Web: WWW.LANDUSCOOPERATIVE.COM

PRODUCTS/OPERATIONS

Selected Departments
Agronomy
Feed
Grain
Seed

COMPETITORS

ADM	Five Star Co-op
Ag Processing Inc.	Gold-Eagle Cooperative
CHS	Heartland Co-op
Cargill	Ingredion
DeBruce Grain	Scoular
Farm Service	Swiss Valley Farms
Cooperative	West Central Co-op
Farmers Cooperative	
Society	

HISTORICAL FINANCIALS

Company Type: Private

Income Statement   FYE: August 31

	REVENUE ($ mil.)	NET INCOME ($ mil.)	NET PROFIT MARGIN	EMPLOYEES
08/10	779	10	1.3%	450
08/09	894	13	1.5%	—
Annual Growth	(12.8%)	(19.9%)	—	—

2010 Year-End Financials

Return on assets: 5.6% Cash ($ mil.): —
Return on equity: 1.3%
Current ratio: —

FARMERS GRAIN TERMINAL, INC.

EXECUTIVES

Pres-Ceo, Steve Nail
Exec V Pres*, Harvey Parrish
V Pres*, C C Craig
V Pres*, John Oakes
Director, Herbert H Huddleston Jr
Manager, Ronnie Ferrell
Customer Manager, Will Weathers
Assistant Manager, Robert Smith
Assistant Elevator Manager, Gary Ballard
Auditors: HUDSON CISNE & CO LLP LITT

LOCATIONS

HQ: FARMERS GRAIN TERMINAL, INC.
 1977 HARBOR FRONT RD, GREENVILLE, MS
 387019588
Phone: 662 332-0987
Web: WWW.FGTCOOP.COM

HISTORICAL FINANCIALS

Company Type: Private

Income Statement   FYE: July 31

	REVENUE ($ mil.)	NET INCOME ($ mil.)	NET PROFIT MARGIN	EMPLOYEES
07/13	929	19	2.1%	102
07/12	615	12	2.1%	—
07/11	471	8	1.8%	—
Annual Growth	40.4%	53.0%	—	—

2013 Year-End Financials

Return on assets: 15.6% Cash ($ mil.): 64
Return on equity: 30.0%
Current ratio: 2.20

FATHER MURRAY NURSING CENTER

EXECUTIVES

Admin, Kim Harrell
Human Resources Manager, Brendon Weill
Auditors: DELOITTE TAX LLP DETROIT MI

LOCATIONS

HQ: FATHER MURRAY NURSING CENTER
 8444 ENGLEMAN, CENTER LINE, MI 480151567
Phone: 586 755-2400
Web: WWW.FATHERMURRAYHCC.COM

HISTORICAL FINANCIALS

Company Type: Private

Income Statement   FYE: June 30

	REVENUE ($ mil.)	NET INCOME ($ mil.)	NET PROFIT MARGIN	EMPLOYEES
06/09	1,562	(1)	—	317
06/08	15	(0)	—	—
Annual Growth	9831.8%	—	—	—

2009 Year-End Financials

Return on assets: (-24.4%) Cash ($ mil.): —
Return on equity: (-293.2%)
Current ratio: 2.10

FCTG HOLDINGS, INC.

EXECUTIVES

Pres, Craig Johnston
Cfo, Derrick Coder
SEC, Carl Neil
Vice President Finance, Lois Burbage

LOCATIONS

HQ: FCTG HOLDINGS, INC.
 10250 SW GREENBURG RD # 200, PORTLAND, OR
 972235461
Phone: 503 246-8500
Web: WWW.FCTG.COM

HISTORICAL FINANCIALS

Company Type: Private

Income Statement   FYE: January 31

	REVENUE ($ mil.)	NET INCOME ($ mil.)	NET PROFIT MARGIN	EMPLOYEES
01/09	1,535	2	0.2%	410
01/08	2,055	1	0.1%	—
01/07	2,798	(0)	—	—
Annual Growth	(25.9%)	—	—	—

2009 Year-End Financials

Return on assets: 2.7% Cash ($ mil.): 3
Return on equity: 11.0%
Current ratio: 1.20

FEDERAL-MOGUL HOLDINGS LLC

Auditors: GRANT THORNTON LLP SOUTHFIELD

LOCATIONS

HQ: FEDERAL-MOGUL HOLDINGS LLC
 27300 W 11 MILE RD # 101, SOUTHFIELD, MI
 480346193
Phone: 248 354-7700
Web: WWW.FEDERALMOGUL.COM

HISTORICAL FINANCIALS

Company Type: Private

Income Statement   FYE: December 31

	REVENUE ($ mil.)	NET INCOME ($ mil.)	NET PROFIT MARGIN	EMPLOYEES
12/16	7,434	90	1.2%	53,700
12/15	7,419	(104)	—	—
12/14	7,317	(161)	—	—
Annual Growth	0.8%	—	—	—

2016 Year-End Financials

Return on assets: 1.3% Cash ($ mil.): 300
Return on equity: 10.2%
Current ratio: 1.70

FIDELITY INV CHARITABLE GIFT FUND

LOCATIONS

HQ: FIDELITY INV CHARITABLE GIFT FUND
 200 SEAPORT BLVD STE 1, BOSTON, MA 022102000
Phone: 617 392-8679
Web: WWW.FUNINBOSTON.COM

HISTORICAL FINANCIALS

Company Type: Private

Income Statement   FYE: June 30

	REVENUE ($ mil.)	NET INCOME ($ mil.)	NET PROFIT MARGIN	EMPLOYEES
06/11	1,874	599	32.0%	1
06/10	1,274	147	11.6%	—
Annual Growth	47.1%	306.7%	—	—

2011 Year-End Financials

Return on assets: 10.7% Cash ($ mil.): 77
Return on equity: 10.8%
Current ratio: 1.90

FINANCIAL INDUSTRY REGULATORY AUTHORITY, INC.

 FINRA is one of the long arms of the law for the securities industry. A non-governmental regulatory authority FINRA regulates all securities firms (roughly 4250) that conduct business in the US. Its activities include writing and enforcing rules; enforcing federal securities laws; licensing and registering brokerages and private equity firms; and providing educational information and arbitration services to investors. The regulator works with the SEC and the Fed and possesses the authority to issue fines and bar violators among other punitive actions. FINRA was formed in 2007 from the consolidation of the National Association of Securities Dealers and certain regulatory and enforcement elements of the NYSE.

Operations

Under the oversight of the SEC FINRA brought 1541 disciplinary actions against registered people and firms in 2012 (an increase of 53 from 2011) levied fines totally more than $69 million and ordered payback in the amount of $34 million to investors (a record amount) that were harmed throughout the year.

Geographic Reach

FINRA operates from Washington DC and New York with 20 regional offices around the US. It also has more than 160000 branch offices and some 635000 registered securities representatives.

Financial Performance

FINRA obviously benefits when lawmakers and regulators crack down on fraud and the breaking of securities laws that led up to the Great Recession. As such the bulk of its revenues (about 80%) come from the collection of regulatory user and contract service fees.

FINRA suffered a net loss of $84 million for 2011 mostly as a result of non-recurring costs related to the development of new data center facilities in New York and Maryland. The net loss was also due to increased integration expenses used to extend FINRA's cross market surveillance capabilities.

EXECUTIVES

Evp And Chief Technology Officer, Martin P. Colburn
Evp And Cio, Steven J. (Steve) Randich
Evp Transparency Services, Steven A. (Steve) Joachim
Evp Market Regulation, Thomas R. Gira
Evp Regulatory Policy And Legal Compliance Officer, Thomas M. (Tom) Selman
Evp Fraud Detection And Market Intelligence, Cameron K. Funkhouser
Evp And Head Of Member Regulation Sales Practice, Michael G. Rufino
Evp Member Regulation Risk Oversight And Operational Regulation (roor), William J. (Bill) Wollman
Evp And Cfo, Todd T. Diganci
Svp And Chief Economist, Jonathan S. Sokobin
Evp Regulatory Operations, Susan F. Axelrod
Evp Enforcement, J. Bradley Bennett
President Finra Foundation, Gerri Walsh
Evp Corporate Communications And Government Relations, F. Gregory Ahern
Chief Risk Officer And Head Of Strategy, Carlo V. di Florio
Evp And Director Dispute Resolution, Richard W. Berry
President And Ceo, Robert W. Cook
Executive Vice President Corporate Communications Government Relat, Gregory Ahern
Senior Vice President And Director Of Mediation Business Strategies And Dispute Resolution, Kenneth Andrichik
Senior Vice President Of Exchange Solutions And Market Regulation, James Price
Vice President, Angela Goelzer
Associate Vice President And Associate General Cou, Kosha Dalal
Vice President And Associate General Counsel Of Regulatory Group, Stephanie Dumont
Vice President, Michael Hourigan
Director Vice President And Director Of Advertising Regulation, Thomas Pappas
Vice President, Joseph Price
Vice President, Katri Arcaro
Associate Vice President, Terri Reicher
Vice President Of Enforcement And Sales Practice, Anthony Cavallaro
Vice President, Geraldine Walsh
Senior Vice President And Investment Officer, James Allen

Vice President, Ethan Lish
Vice President Corporate Governance, Jennifer Mitchell
Senior Vice President Financial Planning And Analysis, Robert Wood
Senior Vice President, Gregory Dean
Vice President, Ornella Bergeron
Vice President, Danny Mileto
Senior Vice President, Holly Lokken
Associate Vice President, Hollie Schwartz
Vice President, Nick Maslavets
Vice President, Justin Tubiolo
Senior Vice President, Jon Kroeper
Vice President Federal Affairs, Jonathan Renfrew
Executive Vice President, Andrew Didden
Vice President, Tigran Khrimian
Assistant Secretary, Jennifer Piorko
Auditors: ERNST & YOUNG LLP MCLEAN VIR

LOCATIONS

HQ: FINANCIAL INDUSTRY REGULATORY AUTHORITY, INC.
1735 K ST NW, WASHINGTON, DC 200061506
Phone: 301 590-6500

PRODUCTS/OPERATIONS

2015 Sales

	$ mil.	% of total
Regulatory revenue	444	45
User revenue	218	22
Contract services revenue	125	13
Fines	93	6
Transparency services revenue	63	4
Dispute resolution revenue	41	1
Other revenue	5	9
Total	**992**	**100**

HISTORICAL FINANCIALS

Company Type: Private

Income Statement   FYE: December 31

	REVENUE ($ mil.)	NET INCOME ($ mil.)	NET PROFIT MARGIN	EMPLOYEES
12/12	878	10	1.2%	3,400
12/11	880	(84)	—	—
12/10	849	54	6.4%	—
Annual Growth	1.7%	(56.1%)	—	—

2012 Year-End Financials

Return on assets: 0.5%   Cash ($ mil.): 356
Return on equity: 0.8%
Current ratio: 2.10

FINANCIAL TRADER CORPORATION

LOCATIONS

HQ: FINANCIAL TRADER CORPORATION
5743 LONGMONT LN, HOUSTON, TX 770572510
Phone: 713 206-4600

HISTORICAL FINANCIALS

Company Type: Private

Income Statement   FYE: December 31

	ASSETS ($ mil.)	NET INCOME ($ mil.)	INCOME AS % OF ASSETS	EMPLOYEES
12/13	398	6	1.7%	1
12/11	10	0	5.6%	—
Annual Growth	525.1%	243.5%	—	—

2013 Year-End Financials

Return on assets: —   Sales ($ mil.): 992
Return on equity: 0.7%

FINCANTIERI MARINE SYSTEMS NORTH AMERICA, INC.

EXECUTIVES

Ceo, Dario Deste
Pres*, Domenico Sorvillo
V Pres-Gen Mgr*, Richard Dinsmore
Treas, Paolo Pezzulo
Contrl, Martha Rosbrough
Manager, Pamela Thomas
Human Resources Coordinator, Ashley Morningstar

LOCATIONS

HQ: FINCANTIERI MARINE SYSTEMS NORTH AMERICA, INC.
800 PRINCIPAL CT STE C, CHESAPEAKE, VA 233203681
Phone: 757 548-6000
Web: WWW.FINCANTIERIMARINESYSTEMS.COM

HISTORICAL FINANCIALS

Company Type: Private

Income Statement   FYE: December 31

	REVENUE ($ mil.)	NET INCOME ($ mil.)	NET PROFIT MARGIN	EMPLOYEES
12/17	35,833	6,670	18.6%	56
12/16	37,567	6,365	16.9%	—
12/14	34,753	2,898	8.3%	—
12/13	0	1,229	—	—
Annual Growth	—	52.6%	—	—

2017 Year-End Financials

Return on assets: 15.1%   Cash ($ mil.): 1,877
Return on equity: 16.7%
Current ratio: 10.10

FLATIRON CONSTRUCTORS, INC.

EXECUTIVES

Ceo, John Diciurcio
Exec V-Pres-Coo*, Robert W French
Cfo*, Paul Driscoll
Coo*, Dale Swanberg
Exec Asst*, Judy Schek
Coo*, Javier Sevilla
Cfo*, Lars Leitner
Accounting Staff, Donna Clardy
Project Manager, Brad Owen
Alternative Delivery Manager, Denny Stoddard
Vice President Special Project, Manuel Rondon
Auditors: DELOITTE & TOUCHE LLP DENVER

LOCATIONS

HQ: FLATIRON CONSTRUCTORS, INC.
385 INTERLOCKEN, BROOMFIELD, CO 80021
Phone: 303 485-4050
Web: WWW.FLATIRONCORP.COM

HISTORICAL FINANCIALS

Company Type: Private

Income Statement

	REVENUE ($ mil.)	NET INCOME ($ mil.)	NET PROFIT MARGIN	EMPLOYEES
12/12	941	(96)	—	611
12/11	1,017	39	3.9%	—
Annual Growth	(7.5%)	—	—	—

FYE: December 31

2012 Year-End Financials

Return on assets: (-18.5%)   Cash ($ mil.): 123
Return on equity: (-55.9%)
Current ratio: 1.60

FLORIDA CLINICAL PRACTICE ASSOCIATION, INC.

EXECUTIVES

Pres, Anthony Mancuso
Exec V Pres, William W Tharp
Information Technology Manager, Aaron Weldon
Director, Stephanie Smith

LOCATIONS

HQ: FLORIDA CLINICAL PRACTICE ASSOCIATION, INC.
1329 SW 16TH ST STE 4250, GAINESVILLE, FL 326081128
Phone: 352 265-8017
Web: WWW.SHANDS.UFL.EDU

HISTORICAL FINANCIALS

Company Type: Private

Income Statement

	REVENUE ($ mil.)	NET INCOME ($ mil.)	NET PROFIT MARGIN	EMPLOYEES
06/17	642	(1)	—	2
06/15	598	19	3.3%	—
06/13	419	2	0.5%	—
06/12	360	(11)	—	—
Annual Growth	12.3%	—	—	—

FYE: June 30

2017 Year-End Financials

Return on assets: (-0.8%)   Cash ($ mil.): 82
Return on equity: (-1.0%)
Current ratio: 9.80

FLORIDA GAS TRANSMISSION COMPANY, LLC

Florida Gas Transmission gasses up the Gulf Coast. The company transports natural gas to co-generation facilities electric utilities independent power producers municipal generators and local distribution companies through a 5400-mile natural gas pipeline extending from south Texas to south Florida. It delivers 3.1 billion cu. ft. of natural gas a day to more than 250 delivery points consisting of more than 50 natural gas-fired electric generation facilities. Florida Gas Transmission is operated by Citrus Corp. which is a joint venture of Energy Transfer Partners and Kinder Morgan.

Operations

Florida Gas Transmission is the primary transporter of natural gas to the Florida energy market delivering more than 64% of the natural gas consumed by Floridians. The pipeline system operates and maintains more than 70 interconnects with major interstate and intrastate natural gas pipelines.

Geographic Reach

Florida Gas Transmission's pipeline system receives natural gas from producing basins in Louisiana and along the Texas Gulf Coast Mobile Bay and offshore in the Gulf of Mexico and transports it to markets in Florida.

Strategy

In 2013 the Florida Public Service Commission approved Florida Power & Light's contracts for a $3.5 billion 600-mile pipeline system. The project due for completion in 2017 will connect Florida's two existing pipelines the larger one owned by Florida Gas Transmission and the other by Gulfstream Natural Gas System LLC.

Upping its pipeline investment in 2012 Kinder Morgan invested about $2 billion in Citrus Corp.

Company Background

In 2008 Florida Power & Light agreed to contract for half the capacity of a $2 billion expansion of a natural-gas pipeline.

EXECUTIVES

Vice President Marketing, Gregg Russell
Vice President Accounting, Mary Simon
Vice President Market Services, Brad Holmes

LOCATIONS

HQ: FLORIDA GAS TRANSMISSION COMPANY, LLC
1300 MAIN ST, HOUSTON, TX 770026803
Phone: 713 989-7000
Web: WWW.ENERGYTRANSFER.COM

COMPETITORS

Columbia Gulf Transmission	Gulf South Pipeline
Enable Oklahoma	Texas Gas Transmission
	Williams Gas Pipeline

HISTORICAL FINANCIALS

Company Type: Private

Income Statement

	REVENUE ($ mil.)	NET INCOME ($ mil.)	NET PROFIT MARGIN	EMPLOYEES
12/18	838	321	38.3%	450
12/17	839	247	29.5%	—
12/16	829	238	28.7%	—
Annual Growth	0.6%	16.1%	—	—

FYE: December 31

FLORIDA HEALTH SCIENCES CENTER INC

Florida Health Sciences Center which does business as Tampa General Hospital (TGH) provides health care services in west-central Florida. The medical center offers general medical and surgical care as well as tertiary offerings including a Level 1 trauma center a burn unit a pediatric ward women's and cardiovascular centers and an organ transplant unit. The not-for-profit hospital has more than 1000 acute-care beds as well as 60 beds in its rehabilitation unit which specializes in helping patients recover from stroke head or spine trauma and other neuromuscular conditions. TGH is the primary teaching hospital for The University of South Florida College of Medicine.

Operations

TGH division Tampa General Medical Group (TGMG) is a multispecialty physician group with locations in Florida's Hillsborough and Pasco counties. Specialties include family practice internal medicine transplant cardiology endocrinology hepatology nephrology and surgery.

Geographic Reach

One of the largest employers in the Tampa Bay region TGH employs about 6300 workers. It also conducts research and operates community care centers in the Tampa area.

Each year TGH treats more than 91000 patients in its emergency department. This includes pediatric chest pain minor emergency and trauma center patients. The hospital also operates a regional helicopter medical transport program.

Strategy

TGH has added new wing to the hospital to expand patient capacity. TGH has added a new emergency/trauma center as well as cardiovascular diagnostic neurology and women's health units.

The hospital also works to stay on top of the latest medical advances. For example in 2014 TGH acquired the ThermoCool SmartTouch catheter a recently launched high-tech device that helps physicians control the amount of contact force applied to the heart wall during treatments for atrial fibrillation.

EXECUTIVES

Vice President Professional Services, David K Robbins
Evp Finance And Cfo, Steve Short
Evp And Coo, Deana L. Nelson
Executive Vice President Chief Medical Officer, Sally H. Houston
Chief Technology Officer, Balaji Ramadoss
Ceo, James R. Burkhart
Executive Vice President Chief Academic Officer, Charles J. Lockwood
Executive Vice President, Judith M Ploszek
Vice President Physician Practice And President Tampa General Medical Group, Lucila Ramiro
Senior Vice President Compliance Legal And Risk Management, Jonathan Dixon
Vice President, Kim Rallis
Vice President Service, Todd Godfrey
Vice President Business Strategy And Compliance, Deirdre A Brown
Chairman, David A. Straz
Pharmacy Secretary, Sonia Burgos
Secretary Unit Management, Linda Starkey
Secretary Unit Management, Markelle Hunt

LOCATIONS

HQ: FLORIDA HEALTH SCIENCES CENTER INC
1 TAMPA GENERAL CIR, TAMPA, FL 336063571
Phone: 813 844-7000
Web: WWW.TGH.ORG

COMPETITORS

All Children's Hospital	Lakeland Regional Medical Center
BayCare Health System	Lee Memorial
Bayfront Health	Manatee Memorial Hospital
DeSoto Memorial	
Florida Hospital Tampa Bay Division	Sarasota Memorial Health Care
HCA	Winter Haven Hospital

HISTORICAL FINANCIALS

Company Type: Private

Income Statement   FYE: September 30

	REVENUE ($ mil.)	NET INCOME ($ mil.)	NET PROFIT MARGIN	EMPLOYEES
09/18	1,325	79	6.0%	8,000
09/17	1,257	98	7.8%	—
09/16	1,055	80	7.6%	—
09/14	1,127	98	8.7%	—
Annual Growth	4.1%	(5.3%)	—	—

2018 Year-End Financials

Return on assets: 4.6%   Cash ($ mil.): 97
Return on equity: 8.0%
Current ratio: 1.20

FLORIDA HOUSING FINANCE CORP

Owning a home in Florida is just a bit easier thanks to Florida Housing Finance Corporation. Established in 1997 by the Florida Legislature as a public corporation Florida Housing's mission is to help Floridians obtain safe decent housing that might otherwise be unavailable to them. Florida Housing pursues its mission through a number of programs that provide financial assistance for first time homebuyers and for developers of multifamily dwellings that serve elderly and low income Floridians. Florida Housing partners with various local state and federal agencies as well as developers and not-for-profit organizations to achieve its goals.

EXECUTIVES

Exec Dir, Stephen Auger
Exec Dir*, Harold Price
Executive Officer, Vicki Robinson
Director of Asset Management, Laura J Cox
Controller, Angie Sellers
Senior Financial Administrator, Melanie Weathers
Bond Accounting Manager, Angela Scott
Homeownership Programs Adminis, Charles White
CIO, David Hearn
Director of Homeownerhip Progr, David Westcott
Federal Loan Program Manager, David Woodward
Auditors: ERNST & YOUNG LLP ORLANDO F

LOCATIONS

HQ: FLORIDA HOUSING FINANCE CORP
227 N BRONOUGH ST # 5000, TALLAHASSEE, FL 323011367
Phone: 850 488-4197
Web: WWW.FLORIDAHOUSING.ORG

PRODUCTS/OPERATIONS

Selected Programs
First Time Homebuyer Program
Down Payment Assistance
Homeownership Loan Program
Mortgage Credit Certificate
Multifamily Development Programs
Multifamily Mortgage Revenue Bonds
Florida Affordable Housing Guarantee Program
HOME Investment Partnerships
Elderly Housing Community Loan Program
Low Income Housing Tax Credits
State Apartment Incentive Loan
Predevelopment Loan Program
State Housing Initiative Partnerships
Demonstration Loans
Affordable Housing Catalyst Program

HISTORICAL FINANCIALS

Company Type: Private

Income Statement   FYE: December 31

	ASSETS ($ mil.)	NET INCOME ($ mil.)	INCOME AS % OF ASSETS	EMPLOYEES
12/17	4,764	206	4.3%	130
12/16	4,567	141	3.1%	—
12/14	5,079	23	0.5%	—
12/12	5,721	0	—	—
Annual Growth	(3.6%)	—	—	—

2017 Year-End Financials

Return on assets: 4.3%   Sales ($ mil): 186
Return on equity: 8.3%

FLORIDA STATE UNIVERSITY

Home to the Florida State Seminoles Florida State University offers more than 300 undergraduate graduate and professionalÂ programs including M.D. (medicine) and J.D. (law) programs.Â TheÂ educational institutionÂ has 16 colleges dedicated to academic fields ranging from liberal arts music visual arts and education to criminology engineering social work and information. A major research institution the university is home to the National High Magnetic Field Laboratory or "Mag Lab" the only national lab in Florida and the only such high-magnetic facility in the US. Florida State was founded in 1851 and is part of the 11-school State University System of Florida.

Operations
Florida State boastsÂ more thanÂ 41000 students andÂ has aÂ student/faculty ratioÂ of 26:1. The school's reputation as a top-notch research schoolÂ stems from its extensive network ofÂ research facilitiesÂ that cover areasÂ such asÂ biological medicine social sciencesÂ and energy. Its facilities alsoÂ include the Center for Advanced Power Systems which is supported by the US Department of Defense and the Department of Energy. The Mag LabÂ is funded by the National Science Foundation.Â Florida State alsoÂ operates the John and Mable Ringling Museum of Art in Sarasota Florida.

Geographic Reach
The main Florida State UniversityÂ campus in Tallahassee covers about 450Â acres. The university also offers degree programs in Sarasota Florida and in the Republic of Panama. It boasts instructional programs in London Florence and Valencia as well as programs in research development and/or services in Costa Rica Croatia and Italy.

Sales and Marketing
The Florida university enrolls students from more than 120 foreign countries.

EXECUTIVES

Asoc In Vice President Research, William Sweeney
Assistant Vice President Faculty Development And Advanced, Jennifer Buchanan
Department Chair Professor, Jeff James
Vice President For Development, Perry Fulkerson
Executive Vice President, John Riveras
Vice President, Vanesa Moreno
Treasurer Mock Trial Team, Gennifer Powell
Secretary, Susan Gay
Secretary, Anne Lamarre
Msf Association Treasurer, Garrett Hilbelink
Auditors: DAVIE W MARTIN CPA TALLAHAS

LOCATIONS

HQ: FLORIDA STATE UNIVERSITY
600 W COLLEGE AVE, TALLAHASSEE, FL 323061096
Phone: 850 644-5482
Web: WWW.FOUNDATION.FSU.EDU

PRODUCTS/OPERATIONS

Selected Colleges
College of Applied Studies
College of Arts and Sciences
College of Business
College of Communication and Information
College of Criminology and Criminal Justice
College of Education
College of Engineering
College of Human Sciences
College of Law
College of Medicine
College of Motion Picture Arts
College of Music
College of Nursing
College of Social Sciences and Public Policy
College of Social Work
College of Visual Arts Theatre and Dance

HISTORICAL FINANCIALS

Company Type: Private

Income Statement   FYE: June 30

	REVENUE ($ mil.)	NET INCOME ($ mil.)	NET PROFIT MARGIN	EMPLOYEES
06/12	654	40	6.1%	13,497
06/11	607	188	31.0%	—
06/10	567	121	21.4%	—
Annual Growth	7.4%	(42.4%)	—	—

2012 Year-End Financials

Return on assets: 1.2%   Cash ($ mil.): 48
Return on equity: 1.4%
Current ratio: 6.00

FLOWORKS INTERNATIONAL LLC

EXECUTIVES

Ceo, Scott Jackson
Cfo, Gary Haire
Pres, Fabrication & Distributi, John Higgins
Pres, Ipvf, Michael Stanwood
Evp, Corp Strategy & Bus Dev, Rob Broyles
Vp & Treas, Rick Hawthorne
SEC, Suzanne Mailes-Dineff
Sr Vp & Chro, Herbert Allen
Vp, Corp Contrl & Acctng Offic, Michael Goldberg
Evp, Ipvf, Jeff Legrand
Pres,valves & Automation, Keith Barnard

Auditors: PRICEWATERHOUSECOOPERS LLP HO

LOCATIONS

HQ: FLOWORKS INTERNATIONAL LLC
3750 HWY 225, PASADENA, TX 77503
Phone: 713 943-3544

HISTORICAL FINANCIALS

Company Type: Private

Income Statement				FYE: February 2
	REVENUE ($ mil.)	NET INCOME ($ mil.)	NET PROFIT MARGIN	EMPLOYEES
02/14*	805	(30)	—	785
06/12	222	(5)	—	
Annual Growth 90.5%		—	—	—

*Fiscal year change

2014 Year-End Financials

Return on assets: (-5.2%)   Cash ($ mil.): 12
Return on equity: (-12.6%)
Current ratio: 4.70

FONTANA UNIFIED SCHOOL DISTRICT

EXECUTIVES

Supt, Leslie Boozer
Human Resources Analyst, Molly Garza
Sergeant, Doug Imhof
Coordinator, Cecilia Henderson
Coordinator, Matt Davis
Strategic Transportation Engin, Kevin Ryan
Administrative Technician, Anna Sinner
Accounting Manager, Dawn Brooks
Superintendent of Schools, Jane Smith
Administrative Aide, Theresa Gardea
Gis Analyst, Angel Gonzalez
Auditors: NIGRO NIGRO & WHITE PC TEMEC

LOCATIONS

HQ: FONTANA UNIFIED SCHOOL DISTRICT
9680 CITRUS AVE, FONTANA, CA 923355571
Phone: 909 357-7600
Web: WWW.FUSD.NET

HISTORICAL FINANCIALS

Company Type: Private

Income Statement				FYE: June 30
	REVENUE ($ mil.)	NET INCOME ($ mil.)	NET PROFIT MARGIN	EMPLOYEES
06/18	543	31	5.7%	3,627
06/17	531	27	5.1%	—
06/16*	525	23	4.5%	—
12/06	0	0	—	—
Annual Growth				

*Fiscal year change

2018 Year-End Financials

Return on assets: 3.0%   Cash ($ mil.): 299
Return on equity: 25.0%
Current ratio: —

FOOD FOR THE POOR, INC.

Food For The Poor feeds spiritual and physicalÂ hunger. The Christian charity provides health social economic and religious services for impoverished people in 17 countries in Latin America andÂ the Caribbean. Food For The Poor believes its organization serves God by helping those most in need distributing requested goods through local churches and charities. The group works through Caritas the American-Nicaraguan Foundation and others to provide vocational training clinic and school construction educational materials feeding programs and medical supplies. Food For The Poor has distributed more than $3 billion in goods since its 1982 inception; the group uses 96% of its funds on programs.

EXECUTIVES

Executive Vice President, Alvaro Pereira
Vice President Of International Operations, Rachmani Domersant
Vice President Major Giving, Natalie Carlisle
Auditors: MAYER HOFFMAN MCCANN PC BOC

LOCATIONS

HQ: FOOD FOR THE POOR, INC.
6401 LYONS RD, COCONUT CREEK, FL 330733602
Phone: 954 427-2222
Web: WWW.FOODFORTHEPOOR.ORG

HISTORICAL FINANCIALS

Company Type: Private

Income Statement				FYE: December 31
	REVENUE ($ mil.)	NET INCOME ($ mil.)	NET PROFIT MARGIN	EMPLOYEES
12/17	948	(1)	—	335
12/16	994	14	1.5%	—
12/15	1,158	(0)	—	—
12/14	913	(0)	—	—
Annual Growth 1.3%		—	—	—

2017 Year-End Financials

Return on assets: (-4.0%)   Cash ($ mil.): 22
Return on equity: (-4.6%)
Current ratio: 4.90

FOOD GIANT SUPERMARKETS, INC.

EXECUTIVES

Pres, Kevin Ladd
V Pres-Oprs*, Gary Duncan
Asst SEC-Treas*, Steve Malone
SEC*, Spencer Coates
Information Technology Manager, Brent Benton
Loan Officer, Dedra Clark
Vice President of Financial SE, Marsha Strobel
Merchandiser, Bill Cook
Area Supervisor, Bruce Broughton
Meat Supervisor, Kevin Stanford
Information Technology Special, Monica Beck

LOCATIONS

HQ: FOOD GIANT SUPERMARKETS, INC.
120 INDUSTRIAL DR, SIKESTON, MO 638015216
Phone: 573 471-3500
Web: WWW.FOODGIANT.COM

HISTORICAL FINANCIALS

Company Type: Private

Income Statement				FYE: October 1
	REVENUE ($ mil.)	NET INCOME ($ mil.)	NET PROFIT MARGIN	EMPLOYEES
10/16	725	22	3.1%	4,500
10/15	757	25	3.4%	—
10/10*	616	22	3.6%	—
09/06	468	108	23.1%	—
Annual Growth 4.5%		(14.6%)	—	—

*Fiscal year change

2016 Year-End Financials

Return on assets: 12.8%   Cash ($ mil.): 18
Return on equity: 14.0%
Current ratio: 1.70

FORDHAM UNIVERSITY

A private Catholic university Fordham offers its more than 16000 students numerous degree programs through about 10 graduate and undergraduate schools. Called the Jesuit University of New York Fordham has multiple locations including the original Rose Hill campus in the Bronx (often the scene of location shooting for movies TV shows and commercials) the Westchester campus and the Lincoln Center campus in Manhattan. It also operates a biological field station in Armonk New York and international centers in China and the UK. Fordham was founded in 1841.

Operations

Fordham offers more than 50 majors in liberal arts sciences and business. It has an undergraduate student/faculty ratio of 15:1. The university has more than 750 full-time instructors (including more than 30 Jesuits). More than 90% of its faculty holds a Ph.D. or other terminal degree.

Some 70% of Fordham's revenue comes from tuition and fees. Auxiliary enterprises bring in more than 10% of revenue. The rest of its income comes from investments contributions and grants and net assets released from restrictions.

Geographic Reach

Fordham's Rose Hill campus is located on 85 acres in the Bronx and offers studies in business liberal arts science and religion. The Lincoln Center campus provides education business administration social services and legal training while the Westchester campus provides graduate programs in a variety of subjects. The Armonk field station is the headquarters for several university research programs.

Financial Performance

In fiscal 2017 (ended June) Fordham had $596.5 million in operating revenues and $738.9 million in endowments and other investments. Operating expenses totaled $592.3 million that year.

Undergraduate tuition in 2016-17 was $47850 per student.

Company Background

The school opened in 1841 as St. John's College. It officially changed its name to Fordham University in 1907.

EXECUTIVES

Vice President Government Relations And Urban Affairs, Thomas Dunne
President, Joseph M. McShane
Provost, Stephen Freedman
Vp Finance, Frank Simio
Vp Technology And Cio, Frank Sirianni
Dean Fordham College At Lincoln Center, Robert R. Grimes
Interim Dean Fordham College At Rose Hill, John Harrington
Dean Gabelli School Of Business, Donna Rapaccioli
Dean Fordham School Of Professional And Continuing Studies, Isabelle Frank
Dean Graduate School Of Arts And Sciences, Eva Badowska
Dean Graduate School Of Education, James J. Hennessy
Dean Graduate School Of Religion And Religious Education, C. Colt Anderson
Dean Graduate School Of Social Service, Debra M. McPhee
Dean School Of Law, Michael M. Martin
Assistant Vice President University Marketing Communications, Kate Spencer
Vice President University Mission And Ministry, Joseph Quinn
Director Of Admissions And Marketing, Glenn S Berman
Associate Vice President Information Technology, Fleur Eshghi
Vice President For Finance, Nicholas Milowski
Assistant Vice President For Development And University Events, Elizabeth Manigan
Associate Vice President, Z Hong
Mba Candidate 18 Vice President Full Time Students, Joe Colandrea
Vice President For Enrollment Admissions, Laurence J Abraham
Assistant Vice President, Tracey Vranich
Former Vice President, Anthony P Carter
Senior Vice President And General Counsel Lockheed Martin Corporation, Maryanne R Lavan
Vice President, John Massarelli
Chairman Board Of Trustees, Robert D. (Bob) Daleo, age 70
Vice Chairman Board Of Trustees, Edward M. Stroz
Secretary, Carla M Parris
Senior Secretary, Sandra Arnold
Secretary, Patricia Crea
Board Member, Lindsay Goodman
Secretary, Alexandra Fisher
Treasurer, Viliam Litavec
Treasurer, Gilda Severiano
Secretary, Nanette Michel
Secretary, Linda Perri
Secretary, Nelson Roman
Soccer Club Treasurer, Alexander Khom
Chairman Emeritus Espn Inc., Herbert A Granath
Secretary, Raj Ghayalod
Auditors: KPMG LLP NEW YORK NY

LOCATIONS

HQ: FORDHAM UNIVERSITY
441 E FORDHAM RD, BRONX, NY 104589993
Phone: 718 817-1000
Web: WWW.FORDHAM.EDU

PRODUCTS/OPERATIONS

2017 Sales

	$ mil.	% of total
Net tuition & fees	424	71
Net auxiliary enterprises	78	13
Investments	27	5
Contributions & private grants	27	4
Government grants	17	3
Net assets released from restrictions	4	1
Other	16	3
Total	596	100

Selected Colleges

Graduate and Professional
  Graduate School of Arts and Sciences
  Graduate School of Business
  Graduate School of Education
  Graduate School of Religion and Religious Education
  Graduate School of Social Services
  School of Law
Undergraduate
  Fordham College at Lincoln Center
  Fordham College at Rose Hill
  Gabelli School of Business
  School of Professional and Continuing Studies

HISTORICAL FINANCIALS

Company Type: Private

Income Statement				FYE: June 30
	REVENUE ($ mil.)	NET INCOME ($ mil.)	NET PROFIT MARGIN	EMPLOYEES
06/18	631	41	6.6%	4,070
06/16	588	(52)	—	—
06/14	566	100	17.7%	—
06/12	518	60	11.6%	—
Annual Growth	3.4%	(5.9%)	—	—

2018 Year-End Financials

Return on assets: 2.1%   Cash ($ mil.): 14
Return on equity: 3.1%
Current ratio: —

FORGE INDUSTRIES, INC.

Forge Industries connects a diverse group of businesses. OperatingÂ viaÂ several subsidiaries theÂ family-owned private holding company distributesÂ thousands ofÂ products from industrial gears and bearings to asphalt and concrete construction equipment.Â Businesses include construction/landscape equipmentÂ maker Miller SpreaderÂ and sister companies Akron Gear & Engineering and Bearing Distributors (BDI)Â Forge's globalÂ product and service distributor. Forge'sÂ lineup includesÂ curb builders and hand tools as well as rebuild and repair gearboxes redesign customer equipment customize gear reducers and machining services.Â Customers work in the automotive package handling food processing and landscape industries.

EXECUTIVES

Chb, William T James II
V Pres*, W Thomas James III
Pres*, Carl G James
Cfo*, Dan Maisonville
Asst SEC*, Gary Davis
Contrl, Robert Ruester
Vice President, John Neuman
Auditors: KPMG LLP

LOCATIONS

HQ: FORGE INDUSTRIES, INC.
4450 MARKET ST, YOUNGSTOWN, OH 445121512
Phone: 330 782-8301

COMPETITORS

Applied Industrial Technologies
Bosch Rexroth
DXP Enterprises

NTN Bearing Corp. of America
WESCO International

HISTORICAL FINANCIALS

Company Type: Private

Income Statement				FYE: December 31
	REVENUE ($ mil.)	NET INCOME ($ mil.)	NET PROFIT MARGIN	EMPLOYEES
12/08	537	6	1.2%	2,000
12/07	605	0	—	—
12/06	0	0	—	—
12/05	404	73	18.1%	—
Annual Growth	9.9%	(56.0%)	—	—

2008 Year-End Financials

Return on assets: 3.1%   Cash ($ mil.): 9
Return on equity: 5.9%
Current ratio: 1.90

FORSYTH COUNTY BOARD OF EDUCATION

EXECUTIVES

Chairperson, Darla Light
Cfo*, Dan Jones
Executive, Amanda Studt
Media Specialist, Jean Lipscomb
Teacher, Amy Knisely
Kindergarten Teacher, Julie Luke
Auditors: MAULDIN & JENKINS LLC ATLANT

LOCATIONS

HQ: FORSYTH COUNTY BOARD OF EDUCATION
1120 DAHLONEGA HWY, CUMMING, GA 300404536
Phone: 770 887-2461
Web: WWW.FORSYTH.K12.GA.US

HISTORICAL FINANCIALS

Company Type: Private

Income Statement				FYE: June 30
	REVENUE ($ mil.)	NET INCOME ($ mil.)	NET PROFIT MARGIN	EMPLOYEES
06/17	526	(16)	—	4,160
06/16	472	21	4.5%	—
06/12	354	(6)	—	—
06/11	346	(10)	—	—
Annual Growth	7.2%	—	—	—

2017 Year-End Financials

Return on assets: (-1.4%)   Cash ($ mil.): 158
Return on equity: (-5.5%)
Current ratio: —

FORT WORTH INDEPENDENT SCHOOL DISTRICT

EXECUTIVES

Sup, Kent Scribner
Executive Officer, Martin Yarobough

Executive Officer, Camille Rodriguez
Executive Officer, Judy Needham
Executive Officer, Blaine Buchenau
Executive Officer, Diana Vargas
Staff, Micheal Lee
Executive Officer, Steven Senevy
Accounting Staff, Deborah Cooper-Boone
Budget Manager, Anna Shelton
Music Teacher, Layne Trent
Auditors: WEAVER AND TIDWELL LLP FORTH

LOCATIONS

HQ: FORT WORTH INDEPENDENT SCHOOL DISTRICT
100 N UNIVERSITY DR, FORT WORTH, TX 761071360
Phone: 817 871-2000
Web: WWW.FWISD.ORG

HISTORICAL FINANCIALS

Company Type: Private

Income Statement   FYE: June 30

	REVENUE ($ mil.)	NET INCOME ($ mil.)	NET PROFIT MARGIN	EMPLOYEES
06/17	924	133	14.4%	10,360
06/16	909	(101)	—	—
06/15	843	64	7.7%	—
06/12	777	(98)	—	—
Annual Growth	3.5%	—	—	—

FORTIS CONSTRUCTION, INC.

Fortis Construction isn't afraid to get its hands dirty. TheÂ fast-growing US construction company offers general contracting preconstruction construction management and environmentally-friendly green building services to customers primarily inÂ Portland OregonÂ and others in the Pacific Northwest. It specializes in remodeling and upgrading corporate offices health care facilitiesÂ retail complexes and schools; it also conducts seismic and structural upgrades. Customers have included Oregon State University Portland State University PPG Industries and StanCorp.

EXECUTIVES

Vice President Information Technology, Mark Callahan
Auditors: ALDRICH CPAS AND ADVISORS LLP

LOCATIONS

HQ: FORTIS CONSTRUCTION, INC.
1705 SW TAYLOR ST STE 200, PORTLAND, OR 972051922
Phone: 503 459-4477
Web: WWW.FORTISCONSTRUCTION.COM

PRODUCTS/OPERATIONS

Selected Services
Construction management
General contracting
Green building
Preconstruction
Web-based collaboration and electronic document management

COMPETITORS

Andersen Construction
Hoffman Corporation
Jacobsen Construction
Panattoni Construction

R&H Construction
S.D. Deacon
Swinerton Builders

HISTORICAL FINANCIALS

Company Type: Private

Income Statement   FYE: December 31

	REVENUE ($ mil.)	NET INCOME ($ mil.)	NET PROFIT MARGIN	EMPLOYEES
12/16	782	30	3.9%	175
12/15	468	18	3.9%	—
12/14	282	14	5.0%	—
Annual Growth	66.6%	48.0%		

2016 Year-End Financials
Return on assets: 20.5%
Return on equity: 75.8%
Current ratio: 1.40

Cash ($ mil.): 41

FRANCISCAN ALLIANCE, INC.

The Franciscan Alliance keeps watch over a family of hospitals. The not-for-profit organization operates more than a dozen hospitals in Indiana and south suburban Chicago. The hospitals house about 3500 beds and include specialist centers for cancer care heart and vascular care weight loss pediatrics and women's health. In addition to inpatient acute care services they operate numerous outpatient facilities and medical practices within their local service areas. Other subsidiaries and affiliates perform clinical laboratory tests offer home health services and provide support services to the system. Franciscan Alliance was founded and is sponsored by the Sisters of St. Francis of Perpetual Adoration.

Operations
Franciscan Alliance's hospitals handle about 100000 inpatient visits annually. The organization also handles about 3 million outpatient visits each year at its hospitals clinics and practice offices. Its physician practice organization includes about 700 doctors.

Along with providing a wide range of health care services Franciscan Alliance educates future health care providers through affiliations with area universities. The schools offer a variety of degree programs in fields including nursing medical technician and pharmacy residency.

Geographic Reach
Franciscan Alliance's hospitals are located in about ten communities in Indiana as well as in southern Chicago suburbs. The facilities serve patients in parts of Michigan as well. The organization also operates hundreds of outpatient clinics and physician offices in the area as well as a data center in Beech Grove Indiana.

Strategy
In 2011 the Sisters of St. Francis of Perpetual Adoration decided to change the name of the health system from Sisters of St. Francis Health Services to Franciscan Alliance to spread brand awareness and illustrate cohesiveness among the system's various facilities. The name change came after several months of consumer research and took about a year to be fully implemented across the entire system.

Franciscan Alliance also expanded through new construction in 2011 with the completion of the first phase of its Indianapolis Campus Expansion project. The health system moved a number of services into the new patient tower there including emergency services surgical suites and a wound

care institute. In 2012 the company closed its Beech Grove hospital and consolidated services to the expanded Indianapolis center. It also opened a new short-stay hospital in Carmel that year.

In 2013 however the company announced that it would explore options to sell all or part of its two Franciscan St. James Health hospitals. The organization sought a partner to invest in capital improvements at the facilities. No buyer stepped forward but economic conditions improved enough by 2014 that the alliance said it was no longer searching for a buyer or investor. It also broke ground on a Hospice facility opened a specialized wound-care center and started a $10.2 million renovation at its St. Margaret facility.

Mergers and Acquisitions
In 2011 Franciscan Alliance grew its outpatient facilities by acquiring Surgical Hospital of Munster which serves as an outpatient surgery center of Franciscan Physicians Hospital.

EXECUTIVES

President Ceo, Kevin Leahy
President And Ceo Franciscan St. Margaret Health, Michael J. Stenger
Ceo Franciscan Health Dyer Franciscan Health Hammond Franciscan Health Munster, Patrick Maloney
Ceo Western Indiana Region, Terrance E. Wilson
Svp And Coo Inpatient Services, Gene Diamond
President And Ceo Crown Point, Barbara Anderson
President And Ceo Franciscan St. Francis Health Indianapolis Mooresville And Carmel, James Callaghan
Corporate Svp Post-acute Services, Thomas Gryzbek
Auditors: I PNCEWATERHOUSECOOPERS LLP

LOCATIONS

HQ: FRANCISCAN ALLIANCE, INC.
3510 PARK PL W STE 200, MISHAWAKA, IN 465453515
Phone: 574 273-3867

PRODUCTS/OPERATIONS

Selected Operations
St. Anthony Health (Crown Point and Michigan City Indiana)
St. Elizabeth Health (Crawfordsville Lafayette Central Lafayette East Indiana)
St. Francis Health (Carmel Indianapolis and Mooresville Indiana)
St. James Health (Chicago Heights and Olympia Fields Illinois)
St. Margaret Health (Hammond and Dyer Indiana)
Franciscan Healthcare Munster (formerly Physicians Hospital; Munster Indiana)

Selected Services
Anticoagulation Clinics
Behavioral Health
Cancer Care
Colon and Rectal Surgery
Diabetes Care
Ear Nose and Throat
Emergency Medicine
Heart & Vascular
Home Health Care
Hospice
Imaging
Joint & Spine Care
Laboratory Services
Neurology
Neurosurgery
Occupational Health
Ophthalmology
Pain Management
Palliative Medicine
Pediatrics
Plastic Surgery
Primary Care Physicians
Pulmonary Medicine
Registered Dietitians

Rehabilitation Services
Robotic Surgery
Senior Services
Sleep Disorders
Sports Medicine
Surgical Services
Urgent Care
Weight Loss/Bariatrics
Women's Health/OBGYN
Wound Care

Selected Hospitals

Franciscan St. Anthony - Crown Point
Franciscan St. Anthony - Michigan City
Franciscan St. Elizabeth - Lafayette Central
Franciscan St. Elizabeth - Lafayette East
Franciscan St. Elizabeth - Crawfordsville
Franciscan St. Francis - Carmel
Franciscan St. Francis - Indianapolis
Franciscan St. Francis - Mooresville
Franciscan St. James - Chicago Heights
Franciscan St. James - Olympia Fields
Franciscan St. Margaret - Dyer
Franciscan St. Margaret - Hammond
Franciscan Healthcare - Munster

COMPETITORS

Advocate Health Care
Ascension Health
Community Health Network
Covenant Ministries
IU Health
Memorial Hospital & Health System
NorthShore University HealthSystem
Northwestern Memorial HealthCare
Porter Health Care System
Riverview Hospital
Rush System for Health
Sinai Health System
St. Bernard Hospital and Health Care Center
Union Hospital (Indiana)
University of Chicago Medical Center

HISTORICAL FINANCIALS

Company Type: Private

Income Statement   FYE: December 31

	REVENUE ($ mil.)	NET INCOME ($ mil.)	NET PROFIT MARGIN	EMPLOYEES
12/18	3,144	14	0.5%	19,000
12/15	2,731	250	9.2%	—
12/14	2,661	274	10.3%	—
12/13	2,588	92	3.6%	—
Annual Growth	4.0%	(31.2%)	—	—

2018 Year-End Financials

Return on assets: 0.3%   Cash ($ mil.): 70
Return on equity: 0.5%
Current ratio: 1.40

FRANCISCAN HEALTH SYSTEM

St. Francis himself may have hailed from Italy but his followers look after the health of the residents of the South Puget Sound area through the Franciscan Health System. The not-for-profit system includes five full-service hospitals. The oldest and largest hospital is St. Joseph Medical Center in Tacoma Washington a 320-bed facility. Its facilities include community hospitals St. Clare Hospital (in Lakewood) and St. Francis Hospital (in Federal Way) as well as a hospice program and numerous primary and specialty care clinics. Its St. Anthony Hospital is an 80-bed full service pharmacy and home medical equipment retail location at Gig Harbor.

Geographic Reach

Franciscan Health System serves patients in Tacoma Washington and surrounding areas.

Financial Performance

The company gets most of its revenues from patient services. Other sources of income includes foundation gifts and investment community benefit charity care and uncompensated care (unreimbursed costs of serving patients enrolled in Medicaid and other state-subsidized programs).

Strategy

Franciscan Health System and Harrison Medical Center are looking to join forces while Franciscan's parent continues in talks to combine its Northwest operations with PeaceHealth of Vancouver Washington. If both plans are approved by regulators Harrison will become part of the largest community hospital system in the Northwest with facilities in Alaska Washington and Oregon. Both the Harrison-Franciscan affiliation and that of Franciscan's parent Catholic Health Initiatives with PeaceHealth is slated to be approved in 2013.

In addition Franciscan Health System is collaborating with the MultiCare Health System and TRA Medical Imaging to build a women's imaging and breast cancer care center.

St. Elizabeth Hospital opened its doors in 2011 in Enumclaw replacing Enumclaw Regional Hospital as that community's acute-care facility.

Company Background

St. Joseph Medical Center in Tacoma (the health system's oldest facility) was founded by the Sisters of St. Francis in 1891.

EXECUTIVES

Pharmacy Manager, Michael Bonck
Director Of Pharmacy, Timothy W Lynch
Medical Director, Martin Cieri
Vice President Of Quality And Associate Chief Marketing Officer, Kimberly Moore
Physical Therapy Director, DAVID LUNDGREN
Medical Director, Paul Darby

LOCATIONS

HQ: FRANCISCAN HEALTH SYSTEM
1717 S J ST, TACOMA, WA 984054933
Phone: 253 426-4101

PRODUCTS/OPERATIONS

Key Facilities and Services

Carol Milgard Breast Center Tacoma
Franciscan Center for Weight Management Federal Way
Franciscan Dialysis Center Eastside Tacoma
Franciscan Medical Group primary-care and specialty-care clinics
Franciscan Hospice House University Place
Franciscan Port Clinic Tacoma
Gig Harbor Medical Pavilion Gig Harbor
Gig Harbor Ambulatory Surgery Clinic Gig Harbor
St. Anthony Hospital Gig Harbor
St. Clare Hospital Lakewood
St. Clare Specialty Center Lakewood
St. Clare Medical Pavilion Lakewood
St. Elizabeth Hospital Enumclaw
St. Francis Hospital Federal Way
St. Francis Outpatient Center Federal Way
St. Joseph Medical Center Tacoma
St. Joseph Outpatient Center Tacoma
St. Joseph Heart & Vascular Center Tacoma
St. Joseph Dialysis Center Tacoma
St. Joseph Dialysis Center Gig Harbor
St. Joseph Dialysis Center Puyallup
St. Joseph Medical Clinic Tacoma
St. Joseph Medical Pavilion Tacoma
Milgard Medical Pavilion at St. Anthony Gig Harbor
Women's Health & Breast Center Federal Way

COMPETITORS

Harrison Medical Center
MultiCare Health System
Overlake Hospital
PeaceHealth
Providence St. Joseph Health
Seattle Children's Hospital
Swedish Health Services
Yakima Valley Memorial

HISTORICAL FINANCIALS

Company Type: Private

Income Statement   FYE: June 30

	REVENUE ($ mil.)	NET INCOME ($ mil.)	NET PROFIT MARGIN	EMPLOYEES
06/16	637	51	8.0%	3,183
06/15	610	56	9.2%	—
06/14	1,190	(106)	—	—
06/10	1,093	71	6.5%	—
Annual Growth	(8.6%)	(5.4%)	—	—

2016 Year-End Financials

Return on assets: 11.2%   Cash ($ mil.): 113
Return on equity: 13.8%
Current ratio: 3.10

FRANCISCAN MEDICAL GROUP

EXECUTIVES

Orthopedic Surgeon, Christo Koulisis
Orthopedic Surgeon, Kevin Schoenfelder
Neurology Specialist, Marc Goldman
Pediatrician, Rachelle Vicencio
Obstetrician, Richelle Olsen
Obstetrician Gynecologist, Robert Holland
Auditors: CATHOLIC HEALTH INITIATIVES E

LOCATIONS

HQ: FRANCISCAN MEDICAL GROUP
1717 S J ST, TACOMA, WA 984054933
Phone: 253 792-4365

HISTORICAL FINANCIALS

Company Type: Private

Income Statement   FYE: June 30

	REVENUE ($ mil.)	NET INCOME ($ mil.)	NET PROFIT MARGIN	EMPLOYEES
06/17	472	9	1.9%	24
06/14	336	55	16.5%	—
06/13	200	(23)	—	—
Annual Growth	23.9%	—	—	—

2017 Year-End Financials

Return on assets: 6.4%   Cash ($ mil.): 1
Return on equity: 14.6%
Current ratio: 1.20

FRANCISCAN MISSIONARIES OF OUR LADY HEALTH SYSTEM, INC.

EXECUTIVES

Pres-Ceo, Richard R Vath
V Pres, Pete Guarisco
SEC-Treas, Sr Helen Cahill
Cfo, Howard Harvill
Manager of Management Informat, Karen Parker
Manager, Brittney Sprague
Information Specialist, Chris Jones
Executive Assistant, Laura Chaney
Information Specialist, Trisha A Tunis
It Security, Becky Davis
Buyer, Carrie Tuftee
Auditors: KPMG LLP BATON ROUGE LA

LOCATIONS

HQ: FRANCISCAN MISSIONARIES OF OUR LADY
 HEALTH SYSTEM, INC.
 4200 ESSEN LN, BATON ROUGE, LA 708092158
Phone: 225 923-2701
Web: WWW.FMOLSISTERS.COM

HISTORICAL FINANCIALS
Company Type: Private

Income Statement				FYE: June 30
	REVENUE ($ mil.)	NET INCOME ($ mil.)	NET PROFIT MARGIN	EMPLOYEES
06/18	2,029	106	5.3%	9,000
06/17	1,911	112	5.9%	—
06/15	122	(34)	—	—
06/14	106	(19)	—	—
Annual Growth	109.1%	—	—	—

2018 Year-End Financials
Return on assets: 3.5%   Cash ($ mil.): 235
Return on equity: 7.5%
Current ratio: 1.60

FRANKLIN COUNTY BOARD OF COMMISSIONERS

EXECUTIVES

Commissioner, Marilyn Brown
Staff, Jenell Williams
Coordinator, Cecilia Weirick
Coordinator, Kris McDaniel
Coordinator, Kysten Palmore
Coordinator, Patti Froehlich
Coordinator, Phyllis Roberts
Contractor, Catherine Richards
Admin SEC, Victoria C
Director of Communications, Amy Lowe
Coordinator, Anne Watson
Auditors: DAVE YOST AUDITOR OF STATE C

LOCATIONS

HQ: FRANKLIN COUNTY BOARD OF COMMISSIONERS
 373 S HIGH ST FL 26, COLUMBUS, OH 432154591
Phone: 614 525-3322
Web: WWW.FRANKLINCOUNTYOHIO.GOV

HISTORICAL FINANCIALS
Company Type: Private

Income Statement				FYE: December 31
	REVENUE ($ mil.)	NET INCOME ($ mil.)	NET PROFIT MARGIN	EMPLOYEES
12/17	1,281	85	6.7%	6,000
12/16	1,226	48	3.9%	—
12/09	1,163	(25)	—	—
12/08	1,169	(38)	—	—
Annual Growth	1.0%	—	—	—

2017 Year-End Financials
Return on assets: 3.0%   Cash ($ mil.): 20
Return on equity: 6.6%
Current ratio: —

FRANKLIN SQUARE HOSPITAL CENTER, INC.

Franklin Square Hospital Center has made a declaration to care for the residents of eastern Baltimore County Maryland. The facility offers a wide range of specialties through some 700 doctors and about 380 beds. Since 1998 the hospital has been part of MedStar Health the region's largest integrated health system. As a teaching hospital Franklin Square offers a number of residency programs including internal and family medicine OB-GYN and surgery. The not-for-profit hospital offers its medical services through half a dozen primary service lines: Medicine Surgery Women's and Children's Care Oncology Behavioral Health and Community Health and Wellness.

Operations
Franklin Square Hospital boasts more than 3000 skilled professions including 1000-plus nurses and 400 staff physicians and more than 750 independently practicing physicians.

Geographic Reach
The only one of its kind in the region Franklin Square's Cancer Institute serves oncology patients by offering education and prevention services research and diagnostic treatment.

Strategy
The hospital which logs one of the highest numbers of cancer admissions in Maryland is working to expand its cancer services as it anticipates admissions to grow.

In fact the company is expanding other services as well also in anticipation of future patient demand. The hospital built a 300-bed patient tower on the campus that includes an expanded emergency department dedicated pediatric and inpatient suites and an expanded 50-bed critical care unit.

EXECUTIVES

Radiology Director, Sandy Winfield
Medical Director, Trudy Hall

LOCATIONS

HQ: FRANKLIN SQUARE HOSPITAL CENTER, INC.
 9000 FRANKLIN SQUARE DR, BALTIMORE, MD
 212373901
Phone: 410 933-2777
Web: WWW.MEDSTARFRANKLINSQUARE.ORG

PRODUCTS/OPERATIONS

Selected Services
Ambulatory & Minimally Invasive Surgery
Cancer Services
Cyberknife
da Vinci Robotic Surgery
Diagnostic Imaging and Radiology
Obstetrics & Neonatology
Orthopedics & Joint Replacement Therapies
Sleep Disorders
Women's Services

COMPETITORS

Anne Arundel Medical Center	LifeBridge Health
Bon Secours Health	MedStar Union Memorial Hospital
GBMC	Sinai Hospital of Baltimore
Good Samaritan Hospital of Maryland	St. Agnes HealthCare
Harbor Hospital	St. Joseph Medical Center
Johns Hopkins Bayview Medical Center	University of Maryland Medical System
Johns Hopkins Health System	Upper Chesapeake Health
Johns Hopkins Medicine	

HISTORICAL FINANCIALS
Company Type: Private

Income Statement				FYE: June 30
	REVENUE ($ mil.)	NET INCOME ($ mil.)	NET PROFIT MARGIN	EMPLOYEES
06/16	506	10	2.1%	3,019
06/15	492	17	3.5%	—
06/11	452	18	4.0%	—
06/10	439	31	7.1%	—
Annual Growth	2.4%	(16.2%)	—	—

2016 Year-End Financials
Return on assets: 3.9%   Cash ($ mil.): 1
Return on equity: 5.1%
Current ratio: 1.20

FREEMAN HEALTH SYSTEM

Freeman Health System (FHS) offers comprehensive health and behavioral health services to the residents of Arkansas Kansas Missouri and Oklahoma through three hospitals with a total of more than 500 beds. Specialty facilities include a full-service cardiothoracic and vascular program at the Freeman Heart Institute and behavioral health services through its Ozark Health Center. Community-owned not-for-profit FHS also operates two urgent care centers a separate sleep center several doctors' office buildings and serves as a teaching hospital with three residency programs (ear nose and throat; emergency medicine; and internal medicine). FHS employs more than 300 physicians in 60 specialties.

Operations
FHS operates three Missouri hospitals - Freeman Hospital West and Freeman Hospital East in Joplin and Freeman Neosho in Neosho. Its Ozark Center provides behavioral health services to patients from Missouri Arkansas Oklahoma and Kansas.

Strategy
Like most health care providers FHS has been working to update it facilities and expand it offerings. To that end in 2013 it opened a transitional

living and life skills assistance center for homeless teens and teamed with an autism support group to design an autism treatment program for its Ozark Center. The prior year it christened Will's Place behavioral health center for children and opened a $2 million sports and rehabilitation center.

Company Background

Located in Joplin Missouri — the site of the deadly E5 tornado that killed 161 people in May 2011— Freeman Health System was the only fully functional hospital in the aftermath of the disaster. Rival St. John's Regional Medical Center just two miles away was destroyed. However Ozark Health Center FHS's behavioral health division lost nine buildings in the disaster.

EXECUTIVES

Pres- Ceo, Paula Baker
Cfo*, Steven Graddy
Exec V Pres*, Joseph Kirk
Cmo*, Richard D Schooler
Cro*, Kevin Gaudette
Specialist, Thomas Coy
Auditors: BKD LLP SPRINGFIELD MISSOUR

LOCATIONS

HQ: FREEMAN HEALTH SYSTEM
   1102 W 32ND ST, JOPLIN, MO 648043503
Phone: 417 347-1111

PRODUCTS/OPERATIONS

Selected Services

Autism Services
Behavioral/mental health
Bladder care
Cancer care
Children's Miracle Network Hospitals
Clinical trials
Cosmetic/reconstructive surgery
Critical Care (ICU)
Diabetes education
Digestive care
Emergency medicine
Family care
Family counseling
Geriatric medicine
Health screenings
Hearing services
Home care
Internal medicine
Internet Addiction Services
Kidney Care
Lung care
Maternity
Neonatal intensive care
Nephrology & dialysis
Neurology & neurosurgery
Occupational medicine
Orthopedics
Pain management
Palliative care
QuickMeds Pharmacy™
Radiology
Rehabilitation
Senior Services
Skilled nursing
Sleep disorders
Sports medicine
Substance abuse services
Surgery
Tobacco cessation
Transitional Care Unit (TCU)
Urgent care
Women's Services
Wound care

Selected Facilities

Freeman Hospital West - Joplin MO
Freeman Hospital East - Joplin MO
Freeman Neosho Hospital - Neosho MO
Freeman Business Center - Joplin MO
Ozark Center - Joplin Missouri

COMPETITORS

Catholic Health Initiatives
Children's Mercy Hospital
Heartland Regional Medical
Mercy Health

HISTORICAL FINANCIALS

Company Type: Private

Income Statement
FYE: March 31

	REVENUE ($ mil.)	NET INCOME ($ mil.)	NET PROFIT MARGIN	EMPLOYEES
03/18	588	51	8.7%	3,887
03/17	564	45	8.1%	—
03/11	452	7	1.7%	—
03/10	474	30	6.5%	—
Annual Growth	2.7%	6.6%		—

2018 Year-End Financials
Return on assets: 8.1%
Return on equity: 12.0%
Current ratio: 1.90
Cash ($ mil.): 43

FRESH MARK, INC.

Fresh Mark is a leading producer of smoked and processed pork products for the domestic and international retail and foodservice industries. From its three plants in Ohio the company makes and markets such products as bacon (raw par-cooked and cooked) deli sausage ham (natural and smoked) hot dogs and lunch meats under the Sugardale and Superior's brands. The company also produces private-label processed meat products for others and supplies the foodservice industry through its Sugardale Food Service business. Founded in 1920 Fresh Mark is owned and operated by the Genshaft family.

EXECUTIVES

Vice President Of Resource Management, Rick Hawley
Vice President, Monica Taylor
Auditors: ERNST & YOUNG LLP AKRON OH

LOCATIONS

HQ: FRESH MARK, INC.
   1888 SOUTHWAY ST SE, MASSILLON, OH 44646
Phone: 330 834-3669
Web: WWW.FRESHMARK.COM

PRODUCTS/OPERATIONS

Selected Products

Bacon
Deli meats
Dry sausage
Ham
Luncheon meats
Specialty meat items
Weiners

COMPETITORS

Birchwood Meat & Provision
Boar's Head
Cargill Meat Solutions
Carl Buddig
Coleman Natural Foods
ConAgra
Farmland Foods
Hormel
Indiana Packers
JBS USA
Johnsonville Sausage
Smithfield Foods
Tyson Foods

HISTORICAL FINANCIALS

Company Type: Private

Income Statement
FYE: January 1

	REVENUE ($ mil.)	NET INCOME ($ mil.)	NET PROFIT MARGIN	EMPLOYEES
01/11*	795	59	7.5%	2,300
12/07	534	31	5.8%	—
12/06	481	21	4.5%	—
12/05	481	23	4.9%	—
Annual Growth	10.6%	20.4%	—	—

*Fiscal year change

2011 Year-End Financials
Return on assets: 3.9%
Return on equity: 7.5%
Current ratio: 0.90
Cash ($ mil.): 4

FRESNO COMMUNITY HOSPITAL AND MEDICAL CENTER

EXECUTIVES

Pres-Ceo, Phillip Hinton
Ceo*, Tim A Joslin
Cfo*, William Grigg
Treas*, Roger Fretwell
Sr V Pres*, Mike Kingbury
Sr V Pres*, Stephen Walter
V Pres*, Les Abercrombie
Network Administrator, Hadi Habib
Network Administrator, Ian Reith
Pacs Administrator, Jason Hulsey
Network Administrator, John Ounesavath
Auditors: MOSS ADAMS LLP STOCKTON CA

LOCATIONS

HQ: FRESNO COMMUNITY HOSPITAL AND MEDICAL CENTER
   2823 FRESNO ST, FRESNO, CA 937211324
Phone: 559 459-3948
Web: WWW.COMMUNITYMEDICAL.ORG

HISTORICAL FINANCIALS

Company Type: Private

Income Statement
FYE: August 31

	REVENUE ($ mil.)	NET INCOME ($ mil.)	NET PROFIT MARGIN	EMPLOYEES
08/15	1,571	139	8.9%	5,045
08/10	1,027	9	0.9%	—
08/09	1,010	65	6.5%	—
Annual Growth	7.6%	13.3%	—	—

2015 Year-End Financials
Return on assets: 7.8%
Return on equity: 13.3%
Current ratio: 0.50
Cash ($ mil.): 62

FRESNO UNIFIED SCHOOL DISTRICT

EXECUTIVES

Supt, Michael Hanson
Asst Supt-Oprs*, Rick Hausman
Magnet School Coordinator, Tammy Townsend
Auditors: PERRY SMITH SACRAMENTO CALIF

LOCATIONS

HQ: FRESNO UNIFIED SCHOOL DISTRICT
2309 TULARE ST, FRESNO, CA 937212287
Phone: 559 457-3000
Web: WWW.FRESNOUNIFIED.ORG

HISTORICAL FINANCIALS

Company Type: Private

Income Statement				FYE: June 30
	REVENUE ($ mil.)	NET INCOME ($ mil.)	NET PROFIT MARGIN	EMPLOYEES
06/10	692	(13)	—	8,400
06/09	757	0	0.1%	—
06/08	771	(40)	—	—
06/07	781	74	9.5%	—
Annual Growth	(3.9%)	—	—	—

2010 Year-End Financials

Return on assets: (-1.5%)   Cash ($ mil.): 221
Return on equity: (-4.6%)
Current ratio: —

FROEDTERT MEMORIAL LUTHERAN HOSPITAL, INC.

Patients in southeastern Wisconsin count on Froedtert Memorial Lutheran Hospital for a full range of health services including trauma transplant sports medicine and senior care. The 500-bed hospital also known as Froedtert & The Medical College of Wisconsin is part of the Froedtert (pronounced "fray-dert") Health system. Specialty units include cancer dermatology neuroscience birthing fertility urology and vein clinics. The hospital also serves as a teaching facility for the Medical College of Wisconsin and it partners with the Children's Hospital of Wisconsin to provide pediatric services. Froedtert Hospital which was founded in 1980 operates the only adult Level I trauma center in the region.

Operations

Froedtert Health offers medical practice care in roughly 25 specialties and sub-specialties. Beyond the hospital's walls it operates four diagnostic imaging centers as well as rehabilitation facilities and a handful of primary care clinics in the community. The Froedtert Health system also includes Community Memorial Hospital in Menomonee Falls Wisconsin; St. Joseph's Hospital in West Bend Wisconsin; and Froedtert Health Medical Group.

Altogether the system's hospitals have 781 beds and see nearly 40000 admissions annually. They also manage more than 900000 outpatient visits each year. In 2014 Froedtert Hospital alone had about 65000 emergency department visits more than 736000 outpatient visits and delivered more than 2000 babies.

Strategy

To help advance the health of its service communities Froedtert Health is investing some $12 million to establish a new 22000-sq.-ft. health clinic in Milwaukee. It is partnering with clinic operator Sixteenth Street Community Health Centers on the project which is intended to address the needs of medically underserved neighborhoods. The facility will provide specialty care cancer prevention and access to cancer clinical trials.

EXECUTIVES

President Froedtert Hospital, Catherine (Cathy) Buck
Svp Finance, Jeffrey Van De Kreeke
President And Ceo Froedtert Health, Catherine A. Jacobson
Chief Medical Officer Froedtert Hospital, Lee Biblo
Coo Froedtert Health And President Community Memorial Hospital, Dennis Pollard
Vp And Cio, Robert DeGrand
Vp Perioperative Services, Gary Colpaert
Vp Supply Chain And Pharmacy, James Klauck
Vp Ambulatory Services, Katherine Bagemihl
Vp Patient Care Services, Kathleen Bechtel
Vp Clinical Integration And Payer Strategies, Patricia Ruff
Evp, Peter Pruessing
Assistant Vice President Finance And Decision Support Services, Timothy Waldoch
Senior Vice President Medical Affair, Andrew J Norton
Medical Director, Lois Connolly
Vice President, Patti Kneiser
Vice President, Julie Kerk
Medical Director Case Management, Pooja Nagpal
Vice President Chief Diversity Officer, Andres Gonzalez
Senior Vice President Chief Human Resources Officer, Eric Humphrey
Vice President Of Marketing And Communications, Kathi Perlewitz
Senior Vice President Service Line And Network Development, Dean Thomas
Executive Medical Director, Douglas Marx
Senior Vice President Chief Experience Officer, Steve Basilotto
Vice President, Ed Hardin
Vice President, Janet Kummeth
Treasurer, Roger D Pierce
Auditors: KPMG LLP COLUMBUS OH

LOCATIONS

HQ: FROEDTERT MEMORIAL LUTHERAN HOSPITAL, INC.
9200 W WISCONSIN AVE, MILWAUKEE, WI 532263522
Phone: 414 805-3000
Web: WWW.FROEDTERT.COM

PRODUCTS/OPERATIONS

Selected Departments Centers and Programs
Clinical Cancer Center
  Blood and Lymph Node Cancer Program
  Blood and Marrow Transplant Program
  Bone and Connective Tissue Cancer Program
  Brain and Spine Tumor Program
  Breast Cancer Program
  Cancer Genetics Screening Program
  Colorectal Cancer Program
  Endocrine Cancer Program
  Eye/Orbital Cancer Program
  Geriatric Oncology
  Gynecologic Cancer Program
  Head and Neck Cancer Program
  Liver Pancreas and Bile Duct Cancer Program
  Neuro-oncology Cognitive Clinic
  Palliative Care Program

  Plastic Surgery Center
  Prostate and Urologic Cancer Program
  Skin Cancer Center
  Thoracic Cancer Program (Lung and Esophageal Cancers)
Heart and Vascular Center
  Adult Congenital Heart Disease
  Advanced Heart Failure and Cardiac Transplantation
  Aortic Disease
  Arrhythmia and Atrial Fibrillation
  Coronary Artery Disease (CAD)
  Hereditary Hemorrhagic Telangiectasia (HHT)
  Hypertrophic Cardiomyopathy (HCM)
  Preventive Cardiology and Lipid Therapy
  Peripheral Arterial Disease (PAD)
  Pulmonary Hypertension
  Valvular Disease
  Venous Thrombotic Disease
  Venous and Vein Disease
  Women and Heart Disease
Neurosciences Center
  Brain Injury Program
  Brain and Spine Tumor Program
  Comprehensive Epilepsy Program
  Comprehensive Spasticity Management Program
  Memory Disorders Program
  Neuro-Oncology Cognitive Clinic
  Normal Pressure Hydrocephalus
  Parkinson's and Movement Disorders Program
  Sleep Disorders Program
  SpineCare Program
  Spinal Cord Injury Center
  Stroke and Neurovascular Program

COMPETITORS

Children's Hospital and Health System
Columbia St. Mary's
Ministry Health Care
ProHealth Care
Rockford Health System
Waukesha Memorial
Wheaton Franciscan Services

HISTORICAL FINANCIALS

Company Type: Private

Income Statement				FYE: June 30
	REVENUE ($ mil.)	NET INCOME ($ mil.)	NET PROFIT MARGIN	EMPLOYEES
06/14	1,164	92	7.9%	3,400
06/11	980	79	8.1%	—
06/10	894	59	6.7%	—
Annual Growth	6.8%	11.6%	—	—

2014 Year-End Financials

Return on assets: 12.3%   Cash ($ mil.): 16
Return on equity: 14.1%
Current ratio: 3.00

FRONTROW CALYPSO LLC

EXECUTIVES

Ceo-Pres, Jens Holstebro
V Pres, John Merline
V Pres, Leo Stearns
SEC, Per Lund
Architectural Consultant, Jaime Mendez
Human Resources Manager, Christy Martinez

LOCATIONS

HQ: FRONTROW CALYPSO LLC
1690 CORPORATE CIR, PETALUMA, CA 949546912
Phone: 707 769-1110
Web: WWW.GOFRONTROW.COM

HISTORICAL FINANCIALS
Company Type: Private

Income Statement   FYE: December 31

	REVENUE ($ mil.)	NET INCOME ($ mil.)	NET PROFIT MARGIN	EMPLOYEES
12/08	1,009	128	12.7%	40
12/07	1,083	214	19.8%	—
12/04	21	(1)	—	—
Annual Growth	162.1%	—	—	—

2008 Year-End Financials
Return on assets: 17.4%   Cash ($ mil.): 26
Return on equity: 126.6%
Current ratio: 0.80

FULTON COUNTY BOARD OF EDUCATION

LOCATIONS
HQ: FULTON COUNTY BOARD OF EDUCATION
6201 POWERS FERRY RD, ATLANTA, GA 303392926
Phone: 404 768-3600
Web: WWW.FULTONSCHOOLS.ORG

HISTORICAL FINANCIALS
Company Type: Private

Income Statement   FYE: June 30

	REVENUE ($ mil.)	NET INCOME ($ mil.)	NET PROFIT MARGIN	EMPLOYEES
06/18	1,268	40	3.2%	10,000
06/17	1,252	14	1.2%	—
06/16	1,201	(32)	—	—
Annual Growth	2.7%	—	—	—

2018 Year-End Financials
Return on assets: 1.5%   Cash ($ mil.): 446
Return on equity: 6.3%
Current ratio: 2.90

GANNETT FLEMING AFFILIATES, INC.

EXECUTIVES
Chb, William Stout
Sr V Pres-V Chm, Robert J Dietz
Treas, Lynn E Knepp
President, Robert Scaer
Director, Beth Petersen
Director, Cort Esch
Director, Greg Ulp
Director, Matt Merrill
Director Transportation Soluti, Nate Reck
Director, Peg Bradley
Vice President, Stu Blankenship
Auditors: STAMBAUGH NESS PC HANOVER P

LOCATIONS
HQ: GANNETT FLEMING AFFILIATES, INC.
1105 N MARKET ST, WILMINGTON, DE 198011216
Phone: 717 763-7211
Web: WWW.GEODECISIONS.COM

HISTORICAL FINANCIALS
Company Type: Private

Income Statement   FYE: December 31

	REVENUE ($ mil.)	NET INCOME ($ mil.)	NET PROFIT MARGIN	EMPLOYEES
12/18	462	17	3.7%	2,000
12/17	423	11	2.6%	—
12/16	386	11	3.0%	—
12/14	331	9	2.7%	—
Annual Growth	8.6%	17.1%	—	—

2018 Year-End Financials
Return on assets: 7.3%   Cash ($ mil.): 6
Return on equity: 21.8%
Current ratio: 2.20

GARDEN GROVE UNIFIED SCHOOL DISTRICT

EXECUTIVES
Supt, Gabriela Mafi
Supt*, Laura Schwalm
Prin*, Coleen Cross
SEC*, Joyan Spraus
Pres*, George West
V Pres*, Lan Quoc Nguyen
Director, Rick Rodriguez
Assistant Director, Steven Nguyen
Accounting Staff, Cathy Joseph
Operations Staff, Marc Aranda
Accounting Staff, Roxanne Linss

LOCATIONS
HQ: GARDEN GROVE UNIFIED SCHOOL DISTRICT
10331 STANFORD AVE, GARDEN GROVE, CA
928406351
Phone: 714 663-6000
Web: WWW.GGUSD.US

HISTORICAL FINANCIALS
Company Type: Private

Income Statement   FYE: June 30

	REVENUE ($ mil.)	NET INCOME ($ mil.)	NET PROFIT MARGIN	EMPLOYEES
06/18	613	(90)	—	5,000
06/17	602	7	1.2%	—
06/16	632	(46)	—	—
06/06	0	0	—	—
Annual Growth	—	—	—	—

2018 Year-End Financials
Return on assets: (-5.3%)   Cash ($ mil.): 531
Return on equity: (-17.1%)
Current ratio: —

GARFF ENTERPRISES, INC.

EXECUTIVES
Chm, Robert Garff
Pres*, John Garff
SEC*, Matthew Garff
V Pres*, Rick Fulkerson
Vice-President Business Develo, Sam Bracken
GMC Sales Consultant, Christina Smith
Director, Rebecca Anderson
Manager, Scott Adams
Auditors: MAYER HOFFMAN MC CANN PC SAL

LOCATIONS
HQ: GARFF ENTERPRISES, INC.
111 E BROADWAY STE 900, SALT LAKE CITY, UT
841115235
Phone: 801 257-3400

HISTORICAL FINANCIALS
Company Type: Private

Income Statement   FYE: December 31

	REVENUE ($ mil.)	NET INCOME ($ mil.)	NET PROFIT MARGIN	EMPLOYEES
12/13	576	14	2.5%	855
12/03	481	10	2.1%	—
12/02	270	4	1.5%	—
12/01	189	0	—	—
Annual Growth	9.7%	—	—	—

2013 Year-End Financials
Return on assets: 1.4%   Cash ($ mil.): 26
Return on equity: 2.5%
Current ratio: 0.20

GARLAND INDEPENDENT SCHOOL DISTRICT

EXECUTIVES
Supt, Dr Bob Morrison
Deputy Supt*, Linda Chance
Information Technology/Interne, Phat Tran
Coordinator, Deb Tietjen
Administrator, Curtis Culwell
Teacher, Shelisa Benton
Coordinator, Tom Brown
Coordinator, Brenda Hass
Coordinator, Kelly Hartmann
Teacher, Mewesette Baker
Business Analyst, Randal Curry
Auditors: WHITLEY PENN LLP HOUSTON TEX

LOCATIONS
HQ: GARLAND INDEPENDENT SCHOOL DISTRICT
501 S JUPITER RD, GARLAND, TX 750427108
Phone: 972 494-8201
Web: WWW.GARLANDISD.NET

HISTORICAL FINANCIALS

Company Type: Private

Income Statement
FYE: August 31

	REVENUE ($ mil.)	NET INCOME ($ mil.)	NET PROFIT MARGIN	EMPLOYEES
08/18	648	(25)	—	7,307
08/17	632	84	13.3%	—
08/16	601	(67)	—	—
Annual Growth	3.8%	—	—	—

2018 Year-End Financials

Return on assets: (-2.0%)
Return on equity: (-16.0%)
Current ratio: —

Cash ($ mil.): 446

GBMC HEALTHCARE, INC.

EXECUTIVES

Pres-Ceo, John B Chessare
V Pres, Richard Borschuk
Cfo, Eric L Melchior
Sr V Pres, John W Ellis
Sr V Pres, Jody Porter
Coo, Keith Poisson
V Pres, Michael A Forthman
V Pres, Deloris Simpson Tuggle
V Pres, Cathy Hamel
V Pres, Jenny Coldiron
V Pres, George Bayless
Auditors: DELOITTE TAX LLP MC LEAN VA

LOCATIONS

HQ: GBMC HEALTHCARE, INC.
6701 N CHARLES ST, BALTIMORE, MD 212046808
Phone: 443 849-2000
Web: WWW.GBMC.ORG

HISTORICAL FINANCIALS

Company Type: Private

Income Statement
FYE: June 30

	REVENUE ($ mil.)	NET INCOME ($ mil.)	NET PROFIT MARGIN	EMPLOYEES
06/18	573	30	5.3%	103
06/17	551	49	9.0%	—
06/15	16	14	88.2%	—
06/14	42	40	95.8%	—
Annual Growth	91.8%	(6.8%)	—	—

2018 Year-End Financials

Return on assets: 3.6%
Return on equity: 5.9%
Current ratio: 1.10

Cash ($ mil.): 34

GCI, LLC

EXECUTIVES

Ceo, Ronald Duncan
Pres, David Morris
Vpres, Wilson Hughes
Vpres, Bruce L Broquet

Exec V Pres, Gregory F Chapados
SEC-Treas, John M Lowber
Sales Staff, Carl St George
Account Manager, John Larson
Network Administrator I, Jordan Blackson
Director, Russ Doig
Technician IV, Daniel Picazo
Auditors: KPMG LLP DENVER COLORADO

LOCATIONS

HQ: GCI, LLC
2550 DENALI ST STE 1000, ANCHORAGE, AK 995032751
Phone: 907 868-5400
Web: WWW.GCI.COM

HISTORICAL FINANCIALS

Company Type: Private

Income Statement
FYE: December 31

	REVENUE ($ mil.)	NET INCOME ($ mil.)	NET PROFIT MARGIN	EMPLOYEES
12/18	739	(917)	—	7
12/17	919	31	3.4%	—
12/16	933	(1)	—	—
12/15	978	(10)	—	—
Annual Growth	(8.9%)	—	—	—

2018 Year-End Financials

Return on assets: (-11.2%)
Return on equity: (-20.5%)
Current ratio: 0.40

Cash ($ mil.): 170

GEISINGER HEALTH

Geisinger Health System provides health care to a large portion of the Keystone State. The health care system serves more than 3 million residents of nearly 50 counties spanning central and northeastern Pennsylvania. Founded in 1915 the organization's flagship facility is Geisinger Medical Center a 400-bed medical-surgical hospital located in Danville. It includes the Janet Weis Children's Hospital. With joint venture partner HealthSouth Geisinger also runs a rehabilitation hospital in Danville. As part of its operations the health system runs the 240-bed Geisinger Wyoming Valley Medical Center as well as numerous outpatient facilities and doctors' offices located throughout the region.

Geographic Reach

Geisinger Health System extends the reach of its health care system to millions of central and northeastern Pennsylvania residents across about 50 counties.

Financial Performance

In fiscal 2014 the hospital reported net revenue of $9.8 billion a $1 billion increase over the prior year.

Strategy

Geisinger Health System has been working to standardize its procedural operations to improve the quality of care at its facilities and cut costs. Initiatives include assigning care coordinators and providing home visits for high-risk patients to avoid repeat hospitalizations. The health network also implemented an electronic medical records system and began using networking technology to reach into rural markets. Known as "telemedicine" the system's networking technologies are used among other things to facilitate remote two-way consultations between system physicians and rural patients. Additionally Geisinger runs the Geisinger Health Plan a not-for-profit HMO with some 230000 members.

In addition to its clinical operations Geisinger Health System also pursues industry partnerships and licensing opportunities through Geisinger Ventures its business development unit. The unit works to commercialize (and sometimes spin off) medical and technology-related innovations.

Mergers and Acquisitions

Geisinger has grown through several strategic acquisitions as of late. The health care system purchased central Pennsylvania's Cancer Care Centers in late 2014 adding four facilities to its network.

EXECUTIVES

Evp And Coo, Frank Trembulak
Evp Finance And Cfo, Kevin F. Brennan
Evp And Chief Medical Officer, Albert Bothe
Evp And Managing Partner Geisinger Consulting Services, Bruce H. Hamory
Evp And System Chief Nursing Officer, Susan M. Robel
Evp Clinical Operations, Lynn Miller
Evp And Chief Scientific Officer, David H. Ledbetter
President And Ceo, David T. Feinberg
President And Ceo Geisinger Health Plans, Steven R. Youso
Chief Medical Executive Geisinger Northeast Region, Robert J. Weil
Vice President Supply Chain Services, Deborah Templeton
Associate Vice President Surgery And Anesthesiology, Kyle Snyder
Senior Vice President Finance, Thomas Sokola
Assistant To Greg Snow Vice President Of Revenue Cycle, Denise Baylor
Vice President Human Resources, Rick Flynn
Vice President Clinical Informatics, Joan Topper
Director Of Pharmacy, David Klinger
Senior Vice President And Chief Inform, Thomas Barna
Executive Vice President, Julie Bordo
Medical Director Government Programs, Perry Meadows
Associate Medical Director, David Withers
Pharmacy Manager, Nannette Leganza
Medical Director, Carrie L Delone
Secretary, Alicia Laskowski
Auditors: KPMG LLP PHILADELPHIA PA

LOCATIONS

HQ: GEISINGER HEALTH
100 N ACADEMY AVE, DANVILLE, PA 178229800
Phone: 800 275-6401
Web: WWW.GEISINGER.ORG

PRODUCTS/OPERATIONS

Selected Services
Adolescent & Young Adult Medicine
Allergy
Anesthesia
Audiology
Bariatric Surgery
Cancer Institute
Cardiology
Colorectal Surgery
Cosmetics Program
Critical Care
Dental Medicine
Dermatology
Ear Nose & Throat
Emergency Medicine
Endocrinology & Metabolism
Fertility Center
Gastroenterology
Gynecology
Gynecologic Oncology
Heart Services
Hip & Knee Center
Imaging Services
Infectious Disease
Internal Medicine
Joint Replacement

Laboratory Medicine
LASIK Surgery
Mammography
Maternal Fetal Medicine
Mental Health
Minimally Invasive Surgery
Mohs Surgery
Neonatology
Nephrology
Neurodevelopmental Pediatrics
Neuroscience Institute
Neurology
Neurosurgery
Obstetrics
Ophthalmology
Orthopaedics
Osteoporosis
Pain Management
Palliative Medicine
Pediatrics (General)
Pediatric Allergy & Immunology
Pediatric Anesthesia & Sedation
Pediatric Cardiology
Pediatric Dental Surgery
Pediatric Dentistry
Pediatric Dermatology
Pediatric Endocrinology
Pediatric Gastroenterology
Pediatric General Surgery
Pediatric Genetics
Pediatric Hematology/Oncology
Pediatric Hospitalists
Pediatric Infectious Disease
Pediatric Intensive Care
Pediatric Interventional Radiology
Pediatric Nephrology
Pediatric Neurology
Pediatric Neuropsychology
Pediatric Neurosurgery
Pediatric Ophthalmology
Pediatric Orthopaedics
Pediatric Otolaryngology
Pediatric Plastic Surgery
Pediatric Psychology & Psychiatry
Pediatric Pulmonology
Pediatric Rehabilitation
Pediatric Rheumatology
Pediatric Transplant Surgery
Pediatric Trauma
Pediatric Urology
Pediatric Weight Management & Nutrition
Plastic & Reconstructive Surgery
Podiatry
Psychiatry
Pulmonary Medicine
Radiology
Rehabilitation
Rheumatology
Sleep Services
Spine Medicine
Sports Medicine
Surgery
Thoracic Surgery
Transplant Surgery
Trauma Center
Urogynecology
Urology
Vascular Surgery
Weight Management Clinic
Women's Health

Selected Facilities

Geisinger HealthSouth Rehabilitation Hospital
   (Danville)
Geisinger Medical Center (Danville)
   The Janet Weis Children's Hospital
Geisinger Wyoming Valley Medical Center (Wilkes-Barre)
   Pearsall Heart Hospital
Geisinger South Wilkes-Barre Outpatient Center
Shamokin Area Community Hospital

COMPETITORS

Ascension Health
Blue Cross of Northeastern Pennsylvania
Capital BlueCross
Community Health Systems
HealthAmerica
Highmark
PinnacleHealth System
UPMC
Universal Health Services
Wyoming Valley Health Care System

HISTORICAL FINANCIALS

Company Type: Private

Income Statement   FYE: June 30

	REVENUE ($ mil.)	NET INCOME ($ mil.)	NET PROFIT MARGIN	EMPLOYEES
06/18	6,536	359	5.5%	13,030
06/17	6,337	552	8.7%	—
06/10	47	31	65.7%	—
06/09	0	0		
Annual Growth	—	—	—	—

2018 Year-End Financials

Return on assets: 4.7%
Return on equity: 8.5%
Current ratio: 1.70

Cash ($ mil.): 363

GEISINGER HEALTH PLAN

EXECUTIVES

Pres, Steve Yosu
V Pres*, Frank J Trembulak
Coordinator, Kevin Boyles
Sales Staff, Stephen Powlus
Director Revenue Cycle Reporti, Karen Hockenbroch
Senior Analyst, Kim Hackenberg
Appeal Coordinator, Mitzie Kerstetter
Nurse Underwriter, Patrice Molesevich
Manager, Bobbi Utt
Customer Team Member, Christine Jaegers
Quality Assurance Manager, Dave Evans

LOCATIONS

HQ: GEISINGER HEALTH PLAN
   100 N ACADEMY AVE, DANVILLE, PA 178229800
Phone: 570 271-8778

HISTORICAL FINANCIALS

Company Type: Private

Income Statement   FYE: June 30

	REVENUE ($ mil.)	NET INCOME ($ mil.)	NET PROFIT MARGIN	EMPLOYEES
06/17	2,337	79	3.4%	900
06/10	875	35	4.0%	—
06/09	827	45	5.5%	—
Annual Growth	13.9%	7.2%	—	—

2017 Year-End Financials

Return on assets: 12.7%
Return on equity: 21.5%
Current ratio: —

Cash ($ mil.): 102

GEISINGER MEDICAL CENTER

EXECUTIVES

Ceo, Glenn D Steele Jr
Exec V Pres*, Frank J Trembulak
Exec V Pres*, Joanne E Wade
Exec V Pres*, Albert Bothe Jr
Exec V Pres*, Lynn Miller
SEC*, Jessica Robertson
Chief Medical Officer*, Rosemary Leeming
Evp-CIO*, Karen Murphy
Evp-Cfo*, Kevin V Roberts
Chief of Emergency, John Skiendzielewski
Customer Representativ, Darren Soles

LOCATIONS

HQ: GEISINGER MEDICAL CENTER
   100 N ACADEMY AVE, DANVILLE, PA 178220001
Phone: 570 271-6211
Web: WWW.GEISINGER.ORG

HISTORICAL FINANCIALS

Company Type: Private

Income Statement   FYE: June 30

	REVENUE ($ mil.)	NET INCOME ($ mil.)	NET PROFIT MARGIN	EMPLOYEES
06/16	1,095	108	9.9%	8,000
06/15	1,058	120	11.4%	—
06/10	815	79	9.7%	—
06/09	735	46	6.3%	—
Annual Growth	5.8%	12.8%	—	—

2016 Year-End Financials

Return on assets: 14.7%
Return on equity: 130.1%
Current ratio: 1.50

Cash ($ mil.): 8

GEISINGER SYSTEM SERVICES

EXECUTIVES

Pres, Glenn D Steele Jr
V Pres System Treas Mgmt, Timothy Fitzgerald
Sr V Pres Treas, Frank J Trembulak
Customer Staff, Randall Hutchison
Vice-President Information Ser, David Macko
Recruiter, Deborah Miller
Coordinator, Paul Venarchick
Director of Fin, Yvonne Knight

LOCATIONS

HQ: GEISINGER SYSTEM SERVICES
   100 N ACADEMY AVE, DANVILLE, PA 178229800
Phone: 570 271-6211
Web: WWW.GEISINGER.ORG

HISTORICAL FINANCIALS
Company Type: Private

Income Statement				FYE: June 30
	REVENUE ($ mil.)	NET INCOME ($ mil.)	NET PROFIT MARGIN	EMPLOYEES
06/15	535	14	2.7%	344
06/14	582	20	3.4%	—
06/13	519	6	1.3%	—
06/10	375	6	1.7%	—
Annual Growth	7.4%	17.1%	—	—

2015 Year-End Financials
Return on assets: 2.2%   Cash ($ mil.): 3
Return on equity: 24.3%
Current ratio: 0.10

GEISINGER WYOMING VALLEY MEDICAL CENTER

EXECUTIVES

Vp, Timothy Fitzgerald
Ceo Pres Chair of Bd, Glenn D Steele Jr
Sr Vp Treasurer, Frank J Trembulak
Chief of Medicine, Steven B Pierdon
Chief of Medicine, Seth Fisher
Internist, Arvind Kumar
Neurologist, Adil Khan
Neurosurgeon, Christoph Griessenauer
Internist, Faiz Subzposh
Records Director, Janet Anderson
Internist, Kiran Fateh

LOCATIONS

HQ: GEISINGER WYOMING VALLEY MEDICAL
CENTER
1000 E MOUNTAIN DR, WILKES BARRE, PA
187110001
Phone: 570 808-7300

HISTORICAL FINANCIALS
Company Type: Private

Income Statement				FYE: June 30
	REVENUE ($ mil.)	NET INCOME ($ mil.)	NET PROFIT MARGIN	EMPLOYEES
06/16	471	25	5.4%	15
06/10	322	11	3.6%	—
Annual Growth	6.6%	14.1%	—	—

2016 Year-End Financials
Return on assets: 8.0%   Cash ($ mil.): 14
Return on equity: 92.6%
Current ratio: 1.50

GENERAL ELECTRIC INTERNATIONAL OPERATIONS COMPANY, INC.

EXECUTIVES

Pres, Robert Smits
Secretary, Kristen Urso
Lead Acct, Kyle Furnish
Auditors: KPMG LLP STAMFORD CT

LOCATIONS

HQ: GENERAL ELECTRIC INTERNATIONAL
OPERATIONS COMPANY, INC.
191 ROSA PARKS ST, CINCINNATI, OH 452022573
Phone: 513 813-9133
Web: WWW.GE.COM

HISTORICAL FINANCIALS
Company Type: Private

Income Statement				FYE: December 31
	REVENUE ($ mil.)	NET INCOME ($ mil.)	NET PROFIT MARGIN	EMPLOYEES
12/17	966	192	19.9%	52
12/16	925	(55)	—	—
12/15	925	(22)	—	—
12/14	760	(8)	—	—
Annual Growth	8.3%	—	—	—

2017 Year-End Financials
Return on assets: 1.9%   Cash ($ mil.): 101
Return on equity: 2.1%
Current ratio: 0.60

GENERAL ELECTRIC INTERNATIONAL, INC.

EXECUTIVES

Pres, Giuseppe Recchi
V Pres*, Candace F Carson
V Pres*, Daniel Janki
SEC*, Pierrot Christophe
SEC*, Kristen Urso-Rio
Treas*, Michael J Geary
Senior Specialist, A Carbone
Power Performance Mana, Jerry King
Fbw Integrator, Joseph Desormeaux
Leader, Tyler Zimmer
Auditors: KPMG LLP CINCINNATI OHIO

LOCATIONS

HQ: GENERAL ELECTRIC INTERNATIONAL, INC.
191 ROSA PARKS ST, CINCINNATI, OH 452022573
Phone: 617 443-3000
Web: WWW.GE.COM

HISTORICAL FINANCIALS
Company Type: Private

Income Statement				FYE: December 31
	REVENUE ($ mil.)	NET INCOME ($ mil.)	NET PROFIT MARGIN	EMPLOYEES
12/17	14,100	685	4.9%	125
12/16	13,364	1,339	10.0%	—
12/15	13,288	82	0.6%	—
12/14	12,884	(304)	—	—
Annual Growth	3.1%	—	—	—

2017 Year-End Financials
Return on assets: 3.5%   Cash ($ mil.): 961
Return on equity: 10.5%
Current ratio: 1.50

GENESIS HEALTH SYSTEM

Genesis Health System operates three acute care hospitals in Iowa and Illinois that have more than 660 beds total and employ some 700 doctors. Genesis Medical Center in Davenport Iowa with more than 500 beds is the system's flagship facility; the hospital offers a range of general surgical and specialist health services. The system's Illini Campus in Silvis Illinois features an assisted-living center. The Genesis Medical Center Dewitt Campus serves that Iowa town and the surrounding area with its 13-bed hospital nursing home and related care facilities. Genesis Health System also operates physician practices outpatient centers and a home health agency.

Operations
Altogether Genesis Health System has more than 100 locations including hospitals convenient care locations Genesis Health Group sites physical rehabilitation clinics and outpatient service centers.

Strategy
In 2014 the system invested $15 million in the new Genesis HealthPlex in Bettendorf.

The following year Genesis Health System entered into a partnership with technology vendor Cerner Corporation to improve its patient care enterprise management systems.

Company Background
Genesis Health System had its genesis in 1869 with the establishment of Mercy Hospital (one of the first hospitals west of the Mississippi) and in the 1895 founding of St. Luke's Hospital. The two hospitals merged in 1994 to form the health system.

EXECUTIVES

Medical Director, Fritz Null Swearingen
Vice President Human Resources, Edwin Maxwell
Medical Records Director, Betsy Tibbitts
Physical Therapy Tech Ii, Katrina Mchugh
Vice President Support Services, Mike Sharp
Director Of Pharmacy, Jeff Houseman
Vp Human Resources, Heidi Kahly Mcmahon
Medical Director Of Emergency Department,
Wayne Gallops
Vice President, Andy Andresen
Medical Director, Linda Delessio
Board Member, Deborah Stafford
Department Secretary, Dana Fox-andrews
Department Secretary, Jennifer Flynn
Secretary, Mary Jo McVey

House Secretary, Mary Lux
Unit Secretary, Leslie Palzkill
Department Secretary, Theresa Czarnetzki
Auditors: MCGLADREY LLP DAVENPORT IA

LOCATIONS

HQ: GENESIS HEALTH SYSTEM
  1227 E RUSHOLME ST, DAVENPORT, IA 528032459
Phone: 563 421-1000
Web: WWW.GENESISHEALTH.COM

PRODUCTS/OPERATIONS

Selected Services
Bariatric Surgery
Behavioral Health
Birthing Services
Cancer
Cardiology
Home Health/Hospice
Neuroscience
Nursing Homes
Physical Medicine & Rehab
Senior Services

COMPETITORS

Blessing Hospital
Catholic Health
  Initiatives
McDonough District
  Hospital
Mercy Health Network
OSF Healthcare System
UnityPoint Health

HISTORICAL FINANCIALS

Company Type: Private

Income Statement				FYE: June 30
	REVENUE ($ mil.)	NET INCOME ($ mil.)	NET PROFIT MARGIN	EMPLOYEES
06/18	511	20	4.1%	5,000
06/16	509	32	6.3%	—
06/15	503	59	11.7%	—
06/14	467	26	5.7%	—
Annual Growth	2.3%	(6.0%)	—	—

2018 Year-End Financials
Return on assets: 2.5%   Cash ($ mil.): 33
Return on equity: 3.6%
Current ratio: 2.30

GENPACT LIMITED

LOCATIONS

HQ: GENPACT LIMITED
  1155 AVENUE OF THE AMERIC, NEW YORK, NY
  100362711
Phone: 212 896-6600
Web: WWW.GENPACT.COM

HISTORICAL FINANCIALS

Company Type: Private

Income Statement				FYE: December 31
	REVENUE ($ mil.)	NET INCOME ($ mil.)	NET PROFIT MARGIN	EMPLOYEES
12/11	1,600	191	11.9%	325
12/10	1,258	149	11.8%	—
12/09	1,120	134	12.0%	—
Annual Growth	19.5%	19.0%	—	—

2011 Year-End Financials
Return on assets: 1.3%   Cash ($ mil.): 408
Return on equity: 11.9%
Current ratio: 1.20

GEOKINETICS INC.

LOCATIONS

HQ: GEOKINETICS INC.
  1500 CITYWEST BLVD # 800, HOUSTON, TX
  770422300
Phone: 713 850-7600
Web: WWW.GEOKINETICS.COM

HISTORICAL FINANCIALS

Company Type: Private

Income Statement				FYE: December 31
	REVENUE ($ mil.)	NET INCOME ($ mil.)	NET PROFIT MARGIN	EMPLOYEES
12/11	763	(222)	—	5,695
12/10	558	(138)	—	—
12/09	510	(5)	—	—
Annual Growth	22.3%	—	—	—

2011 Year-End Financials
Return on assets: (-43.2%)   Cash ($ mil.): 44
Return on equity: —
Current ratio: 1.10

GERBER SCIENTIFIC PRODUCTS INC

LOCATIONS

HQ: GERBER SCIENTIFIC PRODUCTS INC
  83 GERBER RD W, SOUTH WINDSOR, CT 060743230
Phone: 860 648-8300

HISTORICAL FINANCIALS

Company Type: Private

Income Statement				FYE: April 30
	REVENUE ($ mil.)	NET INCOME ($ mil.)	NET PROFIT MARGIN	EMPLOYEES
04/07	574	13	2.4%	300
04/06	530	0	—	—
Annual Growth	8.4%	—	—	—

2007 Year-End Financials
Return on assets: 4.0%   Cash ($ mil.): 8
Return on equity: 9.3%
Current ratio: 1.70

GGP, INC.

Auditors: DELOITTE & TOUCHE LLP CHICAGO

LOCATIONS

HQ: GGP, INC.
  350 N ORLEANS ST STE 300, CHICAGO, IL
  606541607
Phone: 312 960-5000
Web: WWW.GGP.COM

COMPETITORS

CBL & Associates
  Properties
DDR
Glimcher Realty
JMB Realty
Kimco Realty
Lincoln Property
Macerich
Prime Retail
Simon Property Group
Tanger Factory Outlet
Taubman Centers
Trade Street
  Residential
Vornado Realty
Weingarten Realty

HISTORICAL FINANCIALS

Company Type: Private

Income Statement				FYE: December 31
	ASSETS ($ mil.)	NET INCOME ($ mil.)	INCOME AS % OF ASSETS	EMPLOYEES
12/12	27,282	(471)	—	1,500
12/11	29,518	(306)	—	—
12/10	32,367	(256)	—	—
12/09	28,149	(1,304)	—	—
Annual Growth	(1.0%)	—	—	—

2012 Year-End Financials
Return on assets: (-1.7%)   Sales ($ mil.): 2,511
Return on equity: (-6.1%)

GILBANE BUILDING COMPANY

Gilbane Building Company has built a big business constructing for equally large customers. The firm provides construction services consulting subcontracting and facilities management to commercial institutional and governmental markets. Operating as the construction arm of Gilbane the company builds schools hospitals laboratories and prisons serving both the public and private sectors. Its completed projects include the Stroh Center at Bowling Green State University and the National WWII Memorial in Washington DC. Founded in 1873 as a carpentry and general contracting shop the family-owned Gilbane Building Company operates from more than 50 offices around the world.

Operations

The company has worked on a wide range of projects including: the Worcester Recovery Center & Hospital El Paso Corporation Building Renovation New York State Capital Restoration Georgia Tech Carbon Neutral Energy Solutions Laboratory University of North Florida Student Wellness and Sports Albert Einstein Health Network Elmhurst Memorial Healthcare and the University of Puerto Rico Molecular Sciences Building.

As part of its business Gilbane Building Company operates ITSI Gilbane a major provider of engineering and construction services to the US federal government including the Department of Defense Environmental Protection Agency and Department of Energy.

Geographic Reach

With more than 50 offices and 1000 projects underway around the world Gilbane Building Company enjoys a geographic footprint that extends from the US to Japan the United Arab Emirates Ireland South Korea and Afghanistan.

Sales and Marketing

Gilbane Building Company serves several sectors such as healthcare higher education K-12 schools federal and public entities mission critical corporate and sports and recreation. In 2014 the company boasted a 98.4% client satisfaction rate and reported that 65% of its work comes from repeat clients.

Some of its clients have included: Einstein Healthcare Network Google Inc. Operations Mane Inc Wilmington Public School Uihlein Wilson Architects City of Phoenix Crime Lab and the Operating Forces D&C Division.

Strategy
Gilbane Building Company has been busy working on projects in all parts of the country. In 2014 Gilbane secured a $43 million contract for historical renovation work on Pomerene and Oxley Halls on the Ohio State University campus. The firm's 2013 projects included the 131000-sq.-ft. Bergen County Justice Center in Hackensack New Jersey; the Columbus Regional Airport Authority's modernization of concourses B and C at Port Columbus international airports; and Miami University's Kreger Hall Rehabilitation & Addition Project which included the reorganization of 33372 sq. ft. of interior spaces and upgrades to the building's infrastructure as well as a major rehabilitation.

The company also continues to be recognized for its environment-conscious building designs particularly with schools. In early 2015 the company's completed Dunbar High School project — equipped with an advanced geothermal system a 482 kW array of photovoltaic panels and 20000-gallon cisterns — was awarded the LEED for Schools v2009 Platinum certification taking home the highest LEED score on record worldwide. Also in early 2015 the company was awarded the #1 ranking for Education K-12 Building Design and Construction and ranked within the top 5 of green contractor engineers.

It has also extended its reach in Europe in recent years. In 2012 the company formed a joint venture with Ed. Z blinAG known as Z blin Gilbane to pursue and execute projects in Europe.

EXECUTIVES

President And Ceo, Michael C. (Mike) McKelvy, age 59
Vice President Business Development, Randy Lowrance
Senior Vice President Director Human Resources, Pierre La Perriere
Vice President District Manager, Douglas Lim
Vice President Human Resources, Mary A Farrell
Vice President Of Construction Operations For The New England Region, Thomas Comella
Vice President And Regional Operations Manager, Stephen Oaconnor
Vice President, Jay Prybylski
Vice President, James Busam
Vice Chairman, William J. (Bill) Gilbane, age 72
Chairman, Thomas F. (Tom) Gilbane, age 71
Auditors: RSM US LLP BOSTON MASSACHUSE

LOCATIONS

HQ: GILBANE BUILDING COMPANY
7 JACKSON WALKWAY STE 2, PROVIDENCE, RI 029033694
Phone: 401 456-5800
Web: WWW.GILBANECO.COM

PRODUCTS/OPERATIONS

Selected Markets

Convention/cultural

Corporate
Criminal justice
Federal/public
Health care
  Children's hospitals
  Women's centers
  Cardiac-care centers
  Cancer centers
  Clinical and research facilities
Higher education

Research laboratories
Academic facilities
Admissions buildings
Residence halls
Performing arts centers
Sports and recreational centers
Libraries and technology centers
Student unions
K-12 schools
Life sciences
Mission critical
Sports/recreation
Transportation
Water/wastewater

Selected Services

Pre-construction
  Transition planning and management
  Building information modeling
  Conceptual cost modeling
  High-performance building & energy modeling
  Interdisciplinary document coordination
Consulting
  CAT-response
  Facilities management services
  Schedule & risk analysis
  Transition planning & management
Construction
  Construction management at risk
  Construction management as agent
  Lump sum general contracting
  Integrated project delivery

COMPETITORS

Barton Malow	McCarthy Building
Batson-Cook	Peter Kiewit Sons'
Bechtel	Skanska USA Building
Bernards Brothers	Swinerton
Clark Construction	The Pike Company
Group	Thos. S. Byrne
Dimeo Construction	Turner Construction
Fluor	Turner Corporation
KBR	Tutor Perini
L.F. Driscoll	Walbridge Aldinger
MEDCO Construction	Whiting-Turner

HISTORICAL FINANCIALS
Company Type: Private

Income Statement   FYE: December 31

	REVENUE ($ mil.)	NET INCOME ($ mil.)	NET PROFIT MARGIN	EMPLOYEES
12/18	5,453	81	1.5%	2,500
12/17	4,899	63	1.3%	—
12/14	3,840	0	—	—
12/13	4,100	0	—	—
Annual Growth	5.9%	—	—	—

2018 Year-End Financials

Return on assets: 4.3%   Cash ($ mil.): 241
Return on equity: 25.6%
Current ratio: 1.20

GLOBAL HEALTH SOLUTIONS INC

EXECUTIVES

Vice President, T Rosenberger
V Pres, Thomas Rosenberger

LOCATIONS

HQ: GLOBAL HEALTH SOLUTIONS INC
325 SWANTON WAY, DECATUR, GA 300303001
Phone: 404 592-1430
Web: WWW.TASKFORCE.ORG

HISTORICAL FINANCIALS
Company Type: Private

Income Statement   FYE: August 31

	REVENUE ($ mil.)	NET INCOME ($ mil.)	NET PROFIT MARGIN	EMPLOYEES
08/15	1,609	0	—	2
08/14	1,790	0	—	—
08/13	1,574	0	—	—
08/10	1,120	0	0.0%	—
Annual Growth	7.5%	—	—	—

GOOD SAMARITAN HOSPITAL MEDICAL CENTER

The folks at Good Samaritan Hospital Medical Center have plenty of reasons to feel good about their efforts. The hospital is part of Catholic Health Services of Long Island (CHS) and serves the south shore community of West Islip New York. The full-service medical center boasts 900 physicians and 440 acute care beds offering a complete range of health care counseling and rehabilitation services. Good Samaritan provides emergency medicine and trauma care in addition to oncology cardiology pediatric woman's health diagnostic and surgical care. It also operates the Good Samaritan Nursing Home a 100-bed skilled nursing facility as well as satellite clinics and a home health care agency.

Operations
Good Samaritan which contributes about 28% of its parent's revenue logged more than 95000 emergency department visits in 2012. Its ambulatory surgery department treats an average of nearly 300 patients weekly as part of its focus on same-day procedures. Additionally the medical facility in 2012 admitted 27615 patients and logged 2820 births 66000 rehabilitation inpatient visits and 49640 dialysis treatments.

The hospital's outpatient services include same day surgeries pulmonary rehabilitation pediatric specialty visits and physical occupational and speech therapy sessions; it also has satellite locations that provide dialysis treatment. Good Samaritan's palliative care program offers an 11-bed dedicated acute palliative care inpatient unit.

Geographic Reach
Good Samaritan Hospital Medical Center serves those in and around West Islip New York.

Financial Performance
Net patient revenue dragged down Good Samaritan's revenue increases in fiscal 2012 vs. 2011. During the reporting period the medical center posted $579 million in revenue representing a marginal $260000 rise. Net income dropped some 77% to $8.3 million in 2012 vs. 2011 thanks to rising operating expenses from increases in CHS Services.

Strategy
Good Samaritan is recognized for its cancer care and radiology programs as well as its cardiac pediatric and women's health services all of which it has been expanding and enhancing in recent years. For instance the hospital added a nephrology unit in 2011 within its pediatric division to evaluate and treat children with kidney disease. It expanded

its pediatric nephrology unit in 2012 by opening a new 16-bed surgical intensive care unit (SICU). Good Samaritan also added a new diagnostic imaging center in 2012 that provides radiology services including breast imaging.

In addition Good Samaritan is working to add an open-heart surgery program to its cardiology division through a partnership with St. Francis Hospital another member of the CHS organization also known as The Heart Center. In 2013 Good Samaritan became the first facility in the New York metropolitan region to install and offer the GE Innova IGS 530 digital cardiovascular and interventional imaging system in its cardiac catheterization laboratory.

The not-for-profit facility's growth measures are supported in part by its charitable organization The Guilds of Good Samaritan Hospital Medical Center. The Good Samaritan hospital provides some $50 million in community service and charity care each year.

Company Background
Founded in 1959 Good Samaritan became part of the CHS organization in 1997.

EXECUTIVES

Vice President Administration, Joseph Loiacono
Medical Director, Ruth Spector

LOCATIONS

HQ: GOOD SAMARITAN HOSPITAL MEDICAL CENTER
1000 MONTAUK HWY, WEST ISLIP, NY 117954927
Phone: 631 376-3000

PRODUCTS/OPERATIONS

Selected Premier Services
Cancer Care
Cardiac Care
Children's Care
Emergency Services
Satellites
Surgery
Women's Care

Selected Services
Ambulatory Surgery Unit
Audiology/Hearing Aids
BirthPlace
Breast Health Center
Cancer Care
Cancer Surgery
Cardiac Rehabilitation
Cardiology Services
Center for Pediatric Specialty Care
Care Management and Social Work
Child Life Services
da Vinci Surgery
Dentistry
Dermatology
Dialysis Services
Ear Nose and Throat
Emergency Department
Endocrinology
Family Practice
Gastroenterology
Good Samaritan Hospital Foundation
Good Samaritan Nursing Home
Hematology and Oncology
Imaging Services
Infectious Diseases
Inpatient Dialysis
Internal Medicine
Laboratory
Long Term Home Health Care
Managed Care
Martin Luther King Jr. Community Health Center
Maternal Fetal Medicine
Medical Education
Neonatology
Nephrology
Neurosurgery
Nursing at Good Sam
Nutrition and Food Services
Obstetrics and Gynecology
Oncology

Ophthalmology
Oral Surgery
Orthopaedics
Osteoporosis
Palliative Care
Pain Management
Pastoral/Spiritual Care Department
Pathology
Pediatric Services
Perinatal Education
Plastic and Reconstructive Services
Podiatry
Pre-Surgical Testing
Psychiatry
Pulmonary Rehabilitation
Radiation Oncology Center
Rehabilitation Services
Respiratory Care
Safe Haven Program
Sleep Apnea Center
Special Care
Support Groups
Surgery
Thoracic Surgery
Trauma Services
Urology
Vascular Suite
Vascular Surgery
Weight Loss Surgery/Bariatric Surgery
Women's Imaging Center

COMPETITORS

Brookhaven Memorial Hospital Medical Center
CSH
Catholic Healthcare System
Continuum Health Partners
Mather Memorial Hospital
Memorial Sloan-Kettering
New York City Health and Hospitals
NewYork-Presbyterian Healthcare
Northwell Health
Winthrop-University Hospital

HISTORICAL FINANCIALS

Company Type: Private

Income Statement				FYE: December 31
	REVENUE ($ mil.)	NET INCOME ($ mil.)	NET PROFIT MARGIN	EMPLOYEES
12/15	505	28	5.7%	3,774
12/14	488	36	7.5%	—
12/13*	534	(28)	—	—
06/05	118	(1)	—	—
Annual Growth	14.1%	—	—	—

*Fiscal year change

2015 Year-End Financials
Return on assets: 5.6%   Cash ($ mil.): 72
Return on equity: 16.3%
Current ratio: 1.40

GOOD SAMARITAN HOSPITAL OF CINCINNATI

EXECUTIVES

Pres, John S Prout
Chm*, Robert L Walker
Sr V Pres*, John R Robinson
Cfo*, Craig Rucker
Coo*, Gerald Oliphant
Internal Medicine Practitioner, Aleksandr Yultyev

Internal Medicine Practitioner, Ashirf Al-Ghanoudi
Internal Medicine Practitioner, Hiro Kawata
Internal Medicine Practitioner, Irina Gagua
Health Professional, Jiang Wu
Health Professional, Michelle Sotos
Auditors: BKD LLP CINCINNATI OH

LOCATIONS

HQ: GOOD SAMARITAN HOSPITAL OF CINCINNATI
375 DIXMYTH AVE, CINCINNATI, OH 452202489
Phone: 513 569-6251

HISTORICAL FINANCIALS

Company Type: Private

Income Statement				FYE: June 30
	REVENUE ($ mil.)	NET INCOME ($ mil.)	NET PROFIT MARGIN	EMPLOYEES
06/18	579	48	8.3%	3,452
06/15	578	81	14.0%	—
06/13	483	60	12.4%	—
06/10	479	43	9.1%	—
Annual Growth	2.4%	1.2%	—	—

2018 Year-End Financials
Return on assets: 5.1%   Cash ($ mil.): —
Return on equity: 6.1%
Current ratio: 1.30

GOOD SAMARITAN HOSPITAL, L.P.

Good Samaritan Hospital lends a hand to help Silicon Valley'sÂ techies and their neighbors stay healthy. The facility part of the HCA family of for-profit hospitalsÂ administers careÂ throughÂ campusesÂ inÂ San JoseÂ (the main campus) and Los Gatos California. Good Samaritan Hospital provides general acute care as well as a host of tertiary services that includeÂ cardiology and cardiovascular surgery; oncology; obstetrics and gynecology; and psychiatry (both inpatient and outpatient care). The main campus hospital has some 408 patient beds and 600 physicians and the Los Gatos outpatient and short-stay facilityÂ houses approximately 100 beds.

Operations
Each year Good Samaritan admitsÂ 17000 patients (excluding newborns) and handles more than 93500 outpatient visits. More than 4000 deliveries and 8000 surgeries are performed annually in 18 surgical suites.

Strategy
In additionÂ to being aÂ community hospital Good Samaritan is a world-class academic medical center affiliated with both USC and UCLA Schools of Medicine. To cater to theÂ diverse urban population the hospital system servesÂ Good Samaritan'sÂ medical staff and employees speak more than 54 languages/dialects.

Company Background
Good Samaritan Hospital opened its doors in 1965 as an acute care hospital with a staff of about 400.

EXECUTIVES

Vice President Of Operations, Jim Lamar

LOCATIONS

HQ: GOOD SAMARITAN HOSPITAL, L.P.
2425 SAMARITAN DR, SAN JOSE, CA 951243985
Phone: 408 559-2011
Web: WWW.GOODSAMSANJOSE.COM

PRODUCTS/OPERATIONS

Selected Services and Departments

Cardiology
Cardiac Surgery
Comprehensive Sleep Center
Diagnostic Imaging (Radiology)
ENT (Ear Nose & Throat)
Emergency Services
Gamma Knife
Gastroenterology
Laboratory
Neurosciences
Oncology (Cancer)
Opthalmology & Retinal Medicine
Orthopedics
Podiatry
Physical Medicine
Pulmonary Medicine & Respiratory Care
Radiation Oncology
Surgery
Women's Health & Newborn Services
Urology

COMPETITORS

Dignity Health	Stanford Health Care
Mills-Peninsula Health	The Palo Alto Medical
Services	Foundation
Sequoia Healthcare	ValleyCare Health
District	System

HISTORICAL FINANCIALS

Company Type: Private

Income Statement   FYE: January 31

	REVENUE ($ mil.)	NET INCOME ($ mil.)	NET PROFIT MARGIN	EMPLOYEES
01/17	618	141	22.8%	1,800
01/09*	413	30	7.3%	—
05/05	170	0	—	—
12/03	0	0	—	—
Annual Growth	—	—	—	—

*Fiscal year change

2017 Year-End Financials

Return on assets: 53.2%   Cash ($ mil.): —
Return on equity: 37.7%
Current ratio: 2.10

GPM INVESTMENTS, LLC

Convenience is key for GPM Investments which operates or supplies fuel to more than 1100 convenience stores in about 20 US states. The stores sell BP Exxon Marathon and Valero brand gas among others as well as the usual beer smokes and snacks. Some locations also offer fresh made-to-order salads sandwiches and other items or offer branded food from Subway Taco Bell and others. The company which primarily serves the Midwest and eastern US operates or supplies stores under a host of names including Fas Mart Shore Stop Jiffi Stop Young's and Roadrunner Markets.

EXECUTIVES

Vice President Of Facilities And Construction, Mark Wilson
Auditors: GRANT THORNTON LLP RALEIGH

LOCATIONS

HQ: GPM INVESTMENTS, LLC
8565 MAGELLAN PKWY # 400, RICHMOND, VA 232271167
Phone: 276 328-3669
Web: WWW.GPMINVESTMENTS.COM

Selected Locations

Connecticut

Delaware

Maryland
New Jersey
North Carolina
. Pennsylvania
Rhode Island
South Carolina
Tennessee
Virginia

COMPETITORS

7-Eleven	Racetrac Petroleum
Cumberland Farms	Sheetz
Exxon Mobil	Wawa Inc.
Gate Petroleum	

HISTORICAL FINANCIALS

Company Type: Private

Income Statement   FYE: December 31

	REVENUE ($ mil.)	NET INCOME ($ mil.)	NET PROFIT MARGIN	EMPLOYEES
12/08	1,249	(1)	—	2,150
12/07	891	3	0.4%	—
Annual Growth	40.2%	—	—	—

2008 Year-End Financials

Return on assets: 1.7%   Cash ($ mil.): 12
Return on equity: (-0.1%)
Current ratio: 0.40

GRADY MEMORIAL HOSPITAL CORPORATION

EXECUTIVES

Pres-Ceo, John M Haupert
Cfo*, Mark Meyer
Exec V Pres*, Christopher R Mosley
Exec V Pres*, Timothy Jefferson
Exec V Pres*, Curtis Lewis
Vp of Fin, Ozzie Gilbert
Senior Vice-President, Calvin Thomas IV
Grants Manager, David Noble
Security Staff, Donise Musheno
Vice-Chairman, Thomas W Dortch
Accounting Staff, Billy Sawyer
Auditors: KPMG LLP GREENSBORO NC

LOCATIONS

HQ: GRADY MEMORIAL HOSPITAL CORPORATION
80 JESSE HILL JR DR SE, ATLANTA, GA 303033050
Phone: 404 616-4360
Web: WWW.GRADYHEALTH.ORG

HISTORICAL FINANCIALS

Company Type: Private

Income Statement   FYE: December 31

	REVENUE ($ mil.)	NET INCOME ($ mil.)	NET PROFIT MARGIN	EMPLOYEES
12/17	1,494	42	2.9%	4,500
12/16	1,444	47	3.3%	—
12/15	1,230	47	3.9%	—
12/08	358	(56)	—	—
Annual Growth	17.2%	—	—	—

2017 Year-End Financials

Return on assets: 5.2%   Cash ($ mil.): 219
Return on equity: 7.5%
Current ratio: 2.30

GRAHAM ENTERPRISE, INC.

EXECUTIVES

Pres, John C Graham
V Pres, Eugene W Graham III
SEC, Matthew X Graham
Treas, Patrick T Graham
Finance Executive, Donna Greco
Auditors: FGMK LLC BANNOCKBURN ILLINO

LOCATIONS

HQ: GRAHAM ENTERPRISE, INC.
750 BUNKER CT STE 100, VERNON HILLS, IL 600611864
Phone: 847 837-0777
Web: WWW.GRAHAMEI.COM

HISTORICAL FINANCIALS

Company Type: Private

Income Statement   FYE: December 31

	REVENUE ($ mil.)	NET INCOME ($ mil.)	NET PROFIT MARGIN	EMPLOYEES
12/17	638	12	2.0%	350
12/16	596	6	1.1%	—
12/15	662	11	1.7%	—
12/14	866	8	0.9%	—
Annual Growth	(9.7%)	16.5%	—	—

2017 Year-End Financials

Return on assets: 32.4%   Cash ($ mil.): 6
Return on equity: 47.9%
Current ratio: 1.90

GRANDVIEW HEALTH HOMES, INC.

EXECUTIVES

Pres, Jerry E Boone
Admissions Director, Ann McLaughlin
Physical Therapy Rehab Directo, Michele Boone

LOCATIONS

HQ: GRANDVIEW HEALTH HOMES, INC.
78 WOODBINE LN, DANVILLE, PA 178218020
Phone: 570 275-5240
Web: WWW.GRANDVIEWNR.COM

HISTORICAL FINANCIALS

Company Type: Private

Income Statement   FYE: June 30

	REVENUE ($ mil.)	NET INCOME ($ mil.)	NET PROFIT MARGIN	EMPLOYEES
06/09	1,262	4	0.4%	240
06/99	2	2	89.8%	—
06/98	3	0	11.0%	—
Annual Growth	71.5%	25.8%	—	—

2009 Year-End Financials

Return on assets: 92.2%   Cash ($ mil.): —
Return on equity: —
Current ratio: 1.20

GRANITE SCHOOL DISTRICT

EXECUTIVES

Supt, Martin W Bates
SEC*, Mary Lynn
SEC*, Kathy Goodfellow
Information, Anjanette Anderson
Coordinator, Cindy Dunn
Supervisor, Mark Peterson
Manager, Russell Stauffer
Officer, Cole McAfee
Teacher, Brady Martin
Network Engineer, Jason Winn
Network Engineer, Brian Goldsberry
Auditors: SQUIRE & COMPANY PC OREM UT

LOCATIONS

HQ: GRANITE SCHOOL DISTRICT
2500 S STATE ST STE 500, SALT LAKE CITY, UT
841153195
Phone: 385 646-5000
Web: WWW.GRANITESCHOOLS.ORG

HISTORICAL FINANCIALS

Company Type: Private

Income Statement   FYE: June 30

	REVENUE ($ mil.)	NET INCOME ($ mil.)	NET PROFIT MARGIN	EMPLOYEES
06/18	610	79	13.0%	8,000
06/17	571	9	1.7%	—
06/16	561	16	3.0%	—
06/09	528	14	2.7%	—
Annual Growth	1.6%	21.1%	—	—

GRANITE TELECOMMUNICATIONS LLC

Granite Telecommunications carves out an increasing block of telecommunications services to commercial clients in the US and Canada. The company is a wholesaler of local and long distance telephone service as well as broadband internet connections with more than 1.3 million lines provided by network operators. It serves corporate clients many of whom run offices in multiple states offering them no account transfer charges and no term or volume contracts on telephone service. Granite also designs and installs network cabling and security systems and provides loss prevention and risk management services.

Operations
The company serves more than 4800 corporate clients in more than a half a million locations. Its customers include most of the US Fortune 100 companies and its customer retention rate is more than five times higher than the industry average. It has about 1.4 million phone lines; about 1.3 billion lines are business lines and 65000 are data lines. The company uses copper wiring found in traditional telecommunication networks which provide reliable and cost-effective service. Granite's subsidiary Granite Guard is a leading provider of loss prevention and risk management services solely for businesses.

Geographic Reach
Granite serves clients across Canada and the US from offices in Florida Massachusetts Georgia Illinois New York Texas and Rhode Island. It is based in Quincy Massachusetts.

Sales and Marketing
Granite's customers include PepsiCo Toys R Us Quality Distribution Jenny Craig Cardinal Health Southwest Airlines Brookdale Senior Living and Agrium.

Financial Performance
The company reported in 2016 that is annual revenue was more than $1.25 billion and that its revenue increased by more than $100 million.

Strategy
Expanding beyond its role as a reseller of telecom services Granite has rolled out its own Granite Grid. It's a fiber-based network with voice and data services for hospitals shopping malls and other multi-tenant buildings. The Granite-installed and maintained network offers better internet service. Simon Property Group one of the US's biggest mall operators has wired its properties to Granite Grid.

Granite has added clients with expansions in Florida and Georgia where it has built new facilities. It also built a new building at its Quincy Massachusetts headquarters to accommodate more employees.

EXECUTIVES

Svp And Coo, Rand Currier
Founder And Ceo, Robert T. (Rob) Hale
Cfo, Richard Wurman
Vice President Of Operations, Paul Stutzman
National Account Manager, Jonathan Gosian
National Account Manager, Michael Perrone
National Account Manager, William Drago
Svp Client Management, Mark Cameron
Vice President Controller, Mark Prendergast
Vice President, Sam Kline
Senior Vice President Finance, Susan Zahka

Vice President Channels, Charlie Pagliazzo
National Sales Manager, Serge Saint-val
National Sales Manager, Dan Pratt
National Account Manager, Michelle Murphy
National Account Manager, Michael Fricker
National Account Manager, Georgiana Thompson
Assistant Vice President Operations, Victoria King
Regional Vice President Of Sales, Bruce Hoffman
Vice President Talent Management, Kyle Swist
National Account Manager, Jose Villanueva
National Account Manager, Joe Flaherty
National Account Manager, Carlos Mendoza
National Accounts Manager, Paul Sullivan
National Account Manager, Clark Miller
National Sales Manager, Michael Hewatt
National Account Manager, Paul Atwood
National Account Manager, Brent Nelson
Vice President Sales Operations Marketing And Granite University, Anthony Kenneally
National Account Manager, Selwyn Scott
Senior Vice President, Don Macarthur
National Account Manager, Chris Oberg

LOCATIONS

HQ: GRANITE TELECOMMUNICATIONS LLC
100 NEWPORT AVENUE EXT # 1, QUINCY, MA
021712126
Phone: 617 933-5500
Web: WWW.GRANITENET.COM

PRODUCTS/OPERATIONS

Products and Services

Voice
Managed Solutions
Data
Network Integration
Granite Grid

COMPETITORS

5LINX	Rogers Communications
ACN Inc.	Sprint Communications
AT&T	Verizon
BCE	World Communications
EarthLink	

HISTORICAL FINANCIALS

Company Type: Private

Income Statement   FYE: December 31

	REVENUE ($ mil.)	NET INCOME ($ mil.)	NET PROFIT MARGIN	EMPLOYEES
12/12	736	187	25.5%	1,854
12/11	609	143	23.5%	—
12/10	517	109	21.2%	—
Annual Growth	19.3%	31.0%	—	—

2012 Year-End Financials

Return on assets: 110.5%   Cash ($ mil.): 45
Return on equity: 394.1%
Current ratio: 1.40

GREAT RIVER ENERGY

Great River Energy powers up cooperatives along the Great River Road. The utility provides wholesale electricity to 1.7 million people (at 660000 homes businesses and farms) through 28 distribution cooperatives in Minnesota and Wisconsin. It operates more than 4600 miles of transmission lines and has more than 3500 MW of capacity from 12 fossil-fueled hydroelectric and renewable power generation facilities. The company also owns or partially owns more than 100 transmission substations. Great River Energy is the #2 electric utility in Minnesota in terms of generating capacity and one of the top five largest generation and transmission cooperatives in the US (based on assets).

Operations
Great River Energy's 28 co-ops have 88000 miles of distribution line and 555 substations. Its largest distribution co-op member serves more than 125000 consumers while its smallest serves about 2500 end users. Most of the company's power comes from coal with hydro renewable and natural gas making up the rest.

As part of its efforts to increase its green energy output Great River owns Blue Flint Ethanol which includes a 65-million gallon ethanol refinery that uses process steam produced at Great River Energy Coal Creek Station.

Geographic Reach
The company provides power to cooperatives which in turn serve customers in Minnesota and Wisconsin.

Financial Performance
Great River Energy's revenues increased by 4% due to a rise in all segments particularly in electric revenues.

Electric revenues increased due to a drop in member revenues driven by higher member energy and demand unit sales of 1.5% and 0.8% respectively.

The company's net income increased by 21% due to higher net revenues and a decrease in fuel expense related to lower repairs and maintenance of the coal handling system.

Great River Energy's operating cash inflow increased by 33%.

Strategy
The company has a plan to add about 1800 MW of generating resources (including renewable energy) by 2025 to satisfy increasing member demand for electricity. (The State of Minnesota requires utilities to generate 25% of their power from renewable sources by 2025). To support this push Great River Energy has a 30-year power purchase agreement with NextEra Energy Resources to buy 51 MW of output from a wind farm in North Dakota.

In 2014 Manitoba Hydro and Great River Energy also agreed to investigate the sale of up to 600MW) of electricity from Manitoba Hydro to Great River Energy commencing in 2020. An eventual agreement could take advantage of a new Manitoba to Minnesota transmission line also proposed as part of Manitoba Hydro's preferred development plan.

That year Great River Energy announced plans to construct 650 kW of new solar energy installations by mid-2015. The first construction project is a 250 kW solar array slated for land south of Great River Energy's headquarters facility and will include a mix of technologies to help determine how solar energy installations can be integrated into cooperative systems. The remaining 400 kW may include up to 20 individual projects located in its member cooperatives' systems across the state.

In 2014 the company announced plans to undertake the largest transmission refurbishment project with the overhaul and upgrade of the converter stations at either end of the 436-mile high-voltage direct-current transmission line which delivers power to Minnesota from the company's largest power plant located in central North Dakota.

Company Background
In 2013 the company signed a deal with Tangshan Shenzhou Manufacturing Company to make Great River Energy's DryFining technology (for more efficient coal use in power stations) available to utilities in China.

It is also cut costs and increasing efficiency at its own power plants. In 2012 these measures saved Great River Energy more than $8 million.

In 2012 Great River bought the remaining 51% of Blue Flint Ethanol it didn't already own. The move added to its production capabilities and helped push the company to record production that year.

The utility was formed in 1999 through the combination of two Minnesota utilities Cooperative Power and United Power Association.

EXECUTIVES
Vp Generation, Rick Lancaster
Ceo And President, David Saggau
Vp And Cfo, Larry Schmid
Vp Transmission, Will Kaul
Vp And Cio, Jim Jones
Vice President Power Marketing And Asset Utilitzation, Laureen Rossmccalib
Vice Chairman, Sherman Liimatainen
Chairman, Michael Thorson
Board Of Directors, Margaret Schreiner
Board Of Directors, Scott Hughes
Auditors: DELOITTE & TOUCHE LLP MINNEA

LOCATIONS
HQ: GREAT RIVER ENERGY
12300 ELM CREEK BLVD N, MAPLE GROVE, MN 553694718
Phone: 763 445-5000
Web: WWW.GREATRIVERENERGY.COM

PRODUCTS/OPERATIONS

2014 Sales

	% of total
Member	83
Non-member	7
Other	7
Nonutility operations Excluding non-controlling Interest	3
Total	**100**

2014 Sales

	$ mil.	% of total
Electric revenue	952	93
Other operating revenue	68	7
Total	**1,020**	**100**

COMPETITORS

AEP	Entergy
Basin Electric Power	Southern Company
Black Hills	Xcel Energy
DTE	

HISTORICAL FINANCIALS
Company Type: Private

Income Statement   FYE: December 31

	REVENUE ($ mil.)	NET INCOME ($ mil.)	NET PROFIT MARGIN	EMPLOYEES
12/18	1,295	8	0.7%	850
12/17	1,270	18	1.4%	—
12/16	1,022	21	2.1%	—
12/15	983	15	1.5%	—
Annual Growth	9.6%	(17.8%)	—	—

2018 Year-End Financials

Return on assets: 0.2%   Cash ($ mil.): 276
Return on equity: 1.0%
Current ratio: 1.30

GREEN MOUNTAIN POWER CORPORATION

Public utility Green Mountain Power (GMP) lights up the hills of Vermont supplying electricity to more than 250000 customers in the state. The utility also markets wholesale electricity in New England. The company operates several thousand miles of transmission and distribution lines and owns a minority stake in high-voltage transmission operator Vermont Electric Power (VELCO). About half of the generation capacity GMP taps is from hydroelectric and other renewable energy sources. GMP is an indirect subsidiary of Canada's GazMetro. The company absorbed Central Vermont Public Service's assets in 2012.

Operations
GMP produces transmits distributes and sells electricity in Vermont and is a leader in the production of wind and solar energy in that state.

Strategy
In a move to boost its Vermont assets in 2012 parent company GazMetro bought Central Vermont Public Service (CVPS) and is merging it with its GMP operations. CVPS is Vermont's largest electric utility and provides power to more than 159000 customers in 163 communities across the state.

The company is also pursuing a long term initiative to generate power from renewable sources as a way to cut carbon emissions and comply with strict federal clean air requirements. GMP has a preliminary deal to boost green energy sources with Hydro-Quebec as well as plans to to build a wind farm in Lowell make investments in solar power and upgrade its hydroelectric facilities.

While wind and solar only accounted for about 1% of the company's fuel mix for its power stations in 2011 it plans to boost that amount to almost 10% by the end of 2013.

Company Background
GazMetro acquired the company in 2007. The deal boosted Gaz Metro's presence in the Vermont energy market where it has owned Vermont Gas Systems for more than 20 years.

EXECUTIVES

Svp Chief Operating Officer, Brian Otley
Vice President General Counsel And Cor, Donald Rendall
Vp Engineering, Ken Couture
Vice President Of Operations, Gregory White
Auditors: MCSOLEY MCCOY & CO SOUTH BURL

LOCATIONS
HQ: GREEN MOUNTAIN POWER CORPORATION
163 ACORN LN, COLCHESTER, VT 054466611
Phone: 888 835-4672
Web: WWW.GREENMOUNTAINPOWER.COM

COMPETITORS

Avangrid	Maine & Maritimes
Bangor Hydro-Electric	NSTAR
Con Edison	Unitil
DPL	Vermont Gas
Eversource Energy	

HISTORICAL FINANCIALS

Company Type: Private

Income Statement | | | | FYE: December 31

	REVENUE ($ mil.)	NET INCOME ($ mil.)	NET PROFIT MARGIN	EMPLOYEES
12/18	713	80	11.3%	190
12/16	652	69	10.6%	—
Annual Growth	4.5%	7.6%	—	—

2018 Year-End Financials

Return on assets: 3.3%   Cash ($ mil.): 4
Return on equity: 9.9%
Current ratio: 0.70

GREENSTONE FARM CREDIT SERVICES ACA

One of the largest associations in the Farm Credit System GreenStone offers FARM CREDIT SERVICES (FCS) providesÂ short intermediate and long-term loans; equipment and building leases; appraisal services; and life and crop insurance to farmers in Michigan and Wisconsin. ItÂ serves about 15000 members and has nearlyÂ 40 locations. Through an alliance with AgriSolutions a farm software and consulting company Greenstone provides income tax planning and preparation services farm business consulting and educational seminars. FCS Mortgage provides residential loans for rural properties as well as loans for home improvement construction and refinancing.

EXECUTIVES

Executive Vice President Chief Sales And Marketing Officer, Randy Stec
Senior Vice President Chief Information Officer, Steve Junglas
Regional Vice President, Erin Dubois
Regional Vice President, Cindy Birchmeier
Assistant Vice President Credit, Sarah J Morack
Vice President Credit, Kevin Emison
Vice President Commercial Lending, Daniel Gitter
Vice President Credit, Steve Kluemper
Vice President Commercial Lending, Larry Urban
Vice President Credit, Thomas Urban
Regional Vice President Sales And Customer Relations, Ben Mahlich
Regional Vice President Sales And Customer Relations, Melissa Humphrey
Second Vice President, Shane Kenner
Vice President Commercial Lending, Thomas Wilson
Vice President Commercial Lending, Kyle Hurley
Avp Credit And Syndicated Lending, Bonnie Coponen
Vice President Capital Markets, Brad Hibbert
Auditors: PRICEWATERHOUSECOOPERS LLP MI

LOCATIONS

HQ: GREENSTONE FARM CREDIT SERVICES ACA
3515 WEST RD, EAST LANSING, MI 488237312
Phone: 517 324-0213
Web: WWW.GREENSTONEFCS.COM

COMPETITORS

COUNTRY Financial	Rabobank Group
FB BanCorp	

HISTORICAL FINANCIALS

Company Type: Private

Income Statement | | | | FYE: December 31

	ASSETS ($ mil.)	NET INCOME ($ mil.)	INCOME AS % OF ASSETS	EMPLOYEES
12/07	4,317	69	1.6%	380
12/06	3,691	63	1.7%	
Annual Growth	17.0%	8.9%		

GROSSMONT HOSPITAL FOUNDATION

EXECUTIVES

Ex Dir, Elizabeth Morgante
Director of Case Management, Mike Murphey
Public Relations Manager, Sandy Pugliese
Director of Pharmacy, Patrick Craychee
Auditors: ERNST & YOUNG US LLP SAN DIEG

LOCATIONS

HQ: GROSSMONT HOSPITAL FOUNDATION
5555 GROSSMONT CENTER DR, LA MESA, CA 919423077
Phone: 619 740-4200
Web: WWW.GROSSMONTHEALTHCARE.ORG

HISTORICAL FINANCIALS

Company Type: Private

Income Statement | | | FYE: September 30

	REVENUE ($ mil.)	NET INCOME ($ mil.)	NET PROFIT MARGIN	EMPLOYEES
09/16	738	65	8.9%	6
09/09	5	0	8.5%	
09/08	5	0	16.8%	
09/01	1	3	314.9%	
Annual Growth	54.5%	21.8%		

2016 Year-End Financials

Return on assets: 6.9%   Cash ($ mil.): 43
Return on equity: 8.5%
Current ratio: 2.40

GROUP HEALTH COMMUNITY FOUNDATION

EXECUTIVES

Pres-Ceo, Cory Sbarbaro
Chief Inv Officer, Christopher Hanak
Cfo, Mary Wright
Auditors: MOSS ADAMS LLP SEATTLE WA

LOCATIONS

HQ: GROUP HEALTH COMMUNITY FOUNDATION
810 3RD AVE STE 220, SEATTLE, WA 981041614
Phone: 206 788-8900
Web: WWW.KAISERPERMANENTE.ORG

HISTORICAL FINANCIALS

Company Type: Private

Income Statement | | | | FYE: December 31

	REVENUE ($ mil.)	NET INCOME ($ mil.)	NET PROFIT MARGIN	EMPLOYEES
12/17	1,733	1,730	99.8%	23
12/16	3	0	23.9%	—
Annual Growth	45164.5%	189011.8%		

2017 Year-End Financials

Return on assets: 98.7%   Cash ($ mil.): —
Return on equity: 98.7%
Current ratio: —

GROUP O, INC.

The "O" in Group O stands for optimization. It also stands for Ontiveros the family that leads this company. Founded by chairman Robert Ontiveros Group O is one of the largest Hispanic-owned companies in the US. It helps big businesses improve their operations through three divisions: marketing packaging and supply chain. It offers everything from direct mail creation to shrink wrap procurement to warehousing and distribution and business intelligence. It has served clients from various industries including food and beverage (Kerry) consumer goods (P&G) manufacturing (Johnson Controls) pharmaceutical (Bristol-Myers Squibb) and telecommunications (AT&T).

Operations

Group O is a diversified business process outsourcing provider specializing in marketing supply chain packaging and business analytics products.

The company's supply chain division mainly serves heavy equipment and high technology OEMs while its packaging division targets manufacturers and distributors in need of streamlining their packaging processes. It procures and distributes bags stretch films tapes and other materials and also repairs calibrates and upgrades equipment to optimize performance.

Its SMART Audit reporting tool provides realtime reports that monitor production and spending across a plant network so that companies can take appropriate cost reduction actions. Meanwhile its marketing division offers a range of service offerings including marketing analytics customer rewards programs direct mail and e-mail marketing outsourced printing and a customer call center.

The company's Business Analytics unit has experts that can guide companies that seek to make sense out of unstructured and structured data - providing strategists and decision-makers with new insights into customer behavior while maximizing both new and existing channels. The team guides the creation implementation and management of tools in the latest applications and platforms across a comprehensive spectrum of existing systems.

Geographic Reach

Group O maintains a national network of more than 20 facilities mostly concentrated in the Midwest (Illinois Iowa and Minnesota) and Texas. Other sales offices and warehouses are located in California Nevada Pennsylvania and various southern states. It also works with more than 7000 suppliers in more than 30 countries.

Sales and Marketing
The company serves FORTUNE 500 clients across a broad range of industries including food and beverage telecommunications manufacturing consumer packaged goods retail financial services pharmaceutical healthcare technology energy and the public sector.

Strategy
In 2014 Group O launched a new website for its O-vations service offering which is aimed at helping companies optimize the design and operation of enterprise-scale reward programs. Key services range from program design and management technology integration operations and communications value-added services and reporting and analytics.

That year the company also opened its Business Analytics unit in Hyderabad India. The team helps generate customer acquisition and loyalty marketing insights that clients can then use to make better business decisions.

Company Background
Ontiveros established Group O in 1974 as Bi-State Packaging which sold packaging materials and equipment to manufacturers. Today it is one of the top 15 Hispanic-owned businesses in the nation.

EXECUTIVES

Senior Vice President Business Development, Mike De La Cruz
Vice President Marketing Solutions, Candy Wise
Vice President Of Marketing Solutions, Candace Wise
Auditors: HONKAMP KRUEGER & CO PC MO

LOCATIONS

HQ: GROUP O, INC.
4905 77TH AVE E, MILAN, IL 612643250
Phone: 309 736-8100
Web: WWW.GROUPO.COM

PRODUCTS/OPERATIONS

Selected Services

Marketing
Analytics
Consumer and trade fulfillment
Customer call center and workforce management
Direct mail and e-mail optimization
Print management outsourcing
Rewards and loyalty programs
Packaging
Equipment supply and repair (bagging case handling labeling shrinking and stretch wrapping systems)
Materials supply (labels poly bags protective packaging sanitation products shrink and stretch films and tape)
Stretch film equipment auditing
Supply chain
Business process outsourcing
Distribution
Global sourcing
Inventory management
Order management
Supplier management
Warehousing

Selected Industries Served
Food and Beverage
Telecommunications
Manufacturing
Consumer Packaged Goods
Financial Services
Pharmaceutical
Health care
Technology

COMPETITORS

Brightstar Corp.
CEVA Logistics U.S.
Fedex Supply Chain
Jay Group
Kenco Logistics Services
Ozburn-Hessey Logistics
The Bernd Group
UPS Supply Chain Solutions
Weber Logistics

HISTORICAL FINANCIALS
Company Type: Private

Income Statement — FYE: December 31

	REVENUE ($ mil.)	NET INCOME ($ mil.)	NET PROFIT MARGIN	EMPLOYEES
12/13	569	5	1.0%	1,066
12/05	240	5	2.2%	—
Annual Growth	11.4%	0.9%		

2013 Year-End Financials

Return on assets: 87.9%
Return on equity: 1.0%
Current ratio: 0.90
Cash ($ mil.): 7

GROVE ELK UNIFIED SCHOOL DISTRICT

EXECUTIVES

Supt, Steven Ladd
Assc Supt, Richard Odegaard
Technology Manager, Chris Perris
Administrative Assistant, Joanna Corrigan
Director Adult Education, Kathy Hamilton
Senior Administrative Assistan, Libby Sidhu
Computer Resource Teacher, Matthew Gipson
Library Technician, Rebecca Santos
Maintenance Shop Supervisor, Rob Teresi
Administrative Assistant, Shannon Bloodworth
Teacher, Theresa Jones
Auditors: CROWE HORWATH LLP SACRAMENTO

LOCATIONS

HQ: GROVE ELK UNIFIED SCHOOL DISTRICT
9510 ELK GROVE FLORIN RD, ELK GROVE, CA 956241801
Phone: 916 686-5085
Web: WWW.EGUSD.NET

HISTORICAL FINANCIALS
Company Type: Private

Income Statement — FYE: June 30

	REVENUE ($ mil.)	NET INCOME ($ mil.)	NET PROFIT MARGIN	EMPLOYEES
06/17	741	65	8.8%	5,600
06/07	560	(30)	—	—
06/06	0	0	—	—
06/03	454	19	4.4%	—
Annual Growth	3.6%	8.9%	—	—

GROWMARK, INC.

Agricultural and energy cooperative GROWMARK serves more than 250000 farm commercial and residential customers across the US and in parts of Canada. Under the Growmark FS name it offers a host of plant food and crop protection products as well as biotechnology services and training and agricultural marketing and consulting. The company also operates a full-line seed company Seedway and provides grain facility planning and grain marketing services. Lastly GROWMARK's energy business includes the marketing and distribution of fuels lubricants and greases and propane and the Fast Stop convenience stores and gas station chain with 230-plus locations across the Midwest.

Operations
GROWMARK's operations are divided into five major divisions: agronomy energy grain facility planning and logistics.

The agronomy division includes products and services in the areas of seeds plant food crop protection and biotechnology while the energy business includes marketing and distribution services and the Fast Stop convenience store/fuel station chain. GROWMARK provides grain handling and marketing services through its grain division and grain facility planning and consulting through its facility planning division. The company's logistics operations provide for the delivery of more than 150000 truckloads of products annually to local cooperatives.

Geographic Reach
GROWMARK is headquartered in Bloomington Illinois and serves customers in more than 40 US states and Ontario Canada.

Its Seedway business has eight office and warehouse locations in Vermont New York Pennsylvania and Florida.

Financial Performance
Although not required to publicly release full financials GROWMARK reported fiscal 2017 revenue of more than $7 billion.

Strategy
A key element of GROWMARK's strategy is the improvement of its supply chain which has been called out as one of the four major tenets for growth. In 2018 the company added a new executive position focused on supply chain optimization.

Company Background
GROWMARK traces its history back to 1920 and the establishment of local cooperatives by Farm Bureau members. One of those cooperatives Farm Bureau Service Company of Iowa in the early 1960s merged with Illinois Farm Supply Company (founded in 1927) to form the foundation of what is today GROWMARK. The GROWMARK name started being used in 1980.

EXECUTIVES

Chairman And President, John Reifsteck
Ceo, Jeff Solberg
Vice President General Counsel, Brent Bostrom
Vp Eastern Retail Operations, Steve Buckalew
Vp And Cfo, Marshall Bohbrink
Vp Energy, Kevin Carroll
Vp Midwest Retail And Acquisitions, Shelly Kruse
Vp Grain, Brent Ericson
Vice President Human Resources & Compliance, Gary Swango
Vp Agronomy, Mark Orr
Vp Financial And Risk Management, Mike Woods
Vp Member Services, Denny Worth
Vice President Of Human Resources, Ann Kafer
Vice President Systems, George Key
Region Vice President, Barry Schmidt
Vice President Of Information Technology, Rick Norton
Vice President Member Services, Dennis Farmer
Senior Vice President, Jeffrey M Solberg
National Account Manager, Norm Frank
Vice Chairman, Rick Nelson

Vice Chairman, Chet Esther
Assistant Treasurer, Karmy Kays
Treasurer, Jeffrey Lynch
Auditors: ERNST & YOUNG LLP CHICAGO IL

LOCATIONS

HQ: GROWMARK, INC.
  1701 TOWANDA AVE, BLOOMINGTON, IL 617012057
Phone: 309 557-6000
Web: WWW.GROWMARK.COM

COMPETITORS

ADM	Marathon Oil
AGRI Industries	NC Hybrids
Ag Processing Inc.	Orscheln Farm and Home
BP	Pfister Hybrid Corn
Barkley Seed	Pioneer Hi-Bred
Bayer CropScience	Rabo AgriFinance
CHS	Sakata Seed
Cargill	Seed Enterprises
Chevron	Southern States
Costco Wholesale	Terra Nitrogen
DeBruce Grain	Wal-Mart
Exxon Mobil	Wilbur-Ellis

HISTORICAL FINANCIALS
Company Type: Private

Income Statement — FYE: August 31

	REVENUE ($ mil.)	NET INCOME ($ mil.)	NET PROFIT MARGIN	EMPLOYEES
08/18	8,522	65	0.8%	7,000
08/17	7,291	115	1.6%	—
08/16	7,031	101	1.4%	—
08/15	8,727	113	1.3%	—
Annual Growth	(0.8%)	(16.6%)	—	—

2018 Year-End Financials

Return on assets: 2.5%   Cash ($ mil.): 99
Return on equity: 5.4%
Current ratio: 1.70

GRUMA CORPORATION

Gruma is the American subsidiary of giant Mexican food company Gruma S.A.B. de C.V. and the leading tortilla and corn flower producer in the US. The company manufactures and distributes corn flour corn tortillas and related products such as wraps and corn chips through roughly 25 production plants. The company runs the world's largest tortilla plant in Los Angeles; that facility has a production capacity of 25 million tortillas per day. Its highly recognizable brand names include Mission Calidad and Guerrero tortillas and Maseca corn flour. Gruma is its parent company's largest revenue producer.

Strategy

Gruma historically has chased the expanding US Hispanic population which added 63% between 2000 and 2016 but growing general popularity of Mexican food and rising numbers of Mexican food restaurants have led the company to increasingly target non-Hispanic populations (which account for most Mexican food purchases). To that end the company has developed and produced several non-Mexican or Americanized tortilla-like products such as whole wheat and spinach herb wraps and street taco-style tortillas.

Gruma is capitalizing on its market-leading position in corn flour and tortillas and its successful growth by upping its production capacity. Its largest plant launched in 2018 in Dallas Texas; those operations increased its tortilla production

capacity by 10% and created production transportation and logistical efficiencies through adoption of new technologies.

Furthermore the company is moving its product mix toward higher-margin items including health foods value-added products and small-count products. The company's health-conscious alternatives (such as its Mission Organics tortilla chips and gluten-free organic and low-carb Mission wraps) have ridden the wave of the rising popularity of healthy living in the states producing double-digit sales growth.

EXECUTIVES

President And Ceo, Javier Velez Bautista

LOCATIONS

HQ: GRUMA CORPORATION
  5601 EXECUTIVE DR STE 800, IRVING, TX 750382508
Phone: 972 232-5000
Web: WWW.MISSIONFOODS.COM

PRODUCTS/OPERATIONS

Selected Brands and Products

Guerrero
  Chicharron de Cerdo
  Tortillas de Harina (Original and Butter)
  Tortillas de Maíz Blanco
  Tostadas Norte?as Clásicas
  Tostadas Caseras Doraditas
Mission Foods
    96% Fat Free Heart Healthy tortillas
  All Natural Spicy Bean dip
  Caramel Twists
  Carb Balance tortillas
  Cheddar Cheese dip
  Chicharrones (Original BBQ Habanero and Picante)
  Cinnamon Twists
  Chunky Salsa Medium
  Corn tortilla
  Flour tortillas
  Guacamole dip
  Jumbo Taco shells
  Life Balance tortillas
  Multi-Grain Flour tortillas
  Organic Stone-Ground tortilla chips
  Pork Cracklins Plain Tenders
  Restaurant Style Tortilla Triangles (Cilantro Lime Premium White Corn and Salsa Roja)
  Restaurant Style Tortilla Rounds
  Salsa Con Queso
  Salsa Verde Medium
  Sliced Nacho Jalape?o Peppers
  Taco and tostada shells
  Wraps (Original Garden Spinach Jalapeno Cheddar Multi-Grain Sun-dried Tomato Basil and Zesty Garlic Herb)

COMPETITORS

Azteca Foods	Horizon Milling
Bimbo Bakeries	La Gloria Foods
Bob's Red Mill Natural Foods	La Reina
Bunge Milling	La Tortilla Factory
C.H. Guenther & Son	Minsa
Casa de Oro Foods	Ole' Mexican Foods
Don Pancho Authentic Mexican Foods	Organic Milling
	Ruiz Mexican Foods
Flowers Foods	Star of the West
Frito-Lay	Taco Bell
General Mills	Tumaro's Gourmet Tortillas
Grupo Bimbo	Tyson Foods
Hodgson Mill	

HISTORICAL FINANCIALS
Company Type: Private

Income Statement — FYE: December 31

	REVENUE ($ mil.)	NET INCOME ($ mil.)	NET PROFIT MARGIN	EMPLOYEES
12/17	2,050	215	10.5%	7,000
12/16	2,023	179	8.9%	—
12/15	2,086	152	7.3%	—
12/14	2,018	132	6.6%	—
Annual Growth	0.5%	17.5%	—	—

2017 Year-End Financials

Return on assets: 17.7%   Cash ($ mil.): 47
Return on equity: 22.8%
Current ratio: 2.00

GUEST SERVICES, INC.

Guest Services satisfies hungry and sleepy patrons. The company provides contract food services and hospitality-management services nationwide. It operates cafeterias and onsite restaurants and offers catering to businesses hotels hospitals conference centers and government operations including the US Supreme Court the US House of Representatives and the National Park Service. For leisure and resort facilities Guest Services also provides special-event catering and offers management services such as marketing human resources procurement quality-assurance and information technology services. Guest Services was founded in 1917 as a private company to serve governmental agencies.

Operations

Guest Services serves some 250 facilities across the US and more than 25 million guests each year. The company also owns Lancaster Foods one of the largest wholesale produce companies in the mid-Atlantic region.

Additional offerings include corporate accounting systems and food safety and health support.

Geographic Reach

Based in Fairfax Virginia Guest Services serves a variety of customers nationwide.

Sales and Marketing

Guest Services serves several clients including government and business dining facilities museums hotels resorts conference centers luxury condominiums senior living centers health care systems state and national park recreation school and university dining facilities specialty retail stores and full-service restaurants.

Customers have included Washington DC's National Mall and Memorial Park. Guest Services also manages food lodging and recreation services at state parks in West Virginia New York and California.

Strategy

Guest Services has been expanding its portfolio of premium properties. For example it owns and manages the DoubleTree Suites by Hilton Naples. In 2013 Guest Services acquired The Lodge and Spa at Breckenridge which overlooks Colorado's Breckenridge Village. With 45 rooms the property is a popular destination for weddings and corporate events. It's adding food and beverage service in-house catering and event planning to the property's services.

EXECUTIVES

Ceo, Gerard T. Gabrys
President And Coo, Jeffrey A. Marquis

President Lancaster Foods, John Gates
Vp Hotel Division South, Barry G. Trice
Vp Sales And Marketing, Jerry Chadwich
Vp And Cfo, Nico Foris
Vice President, Beverly Frazer
Auditors: PRICEWATERHOUSECOOPERS LLP MC

LOCATIONS

HQ: GUEST SERVICES, INC.
3055 PROSPERITY AVE, FAIRFAX, VA 220312290
Phone: 703 849-9300
Web: WWW.GUESTSERVICES.COM

PRODUCTS/OPERATIONS

Selected Services

Audits
Corporate Support Services
Financial Accounting Systems
Food Safety and Health
Human Resources
IT
Maintenance Support
Management Information Systems
Marketing
Onsite Test Kitchen
PeopleSoft Processing
Procurement
Quality Assurance
Safety
Security
Test Kitchen
Training

COMPETITORS

ARAMARK	Delaware North
Centerplate	Sodexo USA
Compass Group USA	Valley Services

HISTORICAL FINANCIALS

Company Type: Private

Income Statement · FYE: December 31

	REVENUE ($ mil.)	NET INCOME ($ mil.)	NET PROFIT MARGIN	EMPLOYEES
12/17	459	(2)	—	99
12/16	442	1	0.4%	—
12/15	396	3	0.9%	—
12/14	375	0	0.3%	—
Annual Growth	**7.0%**	—	—	—

2017 Year-End Financials

Return on assets: (-1.3%)
Return on equity: (-4.5%)   Cash ($ mil.): 24
Current ratio: 1.20

GUILDNET, INC.

EXECUTIVES

Ceo, Alan R Morse
Chairman, James M Dubin
Treasurer, Lawrence E Goldschmidt
Secretary, Robert B Okun
Administrative Assistant, Angela Rosario
Neurologist, Helen Chang
Technical Consultant, Lok Wong
Occupational Medicine Speciali, Inna Babaeva
Auditors: KPMG LLP NEW YORK NY

LOCATIONS

HQ: GUILDNET, INC.
15 W 65TH ST, NEW YORK, NY 100236601
Phone: 212 769-6200
Web: WWW.JGB.ORG

HISTORICAL FINANCIALS

Company Type: Private

Income Statement · FYE: December 31

	REVENUE ($ mil.)	NET INCOME ($ mil.)	NET PROFIT MARGIN	EMPLOYEES
12/15	950	(24)	—	377
12/14	826	1	0.1%	—
12/13	672	45	6.8%	—
12/12	433	42	9.8%	—
Annual Growth	**29.9%**	—	—	—

2015 Year-End Financials

Return on assets: (-8.5%)
Return on equity: (-19.4%)   Cash ($ mil.): 12
Current ratio: 1.40

GUILFORD COUNTY SCHOOL SYSTEM

EXECUTIVES

Supt, Sharon L Contreras
Co-Interim Supt*, Nora K Carr
CIO*, Terrance Young
Superintendent, Sharon Contreras
Coordinator, April Dixon
Executive of Information Techn, Eric Brown
Security Staff, Les Allison
Coordinator, Todd Baldwin
Co Teacher, Amanda Cobb
Teacher, Amy Dunn
Teacher, Amy Kieffer

LOCATIONS

HQ: GUILFORD COUNTY SCHOOL SYSTEM
712 N EUGENE ST, GREENSBORO, NC 274011622
Phone: 336 370-8100
Web: WWW.GCSNC.COM

HISTORICAL FINANCIALS

Company Type: Private

Income Statement · FYE: June 30

	REVENUE ($ mil.)	NET INCOME ($ mil.)	NET PROFIT MARGIN	EMPLOYEES
06/11	692	(0)	—	10,000
06/09	0	(0)	—	—
06/03	0	0	—	—
06/02	546	69	12.8%	—
Annual Growth	**2.7%**	—	—	—

2011 Year-End Financials

Return on assets: —
Return on equity: (-0.1%)   Cash ($ mil.): 28
Current ratio: 1.10

GUNDERSEN LUTHERAN MEDICAL CENTER, INC.

At the heart of the Gundersen Lutheran health system Gundersen Lutheran Medical Center serves residents of nearly 20 counties that stretch across the upper Midwest. The clinical campus for the University of Wisconsin's medical and nursing schools operates a 325-bed teaching hospital with a Level II Trauma and Emergency Center. Focused on caring for patients in western Wisconsin the hospital boasts several specialty services such as bariatrics behavioral health cancer care orthopedics palliative care pediatrics rehabilitation and women's health. The physician-led not-for-profit medical center is affiliated with a group of regional clinics and specialty centers.

Operations

Gundersen Lutheran Medical Center has a staff of some 800 doctors dentists and other professionals. As part of Gundersen Lutheran (also known as Gundersen Health System) the hospital's sister entities include the Gundersen Clinic and the Gundersen Lutheran Administrative Services entity.

In 2013 the Gundersen Health System reported 1437 births 17000 surgeries and 278000 outpatient hospital visits.

Geographic Reach

From its main campus in La Crosse Wisconsin as well as a satellite outpatient center in Onalaska the hospital serves communities located in 19 counties throughout western Wisconsin northeastern Iowa and southeastern Minnesota.

Strategy

The Gundersen Lutheran organization expands though partnerships such as an alliance with the Allen Hospital in Iowa to enhance regional cardiovascular services in 2013. The medical center is also working to upgrade its infrastructure to enable 100% energy independence in 2014.

To offer advanced training to residents and physicians Gundersen Lutheran Medical Center developed and opened a high-tech training center in 2012. The Cleary Kumm Simulation and Training Labs offer mock operating rooms and simulation labs for use by local doctors and nationwide medical professionals for training or conferences. Gundersen Lutheran Medical Center is banking on the simulation and training facility to draw interest talent and outside funds.

Company Background

Gundersen Lutheran Medical Center was founded in 1995 through the merger of Gunderson Clinic and Lutheran Hospital-La Crosse. The Lutheran Hospital opened in 1902.

EXECUTIVES

Medical Director Emergency Services, Eric Voter
Senior Vice President, Gerald Arndt
Medical Director, Jackie Yaeger
Auditors: KPMG LLP MINNEAPOLIS MN

LOCATIONS

HQ: GUNDERSEN LUTHERAN MEDICAL CENTER, INC.
1900 SOUTH AVE, LA CROSSE, WI 546015467
Phone: 608 782-7300
Web: WWW.GUNDERSENHEALTH.ORG

PRODUCTS/OPERATIONS

Selected Services
Advance care planning
Apnea
Audiology
Autism Spectrum Disorder
BioBank
Brain disorders
Cardiac services
Children's health
Cleft Lip & Palate Clinic
Endocrinology
Hospice
Eye care
Gynecology
Hand surgery
Heart Institute
LASIK eye surgery
Massage
Neck surgery

Neurosciences
Oral and maxillofacial surgery
Pediatrics
Radiation oncology
Rehabilitation
Urgent care
Urology
Weight management
Wound care

COMPETITORS

Dean Health Systems Inc.
Franciscan Skemp Healthcare
Luther Midelfort
Mayo Clinic
Meriter Health Services
Ministry Health Care
Olmsted Medical
Sacred Heart Hospital
Tomah Memorial Hospital
University of Wisconsin Hospital and Clinics

HISTORICAL FINANCIALS

Company Type: Private

Income Statement				FYE: December 31
	REVENUE ($ mil.)	NET INCOME ($ mil.)	NET PROFIT MARGIN	EMPLOYEES
12/17	1,071	112	10.5%	4,500
12/15	980	60	6.1%	—
12/14	894	94	10.6%	—
12/11	431	49	11.5%	—
Annual Growth	16.3%	14.6%	—	—

2017 Year-End Financials

Return on assets: 7.0%
Return on equity: 10.8%
Current ratio: 5.40
Cash ($ mil.): 205

GWINNETT COUNTY BOARD OF EDUCATION

EXECUTIVES

Chairperson, Robert McClure
Accounting Staff, Kathy Stillwell
Teacher, Laurie Pitcock
Business Manager, Gwen Strabala
Payroll, Lori Swilley
Fleet Manager, Roger Brank
Payroll Specialist, Sherry Dudish
Special Education Teacher, Caitlin Cohen
Admin Assistant, Dana Hicks
Teacher, Donna Power
Bookkeeper, Tammy Mackendree
Auditors: MAULDIN & JENKINS LLC ATLANT

LOCATIONS

HQ: GWINNETT COUNTY BOARD OF EDUCATION
437 OLD PEACHTREE RD NW, SUWANEE, GA
300242978
Phone: 678 301-6000
Web: WWW.GWINNETT.K12.GA.US

HISTORICAL FINANCIALS

Company Type: Private

Income Statement				FYE: June 30
	REVENUE ($ mil.)	NET INCOME ($ mil.)	NET PROFIT MARGIN	EMPLOYEES
06/18	1,973	(55)	—	138
06/17	1,868	(2)	—	—
06/16*	1,791	349	19.5%	—
07/10	0	0	11.5%	—
Annual Growth	273.6%	—	—	—

*Fiscal year change

2018 Year-End Financials

Return on assets: (-1.5%)
Return on equity: —
Current ratio: 2.70
Cash ($ mil.): 97

GWINNETT HOSPITAL SYSTEM, INC.

Auditors: KPMG LLP ATLANTA GA

LOCATIONS

HQ: GWINNETT HOSPITAL SYSTEM, INC.
1000 MEDICAL CENTER BLVD, LAWRENCEVILLE,
GA 300467694
Phone: 678 343-3428
Web: WWW.GWINNETTMEDICALCENTER.ORG

HISTORICAL FINANCIALS

Company Type: Private

Income Statement				FYE: June 30
	REVENUE ($ mil.)	NET INCOME ($ mil.)	NET PROFIT MARGIN	EMPLOYEES
06/18	731	12	1.7%	2,050
06/17	729	29	4.1%	—
06/16	735	(31)	—	—
06/15	698	15	2.2%	—
Annual Growth	1.5%	(6.3%)	—	—

2018 Year-End Financials

Return on assets: 1.4%
Return on equity: 2.6%
Current ratio: 2.60
Cash ($ mil.): 54

H. LEE MOFFITT CANCER CENTER AND RESEARCH INSTITUTE HOSPITAL, INC.

The H. Lee Moffitt Cancer Center and Research Institute founded in 1986 is a National Cancer Institute-designated Comprehensive Cancer Center located on the Tampa campus of the University of South Florida. The institute carries it out its stated mission of "contributing to the prevention and cure of cancer" through patient care research and education. It operates a 210-bed medical and surgical facility as well as outpatient treatment programs and a blood and marrow transplant program. Its research programs include study in the areas of molecular oncology immunology risk assessment health outcomes and experimental therapeutics.

Operations
The Moffitt Cancer Center sees more than 9000 cancer inpatients each year; it also handles some 328000 outpatient visits annually. In addition to its 40-bed blood and marrow transplant center which performs 400 annual transplants the hospital includes more than a dozen operating rooms and extensive diagnostic radiology and radiation therapy labs. The Cancer Screening and Prevention Center offers genetic testing for certain kinds of hereditary cancers (breast ovarian colon and melanoma).

The Moffitt Research Institute conducts a wide range of cancer studies and some of its drug discovery research programs are managed through partnerships with pharmaceutical companies and other research laboratories. The research institute also relies on funding grants from organizations such as the National Institutes of Health. It has received more than $80 million in grant funding and participated in some 300 clinical trials.

The Moffitt Cancer Center likewise has educational and health care alliances with a number of Florida hospitals and colleges including a three-way cancer care and research partnership with Shands HealthCare and the University of Florida. Through its affiliated network program (the Moffitt Oncology Network) Moffitt works with community doctors and centers across Florida to provide enhanced cancer services throughout the state. It also operates a number of outpatient clinics in surrounding areas.

Geographic Reach
Through its main campus and numerous outpatient sites Moffitt Cancer Center primarily serves residents of seven Florida counties: Hernando Hillsborough Manatee Pasco Pinellas Polk and Sarasota. It also serves patients from other areas of Florida and neighboring states.

Sales and Marketing
HMO and PPO plans account for about 65% of patient service revenues while reimbursements from Medicare and Medicaid plans account for another 32% of sales.

Financial Performance
Revenue at Moffitt Cancer Center and Research Institute increased 1% to $779 million in 2013 from $772 the previous year due to higher patient service revenues. After a net loss in 2012 the institute reported net income of $26 million due to an increase in net assets and non-operating gains. Cash from operations also grew by $77 million due to the net income increase and cash generated from an estimated third-party settlement.

Strategy
Moffitt Cancer Center conducts expansion and facility improvement projects to enhance services for its cancer patients. For instance it launched construction of a new $74 million outpatient facility at the current McKinley office site in 2013; the location is near the main campus and will provide surgery infusion imaging research and other services. It also formed a partnership with Space Coast Cancer Center Boca Raton Regional Hospital Advinus Therapeutics and Lehigh Valley Health Network to improve cancer care for all the organizations.

EXECUTIVES

Pres, Jack Kolosky
Ex V Pres-Ctr Dir*, Thomas Sellers
Dir*, Willam S Dalton

Vp/Cfo*, Yvette Tremonti
Director Cell-Based Therapies, James J Mul
Stewardship Officer, Jessica Skinner
Project Coordinator Design, Mark Lyon
Public Relations Account Coord, Nicole Drone
Director, Rebecca Young
Auditors: ERNST & YOUNG LLP

LOCATIONS

HQ: H. LEE MOFFITT CANCER CENTER AND
RESEARCH INSTITUTE HOSPITAL, INC.
12902 USF MAGNOLIA DR, TAMPA, FL 336129416
Phone: 813 745-4673
Web: WWW.MOFFITT.ORG

PRODUCTS/OPERATIONS

Selected Services

Chemotherapy

Diagnosis
Emotional Support
Integrative Medicine
Labwork Scans and Biopsy
Other Patient Services
Pain Management
Radiation
Screening and Genetics
Spiritual Support
Surgical Care
Well-Being

Selected Research Fields
Basic Science Division
Cancer Imaging and Metabolism
Drug Discovery
Immunology
Integrated Mathematical Oncology
Molecular Oncology
Tumor Biology
Population Science Division
Biostatistics and Bioinformatics
Cancer Epidemiology
Health Outcomes & Behavior

COMPETITORS

All Children's Hospital	Mayo Clinic Jacksonville
Baptist Hospital of Miami	Memorial Sloan-Kettering
Bay Medical Center	Oak Hill Hospital
Boca Raton Regional Hospital	Roswell Park Cancer Institute
Dana-Farber	Sacred Heart Health System
Fox Chase Cancer Center	South Georgia Medical Center
Jackson County Hospital of Florida	St. Vincent's Health System
MD Anderson Cancer Center	
Manatee Memorial Hospital	

HISTORICAL FINANCIALS

Company Type: Private

Income Statement   FYE: June 30

	REVENUE ($ mil.)	NET INCOME ($ mil.)	NET PROFIT MARGIN	EMPLOYEES
06/14	855	50	5.9%	4,200
06/13	779	26	3.4%	—
06/12	771	(7)	—	—
Annual Growth	5.3%	—	—	—

2014 Year-End Financials
Return on assets: 5.5%   Cash ($ mil.): 96
Return on equity: 10.9%
Current ratio: 1.90

H. LEE MOFFITT CANCER CENTER AND RESEARCH INSTITUTE, INC.

EXECUTIVES

Pres, William Dalton
Svp-Cdio*, Edmondo Robinson
Project Coordinator, Donna Cosenzo
Scientist, Thinh Cao
Assistant Professor, Alfredo A Santillan
Manager, Lee Anne Corbin
Health Professional, Amber Shrewsbury
Assistant Professor, Andrew W Carroll
Scientist, Bin Fang
Pathologist, Santo V Nicosia
Scientist, Shelten G Yuen
Auditors: ERNST & YOUNG LLP TAMPA FLORI

LOCATIONS

HQ: H. LEE MOFFITT CANCER CENTER AND
RESEARCH INSTITUTE, INC.
12902 USF MAGNOLIA DR, TAMPA, FL 336129416
Phone: 813 745-4673
Web: WWW.MOFFITT.ORG

HISTORICAL FINANCIALS

Company Type: Private

Income Statement   FYE: June 30

	REVENUE ($ mil.)	NET INCOME ($ mil.)	NET PROFIT MARGIN	EMPLOYEES
06/18	1,310	178	13.6%	5,500
06/17	1,132	76	6.8%	—
06/15	951	61	6.5%	—
Annual Growth	11.3%	42.7%	—	—

2018 Year-End Financials
Return on assets: 13.5%   Cash ($ mil.): 258
Return on equity: 22.1%
Current ratio: 2.60

HAGGEN, INC.

Haggen showers shoppers in the Pacific Northwest with salmon coffee and other essentials. Formerly one of the area's largest independent grocers Haggen operated some 130 supermarkets in Washington and Oregon as well as California Nevada and Arizona. Most of the stores were acquired from Albertsons in late 2014. In late 2015 Haggen filed for Chapter 11 bankruptcy protection to allow it to reorganize around a reduced number of locations and in 2016 the company agreed to sell its remaining core stores to Albertsons. The chain was founded in 1933 in Bellingham Washington.

EXECUTIVES

Vice President, Mike Lobaugh
Pharmacy Manager, David Muirhead
Vice President, Brad Haggen
Auditors: MOSS ADAMS LLP

LOCATIONS

HQ: HAGGEN, INC.
2211 RIMLAND DR STE 300, BELLINGHAM, WA
982265699
Phone: 360 733-8720
Web: WWW.HAGGEN.COM

2014 Stores

Washington	15
Oregon	2
Total	**0** **17**

COMPETITORS

Costco Wholesale	Smart & Final
Fred Meyer Stores	Target Corporation
Grocery Outlet	Trader Joe's
Quality Food	Wal-Mart
SUPERVALU	Walgreen
Safeway	WinCo Foods

HISTORICAL FINANCIALS

Company Type: Private

Income Statement   FYE: December 31

	REVENUE ($ mil.)	NET INCOME ($ mil.)	NET PROFIT MARGIN	EMPLOYEES
12/07	787	8	1.1%	3,900
12/06	758	6	0.9%	—
12/05	164	0	—	—
Annual Growth	—20237.1%			

2007 Year-End Financials
Return on assets: 4.9%   Cash ($ mil.): 6
Return on equity: 1.1%
Current ratio: 0.30

HAMILTON CHATTANOOGA COUNTY HOSPITAL AUTHORITY

The Chattanooga-Hamilton County Hospital Authority (dba Erlanger Health System) offers a broad range of health service operations including the T.C. Thompson Children's Hospital a cancer treatment facility and centers devoted to heart treatment trauma and eye care. The system comprises five hospital campuses in Tennessee with some 810 acute care beds as well as 50 long-term care beds. A teaching center for the University of Tennessee College of Medicine Erlanger provides tertiary care for a region that includes southeastern Tennessee northern Georgia northern Alabama and western North Carolina.

Operations
Erlanger is the tri-state region's only Level One Trauma Center providing the highest level of trauma care for adults. The Children's Hospital at Erlanger houses the region's only Level III Neonatal Intensive Care Unit as well as a pediatric trauma team Emergency Center and Pediatric Intensive Care Unit

The hospital system treats more than 300000 patients every year. In 2014 Erlanger had 30394 inpatient admissions 230765 outpatient visits to physician practices and 28810 surgical patients. Some 3067 children were admitted to Children's Hospital and 43192 received treatment in the Emergency Department and outpatient surgery.

The LIFE FORCE air ambulance service is is equipped with two EC-135 aircraft capable of single pilot IFR and two Bell 407 aircraft. LIFE FORCE transported 1419 patients in 2014.

Geographic Reach
The Erlanger Health System is a multi-hospital system with five hospitals based in Chattanooga: the University Hospital Children's Hospital at Erlanger Erlanger North Hospital Erlanger East Hos-

pital and Erlanger Bledsoe Hospital located in Pikeville Tennessee. Its LIFE FORCE air ambulance service is stationed in Chattanooga and Sparta in Tennessee and in Calhoun and Blue Ridge in Georgia.

Financial Performance
Medicare accounted for 33% of Erlanger's net patient revenues in fiscal 2014; Commercial insurance 31%; and Medicaid 22%.

Company Background
To extend its patient reach Erlanger entered into a management contract with Hutcheson Hospital located in North Georgia in 2011.

Erlanger was founded in 1889 through the generosity of French nobleman Baron Frederic Emile d'Erlanger who held financial interests in a number of railroads in the region. He donated $5000 (more than $4 million in today's dollars) for a new hospital. It opened with 72 beds in 1899.

EXECUTIVES

Radiology Director, Byron Stutz
Operating Room Dir, Adam Royer
Senior Vice President Physician Services, Steven Burkett
Vice President Human Resources, Floyd Chasse
Svp, Joseph Winick
Director Of Him, Jim Brown
Vice President, Bruce Komiske
Medical Director Of Quality And Safety, Woods Blake
Medical Director, Waleed Mourad
Medical Director, Jenny Mahaffey
Medical Director Infection Prevention And Antimicrobial Stewardship, Jay Sizemore
Clinical Director, Becky Howe
Assistant Vice President Of Oncology, Tony Dotson
Medical Director, Curtis Cary
Medical Director Pediatric Critical Care, Gregory Talbott
Board Member, Brian Ceraolo

LOCATIONS

HQ: HAMILTON CHATTANOOGA COUNTY HOSPITAL AUTHORITY
975 E 3RD ST, CHATTANOOGA, TN 374032147
Phone: 423 778-7000
Web: WWW.ERLANGER.ORG

PRODUCTS/OPERATIONS

Selected Campuses
Dodson Avenue Community Health Center
Erlanger Bledsoe Campus
Erlanger East Campus
Erlanger Medical Center
Erlanger North Campus
Southside Community Health Center
T.C. Thompson Children's Hospital

Selected Medical Services
Breast Imaging
Cancer Services
Cardiology
Chattanooga Lifestyle Center
Community Health Centers
Craniofacial Center
Erlanger Metabolic and Bariatric Surgery Center
Erlanger Pharmacy
Gastroenterology
Heart
Home Health (ContinuCare)
HouseCalls
Hypertension Management Center
Imaging Services
LIFE FORCE
Neurobehavioral and Memory Services
Orthopedics
Radiology
Respiratory Services
Rheumatology
Robotic Surgery
Sleep Disorders Center

Stroke
The Weight Loss Program
Trauma Services
Urgent Care - Adult
Urology
UT Erlanger Kidney Transplant Center
Weight Management
Women's Services
WorkForce Corporate Health
Wound Care and Hyperbaric Oxygen center

COMPETITORS

Catholic Health Initiatives
Community Health Systems
Hutcheson Medical
Parkridge Medical Center
Saint Thomas Rutherford Hospital
Southern Hills
Vanderbilt University Medical Center

HISTORICAL FINANCIALS
Company Type: Private

Income Statement   FYE: June 30

	REVENUE ($ mil.)	NET INCOME ($ mil.)	NET PROFIT MARGIN	EMPLOYEES
06/18	973	26	2.8%	4,700
06/17	888	13	1.6%	—
06/07	499	13	2.7%	—
06/06	439	17	4.0%	—
Annual Growth	6.9%	3.7%	—	—

2018 Year-End Financials
Return on assets: 3.5%   Cash ($ mil.): 43
Return on equity: 9.2%
Current ratio: 1.80

HARBOR-UCLA MEDICAL CENTER

LOCATIONS

HQ: HARBOR-UCLA MEDICAL CENTER
1000 W CARSON ST, TORRANCE, CA 905022059
Phone: 310 222-2301
Web: WWW.LABIOMED.ORG

HISTORICAL FINANCIALS
Company Type: Private

Income Statement   FYE: June 30

	REVENUE ($ mil.)	NET INCOME ($ mil.)	NET PROFIT MARGIN	EMPLOYEES
06/16	637	(268)	—	3,000
06/15	607	(287)	—	—
Annual Growth	5.0%	—	—	—

2016 Year-End Financials
Return on assets: (-33.1%)   Cash ($ mil.): 9
Return on equity: —
Current ratio: 1.40

HARFORD COUNTY BOARD OF EDUCATION (INC)

EXECUTIVES

President, Nancy Reynolds
Vice President, Francis Grambo III
Manager, Carla Fromille
Assistant, Charles Grebe
Assistant, Daniel Hanzelik
Marketing Staff, Mary Stapleton
Auditors: SB & COMPANY HUNT VALLEY MAR

LOCATIONS

HQ: HARFORD COUNTY BOARD OF EDUCATION (INC)
102 S HICKORY AVE, BEL AIR, MD 210143731
Phone: 410 838-7300
Web: WWW.HCPS.ORG

HISTORICAL FINANCIALS
Company Type: Private

Income Statement   FYE: June 30

	REVENUE ($ mil.)	NET INCOME ($ mil.)	NET PROFIT MARGIN	EMPLOYEES
06/13	535	(4)	—	114
06/12	536	1	0.3%	—
06/08	572	(0)	—	—
Annual Growth	(1.3%)	—	—	—

2013 Year-End Financials
Return on assets: (-0.7%)   Cash ($ mil.): 8
Return on equity: (-1.0%)
Current ratio: —

HARLEE MANOR, INC.

EXECUTIVES

Pres, Hardie A Beloff
V Pres*, Leland Beloff
SEC*, Geraldine Barbeau-Leonard
Treasurer, Jean Beloff
Health Care Director, Jennifer Bail

LOCATIONS

HQ: HARLEE MANOR, INC.
218 N DIAMOND ST, CLIFTON HEIGHTS, PA 190181507
Phone: 610 544-2200
Web: WWW.HARLEEMANOR.COM

HISTORICAL FINANCIALS
Company Type: Private

Income Statement   FYE: June 30

	REVENUE ($ mil.)	NET INCOME ($ mil.)	NET PROFIT MARGIN	EMPLOYEES
06/09	1,164	62	5.4%	151
06/98	8	0	6.3%	—
Annual Growth	55.9%	53.6%	—	—

2009 Year-End Financials
Return on assets: 48.8%   Cash ($ mil.): —
Return on equity: 821.7%
Current ratio: 1.80

HARTFORD HEALTHCARE CORPORATION

Hartford Health Care provides a variety of health services to the descendants of our founding fathers. Founded in 1854 the health care system operates a network of hospitals behavioral health centers nursing and rehabilitation facilities medical labs and numerous community programs for residents in northern Connecticut. Medical specialties range from orthopedics and women's health to cancer and heart care. Hartford Health Care's flagship facility is the Hartford Hospital an 870-bed teaching hospital affiliated with the University of Connecticut Medical School. Its network also includes MidState Medical Center (some 155 beds) Windham Hospital (145 beds) and The Hospital of Central Connecticut (415 beds).

Operations

Hartford Health Care provides primary and specialty care services through partnerships with several physician practice organizations and specialist facilities including diagnostic imaging centers and mental health facilities. The company provides medical laboratory services including pathology genetic testing and other diagnostic services through its Clinical Laboratory Partners affiliate. It also provides long-term care through Central Connecticut Senior Health Services as well as home health services through VNA HealthCare.

Financial Performance

In 2013 Hartford Health Care reported a 2% rise in revenue from $1.7 million to $2.1 million due to increased patient service revenue.

Strategy

As it becomes increasingly challenging for hospitals to remain independently profitable in an unstable economic climate especially as health reform changes take effect Hartford has been working to expand its footprint in the Connecticut health care market. In 2012 Hartford Health Care formed an alliance with Backus Corporation which operates the Backus Hospital and other medical care centers in eastern Connecticut. Backus gained access to Hartford's broader resources but continues to manage its own day-to-day operations.

In 2014 Hartford Health Care broke ground on a new 90000-square-foot cancer center at The Hospital of Central Connecticut.

EXECUTIVES

Vice President Medical Director, Kent Stahl
Senior Vice President Finance And Treasurer, Richard Stys
Senior Vice President, Karen Goyette
Executive Vice President, David Whitehead
Senior Vice President Chief Information Officer, Richard T Shirey
Senior Vice President, Gerald Boisvert
Vice President Marketing And Branding, Keith Fontaine
Senior Vice President, Rita Parisi
Vice President Governmental Affairs, Kimberly Harrison
Senior Vice President, Gerard Lupacchino
Senior Vice President Physician Services, Vincent Dibattista
Medical Director, Jason Gluck
Senior Vice President, Daniel Mcintyre
Vice President Quality And Patient Safety, Jamie Roche
Vice Chair Department Of Radiology, Barry Stein
Auditors: ERNST & YOUNG LLP HARTFORD C

LOCATIONS

HQ: HARTFORD HEALTHCARE CORPORATION
1 STATE ST FL 19, HARTFORD, CT 061033102
Phone: 860 696-6248
Web: WWW.HHCHEALTH.ORG

PRODUCTS/OPERATIONS

2013 Sales

	$ mil.	% of total
Net patient revenue	1,906	90
Other operating revenue	211	10
Net asets released from restrctions for operations	10	-
Total	**2,128**	**100**

Selected Facilities

Alliance Occupational Health
Central Connecticut Senior Health Services
Clinical Laboratory Partners
Eastern Rehabilitation Network
Hartford Hospital (acute care)
Hartford Medical Group (primary care)
The Hospital of Central Connecticut (acute care)
Institute of Living (research and psychiatric care)
MidState Medical Center (acute care)
Natchaug Hospital (mental health facility)
Rushford (mental health treatment centers)
VNA HealthCare (home health)
Windham Hospital (acute care)

COMPETITORS

Baystate Medical Center
Berkshire Health Systems
Bristol Hospital
Connecticut Children's Medical Center
Griffin Health
Lawrence & Memorial Hospital
Saint Francis Hospital and Medical Center
St. Vincent's Health Services
University of Connecticut Health Center
Waterbury Hospital
Western Connecticut Health Network
Yale New Haven Health System
Yale-New Haven Hospital Saint Raphael Campus

HISTORICAL FINANCIALS

Company Type: Private

Income Statement				FYE: September 30
	REVENUE ($ mil.)	NET INCOME ($ mil.)	NET PROFIT MARGIN	EMPLOYEES
09/17	2,678	440	16.4%	5,100
09/15	297	(37)	—	—
09/12	2,090	63	3.1%	—
09/11	1,803	138	7.7%	—
Annual Growth	6.8%	21.2%	—	—

2017 Year-End Financials

Return on assets: 11.2%
Return on equity: 21.9%
Current ratio: 1.50
Cash ($ mil.): 215

HARTFORD HOSPITAL

EXECUTIVES

Pres-Ceo, Jeffrey A Flaks
V Pres, Gerry J Boisvert
Sr V Pres, Luis Tavares
Cfo, Tom Marchozzi
Coordinator, Betsy Centeno
Scientist, Michal Assaf
Health Professional, Gada M Abdelhafiz
Scientist, Pamela Tessier
Regional Vice-President, Barry Kriesberg
Coordinator, David Bailey

Assistant Chief, David Chung

LOCATIONS

HQ: HARTFORD HOSPITAL
80 SEYMOUR ST, HARTFORD, CT 061028000
Phone: 860 545-5000
Web: WWW.HARTFORDHOSPITAL.ORG

HISTORICAL FINANCIALS

Company Type: Private

Income Statement				FYE: September 30
	REVENUE ($ mil.)	NET INCOME ($ mil.)	NET PROFIT MARGIN	EMPLOYEES
09/17	1,283	96	7.6%	7,500
09/16	1,031	76	7.5%	—
09/15	993	64	6.5%	—
09/14	986	62	6.3%	—
Annual Growth	9.2%	16.0%		

2017 Year-End Financials

Return on assets: 5.8%
Return on equity: 12.6%
Current ratio: 1.50
Cash ($ mil.): 39

HARVARD MANAGEMENT PRIVATE EQUITY CORPORATION

EXECUTIVES

Pres, Jane L Mendillo
Treas, Robert A Ettl
Human Resources Senior Analyst, Emily Cummings
Human Resources Staff Assistan, Jonathan Mascia
Human Resources Senior, Patricia Lowe
Director of Special Projects, Seth Effron
Instrictor of Environmental MA, Zachary Zevitas
Auditors: RSM MCGLADREY INC CHICAGO IL

LOCATIONS

HQ: HARVARD MANAGEMENT PRIVATE EQUITY CORPORATION
600 ATLANTIC AVE STE 1500, BOSTON, MA 022102203
Phone: 617 523-4400

HISTORICAL FINANCIALS

Company Type: Private

Income Statement				FYE: June 30
	REVENUE ($ mil.)	NET INCOME ($ mil.)	NET PROFIT MARGIN	EMPLOYEES
06/17	663	477	71.9%	6
06/10	1,661	(611)	—	—
Annual Growth	(12.3%)			

HARVARD MEDICAL FACULTY PHYSICIANS AT BETH ISRAEL DEACONESS MEDICAL CENTER, INC.

EXECUTIVES

Ceo, Stuart A Rosenberg
V Pres*, Edward L Grab
Director, Mary Leupold
Manager Technical, Carl Doebler
Neurologist, Robles Lillian
Psychosocial Program Director, Sally Cheek
Instructor In Psychology, Amy Szarkowski
Assistant Professor of Pediatr, Dionne Graham
Researcher Psychologist Assist, Hanson Ellen
Fellow In Patient Safety, Kate Humphrey
Administrative Director, Maxine Milstein
Auditors: LB DELOITTE TAX LLP JERICHO

LOCATIONS

HQ: HARVARD MEDICAL FACULTY PHYSICIANS AT
BETH ISRAEL DEACONESS MEDICAL CENTER, INC.
375 LONGWOOD AVE STE 3, BOSTON, MA
022155395
Phone: 617 632-9755
Web: WWW.HMFPHYSICIANS.ORG

HISTORICAL FINANCIALS

Company Type: Private

Income Statement				FYE: September 30
	REVENUE ($ mil.)	NET INCOME ($ mil.)	NET PROFIT MARGIN	EMPLOYEES
09/15	487	1	0.3%	800
09/14	460	14	3.2%	—
09/08	22	2	11.6%	—
Annual Growth	55.3%	(6.4%)	—	—

2015 Year-End Financials

Return on assets: 0.8%   Cash ($ mil.): 26
Return on equity: 1.4%
Current ratio: 1.40

HAWAI I PACIFIC HEALTH

Hawaii may be paradise but even in paradise's some residents get sick. That's when Hawai'i Pacific Health (HPH) surfs in to save the day. HPH is a not-for-profit health care system consisting of four hospitals (Kapi'olani Medical Center for Women & Children Pali Momi Medical Center Straub Clinic & Hospital and Wilcox Memorial Hospital) across the islands with a combined capacity of 550 beds. The system offers a full array of tertiary specialty and acute care services through its hospitals which also serve as teaching and research centers as well as about 50 outpatient centers. Specialized services offered by HPH include cardiac care maternity services oncology orthopedics and pediatric care.

Operations

HPH supplies a wide range of primary and specialty medical services through its physician organizations. The Kapi'olani Medical Specialists group for instance comprises more than 100 physicians and partners with Kapi'olani Medical Center for Women & Children to care for patients from infancy through adulthood. The center also functions as the women's health and pediatric teaching hospital for the University of Hawaii School of Medicine. Its Visiting Specialists group provides care to the islands where HPH doesn't have primary care facilities.

Strategy

The system has partnered with Surgical Care Affiliates to build an outpatient surgical center in Honolulu in an effort to meet growing demand there. The center dubbed Surgicare of Hawai'i offers an array of medical services including orthopedics pain management ophthalmology general surgery and podiatry.

In 2010 the hospital system embarked on a 6-year $580 million master facility plan to expand and improve some of its primary hospital locations. The first stage included new intensive care units and parking capacity at the Kapi'olani Medical Center.

Company Background

The organization was formed through the 2001 merger of three entities: Kapi'olani Health Straub Clinic & Hospital and Wilcox Health System. Committed to supporting Hawaiian culture and values HPH and its member hospitals honor the Hawaiian language and its use of diacritical marks the glottal stop and the macron (okina and kahako).

EXECUTIVES

Vice President Of General Services, Susan Nonaka
Executive Vice President Chief Financial Officer, David Okabe
Director Of Pharmacy Director Of Pharmacy Services Manager, Kent Kikuchi
Executive Vice President And Chief Information Officer, Steve Robertson
Vice President Operations, Melinda Ashton
Vice President, Warren Chaiko
Board Of Director, Keith Matsumoto
Auditors: ERNST & YOUNG LLP DENVER CO

LOCATIONS

HQ: HAWAI I PACIFIC HEALTH
55 MERCHANT ST STE 2500, HONOLULU, HI
968134306
Phone: 808 949-9355
Web: WWW.HAWAIIPACIFICHEALTH.ORG

PRODUCTS/OPERATIONS

Selected Facilities

Kapi'olani Medical Center for Women & Children (Honolulu)
Kaua'i Medical Clinics (Kaua'i)
Pali Momi Medical Center (Aiea)
Straub Clinic & Hospital (Honolulu)
Straub Family Health Centers (Honolulu)
Visiting Specialists (Hilo Kaua'i Lana'i Maui Moloka'i Walmea)
Wilcox Memorial Hospital (Lihue Kaua'i)

COMPETITORS

Adventist Health System West
Kuakini Health System
Queen's Medical Center
Rehabilitation Hospital of the Pacific

HISTORICAL FINANCIALS

Company Type: Private

Income Statement				FYE: June 30
	REVENUE ($ mil.)	NET INCOME ($ mil.)	NET PROFIT MARGIN	EMPLOYEES
06/17	1,290	153	11.9%	5,400
06/15	159	0	0.3%	—
06/14	145	1	1.1%	—
06/13	130	(3)	—	—
Annual Growth	77.1%	—	—	—

2017 Year-End Financials

Return on assets: 9.5%   Cash ($ mil.): 173
Return on equity: 17.2%
Current ratio: 2.40

HCL AMERICA INC.

EXECUTIVES

Dir, Shiv Nadar
Dir, Prateek Aggarwal
Dir, C Vijayakumar
Dir, Anoop Tiwari
Dir, Robin Abrams
Ceo, Manish Anand
Director Sales, Atul Athavale
Software Manager, John Sklenar
Technical Manager, Lawrence Anand
Technical Lead, Pooja Manocha
Director Strategic Accounts, Rahul Mantri
Auditors: SR BATLIBOI & CO LLP HARY

LOCATIONS

HQ: HCL AMERICA INC.
330 POTRERO AVE, SUNNYVALE, CA 940854194
Phone: 408 733-0480
Web: WWW.HCL.COM

HISTORICAL FINANCIALS

Company Type: Private

Income Statement				FYE: March 31
	REVENUE ($ mil.)	NET INCOME ($ mil.)	NET PROFIT MARGIN	EMPLOYEES
03/17*	3,559	130	3.7%	11,993
06/15	2,815	53	1.9%	—
06/14	2,353	0	0.0%	—
06/13	2,075	35	1.7%	—
Annual Growth	14.4%	37.9%	—	—

*Fiscal year change

2017 Year-End Financials

Return on assets: 8.8%   Cash ($ mil.): 4
Return on equity: 20.2%
Current ratio: 1.10

HDR ENGINEERING, INC.

EXECUTIVES

Ceo, George A Little
Pres, Eric L Keen
Coo, George Little
Cfo, Terence C Cox
Exec V Pres, Terry Cox

Treas, Chad M Hartnett
SEC, Louis J Pachman
SEC, Patty Diggins
Mgr, Gerald T Holmes
Manager, Denis P Gilbert
Director, Kelly Vincent
Auditors: ERNST & YOUNG LLP CHICAGO I

LOCATIONS

HQ: HDR ENGINEERING, INC.
1917 S 67TH ST, OMAHA, NE 681062973
Phone: 402 399-1000
Web: WWW.HDRINC.COM

HISTORICAL FINANCIALS

Company Type: Private

Income Statement   FYE: December 29

	REVENUE ($ mil.)	NET INCOME ($ mil.)	NET PROFIT MARGIN	EMPLOYEES
12/18	1,399	107	7.7%	6,111
12/17	1,707	73	4.3%	—
12/16	1,748	89	5.1%	—
12/15	1,218	100	8.2%	—
Annual Growth	4.7%	2.3%	—	—

2018 Year-End Financials

Return on assets: 9.7%   Cash ($ mil.): 25
Return on equity: 13.1%
Current ratio: 3.90

HDR, INC.

With projects ranging from restoring the Pentagon and the Everglades to working on the Hoover Dam Bypass project HDR has left its mark on the US. HDR is an architecture engineering and consulting firm that specializes in such projects as bridges water- and wastewater-treatment plants and hospitals. The company also provides mechanical and plumbing services construction and project management and utilities planning. It has completed projects nationwide and in some 60 countries through its more than 225 global locations. The employee-owned company was founded as Henningson Engineering in 1917 to build municipal plants in the rural Midwest.

Geographic Reach

Headquartered in Omaha Nebraska HDR has completed projects in 60 countries and maintains some 225 offices worldwide. It operates in the Americas (US and Canada) Asia (China and Mongolia) Australia Europe (Germany and the UK) and the Middle East.

Sales and Marketing

HDR's has performed design and engineering work for a number of clients including: Seattle Public Utilities DEXUS Property Group the Pirbright Institute SeaPort-e TXMAS and Xcel Energy.

Strategy

With the goal of cutting its client costs by 10% through smarter delivery processes in its designed and constructed facilities HDR has spent the past few years expanding its service capabilities through strategic acquisitions. To this end in early 2015 the company purchased Tennessee-based Infrastructure Corporation of America (ICA) which specializes in transport engineering and asset maintenance and management. Additionally it bought the assets of Georgia-based liquid natural gas firm MEI LLC.

The acquisition of architectural practice Rice Daubney in late 2013 enhanced the company's position in the Australian market while purchases in 2012 (Wyoming's Stetson Engineering) and 2011 (New Jersey's HydroQual) extended its water capabilities.

The company also continues to design and engineer big infrastructure projects for city and state governments. In late 2014 Seattle Public Utilities selected HDR develop and evaluate site plan concepts for the South Transfer Station Phase 2 project to create nearly a dozen facilities for recycling and waste-reuse to help the utility reach its goal of 70% solid waste diversion by 2025. Also in late 2014 HDR partnered with Jacobs Engineering Group to lead the engineering for the I-4 Mobility Partners group and will deliver final designs for roadway/traffic control draining structure and intelligent traffic systems for the I-4 Ultimate Project in Florida.

Mergers and Acquisitions

In January 2015 the company acquired both the Infrastructure Corporation of America (ICA) which specializes in transport engineering and asset maintenance and management along with the Georgia-based liquid natural gas firm MEI LLC to broaden its service capabilities.

In 2013 HDR purchased architecture firm Rice Daubney to bolster its design expertise and extend its reach in the Australian market.

In 2012 the company bought Wyoming's Stetson Engineering to broaden its water services.

EXECUTIVES

Chairman And Ceo, George A. Little
Cfo, Terence C. (Terry) Cox
Evp And Director Environmental Resource Management, Elwin Larson
Evp And Director Water Program, Gary L. Bleeker
Vice Chairman; President Hdr Engineering Inc., Eric L. Keen
President Manager, Kevin Keller
President Hdr Architecture Inc., Doug S. Wignall
Cio, Michael Geppert
Evp And Director Transportation, Charles O'Reilly
President Manager Richmond Hill Traffic Practice, David Argue
Associate Vice President, Corrinne Atkinson
Auditors: ERNST & YOUNG LLP CHICAGO IL

LOCATIONS

HQ: HDR, INC.
1917 S 67TH ST, OMAHA, NE 681062973
Phone: 402 399-1000
Web: WWW.HDRINC.COM

PRODUCTS/OPERATIONS

Selected Mergers and Acquisitions

FY2015
Brentwood Tennessee-based Infrastructure Corporation of America (ICA)
FY2103
Rice Daubney (Australia architecture design for healthcare retail defense markets)
FY2012
Stetson Engineering (Wyoming projects in water sewer storm water hydrology and transportation)
FY2011
Amnis Engineering (Canada)
Cooper Medical (Healthcare design/build specialist)
HydroQual (New Jersey water resource management)
Schiff Associates (California engineering)
FY2009
Devine Tarbell & Associates (Maine now named HDR|DTA)
iTrans Consulting (Toronto-based engineering firm)

Selected Markets

Architecture
  Academic
  Civic
  Corporate
  Healthcare
  Justice
  Science and Technology
Energy
  Oil and Gas
  Power Delivery
  Power Generation
  Renewable Energy
Federal
  Federal Architecture
  Federal Engineering
  Federal Planning
  Federal Environmental
  Federal Energy
  Federal Construction
  HDR SeaPort-e
Private Land Development
  Commercial
  Industrial
  Institutional
  Residential
  Resorts and Hotels
Resource Management
  Community Planning & Consulting
  Environmental Sciences & Permitting
  Fisheries Science & Design
  Mining
  Natural Resource Management
  Waste Management and Industrial
Transportation
  Aviation
  Freight Rail
  Highways and Local Roads
  Maritime
  Transit
Water
  Water
  Wastewater
  Water Planning
  Industrial

Selected Services

Analytical consulting
Architectural design
Coastal engineering and restoration
Consulting
Design/build
Environmental monitoring
Finished water storage facility services
Interior design
Landscape architecture
Master planning
Power facility engineering
Pump stations and flow control
Security services
Utility master planning and modeling
Water resources
Water treatment systems

COMPETITORS

AECOM
Black & Veatch
Brown and Caldwell
Epstein
Fuscoe Engineering
Gensler
Geotechnics
HBE Corporation
HKS Inc.
Interior Architects
Jacobs Engineering
KPA Associates
Kimley-Horn and Associates
Lee Burkhart Liu
Leo A Daly
MCG Architects
MWH Global
Michael Baker
Nasland Engineering
Perkowitz + Ruth
RMJM
RTKL Associates
SAIC Energy Environment & Infrastructure
STV
Tetra Tech
The Austin Company
Western Summit Constructors
Willdan Group

HISTORICAL FINANCIALS

Company Type: Private

Income Statement				FYE: December 29
	REVENUE ($ mil.)	NET INCOME ($ mil.)	NET PROFIT MARGIN	EMPLOYEES
12/18	1,762	115	6.5%	10,000
12/17	2,362	82	3.5%	—
12/16	2,230	90	4.0%	—
12/15	2,132	74	3.5%	—
Annual Growth	(6.1%)	15.9%	—	—

2018 Year-End Financials

Return on assets: 7.8%   Cash ($ mil.): 283
Return on equity: 20.1%
Current ratio: 2.00

HEALTH FIRST, INC.

Health First works to keep Florida's Space Coast denizens in tip-top shape. The not-for-profit health system operates four hospitals in Brevard County. Health First's biggest hospital is Holmes Regional Medical Center in Melbourne with more than 500 beds. Its Cape Canaveral Hospital and Palm Bay Community Hospital have 150 and 60 beds respectively. Its Viera Hospital is a 100-bed acute-care hospital. The system also runs outpatient clinics a home health service and a physicians group. Its for-profit subsidiary Health First Health Plans is the county's largest insurer with about 60000 commercial members and 23000 Medicare members.

Operations

The company operates four hospitals (Holmes Regional Medical Center Palm Bay Hospital Cape Canaveral Hospital and Viera Hospital) and offers a wide variety of health insurance plan options for patients in Brevard and Indian River Counties. Health First is the largest multi-specialty physician group on Florida's Space Coast. It also operates to Brevard County's only trauma center and a number of outpatient and wellness services including four pro-health and fitness centers.

Geographic Reach

Health First operates four hospitals and a health insurance company in Brevard County Florida.

Strategy

To expand its capacity Health First makes complementary acquisitions and pursues organic growth.

In 2103 Health First opened of a new center for fracture care at Health First Holmes Regional Medical Center and the center for joint replacement at Health First Viera Hospital. That year it formed a new Small Group Preferred Provider Organization (PPO) Plan offering increased flexibility when it comes to out-of-network coverage and fulfilling the needs of employer groups in its service area.

Mergers and Acquisitions

In 2012 the company acquired Melbourne Internal Medicine Associates (250 physician providers based in Melbourne) to increase patient quality safety and the patient experience. The entity was renamed the Health First Medical Group in 2013.

Company Background

In 2011 Health First partnered with Nemours to expand pediatric care in Brevard County. That year Health First Health Plans opened a new Vero Beach office to serve residents of Indian River County and launch its Medicare Advantage plans to the rest of Indian River County.

Despite an ongoing lawsuit with Wuesthoff Health System (which claims that Health First has an unfair monopoly of hospital services in Brevard County) the company forged ahead with construction of its fourth hospital in the county the Viera hospital campus. The Medical Plaza at Viera Health Park which will includes offices for multi-specialty physicians and a diagnostic/imaging center opened in 2010. And the park's centerpiece Viera Hospital a 100-bed acute-care hospital opened in 2011.

Health First was founded in 1995 through a merger of regional hospitals. The Brevard Hospital (now Holmes Regional Medical Center) first opened in 1937.

EXECUTIVES

Chief Physician Executive, Jeffrey C. Stalnaker
Evp And Coo, J. Stuart Mitchell
Evp Chief Strategy And Growth Officer, Drew Rector
Evp And Cfo, Joseph (Joe) Felkner
President Health First Medical Group, Travis L Douglass
President And Ceo, Steven P. Johnson
Ceo Community Hospitals, Aaron Robinson
Svp And Cio, Alex Popowycz
President Hospital Operations, Bill Calhoun
Chief Nursing Officer, Constance (Connie) Bradley
Vice President And Corporate Attorney, Grant Dearborn
Vice President Marketing And Communications, Matthew Gerrell
Pharmacy Manager, Marta Hamilton
Medical Director Cardiac Electrophysiology, Ken Lee
Physical Therapy Physical Therapy Assistant, Carol Harrington
Chairman, Pamela A. Gatto
Vice Chairman, Kevin B. Steele

LOCATIONS

HQ: HEALTH FIRST, INC.
6450 US HIGHWAY 1, ROCKLEDGE, FL 329555747
Phone: 321 434-4300
Web: WWW.HF.ORG

Selected facilities
Cape Canaveral Hospital (Cocoa Beach)
Holmes Regional Medical Center (Melbourne)
Palm Bay Community Hospital (Palm Bay)
Viera Hospital (Viera)

COMPETITORS

Adventist Health System Sunbelt Healthcare
Aetna
CIGNA
Florida Blue
HCA
Orlando Health
Osceola Regional Medical Center
Tenet Healthcare
Wuesthoff Health System

HISTORICAL FINANCIALS

Company Type: Private

Income Statement				FYE: September 30
	REVENUE ($ mil.)	NET INCOME ($ mil.)	NET PROFIT MARGIN	EMPLOYEES
09/15	1,255	19	1.6%	6,900
09/14	1,136	90	7.9%	—
09/13	1,059	51	4.8%	—
09/11	129	(0)	—	—
Annual Growth	76.5%	—	—	—

2015 Year-End Financials

Return on assets: 1.2%   Cash ($ mil.): 152
Return on equity: 2.7%
Current ratio: 4.30

HEALTH PARTNERS PLANS, INC.

Health Partners wants to partner up with Pennsylvanians in need of health care. The company is a not-for-profit health plan that provides health benefits to some 210000 Medicaid recipients in the Philadelphia area. Its HealthChoices plans for Medicaid participants cover medical dental prescription and vision costs. Its KidzPartners program is provided in partnership with the state of Pennsylvania's Children's Health Insurance Program (CHIP). Its provider network includes about 6000 primary and specialty care doctors and 30 hospitals in the region. The company also provides community outreach and wellness programs. Health Partners was founded in 1985 by a group of hospitals in the Philadelphia area.

Geographic Reach

Health Partners' plans cover members in Philadelphia and in Chester Delaware Bucks and Montgomery counties outside the city.

Strategy

Health Partners signed a provider contract with the University of Pennsylvania Health System that will increase access to care in Philadelphia for Health Partners Medicare members. The agreement increases Health Partners' network to include more than 1300 additional physicians from the Health System's network of practices and four hospitals.

Health Partners has been working to enhance its community health programs in recent years. It launched its Computer Health Care Management Education program to provide free monthly computer lessons combined with tutorials about healthy lifestyle programs.

It also teamed up with the Norcom Community Center to offer HealthChoices and KidzPartners members fitness benefits at the facility; the company has a total of more than 20 fitness centers in its expanding provider network. The KidzPartners program provides free or affordable insurance coverage to children and teens who don't qualify for Medicaid.

Company Background

The area hospitals that own Health Partners are Albert Einstein Medical Center Aria Health Temple University Hospital Episcopal Hospital and two Tenet Healthcare facilities (Hahnemann University Hospital and St. Christopher's Hospital for Children).

EXECUTIVES

President And Ceo, William S. George
Svp Healthcare Management And Chief Medical Officer, Steven E. Szebenyi
Svp Operations And Coo, Lisa Getzfrid
Government Relations, Kearline Jones
Vice President Of Marketing, Caroline Russell
Vice President Finance And Chief Financi, John Sehi
Vice President Government Relations And Compliance, Jones Kearline
Vice President Compliance Medicare Compliance Of, Andy Finkelstein
Executive Vice President Clinical And Provider Management, Denise Croce
Executive Vice President Of Finance And Administration, Eric Huss
Senior Vice President Of Medicare Sales And Actuarial Services, Mark Cary
Vice President Medical Management, Michelle Mattiace
Vice President And Treasurer, Joe Dodi
Auditors: KPMG LLP PHILADELPHIA PENNSY

LOCATIONS

HQ: HEALTH PARTNERS PLANS, INC.
901 MARKET ST STE 500, PHILADELPHIA, PA
191074496
Phone: 215 849-9606
Web: WWW.HEALTHPARTNERSPLANS.COM

COMPETITORS

Aetna	Independence Blue
CIGNA	Cross
Gateway Health Plan	Keystone Mercy
Health Net	UnitedHealth Group
Highmark	

HISTORICAL FINANCIALS

Company Type: Private

Income Statement   FYE: December 31

	REVENUE ($ mil.)	NET INCOME ($ mil.)	NET PROFIT MARGIN	EMPLOYEES
12/14	910	(8)	—	620
12/13	1,000	(0)	—	—
12/12	1,034	(1)	—	—
Annual Growth	(6.2%)	—	—	—

2014 Year-End Financials

Return on assets: (-2.9%)   Cash ($ mil.): 60
Return on equity: (-10.8%)
Current ratio: 0.90

HEALTH QUEST SYSTEMS, INC.

EXECUTIVES

Ceo, Denise George
V Pres, Mary Ann Keppel
Sr V Pres, Ron Tatelbaumm
Sr V Pres, David Ping
Cfo, Yann Kepple
Sr V Pres, Ann Armater
Coordinator, Cheryl Mathieu
Information Specialist, Lew Hulse
Internal Medicine Practitioner, Christopher Panettieri
Coordinator, Carissa Sharp
Chief of Medicine, Imtiaz Mallick
Auditors: PRICEWATERHOUSECOOPERS LLP N

LOCATIONS

HQ: HEALTH QUEST SYSTEMS, INC.
1351 ROUTE 55 STE 200, LAGRANGEVILLE, NY
125405144
Phone: 845 475-9500

HISTORICAL FINANCIALS

Company Type: Private

Income Statement   FYE: December 31

	REVENUE ($ mil.)	NET INCOME ($ mil.)	NET PROFIT MARGIN	EMPLOYEES
12/15	870	39	4.6%	2,000
12/14	796	5	0.6%	—
12/13	706	103	14.6%	—
12/12	692	8	1.2%	—
Annual Growth	7.9%	69.7%	—	—

2015 Year-End Financials

Return on assets: 4.0%   Cash ($ mil.): 109
Return on equity: 8.9%
Current ratio: 3.00

HEALTH RESEARCH, INC.

Health Research Inc. (HRI) knows where the money is. The group is a not-for-profit organization that helps the New York State Department of Health and its affiliated Roswell Park Cancer Institute solicit evaluate and administer financial support. Sources of that support come from federal and state government sources other non-profits and businesses. HRI's Technology Transfer office also assists the Department of Health in sharing its research findings with other public and private institutions and finding ways to create biomedical technologies through private sector development. HRI was founded in 1953 and has administered $7 billion over its lifetime.

EXECUTIVES

Exec Dir, Barbara Ryan
Exec Dir*, Cheryl Mattox
Director of Operations, Tammy Young
Law Specialist, Nicole McMillin
Scientist, Vincent Escuyer
Director of Information Techno, John Bintz
Co Director, Keith Cheung
Director Subcontract Unit, Michelle Coyne
Staff, Mike Varney
Auditors: BONADIO & CO LLP ALBANY NE

LOCATIONS

HQ: HEALTH RESEARCH, INC.
150 BROADWAY STE 560, MENANDS, NY 122042726
Phone: 518 431-1200
Web: WWW.HEALTHRESEARCH.ORG

HISTORICAL FINANCIALS

Company Type: Private

Income Statement   FYE: March 31

	REVENUE ($ mil.)	NET INCOME ($ mil.)	NET PROFIT MARGIN	EMPLOYEES
03/15	677	22	3.3%	1,400
03/14	703	13	1.9%	—
03/13	665	25	3.9%	—
03/12	661	(10)	—	—
Annual Growth	0.8%	—	—	—

2015 Year-End Financials

Return on assets: 4.5%   Cash ($ mil.): 187
Return on equity: 29.8%
Current ratio: —

HEALTHPARTNERS, INC.

EXECUTIVES

Pres-Ceo, Mary Brainerd
Exec V Pres-Chief Mktg Offcr*, Andrea Walsh
Cfo*, David A Dziuk
Cfo*, Todd Hofheins
Analyst, Kathy Rhode
Coordinator, Renee Hannan
Team Leader Appl, Chao Nguyen
Admin Asst, Kristi Brandt
Senior Director, Frank Muller
Senior Vice-President, Scott Schnuckle
Agent, Tim M Haley
Auditors: KPMG LLP MINNEAPOLIS MINNES

LOCATIONS

HQ: HEALTHPARTNERS, INC.
8170 33RD AVE S, BLOOMINGTON, MN 554254516
Phone: 952 883-6000

HISTORICAL FINANCIALS

Company Type: Private

Income Statement   FYE: December 31

	REVENUE ($ mil.)	NET INCOME ($ mil.)	NET PROFIT MARGIN	EMPLOYEES
12/18	7,061	143	2.0%	22,000
12/97	1,247	(2)		
12/96	1,178	9	0.8%	—
12/95	0	0		
Annual Growth	—	—	—	—

2018 Year-End Financials

Return on assets: 2.8%   Cash ($ mil.): 1,003
Return on equity: 4.9%
Current ratio: 2.10

HEARTLAND CO-OP

EXECUTIVES

Pres, Arthur L Churchill
Human Resources Administrator, Katherine Thompson
Manager, Jeff Jones
Staff, Jonathan Lewis
Human Resources Coordinator, Kendra Kehoe
Sales Staff, Shawn Devooght
Manager, Curtis Trimmer
Sales Agronomist, Darryl Bowman
Region 5 Operations Manager Em, John Hohnstein
Location Manager, Lowell Finley
Sales Agronomist, Bob Follis
Auditors: BERGAN PAULSEN & COMPANY PC

LOCATIONS

HQ: HEARTLAND CO-OP
2829 WESTOWN PKWY STE 350, WEST DES MOINES, IA 502661340
Phone: 515 225-1334
Web: WWW.HEARTLANDCOOP.COM

HISTORICAL FINANCIALS

Company Type: Private

Income Statement   FYE: June 30

	REVENUE ($ mil.)	NET INCOME ($ mil.)	NET PROFIT MARGIN	EMPLOYEES
06/18	901	20	2.2%	678
06/17	932	17	1.9%	—
06/16	854	15	1.9%	—
06/15	823	19	2.4%	—
Annual Growth	3.1%	0.2%	—	—

2018 Year-End Financials

Return on assets: 3.8%   Cash ($ mil.): —
Return on equity: 8.8%
Current ratio: 1.50

HEARTLAND HEALTH

Heartland Health provides medical care in the heart of the Midwest. The integrated health care system serves residents of northwest Missouri as well as bordering areas of Kansas and Nebraska. Its flagship facility is Heartland Regional Medical Center a 350-bed acute-care hospital that features an emergency room and Level II trauma center as well as specialty care programs in heart disease cancer and obstetrics. Heartland Health also provides primary care through a multi-specialty medical practice (Heartland Clinic) and it offers home health hospice and long-term care services from the primary medical center facility. The company's Community Health Improvement Solutions unit is an HMO health insurer.

Strategy

In 2012 Heartland Health joined the Mayo Clinic Care Network which will enable to it to tap the knowledge and expertise of Mayo Clinic physicians to better serve its patients.

Company Background

Heartland Health was formed in 1984 through the merger of two St. Joseph Missouri hospital: Methodist Medical Center and St. Joseph's Hospital. The two facilities trace their roots back to 1924 and 1861 respectively.

EXECUTIVES

Ceo, Mark Laney
Pres*, Lowell Kruse
V Pres-Cfo*, John Wilson
Chairman*, Alfred L Purcell
Asst SEC*, Karen Dittemore
Asst Treas-Contrl*, Douglas Brandt
Cmo*, Robert Permet
Chm*, David Solanski
Coo*, Cut Kretzinger
Staff, C R Shumann III
Staff, Monica Ray
Auditors: RSM US LLP DAVENPORT IOWA

LOCATIONS

HQ: HEARTLAND HEALTH
5325 FARAON ST, SAINT JOSEPH, MO 645063488
Phone: 816 271-6000
Web: WWW.MYMOSAICLIFECARE.ORG

PRODUCTS/OPERATIONS

Selected Affiliates
Atchison Hospital (Atchison KS)
Community Hospital (Fairfax MO)
Community Medical Center (Falls City NE)
Dental Clinic (St. Joseph MO)
Laser Cosmedic Center (Platte City MO)
North Kansas City Hospital (North Kansas City MO)
The Surgery Center (St. Joseph MO)

COMPETITORS

Ascension Health
BJC HealthCare
Blue Cross and Blue Shield of Kansas City
Catholic Health Initiatives
Children's Mercy Hospital
CoxHealth
HCA
Mercy Health
Mercy Hospital Springfield
Saint Luke's Health System
Shawnee Mission Medical Center
Sisters of Charity of Leavenworth
Truman Medical Centers
University of Kansas Medical Center

HISTORICAL FINANCIALS
Company Type: Private

Income Statement   FYE: June 30

	REVENUE ($ mil.)	NET INCOME ($ mil.)	NET PROFIT MARGIN	EMPLOYEES
06/18	667	64	9.6%	32,000
06/16	584	(6)	—	—
06/15	577	22	3.9%	—
06/14	560	64	11.4%	—
Annual Growth	4.5%	(0.0%)		

2018 Year-End Financials

Return on assets: 6.5%   Cash ($ mil.): 26
Return on equity: 10.2%
Current ratio: 1.10

HEARTLAND PAYMENT SYSTEMS, LLC

Heartland Payment Systems (HPS) a wholly owned subsidiary of Global Payments Inc. makes sure plastic-card transactions don't get lost along their way. The company performs credit debit and prepaid card processing services at some 300000 locations nationwide. Its client list includes restaurants retailers convenience stores and professional service providers. The Heartland Payroll Solutions segment provides payroll processing such as check printing and direct deposit for more than 10000 customers. Other markets for the firm include K-12 school nutrition programs and payment processing for colleges and universities. Global Payments bought Heartland for $4.3 billion in 2016.

Change in Company Type

Atlanta-based payment technology firm Global Payments acquired Heartland Payment Systems in its largest acquisition to-date in 2016. Through that purchase it expanded its presence in the US small and mid-sized commercial customer market and added new merchant customers. Operating results of HPS are now reported as part of the Global Payments? North American segment.

Operations

Heartland primarily offers card payment processing and related services to small and midsized merchants and network services merchants. Its Campus Solutions unit provides payment processing integrated commerce solutions higher education loan services and open/closed loop payment solutions. Heartland School Solutions provides school nutrition and point-of-sale and related payment services to K-12 schools while Heartland Payroll Solutions provides payroll processing and related tax filing services. Other activities include electronic check processing gift card marketing and processing online payments and the sale and rental of point-of-sale processing equipment.

Geographic Reach

Princeton NJ-based Heartland Payment Systems serves customers throughout the US. The largest centers of its small and medium-sized business merchants are in California Texas Florida New York and Pennsylvania which together represent more than 30% of card processing volume. Its network services merchants are predominantly gas stations located throughout the US.

Sales and Marketing

The company serves small and midsized customers in a variety of businesses including restaurant hospitality education parking and retail. The network service segment primarily serves gas station merchants.

The firm employs sales professionals and relationship managers to build and maintain direct customer relationships.

Strategy

HPS is addressing the fast growth of mobile payments launching a variety of mobile applications in recent years to take advantage of the opportunity. The firm continues to nurture its Heartland Mobile and Online Ordering platform which allows smaller restaurants to accept mobile orders and payments. It also tends to the growth of its OneCard Mobile application which serves as a ?one-for-all? card for university students. The card is issued by campus administrators and serves as a virtual ID card and payment system for all campus services and activities and for permission-based access to events buildings rooms libraries and other facilities.

EXECUTIVES

Ceo, Robert O Carr
Co-Pres*, Michael A Lawler
Co-Pres*, David Gilbert
Cfo*, Samir Zabaneh
Clo-Gen Counsel*, Charles Kallenbach
Coo*, Conan Lane
Cbo*, Michael McMillan
Cso*, Marty Moretti
Cso*, John R South
Cao*, Joseph E White
Cto*, Bryan Thompson
Auditors: DELOITTE & TOUCHE LLP PHILADE

LOCATIONS

HQ: HEARTLAND PAYMENT SYSTEMS, LLC
10 GLENLAKE PKWY STE 324, ATLANTA, GA
303283495
Phone: 609 683-3831
Web: WWW.HEARTLANDPAYMENTSYSTEMS.COM

PRODUCTS/OPERATIONS

Products:
Billing Solutions
E-Commerce
Gift Cards
Internet of Things
Lending
Loyalty Program
Mobile Ordering
Mobile Payment
Payroll Services
Point of Sale
Processing
School Nutrition
School Payment

COMPETITORS

Banc of America Merchant Services
Cardtronics
Chase Paymentech Solutions
Comdata
Deluxe Corporation
ECHO Inc.
Elavon
Fidelity National Information Services
Fifth Third
First Data
Fiserv
Fujitsu America
Total System Services
Vantiv
Wells Fargo
iPayment

HISTORICAL FINANCIALS
Company Type: Private

Income Statement				FYE: December 31
	REVENUE ($ mil.)	NET INCOME ($ mil.)	NET PROFIT MARGIN	EMPLOYEES
12/15	2,682	84	3.2%	3,734
12/14	2,311	31	1.4%	—
12/13	2,135	78	3.7%	—
12/12	2,013	66	3.3%	—
Annual Growth	10.0%	8.4%	—	—

2015 Year-End Financials
Return on assets: 5.5%   Cash ($ mil.): 56
Return on equity: 25.2%
Current ratio: 0.90

HELM FERTILIZER CORPORATION (FLORIDA)

EXECUTIVES

Pres, Dale Miller
Cfo, Chris Carollo
Dir, Hans Christian Sievers
Vice President M, Oliver Koepcke
Auditors: ISRAELOFF TRATTNER & CO PC

LOCATIONS

HQ: HELM FERTILIZER CORPORATION (FLORIDA)
401 E JACKSON ST STE 1400, TAMPA, FL 336025264
Phone: 813 621-8846
Web: WWW.HELMAGRO.COM

HISTORICAL FINANCIALS
Company Type: Private

Income Statement				FYE: December 31
	REVENUE ($ mil.)	NET INCOME ($ mil.)	NET PROFIT MARGIN	EMPLOYEES
12/13	611	5	0.9%	28
12/12	947	11	1.2%	—
12/11	1,056	10	1.0%	—
12/10	667	6	1.0%	—
Annual Growth	(2.9%)	(6.7%)	—	—

2013 Year-End Financials
Return on assets: 7.6%   Cash ($ mil.): —
Return on equity: 24.4%
Current ratio: 1.40

HENDRICK MEDICAL CENTER

Auditors: CONDLEY AND COMPANY LLP ABILE

LOCATIONS

HQ: HENDRICK MEDICAL CENTER
1900 PINE ST, ABILENE, TX 796012432
Phone: 325 670-2000
Web: WWW.HENDRICKHEALTH.ORG

HISTORICAL FINANCIALS
Company Type: Private

Income Statement				FYE: August 31
	REVENUE ($ mil.)	NET INCOME ($ mil.)	NET PROFIT MARGIN	EMPLOYEES
08/18	472	46	9.7%	2,900
08/17	408	40	9.8%	—
08/16	419	44	10.6%	—
08/15	325	15	4.6%	—
Annual Growth	13.3%	45.2%	—	—

2018 Year-End Financials
Return on assets: 6.0%   Cash ($ mil.): 16
Return on equity: 8.0%
Current ratio: 1.90

HENDRICKS COUNTY HOSPITAL

EXECUTIVES

Jd, Ceo, Kevin P Speer
Cfo, Isadore Rivas
Database Administrator, Laura Long
Assistant, Anita Dieckmann
Registered Nurse, Beth Gephart
Coordinator, Stephanie Jones
Materials Manager, Brian Sheets
Anesthesiologist, Clint Myers
Coordinator, Jennifer Herring
Coordinator, Jim Carr
Social Worker, Karen Waltz
Auditors: BLUE & CO LLC INDIANAPOLIS

LOCATIONS

HQ: HENDRICKS COUNTY HOSPITAL
1000 E MAIN ST, DANVILLE, IN 461221991
Phone: 317 745-4451
Web: WWW.HENDRICKS.ORG

HISTORICAL FINANCIALS
Company Type: Private

Income Statement				FYE: December 31
	REVENUE ($ mil.)	NET INCOME ($ mil.)	NET PROFIT MARGIN	EMPLOYEES
12/18	605	(25)	—	1,700
12/17	550	39	7.1%	—
12/16	530	43	8.2%	—
12/15	235	9	4.1%	—
Annual Growth	37.0%	—	—	—

2018 Year-End Financials
Return on assets: (-3.6%)   Cash ($ mil.): 20
Return on equity: (-6.1%)
Current ratio: 1.10

HENRY COUNTY BOARD OF EDUCATION

EXECUTIVES

Chair, Pam Nutt
Supt*, Rodney M Bowler
V Chair*, Mike Griffin
Certified Occupational Therapy, Diana Parden
Coordinator, Jane Cantrell
Coordinator of Learning Suppor, Kent Morrow
Network Coordinator, Chris Davis
Chief Financial Officer, Marc Nicholas

LOCATIONS

HQ: HENRY COUNTY BOARD OF EDUCATION
33 N ZACK HINTON PKWY, MCDONOUGH, GA
302532344
Phone: 770 957-6601
Web: WWW.HENRY.K12.GA.US

HISTORICAL FINANCIALS
Company Type: Private

Income Statement				FYE: June 30
	REVENUE ($ mil.)	NET INCOME ($ mil.)	NET PROFIT MARGIN	EMPLOYEES
06/18	486	(108)	—	2,764
06/17	466	(51)	—	—
06/16	449	254	56.7%	—
06/05	295	(31)	—	—
Annual Growth	3.9%	—	—	—

2018 Year-End Financials
Return on assets: (-9.4%)   Cash ($ mil.): 38
Return on equity: (-233.2%)
Current ratio: —

HENRY FORD ALLEGIANCE HEALTH SYSTEM

EXECUTIVES

Ceo, Georgia Fojtasek
Sr V Pres*, Ondrea Bates
V Pres-Cno*, Wendy Boersma
Chief of Medicine, Reddivalen Nagesh
Coordinator, Deborah Strohaver
Manager, Andrew Caughey
Customer Billing Repre, Brandan Flaws
Assist To The Ceo, Joey Delombarde
Chief of Radiation Biology, Nora Wineland
Executive Director, Tom Lopez
Collaborative Network Manager, Sheri Butters

LOCATIONS

HQ: HENRY FORD ALLEGIANCE HEALTH SYSTEM
205 N EAST AVE, JACKSON, MI 492011753
Phone: 517 205-4800
Web: WWW.HENRYFORD.COM

Company Type: Private

Income Statement   FYE: June 30

	REVENUE ($ mil.)	NET INCOME ($ mil.)	NET PROFIT MARGIN	EMPLOYEES
06/16	477	(11)	—	3,500
06/15	462	(2)	—	—
06/09	371	(63)	—	—
06/08	338	(53)	—	—
Annual Growth	4.4%	—	—	—

2016 Year-End Financials

Return on assets: (-2.4%)   Cash ($ mil.): 26
Return on equity: (-5.3%)
Current ratio: 1.20

HENRY FORD HEALTH SYSTEM

Not-for-profit Henry Ford Health System (HFHS) operates a network of medical facilities in Detroit and nearby communities. The system's half-dozen hospitals — including the flagship Henry Ford Hospital the Henry Ford Wyandotte Hospital and mental health facility Kingswood Hospital — are home to roughly 2400 beds. HFHS also operates a 1300-physician medical group (with more than 40 specialties) as well as nursing homes a hospice provider a home health care network and research and education centers. The system's Health Alliance Plan of Michigan provides managed care and health insurance to more than half a million members.

Strategy

HFHS is working to make health care more affordable for patients by improving efficiencies in both its care model and its business operations. Recent efforts to improve patient services include enacting new safety protocols and promoting virtual (telehealth) patient visits.

The company regularly upgrades or expands its facilities to provide state-of-the-art care and attract new patients and skilled health professionals. It invested $55 million to add a 66-bed patient tower and a medical education center to the Henry Ford Allegiance Health hospital campus in 2018. HFHS also partnered with the Detroit Pistons to construct a sports medicine facility (completed in 2019) and it is constructing a new Detroit cancer center the Brigitte Harris Cancer Pavilion (scheduled to open in 2020).

HFHS seeks to advance the medical profession by providing medical research and training programs. The Henry Ford Innovation Institute allows the network's specialists to engage in clinical research projects. The Henry Ford Hospital serves as an academic training center for the Wayne State University School of Medicine.

The company relies on payments from third parties for the majority of its income with reimbursements from Medicaid Medicare and commercial insurers making up the bulk of revenue. This can result in delayed payments if claims are denied. The company may also be vulnerable to reimbursement reduction decisions or non-payments from self-pay customers.

Company Background

Automaker Henry Ford founded Henry Ford Hospital in 1915.

The Health Alliance Plan became part of the Henry Ford Health System in 1986.

In 2016 Allegiance Health which operated a hospital and other health facilities in Jackson joined the Henry Ford Health System and began operating as Henry Ford Allegiance Health.

EXECUTIVES

Evp; President And Ceo Health Alliance Plan, James M. Connelly
Ceo, Nancy M. Schlichting
Svp And Coo Henry Ford Hospital And Health Network, Robert G. (Bob) Riney
President, Wright L. Lassiter, age 56
Evp And Chief Medical Officer; President And Ceo Henry Ford Hospital, John Popovich
President And Ceo Community Care Services, John J. Polanski
Evp And Cfo, Edward G. (Ed) Chadwick
Evp; Ceo Henry Ford Medical Group, William A. Conway
President And Ceo Henry Ford West Bloomfield Hospital, Lynn M. Torossian
President And Ceo Henry Ford Wyandotte Hospital, Denise Brooks-Williams
Chief Nursing Officer; Coo Henry Ford Hospital, Veronica M. Hall
President And Ceo Henry Ford Macomb Hospitals, Barbara W. Rossmann
Svp Community Health And Equity; Chief Wellness Officer, Kimberlydawn Wisdom
Svp And Cio, Mary Alice Annecharico
Director Of Radiology, Mark C Diamond
Vice President Information Technology Business And Service Integration, Geoff Patterson
Director Of Radiology, Xia Wang
Medical Director, Nabil Khoury
Senior Vice President Is Clinical Integration And Transformation, Michelle Schreiber
Senior Vice President Strategic Business Development, William Schramm
Director Of Radiology, Joseph M Silva
Director Of Radiology, Scott G Sturza
Director Of Radiology, John W Bonnett
Director Of Radiology, Paul A Suiter
Director Of Radiology, Derrick Harper
Director Of Radiology, Pranav S Doshi
Pharmacy Manager Process Improvement, Nadia Haque
Director Of Radiology, Michael J Flynn
Vice President, James O'connor
Senior Vice President And Chief Human Resources Officer, Kathy Oswald
Vice President Corporate Strategic Planning, Joel Keiper
Vice President Clinical Transformation And Information Technology Integration, Matt Walsh
Director Of Radiology, Jay Pearlberg
Director Of Radiology, Mark I Burnstein
Director Of Radiology, Peter J Feczko
Director Of Radiology, Randall R Walter
Director Of Radiology, Riffat K Ahmed
Director Of Radiology, Sabala R Mandava
Director Of Radiology, Sampath Ramachandran
Director Of Radiology, Suresh C Patel
Director Of Radiology, Todd R Aho
Director Of Radiology, Todd R Williams
Director Of Radiology, Syed Arbab Ali
Medical Director, Panayiotis Varelas
Vice President Information Technology, Veeresh Nama
Senior Vice President And Chief Development Officer, Mary Vogt
System Vice President Risk Finance And Insurance Services, John Mucha
Medical Director Of Perioperative Services, Gaylord Alexander
Vice President Of Finance, Asad Malik
Vp Of It Applications, Josephine Molle
Vice President For Research, Margot Lapointe

Director Of Radiology, David Mcvinnie
Director Of Radiology, Daniel Croteau
Medical Records Director, SUSAN GLEASON
Vp And Corporate Controller, Paul Kolpasky
Vice President And Medical Director, Usamah Mossallam
Vice President, Linda Gifford
Executive Vice President And Chief Strategy Officer, Seth Frazier
Medical Director, William O'neill
Svp And Cio, Paul Browne
Regional Vice President, Paul Szilagyi
Vice President Heart And Vascular Services, Ruth Fisher
Medical Director, Gwendolyn Graddy
Director Of Radiology, Zachary Delpropoto
Medical Director, Christopher Lewandowski
Vice President Associate General Counsel, Alice Macdermott
Secretary, Jasmine Parks
Secretary Iii, Alicia Bias
Vice Chairman Department Of Surgery, Arthur Carlin
Secretary, Mary Cantu
Secretary, Barbara Paul
Secretary Ii, Paulette Wojcik
Secretary Iii, Jacqueline Underwood
Medical Secretary, Diana Popp
Auditors: DELOITTE & TOUCHE LLP DETROI

LOCATIONS

HQ: HENRY FORD HEALTH SYSTEM
1 FORD PL, DETROIT, MI 482023450
Phone: 313 916-2600

HOSPITAL LOCATIONS
Henry Ford Allegiance Health
Henry Ford Hospital
Henry Ford Kingswood Hospital
Henry Ford Macomb Hospital - Clinton Township
Henry Ford West Bloomfield Hospital
Henry Ford Wyandotte Hospital

PRODUCTS/OPERATIONS

SELECTED SERVICES
Bariatric Surgery
Cancer
Heart & Vascular
Neurology & Neurosurgery
OptimEyes
Orthopedic Surgery
Primary Care
Transplant Services

COMPETITORS

Ascension Health	OmniCare Health Plan
Beaumont Health System	St. John Health
Crittenton Hospital	Total Health Care
Detroit Medical Center	Trinity Health (Novi)
Garden City Hospital	University of Michigan
Harper-Hutzel Hospital	Health System
McLaren Health Care	
Mount Clemens Regional Medical Center	

HISTORICAL FINANCIALS

Company Type: Private

Income Statement   FYE: December 31

	REVENUE ($ mil.)	NET INCOME ($ mil.)	NET PROFIT MARGIN	EMPLOYEES
12/17	5,977	203	3.4%	23,000
12/14	1,513	(13)	—	—
12/13	4,517	135	3.0%	—
12/09	2,118	26	1.3%	—
Annual Growth	13.8%	28.8%	—	—

2017 Year-End Financials

Return on assets: 4.6%   Cash ($ mil.): 774
Return on equity: 9.9%
Current ratio: 1.60

HENRY FORD MACOMB HOSPITALS

EXECUTIVES

Pres, Stephen J Hathaway
Internal Medicine Practitioner, Dale Scarlett
Director of Patient Accounts, Alicia Letson
Physician, Andrews Kenneth
Administration Executive, Don Johnson
Director of Personnel, Janet Brown
Doctor, Lee Beatty
Sales, Matt Novak
Information Technology Manager, Michael Foster
Manager, Thomas Zamorski
Director of Radiology, Vivian Gordon

LOCATIONS

HQ: HENRY FORD MACOMB HOSPITALS
215 NORTH AVE, MOUNT CLEMENS, MI 480431716
Phone: 586 466-9310

HISTORICAL FINANCIALS

Company Type: Private

Income Statement				FYE: December 31
	REVENUE ($ mil.)	NET INCOME ($ mil.)	NET PROFIT MARGIN	EMPLOYEES
12/17	455	3	0.7%	1
12/16	438	9	2.1%	—
12/15	411	(0)	—	—
12/08	328	12	3.9%	—
Annual Growth	3.7%	(13.9%)	—	—

2017 Year-End Financials

Return on assets: 1.0%   Cash ($ mil.): 3
Return on equity: 3.3%
Current ratio: 1.70

HENRY MODELL & COMPANY, INC.

A model corporate citizen retailer Henry Modell & Company sells sporting goods fitness equipment apparel and brand-name athletic footwear as America's oldest family-owned and -operated sporting goods retailer. Established in 1889 the business also ensures it has local team apparel on hand. Through more than 155 stores that operate under the Modell's Sporting Goods banner the company serves some 10 East Coast states and the District of Columbia. Known for its reasonably priced branded products Modell's locates its stores in malls regional shopping centers and busy urban areas. It also boasts an online presence at Modells.com.

Geographic Reach

New York (home to 69 stores) and New Jersey (with 36 stores) are the sporting goods chain's major markets. The retailer also has stores in Connecticut Pennsylvania Rhode Island Maryland Massachusetts New Hampshire Delaware Virginia and the District of Columbia.

Sales and Marketing

Modell's markets and sells its products through its stores and online.

Strategy

To ensure it has all its bases covered Henry Modell & Company offers licensed products from nearly 30 sports leagues. Also during recent years Henry Modell & Company has focused on designing more appealing and accessible stores. To this end most Modell's locations have been renovated to provide improved accommodations for shoppers. Also the retailer has opened three stores in New York City including its redesigned 20000-sq.-ft. flagship store in Times Square.

To improve wireless performance in all of its stores in 2014 the company partnered with DecisionPoint Systems integrating DecisionPoint's mobile computing and wireless infrastructure system into its operations.

Company Background

Hungarian immigrant Morris Modell first sold menswear from a Lower East Side pushcart in New York City before he founded Henry Modell & Company in 1889. Led by CEO Mitchell Modell the company is operated by the fourth generation of the Modell family.

EXECUTIVES

Ceo, Mitchell B. (Mitch) Modell
Vp Information Technology, Hans Kantor
Vice President Of Operations, Bill Barrett
Vp Of Planning, Rob Stein
Auditors: BDO USA LLP NEW YORK NY

LOCATIONS

HQ: HENRY MODELL & COMPANY, INC.
498 7TH AVE FL 20, NEW YORK, NY 100186704
Phone: 212 822-1000
Web: WWW.MODELLS.COM

2016 Locations

	No.
New York	71
New Jersey	38
Pennsylvania	18
Maryland	9
Connecticut	6
Massachusetts	7
Virginia	5
District of Columbia	2
New Hampshire	2
Delaware	1
Rhode Island	1
Total	**160**

PRODUCTS/OPERATIONS

Selected Product Categories

Accessories
Apparel
Baseball
Basketball
Boxing/martial arts
Camping/hiking
Cycling
Electronics/optics
Fan shop-pro/college
Field hockey
Fishing
Fitness
Football
Footwear
Games
Golf
Ice/roller hockey
In-Line/roller skating
Lacrosse
Optics/telescopes
Outdoor recreation
Paintball
Pilates
Racquetball/squash
Roller hockey
Rugby
Running
Scooters
Skateboarding
Snow sports
Soccer
Softball
Tennis
Water recreation
Winter recreation
Wrestling
Yoga

COMPETITORS

Athleta	Hat World
Dick's Sporting Goods	Olympia Sports
Dunham's	Sears
Eastern Mountain Sports	Sports Authority
Foot Locker	Target Corporation
	Wal-Mart

HISTORICAL FINANCIALS

Company Type: Private

Income Statement				FYE: February 2
	REVENUE ($ mil.)	NET INCOME ($ mil.)	NET PROFIT MARGIN	EMPLOYEES
02/13*	607	0	0.1%	5,430
01/12	570	(3)	—	—
01/11	558	(7)	—	—
Annual Growth	4.3%	—	—	—

*Fiscal year change

2013 Year-End Financials

Return on assets: 0.3%   Cash ($ mil.): 3
Return on equity: 1.7%
Current ratio: 1.10

HENSEL PHELPS CONSTRUCTION CO.

Hensel Phelps Construction builds it all from the courthouse to the big house. The employee-owned general contractor provides a full range of development pre-construction construction and renovation services for commercial institutional and government projects throughout the US and abroad. Its project portfolio includes prisons airports arenas laboratories government complexes offices and more. Major public and private clients have included the US Army Corps of Engineers IBM United Airlines The University of Texas Kodak and Whole Foods. Hensel Phelps founded the eponymous company as a homebuilder in 1937.

Geographic Reach

Colorado-based Hensel Phelps Construction has seven regional offices throughout the continental US including two in California. The company operates internationally most often for US federal projects but also for foreign governments and private enterprises. Its Honolulu branch oversees operations in Hawaii Guam the Marshall Islands and Asia.

Sales and Marketing

Sectors served include aviation commercial education government health care hospitality industrial and justice.

Financial Performance

One of America's largest private companies Hensel Phelps reported $2 billion in revenue in 2014.

Strategy

Hensel Phelps ranks in the top three (by Engineering News Record) among general contractors and construction managers in the US in the aerospace government and "green" government office sectors. The company self-performs (as opposed to subcontracting) most of the work tied to a specific project. That ability helps keep costs and schedules in check. Its construction services include concrete work quality control safety management waste management among others.

In 2016 the company was awarded a contract to build a new 285000-sq.-ft. office tower in Denver. Other notable projects include a new central library in Austin Texas.

EXECUTIVES

President Phelps Development, Eric L. Wilson
Cfo, Stephen J. (Steve) Carrico
Evp, Wayne S. Lindholm
Evp, Jon W. Ball
President And Ceo, Jeffrey K. (Jeff) Wenaas
Evp, Michael J. Choutka
Evp, Richard G. Tucker
President Hensel Phelps Services, Edwin (Glen) Miller
Auditors: KPMG LLP DENVER CO

LOCATIONS

HQ: HENSEL PHELPS CONSTRUCTION CO.
  420 6TH AVE, GREELEY, CO 806312332
Phone: 970 352-6565
Web: WWW.HENSELPHELPS.COM

PRODUCTS/OPERATIONS

Selected Projects
Hilton Hok
Aegis Asho
Regional 0
Guam NAVFAC Bachelor Enlisted Quarters (BEQ)
Mamizu Utilities and Site Improvements Phase I
Samaritan MOB and Parking Structure
Santa Clara Valley Medical Center Receiving and Support Center
Santa Clara Family Justice Center
Santa Clara Valley Medical Center Receiving and Support Center
Rotary PlayGarden
Norman Y. Mineta San José International Airport Terminal Area Improvement Program (TAIP)
Vantage Data Center V2
Vantage Data Center V1

Selected Services
Construction
  Change management
  Construction waste management
  LEED project registration
  Quality control
  Safety management
  Scheduling
  Self-perfoming concrete
  Status reporting
  Subcontractor management
  Sustainability audits
  Quality control
Development
  Feasibility studies
  Financing
  Green building planning/education
  Land acquisition
  Leasing
  Pro forma review
Post-construction
  As-built documentation
  Building operations
  Certificate of occupancy
  Commissioning and warranty programs
  LEED project certification
  Moving services
Preconstruction
  Bid packaging
  Budgeting/cost modeling
  Design management
  Estimating
  Green building and planning/education
  Phasing plans
  Regulatory investigation
  Scheduling
  Status reporting
  Subcontractor prequalification
  Value engineering

Selected Markets
Commercial

Education
High technology
Industrial
International
Justice
Leisure
Medical
Multiresidence
Public
Transportation

COMPETITORS

Balfour Beatty Construction	M. A. Mortenson
C.F. Jordan	McCarthy Building
Clark Construction Group	PCL Employees Holdings
Fluor	Rooney Holdings
Gilbane	Skanska USA Building
Hunt Construction	Turner Corporation
Jacobs Engineering	Tutor Perini
KBR	Walbridge Aldinger
	Walsh Group
	Whiting-Turner

HISTORICAL FINANCIALS
Company Type: Private

Income Statement   FYE: December 31

	REVENUE ($ mil.)	NET INCOME ($ mil.)	NET PROFIT MARGIN	EMPLOYEES
12/17	3,360	80	2.4%	2,000
12/16	3,540	76	2.2%	—
12/15	3,142	70	2.2%	—
12/14	2,507	38	1.5%	—
Annual Growth	10.2%	27.7%	—	—

2017 Year-End Financials
Return on assets: 5.5%   Cash ($ mil.): 281
Return on equity: 34.8%
Current ratio: 1.30

HERITAGE VALLEY HEALTH SYSTEM, INC.

Heritage Valley Health System has a legacy of serving the health care needs of residents of southwestern Pennsylvania eastern Ohio and the West Virginia Panhandle. The two-hospital system includes the flagship Heritage Valley Beaver hospital in Beaver Pennsylvania with more than 330 beds and a smaller facility in nearby Sewickley with roughly 185 beds. In addition to its acute-care facilities the system operates several satellite facilities and provides primary care through a network of three affiliated physician groups. Heritage Valley Health System was formed in 1996 when the two hospitals merged but it has roots going back to 1894.

Operations
Heritage Valley has more than 450 physicians at its two hospitals more than 70 physician offices and 14 community satellite locations. The system's affiliated physician groups are Heritage Valley Medical Group (with specialties including internal medicine family practice cardiology geriatrics and pulmonology) Heritage Valley Pediatrics and Tri-State Obstetrics and Gynecology.

Geographic Reach
The system serves Allegheny Beaver Butler and Lawrence counties in Pennsylvania; eastern Ohio; and the West Virginia Panhandle.

Financial Performance
In fiscal 2014 revenue increased 3% to $444 million on higher net patient service revenues. Net

income rose 237% to $16 million thanks to the higher revenue and declines in employee benefit patient care supplies and drugs expenses.

Strategy
The health system expands its service offerings and increases its geographic reach in part by forming collaborative relationships with health care providers and other organizations. For example it operates immediate care clinics at local Wal-Mart stores to offer patients routine care such as immunizations screenings and treatment of minor injuries and illnesses. Heritage Valley also partners with UPMC to offer radiation therapy and medical oncology services at Heritage Valley Beaver. Additionally Heritage Valley and UPMC Health Plan operate LifeSmart which identifies patients at risk for diabetes connects them with a primary care physician and provides them with lifestyle intervention programs.

Along with increasing its medical offerings through partnerships Heritage Valley hires specialists and adds new services to meet community demand. Some areas of focus include infectious disease endocrinology inpatient rehabilitation and wound care.

In 2015 the system completed the expansion and renovation of one of its network facilities creating its sixth Medical Neighborhood location (in Imperial Pennsylvania). Also that year it opened a new walk-in care clinic under the ConvenientCare brand. The system's sixth ConvenientCare facility it is also located in Imperial.

EXECUTIVES

Board Member, John Wright
Auditors: ARNETT CARBIS TOOTHMAN LLP PI

LOCATIONS

HQ: HERITAGE VALLEY HEALTH SYSTEM, INC.
  1000 DUTCH RIDGE RD, BEAVER, PA 150099727
Phone: 724 728-7000
Web: WWW.HERITAGEVALLEY.ORG

PRODUCTS/OPERATIONS

Selected Medical Services
Advanced Cardiology
Bariatric Surgery
Behavioral Health
Breast Imaging
Cancer Treatment
Cardiac Computed Tomography (Cardiac CT)
Cardiology
Community Advanced Ilness Program (CAIP)
Community Health Services
Diabetes Radiology
Diagnostic Centers
Emergency
Endoscopy Center
Family Planning
Heart and Vascular Center
Inpatient Rehabilitation
Laboratory
LIFE Beaver and Lawrence County
Maternity
MRI Services
Neurology
Nutrition Counseling
Occupational Medicine
Orthopedics Services
Osteoporosis
Pediatric Asthma
Pharmacy retail
Pulmonary Services
Signature BusinessCare
Signature Rehab
Signature SportsCare
Sleep Lab
Surgery Centers
VeinCare
Weight Loss
WoundCare

COMPETITORS

Butler Health System
Children's Hospital of Pittsburgh
Conemaugh Health System
Excela Health
Jefferson Regional Medical Center of Pennsylvania
Kindred Healthcare
Ohio Valley General
Sharon Regional Health System
St. Clair Health
Trinity Health System
UPMC
Weirton Medical Center
West Penn Allegheny Health System

HISTORICAL FINANCIALS

Company Type: Private

Income Statement				FYE: June 30
	REVENUE ($ mil.)	NET INCOME ($ mil.)	NET PROFIT MARGIN	EMPLOYEES
06/18	450	30	6.8%	4,291
06/14	5	4	87.7%	—
06/13	4	3	75.4%	—
06/11	449	40	9.0%	—
Annual Growth	0.0%	(3.9%)	—	—

2018 Year-End Financials
Return on assets: 5.4%
Return on equity: 7.4%
Current ratio: 1.40
Cash ($ mil.): 34

HILAND DAIRY FOODS COMPANY., LLC

Hiland Dairy Foods is a processor and distributor of dairy foods and other beverages. It is a farmer-owned entity giving leverage to its members when negotiating prices and contract terms with buyers of their products. Its farmers' cows produce the raw ingredient for churning out butter ice cream fluid milk cheese yogurt and other dairy products free of artificial growth hormones. Hiland runs ten processing plants and has more than 40 distribution centers. It partners with a larger dairy co-operative Prairie Farms Dairy to market and sell product. Beyond dairy Hiland supplies juices bottled milk and coffee (cravélatté) as well as green tea water and other to-go drinks. It features limited-run specialty items such as peanut butter s'-mores ice cream. Founded in 1938 the farmer-owned venture operates manufacturing plants in the Midwest.

EXECUTIVES

President, Gary L. Aggus
General Manager, Woody Rogers
Auditors: BKD LLP SPRINGFIELD MO

LOCATIONS

HQ: HILAND DAIRY FOODS COMPANY., LLC
1133 E KEARNEY ST, SPRINGFIELD, MO 658033435
Phone: 417 862-9311
Web: WWW.HILANDDAIRY.COM

Selected Plant Locations
Chandler Oklahoma
Fayetteville Arkansas
Fort Smith Arkansas
Kansas City Missouri
Little Rock Arkansas
Norfolk Nebraska
Norman Oklahoma
Omaha Nebraska
Springfield Missouri
Tyler Texas
Wichita Kansas

PRODUCTS/OPERATIONS

Selected Products
Butter
Cheese
Cottage cheese
Cravélatté (milk and coffee)
Creams/Half-and-Half
Dips
Egg nog
Egg substitute
Fruit-flavored drinks
Ice cream
Juice
Lactose-free milk
Lemonade
Milk
Sour cream
Tea
To-go drinks
Water
Yogurt

COMPETITORS

Agri-Mark
Associated Milk
  Producers
Blue Bell
ConAgra
Dairylea
Dean Foods
Dreyer's
Fonterra
Great Lakes Cheese
Hornell Brewing
Land O'Lakes
MMPA
Nestlé
Oberweis Dairy
Organic Valley
Saputo
Sargento
Smith Dairy
Snapple
Wells' Dairy

HILITE INTERNATIONAL, INC.

The highlight of Hilite International's day is to manufacture high-volume high-tech auto components and systems. Its lineup is used in many powertrain (engine and transmission) applications. Hilite's hydraulic and electromagnetic products (on/off valves and variable pressure solenoids) enhance fuel efficiency emissions control and torque. Hilite sells to global auto OEMs such as GM BMW and Honda and brake systems suppliers such as BorgWarner. The company established in 1999 operates through eight locations spanning Asia Europe and North America.

HISTORICAL FINANCIALS

Company Type: Private

Income Statement				FYE: September 30
	REVENUE ($ mil.)	NET INCOME ($ mil.)	NET PROFIT MARGIN	EMPLOYEES
09/11	958	8	0.9%	1,350
09/10	588	24	4.2%	—
09/09	559	39	7.0%	—
Annual Growth	30.8%	(53.0%)	—	—

2011 Year-End Financials
Return on assets: 2.7%
Return on equity: 3.9%
Current ratio: 2.30
Cash ($ mil.): 19

Geographic Reach
Hilite intends to grow its international reach through its three locations in Germany two in the US and three in China.

Strategy
Hilite continues to focus on its bottom line as it places its 2009 bankruptcy in the rear view mirror. In 2012 it sold its heavy duty emissions control operations to auto parts giant Cummins. Hilite made the divestiture in order to focus on growing its core business of powertrain components for passenger cars on a more international scale.

Company Background
Hilite filed for bankruptcy in 2009 emerged the same year and recapitalized with the help of its lenders (primarily Carreras' investment group Carreras Kestner & Co.). It was acquired by 3i Group in 2011 for £112 million (about $181 million). It was subsequently acquired by AVIC Electromechanical Systems Holdings Co. Ltd. (AVIC Systems) in 2014 with the company valued at €473 million ($645 million). AVIC Systems is a subsidiary of Aviation Industry Corporation of China one of the largest industrial conglomerates in China.

EXECUTIVES

Ceo-Pres, Karl Hammer
Cfo, Stefan Eck
Coo, Joerge Feuring
Quality Control Manager, Laura Seidel
Plant Manager, Marco Hernandez
Electrical Engineer, Chris Kendra
Supplier Quality Engineer, Angel Montgomery
Clerk, Anish Kumar
Controller, Chris Curto
Lab Superv, Brad Sanderson
Manufacturing Engineer (engine, Vincent Priest

LOCATIONS

HQ: HILITE INTERNATIONAL, INC.
1671 S BROADWAY ST, CARROLLTON, TX 750067496
Phone: 972 242-2116
Web: WWW.HILITE.COM

PRODUCTS/OPERATIONS

Selected Products

Transmission
Actuators
Control Systems
Automated manual transmissions
Automatic transmissions
Continuous and infinitely variable transmissions
Double clutch transmissions
Differential transmissions
Electromagnetic clutches (all wheel drives)
Integrated solenoids
Sequential
Toroid transmissions
Valves
Valves
Engine valves

COMPETITORS

Aisin Seiki
American Axle &
  Manufacturing
Dana
Dayco Products
Delphi Automotive
  Systems
Magna Powertrain
Meritor
Universal
  Manufacturing
Visteon

HISTORICAL FINANCIALS

Company Type: Private

Income Statement   FYE: December 31

	REVENUE ($ mil.)	NET INCOME ($ mil.)	NET PROFIT MARGIN	EMPLOYEES
12/11	522	(1)	—	1,000
12/10	399	7	2.0%	—
12/09	736	0	—	—
Annual Growth	—	—	—	—

2011 Year-End Financials

Return on assets: 6.5%   Cash ($ mil.): 24
Return on equity: (-0.3%)
Current ratio: 0.90

HILL PHYSICIANS MEDICAL GROUP, INC.

Hill Physicians Medical Group is the doctors' answer to HMOs. The company is an independent practice association (IPA) serving some 300000 health plan members in northern California. The company contracts with managed care organizations throughout the region — including HMOs belonging to Aetna CIGNA and Health Net— to provide care to health plan members through its provider affiliates. Its network includes about 3800 primary care and specialty physicians 38 hospitals and 24 urgent care centers. The company also provides administrative services for doctors and patients. PriMed a management services organization created Hill Physicians Medical Group in 1984 and still runs the company.

Geographic Reach

Hill Physicians Medical Group's member facilities are located in Alameda Contra Costa El Dorado Placer Sacramento San Francisco San Joaquin San Mateo Solano and Yolo counties in northern California.

Financial Performance

Hill Physicians Medical Group reported a 3% increase in 2013 to about $455 million due to higher health plan revenues and investment income. Net income grew by 15% to some $13.6 million that year due to higher revenues and cost savings programs.

Strategy

Hill Physicians Medical Group has been working to enhance its technology systems to improve coordination of care including installing electronic prescription and referral management systems. It is also forming partnerships with area insurers and hospitals to improve communication among regional providers as well as to control overall health care costs. For instance the company teamed up with Dignity Health and Blue Shield of California to form an accountable care organization (ACO).

EXECUTIVES

Obstetrics Andamp; Gynecology Vice President And Chief Administrative Officer, Dan Robinson
Auditors: KPMG LLP SAN FRANCISCO CALIF

LOCATIONS

HQ: HILL PHYSICIANS MEDICAL GROUP, INC.
2409 CAMINO RAMON, SAN RAMON, CA 945834285
Phone: 800 445-5747
Web: WWW.HILLPHYSICIANS.COM

PRODUCTS/OPERATIONS

Selected Health Plan Partners

Aetna of California
Alliance CompleteCare
Anthem/Blue Cross of California
Blue Shield of California
Blue Shield 65 Plus
CIGNA Healthcare of California
Health Net of California
Health Net Medicare
United Healthcare West (formerly Pacificare)
SCAN
Secure Horizons by United Healthcare
Western Healthcare Advantage

COMPETITORS

Alta Bates Summit   Orion HealthCorp
  Medical Center   Prospect Medical
Beaver Medical Group   The Palo Alto Medical
HealthCare Partners   Foundation

HISTORICAL FINANCIALS

Company Type: Private

Income Statement   FYE: December 31

	REVENUE ($ mil.)	NET INCOME ($ mil.)	NET PROFIT MARGIN	EMPLOYEES
12/15	504	6	1.3%	600
12/10	427	5	1.2%	—
12/06	427	5	1.2%	—
12/05	414	7	1.9%	—
Annual Growth	2.0%	(1.3%)	—	—

2015 Year-End Financials

Return on assets: 4.1%   Cash ($ mil.): 46
Return on equity: 7.0%
Current ratio: 1.60

HILL/AHERN FIRE PROTECTION, LLC

EXECUTIVES

MBR, Michelle Colyar
Vice President Building Operat, Harold Hacker
Design Manager, Joe Fabis

LOCATIONS

HQ: HILL/AHERN FIRE PROTECTION, LLC
11045 GAGE AVE, FRANKLIN PARK, IL 601311437
Phone: 847 288-5100
Web: WWW.HILLGRP.COM

HISTORICAL FINANCIALS

Company Type: Private

Income Statement   FYE: December 31

	REVENUE ($ mil.)	NET INCOME ($ mil.)	NET PROFIT MARGIN	EMPLOYEES
12/11	5,669	185	3.3%	100
12/10	2,568	80	3.1%	—
Annual Growth	120.7%	130.7%	—	—

2011 Year-End Financials

Return on assets: 7.3%   Cash ($ mil.): 480
Return on equity: 11.4%
Current ratio: 2.60

HILLCO, LTD.

EXECUTIVES

Pres, Steven Hill
V Pres*, Robert Hill Jr
V Pres*, Greg Hill
SEC-Treas*, Lucy Hill
Office Manager, Kathy Vick
Executive, Cindy DOE
Director Hillco Support Servic, Dannie Kennedy
Supervisor, Evie Blankenburg
Director Production, Stephen Ferrar

LOCATIONS

HQ: HILLCO, LTD.
1435 HWY 258 N, KINSTON, NC 285047208
Phone: 252 523-9094

HISTORICAL FINANCIALS

Company Type: Private

Income Statement   FYE: December 31

	REVENUE ($ mil.)	NET INCOME ($ mil.)	NET PROFIT MARGIN	EMPLOYEES
12/08*	481	18	3.8%	7,000
09/07	481	18	3.8%	—
09/99	1	2	203.9%	—
12/98	1	2	203.9%	—
Annual Growth	79.7%	20.7%	—	—

*Fiscal year change

HILLSBOROUGH COUNTY SCHOOL DISTRICT

EXECUTIVES

Chm, April Griffin
Superintendent*, Maryellen Elia
V Chm*, Cindy Stuart
MBR*, Susan L Valdes
MBR*, Sally Harris
MBR*, Melissa Snively
Building and Grounds Director, Chris Farkas
Manager, David Borisenko
Procurement Officer, Kathy Olsen
Teacher, Jaime Heeman
Principals Secretary, Lara Leto
Auditors: KPMG LLP TAMPA FL

LOCATIONS

HQ: HILLSBOROUGH COUNTY SCHOOL DISTRICT
901 E KENNEDY BLVD, TAMPA, FL 336023502
Phone: 813 272-4000
Web: WWW.SDHC.K12.FL.US

Company Type: Private

Income Statement				FYE: June 30
	REVENUE ($ mil.)	NET INCOME ($ mil.)	NET PROFIT MARGIN	EMPLOYEES
06/16	2,133	(59)	—	25,000
06/15	2,042	(110)	—	—
06/14	1,984	(45)	—	—
06/13	1,878	(44)	—	—
Annual Growth	4.3%	—	—	—

2016 Year-End Financials

Return on assets: (-1.8%)   Cash ($ mil.): 113
Return on equity: (-7.6%)
Current ratio: —

HMH HOSPITALS CORPORATION

Hackensack University Medical Center (HUMC) is an acute care teaching and research hospital that serves northern New Jersey and parts of New York. The hospital has about 775 beds and staffs more than 2200 medical professionals. HUMC administers general medical surgical emergency and diagnostic care. The center also includes specialized treatment centers including a children's hospital a women's hospital a cancer center and a heart and vascular hospital. HUMC is part of the Hackensack University Health Network which also includes a physician practice group and a joint venture that operates two community hospitals. In 2016 the network merged with Meridian Health to create Hackensack Meridian Health.

Operations

HUMC helps train future dentists and doctors through its affiliation with the University of Medicine and Dentistry of New Jersey. It expanded its education programs in 2012 by partnering with the Stevens Institute of Technology to offer joint biomedical training programs.

The hospital also performs research through the David Joseph Jurist Research Center for Tomorrow's Children. The center has roughly 475 research programs in operation at any given time.

Financial Performance

Medicare accounts for 29.5% of HUMC's funding; HMOs 28%; and Blue Cross 28%.

Strategy

The company grows organically and through acquisitions partnerships and affiliations.

To expand its services HUMC broke ground on a $35 million project to expand and renovate its trauma and emergency facilities in 2012 (scheduled to open in 2015).

Hackensack University Health Network is increasing its partnerships and affiliations with other regional care providers following the trend of US hospitals seeking to improve and lower the cost of health care through shared services and resources. The network partnered up with Texas-based LPH Hospital Group in 2012 to reenovate the Pascack Valley Hospital (now HackensackUMC Pascack) in Westwood New Jersey. Hackensack took over the bankrupt facility's ER back in 2007 and in 2012 the joint venture launched a $90 million project to revamp the rest of the 130-bed acute-care community hospital. It reopened in 2013.

Hackensack University Health Network also formed a joint venture with an area physician group to open two ambulatory surgery centers in 2012 and it entered a collaboration with CVS Health's MinuteClinic to open new urgent care centers.

That year HUMC formed a joint venture partnership with community physicians and United Surgical Partners International to buy and operate ambulatory surgery centers in Bergen County: Hackensack Endoscopy Center and the Endoscopy Center of Bergen County.

Mergers and Acquisitions

In 2015 the Hackensack University Health Network agreed to merge with fellow New Jersey care provider Meridian Health. The combined system to be named Hackensack Meridian Health will have 11 hospitals and two children's hospitals. The deal which is one of a number of consolidation efforts by hospitals in the state is pending regulatory approval.

Company Background

To simplify its operations HUMC sold its hospice operations to Amedisys in 2011. The health provider previously sold its home health agency to Amedisys in 2009 to generate revenue and control costs after struggling with financial losses throughout the year due to declining admissions.

HUMC completed construction of its new John Theurer Cancer Center in late 2010 giving it one of the largest comprehensive cancer centers in the US. The center includes diagnostic and treatment units that focus on specific types of cancers.

HUMC was founded as a hospital in 1888 with 12 beds.

EXECUTIVES

Chairman Department Of Ophthamology, Michael Rosenberg
Auditors: PRICEWATERHOUSECOOPERS LLP NE

LOCATIONS

HQ: HMH HOSPITALS CORPORATION
343 THORNALL ST, EDISON, NJ 088372206
Phone: 201 996-2000
Web: WWW.HACKENSACKUMC.ORG

PRODUCTS/OPERATIONS

Selected Services

Donna A. Sanzari Women's Hospital
Emergency Services
Heart & Vascular Hospital
Hospital Services
John Theurer Cancer Center
Joseph M. Sanzari Children's Hospital
Medical
Specialized
Surgical
Tackle Kids Cancer

Selected Facilities

Donna A. Sanzari Women's Hospital
Hackensack University Medical Center Mountainside
Hackensack University Medical Center Pascack
Heart & Vascular Hospital
John Theurer Cancer Center
Joseph M. Sanzari Children's Hospital
Tomorrows Children's Institute for Cancer and Blood Disorders

COMPETITORS

Bergen Regional Medical	Lenox Hill Hospital
Bronx-Lebanon Hospital	Montefiore Medical
Continuum Health Partners	NewYork-Presbyterian Healthcare
Englewood Hospital and Medical Center	Newark Beth Israel Medical Center
Hospital for Special Surgery	St. Joseph's Healthcare System
	Valley Health System

Company Type: Private

Income Statement				FYE: December 31
	REVENUE ($ mil.)	NET INCOME ($ mil.)	NET PROFIT MARGIN	EMPLOYEES
12/18	3,999	220	5.5%	1,100
12/16	1,707	41	2.4%	—
12/15	1,357	83	6.1%	—
12/14	1,309	106	8.1%	—
Annual Growth	32.2%	19.9%	—	—

2018 Year-End Financials

Return on assets: 5.7%   Cash ($ mil.): 202
Return on equity: 8.6%
Current ratio: 1.50

HMO MINNESOTA

EXECUTIVES

Eo, Andrew Czajkowski
Chb*, Jonathon Killmer
Cfo*, Tim Peterson
Psychologist, Kathryn Pearson

LOCATIONS

HQ: HMO MINNESOTA
3535 BLUE CROSS RD, SAINT PAUL, MN 551221154
Phone: 952 456-8434
Web: WWW.BLUECROSSMN.COM

HISTORICAL FINANCIALS

Company Type: Private

Income Statement				FYE: December 31
	REVENUE ($ mil.)	NET INCOME ($ mil.)	NET PROFIT MARGIN	EMPLOYEES
12/16	1,839	(156)	—	40
12/15	918	52	5.7%	—
12/14	850	85	10.1%	—
12/09	978	30	3.1%	—
Annual Growth	9.4%	—	—	—

2016 Year-End Financials

Return on assets: (-18.2%)   Cash ($ mil.): 108
Return on equity: (-36.6%)
Current ratio: —

HOAG MEMORIAL HOSPITAL PRESBYTERIAN

Serving California's Orange County population Hoag Memorial Hospital Presbyterian boasts several hospitals and even more clinics to cater to area residents. The not-for-profit health care system is home to two acute care hospitals seven health centers five urgent care centers and a network of more than 1500 physicians. Its hospitals include Hoag Hospital Irvine and Hoag Hospital Newport Beach in Southern California. Combined the two hospitals have 617 beds and provide a comprehensive range of medical and surgical services with specialized expertise in a number of areas such as oncology cardiovascular disease neuroscience and orthopedics. Hoag is an affiliate of Providence St. Joseph Health.

EXECUTIVES

President And Ceo, Robert Braithwaite
Svp And Cfo, Jennifer Mitzner
Executive Vice President Chief Operating Officer, Michael Ricks
Medical Director, Richard Doering
Vice President Centers Of Excellence, Trish Bartel
Executive Medical Director, Burton Eisenberg
Vice President Operations, Robert Briathwaite
Vice President, Joanne Tucker
Vice President Marketing And Corporate Communications, Nina B Robinson
Assistant Vice President Speciality Business Development, Cathy Major
Vp Operations, Holnagel Dori
Pharm D, Nancy Yano
Director Of Him, Michele Morton
Board Member, Richard Taketa
Board Member, Kris Iyer
Vice Chairman, Robert Evans
Unit Secretary, Marissa Mastromatteo

LOCATIONS

HQ: HOAG MEMORIAL HOSPITAL PRESBYTERIAN
1 HOAG DR, NEWPORT BEACH, CA 926634162
Phone: 949 764-4624
Web: WWW.HOAG.ORG

COMPETITORS

Adventist Health System West	Saddleback Memorial Medical Center
Anaheim Regional Medical Center	St. Joseph Hospital of Orange
Children's Hospital of Orange County	St. Jude Medical Center
Citrus Valley Health Partners	Tenet Healthcare
Dignity Health	Torrance Memorial Medical Center
Long Beach Memorial Memorial Health Services	Trinity Health (Novi)
	Western Medical Center - Santa Ana
Pasadena Hospital Association	

HISTORICAL FINANCIALS
Company Type: Private

Income Statement   FYE: June 30

	REVENUE ($ mil.)	NET INCOME ($ mil.)	NET PROFIT MARGIN	EMPLOYEES
06/16	894	100	11.2%	3,800
06/15	822	107	13.1%	—
/*	0	0	—	—
Annual Growth	—	—	—	—

*Fiscal year change

2016 Year-End Financials

Return on assets: 3.0%   Cash ($ mil.): 189
Return on equity: 5.1%
Current ratio: 1.20

HOBBY LOBBY STORES, INC.

If something wicker this way comes Hobby Lobby Stores may be the source. The craft-and-fabric retailer operates more than 850 stores in the US in more than 45 states selling arts and crafts supplies baskets beads candles frames home-decorating accessories and silk flowers. Hobby Lobby also owns stores in Canada and operates offices in China and Hong Kong. In addition Hobby Lobby operates Mardel Christian and Education Supply which sells Christian educational and homeschooling products. CEO David Green who owns the company founded Hobby Lobby in 1972 and operates it according to biblical principles including closing shop on Sunday.

Strategy

One of America's largest private companies fast-growing Hobby Lobby has been busy expanding its network of stores which average 55000 sq. ft. The company opened 54 stores in 2018 and relocated 20 store locations. In 2019 Hobby Lobby plans to open 65 new stores and relocate 16. The company has been lifted by renewed interest in crafting by younger generations.

Hobby Lobby often sets up shop in second-generation retail sites such as vacated supermarkets and superstores. In recent years the company has put new stores in previous Macy's Toys R Us and OfficeMax locations.

The company has announced the closure of its home furnishings chain Hemispheres admitting the competitive nature of the industry made profitability too difficult.

EXECUTIVES

Vice President Advertising, John Schumacher
Vice President Chief Legal Officer, Peter Dobelbower
Ceo, David Green
Cfo, Jon Cargill
President, Steve Green
Executive Vice President, Stan Lett
Assistant Vice President, Deloris Miller
Department Head, Christi Claxon
Vice President Information Technology, Teddy Amadou
Senior Vice President Operations, Ken Haywood
Vice President Finance, Mandy Rodriguez
Vice President Store Operations, Randy Betts
Vice President Marketing And Advertising, Dolois Smith
Vice President Of Marketing, Timothy Mattingly
Assistant Vice President Controller, Barbara Walke
Assistant Vice President Risk Manager, Rebecca Robinson
Department Head, JEAN STEPHENSON
Regional Vice President Region 9, Joe Guerra
Vice President International Relations, Allen Quine
Assistant Vice President Of Accounting, Barbara A Walke
Administrative Assitant To Vice President Of Information And Interactive Sys, Sherri R Fisher
Vice President, Jessica Mchart
Senior Vice President Information Technology, Francine English
Sec Treas, Mart Green

LOCATIONS

HQ: HOBBY LOBBY STORES, INC.
7707 SW 44TH ST, OKLAHOMA CITY, OK 731794899
Phone: 405 745-1100
Web: WWW.HOBBYLOBBY.COM

PRODUCTS/OPERATIONS

Selected Products
Arts and crafts supplies
Baskets
Candles
Cards
Furniture
Home accent pieces
Jewelry-making supplies
Needlework
Party supplies
Picture frames and framing
Scrapbooking supplies
Seasonal items
Sewing materials (fabric patterns notions)
Silk flowers
Toys
Wearable art

Selected Affiliates
Hemispheres (home furnishings and accessories stores)
Mardel Christian Office & Educational Supply (Christian materials office supplies and educational products)

COMPETITORS

A.C. Moore	Kirkland's
Burnes Home Accents	Michaels Companies
Garden Ridge	Old Time Pottery
Hancock Fabrics	Target Corporation
Jo-Ann Stores	Wal-Mart

HISTORICAL FINANCIALS
Company Type: Private

Income Statement   FYE: December 31

	REVENUE ($ mil.)	NET INCOME ($ mil.)	NET PROFIT MARGIN	EMPLOYEES
12/17	4,544	352	7.8%	30,218
12/06	196	58	29.5%	—
12/04	1,363	88	6.5%	—
12/03	150	58	39.0%	—
Annual Growth	27.5%	13.7%	—	—

2017 Year-End Financials

Return on assets: 11.2%   Cash ($ mil.): —
Return on equity: 20.8%
Current ratio: 2.10

HOLY CROSS HEALTH, INC.

EXECUTIVES

Pres-Ceo, Kevin Sexton
Cfo*, Anne D Gillis
V Pres*, Eileen Cahill
V Pres*, Patrick Connely
Obstetrician, Ronald D Jacobs
Ophthalmology, Benjamin D Magno
Gynecology/Obstetrics, Angela D Thompson
Obstetrician, Oluyemisi O Famuyiwa
Chief of Obstetrics/Gynecology, Laurie Tyau
Home Health Care Director, Margaret Hadley Sr
Information Technology Manager, Patricia Okolie

LOCATIONS

HQ: HOLY CROSS HEALTH, INC.
1500 FOREST GLEN RD, SILVER SPRING, MD 209101460
Phone: 301 754-7000
Web: WWW.HOLYCROSSHEALTH.ORG

HISTORICAL FINANCIALS
Company Type: Private

Income Statement   FYE: June 30

	REVENUE ($ mil.)	NET INCOME ($ mil.)	NET PROFIT MARGIN	EMPLOYEES
06/18	561	43	7.7%	3,270
06/16	434	28	6.6%	—
Annual Growth	13.7%	22.4%	—	—

2018 Year-End Financials
Return on assets: 4.8%   Cash ($ mil.): 282
Return on equity: 10.4%
Current ratio: 4.20

HOLY CROSS HOSPITAL, INC.

Holy Cross Hospital's patients have more than just doctors on their side. Holy Cross is a Catholic community hospital serving the Ft. Lauderdale Florida area. The hospital has about 560 beds and offers inpatient and outpatient medical services along with a cancer treatment center heart and vascular center women's health center orthopedic unit and home health division as well as outpatient imaging centers. It also operates family health and specialist clinics in the region. Sponsored by the Sisters of Mercy Holy Cross Hospital is a part of Trinity Health.

Operations

Holy Cross Hospital employs some 600 physicians including specialists in about 40 medical fields. The organization's Holy Cross Medical Group physician practice group has more than 150 doctors working at about 30 clinics. The hospital also operates the Holy Cross HealthPlex which includes an orthopedic institute a women's health center a wound healing center diagnostic imaging and laboratory facilities and an outpatient surgery center.

Geographic Reach

The hospital operates in South Florida's Broward and Palm Beach counties. In addition to its main campus n Fort Lauderdale the hospital has satellite locations across Broward and Palm Beach counties including Holy Cross Urgent Care and Imaging Centers in Fort Lauderdale and east Boca Raton Holy Cross Medical Group offices and Holy Cross HealthPlex.

Strategy

To enhance service offerings and bring in more area residents Holy Cross Hospital is working to enhance its facilities and improve its technologies.

In 2015 Holy Cross Hospital and Massachusetts General Hospital Cancer Center in Boston entered into a five-year affiliation agreement that expands the collaboration first begun in 2010.

On the innovation front that year the hospital offered its patients the MyCareLink Patient Monitor—a simplified remote monitoring system with global cellular technology that transmits patients' cardiac device diagnostic data to their clinicians from any location where a cellular signal is available.

To align itself with the goals of US federal health reform measures in 2014 Holy Cross Hospital joined the accountable care organization (ACO) facilitated by CIGNA. In 2013 it also joined the ACO facilitated by Blue Cross and Blue Shield of Florida. The ACOs aim to coordinate care for area Medicare residents in order to improve care quality and lower medical costs in the region.

Company Background

Holy Cross Hospital was part of Catholic Health East's (CHE) Southeast division. CHE merged with Michigan-based Trinity Health in 2013.

In 2012 it added a new surgery device for aneurysm embolization treatment procedures. In addition the medical center opened a new meditation chapel and healing garden. The following year Holy Cross Hospital built a new urgent care and diagnostic imaging center in Fort Lauderdale's Rio

Vista community to improve patient access to outpatient services.

The hospital was established in 1953 and opened in 1995.

EXECUTIVES

Vice President Human Resources, Luisa Gutman
Vice President Finance, Matthew Moore
Medical Director Of Emergency Services, Mark Caputo
Clinical Director, Theresa Valern
Vice President Mission Effectiveness Sponsorship, Rita Levasseur
Senior Vice President, Linda Wilford
Secretary, Maureen Gill
Auditors: DELOITTE TAX LLP CINCINNATI

LOCATIONS

HQ: HOLY CROSS HOSPITAL, INC.
4725 N FEDERAL HWY, FORT LAUDERDALE, FL 333084668
Phone: 954 771-8000
Web: WWW.HOLY-CROSS.COM

PRODUCTS/OPERATIONS

Selected Services
Back Pain Management
Bariatrics
Cancer
Center for Optimal Health
Comprehensive Stroke Center
Diagnostic Imaging
Emergency
Epilepsy Monitoring Unit
Heart and Vascular
Heart Research
Home Health
International Services
Maternal/Child Health
Medical Group
Neurology and Spine
Orthopedics
Outpatient Services
Rehabilitation Institute
Robotics
Sleep Disorder Lab
Spine Center
Wellness Pavilion
Women's Center
Wound Healing and Hyperbarics

COMPETITORS

Adventist Health System Sunbelt Healthcare
Ascension Health
Baptist Health South Florida
Broward Health
Florida Hospital Heartland
HCA
Mount Sinai Medical Center of Florida
Northwest Medical Center
South Broward Hospital District
Tenet Healthcare

HISTORICAL FINANCIALS
Company Type: Private

Income Statement				FYE: June 30
	REVENUE ($ mil.)	NET INCOME ($ mil.)	NET PROFIT MARGIN	EMPLOYEES
06/18	470	8	1.9%	2,300
06/15	24	0	4.0%	—
06/14	20	(0)	—	—
Annual Growth	117.8%	—	—	—

HOME PROPERTIES, LIMITED PARTNERSHIP

LOCATIONS

HQ: HOME PROPERTIES, LIMITED PARTNERSHIP
850 CLINTON SQ, ROCHESTER, NY 146041730
Phone: 585 546-4900
Web: WWW.HOMEPROPERTIES.COM

HISTORICAL FINANCIALS
Company Type: Private

Income Statement				FYE: December 31
	ASSETS ($ mil.)	NET INCOME ($ mil.)	INCOME AS % OF ASSETS	EMPLOYEES
12/07	3,216	61	1.9%	1,000
12/06	3,240	110	3.4%	—
12/05	2,977	26	0.9%	—
12/01	1,346	2	0.2%	—
Annual Growth	15.6%	75.1%	—	—

2007 Year-End Financials

Return on assets: 1.9%   Sales ($ mil): 505
Return on equity: 9.2%

HOOSIER ENERGY RURAL ELECTRIC COOPERATIVE INC.

Who's yer daddy? In terms of providing electricity for many Indianans (and some residents of Illinois) that would be Hoosier Energy Rural Electric Cooperative which provides wholesale electric power to 18 member distribution cooperatives in 59 central and southern Indiana counties and 11 counties in southeastern Illinois. These electric cooperatives serve 300000 consumers (650000 residents businesses industries and farms) in a 18000 sq. ml. service area. Hoosier Energy operates six power plants and a 1720-mile transmission system and maintains the Tuttle Creek Reservoir in Southwest Indiana. Hoosier Energy is part of the Touchstone Energy network of electric cooperatives.

Operations

Hoosier Energy operates coal- natural gas- and renewable energy-generation plants. It delivers electricity via a 1720-mile transmission network including 21 major substations and more than 350 delivery points.

Geographic Reach

The company delivers power to member distribution cooperatives in central and southern Indiana and southeastern Illinois.

Financial Performance

In 2013 the power coop's revenues increased by 3% due to higher member revenues and increased sales of electricity. Net income grew by 1% as the result of higher revenues and slight decrease in maintenance costs.

Strategy

To advance its push for more renewable sources Hoosier Energy is pursuing cost-effective generating projects and supply contracts including the Clark-Floyd Landfill Methane Generation plant which has four landfill/coal bed methane projects and which has purchased power agreements for wind and hydropower. These measures are expected to provide 7% of member energy sales annually.

Its recent capital projects include a $400 million multi-year upgrade of the Merom Station investing $18 million in power delivery projects to support growth and reliability and continuing progress toward renewable energy goals with the commercial operation of the Osprey Point coalbed methane plant and the Livingston landfill-methane plant.

Company Background

In 2011 the coop was operating a 2.5 MW landfill methane generation facility in addition to buying 25 MW of wind energy.

Expanding its geographic coverage in 2011 Hoosier Energy began to supply power to the Wayne-White Counties Electric Cooperative when that coop's contract with an independent power supplier ended. The distribution coop serves 13500 residential farm and business consumers in 11 counties in southeastern Illinois.

Hoosier Energy was formed in 1948 as part of the nationwide rural electrification drive initiated by the Roosevelt administration in the 1930s.

EXECUTIVES

Vice President Strategic Business And Diversity Relations, Larry Cox
Auditors: DELOITTE & TOUCHE LLP INDIAN

LOCATIONS

HQ: HOOSIER ENERGY RURAL ELECTRIC COOPERATIVE INC.
2501 S COOPERATIVE WAY, BLOOMINGTON, IN 474035175
Phone: 812 876-2021
Web: WWW.HOOSIERENERGY.COM

PRODUCTS/OPERATIONS

2012 Sales

	$ mil.	% of total
Members	532	82
Nonmembers	115	18
Other	0	-
Total	**647**	**100**

Member Cooperatives

Member Cooperatives
Bartholomew County REMC
Clark County REMC
Decatur County REMC
Daviess-Martin County REMC
Dubois REC Inc.
Harrison REMC
Henry County REMC
Jackson County REMC
Johnson County REMC
Orange County REMC
RushShelby Energy
South Central Indiana REMC
Southeastern Indiana REMC
Southern Indiana Power
Utilities District of Western Indiana REMC
Wayne-White Counties Electric Cooperative
WIN Energy REMC
Whitewater Valley REMC

COMPETITORS

| IPALCO Enterprises | Indiana Municipal |
| Indiana Michigan Power | Power Agency |

HISTORICAL FINANCIALS
Company Type: Private

Income Statement				FYE: December 31
	REVENUE ($ mil.)	NET INCOME ($ mil.)	NET PROFIT MARGIN	EMPLOYEES
12/12	647	27	4.3%	475
12/11	649	30	4.7%	—
12/09	575	16	2.9%	—
Annual Growth	**4.1%**	**18.9%**	—	—

2012 Year-End Financials

Return on assets: 1.6%   Cash ($ mil.): 50
Return on equity: 11.0%
Current ratio: 1.50

HORRY COUNTY SCHOOL DISTRICT

EXECUTIVES

Supt, Dr Rick Maxey
Accounting Staff, Patsy Johnson
Health Professional, Marti Graves
Case Manager, Hope Lupo
Office Assistant, Jennifer Bessant
Athletics Programs Coordinator, Jonathan Carter
Case Management Specialist, Josue Valentin
Nutrition Manager, Kimberly Johnson
Director, Kristin Wilson
Manager, Larry Hamilton
School Resource Officer Horry, Lcpl Anderson
Auditors: MCGREGOR & COMPANY LLP COLUM

LOCATIONS

HQ: HORRY COUNTY SCHOOL DISTRICT
335 FOUR MILE RD, CONWAY, SC 295264506
Phone: 843 488-6700
Web: WWW.HORRYCOUNTYSCHOOLS.NET

HISTORICAL FINANCIALS
Company Type: Private

Income Statement				FYE: June 30
	REVENUE ($ mil.)	NET INCOME ($ mil.)	NET PROFIT MARGIN	EMPLOYEES
06/18	548	(42)	—	5,000
06/17	520	(140)	—	—
06/16	494	218	44.2%	—
06/15	472	9	2.0%	—
Annual Growth	**5.1%**	—	—	—

2018 Year-End Financials

Return on assets: (-3.2%)   Cash ($ mil.): 271
Return on equity: —
Current ratio: —

HOSPITAL OF THE UNIVERSITY OF PENNSYLVANIA

EXECUTIVES

Director, Pamela Mack-Brooks
Coordinator, Alvaro Talavera
Coordinator, Cherlyn Bynum
Coordinator, Denise Amaro
Coordinator, Pete Caldwell
Assistant Professor, Rajat Deo
Assistant Professor, Dennis Hadjiliadis
Nurse Practitioner, Diana Van Houten
Assistant Professor, Lachlan Smith
Coordinator, Barbara Lopez
Staff, Diane Frain

LOCATIONS

HQ: HOSPITAL OF THE UNIVERSITY OF PENNSYLVANIA
3400 SPRUCE ST OFC, PHILADELPHIA, PA 191044208
Phone: 215 301-3776
Web: WWW.PENNMEDICINE.ORG

HISTORICAL FINANCIALS
Company Type: Private

Income Statement				FYE: June 30
	REVENUE ($ mil.)	NET INCOME ($ mil.)	NET PROFIT MARGIN	EMPLOYEES
06/16	2,236	283	12.7%	25
06/15	2,164	320	14.8%	—
Annual Growth	**3.3%**	**(11.5%)**	—	—

2016 Year-End Financials

Return on assets: 9.3%   Cash ($ mil.): 1,091
Return on equity: 13.2%
Current ratio: 9.90

HOUCHENS INDUSTRIES, INC.

Houchens Industries is a supermarket of businesses as well as an operator of supermarkets. The diversified company runs some 400 retail grocery convenience and neighborhood markets across the US. That includes more than 180 conventional supermarkets under the Houchens Food Giant IGA Piggly Wiggly Buehler Foods and Mad Butcher banners. It hass more than 200 Save-A-Lot discount grocery stores in a dozen states that offer limited selections and cover 15000 sq. ft. or less. Outside the grocery store Houchens operates Cohen's Fashion Optical franchise stores and several Sheldon's Express Pharmacy stores. Other businesses include construction financial services real estate restaurants and recycling. Houchens is 100%-owned by its employees.

Operations

Houchens Industries has amassed a diverse portfolio of more than 35 businesses over the years through acquisitions. Beyond the grocery segment Houchen also serves customers in the construction insurance wealth management technology and healthcare industries.

Houchens is the largest franchisee of limited-assortment Save-A-Lot stores in the US. (Grocery retailer and wholesaler SUPERVALU is the parent company of Save-A-Lot.) The company's manufacturing businesses include Stephens Pipe & Steel a leading maker and distributor of fence materials. Southern Recycling collects and processes metals paper glass and plastics. The company also franchises Sonic and Subway quick-serve restaurants. It also operates the Taco Del Mar restaurant chain and Price Less Foods which sells groceries at cost plus 10%.

Geographic Reach

Based in Kentucky Houchens Industries operates grocery stores in Alabama Arkansas Florida Georgia Indiana Illinois Kentucky Mississippi Missouri Tennessee and Virginia. Its diverse other businesses are active almost every US state and about 30 other countries worldwide.

Strategy

Houchens Industries looks to buy assets that have sound management and a history of providing good cash flow that can be bought at a reasonable price. Recent acquisitions include the 14-store family-run White's Fresh Foods chain which operates grocery stores in Tennessee and Virginia and the Bowling Green Kentucky-based two-store drug retailer Sheldon's Express Pharmacy thereby expanding into the drugstore business. Houchens plans to leverage the acquisition to create a regional drugstore chain. The Whites purchase followed the acquisition of Chicago-based Tampico Beverages a maker of refrigerated juice drinks and punches sold in more than 36 countries for an undisclosed amount. Tampico supplies beverages to grocery and convenience stores as well as quick-serve restaurants.

In new version of IGA stores Houchens has made convenience a watchword. The IGA Crossroads brand is set up to help customers get in and out quickly. The stores also contain quick service restaurants. In those and other stores Houchens added to the sandwich mix available bringing Which Wich into its lineup joining Schlotzsky's and Subway.

Company Background

Founded by Ervin Houchens as BG Wholesale in rural Kentucky in 1917 Houchens has been owned by its employees since 1988.

EXECUTIVES

Chairman And Ceo, James (Jimmie) Gipson
President, Spencer A. Coates
Ceo Tampico Beverages, Scott Miller
Cfo, Gordon Minter
President Cohen's Fashion Optical, Bob Cohen
President Hitcents.com, Chris Mills
President And Ceo Food Giant Supermarkets, Ron Watkins

LOCATIONS

HQ: HOUCHENS INDUSTRIES, INC.
700 CHURCH ST, BOWLING GREEN, KY 421011816
Phone: 270 843-3252
Web: WWW.HOUCHENSINDUSTRIES.COM

PRODUCTS/OPERATIONS

Selected Operations

American Sun Systems (tanning salon supplier)
Blake Hart Taylor & Wiseman (insurance)
Buehler's Buy Low (grocery retail)
Cohen's Fashion Optical (optical stores)
Food Giant (grocery retail)
Hilliard Lyons (financial services)
Houchens Markets (grocery retail)
IGA (licensed grocery retail)
Insurance Specialists (insurance)
Jr. Food Stores (convenience stores)
Price Less Foods (grocery retail)
Save-A-Lot (licensed grocery retail)
Scotty's (asphalt paving)
Sheldon's Express Pharmacy (drugstores)
Southern Recycling Inc. (recycling)
Stewart-Richey Construction Inc. (construction management)
Taco Del Mar (fast-food)
Tampico (juice)
TS Trucking (hauling)
Van Meter Insurance (insurance benefits)
White's Fresh Foods (grocery retail)

COMPETITORS

7-Eleven	Meijer
ALDI	Mott's
Ameriprise	Nestlé
CVS	Ocean Spray
Charles Schwab	Odwalla
Citigroup	Old Orchard
Citrus World	Raymond James
Cumberland Farms	Financial
Dole Food	Rite Aid
Dr Pepper Snapple	Sheetz
Group	Southeastern Grocers
E*TRADE Financial	Sunkist
E. W. James	Sunny Delight
Edward D. Jones	TD Ameritrade
FMR	Thorntons Inc.
Faygo	Tree Top
Goya	Tropicana
John Hancock Financial	Visionworks of America
Services	Wal-Mart
Jugos del Valle USA	Walgreen
K-VA-T Food Stores	Weis Markets
Kroger	Welch's
Luxottica Retail	

HISTORICAL FINANCIALS

Company Type: Private

Income Statement				FYE: September 29
	ASSETS ($ mil.)	NET INCOME ($ mil.)	INCOME AS % OF ASSETS	EMPLOYEES
09/18*	1,773	29	1.7%	16,000
10/16	1,976	104	5.3%	—
10/15	2,014	99	5.0%	—
Annual Growth	(4.2%)	(33.4%)	—	—

*Fiscal year change

2018 Year-End Financials

Return on assets: 1.7%   Sales ($ mil): 2,613
Return on equity: 2.3%

HOUSTON INDEPENDENT SCHOOL DISTRICT

EXECUTIVES

Supt, Grenita Lathan
Cfo, Melinda Garrett
SEC-Treas, Diana Davila
Int Cao, Yolanda Rodriguez
Accounting Staff, Glenn Reed
Accounting Staff, Stephanie Matlock
Executive Officer, Manuel Rodriguez
Accounting Staff, David Clardy
Grade Teacher, Anita Atwood
Special Education Teacher, Carol Franklin
Secretary, Chelsi Humes
Auditors: WEAVER AND TIDWELL LLP HOUSTO

LOCATIONS

HQ: HOUSTON INDEPENDENT SCHOOL DISTRICT
4400 W 18TH ST, HOUSTON, TX 770928501
Phone: 713 556-6000
Web: WWW.HOUSTONISD.ORG

HISTORICAL FINANCIALS

Company Type: Private

Income Statement				FYE: June 30
	REVENUE ($ mil.)	NET INCOME ($ mil.)	NET PROFIT MARGIN	EMPLOYEES
06/18	2,695	(250)	—	22,440
06/17	2,329	(39)	—	—
06/16	2,333	266	11.4%	—
06/13	1,876	117	6.3%	—
Annual Growth	7.5%	—	—	—

2018 Year-End Financials

Return on assets: (-3.7%)   Cash ($ mil.): 7
Return on equity: (-22.3%)
Current ratio: —

HOUSTON METHODIST HOSPITAL

EXECUTIVES

Ceo, Marc L Boom
Chm*, Ewing Werlein Jr
Treas*, Carlton E Baucum
SEC*, Gregory V Nelson
Manager, Enrica De Rosa
Information Specialist, Larry Tomazinis
Director, Armand Stansel
Director, Ken Lawson
Vice President, Steve Burns
Network, Brian Simon
Associate Research Member, David Beers

LOCATIONS

HQ: HOUSTON METHODIST HOSPITAL
1213 HERMANN DR STE 300, HOUSTON, TX 770046671
Phone: 713 790-3311
Web: WWW.HOUSTONMETHODIST.ORG

HISTORICAL FINANCIALS

Company Type: Private

Income Statement				FYE: December 31
	REVENUE ($ mil.)	NET INCOME ($ mil.)	NET PROFIT MARGIN	EMPLOYEES
12/17	3,887	681	17.5%	656
12/16	3,746	338	9.0%	—
Annual Growth	3.8%	101.7%	—	—

2017 Year-End Financials

Return on assets: 7.8%   Cash ($ mil.): 102
Return on equity: 10.8%
Current ratio: 1.10

HPS LLC

EXECUTIVES

Mng MBR, Matt Thompson
Cfo-MBR*, Thomas J La Pres
Tres-MBR*, Joseph Schodde
Treas-MBR*, Dwith Gascho
Information Technology Manager, Brian McKinley
Customer Representativ, Tracy Keeler
Regional Manager, Jami Markle
Customer, Anna Hutchinson
Regional Sales Manager, Brian Smith
Computer Support Technician, Eric Daly
Administrative Assistant, Amy McKinley
Auditors: MEYNARD TOLMAN & VENLET PC

LOCATIONS

HQ: HPS LLC
  3275 N M 37 HWY, MIDDLEVILLE, MI 493339126
Phone: 269 795-3308
Web: WWW.HPSGPO.COM

HISTORICAL FINANCIALS
Company Type: Private

Income Statement				FYE: June 30
	REVENUE ($ mil.)	NET INCOME ($ mil.)	NET PROFIT MARGIN	EMPLOYEES
06/18	782	0	0.1%	38
06/16	1,032	0	0.1%	—
06/15	960	0	0.1%	—
06/14	862	0	0.1%	—
Annual Growth	(2.4%)	2.0%	—	—

2018 Year-End Financials
Return on assets: 5.6%   Cash ($ mil.): 4
Return on equity: 7.6%
Current ratio: 1.90

HUMAX USA, INC

Humax USA prefers to connectÂ with its customers through its products. The companyÂ develops and manufacturesÂ flat-panel TV sets and digital set-top boxes for satellite cable and terrestrial connections.Â Humax USA is theÂ US-based subsidiary of Korean consumer electronics manufacturing firm Humax Co. which was founded in 1989.Â The brand has become one of the most popular worldwide among set-top boxes. Humax's products are available in more than 90 countriesÂ as well asÂ in the US. The company primarily serves customers in Asia and Europe.

EXECUTIVES

Ceo, Keehyuk Sung
Corp SEC*, Chong Hong
Manager, Sally Yeo

LOCATIONS

HQ: HUMAX USA, INC
  15641 RED HILL AVE # 150, TUSTIN, CA 927807323
Phone: 714 389-1924

COMPETITORS

DIRECTV   Sony USA
SANYO   Tivo Solutions
Samsung Electronics

Income Statement				FYE: December 31
	REVENUE ($ mil.)	NET INCOME ($ mil.)	NET PROFIT MARGIN	EMPLOYEES
12/17	482	(4)	—	29
12/16	360	(0)	—	—
12/15	373	0	0.1%	—
12/14	448	0	0.1%	—
Annual Growth	2.5%	—	—	—

2017 Year-End Financials
Return on assets: (-1.6%)   Cash ($ mil.): 3
Return on equity: (-97.8%)
Current ratio: 1.00

HUMBLE INDEPENDENT SCHOOL DISTRICT

EXECUTIVES

Supt, Guy M Sconzo
Human Resources Manager, Lorrie Dabbs
Nurse, Lorraine Cano
Psychologist, Carol Reiner
Public Relations Director, Robin McAdams
Administrative Assistant, Ken Hair
Maintenance Director, Kenny Kendrick
Coordinator, Sukari Stredit-Thomas
Network Specialist, Derek Nguyen
Supervisor Records and Documen, Derinda Williams
Coordinator, Diane Henley
Auditors: WHITLEY PENN LLP HOUSTON TEX

LOCATIONS

HQ: HUMBLE INDEPENDENT SCHOOL DISTRICT
  20200 EASTWAY VILLAGE DR, HUMBLE, TX 773382405
Phone: 281 641-1000
Web: WWW.HUMBLEISD.NET

HISTORICAL FINANCIALS
Company Type: Private

Income Statement				FYE: June 30
	REVENUE ($ mil.)	NET INCOME ($ mil.)	NET PROFIT MARGIN	EMPLOYEES
06/18	490	(67)	—	5,000
06/17	462	(11)	—	—
06/16	458	11	2.4%	—
06/13	365	(8)	—	—
Annual Growth	6.1%	—	—	—

HUNTER ROBERTS CONSTRUCTION GROUP LLC

EXECUTIVES

Mbr-Pres-Ceo, James C McKenna
Sr V Pres*, John Alicandri
Executive Vice President*, Kevin Barrett
V Pres*, Mark Lamble
V Pres*, Alex Craig
V Pres*, Dan Dirscherl
Vice President*, Brian Aronne
V Pres-Dir of Purchasing*, Tim Dillon
Exec V Pres-Gen Mgr NY*, Paul Andersen
Vp of Finance*, Robert Belitz
V Pres*, Chuck Petrusky
Auditors: GRASSI & CO JERICHO NEW YOR

LOCATIONS

HQ: HUNTER ROBERTS CONSTRUCTION GROUP LLC
  55 WATER ST FL 51, NEW YORK, NY 100413201
Phone: 212 321-6800
Web: WWW.HRCG.COM

HISTORICAL FINANCIALS
Company Type: Private

Income Statement				FYE: December 31
	REVENUE ($ mil.)	NET INCOME ($ mil.)	NET PROFIT MARGIN	EMPLOYEES
12/13	762	3	0.4%	260
12/12	706	1	0.2%	—
12/10	458	7	1.7%	—
Annual Growth	18.4%	(26.8%)	—	—

2013 Year-End Financials
Return on assets: 1.4%   Cash ($ mil.): 61
Return on equity: 6.4%
Current ratio: 1.20

HUNTINGTON HOSPITAL

LOCATIONS

HQ: HUNTINGTON HOSPITAL
  100 W CALIFORNIA BLVD, PASADENA, CA 911053010
Phone: 626 397-5000
Web: WWW.HUNTINGTONHOSPITAL.ORG

HISTORICAL FINANCIALS
Company Type: Private

Income Statement				FYE: December 31
	REVENUE ($ mil.)	NET INCOME ($ mil.)	NET PROFIT MARGIN	EMPLOYEES
12/17	654	15	2.3%	3,500
12/16	646	6	0.9%	—
12/15	551	3	0.7%	—
12/14	513	1	0.4%	—
Annual Growth	8.4%	102.0%	—	—

2017 Year-End Financials
Return on assets: 1.7%   Cash ($ mil.): 11
Return on equity: 2.6%
Current ratio: 3.30

HUNTSVILLE HOSPITAL HEALTH SYSTEM

EXECUTIVES

Ceo, David Spillers
Coo, Jeff Samz

LOCATIONS

HQ: HUNTSVILLE HOSPITAL HEALTH SYSTEM
101 SIVLEY RD SW, HUNTSVILLE, AL 358014470
Phone: 256 265-1000
Web: WWW.HUNTSVILLEHOSPITAL.ORG

HISTORICAL FINANCIALS

Company Type: Private

Income Statement				FYE: June 30
	REVENUE ($ mil.)	NET INCOME ($ mil.)	NET PROFIT MARGIN	EMPLOYEES
06/16	864	98	11.4%	28
06/15	799	100	12.6%	—
Annual Growth	8.1%	(2.4%)		

2016 Year-End Financials

Return on assets: 7.0%   Cash ($ mil.): 186
Return on equity: 9.7%
Current ratio: 2.10

HUNTSVILLE UTILITIES

EXECUTIVES

Pres, William C Pippin
Staff, Mike Coranet
Vice President, Tim McKee

LOCATIONS

HQ: HUNTSVILLE UTILITIES
112 SPRAGINS ST NW, HUNTSVILLE, AL 358014902
Phone: 256 535-1200
Web: WWW.HSVUTIL.ORG

HISTORICAL FINANCIALS

Company Type: Private

Income Statement				FYE: September 30
	REVENUE ($ mil.)	NET INCOME ($ mil.)	NET PROFIT MARGIN	EMPLOYEES
09/11	493	10	2.1%	634
09/10	456	5	1.3%	—
09/09	451	7	1.6%	—
Annual Growth	4.6%	22.5%		

2011 Year-End Financials

Return on assets: 3.2%   Cash ($ mil.): 11
Return on equity: 4.5%
Current ratio: 1.40

HURON HEALTH CARE CENTER, INC

EXECUTIVES

Admin, Amy Donaldson
Minimum Data Set Coordinator, Shelly Shaffer

LOCATIONS

HQ: HURON HEALTH CARE CENTER, INC
1920 CLEVELAND RD W, HURON, OH 448391211
Phone: 419 433-4990
Web: WWW.ADMIRALS-POINTE.NET

HISTORICAL FINANCIALS

Company Type: Private

Income Statement				FYE: December 31
	REVENUE ($ mil.)	NET INCOME ($ mil.)	NET PROFIT MARGIN	EMPLOYEES
12/09	584	58	10.0%	125
12/98	3	0	—	—
12/97	3	3	97.8%	—
12/96	3	0	—	—
Annual Growth	48.0%	—	—	—

2009 Year-End Financials

Return on assets: 999.9%   Cash ($ mil.): —
Return on equity: 999.9%
Current ratio: 2.20

HY-VEE, INC.

Give Hy-Vee a high five for being one of the largest privately owned US supermarket chains despite serving some modestly sized towns in the Midwest. The company runs some 260 stores in eight Midwestern states. The company's brands include Hy-Vee Hy-Vee Select That's Smart! Baking Stone Bread and Full Circle among others. It distributes products to its stores through several subsidiaries including Lomar Distributing (specialty foods) Perishable Distributors of Iowa (fresh foods) and Florist Distribution (flowers). Other activities include construction and specialty pharmacies. Charles Hyde and David Vredenburg founded the employee-owned firm in 1930. It takes its name from a combination of its founders' names.

Strategy

Looking to leverage the large amount of traffic its website receives in 2018 Hy-Vee partnered with Australian advertising company to insert adverts into search results on its website. The specific nature of its website — buying food and drink — means Hy-Vee has access to a very specific customer segment providing advertisers with a high-value prospect. The move opens up a new revenue stream and monetizes unused screen real estate.

EXECUTIVES

V Pres, Dennis Ausenhus
Assistant Vp Real Estate, David Bailie
Evp And Chief Merchandising Officer, Jon S. Wendel
Chairman President And Ceo, Randy Edeker
Evp And Chief Customer Officer, Sheila Laing
Evp Cfo And Treasurer, Mike Skokan
Vice Chairman Evp And Chief Administrative Officer, Andy McCann
Evp Western Region, Brett Bremser

Evp And Coo, Jay Marshall
Evp Eastern Region, Darren Baty
Vice President Retail Information Technology, Julie Proffitt
Assistant Vice President Operations, Jim Watters
Senior Vice President And Chief Health Officer, Kristin Williams
Pharmacy Manager, Marrianne Ryno
Assistant Vice President Sec, Angie Rosenberger
Assistant Vice President Operations, Rob Eslick
Assistant Vice President Bakery Operations, Tony Byington
Group Vice President Equipment Purchasing, Mark Brauer
Assistant Vice President Engineering And Construction, Dave Kozak
Assistant Vice President Meat Operations, Kenan Judge
Assistant Vice President For Marketing Projects, Erin Bailey
Assistant Vice President Logistics, Jody Sandy
Assistant Vice President, Tony Kaska
Assistant Vice President Western Region, Pat Hensley
Vice President Special Projects, Gary Goodhall
Vice President Government Relations, Noreen Otto
Assistant Vice President Store Setup, Mark Millsap
Vice President Distribution, Tod Hockenson
Vice President Information Technology Operation, Cevin Anderson
Assisant Vice President, Chuck Seaman
Vice President, Karl Kruse
Assistant Vice President Information Technology Operations, Travis Hoover
Assistant Vice President Risk Management, Janet Crocker
Group Vice President Information Technology, Tom Settle
Assistant Vice President, Marshall Sanders
Avp Produce Operations, Mike Orf
Vice President, Aaron Wiese
Assistant Vice President Risk Management, John Brummit
Assistant Vice President Information Technology Projects, Angie Dachenbach
Pharmacy Manager, Jeff Jorgensen
Pharmacy Manager, Brad Moriarty
Pharmacy Manager, Heather Yennie
Vice President Business Development, Kevin Sherlock
Vice President Of Real Estate, Pete Hosch
Vice President Of Human Resources, Karen Boriskey
Assisant Treasurer, Jeff Pierce
Secretary To Greg Frampton, Stacey Groff
Assistant Secretary, Michael Jurgens
Senior Vice President Secretary And General Counsel, Steve Meyer

LOCATIONS

HQ: HY-VEE, INC.
5820 WESTOWN PKWY, WEST DES MOINES, IA 502668223
Phone: 515 267-2800
Web: WWW.HY-VEE.COM

PRODUCTS/OPERATIONS

Selected Subsidiaries

D & D Foods Inc. (salads dips and meats)
Florist Distributing Inc. (flowers plants and florist supplies)
Hy-Vee Construction L.C. (construction)
Hy-Vee Pharmacy Solutions (specialty pharmacy services)
Hy-Vee Weitz Construction L.C. (construction)
Lomar Distributing Inc. (specialty foods)
Midwest Heritage Bank FSB (banking)
Perishable Distributors of Iowa Ltd. (meat fish seafood and ice cream)

COMPETITORS

ALDI	Niemann Foods
Associated Wholesale Grocers	Rite Aid
	Roundy's
Ball's Food	SUPERVALU
CVS	Save-A-Lot Food Stores
Casey's General Stores	Target Corporation
Fareway Stores	Wal-Mart
Kmart	Walgreen
Kroger	

HISTORICAL FINANCIALS
Company Type: Private

Income Statement   FYE: September 30

	REVENUE ($ mil.)	NET INCOME ($ mil.)	NET PROFIT MARGIN	EMPLOYEES
09/18*	10,290	0	—	83,000
12/16	9,842	0	—	—
09/13	8,014	0	—	—
Annual Growth	5.1%			

*Fiscal year change

HYUNDAI TRANSYS GEORGIA POWERTRAIN, INC.

EXECUTIVES

Ceo, Sam Ho Cha
SEC*, Taeeuk Kim
Cfo*, Changyoung Kim
Purchasing Agent, Darren Wiker
Fin & Acct Specialist, Do Hyun Lee
Human Resources, Stephanie Moore
Machining Leader, Jason Aikens
Assistant Manager, Jin Kwak
Associate Professor, Carmello Chris
Senior Specialist J Gen Ral AF, Semin Chun
Manager, Yoosung Jung
Auditors: PK LLP OPELIKA ALABAMA

LOCATIONS

HQ: HYUNDAI TRANSYS GEORGIA POWERTRAIN, INC.
6801 KIA PKWY, WEST POINT, GA 318334937
Phone: 706 902-6800

HISTORICAL FINANCIALS
Company Type: Private

Income Statement   FYE: December 31

	REVENUE ($ mil.)	NET INCOME ($ mil.)	NET PROFIT MARGIN	EMPLOYEES
12/16	1,134	7	0.6%	500
12/15	1,230	12	1.0%	—
12/14	1,250	11	0.9%	—
12/13	1,220	11	0.9%	—
Annual Growth	(2.4%)	(14.3%)	—	—

2016 Year-End Financials
Return on assets: 2.5%   Cash ($ mil.): 22
Return on equity: 6.0%
Current ratio: 1.70

ICAHN SCHOOL OF MEDICINE AT MOUNT SINAI

EXECUTIVES

Ceo, Ken Davis
Dean*, Dennis Charney
Cfo*, Stephen Harvey
Director of Geriatric Srvs, Albert Siu
Nurse Practitioner, Cynthia Esrig
Anesthesiology, Daniel Gainsburg
Assistant Clinical Professor O, Gaetano Bello
Senior Vice President, Jane Maksoud
Director of Information Techno, Kenny Chu
Director of Breast, Laurie Margolies
Rn Director, Maria Vezina
Auditors: ERNST & YOUNG US LLP NEW YORK

LOCATIONS

HQ: ICAHN SCHOOL OF MEDICINE AT MOUNT SINAI
1 GUSTAVE L LEVY PL, NEW YORK, NY 100296504
Phone: 212 241-6500
Web: WWW.MOUNTSINAI.ORG

HISTORICAL FINANCIALS
Company Type: Private

Income Statement   FYE: December 31

	REVENUE ($ mil.)	NET INCOME ($ mil.)	NET PROFIT MARGIN	EMPLOYEES
12/17	2,843	272	9.6%	7,000
12/13	1,625	89	5.5%	—
12/12	1,577	119	7.6%	—
12/11	1,427	(15)	—	—
Annual Growth	12.2%	—	—	—

2017 Year-End Financials
Return on assets: 6.6%   Cash ($ mil.): 681
Return on equity: 13.5%
Current ratio: 0.80

ICREST INTERNATIONAL LLC

EXECUTIVES

Mng MBR, Naoki Ibata
Evp Chief Strategic Officer, Naoti Tsoshima
Cfo, James Katayama
Board of Director, Makoto Sawanoi
Asst Acct Mgr, Christine Tokunaga
Auditors: DELOITTE & TOUCHE LLP LOS AN

LOCATIONS

HQ: ICREST INTERNATIONAL LLC
200 N PACIFIC COAST HWY # 925, EL SEGUNDO, CA 902454340
Phone: 310 760-3200

HISTORICAL FINANCIALS
Company Type: Private

Income Statement   FYE: March 31

	REVENUE ($ mil.)	NET INCOME ($ mil.)	NET PROFIT MARGIN	EMPLOYEES
03/17	516	9	1.9%	35
03/13*	433	8	1.9%	—
12/10	309	9	3.0%	—
12/09	1,396	0	—	—
Annual Growth	(13.2%)	715.2%	—	—

*Fiscal year change

2017 Year-End Financials
Return on assets: 19.4%   Cash ($ mil.): 4
Return on equity: 32.7%
Current ratio: 2.20

IDEMIA IDENTITY & SECURITY USA LLC

MorphoTrust USA builds trust with its credentials and biometrics-based recognition systems. MorphoTrust provides driver's licenses passports voter and other government and corporate-issued IDs as well as related data verification systems. Its biometrics products include face finger and iris recognition scanners. The company which operates in all 50 states serves US federal state and local governments and commercial entities; government contracts represent about 95% of revenues. In addition to its contract-based services MorphoTrust operates a network of more than 1200 ID service centers. It is a subsidiary of Paris-based aerospace components maker SAFRAN.

Geographic Reach
MorphoTrust has 1100 service centers located in Illinois Iowa Indiana Minnesota Massachusetts New Jersey Tennessee Virginia and the District of Columbia.

Sales and Marketing
MorphoTrust caters to more than 3 million customers each year including the Department of Defense the State Department and the Department of Homeland Security.

Financial Performance
The company claims to generate $400 million in annual revenue.

Strategy
MorphoTrust has enjoyed growth from its US federal government activities primarily its FBI products and services involving universal enrollment and weapons permits. However like most companies servicing the public sector it is at the mercy of its clients' budgetary cuts and restrictions.

In 2014 the company won new contracts to provide fingerprint-based background checks for the Massachusetts Executive Office of Public Safety and Security the New Jersey Department of Public Safety the Division of State Police and fingerprint channeling services in Nevada for the Department of Public Safety. It believes these agreements could yield up to $25 million in revenue over the next six years.

EXECUTIVES

Ceo, Robert A. (Bob) Eckel
Vice President, Ben Mallen

LOCATIONS

HQ: IDEMIA IDENTITY & SECURITY USA LLC
11951 FREEDOM DR FL 18, RESTON, VA 201905640
Phone: 978 215-2400

PRODUCTS/OPERATIONS

Selected Products and Services
Biometric-based access control to buildings and
restricted areas
Biometric recognition technologies that accurately
identify individuals
Enrollment centers for processing pre-employment
background checks
Secure credentials that serve as proof of identity
Solving critical issues facing US intelligence and
national security

COMPETITORS

3M Cogent	Edentify
Acsys Biometrics	Entrust DataCard
Allied Security	ImageWare Systems
Innovations	SecuGen
CSSN	Security First
Cross Match	Ultra-Scan
Technologies	Verint Systems
De La Rue	

HISTORICAL FINANCIALS

Company Type: Private

Income Statement				FYE: December 31
	REVENUE ($ mil.)	NET INCOME ($ mil.)	NET PROFIT MARGIN	EMPLOYEES
12/16	708	(7)	—	1,000
12/15	604	0	—	
Annual Growth	17.1%	—	—	—

2016 Year-End Financials
Return on assets: (-0.5%)
Return on equity: (-0.7%)   Cash ($ mil.): 73
Current ratio: 1.70

IHC HEALTH SERVICES, INC.

EXECUTIVES

Pres-Ceo, William Nelson
Svp-Cfo, Bert Zimmerli
V Pres-Pres, Charles Sorenson
Chief Staff, Steven Vannorman
Surgery Director, Brent Hardy
Food Manager, Brent Lamoreaux
Manager Plant Operations, George McGee
Purchasing Agent, Don Cannon
Biomedical Engineer, Bryan White
Womens Health Director, Kenzie Peterson
Family Practitioner, Michael Cascio
Auditors: KPMG LLP SALT LAKE CITY UT

LOCATIONS

HQ: IHC HEALTH SERVICES, INC.
1380 E MEDICAL CENTER DR, ST GEORGE, UT
847902123
Phone: 435 251-2992
Web: WWW.SELECTHEALTH.ORG

HISTORICAL FINANCIALS

Company Type: Private

Income Statement				FYE: December 31
	REVENUE ($ mil.)	NET INCOME ($ mil.)	NET PROFIT MARGIN	EMPLOYEES
12/18	6,037	317	5.3%	4,000
12/17	5,483	884	16.1%	—
12/16	5,275	564	10.7%	—
12/14	394	55	14.2%	—
Annual Growth	97.8%	54.3%	—	—

2018 Year-End Financials
Return on assets: 2.7%
Return on equity: 4.5%   Cash ($ mil.): 658
Current ratio: 1.60

ILWU-PMA WELFARE TRUST

EXECUTIVES

Prin, Michael Ouchida
Auditors: PRICEWATERHOUSECOOPERS LLP WA

LOCATIONS

HQ: ILWU-PMA WELFARE TRUST
1188 FRANKLIN ST STE 101, SAN FRANCISCO, CA
941096852
Phone: 415 673-8500
Web: WWW.ILWU.ORG

HISTORICAL FINANCIALS

Company Type: Private

Income Statement				FYE: June 30
	REVENUE ($ mil.)	NET INCOME ($ mil.)	NET PROFIT MARGIN	EMPLOYEES
06/17	738	5	0.8%	3
06/15	676	27	4.1%	—
06/14	624	(21)	—	—
06/10	585	18	3.1%	—
Annual Growth	3.4%	(15.5%)	—	—

2017 Year-End Financials
Return on assets: 3.0%
Return on equity: 6.5%   Cash ($ mil.): 3
Current ratio: 1.60

IMMIXGROUP, INC.

immixGroup offers a blend of information technology (IT) business development and consulting
services to help tech firms do business with federal
state and local government agencies. Through its
technology sales division the company is a hardware and software reseller for such manufacturers
as IBM Oracle and Hewlett-Packard. It also offers
customized public sector channel development
programs outsourced government contract management and IT consulting and execution. Other
services include market intelligence sales training
and recruiting. immixGroup serves more than 250
tech manufacturers and its government partner
network includes more than 600 resellers systems

integrators and other providers. Arrow Electronics
acquired immixGroup in 2015.

Change in Company Type
Arrow Electronics completed the acquisition of
immixGroup in March 2015. The purchase enables
Arrow to expand its growing IT services business
to the government sector. For immixGroup the
deal puts it in the mix of resources deploye by a
company that sits in the Fortune 150.

Operations
The company operates two subsidiaries: EC
America Inc. and immixTechnology Inc.

Sales and Marketing
immixGroup sells its services with software
providers as partners including Appian Apica
Aruba A10 Networks and Adaptive. Its customers
include federal agencies state governments and
agencies and municipalities. Recent customers are
the Texas Department of Information Resources
NASA and the US Army.

Financial Performance
immixGroup has been the recipient of more than
950 federal contracts and subcontracts from October 2014 through May 2015. The value of the
contracts was more than $90 million.

EXECUTIVES

Ceo-Pres, Art Richer
Evp*, Stephen Charles
Cfo*, Noel N Samuel
Accounting Staff, Doug Kellermann
Sales, David Stewart
General Counsel, Scott Needleman
Marketing, Allan Rubin
Operations, Bill Bottoms
Compliance Staff, Marcelino Lake
Compliance Staff, Nabil Wassel
Information Specialist, Emma Nay

LOCATIONS

HQ: IMMIXGROUP, INC.
8444 WESTPARK DR STE 200, MC LEAN, VA
221025112
Phone: 703 752-0610
Web: WWW.IMMIXGROUP.COM

PRODUCTS/OPERATIONS

Business Services	Channel Development
Contract Management	
Install Base Practice	
Lead Generation	
Leasing	
Market Intelligence	
Marketing	
SLED Program	
Training	
Event Center Usage	
IT Solutions	Cloud Services
Software Solutions	
Information Management	
Project Management & PMO	

COMPETITORS

Accenture
BAE Systems Technology Solutions
Booz Allen
CACI International
Computer Sciences Corp.
DLT Solutions
HP Enterprise Services
Honeywell Technology Solutions
IBM Global Services
Leidos
ManTech
McKinsey & Company
Raytheon Intelligence Information and Services
Unisys

HISTORICAL FINANCIALS
Company Type: Private

Income Statement				FYE: May 31
	REVENUE ($ mil.)	NET INCOME ($ mil.)	NET PROFIT MARGIN	EMPLOYEES
05/13	505	12	2.4%	201
05/12	502	13	2.6%	—
05/11	43	16	37.9%	—
05/10	563	11	2.1%	—
Annual Growth	(3.5%)	0.8%	—	—

2013 Year-End Financials
Return on assets: 25.1%   Cash ($ mil.): 31
Return on equity: 2.4%
Current ratio: 1.00

IMMIXTECHNOLOGY, INC.

EXECUTIVES

Ceo, Art Richer
V Pres*, Skip Liesegang
Exec V Pres*, Steve Charles
V Pres*, Phill Magaro
Cfo*, Noel Samuel
V Pres*, Bill Bottoms
Senior Manager, Jennifer Taylor

LOCATIONS

HQ: IMMIXTECHNOLOGY, INC.
8444 WESTPARK DR STE 200, MC LEAN, VA
221025112
Phone: 703 752-0610

HISTORICAL FINANCIALS
Company Type: Private

Income Statement				FYE: May 31
	REVENUE ($ mil.)	NET INCOME ($ mil.)	NET PROFIT MARGIN	EMPLOYEES
05/10	536	11	2.2%	201
05/09	403	6	1.7%	—
05/05	717	0	—	—
Annual Growth	—	1715.2%	—	—

2010 Year-End Financials
Return on assets: 16.0%   Cash ($ mil.): 10
Return on equity: 2.2%
Current ratio: 1.00

IMPERIAL IRRIGATION DISTRICT

Imperial Irrigation District (IID) keeps the lights on and the water flowing. A public agency IID is the six largest public power utility in the state of California providing generation transmission and distribution services to more than 145000 residential commercial and industrial customers. It is also the largest irrigation district in the US with more than 3000 miles of canals and drains delivering water to active farmland and providing wholesale water to local municipalities primarily in the Southern California desert corridors of Im-perial Valley and Coachella Valley. The district is governed by a five-member board of directors elected by district residents.

Financial Performance
IID saw its revenues increase 6% from $530 million in 2011 to $562 million in 2012. The growth was driven by a 12% surge in water revenue; this was due to a rise in water transfer rates and a volume increase in water transferred to the San Diego County Water Authority and the Coachella Valley Water District of about $5 million. Power revenues also climbed 4% in 2012 due to a spike in energy sales mainly from residential customers.

Strategy
In the area of renewable energy IID is part of a statewide effort to significantly increase solar energy development and production by the year 2017. In 2011 it announced a public-private partnership with renewable energy generators. The partnership involves the signing of interconnection and transmission service agreements among IID CalEnergy Generation 8minuteenergy Ormat Technologies and the Los Angeles Department of Water and Power. It's the first step in a renewable energy transmission expansion plan to increase capacity enough to support more than a dozen renewable energy construction projects.

In addition IID offers a variety of programs to assist its customers in reducing their personal energy consumption including rebates for buying select energy efficient products online home energy audits and funding for residential projects that involve installing solar technologies such as photovoltaic (PV) systems.

Company Background
Founded in 1911 IID acquired properties from the financially struggling California Development Company and its Mexican subsidiary. By 1922 it had purchased 13 mutual water companies each of which had developed and operated distribution canals in the Imperial Valley. Principal water customers today include farm operators and municipalities that treat the water and resell it to their residential and business customers. The district entered the power business in 1936 to utilize the hydroelectric generation of the All-American Canal. Since that time IID has added geothermal natural gas coal and solar to its energy generation portfolio. Its electric services account for majority of IID's annual revenues.

EXECUTIVES

Vice President, Alfonso Juarez
Vice President Customer, Efrain Macias
Secretary Admin, Angelita Alvarado
Secretary Admin, Angelica Velasquez

LOCATIONS

HQ: IMPERIAL IRRIGATION DISTRICT
333 E BARIONI BLVD, IMPERIAL, CA 922511773
Phone: 800 303-7756
Web: WWW.IID.COM

HISTORICAL FINANCIALS
Company Type: Private

Income Statement				FYE: December 31
	REVENUE ($ mil.)	NET INCOME ($ mil.)	NET PROFIT MARGIN	EMPLOYEES
12/18	615	48	7.9%	1,300
12/17	634	3	0.5%	—
12/16	631	(16)	—	—
12/07	524	151	29.0%	—
Annual Growth	1.5%	(9.8%)	—	—

2018 Year-End Financials
Return on assets: 1.8%   Cash ($ mil.): 75
Return on equity: 3.0%
Current ratio: 1.60

INDEPENDENT PHARMACY COOPERATIVE

EXECUTIVES

Pres, Don Anderson
Director of Marketing/Sales, Linda Reedy Sr
Sales and Marketing Staff, Jake Lewis
Staff, Vickie Miller
Human Resources Executive, Michelle R Johnson
Government Relations Director, John Covello
Sales Associate, Nicole Burbach
Sales Associate, Tammy Riley
Marketing Coordinator, Emily Gutgesell
Director Regional Sales, Stacy Hall
Administration Staff, Susan Oechsner
Auditors: GRANT THORNTON LLP APPLETON

LOCATIONS

HQ: INDEPENDENT PHARMACY COOPERATIVE
1550 COLUMBUS ST, SUN PRAIRIE, WI 535903901
Phone: 800 755-1531
Web: WWW.IPCRX.COM

HISTORICAL FINANCIALS
Company Type: Private

Income Statement				FYE: December 31
	REVENUE ($ mil.)	NET INCOME ($ mil.)	NET PROFIT MARGIN	EMPLOYEES
12/16	1,427	30	2.1%	160
12/14	1,052	2	0.2%	—
12/13	1,058	2	0.2%	—
12/11	806	1	0.2%	—
Annual Growth	12.1%	73.9%	—	—

2016 Year-End Financials
Return on assets: 12.5%   Cash ($ mil.): 40
Return on equity: 60.7%
Current ratio: 1.20

INDEPENDENT SCHOOL DIST 625

EXECUTIVES

Spdt, Joe Gothard
Mgmt Specialist, Andrew Mosca
Executive of Information Techn, Cathy Bloomquist
Executive of Information Techn, Jim Litwin
Accounting Staff, Shirley Davis
Accounting Staff, Patty Kelly
Accounting Staff, Gloria Thompson
Project Coordinator, Deb Campobasso
Chief Information Officer, Julie Huppertz
Manager, Margaret Vanderhoff
Accounting Staff, Julie Martinez
Auditors: MALLOY MONTAGUE KARNOWSKI R

LOCATIONS

HQ: INDEPENDENT SCHOOL DIST 625
360 COLBORNE ST, SAINT PAUL, MN 551023228
Phone: 651 767-8100
Web: WWW.SPPS.ORG

HISTORICAL FINANCIALS
Company Type: Private

Income Statement				FYE: June 30
	REVENUE ($ mil.)	NET INCOME ($ mil.)	NET PROFIT MARGIN	EMPLOYEES
06/18	711	17	2.5%	6,500
06/17	706	49	7.0%	—
06/16	693	(37)	—	—
06/08	608	(1)	—	—
Annual Growth	1.6%	—	—	—

INDIAN PRAIRIE COMMUNITY UNIT SCHOOL DISTRICT

EXECUTIVES

Supt, Kathryn Birkett
Staff, Adam Schlipmann
Staff, Beth Schmitdgall
Staff, Adreanne Oneal
Staff, Bill Jastrow
Staff, Bill Roller
Staff, Andrew Himes
Staff, Marchel Rogers
Staff, Jennifer Claussen
Staff, Jennifer Schmauderer
Staff, Colleen Ellis

LOCATIONS

HQ: INDIAN PRAIRIE COMMUNITY UNIT SCHOOL DISTRICT
780 SHORELINE DR, AURORA, IL 605046192
Phone: 630 375-3000
Web: WWW.IPSD.ORG

HISTORICAL FINANCIALS
Company Type: Private

Income Statement				FYE: June 30
	REVENUE ($ mil.)	NET INCOME ($ mil.)	NET PROFIT MARGIN	EMPLOYEES
06/18	450	10	2.3%	3,000
06/16	434	2	0.6%	—
06/05	0	0	—	—
06/03	237	14	6.0%	—
Annual Growth	4.4%	(2.2%)	—	—

INDIANA MUNICIPAL POWER AGENCY

Indiana Municipal Power Agency (IMPA) supplies bulk electricity to 53 community-owned distribution utilities throughout Indiana. IMPA members deliver electric service to households businesses and industries across Indiana. The company has interests in fossil-fueled power plants that give it nearly 820 MW of generating capacity; it also buys electricity through supply contracts and through purchases on the wholesale market. IMPA also owns power tranmission assets and it provides utility engineering and consulting services through its ISC subsidiary. The state's 72 public power systems provide about 6% of the state's power capacity.

EXECUTIVES

Ceo, Raj RAO
Sr V Pres, Jack Alvey
Cfo, Chris Rettig
Coordinator, Brodie Williams
Coordinator, Rob Rucker
Accounting Staff, Lezli Lingerfeldt
Manager, Eric Burch
Electrical Supervisor, Jeff Henderson
Operations Security Manager, John R Lloyd
Senior Vice President, Peter Prettyman
Crew Foreman, Rob Doty
Auditors: PRICEWATERHOUSECOOPERS LLP CO

LOCATIONS

HQ: INDIANA MUNICIPAL POWER AGENCY
11610 N COLLEGE AVE, CARMEL, IN 460325602
Phone: 317 573-9955
Web: WWW.IMPA.COM

HISTORICAL FINANCIALS
Company Type: Private

Income Statement				FYE: December 31
	REVENUE ($ mil.)	NET INCOME ($ mil.)	NET PROFIT MARGIN	EMPLOYEES
12/18	461	37	8.1%	84
12/17	423	23	5.5%	—
12/16	452	28	6.3%	—
12/14	456	26	5.8%	—
Annual Growth	0.2%	9.0%	—	—

2018 Year-End Financials
Return on assets: 2.0%   Cash ($ mil.): 166
Return on equity: 10.4%
Current ratio: 2.00

INDIANA UNIVERSITY

EXECUTIVES

Teacher, Bob Eckert
Staff, Emily Tenney

LOCATIONS

HQ: INDIANA UNIVERSITY
1020 E KIRKWOOD AVE, BLOOMINGTON, IN 474057103
Phone: 812 855-7581
Web: WWW.IU.EDU

HISTORICAL FINANCIALS
Company Type: Private

Income Statement				FYE: June 30
	REVENUE ($ mil.)	NET INCOME ($ mil.)	NET PROFIT MARGIN	EMPLOYEES
06/14	2,195	201	9.2%	31
06/13	2,146	189	8.8%	—
Annual Growth	2.3%	6.3%	—	—

2014 Year-End Financials
Return on assets: 10.0%   Cash ($ mil.): 313
Return on equity: 9.2%
Current ratio: 1.10

INDIANA UNIVERSITY HEALTH, INC.

Indiana University Health (IU Health) is one of the largest health systems in Indiana. Not-for-profit IU Health owns or is affiliated with more than 20 hospitals throughout the state including three major facilities ? Methodist Hospital Indiana University Hospital and Riley Hospital for Children ? in downtown Indianapolis. The hospitals serve as teaching facilities for Indiana University's medical school. The largest Methodist Hospital features the Methodist Research Institute which conducts research and clinical trials. The 2700-bed IU Health system also includes primary and specialty care clinics surgery and urgent care centers a health insurance provider and a home health agency.

Financial Performance

IU Health reported relatively flat revenue in 2018. Sales increased a little over 1% to some $6.4 billion as a 7% increase in patient service revenue (accounting for most of sales) was offset by a 70% decline in member premium (health plan) revenue.

Excess of revenue over expenses was $296.2 million in 2018 down from $989.3 million in 2017 due to investment losses.

The company ended 2018 with $345 million in cash down $69.6 million from 2017. Operating activities contributed $178.2 million while investing activities used $265.8 million (on property and equipment) and financing activities contributed $18 million via issuance of long-term debt.

Strategy

The system's growth strategy includes expanding into Indianapolis' suburbs and other growing areas of Indiana through construction efforts acquisitions and affiliation agreements. It also regularly improves upon existing facilities to enhance services for area residents.

Current projects include the construction of the $344 million Bloomington Regional Academic Health Center which will replace and expand the existing Bloomington Hospital (opening in 2021) and the addition of a $104 million patient tower at the Ball Memorial Hospital (scheduled for completion in 2022). IU Health has announced plans to construct a new Academic Health Center to replace some aging assets in downtown Indianapolis. It is opening new urgent and ambulatory care centers to increase outpatient revenue as industry service models shift towards non-inpatient care.

IU Health also works to improve the health of Indiana residents through research education and community outreach programs. Recent initiatives include improving access to affordable care behavioral health care and obesity prevention services.

While it continues to expand the organization is also working to reduce expenses during a time when US health providers and regulatory agencies look to control medical spending.

Company Background

The organization was formed in 1997 as Clarian Health Partners through the merger of University Hospital and Riley Hospital (operated by the Trustees of Indiana University) with the Methodist Hospital (operated by Methodist Health Group).

The company changed its name from Clarian Health Partners to Indiana University Health (IU Health) in 2011 to reflect its relationship with the university.

EXECUTIVES

Ceo Iu Health Arnett Hospital, Al W. Gatmaitan
Evp And Chief Medical Executive, Jonathan E. Gottlieb
Evp And Coo, Dennis M. Murphy
Svp And Cio, Mark Lantzy
Svp Engagement And External Affairs, Ron Stiver
President And Ceo Iu Health Ball Memorial Hospital, Michael Haley
Chief Nurse Executive, Michelle Janney
Evp And Chief Administrative Officer, Ryan C. Kitchell
President And Ceo Iu Health North Hospital And Iu Health Saxony Hospital, Jonathan Goble
President Iu Health South Central Region, Matt Bailey
President And Ceo Iu Health Tipton Hospital, Michael Harlowe
Ceo Iu Health Paoli Hospital, Larry Bailey
President And Ceo Iu Health Bedford Hospital, Bradford W. Dykes
President Iu Health Arnett Hospital, Donald E. Clayton
President Iu Health West Hospital, Doug Puckett
President Riley Hospital For Children, Matthew Cook
Coo And Chief Medical Officer Iu Health Ball Memorial Hospital., Jeff Bird
Interim President And Chief Medical Officer Iu Health Methodist And University, Ryan Nagy
Vice President Latino Alumni Association, Adam Karcz
Vice President Of Clinical Excellence, Lisa Sparks
Vice President Quality And Patient Safety, James Bien
Vice President Revenue Cycle Services And Treasurer, Jennifer Alvey
Vice President Cno, Linda Chase
Vice President Revenue Cycle Services, Jonathan Vanator
Radiology Director, Shelli Kordes
Vice President Physician Recruitment, Jenny Garver
Vice President Retail Health Services, David Kogan
Vice President Strategic Planning And Market Insights, Ryan Ross
Senior Vice President And Chief Health Information Officer, Joseph Hschneider
Vp Marketing And Community Relations, Teri Dematas
Evp Mission And Values And Chief Of Staff, Kevin R Armstrong
Vp It And Innovation, Sulabh Srivastava
Vice President Clinical Strategy And Integration, Andrea Kessler
Vice President Supply Chain Operations, Dennis Mullins
Medical Director, Jeffrey Nace
Vice President Human Resources Total Rewards, Lauren Zink
Vice President Of Rehabilitation Wound C, Tara Roberts
Vice President Finance And Operations, Joseph Traeger
Director Of Pharmacy, Pat Schneider
Chairman, Anne Nobles
Cpe Secretary, Lorie Vaughn
Secretary Administrative, Valerie Craig
Auditors: ERNST & YOUNG LLP INDIANAPOLI

LOCATIONS

HQ: INDIANA UNIVERSITY HEALTH, INC.
340 W 10TH ST, INDIANAPOLIS, IN 462023082
Phone: 317 962-2000

PRODUCTS/OPERATIONS

Selected Facilities
INDIANAPOLIS-AREA HOSPITALS
Indiana University Hospital (dba IU Health University Hospital Indianapolis)
Methodist Hospital (dba IU Health Methodist Hospital Indianapolis)
Riley Hospital for Children (dba Riley Hospital for Children at IU Health Indianapolis)
IU Simon Cancer Center
Clarian North Medical Center (dba IU Health North Hospital Carmel)
Clarian West Medical Center (dba IU Health West Hospital Avon)
STATEWIDE PARTNERS
Clarian Arnett Health (dba IU Health Arnett Hospital Lafayette)
Ball Memorial Hospital (dba IU Health Ball Memorial Hospital Muncie)
Bedford Regional Medical Center (dba IU Health Bedford Hospital Bedford)
Blackford Community Hospital (dba IU Health Blackford Hospital Hartford City)
Bloomington Hospital (dba IU Health Bloomington Hospital Bloomington)
Bloomington Hospital of Orange County (dba IU Health Paoli Hospital Paoli)
Goshen Health System (dba IU Health Goshen Hospital Goshen)
LaPorte Regional Health System (dba IU Health LaPorte Hospital La Porte)
Midwest Proton Radiotherapy Institute (dba IU Health Proton Therapy Center Bloomington)
Starke Memorial Hospital (dba IU Health Starke Hospital Knox)
Tipton Hospital (dba IU Health Tipton Hospital Tipton)
METHODIST MEDICAL PLAZAS (outpatient centers)
Georgetown Medical Plaza
Methodist Medical Plaza Eagle Highlands
Methodist Medical Plaza East
Methodist Medical Plaza North
Methodist Medical Plaza South

COMPETITORS

Ascension Health	Henry County Memorial
Banner Health	Hospital
Catholic Health	MedStar Health
Initiatives	Riverview Hospital
Community Health	St. Elizabeth Regional
Network	Health
Community Hospital	St. Vincent Health
Anderson	Tenet Healthcare
Daviess Community	Union Hospital
Hospital	(Indiana)
Franciscan Alliance	
Good Samaritan	
Hospital (IN)	

HISTORICAL FINANCIALS
Company Type: Private

Income Statement				FYE: December 31
	REVENUE ($ mil.)	NET INCOME ($ mil.)	NET PROFIT MARGIN	EMPLOYEES
12/08	1,889	(23)	—	17,242
12/06	2,478	159	6.4%	—
12/05	2,281	68	3.0%	—
Annual Growth	(6.1%)	—	—	—

2008 Year-End Financials
Return on assets: (-1.3%)   Cash ($ mil.): 237
Return on equity: (-1.8%)
Current ratio: 0.90

INFINITE ENERGY, INC.

Infinite wisdom? No. Infinite energy? Yes. Infinite Energy does not provide its customers with the natural high of endorphins or with the latest health diet but with the more prosaic commodity of natural gas. The company supplies natural gas to clients in Florida Georgia and New York. Wholesale customers include municipalities institutions and utilities; Infinite Energy also sells to large and small commercial establishments (including restaurants) and to residential customers.

EXECUTIVES

Ceo, Darin Cook
Pres, Richard Blaser
Administrative Director, Martha McCullough
Dir, Jason Cook
Purchasing Director, Richard Trachet
Director, August Bianchi
Accounting Staff, Karen Nelsen
Account Manager, Dennis Connolly
Executive Assistant, Kelly Haven
Legal Supervisor, Andrea McHenry
Business Application Developme, Dave Weldy

LOCATIONS

HQ: INFINITE ENERGY, INC.
7001 SW 24TH AVE, GAINESVILLE, FL 326073704
Phone: 352 331-1654
Web: WWW.INFINITEENERGY.COM

COMPETITORS

Eversource Energy	New Jersey Natural Gas
Florida Gas	Piedmont Natural Gas
Transmission	SCANA
National Grid USA	

HISTORICAL FINANCIALS
Company Type: Private

Income Statement				FYE: December 31
	REVENUE ($ mil.)	NET INCOME ($ mil.)	NET PROFIT MARGIN	EMPLOYEES
12/09	477	13	2.7%	10
12/05	583	4	0.8%	—
12/04	474	8	1.8%	—
12/03	335	3	0.9%	—
Annual Growth	6.0%	26.7%	—	—

2009 Year-End Financials
Return on assets: 10.2%   Cash ($ mil.): 12
Return on equity: 172.3%
Current ratio: 1.00

INFIRMARY HEALTH SYSTEM, INC.

EXECUTIVES

Ceo, D Mark Nix
Pres*, E Chandler Bramlett
Contrl, Jim Mitchell
Human Resources Information MA, Stephanie Andrews
Controller, Becky Michels
Information Technology/Interne, Curtis Rye
Administrative Assistant, Dana Thomas
Executive Vice-President, Alan Whaley
Director of Radiology, Anthony Mosley
Coordinator, Alex Oditt
Coordinator, Allan Farnum

LOCATIONS

HQ: INFIRMARY HEALTH SYSTEM, INC.
   5 MOBILE INFIRMARY CIR, MOBILE, AL 366073513
Phone: 251 435-3030
Web: WWW.DEBAKEYDRUGEDUCATION.COM

HISTORICAL FINANCIALS
Company Type: Private

Income Statement — FYE: March 31

	REVENUE ($ mil.)	NET INCOME ($ mil.)	NET PROFIT MARGIN	EMPLOYEES
03/18	727	35	4.8%	5,000
03/17	696	70	10.2%	—
03/15	58	(4)	—	—
03/14	51	(4)	—	—
Annual Growth	93.6%	—	—	—

2018 Year-End Financials
Return on assets: 4.0%   Cash ($ mil.): 68
Return on equity: 8.6%
Current ratio: 4.80

INLAND COUNTIES REGIONAL CENTER, INC.

EXECUTIVES

Ceo, Carol A Fitzgibbons
Exec Dir*, Carol Fitzgibbons
Manager, Mary Hernandez
Manager, Elizabeth Stroh
Program Manager, Mia Gurri
Counselor, Amber Hernandez
Director, Denise Fanelli
Counselor, Melissa Guzman
Counselor, Robert Romero
Office Assistant, Stephen Hughes
Doctor, Sharrie Mills
Auditors: WINDES INC LONG BEACH CA

LOCATIONS

HQ: INLAND COUNTIES REGIONAL CENTER, INC.
   1365 S WATERMAN AVE, SAN BERNARDINO, CA
   924082804
Phone: 909 890-3000
Web: WWW.INLANDRC.ORG

HISTORICAL FINANCIALS
Company Type: Private

Income Statement — FYE: June 30

	REVENUE ($ mil.)	NET INCOME ($ mil.)	NET PROFIT MARGIN	EMPLOYEES
06/18	502	(0)	—	586
06/17	463	(39)	—	—
06/16	402	(7)	—	—
06/15	378	4	1.1%	—
Annual Growth	9.9%	—	—	—

2018 Year-End Financials
Return on assets: (-0.2%)   Cash ($ mil.): 24
Return on equity: —
Current ratio: 1.10

INNOVATIVE AG SERVICES CO.

EXECUTIVES

Ceo, Rick Vaughan
Pres*, Randy Blake
1st Vp*, Paul Cook
Cfo*, Brenda Hoefler
Human Resources Staff, Marilyn E Ewing
Manager, Mike Bachman
Bookkeeper, Jill Manternach
Associate Director, Allen Jaspers
Vice President of Human Resour, Carla Elliott
Location Manager, Gerald Severson
Associate Director, Jeff Lindsay
Auditors: MERIWETHER WILSON & COMPANY

LOCATIONS

HQ: INNOVATIVE AG SERVICES CO.
   2010 S MAIN ST, MONTICELLO, IA 523107707
Phone: 319 465-3501
Web: WWW.INNOVATIVEAG.COM

HISTORICAL FINANCIALS
Company Type: Private

Income Statement — FYE: August 31

	REVENUE ($ mil.)	NET INCOME ($ mil.)	NET PROFIT MARGIN	EMPLOYEES
08/18	649	11	1.8%	500
08/17	615	15	2.6%	—
08/16	682	10	1.6%	—
08/15	657	18	2.8%	—
Annual Growth	(0.4%)	(14.7%)	—	—

2018 Year-End Financials
Return on assets: 3.9%   Cash ($ mil.): 2
Return on equity: 7.1%
Current ratio: 1.80

INOVA HEALTH CARE SERVICES

EXECUTIVES

Chm, Nicholas Carosi
Pres, John Knox Singleton
V Pres, Richard C Magenheimer
V Pres, James Hughes
V Pres, H Patrick Walters
SEC, Shannon Sinclair
Tres, Lydia Thomas
SEC, Tony Nader
Vice-President Information Ser, Maggie Cornett
Coordinator, Roxanne Wright
Manager, Sandra White

LOCATIONS

HQ: INOVA HEALTH CARE SERVICES
   8110 GATEHOUSE RD 200E, FALLS CHURCH, VA
   220421217
Phone: 703 289-2000
Web: WWW.INOVACAREERS.ORG

HISTORICAL FINANCIALS
Company Type: Private

Income Statement — FYE: December 31

	REVENUE ($ mil.)	NET INCOME ($ mil.)	NET PROFIT MARGIN	EMPLOYEES
12/13	2,134	145	6.8%	13,000
12/09	1,663	200	12.0%	—
12/03	1,012	46	4.6%	—
12/02	1	(0)		
Annual Growth	96.8%	—	—	—

2013 Year-End Financials
Return on assets: 3.9%   Cash ($ mil.): 203
Return on equity: 7.8%
Current ratio: 0.30

INOVA HEALTH SYSTEM FOUNDATION

Inova Health Foundation provides financial support and assistance to the Inova Health System which operates a network of not-for-profit community hospitals in northern Virginia. It also supports home health services heart care programs clinical research and trials emergency and urgent care centers family practice locations and rehabilitation centers. To raise funds for the hospital system the foundation organizes special events such as galas golf tournaments and silent auctions. Donors can also make contributions through the Inova website. The foundation took in $15.8 million in contributions in 2012.

EXECUTIVES

Cfo, Richard Magenheimer
Ceo, John Niederhuber
Director Of Pharmacy, Gill Abernathy
Radiology Director, Deborah Berg
Chief People Officer, Terri Feely
Assistant Vice President Building And Support Services, Cheryll Battle
Chairman, Terry D. McCallister
Executive Assistant To The Chair And Vice Chairs Department Of Medicine, Barbara Perry

LOCATIONS

HQ: INOVA HEALTH SYSTEM FOUNDATION
   8110 GATEHOUSE RD 200E, FALLS CHURCH, VA
   220421217
Phone: 703 289-2069
Web: WWW.INOVA.ORG

HISTORICAL FINANCIALS
Company Type: Private

Income Statement — FYE: December 31

	REVENUE ($ mil.)	NET INCOME ($ mil.)	NET PROFIT MARGIN	EMPLOYEES
12/17	765	717	93.6%	16,000
12/15	2,972	234	7.9%	—
Annual Growth	(49.2%)	74.8%	—	—

2017 Year-End Financials
Return on assets: 14.1%   Cash ($ mil.): —
Return on equity: 25.6%
Current ratio: 8.40

INSPIRA MEDICAL CENTERS, INC.

EXECUTIVES

Pres, John D'Angelo
Coo*, Wayne Schiffner
Accounting Staff, Donna Anthony
Information, David C Mills
Coordinator, Joanna Galletta
Coordinator, Cari Schenkel
Coordinator, Colleen Zboray
Chief Information Offi, Greg Herman
Assistant Vice President Cardi, Paul Abrams
Training, Francois Bodhuin
Analyst, Jeanne Goss
Auditors: WITHUMSMITHBROWN PC
MORRISTOW

LOCATIONS

HQ: INSPIRA MEDICAL CENTERS, INC.
333 IRVING AVE, BRIDGETON, NJ 083022123
Phone: 856 575-4500
Web: WWW.INSPIRAHEALTHNETWORK.ORG

HISTORICAL FINANCIALS

Company Type: Private

Income Statement				FYE: December 31
	REVENUE ($ mil.)	NET INCOME ($ mil.)	NET PROFIT MARGIN	EMPLOYEES
12/17	487	75	15.6%	3,063
12/13	412	22	5.4%	—
Annual Growth	4.3%	35.9%	—	—

2017 Year-End Financials

Return on assets: 7.8%
Return on equity: 12.8%
Current ratio: 0.50
Cash ($ mil.): 72

INTEGRIS BAPTIST MEDICAL CENTER, INC.

INTEGRIS Baptist Medical Center seeks integrity by caring for citizens from across the state of Oklahoma.Â The Oklahoma City-based medical center is the flagship hospitalÂ of the not-for-profit INTEGRIS Health system. WithÂ about 510 beds INTEGRIS Baptist is home to specialty care facilities for burns women's and children's health infertility stroke treatment cardiac care organ transplantation cancer treatmentÂ and more. The company also has centers for wellness hearing sleep disorders senior health and weight loss and itÂ provides medicalÂ training and residencyÂ programs.Â INTEGRIS Baptist Medical Center opened its doors in 1959 with 200 beds.

EXECUTIVES

Secretary, Stacey Turner

LOCATIONS

HQ: INTEGRIS BAPTIST MEDICAL CENTER, INC.
3300 NW EXPRESSWAY, OKLAHOMA CITY, OK
731124418
Phone: 405 949-3011
Web: WWW.INTEGRISOK.COM

PRODUCTS/OPERATIONS

Selected Centers and Services

Advanced Cardiac Care
Anticoagulation Clinics
Bariatrics
Bennett Fertility Institute
Bones and Joints
Breast Care
Burn Center
Cancer Care
Cardiology
Case Management
Children's Health
Comprehensive Breast Center of Oklahoma
Continuing Medical Education
Corporate Assistance Program
Diabetes
Diagnostic Services
Digestive Health
Emergency Department
Fertility
General Heart Care
General Pediatrics
Home Care
Hospice
Hospitalist Program
Hough Ear Institute
Hyperbaric Medicine and Wound Care
James R. Daniel Cerebrovascular and Stroke Center
Jim Thorpe Rehabilitation Center
Labor and Delivery
Men's Health
Nazih Zuhdi Transplant Institute
Neonatal Intensive Care Unit (NICU)
Orthopedics
PACER Fitness Center
Pastoral Care
Pediatric Intensive Care Unit (PICU)
Pediatric Neurology
Pharmacy
Radiology Services
Senior Health
Sleep Disorders Center of Oklahoma
Stroke Center
Surgical Services
TeleHealth
Urogynecology
Weight Loss

COMPETITORS

Deaconess Health Care
Hillcrest Medical Center
Jackson County Memorial Hospital
Marian Health System
Mercy Health
Norman Regional Health
SSM Health Care
Saint Francis Health System
Texas Health Denton
Universal Health Services

HISTORICAL FINANCIALS

Company Type: Private

Income Statement				FYE: June 30
	REVENUE ($ mil.)	NET INCOME ($ mil.)	NET PROFIT MARGIN	EMPLOYEES
06/18	814	67	8.3%	2,700
06/16	701	6	1.0%	—
06/09*	582	22	3.9%	—
12/08	0	0	—	—
Annual Growth	—	—	—	—

*Fiscal year change

2018 Year-End Financials

Return on assets: 5.4%
Return on equity: 12.2%
Current ratio: 2.70
Cash ($ mil.): 339

INTEGRIS HEALTH, INC.

INTEGRIS Health provides a range of health services to residents throughout the Sooner state. The company one of Oklahoma's largest not-for-profit health care organization operates 16 hospitals with some 1500 combined beds in both urban and rural communities. The hospitals provide services including primary diagnostic emergency surgical behavioral therapeutic and rehabilitative care. INTEGRIS also operates specialty facilities for the treatment of hearing disorders and neuromuscular ailments and for rehabilitation care. The company operates assisted living centers and a home health agency plus a network of physician clinics and ambulatory care centers.

Operations

Operations include INTEGRIS Baptist Medical Center (the system's largest with 629 beds) INTEGRIS South Oklahoma City (dba INTEGRIS Southwest Medical Center 389 beds) and INTEGRIS Rural Health facilities INTEGRIS Baptist Regional Health Center INTEGRIS Bass Baptist Health Center and INTEGRIS Grove Hospital.

INTEGRIS Health has approximately 1400 physicians in its system.

Sales and Marketing

Managed care payments account for more than half of net patient service revenue; Medicare and Medicaid combined account for around a third.

INTEGRIS Health offers community residents with more life experience such services as senior seminars and classes health screenings support groups and technology classes to help stay up-to-date on computer use. The idea is to help keep the elderly as independent as possible for as long as possible.

Financial Performance

The company's revenue increased slightly in fiscal 2015 rising 1% to $1.4 billion. This was due to growth in net patient service revenues. However INTEGRIS Health reported a net loss of $150 million (versus a net gain in 2014) due to factors that included higher operating expenses (salaries supplies) and higher pension liability adjustments. This in turn led to a 60% drop in cash flow from operations which totaled $49 million.

EXECUTIVES

President Integris Southwest Medical Center, James D. Moore
Chief Medical Officer, James White
Evp And Coo, Chris Hammes
President And Ceo, Bruce Lawrence
Cfo, David Hadley
President Integris Baptist Medical Center, Tim Johnsen
President Integris Bass Baptist Health Center Enid, Eddie Herrman
President Integris Baptist Regional Health Center Miami, Jordan Cash
President Integris Canadian Valley Hospital Yukon, Rex Van Meter
President Integris Cancer Institute Of Oklahoma, Phil Lance
President Integris Health Edmond, Avilla Williams
President Integris Health Partners, Carl Raczkowski
President Integris Heart Hospital, R. Mel Clark
President Integris Medical Group, Jeff Cruzan
President Lakeside Women's Hospital, Kelley Brewer
President And Coo Integris Mental Health And James L. Hall Jr. Center For Mind Body And Spirit, R. Murali Krishna
Vp Integris Nazih Zuhdi Transplant Insitute Integris Advanced Cardiac Care, Kathie Calbone

President Integris Grove Hospital, Tim Bowen, age 36
Clinical Director, Cindy Penland
Clinical Director, Terri Preston
Director Of Radiology, Amy Brown
Radiology Director, Kirsten Runyan
Vice President Integris Jim Thorpe Rehabilitation, Keith Wilton
Vice President Integris Health Partners, Jeff Brown
Vice President, Paul Szymanski
Vice President Administrator Mental Health, Jim Igo
Executive Vice President And Chief Financial Officer, Doug Smith
Pharmacy Manager, Jennifer Maune
Clinical Director, Lisa Aishman
Director Of Pharmacy, Larry Anderson
Assistant Vice President, Lynda Van
System Vp Finance, Jaquetta Clemons
Radiology Director, Maggie Kane
Executive Vice President And Chief Physician Executive, Tommy Ibrahim
Auditors: KPMG LLP OKLAHOMA CITY OKLAH

LOCATIONS

HQ: INTEGRIS HEALTH, INC.
3300 NW EXPRESSWAY, OKLAHOMA CITY, OK 731124418
Phone: 405 949-6066
Web: WWW.INTEGRISOK.COM

PRODUCTS/OPERATIONS

2015 Sales

	$ mil.	% of total
INTEGRIS Baptist Medical Center Inc.	635	39
INTEGRIS South Oklahoma City Hospital Corporation	244	15
INTEGRIS Rural Health Inc.	227	14
INTEGRIS Health Edmond	48	3
All others	459	29
Eliminations	(229.7)	-
Total	**1,384**	**100**

Selected Facilities

Baptist Medical Center
Baptist Regional Health Center
Bass Baptist Health Center
Blackwell Regional Hospital
Canadian Valley Regional Hospital
Cancer Institute of Oklahoma
Clinton Regional Hospital
Grove General Hospital
Health Edmond
Hospice House
Jim Thorpe Rehabilitation
Marshall County Medical Center
Mayes County Medical Center
Mental Health Spencer
Seminole Medical Center
Southwest Medical Center

COMPETITORS

Ardent Health Services
Deaconess Health Care
Fairview Health
HealthEast Care System
Hillcrest Medical Center
Marian Health System
Mercy Health
Norman Regional Health
Saint Francis Health System
St. John Health System

HISTORICAL FINANCIALS

Company Type: Private

Income Statement
FYE: June 30

	REVENUE ($ mil.)	NET INCOME ($ mil.)	NET PROFIT MARGIN	EMPLOYEES
06/18	1,673	53	3.2%	9,500
06/17	1,558	111	7.2%	—
06/15	1,384	(90)	—	—
06/06	1,067	89	8.4%	—
Annual Growth	3.8%	(4.2%)	—	—

2018 Year-End Financials

Return on assets: 2.4%
Return on equity: 5.1%
Current ratio: 1.60
Cash ($ mil.): 76

INTERACTIVE DATA CORPORATION

EXECUTIVES

Pres, Scott A Hill
Treasurer, Martin Hunter
Secretary, Octavia Spencer
Vice President, Chuck Adkins
Database Programmer, Harsh Nayak
Director, Michael Scotland
Assistant General Counsel, Nathan Bouley
Vice President Information TEC, Scott Caudell
Director Evaluated Op, Steve Miano
Senior Business Analyst, Tim Sweeney
Senior Director, Bob Leone

LOCATIONS

HQ: INTERACTIVE DATA CORPORATION
32 CROSBY DR STE 100, BEDFORD, MA 017301448
Phone: 781 687-8500
Web: WWW.THEICE.COM

HISTORICAL FINANCIALS

Company Type: Private

Income Statement
FYE: December 31

	ASSETS ($ mil.)	NET INCOME ($ mil.)	INCOME AS % OF ASSETS	EMPLOYEES
12/13	3,968	33	0.8%	2,600
12/12	3,962	1	0.0%	—
12/11	4,093	(29)	—	—
Annual Growth	(1.5%)	—	—	—

2013 Year-End Financials

Return on assets: 0.8%
Return on equity: 2.8%
Sales ($ mil): 905

INTERBOND CORPORATION OF AMERICA

Interbond Corporation of America (doing business as BrandsMart USA)Â boasts more than 500 brand namesÂ across its nearly 50000 electronics and entertainment products. It sells them in the US and internationally. It offers low-priced appliancesÂ computers TVs car stereos mobile phones personal care gadgets movie music games and more. The retailer runs aboutÂ 10 electronics stores under the BrandsMart USA banner in the South Florida and Atlanta metropolitan areas. Each stocksÂ more than $8 million in merchandise. BrandsMart USA alsoÂ sells products online providing shipping for orders placed throughout the US Latin America and the Caribbean. Chair-

man Robert Perlman founded the company in 1977.

Operations

BrandsMart USA is one of the nation's largest volume-per-store retailers. With help from its low-price strategy the retailerÂ has performedÂ relatively well in the consumerÂ electronics nicheÂ which once included bankrupt rivals such as Circuit City.

The company operates in Latin America and the Caribbean through a marketing agreement with shopping facilitator Punto Mio. Using Punto Mio's integration technology international customers accessing BrandsMart USA's website can browse products listed in their local currencies (purchase prices include applicable delivery fees and taxes).

Geographic Reach

Aside from its home office and warehouse facilities in Hollywood Florida BrandsMart USA operates stores in South Florida and in Georgia providing some 2600 jobs. Its clearance center is located in Florida's South Broward County.

Sales and Marketing

BrandsMart USA stores are known for their brightly lit interiors and neon price tags as well as their noisy bustling atmospheres. The simple presentation scheme helps to keep price tags low and to move crowds of customers. The retailerÂ faces competition from the likes of Best Buy hhgreggÂ and Wal-Mart.

To promote an eco-friendly message Brands-Mart USA runsÂ a Go Green Trade In ProgramÂ a take-backÂ initiative in partnership with the Consumer Electronics Exchange. The program issues BrandsMart USA gift cards to shoppers who trade in their unwanted electronics (includingÂ gaming consoles MP3 players and mobile phones) which are then recycled byÂ the Consumer Electronics Exchange.

EXECUTIVES

Senior Vice President Chief Information Officer, Vincent Visco
Vice President Sales, Neil Anello
Vice President Customer Operations, Eydie Bowe
Auditors: KAUFMAN ROSSIN & CO PA MIAM

LOCATIONS

HQ: INTERBOND CORPORATION OF AMERICA
3200 SW 42ND ST, HOLLYWOOD, FL 33020
Phone: 954 797-4000
Web: WWW.BRANDSMARTUSA.COM

2013 Stores

	No.
Florida	5
Georgia	4
Total	**9**

PRODUCTS/OPERATIONS

Selected Products

Appliances
Blu-rays & DVDs
Headphones
Home audio
Car audio & GPS
Computers
Fitness
Games
Home security
Mobile phones
Office products
Personal care
Tablets
Toys
TVs
Wellness

Selected Brands

Bose
Dell
Electrolux
Epson
Frigidaire
iRobot
LG
Logitech
Samsung
Sharp
Sony

COMPETITORS

Best Buy	RadioShack
Costco Wholesale	Sears
Fry's Electronics	Wal-Mart
Home Depot	

HISTORICAL FINANCIALS

Company Type: Private

Income Statement   FYE: September 24

	REVENUE ($ mil.)	NET INCOME ($ mil.)	NET PROFIT MARGIN	EMPLOYEES
09/11	743	3	0.5%	2,400
09/10	800	7	0.9%	—
09/08	936	19	2.1%	—
Annual Growth	(7.4%)	(43.3%)	—	—

2011 Year-End Financials

Return on assets: 1.3%   Cash ($ mil.): 1
Return on equity: 2.2%
Current ratio: 1.00

INTERMOUNTAIN HEALTH CARE INC

If you whoosh down the side of one of Idaho's majestic mountains and take a nasty spill Intermountain Health Care (dba Intermountain Healthcare) can pick you up and put you back together. From air ambulance services to urgent care clinics and general hospitals Intermountain has all the tools to mend skiers (and non-skiers alike) in Utah and southern Idaho. With about 1600 physicians the not-for-profit health system operates 22 hospitals and some 180 clinics as well as urgent care centers and rehabilitation centers. Intermountain also has an insurance arm named SelectHealth.

Operations

Intermountain Healthcare's hospitals range from general surgical to specialty care including orthopedic and pediatric facilities. Along with the full spectrum of physical health care services Intermountain also offers comprehensive mental health and substance abuse programs for patients of all ages. The organization's spectrum of care includes acute inpatient residential treatment day treatment chemical dependency inpatient/detoxification and intensive outpatient programs.

The system conducts cancer research through its partnership with Huntsman Cancer Institute at the University of Utah. The two share data best practices funding and co-conduct clinical trials. They also operate a number of cancer-specific treatment centers including multi-disciplinary tumor-specific clinics designed to provide one-stop service for cancer patients to meet with different cancer specialists on the same day for a more comprehensive treatment plan. Other areas of research include cardiovascular intensive medicine surgical care and behavioral health.

On the physician side the Intermountain Medical Group administers multi-specialty health care services in clinics located throughout the region. The group also operates urgent care clinics under the InstaCare and KidsCare banners.

Entering itself into the "what doesn't Intermountain do?" category the health system also provides health and dental insurance plans through its SelectHealth division.

Geographic Reach

Intermountain Healthcare serves the health care needs of Utah and Idaho residents.

Financial Performance

In 2016 Intermountain Healthcare's revenue grew 14% to $7.6 billion in fiscal 2016. This was due to increases in net patient services income non-patient activity income and investment income. Net patient services accounted for 63% of the system's total revenue that year.

The company used $7 billion of that revenue towards operating expenses including salaries and benefits medical supplies and facilities maintenance and other business services as well as towards funds dedicated to future needs.

Strategy

Intermountain Healthcare uses its dedicated supply chain organization to continuously improve system efficiency. In addition to delivering medical supplies the unit also oversees hospital vehicles.

The system partners with several leading IT companies (including Xi3 Intel Dell and NetApp) to operate its Healthcare Transformation Lab on the campus of its flagship hospital Intermountain Medical Center in Murray Utah. The lab researches develops and measures new ideas to improve patient care.

In 2016 the system launched Navican Genomics its genomics research and testing arm. Also that year it partnered with the Stanford Genome Technology Center to establish a collaborative research program.

Intermountain has a number of projects underway to add expand or replace existing facilities.

Company Background

Intermountain was formed in 1975 when the Church of Jesus Christ of Latter Day Saints donated 15 hospitals to local communities.

EXECUTIVES

Senior Vice President Community Health, Mikelle Moore
Senior Vice President, Greg Poulsen
Ceo Intermountain Medical Group And Vp Physician Division, Linda C. Leckman
President And Ceo Selecthealth, Patricia R. Richards
Evp And Cfo, Bert R. Zimmerli
Evp And Coo, Laura S. Kaiser
Regional Vp Central Region, Moody L. Chisholm
Vp And Cio, Marc Probst
President And Ceo, A. Marc Harrison, age 55
Regional Vp Soutwest Region, Terri Kane
Svp And Coo, Robert Allen
Vp Clinical Operations And Chief Nursing Officer, Kim Henrichsen
Regional Vp North Region, Timothy T. Pehrson
Chief Medical Officer, Brent E. Wallace
Ceo Primary Childrenâ's Medical Center, Katherine A. (Katy) Welkie
Regional Vp South Region, Steve Smoot
Vp Supply Chain And Support Services, Joe Walsh
Assistant Vice President Of Risk Management Services, Harlan Hammond
Assistant Vice President Investments, Stacy Jennings
Assistant Vice President Communications, Tom Vitelli
Assistant Vice President Compensation And Benefits, David Adams

Medical Director Utah County Region Intermountain Medical Group, Gordon Harkness
Vice President Healthcare Transformation, Joe Mott
Vice President, George Null Hamilton
Director Of Pharmacy, Scott Yardley
Medical Director, Dean Mayer
Assistant Vice President, Ray Morales
Medical Director, Scott Whittle
Vice President Of Pharmacy Affairs, Eric Cannon
Vice President Human Resources, Dan Zuhlke
Vice President And General Counsel, Doug Hammer
Medical Director, Tamara Lewis
Avp Pharmacy Services, Nannette Berensen
Assistant Vice President Clinical Is Operations, Tammy Madsen
Medical Director Community Health And Prevention, Tamara Sheffield
Pharmacy Manager, Robb Dengg
Pharmacy Manager, Bevan Jensen
Director Of Him, Mary Staub
Pharmacy Manager, Heather Hansen
Assistant Vice President Telehealth Services, Brian Wayling
Medical Director Clinical Genetics Institute, Steven Bleyl
Clinical Director Primary Children's Pediatric Behavioral Health Clinic, Nancy Cantor
Nursing Director, David Hurst
Vice President Of Operational Finance, Mark Runyon
Medical Director Informatics, Farukh Usmani
Pharmacy Manager, Lara Nye
Medical Director Palliative Medicine Mckay Dee Hospital, April Krutka
Pharmacy Director Vice President Of Pharmacy Services, Matt Mitchell
Vice Chairman, Bruce T. Reese
Chairman, A. Scott Anderson
Secretary, Nicole Houghton
Secretary, Jeri Lay
Secretary, Sheri Jones
Medical Secretary, Janet Staker
Medical Secretary, Renee Harston
Scheduling Secretary, Jeanine Price
Secretary, JoAnn Fountain
Medical Secretary, Sherri Longhurst
Secretary, Stephanie Stromberg
Secretary, Jodi Simmons
Auditors: KPMG LLP SALT LAKE CITY UT

LOCATIONS

HQ: INTERMOUNTAIN HEALTH CARE INC
36 S STATE ST STE 1600, SALT LAKE CITY, UT 841111633
Phone: 801 442-2000
Web: WWW.INTERMOUNTAINHEALTHCARE.ORG

PRODUCTS/OPERATIONS

2016 Sales

	$ mil.	% of total
Net patient services	4,368	57
Non-patient activities	3,010	40
Non-operating income	237	3
Total	**7,617**	**100**

Selected Hospitals

Alta View Hospital (Sandy UT)
American Fork Hospital (Utah)
Bear River Valley Hospital (Tremonton UT)
Cassia Regional Medical Center (Burley ID)
Delta Community Medical Center (Utah)
Dixie Regional Medical Center (St. George UT)
Fillmore Community Medical Center (Utah)
Garfield Memorial Hospital (Panguitch UT)
Heber Valley Medical Center (Heber City UT)
Intermountain Medical Center (Murray UT)
LDS Hospital (Salt Lake City)
Logan Regional Hospital (Orem UT)
McKay-Dee Hospital Center (Ogden UT)
   McKay-Dee Behavioral Health Institute

Orem Community Hospital (Utah)
Park City Medical Center (Park City UT)
Primary Children's Medical Center (Salt Lake City)
Riverton Hospital (Riverton UT)
Sanpete Valley Hospital (Mt. Pleasant UT)
Sevier Valley Hospital (Richfield UT)
TOSH - The Orthopedic Specialty Hospital (Murray UT)
Utah Valley Regional Medical Center (Provo UT)
Valley View Medical Center (Cedar City UT)

COMPETITORS

CHRISTUS Health	Regence BlueCross
Encompass Health	BlueShield of Utah
HCA	St. Mark's
LifePoint Health	University of Utah
Ogden Regional Medical	Hospitals & Clinics
Center	

HISTORICAL FINANCIALS

Company Type: Private

Income Statement   FYE: December 31

	REVENUE ($ mil.)	NET INCOME ($ mil.)	NET PROFIT MARGIN	EMPLOYEES
12/18	7,724	420	5.4%	35,000
12/17	6,940	1,061	15.3%	—
12/16	6,716	606	9.0%	—
12/15	6,058	155	2.6%	—
Annual Growth	8.4%	39.3%	—	—

2018 Year-End Financials

Return on assets: 3.3%
Return on equity: 5.3%
Current ratio: 1.40

Cash ($ mil.): 723

INTERNATIONAL RESCUE COMMITTEE, INC.

EXECUTIVES

Pres-Ceo, David Miliband
General Counsel*, Ricardo Castro
Cfo*, Danusia Dzierzbinski
Project Coordinator, Emelina Cesheshyan
Programmer Analyst, Adnan Suvalic
Director, Amanya Michael
Human Resources Administrator, Milagros Cruz
Human Resources Manager, Sead Eminovic
Procurement Staff, Sherif Blaku
Regional Director, Amanya Ebye
Benefits Coordinator, Carolyn Brodowski
Auditors: KPMG LLP NEW YORK NY

LOCATIONS

HQ: INTERNATIONAL RESCUE COMMITTEE, INC.
122 E 42ND ST, NEW YORK, NY 101680002
Phone: 212 551-3000
Web: WWW.RESCUE.ORG

HISTORICAL FINANCIALS

Company Type: Private

Income Statement   FYE: September 30

	REVENUE ($ mil.)	NET INCOME ($ mil.)	NET PROFIT MARGIN	EMPLOYEES
09/18	744	2	0.3%	8,000
09/17	753	44	5.9%	—
09/14	562	9	1.7%	—
09/11	397	11	2.9%	—
Annual Growth	9.4%	(19.9%)	—	—

2018 Year-End Financials

Return on assets: 0.6%
Return on equity: 1.1%
Current ratio: 1.60

Cash ($ mil.): 99

INTERNATIONAL WIRE GROUP, INC.

International Wire Group (IWG) bares it all in the wire business. Through three divisions — Bare Wire Products Engineered Products - Europe and High Performance Conductors — IWG makes multi-gauge bare silver- nickel- and tin-plated copper wire as well as engineered wire products and performance conductors. The company's customers (General Cable is one of its largest) include suppliers and OEMs. IWG's wire products are used in industrial/energy consumer electronics aerospace and defense medical electronics automotive and appliance applications.

Operations

The company's Bare Wire Products (or conductors) are used to transmit digital video and audio signals or conduct electricity and are sold to more than 1000 insulated wire manufacturers and various industrial OEMs for use in computer and data communications products general industrial energy appliances automobiles and other applications.

IWG's Engineered Products - Europe makes bare copper wire products which are sold to a diverse customer base of various OEMs in Europe.

Its High Performance Conductors include tin nickel and silver plated copper and copper alloy conductors including standard and customized conductors as well as specialty film insulated conductors and miniature tubing products.

Subsidiaries include US-based Continental Cordage a leading maker of braided wire for a wide range of commercial military and industrial applications and Tresse Metallique J. Forissier SAS and Italtrecce leading European makerd of bare copper wire products.

Geographic Reach

The company maintains 18 manufacturing plants and two distribution facilities in the US and Europe (Belgium France Italy and Poland). IWG makes the majority of its sales in the US.

Sales and Marketing

IWG serves customers in the electrical appliances power supplies aircraft railway and automotive system sectors. The volatile pricing of raw materials especially copper is a lingering concern for IWG. The company depends on four leading suppliers for copper and does not have long-term supply contracts with any of them creating concern about the reliability of IWG's copper supply chain. Many of the company's customers have their own captive (in-house) wire production facilities and

they could exclusively turn to those facilities reducing orders to IWG.

Mergers and Acquisitions

In 2011 the company expanded its operations through the purchase of the machinery and equipment of Ffhoenix Cuivre LLC in Santa Teresa New Mexico expanding the IWG's manufacturing capacity in the US Southwest. In addition IWG opened a new plant in Dabrowa Gornicza Poland allowing the company to better serve a growing customer base in Eastern Europe. Initial investment for these expansions totaled $14.5 million.

EXECUTIVES

Chb, Rodney D Kent
Sr V Pres-Cfo-Sec*, Glenn J Holler
V Pres Fin*, Donald F Dekay
V Pres Purchasing & Logistics*, Geoff Kent
Customer Representativ, Brett Charbonneau

LOCATIONS

HQ: INTERNATIONAL WIRE GROUP, INC.
12 MASONIC AVE, CAMDEN, NY 133161202
Phone: 315 245-2000
Web: WWW.INTERNATIONALWIREGROUP.COM

PRODUCTS/OPERATIONS

Selected Products

Bare wire products
  Bare and tin-plated copper wire (or conductors)
    Engineered
  Bare copper wire (to conduct electricity)
High performance conductors
  Conductors

COMPETITORS

A.E. Petsche	Nexans
Cerro Wire	Okonite
Driver-Harris	Owl Wire & Cable
Encore Wire	Prestolite Wire
LEONI	Republic Wire
LS Cable	Southwire
Loos & Co.	

HISTORICAL FINANCIALS

Company Type: Private

Income Statement   FYE: December 31

	REVENUE ($ mil.)	NET INCOME ($ mil.)	NET PROFIT MARGIN	EMPLOYEES
12/08	736	6	0.9%	1,600
12/07	730	15	2.2%	—
12/06	1,789	0	—	—
Annual Growth	—	13597.3%	—	—

2008 Year-End Financials

Return on assets: 1.8%
Return on equity: 3.6%
Current ratio: 2.10

Cash ($ mil.): 7

INVACARE CORPORATION (TW)

LOCATIONS

HQ: INVACARE CORPORATION (TW)
39400 TAYLOR PKWY, NORTH RIDGEVILLE, OH 440356270
Phone: 440 329-6000
Web: WWW.INVACARE.COM

HISTORICAL FINANCIALS
Company Type: Private

Income Statement				FYE: December 31
	REVENUE ($ mil.)	NET INCOME ($ mil.)	NET PROFIT MARGIN	EMPLOYEES
12/11	1,801	(4)	—	45
12/10	1,722	25	1.5%	—
12/09	1,693	41	2.4%	—
Annual Growth	3.1%	—	—	—

2011 Year-End Financials
Return on assets: (-0.3%)   Cash ($ mil.): 34
Return on equity: (-0.7%)
Current ratio: 1.80

IOWA HEALTH SYSTEM

The land where the tall corn grows is also the land of Iowa Health System (IHS) which does business as UnityPoint. The integrated health care system operates some 15 acute care hospitals that serve large communities throughout Iowa as well as parts of western Illinois and Madison Wisconsin. UnityPoint also supports about a dozen rural hospitals and it manages about 300 physician clinics located in rural and suburban areas. The system's hospitals provide general medical-surgical care as well as care in a number of medical specialties such as cardiovascular disease and home health services. Founded in 1993 UnityPoint has about 3700 licensed beds.

Operations
In 2014 the system had about 155000 patient admissions facilitated 20000 births and saw a total of some 4.5 million patients.

Geographic Reach
UnityPoint Health includes a dozen hospitals in 10 Iowa cities four in Illinois and another in Wisconsin. Its largest geographic markets served are Anamosa Cedar Rapids Des Moines Dubuque Fort Dodge Sioux City and Waterloo Iowa; the Quad Cities/Muscatine region in Iowa and Illinois; Peoria Illinois; and Madison Wisconsin.

Strategy
In early 2013 Iowa Health System rebranded itself UnityPoint to showcase its mission to be a point of unity for patient care. It probably also helped that the company was expanding and including health care facilities in other states. That same year it picked up new affiliates in Illinois expanded its broadband Internet access program across Iowa and added Meriter Health Services of Madison Wisconsin. The health system operates many of its member hospitals through similar affiliation agreements where it provides administration contracting billing legal recruitment information technology and other central services. In 2015 the system built a new primary care facility in Cedar Falls Iowa.

The system is also expanding in areas beyond its physical locations. In 2015 it partnered with MDLive to begin offering telehealth services in Iowa and it added a plane to its air ambulance fleet. UnityPoint also plans to launch a new insurance firm with not-for-profit organization Health-Partners.

EXECUTIVES

President And Ceo Unitypoint Health -des Moines, Eric Crowell
Vp And Cio, Joy M. Grosser
Ceo, Kevin Vermeer

Vp Supply Chain Management, Katie Marchik
Svp And Cfo, Mark Johnson
Evp And Coo; President And Ceo Meriter-unitypoint Health Madison, Arthur Nizza
Vp Payor Innovation; Ceo Unitypoint At Work, Brian Jones
Ceo Unitypoint Health -st. Luke's -sioux City, Lynn Wold
Ceo Jones Regional Medical Center Anamosa, Eric Briesemeister
President And Ceo Unitypoint Health -dubuque, David Brandon
President And Ceo Unitypoint Health -peoria, Debbie Simon
President And Ceo Unitypoint Health -trinity (quad Cities Muscatine), Rick Seidler
President And Ceo Unitypoint Health -waterloo, Pam Delagardelle
President And Ceo St. Luke's -cedar Rapids, Ted Townsend
Ceo Unitypoint Health Partners, David Williams
Svp Insurance Division And Ceo Physicians Plus Insurance Corporation (ppic), Troy Caraway
Evp And Coo Unitypoint Health Des Moines And Interim Ceo Unitypoint Clinic, Steve Stephenson
Svp Integration And Optimization And Interim Ceo Unitypoint At Home, Susan K. Thompson
President And Ceo Unitypoint Health Fort Dodge, Mike Dewerff
Vice President People Excellence, Emily Porter
Vice President Of Practice Operations, Matt Behrens
Vice President Network Business Services Development, Lori Weih
Medical Director Finley Wound Care Center, David Arnold
Chairman, Mike Williams
Vice Chair, Mike Stone
Secretary, Lucinda Barnes
Department Secretary, Allison Kamerling
Department Secretary, Diane Hagan
Auditors: BKD LLP KANSAS CITY MO

LOCATIONS

HQ: IOWA HEALTH SYSTEM
  1776 WEST LAKES PKWY # 400, WEST DES MOINES, IA 502668377
Phone: 515 241-6161
Web: WWW.UNITYPOINT.ORG

PRODUCTS/OPERATIONS

Selected Facilities
Metropolitan Hospitals
  Allen Memorial Hospital Corporation (Waterloo Iowa)
  Iowa Lutheran Hospital (Des Moines Iowa)
  Iowa Methodist Medical Center (Des Moines Iowa)
  Blank Children's Hospital (Des Moines Iowa)
  Methodist Medical Center of Illinois (Peoria Illinois)
  Methodist West Hospital (West Des Moines Iowa)
  St. Luke's Hospital (Cedar Rapids Iowa)
  St. Luke's Regional Medical Center (Sioux City Iowa)
  Jones Regional Medical Center (Anamosa Iowa)
  The Finley Hospital (Dubuque Iowa)
  Trinity Bettendorf (Bettendorf Iowa)
  Trinity Moline (Moline Illinois)
  Trinity Muscatine (Muscatine Iowa)
  Trinity Regional Medical Center (Fort Dodge Iowa)
  Trinity Rock Island (Rock Island Illinois)
Rural Hospitals
  Buena Vista Regional Medical Center (Storm Lake Iowa)
  Clarke County Hospital (Osceola Iowa)
  Community Memorial Hospital (Sumner Iowa)
  Greater Regional Medical Center (Creston Iowa)
  Greene County Medical Center (Jefferson Iowa)
  Grundy County Memorial Hospital (Grundy Center Iowa)
  Guthrie County Hospital (Guthrie Center Iowa)
  Guttenberg Municipal Hospital (Guttenberg Iowa)
  Humboldt County Memorial Hospital (Humboldt Iowa)
  Loring Hospital (Sac City Iowa)
  Pocahontas Community Hospital (Pocahontas Iowa)

COMPETITORS

Avera Health	Mercy Health Network
Blessing Hospital	Methodist Health
CHI Health	System
Genesis Health System	OSF Healthcare System
McDonough District Hospital	

HISTORICAL FINANCIALS
Company Type: Private

Income Statement				FYE: December 31
	REVENUE ($ mil.)	NET INCOME ($ mil.)	NET PROFIT MARGIN	EMPLOYEES
12/17	4,157	229	5.5%	18,923
12/16	4,054	148	3.7%	—
Annual Growth	2.5%	54.4%	—	—

2017 Year-End Financials
Return on assets: 4.1%   Cash ($ mil.): 251
Return on equity: 6.8%
Current ratio: 1.50

IOWA PHYSICIANS CLINIC MEDICAL FOUNDATION

EXECUTIVES

Pres, Daniel P Allen
Cfo, Robin McNichols
SEC, Kenneth W Anderson

LOCATIONS

HQ: IOWA PHYSICIANS CLINIC MEDICAL FOUNDATION
  8101 BIRCHWOOD CT UNIT N, JOHNSTON, IA 501312930
Phone: 515 471-9200

HISTORICAL FINANCIALS
Company Type: Private

Income Statement				FYE: December 31
	REVENUE ($ mil.)	NET INCOME ($ mil.)	NET PROFIT MARGIN	EMPLOYEES
12/17	600	17	3.0%	1,000
12/00	76	(13)	—	—
12/99	8	2	31.3%	—
12/98	61	(19)	—	—
Annual Growth	12.8%	—	—	—

2017 Year-End Financials
Return on assets: 8.6%   Cash ($ mil.): 11
Return on equity: 26.0%
Current ratio: 2.30

IOWA STATE UNIVERSITY OF SCIENCE AND TECHNOLOGY

Home to the Cyclones athletics teams Iowa State University of Science and Technology (ISU) can be a whirlwind experience for some. ISU is a public land-grant institution offering higher education courses and programs with an emphasis on science technology and related areas. ISU's eight colleges offer more than 100 undergraduate degrees and nearly 200 fields of study leading to graduate and professional degrees. The university has an enrollment of more than 31000 students and charges more than $7720 in tuition and fees for resident students for two semesters.

Operations
In fiscal 2012 Iowa State received $360.2 million in grants contracts co-operative agreements and gifts of which about 60% is utilized for research purpose. The university's research park has about 20000 square feet of incubators space including office and laboratories.

Geographic Reach
The university enrolls students from 50 states and more than 100 countries.

Financial Performance
The 6% increase in revenues in 2012 was due to higher tuition and fees sales and services of educational activities and auxiliary enterprise revenues. The tuition revenue increase was to a 5% hike in the resident tuition rate coupled with record enrollments. The increase in sales and services of educational activities was due to large one-time events ISU farms and the Vet Diagnostic Lab. ISU's auxiliary enterprises reported revenue growth thanks to new revenue sources and a record number of students in the residence system.

ISU's net income increased by 47% in 2012 thanks to higher operating expenses and a decline in non-operating revenues. Non-operating revenues decreased $24.4 million thanks to an $11 million decrease in funding from education appropriations. Investment income also dropped $16.3 million or 49% mainly due to an unrealized loss in the value of investments.

Company Background
Chartered as Iowa Agriculture College in 1858 the school first officially opened for classes in 1869. Among ISU's notable alumni is scientist and inventor George Washington Carver.

EXECUTIVES

Vice President, Atalie Ruhnke
Vice President, Karen Bramow
Vice President Membership Development, Tyler Brodeur
Medical Director, Jeffrey Rayl
Department Chair Lynn Gleason Professor Of Interdisciplinary Engineering, Caroline Hayes
Director Of Nursing, Laura Knowles
Associate Vice President For Student Affairs, Vernon Hurte
Vice President, Aline Sartor-chicowski
Vice President, Parker Bibus
Secretary, Lina Doering
Secretary, Joyce Wray
Secretary, Traci Stewart
Secretary Department Of Agricultural And Biosystems Engineering, Kristine Bell
Secretary, Nancy Paris
Secretary, Suzanne Wirth
Secretary, Paula Kokemiller
Secretary, Katherine Petersen
Secretary, Annmarie Butler
Secretary, Jane E Blair
Auditors: MARY MOSIMAN CPA DES MOINES

LOCATIONS

HQ: IOWA STATE UNIVERSITY OF SCIENCE AND TECHNOLOGY
515 MORRILL RD, AMES, IA 500112105
Phone: 515 294-6162
Web: WWW.IASTATE.EDU

PRODUCTS/OPERATIONS

Colleges
Agriculture and Life Sciences
Business
Design
Engineering
Graduate
Human Sciences
Liberal Arts and Sciences
Veterinary Medicine

HISTORICAL FINANCIALS
Company Type: Private

Income Statement FYE: June 30

	REVENUE ($ mil.)	NET INCOME ($ mil.)	NET PROFIT MARGIN	EMPLOYEES
06/18	948	58	6.2%	5,800
06/17	920	77	8.4%	—
06/16	902	67	7.5%	—
06/15	858	67	7.8%	—
Annual Growth	3.4%	(4.3%)	—	—

2018 Year-End Financials
Return on assets: 2.2%   Cash ($ mil.): 28
Return on equity: 3.7%
Current ratio: 1.10

IRVINE UNIFIED SCHOOL DISTICT

EXECUTIVES

Superintendent, Terry Walker
Ceo*, Michael B Regele
Director of Operations Seconda, Allison Robbins
Assistant, Amy Paulsen
Programmer Analyst, Anna Arkof
Teacher Humanities, Barbara Hall
Administrative Assistant, Becca Lane
Financial Analyst, Becky Myers
Coordinator Visual, Brad Van Patten
5th Grade Teacher, Carrie Eaton
Principals Secretary, Christina Sanchez
Auditors: VAVRINEK TRINE DAY & CO LL

LOCATIONS

HQ: IRVINE UNIFIED SCHOOL DISTICT
5050 BARRANCA PKWY, IRVINE, CA 926044698
Phone: 949 936-5000
Web: WWW.IUSD.ORG

HISTORICAL FINANCIALS
Company Type: Private

Income Statement FYE: June 30

	REVENUE ($ mil.)	NET INCOME ($ mil.)	NET PROFIT MARGIN	EMPLOYEES
06/18	497	(1)	—	2,212
06/17	380	138	36.5%	—
06/16	360	(61)	—	—
06/09	278	19	7.0%	—
Annual Growth	6.7%	—	—	—

J M SMITH CORPORATION

J M Smith Corporation has gone from corner drugstore to supplying drugstores and more. The family-owned holding company's primary subsidiary is Smith Drug which provides purchasing and distribution services for more than 1000 independent pharmacies in more than 20 US states. It also operates through QS/1 Data Systems and Integral Solutions both of which offer data management software and services for pharmacies care providers and government agencies. Smith Premier provides prescription benefit management while other divisions offer automated dispensing systems for pharmacies and marketing services for drugmakers. Other units include Norgenix and RxMedic Systems.

Operations
The company operates through six business units: Smith Drug Company QS/1 Smith Premier Services Integral Solutions Group Norgenix and RxMedic Systems.

In addition to being its oldest subsidiary J M Smith's core Smith Drug unit is one of the top private wholesale drug distributors in the US. The company's Smith Premier unit also has a nationwide presence providing prescription management services through some 57000 contracted pharmacies.

Meanwhile the growing QS/1 division has installed more than 12000 health care and pharmacy automation systems and has more than 20 service offices across the US. The Integral Solutions unit which has about 15 offices scattered across the nation offers communication networking systems for universities banks and manufacturers in addition to health care customers.

J M Smith newest subsidiary Norgenix is a specialty pharmaceutical medical device and biotech company that engages in the development commercialization and sales of pharmaceutical products that serve the unmet needs within women's health. It acquires or licenses rights for select pharmaceuticals which it then markets through its direct sales force in North America. Norgenix is focused on the women's health markets and began marketing its first hormone replacement therapy in 2009.

RxMedic Systems provides leading-edge dispensing technology to pharmacies.

Geographic Reach
Smith Drug serves customers in 21 states primarily in the southern US as well as Washington DC and the Virgin Islands.

Sales and Marketing
The company supplies products services and technologies to pharmacies institutions local government agencies and businesses across the US.

Strategy

J M Smith's cornerstone Smith Drug subsidiary continues to be a key growth component doubling the number of states in which it operates over the last decade. However the company is also extolling its energies towards developing and introducing innovative data management and technology solutions through other subsidiaries to meet the rising demand for such solutions in the health care market.

Smith Premier is working to help customers go paperless by offering electronic prescription processing while RxMedic's dispensing systems allow pharmacies to increase productivity with its robotic counting and dispensing equipment.

The company's QS/1 subsidiary has experienced rapid growth in recent years as pharmacies and care providers increasingly look to automate processes and the Integral Solutions unit also benefits from recent trends in the health care market to improve electronic communication systems.

Partnerships are also key to J M Smith's growth. In 2014 Norgenix partnered with CrossBay Medical for the co-promotion of the SonoSure a device for use to access the uterine cavity for saline infusion sonohysterography and to obtain an endometrial biopsy if needed using the same device.

Mergers and Acquisitions

In late 2016 the company agreed to buy Vermont-based Burlington Drug Company which serves community pharmacies in New England and New York as well as certain assets of Pharmacy Health Services. The moves will broaden J M Smith's presence in the Northeast a target market for the company.

Company Background

In 2010 Smith expanded by acquiring health equipment manufacturing firm RxMedic. Through the purchase the company entered the automated dispensing system market.

J M Smith was founded in 1943 by drugstore proprietor James Smith and is run by the Smith family.

EXECUTIVES

President Integral Solutions Group (isg), Joe Strayer
President Smith Drug Company, Jeff Foreman
President Integra Ltc Solutions Llc, Kevin Welch
Chairman And Ceo, A. Alan Turfe
President Qs/1, Saul Factor
Cfo And Treasurer, Philip J. Ryan
Senior Vice President Business Development, Rick Simerly
Vice President General Counsel And Corporate Secretary, Robert Barrett
Vice President Global Services, Donna Johnson

LOCATIONS

HQ: J M SMITH CORPORATION
101 W SAINT JOHN ST # 305, SPARTANBURG, SC
293065150
Phone: 864 542-9419
Web: WWW.JMSMITHCORP.COM

Selected Office Locations
Altamonte Springs FL
Brandon MS
Columbia SC
Dallas TX
Fairmont WV
Gray ME
Hermitage PA
Houston TX
Indianapolis IN
Lexington KY
Mechanicsburg PA
Miami FL
Morrisville GA
Paragould AR
Perry GA
Pleasant Hill MO

Richmond VA
Seattle WA
Spartanburg SC
St. Paul MN
Sturbridge MA
Valdosta GA
Valencia CA
Wake Forest NC

PRODUCTS/OPERATIONS

Selected Divisions
Integral Solutions Group
Norgenix Pharmaceuticals
QS/1
RxMedic
Smith Drug Company
Smith Premier Services

COMPETITORS

AmerisourceBergen
CVS
Cardinal Health
Express Scripts
Fiserv
H. D. Smith Wholesale Drug

HP Enterprise Services
Kinray
McKesson
PharMerica

HISTORICAL FINANCIALS

Company Type: Private

Income Statement				FYE: February 28
	REVENUE ($ mil.)	NET INCOME ($ mil.)	NET PROFIT MARGIN	EMPLOYEES
02/15	2,566	47	1.8%	235
02/14	2,370	38	1.6%	—
02/13	2,362	26	1.1%	—
Annual Growth	4.2%	33.8%	—	—

2015 Year-End Financials
Return on assets: 8.1%
Return on equity: 16.0%
Current ratio: 1.60
Cash ($ mil.): 142

J.E. DUNN CONSTRUCTION COMPANY

From first building designs to the last brick J.E. Dunn Construction helps make building plans a done deal. The contractor offers general construction services construction management and design/build services nationwide. It's known for its work on campus health care and commercial projects including the Mizzou Arena at the University of Missouri the H&R Block headquarters the Topfer Theatre at ZACH and the National Nuclear Security Administration campus. Founded in 1924 the company is one of Kansas City's top commercial construction firms and has been listed as one of the nation's top 10 general building companies. It operates as a subsidiary of J.E. Dunn Construction Group.

Operations

JE Dunn has ranked as one of the top 15 largest general building companies in the US in recent years. It counts several noteworthy projects among its portfolio such as CyrusOne Phoenix Data Center Tucson Medical Center West Campus CCA La Palma Correctional Center Lone Butte Casino

Oasis Hospital Mountain Vista Medical Center and West Valley Medical Center Hospital.

Geographic Reach

Based in Kansas City Missouri JE Dunn operates about 20 offices throughout the US.

Sales and Marketing

JE Dunn works on projects for clients in several sectors including projects related to: science and technology corporate environments healthcare hospitality government and military energy and utility education and multifamily residential properties among others.

Financial Performance

While full financial information of the privately-held company were not available the company reported that it brings in annual revenue of $2.7 billion as of early 2015.

Strategy

J.E. Dunn Construction Company has been busy working on a variety of different projects in recent years. As of early 2015 JE Dunn's project portfolio included: the Health Care Patient Tower at the University of Missouri the Jennie Smoly Caruthers Biotechnology Building at the University of Colorado at Boulder the National Renewable Energy Laboratory (NREL) Energy System Integration Facility (Phase I) the Outpatient Cancer Center and parking garage for the Georgia Regents Health System and the new headquarters for the school-improvement group AdvancED. In 2013 JE Dunn completed a $300-million-plus renovation of the Kansas Capitol Building which involved renovating underground areas previously occupied by storage and maintenance areas into new space with improved ventilation technology and security.

JE Dunn is also adding offices to position itself near new target growth areas. To this end in early 2013 it opened an office in Williston North Dakota.

Company Background

In the past JE Dunn grew through acquisitions purchasing RJ Griffin & Co. (Atlanta) in 2000 Witcher Construction (Minneapolis) in 1990 and Drake Construction (Portland Oregon) in 1992.

EXECUTIVES

President & Chief Executive Officer, Gordon E. Lansford
Midwest Regional President, Dirk Schafer
Evp And Chief Risk Officer, Casey S. Halsey
Evp And Chief Legal Officer, Thomas F. (Tom) Whittaker
President Je Dunn Rocky Mountain, Steve Hamline
East Regional President, Dan Kaufman
Cio, John Jacobs
South Central Regional President, Greg Lorei
Cfo, Beth Soukup
Evp And Chief Marketing Officer, Greg Nook
Vice President, Tom Heger
Vice President, Mike Cloud
Vice President, Brent Ferguson
Assistant Vice President Field Operations, Bob Jacquinot
Senior Vice President, Bill Edwards
Vice President, Dave Ruf
Senior Vice President, Randall Bredar
Vice President Of Audit, John Conley
Vice President Systems Quality Assurance, Michael Clippinger
Vice President Preconstruction, Justin Griffin
Vice President, Curtis Golba
Vice President Operations, Marc Hutson
Vice President Engineering Services, David Barber
Senior Vice President, James Miller
Vice President Marketing, Diane Miller
Vice President, Chris Cole
Executive Vice President Field Operations, Dan Hotchkiss
Vice President, Jeff Blaesing

Senior Vice President Risk Management, Robert Jacquinot
Vice President Healthcare, Bill Igel
Vice President, Donnie Lindstrom
Vice President, Jim Ray
Vice President Group Manager, Jake Nellis
Vice President Industrial Group, Brent Strength
Vice President, Angela Talbot
Vice President Of Communications, Emily Gallagher
Vice President Of Operations, Matthew Braun
Vice President, Gene Mccarthy
Vice President East Region, Pat Arrington
Vice President, Patrick Oaks
Vice President Chc, Todd Freed
Vice President Division Manager, Paul Fenzel
Vice President Business Development, Keith Knight
Vice President Project Manager, Eugene Smith
Senior Vice President, Jeff Hicks
Sr. Vp Business Development, Bob Maxwell
Senior Vice President, Kevin O'gara
Vice President Group Manager, Sean Buck
Vice President, Jeff Camplwell
Vp Director Of Real Estate Investment And Business Development, Michael Collins
Vp Diversity Inclusion And Compliance, Pete Burney
Vice President, Terry Dunn
Vice Chair, William H Dunn
Chairman, Steve Dunn
Secretary, Barbara Hachey
Secretary, Barb Hachey
Auditors: KPMG LLP KANSAS CITY MISSOU

LOCATIONS

HQ: J.E. DUNN CONSTRUCTION COMPANY
  1001 LOCUST ST, KANSAS CITY, MO 641061904
Phone: 816 474-8600
Web: WWW.JEDUNN.COM

PRODUCTS/OPERATIONS

Selected Project Delivery Methods
Competitive Bid
Construction Management (Agency)
Design-Build
General Contracting/CM At Risk
Integrated Project Delivery
Project Management

COMPETITORS

Adolfson & Peterson Inc.	H.J. Russell
Barnhart	Hensel Phelps Construction
Boran Craig Barber Engel	Korte
C.F. Jordan	M. A. Mortenson
CORE Construction	MEDCO Construction
Clarkson Construction	Skanska USA Building
Flintco	Turner Corporation
	Weitz

HISTORICAL FINANCIALS

Company Type: Private

Income Statement				FYE: December 31
	REVENUE ($ mil.)	NET INCOME ($ mil.)	NET PROFIT MARGIN	EMPLOYEES
12/17	2,945	0	—	1,635
12/16	2,909	0	—	—
12/15	2,909	0	—	—
12/14	2,242	0	—	—
Annual Growth	9.5%	—	—	—

2017 Year-End Financials

Return on assets: —
Return on equity: —
Current ratio: 1.10
Cash ($ mil.): 29

J.E. DUNN CONSTRUCTION GROUP, INC.

Owned by descendants of founder John Ernest Dunn J.E. Dunn Construction Group operates as the holding company for a group of construction firms that includes flagship J.E. Dunn Construction and Atlanta-based R.J. Griffin & Company. Founded in 1924 it builds institutional commercial and industrial structures nationwide. It also provides construction and program management and design/build services. J.E. Dunn Construction which is among the largest US general builders was one of the first contractors to offer the construction management delivery method. Some of its major projects have included an IRS facility and the world headquarters for H&R Block both located in Kansas City Missouri.

Operations
Besides its primary operations of J.E. Dunn Construction and R.J. Griffin & Company the construction company runs Dunn Project Solutions a construction services unit that tackles projects ranging in size from $50000 to $5 million. The business focuses on projects related to corporate interiors retail improvements historic rehabilitation additions fixtures and equipment building upgrades maintenance work and small office projects.

The company's ranked as the 10th largest general building company in the US in 2015.

Geographic Reach
Headquartered in Kansas City Missouri J.E. Dunn operates some 20 offices across the nation. It has offices in Georgia Texas North Carolina Colorado Iowa Missouri Minnesota Tennessee Oklahoma Nebraska Arizona Oregon Kansas and North Dakota.

Sales and Marketing
The company works on corporate environments mission critical correctional/justice and mixed use/retail projects among others.

Financial Performance
J.E. Dunn Construction last reported annual revenues of more than $2.6 billion in 2014.

Strategy
Some of the group's more recent projects projects include work on the North Dakota governor's residence and the new Bank of North Dakota Financial Center in Bismark (2016); the Harold Newman Arena in Jamestown (2016); the Trinity High School reconstruction and expansion project (2016); the building of the 378000 sq. ft. Cambridge North Tower at The University of Kansas Hospital (September 2017); the 92000 sq. ft. entertainment of the arts at the University of Colorado; the 151000 sq. ft. expansion project on an inpatient pavilion at the UCHealth University of Colorado Hospital (May 2015); the 92000 sq. ft. Fallen Fire Fighter Memorial in Colorado Springs (June 2015); and the 160000 sq. ft. CHI St. Joseph's Hospital and Health Center (October 2014).

Past projects include work on the Charles R. Drew Charter School Senior Academy the Kauffman Center for the Performing Arts the Topfer Theatre at ZACH the Energy Systems Integration Facility (ESIF) the Collaborative Life Sciences Building & Skourtes Tower and the Georgia Regents Health System Outpatient Cancer. Other past projects have included Baylor Scott & White Cancer Center Hotel Sorella GSA National Nuclear Security Administration City of Houston Bethel Park Renovation and the B.E. Smith Corporate Headquarters Renovation.

Company Background
A bigwig particularly in the Midwest the group regularly bids on federal government projects. J.E. Dunn won a major contract from the US Army Corps of Engineers to build a regional correctional facility at Fort Leavenworth Kansas that replaced smaller prisons in Texas Kentucky and Oklahoma.

In 2012 the company earned the designation of having the first ever LEED Gold Certified building in downtown Kansas City.

The descendants of John Ernest Dunn hold a majority stake in the company.

EXECUTIVES

Evp And Cfo, Gordon E. Lansford
President Midwest Region, Dirk Schafer
Evp, William H. (Bill) Dunn
Evp And Chief Risk Officer, Casey S. Halsey
President West Region, Steve Hamline
Evp Marketing, Gregory E. (Greg) Nook
President East Region, Dan Kaufman
Evp And Chief Legal Officer, Tom Whittaker
Cio, John Jacobs
President South Central, Greg Lorei
Cfo, Beth Soukup
Vice President, Mike Barr
Senior Vice President, David L Disney
Senior Vice President, Patrick Dennis
Assistant Vice President And Director Of Compensation And Benefits, Stephen Best
Senior Vice President, Bob Dunn
Chairman, Stephen D. (Steve) Dunn
Auditors: KPMG LLP KANSAS CITY MISSOUR

LOCATIONS

HQ: J.E. DUNN CONSTRUCTION GROUP, INC.
  1001 LOCUST ST, KANSAS CITY, MO 641061904
Phone: 816 474-8600
Web: WWW.JEDUNN.COM

PRODUCTS/OPERATIONS

Selected Group Companies
JE Dunn Midwest
JE Dunn North Central
JE Dunn Northwest
JE Dunn Rocky Mountain
JE Dunn South Central
R.J. Griffin & Company

Selected Services
Preconstruction
  Constructability review
  Feasibility studies
  Market analysis
  Mechanical electrical plumbing review
  Preconstruction estimating
  Quality control
  Risk management
  Scheduling
Construction
  Change order management
  Labor relations
  Progress monitoring
  Quality control and testing
Post Construction
  Commissioning
  Final closeout
  Lien releases
  One-year walkthrough
  Operations and maintenance manuals

COMPETITORS

Alberici	Skanska USA Building
Clark Enterprises	Sundt
Hensel Phelps Construction	Turner Corporation
Hunt Construction	Tutor Perini
McCarthy Building	Weitz
	Whiting-Turner

HISTORICAL FINANCIALS
Company Type: Private

	REVENUE ($ mil.)	NET INCOME ($ mil.)	NET PROFIT MARGIN	EMPLOYEES
				FYE: December 31
12/17	2,947	0	—	2,080
12/15	2,910	0	—	—
12/14	2,243	0	—	—
12/13	2,243	0	—	—
Annual Growth	7.1%	—	—	—

JACKSON ELECTRIC MEMBERSHIP CORPORATION

Jackson EMC distributes electricity to more than 197800 individual customers (more than 210200 meters) in 10 counties around Atlanta and in northeastern Georgia. The majority of customers are residential with commercial and industrial customers accounting for 42% of fiscal year 2013 revenues. One of the largest nonprofit power cooperatives in the US and the largest electric cooperative in Georgia Jackson EMC is owned by its members. The cooperative's generation and transmission partners include Oglethorpe Power Corp. Georgia Systems Operation and Georgia Transmission Corp.

Operations
Jackson EMC operates 86 substations and more than 13550 miles of power line.

Financial Performance
In fiscal 2013 the coop reported a revenue increased of 1%. Net income declined slightly by 0.3%. That year the non-profit coop returned $5.5 million in margin refunds to nearly 201000 members.

Strategy
Among other initiatives Jackson EMC is promoting conservation and green energy options as a way to slow energy growth and reduce greenhouse gas emissions. Initiatives include advocating the use of more efficient light bulbs and the widespread use of solar panels for power generation.

Company Background
Although the county of Jackson is named after a Georgia statesman from the Revolutionary War era Jackson Electric Membership Corporation (Jackson EMC) can trace its roots more directly to US president Franklin Roosevelt whose frequent trips to Warm Springs alerted him to the shortage of affordable electric power outside of major cities. Jackson EMC was founded in 1938 as part of the Roosevelt government's national rural electrification drive.

EXECUTIVES

Vp Of Marketing, Stefano Sandoval
Auditors: MCNAIR MCLEMORE MIDDLEBROOKS &

LOCATIONS

HQ: JACKSON ELECTRIC MEMBERSHIP CORPORATION
850 COMMERCE RD, JEFFERSON, GA 305493329
Phone: 706 367-5281
Web: WWW.JACKSONEMC.COM

HISTORICAL FINANCIALS
Company Type: Private

	REVENUE ($ mil.)	NET INCOME ($ mil.)	NET PROFIT MARGIN	EMPLOYEES
				FYE: May 31
05/18	548	37	6.8%	445
05/17*	518	28	5.5%	—
12/15	541	0	—	—
12/14	527	0	—	—
Annual Growth	1.3%	—	—	—

*Fiscal year change

2018 Year-End Financials

Return on assets: 3.7% Cash ($ mil.): 27
Return on equity: 8.6%
Current ratio: 1.30

JACKSON HEALTHCARE, LLC

Jackson Healthcare can help find physicians to work at hospitals and help keep track of patients as they enter and leave hospitals. Its staffing businesses offer job search recruiting and placement services for physicians and other health care professionals; provide anesthesiologists; and coordinate the work of traveling nurses. Jackson Healthcare's physician job boards attract thousands of visitors per month giving it a reputation for filling openings quickly. Subsidiary Patient Placement Systems manages patient flow through the medical system and Care Logistics provides patient tracking software. Richard Jackson formed the company in 1978.

Operations
Jackson Healthcare operates more than a dozen subsidiaries and operations units and serves more than 7 million patients spread throughout 1300 health care facilities.

Subsidiaries and divisions include Premier Anesthesia Jackson Therapy Partners LucumTenens.com Jackson Nurse Professionals and Jackson & Coker. Other operations include AdvancedPractice.com Jackson Surgical Assistants Jackson Pharmacy Professionals Tyler & Company and Parker HealthcareIT.

Its health care software and technology portfolio is managed by Care Logistics and Patient Placement Systems.

Mergers and Acquisitions
Jackson Healthcare's growth strategy involves acquiring other staffing businesses to augment its geographical reach. In 2014 it purchased Sullivan Healthcare Consulting (SHC) a Michigan-based firm focused on improving the performance of the hospital's perioperative suite.

EXECUTIVES

Managing Director Jackson Healthcare, Paul D. Foster
President And Ceo Jackson Therapy Partners, Scott L'Heureux
Ceo, Richard L. Jackson
President Jackson Healthcare And Locumtenens.com, R. Shane Jackson
Vp Human Resources, Michael Hiffa
Cto, Tim Aligheri
Cfo, Douglas B. Kline
President Care Logistics, Karl Straub
President Premier Anesthesia, Kerry Teel

President Advancedpractice.com, Susan Mesa
President Jackson & Coker Permanent Placement, Tony Stajduhar
President And Ceo Parker Health Care It, Debbie Crandall
President Healthit Project Managers, Jack Williams
Vp And General Manager Healthcare Staffing Technologies, Karyn Mullins
Vp Advancedpractice.com And Jackson Pharmacy Professionals, David McAnally
Vp And General Manager Patient Placement Systems, Doug Walker
Cio, Ryan Esparza
Vice President Property Management, Leslie Harrell
Vice President Human Resources, Matthew Harrison
National Accounts Manager, Julie Ianni
Vice Chairman, William H. Franklin

LOCATIONS

HQ: JACKSON HEALTHCARE, LLC
2655 NORTHWINDS PKWY, ALPHARETTA, GA 300092280
Phone: 770 643-5500
Web: WWW.JACKSONHEALTHCARE.COM

PRODUCTS/OPERATIONS

Selected Subsidiaries and Operating Units
Jackson Healthcare Staffing
  AdvancedPractice.com (a full-service locum tenens agency dedicated to physician assistants and nurse practitioners)
  Healthcare Staffing Technologies (provider of career concierge sites in the healthcare market)
  HealthIT Project Managers (provider of experienced IT project management contractors to hospitals)
  Jackson & Coker (locum tenens and permanent recruitment firm for physicians)
  Jackson Nurse Professionals (specializes in the placement of registered nurses in healthcare settings nationwide)
  Jackson Pharmacy Professionals (national pharmacy-only staffing and recruiting company)
  Jackson Surgical Assistants (staffing of certified surgical assistants to surgeons and hospitals)
  Jackson Therapy Partners (staffing of rehabilitation therapists and other allied healthcare professionals)
  LocumTenens.com (locum tenens physician recruitment agency)
  Parker HealthcareIT (provider of supplemental IT staffing)
  Premier Anesthesia (anesthesia department management company)
Jackson Healthcare Technology
  Care Logistics (firm that helps hospitals transform their operations to deliver hospital efficiency)
  Patient Placement Systems (supplier of continuing care provider software)

COMPETITORS

AMN Healthcare	Gentiva
ATC Healthcare	Kelly Services
Adecco	ManpowerGroup
CHG Healthcare	On Assignment
CompHealth	RehabCare
Cross Country Healthcare	TeamStaff
	inVentiv Health

HISTORICAL FINANCIALS
Company Type: Private

	REVENUE ($ mil.)	NET INCOME ($ mil.)	NET PROFIT MARGIN	EMPLOYEES
				FYE: December 31
12/17	949	99	10.5%	949
12/16	838	93	11.1%	—
12/15	696	70	10.2%	—
12/07	384	18	4.8%	—
Annual Growth	9.5%	18.4%	—	—

2017 Year-End Financials

Return on assets: 25.6% Cash ($ mil.): 65
Return on equity: 132.6%
Current ratio: 3.60

JACKSON-MADISON COUNTY GENERAL HOSPITAL DISTRICT

EXECUTIVES

Pres-Ceo, James Ross
Chm*, Phil Bryant
Cfo*, Jeffrey Blankenship
Coordinator, Trisha Ross
Executive Director, Bart Teague
Director, Mary Bryant
Director, Angela Holmes
Engineer, Kris Lee-Vester
Marketing Manager, Cathy Sudbury
Information Technology Manager, Currie Higgs
Registered Nurse, Keith McGuire

LOCATIONS

HQ: JACKSON-MADISON COUNTY GENERAL
  HOSPITAL DISTRICT
  620 SKYLINE DR, JACKSON, TN 383013923
Phone: 731 541-5000
Web: WWW.WTH.ORG

HISTORICAL FINANCIALS

Company Type: Private

Income Statement				FYE: June 30
	REVENUE ($ mil.)	NET INCOME ($ mil.)	NET PROFIT MARGIN	EMPLOYEES
06/16	597	10	1.8%	6,000
06/15	554	20	3.7%	—
06/04	429	37	8.6%	—
06/03	307	247	80.4%	—
Annual Growth	5.3%	(21.4%)	—	—

2016 Year-End Financials

Return on assets: 1.2% Cash ($ mil.): 20
Return on equity: 2.3%
Current ratio: 3.70

JACO OIL COMPANY

Jaco Oil Company is jockeying for its piece of the convenience store pie. The company's Fastrip Food Stores subsidiary operates more than 50 convenience stores and gas stations primarily in and around Bakersfield California but also in Arizona. Besides offering customers traditional convenience-store fare which includes coffee milk beer snacks tobacco and the like the Fastrip chain stocks a full range of grocery items and provides in-store financial service centers. Financial services include check cashing payday loans wire transfer services via The Western Union Company refund anticipation loans and other services at many locations. Jaco Oil Company was founded in 1970.

Operations

The company operates nearly 50 stores in Bakersfield and Kern counties as well as in Fresno Sacramento and the Chico area. It also has four stores in Arizona located in Bullhead Casa Grande and Nogales. As part of its business Jaco Oil offers food beverages and financial services such as payday loans wire transfer services and tax preparation services.

Geographic Reach

Jaco Oil owns and operates gasoline service stations and convenience stores in the Western US.

Strategy

Fastrip works to distinguish itself from other convenience store chains by stocking a complete assortment of grocery items including such staples as sugar flour salt cake mix and even green beans. The chain bills itself as a Mini Grocery Store a strategy that other retailers including Dollar General and drugstore-giant Walgreen have adopted. It's also always open (24/7/365).

EXECUTIVES

Ceo, T J Jamieson
V Pres*, Charles Mc Can
SEC-Treas*, Lee Jamieson
Cfo*, Brian Busacca
Auditors: MOSS ADAMS LLP LOS ANGELES C

LOCATIONS

HQ: JACO OIL COMPANY
  3101 STATE RD, BAKERSFIELD, CA 933084931
Phone: 661 393-7000
Web: WWW.FASTRIP.COM

2013 Stores

	No.
California	49
Arizona	4
Total	**53**

PRODUCTS/OPERATIONS

Selected Services
Check cashing
EBT
Ice
Liquor
Lottery
Money orders
Money transfers
Phone cards
Quick serve restaurant
Restrooms
WIC

Selected Products
Alcoholic beverages
Beverages
Coffee
Dairy
Food
Fountain drinks
Groceries
Snacks
Tobacco products

COMPETITORS

7-Eleven	Ralphs Grocery
Chevron	Stater Bros.
Couche-Tard	Vons
Dollar General	Walgreen
Exxon Mobil	

HISTORICAL FINANCIALS

Company Type: Private

Income Statement				FYE: December 31
	REVENUE ($ mil.)	NET INCOME ($ mil.)	NET PROFIT MARGIN	EMPLOYEES
12/18	636	19	3.1%	350
12/17	506	13	2.7%	—
12/16	429	17	4.0%	—
12/15	442	17	3.9%	—
Annual Growth	12.9%	4.4%	—	—

2018 Year-End Financials

Return on assets: 13.4% Cash ($ mil.): 90
Return on equity: 16.0%
Current ratio: 3.00

JARDEN LLC

EXECUTIVES

Chair, Patrick D Campbell
Ceo, Debra A Crew
Pres, Ravi Saligram
National Account Sales Manager, Joe Cunningham
Auditors: PRICEWATERHOUSECOOPERS LLP NE

LOCATIONS

HQ: JARDEN LLC
  221 RIVER ST, HOBOKEN, NJ 070305989
Phone: 201 610-6600
Web: WWW.NEWELLBRANDS.COM

COMPETITORS

AZZ	Johnson Outdoors
Academy Sports	Kaz
Amazon.com	Kellwood
Amer Sports	Lasko Products
Andis	Lifetime Brands
BWAY	Lowe's
Bass Pro Shops	MEGA Brands
Bauer Hockey	Mattel
Bed Bath & Beyond	Mayborn Group
Burton	Mizuno
Cabela's	NACCO Industries
CalCedar	NIKE
Canadian Tire	New Balance
Carrefour	Newell Rubbermaid
Church & Dwight	Owens-Illinois
Conair Consumer	Patch Products
Products	Philips Avent
Costco Wholesale	Procter & Gamble
Crayola	Quiksilver
Daiwa	REI
De'Longhi	Richco
Deswell	Rollerblade
Dick's Sporting Goods	Rossignol
EBSCO	Russell Hobbs
Easton-Bell Sports	SEB
Elmer's Products	Sealy
Energizer Holdings	Simmons
Evenflo	Spectrum Brands
Female Health	Suncast
Gaming Partners	Target Corporation
International	Tecnica
Gerber Products	Tegrant
Habasit America	UTC Climate Controls
Hamilton Beach	& Security
Hanesbrands	Universal Security
Head N.V.	Instruments
Hillerich &	VF Corporation
Bradsby	W.C. Bradley Co.
HoMedics	Wahl Clipper
Home Depot	West Pharmaceutical
Honeywell ACS	Services
Igloo Products	Whirlpool
Intex DIY	Worthington Industries
Invensys	adidas
Johnson & Johnson	

HISTORICAL FINANCIALS
Company Type: Private

Income Statement   FYE: December 31

	REVENUE ($ mil.)	NET INCOME ($ mil.)	NET PROFIT MARGIN	EMPLOYEES
12/15	8,603	146	1.7%	17,000
12/14	8,287	242	2.9%	—
12/13	7,355	203	2.8%	—
12/12	6,696	243	3.6%	—
Annual Growth	8.7%	(15.6%)	—	—

2015 Year-End Financials
Return on assets: 1.0%
Return on equity: 3.6%
Current ratio: 2.00

Cash ($ mil.): 1,298

JEA

As long as sparks are flying in Jacksonville everything is A-OK with JEA. The community-owned not-for-profit utility provides electricity to 438000 customers in Jacksonville and surrounding areas in northeastern Florida. Managing an electric system that dates back to 1895 JEA has a net generating capacity of 3747 MW. It owns an electric system with five primarily fossil-fueled generating plants. JEA also gets 12.8 MW of generating capacity from two methane-fueled landfill plants. The company resells electricity to other utilities including NextEra Energy. JEA also provides water and wastewater services; it serves 321600 water customers and 247500 wastewater customers.

Operations
JEA is the largest community-owned utility in Florida and the eighth largest in the US.

The company operates in four segments: the Electric System and Bulk Power Supply System; the St. Johns River Power Park System System; the Water and Sewer System; and the District Energy System.

The Electric System operates five generating plants in Florida (and holds a stake in a power plant in Georgia) and all transmission and distribution facilities including more than 745 miles of transmission lines and more than 6500 miles of distribution lines. It purchases power locally from a solar field and a landfill gas facility. This segment accounted for 77% of the company's 2014 revenues.

JEA's Water System consists of 134 artesian wells that tap into the Floridan aquifer. Water is distributed through 37 water treatment plants and more than 4300 miles of water lines. Wastewater is collected through more than 3800 miles of wastewater collection lines and treated at seven regional treatment plants.

The company's operations are funded by three enterprise funds: the Electric Enterprise Fund the Water and Sewer Fund and the District Energy System The Electric Enterprise Fund is comprised of the JEA Electric System Bulk Power Supply System and St. Johns River Power Park System.

Geographic Reach
The cooperative serves customers in Northeast Florida.

Financial Performance
In 2014 JEA's revenues increased by 3% due to a 3% growth in electric sales as the result of higher consumption (primarily 4.3% in residential sales). Water and sewer sales increased by 1% related to a rise in customers and District Energy System sales increased by 2%. Approximately 47% of JEA's electric 2014 revenues came from its 375000 residential customers 50% from 48000 commercial and industrial customers and 3% from one wholesale customer.

The company's net income increased by 97% due to higher investment returns and a decline in loss from interest on debt.

JEA's operating cash flow decreased by 4% due to higher payments to suppliers.

Strategy
To help meet state regulations for carbon emission control JEA plans to get 10% of its energy requirements from nuclear energy by 2018 and 30% by 2030. In this regard JEA has signed a purchase power agreement to get 206 MW from a nuclear plant beginning in 2016 and is pursuing additional purchased power contracts.

JEA is also building out more fossil fuel capacity.

Company Background
The electric utility grew from a department of city of Jacksonville into an independent authority created by city and county government consolidation in 1967. In 1997 the water and sewer systems (which had been operated by the city since 1880) were also placed under JEA management.

In 2011 it completed the Greenland Energy Center which included two 175-MW natural gas-fired combustion turbines.

EXECUTIVES
Ceo, Paul McElroy
V Pres*, Mike Brost
V Pres*, Brian Roche
Exec Pres*, James Chancellor
Exec V Pres*, James Dickenson
Mng Dir*, Walter Bussells
CIO*, Ron Baker
Cfo*, Melissa Dykes
Staff, William Adams
Project Coordinator, Bradley W Collier
Human Resources Assistant, Jaime Obermeyer

LOCATIONS
HQ: JEA
21 W CHURCH ST FL 1, JACKSONVILLE, FL 322023158
Phone: 904 665-6000
Web: WWW.JEA.COM

PRODUCTS/OPERATIONS

2014 Sales

	$ mil.	% of total
Electric	1,431	77
Water & wastewater	383	21
District Energy System	8	-
Other	38	2
Total	**1,861**	**100**

COMPETITORS

Chesapeake Utilities	Seminole Electric
Florida Power & Light	Southern Company
Florida Public Utilities	TECO Energy
NextEra Energy	United Water Inc.
Progress Energy	Utilities Inc.

HISTORICAL FINANCIALS
Company Type: Private

Income Statement   FYE: September 30

	REVENUE ($ mil.)	NET INCOME ($ mil.)	NET PROFIT MARGIN	EMPLOYEES
09/18	1,789	126	7.1%	2,356
09/17	1,875	254	13.6%	—
09/16*	1,782	210	11.8%	—
06/09	1,319	71	5.4%	—
Annual Growth	3.4%	6.5%	—	—

*Fiscal year change

2018 Year-End Financials
Return on assets: 1.5%
Return on equity: 4.6%
Current ratio: 4.20

Cash ($ mil.): 441

JEFFERSON COUNTY BOARD OF EDUCATION

EXECUTIVES
Supt, Donna Hargenes
Supt*, Donna Hargens
Supt*, Steven Daeschner PHD
Coordinator, Linda Spencer
Coordinator, Sue Carmouche
Computer Lab Tech, Bonni Lincoln
Science Department Chair, Kelly Denton
Executive SEC, Sherry Fields
Auditors: STROTHMAN & COMPANY PSC LOUI

LOCATIONS
HQ: JEFFERSON COUNTY BOARD OF EDUCATION
3332 NEWBURG RD, LOUISVILLE, KY 402182414
Phone: 502 485-3011
Web: WWW.KYSCHOOLS.US

HISTORICAL FINANCIALS
Company Type: Private

Income Statement   FYE: June 30

	REVENUE ($ mil.)	NET INCOME ($ mil.)	NET PROFIT MARGIN	EMPLOYEES
06/18	1,400	(56)	—	14,000
06/17	1,274	18	1.4%	—
06/16	1,251	31	2.5%	—
06/14	1,158	24	2.1%	—
Annual Growth	4.9%	—	—	—

2018 Year-End Financials
Return on assets: (-4.3%)
Return on equity: —
Current ratio: —

Cash ($ mil.): 247

JEFFERSON COUNTY SCHOOL DISTRICT NO. R-1

EXECUTIVES

Supt, Dan McMinimee
Supt*, Cindy Stevenson
Office Aid, Grease Butte
Coordinator, Kay Bridges
Coordinator, Mary J Abbott
Executive Director, Amy Weber
Teacher, Dakota Ridge
Director of Infras, Scott Bell
Director of Purchasing, Betty Standley
Data Analyst, Carlos Angulo
Education, Michael Collins
Auditors: CLIFTONLARSONALLEN LLP BROOMF

LOCATIONS

HQ: JEFFERSON COUNTY SCHOOL DISTRICT NO. R-1
1829 DENVER WEST DR # 27, GOLDEN, CO
804013120
Phone: 303 982-6500
Web: WWW.JEFFCOPUBLICSCHOOLS.ORG

HISTORICAL FINANCIALS

Company Type: Private

Income Statement   FYE: June 30

	REVENUE ($ mil.)	NET INCOME ($ mil.)	NET PROFIT MARGIN	EMPLOYEES
06/18	848	(4)	—	12,000
06/17	808	(40)	—	—
06/15	801	(18)	—	—
06/14	785	(14)	—	—
Annual Growth	1.9%	—	—	—

2018 Year-End Financials

Return on assets: (-0.2%)   Cash ($ mil.): 4
Return on equity: —
Current ratio: —

JEFFERSON PARISH SCHOOL BOARD INC

EXECUTIVES

Pres, Mark Morgan
Attorney, Jack Grant
Counselor, Monica Baltodano-Dubey
Auditors: MIKE B GILLESPIE CPA JENNIN

LOCATIONS

HQ: JEFFERSON PARISH SCHOOL BOARD INC
501 MANHATTAN BLVD, HARVEY, LA 700584443
Phone: 504 349-7803
Web: WWW.JPSCHOOLS.ORG

HISTORICAL FINANCIALS

Company Type: Private

Income Statement   FYE: June 30

	REVENUE ($ mil.)	NET INCOME ($ mil.)	NET PROFIT MARGIN	EMPLOYEES
06/11	556	3	0.7%	1,260
06/09	501	(70)	—	—
06/08	521	22	4.2%	—
Annual Growth	2.2%	(43.9%)	—	—

2011 Year-End Financials

Return on assets: 0.7%   Cash ($ mil.): 242
Return on equity: 1.5%
Current ratio: —

JERSEY CENTRAL POWER & LIGHT COMPANY

New Jersey native son Bruce Springsteen may be The Boss but Jersey Central Power & Light (JCP&L) electrifies more fans than he does every day. The company a subidiary of multi-utility holding company FirstEnergy transmits and distributes electricity to 1.1 million homes and businesses in 13 counties in central and northern New Jersey. JCP&L operates 22670 miles of distribution lines; its 2550-mile transmission system is overseen by regional transmission organization (RTO) PJM Interconnection. The utility also has some power plant interests.

Operations
The company provides regulated electric transmission and distribution services. JCP&L also has an ownership interest in a hydroelectric generating facility.

Geographic Reach
JCP&L conducts business in 3200 square miles of east central northern and western New Jersey. The area it serves has a population of approximately 2.7 million.

Financial Performance
Revenues decreased by 18% in 2011 due to a rate adjustment for all customer classes and lower power deliveries. The lower power delivery to residential customers was the result of decreased weather-related usage in 2011. Lower distribution deliveries to commercial and industrial customers that year reflected the impact of economic conditions in JCP&L's service territory. A decrease in retail generation revenues was due to lower generation power sales in all customer classes primarily due to an increase in customers shopping around for alternative providers. Wholesale generation revenues decreased due to a drop in PJM spot market energy sales.

JCP&L's net income decreased by 39% in 2011 due to lower revenues offset by reductions in purchased power costs and amortization of regulatory assets.

Company Background
The utility was organized under the laws of the State of New Jersey in 1925.

EXECUTIVES

Pres-Ceo, Donald M Lynch
Cfo-Cao-Controller*, Marlene A Barwood
Director, Ernest J Novak Jr
Director, Jesse T Williams Sr
Vp Corporate Risk and Chief R, William D Byrd
V Pres External Affairs, Mark A Jones
Customer Staff, Sandra Rudolph
Vp-Operations, Alex Patton
General Manager, Chad Hampson
Staff Nuclear Specialist, Fulton Schaffner
Customer, Steve Paiewonsky
Auditors: PRICEWATERHOUSECOOPERS LLP C

LOCATIONS

HQ: JERSEY CENTRAL POWER & LIGHT COMPANY
76 S MAIN ST, AKRON, OH 443081812
Phone: 800 736-3402
Web: WWW.FIRSTENERGYCORP.COM

PRODUCTS/OPERATIONS

Selected Services
Electrical services
Outdoor lighting
Professional tree services

COMPETITORS

Conectiv Power Delivery
New Jersey Natural Gas
Orange & Rockland Utilities
Public Service Electric and Gas
South Jersey Gas
Southern Company Gas

HISTORICAL FINANCIALS

Company Type: Private

Income Statement   FYE: December 31

	REVENUE ($ mil.)	NET INCOME ($ mil.)	NET PROFIT MARGIN	EMPLOYEES
12/17	1,801	115	6.4%	1,413
12/16	1,787	80	4.5%	—
12/11	2,495	144	5.8%	—
12/10	3,027	192	6.3%	—
Annual Growth	(7.1%)	(7.1%)	—	—

2017 Year-End Financials

Return on assets: 1.3%   Cash ($ mil.): 251
Return on equity: 3.6%
Current ratio: 2.20

JEWISH COMMUNAL FUND

EXECUTIVES

Pres, Zoya Raynes
V Pres, Susan F Dickman
Sr V Pres, Jose Virella
Coordinator, Claudia Pinto
Director of Grants, Karla Floris
Chief Operations Officer, Beth Wohlgelernter
Senior Director, Michelle Lebowits
Auditors: EISNERAMPER LLP NEW YORK NY

LOCATIONS

HQ: JEWISH COMMUNAL FUND
575 MADISON AVE STE 703, NEW YORK, NY
100228591
Phone: 212 752-8277
Web: WWW.JCFNY.ORG

HISTORICAL FINANCIALS
Company Type: Private

Income Statement   FYE: June 30

	ASSETS ($ mil.)	NET INCOME ($ mil.)	INCOME AS % OF ASSETS	EMPLOYEES
06/17	1,558	55	3.6%	14
06/13	1,179	110	9.3%	—
06/12	1,012	(57)	—	—
06/11	1,086	42	3.9%	—
Annual Growth	6.2%	4.6%	—	—

2017 Year-End Financials
Return on assets: 3.6%   Sales ($ mil): 461
Return on equity: 3.6%

JFK HEALTH SYSTEM, INC.

EXECUTIVES

Pres-Ceo, Raymond Fredericks
Chm*, Dr Michael Kleiman
Plant Manager, Mark Di Geronimno
Vice President Finance, Louis Perillo
Coordinator, John Schenk
Director, Cindy Kaiser
Senior Manager, Frank Esposito
Osteopathic Physician, Richard Malone
Media Relations Mgr, Mary Jo Layton
Neuroscience Supervisor, Zahra Jiwani
Interior Designer, Asid Persico

LOCATIONS

HQ: JFK HEALTH SYSTEM, INC.
   80 JAMES ST, EDISON, NJ 088203938
Phone: 732 321-7000
Web: WWW.JFKJOHNSON.ORG

COMPETITORS

Atlantic Health
 Barnabas Health
 Catholic Health East
 CentraState Healthcare
  System
 Continuum Health
  Partners
 East Orange General
  Hospital
 NewYork-Presbyterian
  Healthcare
 Newark Beth Israel
  Medical Center
 Raritan Bay Medical
  Center

Robert Wood Johnson
 University Hospital
 Saint Peter's
  University Hospital
 Somerset Medical
  Center
 St. Joseph's
  Healthcare System
 Staten Island
  University Hospital
 Trinitas Regional
  Medical Center

HISTORICAL FINANCIALS
Company Type: Private

Income Statement   FYE: December 31

	REVENUE ($ mil.)	NET INCOME ($ mil.)	NET PROFIT MARGIN	EMPLOYEES
12/18	591	128	21.7%	6,735
12/17	0	(0)	—	—
12/15	0	0	—	—
12/14	0	0	—	—
Annual Growth	—	—	—	—

2018 Year-End Financials
Return on assets: 33.7%   Cash ($ mil.): 35
Return on equity: 74.5%
Current ratio: 0.70

JOERIS GENERAL CONTRACTORS, LTD.

EXECUTIVES

Gen Ptnr, Gary Joeris
Ptnr, Stephen Walter
Ptnr, Michelle Seward
Project Manager, Samantha Lyman
Project Manager, Sysun Howell
Technical Staff, Danny Murray
Executive Assistant, Gloriane Quintanilla
Project Manager, Matthew Haddox
Senior Project Manager, Michael Willy
Project Manager, Curtis Stavinoha
Director of Preconstruction, Kristian Pearson
Auditors: RSM SAN ANTONIO TEXAS

LOCATIONS

HQ: JOERIS GENERAL CONTRACTORS, LTD.
   823 ARION PKWY, SAN ANTONIO, TX 782162922
Phone: 210 494-1638
Web: WWW.JOERIS.COM

HISTORICAL FINANCIALS
Company Type: Private

Income Statement   FYE: October 31

	REVENUE ($ mil.)	NET INCOME ($ mil.)	NET PROFIT MARGIN	EMPLOYEES
10/18	463	0	0.2%	415
10/17	552	4	0.8%	—
10/16	0	0	—	—
10/12	188	0	—	—
Annual Growth	16.2%	—	—	—

2018 Year-End Financials
Return on assets: 0.7%   Cash ($ mil.): 22
Return on equity: 3.7%
Current ratio: 1.20

JOHN C. LINCOLN HEALTH NETWORK

John C. Lincoln Health Network takes care of the health of John Q. Public in Arizona. The not-for-profit health care network serves the northern Phoenix area and is home to two hospitals: John C. Lincoln Deer Valley Hospital with more than 200 beds and John C. Lincoln North Mountain Hospital with roughly 260 beds (the Valley's first Magnet nursing hospital an accredited Chest Pain Center and the host of a Level 1 Trauma Center). The system also features a children's care facility various physician and dental clinics a food bank and assisted living facilities for the elderly all operating under the Desert Mission moniker. John C. Lincoln Health Network is part of the Scottsdale Lincoln Health Network along with Scottsdale Healthcare.

Operations
John C. Lincoln Health Network has a staff of about 1100 physicians.

In addition to its hospital locations the network includes physician practices for primary and specialty care as well as medical imaging and research centers. John C. Lincoln's facilities serve about 750000 patients each year and provide specialty services in fields including cardiology pulmonary care neuroscience and women's health. The Deer Valley Hospital is also home to Mendy's Place the North Valley's only 24-hour hospital emergency center exclusively for children and an accredited Chest Pain Center.

In 2012 John C. Lincoln Health Network had 748019 patient visits to its hospitals and physicians and specialty practices; 26868 exams at the breast health and research center; and 8719 adult day health care visits.

Its specialized medical services includes heart care pulmonary care neurosciences emergency care and a Breast Health and Research Center. Community services include Desert Mission Food Bank a dental clinic for uninsured children a resource center for families in crisis and a child care center. The John C. Lincoln Health Foundation conducts philanthropic efforts.

The health system's Desert Mission Food Bank distributed roughly 41000 emergency food boxes to members of its community in 2012. Other locations providing community outreach services include the Community Health Center Children's Dental Clinic Lincoln Learning Center Adult Day Health Care and Neighborhood Renewal. The Marley House Behavioral Health Clinic provides mental health and related services for children and adults on a sliding scale basis in English and Spanish.

Strategy
In 2013 John C. Lincoln expanded its infrastructure opening the John C. Lincoln Sonoran Health and Emergency Center a new emergency center and outpatient clinic in Phoenix. The $18 million project includes an emergency department medical practice and diagnostic imaging facilities.

Upgrading its technology in 2012 John C. Lincoln Deer Valley Hospital added the da Vinci Si Robotic Surgical System. To help it improve its medical record keeping that year the health system's primary care offices launched JCL Connect electronic health records software.

Mergers and Acquisitions
To strengthen its footing in the Arizona marketplace in 2014 John C. Lincoln formed an affiliation with Scottsdale Healthcare. The combined networks operating under the moniker Scottsdale Lincoln Health Network include five hospitals with some 3700 affiliated physicians and an extensive outpatient services network.

Company Background
The hospital gained its first real funding in 1933 from millionaire entrepreneur John C. Lincoln the founder of Lincoln Electric.

LOCATIONS

HQ: JOHN C. LINCOLN HEALTH NETWORK
   2500 E DUNLAP AVE, PHOENIX, AZ 85020
Phone: 602 870-6060

Hospitals
Deer Valley Hospital: Phoenix Arizona
North Mountain Hospital: Phoenix Arizona

PRODUCTS/OPERATIONS

Selected Centers and Services
Breast Health and Research Center
Cancer Treatment
Cardiac Care
Deep Vein Thrombosis Program
Emergency Care
Heartburn Program

Level I Trauma Center
Medical Imaging
Neurosciences
Orthopedics
Outpatient Surgery Centers
Pediatrics
Pulmonary Program
Reconstructive Plastic Surgery
Scarless Surgery
Uterine Fibroid Treatment
Varicose Vein Treatment

COMPETITORS

Banner Health
Community Health
  Systems
Dignity Health
Flagstaff Medical
  Center
Northern Arizona
  Healthcare
Phoenix Children's
  Hospital

Scottsdale Healthcare
Universal Health
  Services
University of Arizona
  Health Network
Yuma Regional Medical
  Center

HISTORICAL FINANCIALS
Company Type: Private

Income Statement				FYE: December 31
	REVENUE ($ mil.)	NET INCOME ($ mil.)	NET PROFIT MARGIN	EMPLOYEES
12/13	584	44	7.6%	3,500
12/12	509	32	6.4%	—
12/11	486	17	3.6%	—
12/10	551	19	3.5%	—
Annual Growth	2.0%	31.3%	—	—

2013 Year-End Financials
Return on assets: 4.7%   Cash ($ mil.): 40
Return on equity: 7.6%
Current ratio: 1.30

JOHN MUIR HEALTH

Named after famed naturalist and champion of wilderness preservation John Muir John Muir Health provides health care throughout the scenic San Francisco Bay area. The not-for-profit system operates three hospitals eight outpatient and urgent care centers two surgery centers a physician practice organization and several community health foundations. The John Muir Medical Center Walnut Creek Campus has more than 570 beds and specializes in neurological and obstetrics care. The Concord Campus has about 315 beds and specializes in cardiac and cancer care. The John Muir Behavioral Health Center is a 70-bed psychiatric hospital. John Muir Health also offers home health rehabilitation and wellness programs.

Operations
John Muir Health's network of outpatient facilities include physical therapy and occupational therapy centers as well as specialty pediatric women's health and diabetes centers. The system also includes medical imaging centers and the MuirLab division which performs a full range of clinical and anatomic pathology laboratory testing at more than a dozen locations.

The system has 900 physicians associated with the John Muir Physician Network which owns and operates two dozen locations.

John Muir Health partners include Aetna Anthem Blue Cross Blue Shield of California and CIGNA.

Geographic Reach
The company's hospitals are located in California's Contra Costa County (Concord and Walnut Creek); outpatient centers are located in Brentwood Concord Walnut Creek and Walnut Creek gated community Rossmoor.

Financial Performance
John Muir Health reported $1.41 billion in revenues for 2012 a total that was slightly down from the $1.44 billion it reported in 2011.

Strategy
To better serve residents of the growing San Francisco Bay area John Muir Health has made additions to its existing facilities including increasing bed counts and upgrading its IT infrastructure. Other initiatives that aim to improve patient care — and ultimately to lower the overall cost of care and meet federal reform guidelines — include upgrading medical equipment coordinating regional care establishing joint ventures and attracting and retaining skilled physicians. In 2015 the system partnered with Stanford Children's Health to open a new pediatric intensive care unit at its Walnut Creek medical center.

Also that year John Muir Health joined together with Health Net of California to form an Accountable Care Organization (ACO) serving Health Net's members from the system's medical centers.

In 2013 John Muir Health established a joint venture with Tenet Healthcare Corporation that created a partnership with San Ramon Regional Medical Center. Through this partnership John Muir Health is spending $100 million to acquire a 49% ownership interest in San Ramon Regional Medical Center. Together the two organizations will expand and improve the efficiency and coordination of care in the TriValley area and nearby communities including San Ramon. The new partnership will also increase patient access to a stronger network of services and align outpatient and physician-focused health care in the region. In 2014 the partnership invested in a 92000 sq. ft. building slated to become a new outpatient center in Pleasanton California.

Company Background
John Muir Health was formed from the 1997 merger of the John Muir Medical Center (the Walnut Creek Campus which dates back to 1965) and the Mt. Diablo Medical Center (now the Concord Campus dating back to 1930 as the Concord Hospital).

EXECUTIVES

President And Ceo, Calvin (Cal) Knight
President And Chief Administrative Officer John Muir Medical Center Walnut Creek Campus, Jane A. Willemsen
President And Chief Administrative Officer John Muir Medical Center Concord Campus, Michael S. Thomas
President Cao Of John Muir, Lee Huskins
President John Muir Health Foundation, Patrick J. Carew
Interim Cfo, Chris Pass
Svp And Cio, Jon Russell
Associate Cio Vp Of It Operations, William Hudson
Chairman, David L. Goldsmith
Vice Chairman, Thomas Rundall
Treasurer, Malcolm McAuley
Auditors: KPMG LLP SAN FRANCISCO CALIF

LOCATIONS

HQ: JOHN MUIR HEALTH
  1601 YGNACIO VALLEY RD, WALNUT CREEK, CA
  945983122
Phone: 925 947-4449
Web: WWW.JOHNMUIRHEALTH.COM

PRODUCTS/OPERATIONS

Selected California Locations
Behavioral Health Center (Concord)
Breast Health Center (Walnut Creek)
Caring Hands Volunteer Program (Walnut Creek)
Clinical Research Centers (Concord)
Diabetes Center (Walnut Creek)
Garret Thrift Shop (Walnut Creek)
John Muir Medical Center (Concord)
John Muir Medical Center (Walnut Creek)
John Muir Outpatient Center (Brentwood Tice
  Valley/Rossmoor)
Medical Imaging (Brentwood Concord San Ramon
  Walnut Creek)
MuirLab (Regional)
Occupational Medicine (Brentwood Concord Walnut
  Creek)
Physical Rehabilitation Center (Concord Pleasant Hill)
Urgent Care Centers (Brentwood Concord San Ramon
  Walnut Creek)
Women's Health Center (Walnut Creek)
Wound Care Center (Walnut Creek)

Selected Services
Behavioral Health
Cancer
Cardiovascular Services
Chemical Dependency
Children's Services
Emergency Services
Lab Services
Medical Imaging
Orthopedics
Neurosciences
Physical Rehabilitation
Pregnancy & New Parent
Primary Care
Urgent Care

COMPETITORS

Alta Bates Summit Medical Center
California Pacific Medical Center
Children's Hospital & Research Center at Oakland
Community Hospital of the Monterey Peninsula
Dignity Health
Healdsburg District Hospital
Hill Physicians Medical Group
Marin General Hospital
Mills-Peninsula Health Services
Sequoia Healthcare District
Stanford Health Care
Sutter Health
Tenet Healthcare
The Palo Alto Medical Foundation
UCSF Medical
ValleyCare Health System

HISTORICAL FINANCIALS
Company Type: Private

Income Statement				FYE: December 31
	REVENUE ($ mil.)	NET INCOME ($ mil.)	NET PROFIT MARGIN	EMPLOYEES
12/17	1,831	92	5.0%	2,200
12/16	1,734	107	6.2%	—
Annual Growth	5.6%	(14.0%)	—	—

2017 Year-End Financials
Return on assets: 3.1%   Cash ($ mil.): 72
Return on equity: 5.0%
Current ratio: 1.10

JOHNS HOPKINS BAYVIEW MEDICAL CENTER, INC.

If you've just been pulled from the bay like an old emptyÂ crab trap Johns Hopkins Bayview might be the first place you're taken. One of five member institutions in the Johns Hopkins Health System Johns Hopkins Bayview Medical Center is a community teaching hospital. Its Baltimore-based operations include a neonatal intensive care unit as well as centers devoted to trauma geriatrics sleep disorders and weight management. It also features the state's onlyÂ regional burn center.Â The facilityÂ includes a meditation labyrinth for patients families and staff to walk. Established in 1773 the medical center has more than 560 beds.

Operations

As an academic teaching hospital all of the physicians at Johns Hopkins Bayview are also full-time faculty at the Johns Hopkins School of Medicine. Students from TheÂ Johns Hopkins University School of Nursing also come to the medical center for hospital-based instruction in acute and long term care.

EXECUTIVES

Vice President Support Services, Cheryl Koch
Auditors: PRICEWATERHOUSECOOPERS LLP BA

LOCATIONS

HQ: JOHNS HOPKINS BAYVIEW MEDICAL CENTER, INC.
4940 EASTERN AVE, BALTIMORE, MD 212242735
Phone: 410 550-0100
Web: WWW.HOPKINSMEDICINE.ORG

PRODUCTS/OPERATIONS

Selected services
Primary Care Services
    General Internal Medicine
    Obstetrics/Gynecology
    Pediatrics
Specialty Services
    Bariatrics
    Burn
    Cardiology
    Clinical Nutrition
    Dermatology
    Endocrinology
    Gastroenterology
    General Surgery
    Hematology/Oncology
    Imaging (X-ray mammography ultrasound etc)
    Minor Surgery
    Neurodiagnostic Lab
    Neurology
    Ophthalmology
    Otolaryngology (ear nose and throat)
    Orthopaedics
    Plastic Surgery
    Podiatry
    Urology
    Vascular Lab

COMPETITORS

Franklin Square	Sinai Hospital of
Hospital Center	Baltimore
GBMC	St. Agnes HealthCare
Good Samaritan	St. Joseph Medical
Hospital of Maryland	Center
Harbor Hospital	University of Maryland
Levindale Hospital	Medical System
LifeBridge Health	

HISTORICAL FINANCIALS
Company Type: Private

Income Statement   FYE: June 30

	REVENUE ($ mil.)	NET INCOME ($ mil.)	NET PROFIT MARGIN	EMPLOYEES
06/18	628	12	1.9%	3,300
06/16	544	11	2.1%	—
06/15	507	16	3.2%	—
06/14	541	11	2.2%	—
Annual Growth	3.8%	0.7%	—	—

2018 Year-End Financials
Return on assets: 2.8%   Cash ($ mil.): 20
Return on equity: 20.6%
Current ratio: 1.10

JOHNS HOPKINS HOSPITAL

EXECUTIVES

Pres, Ronald Peterson
Cfo, Ronald Werthman
Ophthalmologist, Albert Jun
Health Professional, Tonya Bradley
Gynecologic Oncologist, Edward Tanner III
Hematology, Josh Lauring
Endocrinology, Sheila Roman
Physical Therapist, Perticone Greg
Director of Pharmacy, Rhiannon Fitzsimmons
MD, Daniel P Judge
Patient Care Manager, Vicki Minor

LOCATIONS

HQ: JOHNS HOPKINS HOSPITAL
1800 ORLEANS ST, BALTIMORE, MD 212870010
Phone: 410 550-0730
Web: WWW.HOPKINSMEDICINE.ORG

HISTORICAL FINANCIALS
Company Type: Private

Income Statement   FYE: June 30

	REVENUE ($ mil.)	NET INCOME ($ mil.)	NET PROFIT MARGIN	EMPLOYEES
06/18	2,422	98	4.1%	12,000
06/16	1,968	80	4.1%	—
06/15	1,879	68	3.6%	—
06/12	1,791	(238)	—	—
Annual Growth	5.2%	—	—	—

2018 Year-End Financials
Return on assets: 3.2%   Cash ($ mil.): 80
Return on equity: 7.0%
Current ratio: 1.50

JOHNS HOPKINS UNIVERSITY

Founded in 1876 with a $7 million bequest from its namesake The Johns Hopkins University has established its reputation by molding itself in the image of a European research institution. While renowned for its School of Medicine the private university offers 260 academic programs spanning fields of study including arts and sciences business and international studies. The university enrolls more than 24000 full- and part-time students. Johns Hopkins has about a half-dozen campuses in Maryland and Washington DC as well as facilities in China and Italy. The student-teacher ratio is 13:1. The affiliated Johns Hopkins Health System provides health care from its three Baltimore-area hospitals.

Operations

Johns Hopkins University a private and non-profit institution with 1700 non-medical and 2800 medical faculty members offers education research and professional medical services. Its research and related services are offered through about 1800 government and private sponsors.

Keenly focused on research Johns Hopkins is engaged in a range of disciplines including health and medicine social sciences humanities the arts natural sciences engineering and technology. Projects include researching alternatives to animal testing disease treatments and chemical and biomolecular engineering topics among others.

The Johns Hopkins University offers graduate programs in business finance and real estate through its relatively new Carey Business School. Trustee emeritus William Polk Carey chairman of W. P. Carey & Co. partially funded the $100 million development of the school with $50 million which was completed in 2007.

Notable alumni of the school include 28th US president Woodrow Wilson Michael Bloomberg and horror film director Wesley Craven.

Geographic Reach

The university boasts three major campuses in Baltimore as well as single campus locations in (Montgomery County) Maryland and Washington DC. Johns Hopkins also operates facilities in the Baltimore-Washington area and abroad in China and Italy.

Strategy

Johns Hopkins is mid-way through its Ten By Twenty program — comprising 10 goals to achieve by 2020 — launched in 2013. The 10 goals are divided into four categories: One University (forging collaboration across disciplines); Individual Excellence (supporting faculty students and staff); Commitment to Our Communities (enriching ties to Baltimore the US and the world); and Institution Building (building a stronger university). In its 2017 progress report some of the achievements listed are more robust mental health resources; smaller class sizes; around 25 (out of a goal of 50) hires of interdisciplinary scholars; improved diversity and inclusion; and raised $4.6 billion in donations.

EXECUTIVES

Cio And Vice Provost Information Technology, Stephanie L. Reel
President, Ronald J. (Ron) Daniels
Svp Finance And Administration, Daniel G. Ennis
Svp Academic Affairs And Provost, Sunil Kumar
Vice President, Joseph Zolenas
Medical Director, Haig Kazazian
Senior Vice President Patient Care Services, Laura Wood
Vice President, Ben Myers
Medical Director Wilmer Eye Instructor At Columbia, Dean Glaros
Medical Director, Jeanette Nazarian
Pharmacy Manager, Michael Brown
Clinical Director, Peter Hill
Pharmacy Manager, Charles Wells
Vice President, Keith Hill

Medical Director Of Care Coordination, Joseph Perno
Vice President For Quality, Renee Demski
Senior Vice President Human Resources (john Hopkins Health System), Inez Stewart
Vice President And Chief Administrator, Sowell Ashlyn
Vice President Human Resources, Marcos Deleon
Director Of Nursing, Laurie Saletnik
Director Of Nursing, Deborah Baker
Senior Vice President Health Care Transformation And Strategic Planning, John Colmers
Vice President For Finance, Sidd Patel
Secretary Iii, Kristy Stewart
Medical Secretary, Samantha Boeshore
Medchi Vice Chair, Pranjal Gupta

LOCATIONS

HQ: JOHNS HOPKINS UNIVERSITY
3400 N CHARLES ST, BALTIMORE, MD 212182680
Phone: 410 516-8000

PRODUCTS/OPERATIONS

Selected Schools and Colleges
Bloomberg School of Public Health
Carey Business School
Krieger School of Arts and Sciences
Peabody Institute
School of Advanced International Studies
School of Education
School of Medicine
School of Nursing
Whiting School of Engineering

Selected Centers and Institutes
American Institute for Contemporary German Studies
Bloomberg School of Public Health Department of Health Policy and Management Fall Institute in Barcelona Spain
Bloomberg School of Public Health Research Centers
Center for Africana Studies
Center for Communication Programs
Center for Constitutional Studies and Democratic Development
Center for Clinical Global Health Education
Center for Global Health
Center for International Business and Public Policy
Center for Language Education
Center for Talented Youth
Center for Transatlantic Relations
Central Asia Caucasus Institute
Foreign Policy Institute
Hopkins Nanjing Center
Institute for Global Studies in Culture Power and History
Institute for Policy Studies
Johns Hopkins SAIS Bologna Center
Office of Global Nursing
SAIS Research Centers
Summer Language Institute
The Institute for Johns Hopkins Nursing
Yeung Center for Collaborative China Studies

Selected Campuses
Columbia Center - Columbia Maryland
East Baltimore Campus - Baltimore
Harbor East - Downtown Baltimore
Homewood Campus - Baltimore
Hopkins-Nanjing Center - Nanjing Jiangsu Province People's Republic of China
Johns Hopkins University Applied Physics Laboratory - Laurel MD; Baltimore and Washington
Johns Hopkins University Zanvyl Krieger School of Arts & Sciences Advanced Academic Programs - Washington DC
Montgomery County Center - Rockville Maryland
Nitze School of Advanced International Studies (SAIS) - Washington D.C
Peabody Campus - Baltimore
School of Advanced International Studies - Bologna Italy

HISTORICAL FINANCIALS
Company Type: Private

Income Statement — FYE: June 30

	REVENUE ($ mil.)	NET INCOME ($ mil.)	NET PROFIT MARGIN	EMPLOYEES
06/18	6,020	705	11.7%	37,600
06/13	4,793	526	11.0%	—
06/11	4,369	826	18.9%	—
06/05	788	0	—	—
Annual Growth	16.9%	—	—	—

2018 Year-End Financials
Return on assets: 6.6%   Cash ($ mil.): 262
Return on equity: 9.8%
Current ratio: —

JOHNSON & JOHNSON PATIENT ASSISTANCE FOUNDATION INC

EXECUTIVES

Prin, Nancy Moyer
Manager, Katherine Edwards

LOCATIONS

HQ: JOHNSON & JOHNSON PATIENT ASSISTANCE FOUNDATION INC
1 JOHNSON AND JOHNSON PLZ, NEW BRUNSWICK, NJ 089330001
Phone: 732 524-1394
Web: WWW.JJPAF.ORG

HISTORICAL FINANCIALS
Company Type: Private

Income Statement — FYE: December 31

	REVENUE ($ mil.)	NET INCOME ($ mil.)	NET PROFIT MARGIN	EMPLOYEES
12/14	787	(16)	—	13
12/13	741	13	1.8%	—
12/10	425	(6)	—	—
12/09	355	(2)	—	—
Annual Growth	17.2%	—	—	—

2014 Year-End Financials
Return on assets: (-23.4%)   Cash ($ mil.): 31
Return on equity: (-23.4%)
Current ratio: —

JOHNSON CONTROLS FIRE PROTECTION LP

SimplexGrinnell handles emergencies well. The company provides integrated security alarm fire suppression healthcare communications and emergency lighting systems. SimplexGrinnell reaches some 1 million customers in the US and Canada through more than 150 district offices located in the Americas Europe Asia and other regions. In addition to providing security and fire related products SimplexGrinnell operates a service division devoted to test and inspection preventive maintenance central station monitoring and emergency services. The company's clients include members of local state and federal government agencies corporations oil and gas companies hospitals and educational facilities.

Operations
The company's communications segment provides mass notification and commercial paging as well as intercom and other sound systems. The company also provides healthcare communications such as infant security nurse call and emergency alert units.

Strategy
SimplexGrinnell launched a new website to give its customers a fast and convenient way to purchase many of its products that do not require installation support.

EXECUTIVES

President, Robert F. (Bob) Chauvin
Ceo, George Oliver
Vice President, Scott Roberts

LOCATIONS

HQ: JOHNSON CONTROLS FIRE PROTECTION LP
6600 CONGRESS AVE, BOCA RATON, FL 334871213
Phone: 561 988-7200
Web: WWW.TYCOSIMPLEXGRINNELL.COM

PRODUCTS/OPERATIONS

Selected Products and Services
Fire Detection and Alarm
Control Panels
Notification
Network Solutions
Smoke Detector and Carbon Monoxide Detection
Sound and Communication
Healthcare Communications
Emergency Communications
Public Address and Intercom
Sound Reinforcement
Telephone Networks
Integrated Security
Access Control
Intrusion Detection
Property Surveillance
Mass Notification
Fire Sprinkler and Suppression
Fire Extinguisher
Special Hazards
Sprinkler

COMPETITORS

APi Group
Brink's
COSCO Fire Protection
Honeywell International
Ingersoll-Rand Security Technologies
Protection One

HISTORICAL FINANCIALS
Company Type: Private

Income Statement — FYE: September 30

	REVENUE ($ mil.)	NET INCOME ($ mil.)	NET PROFIT MARGIN	EMPLOYEES
09/16	1,871	182	9.7%	9,500
09/09	1,750	0	—	—
Annual Growth	1.0%	—	—	—

JOHNSON CONTROLS, INC.

EXECUTIVES

Ceo, Alberto Ventura
Pres-Coo*, George R Oliver
Exec V Pres-Cfo*, Brian Stief
V Pres-Gen Counsel-Sec*, Brian J Cadwallader
V Pres-Corp Contrl*, Suzanne M Vincent
Cpo-V Pres of Controls Operati*, Michael Bartschat
Coordinator, Bob Anders
Designer, Ed Stevens
Coordinator, Debra Morley
Coordinator, Mary Moore
Compliance Staff, Melissa Goetz-Krummel
Auditors: PRICEWATERHOUSECOOPERS LLP MI

LOCATIONS

HQ: JOHNSON CONTROLS, INC.
5757 N GREEN BAY AVE, MILWAUKEE, WI 532094408
Phone: 414 524-1200
Web: WWW.JOHNSONCONTROLS.COM

COMPETITORS

3M	Honeywell
A123 Systems	International
Addison	Illinois Tool Works
Alcoa	Inci Aku
Building Technologies	International Paper
Caterpillar	Invensys
Comfort Systems USA	Lear Corp
DENSO	Lennox
Deere	Lockheed Martin
Delphi Automotive	Magna International
Systems	Northrop Grumman
Dow Chemical	Paloma Group
DuPont	Raytheon
Eagle-Picher	Rieter Automotive
East Penn	North America
Manufacturing	Robert Bosch
Eaton	SPX
Emerson Electric	Trane Inc.
Exide	United Technologies
Faurecia	Valeo
GS Yuasa	Visteon
General Dynamics	Whirlpool
General Motors	Yazaki North America
Goodman Global	
Goodyear Tire & Rubber	

HISTORICAL FINANCIALS

Company Type: Private

Income Statement				FYE: September 30
	REVENUE ($ mil.)	NET INCOME ($ mil.)	NET PROFIT MARGIN	EMPLOYEES
09/15	37,179	1,679	4.5%	139,000
09/14	42,828	1,335	3.1%	—
09/13	42,730	1,297	3.0%	—
Annual Growth	(6.7%)	13.8%	—	—

2015 Year-End Financials
Return on assets: 5.7%   Cash ($ mil.): 597
Return on equity: 15.9%
Current ratio: 1.10

JORDAN SCHOOL DISTRICT

EXECUTIVES

Supt, Patrice Johnson
Bus Admin*, Burke Jolley
V Pres*, Leah Voorhies
Prin*, Richard S Osborn
Prin*, Susan Pulsipher
Payroll Staff, Ladenea Jenkins
Director, Darby Cowles
Technology/Computer Coord, Mark Sowa
Secretary, Dianne Christensen
Administrative Assistant, Natalie Miles
Assistant, Amber Zdunich
Auditors: SQUIRE & COMPANY PC OREM UT

LOCATIONS

HQ: JORDAN SCHOOL DISTRICT
7387 S CAMPUS VIEW DR, WEST JORDAN, UT 840845500
Phone: 801 280-3689
Web: WWW.JORDANDISTRICT.ORG

HISTORICAL FINANCIALS

Company Type: Private

Income Statement				FYE: June 30
	REVENUE ($ mil.)	NET INCOME ($ mil.)	NET PROFIT MARGIN	EMPLOYEES
06/18	454	11	2.5%	5,900
06/16	415	27	6.6%	—
06/15	391	9	2.3%	—
06/14	378	(3)	—	—
Annual Growth	4.6%	—	—	—

JP ENERGY PARTNERS LP

EXECUTIVES

Pres-Ceo, J Patrick Barley
Evp-Cfo, Patrick J Welch
Sr Vp-Cao, Shiming Chen
Vp-Corp Controller-Cao, Michael Croney
Executive Vice President Chief, Patrick Welch
Auditors: PRICEWATERHOUSECOOPERS LLP DA

LOCATIONS

HQ: JP ENERGY PARTNERS LP
600 LAS COLINAS BLVD E # 2000, IRVING, TX 750395607
Phone: 972 444-0300

HISTORICAL FINANCIALS

Company Type: Private

Income Statement				FYE: December 31
	REVENUE ($ mil.)	NET INCOME ($ mil.)	NET PROFIT MARGIN	EMPLOYEES
12/16	493	(34)	—	105
12/14	1,693	(53)	—	—
Annual Growth	(46.0%)	—	—	—

2016 Year-End Financials
Return on assets: (-5.1%)   Cash ($ mil.): 2
Return on equity: (-8.0%)
Current ratio: 1.20

K & M TIRE, INC.

EXECUTIVES

Pres, Ken Langhals
V Pres-SEC*, Cheryl Gossard
Sales Manager, Mel Donnelly
Assistant Project Manager, Michael Mesker
Programming Supervisor, Kathryn Reynolds
Account Manager, Kelly Schimmoller
Communications Representative, Mark Ciarlariello
Auditors: BKD LLP FORT WAYNE INDIANA

LOCATIONS

HQ: K & M TIRE, INC.
965 SPENCERVILLE RD, DELPHOS, OH 458332351
Phone: 419 695-1061
Web: WWW.KMTIRE.COM

HISTORICAL FINANCIALS

Company Type: Private

Income Statement				FYE: September 30
	REVENUE ($ mil.)	NET INCOME ($ mil.)	NET PROFIT MARGIN	EMPLOYEES
09/18	512	22	4.4%	500
09/17	451	21	4.7%	—
Annual Growth	13.6%	6.9%	—	—

2018 Year-End Financials
Return on assets: 14.1%   Cash ($ mil.): —
Return on equity: 26.9%
Current ratio: 4.20

KADLEC REGIONAL MEDICAL CENTER

Kadlec Regional Medical Center is an acute care hospital facility serving southeastern Washington and northeastern Oregon. In addition to providing comprehensive medical surgical and emergency services the hospital provides neonatal intensive care cardiopulmonary rehabilitation interventional cardiology neurology cancer care and other specialist services. Not-for-profit Kadlec Regional has some 270 inpatient beds including pediatric intensive intermediate and critical care capacity. It also operates outpatient physician offices and clinics in surrounding areas.

Operations

Kadlec Regional's cardiovascular programs include open heart surgery and interventional cardiology. The hospital also operates an all-digital outpatient imaging center and the region's only level III neonatal intensive care unit (NICU). Kadlec was is also designated as a Level 1 Cardiac Center and a Level 2 Stroke Center. Area specialist practices include centers for dermatology colorectal surgery nephrology pediatrics women's health ENT (ear nose and throat) and foot and ankle practices.

Kadlec Regional also operates satellite urgent care and family practice clinics.

The Kadlec Neuroscience Center offers a wide range of services to treat and diagnose conditions related to the brain spine spinal cord & peripheral nervous system.

In 2013 the hospital reported more than 2700 births 66000 emergency department visits and about 15000 admissions.

That year Kadlec Regional provided $27 million in charity care.

Geographic Reach
Kadlec Regional has hospital and clinic locations in Hermiston Kennewick Pasco Pendleton Prosser and Richland.

Financial Performance
The hospital reported revenue of $312 million in 2012 consisting of $305 million in net patient service earnings and other revenue of some $7.5 million. Kadlec Regional brought in profits of some $29 million.

Strategy
The hospital has undergone aggressive expansion efforts adding a new patient tower with diagnostic outpatient and intermediate care and surgery rooms. Kadlec Regional is enhancing its specialty service units in fields to attract specialists and increase revenue. The organization launched a $10 million project to expand its NICU unit in 2013. It will add 27 private and semi-private rooms and new observation gathering and lactation areas.

It is also expanding outpatient service facilities such as a new $19 million three-story specialty physician practice office that opened in Richland in 2013. The new building increases collaboration between various surgical and medical specialists in the Kadlec Regional clinic network.

The year the company also expanded its emergency room offerings through the opening of the Kadlec ER in Kennewick. The new 15-bed ER is the first in the region to operate as a freestanding facility like traditional hospital-based ERs.

Mergers and Acquisitions
Kadlec Regional also absorbs other area providers. In 2013 Inland Cardiology Associates become part of the Kadlec Regional health system. The region's largest independent group of experienced cardiologists Inland provides comprehensive invasive noninvasive and interventional services throughout southeast Washington and northeast Oregon.

Company Background
In 2011 it partnered with the nearby PMH Medical Center to increase collaboration and specialist referrals between the two hospitals. The partnership extends the reach of Kadlec Regional's medical specialists to additional communities and brings PMH online with Kadlec Regional's electronic health record system. Both hospitals remained independently run.

The hospital system was founded in 1944.

EXECUTIVES

Vice President Finance Chief Financial Officer, Julie Meek
Secretary And Director, David Merkley

LOCATIONS

HQ: KADLEC REGIONAL MEDICAL CENTER
888 SWIFT BLVD, RICHLAND, WA 993523514
Phone: 509 946-4611
Web: WWW.KADLEC.ORG

PRODUCTS/OPERATIONS

Selected Services
The Birth Center
Bloodless Medicine and Surgery
Cancer Care
Cardiac Care

Cardiac Catheterization
CardioPulmonary Rehabilitation
Cardiovascular and Thoracic Surgery
CaringBridge
Clinical Decision Unit
Coumadin Clinic
Diabetes Learning Center
Diagnostic Imaging
Don and Lori Watts Pediatric Center
Emergency Department
Emergency Room-Kennewick
Home Health Care
Imaging
Inpatient Rehabilitation and Therapy
Intensive Care Unit
Joint Care Center
Kadlec Academy
Kadlec Healthy Ages
Kadlec Medical Associates
Neonatal Intensive Care Unit
Occupational Medicine
Occupational Therapy
Ostomy Support Group
Outpatient Imaging Center
Outpatient Procedures
Physical Therapy
Planetree
Rehabilitation and Therapy Services
Speech Therapy
Urgent Care
Water Therapy
Wound Healing Center

COMPETITORS

Adventist Health System West
Asante Health System
Legacy Health System
PeaceHealth
Providence Health & Services-Washington
Providence St. Joseph Health
Salem Hospital
Wenatchee Valley Medical Center
Yakima Valley Memorial

HISTORICAL FINANCIALS
Company Type: Private

Income Statement			FYE: December 31	
	REVENUE ($ mil.)	NET INCOME ($ mil.)	NET PROFIT MARGIN	EMPLOYEES
12/17	595	87	14.7%	2,668
12/16	534	9	1.9%	—
12/15	504	(7)	—	—
12/14	417	190	45.7%	—
Annual Growth	12.6%	(23.0%)	—	—

2017 Year-End Financials
Return on assets: 14.0%
Return on equity: 28.3%
Current ratio: 5.60
Cash ($ mil.): 139

KAISER FDN HEALTH PLAN OF COLORADO

Auditors: PRICEWATERHOUSECOOPERS LLP PH

LOCATIONS

HQ: KAISER FDN HEALTH PLAN OF COLORADO
1 KAISER PLZ STE 15L, OAKLAND, CA 946123610
Phone: 510 271-6611

HISTORICAL FINANCIALS
Company Type: Private

Income Statement				FYE: December 31
	REVENUE ($ mil.)	NET INCOME ($ mil.)	NET PROFIT MARGIN	EMPLOYEES
12/13	3,197	115	3.6%	14
12/09	2,374	32	1.4%	—
Annual Growth	7.7%	37.5%	—	—

2013 Year-End Financials
Return on assets: 7.2%
Return on equity: 14.7%
Current ratio: 0.50
Cash ($ mil.): 3

KAISER FOUNDATION HOSPITALS INC

Kaiser Foundation Hospitals is on a roll. The hospital group operates nearly 40 acute care hospitals and 680 medical offices in eight states (California Colorado Georgia Hawaii Maryland Oregon Virginia and Washington) and Washington D.C. The company's largest presence is in California where the majority of its hospitals are located. Kaiser Foundation Hospitals employs more than 21000 physicians representing all medical specialties. Kaiser Foundation Hospital's doctors group is controlled by Permanente Medical Groups and its HMO is offered through Kaiser Foundation Health Plan. Altogether the group provides care for about 11.7 million members.

Operations
Kaiser Foundation Hospitals works with other organizations to tackle such issues as obesity access to care and violence. It also works to promote health in the communities it serves through wellness programs.

In 2016 Kaiser Foundation Hospitals logged 44 million office visits. It facilitated 106000 births performed 129000 surgeries and filled 90 million prescriptions.

Company Background
Kaiser Foundation Hospitals was founded in 1945.

EXECUTIVES

Evp Kaiser Foundation Hospitals And Health Plan; Group President Kaiser Permanente Northern California And Mid-atlantic States; President Kaiser Permanente Northern California, Gregory A. Adams
Evp Kaiser Foundation Hospitals And Health Plan; Group President Kaiser Permanente Southern California And Hawaii; President Kaiser Permanente Southern California, Benjamin K. Chu
Chairman Southern California Permanente Medical Group And Executive Medical Director, Edward Ellison
Senior Management Senior Vice President General Manager Director, Anne Mcnealis
Managing Director Special Projects, Ann Cahill

LOCATIONS

HQ: KAISER FOUNDATION HOSPITALS INC
1 KAISER PLZ, OAKLAND, CA 946123610
Phone: 510 271-6611
Web: WWW.HEALTHY.KAISERPERMANENTE.ORG

PRODUCTS/OPERATIONS

Selected Hospitals

Antioch Medical Center
Fremont Medical Center
Fresno Medical Center
Hayward Medical Center
Manteca Medical Center
Modesto Medical Center
Oakland Medical Center
Redwood City Medical Center
Richmond Medical Center
Roseville Women and Children's Center
San Jose Medical Center
Santa Clara Medical Center
Sacramento Medical Center
South San Francisco Medical Center
South Sacramento Trauma Center
Santa Rosa Medical Center
San Francisco Medical Center
San Rafael Medical Center
Vacaville Medical Center
Vallejo Medical Center
Walnut Creek Medical Center
Baldwin Park Medical Center
Downey Medical Center
Fontana Medical Center
Los Angeles Medical Center
Moreno Valley Community Hospital
Orange County - Anaheim Medical Center
Orange County - Irvine Medical Center
Panorama City Medical Center
Riverside Medical Center
San Diego Medical Center
Harbor City (South Bay Medical Center)
Woodlands Hills Medical Center
West Los Angeles Medical Center
Sunnyside Medical Center (Portland Oregon area)
Moanalua Medical Center (Hawaii)

COMPETITORS

Adventist Health System West	Dignity Health
Ascension Health	HCA
Banner Health	LifePoint Health
CHRISTUS Health	Sutter Health
Catholic Health Initiatives	Tenet Healthcare
Community Health Systems	The Cleveland Clinic
	Universal Health Services

HISTORICAL FINANCIALS

Company Type: Private

Income Statement   FYE: December 31

	REVENUE ($ mil.)	NET INCOME ($ mil.)	NET PROFIT MARGIN	EMPLOYEES
12/09	14,795	429	2.9%	175,668
12/08	0	0	99.0%	—
12/05	9,852	774	7.9%	—
Annual Growth	**10.7%**	**(13.7%)**	**—**	**—**

2009 Year-End Financials

Return on assets: —
Return on equity: 2.9%
Current ratio: —

Cash ($ mil.): 57

KALEIDA HEALTH

Kaleida Health provides a kaleidoscope of services to residents of western New York. The health system operates five acute care hospitals including Buffalo General Hospital and Gates Vascular Institute (combined with about 550 beds) The Women & Children's Hospital of Buffalo (200) DeGraff Memorial Hospital (70) and Millard Fillmore Suburban Hospital (260). Community health needs are met through a network of some 80 medical clinics.

Kaleida Health also operates skilled nursing care facilities and provides home health care through its Visiting Nursing Association. To help train future medical professionals Buffalo General Hospital is a teaching affiliate of the State University of New York.

Operations

Kaleida Health is also home to the Deaconess Center and Waterfront long-term care facilities. Along with primary care the system's network of outpatient centers offers medical and surgical subspecialty care dental and oral surgery services and behavioral health and outpatient alcohol treatment services. Kaleida Health also operates the Pediatric Trauma Center and Pediatric HIV/AIDS Center for the Western New York (WNY).

In 2012 the health system had 55125 inpatient discharges 158902 emergency department visits and 2.3 million clinic and lab visits.

Financial Performance

The company's revenues grew by 3% to $1.2 billion in 2012 thanks to higher net patient service revenues and other revenues (including increases from a medical resident tax refund and HITECH incentive funds). It reported that 37% of net patient service revenues came from Medicare; 21% from New York State Medicaid; and 38% from commercial insurance plans.

Kaleida Health saw net income of $52 million in 2012 (compared to a net loss in 2011) as the result of higher revenues and an increase in investment returns (including a gain from a net change in unrealized gains and losses on investments).

Strategy

In an effort to draw in more patients to the eight communities in which it already operates in the US Kaleida Health has become one of a handful of US medical providers to market itself to patients north of the border in Canada. The organization launched a marketing campaign in Ontario over the years that included a website aimed at pulling in Canadian patients seeking bariatric care for obesity gastrointestinal services (such as colonoscopies) joint replacement or spinal surgery pediatric care and radiology services. Overall Kaleida is focused on attracting Canadian patients who can either pay out-of-pocket or patients seeking non-emergency services covered in the US by the Ontario Health Insurance Program.

Growing its operations in 2013 The Kaleida Health Laboratories (which performs more than 4 million tests a year) opened four new patient service centers in New York (Tonawanda Lancaster Buffalo and Cheektowaga).

Teaming up with Olean General Hospital (OGH) in 2013 Kaleida Health and OGH opened their new interventional cardiac catheterization lab joint-venture in the Southern Tier of New York.

Kaleida Health and The University at Buffalo opened a new 10-story vascular institute and research building in 2012. The $291 million Gates Vascular Institute and the University at Buffalo's Clinical and Translational Research Center integrates Kaleida Health's physicians and UB researchers in a collaborative effort to deliver clinical care investigate the causes of a wide range of human diseases and spin-off new biotechnology businesses and jobs.

In 2012 Kaleida Health's Visiting Nursing Association of Western New York received regulatory approval to expand into four additional counties.

To raise cash in 2013 Kaleida Health sold the former Millard Fillmore Gates Circle Hospital to TM Montante Development for commercial development.

Mergers and Acquisitions

In 2013 The Visiting Nursing Association of Western New York was selected as the provider of choice to buy the Livingston County Certified Home Health Agency. In 2012 it was selected as

the provider of choice to purchase the Wyoming Certified Home Health Agency.

Company Background

Along with trying to grab a share of the Canadian market Kaleida is working to renovate and refurbish its current locations to draw in more patients. In late 2011 the system completed renovations of its maternity services at Women & Children's Hospital of Buffalo. The new Mother-Baby Unit offers 14 additional single rooms with private showers and enhanced amenities. The health system underwent another complete renovation that serves as an additional Mother-Baby Unit as well as inpatient beds for the Perinatal Center gynecology and other women's services.

EXECUTIVES

Senior Vice President Business Development, Michael P Hughes
Doctor Of Pharmacy, William Loeffler
Vice President And Chief Officer Information Technology, Cletis Earle
Director Of Nursing, Sandra Boneberg
Medical Records Director, Tanya Parlato
Ambulatory Services Dir, Melissa Hockenberry
Executive Vice President And Chief Financial Officer, Robert J Nesselbush
Clinical Director, Laurie Sadler
Operating Room Dir, Christina Leo
Vice President Physician Quality, Kenneth Snyder
Medical Secretary, Veronica Baker
Medical Secretary, Patti Carpino

LOCATIONS

HQ: KALEIDA HEALTH
726 EXCHANGE ST, BUFFALO, NY 142101484
Phone: 716 859-5600
Web: WWW.KALEIDAHEALTH.ORG

PRODUCTS/OPERATIONS

Selected Facilities

Buffalo General Hospital (Buffalo)
Deaconess Center (Buffalo)
DeGraff Memorial Hospital (North Tonawanda)
Gates Vascular Institute (Buffalo)
Millard Fillmore Suburban Hospital (Williamsville)
VNA Home Care Services (Allegany County Chautauqua County Erie County Genesee County Niagara County)
Women and Children's Hospital of Buffalo (Buffalo)

Selected Services

Admissions
Adult Day Services
Allergy & Immunology Clinic
Anesthesia
Bariatric Program
Bereavement Services
Blood Draw Labs
Breast Reconstruction Surgery Information
Buffalo Niagara MRI Center
Cardiac Program
Center for Asthma & Environmental Exposure
Center for Wound Care
Chest Pain Center
Colorectal Surgery
Community Health
Department
DeGraff Skilled Nursing Facility
Diabetes-Endocrinology Center of Western New York
Dialysis Treatments
Diversity & Inclusion
Ear Nose and Throat Center/Otolaryngology
Easy Referrals
Emergency Department
Epilepsy Family Planning Center
Gastroenterology
Geriatric Center of Western New York
Hernia Center
Imaging Services
Immunology Laboratory
Laboratory and Pathology
Maternity Services
Minimally Invasive Surgery
Minor Surgery

Multiple Sclerosis
Neonatology
Neuropsychology
Neurosciences
Neurosurgery and Procedures
Obstetrics and Gynecology
Occupational Therapy
Orthopedics
Parkinson's Disease Comprehensive Movement Disorder
   Center
Pastoral Care
Personal Care Services
Personal Response System (Lifeline)
Pharmacy - High Street
Pharmacy Pharmacy - Suburban Family Pharmacy
Pharmacy Residency Program
Physical Therapy Prenatal Testing
Primary Care
Rehabilitation Medicine - Acute Medical
Rehabilitation Rehabilitation Services
Retinal
Surgical Services
Robotic Surgery
School Based Health Centers
Security
Speech Therapy - Outpatient
Spirit of Women
Stroke Program
Subacute Rehabilitation
Surgical Services
Telehealth Home Monitoring
The Greater Buffalo
United Accountable Healthcare
Urology Services
Vascular Lab
Vascular Services
Visiting Nursing Association of WNY
VNA Diabetes Program
Women's Services
Wound Care

COMPETITORS

Catholic Health System	St. Joseph's Hospital
Ellis Hospital	Health Center
Hamot Medical Center	St. Peter's Health
Kane Community	Partners
Hospital	St. Vincent Health
Lifetime Health	System
Oneida Healthcare	Titusville
Center	United Health Services
SUNY Upstate Medical	Hospitals
University	

HISTORICAL FINANCIALS
Company Type: Private

Income Statement				FYE: December 31
	REVENUE ($ mil.)	NET INCOME ($ mil.)	NET PROFIT MARGIN	EMPLOYEES
12/17	1,331	60	4.5%	9,000
12/13	1,139	(14)	—	—
12/09	1,155	75	6.5%	—
Annual Growth	1.8%	(2.7%)	—	—

2017 Year-End Financials
Return on assets: 4.3%   Cash ($ mil.): 16
Return on equity: 19.6%
Current ratio: 1.40

KALISPELL REGIONAL HEALTHCARE SYSTEM

EXECUTIVES

Pres-Ceo, Pamela Robertson
Chb, Doug Nelson
Pres, Velinda Stevens
Treas, Charles T Pearce
Cfo, Craig Boyer
Manager Supply/Materials Mgmt, Dave Brabham
Network Engineer, Aaron Turner
Phlebotomist, Doreen Hatcher
Chief Pilot, Matthew Weller
Mpd Coding Manager, Lauren Krass
Telecommunications Analyst, Tom Watts
Auditors: JORDAHL & SLITER PLLC KALISPE

LOCATIONS

HQ: KALISPELL REGIONAL HEALTHCARE SYSTEM
   310 SUNNYVIEW LN, KALISPELL, MT 599013129
Phone: 406 752-8991
Web: WWW.KRH.ORG

HISTORICAL FINANCIALS
Company Type: Private

Income Statement				FYE: March 31
	REVENUE ($ mil.)	NET INCOME ($ mil.)	NET PROFIT MARGIN	EMPLOYEES
03/18	571	(21)	—	3,100
03/14	2	(2)	—	—
03/12	2	(1)	—	—
03/11	1	(1)	—	—
Annual Growth	126.9%	—	—	—

2018 Year-End Financials
Return on assets: (-3.7%)   Cash ($ mil.): 50
Return on equity: (-8.2%)
Current ratio: 1.10

KANSAS STATE UNIVERSITY

K-State is a big deal in the Little Apple. Located in Manhattan Kansas (aka the Little Apple) Kansas State University (K-State) is a land grant institution that has an enrollment of some 24000 students. It offers more than 250 undergraduate majors 65Å master's degrees 45 doctoral degrees and more than 20 graduate certificate programs. Major fields of study include agriculture technologyÅ and veterinary medicine.Å Notable alumni include former White House press secretary Marlin Fitzwater and actor Gordon Jump. Along with the University of Kansas and other universities technical schools and community collegesÅ in the state K-State is governed byÅ TheÅ Kansas Board of Regents.

Operations
With a student-to-faculty ratio of 20:1 K-State ranks among top US colleges and has one of the highest levels of prestigious scholarship winners (including Rhodes Marshall and Truman scholars) in the US. The university also has several notable research organizations in fields including agriculture and genetic science.

K-State is also big on sports and is part of the Big 12 Conference of collegiate athletics.

Geographic Reach
K-State has its main campus on 670-acres in Manhattan Kansas. It also has satellite campuses in Salina and Olathe. It also hasÅ agricultural and researchÅ centersÅ at five KansasÅ locations.Å The university's students come from all 50 US states and more than 90 countries.

Financial Performance
K-State increased revenues by 9% to $541 millionÅ in 2012 due toÅ higher income fromÅ student fees; government and non-government grants and contracts (for research and athletic activities); and auxiliary enterprises. Net income decreased 24% to $47 millionÅ due to higher operating expenses and lower non-operating revenues which was attributed to lower state appropriation levels and higher interest expenses.

Strategy
K-State is expanding its facilities and programs to meet the needs of its students. It completed the first $22 million phase of its National Bio and Agro-Defense Facility in 2012 as well as work on a new student recreational housing classroom and athletics facilities. In 2011 it added a new bachelor's degree program in social work. It also expanded its partnership with the Chinese scholarship council to allow additional students from China to study at K-State.

Company Background
K-State was established in 1858 as Bluemont Central College; five years later it was one of the firstÅ colleges in the USÅ to be designated a land-grant school.

EXECUTIVES

Senior Vice President Of Business Develo, David Pacey
Vice President Marketing And Brand Development, Jackie Coletta
Chapter Treasurer Spring 2017, Dan Baker
Interior Design Business Minor Treasurer, Tarah Shane

LOCATIONS

HQ: KANSAS STATE UNIVERSITY
   ANDERSON HALL 110 1301 MI, MANHATTAN, KS 66506
Phone: 785 532-6011
Web: WWW.OLATHE.K-STATE.EDU

PRODUCTS/OPERATIONS

Selected Colleges and Departments
College of Agriculture
   Agricultural Economics
   Agronomy
   Animal Sciences and Industry
   Entomology
   Food Science Institute
   Grain Science and Industry
   Plant Pathology
College of Architecture Planning and Design
   Architecture
   Interior Architecture and Product Design
   Landscape Architecture/Regional and Community Planning
College of Arts and Sciences
   Aerospace Studies
   American Ethnic Studies
   Art
   Biochemistry
   Chemistry
   Economics
   English
   Geography
   Geology
   History
   International and Area Studies
   Journalism and Mass Communications
   Kinesiology
   Mathematics
   Military Science

Modern Languages
Music
Philosophy
Physics
Political Science
Psychology
Statistics
Women's Studies
College of Business Administration
Accounting
Finance
Management
Marketing
College of Education
Educational Leadership
Elementary Education
Secondary Education
Special Education Counseling and Student Affairs
College of Engineering
Architectural Engineering and Construction Science
Biological and Agricultural Engineering
Chemical Engineering
Computing and Information Science
Electrical and Computer Engineering
Mechanical and Nuclear Engineering
College of Human Ecology
Apparel Textiles and Interior Design
Gerontology
Human Nutrition
College of Technology and Aviation
Arts Sciences and Business
Aviation Technology
College of Veterinary Medicine
Anatomy and Physiology
Clinical Sciences

COMPETITORS

Baylor University
Iowa State University
Oklahoma State
Texas A&M
Texas Tech
The University of
   Kansas

University of Colorado
University of Missouri
University of Nebraska
University of Oklahoma
University of Texas
Wichita State
   University

HISTORICAL FINANCIALS

Company Type: Private

Income Statement				FYE: June 30
	REVENUE ($ mil.)	NET INCOME ($ mil.)	NET PROFIT MARGIN	EMPLOYEES
06/17	620	50	8.2%	5,168
06/10	459	50	11.0%	—
06/09	420	10	2.6%	—
Annual Growth	5.0%	21.4%	—	—

2017 Year-End Financials

Return on assets: 3.5%   Cash ($ mil.): 150
Return on equity: 6.8%
Current ratio: 1.90

KAST CONSTRUCTION COMPANY LLC

EXECUTIVES

Mng MBR-Pres, Michael Neal
MBR*, Robert Julien
MBR*, Eric Plotke
MBR*, Roger Whitman
MBR*, Robert Vail
MBR*, David Demay
MBR*, Chandler Aden
MBR*, Zachary Young
Auditors: EF ALVAREZ & COMPANY PA M

LOCATIONS

HQ: KAST CONSTRUCTION COMPANY LLC
   701 NRTHPINT PKWY STE 400, WEST PALM BEACH,
   FL 33407
Phone: 561 689-2910
Web: WWW.KASTBUILD.COM

HISTORICAL FINANCIALS

Company Type: Private

Income Statement				FYE: December 31
	REVENUE ($ mil.)	NET INCOME ($ mil.)	NET PROFIT MARGIN	EMPLOYEES
12/17	511	1	0.2%	213
12/13	87	0	0.0%	—
12/07	95	3	3.8%	—
12/06	30	0	1.2%	—
Annual Growth	29.3%	12.1%	—	—

2017 Year-End Financials

Return on assets: 0.8%   Cash ($ mil.): 36
Return on equity: 8.5%
Current ratio: 1.10

KATY INDEPENDENT SCHOOL DISTRICT

EXECUTIVES

Pres, Bryan Michalsky
Pres-SEC*, Rebecca Fox
V Pres*, Henry Dibrell
V Pres*, Joe M Adams
Supt*, Alton Fraley
Treas*, Charles Griffin
Cfo*, William L Moore
Coordinator, Howard Grimet
Reading Specialist, Janet Sutherland
Secretary To Director, Tabitha Turner
Teacher, Brandy Williams

LOCATIONS

HQ: KATY INDEPENDENT SCHOOL DISTRICT
   6301 S STADIUM LN, KATY, TX 774941057
Phone: 281 396-6000
Web: WWW.KATYISD.ORG

HISTORICAL FINANCIALS

Company Type: Private

Income Statement				FYE: August 31
	REVENUE ($ mil.)	NET INCOME ($ mil.)	NET PROFIT MARGIN	EMPLOYEES
08/18	922	0	0.1%	6,631
08/16	841	15	1.9%	—
08/11*	601	123	20.5%	—
12/09	540	(2)	—	—
Annual Growth	6.1%	—	—	—

*Fiscal year change

2018 Year-End Financials

Return on assets: —   Cash ($ mil.): 492
Return on equity: —
Current ratio: —

KAWEAH DELTA HEALTH CARE DISTRICT

EXECUTIVES

Ceo, Donna Archer
Ceo*, Lindsay K Mann
V Pres-Cfo*, Gary Herbst
Vice-President Finance, Jennifer Stockton
Director, Thomas L Gray
Information Technology/Interne, Christine
   Muldoon
Information Technology/Interne, Danny Desimas
Human Resources Administrator, Jaime Thomason
Marketing Director, Dru Quesnoy
Controller, Bill Blair
Administrative Secretary, Cindy Moccio

LOCATIONS

HQ: KAWEAH DELTA HEALTH CARE DISTRICT
   400 W MINERAL KING AVE, VISALIA, CA 932916237
Phone: 559 624-2000
Web: WWW.KAWEAHDELTA.ORG

HISTORICAL FINANCIALS

Company Type: Private

Income Statement				FYE: June 30
	REVENUE ($ mil.)	NET INCOME ($ mil.)	NET PROFIT MARGIN	EMPLOYEES
06/18	710	28	4.1%	3,200
06/16	537	52	9.8%	—
06/15	475	26	5.7%	—
06/08	370	16	4.5%	—
Annual Growth	6.7%	5.7%	—	—

2018 Year-End Financials

Return on assets: 3.3%   Cash ($ mil.): 5
Return on equity: 6.4%
Current ratio: 2.00

KCP&L GREATER MISSOURI OPERATIONS COMPANY

EXECUTIVES

Ceo, Terry D Bassham
Sr V Pres*, Paul Perkins
V Pres*, Maria Jenks
V Pres*, Marvin L Rollison
V Pres*, Chuck Tickles
V Pres*, Stephen T Easley
V Pres*, Scott Heidtbrink
V Pres*, Lori A Wright
V Pres*, Jim Alberts
V Pres*, Kevin E Bryant
V Pres*, Lora C Cheatman

LOCATIONS

HQ: KCP&L GREATER MISSOURI OPERATIONS
   COMPANY
   1200 MAIN ST FL 30, KANSAS CITY, MO 641052122
Phone: 816 556-2200
Web: WWW.KCPL.COM

HISTORICAL FINANCIALS

Company Type: Private

Income Statement				FYE: December 31
	REVENUE ($ mil.)	NET INCOME ($ mil.)	NET PROFIT MARGIN	EMPLOYEES
12/18	833	27	3.3%	2,213
12/17	818	(40)	—	—
12/16	801	60	7.6%	—
Annual Growth	2.0%	(32.8%)	—	—

2018 Year-End Financials

Return on assets: 0.8%
Return on equity: 2.3%
Current ratio: 2.50

Cash ($ mil.): 1

KENNEDY MEMORIAL HOSPITAL UNIVERSITY MEDICAL CENTER INC

LOCATIONS

HQ: KENNEDY MEMORIAL HOSPITAL UNIVERSITY
MEDICAL CENTER INC
1099 WHITE HORSE RD FL 3, VOORHEES, NJ
080434405
Phone: 856 566-2000

HISTORICAL FINANCIALS

Company Type: Private

Income Statement				FYE: December 31
	REVENUE ($ mil.)	NET INCOME ($ mil.)	NET PROFIT MARGIN	EMPLOYEES
12/09*	455	17	3.8%	2
09/09	339	9	2.8%	—
12/08	426	(14)	—	—
12/07	372	9	2.4%	—
Annual Growth	10.5%	37.6%	—	—

*Fiscal year change

2009 Year-End Financials

Return on assets: 4.6%
Return on equity: 8.5%
Current ratio: 0.70

Cash ($ mil.): 9

KENNESTONE HOSPITAL AT WINDY HILL, INC.

Kennestone cures kidney stones and other ailments for residents of Cobb County Georgia. WellStar Kennestone Hospital has more than 630 beds and a full range of specialty services. The hospital's physicians provide cardiac care inpatient and outpatient surgery and rehabilitation trauma diabetes care oncology dialysis and home health care. The hospital also operates centers specializing in women's health senior living facilities diagnostic clinics and a wellness and fitness center. WellStar Kennestone Hospital is part of the not-for-profit WellStar Health System which operates hospitals and other medical facilities throughout Georgia.

Operations

WellStar Kennestone Hospital is the anchor of the group's WellStar Kennestone Regional Medical Center division. WellStar Kennestone Hospital handles about 37000 inpatient admissions each year as well as more than 400000 outpatient appointments and 120000 emergency room visits. It also conducts about 23000 inpatient and outpatient surgeries and 9000 births annually and operates a level II regional trauma center. The hospital has been recognized in a number of specialist fields such as orthopedics neurology and gastroenterology.

Geographic Reach

Located in Marietta Georgia WellStar Kennestone Hospital primary serves northern and central Cobb County.

Strategy

The hospital is undergoing renovation and expansion efforts including construction of a new hospital tower with all private patient rooms; the tower was completed and opened in early 2013. Two years later the hospital opened a new inpatient pediatric unit. It also began renovations of its cancer center.

WellStar Kennestone also regularly upgrades its medical technology systems and tools such as robotic surgery systems and data management programs.

EXECUTIVES

Director Of Him, Beth Kost
Asst Vice President Hr Information Systems, Todd Hamilton
Medical Director Critical Care Medicine Kennestone Re, Asif Saberi
Secretary Labor And Delivery, Miriam Murray

LOCATIONS

HQ: KENNESTONE HOSPITAL AT WINDY HILL, INC.
677 CHURCH ST NE, MARIETTA, GA 300601101
Phone: 770 793-5000
Web: WWW.WELLSTAR.ORG

COMPETITORS

Adventist Health System Sunbelt Healthcare
Children's Healthcare of Atlanta
DeKalb Medical
Emory Healthcare
Grady Health System
Northside Hospital
Piedmont Healthcare
Redmond Regional Medical Center
Regency Hospital
Shepherd Center
SunLink Health Systems
The Fulton-DeKalb Hospital Authority
West Georgia Health System

HISTORICAL FINANCIALS

Company Type: Private

Income Statement				FYE: June 30
	REVENUE ($ mil.)	NET INCOME ($ mil.)	NET PROFIT MARGIN	EMPLOYEES
06/15	821	106	12.9%	2,950
06/05	481	54	11.2%	—
06/04	877	50	5.7%	—
06/03	792	24	3.1%	—
Annual Growth	0.3%	12.9%	—	—

2015 Year-End Financials

Return on assets: 20.5%
Return on equity: 38.2%
Current ratio: 8.90

Cash ($ mil.): —

KENNESTONE HOSPITAL INC

Auditors: PRICEWATERHOUSECOOPERS LLP PH

LOCATIONS

HQ: KENNESTONE HOSPITAL INC
805 SANDY PLAINS RD, MARIETTA, GA 300666340
Phone: 770 792-5023
Web: WWW.WELLSTAR.ORG

HISTORICAL FINANCIALS

Company Type: Private

Income Statement				FYE: June 30
	REVENUE ($ mil.)	NET INCOME ($ mil.)	NET PROFIT MARGIN	EMPLOYEES
06/15	948	182	19.2%	15
06/14	836	113	13.5%	—
06/13	791	123	15.6%	—
06/10	800	123	15.5%	—
Annual Growth	3.5%	8.0%	—	—

2015 Year-End Financials

Return on assets: 29.0%
Return on equity: 48.5%
Current ratio: 8.60

Cash ($ mil.): —

KENT STATE UNIVERSITY

Kent State University (KSU) knows all about learning from history. The school offers some 300 degrees in art business management technology medicine biology psychology and other fields. Through eight campuses located in northeastern Ohio KSU educates some 43000 students making it Ohio's second-largest public university (behind Ohio State). Its campuses include more than 24 residence halls and the university encourages on-campus living. The school has a student-teacher ratio of about 20:1 and it offers both graduate and undergraduate degrees. KSU was founded in 1910 for teacher training and is one of the state's oldest universities.

Operations

With 43000 students — 28000 of which attend classes on the main university campus — KSU has 600 full-time and 1300 part-time faculty members.

The university also has a number of research institutes across a variety of topics. Its Liquid Crystal Institute for instance focuses on developing new technologies for digital TVs laptops and other devices.

Geographic Reach

The main KSU campus located in Kent Ohio; the university has satellite locations in the Ohio communities of Ashtabula East Liverpool Geauga Salem Stark Trumbull and Tuscarawas.

Sales and Marketing

KSU uses television commercials to market its educational programs.

Financial Performance

In 2012 KSU improved operating revenues by 3% due to higher income from tuition and fees both as a result of increased enrollment and higher tuition levels. The university also reported an increase in auxiliary activity revenue. Net income fell 92% that year however due to an increased allowance for bad debt an investment loss and higher expenses associated with a telecommunications upgrade.

Strategy

As the KSU system strives to attract and retain students through a number of strategic programs. It is implementing timetable tracking and recruitment and retention analysis tools via its IT department and it is also working to enhance its student recreation community involvement and athletics programs. KSU is also conducting capital improvement programs at many of its campuses to improve facilities in areas including science research electronics and athletics and it is also seeking to partner with new external entities (businesses and government agencies) to conduct research in new fields.

In addition the university is enhancing curriculum and teacher resources to improve the quality of its academic programs. It is also expanding facilities such as a new $18 million construction project launched in 2012 to build a new center for the College of Applied Engineering Sustainability and Technology. To extend study abroad programs KSU formed an international exchange program with the University of W rzburg in Germany in 2012.

Company Background

KSU's Center for Peaceful Change (later renamed the Center for Applied Conflict Management) was formed after four KSU students were killed and nine wounded by the Ohio National Guard in 1970 amidst a protest of the US invasion of Cambodia. The incident has long been referred to as the Kent State shootings or Kent State massacre.

EXECUTIVES

Vice President And University Secretary, Charlene Reed
Vice President Operations, Tim Monroe
Vice President, John Abraham
Associate Vice President Univ Comm And Marketing, Rebecca S Murphy
Vice President, Leslie Heaphy
Vice President Of Public Relations, Cody Huntsberry
Senior Secretary, Betty Walker
Senior Secretary, Diana Fields
Secretary, Donna Warner
Secretary, Joan Lash
Senior Secretary, Jane Ickes
Auditors: DAVE YOST COLUMBUS OHIO

LOCATIONS

HQ: KENT STATE UNIVERSITY
  1500 HORNING RD, KENT, OH 442420001
Phone: 330 672-3000
Web: WWW.KENT.EDU

PRODUCTS/OPERATIONS

2012 Sales

	$ mil.	% of total
Student tuition & fees	295	68
Auxiliary activities	88	20
Federal grants & contracts	27	6
State local & nongovernment grants and contracts	13	3
Educational departments sales & services	9	3
Total	**433**	**100**

Selected Ohio Campuses

Kent State University (main campus in Kent)
Kent State University at Ashtabula
Kent State University at East Liverpool
Kent State University at Geauga
Kent State University at Salem
Kent State University at Stark
Kent State University at Trumbull
Kent State University at Tuscarawas

HISTORICAL FINANCIALS

Company Type: Private

Income Statement   FYE: June 30

	REVENUE ($ mil.)	NET INCOME ($ mil.)	NET PROFIT MARGIN	EMPLOYEES
06/13	460	54	11.9%	5,466
06/11	420	107	25.5%	—
06/09	358	(63)	—	—
Annual Growth	**6.4%**	—	—	—

2013 Year-End Financials

Return on assets: 3.4%   Cash ($ mil.): 116
Return on equity: 6.1%
Current ratio: 3.00

KERN HIGH SCHOOL DST

EXECUTIVES

Supt, Donald E Carter
Principal, Robert Schneider
Principal, Jim Caswell
Payroll Staff, Gregory Vasquez
Superintendent, Don Carter
School Secretary, Christa Burton
Staff Secretary I, Ghada Akroush
Director of Human Resources, Jason George
Teacher, Jesse Aguilar
Categorical Programs Administr, Krista Twist
Resource Center Director, Lorri Michael
Auditors: MAYER HOFFMAN MCCANN PC BAK

LOCATIONS

HQ: KERN HIGH SCHOOL DST
  5801 SUNDALE AVE, BAKERSFIELD, CA 933097908
Phone: 661 827-3100
Web: WWW.KERNHIGH.ORG

HISTORICAL FINANCIALS

Company Type: Private

Income Statement   FYE: June 30

	REVENUE ($ mil.)	NET INCOME ($ mil.)	NET PROFIT MARGIN	EMPLOYEES
06/18	557	40	7.3%	2,000
06/17	518	40	7.8%	—
06/16	507	44	8.7%	—
06/13	405	(11)	—	—
Annual Growth	**6.6%**	—	—	—

KETTERING ADVENTIST HEALTHCARE

Kettering Adventist Healthcare dba Kettering Health Network and named for famed inventor Charles F. Kettering is an Ohio-based health care system. It comprises about 120 outpatient facilities including seven acute care hospitals: Kettering Medical Center Grandview Medical Center Sycamore Medical Center Southview Medical Center Fort Hamilton Hospital Greene Memorial Hospital and Soin Medical Center. Other facilities include Kettering Behavioral Hospital and multiple outpatient diagnostic senior care and urgent care clinics. Among its specialized services are heart care rehabilitation orthopedics women's health and emergency medicine.

Operations

Several times in recent years Kettering Health has been named by Thomson Reuters as one of the Top 10 US Healthcare Systems.

The system operates nine radiology centers 10 pharmacies eight outpatient rehab centers seven sleep centers 13 sports medicine centers and five wound centers.

Kettering Health provides community care benefits including health screenings education programs charity care for uninsured patients and coverage of Medicare/Medicaid shortfalls for under-insured patients.

Geographic Reach

Kettering Health's facilities are located in Dayton Ohio and the surrounding towns of Beavercreek Centerville Hamilton Kettering Miamisburg and Xenia.

Financial Performance

Revenue totaled $1.4 billion in 2014.

Strategy

Kettering makes capital investments in its medical centers to better serve its communities. It works to improve specialty units and equipment at its existing inpatient hospitals as well as technologically advanced hospitals tend to attract better physicians (and therefore patients). Kettering is adding new freestanding emergency room facilities in Franklin and in Eaton to the tune of $19 million. In 2015 it broke ground on a $49 million five-story cancer center at Kettering Medical Center.

The health network is also intent on expanding its outpatient facility network.

It's expanding in Ohio as well through a 2014 collaboration with Health Innovations of Ohio. To keep its database up to date Kettering in 2014 enlisted the help of ProVation Order Sets to oversee its clinical content management system.

EXECUTIVES

Clinical Director, Donna Arand
Vice President For Patient Car, Belinda Mallett
Radiology Director, Mark Rita
Medical Director, Rajinder Singh
Vice President Medical Affairs Chief Medical Officer, Robert Smith
Pharmacist Manager, Rachael Schlechty
Pharmacy Manager, Wayne Hoover
Director Of Radiology, Max Grady
Medical Secretary, Sharon Stamas
Secretary, Valarie Pyles

LOCATIONS

HQ: KETTERING ADVENTIST HEALTHCARE
  3535 SOUTHERN BLVD, DAYTON, OH 454291221
Phone: 937 298-4331
Web: WWW.KETTERINGHEALTH.ORG

PRODUCTS/OPERATIONS

Selected Ohio Facilities

Acute Care Hospitals
  Fort Hamilton Hospital (Hamilton)
  Grandview Medical Center (Dayton)
  Greene Memorial Hospital (Xenia)
  Kettering Medical Center (Kettering)
  Soin Medical Center (Beavercreek)
  Southview Medical Center (Dayton)
  Sycamore Medical Center (Miamisburg)
Other
  Adolescent Recovery Center of Hope
  Beavercreek Health Center
  Beavercreek Health Park
  Charles H. Huber Health Center
  Corwin M. Nixon Health Center
  Englewood Community Medical Center
  Kettering Behavioral Hospital (Dayton)
  Sugarcreek Health Center

Sycamore Glen Health Center
Sycamore Glen Retirement Center
Sycamore Primary Care Center
Urgent Care Centers (regional)

Selected Services

Assisted Living
Back Pain
Bariatric
Behavioral Health
Bladder Confidence
Breast Health
Cancer Care
Cardiovascular
Corporate Wellness
Community Outreach
Counseling
Diabetes
Emergency
Epilepsy
Executive Health
Fertility
Gamma Knife
Heart Care
Home Care
Hyperbaric Medicine
Imaging
Independent Living
Mammography
Maternity
Mental Health
Minimally Invasive Surgery
Neonatal Care
Neuroscience
NeuroRehab
Nutrition Counseling
Obstetrics
Oncology
Orthopedics
Pain Management
Palliative Care
Pastoral Care
Pelvic Control
Physical Therapy
Pulmonary Rehab
Radiology
Rehab Therapy
Reproductive
Robotic Surgery
Senior Living
Short-term Rehab
Skilled Nursing
Sleep
Spine
Spiritual Services
Sports Medicine
Stroke
Surgery
Urgent Care
Weight Loss
Wound Care

COMPETITORS

AdCare	OhioHealth
Adena Health System	Premier Health
Cincinnati Children's	Partners
Hospital	Regency Hospital
Fairfield Medical	Select Medical
Center	TriHealth
Licking Memorial	UC Health
Health Systems	University Hospitals
MetroHealth System	Health System
Mount Carmel Health	

HISTORICAL FINANCIALS

Company Type: Private

Income Statement				FYE: December 31
	REVENUE ($ mil.)	NET INCOME ($ mil.)	NET PROFIT MARGIN	EMPLOYEES
12/18	1,863	70	3.8%	6,800
12/17	1,753	171	9.8%	—
12/16	1,577	98	6.2%	—
Annual Growth	8.7%	(15.4%)	—	—

Return on assets: 2.9%   Cash ($ mil.): 63
Return on equity: 5.2%
Current ratio: 1.60

KETTERING MEDICAL CENTER

EXECUTIVES

Ceo, Jarrod McNaughton
Ceo, Fred Manchur
Pres, Roy Chew
Cfo, Russell Wetherell
Coordinator, Sandy West
Pres, Terri Day
Pres, Walter Sackett
Coordinator, Kara Paxson
Human Resources Executive, Edward Mann
Prin, Jay E Locke
Recruiter, Gloria Hopkins
Auditors: CLARK SCHAEFER HACKETT & CO D

LOCATIONS

HQ: KETTERING MEDICAL CENTER
   3535 SOUTHERN BLVD, KETTERING, OH 454291298
Phone: 937 298-4331
Web: WWW.KETTERINGHEALTH.ORG

COMPETITORS

AdCare	MetroHealth System
Adena Health System	Mount Carmel Health
Catholic Health	OhioHealth
Partners	Premier Health
Cincinnati Children's	Partners
Hospital	Regency Hospital
Fairfield Medical	Select Medical
Center	TriHealth
Licking Memorial	UC Health
Health Systems	University Hospitals
MedCath	Health System

HISTORICAL FINANCIALS

Company Type: Private

Income Statement				FYE: December 31
	REVENUE ($ mil.)	NET INCOME ($ mil.)	NET PROFIT MARGIN	EMPLOYEES
12/09	531	40	7.6%	3,100
12/04	628	40	6.4%	—
12/03	568	561	98.6%	—
12/02	496	5	1.1%	—
Annual Growth	1.0%	33.4%	—	—

2009 Year-End Financials

Return on assets: 5.7%   Cash ($ mil.): 13
Return on equity: 12.0%
Current ratio: 0.30

KEY COOPERATIVE

EXECUTIVES

Pres, Bob Finch
V Pres, Rick Fopma
Treas, Dave Vander Pol
SEC, David Hassebrock

Accountant, Kim Staecker
Customer Staff, Morgan Moore
Customer Staff, Bev Pothoven
Sales Staff, Art Beck
Customer Staff, Betty Tice
Sales Staff, Chris McIlrath
Sales Staff, Mike Wormley

LOCATIONS

HQ: KEY COOPERATIVE
   13585 620TH AVE, ROLAND, IA 502368061
Phone: 515 388-4341
Web: WWW.KEYCOOP.COM

HISTORICAL FINANCIALS

Company Type: Private

Income Statement				FYE: September 30
	REVENUE ($ mil.)	NET INCOME ($ mil.)	NET PROFIT MARGIN	EMPLOYEES
09/13	531	10	2.0%	180
09/12	541	8	1.5%	—
09/11	451	5	1.3%	—
Annual Growth	8.5%	33.1%	—	—

2013 Year-End Financials

Return on assets: 8.3%   Cash ($ mil.): 4
Return on equity: 16.2%
Current ratio: 1.60

KEY FOOD STORES CO-OPERATIVE, INC.

Key Food Stores Co-Operative is a friend to independent New York area grocers. The co-op provides retail support and other services to 150 independently owned food retailers in the New York City area. Key Food's member-owners run stores mainly in Brooklyn and Queens but also in the other boroughs and surrounding counties. It operates stores primarily under the Key Food banner but it also has Key Food Marketplace locations that feature expanded meat deli and produce departments. In addition the co-op supplies Key Foods-branded products to member stores. Among its members are Pick Quick Foods Dan's Supreme Super Markets Gemstone Supermarkets and Queens Supe rmarkets. Key Foods was founded in 1937.

Geographic Reach

Staten Island-based Key Food Stores Co-Operative operates supermarkets across the five boroughs and on Long Island in upstate New York and in New Jersey and Pennsylvania.

Financial Performance

Key Foods Stores has annual sales of about $1.5 billion.

Strategy

Key Food has been expanding in Queens and Brooklyn and on Long Island after scaling back in Manhattan — where many of its stores were converted to Duane Reade drugstores as the pharmacy chain expanded and took over individual locations. To that end in late 2013 the regional grocer launched a new banner called Urban Market in Brooklyn. The 16000-square foot store in Williamsburg was the co-op's 150th location. The cooperative is expanding aggressively adding more than 30 locations under the Key Food Key Fresh & Natural and Food Dynasty banners including stores in Harlem and the Bronx. It also recently reopened a store in Coney Island that was destroyed by Hurricane Sandy in 2012.

EXECUTIVES

Vice President, George Knobloch
Vice President Finance, Sharon Konzelman
Auditors: ANCHIN BLOCK & ANCHIN LLP N

LOCATIONS

HQ: KEY FOOD STORES CO-OPERATIVE, INC.
  1200 SOUTH AVE, STATEN ISLAND, NY 103143413
Phone: 718 370-4200

PRODUCTS/OPERATIONS

Selected Banners
Food Dynasty
Food World
Holiday Farms
Key Food
Key Food Marketplace
Key Fresh & Natural
Locust Valley
Milford Farms
Urban Market
Vitelio's Marketplace

COMPETITORS

A&P
 D'Agostino
  Supermarkets
 Fresh Direct

Gristede's Foods
King Kullen Grocery
Walgreen

HISTORICAL FINANCIALS

Company Type: Private

Income Statement				FYE: April 25
	REVENUE ($ mil.)	NET INCOME ($ mil.)	NET PROFIT MARGIN	EMPLOYEES
04/15	893	(0)	—	84
04/14	753	0	0.0%	—
04/11	537	(0)	—	—
04/10	0	0	—	—
Annual Growth	—	—	—	—

2015 Year-End Financials
Return on assets: (-0.6%)
Return on equity: (-2.7%)
Current ratio: 1.10
Cash ($ mil.): 4

KEYSTOPS, LLC

EXECUTIVES

Mmbr, Lester Key
MBR*, Rex Hazelip
MBR*, Richard Shepherd
MBR*, Kent Pyle
MBR*, Charles Key
Distribution Shipping Transpor, George Cole
Auditors: BKD LLP BOWLING GREEN KENTUC

LOCATIONS

HQ: KEYSTOPS, LLC
  376 REASONOVER AVE, FRANKLIN, KY 421344003
Phone: 270 586-8283
Web: WWW.KEYSTOPS.COM

HISTORICAL FINANCIALS

Company Type: Private

Income Statement				FYE: September 30
	REVENUE ($ mil.)	NET INCOME ($ mil.)	NET PROFIT MARGIN	EMPLOYEES
09/18	578	0	0.1%	200
09/17	500	2	0.5%	—
09/16	430	4	1.0%	—
09/15	584	6	1.2%	—
Annual Growth	(0.4%)	(55.1%)	—	—

2018 Year-End Financials
Return on assets: 0.6%
Return on equity: 1.2%
Current ratio: 2.40
Cash ($ mil.): 1

KFHP OF THE MID-ATLANTIC STATES INC.

Auditors: PRICEWATERHOUSECOOPERS LLP PH

LOCATIONS

HQ: KFHP OF THE MID-ATLANTIC STATES INC.
  1 KAISER PLZ 15L, OAKLAND, CA 946123610
Phone: 510 271-6611

HISTORICAL FINANCIALS

Company Type: Private

Income Statement				FYE: December 31
	REVENUE ($ mil.)	NET INCOME ($ mil.)	NET PROFIT MARGIN	EMPLOYEES
12/13	2,511	(13)	—	2
12/09	2,089	(10)	—	—
Annual Growth	4.7%	—	—	—

2013 Year-End Financials
Return on assets: 7.1%
Return on equity: (-0.5%)
Current ratio: 0.60
Cash ($ mil.): 7

KGBO HOLDINGS, INC

Total Quality Logistics sets a high standard for moving merchandise. The third-party logistics (non-asset based) provider specializes in arranging freight transportation using reefers (refrigerated trucks) vans and flatbeds — moving in excess of 500000 loads each year. The trucking brokerage company serves more than 7000 clients across the US Canada and Mexico ranging from small businesses to Fortune 500 organizations. Founded in 1997 by company president Ken Oaks Total Quality Logistics (TQL) has contracts with carriers that include single owner operators and large fleets. Customers have included Kroger Dole Food and Laura's Lean Beef.

Operations

The company began as a produce shipper — not a popular item for most brokers because it is perishable — and expanded into flatbed shipments and other dry freight. As a non-asset-based business TQL does not own trucks or warehouses nor does it employ drivers. Rather it arranges for independent carrier companies and owner/operators to transport its customers' freight; TQL manages the shipment while it is on the road. Additionally the company has no expensive overhead and is not limited by fleet size equipment or shipping routes allowing more flexibility for its customers.

Geographic Reach

TQL largely caters to customers in the Greater Cincinnati Area where it has nearly five offices. It has about 25 satellite locations located in Chicago; Cleveland; Charlotte North Carolina; Charleston South Carolina; Detroit; Indianapolis; Denver; Columbus Ohio; Houston; Lexington Kentucky; Louisville; Nashville Tennessee; Orlando Florida; Dayton Ohio; Erlanger Kentucky; Pittsburgh; Tampa; and Austin Texas.

Sales and Marketing

The company serves more than 10000 customers and 50000 carriers across North America to move more than 800000 loads each year. Customers include Dole Food Wholesalers and Kroger.

Financial Performance

TOL posted $1.6 billion in annual sales for 2013 up from the $1.4 billion it posted the previous year. With no expense overhead to bog down its balance sheet the company has enjoyed three straight years of sizable growth.

Strategy

TQL grows its business by gradually launching additional locations and sales offices in key cities across the country. In 2013 it expanded its sales office in Charlotte North Carolina and moved its operations in Lexington Kentucky to a larger space. Also that year TQL launched a new sales office in Orlando Florida. In 2012 the company opened new offices in the key metropolitan areas of Cleveland Detroit and Pittsburgh. In 2014 it announced plans to launch a new office in Nashville Tennessee.

EXECUTIVES

Pres, Kenneth Oaks
Controller, Kate Lucas Stump
Distribution/Shipping/Transpor, Aaron Schaeffer
It Support Technician, Wesley Barnette
Auditors: BARNES DENNIG & CO LTD CI

LOCATIONS

HQ: KGBO HOLDINGS, INC
  4289 IVY POINTE BLVD, CINCINNATI, OH 452450002
Phone: 513 831-2600
Web: WWW.TQL.COM

COMPETITORS

Alliance Shippers
C.H. Robinson Worldwide
Echo Global
MIQ Logistics
Roadrunner Transportation Systems
Ryder System
Schneider Logistics
Transplace
UPS Supply Chain Solutions

HISTORICAL FINANCIALS

Company Type: Private

Income Statement				FYE: December 30
	REVENUE ($ mil.)	NET INCOME ($ mil.)	NET PROFIT MARGIN	EMPLOYEES
12/12	1,387	0	—	4,077
12/11	1,046	0	—	—
12/10	762	0	—	—
Annual Growth	34.9%	—	—	—

KIEWIT BUILDING GROUP INC.

EXECUTIVES

Pres-Ceo, Joseph R Lempka
Sr V Pres*, Michael J Colpack
Sr V Pres*, Ronald C Duce
Sr V Pres*, J D Vetter
Sr V Pres*, Kevin P Welker
Sr V Pres*, Lance K Wilhelm
V Pres*, Becky S Golden
V Pres*, Raymond D Hallquist
V Pres*, Michael J Piechoski
V Pres*, Herb J Reuss
V Pres*, Tobin A Schropp
Auditors: KPMG LLP OMAHA NE

LOCATIONS

HQ: KIEWIT BUILDING GROUP INC.
160 INVERNESS DR W # 110, ENGLEWOOD, CO
801125005
Phone: 402 977-4500
Web: WWW.KIEWIT.COM

HISTORICAL FINANCIALS

Company Type: Private

Income Statement				FYE: December 29
	REVENUE ($ mil.)	NET INCOME ($ mil.)	NET PROFIT MARGIN	EMPLOYEES
12/12	649	12	1.9%	1,047
12/11	860	85	10.0%	—
12/10	1,280	124	9.7%	—
Annual Growth	(28.8%)	(68.3%)	—	—

2012 Year-End Financials

Return on assets: 4.5%   Cash ($ mil.): 47
Return on equity: 9.2%
Current ratio: 1.80

KIEWIT CORPORATION

EXECUTIVES

Ceo, Bruce E Grewcock
Exec V Pres, Richard W Colf
Exec V Pres, Douglas E Patterson
Exec V Pres, Scott L Cassels
Sr V Pres, Steven Hansen
Treas, Stephen S Thomas
SEC, Michael F Norton
Major Project Mana, Joe Wingerter
Career, Heather Semple
Vice-President, Larry Cochran
Senior Manager, Michael Ramsey
Auditors: KPMG LLP OMAHA NE

LOCATIONS

HQ: KIEWIT CORPORATION
3555 FARNAM ST STE 1000, OMAHA, NE 681313302
Phone: 402 342-2052
Web: WWW.KIEWIT.COM

HISTORICAL FINANCIALS

Company Type: Private

Income Statement				FYE: December 28
	REVENUE ($ mil.)	NET INCOME ($ mil.)	NET PROFIT MARGIN	EMPLOYEES
12/13	11,826	796	6.7%	10,441
12/12	11,220	512	4.6%	—
12/11	10,381	796	7.7%	—
Annual Growth	6.7%	(0.0%)	—	—

KIEWIT INDUSTRIAL GROUP INC

EXECUTIVES

Pres, Douglas E Patterson
Ex V Pres, Richard A Lanoha
Auditors: KPMG LLP OMAHA NE

LOCATIONS

HQ: KIEWIT INDUSTRIAL GROUP INC
3555 FARNAM ST, OMAHA, NE 681313311
Phone: 402 342-2052

HISTORICAL FINANCIALS

Company Type: Private

Income Statement				FYE: December 28
	REVENUE ($ mil.)	NET INCOME ($ mil.)	NET PROFIT MARGIN	EMPLOYEES
12/13	3,474	241	6.9%	20
12/12	3,397	110	3.2%	—
12/11	2,445	118	4.8%	—
12/10	2,546	173	6.8%	—
Annual Growth	10.9%	11.5%	—	—

2013 Year-End Financials

Return on assets: 13.8%   Cash ($ mil.): 324
Return on equity: 26.4%
Current ratio: 1.80

KIEWIT INFRASTRUCTURE CO.

EXECUTIVES

Pres, Bruce Grewcock
Prin, Scott L Cassels
Exec V Pres, H E Adams
Exec V Pres, David J Miles
Snr V Pres, Parke D Ball
Snr V Pres, Craig A Briggs
Cfo, Michael J Piechoski
V Pres, Stephen P Allen
V Pres, Michael K Breyer
Cntrl, Michael J Whetstine
Asst Cntrl, Jean Dulmaine

LOCATIONS

HQ: KIEWIT INFRASTRUCTURE CO.
KIEWIT PLZ, OMAHA, NE 68131
Phone: 402 342-2052
Web: WWW.KIEWIT.COM

HISTORICAL FINANCIALS

Company Type: Private

Income Statement				FYE: December 31
	REVENUE ($ mil.)	NET INCOME ($ mil.)	NET PROFIT MARGIN	EMPLOYEES
12/12	857	55	6.5%	9,000
12/11	1,127	74	6.6%	—
12/10	3,516	269	7.7%	—
Annual Growth	(50.6%)	(54.6%)	—	—

2012 Year-End Financials

Return on assets: 6.9%   Cash ($ mil.): —
Return on equity: 10.3%
Current ratio: 2.30

KIEWIT INFRASTRUCTURE SOUTH CO.

EXECUTIVES

Pres, David J Miles
V Pres, Jeffrey P Petersen
V Pres, Randall P Sanman
V Pres, Keith N Sasich
V Pres, S Van Groves
V Pres, Howard L Barton Jr
V Pres, Stephen Paul Carter Jr
V Pres, Timothy J Cleary
V Pres, Ricardo Cummings
V Pres, William D Glaser
V Pres, Mark D Langford
Auditors: KPMG LLP OMAHA NEBRASKA

LOCATIONS

HQ: KIEWIT INFRASTRUCTURE SOUTH CO.
KIEWIT PLZ NO 1044, OMAHA, NE 68131
Phone: 402 342-2052
Web: WWW.KIEWIT.COM

HISTORICAL FINANCIALS

Company Type: Private

Income Statement				FYE: December 29
	REVENUE ($ mil.)	NET INCOME ($ mil.)	NET PROFIT MARGIN	EMPLOYEES
12/12	549	85	15.6%	333
12/11	901	135	15.0%	—
12/10	1,009	126	12.6%	—
Annual Growth	(26.2%)	(17.8%)	—	—

2012 Year-End Financials

Return on assets: 21.0%   Cash ($ mil.): 127
Return on equity: 39.7%
Current ratio: 2.00

KIEWIT INFRASTRUCTURE WEST CO.

EXECUTIVES

Pres, Scott L Cassels
Exec V Pres, H E Adams
Exec V Pres, David J Miles
Exec V Pres, Alfredo E Sori
Sr V Pres, Jeffrey P Petersen
Sr V Pres, Eric M Scott
Sr V Pres, A T Skoro
Sr V Pres, Matt L Swinton
Sr V Pres, Eugene D Van Wagner III
Sr V Pres, J D Vetter
Sr V Pres, Jamie D Wisenbaker
Auditors: KPMG LLPOMAHA NEBRASKA

LOCATIONS

HQ: KIEWIT INFRASTRUCTURE WEST CO.
3555 FARNAM ST, OMAHA, NE 681313311
Phone: 402 342-2052
Web: WWW.KIEWIT.COM

HISTORICAL FINANCIALS

Company Type: Private

Income Statement				FYE: December 29
	REVENUE ($ mil.)	NET INCOME ($ mil.)	NET PROFIT MARGIN	EMPLOYEES
12/12	1,512	(126)	—	2,625
12/11	1,209	85	7.1%	—
12/10	945	31	3.3%	—
Annual Growth	26.5%	—	—	—

2012 Year-End Financials
Return on assets: (-13.5%)   Cash ($ mil.): 152
Return on equity: (-47.1%)
Current ratio: 1.20

KILLEEN INDEPENDENT SCHOOL DISTRICT

EXECUTIVES

Supt, John Craft
Pres*, Carlos Cole Jr
V Pres*, Joshua Ayers
Dir*, Tia Perry
Dir*, Javoris Jordan
Dir*, Jamal Wright
Cfo*, Megan Bradley
Tech Prep Coordinator, Marvin Rainwater
Coordinator, Julie Reynolds
Teacher, Ellen Keaney
Coordinator, Steven McKissick
Auditors: LOTT VERNON & COMPANY PC K

LOCATIONS

HQ: KILLEEN INDEPENDENT SCHOOL DISTRICT
200 N W S YOUNG DR, KILLEEN, TX 765434025
Phone: 254 336-0000
Web: WWW.KILLEENISD.ORG

HISTORICAL FINANCIALS

Company Type: Private

Income Statement				FYE: August 31
	REVENUE ($ mil.)	NET INCOME ($ mil.)	NET PROFIT MARGIN	EMPLOYEES
08/18	456	316	69.3%	6,200
08/17	436	(30)	—	—
08/16	438	7	1.7%	—
08/15	418	21	5.2%	—
Annual Growth	2.9%	144.8%	—	—

2018 Year-End Financials
Return on assets: 31.8%   Cash ($ mil.): 160
Return on equity: 91.3%
Current ratio: —

KIMBALL HILL INC

LOCATIONS

HQ: KIMBALL HILL INC
5999 NEW WILKE RD STE 306, ROLLING
MEADOWS, IL 600084503
Phone: 847 364-7300

HISTORICAL FINANCIALS

Company Type: Private

Income Statement				FYE: September 30
	REVENUE ($ mil.)	NET INCOME ($ mil.)	NET PROFIT MARGIN	EMPLOYEES
09/07	900	(220)	—	900
09/05	1,146	86	7.6%	—
09/04	927	55	6.0%	—
09/03	786	37	4.8%	—
Annual Growth	3.4%	—	—	—

2007 Year-End Financials
Return on assets: (-25.0%)   Cash ($ mil.): 31
Return on equity: (-144.4%)
Current ratio: —

KING COUNTY PUBLIC HOSPITAL DISTRICT 2

EXECUTIVES

Ceo, Bob Malte
Sr V Pres*, Neil Johnson
V Pres*, Jack Handley
Scientist, Deanne Gilbert
Chief of Medicine, James D Brown
Analyst, Cheryl Riley
Information Specialist, Dana Tran
Physician, Aileen Mickey
Staff Coordinator, Christine Abraham
Director, Francis X Riedo
Doctor, Jennifer Porter

LOCATIONS

HQ: KING COUNTY PUBLIC HOSPITAL DISTRICT 2
12040 NE 128TH ST, KIRKLAND, WA 980343013
Phone: 425 899-2769
Web: WWW.EVERGREENHEALTH.COM

HISTORICAL FINANCIALS

Company Type: Private

Income Statement				FYE: December 31
	REVENUE ($ mil.)	NET INCOME ($ mil.)	NET PROFIT MARGIN	EMPLOYEES
12/17	713	14	2.0%	2,400
12/16	597	(3)	—	—
12/15	565	3	0.7%	—
12/06	273	16	6.2%	—
Annual Growth	9.1%	(1.4%)	—	—

2017 Year-End Financials
Return on assets: 2.1%   Cash ($ mil.): 44
Return on equity: 4.4%
Current ratio: 1.70

KING COUNTY PUBLIC HOSPITAL DISTRICT 2

LOCATIONS

HQ: KING COUNTY PUBLIC HOSPITAL DISTRICT 2
12040 NE 128TH ST, KIRKLAND, WA 980343013
Phone: 425 899-2646
Web: WWW.EVERGREENHEALTH.COM

HISTORICAL FINANCIALS

Company Type: Private

Income Statement				FYE: December 31
	REVENUE ($ mil.)	NET INCOME ($ mil.)	NET PROFIT MARGIN	EMPLOYEES
12/14	511	4	0.8%	4,000
12/08	312	5	1.7%	—
Annual Growth	8.5%	(4.0%)	—	—

2014 Year-End Financials
Return on assets: 4.1%   Cash ($ mil.): 21
Return on equity: 0.8%
Current ratio: 1.20

KING'S DAUGHTERS HEALTH SYSTEM, INC.

EXECUTIVES

Ceo, Fred Jackson
SEC*, Sheryl Mahaney
Treasurer*, Jeff Treasure
Director, Ray Mecca
Directors, Charlie Borders
Assistant Chief Office, Charbel Salem
Administrator, David McDonald
Human Resources Business Partn, Earnie Duty
Network Engineer, Greggory Howard
Manager, Larry Sites
Manager, Maggie Hymer
Auditors: BAKER TILLY VIRCHOW KRAUSE LLP

LOCATIONS

HQ: KING'S DAUGHTERS HEALTH SYSTEM, INC.
2201 LEXINGTON AVE, ASHLAND, KY 411012843
Phone: 606 408-4000
Web: WWW.KINGSDAUGHTERSHEALTH.COM

HISTORICAL FINANCIALS

Company Type: Private

| Income Statement | | | FYE: September 30 |
	REVENUE ($ mil.)	NET INCOME ($ mil.)	NET PROFIT MARGIN	EMPLOYEES
09/18	485	(1)	—	4,200
09/17	475	3	0.8%	—
09/16	459	(8)	—	—
09/14	0	0	—	—
Annual Growth	—	—	—	—

2018 Year-End Financials

Return on assets: (-0.3%)   Cash ($ mil.): 30
Return on equity: (-0.6%)
Current ratio: 2.10

KIRBY - SMITH MACHINERY, INC.

EXECUTIVES

Pres, Ed Kirby
Coordinator, Alan Soab
Division Manager, Kevin D Phillips
Vice President of Human Resour, Seth McColley
Tulsa Rental Manager, Brian Burris
Vice President and General Man, Joe Trapani
Vice President, Rickey Bailey
Territory Manager, Ron Weaver
Account Manager Pipeline Servi, Woody Ferrell
Parts Sales, Bret Bryant
Technical Communicator, Cash Still
Auditors: EIDE BAILLY OKLAHOMA CITY OK

LOCATIONS

HQ: KIRBY - SMITH MACHINERY, INC.
6715 W RENO AVE, OKLAHOMA CITY, OK 731276590
Phone: 888 861-0219
Web: WWW.KIRBY-SMITH.COM

HISTORICAL FINANCIALS

Company Type: Private

| Income Statement | | | FYE: December 31 |
	REVENUE ($ mil.)	NET INCOME ($ mil.)	NET PROFIT MARGIN	EMPLOYEES
12/18	666	52	7.9%	516
12/17	421	36	8.6%	—
12/16	312	25	8.2%	—
12/15	321	33	10.5%	—
Annual Growth	27.5%	16.1%	—	—

2018 Year-End Financials

Return on assets: 10.8%   Cash ($ mil.): —
Return on equity: 25.1%
Current ratio: 1.40

KLEIN INDEPENDENT SCHOOL DISTRICT

EXECUTIVES

Supt, Bret A Champion
Pres, Steven E Smith
V Pres, Ronnie K Anderson
SEC, Stephen J Szymczak
Building) Instructional Office, Pat Braunagel
Accounting Staff, Heather Cummings
Coordinator, Karri Clark
Coordinator, Kim Huseman
Teacher, Gary Jackson
Auditors: HEREFORD LYNCH SELLARS & KIR

LOCATIONS

HQ: KLEIN INDEPENDENT SCHOOL DISTRICT
7200 SPRING CYPRESS RD, SPRING, TX 773793215
Phone: 832 249-4000
Web: WWW.KLEINISD.NET

HISTORICAL FINANCIALS

Company Type: Private

| Income Statement | | | FYE: August 31 |
	REVENUE ($ mil.)	NET INCOME ($ mil.)	NET PROFIT MARGIN	EMPLOYEES
08/18	594	2	0.4%	5,691
08/17	548	8	1.5%	—
08/16	539	(135)	—	—
08/15	511	186	36.5%	—
Annual Growth	5.2%	(76.7%)	—	—

2018 Year-End Financials

Return on assets: 0.2%   Cash ($ mil.): 220
Return on equity: —
Current ratio: —

KMM TELECOMMUNICATIONS

EXECUTIVES

Ceo, Katherine McConvey
Cfo, Kofi Badu
Pres, Nick Shanker
Corporate Communications Staff, Sarah McNab
Accnt, Brad Van Kalsbeck
Auditors: DORFMAN ABRAMS MUSIC LLC SAD

LOCATIONS

HQ: KMM TELECOMMUNICATIONS
1900 LAKEWAY DR STE 100, LEWISVILLE, TX 750576012
Phone: 844 566-8488
Web: WWW.KMMCORP.NET

HISTORICAL FINANCIALS

Company Type: Private

| Income Statement | | | FYE: December 31 |
	REVENUE ($ mil.)	NET INCOME ($ mil.)	NET PROFIT MARGIN	EMPLOYEES
12/08	868	13	1.5%	190
12/07	789	17	2.2%	—
12/06	483	0	0.0%	—
Annual Growth	34.0%	70961.0%	—	—

2008 Year-End Financials

Return on assets: 13.3%   Cash ($ mil.): 3
Return on equity: 57.5%
Current ratio: 1.30

KNIGHTS OF COLUMBUS

Good Knight! The Knights of Columbus is a formidable volunteer group boasting more than 15300 councils made up of 1.9 million Roman Catholic male members in the US Canada Mexico Cuba the Philippines Poland and several other countries. The fraternal organization is also a force to be reckoned with in the insurance world providing life insurance annuities and long-term care insurance to its members and their families. More than 1500 full-time insurance agents work across the United States and Canada. In addition the group manages the Knights of Columbus Museum in New Haven Connecticut featuring exhibits of religious art and history. The group was founded in 1882 by Father Michael J. McGivney.

Operations

The Knights of Columbus (KoC) was formed to render financial aid to members and their families. Mutual aid and assistance are offered to sick disabled and needy members and their families. Social and intellectual fellowship is promoted among members and their families through educational charitable religious social welfare war relief and public relief works. KoC is also engaged in religious education the support of public policy issues and charitable activities such as disaster relief.

The entity is a Catholic family fraternal service organization. This theme permeates the entire Service Program: all Church community council family culture of life and youth activities. The Service Program is designed to establish each council as an influential and important force within the community elevate the status of the programming personnel provide more meaningful and relevant programs of action establish direct areas of responsibility build leadership and ensure the success of council programs.

The group's supreme council has more than 75 state council organizations.

Geographic Reach

The Knights of Columbus is made up of local councils throughout the US Canada Mexico Puerto Rico Guam Saipan and the US Virgin Islands. It also has councils in the Bahamas Cuba the Dominican Republic Guatemala Lithuania Panama the Philippines Poland South Korea and Ukraine. The United States Canada and the Philippines have the largest membership numbers.

Financial Performance

In 2019 its Knights of Columbus Insurance reported $8.6 billion in annual sales and more than $26?billion in assets under management. The organization gave $185.7 million to charity and donated 76.7 million hours of hands-on service in 2018.

Strategy

Known for its charitable giving the Knights of Columbus is also an insurance company providing insurance to its membership.

The organization has 1500 agents who are also members of the Knights. In 2018 Knights of Columbus Insurance issued $8.6 billion of new life insurance provided $1 billion in benefits including $441 million in death benefits and $262 million in refunds to members. Once the company?s revenue covers operational costs and refunds (dividends) to its membership the remaining profits are directed to charity.

The Knights of Columbus wants to attract younger members to the organization and has made some adjustments such as offering streamlined online memberships and eliminating some of its longstanding uniform requirements.

Company Background

The Knights of Columbus was founded in New Haven by Father Michael J. McGivney in 1882 and has been selling insurance since its founding.

EXECUTIVES

Supreme Knight, Carl A. Anderson
Supreme Secretary, Michael J. (Mike) O'Connor
Supreme Chaplain, William E. Lori
Deputy Supreme Knight, Patrick E. Kelly
Supreme Treasurer, Ronald F. Schwarz
Vice President Communications And Strategic Planning, Andrew Walther
Assistant Vice President Of Application Development, Niki Kratzert
Vice President, Gary Nolan
Vice President Actuary, Marc Andre-Brunet
Senior Vice President Chief Communications Officer, Kevin Shinkle
Vice President Portfolio Manager, Gil Marchand
Treasurer, Logan Ludwig
Treasurer, Keith Ryan
Treasurer, Ron Schwarz

LOCATIONS

HQ: KNIGHTS OF COLUMBUS
1 COLUMBUS PLZ STE 1700, NEW HAVEN, CT 065103326
Phone: 203 752-4000
Web: WWW.KOFC.ORG

HISTORICAL FINANCIALS
Company Type: Private

Income Statement			FYE: December 31	
	ASSETS ($ mil.)	NET INCOME ($ mil.)	INCOME AS % OF ASSETS	EMPLOYEES
12/13	20,534	113	0.6%	2,300
12/12	19,401	127	0.7%	—
12/11	18,026	81	0.4%	—
12/10	16,861	86	0.5%	—
Annual Growth	6.8%	9.5%	—	—

2013 Year-End Financials

Return on assets: 0.6% Sales ($ mil): 2,115
Return on equity: 6.0%

KOOTENAI HOSPITAL DISTRICT

EXECUTIVES

Prin, Jon Ness
Cfo*, Kim Webb
V Pres*, Jeremy S Evans
Accounting Staff, Jenny Lea
Chief Staff, Thomas Nickol
Physician Recruitment Manager, Brian S Jerome
Manager, Charlie Linder
Phlebotomist, Daphne Kaiser
Administrative Assistant, Kali Singleton
Coordinator, Megan Clevenger
Project Coordinator, Rachel Maly

LOCATIONS

HQ: KOOTENAI HOSPITAL DISTRICT
2003 KOOTENAI HEALTH WAY, COEUR D ALENE, ID 838146051
Phone: 208 625-4000
Web: WWW.KH.ORG

HISTORICAL FINANCIALS
Company Type: Private

Income Statement			FYE: December 31	
	REVENUE ($ mil.)	NET INCOME ($ mil.)	NET PROFIT MARGIN	EMPLOYEES
12/17	506	35	6.9%	2,776
12/16	467	15	3.4%	—
12/15	398	35	9.0%	—
12/14	368	30	8.3%	—
Annual Growth	11.1%	4.6%	—	—

2017 Year-End Financials

Return on assets: 5.8% Cash ($ mil.): 80
Return on equity: 8.4%
Current ratio: 2.80

KRAMM HEALTHCARE CENTER, INC

EXECUTIVES

President, Jeffrey Kramm
Principal, Randall L Kramm
Principal, Steven Kramm DMD
Food Director, Carla Kline

LOCATIONS

HQ: KRAMM HEALTHCARE CENTER, INC
743 MAHONING ST, MILTON, PA 178472232
Phone: 570 742-2681
Web: WWW.KRAMMHEALTHCARE.ORG

HISTORICAL FINANCIALS
Company Type: Private

Income Statement			FYE: June 30	
	REVENUE ($ mil.)	NET INCOME ($ mil.)	NET PROFIT MARGIN	EMPLOYEES
06/09	925	98	10.7%	330
06/00	5	0	3.8%	—
06/98	1	0	—	—
06/97	4	0	1.8%	—
Annual Growth	56.0%	80.8%	—	—

2009 Year-End Financials

Return on assets: 688.1% Cash ($ mil.): —
Return on equity: 582.5%
Current ratio: 1.10

KRATON POLYMERS U.S. LLC

EXECUTIVES

Mng MBR, Kevin M Fogarty
MBR*, David A Bradley
MBR -Exec V Pres*, Stephen E Tremblay
MBR*, Stephen W Duffy
Vice-President*, Richard A Ott
MBR*, Lothar P Freund
MBR*, G Scott Lee
MBR*, Holger R Jung
Associate Director of Human RE, Joop Oranje
Sales Manager, Owen Frawley
Member, Anna Catalano

LOCATIONS

HQ: KRATON POLYMERS U.S. LLC
15710 JOHN F KENNEDY BLVD # 300, HOUSTON, TX 770322347
Phone: 281 504-4700
Web: WWW.KRATON.COM

HISTORICAL FINANCIALS
Company Type: Private

Income Statement			FYE: December 31	
	REVENUE ($ mil.)	NET INCOME ($ mil.)	NET PROFIT MARGIN	EMPLOYEES
12/08	1,226	28	2.3%	520
12/07	1,089	(43)	—	—
12/06	0	0	—	—
12/05	975	166	17.1%	—
Annual Growth	7.9%	(44.6%)	—	—

2008 Year-End Financials

Return on assets: 6.1% Cash ($ mil.): 101
Return on equity: 2.3%
Current ratio: 1.10

KRUEGER INTERNATIONAL, INC.

Krueger International can be found in cubicles classrooms cafeterias and college dorms. The company which does business as KI makes ergonomic seating cabinets and other furniture used by businesses healthcare organizations government agencies and educational institutions. The company offers everything from benches and beds to desks and tables not to mention shelving filing systems movable walls and trash bins. KI markets its products through sales representatives furniture dealers architects and interior designers worldwide. Founded in 1941 KI was purchased in the 1980s by its managers who later allowed employees to buy stock. Today KI is 100% employee owned.

Operations
Boasting $700 million in sales and the title of sixth-largest contract furniture manufacturer in the industry KI operates a variety of subsidiaries including KI UK Ltd. KI East Asia Sdn. Bhd KI Nova Scotia KI Canada KI-Sebel and KI India.

KI also owns three subsidiaries: AWP Wood Products Pallas Textiles and Spacesaver. Quebec-based AWP Wood Products makes architectural wood doors for the office partition industry. Pallas Textiles which operates out of Wisconsin creates textile products for contract upholstery panel systems and wall-coverings healthcare environments and casements. Spacesaver Corporation also located in Wisconsin makes high-density mobile storage systems for office institutional and industrial applications and is a major supplier of steel shelving systems rotary storage systems and storage accessories.

The company maintains nine manufacturing sites around the globe. Besides its four locations in Wisconsin (in Bonduel Fort Atkinson Green Bay and Manitowoc) KI operates production facilities in High Point North Carolina; Penmroke Ontario Canada; and Tupelo Mississippi. In 2012 KI expanded its Green Bay Wisconsin plant (at the tune of $3.3 million) by more than 100000 sq. ft. for additional elbow room devoted to manufacturing shipping receiving and warehousing.

Geographic Reach
Based in Wisconsin KI sells its products worldwide and operates manufacturing facilities and sales offices in the US Canada China and India as well as throughout Europe Latin America and Asia. It has subsidiaries based in the UK Canada India and Malaysia. Its showrooms are in several metropolitan areas across the US Toronto and London.

Sales and Marketing
KI sells its products globally through furniture dealers sales representatives architects and interior designers. It primarily serves the educational university healthcare business and government markets.

The company staffs direct sales offices around the world and also boasts showrooms in metropolitan areas to display its products to potential business and individual customers.

Strategy
KI is well-regarded in the classroom furniture market and is a leading supplier for both K-12 schools and universities. The company has outfitted classrooms lecture halls administrative offices computer labs media centers residence halls and student unions. KI has been a government vendor for more than six decades providing furnishings for an assortment of federal agencies including all branches of the military. KI's corporate products are ergonomically designed to help individuals work more comfortably and efficiently. In addition to these core customer groups KI has also installed its furnishings in outdoor public spaces sports arenas conference centers and airports.

It regularly rolls out new products. In 2013 KI launched the Grazie Seating Collection through a collaboration between renowned designer Giancarlo Piretti and in 2012 introduced the elegant and sophisticated Affina Collection an expansive seating and table line designed by Paul James and Dan Cramer. KI also expanded its existing product licensing agreement with UK seating industry leader Boss Design in 2013 to give Boss Design an extended reach into the US market and KI a broader portfolio of lounge task seating and occasional table items.

Company Background
The company has expanded its network of showrooms in the US and abroad over the years. KI added a showroom in Houston in 2010 to boost its US presence which includes about 10 locations in half a dozen states. To better serve its Asian and European customers the company operates through a showroom in Shanghai China. KI has international showrooms in London Malaysia Mexico Puerto Rico and Toronto. To support its growth KI completed a $3.3-million 100000-sq.-ft. plant expansion in 2012 to reduce costs and streamline its business. The move boosts its manufacturing shipping receiving and warehousing space.

As its showroom presence grew KI also formed new sales partnerships. The company tapped Heartland Furniture Group a contract furniture representative in 2011 to take care of existing customer accounts and broker sales in Kansas Missouri and southern Illinois.

It's also looked to acquisitions to extend the reach of its business. In 2011 KI purchased Sebel Furniture Limited from GWA Group Ltd. a top supplier of building fixtures in Australia. The $24 million deal has given KI a foothold in the commercial furniture business in Australia New Zealand the UK and Hong Kong.

EXECUTIVES

Chairman And Ceo, Richard J. (Dick) Resch
President, Brian Krenke
Vice President Oei Sales And Operations, Patrick Morris
Vice President Corporate Communications, Joe Burkard
Vice President Architectural Wall Operations, Ryan Usiak
Vice President Marketing, Tom Abrahamson
Vice President, Don Gust
Assistant Secretary, Michael Pum
Auditors: BAKER TILLY VIRCHOW KRAUSE LL

LOCATIONS

HQ: KRUEGER INTERNATIONAL, INC.
1330 BELLEVUE ST, GREEN BAY, WI 543022197
Phone: 920 468-8100
Web: WWW.KI.COM

PRODUCTS/OPERATIONS

Selected Products
Auditorium seating
Beds
Benches
Bookcases
Carrels
Chairs
Desks
File cabinets
Lecterns
Movable walls
Planters
Power and data connections
Receptacles
Recliners
Residence hall furniture
Sleepers
Special events seating
Stools
Tables

COMPETITORS

ABCO Office Furniture	Kewaunee Scientific
Allsteel	Kimball International
Bretford	Knoll Inc.
CFGroup	La-Z-Boy
Columbia Manufacturing	Norstar Office
Edsal Manufacturing	Products
Global Group	Sagus
HNI	Steelcase
Haworth Inc.	Trendway
Herman Miller	Virco Mfg.
Inscape corp	

HISTORICAL FINANCIALS
Company Type: Private

Income Statement — FYE: December 31

	REVENUE ($ mil.)	NET INCOME ($ mil.)	NET PROFIT MARGIN	EMPLOYEES
12/17	649	47	7.4%	2,300
12/15	617	53	8.6%	—
12/11	649	56	8.8%	—
12/10	40	0		
Annual Growth	—	462.7%	—	—

2017 Year-End Financials
Return on assets: 18.5%   Cash ($ mil.): 2
Return on equity: 45.8%
Current ratio: 1.20

KWIK TRIP, INC.

Midwesterners who need to make a quick trip to get gas or groceries cigarettes or donuts race on over to Kwik Trip stores. Kwik Trip owns and operates more than 600 Kwik Trip and Kwik Star convenience stores in Iowa Minnesota and Wisconsin. Kwik Trip owns in-house dairy and bakery operations and makes many of its products in-house; popular products include Glazers donuts and Karuba Coffee. All Kwik Trip stores built since 1990 are owned by Convenience Store Investments a separate firm which leases the land and stores to Kwik Trip. Kwik Trip which opened its first store in 1965 in Eau Claire Wisconsin is owned by the family of CEO Don Zietlow.

Strategy
Kwik Trip's main route to growth is opening new stores. It's currently adding store at a rate of roughly 40 each year.

The company is always looking at ways to improve its food and drink offering. Initiatives have included a new line of take-home meals produced each day in house and a tie-up with delivery service EatStreet that allows customers near select locations to order up to 400 items.

Company Background
The John Hansen family founded Kwik Trip in Eau Claire Wisconsin in 1965. In 2000 the Hansens sold their interest in Kwik Trip to the Zietlow family for $120 million. The two families had jointly owned Kwik Trip since 1972.

EXECUTIVES

President And Ceo, Donald P. (Don) Zietlow
Vp And Director Petroleum Operations, Steve Zietlow

Vice President Retail Operations, Greg Olson
Vice President Of Operations Support, Steve
 Loehr
Vice President, Neil Fletcher
Auditors: MCGLADREY & PULLEN LLP MINNE

LOCATIONS

HQ: KWIK TRIP, INC.
 1626 OAK ST, LA CROSSE, WI 546032308
Phone: 608 781-8988
Web: WWW.KWIKTRIP.COM

PRODUCTS/OPERATIONS

Selected Banners
Hearty Platter
Kwik Star
Kwik Trip
Tobacco Outlet Plus

COMPETITORS

7-Eleven	Denny's
Brinker	Exxon Mobil
Carlson Restaurants	Hy-Vee
Casey's General Stores	Krause Gentle
Chevron	Northern Tier Energy
Couche-Tard	Roundy's
Cub Foods	

HISTORICAL FINANCIALS

Company Type: Private

Income Statement				FYE: September 27
	REVENUE ($ mil.)	NET INCOME ($ mil.)	NET PROFIT MARGIN	EMPLOYEES
09/08	3,640	23	0.7%	10,500
09/04	1,887	24	1.3%	—
09/03	1,651	24	1.5%	—
Annual Growth	17.1%	(0.2%)	—	—

2008 Year-End Financials
Return on assets: 3.6%   Cash ($ mil.): 1
Return on equity: 20.3%
Current ratio: 0.70

LAFAYETTE GENERAL HEALTH SYSTEM, INC.

EXECUTIVES

Chb, Clay M Allen
Pres-Ceo*, David Callecod
Svp-Cmo*, Amanda Logue
Cmio*, Fallon Strother McManus
Svp and Chief Administrative O, Al Patin
Svp, Gordon Rountree
Svp, Marisa M Alack
Vp, Michael Dozier
Evp, Patrick W Gandy
Vp, Paul Molbert
Svp, Roger Mattke

LOCATIONS

HQ: LAFAYETTE GENERAL HEALTH SYSTEM, INC.
 1214 COOLIDGE BLVD, LAFAYETTE, LA 705032621
Phone: 337 289-8125
Web: WWW.LAFAYETTEGENERAL.COM

HISTORICAL FINANCIALS

Company Type: Private

Income Statement				FYE: September 30
	REVENUE ($ mil.)	NET INCOME ($ mil.)	NET PROFIT MARGIN	EMPLOYEES
09/18	758	14	1.9%	2,600
09/16	700	13	1.9%	—
09/15	585	18	3.2%	—
09/14	495	24	5.0%	—
Annual Growth	11.2%	(11.9%)	—	—

2018 Year-End Financials
Return on assets: 2.2%   Cash ($ mil.): 79
Return on equity: 4.7%
Current ratio: 2.70

LAFAYETTE GENERAL MEDICAL CENTER, INC.

Serving the people of Acadiana (southern Louisiana) Lafayette General Medical Center (LGMC) provides general inpatient medical and surgical care as well as specialized trauma care and neonatal intensive care. The nonprofit hospital which has 365 beds also offers a cancer center home health services outpatient care occupational medicine and mental health care. As part of umbrella group Lafayette Health LGMC is affiliated with Lafayette General Surgical Hospital Lafayette General Southwest St. Martin Hospital Acadia General Hospital University Hospital and Clinics and Abrom Kaplan Memorial Hospital. It's also a teaching hospital for LSU. Non-profit foundation Lafayette General Foundation supports and governs Lafayette Health.

EXECUTIVES

Svp Of Human Resource, David Muldowney

LOCATIONS

HQ: LAFAYETTE GENERAL MEDICAL CENTER, INC.
 1214 COOLIDGE BLVD, LAFAYETTE, LA 705032621
Phone: 337 289-7991
Web: WWW.LAFAYETTEGENERAL.COM

COMPETITORS

Baton Rouge General	LifePoint Health
CHRISTUS St. Frances	Our Lady of Lourdes
Cabrini Hospital	Women & Children's Hospital
HCA	

HISTORICAL FINANCIALS

Company Type: Private

Income Statement				FYE: September 30
	REVENUE ($ mil.)	NET INCOME ($ mil.)	NET PROFIT MARGIN	EMPLOYEES
09/18	480	45	9.4%	1,626
09/17	465	44	9.5%	—
09/16	454	50	11.2%	—
09/15	428	55	12.9%	—
Annual Growth	3.8%	(6.7%)	—	—

2018 Year-End Financials
Return on assets: 9.5%   Cash ($ mil.): 13
Return on equity: 10.0%
Current ratio: 16.10

LAHEY CLINIC HOSPITAL, INC.

EXECUTIVES

Ceo, Howard R Grant JD
Ceo, David Barrett
Chm, Bernard Gordon
V Chm, John Libertino
V Pres, Donna Cameron
Director of Comm & Mktg, Scott V Hartman
Internal Medicine Practitioner, Anu Diddee
Ophthalmologist, Paul R Cotran
Laboratory Director, Barbara Sacco
Director Education, Donna Ales
Chief of Anesthesiology, Sana Ata

LOCATIONS

HQ: LAHEY CLINIC HOSPITAL, INC.
 41 MALL RD, BURLINGTON, MA 018050002
Phone: 781 273-5100
Web: WWW.LAHEY.ORG

HISTORICAL FINANCIALS

Company Type: Private

Income Statement				FYE: September 30
	REVENUE ($ mil.)	NET INCOME ($ mil.)	NET PROFIT MARGIN	EMPLOYEES
09/15	816	(17)	—	1
09/14	800	(0)	—	—
09/13	774	228	29.5%	—
09/12	796	192	24.1%	—
Annual Growth	0.8%	—	—	—

2015 Year-End Financials
Return on assets: (-2.3%)   Cash ($ mil.): 105
Return on equity: (-12.0%)
Current ratio: 2.40

LAKELAND REGIONAL HEALTH SYSTEMS, INC.

EXECUTIVES

Pres & Ceo, Elaine Thompson
Vp-Coo, Sarah Bhagat
Exec Vp-Cfo, Evan C Jones
Vp & Chief Public Relations, Timothy J Boynton
Svp & Chief Hr, Scott W Dimmick
Evp & Coo, Danielle Drummond
Evp & Chief Nurse Executive, Janet Fansler
Vp & Chief Analytics Officer, Caroline Gay
Vp Finance, Lance Green
Exec Dir & Chief Academic Offi, Graham F
 Greene
Evp & Chief Legal Officer, Jonn D Hoppe
Auditors: KPMG LLP TAMPA FL

LOCATIONS

HQ: LAKELAND REGIONAL HEALTH SYSTEMS, INC.
 1324 LAKELAND HILLS BLVD, LAKELAND, FL 338054543
Phone: 863 687-1100
Web: WWW.MYLRH.ORG

HISTORICAL FINANCIALS
Company Type: Private

Income Statement				FYE: September 30
	REVENUE ($ mil.)	NET INCOME ($ mil.)	NET PROFIT MARGIN	EMPLOYEES
09/14	685	67	9.9%	3,124
09/13	24	(13)	—	—
09/12	582	67	11.6%	—
Annual Growth	8.5%	0.4%	—	—

2014 Year-End Financials
Return on assets: 7.2% Cash ($ mil.): 22
Return on equity: 10.9%
Current ratio: 1.40

LAKELAND REGIONAL MEDICAL CENTER, INC.

Lakeland Regional Medical Center (LRMC) serves Florida's Polk County (roughly between Kissimmee and Tampa) through an acute care hospital with approximately 850 beds. Among its specialty services are cardiac care cancer treatment senior care urology emergency medicine orthopedics women's and children's health care and surgery. LRMC also operates general care and specialty outpatient clinics. Additionally the hospital provides medical training programs for radiology specialists. Its LRMC Foundation offers financial support for indigent patients facing ongoing treatment.

Operations
LRMC is part of Lakeland Regional Health System a not-for-profit organization that also includes Lakeland Regional Cancer Center Lakeland Regional Family Health Center and Lakeland Regional Health Medical Group.

Annually LRMC has more than 41000 admissions and performs more than 15000 surgeries. Its emergency department treats more than 200000 patients each year.

Financial Performance
Revenue in 2014 totaled $633 million (representing 92% of Lakeland Regional Health System's revenue) while net income totaled $67 million.

LRMC funds its activities through charges to patients for inpatient and outpatient services as well as from non-hospital activities such as its cafeteria gift and uniform shops and physicians' answering service. Although the hospital also receives payment from federal agencies such as Medicaid and Medicare they along with other managed care entities have cut their reimbursement levels causing LRMC's charity care levels to increase.

Strategy
The hospital has been undergoing facility and data systems improvement efforts to enhance care and increase efficiencies. It recently expanded its intensive care department and upgraded technology in areas including radiology orthopedics and chemotherapy.

In 2014 Lakeland Regional Health System announced plans to build an eight-story women and children pavilion at LRMC. The $250 million addition will include 300000 sq. ft. of space including 32 private rooms for mothers and newborns a 30-bed neonatal intensive care unit 64 private rooms for women's surgical and medical care three surgical suites and 12 private suites for labor delivery and recovery. It will also have an education and conference center. The pavilion is expected to open in 2017.

EXECUTIVES
President And Chief Medical Officer, Mack Reavis
Rph, Louis Frescura
Director Of Radiology, Fakhir F Elmasri
Medical Director, Sharlet Cochran
Executive Medical Director, Natalie Adsuar
Secretary, Christine Johnston
Auditors: PERSHING YOAKLEY & ASSOCIATES

LOCATIONS
HQ: LAKELAND REGIONAL MEDICAL CENTER, INC.
1324 LAKELAND HILLS BLVD, LAKELAND, FL 338054500
Phone: 863 687-1100
Web: WWW.LRMC.COM

PRODUCTS/OPERATIONS

Selected Facilities
Lakeland Regional Cancer Center
Lakeland Regional Medical Center (LRMC) Foundation
Lakeland Regional Orthopedics Associates
Lakeland Regional Rehabilitation and Sports Medicine Clinic

Selected Services and Centers
Emergency
Family health center
Gastroenterology
Heart center
Mental health & addictions
Neurosurgery
Nursing
Oncology care
Orthopedic care
Palliative care
Pharmacy
Rehabilitation and sports medicine clinic
Robotic surgery
School of radiologic technology
Stroke center
Surgery
Trauma services
Women and children
Wound center

COMPETITORS
Adventist Health System Sunbelt Healthcare
All Children's Hospital
Baptist Health South Florida
BayCare Health System
Bayfront Health
DeSoto Memorial
Florida Hospital Tampa Bay Division
HCA
Manatee Memorial Hospital
Sarasota Memorial Health Care
Tampa General Hospital
Winter Haven Hospital

HISTORICAL FINANCIALS
Company Type: Private

Income Statement				FYE: September 30
	REVENUE ($ mil.)	NET INCOME ($ mil.)	NET PROFIT MARGIN	EMPLOYEES
09/16	790	84	10.7%	3,100
09/15	674	68	10.2%	—
09/14	618	66	10.8%	—
09/13	584	55	9.4%	—
Annual Growth	10.6%	15.3%	—	—

2016 Year-End Financials
Return on assets: 10.5% Cash ($ mil.): 1
Return on equity: 25.6%
Current ratio: —

LAMEX FOODS INC.

EXECUTIVES
Ceo, Phillip O Wallace
Pres*, Steven Anderson
V Pres*, Mark Barrett
Sr Dir*, Mark Ryder
Accounting Manager, Lisa Henkel
Latin America Trade Manager, Robert Preska
Trading Manager, Robert Lucas
Import Logistics Manager, Samantha Zarske
Sales Team Member, Eileen Wang
Export Coordinator, Danielle Waterhouse
Director, Paul Wallace

LOCATIONS
HQ: LAMEX FOODS INC.
8500 NORMANDALE, BLOOMINGTON, MN 55437
Phone: 952 844-0585
Web: WWW.LAMEXFOODS.EU

HISTORICAL FINANCIALS
Company Type: Private

Income Statement				FYE: March 31
	REVENUE ($ mil.)	NET INCOME ($ mil.)	NET PROFIT MARGIN	EMPLOYEES
03/15	592	7	1.3%	80
03/05	103	1	1.0%	—
03/04	76	0	0.9%	—
Annual Growth	20.4%	24.8%	—	—

2015 Year-End Financials
Return on assets: 7.2% Cash ($ mil.): —
Return on equity: 20.8%
Current ratio: 1.50

LANE INDUSTRIES INCORPORATED

EXECUTIVES
Pres-Ceo, Mark Schiller
Chb, Robert Alger
Treas-Asst SEC, Vincent Caiola
Exec V Pres, Kirk Junco
V Pres, David Benton
Exec V Pres, Mike Cote
Auditors: KPMG LLP HARTFORD CT

LOCATIONS
HQ: LANE INDUSTRIES INCORPORATED
90 FIELDSTONE CT, CHESHIRE, CT 064101212
Phone: 203 235-3351
Web: WWW.LANECONSTRUCT.COM

HISTORICAL FINANCIALS
Company Type: Private

Income Statement				FYE: December 31
	REVENUE ($ mil.)	NET INCOME ($ mil.)	NET PROFIT MARGIN	EMPLOYEES
12/18	856	(68)	—	4,500
12/17	1,592	14	0.9%	—
12/16	1,292	36	2.8%	—
12/15	1,197	(13)	—	—
Annual Growth	(10.6%)	—	—	—

2018 Year-End Financials

Return on assets: (-6.9%)   Cash ($ mil.): 137
Return on equity: (-13.8%)
Current ratio: 1.80

LARSEN & TOUBRO INFOTECH LIMITED

EXECUTIVES

Ceo, Sanjay Jalona
Cfo, Ashok Sonthalia
Exec Vp, Sunil Pande
Executive Engineer Procurement, Ankush Singh
Technical, Kishore Dhanapal
Software Engineer, Maya Mohan
Senior Consultant, Alok Jain
Senior Software Engineer, Soumyadeep Mishra
Senior Account Director, Brijesh Gopinath
Senior Consultant, Mandar Chandratre
Project Manager, Prashant Ardalkar
Auditors: RAMESH SARVA CPA PC FOR

LOCATIONS

HQ: LARSEN & TOUBRO INFOTECH LIMITED
2035 STATE ROUTE 27 # 3000, EDISON, NJ
088173351
Phone: 732 248-6111
Web: WWW.LNTINFOTECH.COM

HISTORICAL FINANCIALS

Company Type: Private

Income Statement				FYE: March 31
	REVENUE ($ mil.)	NET INCOME ($ mil.)	NET PROFIT MARGIN	EMPLOYEES
03/15	478	8	1.7%	20,000
03/13	398	7	1.8%	—
Annual Growth	9.6%	8.6%	—	—

2015 Year-End Financials

Return on assets: 6.9%   Cash ($ mil.): 6
Return on equity: 18.2%
Current ratio: 1.60

LAWRENCE WHOLESALE, LLC

EXECUTIVES

Ceo, Mark Liszt
Cfo, Robert Francis
Coo, Max Liszt
Sales Team, Lawrence Wholesale
It Manager, Walter Aceituno
Controller, Dannette Soto
Auditors: MOSS ADAMS LLP LOS ANGELES

LOCATIONS

HQ: LAWRENCE WHOLESALE, LLC
4353 EXCHANGE AVE, VERNON, CA 900582619
Phone: 323 235-7535
Web: WWW.LAWRENCEWHOLESALE.COM

HISTORICAL FINANCIALS

Company Type: Private

Income Statement				FYE: December 31
	REVENUE ($ mil.)	NET INCOME ($ mil.)	NET PROFIT MARGIN	EMPLOYEES
12/18	698	7	1.0%	100
12/17	810	8	1.0%	—
12/16	741	9	1.2%	—
Annual Growth	(2.9%)	(10.2%)	—	—

2018 Year-End Financials

Return on assets: 6.3%   Cash ($ mil.): 5
Return on equity: 23.2%
Current ratio: 1.40

LEANDER INDEPENDENT SCHOOL DISTRICT

EXECUTIVES

Supt, Bret A Champion
Acct, Dana Paulson
Assistant Director, Gina Mitschke
Manager, Tami Rust
Officer, Carmen Lawson
Network Engineer, James Watson
Reading Specialist, Robyn Cooper
Pathologist, Darolyn Gonzales
Coordinator, Denise Geiger
Coordinator, Mary Kluga
Director, Peter Warshaw

LOCATIONS

HQ: LEANDER INDEPENDENT SCHOOL DISTRICT
204 W SOUTH ST, LEANDER, TX 786411719
Phone: 512 570-0000
Web: WWW.LEANDERISD.ORG

HISTORICAL FINANCIALS

Company Type: Private

Income Statement				FYE: August 31
	REVENUE ($ mil.)	NET INCOME ($ mil.)	NET PROFIT MARGIN	EMPLOYEES
08/18	462	85	18.6%	2,700
08/17	440	(29)	—	—
08/16	414	(36)	—	—
08/07	239	9	3.8%	—
Annual Growth	6.1%	22.5%	—	—

2018 Year-End Financials

Return on assets: 5.3%   Cash ($ mil.): 11
Return on equity: —
Current ratio: —

LEE MEMORIAL HEALTH SYSTEM FOUNDATION, INC.

Not feeling so bright in the Sunshine State? Lee Memorial Health System can help. Serving residents of Fort Myers and surrounding areas in Southwestern Florida's Lee County the community-owned not-for-profit health care system is home to four acute care hospitals (with a total of more than 1400 beds) a home health agency a 112-bed nursing home and numerous outpatient treatment and diagnostic centers. The flagship Lee Memorial Hospital also houses a 60-bed inpatient rehabilitation hospital and the HealthPark Medical Center location includes a dedicated 100-bed children's hospital. Lee Memorial Health Systems' corporate services include pre-employment screenings drug screens and wellness programs.

Operations

The system's facilities include the flagship Lee Memorial Hospital (355 beds) HealthPark Medical Center (270 beds) Gulf Coast Medical Center (350 beds) and Cape Coral Hospital (290 beds). Lee Memorial Health System employs more than 1200 doctors including primary and specialty care practitioners that are members of the affiliated Lee Physician Group. Patient service revenues account for nearly all of the company's revenues.

Lee Memorial Hospital is the only level II trauma center between Tampa and Miami.

Altogether the system has more than 1 million patient contacts each year.

Geographic Reach

Three of the systems' hospitals are located in Fort Myers Florida. Its fourth hospital (Cape Coral Hospital) is located in Cape Coral Florida.

Sales and Marketing

Medicare payments accounted for a third of the system's net patient service revenues in fiscal 2014 while Medicaid accounted for 15%. Self-pay accounted for 26% followed by managed care (20%) and commercial insurance (6%).

Financial Performance

Revenue increased 8% to $1.4 billion in fiscal 2014 (ended September) as net patient service revenues grew. This in turn led to an increase in net income which grew 31% to $158 million. Decreased interest expenses also helped boost profits.

Cash flow from operations increased 49% to $225 million that year largely due to cash received from patient care services.

Strategy

Lee Memorial Health System is a not-for-profit organization that proclaims its fiscal mission is to reinvest its profits back into the community it serves through facility and equipment upgrades and other measures. The system has undertaken a number of expansion projects at its hospitals in recent years to add specialty services and private patient rooms and has also opened a number of new community outpatient centers. In addition it is enhancing existing facilities to improve quality safety and financial performance.

In 2015 the system approved a $315 million expansion plan that will add 275 patient beds to Gulf Coast Medical Center. Construction on the project is expected to begin in 2017.

Lee Memorial Health System is also upgrading its IT systems to provide coordinated and efficient care. It has installed electronic health record programs (using EHR software from Epic Systems) at most of its facilities and it is improving other tools to streamline business systems and improve health care delivery processes.

Company Background

Tracing its roots to 1916 Lee Memorial Health System is a public health care system created by special act of the Florida Legislature in 1963. Its governing board is composed of 10 members elected by the public.

EXECUTIVES

Nursing Director, Tomaso Vicki
Nursing Director, Kristina Desfosses
Assistant Vice President Of Operations, Sheila Dupuy
Treasurer, Pablo Veintimilla
Secretary, Jennifer Parisi
Secretary, Janine Mcelroy

LOCATIONS

HQ: LEE MEMORIAL HEALTH SYSTEM FOUNDATION, INC.
2776 CLEVELAND AVE, FORT MYERS, FL 339015864
Phone: 239 343-2000
Web: WWW.LEEHEALTH.ORG

PRODUCTS/OPERATIONS

2014 Sales by Segment

	$ mil.	% of total
Lee Memorial Hospital	682	50
Gulf Coast Memorial Center	302	22
Cape Memorial Hospital	206	15
Physicians	133	10
Health Park Care Center	13	1
Lee Memorial Home Health	8	1
Lee Memorial Health System Foundation	3	-
Lee County Trauma Services District	3	-
Lee Community Health Care	1	-
Other	9	1
Total	**1,363**	**100**

Selected Florida Hospitals
Blood Centers
Cardiac Care (Heart Services)
Community Health Centers/United Way Houses
Convenient Care
Emergency Services
Home Health Services
The Kidney Transplant Center
Lee Physician Group
Mental Health Services
Neuroscience Services
Nursing Home
Occupational Health Services
Orthopedic and Spine Services
Palliative Services
Patient Services
Pediatric Services
Pulmonary Services
Rehabilitation Services
Sleep Disorder Center
Surgical Services
Volunteer Services
Wellness and Nutrition Services
Women's Health Services
Wound Care and Hyperbaric Medicine

COMPETITORS

Adventist Health System Sunbelt Healthcare
All Children's Hospital
BayCare Health System
Bayfront Health
DeSoto Memorial
H. Lee Moffitt Cancer Center & Research Institute
HCA
NCH Healthcare
Sarasota Memorial Health Care
St. Joseph's-Baptist Health Care
Tampa General Hospital

HISTORICAL FINANCIALS
Company Type: Private

Income Statement
FYE: September 30

	REVENUE ($ mil.)	NET INCOME ($ mil.)	NET PROFIT MARGIN	EMPLOYEES
09/18	1,789	101	5.6%	7,870
09/04	585	46	8.0%	—
09/03	522	50	9.8%	—
09/02	477	7	1.6%	—
Annual Growth	**8.6%**	**17.4%**	—	—

2018 Year-End Financials
Return on assets: 4.1%   Cash ($ mil.): 33
Return on equity: 6.6%
Current ratio: 5.40

LEE MEMORIAL HOSPITAL, INC.

EXECUTIVES

President, Jim Nathan
Coordinator, Shari Trivett
Executive Officer, Ken Szymanski
Assistant, Donna Shapiro
Health Professional, Furhan Qureshi
Manager, Patricia Hurttbateman
Internal Medicine Practitioner, Iasmina Jivanov
Internal Medicine Practitioner, Nadia Parchment
Secretary, Nancy McGovern
Family Practitioner, Asif Azam
Senior Recruiter, Barbara Pretasky

LOCATIONS

HQ: LEE MEMORIAL HOSPITAL, INC.
2776 CLEVELAND AVE, FORT MYERS, FL 339015855
Phone: 239 343-2000

HISTORICAL FINANCIALS
Company Type: Private

Income Statement
FYE: September 30

	REVENUE ($ mil.)	NET INCOME ($ mil.)	NET PROFIT MARGIN	EMPLOYEES
09/14	688	163	23.8%	1,159
09/13	632	135	21.4%	—
09/12	613	105	17.3%	—
Annual Growth	**6.0%**	**24.4%**	—	—

2014 Year-End Financials
Return on assets: 10.8%   Cash ($ mil.): 32
Return on equity: 21.1%
Current ratio: 7.30

LEGACY EMANUEL HOSPITAL & HEALTH CENTER

Legacy Emanuel Hospital and Health Center part of the Legacy Health System provides acute and specialized health care to residents of Portland Oregon and surrounding communities. The 420-bed teaching hospital's operations include centers devoted to trauma treatment burn care oncology birthing neurosurgery orthopedics and cardiology. It also houses a pediatric hospital and operates the region's Life Flight Network service which is owned by a consortium of local hospitals. Legacy Emanuel's emergency department handles more than 15600 visits every year.

Operations

Legacy Emanuel's trauma and burn centers are level I designated facilities meaning they receive severe trauma and burn cases from other area hospitals. The hospital's burn center is the only one of its kind in an area stretching from Seattle to Sacramento and Salt Lake City. Other specialist facilities at Legacy Emanuel include its maternity center and its diagnostic imaging and screening units.

The medical center sees more than 18000 inpatients each year. Its staff includes about 140 full-time doctors and dentists as well as 700 full-time registered nurses. The Randall Children's Hospital located within Legacy Emanuel has about 600 affiliated pediatricians and specialists on its staff and handles about 100000 patient encounters each year including 20000 emergency room visits.

Strategy

The hospital has undergone massive expansion efforts. The hospital has completed construction of the new Randall Children's Hospital facilities making it one of the largest pediatric facilities in the state. The new pediatric center is four times as large as the past facilities. Other expansion efforts in recent years include new acute and intensive care capacity.

Company Background

To expand its medical transportation services Legacy Emanuel and other owners of LFN teamed up to purchase 15 new helicopters in 2012.

Legacy Emanuel Hospital was established in 1912 by the Lutheran Church.

EXECUTIVES

Senior Vice President And Chief Development Officer, Maureen Bradley

LOCATIONS

HQ: LEGACY EMANUEL HOSPITAL & HEALTH CENTER
2801 N GANTENBEIN AVE, PORTLAND, OR 972271623
Phone: 503 413-2200
Web: WWW.LEGACYHEALTH.ORG

PRODUCTS/OPERATIONS

Selected Centers and Services
Burn care
Cancer care
Children's care
Diabetes and nutrition
Emergency services
Family birth center
Gardens
High-risk obstetrics
Imaging
Injury prevention

Intensive care
Interventional and diagnostic cardiology
Level I trauma center
Life flight network
Maternal-fetal medicine
Neurology and neurosurgery including spine surgery
Orthopedics
Pediatrics
Rehabilitation (inpatient and outpatient)
Radiation oncology
Stroke
Surgery (including minimally invasive surgery)
Vascular clinic
Wound and ostomy clinic
Wound care and outpatient burn clinic

COMPETITORS

Adventist Health	PeaceHealth
System West	PeaceHealth Southwest
Asante Health System	Medical Center
Dignity Health	Providence St. Joseph
Kadlec Regional	Health
Medical Center	Salem Hospital

HISTORICAL FINANCIALS
Company Type: Private

Income Statement   FYE: March 31

	REVENUE ($ mil.)	NET INCOME ($ mil.)	NET PROFIT MARGIN	EMPLOYEES
03/15	705	29	4.2%	3,619
03/14	649	30	4.8%	—
03/13	566	6	1.1%	—
03/12	571	(6)	—	—
Annual Growth	7.3%	—	—	—

LEGACY HEALTH

Legacy Health strives to promote positive health in the Portland/Vancouver metropolitan area. A not-for-profit provider of health care services in Oregon and Washington the health system operates half a dozen hospitals including Legacy Emanuel Medical Center and Legacy Good Samaritan Medical Center as well as the Randall Children's Hospital at Legacy Emanuel. Legacy Health has more than 1200 total beds and its facilities provide such services as acute and critical care behavioral health and outpatient and health education programs. It also operates home health hospice and research facilities; emergency transportation helicopters; and a number of regional clinics and labs.

Operations
Legacy Health's hospitals include Legacy Emanuel Medical Center Randall Children's Hospital Legacy Good Samaritan Medical Center Legacy Meridian Park Medical Center Legacy Mount Hood Medical Center and Legacy Salmon Creek Medical Center in Washington.

Legacy Medical Group includes more than 300 affiliated physicians operating nearly 30 primary care clinics in the region as well as a number of specialty care centers in fields such as obstetrics pediatrics cardiology neurology and orthopedics.

In addition to providing medical care Legacy Health partners with government and commercial entities to conduct medical research studies.

Geographic Reach
Legacy Health System operates six hospitals some 70 outpatient clinics and a number of hospice research and diagnostic facilities in the Portland/Vancouver metropolitan area. It has three hospitals located in Portland as well as one each in Gresham Oregon; Tualatin Oregon; and Vancouver Washington.

Financial Performance
Legacy Health had an 8% increase in net operating revenue to some $2.1 billion in fiscal 2018 (ended March) marking several straight years of rising revenues due to organic growth.

However revenues in excess of expenses declined 20% to $100.2 million that year as operating income and non-operating gains fell significantly. Part of that decline was due to costs related to providing services to patients unable to pay for health care.

Strategy
Legacy Health is focused on improving its existing hospitals. It is also opening new general care and specialty clinics partly through partnerships with area physicians. The addition of new clinics is designed not only to service the needs of small communities but also to ensure that referrals from area doctors help to sustain its nearby hospitals. New facilities also allow Legacy to broaden its Portland-area offerings by providing pediatric orthopedic diagnostic and sports medicine services among others.

In 2017 the system joined together with OHSU Kaiser Permanente Northwest and Adventist Health to open the first comprehensive full-time behavioral health care center in the area. Unity Center for Behavioral Health offers psychiatric emergency care for adults and operates a 107-bed inpatient facility for adults and adolescents. The state of Portland began investigating complaints from the center's employees in 2018 which led the facility to temporarily close its doors to new patients.

Company Background
Legacy Health was founded through the 1989 merger of HealthLink and Good Samaritan Hospital.

EXECUTIVES

Svp And Chief Nursing Officer, Carol Bradley
President And Ceo, George J. Brown
Chief Administrative Officer Legacy Meridian Park Medical Center, Allyson Anderson
Chief Administrative Officer Legacy Good Samaritan Medical Center, Jonathan Avery
Svp And Cio, John Kenagy
Chief Admnistrative Officer Randall Children's Hospital At Legacy Emanuel, Bronwyn Houston, age 50
Svp And Coo, Mike Newcomb
Svp And Chief Medical Officer, Lewis Low
Chief Administrative Officer Legacy Mount Hood Medical Center, Gretchen Nichols
Svp And Cfo, Linda Hoff
Chief Administrative Officer, Bryce Helgerson
Vice President Finance, Gordon Edwards
Clinical Vice President Womens Services And Surgical Services, Duncan Neilson
Vice President Human Resources, Sonja Steves
Auditors: KPMG LLP PORTLAND OREGON

LOCATIONS
HQ: LEGACY HEALTH
1919 NW LOVEJOY ST, PORTLAND, OR 972091503
Phone: 503 415-5600
Web: WWW.LEGACYHEALTH.ORG

PRODUCTS/OPERATIONS

Selected Facilities

Hospitals
Legacy Emanuel Medical Center (Portland Oregon)
Legacy Good Samaritan Medical Center (Portland Oregon)
Legacy Meridian Park Medical Center (Tualatin Oregon)
Legacy Mount Hood Medical Center (Gresham Oregon)
Legacy Salmon Creek Medical Center (Vancouver Washington)
Randall Children's Hospital At Legacy Emanuel (Portland Oregon)

Clinics
Legacy Med
Legacy Med
Legacy Med
Legacy Med
Legacy Med
Legacy Medical Group - Fisher's Landing
Legacy Medical Group - Good Samaritan
Legacy Medical Group - Lake Oswego
Legacy Med
Legacy Med
Legacy Medical Group - Salmon Creek Family Medicine (Vancouver Washington)
Legacy Medical Group - Salmon Creek Internal Medicine (Vancouver Washington)
Legacy Med
Legacy Medical Group - West Linn
Legacy Med

COMPETITORS

Adventist Health	Oregon Health &
System West	Science University
Asante Health System	PeaceHealth
Kadlec Regional	Providence St. Joseph
Medical Center	Health
Kaiser Foundation	Salem Hospital
Hospitals	

HISTORICAL FINANCIALS
Company Type: Private

Income Statement   FYE: March 31

	REVENUE ($ mil.)	NET INCOME ($ mil.)	NET PROFIT MARGIN	EMPLOYEES
03/18	2,117	100	4.7%	10,675
03/17	1,965	172	8.8%	—
03/15	1,658	156	9.4%	—
03/14	183	9	5.2%	—
Annual Growth	84.4%	80.0%	—	—

2018 Year-End Financials
Return on assets: 4.0%   Cash ($ mil.): 67
Return on equity: 6.7%
Current ratio: 1.70

LEHIGH GAS CORPORATION

EXECUTIVES

Pres, David Hrinak
V Pres*, Lowell Brogan
SEC-Treas*, Howard J Krapf
Director, Anne Boran
Senior Manager of Information, Wayne Maresch

LOCATIONS
HQ: LEHIGH GAS CORPORATION
702 HAMILTON ST STE 203, ALLENTOWN, PA 181012469
Phone: 610 791-3800

Company Type: Private

Income Statement				FYE: December 31
	REVENUE ($ mil.)	NET INCOME ($ mil.)	NET PROFIT MARGIN	EMPLOYEES
12/07	1,034	4	0.5%	200
12/05*	53	(0)	—	—
06/04	116	1	1.2%	—
Annual Growth	72.5%	36.5%	—	—

*Fiscal year change

2007 Year-End Financials

Return on assets: 2.5% Cash ($ mil.): 1
Return on equity: 46.7%
Current ratio: 0.80

LEHIGH VALLEY HEALTH NETWORK, INC.

Residents of the Lehigh Valley seeking medical care head uptown to facilities operated by the Lehigh Valley Health Network (LVHN). The not-for-profit health care provider operates through four full-service hospital campuses housing a total of about 1000 licensed beds. The medical center serves as a regional referral center for trauma and burn care and organ transplantation as well as specialty care in numerous areas such as cardiology women's health and pediatric surgery. LVHN also boasts a network of physician practices and community health centers as well as home health and hospice units.

Operations

The company's hospitals provide care in about 95 specialist fields including pediatric care burn treatment trauma care organ transplant cardiovascular care oncology and neurology. Its children's hospital includes inpatient emergency and specialist units. LVHN also conducts medical training programs and performs research in a range of different areas including cancer cardiovascular and infectious disease; a number of these programs are conducted through partnerships with entities including the H. Lee Moffitt Cancer Center and the University of South Florida's Morsani College of Medicine.

In addition to its core hospital operations the health organization has an alliance with the Sacred Heart Hospital of Allentown through which it provides Sacred Heart with certain services in the areas of cardiac care primary care telehealth services and mental health care. The two hospitals discussed but ultimately dismissed the possibility of a formal merger settling on being affiliated instead.

LVHN's 40 community clinics administer primary and specialty care for area residents including facilities for low-income patients. For patients (insured or not) who need care for minor ailments and routine tests LVHN operates a handful of retail health clinics under the Careworks brand. In addition the network includes a system of medical laboratories (Health Network Laboratories).

Geographic Reach

The LVHN system's main facilities are located in Allentown Bethlehem and Hazleton. With more than a dozen additional health centers the network provides services to residents of a five-county territory in Pennsylvania.

Financial Performance

Revenues increased 8% to $1.7 billion in 2014 on higher patient service and supporting operations revenues as well as higher investment earnings. Net income increased 59% to $95.5 million that year.

Strategy

LVHN opened the region's first pediatric emergency department at its Cedar Crest campus in 2011. The center houses about a dozen beds and is staffed by pediatric emergency physicians and nurses as well as a child life specialist. To further expand its emergency capabilities in 2013 the organization added emergency transportation services to its offerings.

In early 2014 LVHN merged with Greater Hazleton Health Alliance adding Hazleton General Hospital (now Lehigh Valley Hospital-Hazleton) to its network of facilities. The merger also added a physician group a hospital-based home health agency and a health and wellness center all in Hazleton

To promote care coordination and communication LVHN entered into a clinical affiliation with CVS Health in 2015. Through the partnership information on patient visits and prescriptions is accessible to care providers through secure electronic health record (EHR) systems.

EXECUTIVES

President And Ceo, Brian A. Nester
Coo, Terry Capuano
Evp And Chief Medical Officer, Thomas V. Whalen
Svp And Cfo, Edward O'Dea
Acting President Lehigh Valley Hospital Pocono, Elizabeth Wise
President Lehigh Valley Health Network Medical Staff And Trustee, Joseph Patruno
President Lehigh Valley Hospital-hazleton Medical Staff And Trustee, Anthony P. Veglia
Svp Patient Care Services And Chief Nursing Officer, Marie K. (Kim) Jordan
Vice Chair, William F. Hecht, age 76
Chairman, John D. Stanley, age 62
Vice Chair, Jefferson K. (Jeff) Aiken
Secretary, Vicki Bush
Auditors: KPMG LLP PHILADELPHIA PENNSY

LOCATIONS

HQ: LEHIGH VALLEY HEALTH NETWORK, INC.
1247 S CEDAR CREST BLVD, ALLENTOWN, PA 181036298
Phone: 610 402-8000
Web: WWW.LVH.COM

PRODUCTS/OPERATIONS

Selected Facilities

Community Health Centers
  Hamburg Community Health Center
  Lehigh Valley Health Center at Bath
  Lehigh Valley Health Center at Bethlehem Township
  Lehigh Valley Health Center at Hellertown
  Lehigh Valley Health Center at Kutztown
  Lehigh Valley Health Center at Saucon Valley
  Lehigh Valley Health Center at Trexlertown
  Upper Bucks Health & Diagnostic Center (in partnership with Grand View Hospital Quakertown)
Hospitals
  Lehigh Valley Hospital - 17th St. (short-stay hospital Salisbury Township in Allentown)
  Lehigh Valley Hospital - Cedar Crest (Allentown)
  Lehigh Valley Hospital - Muhlenberg (Bethlehem)

COMPETITORS

Abington Memorial Hospital
Ascension Health
Community Health Systems
Doylestown Hospital
Grand View
Main Line Health System
Mercy Health System
Moses Taylor Hospital
North Philadelphia Health System
Pennsylvania Hospital
Reading Hospital and Medical Center
Sacred Heart Hospital of Allentown
Shore Memorial Hospital
St. Luke's University Health Network
Tenet Healthcare
University of Pennsylvania Health System
Wyoming Valley Health Care System

HISTORICAL FINANCIALS

Company Type: Private

Income Statement				FYE: June 30
	REVENUE ($ mil.)	NET INCOME ($ mil.)	NET PROFIT MARGIN	EMPLOYEES
06/18	2,739	106	3.9%	12,000
06/17	2,432	409	16.8%	—
06/12	1,620	(63)	—	—
06/11	1,524	314	20.6%	—
Annual Growth	8.7%	(14.3%)	—	—

2018 Year-End Financials

Return on assets: 3.1% Cash ($ mil.): 109
Return on equity: 6.0%
Current ratio: 1.70

LELAND STANFORD JUNIOR UNIVERSITY

Prospectors panning for gold in higher education can strike it rich at The Leland Stanford Junior University. The school known as Stanford University is one of the premier educational institutions in the US boasting respected programs in business engineering law and medicine among others. Stanford serves more than 16300 students (taught by 2180 faculty members) and a student-teacher ratio of about 4:1. A private institution Stanford is supported through an endowment of some $22.4 billion one of the largest in the US. The university was established in 1885 by Leland Stanford Sr. who made his fortune selling provisions to California gold miners; it was named after his son Leland Stanford Jr.

Operations

Stanford University is widely recognized as one of the top US research universities and sports a host of laboratories and research centers including the Stanford Institute for Economic Policy Research and the Stanford Linear Accelerator Center. Its faculty members include around 20 Nobel Prize winners a handful of Pulitzer Prize winners and more than 20 MacArthur fellows.

The university also offers 35 varsity sports and 20 club sports; it boasts more than 110 NCAA team championships.

Geographic Reach

Stanford is located in the heart of California's Silicon Valley known worldwide as an epicenter for technology and research ventures. Google (headquartered in Silicon Valley) got its start at Stanford when Sergey Brin and Larry Page developed the page-rank algorithm while they were still computer science graduate students.

The university is located on 8180 contiguous acres and has almost 700 major buildings.

Financial Performance

Stanford University reported revenues of some $9.8 billion in fiscal 2016 up from $9.1 billion in 2015 due to an increase in student income higher patient service revenues (from the Stanford Hospitals and Clinics organization) sponsored research funding and increased returns on its investment portfolio assets.

Net income fell to $490 million in 2016 (versus $700 million in 2015) as expenses including salaries and benefits rose especially within the medical school. Other expenditures that year such as facilities and infrastructure maintenance and higher depreciation also impacted net income.

The university has received sizable donations from notable alumni such as Jerry Yang (cofounder of Yahoo!) Charles Schwab Texas billionaire Robert Bass and William Hewlett (of Hewlett-Packard who has since died).

Strategy

To further widen its student resources Stanford has recently completed renovation and construction efforts on some 40 campus buildings and added a number of new faculty and fellowship positions. The university is also exploring options to establish a satellite-applied science and engineering campus in another US city. In addition Stanford is examining whether it might begin to offer courses through an online platform.

In 2017 Stanford launched a new major in aeronautics and astronautics (allowing students to work with unmanned aerial vehicles satellites autonomous systems and other flight technologies).

HISTORY

In 1885 Leland Stanford Sr. and his wife Jane established Leland Stanford Junior University in memory of their son Leland Jr. who had died of typhoid at age 15. Stanford made his fortune selling provisions to California gold miners and as a major investor in the Central Pacific Railroad one of the two companies that built the first transcontinental railway. It was Stanford who connected the tracks laid eastward by Central Pacific and westward by Union Pacific with a gold railway spike in 1869. He also served as California's governor and as a US senator.

The Stanfords donated more than 8000 acres of land from their own estate to establish an unconventional university one that was coeducational and nondenominational with a focus on preparing students for a profession. Stanford opened its doors in 1891 to a freshman class of 559 students. It awarded its first degrees four years later and among the graduates was future US president Herbert Hoover.

Leland Stanford Sr. died in 1893 and in 1903 Jane Stanford turned the university over to the board of trustees. After weathering significant damage in 1906 from the Great San Francisco Earthquake the university established a law school in 1908 and its medical school five years later.

During WWI the university mobilized half of its students into the Students' Army Training Corps. The School of Education was established in 1917 followed by the School of Engineering and Graduate School of Business eight years later. In 1933 a rule limiting the number of women admitted to Stanford was abolished.

Wallace Sterling who became president of the university after WWII initiated the transformation of Stanford into a world-class institution with a reputation for teaching and research. Under Sterling the university initiated development on the Stanford Research Park.

In 1958 Stanford opened its first overseas campus (near Stuttgart Germany) and the Stanford Medical Center was completed the following year. The university created a computer science department in 1965 and two years later opened the Stanford Linear Accelerator Center dedicated to physics research.

Donald Kennedy became president in 1980. The next year students voted to abandon the university's official mascot the "Indians" in response to concerns raised by Native American students. The nickname "Cardinal" was adopted in its place. The term refers to the school's color cardinal red.

Also during Kennedy's tenure it was revealed that Stanford had overcharged the Office of Naval Research for indirect costs associated with research. The scandal led to Kennedy's resignation in 1992 and in 1994 the Office of Naval Research and the university settled a related lawsuit for $1.2 million and a stipulation that Stanford had not committed any wrongdoing. Gerhard Casper succeeded Kennedy as president.

In 1997 Stanford and the University of California at San Francisco combined their teaching hospitals in a public/private merger. Two years later after the controversial experiment had harmed both hospitals' financial pictures the merger was terminated and the two hospitals agreed to go their separate ways.

In 1999 Casper announced his intention to resign as president. The school tapped provost John Hennessy as his replacement. Soon after his appointment in 2000 Hennessey launched a campaign to raise $1 billion. Former Stanford professor and Netscape co-founder Jim Clark donated $150 million later that year to support Stanford's biomedical engineering and sciences program. The school also launched a new company SKOLAR which developed an online search engine for the medical industry.

EXECUTIVES

President, John L. Hennessy
Provost, John W. Etchemendy
Dean School Of Humanities And Science, Richard P. Saller
Vp Business Affairs And Cfo, Randall S. (Randy) Livingston
Dean School Of Earth Energy And Environmental Sciences, Pamela Matson
Associate Vp It Services, Bill Clebsch
President And Ceo Stanford Health Care, Amir Dan Rubin
Vice Provost And Dean Of Research, Ann Margaret Arvin
Dean Graduate School Of Business, Garth Saloner
Dean Graduate School Of Education, Deborah Stipek
Dean School Of Engineering, Persis S. Drell
Dean Law School, M. Elizabeth Magill
Dean School Of Medicine, Lloyd Minor
President And Ceo Stanford Children's Health, Christopher Dawes
Assistant Vice President And Chief Information Security Officer, Michael Duff
Vice President Human Resources, David Jones
Vice President, Britt Hedman
Vice President, Philip Scherrer
Associate Vice President For Government Relations, Ryan Adesnik
Vice President, Stephen Krasner
Associate Vice President, Anne Hannigan
Vice President Information Technology, Stephen Wong
Vice Provost Budget, Tim R Warner
M.s. Candidate In Computer Science Audit Intern Vice President Of Board Games, Hana Lee
Professor And Associate Chair Department Of Psychiatry And Behavioral Sciences, Bruce Arnow

Associate Vice President Of Sponsored Research, Russell Brewer
Medical Director, Kirsti Weng
Assoc. Vice President Of Human Resources Benefits, Leslie Schlaegel
Senior Vice President Human Resources, Rosemary Monroe
Assistant Vice President Medical Center Development, Jennifer Kitt
Vice President Human Resources, Elizabeth Zacharias
B.s. Candidate Computer Science Vice President Of External Affairs Co Director Spectra Hackathon, Cynthia Yin
Associate Vice President For The Arts, Matthew Tiews
Medical Director Emergency Medicine, Sam Shen
B.s. Candidate Product Design Blackstage Vice President, Adriana Ganem
Vice President Accountable Care, Thomas Williams
Vice President Of External Relations, Tina Jiang
Medical Director Vaden Health Center, Robyn Tepper
Medical Director, James Lau
Clinical Director Ibd, Sarah Streett
Vice President Communications And Marketing Publisher, Edie Feilce Barry
Associate Vice President Human Resources Communications, Melissa Mcvicker
Executive Vice President Technology, Ruth Ohara
Vice President And Corporate Controller, James Martin
Chairs Secretary, Debbi Barley
Secretary Of State, Condoleezza Rice
Vice Chair, Mary Goldstein
Board Member, Udai Baisiwala
Auditors: PRICEWATERHOUSECOOPERS LLP SA

LOCATIONS

HQ: LELAND STANFORD JUNIOR UNIVERSITY
450 SERRA MALL, STANFORD, CA 943052004
Phone: 650 723-2300
Web: WWW.STANFORD.EDU

PRODUCTS/OPERATIONS

2014 Sales

	$ mil.	% of total
Healthcare services	3,942	50
Sponsored reseach support	1,266	16
Investment income	1,181	15
Student income	533	7
Special program fee and other income	641	7
Gifts	212	3
Net assets released from restrictions	146	2
Total	**7,924**	**100**

Selected Schools

Undergraduate
  School of Earth Sciences
  School of Engineering
  School of Humanities and Sciences
Graduate
  School of Business
  School of Earth Sciences
  School of Education
  School of Engineering
  School of Humanities and Sciences
  School of Law
  School of Medicine

Selected Interdisciplinary Research Centers

Alliance for Innovative Manufacturing at Stanford
Center for Computer Research in Music and Acoustics
Center for Integrated Facility Engineering
Center for Integrated Systems

Selected Laboratories Centers and Institutes

Center for Research on Information Storage Materials
Center for the Study of Language and Information
Edward L. Ginzton Laboratory
Institute for International Studies
Institute for Research on Women and Gender
John and Terry Levin Center for Public Service and Public Interest Law

Stanford Center for Buddhist Studies
Stanford Humanities Center
Stanford Institute for Economic Policy Research
W.W. Hansen Experimental Physics Laboratory

Selected Medical Research Facilities
Center for Biomedical Ethics
Center for Research in Disease Prevention
Human Genome Center
Richard M. Lucas Center for Magnetic Resonance
   Spectroscopy & Imaging
Sleep Disorders Center
Other Selected Research Facilities
Hoover Institution on War Revolution and Peace
Hopkins Marine Station
Martin Luther King Jr. Papers Project
Stanford Linear Accelerator Center

HISTORICAL FINANCIALS
Company Type: Private

Income Statement   FYE: August 31

	REVENUE ($ mil.)	NET INCOME ($ mil.)	NET PROFIT MARGIN	EMPLOYEES
08/18	11,311	2,653	23.5%	15,000
08/17	5,604	2,972	53.0%	—
08/06	4,511	3,007	66.7%	—
08/05	4,162	2,896	69.6%	—
Annual Growth	8.0%	(0.7%)	—	—

2018 Year-End Financials
Return on assets: 4.8%   Cash ($ mil.): 1,199
Return on equity: 6.1%
Current ratio: —

LENOX HILL HOSPITAL

LOCATIONS
HQ: LENOX HILL HOSPITAL
   210 E 64TH ST FL 4, NEW YORK, NY 100657471
Phone: 212 472-8872
Web: WWW.LENOXHILL.ORG

HISTORICAL FINANCIALS
Company Type: Private

Income Statement   FYE: December 31

	REVENUE ($ mil.)	NET INCOME ($ mil.)	NET PROFIT MARGIN	EMPLOYEES
12/16	960	21	2.3%	41
12/15	885	6	0.7%	—
Annual Growth	8.5%	244.8%	—	—

2016 Year-End Financials
Return on assets: 1.8%   Cash ($ mil.): —
Return on equity: 4.7%
Current ratio: 0.80

LESTER E. COX MEDICAL CENTERS

Lester E. Cox Medical Centers (dba CoxHealth) provides a myriad of medical services to people in Missouri and Arkansas. CoxHealth's network includes six acute care hospitals (with more than 1000 beds) and more than 80 physician clinics. Centers for cardiac care cancer treatment ortho-pedics mental health and women's health are among CoxHealth's specialized care options. Other operations include an ambulance service offering both ground and air transportation the Cox Health Systems HMO the Oxford HealthCare home health agency and educational programs. The organization was named after its primary fundraiser in the 1940s.

Operations
Each year CoxHealth handles about 500000 outpatient visits; 205000 emergency urgent care and trauma visits; 32000 ground ambulance transports; and nearly 4000 births. Its hospitals include Cox Medical Center South Cox Medical Center Branson Cox North Hospital Cox Monett Hospital and the Meyer Orthopedic and Rehabilitation Hospital. Its specialty clinics include centers for cancer orthopedics cardiovascular care women's and children's health outpatient surgery and diagnostic imaging.

Geographic Reach
CoxHealth serves about 25 communities in 25 counties in southwestern Missouri and northwestern Arkansas. Major facilities are in Branson Monett and Springfield Missouri.

Sales and Marketing
CoxHealth primarily serves families children women seniors and athletes.

Strategy
Enduring through blizzards and tornadoes CoxHealth strives to improve its services and the health of its community. The system typically grows by adding or expanding facilities. In late 2018 it announced plans to build a $42 million hospital in rural Monett Missouri. The facility will replace its existing 60-year old hospital in the area.

Other initiatives include upgrading clinical processes and information technology systems.

Company Background
CoxHealth was founded as Burge Deaconess Hospital in 1908. It became Lester E. Cox Medical Centers in 1968 following the death of Cox a St. Louis businessman who led a series of major fundraising campaigns in the 1940s critical to the survival and growth of the hospital.

EXECUTIVES

Vice President And Chief Medical Officer; And Medical Director Oxford Hospice, Dan Sontheimer
Senior Vice President Chief Hospital Officer, John Duff
Vice President And Chief Nursing Officer, Karen Kramer
Svp And Cfo, Jacob McWay
Vice President And Chief Information Officer, Bruce Robison
President Cox Healthplans, Jeffrey C. (Jeff) Bond
Vice President And Chief Clinical Officer, Ron Prenger
Vice President; President Cox Monett, Genny Maroc
Vice President; President Oxford Healthcare, Karen Thomas
Chairman Joint Operations Committee And Chief Integrated Physicians, Kenneth Powell
Vice President President Home Parenteral Services, H. Lynn Kelley
President And Ceo; Director, Steven D. (Steve) Edwards
President Coxhealth Foundation, Lisa Alexander
President Cox College, Anne Liners Brett
Vice President Clinical Services, Amanda Hedgpeth
Director Of Respiratory Therapy, Martin Rohrer
Vice President Of Corporate Integrity, Betty Breshears
Vice President Clinical Services, Jeff Hawkins
Pharmacy Manager, Kirsten Dougherty
Cno Vice President Clinical Services Enterprise Nursing Informatics Coxhealth Branson, Lynne Yaggy
Pharmacy Manager, Steven Crain
Director Of Pharmacy, Rhonda Flannery
Board Member, Charles Woodall
Department Secretary I, Regina Barfield

LOCATIONS
HQ: LESTER E. COX MEDICAL CENTERS
   1423 N JEFFERSON AVE, SPRINGFIELD, MO 658021917
Phone: 417 269-3000
Web: WWW.COXHEALTH.COM

PRODUCTS/OPERATIONS

Selected Services
Air Care
Alzheimer's Disease
Behavioral Health
Brain and Spine Disorders
Breast Care
Cancer Services
Children's Health
Diabetes
Dialysis
Ear Nose and Throat (ENT)
Emergency Department
Fitness Centers
Food and Nutrition
Heart and Vascular
Home Health
Hyperbaric Medicine and Wound Care
Neuroscience
Occupational Medicine
Orthopedics
Parenting
Parkinson's Clinic
Pharmacy
Physical Medicine
Pregnancy
Radiology
Rehabilitation
Respiratory Care
Robotic Surgery
Sleep Disorders
Smoking Cessation
Specialty Services
Sports Medicine
Stroke
Trauma Services
Urgent Care
Weight Loss
Wellness Consultations
Women's Health
Workers' Compensation

COMPETITORS

Ascension Health
BJC HealthCare
Catholic Health Initiatives
Children's Mercy Hospital
HCA
Mercy Health
Mercy Hospital Springfield
Saint Luke's Health System
Shawnee Mission Medical Center
Sisters of Charity of Leavenworth
St. Anthony's Medical Center
Tenet Healthcare
Truman Medical Centers
Universal Health Services
University of Kansas Medical Center

HISTORICAL FINANCIALS
Company Type: Private

Income Statement   FYE: September 30

	REVENUE ($ mil.)	NET INCOME ($ mil.)	NET PROFIT MARGIN	EMPLOYEES
09/14	898	50	5.6%	11,000
09/13	858	105	12.3%	—
09/12	843	66	7.9%	—
Annual Growth	3.2%	(13.0%)	—	—

2014 Year-End Financials

Return on assets: 3.6%   Cash ($ mil.): 61
Return on equity: 7.3%
Current ratio: 2.00

LEVI STRAUSS & CO.

Pioneering American apparel maker Levi Strauss & Co. has jeans in its genes. A global manufacturer of brand-name clothing Levi Strauss sells jeans and sportswear under the Levi's Dockers Signature by Levi Strauss and Denizen labels in more than 110 countries. It also markets men's and women's underwear and loungewear. The company distributes its brand products through more than 800 company-operated stores located in over 30 countries and through the third-party and first-party online stores. Levi Strauss makes some 70% of its revenue from Levi's branded men's pants. The company went public (again) in early 2019 although the Haas family (descendants of founder Levi Strauss) still controls it.

IPO

In early 2019 Levi Strauss raised some $625 million in a public offering. The company plans to use the proceeds to support store expansion and developing its online business.

Operations

Levi Strauss & Co (LS&CO). designs markets and sells jeans casual and dress pants tops shorts skirts jackets footwear and related accessories for men women and children. It has two principal brands Levi's which is known best for its jeans but makes a full wardrobe besides; and Dockers which makes business casual clothing mainly for men. Sales of the Levi's brand accounts for 85% of the total sales of menswear accounts for 70% and sales of pants represents 70% of sales as well.

LS&CO reaches customers indirectly through third-party wholesale customers such as department stores and directly through owned and operated freestanding physical stores concession stands in departments stores and e-commerce sites. The wholesale channel generates two-thirds of LS&CO's sales. Within the direct channel which accounts for the other third of sales physical retail represents nearly 25% and e-commerce nearly 15%.

Outside the US LS&CO operates a franchise model consisting of around 1200 stores.

Geographic Reach

LS&CO. sells its products in more than 110 countries. It operates manufacturing distribution and finishing facilities in the Americas Europe and Asia/Pacific regions. The company's Americas segment contributes about 55% of total revenue while its Europe and Asia (which includes the Middle East and North Africa) segments contributed about 30% and 15% respectively. Its key markets are the US France Germany Mexico and the UK.

Sales and Marketing

A multi-channel marketer LS&CO. sells its products in more than 50000 retail locations worldwide. Its brands lend themselves to a variety of retail formats including chain retailers (Wal-Mart and Target) department stores (Nordstrom and Bloomingdale's) and company-operated e-commerce sites and online stores of other retailers. Sales to its top 10 wholesale customers account for more than 25% of revenues.

The company distributes its products through a wide variety of retail formats around the world including chain and department stores franchise stores and shop-in-shops company-operated retail network multi-brand specialty stores mass channel

retailers and both company-operated and retailer ecommerce sites.

Extremely successful marketing means Levi's jeans are much more expensive in Europe where they are considered a luxury brand than in the US where they have a more workmanlike image.

LS&CO. records a high marketing spend of roughly 10% of total sales. Advertising expenses were $400 million in 2018 up from $325 million in 2017.

Financial Performance

After a difficult spell Levi Strauss & Co.'s sales growth has kicked up a gear. In 2018 the company's revenue grew 14% to $5.6 billion thanks to surging sales in Europe a broader product range and new store additions. LS&CO. grew its range of women's clothes expanded its Signature label and added 21 stores in the Americas 17 in Europe and 36 in the Asia/Pacific region.

Net income was materially unchanged in 2018 at $285.3 million as higher sales were offset by a sharp increase in income taxes. LS&CO. paid $214.8 million in tax up from $64.2 million in 2017 due to a one-off charge from the US Tax Cuts and Jobs Act.

LS&CO.'s cash on hand grew $79.5 million during 2018 ending the year at $633.6 million. The company's operations generated $420.4 million partially offset by $179.4 million used in its investing activities and $148.2 million used in its financing. LS&CO.'s main cash uses were capital expenditures dividends and share repurchases.

Strategy

Levi Strauss & Co.'s strategy is two-fold: increase direct sales to offset declines in the department store sector; and expand its product lines including a greater focus on women.

The well-documented difficulties of the department store sector which is taking a hammering from e-commerce (among other things) is having a material impact on LS&CO.'s wholesale division. Wholesale has historically accounted for around two-thirds of its sales and is declining by a few percent annually. To mitigate the threat the company is growing its direct-to-consumer channel. It has accelerated its store opening program across all geographies adding around 75 stores in 2018 and improved its online business through new features and new websites such as a website serving the Indian market in 2018.

But LS&CO is also finding ways e-commerce can help slow the decline in its wholesale channel. LS&CO partnered with Amazon to establish what is essentially a Levi's shop-in-shop concession stand (albeit a digital one).

Long dependent on the men's bottoms category LS&CO. is expanding its women's and tops ranges. Logo t-shirts have been growing strongly as are fleece sweatshirts and trucker jackets. The strategy appears to be working: Pants are declining as a proportion of total sales fairly rapidly down from 77% in 2016 to 68% in 2018 while men's products are declining at a similar rate.

HISTORY

Levi Strauss arrived in New York City from Bavaria in 1847. In 1853 he joined his brother-in-law David Stern in San Francisco selling dry goods to the gold rushers. Shortly after a prospector told Strauss of miners' problems in finding sturdy pants. Strauss made a pair out of canvas for the prospector; word of the rugged pants spread quickly.

Strauss continued his dry-goods business in the 1860s. During this time he switched the pants' fabric to a durable French cloth called serge de Nimes soon known as denim. He colored the fabric with indigo dye and adopted the idea from Nevada tailor Jacob Davis of reinforcing the pants with

copper rivets. In 1873 Strauss and Davis produced their first pair of waist-high overalls (later known as jeans). The pants soon became de rigueur for lumberjacks cowboys railroad workers oil drillers and farmers.

Strauss continued to build his pants and wholesaling business until he died in 1902. Levi Strauss & Co. passed to four Stern nephews who carried on their uncle's jeans business while maintaining the company's philanthropic reputation.

After WWII Walter Haas and Peter Haas (a fourth-generation Strauss family member) assumed leadership of LS&CO. In 1948 they ended the company's wholesaling business to concentrate on Levi's clothing. In the 1950s Levi's jeans ceased to be merely functional garments for workers; they became the uniform of American youth. In the 1960s LS&CO. added women's attire and expanded overseas.

The company went public in 1971. That year it added a women's career line and bought Koret sportswear (sold in 1984). By the mid-1980s profits declined. Peace Corps-veteran-turned-McKinsey-consultant Robert Haas (Walter's son) grabbed the reins of LS&CO. in 1984 and took the company private the next year (he became chairman in 1989). He also instilled a touchy-feely corporate culture often at odds with the bottom line.

In 1986 LS&CO. introduced Dockers casual pants. The company's sales began rising in 1991 as consumers forsook the designer duds of the 1980s for more practical clothes. LS&CO. says seven out of every 10 American men own a pair of Dockers. However LS&CO. missed out on the birth of another trend: the split between the fashion sense of US adolescents and their Levi's-loving baby boomer parents.

In 1996 the company introduced Slates dress slacks. That year LS&CO. bought back nearly one-third of its stock from family and employees for $4.3 billion. Grappling with slipping sales and debt from the buyout in 1997 LS&CO. closed 11 of its 37 North American plants laying off 6400 workers and 1000 salaried employees; it granted generous severance packages even to those earning minimum wage.

In 1998 citing improved labor conditions in China LS&CO. announced it would step up its use of Chinese subcontractors. Further restructuring added a third of its European plants to the closures list that year. LS&CO.'s sales fell 13% in fiscal 1998. Also that year Haas handed his CEO title to Pepsi executive Philip Marineau; Haas remained chairman.

LS&CO. closed 11 of 22 remaining North American plants in 1999. It also unleashed several new jeans brands that eschewed the company's one-style-fits-all approach of old.

In April 2002 LS&CO. announced it would close six of its last eight US plants and cut 20% of its worldwide staff (3300 workers). In September 2003 it cut another 5% of its global staff (650 workers). That month the company opened its first girls-only store located in Paris. In December LS&CO. replaced CFO Bill Chiasson with an outside turnaround specialist.

Pinpointing 2006 as the best time to step down as the company's chief executive Philip Marineau retired at the end of 2006. John Anderson president of LS&CO.'s Asia/Pacific division and head of the firm's global supply chain unit replaced Marineau as president and CEO.

Levi Strauss chairman Robert Haas retired in 2008 after 18 years in that role. His successor was Dryer's ice cream executive T. Gary Rogers who became the first leader in the company's history who was not a descendant of the founder. In August 2008 CFO Hans Ploos van Amstel left the company the and was replaced by Heidi Manes its corporate controller and principal accounting officer.

Looking to gain a more active role in its store business LS&CO. in July 2009 bought the operating rights for more than 70 Levi's and Dockers Outlet locations from store operator Anchor Blue Retail Group which had filed for bankruptcy for $72 million. Anchor Blue said the US recession and drop in consumer spending especially among teens severely affected its financial performance. LS&CO. said the acquisition will enable it to better manage its brands' positioning.

Rogers retired in late 2009 and Richard Kauffman became chairman.

EXECUTIVES

Executive Vice President And President Europe, Seth M. Ellison, age 60, $609,808 total compensation
President & Ceo Director, Charles V. (Chip) Bergh, age 61, $1,343,077 total compensation
Evp And Cfo, Harmit J. Singh, age 55, $746,538 total compensation
Executive Vice President And General Counsel, Seth R. Jaffe
Chief Human Resources Officer, Elizabeth Wood
Executive Vice President And President Of Direct-to-consumer (dtc), Marc Rosen, age 50
Executive Vice President And President Of Levi Strauss Asia Middle East And Africa, David Love, age 56, $580,387 total compensation
Senior Vice President And Chief Communications Officer, Kelly McGinnis
Executive Vice President And President Levi Strauss Americas, Roy Bagattini, age 55, $690,433 total compensation
Executive Vice President And President Product Innovation And Supply Chain, Liz O'Neill
Senior Vice President & Chief Marketing Officer, Jennifer (Jen) Sey
Vice President Global Mand D Plng And Operations, Barb Gollert
Vice President Sustainability, Michael Kobori
Vice President Human Resources, Karthik Sarma
Vice President Sales, Donna Null Paulo
Vice President Global Logistics, Doug Flores
Vp Purchasing, Dean Edwards
Vice President Dtc Merchandising, Simon Haskell
Senior Vice President Global Distribution And Logistics, Stephen Berube
Vice President Managing Director South Europe, Diana Dimitian
Vice President Merchandising Levi's Wome, Julie Pike
Executive Vice President President, Levi Strauss Americas
Chairman, Stephen C. Neal, age 69
Auditors: PRICEWATERHOUSECOOPERS LLP SA

LOCATIONS

HQ: LEVI STRAUSS & CO.
1155 BATTERY ST, SAN FRANCISCO, CA 941111264
Phone: 415 501-6000
Web: WWW.LEVISTRAUSS.COM

2018 Stores

	#
Americas region	268
Europe region	300
Asia/Pacific region	256
Total	**0 697**

2018 Sales

	$ mil.	% of total
Americas	3,042	55
Europe	1,646	29
Asia/Pacific region	886	17
Total	**5,575**	**100**

PRODUCTS/OPERATIONS

2018 Sales

	% of total
Levi's brand	86
Dockers brand	7
Signature by Levi Strauss & Denizen brands	7
Total	**100**

Selected Brands
Denizen
Dockers
 Dockers Alpha Khaki
 Dockers for Men
 Dockers for Women
Levi's
 Levi's 501 Original
 Levi's 505 Straight
 Levi's 511 Skinny
 Levi's 513 Slim
 Levi's 514 Slim Straight
 Levi's Curve ID
Signature by Levis Strauss & Co.
Intro
Waterless
Wellthread
Wasteless

COMPETITORS

Abercrombie & Fitch	Nine West
American Eagle	OshKosh B'Gosh
Outfitters	Oxford Industries
Benetton	PVH
Calvin Klein	Perry Ellis
Diesel SpA	International
Fast Retailing	Ralph Lauren
Fruit of the Loom	Sean John
Guess?	Sears
Haggar	Target Corporation
Hugo Boss	The Gap
Inditex	True Religion Apparel
J. Crew	Under Armour
Jockey International	VF Corporation
Joe's Jeans	Victoria's Secret
Kmart	Stores
Kohl's	Wacoal
Lands' End	Wal-Mart
Macy's	Warnaco Group
NIKE	adidas
Nautica Apparel	

HISTORICAL FINANCIALS
Company Type: Private

Income Statement
FYE: November 25

	REVENUE ($ mil.)	NET INCOME ($ mil.)	NET PROFIT MARGIN	EMPLOYEES
11/18	5,575	285	5.1%	14,400
11/17	4,904	284	5.8%	—
11/16	4,552	291	6.4%	—
11/15	4,494	209	4.7%	—
Annual Growth	**7.4%**	**10.8%**	**—**	**—**

2018 Year-End Financials
Return on assets: 8.1% Cash ($ mil.): 713
Return on equity: 42.7%
Current ratio: 2.20

LEXA INTERNATIONAL CORPORATION

EXECUTIVES

Chb-Pres, Antonia Axson Johnson
V Chb, P Goeran Ennerfelt
V Pres-Contrl, Charles W Seitz
V Pres, John Pascale
Dir, William I Turner
Asst Treas-Dir of Credit, Kory Arthur
Vice-Chairman, Goeran P Ennerfelt
Investment Manager, Frank Ingarra
General Manager, Nelson Weinstein
Auditors: CITRIN COOPERMAN & COMPANY LL

LOCATIONS

HQ: LEXA INTERNATIONAL CORPORATION
1 LANDMARK SQ STE 407, STAMFORD, CT 069012601
Phone: 203 326-5200
Web: WWW.AXELJOHNSON.COM

HISTORICAL FINANCIALS
Company Type: Private

Income Statement
FYE: December 31

	REVENUE ($ mil.)	NET INCOME ($ mil.)	NET PROFIT MARGIN	EMPLOYEES
12/09	2,598	6	0.2%	1,204
12/08	4,312	4	0.1%	—
12/07	4,003	(21)	—	—
Annual Growth	**(19.4%)**	**—**	**—**	**—**

2009 Year-End Financials
Return on assets: 0.6% Cash ($ mil.): 43
Return on equity: 3.1%
Current ratio: 1.80

LEXINGTON COUNTY HEALTH SERVICES DISTRICT, INC.

EXECUTIVES

Pres, Michael Biediger
V Pres*, Melinda P Kruzner
Coo*, Tod Augsburger
Infection Control Manager, Janet Foster
Clinical Applications Analyst, Janet Paul
Auditors: KPMG LLP ATLANTA GA

LOCATIONS

HQ: LEXINGTON COUNTY HEALTH SERVICES DISTRICT, INC.
2720 SUNSET BLVD, WEST COLUMBIA, SC 291694810
Phone: 803 791-2000

HISTORICAL FINANCIALS

Company Type: Private

Income Statement

FYE: September 30

	REVENUE ($ mil.)	NET INCOME ($ mil.)	NET PROFIT MARGIN	EMPLOYEES
09/10	576	59	10.4%	6,000
09/09	528	57	10.9%	—
09/08	491	35	7.2%	—
Annual Growth	8.3%	29.8%	—	—

2010 Year-End Financials

Return on assets: 7.3%
Return on equity: 11.6%
Current ratio: 4.70

Cash ($ mil.): 170

LEXINGTON MEDICAL CENTER

Lexington Medical Center is a not-for-profit health care organization serving the residents of South Carolina's Lexington County. Established in 1971 the medical center has some 415 beds and provides general emergency surgical and diagnostic services. Specialty services include cancer treatment cardiovascular care women's health and rehabilitation. Lexington Medical Center also operates a skilled nursing center as well as a network of affiliated community health centers urgent care clinics and affiliated physician practices. The hospital is managed by the Lexington County Health Service District.

Operations
The 414-bed facility is home to the largest extended-care facility in the Carolinas. It sees about 100000 emergency department visits each year.

Altogether the Lexington Medical Center's network of facilities — which includes six community clinics an occupational health center an Alzheimer's care center and 60 doctors' offices — employs some 5900 health professionals.

Strategy
Lexington Medical Center is expanding its facilities to better serve the growing population in its service territory. In 2015 it opened a new cardiac rehabilitation program at its Irmo Medical Park campus. The program — the first of its kind in the area — provides services to patients with a history of heart attack angioplasty heart failure heart transplant bypass surgery or the like.

In 2014 Lexington's physician practice opened a third sleep lab where clinicians can diagnose such conditions as hypersomnia insomnia narcolepsy restless leg syndrome snoring and sleep apnea.

EXECUTIVES

Vice President Pateint Care Services, Cindy Rhoman
Assistant Vice President, Lang Spotts
Vice President And Chief Officer Medical Informatics, Anna Shalkham
Assistant Vice President Revenue Cycle Integrity, Deborah Hunt
Vice President Patient Care, Cindy Rohman
Vice President Physician Network, Matthew Cogdill
Pharmacy Manager, Lee Stabler
Auditors: KPMG LLP ATLANTA GA

LOCATIONS

HQ: LEXINGTON MEDICAL CENTER
2720 SUNSET BLVD, WEST COLUMBIA, SC
291694810
Phone: 803 791-2000
Web: WWW.LEXMED.COM

PRODUCTS/OPERATIONS

Selected Services
Patient Care
Alzheimer's Care
Birth Center
Extended Care
Family Medicine
General Surgery
Imaging
Laboratory & Pathology
Occupational Health
Weight-Loss Surgery
Health & Wellness
Community Health Screenings
Health Directions Wellness Center
Nutrition Therapy
Sleep Solutions

Selected Facilities
Community Medical Centers
  LMC Batesburg-Leesville
  LMC Chapin
  LMC Gilbert
  LMC Irmo
  LMC Lexington
  LMC Swansea
Hospital Units
  Alzheimers Care Center
  Birth Center
  Cancer Center
  Emergency Care
  Extended Care
  Heart Center
  Obesity Surgery Center
  Urgent Care
  Women's Services

COMPETITORS

Carolinas HealthCare System
Carolinas Hospital System
Georgetown Hospital System
Grand Strand Regional Medical Center
Laurens County Hospital
McLeod Health
Palmetto Health
Upstate Affiliate

HISTORICAL FINANCIALS

Company Type: Private

Income Statement

FYE: September 30

	REVENUE ($ mil.)	NET INCOME ($ mil.)	NET PROFIT MARGIN	EMPLOYEES
09/17	953	(9)	—	5,616
09/16	906	21	2.3%	—
09/15	863	86	10.0%	—
09/14	781	95	12.2%	—
Annual Growth	6.8%	—	—	—

2017 Year-End Financials

Return on assets: (-0.6%)
Return on equity: (-3.2%)
Current ratio: 2.80

Cash ($ mil.): 173

LHH CORPORATION

When Manhattanites are looking for health care many of them head for the hill: Lenox Hill Hospital to be exact. The 650-bed facility provides care to patients on Manhattan's Upper East Side — about 45% of its patient base is from Manhattan the rest from surrounding boroughs. Services include cardiac care high-risk obstetrics pediatrics and orthopedics and sports medicine. Lenox Hill serves as a teaching affiliate for NYU Medical Center and also owns Manhattan Eye Ear and Throat Hospital a provider of specialty care for vision hearing and speech disorders. Today it's part of North Shore-Long Island Jewish Health System.

Operations
As part of the North Shore-LIJ system Lenox Hill has access to the larger organization's resources. North Shore-LIJ one of the largest health care providers in New York State; Lenox Hill is its first hospital in the New York metropolitan area.

Lenox Hill Hospital operates a handful of outpatient locations that provide medical surgical and specialized services. Its center for mental health administers a wide range of inpatient and ambulatory psychiatric services for adults and children. To provide quality services to a diverse population Lenox Hill provides multi-lingual translators.

The hospital treats more than 325000 patients a year.

Geographic Reach
The hospital serves patients from Manhattan and surrounding neighborhoods from two campuses in New York City and one in Westchester County.

Financial Performance
In 2012 Lenox Hill reported revenues of $729 million and a net loss of $37 million.

Strategy
Lenox Hill Hospital has also expanded in recent years by opening primary care center and urgent care centers in Manhattan and upgrading and enhancing some of its existing facilities such as its emergency care center to accommodate a growing number of patients. In 2012 it opened a new pediatric inpatient care unit for general and surgical care as well as new head and neck and cranial base surgery centers. In 2013 it opened a new reproduction clinic for fertility services.

Expanding its medical services outside of North Shore-LIJ system's 16 hospitals and into community settings in 2013 Lenox Hill opened the 3200-sq.-ft. Heart and Vascular Institute in Yorktown Heights — the first facility for the hospital system in Westchester County.

In 2012 Lenox Hill became the first in the New York area to perform minimally invasive heart valve replacement.

Company Background
US News & World Report has ranked Lenox Hill as one the top 50 in Cardiology and Heart Surgery and Ear Nose and Throat facilities in the US and among the top 10 hospitals in New York state.

In 2010 the hospital expanded its service offerings by adding palliative care to its medical roster. The services are aimed at relieving pain symptoms and stress related to serious illness. In many cases palliative care specialists provide care to patients who are not eligible for or don't want hospice care when facing a fatal illness.

It performed the first coronary angioplasty in the US (in 1978) and the first angiocardiogram (in 1938).

The hospital was established in 1857 as the German Dispensary.

EXECUTIVES

Radiology Director, Fred Desarno

LOCATIONS

HQ: LHH CORPORATION
100 E 77TH ST, NEW YORK, NY 100751850
Phone: 212 434-2000

PRODUCTS/OPERATIONS

Selected Services
Bariatric surgery
Cardiothoracic surgery
Cardiovascular care
Colorectal surgery
Critical care
Maternal and child health
Manhattan Ear Eye and Throat Institute
Mental health
Neurosurgery
Palliative care
Pathology
Plastic and reconstructive surgery
Primary care
Radiology
Rehabilitation
Robotic surgery

COMPETITORS

Beth Israel Medical Center
Bronx-Lebanon Hospital
Catholic Health Services of Long Island
Catholic Healthcare System
Lutheran HealthCare
Maimonides Medical Center
Memorial Sloan-Kettering
Montefiore Medical
New York City Health and Hospitals
NewYork-Presbyterian Hospital

HISTORICAL FINANCIALS
Company Type: Private

Income Statement				FYE: December 31
	REVENUE ($ mil.)	NET INCOME ($ mil.)	NET PROFIT MARGIN	EMPLOYEES
12/16	960	21	2.3%	2,955
12/14	790	3	0.4%	—
Annual Growth	10.2%	160.9%	—	—

2016 Year-End Financials
Return on assets: 1.8%
Return on equity: 4.7%
Current ratio: 0.80
Cash ($ mil.): —

LIBERTY UNIVERSITY, INC.

EXECUTIVES

Pres, Jerry Lamon Falwell Jr
Sr V Pres*, Mark Hine
Cfo*, Don Moon
Cao*, Ronald E Hawkins
Coo*, Randy Smith Randy Smith
SEC*, David M Corry
Project Coordinator, William Mailand
Assistant Professor, Bruce M Kirk
Assistant Professor, Danielle E Scholten
Assistant Professor, Michael R Mitchell
Accounting Staff, Michael Ohemeng-Dapaah
Auditors: DIXON HUGHES GOODMAN LLP RICH

LOCATIONS

HQ: LIBERTY UNIVERSITY, INC.
1971 UNIVERSITY BLVD, LYNCHBURG, VA 245150002
Phone: 434 582-2000
Web: WWW.LIBERTY.EDU

HISTORICAL FINANCIALS
Company Type: Private

Income Statement				FYE: June 30
	REVENUE ($ mil.)	NET INCOME ($ mil.)	NET PROFIT MARGIN	EMPLOYEES
06/18	896	276	30.8%	7,200
06/17	961	289	30.1%	—
06/15	1,001	223	22.3%	—
06/11	628	203	32.4%	—
Annual Growth	5.2%	4.5%	—	—

2018 Year-End Financials
Return on assets: 9.8%
Return on equity: 11.6%
Current ratio: —
Cash ($ mil.): 267

LIFEBRIDGE HEALTH, INC.

LifeBridge Health links patients to healthcare. Serving the Baltimore region the not-for-profit company operates two general hospitals — Sinai Hospital of Baltimore and Northwest Hospital — with specialties including oncology neurology pediatrics and sports medicine. The LifeBridge Health network also provides long-term care at the Levindale Hebrew Geriatric Center and Hospital (nursing subacute and adult day care services) and the Courtland Gardens Nursing & Rehabilitation Center. Altogether the health system boasts some 1190 beds. LifeBridge's Health Wellness division includes a health and fitness program and community fitness center.

Operations
Sinai Hospital is a teaching hospital with residency programs for medical students training at Johns Hopkins University and University of Maryland. Levindale also serves as a teaching facility for medical dental nursing and social work students pursuing training to serve geriatric populations.

EXECUTIVES

Executive Vice President, Leslie Simmons
Board Of Directors, Sinai Price
Auditors: KPMG LLP BALTIMORE MD

LOCATIONS

HQ: LIFEBRIDGE HEALTH, INC.
2401 W BELVEDERE AVE, BALTIMORE, MD 212155216
Phone: 410 601-5653

PRODUCTS/OPERATIONS

Selected Locations
Courtland Gardens Nursing & Rehabilitation Center
Levindale Hebrew Geriatric Center and Hospital
Northwest Hospital
Sinai Hospital

Selected Services
Bariatric and Minimally Invasive Surgery
Brain & Spine Institute
Cancer Institute
Hospitalist Program
Rubin Institute for Advanced Orthopedics
Vascular Institute

COMPETITORS

Anne Arundel Medical Center	Johns Hopkins Health System
Ascension Health	MedStar Health
Bon Secours Health	MedStar Union Memorial Hospital
Franklin Square Hospital Center	University of Maryland Medical System
GBMC	

HISTORICAL FINANCIALS
Company Type: Private

Income Statement				FYE: June 30
	REVENUE ($ mil.)	NET INCOME ($ mil.)	NET PROFIT MARGIN	EMPLOYEES
06/17	1,527	111	7.3%	6,000
06/15	145	0	0.5%	—
06/13	1,033	53	5.2%	—
06/11	99	(3)	—	—
Annual Growth	57.5%	—	—	—

2017 Year-End Financials
Return on assets: 5.4%
Return on equity: 10.4%
Current ratio: 2.30
Cash ($ mil.): 356

LIFEWAY CHRISTIAN RESOURCES OF THE SOUTHERN BAPTIST CONVENTION

LifeWay Christian Resources of the Southern Baptist Convention helps to spread the teachings of Jesus. The company is a not-for-profit Christian publisher. It also sells Bibles CDs gifts software church furniture signs and other supplies. In addition to its roughly 200 LifeWay Christian Stores located in more than 25 states the retailer sells products online and through its catalog. LifeWay operates two of the nation's largest Christian conference facilities and summer camps. LifeWay Ridgecrest Conference Center in North Carolina and LifeWay Glorieta Conference Center in New Mexico together welcome some 2000 conference and overnight guests each year. LifeWay was founded in 1891 by Dr. J.M. Frost.

Operations
The B&H Publishing Group produces Bibles books Sunday school teaching materials and audio and video products which are sold to bookstores and other retailers. Its Holman Christian Standard Bible is one of the best-selling versions in the US. As part of its digital outreach efforts Lifeway provides ministry services-related Digital Church which can be accessed through Lifeway's website and offers an array of resources for ministries including downloadable worship music and a video publishing utility.

Its Executive Communications and Relations division produces LifeWay's news and information services directs corporate events builds corporate relations and supports the office of the president. It works with state conventions and other evangelical organizations as well. The Technology division offers strategic retail enterprise and Internet services. The company's Research and Ministry Development division is where LifeWay conducts its research and explores new ministry ventures it calls "blue oceans." LifeWay's Finance and Business Services division which runs a conference center in Ridgecrest North Carolina oversees the company's financial policies and general accounting as well as directs business services such as legal investment purchasing real estate strategic planning corporate services and human resources.

Geographic Reach

Based in Nashville LifeWay boasts offices and conference centers in three states: Tennessee New Mexico and North Carolina. In Nashville the company has more than 1.3 million sq. ft. of office retail parking conference and warehouse space that covers 14.6 acres. As part of its operations LifeWay has a 350000-sq.-ft. warehouse on 44 acres in Lebanon Tennessee that supports the Life-Way Christian Stores the company operates nationwide in more than 25 states and extends its reach globally through its website and catalogs.

EXECUTIVES

Vp Lifeway Christian Stores, Tim Vineyard
Vp Finance And Business Services; Cfo, Jerry Rhyne
President And Ceo, Thom S. Rainer
Evp, Brad Waggoner
Vp B&h Publishing Group, Selma Wilson
Vp Insights Division, Ed Stetzer
Vp Church Resources Division, Eric Geiger
Vp And Cio, Tim Hill
Senior Vice President Ancillary Services, Cathy A Brown
Vice President Marketing And Sales, Jim Baird
Associate Vice President Church Resources, Earl Roberson
Vice President Sales Mass Market And Specialty Accounts, David Humphrey
Vice President Human Resources, Connia Nelson
Auditors: LBMC BRENTWOOD TENNESSEE

LOCATIONS

HQ: LIFEWAY CHRISTIAN RESOURCES OF THE SOUTHERN BAPTIST CONVENTION
1 LIFEWAY PLZ, NASHVILLE, TN 372341001
Phone: 615 251-2000
Web: WWW.LIFEWAY.COM

2013 Stores

	No.
Texas	26
Tennessee	21
North Carolina	14
Alabama	11
Georgia	11
Virginia	9
Florida	8
Kentucky	8
Arkansas	6
Mississippi	6
South Carolina	6
Louisiana	5
Minnesota	5
Missouri	5
Ohio	4
Pennsylvania	3
California	2
Illinois	2
Kansas	2
Maryland	2
Oklahoma	2
Washington	2
Colorado	1
Indiana	1
New Mexico	1
Oregon	1
Utah	1
Total	**165**

PRODUCTS/OPERATIONS

Selected Divisions
B&H Publishing Group
Church Resources
Executive Communications and Relations
Finance and Business Services
LifeWay Christian Stores
Research and Ministry Development
Technology

Selected Products
Apparel
Audio
Bibles
Books
Church supplies
Curriculum
eBooks
Events
Gifts
Magazines
Movies
Music
Video

COMPETITORS

Amazon.com	United Methodist
Baker Publishing	Publishing
Barnes & Noble	Wal-Mart
Deseret Management	

HISTORICAL FINANCIALS

Company Type: Private

Income Statement — FYE: September 30

	REVENUE ($ mil.)	NET INCOME ($ mil.)	NET PROFIT MARGIN	EMPLOYEES
09/17	476	43	9.2%	5,000
09/16	502	8	1.6%	—
09/15	487	(67)	—	—
09/14	500	(25)	—	—
Annual Growth	**(1.6%)**	—	—	—

2017 Year-End Financials

Return on assets: 9.7%   Cash ($ mil.): 1
Return on equity: 33.1%
Current ratio: 2.10

LIMETREE BAY TERMINALS LLC

HOVENSA brings together US and Latin American know-how and operations to handle oil products in the US Virgin Islands. HOVENSA is a joint venture of Hess and Venezuelan oil giant PDVSA (its major crude oil supplier). Once the largest private employer in the US Virgin Islands the company operated a 500000-barrels-per-day crude oil refinery on St. Croix along with two specialized oil processing complexes a 150000-barrels-per-day fluid catalytic cracking unit and a 58000-barrels-per-day delayed coker unit. However the St. Croix refinery had run up losses for years; it was shut down in 2012 and was put up for sale in 2013.

Strategy

Citing high operating and maintenance costs (the refinery was fueled by oil not the cheaper natural gas) and the growth of lower-cost refineries in emerging markets HOVENSA has posted $1.3 billion in losses since 2009. As a result the company decided to cut its losses by converting the refinery into an oil storage terminal which can take advantage of St. Croix's strategic location. Its 55-

ft. deep harbor enables it to receive crude oil tanker deliveries from Venezuela and around the world. The storage terminal employs about 100 workers. The shutdown of the refinery resulted in more than 2000 employes being laid off.

Company Background

In 2009 the global economic downturn depressed demand for oil caused a dip in production and prompted the company to lay off 270 employees (about 21% of its total contract workers).

Crude thoughput has declined steadily at HOVENSA due to weaker refining margins and planned and unplanned maintenance from 402000 barrels per day (bpd) in 2009 to 390000 bpd in 2010 to 284000 bpd in 2011.

Auditors: ERNST & YOUNG LLP NEW YORK N

LOCATIONS

HQ: LIMETREE BAY TERMINALS LLC
1 ESTATE HOPE, CHRISTIANSTED, VI 00820
Phone: 340 692-3000

COMPETITORS

Chevron	Royal Dutch Shell
ConocoPhillips	Sunoco
Exxon Mobil	Valero Energy
Marathon Oil	

HISTORICAL FINANCIALS

Company Type: Private

Income Statement — FYE: December 31

	REVENUE ($ mil.)	NET INCOME ($ mil.)	NET PROFIT MARGIN	EMPLOYEES
12/09	10,048	(451)	—	1,300
12/08	17,479	94	0.5%	—
Annual Growth	**(42.5%)**	—	—	—

2009 Year-End Financials

Return on assets: 3.2%   Cash ($ mil.): 77
Return on equity: (-4.5%)
Current ratio: 0.20

LINCOLN MEDICAL AND MENTAL HEALTH CENTER

EXECUTIVES

Exec Dir, Milton Nunez
Marketing Director, Cheryl Simmons-Oliver
Anesthesiologist, Jean R Maurice
Infectious Disease Specialist, Chung Kim
Doctor, Karen Hennessey
Emergency Medicine Specialist, Karlene Hosford
Emergency Medicine Specialist, Lee Donner
Case Management Director, Andrina Campbell
Obstetrician Gynecologist, Manisha Jain
Infection Control Director, Melba Talan
Emergency Medicine Specialist, Andaleeb H Raja

LOCATIONS

HQ: LINCOLN MEDICAL AND MENTAL HEALTH CENTER
234 E 149TH ST, BRONX, NY 104515504
Phone: 718 579-5000

HISTORICAL FINANCIALS

Company Type: Private

Income Statement

FYE: June 30

	REVENUE ($ mil.)	NET INCOME ($ mil.)	NET PROFIT MARGIN	EMPLOYEES
06/16	616	120	19.6%	79
06/15	530	20	3.9%	—
Annual Growth	16.2%	488.5%	—	—

2016 Year-End Financials

Return on assets: 14.0%
Return on equity: 50.4%
Current ratio: 1.40

Cash ($ mil.): —

LOGICALIS US HOLDINGS, INC.

EXECUTIVES

Ceo, Vince Deluca
Sr V Pres, Dan Sytsma
Exec V Pres, Eric Tilds
Cfo, Rich Pirrotta
Coo, Michael Souders
Cso, Mike Houghton
Director of Storage, Brian Dittmar
Account Executive Goved Southe, Lisa Waelde
Auditors: DELOITTE & TOUCHE LLP DETROIT

LOCATIONS

HQ: LOGICALIS US HOLDINGS, INC.
  1 PENN PLZ, NEW YORK, NY 101190002
Phone: 212 596-7160
Web: WWW.LOGICALIS.COM

HISTORICAL FINANCIALS

Company Type: Private

Income Statement

FYE: February 28

	REVENUE ($ mil.)	NET INCOME ($ mil.)	NET PROFIT MARGIN	EMPLOYEES
02/17	452	9	2.2%	702
02/16	465	6	1.4%	—
Annual Growth	(2.8%)	47.4%	—	—

2017 Year-End Financials

Return on assets: 3.9%
Return on equity: 10.6%
Current ratio: 0.70

Cash ($ mil.): 1

LOGISTICARE SOLUTIONS, LLC

LogistiCare is a go-between for getting from your house to the doctor's office and back. The company brokers non-emergency transportation services for commercial health plans government entities (such as state Medicaid agencies) and hospitals throughout the US. Using its nearly 20 call centers and a network of some 1500 independent contracted transportation providers the company coordinates the medical-related travel arrange-

ments of its clients' members. In addition it contracts with local school boards to coordinate transportation for special needs students. The company provides more than 26 million trips each year for clients in some 40 states. LogistiCare is a subsidiary of Providence Service.

Operations

LogistiCare also known as Charter LCI has contracts with clients including metro transit authorities HMOs and commercial insurance firms. OtherÂ services include finance and consulting to help companies with billing management and claims adjudication customer reimbursement risk management and discount programs for patients requesting noncovered services. LogistiCare's eligibility and authorization services include call screening to determine client-provided benefit criteria as well as screening to determine type of transport needed.

The company operates more than a dozen regional call centers that match incoming requests with subcontracted transportation providers including local taxi and ambulance companies. Transportation customers often include the elderly or those with disabilities that prevent self-transportation.

Strategy

A major part of LogistiCare's growth strategy is to secure contracts with state and local authorities to become the sole Medicaid or Medicare transportation provider. It scored one such contract in late 2010 with Sussex County Delaware. Under terms of that agreement LogistiCare became the statewide broker for all Medicaid medical transportation.

EXECUTIVES

Vice President Human Resources, Jenny Southern
Vice President Finance, Ken Shepard

LOCATIONS

HQ: LOGISTICARE SOLUTIONS, LLC
  1275 PEACHTREE ST NE FL 6, ATLANTA, GA
  303093580
Phone: 404 888-5831
Web: WWW.LOGISTICARE.COM

PRODUCTS/OPERATIONS

Selected Services

Billing and claims management
Call center management
Credentialing
Data management and reporting
Eligibility and authorization services
Logistics
Non-emergency transportation management
  (ambulatory/livery vans wheel chair vans stretcher vans)
Provider payment
Quality assurance

COMPETITORS

AMR	National Express Group
Coach USA	Safe Ride Services
FirstGroup America	Veolia Transportation
MV Transportation	

HISTORICAL FINANCIALS

Company Type: Private

Income Statement

FYE: December 31

	REVENUE ($ mil.)	NET INCOME ($ mil.)	NET PROFIT MARGIN	EMPLOYEES
12/17*	1,318	35	2.7%	2,000
04/17	1,234	44	3.6%	—
12/15	1,083	40	3.7%	—
12/14	884	71	8.1%	—
Annual Growth	14.2%	(21.0%)	—	—

*Fiscal year change

2017 Year-End Financials

Return on assets: 19.1%
Return on equity: 73.8%
Current ratio: 1.10

Cash ($ mil.): 26

LONE STAR NGL PIPELINE LP

EXECUTIVES

Ptnr-Ceo, Kelcy L Warren
Ptnr-Pres-Coo, Marshall S McCrea III
Ptnr-Cfo, Martin Salinas Jr
Sr Dir, Josie Castrejana
Vice-President, Brad Burmaster

LOCATIONS

HQ: LONE STAR NGL PIPELINE LP
  1300 MAIN ST 10, HOUSTON, TX 770026803
Phone: 210 403-7300

HISTORICAL FINANCIALS

Company Type: Private

Income Statement

FYE: December 31

	REVENUE ($ mil.)	NET INCOME ($ mil.)	NET PROFIT MARGIN	EMPLOYEES
12/17	471	366	77.7%	200
12/16	360	302	83.8%	—
Annual Growth	30.7%	21.2%	—	—

LONG BEACH MEMORIAL MEDICAL CENTER

Long Beach Memorial Medical Center (LBMMC) is an old-timer in the Long Beach health care market. A subsidiary of Memorial Health Services LBMMC provides a full range of health services to residents of the Long Beach California area. The medical center a 420-bed acute-care hospital was founded in 1907 and is one of the largest private hospitals on the West Coast. Services include primary emergency diagnostic surgical therapeutic and rehabilitative care. The hospital is home to centers for treatment of cancer heart stroke and women's and children's health concerns. It also provides home and hospice care programs as well as occupational health services.

Operations

LBMMC comprises a breast center cancer institute center for women heart and vascular institute imaging center joint replacement center rehabilitation institute and stroke center. The medical center is a 420-bed acute-care hospital.

Geographic Reach

Long Beach Memorial Medical Center (LBMMC) is one of the nation's largest private hospitals on the West Coast.

Strategy

LBMMC boasts an electronic medical record (EMR) system that connects the hospital and all of its affiliated physicians and pharmacies so that they can transfer patient information electronically between different care providers and locations.

Hospitals that use an EMR are eligible for incentives and higher reimbursements from the federal government. Additionally EMRs help to reduce medical errors and increase patient safety by eliminating things like medication interactions and duplicate patient records.

LBMMC expanded its cancer services by building a new $31 million dedicated outpatient cancer facility. The MemorialCare Todd Cancer Institute at Long Beach Memorial which was completed in mid-2013 serves to supplement its current center which had reached capacity. With the new 65000-sq.-ft. MemorialCare Todd Cancer Institute pavilion LBMMC enhances its cancer care technology and capacity.

LBMMC has also expanded its robotics program beyond cardiology. The hospital recently established a new intensivist program in the Intensive Care Unit (ICU). The ICU program integrates teaching from the University of California Irvine residents and interns.

EXECUTIVES

Cio, Scott Joslyn
Cfo, Wendy Dorchester
President And Ceo, Barry Arbuckle
Director Of Nursing, Mary Jorgensen
Vice President Of Quality, Donna Hartman
Vice President Material Resources, Gerald Olson
Medical Director Ed, Gary Moreau
Vice President Human Resource, Kerri Jo Cooper
Medical Director Pediatric Cardiology, Saar Danon
Operating Room Dir, Deborah Ebert
Secretary Executive, Donna Gorman
Secretary Executive, Donna Reyes
Secretary Executive, Kathleen Webster
Secretary Executive, Barbara Steinhauser
Secretary Executive, Kelly Ambrose
Secretary Department Medical, Heather Lawrence
Secretary Executive, Evelyn Satele
Secretary Admin, Carmencita De Jesus
Secretary Admin, Carol Fraser
Secretary Department Medical, Deborah Ruman
Unit Secretary, Gabrielle Ray
Unit Secretary, Mary Fernandez

LOCATIONS

HQ: LONG BEACH MEMORIAL MEDICAL CENTER
2801 ATLANTIC AVE FL 2, LONG BEACH, CA
908061701
Phone: 562 933-2000
Web: WWW.MEMORIALCARE.ORG

PRODUCTS/OPERATIONS

Selected Institutes and Centers
Certified Comprehensive Stroke Center
Long Beach Adult & Pediatric Sleep Center
MemorialCare Breast Center at Long Beach Medical Center
MemorialCare Heart & Vascular Institute
MemorialCare Imaging Center
MemorialCare Joint Replacement Center
MemorialCare Rehabilitation Institute
MemorialCare Todd Cancer Institute
Spine Center at Long Beach Memorial
Trauma Center at Long Beach Medical Center

Selected Services
Blood Donation Center
Diabetes Care
Digestive Care
Emergency Department
Gynecological Care at Long Beach Medical Center
Lung & Respiratory Care
Minimally Invasive Surgery at Long Beach Memorial
Palliative Care Program at Long Beach Medical Center
Pharmacy at Long Beach Medical Center
Robotic-Assisted Surgery at Long Beach Memorial
Surgical Care
Wound Healing & Hyperbaric Medicine at Long Beach Medical Center

COMPETITORS

Adventist Health System West
Aptium Oncology
Brotman Medical Center
Cedars-Sinai Medical Center
Dignity Health
Good Samaritan Hospital (Los Angeles)
HCA
Hoag Memorial Hospital
Hollywood Presbyterian Medical Center
Methodist Hospital of Southern California
Newhall Memorial Hospital
Pasadena Hospital Association
Providence Health System Southern California
Sutter Health
Tenet Healthcare
Torrance Memorial Medical Center
Trinity Health (Novi)
Western Medical Center - Santa Ana

HISTORICAL FINANCIALS
Company Type: Private

Income Statement				FYE: June 30
	REVENUE ($ mil.)	NET INCOME ($ mil.)	NET PROFIT MARGIN	EMPLOYEES
06/16	618	88	14.4%	6,000
06/15	624	93	15.0%	—
06/11	1,083	63	5.9%	—
06/09	446	53	12.0%	—
Annual Growth	4.8%	7.5%	—	—

2016 Year-End Financials
Return on assets: 7.7%   Cash ($ mil.): —
Return on equity: 8.2%
Current ratio: 18.90

LONG ISLAND JEWISH MEDICAL CENTER

Long Island Jewish Medical Center serves the western edge of Long Island and the eastern edge of the greater metropolitan New York area. The medical center campus includes Long Island Jewish Hospital a general acute care hospital; Cohen Children's Medical Center of New York Hospital which provides a full range of pediatric care services; and The Zucker Hillside Hospital a psychiatric hospital for patients of all ages. The medical center's staff includes 1200 physicians. Long Island Jewish Medical Center is the primary clinical and medical training facility of Northwell Health.

Operations
The Long Island Jewish Medical Center's main activities are centered at the Long Island Jewish Hospital which provides emergency diagnostic surgical inpatient and outpatient services. The hospital has centers for cancer treatment cardiac surgery and women's health as well as units specializing in hearing loss stroke recovery sleep disorders and hemophilia treatment. As an affiliate of Hofstra University the Long Island Jewish Hospital also provides graduate medical education programs.

Geographic Reach
Long Island Jewish Medical Center is located on a 48-acre campus on the border of New York's Queens and Nassau counties about 15 miles east of Manhattan.

EXECUTIVES

Medical Records Director, Patricia Hennelly

LOCATIONS

HQ: LONG ISLAND JEWISH MEDICAL CENTER
27005 76TH AVE, NEW HYDE PARK, NY 110401496
Phone: 516 465-2600

PRODUCTS/OPERATIONS

Selected Facilities
Long Island Jewish Hospital (490 beds)
The Steven and Alexandra Cohen Children's Medical Center (160 beds)
The Zucker Hillside Hospital (240 beds)

Selected Services
Anesthesiology
Cardiac Services
Center for Maternal-Fetal Health
Dental Medicine
Emergency Medicine
Medicine
Neurosciences
Obstetrics
Ophthalmology
Orthopaedic Surgery
Otolaryngology
Pathology
Radiation Oncology
Radiology
Rehabilitation
Surgery
Thoracic Surgery
Urogynecology
Urology: The Arthur Smith Insitute for Urology

COMPETITORS

Catholic Health Services of Long Island
Mercy Medical Center (NY)
North Shore University Hospital
NuHealth
St. Francis Hospital Roslyn
Winthrop-University Hospital

HISTORICAL FINANCIALS
Company Type: Private

Income Statement				FYE: December 31
	REVENUE ($ mil.)	NET INCOME ($ mil.)	NET PROFIT MARGIN	EMPLOYEES
12/17	2,222	154	6.9%	1,214
12/16	2,093	162	7.8%	—
12/15	1,524	44	2.9%	—
12/14	1,446	96	6.7%	—
Annual Growth	15.4%	16.9%	—	—

2017 Year-End Financials
Return on assets: 5.4%   Cash ($ mil.): 61
Return on equity: 18.9%
Current ratio: 2.40

LONG ISLAND POWER AUTHORITY

The long and short of it is that Long Island Power Authority (LIPA) owns the electric transmission and distribution system on Long Island that delivers power to more than 1.1 million retail customers. The company's network which is managed and operated by the National Grid USA consists of nearly 14000 miles of overhead and underground lines. LIPA offers energy conservation products and services as well as incentive programs to encourage customers to purchase energy from "green" (environmentally friendly) power generation sources. LIPA is a municipally owned not-for-profit utility company.

EXECUTIVES

Ceo-Coo, Michael D Hervey
Gen Counsel-Sec*, Lynda Nicolino
V Pres-Envrnm Affrs*, Michael Deering
V Pres-Cfo*, Herbert L Hogue
V Pres*, Kenneth Kane
Enterise Risk Manager, Jessica Swenson
Procurement Director, Maria Gomes
Auditors: KPMG LLP NEW YORK NEW YORK

LOCATIONS

HQ: LONG ISLAND POWER AUTHORITY
333 EARLE OVINGTON BLVD # 403, UNIONDALE, NY
115533606
Phone: 516 222-7700
Web: WWW.LIPOWER.ORG

PRODUCTS/OPERATIONS

Energy Conservation Products and Services
Commercial energy analysis
Construction and renovation incentives
Energy Star labeled homes program
Geothermal rebates
HVAC upgrades
Lighting and appliance solutions
Peak demand reduction programs
Residential energy affordability program
Residential energy audit
Solar Pioneer program
Wind energy development initiatives

COMPETITORS

Avangrid
CH Energy
Con Edison

New York Power
Authority

HISTORICAL FINANCIALS

Company Type: Private

Income Statement				FYE: December 31
	REVENUE ($ mil.)	NET INCOME ($ mil.)	NET PROFIT MARGIN	EMPLOYEES
12/18	3,576	22	0.6%	100
12/16	3,399	(26)	—	—
12/09	3,312	40	1.2%	—
Annual Growth	0.9%	(6.3%)	—	—

2018 Year-End Financials
Return on assets: 0.2%   Cash ($ mil.): 327
Return on equity: 4.6%
Current ratio: 2.00

LOS ANGELES COUNTY OFFICE OF EDUCATION

EXECUTIVES

Ceo, Rudell S Freer
Pres*, Rebecca J Turrentine
V Pres*, Katie Braude
E-Business Point of Contact, Roberta Gerarde
Executive Officer, Ronald Reynolds
Consultant, Carolina Alvarez
Board of Directors, Maria Yepes
Program Manager, Anna Whalen
Programmer Analyst, Gregory Brignoni
Consultant, Amy Honculada
Coordinator, Gerald Yarbrough
Auditors: VAVRINEK TRINE DAY & CO LL

LOCATIONS

HQ: LOS ANGELES COUNTY OFFICE OF EDUCATION
9300 IMPERIAL HWY, DOWNEY, CA 902422813
Phone: 562 922-6111
Web: WWW.LACOE.EDU

HISTORICAL FINANCIALS

Company Type: Private

Income Statement				FYE: June 30
	REVENUE ($ mil.)	NET INCOME ($ mil.)	NET PROFIT MARGIN	EMPLOYEES
06/18	657	22	3.4%	4,000
06/17	646	17	2.6%	—
06/16	661	7	1.2%	—
06/08	6	0	1.4%	—
Annual Growth	57.5%	71.9%	—	—

LOS ANGELES DEPARTMENT OF WATER AND POWER

The Los Angeles Department of Water and Power (LADWP) keeps the movie cameras running and the swimming pools full. The largest municipally owned utility in the US LADWP provides electricity to 1.4 million residential and business customers and water to 674000 customers. The company has power plant interests that give it more than 7220 MW of generating capacity; it also buys and sells wholesale power. Most of the city's water supply is transported through two aqueduct systems from the Sierra Nevada Mountains; other water sources include wells and local groundwater basins. Because LADWP is city-owned its retail monopoly status has been unaffected by utility deregulation in California.

Operations
The department has 114 tanks and reservoirs 78 pump stations a distribution main of 7263 miles of pipe and storage capacity of 315245 acre-feet.

It has a budget of $1.5 billion of which $422 million is for operations and maintenance; $722 million for capital projects; and $343 million for purchased water.

Financial Performance
LADWP's operations are entirely financed by the sale of water and electric services. The multi-utility transfers about 7% of its annual electric revenues and 5% of its water revenues to the City of Los Angeles general fund.

Strategy
Residential customers form the largest client group of the utility's water service unit; commercial customers the largest customer class of the power segment. To enhance operating efficiencies and conserve energy the department has launched a 10-year $1 billion Smart Grid program to automate and upgrade the City's grid.

It is also pushing to increase the amount of energy it generates from renewable sources (mainly wind and solar power) to meet state and federal clean air goals. LADWP got only 5% of it power from renewables in 2005 but has upped that amount to more than 20% by 2014. LADWP sold ts Navajo Generating Station in Arizona in 2015 which cut carbon emissions by a further 26%.

In 2013 LADWP signed a decade-long power purchase agreement to purchase renewable geot-hermal power (about 34 MW) from the Imperial Valley (enough to provide enough clean energy to serve 47600 Los Angeles homes).

In addition as the Western US states battle a prolonged drought the utility is negotiating with water agencies across the region to ensure a reliable future supply for its citizens.

Proposed rate changes for residential customers see an increase of about 3% for water and power on bills each year for five years. This reflects an average monthly bill increase of $4.20 each year from 2016 through 2020.

Company Background
LADWP was founded in 1902.

EXECUTIVES

Chief Administrative Officer, David H. Wiggs
Senior Assistant General Manager Power System,
David H. (Dave) Wright
General Manager, Marcie L. Edwards
Senior Assistant General Manager Water System,
Martin L. Adams
Chief Sustainability And Economic Development Officer, Nancy Sutley
Cfo, Phil Leiber
Fac Vice President, Kevin Brown
Vice President, Ann Unkcd Santilli
Vice President Information Technology, Dan
Raftevold
Legal Secretary, Patricia Stanard
Vice President Of Market Strategy, John Poplawski
Medical Director, Leslie Israel
President Board Of Commissioners, Mel Levine
Vp Board Of Commissioners, William W.
Funderburk
Secretary To Executive Vice President, Javier
Romero
Secretary, Lisa Solomon
Secretary, Clariza Valdovinos
Secretary, Chris Reinhart
Auditors: KPMG LLP LOS ANGELES CA

LOCATIONS

HQ: LOS ANGELES DEPARTMENT OF WATER AND
POWER
111 N HOPE ST, LOS ANGELES, CA 900122607
Phone: 213 367-4211
Web: WWW.LADWP.COM

COMPETITORS

AES
American States Water
Avista
California Water
Service
Calpine
Duke Energy

Edison International
PG&E Corporation
Sacramento Municipal
Utility
Sempra Energy
SouthWest Water

HISTORICAL FINANCIALS

Company Type: Private

Income Statement				FYE: June 30
	REVENUE ($ mil.)	NET INCOME ($ mil.)	NET PROFIT MARGIN	EMPLOYEES
06/17	1,118	140	12.6%	9,500
06/11	3,125	57	1.8%	—
06/10	812	67	8.3%	—
Annual Growth	4.7%	11.1%	—	—

2017 Year-End Financials
Return on assets: 1.4%   Cash ($ mil.): 320
Return on equity: 4.5%
Current ratio: 1.20

LOS ANGELES LOMOD CORPORATION

EXECUTIVES

Pres, Nancy Wesoff
Dir*, Lucelia Hooper
President*, Connie Loyola
Principal*, Ben Besley
Principal*, Erica Jacquez
Information Technology Manager, Robin Fox
Auditors: MACIAS GINI & O'CONNELL LLP L

LOCATIONS

HQ: LOS ANGELES LOMOD CORPORATION
2600 WILSHIRE BLVD, LOS ANGELES, CA 900573400
Phone: 213 252-2510

HISTORICAL FINANCIALS
Company Type: Private

Income Statement				FYE: December 31
	REVENUE ($ mil.)	NET INCOME ($ mil.)	NET PROFIT MARGIN	EMPLOYEES
12/17	534	12	2.4%	44
12/13	405	6	1.5%	—
12/09	356	5	1.4%	—
12/08	316	0	—	—
Annual Growth	6.0%	—	—	—

2017 Year-End Financials
Return on assets: 36.4%
Return on equity: 37.3%
Current ratio: —
Cash ($ mil.): 30

LOS ROBLES HOSPITAL & MEDICAL CENTER

EXECUTIVES

Ceo, Greg Angle
Director of Mis/Is, Alex Bryar
Dermatologist, Michael Bodnar
Respiratory Therapy Director, Pam Whitener
Dermatologist, Ralph Kamell
Surgeon, Alan Mintz
Internal Medicine Practitioner, Anna Stewart
Ceo Assistant, Maureen Nicols
Orthopedic Surgeon, Pierre Durand
Pathologist, Wayne M Schultheis
Pacs Admin, Don Adler

LOCATIONS

HQ: LOS ROBLES HOSPITAL & MEDICAL CENTER
215 W JANSS RD, THOUSAND OAKS, CA 913601899
Phone: 805 497-2727
Web: WWW.LOSROBLESHOSPITAL.COM

HISTORICAL FINANCIALS
Company Type: Private

Income Statement				FYE: December 31
	REVENUE ($ mil.)	NET INCOME ($ mil.)	NET PROFIT MARGIN	EMPLOYEES
12/16	474	107	22.7%	1,700
12/15	465	97	20.9%	—
12/08	276	25	9.3%	—
12/04	0	0	7.8%	—
Annual Growth	103.1%	122.0%	—	—

2016 Year-End Financials
Return on assets: 35.5%
Return on equity: 44.7%
Current ratio: 3.10
Cash ($ mil.): —

LOUDOUN COUNTY PUBLIC SCHOOL DISTRICT

EXECUTIVES

Supt, Eric Williams
Coordinator, Mark Taylor
Assistant Superintendent, Mary V Kealy
Coordinator, Paige Neeley
Finance Assistant, Diane Aaronson
Sergeant, Linda Cerniglia
Information Technology Manager, Andrew Leith
Auditors: CHERRY BEKAERT LLP TYSONS COR

LOCATIONS

HQ: LOUDOUN COUNTY PUBLIC SCHOOL DISTRICT
21000 EDUCATION CT, BROADLANDS, VA 201485526
Phone: 571 252-1000
Web: WWW.LCPS.ORG

HISTORICAL FINANCIALS
Company Type: Private

Income Statement				FYE: June 30
	REVENUE ($ mil.)	NET INCOME ($ mil.)	NET PROFIT MARGIN	EMPLOYEES
06/16	1,130	14	1.3%	9,822
06/15	1,080	19	1.8%	—
Annual Growth	4.7%	(28.6%)	—	—

LOUISIANA CHILDRENS MEDICAL CENTER, INC

EXECUTIVES

Pres-Ceo, Mary Perrin
Cfo*, Jenny Barnett-Sarpalius
Coordinator, Susan Wack MBA
Coordinator, Jennifer Turner
Physician, Stephen Levine

LOCATIONS

HQ: LOUISIANA CHILDRENS MEDICAL CENTER, INC
200 HENRY CLAY AVE, NEW ORLEANS, LA 701185720
Phone: 504 896-9581
Web: WWW.CHNOLA.ORG

HISTORICAL FINANCIALS
Company Type: Private

Income Statement				FYE: December 31
	REVENUE ($ mil.)	NET INCOME ($ mil.)	NET PROFIT MARGIN	EMPLOYEES
12/18	1,617	(34)	—	6,100
12/14	21	0	—	—
12/13*	926	285	30.8%	—
03/13	500	10	2.1%	—
Annual Growth	21.6%	—	—	—
*Fiscal year change				

2018 Year-End Financials
Return on assets: (-1.3%)
Return on equity: (-2.3%)
Current ratio: 1.20
Cash ($ mil.): 104

LOWELL GENERAL HOSPITAL

EXECUTIVES

Ceo, Joseph White III
V Pres*, Amy Hoey
Prin*, William Wyman
Director, William J Galvin II
Human Resources, Nancy Dale
Director of Risk Management, Tatiana Schultz
Director of Quality Improvemen, Gina O'Connor
Chief of Radiology, Scott Abel
Coordinator, Andrea Jackson
Staff, Bill Charette
Program Director, Christine Labrecque
Auditors: DELOITTE & TOUCHE LLP BOSTON

LOCATIONS

HQ: LOWELL GENERAL HOSPITAL
295 VARNUM AVE, LOWELL, MA 018542193
Phone: 978 937-6000
Web: WWW.LOWELLGENERAL.ORG

HISTORICAL FINANCIALS
Company Type: Private

Income Statement				FYE: September 30
	REVENUE ($ mil.)	NET INCOME ($ mil.)	NET PROFIT MARGIN	EMPLOYEES
09/18	472	1	0.2%	3,000
09/16	441	1	0.3%	—
09/15	419	10	2.6%	—
09/14	405	17	4.3%	—
Annual Growth	3.9%	(49.7%)	—	—

2018 Year-End Financials
Return on assets: 0.2%
Return on equity: 0.7%
Current ratio: 1.20
Cash ($ mil.): 46

LOWER COLORADO RIVER AUTHORITY

The stars at night may be big and bright but more than 1 million people deep in the heart of Texas still need electricity from the Lower Colorado River Authority (LCRA). Serving 80 counties along the lower Colorado River between Central Texas and the Gulf of Mexico the not-for profit state-run entity supplies wholesale electricity to more than 40 retail utilities (primarily municipalities and cooperatives). It operates three fossil-fuel powered plants and six hydroelectric dams that give it a production capacity of about 3800 megawatts; it also purchases electricity from Texas wind farms. The LCRA provides water and wastewater utility services to more than 30 communities as well.

Operations
Founded by the Texas Legislature in 1934 the LCRA has pursued two complementary goals — providing reliable low-cost utility and public services and ensuring the protection of the area's natural resources. In the latter role the LCRA owns or operates more than 40 public recreation areas comprising more than 16400 acres; it also monitors the water quality and levels of the lakes formed by its dams.

Sales and Marketing
Sales of electricity to one major customer represented 25% of its total electric revenue for 2014.

Financial Performance
LCRA receives no state tax revenues but operates by selling electricity electric transmission and water services at cost. It does not levy taxes or receive specific appropriations from any government. Its net income for fiscal year 2014 increased 1% over 2013 while its revenues remained flat.

Strategy
LCRA's capital improvement and expansion programs from fiscal year 2015 through 2019 totals at $1.2 billion with $0.8 billion or 67% to be debt funded. The majority of the forecasted capital costs will go toward expansion of transmission services dam improvements and the construction of a new water reservoir. LCRA continues to increase its transmission system investment due to the need for additional electric transmission capability statewide.

EXECUTIVES

Deputy General Manager, Ross Phillips
General Manager And Ceo, Phil Wilson
Treasurer, Brady Edwards
Manager Information Services And Strategy, Debbie Dunn-Krause
Vice President Governmental Regional Affairs, Victoria Miller
Chairman, Timothy T. Timmerman, age 58
Vice Chairman, John C. Dickerson
Auditors: BAKER TILLY VIRCHOW KRAUSE LLP

LOCATIONS

HQ: LOWER COLORADO RIVER AUTHORITY
3700 LAKE AUSTIN BLVD, AUSTIN, TX 787033504
Phone: 512 473-3200
Web: WWW.LCRA.ORG

PRODUCTS/OPERATIONS

Selected Subsidiaries and Affiliates
Fayette Power Project (coal-fired power generating units)
GenTex Power Corporation (power generation)
LCRA Transmission Services Corporation (power transmission services)

HISTORICAL FINANCIALS
Company Type: Private

Income Statement   FYE: June 30

	REVENUE ($ mil.)	NET INCOME ($ mil.)	NET PROFIT MARGIN	EMPLOYEES
06/15	1,021	15	1.5%	1,800
06/12	1,261	101	8.0%	—
06/11	1,185	48	4.1%	—
06/10	1,244	110	8.9%	—
Annual Growth	(3.9%)	(32.5%)	—	—

2015 Year-End Financials

Return on assets: 0.3%   Cash ($ mil.): 182
Return on equity: 1.2%
Current ratio: 1.20

LOYOLA UNIVERSITY MEDICAL CENTER

Auditors: PRICEWATERHOUSECOOPERS LLP WA

LOCATIONS

HQ: LOYOLA UNIVERSITY MEDICAL CENTER
2160 S 1ST AVE, MAYWOOD, IL 601533328
Phone: 708 216-9000
Web: WWW.LOYOLAHEALTH.ORG

HISTORICAL FINANCIALS
Company Type: Private

Income Statement   FYE: June 30

	REVENUE ($ mil.)	NET INCOME ($ mil.)	NET PROFIT MARGIN	EMPLOYEES
06/11	938	14	1.6%	4
06/10	917	8	0.9%	—
Annual Growth	2.3%	75.7%	—	—

2011 Year-End Financials

Return on assets: —   Cash ($ mil.): 65
Return on equity: 1.6%
Current ratio: 0.30

LOYOLA UNIVERSITY OF CHICAGO INC

Loyola University is a Jesuit Catholic university with a reach that extends far beyond the Windy City. In addition to its three Chicago-area campuses the university also maintains an undergraduate campus in Italy and a study center in Beijing China. Loyola University's nearly 16000 students can choose from about 80 undergraduate 85 master's 30 doctoral and about two dozen graduate-level certificate programs. With about 1550 full-time staff members the not-for-profit school has a 14:1 student-teacher ratio. Notable alumni include actor Bob Newhart and writer Sandra Cisneros. Established in 1870 by a group of Jesuit priests the university turned its medical center into a separate subsidiary in 1995.

Geographic Reach
Loyola University three Chicago campuses include Lake Shore Water Tower and Health Sciences as well as the John Felice Rome Center in Italy. It is home to 10 schools and colleges that include arts and sciences business administration communication education graduate studies law medicine nursing continuing and professional studies and social work.

Loyola also features course locations in Beijing China and Saigon-Ho Chi Minh City Vietnam.

Strategy
In 2013 Loyola University Chicago broke ground on a new $137 million medical research and education building at its Health Sciences Campus. Named the Loyola University Chicago Center for Translational Research and Education the building will include laboratory space and a 250-seat auditorium. It is scheduled to open in mid-2016.

In 2011 the Loyola University Health System (LUHS) was sold to Trinity Health one of the largest Catholic health care systems in the US. LUHS and its half-dozen hospitals had not been profitable and the sale allowed it to pay less in subsidies to Loyola University's medical school in exchange for the university getting out from underneath the health system's debt.

EXECUTIVES

Svp Administrative Services And Chief Hr Officer, Thomas Kelly
President And Ceo, Michael J. Garanzini
Provost, John Pelissero
Government Relations, Philip Hale
Vice President Of University Marketing And Communications, Kelly Shannon
Vice President Spence And Elster, Nanette Elster
Vice President Of Professional Development, Lisa Marks
Vice President Strategic Capital Planning, Wayne F Magdziarz
Senior Vice President For Academic Affairs, Larry Braskamp
Chairman, Robert L. Parkinson
Vice Chairman, Mary Ann Zollmann
Senior Vice President Finance Of Cfo And Treasurer, William Laird
Treasurer, Susan Bodin
Board Member, Carolyn Saari
Secretary, Carol Grimm
Auditors: DELOITTE & TOUCHE LLP CHICAG

LOCATIONS

HQ: LOYOLA UNIVERSITY OF CHICAGO INC
1032 W SHERIDAN RD, CHICAGO, IL 606601537
Phone: 773 274-3000
Web: WWW.LUC.EDU

PRODUCTS/OPERATIONS

Selected Schools & Colleges
College of Arts and Sciences
Graduate School of Business
Institute of Pastoral Studies
Marcella Niehoff School of Nursing
Quinlan School of Business
School of Communication
School of Continuing and Professional Studies
School of Education
School of Law
School of Social Work
Stritch School of Medicine
The Graduate School

HISTORICAL FINANCIALS
Company Type: Private

Income Statement				FYE: June 30
	REVENUE ($ mil.)	NET INCOME ($ mil.)	NET PROFIT MARGIN	EMPLOYEES
06/18	594	109	18.4%	10,500
06/17	582	109	18.7%	—
06/13	509	87	17.2%	—
06/12	490	74	15.3%	—
Annual Growth	3.3%	6.5%	—	—

2018 Year-End Financials
Return on assets: 5.0%
Return on equity: 6.9%
Current ratio: —

Cash ($ mil.): 70

LUBBOCK COUNTY HOSPITAL DISTRICT

EXECUTIVES

Pres-Ceo, David Allison
Coordinator, Carol Cloud
Coordinator, Ace Garcia
Coordinator, Jayton Zachary
Coordinator, Jillian Edge
Coordinator, Kelsey Thrasher
Chief of Medicine, Werner De Riese
Staff, Elsie Foli
Coordinator, Jeffrey Fuerstenberg
Senior Manager, Andrew Ochoa
Director, Barbara Condren

LOCATIONS

HQ: LUBBOCK COUNTY HOSPITAL DISTRICT
602 INDIANA AVE, LUBBOCK, TX 794153364
Phone: 806 775-8200
Web: WWW.UMCHEALTHSYSTEM.COM

HISTORICAL FINANCIALS
Company Type: Private

Income Statement				FYE: December 31
	REVENUE ($ mil.)	NET INCOME ($ mil.)	NET PROFIT MARGIN	EMPLOYEES
12/16	463	57	12.4%	2,000
12/15	444	49	11.2%	—
12/14*	473	33	7.0%	—
05/05	0	(0)	—	—
Annual Growth	77.6%	—	—	—

*Fiscal year change

2016 Year-End Financials
Return on assets: 8.4%
Return on equity: 9.4%
Current ratio: 5.40

Cash ($ mil.): 141

LUCILE SALTER PACKARD CHILDREN'S HOSPITAL AT STANFORD

EXECUTIVES

Pres-Ceo, Christopher Dawes
Cfo*, Timothy W Carmack
Coordinator, Arlene Sheehan
Coordinator, Sonja Avery
Chief Information Security Off, Auston Davis
Coordinator, Carrie Johnson
Coordinator, Erin Murphy
Coordinator, Jennifer Cctc
Occupational Specia, Quiara Smith
Manager, Anne Badame
Technology Director, Donald Fisher
Auditors: PRICEWATERHOUSECOOPERS LLP BO

LOCATIONS

HQ: LUCILE SALTER PACKARD CHILDREN'S HOSPITAL AT STANFORD
725 WELCH RD, PALO ALTO, CA 943041601
Phone: 650 497-8000
Web: WWW.STANFORDCHILDRENS.ORG

HISTORICAL FINANCIALS
Company Type: Private

Income Statement				FYE: August 31
	REVENUE ($ mil.)	NET INCOME ($ mil.)	NET PROFIT MARGIN	EMPLOYEES
08/18	1,637	22	1.4%	1,100
08/17	1,486	227	15.3%	—
08/16	1,402	157	11.2%	—
08/14	1,135	98	8.7%	—
Annual Growth	9.6%	(30.7%)	—	—

2018 Year-End Financials
Return on assets: 0.6%
Return on equity: 0.9%
Current ratio: 2.00

Cash ($ mil.): 288

LUKOIL PAN AMERICAS, LLC

EXECUTIVES

Ceo, Timothy Bullock
Dir*, Simon Fenner

LOCATIONS

HQ: LUKOIL PAN AMERICAS, LLC
1095 AVE OF THE AMERICAS, NEW YORK, NY 100366797
Phone: 646 562-3600
Web: WWW.LITASCO.COM

HISTORICAL FINANCIALS
Company Type: Private

Income Statement				FYE: December 31
	REVENUE ($ mil.)	NET INCOME ($ mil.)	NET PROFIT MARGIN	EMPLOYEES
12/08	4,745	5	0.1%	58
12/07	4,717	3	0.1%	—
12/06	3,021	23	0.8%	—
12/05	2,788	21	0.8%	—
Annual Growth	19.4%	(37.8%)	—	—

2008 Year-End Financials
Return on assets: —
Return on equity: 0.1%
Current ratio: 0.40

Cash ($ mil.): 1

M. F. A. OIL COMPANY

Many farmers appreciate MFA Oil. The energy cooperative controlled by its 40000 farmer-members produces fuel and lubrication products and manages bulk petroleum and propane plants in the Central and Western US. Operating 140 propane plants the company sells more propane for farm use and home heating than any other company in Missouri. It also operates nearly 100 oil and lubricant bulk plants and serves customers in Arkansas Iowa Kansas and Oklahoma. Additionally the company operates 76 convenience stores under the Break Time brand (in Arkansas and Missouri) more than 160 Petro-Card 24 fueling locations and owns 10 Jiffy Lube and a dozen Big O Tire franchises.

Geographic Reach

MFA Oil serves customers in Arkansas Colorado Kansas Kentucky Indiana Iowa Missouri Nebraska Oklahoma Virginia and Wyoming.

Strategy

While not a pure vertically integrated enterprise over time the cooperative has developed multiple complementary business lines to enable it to respond to a wide range of its members' fuel transportation and food service needs. In this tradition in 2011 MFA Oil teamed up with biofuel developer Aloterra Energy to form MFA Oil Biomass LLC. The partnership aims to help farmers to produce a renewable energy crop that can be used as biomass for an alternative cleaner burning energy supply for use in power generation plants as well as a liquid fuel. In 2011 about 250 farmers had signed letters of intent to grow miscanthus (a perennial grass) on more than 21000 acres as part of this initiative.

Mergers and Acquisitions

Expanding its geographic network in 2013 MFA Oil acquired Kansas-based American Petroleum Marketers which distributes fuel to more than 60 Cenex branded sites along with unbranded fuel in six states.

Company Background

MFA Oil has grown well beyond its Missouri roots where it was founded by farmers in 1929. The company's first bulk plant was located at Wright City Missouri.

EXECUTIVES

Vice President Of Logistics, Larry Ehrman
Auditors: WILLIAMS-KEEPERS LLC COLUMBIA

LOCATIONS

HQ: M. F. A. OIL COMPANY
1 RAY YOUNG DR, COLUMBIA, MO 652013506
Phone: 573 442-0171
Web: WWW.MFAOIL.COM

COMPETITORS

Ag Processing Inc.	Lykins
Green Brick Partners	Shell Oil Products
Green Plains	Valero Energy
Jordan Oil Company	WilcoHess

HISTORICAL FINANCIALS

Company Type: Private

Income Statement   FYE: August 31

	REVENUE ($ mil.)	NET INCOME ($ mil.)	NET PROFIT MARGIN	EMPLOYEES
08/18	1,086	20	1.9%	1,500
08/17	900	8	0.9%	—
08/16	800	24	3.1%	—
08/15	1,045	48	4.6%	—
Annual Growth	1.3%	(24.7%)	—	—

2018 Year-End Financials

Return on assets: 4.7%   Cash ($ mil.): 22
Return on equity: 6.5%
Current ratio: 2.30

MACDONALD MOTT GROUP INC

Hatch Mott MacDonald (HMM) is the consulting engineering subsidiary of Mott MacDonald and offers planning project development analysis design construction management facility maintenance and facility management for all types of infrastructure projects to public and private clients across North America. It specializes in tunnels wastewater systems pipelines rail and transit systems buildings and utilities. Customers are both private companies and municipalities. HMM strategically acquires specialized engineering firms in new regions to expand its service offerings and geographic market reach. Formed in 1996 HHM now boasts a staff of 25000 and has more than 75 offices in the US and Canada.

Geographic Reach

New Jersey-based Hatch Mott MacDonald has offices in about two dozen US states including California Florida Massachusetts New York and Texas as well as in Alberta British Columbia New Brunswick Newfoundland and Labrador Nova Scotia and Ontario Canada.

Strategy

Hatch Mott MacDonald (HMM) continued in 2016 to work on infrastructure and other large projects for public (including municipalities and airports) and private sector clients across North America. Some of its recent projects have included Sacramento's Bradshaw Interceptor Pipeline work for the District of Columbia Water and Sewer Authority the Nipigon River Bridge the Halton Booster Pumping Station the JFK Airport Deicing Facility the Genesee Street ITS Corridor and the New York Harbor Water Siphon Replacement project.

The engineering firm has historically grown by acquiring smaller engineering firms across a variety of specialty practices and regions to expand its service offerings and bolster its expertise.

Mergers and Acquisitions

In 2014 HMM purchased Coast & Harbor Engineering which focuses on protecting and restoring coastlines and developing port and harbor infrastructure. The deal also adds the smaller company's offices in New Orleans (a top market for HMM) San Francisco Austin Delray Beach and Edmonds Washington.

Company Background

In May 2012 the company acquired Canadian consulting specialist Engineering Northwest. The Thunder Bay Ontario-based firm focused on highway municipal water and wastewater engineering and project and construction management services. Also in 2012 HMM extended its reach to New Orleans with the purchase of Lambert Engineers an engineering and architectural firm there. With its extensive infrastructure needs New Orleans was a fertile market for HMM's services and complemented the firm's other Gulf Coast offices from Florida to Texas.

In 2011 HMM acquired Richard P. Arber Associates a professional consulting engineering firm in Lakewood Colorado to expand its water and wastewater practice in the western US. Also that year it purchased North Carolina-based transportation firm Gibson Engineers.

EXECUTIVES

Principal, John Davenport
Owner, Mott MacDonald
Ceo President, Nicholas DeNichilo
Auditors: BDO USA LLP WOODBRIDGE NJ

LOCATIONS

HQ: MACDONALD MOTT GROUP INC
111 WOOD AVE S STE 5, ISELIN, NJ 088302700
Phone: 973 379-3400
Web: WWW.MOTTMAC.COM

PRODUCTS/OPERATIONS

Selected Services

Asset management
Aviation
Environment
Highways & bridges
Information management
Life-safety & security
Model-based Design/BIM
Pipelines
Ports
Project delivery
Rail & transit
Site development
Sustainability
Transportation planning
Tunnels
Wastewater
Water

COMPETITORS

3i Infrastructure	E M C Engineers
Bechtel	Fagen Inc.
Black & Veatch Ltd.	Fluor
Burns and Roe	Lauren Engineers
CDI Engineering Solutions	Sargent & Lundy

HISTORICAL FINANCIALS

Company Type: Private

Income Statement   FYE: December 31

	REVENUE ($ mil.)	NET INCOME ($ mil.)	NET PROFIT MARGIN	EMPLOYEES
12/12	477	27	5.7%	2,500
12/11	440	25	5.8%	—
12/10	374	20	5.5%	—
Annual Growth	13.0%	14.8%	—	—

2012 Year-End Financials

Return on assets: 14.0%   Cash ($ mil.): 25
Return on equity: 33.2%
Current ratio: 1.40

MAGEE-WOMENS HOSPITAL OF UPMC

EXECUTIVES

Pres, Leslie C Davis
Chb*, William Pietragallo
Treas*, Peter Eisenbrandt
SEC*, Claire Williams
Oncology, Margaret V Ragni
Project Coordinator, Meredith Colaizzi
Information Specialist, Michele King
Director, Dan Pototo
Obstetrician Gynecologist, Jamie Wright
Obstetrician Gynecologist, Katherine Cook
Obstetrician Gynecologist, Pamela Moalli

LOCATIONS

HQ: MAGEE-WOMENS HOSPITAL OF UPMC
300 HALKET ST, PITTSBURGH, PA 152133108
Phone: 412 641-1000
Web: WWW.UPMC.COM

HISTORICAL FINANCIALS

Company Type: Private

Income Statement   FYE: June 30

	REVENUE ($ mil.)	NET INCOME ($ mil.)	NET PROFIT MARGIN	EMPLOYEES
06/16	838	92	11.1%	2,300
06/15	823	62	7.6%	—
06/00	7	7	98.8%	—
Annual Growth	33.9%	16.8%	—	—

2016 Year-End Financials

Return on assets: 17.7%   Cash ($ mil.): 1
Return on equity: 19.0%
Current ratio: 9.40

MAGELLAN PIPELINE COMPANY, L.P.

EXECUTIVES

Ptnr-Pres-Ceo, Don Wellendorf
Ptnr-V Pres-Tres,, Jeff Holman
Analyst, Tj Simmons
Facility Maintenance Superviso, Kevan Heil
Senior Technician, Chris Sullivan
Tech, Dan Sotelo
Accounting Staff, Dana Taylor
Director, Doug Chabino
Analyst Senior, Glen Jackson
Area Supervisor, James Bacon
Information Technology Contrac, Kenny Williams

HQ: MAGELLAN PIPELINE COMPANY, L.P.
1 WILLIAMS CTR, TULSA, OK 741720140
Phone: 918 574-7000
Web: WWW.MAGELLANLP.COM

HISTORICAL FINANCIALS

Company Type: Private

Income Statement				FYE: December 31
	REVENUE ($ mil.)	NET INCOME ($ mil.)	NET PROFIT MARGIN	EMPLOYEES
12/17	828	396	47.9%	435
12/16	911	339	37.2%	—
Annual Growth	(9.1%)	17.0%		

2017 Year-End Financials

Return on assets: 18.5%   Cash ($ mil.): 15
Return on equity: 20.9%
Current ratio: 0.60

MAIMONIDES MEDICAL CENTER

Maimonides Medical Center a not-for-profit hospital offers emergency medicine surgical procedures psychiatric treatment and other traditional hospital services to patients in Brooklyn New York. It has more than 710 beds and more than 70 subspecialty treatment programs for a range of conditions including cancer cardiac stroke neurological pediatric and women's health ailments. It also operates outpatient family health and specialty clinics. Maimonides Medical Center is an independent teaching hospital that serves as a training facility for SUNY-Brooklyn St. George's University and other schools.

Financial Performance

In fiscal 2015 revenue remained flat at $1.1 billion compared to 2014. Although net patient service revenue rose 1% the hospital saw a 23% decline in "other" revenue. Net income fell 78% to $11 million that year as expenses rose; the center also reported accrued benefits liabilities to be recognized in future periods.

Despite the decline in profits operating cash flow increased 203% to $33 million primarily due to a change in receivables for patient fare.

Strategy

Maimonides Medical Center works to keep its utilization rates up (the number of patients it sees) and make itself attractive to doctors by making capital investments in its facilities and technology systems on a regular basis. In 2015 it established a partnership with North Shore-LIJ Health System (now Northwell) through which the systems will share services infrastructure and expertise; Northshore will also provide Maimonides with funding.

The hospital uses a fully-implemented electronic health record (EHR) system that includes a computerized physician order entry system (CPOE) that reduces prescription errors and a picture archival communications system (PACS) to store digital radiology images. The use of such technology is becoming increasingly tied to how the government reimburses hospitals for the services they provide especially in the new health care reform laws.

Company Background

Maimonides Medical Center traces its roots to the New Utrecht Dispensary which opened in 1911. The medical center later merged with Beth Moses and United Israel Zion hospitals in 1947. It is named after 12th-century philosopher Rabbi Moshe Ben Maimon.

EXECUTIVES

Evp And Cfo, Robert Naldi
Vp Management Information Systems And Cio, Walter J. Fahey
Executive Vice President Clinical Affairs & Affiliations, David I. Cohen
Evp And Coo, Dominick Stanzione
President And Ceo, Kenneth Gibbs
Senior Vice President, Karen Nelson
Senior Vice President, Thomas Doherty
Medical Director, Elie Hamaoui
Assistant Vice President Heart And Vascular Center, Lorraine Carroll
Avp Mis, Nancy Daurio
Assistant Vice President, William Howe
Vice President Physician Enterprise, Gail Simhon
Vice President Support Services, Bob Cruz
Assistant Vice President Human Resources, Paul Stuart
Vice President For Legal Affairs, Anthony Mancuso
Vice President Of Research And Development, Rich Casazza
Director Of Hospitalist Service, Ping Zhou
Interim Vp Human Resources, Mary Cataudella
Director Of Pharmacy And Compliance, Neal Neumann
Medical Director, Robert Adler
Vp Analytics And Business Operations, Rob Cimino
Chairman, Eugene J. Keilin
Secretary, Rosalyn Levin
Secretary, Larisa Zmoyro
Medical Secretary, Elizabeth Bowen
Vice Chairman Orthopedics, Afshin Razi

LOCATIONS

HQ: MAIMONIDES MEDICAL CENTER
4802 10TH AVE, BROOKLYN, NY 112192916
Phone: 718 581-0598
Web: WWW.MAIMONIDESMED.ORG

PRODUCTS/OPERATIONS

2014 Sales

	$ mil.	% of total
Net patient revenue less provision for bad debts	1,001	95
Net assets released from restrictions	0	-
Other revenue	48	5
Total	**1,051**	**100**

Selected Services

Adult Primary Care
Ambulatory Health Services
Bay Parkway Multi-Specialty
Manfredi Family Health Center
Newkirk Family Health Center
Outpatient Eye Clinic
Pediatric Primary Care
Primary Health Services
Sheepshead Bay
Women's Primary Care Services

COMPETITORS

Beth Israel Medical Center
Bronx-Lebanon Hospital
Brookdale University Hospital
Brooklyn Hospital Center
Catholic Healthcare System
Continuum Health Partners
Jamaica Hospital Medical Center
Kingsbrook Jewish Medical Center
Long Island College Hospital
Lutheran HealthCare
Montefiore Medical
New York City Health and Hospitals
New York Methodist Hospital
NewYork-Presbyterian Hospital
North Shore University Hospital
SUNY Downstate
Staten Island University Hospital
Wyckoff Heights Medical Center

HISTORICAL FINANCIALS

Company Type: Private

Income Statement				FYE: December 31
	REVENUE ($ mil.)	NET INCOME ($ mil.)	NET PROFIT MARGIN	EMPLOYEES
12/17	958	19	2.0%	6,382
12/16	940	20	2.2%	—
12/15	890	(2)		—
12/14	884	10	1.2%	—
Annual Growth	2.7%	23.2%	—	—

2017 Year-End Financials

Return on assets: 1.5%   Cash ($ mil.): 16
Return on equity: 7.1%
Current ratio: 1.50

MAIN LINE HEALTH SYSTEM

Main Line Health is a not-for-profit network that includes four acute care hospitals a drug and alcohol recovery treatment center home care outpatient centers a physician network and a biomedical research organization all serving the greater Philadelphia area. Its hospitals — Lankenau Medical Center Bryn Mawr Hospital Paoli Hospital and Riddle Hospital — are accredited as primary stroke care centers comprehensive breast centers and chest pain centers. Other specialties include diabetes and endocrinology orthopedics and cardiovascular care. Bryn Mawr Hospital offers residency programs in family practice radiology and surgical podiatry. Main Line Health was founded in 1985.

EXECUTIVES

Pres-Ceo, Jack Lynch
Sr V Pres*, Thomas Mendicino
Hris Analyst, Michelle Massaro
Recruiter, Connie Samulewicz
Manager, Dominic Kayatta
Senior Recruiter, Krystin Walker
Benefits Administrator, Mark Wallace
Manager, Annemarie Cellucci
Lead Recruiter, Cheryl Remolde
Manger Graphic Designer, Damien Lubeski
Recruiter, Katie Kealey

LOCATIONS

HQ: MAIN LINE HEALTH SYSTEM
240 N RADNOR CHESTER RD, RADNOR, PA 190875170
Phone: 610 225-6200

COMPETITORS

Abington Memorial Hospital
Albert Einstein Healthcare Network
Crozer-Keystone Health System
LVHN
Lancaster General
Memorial Hospital (PA)
Mercy Health System
North Philadelphia Health System
TUHS
University of Pennsylvania Health System
Virtua Health

HISTORICAL FINANCIALS

Company Type: Private

Income Statement				FYE: June 30
	REVENUE ($ mil.)	NET INCOME ($ mil.)	NET PROFIT MARGIN	EMPLOYEES
06/18	1,742	267	15.4%	17,485
06/17	1,695	51	3.0%	—
06/16	1,660	(130)	—	—
06/15	1,586	121	7.6%	—
Annual Growth	3.2%	30.2%	—	—

2018 Year-End Financials

Return on assets: 7.1%   Cash ($ mil.): 113
Return on equity: 9.7%
Current ratio: 2.30

MAIN LINE HOSPITALS, INC.

Bryn Mawr Hospital a member of the Main Line not-for-profit health network is an acute care facility providing a variety of inpatient and outpatient services in the western suburbs of Philadelphia. With some 320 beds Bryn Mawr Hospital is recognized nationally for its orthopedic program. Founded in 1893 by Dr. George Gerhard the teaching hospital also provides cancer cardiac surgical pediatric reproductive health diagnostic imaging psychiatric bariatric and wound care services. The hospital also operates the Main Line Health Center outpatient facility (which includes a comprehensive breast center) in Newtown Square.

EXECUTIVES

Medical Director Of The Main Line Health Stroke Program, Gary Friday
Vice President Of Finance And Treasurer, Michael Bouongiono
Vice President Planning And Business Development, Joel Port
Vice President And Chief Medical Information Officer, Harm Scherpbier
Director Of Nursing, Michael Buongiorno
Vice President Management, Phillip Kim

LOCATIONS

HQ: MAIN LINE HOSPITALS, INC.
130 S BRYN MAWR AVE, BRYN MAWR, PA 190103121
Phone: 610 526-3000
Web: WWW.BRYNMAWRUROLOGY.COM

COMPETITORS

Abington Memorial Hospital
Albert Einstein Healthcare Network
Christiana Care
Crozer-Keystone Health System
Doylestown Hospital
Memorial Hospital (PA)
Moses Taylor Hospital
North Philadelphia Health System
Tenet Healthcare
University of Pennsylvania Health System
Virtua Memorial

HISTORICAL FINANCIALS

Company Type: Private

Income Statement				FYE: June 30
	REVENUE ($ mil.)	NET INCOME ($ mil.)	NET PROFIT MARGIN	EMPLOYEES
06/18	1,193	100	8.4%	5,840
06/16	327	36	11.0%	—
Annual Growth	90.9%	67.0%	—	—

2018 Year-End Financials

Return on assets: 3.5%   Cash ($ mil.): 68
Return on equity: 4.4%
Current ratio: 4.70

MAINEGENERAL MEDICAL CENTER

EXECUTIVES

Ceo, Chuck Hays
Princ*, Paul Stein
Officer*, Charles Hays
Supervisor, Joy Leach
Administrative Assistant, Chris Hoffman
Senior Network Engineer, Dan Ottman
Director of Communications, Paul Tobey
Director, Michael Koziol
Director of Finance, Gregory Pizzo
Oncologist, David Frost
Doctor, Rebecca Brackett
Auditors: BAKER NEWMAN & NOYES PORTLAN

LOCATIONS

HQ: MAINEGENERAL MEDICAL CENTER
35 MEDICAL CENTER PKWY, AUGUSTA, ME
043308160
Phone: 207 626-1289
Web: WWW.MAINEGENERAL.ORG

HISTORICAL FINANCIALS

Company Type: Private

Income Statement				FYE: June 30
	REVENUE ($ mil.)	NET INCOME ($ mil.)	NET PROFIT MARGIN	EMPLOYEES
06/18	476	13	2.8%	2,200
06/13	378	40	10.6%	—
06/11	372	39	10.7%	—
06/10	336	10	3.2%	—
Annual Growth	4.5%	3.0%	—	—

2018 Year-End Financials

Return on assets: 2.2%   Cash ($ mil.): 20
Return on equity: 5.7%
Current ratio: 2.50

MAINEHEALTH

Maine Medical Center (MMC) makes healing happen for the residents of northern New England. Part of MaineHealth the not-for-profit medical center consists of a tertiary care community hospital The Barbara Bush Children's Hospital and outpatient clinics. Specialty services include cancer care geriatrics emergency medicine cardiovascular care rehabilitation neurology orthopedics and women's health. Through its partnership with the Tufts University School of Medicine the 640-bed teaching hospital provides a variety of medical education and training programs. MMC also conducts research through the Maine Medical Center Research Institute. The medical center was founded in 1874 with 40 beds.

Operations

MMC boasts a large ever-expanding outpatient segment that provides day surgery cardiac catheterization laboratory services and rehabilitation services. It also operates about three dozen outpatient clinics. MMC provides preventive and consultation services including the MMC Diabetes Center the AIDS Consultation Service and the Center for Lipids and Cardiovascular Health.

MMC is expanding the surgical facilities at its main campus. Due for completion in 2015 the medical center embarked on a $40-million expansion plan that will add five modern operating rooms including a cardiac hybrid operating room and 20 perioperative spaces for patient prep and recovery.

The medical center is one of the largest employers in its service territory with a workforce of some 6500. Its Maine Medical Partners physician organization maintains about 175 doctors who provide care at some 30 primary and specialty care centers. MMC also provides more than 20% of charity care for uninsured or underinsured patients in the state.

Geographic Reach

Located in Portland the MMC serves the northern New England area.

Strategy

In keeping with its reputation of being technologically forward the hospital operates a Telestroke Network that provides area residents with around-the-clock access to MMC's neurology and ER physicians. The Telestroke Network is a form of telemedicine an increasingly popular way of expanding access to care by allowing patients to "visit" physicians either telephonically or via streaming web and video. MMC is also one of a growing number of teaching hospitals to use high-tech simulation rooms to train medical students.

To improve the quality of care MMC is enacting evidence-based medicine programs. Through such programs hospitals seek to lower medical expenses and improve patient outcomes through data exchange systems that allow physicians to review best practices in specific medical fields. The hospital is also looking to expand its research programs by partnering with other area medical R&D firms.

EXECUTIVES

Assistant Vice President Benefits, Keith Kolodgie
President And Ceo, Richard W. (Rich) Petersen
Senior Vice President Chief Information Officer, Barry Blumenfeld
Svp Planning And Marketing Maine Medical Center And Mainehealth, Mark A. Harris
Vp Medical And Academic Affairs; Chief Medical Officer And Academic Dean Tufts University School Of Medicine Medical School Program, Peter W. Bates
Evp And Coo, Jeffrey D. (Jeff) Sanders
President Medical Staff, M. Parker Roberts

President And A Principal Of Cbre|boulos
  Property Management, Morris Fisher
President Mainehealth, William L. Caron
Vice President For Development, Susan Doliner
Medical Director, Kate Zimmerman
Vice President Of Strategy And Business
  Development, Edward Farrell
Senior Vice President Of Finance, Lugene Inzana
Vice President Finance, Jeffrey Kirby
Nursing Director, Deborah Bachand
Vice President Revenue Cycle, Chausse Paul
Medical Director Of Care Coordination, Chris
  Wellins
Associate Vice President Of Nursing, Kathleen
  Hale
Nursing Director, Peggy Doliner
Vice President, Eric Tweedie
Medical Director, Tammi Schaeffer
Vice President Cardiovascular Services, Tim Kafer
Medical Director, Mark Fulton
Vice President Global Information Technology,
  Belinda Broome
Vice President, Melissa Norton
Chairman, Christopher W. Emmons
Secretary, Kay Mullen
Department Secretary, Andrea Fletcher
Auditors: KPMG LLP BOSTON MA

LOCATIONS

HQ: MAINEHEALTH
  22 BRAMHALL ST, PORTLAND, ME 041023134
Phone: 207 662-0111
Web: WWW.MAINEHEALTH.ORG

PRODUCTS/OPERATIONS

Selected Specialty Centers
Cancer Institute
Cardiovascular Institute
Emergency Medicine
Family Birth Center
Joint Replacement Center
Neuroscience Institute
The Barbara Bush Children's Hospital

COMPETITORS

Eastern Maine	MaineGeneral Health
Healthcare Systems	Mercy Health System of
Franklin Community	Maine
Health Network	St. Joseph Healthcare
Maine Coast Memorial	
Hospital	

HISTORICAL FINANCIALS

Company Type: Private

Income Statement				FYE: September 30
	REVENUE ($ mil.)	NET INCOME ($ mil.)	NET PROFIT MARGIN	EMPLOYEES
09/18	2,523	205	8.2%	2,000
09/17	1,236	152	12.4%	—
09/16	1,126	3	0.3%	—
09/15	1,023	(39)	—	—
Annual Growth	35.1%			

2018 Year-End Financials

Return on assets: 6.6%   Cash ($ mil.): 353
Return on equity: 11.7%
Current ratio: 3.20

MAINLINE INFORMATION SYSTEMS, INC.

EXECUTIVES

Chm, Rick Kearney
Pres-Ceo, John McCarthy
Exec V Pres-Sls, Eric Mann
V Pres-Services, Jeff Dobbelaere
Cfo, Joe Elebash
V Pres-Ops, Krista Campbell
Gen Counsel, Brian Showman
V Pres-Hr, Beth Oberacker
Senior Sales Representative, Amanda Lockwood
Inside Sales Representative We, Amy Beason
Senior Engineer, Andy Foster
Auditors: KPMG LLP JACKSONVILLE FL

LOCATIONS

HQ: MAINLINE INFORMATION SYSTEMS, INC.
  1700 SUMMIT LAKE DR, TALLAHASSEE, FL
  323177942
Phone: 850 219-5000
Web: WWW.MAINLINE.COM

HISTORICAL FINANCIALS

Company Type: Private

Income Statement				FYE: December 31
	REVENUE ($ mil.)	NET INCOME ($ mil.)	NET PROFIT MARGIN	EMPLOYEES
12/12	520	35	6.8%	568
12/11	567	26	4.6%	—
12/10	576	26	4.7%	
Annual Growth	(5.0%)	15.1%	—	—

2012 Year-End Financials

Return on assets: 17.4%   Cash ($ mil.): 18
Return on equity: 58.8%
Current ratio: 1.50

MANAGEMENT & TRAINING CORPORATION

Management & Training Corporation (MTC) prepares prison inmates for re-entry into society. It provides a variety of academic vocational and social-skills training in rehabilitation-oriented private prisons. Its holistic education model offers programs to help inmates avoid substance abuse as they also boost their engagement in community service find work and increase their cognitive skills. As part of its services MTC operates about two dozen correctional facilities in eight states through a contract with the Department of Labor. The company also operates Job Corps centers and provides healthcare-related services to correctional facilities.

Operations

MTC operates through four divisions: Correctional Education & Training MTC Medical and Economic & Social Development. Its correctional division operates facilities that house more than 31100 inmates and is one of the largest US correctional contractors for the Department of Labor. The Education & Training division trains some 14000 young adults each year at 23 Job Corps centers.

The company's MTC Medical unit provides subcontracted healthcare services to correctional facilities by employing a range of medical providers including dentists optometrists psychiatrists and psychologists and physicians. The Economic & Social Development division which offers research retraining and vocational training through contracts with other organizations has provided vocational training to citizens in Iraq and research and retraining efforts in China Haiti Mongolia Southern Sudan Tunisia Pakistan Indonesia Jordan and Palestine.

The company trains its supervisors senior managers and executives through its MTC Corporate University while its MTC Institute performs research into forming best practices related to addressing issues facing those who work with Job Corps youth and prison inmates.

Geographic Reach

The company's main offices are located in Centerville Utah and it has satellite centers in Georgia Texas and Washington DC. MTC operates through more than 60 contracts in about 20 states including correctional facility contracts in Arizona California Florida Idaho Ohio New Mexico Mississippi and Texas.

MTC operates internationally providing governments NGOs ministries and private entities with customized training programs designed to help develop workforces. Its international unit has assisted clients in Africa Asia Australia the Middle East and North America.

Sales and Marketing

In addition to the Department of Labor the company has held contracts with the US Agency for International Development the African Development Bank UNICEF and other organizations. It also serves state agencies such as the Texas Department of Criminal Justice.

Strategy

MTC expands by recruiting and retaining quality educators health professionals and international consultants. To maximize its employees' potential the company conducts leadership development programs for all of its employees. MTC also expands by adding new contracts with state correctional agencies.

Working with MTC in 2014 Georgia's Wilkinson County Correctional Facility started a new program to help inmates deal with anger issues. The following year MTC was granted a contract to operate the Polk Secure Adult Detention Center in Livingston Texas.

Company Background

MRC was founded in 1981.

EXECUTIVES

President, R. Scott Marquardt
Vice President Corrections Marketing, Mike Murphy
Senior Vice President Business Development And Administration, Sergio Molina
Vice President, Lowder Korey
Chairman, Robert Marquardt
Secretary Programs, Shondra Hampton
Auditors: KPMG LLP SALT LAKE CITY UTAH

LOCATIONS

HQ: MANAGEMENT & TRAINING CORPORATION
  500 N MARKET PLACE DR # 100, CENTERVILLE, UT
  840141711
Phone: 801 693-2600
Web: WWW.MTCTRAINS.COM

PRODUCTS/OPERATIONS

Selected Services
Communicate through formal and informal channels
Develop custom training for students clients & offenders
Manage facilities
Provide community connections
Provide data solutions

COMPETITORS

Avalon Correctional Services
Community Education Centers
Conmed Healthcare
Corizon
Corrections Corporation of America
G4S
GEO Group
MHM Services
Res-Care
Wexford Health

HISTORICAL FINANCIALS

Company Type: Private

Income Statement				FYE: December 31
	REVENUE ($ mil.)	NET INCOME ($ mil.)	NET PROFIT MARGIN	EMPLOYEES
12/17	667	49	7.5%	9,500
12/15	753	30	4.0%	—
12/13	735	50	6.9%	—
12/12	704	45	6.5%	—
Annual Growth	(1.1%)	1.8%		—

2017 Year-End Financials
Return on assets: 20.3%   Cash ($ mil.): 2
Return on equity: 35.5%
Current ratio: 1.40

MANAGEMENT-ILA MANAGED HEALTH CARE TRUST FUND

EXECUTIVES

MGT, Jason Cury
Accounting Director, Robin Csabon
Auditors: DESENA & COMPANY CPAS EAST HA

LOCATIONS

HQ: MANAGEMENT-ILA MANAGED HEALTH CARE TRUST FUND
111 BROADWAY FL 5, NEW YORK, NY 100061901
Phone: 212 766-5700
Web: WWW.MILAMHCTF.COM

HISTORICAL FINANCIALS

Company Type: Private

Income Statement				FYE: December 31
	REVENUE ($ mil.)	NET INCOME ($ mil.)	NET PROFIT MARGIN	EMPLOYEES
12/17	675	64	9.6%	3
12/14	492	(39)	—	—
12/13	491	24	5.0%	—
Annual Growth	8.3%	27.3%		—

2017 Year-End Financials
Return on assets: 6.9%   Cash ($ mil.): 28
Return on equity: 7.5%
Current ratio: 1.90

MANN+HUMMEL FILTRATION TECHNOLOGY INTERMEDIATE HOLDINGS INC.

EXECUTIVES

Pres-Ceo, Keith A Wilson
Chb, James S McElya
Sr V Pres-Cfo-Treas, Steven P Klueg
CIO, Karl J Westrick
Sr V Pres Hr, Kay Teixeira
Sr Vpres-General Counsel-Sec, David E Sturgess
Auditors: DELOITTE & TOUCHE LLP CHARLOT

LOCATIONS

HQ: MANN+HUMMEL FILTRATION TECHNOLOGY INTERMEDIATE HOLDINGS INC.
1 WIX WAY, GASTONIA, NC 280546142
Phone: 704 869-3300
Web: WWW.MANN-HUMMEL.COM

HISTORICAL FINANCIALS

Company Type: Private

Income Statement				FYE: December 31
	REVENUE ($ mil.)	NET INCOME ($ mil.)	NET PROFIT MARGIN	EMPLOYEES
12/15	899	(72)	—	5,577
12/14	1,396	82	5.9%	—
12/13	1,361	10	0.7%	—
12/12	1,453	(102)	—	—
Annual Growth	(14.8%)	—	—	—

2015 Year-End Financials
Return on assets: (-12.2%)   Cash ($ mil.): 28
Return on equity: —
Current ratio: 0.90

MAP INTERNATIONAL (INC.)

EXECUTIVES

Pres/Ceo, Steve Stirling
Int Pres-Ceo*, Chok-Pin Foo
Cfo*, Daniel C Reed
Chm*, Immanuel Phangaraj
VCM*, Edwin G Corr
SEC*, Ingrid M Mail
Asst SEC*, Carrene G Rosser
Coordinator, Connie Reed
Consultant, Alan Ichikawa
Deputy Director, Allen Craig
Director, James Sirleaf
Auditors: CAPIN CROUSE LAWRENCEVILLE G

LOCATIONS

HQ: MAP INTERNATIONAL (INC.)
315 W PNCE DE LEON AVE, BRUNSWICK, GA 31520
Phone: 912 265-6010
Web: WWW.MAP.ORG

HISTORICAL FINANCIALS

Company Type: Private

Income Statement				FYE: September 30
	REVENUE ($ mil.)	NET INCOME ($ mil.)	NET PROFIT MARGIN	EMPLOYEES
09/18	575	11	2.1%	200
09/17	598	(40)	—	—
09/16	606	87	14.5%	—
09/15	547	60	11.1%	—
Annual Growth	1.7%	(41.7%)		—

2018 Year-End Financials
Return on assets: 6.0%   Cash ($ mil.): 2
Return on equity: 6.0%
Current ratio: 189.10

MARIETTA AREA HEALTH CARE INC

EXECUTIVES

Exec Dir-Pres, Larry Unroe
Administrator, Susan Crozier

LOCATIONS

HQ: MARIETTA AREA HEALTH CARE INC
401 MATTHEW ST, MARIETTA, OH 457501635
Phone: 740 374-1400
Web: WWW.MHSYSTEM.ORG

HISTORICAL FINANCIALS

Company Type: Private

Income Statement				FYE: September 30
	REVENUE ($ mil.)	NET INCOME ($ mil.)	NET PROFIT MARGIN	EMPLOYEES
09/18	472	10	2.3%	15
09/17	448	5	1.1%	—
09/12	267	(0)	—	—
09/11	271	1	0.6%	—
Annual Growth	8.2%	31.0%		—

2018 Year-End Financials
Return on assets: 2.2%   Cash ($ mil.): 26
Return on equity: 7.3%
Current ratio: 1.20

MARIN GENERAL HOSPITAL

Serving Northern California's Marin County Marin General Hospital is the county's largest acute-care health care facility with some 235 beds. Opened in 1952 Marin General Hospital has been a member of Sutter Health since 1996. It operates the Marin Cancer Institute the Haynes Cardiovascular Institute the Surgery Center of Marin and The Institute for Health & Healing which provides holistic care within the hospital setting. Other services include adult psychiatric care a level III trauma center a family birthing center neonatal intensive care pediatrics and a cardiac catheterization lab.

EXECUTIVES

Director Of Him And Patient Access, Celia Lenson
Director Of Nursing, Karin Reese
Medical Director Inpatient Psychiatric Services, Stephen Allison
Medical Director, Adrienne M Fratini

LOCATIONS

HQ: MARIN GENERAL HOSPITAL
250 BON AIR RD, KENTFIELD, CA 949041784
Phone: 415 925-7000

COMPETITORS

California Pacific Medical Center
Dignity Health
The Palo Alto Medical Foundation
UCSF Medical

HISTORICAL FINANCIALS
Company Type: Private

Income Statement				FYE: December 31
	REVENUE ($ mil.)	NET INCOME ($ mil.)	NET PROFIT MARGIN	EMPLOYEES
12/18	470	4	0.9%	1,100
12/17	370	17	4.8%	—
12/16	350	6	1.8%	—
12/15	342	20	6.1%	—
Annual Growth	11.1%	(41.6%)	—	—

2018 Year-End Financials
Return on assets: 0.8%   Cash ($ mil.): 87
Return on equity: 2.1%
Current ratio: 4.60

MARINA DISTRICT DEVELOPMENT COMPANY, LLC

EXECUTIVES

Pres-Coo, Tom Ballance
MBR, Bob Boughner
MBR, Auggie Cipollini
V Pres of Fin, Hugh Turner
Executive Officer, Cassie Fireman
Manager, Colleen Hermann
Corporate Communications Staff, Kathy Mick
Vice-President, Signe Huff
Manager, David Powell
Manager, Sarah Kimble
Director, Jennifer Bowen

LOCATIONS

HQ: MARINA DISTRICT DEVELOPMENT COMPANY, LLC
1 BORGATA WAY, ATLANTIC CITY, NJ 084011946
Phone: 609 317-1000
Web: WWW.THEBORGATA.COM

HISTORICAL FINANCIALS
Company Type: Private

Income Statement				FYE: December 31
	REVENUE ($ mil.)	NET INCOME ($ mil.)	NET PROFIT MARGIN	EMPLOYEES
12/10	738	44	6.0%	7,000
12/09	777	108	13.9%	—
12/08	830	83	10.0%	—
Annual Growth	(5.7%)	(27.1%)	—	—

2010 Year-End Financials
Return on assets: 3.1%   Cash ($ mil.): 42
Return on equity: 9.6%
Current ratio: 0.80

MARITZ HOLDINGS INC.

Maritz Holdings designs employee incentive and reward programs including incentive travel rewards and customer loyalty programs. The company also plans corporate trade shows and events and offers traditional market research services such as the creation of product launch campaigns. Its programs are designed to help its clients improve workforce quality and customer satisfaction. The company operates through a number of subsidiaries including Maritz Motivation Solutions (services for marketing sales HR) MaritzCX (customer experience) Maritz Global Events (meeting and event industry professionals). The company is owned by Steve Maritz.

Strategy

One of Maritz's competitive strengths is its widely diversified customer base which makes it less susceptible to regional or industry-specific economic downturns. Its customers come from large and small businesses in the automotive financial services health care retail pharmaceutical telecommunications and professional and business services industries.

From time to time the company also makes acquisitions to strengthen its offerings to keep its competitive edge.

EXECUTIVES

Chairman And Ceo, W. Stephen (Steve) Maritz, age 62
President And Coo, Dennis Hummel
Cfo, Rick Ramos
President Of Maritz Travel Company, David Peckinpaugh
Senior Vice President Sales And Marketing, Charlie Ferbet
Vice President Human Resources, David Estes
Vice President Managing Director, Alfredo Legoretta
Vice President And Managing Consultant For Channel Effectiveness Practice, Mike Spellecy
Senior Vice President And Corporate Controller, Holly Francois
Vice President, Mike Mcclernon
Vice President Of Sales And Marketing, Carrie Nolan
Division Vice President, Kari Mcgraw
Vice President Group Business Manager, Terry Erwin
Vice President And Corporate Real Estate And Property Services, Mark Alspaw
Vice President Experience Design, Greg Bogue
Vice President Financial Shared Services, Gwen Sommerville

Vice President Global Business Manager, Joel Barone
Vice President Corporate Controller, Greg Dunn
Vice President Major Account Sales, Bill Moulder
Vice President Corporate Infrastructure Team Solutions, Jason Hampton
Vice President Of Engagement Marketing, Jen Hunter
Division Vice President, Kimberly Clark
Vice President, Dave Harwood
Vp Of Business Development, Jason Mauser
Board Member, Karen Staten
Board Member, Debbie Juntti
Auditors: KPMG LLP ST LOUIS MO

LOCATIONS

HQ: MARITZ HOLDINGS INC.
1375 N HIGHWAY DR, FENTON, MO 630990001
Phone: 636 827-4000
Web: WWW.MARITZ.COM

PRODUCTS/OPERATIONS

Selected Services
Marketing Research
  Custom marketing research
  Customer satisfaction and customer value analysis
  Data collection (focus groups telephone interviews)
  Maritz Polls and Maritz Research Reports
  Syndicated buyer research
  Telecommunications research
Performance Improvement
  Communications
  e-Learning
  Fulfillment
  Internet consulting
  Loyalty marketing
  Measurement and feedback
  Rewards and recognition
Travel
  Consulting services
  Corporate travel management
  Group travel services
  Travel award programs

COMPETITORS

Franklin Covey
Gallup
GiftCertificates.com
Harris Interactive
IMS Health
Information Resources Inc.
J.D. Power
JTB Corp.
Kantar Group
Motivcom
Nielsen
ORC International

HISTORICAL FINANCIALS
Company Type: Private

Income Statement				FYE: March 31
	REVENUE ($ mil.)	NET INCOME ($ mil.)	NET PROFIT MARGIN	EMPLOYEES
03/17	1,217	(30)	—	4,646
03/16	1,274	(16)	—	—
03/13	1,256	42	3.3%	—
03/12	1,155	47	4.1%	—
Annual Growth	1.1%	—	—	—

2017 Year-End Financials
Return on assets: (-4.3%)   Cash ($ mil.): 139
Return on equity: (-53.1%)
Current ratio: 0.80

MARQUETTE UNIVERSITY

A member of the Association of Jesuit Colleges and Universities Marquette University provides undergraduate graduate and professional courses and programs. It specializes in business engineering arts and sciences nursing law dentistry and other fields. The university offers undergraduates some 75 majors and 65 minors and post-graduate students about 50 doctoral and master's degree programs. With an enrollment of more than 11700 students Marquette University boasts a student/faculty ratio of 14:1. Its student population consists of students from all 50 US states and nearly 70 countries. Founded in 1881 the university is named after French missionary explorer Father Jacques Marquette.

Operations
Marquette University an independent coeducational and not-for-profit institution of higher learning and research consists of a dozen separate colleges and schools.

Geographic Reach
Based in Milwaukee Wisconsin the Marquette University campus attracts students across the nation and from nearly 70 countries worldwide.

Financial Performance
The educational institution logged a marginal 1% increase in revenue in fiscal 2012 as compared to 2011 due to rising tuition and fees contributions government and private grants and endowment income used in operations. Net income during the same reporting period dropped some 90% thanks to increases in operating expenses and declines in endowment gains in excess of the amount designated for current operations (net other).

Strategy
To boost its healthcare presence the Marquette University College of Nursing opened the Wheaton Franciscan Healthcare Center for Clinical Simulation in late 2012. The facility features a six-bed hospital suite with a pair of intensive care rooms two medical surgical rooms one pediatrics room and one labor and delivery suite.

EXECUTIVES

Vp Finance, John Lamb
Executive Vice President Learning And Development, Christopher Longstreet
Vice President Technology, Alice Gormley
Vice President, Rachael Hefel
Associate Vice President For Research And Innovation Research Associate Professor, Carmel Ruffolo
Associate Vice President University Advancement, Paul Milakovich
Vice President, Kendra Jorandby
Vice President Of Communication, Stephanie Cleary
Vice President Student Affairs, Andrew J Thon
Evp For Operations And Interim Vp For University Advancement, Dave Lawlor
Vice President Of Recruitment, Chris Alaimo
Associate Department Chair, Robert Paxton
Vice President, Chris Miller
Vice President Information Technology, Gregg Tushaus
Vice President Of Provo Academic Affairs, John Su
Managing Director Annual Giving, Sara Harvey
Secretary, Joe Foti
Secretary, Greg Merkel
Auditors: KPMG LLP MILWAUKEE WI

LOCATIONS
HQ: MARQUETTE UNIVERSITY
1250 W WISCONSIN AVE, MILWAUKEE, WI 532332225
Phone: 414 288-7250
Web: WWW.MARQUETTE.EDU

PRODUCTS/OPERATIONS

Selected Schools and Colleges
College of Business Administration
College of Education
College of Engineering
College of Health Sciences
College of Nursing
College of Professional Studies
Graduate School
Graduate School of Management
Helen Way Klingler College of Arts and Sciences
J. William and Mary Diederich College of Communications
Law School
School of Dentistry

HISTORICAL FINANCIALS
Company Type: Private

Income Statement				FYE: June 30
	REVENUE ($ mil.)	NET INCOME ($ mil.)	NET PROFIT MARGIN	EMPLOYEES
06/18	463	57	12.4%	3,000
06/17	434	67	15.4%	—
06/15	548	48	8.8%	—
06/13	391	37	9.5%	—
Annual Growth	3.4%	9.2%		

2018 Year-End Financials
Return on assets: 3.9% Cash ($ mil.): 63
Return on equity: 5.2%
Current ratio: —

MARSHFIELD CLINIC HEALTH SYSTEM, INC.

Marshfield Clinic Health System (MCHS) is a private group medical practice that operates more than 50 medical locations across Wisconsin. The network provides primary secondary and tertiary care through its more than 700 physicians who represent about 80 medical specialties. Through three hospitals — Marshfield Medical Center Flambeau Hospital and Lakeview Medical Center — and dozens of clinics MCHS annually serves hundreds of thousands of patients and handles millions of patient encounters. Other parts of the network include Marshfield Labs and Security Health Plan of Wisconsin as well as medical education and research organizations.

Operations
MCHS's Security Health Plan of Wisconsin provides a variety of health insurance options to more than 230000 members in much of central northern and western Wisconsin. Marshfield Labs is one of the largest private full-service laboratory systems in the nation conducting clinical and veterinary lab work research testing and toxicology services and providing lab student education.

The flagship Marshfield Medical Center is a 500-bed hospital that features a Level II trauma center a children's hospital and more than 80 medical specialties.

Flambeau Hospital is a small Critical Access Hospital and provides 24-hour care emergency ambulance services and home health and hospice service. Flambeau Hospital is jointly sponsored by Ministry Health Care and Marshfield Clinic.

Lakeview Medical Center is a 40-bed not-for-profit community hospital and provides 24-hour care and emergency ambulance services.

Marshfield Clinic runs some 50 general and specialty medical clinics and dental offices in its service territory. It also has an outreach services program that collaborates with 1200 medical sites to provide care in surrounding regions.

The Marshfield Clinic Education Foundation programs for medical school graduates include internal medicine pediatrics dermatology and surgery. MCHS's research division Marshfield Clinic Research Institute focuses on clinical research agricultural health and safety human genetics epidemiology and biomedical informatics.

Geographic Reach
MCHS operates about 50 clinic locations and two hospitals in central western and northern Wisconsin. Its main hospital campuses are located in Park Falls and Rice Lake.

Sales and Marketing
Features of MCHS's Security Health Plan include contacting members through reminder mailings and personal phone calls to aid with their health maintenance. Additionally affiliated home health nurses visit members at home or in the hospital to answer their questions about their medications or care and to provide needed resources for their recuperation.

Strategy
MCHS is expanding its care giving capabilities through expansions of some of its facilities and acquisitions of others. For example it is building a new hospital in Minocqua; the hospital will feature advanced computer technology and state-of-the-art equipment. In 2017 it acquired Saint Joseph's Hospital since renamed Marshfield Medical Center. In 2018 the company began construction of additional surgical suites at its Wausau Center clinic and it is building a new cancer center and hospital in Eau Claire. The additions of new hospitals allows the health system to provide a fuller range of care in an integrated manner.

The system has a rich history in health information technology and software development. The Clinic has used a computer-based electronic health record for more than 20 years. Cattails Software Suite Marshfield Clinic's homegrown electronic health record was developed in conjunction with Clinic providers and the Information Systems Department.

Company Background
Marshfield Clinic was founded in 1916.

EXECUTIVES

Executive Director, Narayana S. Murali
Ceo, Susan L. Turney
Coo, Daniel J. Ramsey
Cfo, Gordon T. Edwards
Pharmacy Manager, Adam Maguire
Vice Chairman, Mark J. Bradley
Chairman, Mark D. Bugher
Secretary Treasurer, Kevin McEwen
Auditors: KPMG LLP MINNEAPOLIS MN

LOCATIONS
HQ: MARSHFIELD CLINIC HEALTH SYSTEM, INC.
1000 N OAK AVE, MARSHFIELD, WI 544495702
Phone: 715 387-5511
Web: WWW.MARSHFIELDCLINIC.ORG

PRODUCTS/OPERATIONS

Selected Services
Allergy and Asthma
Ambulatory Surgery
Anesthesia
Athletic Training
Audiology
Bariatric Surgery
Cancer Care
Cardiology (Heart Care)
Center for Community Outreach
Child Development Center
Dental Care
Dermatology
Diabetes Education
Ear Nose and Throat (ENT)
Emergency Medicine
Endocrinology (Diabetes and Metabolism)
Family Medicine
Gastroenterology (Digestive Care)
General Surgery
Genetic Services
Hospitalists (Hospital Care)
Infectious Diseases
Internal Medicine
Nephrology (Kidney Care)
Neurosciences (Neurology)
Nutrition Services
Obstetrics and Gynecology (OB/GYN)
Occupational Health
Oncology (Cancer Care)
Ophthalmology and Optometry (Eye Care)
Optical
Oral and Maxillofacial Surgery
Orthopedics
Orthotics and Prosthetics
Pain Management
Palliative Medicine
Pediatrics
Pharmacy
Physical and Occupational Therapy
Physical Medicine and Rehabilitation
Plastic and Cosmetic Surgery
Podiatry
Primary Care
Psychiatry and Psychology
Pulmonary Medicine (Lung Care)
Radiology
Rheumatology and Arthritis Care
Sports Medicine
TeleHealth
Urgent Care
Urology
Wound Healing

COMPETITORS

Blue Cross Blue Shield of Wisconsin
Compcare Health Services Insurance Corporation
Dean Health Systems Inc.
Group Health Cooperative
Luther Midelfort
Meriter Health Services
Ministry Health Care
ThedaCare Inc.
University of Wisconsin Hospital and Clinics

HISTORICAL FINANCIALS
Company Type: Private

Income Statement				FYE: September 30
	REVENUE ($ mil.)	NET INCOME ($ mil.)	NET PROFIT MARGIN	EMPLOYEES
09/18	2,430	(3)	—	363
09/15	0	(3)	—	—
Annual Growth	1820.8%	—	—	—

2018 Year-End Financials
Return on assets: (-0.2%)   Cash ($ mil.): 133
Return on equity: (-0.3%)
Current ratio: 1.40

MARSHFIELD CLINIC, INC.

EXECUTIVES

Pres, Brian H Ewert
Treasurer Oncology, Douglas Reding
Cfo, Gary Jankowski
V Pres, C Todd Stewart
Treas, Mark A Lepage
Urology Specialist, Gregory A Anderson
Ophthalmologist, Richard B Patchett
Manager, Teri Herr-Wilczek
General Counsel and Compliance, Barbara A Kuhl
Director Facilities and Proper, James D Colburn
Dir Buss Devlopment, Victoria L Strobel
Auditors: KPMG LLP MINNEAPOLIS MN

LOCATIONS

HQ: MARSHFIELD CLINIC, INC.
   1000 N OAK AVE, MARSHFIELD, WI 544495702
Phone: 715 387-5511
Web: WWW.MARSHFIELDRESEARCH.ORG

HISTORICAL FINANCIALS
Company Type: Private

Income Statement				FYE: September 30
	REVENUE ($ mil.)	NET INCOME ($ mil.)	NET PROFIT MARGIN	EMPLOYEES
09/15	1,211	24	2.0%	363
09/09	1,062	78	7.4%	—
09/08*	102	6	5.9%	—
06/06	813	23	2.9%	—
Annual Growth	4.5%	0.5%	—	—

*Fiscal year change

2015 Year-End Financials
Return on assets: 2.3%   Cash ($ mil.): 96
Return on equity: 4.5%
Current ratio: 0.70

MARTIN & BAYLEY, INC.

Martin & Bayley (dba Huck's Food and Fuel) operates 115 Huck's convenience stores and a number travel centers in mostly in Illinois and Indiana but also in Missouri Kentucky and Tennessee. Half of its outlets are in Illinois. The company operates a commissary at its warehouse in Carmi Illinois to supply sandwiches chicken and other food items to its stores. Some stores sell Godfather's Pizza. Family-owned since its inception Martin & Bayley became a 100% employee-owned firm when the Martin and Bayley families sold their stakes in the company.

Geographic Reach
Martin & Bayley owns and operates convenience stores in Illinois Indiana Missouri Kentucky and Tennessee.

Sales and Marketing
The company's vendor includes Fritolay Jack Link's Kraft MillerCoors Nestle Pepsi Red Bull and Wonka.

The convenience store operator is growing in the south with new Hucks locations opening in Huntingdon Tennessee and Paducah and Hopkinson Kentucky.

Company Background
Founders Bob Martin and Frank Bayley formed a partnership in 1960. In 1974 they opened the first Huck's convenience store in Illinois. The Martins and the Bayleys sold the company to its employees in 2001.

EXECUTIVES

Vice President Marketing, Tim Tilford
Vice President Of Operations, Mark Mckinney
Vice President Real Estate, Jim Whetstone
Vice President Foodservice, Ken Pearson
Auditors: HARDING SHYMANSKI & COMPANY

LOCATIONS

HQ: MARTIN & BAYLEY, INC.
   1311A W MAIN ST, CARMI, IL 628211389
Phone: 618 382-2334
Web: WWW.ROVERTOWN.COM

PRODUCTS/OPERATIONS

2013 Stores

	No.
Illinois	55
Indiana	26
Kentucky	18
Missouri	14
Tennessee	2
Total	**115**

Selected Product Lines
Godfathers Pizza
5 Buck Huck
Bigg Swigg
Coffee
Deli Express
Fresh Brewed Ice Tea
Hot to Go at Huck's
Sweet Street

COMPETITORS

7-Eleven	Exxon Mobil
Casey's General Stores	Krause Gentle
Chevron	TravelCenters of
Couche-Tard	America

HISTORICAL FINANCIALS
Company Type: Private

Income Statement				FYE: March 27
	REVENUE ($ mil.)	NET INCOME ($ mil.)	NET PROFIT MARGIN	EMPLOYEES
03/18	523	8	1.6%	1,500
03/11	528	7	1.4%	—
03/10	466	5	1.1%	—
03/09	1,579	0	—	—
Annual Growth	—	193.4%	—	—

2018 Year-End Financials
Return on assets: 6.0%   Cash ($ mil.): 11
Return on equity: 10.8%
Current ratio: 1.40

MARTIN MEMORIAL HEALTH SYSTEMS, INC.

EXECUTIVES

Pres, Robert L Lord Jr
Cfo, Mike Moerhing
Vp, Fernando Patry
Coordinator, Micaela Wolfe
Periop Manager, Chris Sweeney
Communications Specialist, Donna Murphy
Emergency Medicine Specialist, Jason A Ravanzo

Diagnostic Radiologist, Jeffrey Hillmann
Manager, Jenny Flaugh
Corporate Compliance Administr, Linda Durgin
Assistant Vice President Pract, Tom Hannon

LOCATIONS

HQ: MARTIN MEMORIAL HEALTH SYSTEMS, INC.
200 SE HOSPITAL AVE, STUART, FL 349942346
Phone: 772 287-5200
Web: WWW.MARTINHEALTH.ORG

HISTORICAL FINANCIALS

Company Type: Private

Income Statement				FYE: September 30
	REVENUE ($ mil.)	NET INCOME ($ mil.)	NET PROFIT MARGIN	EMPLOYEES
09/18	586	16	2.8%	4,300
09/17	559	30	5.4%	—
09/16	542	25	4.6%	—
Annual Growth	4.0%	(19.5%)	—	—

2018 Year-End Financials

Return on assets: 2.1%   Cash ($ mil.): 27
Return on equity: 4.9%
Current ratio: 4.10

MARTIN MEMORIAL MEDICAL CENTER, INC

EXECUTIVES

Pres, Mark Robitaille
V Pres-Cfo*, L Mark Cocorullo
Treas*, John Lowenberg
Secr*, James Orr III
Sr V Pres*, Donna H Griffith
V Pres*, Craig Chindemi
Cfo*, Chuck Cleaver
Chief of Pediatric, Kristen Walker
Executive Officer, Cindy Pingolt
Consultant, Stacey Rhodewalt
Assistant Vice-President, Candice Tettamanti

LOCATIONS

HQ: MARTIN MEMORIAL MEDICAL CENTER, INC
200 SE HOSPITAL AVE, STUART, FL 349942346
Phone: 772 287-5200
Web: WWW.MARTINHEALTH.ORG

HISTORICAL FINANCIALS

Company Type: Private

Income Statement				FYE: September 30
	REVENUE ($ mil.)	NET INCOME ($ mil.)	NET PROFIT MARGIN	EMPLOYEES
09/18	506	20	4.0%	2,972
09/17	490	26	5.3%	—
09/14	910	545	59.9%	—
Annual Growth	(13.6%)	(56.2%)	—	—

2018 Year-End Financials

Return on assets: 2.9%   Cash ($ mil.): 21
Return on equity: 7.1%
Current ratio: 4.20

MARTIN PRODUCT SALES LLC

EXECUTIVES

Pres, Ruben S Martin III
MBR-V Pres*, Chris Booth
Coo*, Randall L Tauscher
Exec V Pres*, Robert D Bondurant
MBR, Don Liles

LOCATIONS

HQ: MARTIN PRODUCT SALES LLC
4200 STONE RD, KILGORE, TX 756626935
Phone: 903 983-6200

HISTORICAL FINANCIALS

Company Type: Private

Income Statement				FYE: December 31
	REVENUE ($ mil.)	NET INCOME ($ mil.)	NET PROFIT MARGIN	EMPLOYEES
12/07	1,204	8	0.7%	206
12/02*	156	1	0.7%	—
06/01	260	3	1.4%	—
06/99	132	0	0.2%	—
Annual Growth	27.8%	46.7%	—	—

*Fiscal year change

2007 Year-End Financials

Return on assets: 2.0%   Cash ($ mil.): 5
Return on equity: 21.2%
Current ratio: 1.80

MARTIN RESOURCE MANAGEMENT CORPORATION

Martin Resource Management likes to push around petroleum products. The employee-owned company's flagship affiliate Martin Midstream Partners offers transportation storage marketing and logistics management services for petroleum products including sulfur sulfur derivatives fuel oil liquefied petroleum gas asphalt and other bulk tank liquids primarily in the southern US. Martin Resource also manufactures and markets fertilizer and other processed sulfur products. Through its Martin Energy Services unit the company offers inland marine fuel supply and offshore support services. Other units include The Brimrock Group (sulfur) Cross Oil Refining & Marketing and Martin Asphalt.

Operations

Each year the company markets more than 250 million gallons of diesel fuel and lubricants along the Gulf Coast and 1.5 million barrels of naphthenic lubricants and base oils across the US. In addition Martin Resource also provides surface transportation services for products such as molten sulfur sulfuric acid fuel oil natural gas liquids (NGLs) asphalt paper mill liquids and other bulk tank liquids.

The company's more than $550 million of assets include a fleet of truck trailers and tractors. Its Martin Transport subsidiary has about 25 termi-

nals in the Southeast and Southern US with more than 850 trucks and 1200 trailers. Martin Product Sales LLC markets and distributes petroleum-based products including asphalt fuel oil and sulfuric acid.

Martin Resource owns a 28.0% limited partnership interest and a 2% general partnership interest in its flagship operating company Martin Midstream Partners. Its Martin Energy Services subsidiary offers marine fuel supply and offshore support services.

Sales and Marketing

The company's customers include agriculture petrochemical petroleum and utility companies.

Strategy

Martin Resource markets oil and gas and by-products through facilities located throughout the Gulf Coast region. It acquires other companies or forms joint ventures to develop its portfolio. It also redistributes operating assets to its major subsidiaries to improve their performance.

In 2013 Canadian subsidiary Brimrock signed an engineering service agreement with Keyera to act as the engineering management and technology provider for Keyera's planned sulphur forming and materials handling facilities upgrade.

That year Martin Resource sold a 49% voting interest in MMGP Holdings LLC a newly-formed sole member of Martin Midstream GP LLC the general partner of Martin Midstream Partners to Alinda Capital Partners.

In 2012 Martin Midstream Partners also sold its East Texas and Northwest Louisiana natural gas gathering and processing assets to CenterPoint Energy Field Services for $275 million.

Streamlining its businesses in 2012 the company formed Martin Energy Services LLC combining the entities of Midstream Fuel Service LLC L & L Oil and Gas Services L.L.C. and PEPCO into one entity for improved service and growth.

Mergers and Acquisitions

In 2013 Martin Midstream Partners' subsidiary Martin Operating Partnership L.P bought Kansas City Missouri-based NL Grease LLC a grease manufacturer that specializes in private-label packaging of commercial and industrial greases.

Boosting its NGL handling capabilities that year Martin Midstream Partners purchased six liquefied petroleum gas pressure barges and two commercial push boats from affiliates of Florida Marine Transporters for $51 million.

In 2012 Martin Midstream Partners acquired Gulf Coast fuels and lubricants provider Talen's Marine & Fuel LLC. The transactions boosted the company's marine terminal infrastructure adding ten marine terminals between Houston/Galveston and Port Fourchon in Louisiana with total tankage of 300000 barrels and an additional 4000 feet of water-accessible bulkhead.

In 2012 Martin Midstream Partners bought the remaining equity interests in Redbird Gas Storage LLC for $150 million. (In 2011 Martin Resource and Martin Midstream Partners formed the Redbird Gas Storage natural gas storage joint venture to invest in Cardinal Gas Storage Partners a joint venture between Redbird and Energy Capital Partners focused on the development of natural gas storage facilities across North America).

Company Background

The acquisition of L & L Oil and Gas L.L.C. by Midstream Fuel Service in 2011 increased Martin Resources' capability along the U.S. Gulf Coast to 31 facilities for offshore fuels lubricants and logistical services including land based commercial and industrial fuels and lubricants.

In 2011 Martin Resource and Martin Midstream Partners formed the Redbird Gas Storage natural gas storage joint venture to invest in Cardinal Gas Storage Partners. Cardinal is a joint venture between Redbird and Energy Capital Partners that is focused on the development construction operation and management of natural gas storage facilities across North America.

To raise cash and boost the Martin Midstream Partners' storage segment in 2011 Martin Resource sold 13 terminals to that unit for $36.5 million.

Founded in 1951 by R. S. Martin Jr. Martin Resource also holds a stake in Ican Energy an LPG distributor. To raise cash and increase its financial flexibility in 2002 the company spun off a portion of its assets.

EXECUTIVES

Vice President Of Human Resources, Melanie Mathews

Senior Vice President Of Surface Transportation, Johnnie Murry

Vice President, Mike Lawrence
Auditors: KPMG LLP DALLAS TEXAS

LOCATIONS

HQ: MARTIN RESOURCE MANAGEMENT CORPORATION
4200 STONE RD, KILGORE, TX 756626935
Phone: 903 983-6200

PRODUCTS/OPERATIONS

Selected Companies
Altec Environmental Consulting
Commercial & Industrial Fuels & Lubricants
Commercial & Industrial Tanks & Equipment
Cross Oil Refining & Marketing Inc.
Marine Lubricants & Specialty Products
Martin Crude Marketing Company
Martin Energy Services LLC
Martin Product Sales LLC
Martin Transport Inc
Roddey engineering services Inc.

COMPETITORS

Enterprise Products	Penn Octane
George Warren	Sun Coast Resources
Global Partners	Williams Companies
Gulf Oil	

HISTORICAL FINANCIALS

Company Type: Private

Income Statement			FYE: December 31
	REVENUE ($ mil.)	NET INCOME ($ mil.)	NET PROFIT MARGIN	EMPLOYEES
12/15	2,493	27	1.1%	2,300
12/11	2,985	37	1.3%	—
12/09	1,537	23	1.5%	—
12/08	2,903	5	0.2%	—
Annual Growth	(2.1%)	24.9%	—	—

2015 Year-End Financials
Return on assets: 1.5%
Return on equity: 6.9%
Current ratio: 1.80
Cash ($ mil.): 13

MARTIN'S POINT HEALTH CARE, INC.

EXECUTIVES

Ceo-Pres, David Howes
Chb*, Robert Moore
Cfo*, Daniel Chojnowski

Coordinator, Elizabeth Chadbourne
Coordinator, INA Levasseur
Coordinator, Jeanne Richards
Coordinator, Sheryl Fossett
Vice-President, Jeffry Bland
Nurse Practitioner, Robin Baier
Information Specialist, Brandon Bergman
Specialist, Lisa Dellinger
Auditors: BAKER NEWMAN & NOYES LLC POR

LOCATIONS

HQ: MARTIN'S POINT HEALTH CARE, INC.
331 VERANDA ST STE 1, PORTLAND, ME 041035544
Phone: 207 774-5801
Web: WWW.MARTINSPOINT.ORG

HISTORICAL FINANCIALS

Company Type: Private

Income Statement			FYE: December 31
	ASSETS ($ mil.)	NET INCOME ($ mil.)	INCOME AS % OF ASSETS	EMPLOYEES
12/16	386	17	4.6%	839
12/14	351	3	1.0%	—
12/13	345	10	3.0%	—
12/09	247	30	12.2%	—
Annual Growth	6.6%	(7.2%)	—	—

2016 Year-End Financials
Return on assets: 4.6%
Return on equity: 6.6%
Sales ($ mil): 704

MARYLAND AND VIRGINIA MILK PRODUCERS COOPERATIVE ASSOCIATION, INCORPORATED

Milk is "Mar-VA-lous" for the members of the Maryland & Virginia Milk Producers Cooperative Association. Known as Maryland & Virginia the co-op processes and sells milk for nearly 1500 member/farmers with dairy herds in the southeastern US and mid-Atlantic region. Maryland & Virginia produces fluid milk ice cream and cultured dairy products for retail sale under the Marva Maid Maola and Valley Milk brands. Its butter condensed milk and milk-powder products are sold primarily to food manufacturers. As a co-op it also offers agricultural supplies to its members. Maryland & Virginia operates three fluid-milk processing plants a manufacturing plant and an equipment-supply warehouse.

Operations

Maryland & Virginia operates three fluid processing plants a single manufacturing plant and a farm supply equipment division. It also owns a majority stake in Valley Milk LLC. The co-op transports more than 300 tanker truckloads of milk daily to nearly 30 different plants. Member farms range in size from fewer than 100 cows to more than 2000. Combined Maryland & Virginia mem-

bers produce three billion pounds of milk annually.

Geographic Reach

The co-op gets its milk from member farmers in Delaware Florida Georgia Kentucky Maryland North Carolina Ohio Pennsylvania South Carolina Tennessee Virginia and West Virginia. Its fluid processing plants are located in Newport News Virginia; Landover Maryland; and New Bern North Carolina. It has manufacturing facilities in Laurel Maryland and Strasburg Virginia and a warehouse in Frederick Maryland.

Sales and Marketing

In addition to supermarkets the co-op counts customers such as Walgreens Starbucks Sheetz convenience stores and Dairy Queen among its customers.

Financial Performance

The co-op's revenue decreased by 5% to $1.3 billion in 2012 versus $1.4 billion in 2011 due to a decline in milk dairy and other products as well as sales of equipment and supplies partially offset by an increase in sales of its members' and non-members' raw milk. Despite the decline in sales the Maryland & Virginia reported a profit of $5.5 million in 2012 versus a loss of $2.8 million the prior year. Like other milk producers Maryland & Virginia has been contending with sluggish milk sales due to decreasing milk consumption beginning in the 1970s.

EXECUTIVES

Pres, Dwayne Myers
Cfo*, Jorge Gonzalez
Treas*, Jay Bryant
Corp SEC*, Barbara Campbell
V Pres*, R Steven Graybeal
V Pres*, Richard Mosemann
Operations Manager, Craig Gentry
Executive of Sales, Michael Curtis
Chief Financial Officer, Jan Tenpas
Director, Troye Cooper
Chief Operating Officer, Brian Linney
Auditors: HERLIEM & COMPANY INC READING

LOCATIONS

HQ: MARYLAND AND VIRGINIA MILK PRODUCERS COOPERATIVE ASSOCIATION, INCORPORATED
1985 ISAAC NEWTON SQ W # 200, RESTON, VA 201905031
Phone: 703 742-6800
Web: WWW.MDVAMILK.COM

COMPETITORS

Associated Milk Producers	Dairylea
Dairy Farmers of America	Dean Foods
Dairy Manufacturers	Foremost Farms
	Land O'Lakes

HISTORICAL FINANCIALS

Company Type: Private

Income Statement			FYE: December 31
	REVENUE ($ mil.)	NET INCOME ($ mil.)	NET PROFIT MARGIN	EMPLOYEES
12/12	1,296	5	0.4%	550
12/11	1,362	(2)	—	—
12/10	1,219	8	0.7%	—
Annual Growth	3.1%	(20.4%)	—	—

2012 Year-End Financials
Return on assets: 3.4%
Return on equity: 14.9%
Current ratio: 0.80
Cash ($ mil.): —

MARYLAND DEPARTMENT OF TRANSPORTATION

Traveling in Maryland? You can thank (or curse) the Maryland Department of Transportation (MDOT). MDOT is responsible for building operating and maintaining a safe and seamless transportation network that includes highway transit maritime and aviation facilities. The Department of Transportation is organized along various administrative groups including the Maryland Motor Vehicle Administration Transit Administration Port Administration Aviation Administration and Highway Administration. MDOT annual budget of about $1.5 billion is funded through the state's Transportation Trust Fund and federal aid.

EXECUTIVES

SEC, Pete K Rahn
SEC, John Porcari
Prin, Donald A Halligan
Prin, Robert Ehrlich
Bay Bridge Facility Administra, Richard Jaramillo
Coordinator, Cathy Kahl
Coordinator, Colleen Johnson
Policy, Jeff Tosi
Deputy Director, Sandy Hertz
Support Specialist, Wayne Hudson
Auditors: SB & COMPANY LLC HUNT VALLEY

LOCATIONS

HQ: MARYLAND DEPARTMENT OF TRANSPORTATION
7201 CORPORATE CENTER DR, HANOVER, MD
210761415
Phone: 410 865-1037

HISTORICAL FINANCIALS
Company Type: Private

Income Statement				FYE: June 30
	REVENUE ($ mil.)	NET INCOME ($ mil.)	NET PROFIT MARGIN	EMPLOYEES
06/18	4,407	(189)	—	1,000
06/17	4,490	85	1.9%	—
06/16	4,170	(232)	—	—
06/14	3,890	58	1.5%	—
Annual Growth	3.2%	—	—	—

2018 Year-End Financials
Return on assets: (-0.9%) Cash ($ mil.): 1
Return on equity: (-1.3%)
Current ratio: —

MARYLAND SOUTHERN ELECTRIC COOPERATIVE INC

Historic Southern Maryland gets it power via the South Maryland Electric Cooperative (SMECO) which distributes electricity to about 154000 residential commercial and industrial customers in four counties via about 11360 miles of power line and 54 electric substations. One of the ten largest electric cooperatives in the US the member-owned enterprise gets its wholesale power supply through its membership in wholesale energy trading and risk management service company ACES Power Marketing. Overseen by a board of directors SMECO's single mission is to provide reliable competitively priced energy and related services to its members.

Geographic Reach
SMECO's 1150 sq. ml. service area includes all of Charles and St. Mary's counties and parts of of Calvert and Prince George's counties. Cities covered include Hughesville Leonardtown Prince Frederick and White Plains.

Financial Performance
In 2012 SMECO revenues decreased by 7% due to weaker residential power demand and lower costs paid for third-party purchased power. The coop's net income decreased by 15%.

Strategy
Like other coops SMECO is pushing conservation the use of green energy and smart technology to reduce power costs. It is also promoting the development of solar and wind energy and integrating it into the power supply it makes available to its members.

In addition SMECO is constructing the Southern Maryland Reliability Project which aims to upgrade SEMCOs existing 69000-volt transmission line to 230000 volts by 2015. The Project's expanded capacity will ensure a more reliable supply.

Company Background
In 1937 as part of the national rural electrification drive of the Roosevelt government a local committee in St. Mary's county and one representing Charles and Prince George's counties merged to form the Southern Maryland Tri-County Cooperative Association. The members converted this association into a non-profit membership cooperative in 1942 and changed its name to Southern Maryland Electric Cooperative.

In 2011 the coop's service areas felt the full brunt of Hurricane Irene which knocked out 11 transmission circuits and cut power 108000 customers and caused $7 million of damage to the coop's electric system.

EXECUTIVES

Senior Vice President And General Counsel, Mark Macdougall
Vice President And Chief Information Officer, Andrew Yeskie
Vice President Transmission And Substation Operations, Kingsley Chip
Auditors: I ADAMS JENKINS CHEATHAM PC

LOCATIONS

HQ: MARYLAND SOUTHERN ELECTRIC COOPERATIVE INC
15035 BURNT STORE RD, HUGHESVILLE, MD
206372699
Phone: 301 274-3111
Web: WWW.SMECO.COOP

HISTORICAL FINANCIALS
Company Type: Private

Income Statement				FYE: December 31
	REVENUE ($ mil.)	NET INCOME ($ mil.)	NET PROFIT MARGIN	EMPLOYEES
12/15	451	4	1.0%	375
12/14	490	1	0.3%	—
12/10	492	17	3.5%	—
12/09	462	3	0.7%	—
Annual Growth	(0.4%)	5.6%	—	—

2015 Year-End Financials
Return on assets: 0.5% Cash ($ mil.): 4
Return on equity: 3.4%
Current ratio: 3.50

MARYLAND TRANSPORTATION AUTHORITY

EXECUTIVES

Governor, Larry Hogan
Director of Communications, Ashley Fails
Recruiter, Paige Ryder

LOCATIONS

HQ: MARYLAND TRANSPORTATION AUTHORITY
2310 BROENING HWY, BALTIMORE, MD 212246639
Phone: 410 537-7833
Web: WWW.MARYLAND.GOV

HISTORICAL FINANCIALS
Company Type: Private

Income Statement				FYE: June 30
	REVENUE ($ mil.)	NET INCOME ($ mil.)	NET PROFIT MARGIN	EMPLOYEES
06/18	862	309	35.9%	77
06/17	869	332	38.3%	—
Annual Growth	(0.8%)	(6.9%)	—	—

2018 Year-End Financials
Return on assets: 4.3% Cash ($ mil.): 75
Return on equity: 6.8%
Current ratio: 1.60

MASSACHUSETTS INSTITUTE OF TECHNOLOGY

Massachusetts Institute of Technology (MIT) takes the prize for breeding ingenuity. A leading research institution the school is typically granted more patents annually than any other university and about 90 people associated with MIT are Nobel Prize recipients. Blending that science and engineering acumen with top business programs (including the Sloan School of Management) MIT graduates have started more than 30000 active companies. MIT has more than 11000 students more than 60% of whom attend graduate school. The faculty of the nearly three dozen academic departments includes more than 1000 professors. The school's student teacher ratio is 3:1 (undergraduates). Founded in 1865 MIT is privately endowed.

Operations
MIT's research is conducted both through its academic facilities which employ more than 3700 researchers and engage some 2500 graduate stu-

dents and through its Lincoln Laboratory in Lexington Massachusetts. The Lincoln Laboratory has approximately 3200 workers focused on federally funded research programs in areas of national security such as information communication and decision making. Lincoln Laboratory specialized in sensors signal processing and embedded computer systems.

The university offers 46 major and 49 minor undergraduate programs. Its undergraduate tuition for academic year 2016-2017 was about $48000. MIT's libraries have more than 5 million items in print and digital formats.

MIT is one of a growing number of universities to begin offering OpenCourseWare which makes teaching materials used in MIT undergraduate and graduate courses available on the internet free of charge to any user anywhere in the world for uses ranging from curriculum development to self-learning.

Geographic Reach

MIT is located on 168 acres in Cambridge Massachusetts and includes 18 student residences and 26 acres of athletic fields.

MIT enrolled students from all 50 states and the District of Columbia three territories and about 100 foreign nations in the academic year ending 2017.

Financial Performance

MIT clearly has a strong emphasis on procuring funding for its technology research programs. The institute receives grants from a variety of commercial and non-commercial entities bringing in a total of $1.7 billion in sponsored funding each year. The Department of Defense and Department of Health and Human Services and the largest sponsors. Other sponsors include the Department of Energy National Science Foundation NASA local government agencies and not-for-profit entities. MIT also conducts $100 million in contracted general industry research each year.

Annual revenue for MIT in fiscal 2017 was $3.5 billion up from about $3.4 billion in 2016. About 50% of revenue comes from research funding. About 10% comes from tuition.

Strategy

MIT's primary goal is to advance science and technology both among its students and on a worldwide scale. It aims to make discoveries in areas including energy economics and medicine. To take its efforts to the broader population MIT licenses more technologies to startups than any other university. Its licensing office enters about 100 licensing and option agreements each year with about a quarter of those going to startup technology firms.

While MIT is well-known for students and graduates who create businesses the university has created a fund to help early stage enterprises along. The Engine as the fund is called invests in university-related startups in their early stages. It steps in where venture capital funds usually don't go technologies that require time to commercialize. Main areas of investment include robotics biotechnology manufacturing and materials and energy. The fund has about $200 billion for investment.

Company Background

MIT has some extraordinary alumni who include former chairman of the Federal Reserve Ben Bernanke former US Representative Pete Stark former National Economic Council chairman Lawrence H. Summers and former Council of Economic Advisors chairwoman Christina Romer. Outside of politics MIT alumni founded or co-founded several notable companies such as Intel Hewlett-Packard Texas Instruments Qualcomm Bose and Campbell Soup.

EXECUTIVES

Dean Digital Learning, Sanjay Sarma
President, L. Rafael Reif
Dean Sloan School Of Management, David C. Schmittlein
Evp And Treasurer, Israel Ruiz
Dean School Of Engineering, Ian A. Waitz
Dean Graduate Education, Christine Ortiz
Dean Undergraduate Education, Dennis M. Freeman
Dean Student Life, Costantino (Chris) Colombo
Chancellor, Cynthia Barnhart
Provost, Martin A. Schmidt
Dean School Of Architecture And Planning, Hashim Sarkis
Dean School Of Humanities Arts And Social Sciences, Melissa Nobles
Dean School Of Science, Michael Sipser
Vp Information Systems And Technology, John Charles
Associate Vice President For Communications, Nate Nickerson
Associate Vice President For Human Resources, Meg Regan
Vice President, Susan Hockfield
Associate Vice President And Chief Operating Officer, David Woodruff
Vice President Product, Nadav Aharony
Senior Vice President Of Information Technology, Ed Gazarian
Vice President For Open Learning, Laura White
Senior Advisor To The Senior Vice President, Kathryn Liede
Vice President, Ann Drumm
Department Head, Maria Zuber
Vice President, Chris Huson
Vice President Of Sales, Andrew Mcinnes
Vice President For Institute Affairs And Secretary Of The Corporation, Jennifer Walsh
Executive Vice President, James Hodges
Vice President, Haizheng Zhang
Senior Advisor Office Of The Vice President For Research, Tom Kiley
Vice President Information Technology, Lisa Mandel
Vice President, Sreehari Rayavarapu
Medical Director, Cecilia Stuopis
Vice President, Sandro Salgueiro
Vice President Strategy And Analysis, Amanda Chiu
Vice President Of Conference, Zeng Qingying
Vice President Sales, James Dunn
Vice President For Students Affairs, Allison Dolan-wilson
Chairman, Robert B. Millard, age 69
Vice Chair, Judy Pederson
Secretary, Richard Zhang
Board Member, James Harland
Deputy Treasurer And Director Of Investments, Allan Bufferd

LOCATIONS

HQ: MASSACHUSETTS INSTITUTE OF TECHNOLOGY
77 MASSACHUSETTS AVE, CAMBRIDGE, MA
021394307
Phone: 617 253-1000
Web: WWW.WWW-MATH.MIT.EDU

PRODUCTS/OPERATIONS

2014 Sales

	$ mil.	% of total
Reseach revenue	1,528	49
Support from investment	625	20
Tuition and similar revenue	324	10
Fee and services	176	6
Gifts	162	5
Auxiliary enterprises	120	4
Other program	117	4
Net asset reclassification	69	2
Total	**3,124**	**100**

Schools and Areas of Study

Schools and Areas of Study
School of Architecture and Planning
  Architecture
  Media Arts and Sciences
  Urban Studies and Planning
School of Engineering
  Aeronautics and Astronautics
  Biological Engineering
  Chemical Engineering
  Civil and Environmental Engineering
  Electrical Engineering and Computer Science
  Engineering Systems Division
  Materials Science and Engineering
  Mechanical Engineering
  Nuclear Science and Engineering
School of Humanities Arts and Social Sciences
  Anthropology
  Comparative Media Studies
  Economics
  Foreign Languages and Literatures
  History
  Humanities
  Linguistics and Philosophy
  Literature
  Music and Theater Arts
  Political Science
  Science Technology and Society
  Writing and Humanistic Studies
Sloan School of Management
  Management
School of Science
  Biology
  Brain and Cognitive Sciences
  Chemistry
  Earth Atmospheric and Planetary Sciences
  Mathematics
  Physics
Whitaker College of Health Sciences and Technology
  Harvard-MIT Division of Health Sciences and Technology
MIT-WHOI Joint Program in Oceanography and Applied Ocean Science and Engineering
Degrees Offered
Bachelor of Science (SB)
Master of Architecture (MArch)
Master of Business Administration (MBA)
Master in City Planning (MCP)
Master of Engineering (MEng)
Master of Finance (MFin)
Master of Science (SM)
Engineer (degree designates the field)
Doctor of Philosophy (PhD)
Doctor of Science (ScD)

HISTORICAL FINANCIALS

Company Type: Private

Income Statement

	REVENUE ($ mil.)	NET INCOME ($ mil.)	NET PROFIT MARGIN	EMPLOYEES
06/18	3,626	2,391	65.9%	12,000
06/17	3,551	2,195	61.8%	—
06/10	2,727	(199)	—	—
06/09	1,647	0	—	—
Annual Growth	9.2%	—	—	—

FYE: June 30

2018 Year-End Financials

Return on assets: 9.2%   Cash ($ mil.): 428
Return on equity: 11.1%
Current ratio: —

MASSACHUSETTS PORT AUTHORITY

Massachusetts Port Authority (Massport) operates three airports: Boston Logan International Hanscom Field and Worcester Regional. Logan is home to 50 airlines and is New England's largest airport and the first port of call for many international flights entering the US. (It accounts for the majority of Massport's revenues.) Hanscom Field operates as the region's main aviation airport and offers niche commercial services while Worcester Regional primarily supports commercial flight services. Massport also oversees various waterfront properties of the Port of Boston. The agency was created by the Commonwealth of Massachusetts in 1956. The governor of Massachusetts appoints the agency's board members.

Operations

Massport's business consists of two distinct operating departments: Aviation and the Port. Logan airport catered to 29.4 million aviation passengers and 369000 cruise passengers in 2013. Its shipping operations serviced more than 110000 containers of products at its port.

Financial Performance

Massport's net revenues have steadily climbed over the years. Revenues jumped 2% from $1.78 billion in 2012 to $1.83 billion in 2013 thanks mainly to parking concession ground services and other revenue from nearly 125000 more passengers at Logan. The overall revenue increase for 2013 was generated by operating revenues exceeding operating expenses by $2.4 million.

EXECUTIVES

Secretary, Rita Hannon

LOCATIONS

HQ: MASSACHUSETTS PORT AUTHORITY
1 HARBORSIDE DR STE 200S, BOSTON, MA 021282905
Phone: 617 561-1600
Web: WWW.MASSPORT.COM

HISTORICAL FINANCIALS

Company Type: Private

Income Statement				FYE: June 30
	REVENUE ($ mil.)	NET INCOME ($ mil.)	NET PROFIT MARGIN	EMPLOYEES
06/16	699	105	15.1%	1,102
06/15	662	107	16.2%	—
Annual Growth	5.5%	(2.0%)	—	—

2016 Year-End Financials

Return on assets: 2.5%   Cash ($ mil.): 63
Return on equity: 5.1%
Current ratio: 1.50

MASSACHUSETTS SCHOOL BUILDING AUTHORITY

EXECUTIVES

Exec Director, Katherine Craven
Accounting Staff, Audrey Cushman
Executive Board Member, Matthew Deninger
Associate General Counsel, Brian Kelley

LOCATIONS

HQ: MASSACHUSETTS SCHOOL BUILDING AUTHORITY
40 BROAD ST STE 500, BOSTON, MA 021094371
Phone: 617 720-4466
Web: WWW.MASSSCHOOLBUILDINGS.ORG

HISTORICAL FINANCIALS

Company Type: Private

Income Statement				FYE: June 30
	REVENUE ($ mil.)	NET INCOME ($ mil.)	NET PROFIT MARGIN	EMPLOYEES
06/18	891	252	28.3%	8
06/17	828	148	17.9%	—
06/16	908	237	26.1%	—
Annual Growth	(0.9%)	3.2%	—	—

MAXIFACIAL DENTAL SURGERY

Auditors: ERNST & YOUNG US LLP INDIAN

LOCATIONS

HQ: MAXIFACIAL DENTAL SURGERY
1 MEDICAL CENTER DR, LEBANON, NH 037561000
Phone: 603 650-5000
Web: WWW.HITCHCOCK.ORG

HISTORICAL FINANCIALS

Company Type: Private

Income Statement				FYE: September 30
	REVENUE ($ mil.)	NET INCOME ($ mil.)	NET PROFIT MARGIN	EMPLOYEES
09/09	1,147	27	2.4%	7,500
09/06	913	15	1.7%	—
Annual Growth	7.9%	20.7%	—	—

2009 Year-End Financials

Return on assets: 2.3%   Cash ($ mil.): 40
Return on equity: 10.6%
Current ratio: 1.30

MAXIM HEALTHCARE SERVICES, INC.

Maxim Healthcare Services aims to promote good health by offering medical staffing and home health care as well as immunizations and other wellness services to clients nationwide. The company provides medical and administrative personnel for hospitals school systems nursing homes and correctional facilities. The company's staffing division offers contract per diem and travel assignments. Maxim Healthcare's consultants are available 24 hours a day seven days a week to provide assistance for clients. The company which operates from more than 360 locations nationwide was established in 1988.

Operations

The company's Maxim Health Systems division established in 1996 provides immunizations health screenings and health fairs. Each year the division's immunization program is responsible for vaccinating millions of people across more than 40000 clinics.

Other major Maxim Healthcare divisions include Maxim Staffing Solutions (Nurse Allied Health and Administrative Staffing) Maxim Government Services Maxim Physician Resources Timeline Recruiting Maxim Coders Maxim Pediatric Services; Logix Healthcare Search Partners and StaffAssist.

EXECUTIVES

Cio, Kevin Apperson
Coo Maxim Staffing Solutions, Chris Powell
Ceo, W. Bradley (Brad) Bennett
Vp Chief Medical Officer And Chief Quality Officer, W. John Langley
Cfo, Raymond (Ray) Carbone
Area Vice President Regional Account Manager, Jimmy Nichols
Director Of Clinical Services, Denise Sutton
Vice President Of Compliance, Shane Campbell
Director Of Clinical Services, Ann Lopez
Vice President, Andrew Friedell
Director Of Clinical Services, Lisa Malone
Director Of Clinical Services, Jolinda Jackson
Area Vice President, John Smalley
Senior Vice President And Chief Medical Officer, John Langley
Director Of Clinical Services, Jean Jacks
Area Vice President, Mike Beams
Area Vice President, Haven Andrews
Director Of Clinical Services, Susan Gibala
Area Vice President, Chris Bodmer
Area Vice President Southeast, Matt Rozelle
Area Vice President, Jeremy Markewicz
Director Of Clinical Services, Tina Marquez
Area Vice President Of Clinical Operations, Kathy Mandeville
Vice President Of Finance, Steve Walsh
Area Vice President Of Clinical Operations, Savannah Moose
Vice President Human Resources, Kelly Bart
Director Of Clinical Services, Jane Robinson
Director Of Clinical Services, Diane Charboneau
Director Of Clinical Services, Jennifer Turner
Auditors: PRICEWATERHOUSECOOPERS LLP BA

LOCATIONS

HQ: MAXIM HEALTHCARE SERVICES, INC.
7227 LEE DEFOREST DR, COLUMBIA, MD 210463236
Phone: 410 910-1500
Web: WWW.MAXIMHEALTHCARE.COM

PRODUCTS/OPERATIONS

Selected Services

Allied Health staffing
Facility nurse staffing
Flu and wellness services
Government services
Health information services
International nursing
Home healthcare
HME/pharmacy services
Habilitation services
Physician services
Travel nursing

Selected Divisions

CareFocus
CareFocus Companion Services
Centrus Premier Homecare
Logix Healthcare Search Partners
Maxim Coders
Maxim Government Services
Maxim Health Information Services
Maxim Health Systems
Maxim Healthcare Services (Homecare)
Maxim Home Health Resources

Maxim Pediatric Services
Maxim Physician Resources
Maxim Staffing Solutions - Administrative Staffing
Maxim Staffing Solutions - Allied Health
Maxim Staffing Solutions - Nurse Staffing
Orbis Clinical
Reflectx Services
StaffAssist
TimeLine Recruiting
TravelMax

COMPETITORS

American HomePatient	PHS Correctional
Apria Healthcare	Healthcare
Cross Country	Team Health
Healthcare	TeamStaff
MedStaff	
Medsearch Staffing	
Services	

HISTORICAL FINANCIALS
Company Type: Private

Income Statement				FYE: December 31
	REVENUE ($ mil.)	NET INCOME ($ mil.)	NET PROFIT MARGIN	EMPLOYEES
12/17	1,510	38	2.5%	35,000
12/15	1,382	11	0.8%	—
12/14	1,269	4	0.4%	—
12/13	1,226	(1)	—	—
Annual Growth	5.3%	—	—	—

2017 Year-End Financials
Return on assets: 14.2%   Cash ($ mil.): 8
Return on equity: 71.1%
Current ratio: 1.40

MAYER ELECTRIC SUPPLY COMPANY, INC.

Mayer Electric Supply helps to light up those southern nights. The company is one of the nation's largest distributors of electrical supplies with about 50 branch locations in the southeastern US. It offers some 40000 items made by leading manufacturers such as 3M GE Littelfuse and Schneider Electric. Products include conduit circuit breakers controls and switches fire and safety products LED and low-voltage lighting systems motors power tools transformers and wire and cable. Mayer Electric supplies customers in the construction datacomm government industrial and utility industries. The Collat family including CEO Nancy Collat Goedecke owns Mayer Electric.

Operations
Besides distributing electrical supplies Mayer Electric offers several services. Its Mayer Project Management group works to lower cost for construction contractors by providing on-site storage and inventory management. Other services include lamp and battery recycling conduit bending and threading and wire and cable cutting. The company also specializes in factory automation energy efficiency and datacomm systems.

Geographic Reach
Mayer Electric serves customers through locations in Alabama Florida Georgia Mississippi the Carolinas Texas Tennessee and Virginia.

Sales and Marketing
The electrical supplies distributor serves multiple customer segments including those in the construction government industrial datacomm and utility industries through about 51 branch locations across US Southeast.

Strategy
Growing its geographic presence in 2013 Mayer Electric opened a branch location in the Houston area.

Mergers and Acquisitions
Looking to expand further in the southeastern US Mayer Electric in 2012 acquired Mustang Electric Supply based outside Dallas in Lewisville Texas. Established in 1998 Mustang Electric serves commercial and residential contractors across the Dallas and Fort Worth area allowing Mayer Electric to expand to the dynamic and lucrative Dallas market. The purchase included Mustang Electric's 40000-sq.-ft. facility in Lewisville.

Company Background
The recession hit companies like Mayer Electric hard as residential and commercial construction efforts were backburnered. Sales for Mayer Electric dropped by about 21% in 2009 compared to the prior year. Rather than responding by laying off employees or shuttering branches the company planned for break-even results or a small loss for the year. Indeed the company made a small profit in 2009.
Mayer Electric was founded in 1930.

EXECUTIVES

Chb-Ceo, Nancy Collat Goedecke
Pres*, Wes Smith
Exec V Pres-Coo*, Charles A Collat Jr
Exec V Pres*, Glenn Goedecke
Executive Officer, Mike Dunaway
Staff, Steve Poremba
Human Resources, Melissa Hill
Outside Account Manager, Jake Gray
Project Sales Support, Julie Kelly
Commercial Outside Sales, Marcus Abdo
Purchasing Manager, Dennis Shirley

LOCATIONS

HQ: MAYER ELECTRIC SUPPLY COMPANY, INC.
   3405 4TH AVE S, BIRMINGHAM, AL 352222300
Phone: 205 583-3500
Web: WWW.MAYERELECTRIC.COM

PRODUCTS/OPERATIONS

Selected Services
Basic distributor services
Construction partner
Maintenance repair and operations

Selected Products
Ballasts
Batteries
Cable and wire
Circuit breakers
Conduit
Factory automation products
Fan boxes
Fasteners
Fuses
LED lighting systems
Lenses
Lighting fixtures
Locks
Low-voltage lighting systems
Meters
Motors
Panelboards
Power supplies
Relays
Switches
Surge protection devices
Terminal blocks
Tools
Transformers
Voltage regulators

COMPETITORS

Anixter International	Independent Electric
Consolidated	Supply
Electrical	Rexel Inc.
Crescent Electric	W.W. Grainger
Supply	WESCO International
Gexpro	Wholesale Supply Group
Graybar Electric	

HISTORICAL FINANCIALS
Company Type: Private

Income Statement				FYE: December 30
	REVENUE ($ mil.)	NET INCOME ($ mil.)	NET PROFIT MARGIN	EMPLOYEES
12/17	911	11	1.2%	900
12/16	812	5	0.7%	—
12/15	811	7	0.9%	—
12/14	737	6	0.9%	—
Annual Growth	7.3%	18.5%	—	—

2017 Year-End Financials
Return on assets: 3.6%   Cash ($ mil.): 4
Return on equity: 11.9%
Current ratio: 2.20

MAYO CLINIC HEALTH SYSTEM-FRANCISCAN MEDICAL CENTER, INC.

EXECUTIVES

Pres-Ceo, Robert Nesse
Cfo*, Thomas Tiggelaar
Crna, Bradley J Lassa
Crna, Darla J Brodigan
Anp, Alayna M Ruhbusch
MD, Bradly J Narr
Chief of Anesthesiology, Brian Larsen
Crna, Cole B Dolan
MD, Jennifer L Brumm
MD, Jonathan Ticku
Crna, Kim M Oldenburg

LOCATIONS

HQ: MAYO CLINIC HEALTH SYSTEM-FRANCISCAN
   MEDICAL CENTER, INC.
   700 WEST AVE S, LA CROSSE, WI 546014783
Phone: 608 785-0940
Web: WWW.MAYO.EDU

HISTORICAL FINANCIALS
Company Type: Private

Income Statement				FYE: December 31
	REVENUE ($ mil.)	NET INCOME ($ mil.)	NET PROFIT MARGIN	EMPLOYEES
12/14	452	19	4.3%	3,300
12/08	363	0	—	—
12/05	223	200	89.5%	—
12/04	2,103	0	—	—
Annual Growth	—	—	—	—

2014 Year-End Financials
Return on assets: 7.3%   Cash ($ mil.): —
Return on equity: 12.1%
Current ratio: 1.30

MAYO CLINIC HOSPITAL-ROCHESTER

Multidisciplinary teamwork with coordinated care is Mayo Clinic's secret sauce. The not-for-profit Mayo Clinic provides health care most notably for complex medical conditions through its clinics in Rochester Minnesota Arizona and Florida. The clinics' multidisciplinary approach to care attracts more than a million patients a year from around the globe. For less specialized care the Mayo Clinic Health System operates a regional network of affiliated community hospitals and clinics in Minnesota Iowa and Wisconsin. Mayo Clinic also conducts research and trains physicians nurses and other health professionals. The Mayo Clinic is named for Dr. William Worrall Mayo who settled in Rochester in 1863.

Operations

Mayo Clinic Health System's regional network operates more than a dozen hospitals that combined are home to about 1000 beds and 3800 staff physicians medical scientists and clinical and research associates. The system also includes roughly 70 clinics in northern Iowa western Wisconsin and southeastern Minnesota. To manage its patient load Mayo forms referral alliances with other hospital groups HMOs and other organizations.

The clinic's education programs include the Mayo Medical School Mayo Graduate School and the Mayo School of Health Sciences; some medical training programs are conducted through partnerships with universities including the University of Minnesota. It also provides continuing education programs to medical professionals.

Financial Performance

The Mayo Clinic's revenue increased by nearly 7% in 2011 vs. 2010 while net income declined 18% over the same period. Indeed revenue gains and other support has steadily increased in recent years to nearly $8.5 billion in 2011. Sales of medical services (which account for about 85% of the Mayo Clinic's total) grew by 6% vs. the prior year. The Mayo Clinic list more than $10 billion in total assets.

Strategy

Already a giant in health care in the Midwest the Mayo Clinic continues to grow in other regions. In 2018 it announced plans to invest some $648 million in its Phoenix campus over the next five years. The project will roughly double the size of the campus allowing the system to meet growing demand for complex health care services in the Southwest. Similarly Mayo Clinic is investing some $144 million in its Jacksonville Florida campus.

Mayo Clinic strives to accommodate patients who travel to get to its facilities and will schedule multiple appointments and tests tightly together to make the most of patient's time. Rather than paying physicians based upon the quantity of patients seen the clinic's doctors are paid salaries as an incentive to quality care. These and other innovations have drawn attention to the clinic's patient-centered model of care. It has created a Center for the Science of Health Care Delivery and collaborates with other innovators including Cleveland Clinic and Intermountain Healthcare.

To reach remote areas Mayo Clinic in Arizona pioneered a telemedicine program that places robots in rural hospitals allowing local doctors and hospital staff to communicate with Mayo doctors in real time as they treat patients with such conditions as stroke or collapsed lungs.

EXECUTIVES

Regional Vice President, Annie Sadosty
Vice President, Brian Arendt
Assistant Treasurer, Paul A Gorman
Medical Secretary, Judy Jerabek
Vice Chair Dermatology, Marian Mcevoy
Medical Secretary, Deborah Stark
Medical Secretary, Mark Wojahn
Medical Secretary, Gina Robertson
Auditors: ERNST & YOUNG LLP MINNEAPOLIS

LOCATIONS

HQ: MAYO CLINIC HOSPITAL-ROCHESTER
200 1ST ST SW, ROCHESTER, MN 559050002
Phone: 507 284-2511
Web: WWW.MAYOCLINIC.ORG

Selected Locations and Affiliates
Direct subsidiaries
 Arizona
 Mayo Clinic Hospital (Phoenix)
 Mayo Clinic Scottsdale
 Florida
 Mayo Clinic Hospital (Jacksonville)
 Mayo Clinic Jacksonville
 Minnesota
 Mayo Clinic Rochester
 Rochester Methodist Hospital
 Saint Marys Hospital (Rochester)
 Mayo Eugenio Litta Children's Hospital
Mayo Health System affiliates
 Iowa
 Armstrong Clinic
 Decorah Clinic
 Lake Mills Clinic
  Franciscan
 Swea City Clinic
 Minnesota
 Fountain Centers in Fairmont
 Fountain Centers in Waseca
  FamilyHeal
 FamilyHealth Medical Clinic - Northfield Hospital
 Franciscan Healthcare in Caledonia
 Franciscan Healthcare La Crescent Clinic
 Mayo Clinic Health System - Albert Lea
  Mayo Clini
  Mayo Clini
  Mayo Clini
  Mayo Clini
 Wisconsin
 Chippewa Valley in Bloomer
 Chippewa Valley in Chippewa Falls
 Chippewa Valley in Colfax
 Eau Claire Home Health & Hospice
 Franciscan Healthcare Arcadia Campus
 Franciscan Healthcare Holmen Clinic
 Franciscan Healthcare Lake Tomah Clinic
 Franciscan Healthcare Onalaska Clinic
 Franciscan Healthcare Prairie du Chien Clinic
 Franciscan Healthcare Sparta Campus
 Northland in Barron
 Red Cedar in Elmwood
 Red Cedar in Glenwood
 Red Cedar in Menomonie

PRODUCTS/OPERATIONS

2015 Revenues

	$ mil.	% of total
Medical services	8,620	84
Grants & contracts	386	4
Investment return	233	2
Contributions	211	2
Premiums	144	1
Other	721	6
Total	**8,476**	**100**

COMPETITORS

Allina Hospitals
Ascension Health
Beth Israel Deaconess Medical Center
CentraCare Health
Children's Hospitals and Clinics of Minnesota
Dana-Farber
Fairview Health
Fox Chase Cancer Center
Gundersen Lutheran
HCA
Henry Ford Health System
Intermountain Health Care
Johns Hopkins Medicine
MD Anderson Cancer Center
Memorial Sloan-Kettering
North Memorial Health Care
Olmsted Medical
Park Nicollet Health Services
Roswell Park Cancer Institute
Scottsdale Healthcare
Tenet Healthcare
The Cleveland Clinic
Wistar Institute

HISTORICAL FINANCIALS

Company Type: Private

Income Statement   FYE: December 31

	REVENUE ($ mil.)	NET INCOME ($ mil.)	NET PROFIT MARGIN	EMPLOYEES
12/17	11,993	856	7.1%	32,271
12/16	10,998	(480)	—	—
Annual Growth	9.0%	—	—	—

2017 Year-End Financials

Return on assets: 5.2%   Cash ($ mil.): 66
Return on equity: 10.7%
Current ratio: 1.00

MAYO CLINIC JACKSONVILLE (A NONPROFIT CORPORATION)

With more than 370 doctors and scientists on staff Mayo Clinic Jacksonville offers a broad range of medical surgical and research services. The clinic part of the larger Mayo Clinic network and one of its four major campuses offers specialty services such as organ transplantation neurology and oncology therapy. Most patients provided care from the clinic are treated on an outpatient basis; those who require hospitalization are admitted to the adjacent Mayo Clinic Hospital a 214-bed acute care facility. The Jacksonville campus also includes the Birdsall Medical Research center and the Griffin Cancer Research building.

Geographic Reach

While it draws heavily from the local population Mayo Clinic Jacksonville is also a destination for interregional and international patients seeking the coordinated treatment services that are ingrained in the Mayo approach to care.

Strategy

In recent years May Clinic Jacksonville has boosted its presence across the Northeast Florida region. The move includes its $80-million capital improvement of the hospital off San Pablo Road which added two floors and 90 beds in 2013.

Mayo Clinic Jacksonville has also been busy in 2014 opening primary care centers throughout the region including those on the city's Southside Jacksonville Beach and St. Augustine areas.

Since its opening in 1986 the Jacksonville campus has steadily added new facilities. It built and opened the Mayo Clinic Hospital building in 2008 on its current campus. In 2011 it opened a sleep disorder center and a simulation training center where physicians can improve their skills in risk-free environment. Because so many patients travel to receive treatment at Mayo Clinic Jacksonville the clinic also houses two hotels on its campus as well as the extended-stay Gabriel House of Care.

Company Background

The Jacksonville clinic originally provided acute care services at St. Luke's Hospital. The clinic sold St. Luke's to St. Vincent's Medical Center (one of the members of Jacksonville's St. Vincent's Health System) in 2005. The Mayo Clinic leased back the St. Luke's hospital until its new facility was completed in 2008.

EXECUTIVES

Ceo, Kent R Thielen
Cfo*, Mary J Hoffman
Admin, Paul Haines

LOCATIONS

HQ: MAYO CLINIC JACKSONVILLE (A NONPROFIT CORPORATION)
4500 SAN PABLO RD S, JACKSONVILLE, FL 322241865
Phone: 904 953-2000

PRODUCTS/OPERATIONS

Selected Facilities

Birdsall Medical Research Building
Cannaday Building
Gabriel House of Care
Griffin Cancer Research Building
Mayo Clinic Hospital
The Inn at Mayo Clinic

COMPETITORS

Baptist Health System
Florida Hospital Tampa Bay Division
H. Lee Moffitt Cancer Center & Research Institute
Lawnwood Medical Center
Nemours Foundation
North Florida Regional Medical Center
Ocala Regional Medical Center
Palms West Hospital
St. Vincent's Health System
UF Health Jacksonville
UF&Shands

HISTORICAL FINANCIALS

Company Type: Private

Income Statement   FYE: December 31

	REVENUE ($ mil.)	NET INCOME ($ mil.)	NET PROFIT MARGIN	EMPLOYEES
12/16	520	94	18.2%	5,500
12/15	457	65	14.3%	—
12/13	657	(0)	—	—
12/09	340	(4)	—	—
Annual Growth	6.2%	—	—	—

2016 Year-End Financials

Return on assets: 11.5%   Cash ($ mil.): —
Return on equity: 17.8%
Current ratio: 2.00

MAYO FOUNDATION FOR MEDICAL EDUCATION AND RESEARCH

EXECUTIVES

Pres-Ceo, William Litchy
Pres and Ceo*, John H Noseworthy
Operations Administrator, Adrienne Palmer Fache
Senior Analyst Programmer, Craig Robert Stancl
Information, Gerhardt Hartke
Information Technology/Telecom, Jeralyn Waller Smith
Information Project Sp, Joe Woodie
Information Unit Head, Karen Laures
Assistant To Chief Technology, Kristin Olson
Net, Neal Briest
Information, Calvin Beebe

LOCATIONS

HQ: MAYO FOUNDATION FOR MEDICAL EDUCATION AND RESEARCH
200 1ST ST SW, ROCHESTER, MN 559050001
Phone: 507 284-2511

HISTORICAL FINANCIALS

Company Type: Private

Income Statement   FYE: December 31

	REVENUE ($ mil.)	NET INCOME ($ mil.)	NET PROFIT MARGIN	EMPLOYEES
12/13	1,069	6	0.6%	60,000
12/05	5,802	505	8.7%	—
12/03	4,822	348	7.2%	—
12/02	0	0	—	—
Annual Growth	—	—	—	—

2013 Year-End Financials

Return on assets: 75.4%   Cash ($ mil.): 496
Return on equity: 0.6%
Current ratio: 0.70

MCCARTHY BUILDING COMPANIES, INC.

A company that was in construction before Reconstruction McCarthy Building Companies is one of the oldest and largest privately-held builders in the US. The general contractor and construction manager ranks among the top builders of health care education and green building facilities in the country. Contracts include heavy construction projects (bridges and water- and waste-treatment plants) commercial projects (retail and office buildings) and institutional projects (airports schools and prisons). Subsidiary MC Industrial handles energy auto and other manufacturing projects. Founded by Timothy McCarthy in 1864 the company is 100% employee owned and generates $3 billion in annual revenues.

Operations

As of 2016 nearly half of the builder's project portfolio was made up of Construction Manager at Risk projects while around a quarter of the portfolio consisted of Hard Bid projects. The rest was made up of Design/Build Construction Manager Owner Agent and Negotiated General Contracting

projects. About 70% of its work came from repeat clients.

That year the company reported that it had 1600 full-time salaried and 1200 weekly payroll employees.

Geographic Reach

Headquartered in Saint Louis McCarthy Building Companies has worked on projects in 44 US states. Its offices are in Newport Beach San Francisco Sacramento and San Diego California; Albuquerque New Mexico; Las Vegas; Phoenix; St. Louis; Atlanta; Dallas; Houston; and Illinois. It does business in about 45 states.

Sales and Marketing

The firm gets more than 70% of its work from repeat clients which have included Kaiser Permanente California State University and Bally's Casino Resort.

Financial Performance

Ranked among the Top 10 commercial builders in the US McCarthy generates about $3 billion in annual revenues (as of 2016).

Strategy

McCarthy Building Companies has been steadily building its presence with new office openings in strong building markets across the US over the past few years with one of its most recent being an office in Lakewood Colorado in mid 2015. The company has also been growing through acquisitions of smaller companies that complement its existing service lines.

Some of the company's more recent contracts (around early 2016) include: the Genome Lab for J. Craig Venter Institute; the Chino Valley Solar project for Arizona Public Service; the Dallas City Performance Hall for the City of Dallas; the McCarran International Airport for Clark County; the Sacramento Recreation & Wellness Center for California State University; the San Diego and Paramount Unified School Districts in California; and the Lake Pleasant Water Treatment Plant for the City of Phoenix among others.

Some of its past projects include The Platinum condominium/hotel tower in Las Vegas expansion at M.D. Anderson Cancer Center and renovation and expansion of the National Baseball Hall of Fame and Museum in Cooperstown New York.

Mergers and Acquisitions

In October 2014 McCarthy bought St. Louis-based Castle Contracting and its subsidiary CastleGPS. Castle provided turnkey civil services utilities earthwork and trenchless technology directly to owners general contractors and mechinncal electrical and plumbing contractors. Castle's GPS technology provides "industry-leading" subsurface 3-Dimensional utility mapping. The acquired company would continue using the Castle brand name.

EXECUTIVES

Chairman And Ceo, Michael D. (Mike) Bolen
President And Coo, Derek W. Glanvill
President Northern Pacific Division, Richard A. (Rich) Henry
President Southwest Region, Robert (Bo) Calbert
President Texas Division, Michael J. McWay
President Southeast Division, Kevin Kuntz
President Mc Industrial, Tom Felton
Corporate President And Coo, Scott Wittkop
Evp, Ray Sedey
Evp Operations, Robert Betz
Vp And Cio, Mike Oster
Cfo, Doug Audiffred
President Central Division, John Buescher
Vice President Operations, Ben Johanneman
Vice President, Drew Jackson
Senior Vice President General Counsel, Matt Lawson

Vice President Business Development Houston, Wendell Rychlik
Senior Vice President Atlanta, Bobby Campbell
Vice President Finance Southwest Region, Christine Mostaert
Auditors: RUBINBROWN LLP SAINT LOUIS M

LOCATIONS

HQ: MCCARTHY BUILDING COMPANIES, INC.
  1341 N ROCK HILL RD, SAINT LOUIS, MO 631241441
Phone: 314 968-3300
Web: WWW.MCCARTHY.COM

PRODUCTS/OPERATIONS

Selected Markets

Commercial
Education K-12
Health care
Heavy/civil/transportation
Higher education
High performance/green
Hospitality/entertainment
Industrial
Native American
Parking structures
Science and technology
Water/wastewater

Selected Services
Negotiated general contracting
Construction management
Hard bid (lump sum contract for services)
Design/build
Construction management/general contracting

COMPETITORS

Alberici	Korte
Barton Malow	Peter Kiewit Sons'
Bechtel	Primus Builders
Clayco	S. M. Wilson
DPR Construction	Skanska
Gilbane	Swinerton
HBE Corporation	Turner Corporation
Hensel Phelps	Tutor Perini
Construction	

HISTORICAL FINANCIALS

Company Type: Private

Income Statement				FYE: December 31
	REVENUE ($ mil.)	NET INCOME ($ mil.)	NET PROFIT MARGIN	EMPLOYEES
12/18	3,852	0	—	4,025
12/17	3,574	0	—	—
12/16	3,265	0	—	—
12/15	2,719	0	—	—
Annual Growth	12.3%	—	—	—

2018 Year-End Financials

Return on assets: —
Return on equity: —
Current ratio: 1.40
Cash ($ mil.): 451

MCCARTHY HOLDINGS, INC.

EXECUTIVES

Ceo, Raymond J Sedey
Chb, Michael D Bolen
Pres-Coo*, Scott Wittkop
Exec V Pres-Cfo-Sec*, J Douglas Audiffred
Sr V Pres-Gen Counsel*, Matthew Lawson

Treas-Asst SEC*, Danel Dillon
Project Engineer, Adam Lampe
Project Engineer, Adam Walter
Senior Project Engineer, Alex Wright
Engineer, Amanda Morgan
Assistant Project Manager, Amanda Nichols
Auditors: RUBINBROWN LLP SAINT LOUIS M

LOCATIONS

HQ: MCCARTHY HOLDINGS, INC.
  1341 N ROCK HILL RD, SAINT LOUIS, MO 631241441
Phone: 314 968-3300
Web: WWW.MCCARTHY.COM

HISTORICAL FINANCIALS

Company Type: Private

Income Statement				FYE: December 31
	REVENUE ($ mil.)	NET INCOME ($ mil.)	NET PROFIT MARGIN	EMPLOYEES
12/18	3,925	0	—	4,600
12/17	3,666	0	—	—
12/16	3,481	0	—	—
12/15	2,837	0	—	—
Annual Growth	11.4%	—	—	—

2018 Year-End Financials

Return on assets: —
Return on equity: —
Current ratio: 1.30
Cash ($ mil.): 90

MCLANE COMPANY, INC.

McLane Company is one of the largest wholesale suppliers of grocery and food products in the US serving some 50000 retail locations and 35000 restaurants across all 50 states. It delivers more than 50000 different consumer products to customers such as convenience and discount stores mass merchandisers wholesale clubs drug stores military bases and quick-service and casual dining restaurants. The company also distributes alcoholic beverages in the southeastern US and Colorado through subsidiaries. McLane is owned by Warren Buffett's Berkshire Hathaway and accounts for about a fifth of its revenue.

Operations

McLane operates through three business units: grocery distribution foodservice distribution and beverage distribution.

Its grocery business which accounts for about two-thirds of sales serves convenience stores and other retailers nationwide. The company's foodservice business focuses on restaurants across the country while subsidiaries such as Empire Distributors and Baroness Small Estates provide spirits wine and beer to more than 25000 retail locations in the southeastern US and Colorado. Food and beverage distribution together generates about a third of sales.

Geographic Reach

McLane has an extensive distribution network of some 80 facilities across the country with reach in all 50 US states. Its headquarters and grocery operations are based in Temple Texas while its Foodservice operation is based in Carrollton Texas.

The company supplies alcoholic beverages throughout the southeastern US and in Colorado through distribution centers in Colorado Georgia North Carolina and Tennessee.

Sales and Marketing

McLane is a leading supplier to convenience stores; other customers include discount and drug stores mass merchants wholesale clubs military

bases and quick-service and casual dining restaurants.

The company is heavily reliant on former parent Walmart which generates about 20% of its revenue; 7-Eleven and Yum! Brands each account for about 10% of revenue.

Financial Performance

McLane's revenue has grown slightly over the past several years up 4% since 2016 amid intense competition.

The company reported 2018 revenue of about $50 billion up less than a percent from the prior year. A slight rise in grocery sales was mostly offset by a decline in foodservice sales because of a net loss in customers.

Strategy

Although McLane is one of the leaders in grocery and food distribution the business is low-margin and intensely competitive. As the company continues to expand by opening new distribution centers it is focused on technology and automation that can improve service while reducing costs. In late 2017 it opened what was its most technologically advanced distribution center in Findlay Ohio. The facility makes use of automation robotics and artificial intelligence among other technologies. McLane has continued opening distribution centers since then including a 2018 opening in Fort Worth Texas and a 2019 opening in Ocala Florida.

In addition to distribution center technology the company has also introduced a new mobile app (Mobile Virtual Trade Show or Mobile VTS) to simplify the ordering process for convenience store retailers.

Company Background

Starting as a family-owned grocery store in 1894 McLane expanded into wholesale distribution in the early 1900s. The McLane family including former Houston Astros owner Drayton McLane sold the business to Wal-Mart Stores in the 1990s. Conglomerate Berkshire Hathaway acquired McLane Company in 2003 for about $1.5 billion.

EXECUTIVES

President Mclane Grocery, Mike Youngblood
Evp Administration, James L. (Jim) Kent
President And Ceo, W. Grady Rosier
President Southeast Southern And Dothan Divisions, Ron Clark
President Mclane Carolina And Mid-atlantic Divisions, George Bolts
President Southwest And High Plains Divisions, Scott Braden
Svp And Chief Marketing Officer, Tom Sicola
Vice President Of Information Technology, Mona Huffman
Vice President Of Sales, Jimmy Morales
Vice President Distribution, Curtis Carpenter
Senior Vice President, Charles Freeman
Senior Vice President, Julie Norris
Vice President National Accounts, Jeff Hayes
Vice President Of Logistics, Robbie Wainwright
Vice President Of Sales Convenience And Military Executive, Vito Maurici
Division Vice President, John Havel
Region Vice President, Calvin Parker
Senior Vice President Midwest Division, Tim Donahoe
Senior Vice President Midwest Division, Matt Bowen
Vice President Information Systems, Melanie Lewis

LOCATIONS

HQ: MCLANE COMPANY, INC.
  4747 MCLANE PKWY, TEMPLE, TX 765044854
Phone: 254 771-7500
Web: WWW.MCLANECO.COM

COMPETITORS

AMCON Distributing	MAINES
Associated Wholesale Grocers	Performance Food Group
Ben E. Keith	Reinhart FoodService
C&S Wholesale	SUPERVALU
Core-Mark	Southern Glazer's Wine and Spirits
Eby-Brown	Sysco
GSC Enterprises	US Foods
Golden State Foods	United Natural
Gordon Food Service	Wakefern Food
H. T. Hackney	

HISTORICAL FINANCIALS
Company Type: Private

Income Statement
FYE: December 30

	REVENUE ($ mil.)	NET INCOME ($ mil.)	NET PROFIT MARGIN	EMPLOYEES
12/16*	48,016	0	—	20,128
01/16	48,144	0	—	—
12/12	37,389	0	—	—
01/09	29,800	0	—	—
Annual Growth	6.1%	—	—	—

*Fiscal year change

2016 Year-End Financials
Return on assets: —
Return on equity: —
Current ratio: 1.40
Cash ($ mil.): 122

MCNAUGHTON-MCKAY ELECTRIC CO.

Getting connected at work has a completely different meaning at McNaughton-McKay. Its more than 10000 customers can buy electrical supplies sensors and controls and automation and security software online or through 23 branches in five US states and two offices in Germany and Brazil. One of the largest employee-owned companies in the US McNaughton-McKay distributes some 300 product lines from manufacturers such as Hubbell GE Brady Belden Coleman Cable Leviton Thomas & Betts Cognex Specter Instruments and Rockwell Automation. It sells to the construction commercial government and industrial automation markets.

Geographic Reach
The company serves more than 10000 customers through 23 branches in the US Germany and Brazil.

Sales and Marketing
The company sells its products from its sales offices and as well as eSales Centers. In addition to the industrial automation commercial and construction markets McNaughton-McKay supports government customers on a Federal State and Local level by providing hundreds of electrical products and MRO supplies with local support and inventory. McNaughton-McKay's customers include supplyFORCE Vanguard National Alliance and Vantage Group.

Strategy
McNaughton-McKay — informally known as Mc-Mc — has grown by expanding its product lineup and increasing its purchasing power through buying and marketing groups such as Affiliated Distributors supplyFORCE and Vantage Group. The distributor has also added a group dedicated to green products primarily energy-efficient lighting and power distribution products along with an Engineered Solutions Group that sells and installs solar and wind energy through partnerships with companies that include Schletter and Ohio Green Wind.

Company Background
Founded in 1910 the Bull and McNaughton families ran McNaughton-McKay until 2006. It established a sales office in Germany in 2004.

EXECUTIVES

Evp And, Donald D. (Don) Slominski
Evp Sales And Marketing, Richard (Rick) Dahlstrom
Vp Information Technology, Gregory H. (Greg) Chun
Vice President Human Resources, John D. Kuczmanski
Corporate Purchasing Manager, Maridee Curry
Auditors: KPMG LLP

LOCATIONS

HQ: MCNAUGHTON-MCKAY ELECTRIC CO.
1357 E LINCOLN AVE, MADISON HEIGHTS, MI 480714126
Phone: 248 399-7500
Web: WWW.MC-MC.COM

PRODUCTS/OPERATIONS

Selected Products
Bar code scanners and systems
Communication input/output (I/O) networks
Computers and peripherals
Convenience panels (cables and equipment)
Cordsets
Data-collection terminals and software
Drives and motor controllers
Engineered products
I/O products (AC/DC modules)
Motion-control products
  CNC controls
  Servos
  Spindles
Motors (AC)
PLC processors
Radio-frequency identification (RFID) products
Safety products
  Gate switches
  Light curtains
  Mats
  Relays
Sensors
Software
Vision products (inspection equipment)

COMPETITORS

Anixter International	Kendall Electric
Border States Electric	Madison Electric
Consolidated Electrical	Medler Electric
Crescent Electric Supply	OneSource Distributors
	Rexel Inc.
Dealers Electrical	SUMMIT Electric Supply
Electrocomponents	Steiner Electric
Graybar Electric	Stuart C. Irby
Hite Company	W.W. Grainger
	WESCO International

HISTORICAL FINANCIALS
Company Type: Private

Income Statement
FYE: December 31

	REVENUE ($ mil.)	NET INCOME ($ mil.)	NET PROFIT MARGIN	EMPLOYEES
12/17	822	0	—	854
12/16	724	0	—	—
12/15	702	0	—	—
12/14	689	0	—	—
Annual Growth	6.1%	—	—	—

2017 Year-End Financials
Return on assets: —
Return on equity: —
Current ratio: 4.60
Cash ($ mil.): 26

MED AMERICA HEALTH SYSTEMS CORPORATION

EXECUTIVES

Pres, T G Breitenbach
SEC*, Dale Creech
Cfo*, Timothy Jackson
Coordinator, Evan Ichikawa
Coordinator, Kimiko Johnson

LOCATIONS

HQ: MED AMERICA HEALTH SYSTEMS CORPORATION
1 WYOMING ST, DAYTON, OH 454092722
Phone: 937 223-6192

HISTORICAL FINANCIALS
Company Type: Private

Income Statement
FYE: December 31

	REVENUE ($ mil.)	NET INCOME ($ mil.)	NET PROFIT MARGIN	EMPLOYEES
12/11	919	24	2.7%	10,700
12/10	843	67	8.1%	—
12/08	790	(153)	—	—
Annual Growth	5.1%	—	—	—

2011 Year-End Financials
Return on assets: 1.7%
Return on equity: 3.5%
Current ratio: 1.90
Cash ($ mil.): 42

MEDCO, L.L.C.

EXECUTIVES

Admin, Archie J Chapman
Office Manager, Henry Williams

LOCATIONS

HQ: MEDCO, L.L.C.
3701 DADEVILLE RD, ALEXANDER CITY, AL 350109075
Phone: 256 215-3889
Web: WWW.CHAPMANHEALTHCARE.NET

HISTORICAL FINANCIALS
Company Type: Private

Income Statement
FYE: June 30

	REVENUE ($ mil.)	NET INCOME ($ mil.)	NET PROFIT MARGIN	EMPLOYEES
06/09*	854	(173)	—	225
09/02	4	0	13.6%	—
09/00	2	0	13.7%	—
12/99	0	0	—	—
Annual Growth	—	—	—	—

*Fiscal year change

2009 Year-End Financials
Return on assets: (-999.9%)
Return on equity: (-999.9%)
Current ratio: 1.40
Cash ($ mil.): —

MEDICAL UNIVERSITY HOSPITAL AUTHORITY

EXECUTIVES

Exec Dir, Patrick Pawley
Auditors: KPMG LLP ATLANTA GA

LOCATIONS

HQ: MEDICAL UNIVERSITY HOSPITAL AUTHORITY
169 ASHLEY AVE, CHARLESTON, SC 294258905
Phone: 843 792-1414
Web: WWW.MUSCKIDS.ORG

HISTORICAL FINANCIALS

Company Type: Private

Income Statement				FYE: June 30
	REVENUE ($ mil.)	NET INCOME ($ mil.)	NET PROFIT MARGIN	EMPLOYEES
06/08	821	(19)	—	4,000
06/07	749	26	3.5%	—
06/06	0	0	—	—
Annual Growth	—	—	—	—

2008 Year-End Financials

Return on assets: (-2.2%)
Return on equity: (-8.3%)
Current ratio: 1.50
Cash ($ mil.): 14

MEDSTAR HEALTH, INC.

Whether you're seeing stars or are just plain sickly MedStar Health can cater to you. The not-for-profit organization runs 10 hospitals and about 20 other health-related businesses across Maryland and the Washington DC area including Union Memorial and Georgetown University Hospital. With more than 3000 beds and 6000 affiliated physicians MedStar has a comprehensive service offering including acute and long-term sub-acute care emergency services home health care and rehabilitation. It also operates emergency clinics and assisted living and nursing homes maintains a primary care and specialist physician network (MedStar Physician Partners) and conducts research and medical education activities.

Operations

Along with its 10 hospitals and a dizzying array of inpatient and outpatient services MedStar Health also operates a Medicaid managed care program called MedStar Family Choice.

Its Nascott Orthotics and Prosthetics division provides adult and pediatric prosthetic services and devices to patients in Washington DC and Baltimore. The company provides a continuum of care from initial measurement to fabrication of the device and maintenance through four locations scattered throughout the service areas.

MedStar Health's Visiting Nurse Association (VNA) administers home health care infusion services private duty nursing and hospice as well as immunizations. The VNA also uses telemonitoring services to keep tabs on home care patients without having to physically visit each patient's home.

In 2014 the system had 148685 inpatient admissions and nearly 4 million outpatient visits.

Financial Performance

In fiscal 2014 MedStar Health's net operating revenue totaled $4.6 billion.

Strategy

Despite its already hefty size MedStar Health is not adverse to getting bigger. It grows usually through acquisitions of existing facilities but also through alliances with other health care providers. MedStar Health has acquired several hospitals in recent years including St. Mary's Hospital with 100 beds in southern Maryland and Montgomery General Hospital a 150-bed general acute care facility located in Montgomery County Maryland.

The company also grows by establishing new facilities. In 2014 it opened an integrated multi-specialty care center in downtown Baltimore as well as four new PromptCare locations in Maryland and Virginia. That year it began work on a new ambulatory care center at the 16-acre MedStar Health Bel Air Medical Campus. MedStar is also developing a new ambulatory care center at Lafayette Centre in northwest Washington DC.

MedStar Health has also entered the growing quick-care and urgent care market by partnering with Rite Aid to establish walk-in health clinics in a number of Rite Aid pharmacies throughout the Baltimore and Washington DC markets.

In 2015 the system expanded its Medicare Choice plan into Baltimore City and Anne Arundel Baltimore Charles Prince George's and St. Mary's counties.

EXECUTIVES

Evp Insurance And Diversified Operations, Eric R. Wagner
Evp And Chief Administrative Officer, Michael J. Curran
Evp And Coo, M. Joy Drass
President Medstar Ambulatory Services, Bob Gilbert
Svp And President Medstar Good Samaritan Hospital And Medstar Union Memorial Hospital, Bradley S. Chambers
Svp And Chief Nursing Officer, Maureen P. McCausland
President Medstar Medical Group, Richard Goldberg
President Ceo And Director, Kenneth A. Samet
President Medstar Visiting Nurse Association, Traci K. Anderson
Evp Medical Affairs And Chief Medical Officer, Stephen R. T. Evans
Svp And President Medstar National Rehabilitation Network, John D. Rockwood
President Medstar Health Research Institute, Neil J. Weissman
Svp And President Medstar Southern Maryland Hospital Center And St. Mary's Hospital, Christine R. Wray
Svp And President Medstar Franklin Square Medical Center, Samuel E. Moskowitz
Evp And General Counsel, Oliver M. Johnson
Svp And President Medstar Washington Hospital Center, John Sullivan
Svp Marketing And Strategy, Kevin P. Kowalski
Evp And Cfo, Susan K. Nelson
Vp Applications And Interim Cio, Mark K. Schneider
Svp And President Medstar Georgetown University Hospital, Michael C. Sachtleben
Svp And President Medstar Montgomery Medical Center, T. J. Senker
Vice President Digital Marketing, Sameer Kasargod
Chairman, William R. Roberts
Vice Chairman, William J. Oetgen
Auditors: KMPG LLP BALTIMORE MD

LOCATIONS

HQ: MEDSTAR HEALTH, INC.
10980 GRANTCHESTER WAY WA, COLUMBIA, MD 210446097
Phone: 410 772-6500
Web: WWW.MEDSTARHEALTH.ORG

Selected Facilities

Maryland
Franklin Square Hospital Center (Baltimore)
Good Samaritan Hospital (Baltimore)
Harbor Hospital (Baltimore)
Montgomery General Hospital (Olney)
St. Mary's Hospital (Leonardtown)
Union Memorial Hospital (Baltimore)

Washington DC
Georgetown University Hospital
National Rehabilitation Hospital
Washington Hospital Center

PRODUCTS/OPERATIONS

Selected Affiliates/Operations

Clinical Research
Georgetown University Medical Center (Washington DC)
MedStar Research Institute (Hyattsville Maryland)
Home Health Care
MedStar Health VNA (Washington DC)
MedStar Health Infusion (Elkridge Maryland)
MGH Community Health (Olney Maryland)
Managed Care
MedStar Family Choice (Baltimore Maryland)
Nursing Homes/Senior Living
Franklin Woods (Rosedale Maryland)
Good Samaritan Nursing Center (Baltimore Maryland)
Belvedere Green (Baltimore Maryland)
Woodbourne Woods (Baltimore Maryland)
Primary Care
MedStar Physician Partners (Washington DC)
Outpatient Surgery Centers
MedStar Surgery Center (Washington DC)
Harbor Hospital HealthPark (Pasadena Maryland)
SurgiCenter at Pasadena (Pasadena Maryland)

COMPETITORS

Adventist HealthCare
Anne Arundel Medical Center
Ascension Health
Bon Secours Health
Carilion Clinic
Children's National Medical Center
Christiana Care
Civista Health
Franklin Square Hospital Center
GBMC
Harbor Hospital
Inova
Johns Hopkins Health System
Johns Hopkins Medicine
Kaiser Foundation Health Plan of the Mid-Atlantic
Levindale Hospital
LifeBridge Health
MedStar Union Memorial Hospital
Sinai Hospital of Baltimore
Suburban Hospital
Trinity Health (Novi)
University of Maryland Medical System
Valley Health
Virginia Hospital Center

HISTORICAL FINANCIALS

Company Type: Private

Income Statement				FYE: June 30
	REVENUE ($ mil.)	NET INCOME ($ mil.)	NET PROFIT MARGIN	EMPLOYEES
06/18	5,604	324	5.8%	33,000
06/13	4,217	311	7.4%	—
06/11*	4,011	271	6.8%	—
12/09	1,936	200	10.4%	—
Annual Growth	14.2%	6.2%	—	—

*Fiscal year change

Return on assets: 5.7%   Cash ($ mil.): 692
Return on equity: 16.3%
Current ratio: 1.30

MEDSTAR-GEORGETOWN MEDICAL CENTER, INC.

Medstar-Georgetown Medical Center (dba as Medstar Georgetown University Hospital as a part of MedStar Health) is a 609-bed acute care teaching hospital serving residents of the greater Washington DC area including Maryland and Virginia. The hospital's staff of more than 1100 physicians represents a wide range of medical specializations including cardiology oncology neurology/neurosurgery and surgical transplantation. Medstar Georgetown provides a comprehensive array of inpatient outpatient surgical and rehabilitative care services. The hospital is part of a local network of affiliated primary care providers.

Operations
Medstar Georgetown's Transplant Institute is one of a handful of centers in the US that offers living-donor liver transplants; it opened a new medical space in 2014. Also Georgetown Neurosciences is the sixth unit nationwide to provide CyberKnife stereotactic radiosurgery for the treatment of tumors and lesions of the brain neck and spine.

Strategy
In 2015 Medstar Georgetown submitted a letter of intent with the District of Columbia State Health Planning and Development Agency seeking approval to modernize its existing medical facility by constructing a new state-of-the-art medical surgical pavilion. The pavilion will house surgical critical care and emergency departments as well as related administrative functions.

In 2014 MedStar Georgetown became the first center in Washington DC to perform a two-level artificial disc replacement in a patient's neck.

Company Background
In 2011 Medstar Georgetown became the first health system in the area to offer bloodless surgery to patients who prefer not to receive someone else's blood usually for religious reasons. There are three primary approaches to performing bloodless surgeries: before during and after surgery. Before surgery the hospital gives the patient medications such as iron supplements or epoprotein to boost the blood's hemoglobin level. During surgery the hospital is precise as it can be with its surgical techniques to limit blood loss and there are anesthesia techniques to lower blood pressure so patients bleed less. There is also a machine called Cell Saver that is used during surgery that collects blood lost suctions it into a canister washes and filters it and then returns it directly into the patient as a product that is about 60-percent pure red blood cells. After surgery medications are used to raise blood levels and medical providers avoid taking multiple blood draws for blood tests.

The hospital was founded in 1898 to promote health through education research and patient care. The current hospital/medical center was opened in 1947.

EXECUTIVES

Medical Director, Maral Skelsey

LOCATIONS

HQ: MEDSTAR-GEORGETOWN MEDICAL CENTER, INC.
3800 RESERVOIR RD NW, WASHINGTON, DC 200072113
Phone: 202 444-2000
Web: WWW.MEDSTARGEORGETOWN.ORG

PRODUCTS/OPERATIONS

Selected Services
Anesthesiology
Audiology
Bloodless Medicine and Surgery Program
Bone Marrow Transplant
Breast Cancer
Breast Health Program
Cancer Care
Cardiology
Cerebrovascular Center
Colon and Rectal Surgery
Ear Nose and Throat (ENT)
Emergency Urgent Care and Trauma
Endocrinology
Epilepsy
Family Medicine
Fracture Liaison
Head and Neck Cancer
Headache Center
Hematology
Hospital Medicine
Huntington Disease Center
Hyperbaric Oxygen Therapy
Ophthalmology
Orthopaedics
Ostomy Clinic
Otolaryngology
Pastoral Care
Pediatrics
Pharmacy
Physical Medicine
Plastic Surgery
Primary Care
Prostate Cancer

COMPETITORS

Adventist HealthCare
Bon Secours Health
Calvert Memorial Hospital
Children's National Medical Center
Chindex International
Dimensions Healthcare
Doctors Community Hospital
Inova Alexandria Hospital
Providence St. Joseph Health
Suburban Hospital
Upper Chesapeake Health

HISTORICAL FINANCIALS
Company Type: Private

Income Statement   FYE: June 30

	REVENUE ($ mil.)	NET INCOME ($ mil.)	NET PROFIT MARGIN	EMPLOYEES
06/16	801	104	13.1%	4,000
06/15	774	98	12.7%	—
06/11	809	43	5.4%	—
06/10	782	45	5.8%	—
Annual Growth	0.4%	15.0%	—	—

2016 Year-End Financials
Return on assets: 23.6%   Cash ($ mil.): 5
Return on equity: 31.3%
Current ratio: 1.90

MEGA BRANDS AMERICA, INC.

LOCATIONS

HQ: MEGA BRANDS AMERICA, INC.
333 CONTINENTAL BLVD, EL SEGUNDO, CA 902455032
Phone: 949 727-9009
Web: WWW.ROSEART.COM

HISTORICAL FINANCIALS
Company Type: Private

Income Statement   FYE: December 31

	REVENUE ($ mil.)	NET INCOME ($ mil.)	NET PROFIT MARGIN	EMPLOYEES
12/07	524	(97)	—	1,600
12/05	337	37	11.2%	—
Annual Growth	24.7%	—	—	—

2007 Year-End Financials
Return on assets: (-13.7%)   Cash ($ mil.): 8
Return on equity: (-43.7%)
Current ratio: 1.30

MEGLOBAL AMERICAS INC.

EXECUTIVES

Pres, Ramesh Ramachandran
Cfo, Niklaus Meier
Treas, Sumit Pathak
Contrl, William Leikhim
Customer Staff, Nicole Hunt

LOCATIONS

HQ: MEGLOBAL AMERICAS INC.
2150 TOWN SQUARE PL # 750, SUGAR LAND, TX 774791465
Phone: 844 634-5622

HISTORICAL FINANCIALS
Company Type: Private

Income Statement   FYE: December 31

	REVENUE ($ mil.)	NET INCOME ($ mil.)	NET PROFIT MARGIN	EMPLOYEES
12/13	596	10	1.7%	15
12/12	597	13	2.2%	—
12/11	743	20	2.7%	—
Annual Growth	(10.4%)	(29.9%)	—	—

2013 Year-End Financials
Return on assets: 13.6%   Cash ($ mil.): 5
Return on equity: 107.6%
Current ratio: 1.10

MEMORIAL HEALTH CARE SYSTEM, INC.

EXECUTIVES

Pres, James M Hobson
Pres*, Shawn Morrow
Sr V Pres*, Debra L Moore
Cfo*, Cheryl A Sadro
V Pres*, Leigh Bertholf
V Pres*, Diona Brown
Auditors: CATHOLIC HEALTH INITIATIVES E

LOCATIONS

HQ: MEMORIAL HEALTH CARE SYSTEM, INC.
2525 DESALES AVE, CHATTANOOGA, TN 374041161
Phone: 423 495-2525
Web: WWW.MEMORIAL.ORG

HISTORICAL FINANCIALS
Company Type: Private

Income Statement				FYE: June 30
	REVENUE ($ mil.)	NET INCOME ($ mil.)	NET PROFIT MARGIN	EMPLOYEES
06/16	545	22	4.1%	8,800
06/15	527	34	6.6%	—
06/14	557	25	4.6%	—
Annual Growth	(1.1%)	(6.0%)	—	—

2016 Year-End Financials
Return on assets: 2.9%   Cash ($ mil.): 238
Return on equity: 4.8%
Current ratio: 3.70

MEMORIAL HEALTH SERVICES

Where do you go after you get sick riding the tea cups at Disneyland? Not-for-profit Memorial Health Services (known as MemorialCare) owns six hospitals in Southern California including Long Beach Memorial Medical Center Miller Children's Hospital Orange Coast Memorial Medical Center and Saddleback Memorial Medical Center. The facilities have a total of more than 1500 beds and offer a full spectrum of medical services including rehabilitation diagnostic/radiology and emergency services. MemorialCare also operates women's health facilities and other specialty and general practice clinics as well as home health and hospice programs. The organization was founded in 1907.

Operations
MemorialCare's outpatient facilities include the physician practices of the MemorialCare Medical Group the Memorial Prompt Care urgent care centers and the MemorialCare HealthExpress clinics. The network also includes the affiliated practices of the Greater Newport Physicians organization. In addition to inpatient outpatient and home medical care the organization provides clinical training and graduate medical education programs.

Altogether the system's facilities employ 2600 physicians and serve 70000 inpatients each year. They also handle some 35000 surgeries 10000 births 200000 emergency room visits and 40000 home health visits.

Geographic Reach
MemorialCare's facilities are located in Los Angeles County and Orange County in Southern California.

Financial Performance
MemorialCare reported $1.9 billion in revenues and $83 million in net income in 2012. Most of the organization's revenues come from patient services.

Strategy
MemorialCare is expanding to meet continued demand throughout its service area. It has several projects either going on or recently completed that have added operating rooms neonatal beds more advanced technology and centers of excellence in imaging cardiac cancer and obesity at several of its hospitals. In 2014 it opened the new Lung Nodule Center at The MemorialCare Todd Cancer Institute part of Long Beach Memorial.

The organization is also expanding its outpatient care facilities. For instance MemorialCare has joined the growing trend of hospitals partnering with retailers to open in-store retail clinics (under the HealthExpress brand) that offer basic after-hours medical care through physicians and nurse practitioners. It has recently opened four new outpatient surgery centers and launched a couple of new physician locations in affiliation with UC Irvine Health.

EXECUTIVES

Senior Vice President Chief Financial Officer, Cheryl Sadro
President Ceo, James Hobson
Information Technology Vice President, Steven Beal
Medical Director, Adam Wass
Medical Director Of Breast Surgery, Jane Kakkis
Vice President Facilities Committee Chair Project Manager, Denyse Jennings
Chairman, Keith Nelson
Secretary Admin, Paula Spas
Auditors: PRICEWATERHOUSECOOPERS LLP LO

LOCATIONS

HQ: MEMORIAL HEALTH SERVICES
17360 BROOKHURST ST # 160, FOUNTAIN VALLEY, CA 927083720
Phone: 714 377-6748
Web: WWW.MEMORIALCARE.ORG

Selected Facilities
Long Beach Memorial Medical Center (Long Beach California)
Miller Children's Hospital (Long Beach California)
Community Hospital (Long Beach California)
Orange Coast Memorial Medical Center (Fountain Valley California)
Saddleback Memorial Medical Center (San Clemente California)
Saddleback Memorial Medical Center (Laguna Hills California)
MemorialCare Medical Group (regional)
MemorialCare HealthExpress (regional)
MemorialCare Imaging Centers (regional)
Memorial Prompt Care (regional)

PRODUCTS/OPERATIONS

Selected Services
Blood Donation
Diabetes Care
Heart and Vascular Care
Joint Replacement
Neonatal Intensive Care
Rehabilitation and Therapy
Wellness Care
Cancer Care
Gynecological Care
Imaging and Radiology
Maternity Care
Orthopedic Care
Stroke Care
Wound Healing

Breast Care
Express Care
Hyperbaric Medicine
Laboratory Services
Pediatric Care
Surgical Care
Women's Care

COMPETITORS

Adventist Health System West
Cedars-Sinai Medical Center
Childrens Hospital Los Angeles
Community Health Systems
Dignity Health
Good Samaritan Hospital (IN)
Good Samaritan Hospital (Los Angeles)
HCA
HealthCare Partners
Hollywood Presbyterian Medical Center
LifePoint Health
Methodist Hospital of Southern California
Pasadena Hospital Association
Prospect Medical
Providence St. Joseph Health
St. Jude Medical Center
Sutter Health
Tenet Healthcare
Trinity Health (Novi)
Western Medical Center - Santa Ana

HISTORICAL FINANCIALS
Company Type: Private

Income Statement				FYE: June 30
	REVENUE ($ mil.)	NET INCOME ($ mil.)	NET PROFIT MARGIN	EMPLOYEES
06/18	2,232	101	4.5%	6,000
06/15	215	26	12.3%	—
Annual Growth	117.8%	56.3%	—	—

2018 Year-End Financials
Return on assets: 2.8%   Cash ($ mil.): 122
Return on equity: 4.2%
Current ratio: 0.70

MEMORIAL HEALTH, INC.

Auditors: DIXON HUGHES GOODMAN LLP ASHE

LOCATIONS

HQ: MEMORIAL HEALTH, INC.
4700 WATERS AVE, SAVANNAH, GA 314046220
Phone: 912 350-8000
Web: WWW.MEMORIALHEALTH.COM

HISTORICAL FINANCIALS
Company Type: Private

Income Statement				FYE: December 31
	REVENUE ($ mil.)	NET INCOME ($ mil.)	NET PROFIT MARGIN	EMPLOYEES
12/16	581	(38)	—	4,500
12/14	42	(11)	—	—
12/13	24	0	—	—
Annual Growth	185.6%	—	—	—

2016 Year-End Financials
Return on assets: (-6.8%)   Cash ($ mil.): 16
Return on equity: (-28.3%)
Current ratio: 1.50

MEMORIAL HERMANN HEALTH SYSTEM

EXECUTIVES

Ceo, Charles Stokes
Cfo*, Dennis Laraway
Svp-Cceo*, Alexander Greengold
Chief of Medicine, Todd M Price
Coordinator, Melissa Aing
Director of Radiology, Alla Vargo
Educator, Linda Whitson
Obstetrics, Jennifer Weber
Director, Scott Pruzan
Human Resources Manager, Shanobia Stovall
Director of Business Developme, Amanda
 Spielman
Auditors: ERNST & YOUNG LLP HOUSTON TX

LOCATIONS

HQ: MEMORIAL HERMANN HEALTH SYSTEM
 929 GESSNER RD STE 1900, HOUSTON, TX
 770242317
Phone: 713 242-3000
Web: WWW.MEMORIALHERMANN.ORG

HISTORICAL FINANCIALS
Company Type: Private

Income Statement   FYE: June 30

	REVENUE ($ mil.)	NET INCOME ($ mil.)	NET PROFIT MARGIN	EMPLOYEES
06/18	5,258	318	6.1%	14,000
06/17	5,061	313	6.2%	—
06/14	3,741	454	12.1%	—
06/13	3,285	230	7.0%	—
Annual Growth	9.9%	6.6%	—	—

2018 Year-End Financials

Return on assets: 4.5%   Cash ($ mil.): 371
Return on equity: 8.9%
Current ratio: 1.00

MEMORIAL HERMANN HEALTHCARE SYSTEM

Memorial Hermann Healthcare System is a Texas-sized operation. As Houston's largest not-for-profit health care system it includes 15 hospitals (including a children's hospital an orthopedic hospital and two rehabilitation hospitals) with more than 4000 beds and dozens of specialty treatment centers. The system also has joint ventures with four other hospitals in the Greater Houston metropolitan area (located in First Colony Kingwood and Tomball). Memorial Hermann provides medical training in affiliation with The University of Texas Health Science Center Medical School. Other services and programs include home health services air ambulances and imaging; it also offers health insurance coverage. In early 2019 Memorial Hermann canceled plans to merge with fellow Texas health care provider Baylor Scott & White Health.

Operations
Memorial Hermann's 15 hospitals include 11 acute care hospitals a children's hospital two rehabilitation hospitals and an orthopedic hospital. Its flagship location in the Texas Medical Center has a Level I trauma center and houses the Life Flight air ambulance. The system also operates three Heart & Vascular Institutes the Mischer Neuroscience Institute four IRONMAN Sports Medicine Institute locations imaging and surgery centers sports medicine and rehabilitation centers outpatient laboratories a chemical dependency treatment center a home health agency and a senior living community.

In the insurance arena the company's Memorial Hermann Health Insurance Company subsidiary provides HMO and PPO health plans as well as Medicare Advantage plans. Memorial Hermann chose to start offering health care benefits as a way to help employers and individuals cut healthcare costs.

Memorial Hermann has 5500 affiliated physicians.

Geographic Reach
Memorial Hermann's various facilities serve Southeast Texas and the Greater Houston community.

Sales and Marketing
Memorial Herman markets its services through a variety of outlets including social media.

Strategy
As Houston (one of the nation's largest cities) sprawls into the suburbs so has Memorial Hermann. The system's facilities were previously confined to the downtown medical plaza known as Texas Medical Center and other metropolitan locations but Memorial Hermann has branched out to serve surrounding areas and now operates several suburban hospitals. Partnerships with other area providers are another way in which Memorial Hermann enhances its service offerings.

The system's Breaking New Ground initiative is designed to expand access to health care throughout the Greater Houston area. Its flagship location Memorial Hermann-Texas Medical Center is undergoing a major renovation which will add more than 1 million sq. ft. of space. The project includes the construction of a 17-floor patient care tower and later on an expanded emergency center.

Other new or recently updated facilities include the 250000-sq.-ft. Memorial Hermann Pearland Hospital (opened in 2016) Memorial Hermann Katy Hospital (which features a new six-story patient care tower Memorial Hermann Sugar Land Hospital (which also received a new six-story patient care tower) and Memorial Hermann Cypress Hospital (opened in 2017). Additionally the system has opened new urgent care facilities and convenient care centers as well as its fourth IRONMAN Sports Medicine Institute.

Memorial Hermann is also expanding its trauma operations by pursuing Level II trauma verification at two of its facilities. Gaining this designation will help ease the burden on the system's Level I trauma center which is the nation's busiest trauma center.

Additionally the system has been upping its digital game to better serve patients. Its Everyday Well system co-developed with Cerner allows patients to schedule appointments check for lab results contact their doctor and pay their bill for example. This convenience has paid off for Memorial Hermann: The system has seen hikes in self-service collection activities and in overall payments collected.

In 2017 Memorial Hermann faced financial pressures from rising costs declining reimbursements and a softened local economy. In response it initiated two rounds of layoffs affecting more than 450 employees.

In 2019 the system agreed to merge with Baylor Scott & White Health. The combined firm would have been the largest hospital system in Texas with some 70 hospital campuses in more than 30 counties.

EXECUTIVES

President And Ceo, Daniel J. Wolterman
Evp And Coo, Charles D. (Chuck) Stokes
Evp And Chief Clinical Officer, M. Michael Shabot
Ceo Memorial Hermann Memorial City Medical
 Center, Paul O'Sullivan

LOCATIONS

HQ: MEMORIAL HERMANN HEALTHCARE SYSTEM
 929 GESSNER RD, HOUSTON, TX 770242515
Phone: 713 242-3000
Web: WWW.MEMORIALHERMANN.ORG

PRODUCTS/OPERATIONS

Selected Facilities
Children's Memorial Hermann Hospital
Memorial Hermann Katy Hospital
Memorial Hermann Memorial City Medical Center
Memorial Hermann Northeast Hospital
Memorial Hermann Northwest Hospital
                Memorial H
Memorial Hermann Southeast Hospital
Memorial Hermann Southwest Hospital
Memorial Hermann Sugar Land Health Center
Memorial Hermann - Texas Medical Center
Memorial Hermann The Woodlands Hospital
Memorial Hermann Wellness Center and Garden Spa
Neighborhood Health Center
TIRR Memorial Hermann (Houston)
University Place Retirement Community and Nursing
 Center (Houston)

COMPETITORS

CHRISTUS Health	Methodist Hospital
Dynacq Healthcare	System
HCA	St. Luke's Episcopal
LifePoint Health	Health System
MD Anderson Cancer	Tenet Healthcare
Center	Texas Children's
Memorial	Hospital
Sloan-Kettering	

HISTORICAL FINANCIALS
Company Type: Private

Income Statement   FYE: June 30

	REVENUE ($ mil.)	NET INCOME ($ mil.)	NET PROFIT MARGIN	EMPLOYEES
06/08	2,841	16	0.6%	24,000
06/07	2,506	209	8.4%	—
Annual Growth	13.4%	(92.3%)	—	—

2008 Year-End Financials

Return on assets: 4.0%   Cash ($ mil.): 327
Return on equity: 0.6%
Current ratio: 1.20

MEMORIAL HOSPITAL CORPORATION

Memorial Hospital tries to keep good health more than a memory for the patients in its care. The hospital is a 520-bed general hospital which provides a range of children's and adult health-care services and specialties including cardiac care cancer treatment trauma care women's services pediatric medicine and rehabilitation. The hospital has about 700 physicians on its medical staff. Memorial Hospital also includes the 100-bed Memorial Hospital North and Children's Hospital Colorado as well as outpatient clinics throughout the Colorado Springs area. In 2012 it became an affiliate of University of Colorado Health.

EXECUTIVES

Vice President Sales And Marketing, Char
Longwell
Vp Of Physician Services, Vivek Abhyankar
Vice President Finance, Michael Ryan

LOCATIONS

HQ: MEMORIAL HOSPITAL CORPORATION
1400 E BOULDER ST, COLORADO SPRINGS, CO
809095599
Phone: 719 365-5000
Web: WWW.UCHEALTH.ORG

COMPETITORS

Banner Health
Centura Health
Exempla Healthcare
HealthONE
Poudre Valley Health
System

The Memorial Hospital
University of Colorado
Hospital
Valley View Hospital

HISTORICAL FINANCIALS

Company Type: Private

Income Statement   FYE: June 30

	REVENUE ($ mil.)	NET INCOME ($ mil.)	NET PROFIT MARGIN	EMPLOYEES
06/16	693	25	3.7%	2,438
06/15	612	34	5.6%	—
/* 0	0	—	—	—
Annual Growth	—	—	—	—

*Fiscal year change

2016 Year-End Financials

Return on assets: 4.8%   Cash ($ mil.): 4
Return on equity: —
Current ratio: 0.80

MEMORIAL HOSPITAL FOR CANCER AND ALLIED DISEASES

EXECUTIVES

Ceo, Craig B Thompson
Pacs Administrator, Peter Kijewski
Finance Manager, Brendan Phalan
Project Manager, Silvino Tanchoco
Information Senior Man, Susan Shadwick

LOCATIONS

HQ: MEMORIAL HOSPITAL FOR CANCER AND ALLIED
DISEASES
1275 YORK AVE, NEW YORK, NY 100656094
Phone: 212 639-2000
Web: WWW.MSKCC.ORG

HISTORICAL FINANCIALS

Company Type: Private

Income Statement   FYE: December 31

	REVENUE ($ mil.)	NET INCOME ($ mil.)	NET PROFIT MARGIN	EMPLOYEES
12/14	2,035	71	3.5%	5,000
12/08	1,236	(51)	—	—
Annual Growth	8.7%	—	—	—

Return on assets: 3.5%   Cash ($ mil.): —
Return on equity: 7.4%
Current ratio: 0.90

MEMORIAL SLOAN-KETTERING CANCER CENTER

Memorial Sloan-Kettering Cancer Center
(MSKCC) leads the way in cancer research and
treatment. The center includes the 500-bed Memorial Hospital for Cancer and Allied Diseases providing pediatric and adult cancer care and the
Sloan Kettering Institute for cancer research activities. Memorial Hospital specializes in bone-mar-
row transplants radiation therapy and chemotherapy. It also offers programs in cancer prevention
diagnosis treatment research and education. The
Sloan Kettering Institute conducts medical and
clinical laboratory research on cancer genetics and
therapeutics. In addition to the main cancer center
and research facilities in New York City MSKCC
operates clinics in New York New Jersey and Long
Island.

Financial Performance

MSKCC has showed steadily increasing sales in
recent years as it has expanded its care network.
Revenue increased each year between 2014 and
2018 showing an overall gain of 46% over the period.

Revenue grew 11% in 2018 to some $4.9 billion.
Patient care which accounts for about 80% of sales
showed a 12% improvement. Grants and contracts
revenue grew 13% while contributions declined
12%.

Strategy

MSKCC is the largest private cancer center
worldwide and ranks among the top cancer centers
in the US. It is one of 50 facilities designated as a
Comprehensive Cancer Center by the National
Cancer Institute. To maintain its position the company invests in cutting-edge cancer technologies
and conducts extensive research into next-generation medical treatments.

MSKCC has expanded its network over the
years by renovating existing centers and adding
new outpatient facilities. The company opened the
Memorial Sloan Kettering Bergen outpatient treatment center in Montvale New Jersey in 2018. The
facility offers chemotherapy immunotherapy radiation and other treatments to cancer patients.

Sloan Kettering Institute researchers work with
physicians to develop more comprehensive and effective cancer care techniques. The institute also
conducts clinical trials to develop new cancer pharmaceuticals; it is typically engaged in hundreds of
pediatric and adult clinical trials.

To keep its various projects and clinical trials
funded MSKCC counts on grants from a number
of biomedical research institutions including the
National Institutes of Health and the National Cancer Institute. It also receives a good portion of its
cash through fundraising efforts and philanthropic
donations.

Company Background

Memorial Hospital was founded in 1884 as the
New York Cancer Center by a group that included
John and Charlotte Astor. Sloan Kettering Institute
was founded in 1945 by Alfred Sloan and Charles

Kettering to research new cancer cures; the institute was located adjacent to Memorial Hospital.
The two entities formed a coordinating corporate
entity (Memorial Sloan Kettering Cancer Center)
in 1960 and officially merged in 1980.

EXECUTIVES

Svp Information Systems And Cio, Patricia C.
Skarulis
Evp And Cfo, Michael P. Gutnick
Coo, Kathryn Martin
Vp Facilities Management, Edward J. Mahoney
**Vp International Programs And Benno C.
Schmidt Chair In Clinical Oncology,** Murray F.
Brennan, age 78
President And Ceo, Craig B. Thompson, age 66
**Vice President Research And Technology
Management,** Eric M. Cottington
Svp And Chief Investment Officer, Jason Klein
**Physician-in-chief And Chief Medical Officer
Memorial Hospital,** José Baselga
Chairman Department Of Surgery, Jeffrey A.
Drebin
Evp And Hospital Administrator, Ned Groves
Evp And General Counsel, Jorge Lopez
Radiology Director, Michelle Ginsberg
Vice President Human Resources, Kerry Bessey
**Vice President Human Resources Operations And
Information Systems,** Bill Morgan
Respiratory Therapy Director, Carmela Cunneen
**Vice President Director Of Other Admin Financial
Depts,** Melvin McLean
Senior Vice President Patient Revenues, Ruth
Lande
Director Of Radiology, Chester Mah
Director Of Radiology, Stefanie Jacobs
Director Of Radiology, Linda Aboody
**Senior Vice President And Chief Information
Technology Officer,** Anna A Spitzer
Senior Vice President Strategic Partnerships,
James Harden
Vice President Environmental Health And Safety,
Erik Talley
Vice President Finance, Anthony Diasio
Vice President Marketing, Ken Marians
**Vice President And Chief Information Security
Officer,** Michael Czumak
Svp And Chief Development Officer, Kenneth
Manotti
Secretary, Sharlene Pothemont
Reuters Secretary, Maureen Flaherty
Secretary Iii, Debra Alston
Secretary Iii, Pascale Presendor
Secretary Iii, Mahon Ledgister
Secretary, Svetlana Visotski
Med Secretary Iv (g), Michel Barbagallo
Secretary Iv, Sorita Alvarez
Secretary Iv, Nanci Prefach
Secretary, Simone Joseph
Medical Secretary, Tashara Mason
Medical Secretary, Bonnie Correa
Board Member, J Stewart
Secretary, Maire Brennan
Secretary, Danielle Bridges
Board Member, Paul Nurse

LOCATIONS

HQ: MEMORIAL SLOAN-KETTERING CANCER
CENTER
1275 YORK AVE, NEW YORK, NY 100656007
Phone: 212 639-2000
Web: WWW.MSKCC.ORG

PRODUCTS/OPERATIONS

2013 Sales

	$ mil.	% of total
Patient care	2,367	78
Grants and contracts	202	7
Other	455	15
Total	**3,025**	**100**

COMPETITORS

Aptium Oncology	NewYork-Presbyterian
City of Hope	Healthcare
Columbia University	Northwell Health
Continuum Health	Partners HealthCare
Partners	Roswell Park Cancer
Dana-Farber	Institute
Fox Chase Cancer	Sandford Burnham
Center	Institute
Johns Hopkins Medicine	St. Jude Children's
MD Anderson Cancer	Research Hospital
Center	Wistar Institute
Mayo Clinic	
New York City Health	
and Hospitals	

HISTORICAL FINANCIALS

Company Type: Private

Income Statement   FYE: December 31

	REVENUE ($ mil.)	NET INCOME ($ mil.)	NET PROFIT MARGIN	EMPLOYEES
12/17	4,499	314	7.0%	9,325
12/13	582	0	0.2%	—
12/09	2,105	(195)	—	—
12/06	1,622	320	19.8%	—
Annual Growth	9.7%	(0.2%)	—	—

2017 Year-End Financials

Return on assets: 3.0%   Cash ($ mil.): 1,139
Return on equity: 5.2%
Current ratio: 1.00

MENTOR GRAPHICS CORPORATION

Mentor Graphics lends a hand to guide engineers who design electronic components. The company is a leading global developer of electronic design automation (EDA) software and systems used by engineers to design simulate and test electronic components such as integrated circuits (IC's) wire harness systems and printed circuit boards (PCBs). Products include PADS (PCB design) Nucleus (operating system) and Calibre (IC design). Its software is used to design components for such products as computers and wireless handsets. Clients come from the aerospace IT telecommunications and increasingly transportation industries. Mentor Graphics was acquired by Siemens for $4.5 billion in 2017.

Change in Company Type

Mentor Graphics supplies a crucial set of software products to help Siemens fill out its portfolio. The companies agreed to the $4.5billion deal in 2016 and it was finalized in 2017. Mentor Graphics became part of the Siemens PLM Software business in the Siemens Digital Factory division. Mentor's system design product portfolio adds to Siemens' Digital Enterprise strategy bolstering model-driven design methodologies with Mentor's electronic system design expertise.

Operations

Mentor Graphics creates system and software products most of which are sold through term software license contracts. It also provides service and support including professional services consulting training and other services.

Geographic Reach

Based in Wilsonville Oregon Mentor Graphics has US research and development operations in Colorado Washington Alabama and Massachu-

setts. It also conducts R&D in Armenia Egypt France Germany Hungary India Israel Pakistan Poland Russia Taiwan and the UK.

Financial Performance

Mentor Graphics reported increases in revenue and profit in 2017 (ended January). The company's sales rose 9% to $1.3 billion in 2017 from 2016 and profit shot up 60% to $155 million for the year. The company had robust growth in all geographic markets except for the US its biggest market with about 40% of sales. Japan was particularly strong in 2017 with sales jumping more than 35% while sales rose about 15% each in the Pacific Rim and Europe. The company credited the overseas growth to the timing of contract renewals and blamed the North America decline of 3% on weaker sales of emulation hardware systems and a slower rate of contract renewals for the year.

The 60% rise in profit to $1.3 billion in 2017 resulted from higher sales combined with lower special charges in 2017 from 2016. The higher profit helped boost cash flow from operations to $322 million in 2017 from $228 million in 2016.

Strategy

Mentor Graphics is moving to apply its processes to new businesses. The automotive business is one example. It has grown to 20% of Mentor Graphics' revenue in several years. The company is keen on driving its products into other transportation areas such as the design of electronic components in airplanes and trains.

HISTORY

Mentor Graphics was founded in 1981 by a group from instrument maker Tektronix to market desktop computers to design engineers. Throughout the 1980s the company was a leader in electronic design automation (EDA) software but the early 1990s found it in trouble. Revenues fell because of delays in upgrade releases and a worldwide recession.

In 1992 Mentor Graphics began phasing out hardware sales further disrupting operations. Texas Instruments veteran Walden Rhines became CEO in 1993. That year the company acquired CheckLogic a maker of testing software for integrated circuit (IC) design. By 1994 cost-cutting and product line restructuring returned Mentor to profitability.

The company bought ANACAD which developed design software for analog and mixed-signal ICs and Model Technology a very-high-density logic simulation tool firm in 1994. It acquired 14 more companies in 1995 and 1996 including embedded software tool developer Microtec Research (1996) which moved Mentor into the market for software development tools.

EXECUTIVES

Vice President, Henry Potts
Vice President Global Accounts, Don Cantow
President, Gregory K. (Greg) Hinckley, $619,000 total compensation
Chairman And Ceo, Walden C. (Wally) Rhines, $761,000 total compensation
Vp And General Manager Deep Submicron Division, Robert Hum, $319,725 total compensation
Vp Corporate Marketing, Brian Derrick, $350,000 total compensation
Vp Europe And India, Hanns Windele
Vp And General Manager Design-to-silicon, Joseph D. (Joe) Sawicki, $345,000 total compensation
Vp And General Manager Mentor Emulation, Eric Selosse
General Manager System-level Engineering, Serge Leef
Vp And General Manager Embedded Software Division, Glenn Perry

Vp Pacrim, Danny Perng
Vp Worldwide Consulting, Paul Hofstadler
Vp And Cio, Ananthan Thandri
Vp Focus Products Organization, Erich Buergel
President And Managing Director Mentor Graphics Japan Co. Ltd., Yukio Tsuchida
Vp And General Manager Board Systems Division, A.J. Incorvaia
Vp And General Manager Integrated Electrical Systems Division, Martin OÂ'Brien
Senior Vice President, John Sturtevant
Vice President Manager Diretor, Subba Somanchi
Vp Human Resources, Paul Sale
Senior Vice President World Trade, Don Maulsby
Vice President, Ethan Manuel
Vice President Of Engineering, Guy Insley
Vice President Engineering, Juan Rey
Vice President, Dean Freed
Vice President General Manager Design To Silicon Division, Joe Sawicki
Vice President Americas, Veronica Watson
Treasurer, Dennis Weldon
Board Member, Kurt Takara
Auditors: KPMG LLP PORTLAND OREGON

LOCATIONS

HQ: MENTOR GRAPHICS CORPORATION
8005 SW BOECKMAN RD, WILSONVILLE, OR 970707777
Phone: 503 685-7000
Web: WWW.MENTOR.COM

2016 Sales

	$ mil.	% of total
United States	488	41
Europe	254	22
Japan	87	7
Pacific Rim	335	29
Other	15	1
Total	**1,181**	**100**

PRODUCTS/OPERATIONS

2017 Sales

	$ mil.	% of total
System and software	794	62
Service & support	488	38
Total	**1,282**	**100**

Selected Products

Embedded software development
  Compilers
  Debugger
  Real-time operating system
Integrated circuit (IC) design and verification
  Analog/mixed signal
  Custom design
  Design-for-test
  Field-programmable gate array/application-specific IC design
  Formal verification
  High-capacity circuit simulation
  Interconnect modeling
  Physical optimization
  Physical verification & manufacturability
  Resolution enhancement technologies
  Static timing
  Synthesis
Printed circuit board design and analysis
  Design tools
  Digital high-speed
  Integration interfaces and viewers
  Layout
  Library management
  Radio-frequency/mixed-signal
  Simulation and analysis
System-level design and verification
  Accelerated system verification
  Cabling design and analysis
  Design creation
  Digital simulation
  Hardware emulation and simulation
  Intellectual property
  Process management
  System-on-a-chip
  Web-based development system

COMPETITORS

ANSYS	Intrinsix
Altium	PDF Solutions
Autodesk	QNX Software Systems
Blue Ridge Numerics	Silvaco
Cadence Design	Synopsys
CollabNet	Wind River Systems
Green Hills Software	Zuken
Interra Systems	

HISTORICAL FINANCIALS

Company Type: Private

Income Statement — FYE: January 31

	REVENUE ($ mil.)	NET INCOME ($ mil.)	NET PROFIT MARGIN	EMPLOYEES
01/17	1,282	154	12.1%	5,700
01/16	1,180	94	8.0%	—
01/15	1,244	145	11.7%	—
01/14	1,156	153	13.3%	—
Annual Growth	3.5%	0.3%	—	—

2017 Year-End Financials

Return on assets: 6.8% Cash ($ mil.): 441
Return on equity: 11.3%
Current ratio: 1.30

MERCY CARE

Mercy Care is a not-for-profit provider of managed health care services in Arizona. The Mercy Care Plan provides these services under a contract with the Arizona Health Care Cost Containment System the state of Arizona's Medicaid program. The plan provides health coverage and prescription drug benefits to some 300000 members. The company founded in 1985 is affiliated with St. Joseph's Hospital & Medical Center (which is part of Catholic Healthcare West) Dignity Health and Carondelet Health Network. The plan is administered by health care management firm Schaller Anderson.

Operations

Mercy Care provides coverage to families children the elderly and the developmentally disabled. In addition to traditional HMO coverage the company also offers disease management and preventative health care services.

Along with the Centers for Medicare & Medicaid Services (CMS) Mercy Care provides qualified members with medical and prescription drug benefits. Its Mercy Care Long Term Care (MCLTC) offers services to those covered by the AHCCCS Arizona Long Term Care System (ALTCS) which accounts for 22% of revenue.

The Division of Developmental Disabilities Long Term Care serves members who are enrolled through the Arizona Department of Economic Security/Division of Development Disabilities (DES/DDD) which generates approximately 2% of SCHN's revenue. Through a contract with the DES/DDD the company provides medical care to qualified members.

Geographic Reach

Mercy Care serves the Arizona counties of Maricopa Pima Graham Greenlee and Cochise providing covered services to enrolled members.

Sales and Marketing

As part of its business Mercy Care provides patients with prescriptions through retail pharmacies mail order pharmacies home infusion pharmacies long-term care pharmacies and Indian Health Service/Tribal/Urban Indian Health Program (I/T/U) pharmacies.

EXECUTIVES

Vice President Of Health Plan Operations, John Monte

LOCATIONS

HQ: MERCY CARE
4755 S 44TH PL, PHOENIX, AZ 850408895
Phone: 602 263-3000
Web: WWW.MERCYCAREAZ.ORG

COMPETITORS

Aetna	Health Net
Blue Cross Blue Shield of Arizona	UnitedHealth Group
CIGNA HealthCare of Arizona	

HISTORICAL FINANCIALS

Company Type: Private

Income Statement — FYE: June 30

	REVENUE ($ mil.)	NET INCOME ($ mil.)	NET PROFIT MARGIN	EMPLOYEES
06/14	1,808	41	2.3%	500
06/12	1,747	28	1.6%	—
06/11	1,939	58	3.0%	—
06/10	1,904	49	2.6%	—
Annual Growth	(1.3%)	(3.8%)	—	—

2014 Year-End Financials

Return on assets: 12.6% Cash ($ mil.): 46
Return on equity: 23.5%
Current ratio: 1.20

MERCY CHILDREN'S HOSPITAL

Children's Mercy Kansas City is a not-for-profit health system providing care services for youngsters in and around Kansas City Missouri. The system has two hospitals three urgent care facilities and five campuses featuring primary care offices and more than 25 specialty clinics. Among its specialized services are diabetes and endocrinology genetics heart surgery neonatology and rehabilitation. Children's Mercy also offers medical training and research facilities. Founded in 1897 the system today has some 500000 patient visits annually.

Operations

Children's Mercy has a medical staff of roughly 750 pediatric specialists. Its main campus Children's Mercy Adele Hall has 355 beds; there are an additional 53 at the Children's Mercy Hospital Kansas suburban campus.

The system performs roughly 20000 surgeries annually; it has around 200000 emergency room visits each year.

Geographic Reach

Children's Mercy Adele Hall is the only Level I pediatric trauma center between St. Louis Missouri and Denver Colorado.

It is a teaching hospital affiliated with University of Missouri-Kansas City School of Medicine University of Kansas School of Medicine and the Kansas City University of Medicine and Biosciences among others.

Sales and Marketing

Children's Mercy has recently begun advertising for the first time. It uses its marketing campaign in part to solicit donations as it relies heavily on philanthropy to manage operating costs.

Financial Performance

In 2017 Children's Mercy had revenue of $1.3 billion about 95% of which came from patient care services.

Strategy

Children's Mercy is in the midst of a multi-year $800 million expansion plan designed to more than double the size of the main hospital increase the number of patient beds by 50% add a new emergency room six new operating rooms new heart catheterization labs new educational buildings clinics and doctors' offices. A nine-story research tower will also be built atop an existing parking garage at the hospital's campus.

A large part of the funding for the expansion comes from philanthropic donations. Since the project began growth at the health system has included new urgent and specialty care centers a Pediatric Research Center new primary care centers and additional patient units and beds. The hospital has also undergone remodeling and expansion of certain existing facilities.

Children's Mercy has been expanding its research activities. It recently launched the Children's Research Institute to manage its research portfolio which includes gene therapy trials for leukemia and a cancer research partnership.

The system is vulnerable to potential reimbursement cutbacks that could result from the termination or reduction of the federal Children's Health Insurance Program (CHIP). Funding for the program temporarily ran out in 2017 as Congress deliberated on CHIPs future. Other public health care programs could also be shut down which would impact the system's ability to provide services to low-income families.

Company Background

Children's Mercy is a not-for-profit free-standing pediatric health system that offers low-income families a low- or no-cost health plan through the Take CARE benefit plans.

EXECUTIVES

President Ceo And Director, Randall L. O'Donnell
Svp Patient Care Services, Karen Cox
Evp And Co-coo, Jo Stueve
Evp And Cfo, Sandra A. J. Lawrence
Vp And Chief Nursing Officer, Cheri Hunt
Vp Market Development And Outreach, Warren Dudley
Surgeon-in-chief, George W. Holcomb
Pediatrician-in-chief, Michael Artman
Medical Director, Mamta Reddy
Medical Director, Ashley Daly
Vice President General Counsel, Sally B Surridge
Vice President Of Supply Chain, Laurisa Jackson
Medical Director Office Of Equity And, John Cowden
Vice President, Kim Brown
Medical Director, Jeanette Higgins
Medical Director Geriatric Programs, Krista Nelson
Chairman, Jack Ovel
Board Member, Kristi Canty
Assistant Treasurer Honorary Directors, David White

LOCATIONS

HQ: MERCY CHILDREN'S HOSPITAL
2401 GILLHAM RD, KANSAS CITY, MO 641084619
Phone: 816 234-3000
Web: WWW.CHILDRENSMERCY.ORG

Selected locations
Children's Mercy Adele Hall Campus (Kansas City MO)
Children's Mercy Blue Valley (Overland Park KS)
Children's Mercy Broadway (Kansas City)
Children's Mercy College Boulevard (Overland Park KS)
Children's Mercy East (Independence MO)
Children's Mercy Hospital Kansas (Overland Park KS)
Children's Mercy Northland (Kansas City MO)

Children's Mercy Olathe (Olathe KS)
Children's Mercy West (Kansas City KS)
Children's Mercy Sports Medicine Center at Village West
 (Kansas City KS)

COMPETITORS

Ascension Health	Shriners Hospitals For
CoxHealth	Children
Liberty Hospital	Sisters of Charity of
Saint Luke's Health	Leavenworth
System	Truman Medical Centers
Shawnee Mission	University of Kansas
Medical Center	Medical Center

HISTORICAL FINANCIALS
Company Type: Private

Income Statement   FYE: June 30

	REVENUE ($ mil.)	NET INCOME ($ mil.)	NET PROFIT MARGIN	EMPLOYEES
06/16	1,020	35	3.5%	7,000
06/15	978	79	8.1%	—
06/13	9	(0)	—	—
06/11	816	13	1.6%	—
Annual Growth	4.5%	22.3%		

2016 Year-End Financials

Return on assets: 2.8%   Cash ($ mil.): 63
Return on equity: 4.0%
Current ratio: 1.70

MERCY HEALTH

Mercy Health formerly known as the Sisters of Mercy Health System provides a range of health care and social services through its network of facilities and service organizations. The organization operates some 35 acute care hospitals (including four specialty heart hospitals and two children's hospitals) with more than 4200 licensed beds as well as 700 clinics and outpatient facilities in four Midwestern states. Its hospital groups include facilities for nursing homes medical practices and outpatient centers. Mercy Health also operates Resource Optimization & Innovation (ROi) its industry-leading health care supply chain organization and health outreach organizations in Louisiana Mississippi and Texas.

Operations

Mercy Health also operates three rehabilitation hospitals and two orthopedic hospitals. The system has more than 2000 Mercy Clinic physicians.

In 2014 Mercy Health had 150696 acute inpatient discharges; 158911 inpatient and outpatient surgeries; 631444 emergency department visits; 23213 births; and nearly 8.4 million outpatient visits.

Geographic Reach

The system operates in Arkansas Kansas Missouri and Oklahoma.

Mercy Health's outreach efforts include Mercy Ministries of Laredo a group providing primary health care and social services to residents of Laredo Texas. In New Orleans Mercy Health sponsors Mercy Family Center which provides mental health services; in Mississippi it funds a health care advocacy group.

Sales and Marketing

Commercial and other third-party payments accounted for 44% of net patient service revenue while Medicare and Medicaid combined accounted for 51%.

Financial Performance

Mercy Health's operating revenue increased 14% to $4.5 billion in 2014 as net patient and other revenues grew. However the system reported a net loss of $6.5 million that year (versus net income in 2013) as a result of interest rate swap agreement losses and higher expenses as well as lower investment earnings.

Cash flow from operations fell 46% to $354 million in 2014.

Strategy

In 2013 Mercy Health opened new facilities in Missouri (St. Charles and Wentzville) as well as a new heart and vascular center that centralized its outpatient heart and vascular offerings. The following year it opened a new orthopedic hospital in Fort Smith and a 60-bed rehabilitation hospital.

The system acquired Lincoln County Medical Center (renamed Mercy Hospital Lincoln) and its eight affiliated clinics in 2015 expanding its presence in eastern Missouri.

Despite its various expansions the Mercy system experienced the same industry challenges as its health care brethren including escalating medical and pharmaceutical costs and increasing self-pay bad debts (uninsured patients who leave their medical bills unpaid). Several of the health system's facilities have seen a decline in discharges.

Company Background

The organization was founded by the Sisters of Mercy of the St. Louis Regional Community in 1986 and operated under that model until 2008 when its sponsorship was transferred from the Sisters of Mercy of the St. Louis Regional Community to a new entity Mercy Health Ministry. The shift to the new sponsorship organization was made to allow lay members to join the Sisters of Mercy in sponsoring the ministry. It also reflected the growing number of lay people holding executive positions at the system's hospitals and on the board of directors.

EXECUTIVES

Pres-Ceo, Lynn Britton
Evp-Coo*, Michael McCurry
Evp-Cfo*, Shannon Sock
Vp of Information, Mike Mc Creary
Vp of Operations, Mike Mc Curry
Health Professional, Lora Petty
Chief Information Security Off, David Westman
Chief of Medicine, Edson Carrel
Information, Jon Allen
Project Manager Information Sy, Adam Williams
Vp For Audiology, Amanda Moore
Auditors: ERNST & YOUNG LLP ST LOUIS

LOCATIONS

HQ: MERCY HEALTH
 14528 SOUTH OUTER 40 RD # 100, CHESTERFIELD, MO 630175743
Phone: 314 579-6100

Selected Locations

Arkansas
 Berryville
 Fort Smith
 Hot Springs
 Ozark
 Paris
 Rogers
 Waldron
Kansas
 Columbus
 Fort Scott
 Independence
Missouri
 Aurora
 Cassville
 Joplin
 Lebanon
 Mountain View

St. Louis
Springfield
Washington
Oklahoma
 Ada
 Ardmore
 El Reno
 Guthrie
 Healdton
 Kingfisher
 Marietta
 Oklahoma City
 Tishomingo
 Watonga

PRODUCTS/OPERATIONS

2014 Sales

	$ mil.	% of total
Net patient service revenue less provision for bad debts	3,838	85
Member revenue	477	11
Other revenue	194	4
Total	**4,510**	**100**

Selected Facilities

Arkansas
 Mercy Hospital Berryville
 Mercy Hospital Fort Smith
 Mercy Hospital Hot Springs
 Mercy Hospital Northwest Arkansas
 Mercy Hospital of Scott County
 Mercy Hospital Ozark
 Mercy Hospital Paris
 Mercy Hospital Waldron
Kansas
 Mercy Health Center
 Mercy Hospital Fort Scott
 Mercy Hospital Independence
 Mercy Maude Norton Hospital Columbus
Missouri
 Mercy Hospital Aurora
 Mercy Hospital Cassville
 Mercy Hospital Joplin
 Mercy Hospital Lebanon
 Mercy Hospital St. Louis
 Mercy Children's Hospital St. Louis
 Mercy Heart and Vascular Hospital St. Louis
 Mercy Heart Hospital St. Louis
 Mercy Rehabilitation Hospital St. Louis
 Mercy Hospital Springfield
 Mercy Children's Hospital Springfield
 Mercy Hospital Washington
 Mercy McCune-Brooks Hospital
 Mercy St. Francis Hospital
Oklahoma
 Arbuckle Memorial Hospital
 Mercy Health Love County
 Mercy Hospital Ardmore
 Mercy Hospital El Reno
 Mercy Hospital Healdton
 Mercy Hospital Logan County
 Mercy Hospital Oklahoma City
 Mercy Hospital - Tishomingo
 Valley View Regional Hospital
 Watonga Municipal Hospital

COMPETITORS

Ascension Health	SSM Health Care
BJC HealthCare	Saint Luke's Health
Baptist Health	System
(Arkansas)	Shawnee Mission
Barnes-Jewish Hospital	Medical Center
CHRISTUS Health	Sisters of Charity of
Christian Hospital	Leavenworth
Community Health	St. Anthony's Medical
Systems	Center
CoxHealth	St. Vincent Health
HCA	System
INTEGRIS Health	Tenet Healthcare
Memorial Hospital	Universal Health
(Illinois)	Services
RehabCare	

HISTORICAL FINANCIALS
Company Type: Private

Income Statement   FYE: June 30

	REVENUE ($ mil.)	NET INCOME ($ mil.)	NET PROFIT MARGIN	EMPLOYEES
06/18	6,254	243	3.9%	8,800
06/17	5,527	558	10.1%	—
06/10*	18	7	38.4%	—
03/09	2,936	(196)	—	—
Annual Growth	8.8%	—	—	—

*Fiscal year change

2018 Year-End Financials
Return on assets: 3.2%   Cash ($ mil.): 481
Return on equity: 6.0%
Current ratio: 1.50

MERCY HEALTH

EXECUTIVES

Ceo-Pres, John M Starcher Jr
Coordinator, Fiona McCloy
Chief Officer and Pres, Randy Curnow
Scientist, Larry Jackson
Purchasing Agent, Carlos Ballinas
Vice President, Cathy Follmer
Director, Christine Swyres
Information Technology Project, Brooke Fender
Chief Financial Officer, Dave Nowiski
Information Technology, David Laytart
Information Technology Project, Elizabeth Vanderleest
Auditors: ERNST & YOUNG LLP CINCINNATI

LOCATIONS

HQ: MERCY HEALTH
   1701 MERCY HEALTH PL, CINCINNATI, OH
   452376147
Phone: 513 639-2800

HISTORICAL FINANCIALS
Company Type: Private

Income Statement   FYE: December 31

	REVENUE ($ mil.)	NET INCOME ($ mil.)	NET PROFIT MARGIN	EMPLOYEES
12/18	4,860	(978)	—	35,000
12/17	4,737	456	9.6%	—
Annual Growth	2.6%	—	—	—

MERCY HEALTH PARTNERS

EXECUTIVES

Pres, Gordon A Mudler
V Pres, David Gingras
Chb, Richard C Lague
Treas, H Richard Morgenstern
SEC, Patrick T Kirk
Staff Rn, Erica Cousins
Executive Assistant, Mandy McCarl
Physician Pcn, Byron Varnado
Business Manager, Toni Pruitt

LOCATIONS

HQ: MERCY HEALTH PARTNERS
   1675 LEAHY ST STE 101, MUSKEGON, MI 494425538
Phone: 231 728-4032
Web: WWW.MERCYHEALTH.COM

HISTORICAL FINANCIALS
Company Type: Private

Income Statement   FYE: June 30

	REVENUE ($ mil.)	NET INCOME ($ mil.)	NET PROFIT MARGIN	EMPLOYEES
06/18	666	36	5.5%	1,500
06/08	0	0	81.1%	—
06/06	0	0	50.7%	—
06/04	0	(0)	—	—
Annual Growth	96.2%	—	—	—

MERCY HEALTH SERVICES, INC.

EXECUTIVES

Pres, Thomas Mullen
Vice President Finance, John Lepley
Senior Vice President, Scott Spier
Auditors: DIXON HUGHES GOODMAN LLP TYSO

LOCATIONS

HQ: MERCY HEALTH SERVICES, INC.
   301 SAINT PAUL ST, BALTIMORE, MD 212022102
Phone: 410 332-9000
Web: WWW.MDMERCY.COM

HISTORICAL FINANCIALS
Company Type: Private

Income Statement   FYE: June 30

	REVENUE ($ mil.)	NET INCOME ($ mil.)	NET PROFIT MARGIN	EMPLOYEES
06/18	737	31	4.2%	1
06/17	705	50	7.1%	—
06/14	9	1	16.3%	—
06/13	602	15	2.6%	—
Annual Growth	4.1%	14.9%	—	—

2018 Year-End Financials
Return on assets: 2.9%   Cash ($ mil.): 110
Return on equity: 6.9%
Current ratio: 1.90

MERCY HEALTH SERVICES-IOWA, CORP.

EXECUTIVES

Ceo, Jack Weiner
Pres-Ceo*, Joseph Swevish
Pres*, Daniel Varnum
Cfo*, James Peppiatt-Combes
Gen Counsel*, Daniel G Hale
Prin*, Scott Leighty

Director, Colleen Flynn
Executive Director, Anne Voeke
Employee, Cheri Bowman
Director, Mary West

LOCATIONS

HQ: MERCY HEALTH SERVICES-IOWA, CORP.
   20555 VICTOR PKWY, LIVONIA, MI 481527031
Phone: 734 343-1000
Web: WWW.TRINITY-HEALTH.ORG

HISTORICAL FINANCIALS
Company Type: Private

Income Statement   FYE: June 30

	REVENUE ($ mil.)	NET INCOME ($ mil.)	NET PROFIT MARGIN	EMPLOYEES
06/18	969	31	3.3%	2,471
06/14	665	2	0.4%	—
06/05	546	23	4.3%	—
Annual Growth	4.5%	2.3%	—	—

MERCY HEALTH SERVICES-IOWA, CORP.

EXECUTIVES

Prin, Robin Edgar
Internal Medicine Practitioner, Natalia F Gabilondo
Family Practitioner, Teresa A Mock
Emergency Medicine Specialist, Javeria Iqbal
Internist, Kenosa Okafor
Nephrologist, Mark Hong
Internist, Maureen Muke
Ob Gyn Surg Director, Molly Verstegen
Physician, Mark Johnson
Information Technology Relatio, Andy Adams
Marketing Specialist, Angie Creger

LOCATIONS

HQ: MERCY HEALTH SERVICES-IOWA, CORP.
   1000 4TH ST SW, MASON CITY, IA 504012800
Phone: 641 428-7000
Web: WWW.MERCYNORTHIOWA.COM

HISTORICAL FINANCIALS
Company Type: Private

Income Statement   FYE: June 30

	REVENUE ($ mil.)	NET INCOME ($ mil.)	NET PROFIT MARGIN	EMPLOYEES
06/11	649	17	2.7%	—
06/10	632	19	3.0%	—
Annual Growth	2.7%	(7.9%)	—	—

2011 Year-End Financials
Return on assets: 2.2%   Cash ($ mil.): 10
Return on equity: 3.5%
Current ratio: 0.40

MERCY HEALTH ST VINCENT MED LLC

EXECUTIVES

President, Tim Koder
Pres*, Steven Mickus
Chb*, Beverly J McBride
SEC*, Julie Higgins
Treas*, Robert A Sullivan
Occupational Specia, Amy M Smith
Clinical Coordinator Pharmacy, Andrea Decker
Clinical Coordinator, Colleen Harrell
Health Professional, Mandasmitha Sowmarpet
Internal Medicine Practitioner, Vandana Gambhir
Administrator, Imran A Andrabi

LOCATIONS

HQ: MERCY HEALTH ST VINCENT MED LLC
2213 CHERRY ST, TOLEDO, OH 436082603
Phone: 419 251-3232
Web: WWW.MERCY.COM

HISTORICAL FINANCIALS

Company Type: Private

Income Statement				FYE: December 31
	REVENUE ($ mil.)	NET INCOME ($ mil.)	NET PROFIT MARGIN	EMPLOYEES
12/16	478	24	5.1%	6,000
12/15	467	22	4.8%	—
12/00	333	5	1.5%	—
12/99	327	(7)	—	—
Annual Growth	2.3%	—	—	—

MERCY HEALTH SYSTEM CORPORATION

EXECUTIVES

Ceo, Javon R Bea
V Pres-Cfo*, Joseph Nemeth
Optometrists, Kevin Walter
Optometrists, Becky Trujillo
Public Relations Director, Ronald Del Ciello
Procurement Staff, Steve Walker
Training and Direc, Wynn Biedermann
Coordinator, Kristin Hansberry
Coordinator, Karen Ellis
Coordinator, Jennifer Bestland
Controller, Carol May
Auditors: WIPFLI LLP MILWAUKEE WISCONS

LOCATIONS

HQ: MERCY HEALTH SYSTEM CORPORATION
1000 MINERAL POINT AVE, JANESVILLE, WI
535482940
Phone: 608 741-6891
Web: WWW.MERCYHEALTHSYSTEM.ORG

HISTORICAL FINANCIALS

Company Type: Private

Income Statement				FYE: June 30
	REVENUE ($ mil.)	NET INCOME ($ mil.)	NET PROFIT MARGIN	EMPLOYEES
06/16	559	19	3.5%	2,200
06/15	523	12	2.3%	—
06/14	478	39	8.2%	—
06/13	473	21	4.5%	—
Annual Growth	5.7%	(2.5%)	—	—

2016 Year-End Financials

Return on assets: 4.0%   Cash ($ mil.): 66
Return on equity: 10.9%
Current ratio: 0.60

MERCY HEALTH SYSTEM OF SOUTHEASTERN PENNSYLVANIA

EXECUTIVES

Chb, Christine McCann
Ceo*, H Ray Welch
Cfo*, Joseph Bradley
Asst Acct, Lia Onell
Scientist, Patricia Daly
Compliance Staff, Maryann L Cannon
Data Analyst, Carolyn Schenkel
Director Info Technology, Charles Welsh
Director of Organizational Dev, Cynthia Nelson
Information Technology Applica, Debra McCombs
Assistant To President, Janet Borger
Auditors: DELOITTE TAX LLP PHILADELPHIA

LOCATIONS

HQ: MERCY HEALTH SYSTEM OF SOUTHEASTERN
PENNSYLVANIA
1 W ELM ST STE 100, CONSHOHOCKEN, PA
194284108
Phone: 610 567-6000
Web: WWW.MERCYHEALTH.ORG

HISTORICAL FINANCIALS

Company Type: Private

Income Statement				FYE: June 30
	REVENUE ($ mil.)	NET INCOME ($ mil.)	NET PROFIT MARGIN	EMPLOYEES
06/18	745	64	8.7%	8,050
06/15	88	10	11.8%	—
Annual Growth	103.6%	83.7%	—	—

MERCY HOSPITAL SOUTH

St. Anthony's Medical Center applies its skills to medical cases in the Midwest. The hospital serves residents in the areas surrounding St. Louis Missouri as well as portions of southwestern Illinois.

With about 770 beds and some 800 affiliated physicians the hospital provides a comprehensive offering including inpatient and outpatient medical surgical diagnostic and behavioral health care. The hospital operates a level II trauma center cancer and chest pain units and a pediatric emergency center as well as several urgent care facilities. It also offers home health hospice laboratory and pharmacy services. St. Anthony's Medical Center was founded in 1900 by the Franciscan Sisters of Germany.

Operations

St. Anthony's Medical Center's ER is staffed by an independently owned group of emergency physicians (Emergency Physicians of St. Louis) who provide services to the hospital on a contract bases. The physician-group model of employment aims to improve patient flow and reduce waiting times at the ER.

In fiscal 2015 (ended June) the hospital had some 27000 inpatient admissions and more than 77700 emergency department visits delivered more than 1100 babies and performed more than 13000 surgeries.

Geographic Reach

St. Anthony's Medical Center is one of the largest hospitals in the St. Louis metropolitan area. It serves a population base of more than 900000 people in 10 counties in Missouri and Illinois. It also operates four urgent care centers in surrounding communities of Arnold Big Bend Fenton and Lemay.

Strategy

In 2014 St. Anthony's Medical Center became one of the first hospitals in the nation to implant the newly approved Medtronic Reveal LINQ Insertable Cardiac Monitor System a miniature cardiac monitor in a stroke patient.

EXECUTIVES

Assistant Secretary Board Of Directors, Kelly Kothe
Auditors: BKD LLP SAINT LOUIS MO

LOCATIONS

HQ: MERCY HOSPITAL SOUTH
10010 KENNERLY RD, SAINT LOUIS, MO 631282106
Phone: 314 525-1000
Web: WWW.MERCY.NET

PRODUCTS/OPERATIONS

Selected Services
Acute Rehabilitation
Audiology/Hearing
Behavioral Health
Breast Center
Cancer Care Center
Diabetes Education
Emergency/Trauma
Heart Specialty Center
Home Care
Hospice Field Program
Hyland Behavioral Health
Long-term Acute Care
Neuroscience and Stroke
Occupational Medicine
Oncology
Orthopedics
Ostomy Clinic
Outpatient Imaging
Pediatric Services
Physical Therapy
Pregnancy and Birth
Pharmacy
Pulmonary
Radiology/Imaging Centers
Rehabilitation (cardiac and acute)
Senior Services
Sleep Disorder Center
Social Services (Care Management)
Speech Therapy
Sports & Therapy

Stroke
Surgery
Urgent Care Centers
Urological Gynecology
Vestibular Rehab
Weight Management
Women's Medical/Surgical Unit
Wound Treatment

COMPETITORS

Ascension Health	Mercy Hospital St.
BJC HealthCare	Louis
Barnes-Jewish Hospital	RehabCare
Christian Hospital	SSM Health Care
CoxHealth	Saint Francis Medical
HCA	Center
Memorial Hospital	St. Luke's Hospital
(Illinois)	(MO)
Mercy Health	Tenet Healthcare

HISTORICAL FINANCIALS
Company Type: Private

Income Statement				FYE: June 30
	REVENUE ($ mil.)	NET INCOME ($ mil.)	NET PROFIT MARGIN	EMPLOYEES
06/17	451	(43)	—	3,900
06/15	482	1	0.3%	—
06/14	424	13	3.1%	—
06/13	443	38	8.7%	—
Annual Growth	0.5%	—	—	—

2017 Year-End Financials
Return on assets: (-9.0%)   Cash ($ mil.): 17
Return on equity: (-10.9%)
Current ratio: 2.50

MERCY HOSPITAL SPRINGFIELD

Mercy Hospital Springfield is an 890-bed acute-care hospital in the Mercy Health system. The facility provides health care to southwestern Missouri and northwestern Arkansas and includes the Mercy Children's Hospital Springfield. Other hospital specialties include cardiology and stroke care as well as women's and seniors' health cancer emergency trauma burn neuroscience rehabilitation and sports medicine. In addition to its hospital in Springfield Mercy Hospital Springfield operates a number of community clinics and specialty care centers in the area.

Operations
Mercy Hospital Springfield has about 700 doctors on its medical staff. The center sees some 441000 outpatient visits per year as well as 94000 emergency room visits and 37000 surgeries. It also enables more than 3000 births Specialty units feature a level I trauma and burn center (the highest ranking in the US) a neonatal intensive care unit a nationally certified stroke center and high-tech surgery suites (including da Vinci robotic surgery and CyberKnife radiosurgery centers). It also operates an air ambulance service.

Geographic Reach
The hospital serves patients in southwest Missouri and northwest Arkansas.

Financial Performance
The hospital's revenues decreased by 1% in 2014 due to 1% drop in net patient service revenue (which contributed 98% of the revenue) and a 11% decrease in revenues from other sources.

In 2014 the company provided charity care of about $26 million along with unreimbursed Medicaid expenses of around $17 million.

Strategy
That year Mercy Hospital Springfield opened the 60-bed Mercy Rehabilitation Hospital Springfield which is spread across a 63000-square-feet facility. The new $28 million building allows for more options for patient rehabilitation and will also serve as the region's only burn unit.

In 2014 the company also opened Phase II of its Betty and Bobby Allison Neonatal Intensive Care Unit (NICU) which expands the number of beds under NICU to 46. With this final phase complete Mercy permanently closed its former NICU.

Company Background
Formerly St. John's Regional Health Center the hospital's name changed to Mercy Hospital Springfield in 2012; the move coincided with the parent organization's efforts to to unify its brand identity. (The parent group's named changed as well from Sisters of Mercy Health System to Mercy Health.)

The hospital was founded in 1891 by the Sisters of Mercy.

EXECUTIVES

Executive Vice President Operations, Donn Sorensen
Senior Vice President, Joseph J Kelly
Senior Vice President General Counsel, Philip Wheeler

LOCATIONS

HQ: MERCY HOSPITAL SPRINGFIELD
1235 E CHEROKEE ST, SPRINGFIELD, MO 658042203
Phone: 417 820-2000
Web: WWW.MERCY.NET

PRODUCTS/OPERATIONS

Selected Services
Bariatric Surgery
Cancer Care
Children's Care
Heart Care
Integrative Medicine
Mother and Baby Care
Neurosciences
Orthopedic and Sport Care
Palliative Care
Pastoral Care
Senior Care
Trauma and Burn Care
Women's Care

COMPETITORS

Ascension Health	HCA
BJC HealthCare	Heartland Health
Boone Hospital Center	Liberty Hospital
Catholic Health	Tenet Healthcare
Initiatives	Truman Medical Centers
Christian Hospital	University of Kansas
CoxHealth	Medical Center

HISTORICAL FINANCIALS
Company Type: Private

Income Statement				FYE: June 30
	REVENUE ($ mil.)	NET INCOME ($ mil.)	NET PROFIT MARGIN	EMPLOYEES
06/16	1,024	104	10.2%	4,400
06/15	948	93	9.9%	—
06/14	964	42	4.4%	—
06/13	965	87	9.1%	—
Annual Growth	2.0%	6.1%	—	—

2016 Year-End Financials
Return on assets: 24.4%   Cash ($ mil.): 25
Return on equity: 27.5%
Current ratio: 4.60

MERCY HOSPITALS EAST COMMUNITIES

EXECUTIVES

President, Jeffrey Johnston
Vice President*, Paul Hintze
Attorney, Melissa Jackson
Obstetrician Gynecologist, Marcus Gunter
Director, Mary Burton
Account Coordinator III, Vereena Peart

LOCATIONS

HQ: MERCY HOSPITALS EAST COMMUNITIES
615 S NEW BALLAS RD, SAINT LOUIS, MO 631418221
Phone: 314 251-6000

COMPETITORS

BJC HealthCare	St. Anthony's Medical
Memorial Hospital	Center
(Illinois)	St. Luke's Hospital
SSM Health Care	(MO)

HISTORICAL FINANCIALS
Company Type: Private

Income Statement				FYE: June 30
	REVENUE ($ mil.)	NET INCOME ($ mil.)	NET PROFIT MARGIN	EMPLOYEES
06/16	1,023	184	18.0%	10,000
06/15	940	132	14.1%	—
06/14	1,177	118	10.1%	—
06/13	840	82	9.8%	—
Annual Growth	6.8%	30.9%	—	—

2016 Year-End Financials
Return on assets: 29.1%   Cash ($ mil.): 22
Return on equity: 31.5%
Current ratio: 4.90

MERCY HOUSING, INC.

EXECUTIVES

Pres, Jane Graf
V Pres-Fin*, Vince Dodds
V Pres*, Michele Mamet
Sr V Pres*, L Steven Spears
Sr V Pres*, Cindy Holler
Sr V Pres*, Carol Breslau
Compliance Staff, Shana Morgan
Coordinator, Kathryn McBride
Coordinator, Marco Cheng
Coordinator, Helen Scalzo
Director, Alva Winfrey

LOCATIONS

HQ: MERCY HOUSING, INC.
1600 BROADWAY STE 2000, DENVER, CO 802024929
Phone: 303 830-3300
Web: WWW.MERCYHOUSING.ORG

HISTORICAL FINANCIALS
Company Type: Private

Income Statement				FYE: December 31
	REVENUE ($ mil.)	NET INCOME ($ mil.)	NET PROFIT MARGIN	EMPLOYEES
12/16	495	(109)	—	1,490
12/15	16	(1)	—	
12/14	13	5	44.9%	
Annual Growth	517.2%	—	—	

2016 Year-End Financials
Return on assets: (-4.4%)　　Cash ($ mil.): 61
Return on equity: (-13.5%)
Current ratio: 0.70

MERCY MEDICAL CENTER, INC.

EXECUTIVES

Chb, Sister Helen Amos
Ceo*, Thomas R Mullen
Exec V Pres-Cfo*, John E Topper
Exec V Pres*, Amy Freeman
Sr V Pres Medical Affairs*, Dr Scott Spier
Coordinator, Rona Kassem
Scientist, Ruth Bates
Internal Medicine Practitioner, Robert G Davidson
Coordinator, Eric Barbieri
Coordinator, Erin Pollitt
Internal Medicine Practitioner, Matthew Croley
Auditors: DIXON HUGHES GOODMAN LLP ROCK

LOCATIONS

HQ: MERCY MEDICAL CENTER, INC.
　345 SAINT PAUL ST, BALTIMORE, MD 212022123
Phone: 410 332-9000
Web: WWW.MERCYRESIDENCY.ORG

HISTORICAL FINANCIALS
Company Type: Private

Income Statement				FYE: June 30
	REVENUE ($ mil.)	NET INCOME ($ mil.)	NET PROFIT MARGIN	EMPLOYEES
06/18	502	25	5.1%	2,139
06/16	446	(16)	—	
06/10	387	36	9.3%	
06/09	374	0	—	
Annual Growth	3.3%	—	—	

2018 Year-End Financials
Return on assets: 2.7%　　Cash ($ mil.): 95
Return on equity: 7.3%
Current ratio: 1.80

MERCY SCRIPPS HOSPITAL

EXECUTIVES

Prin, Andrew C Ping
Coordinator, Callie Huza
General Surgery, Alan Wittgrove
Security Manager, Anthony Roman
Manager Surgical, Dorothea Meyers
Manager of Patient Access, Erlinda Medina
General Manager, Jerry Cunningham
Chief Staff, Jerry Glassman
Risk Manager, Kathy Maroni
General Surgery, Kimberly Peck
General Surgery, Mary Murphy

LOCATIONS

HQ: MERCY SCRIPPS HOSPITAL
　4077 5TH AVE MER35, SAN DIEGO, CA 921032105
Phone: 619 294-8111
Web: WWW.SCRIPPS.ORG

HISTORICAL FINANCIALS
Company Type: Private

Income Statement				FYE: September 30
	REVENUE ($ mil.)	NET INCOME ($ mil.)	NET PROFIT MARGIN	EMPLOYEES
09/15	750	44	5.9%	77
09/14	623	3	0.6%	
09/13	700	41	5.9%	
Annual Growth	3.5%	3.7%	—	—

MERIDIAN HOSPITALS CORPORATION

Auditors: PRICEWATERHOUSECOOPERS LLP NE

LOCATIONS

HQ: MERIDIAN HOSPITALS CORPORATION
　1945 ROUTE 33, NEPTUNE, NJ 077534859
Phone: 732 751-7500

HISTORICAL FINANCIALS
Company Type: Private

Income Statement				FYE: December 31
	REVENUE ($ mil.)	NET INCOME ($ mil.)	NET PROFIT MARGIN	EMPLOYEES
12/16	1,667	244	14.7%	5,200
12/15	674	64	9.5%	
12/09	929	94	10.2%	
12/08	873	(140)	—	
Annual Growth	8.4%	—	—	—

2016 Year-End Financials
Return on assets: 9.6%　　Cash ($ mil.): 257
Return on equity: 18.4%
Current ratio: 2.80

MERITER HOSPITAL, INC.

EXECUTIVES

Ceo, James L Woodward
Pres, Robert Turngren
V Pres, Sue Erickson
Cfo, Kevin Boren
Chief of Medicine, Geoffrey Priest
Coordinator, Amy Schwarz
Internal Medicine Practitioner, Jeremy W Jaskunas
Payroll Staff, Marcia Virgil
Staff, Mussallem Matthew
Health Professional, Nicole Kemp
Facilities Manager, Alice Butler

LOCATIONS

HQ: MERITER HOSPITAL, INC.
　202 S PARK ST, MADISON, WI 537151596
Phone: 608 417-6000
Web: WWW.UNITYPOINT.ORG

HISTORICAL FINANCIALS
Company Type: Private

Income Statement				FYE: December 31
	REVENUE ($ mil.)	NET INCOME ($ mil.)	NET PROFIT MARGIN	EMPLOYEES
12/17	452	34	7.7%	2,548
12/15	402	52	13.0%	
12/14	434	47	11.0%	
12/13	454	56	12.5%	
Annual Growth	(0.1%)	(11.3%)	—	—

2017 Year-End Financials
Return on assets: 4.6%　　Cash ($ mil.): 39
Return on equity: 7.3%
Current ratio: 1.80

MERRILL CORPORATION

Document services company Merrill is no relation to financial services giant Merrill Lynch but the companies do share an interest in SEC paperwork. Merrill Corporation is a provider of outsourced document management branded marketing services and other information management services. It helps clients gather organize and manage confidential and time-sensitive information for legal and financial transactions. In addition the company provides marketing and communication services such as document composition printing fulfillment and digital delivery as well as technology integration.

Operations

Merrill's Legal and Financial Transaction Services (LFTS) offers legal financial and corporate professionals a suite of advanced services and web-based tools to gather organize and manage transactional information. The company's Marketing and Communication Solutions (MCS) segment specializes in technology-enabled marketing and compliance communications.

Geographic Reach

Merrill operates through more than 40 offices in the US and about 20 international locations. It also has an IT Technology Center in Chennai India and another IT-focused facility in Coimbatore India.

Strategy

While Merrill continues to print individual annual reports brochures catalogs and other publications it has diversified beyond its traditional printing business through numerous acquisitions and strategic alliances to position itself as a business process outsourcing company. It sees growth opportunities in its legal solutions offerings which include managing electronic data discovery and in Merrill Datasite which provides online hosting of documents related to mergers and acquisitions.

In addition to acquisitions Merrill also divests assets from time to time to support its ongoing strategic repositioning efforts in the business process outsourcing marketplace. In 2016 it sold its language services subsidiary Merrill Brink International to United Language Group Inc. The same year it divested its real Estate and Franchise Business selling it to direct marketing technologies firm Xpressdocs Holdings.

HISTORY

Kenneth Merrill founded K. F. Merrill with his wife Lorraine in 1968 and grew the company into a major regional printer. He turned over the reins in 1984 to John Castro who had worked his way up from production manager. The company went public two years later.

EXECUTIVES

Managing Director Asia, Nancy Yu
Chief Product Officer, Thomas Fredell, age 49
Evp And Chief Administrative Officer, Brenda J. Vale
Coo Marketing And Communications Solutions, Roy Gross
Coo, Rodney D. Johnson
Regional Managing Director Europe Middle East Africa (emea), Alun Baker
Ceo, James (Rusty) Wiley
Cfo, Thomas Donnelly
Cio, Brad Smuland
Vice President Sales, Laura Lipani
Senior Vice President Of Sales, Elin Lawrence
Senior Vice President Sales, Scott Taylor
Vice President Sales, Lori Frederick
Senior Vice President, Jean Gardner
Vice President Finance, John Gyurci
Vice President, Raul Varela
Senior Vice President Sales, Andrea Sparke
Senior Vice President, Nancy Skluth
Vice President Sales, Phillip Juett
Vice President Sales, Mark Stefonek
Senior Vice President, Tom Killeen
Senior Vice President, Mark Lederman
Senior Vice President, Eric Polans
Senior Vice President Business Solutions, Cathleen Napoli
Vice President Regional Sales Manager, Christy Vierzba
Senior Vice President Sales, Michelle Fenley
Vice President Sales, Colin Schopbach
Executive Vice President Client Services, Deven Lindemann
Senior Vice President Controller And Chief Accounting Officer, Cathy Miller
Vice President, Axel Kirstetter
Senior Vice President, Mike Sabutis
Senior Vice President Product Management, Christian Idiodi
Senior Vice President Sales, Steve Piccone
Senior Vice President, Neal Davies
Senior Vice President, Clark Graebner
Vice President, Michael Keating
Vice President Business Solutions, Jean Goodwin
Chairman, James V. (Jim) Continenza, age 56
Auditors: PRICE WATER HOUSE COOPER LLP

LOCATIONS

HQ: MERRILL CORPORATION
  1 MERRILL CIR, SAINT PAUL, MN 551085264
Phone: 651 646-4501
Web: WWW.MERRILLCORP.COM

PRODUCTS/OPERATIONS

SERVICES
Capital Transactions
Contract Management
Data Warehousing
Elections
Financial Services Marketing & Communications
Healthcare Member Communications
Intellectual Property Management
M&A Reorganizations & Exchange Offers
Merrill IFN
Portfolio Management
Regulatory Disclosure

COMPETITORS

Applied Discovery	Pitney Bowes
Diebold	R.R. Donnelley
Harte-Hanks	Ricoh USA
IntraLinks	St Ives
Kroll Ontrack	Williams Lea
Lionbridge	Xerox

HISTORICAL FINANCIALS
Company Type: Private

Income Statement

	REVENUE ($ mil.)	NET INCOME ($ mil.)	NET PROFIT MARGIN	EMPLOYEES
				FYE: January 31
01/16	579	78	13.5%	5,418
01/15	691	64	9.3%	—
01/14	815	24	3.0%	—
01/13	851	(9)	—	—
Annual Growth	(12.0%)	—	—	—

2016 Year-End Financials
Return on assets: 24.3%   Cash ($ mil.): 31
Return on equity: —
Current ratio: 2.20

MESA UNIFIED SCHOOL DISTRICT 4

EXECUTIVES

Supt, Amber Conley
Site Manager, Theresa Chucri
Exec Asst, Alice Swinehart
Department Head, Allison Miller
Risk Management Specialist, Carmen Rocha
Secretary, Cheryl Farney
Specialist, Christine Niven
Band Director, Dennis Marcum
Music Technology Director, Douglas Akey
Counselor, Gary Ingle
Specialist, Holly Benza
Auditors: HEINFELD MEECH & CO PC P

LOCATIONS

HQ: MESA UNIFIED SCHOOL DISTRICT 4
  63 E MAIN ST STE 101, MESA, AZ 852017422
Phone: 480 472-0200
Web: WWW.MPSAZ.ORG

HISTORICAL FINANCIALS
Company Type: Private

Income Statement

	REVENUE ($ mil.)	NET INCOME ($ mil.)	NET PROFIT MARGIN	EMPLOYEES
				FYE: June 30
06/18	580	8	1.4%	9,621
06/16	549	(22)	—	—
06/15	531	(19)	—	—
06/14	520	(25)	—	—
Annual Growth	2.8%	—	—	—

MESQUITE INDEPENDENT SCHOOL DISTRICT

EXECUTIVES

RES, Robert Seward
Supt*, David Vroonland
Vp*, Greg Everett
SEC*, Archimedes Faulkner
Exec Drt*, Mandy Burns
Coordinator, Betty Wisdom
Coordinator, Bob Ankrum
Coordinator, Carolyn Pyles
Coordinator, Ella Wilcox
Coordinator, Leigh Farley
Coordinator, Nancy Gray
Auditors: WEAVER AND TIDWELL LLP DALLA

LOCATIONS

HQ: MESQUITE INDEPENDENT SCHOOL DISTRICT
  3819 TOWNE CROSSING BLVD, MESQUITE, TX 751502799
Phone: 972 288-6411
Web: WWW.MESQUITEISD.ORG

HISTORICAL FINANCIALS
Company Type: Private

Income Statement

	REVENUE ($ mil.)	NET INCOME ($ mil.)	NET PROFIT MARGIN	EMPLOYEES
				FYE: August 31
08/18	463	31	6.9%	4,200
08/17	447	115	25.8%	—
08/16	432	52	12.1%	—
08/15	414	9	2.2%	—
Annual Growth	3.7%	51.4%	—	—

2018 Year-End Financials
Return on assets: 2.6%   Cash ($ mil.): 188
Return on equity: 23.8%
Current ratio: 6.90

MESSER CONSTRUCTION CO.

From casinos and courthouses to laboratories and dormitories Messer Construction has built them all. The builder provides commercial construction services (including design/build and project management) for projects in Indiana Kentucky Ohio North Carolina and Tennessee. Messer completes over $830 million worth of projects each year for clients in the life sciences higher education senior living commercial manufacturing/industrial public and health care sectors among others. Its projects have included one of the US's only LEED-certified research buildings (at the University of Louisville) and the Newport Aquarium in Kentucky. Founded in 1932 employee-owned Messer boasts a return-customer rate of 80%.

Operations

Messer Construction offers a range of commercial construction services including building information modeling cost planning and estimating integrated project delivery lean construction and safety programs. It also offers prefabrication services such as mechanical/electrical/plumbing services bathroom pods and health care headwall assemblies.

Geographic Reach

Based in Cincinnati Ohio Messer operates regional offices in North Carolina (Charlotte) Ohio (Cincinnati Columbus and Dayton) Indiana (Indianapolis) Tennessee (Knoxville and Nashville) and Kentucky (Lexington and Louisville).

Sales and Marketing

Messer Construction has served customers from a variety of industries including clients such as: Aisin Automotive Casting Cummins DHL Express Dow AgroSciences Forest Pharmaceuticals Gannett Co General Motors Honda of America Praxair Procter & Gamble Sonoco and Worthington Steel.

Strategy

Messer continues to work on high-value projects across a wide range of industries in the Midwest particularly in secure industries such as healthcare government and education.

During 2015 for example it worked on the 70000-square-foot expansion to Cincinnati Children's Hospital Medical Center (CCHMC) adding a fourth floor 30 beds kitchen full-service cafeteria expanded medical and surgery specialty clinics a gift shop and more. That year it also worked on the $24.1 million- expansion at the National Air and Space Intelligence Center's (NASIC) Foreign Materials Exploitation Laboratory in Dayton for the US Department of Defense as well as the University of Kentucky's $175 million- Student Center Transformation Project (to be completed in 2017) which will span 360000 square feet and include updated student activity and study spaces dining and retail outlets parking a bookstore and more.

Company Background

Formerly known as Frank Messer & Sons Inc. the company changed its name to Messer Construction Co. in March 2002.

EXECUTIVES

President And Ceo, Thomas M. (Tom) Keckeis
Svp And Cfo, E. Paul Hitter
Vp And Cio, Richard A. Hensley
Vice President, Karen Pawsat
Finance Vice President, Brian Doyle
Vice President Leed Ap, Robert Williams
Operations Vice President, Richard Zoller
Vice President Of Sales Development, Mike Malone

Senior Vice President, Jim Hess
Assistant Treasurer, Thomas T Kmiecik
Auditors: DELOITTE & TOUCHE LLP CINCINN

LOCATIONS

HQ: MESSER CONSTRUCTION CO.
643 W COURT ST, CINCINNATI, OH 452031511
Phone: 513 242-1541
Web: WWW.MESSER.COM

PRODUCTS/OPERATIONS

Selected Projects
Health Care
  Norton Healthcare
  Knoxville Orthopedic Clinic
Life Sciences
  Indiana University
  University of Kentucky
Higher Education
  Xavier University
  Western Kentucky University
Senior Living
  Graceworks Lutheran Services
  Episcopal Retirement Homes
Commercial
  IGS Energy
  Penn National Gaming
Manufacturing & Industrial
  Aisin Automotive Casting Tennessee Inc.
  DHL Express Inc.
Public/Institutional
  The Ohio Building Authority
  Commonwealth of Kentucky

COMPETITORS

Albert M. Higley	Shook National
Danis	Skanska USA Building
F.A. Wilhelm	The Austin Company
Gray Construction	Turner Corporation
Hunt Construction	Tutor Perini
Pepper Construction	

HISTORICAL FINANCIALS
Company Type: Private

Income Statement   FYE: September 30

	REVENUE ($ mil.)	NET INCOME ($ mil.)	NET PROFIT MARGIN	EMPLOYEES
09/17	1,092	0	—	900
09/15	1,167	0	—	—
09/14	1,029	0	—	—
09/13	831	0	—	—
Annual Growth	7.0%	—	—	—

2017 Year-End Financials

Return on assets: —
Return on equity: —
Current ratio: 1.20
Cash ($ mil.): 83

METALDYNE PERFORMANCE GROUP INC.

EXECUTIVES

Ceo, George Thanopoulos
Chb*, Kevin Penn
Pres-Coo*, Douglas Grimm
Cfo*, Mark Blaufuss
Exec V Pres-Gen Counsel-Sec*, Thomas M Dono Jr

Exec V Pres Sls*, Russell Bradley
V Pres-Cao-Controller*, Gary Ford
Plant Manager, Carl Koerschner
Auditors: DELOITTE & TOUCHE LLP DETROIT

LOCATIONS

HQ: METALDYNE PERFORMANCE GROUP INC.
1 TOWNE SQ STE 550, SOUTHFIELD, MI 480763710
Phone: 248 727-1800

HISTORICAL FINANCIALS
Company Type: Private

Income Statement   FYE: December 31

	REVENUE ($ mil.)	NET INCOME ($ mil.)	NET PROFIT MARGIN	EMPLOYEES
12/16	2,790	96	3.5%	12,000
12/15	3,047	125	4.1%	—
12/14	2,717	73	2.7%	—
Annual Growth	1.3%	15.0%	—	—

2016 Year-End Financials

Return on assets: 3.0%
Return on equity: 14.3%
Current ratio: 2.00
Cash ($ mil.): 209

METHODIST HEALTH CARE SYSTEM

EXECUTIVES

Pres, Larry L Mathis
Pres*, Mauro Ferrari
V Pres*, S Jeffrey Atcherman
Operations Administrator, Laura Espinosa PHD Rn
Chief of Medicine, Bruce Kennedy
Staff, Korsh Jafarnia
Health Professional, Sherrie Alexander
Scientist, David Raskin
Consultant, Brian Schapper
Epic Consultant, Kathryn Buchanan
Acdm Special Projects Coordina, Crystal Morgan
Auditors: GRANT THORNTON LLP DALLAS TX

LOCATIONS

HQ: METHODIST HEALTH CARE SYSTEM
6565 FANNIN ST D200, HOUSTON, TX 770302703
Phone: 713 793-1602

HISTORICAL FINANCIALS
Company Type: Private

Income Statement   FYE: September 30

	REVENUE ($ mil.)	NET INCOME ($ mil.)	NET PROFIT MARGIN	EMPLOYEES
09/17	1,536	161	10.5%	30
09/14*	1,199	151	12.6%	—
06/05	17	0	1.9%	—
Annual Growth	45.4%	67.8%	—	—

*Fiscal year change

2017 Year-End Financials

Return on assets: 6.8%
Return on equity: 10.0%
Current ratio: 9.10
Cash ($ mil.): 58

METHODIST HEALTHCARE MEMPHIS HOSPITALS

EXECUTIVES

Ceo, David Baytos
Pres*, Meri Armour
Chief of Medicine, Karen Hopper
Executive Officer, Willeen Hasting
Co-Minimum Data Set Coordinato, Shelly Neal
Scientist, Keeba Hudson
Coordinator, Teresa Berkley
Executive Officer, Cato Johnson
Manager of Treasury, Mark Barbieri
Information Technology Manager, Wanda Turner
Director, Bob Plunk
Auditors: DIXON HUGHES GOODMAN LLP ASHE

LOCATIONS

HQ: METHODIST HEALTHCARE MEMPHIS
HOSPITALS
1265 UNION AVE, MEMPHIS, TN 381043415
Phone: 901 516-7000
Web: WWW.METHODISTMD.ORG

HISTORICAL FINANCIALS
Company Type: Private

Income Statement				FYE: December 31
	REVENUE ($ mil.)	NET INCOME ($ mil.)	NET PROFIT MARGIN	EMPLOYEES
12/17	2,101	101	4.8%	7,000
12/02	784	(26)	—	—
12/01	717	(28)	—	—
Annual Growth	6.9%	—	—	—

METRO-NORTH COMMUTER RAILROAD CO INC

Part of New York's Metropolitan Transportation Authority Metro-North Commuter Railroad carries passengers between New York City and its New York and Connecticut suburbs. The company known as MTA Metro-North Railroad or Metro-North covers 795 miles of track and serves a ridership of about 83 million. Three of the company's lines operate from Grand Central Terminal in New York City; the other two operate from Hoboken New Jersey. MTA Metro-North Railroad serves more than 120 stations in seven counties in New York State (Bronx Dutchess New York Orange Putnam Rockland and Westchester) and two in Connecticut (Fairfield and New Haven). The railroad 2014 operating annual budget was $1.4 billion.

Operations

MTA Metro-North Railroad also manages The Hudson Rail Link feeder bus service in the Bronx and The Haverstraw-Ossining and Newburgh-Beacon ferries all of which connect with the major Hudson line. In 2012 the railroad reported a system-wide on-time performance of 97.6%.

Geographic Reach

The company operates rail lines in Westchester Putnam Dutchess Orange and Rockland counties and in Connecticut and New York City.

Financial Performance

MTA Metro-North Railroad's passenger revenues increased in 2013 by 5.4% and ridership in 2013 increased by 0.7%. This increase is primarily a reflection of a 5% Connecticut fare increase implemented in January 2013 and a 7.5% yield New York State fare increase implemented in March 2013.

Strategy

The company's investments include the purchase of two new catenary maintenance vehicles investments in critical warehouse inventory management system components replacement of power system electrical components to maintain the reliability of 3rd rail traction and other infrastructure Improvements.

In 2014 MTA Metro-North Railroad completed a major track reconstruction of lines through the central Bronx used by New Haven Line and Harlem Line trains. The complete rebuilding of this section of track is a major milestone in our ongoing effort to improve track conditions systemwide.

In 2013 the company planned to build 500-car Parking Garage in North White Plains which replaces an existing garage. The project is the outcome of planning studies that began in 2003 and will accommodate the projected demand for parking at the North White Plains railroad station which is used by more than 2200 people each weekday. After completion the garage will be equipped with six electric car charging stations. The garage also will have a storefront retail space along Haarlem Avenue which may provide coffee and newspapers or other service.

That year MTA Metro-North Railroad completed major station renovations at Peekskill and Croton-Harmon that include the installation of new site-specific art work at each location.

In 2013 a seven-car train derailment as the result of a Manhattan-bound commuter train running off the tracks while rounding a sharp curve in the Bronx killed four people and injured 11 critically. As a result a portion of the MTA Metro-North Railroad line between the Bronx and part of Westchester County was closed for a week while the track was repaired.

In the IT realm in 2012 MTA Metro-North Railroad tested an application for purchasing tickets on iPhone Android or BlackBerry phones. The electronic ticket appearing on a smartphone screen can be checked by a conductor visually or scanned by a conductor's handheld device.

Company Background

As part of the largest service expansion in MTA Metro-North Railroad's history in 2011 the company added 230 trains a week mostly for weekend and off-peak non-commuter travel which has been growing faster than AM-peak inbound travel. Improvement projects undertaken by railroad include the $10.5 million replacement of the Park Avenue bridge in 2011 and the $145000 refurbishment of two bridges in Mount Vernon.

Although MTA Metro-North Railroad was founded in 1983 when the MTA assumed control of Conrail commuter operations in New York and Connecticut its roots can be traced back to the New York & Harlem Railroad which began as a horse-car line in lower Manhattan in 1832.

EXECUTIVES

Pres, Howard Permut
Sr V Pres*, George Walker
V Pres*, Kim Porcelain
SEC*, Greg Bradley
Treas*, Robert Maclagger
Press Secretary, Marjorie Anders
Director Project Controls, Bernadette Vero
It Manager Database Administra, Diana Garcia
Assistant Deputy Director Proc, James Sheridan
Asst Director, Karen Oles
Assistant Chief Engineer, Matthew Youssef

LOCATIONS

HQ: METRO-NORTH COMMUTER RAILROAD CO INC
420 LEXINGTON AVE FL 12, NEW YORK, NY
101701200
Phone: 212 878-7000
Web: WWW.RAILROAD.NET

HISTORICAL FINANCIALS
Company Type: Private

Income Statement				FYE: December 31
	REVENUE ($ mil.)	NET INCOME ($ mil.)	NET PROFIT MARGIN	EMPLOYEES
12/08	538	186	34.7%	5,564
12/06	490	152	31.1%	—
12/05	470	226	48.2%	—
12/04	433	246	57.0%	—
Annual Growth	5.6%	(6.7%)	—	—

2008 Year-End Financials

Return on assets: 4.3%   Cash ($ mil.): 27
Return on equity: 4.7%
Current ratio: 0.90

METROHEALTH MEDICAL CENTER

LOCATIONS

HQ: METROHEALTH MEDICAL CENTER
2500 METROHEALTH DR, CLEVELAND, OH
441091900
Phone: 216 778-7800
Web: WWW.METROHEALTH.ORG

HISTORICAL FINANCIALS
Company Type: Private

Income Statement				FYE: December 31
	REVENUE ($ mil.)	NET INCOME ($ mil.)	NET PROFIT MARGIN	EMPLOYEES
12/16	883	(8)	—	6,000
12/15	795	35	4.5%	—
12/14	782	32	4.2%	—
Annual Growth	6.3%	—	—	—

2016 Year-End Financials

Return on assets: (-0.8%)   Cash ($ mil.): 11
Return on equity: (-4.9%)
Current ratio: 1.30

METROPOLITAN EDISON COMPANY

Metropolitan Edison is an electric company and it knows a thing or two about serving cities and surrounding communities. The company a subsidiary of holding company FirstEnergy provides electric services to a population of 1.3 million in a 3300-sq. ml. service area in south central and eastern Pennsylvania. Metropolitan Edison or Met-Ed as it is sometimes referred to operates almost 16500 miles of power transmission and distribution lines. Although the company's primary source of electricity is derived from oil-and gas-fired units its York Haven Power Company generates hydroelectric power.

EXECUTIVES

Pres, Charles E Jones
Exec V Pres-Cfo, Mark T Clark
V Pres-Controller-Cao, Harvey L Wagner
Exec V Pres-Gen Counsel, Leila L Vespoli
V Pres-Treas, James F Pearson
Real Estate Conultant, Craig Correll
Clerk, Michelle Frey
Supervisor Engineering, Alfred Nerino
Customer Associate, Matthew Kemp
Manager Forestry, Doug Kinyo
Manager Regional Operations, James Frey
Auditors: PRICEWATERHOUSECOOPERS LLP CL

LOCATIONS

HQ: METROPOLITAN EDISON COMPANY
76 S MAIN ST, AKRON, OH 443081812
Phone: 800 736-3402
Web: WWW.FIRSTENERGYCORP.COM

COMPETITORS

Columbia Gas of Pennsylvania	PECO Energy
Direct Energy	PPL Electric

HISTORICAL FINANCIALS

Company Type: Private

Income Statement   FYE: December 31

	REVENUE ($ mil.)	NET INCOME ($ mil.)	NET PROFIT MARGIN	EMPLOYEES
12/17	837	97	11.6%	678
12/16	865	87	10.1%	—
12/10	1,818	58	3.2%	—
12/09	1,688	55	3.3%	—
Annual Growth	(8.4%)	7.3%	—	—

2017 Year-End Financials

Return on assets: 2.7%   Cash ($ mil.): —
Return on equity: 10.4%
Current ratio: 1.50

METROPOLITAN TRANSPORTATION AUTHORITY

The largest public transportation system in the US New York City's Metropolitan Transportation Authority (MTA) provides about 2.6 billion passenger trips and sees about 380 million vehicles travel its system annually. The MTA's largest agency the New York City Transit Authority operates about 8700 rail and subway cars that provide service across New York's five boroughs; it also runs a fleet of some 5900 buses. Other MTA units offer bus and rail service to Connecticut and Long Island and operate the Triborough system of toll bridges and tunnels.

Strategy
The government-owned MTA a public-benefit corporation chartered by the New York Legislature in 1965 operates with an annual budget of $12.6 billion. The system has been working to become more self-sufficient in recent years but it has battled persistent operating losses brought on by among other causes high operating costs and the struggling US economy. In an attempt to reduce its expenses the company in 2010 cut payroll by 20% at its headquarters and 15% at other agencies. The MTA has also bolstered its revenue through increased fares and tolls and freed up capital by restructuring its debt at lower interest rates.

While it is making cuts in some areas the MTA is investing in capital improvements to its system including extending the Long Island Rail Road to Grand Central Station and creating a direct link between John F. Kennedy Airport and downtown Manhattan. Other key projects have included the construction of the Second Avenue Subway and renovations at the Fulton Street Transit Center. The MTA also is looking at installing wireless Internet access on its Metro-North and Long Island rail lines' trains.

EXECUTIVES

Cfo, Robert E. (Bob) Foran
Executive Officer Corporate Communications Marketing And Branding, John McKay
Director Security, Raymond Diaz
Coo, Phil Eng
Interim Executive Director, Veronique Hakim
President Mta Bridges And Tunnels, Cedrick Fulton
Chairman, Joseph J. Lhota
Auditors: DELOITTE & TOUCHE LLP NEW YOR

LOCATIONS

HQ: METROPOLITAN TRANSPORTATION AUTHORITY
2 BROADWAY BSMT B, NEW YORK, NY 100043354
Phone: 212 878-7000

PRODUCTS/OPERATIONS

Selected Operations

Bus
Long Island Bus
MTA Bus Company
New York City Transit
Commuter Rail
Long Island Rail Road
Metro-North Railroad
Staten Island Railway

HISTORICAL FINANCIALS

Company Type: Private

Income Statement   FYE: December 31

	REVENUE ($ mil.)	NET INCOME ($ mil.)	NET PROFIT MARGIN	EMPLOYEES
12/18	8,736	(145)	—	67,457
12/17	8	(0)	—	—
12/16	8,527	(271)	—	—
12/15	8,408	370	4.4%	—
Annual Growth	1.3%	—	—	—

2018 Year-End Financials

Return on assets: (-0.2%)   Cash ($ mil.): 541
Return on equity: (-3.7%)
Current ratio: 0.90

METROPOLITAN WATER RECLAMATION DISTRICT OF GREATER CHICAGO

EXECUTIVES

Exec Dir, Brian Perkovich
V Pres, Kathleen Meany
Chief of Mno, Thomas O Conner
Principal, Jeff Weber
Actng Public Info Coordinat, Mary Carroll
Acting Director, Ellen Barry
Accounting Staff, Marilyn Torres
Scientist, Weizhe An
Executive Officer, Joe Cannici
Scientist, Ali Oskouie
Program Inspector, Dwayne Logan
Auditors: RSM US LLP CHICAGO ILLINOIS

LOCATIONS

HQ: METROPOLITAN WATER RECLAMATION DISTRICT OF GREATER CHICAGO
100 E ERIE ST, CHICAGO, IL 606112829
Phone: 312 751-5600
Web: WWW.MWRDECU.ORG

HISTORICAL FINANCIALS

Company Type: Private

Income Statement   FYE: December 31

	REVENUE ($ mil.)	NET INCOME ($ mil.)	NET PROFIT MARGIN	EMPLOYEES
12/18	755	107	14.2%	2,259
12/17	719	76	10.6%	—
12/16	703	10	1.5%	—
12/15	679	37	5.6%	—
Annual Growth	3.6%	41.6%	—	—

2018 Year-End Financials

Return on assets: 1.2%   Cash ($ mil.): 264
Return on equity: 2.3%
Current ratio: 0.20

MFA INCORPORATED

Agricultural cooperative MFA brings together 45000 farmers in Missouri and adjacent states. One of the US' oldest regional co-ops supplying its member/owners with agronomy distribution financing and purchasing services it runs more than 145 retail farm supply centers and works with independent dealers. MFA supplies animal feeds seed fertilizer and crop protection products. The co-op also provides its members with agronomy services animal-health products and farm supplies. It also offers marketing services and is the publisher of Today's Farmer. Agmo Corporation MFA's finance company provides co-op members longer credit terms for purchases made through MFA's retail outlets.

Operations
MFA's plant food sales exceed 1 million tons each year.

Geographic Reach
The coop has fertilizer terminals on the Mississippi River as well as on the Missouri and Arkansas rivers.

Sales and Marketing
The coop sells through 400 independent dealers.

Strategy
Part of MFA's strategy is to focus on growth initiatives and find opportunistic products and services to provide to its customers. Strategic river terminals and other bulk facilities give it capacity to deliver bulk quantities of plant food. It also invests in rolling stock trucks and application equipment to ensure bulk products are efficiently delivered to retail customers.

In 2016 the coop formed a joint venture with MFA Oil Company a farmer-owned energy supply cooperative to build a shuttle-loader facility on the Union Pacific Railroad line about 5 miles east of Hamilton Missouri. The grain-handling facility will consist of 2 million bushels of permanent storage and 1.5 million bushels of temporary storage along with a loop rail siding to accommodate a 110-railroad-car 'shuttle' unit. Once completed the structure will allow farmers in north central Missouri and southern Iowa to deliver crops to a modern high-speed grain facility.

Company Background
Expanding its assets in 2013 MFA acquired Producers Grain Company's assets in El Dorado Springs Walker Bronaugh and Nevada in Missouri.

The co-op was established in 1914 when seven Missouri farmers got together to buy binder twine.

EXECUTIVES

Svp Corporate And Member Services And Corporate Secretary, Janice Schuerman
Svp Corporate Operations, J. Brian Griffith
President And Ceo, Bill Streeter
Vp Feed Division, Alan Wessler
Svp And Cfo, Ernie Verslues
Vp Plant Foods And Transportation, Bill Coen
Vp Crop Protection Seed And Farm Supply, Don Houston
Vp Agri Services, Craig Childs
Vice President Mill Operations, Tom Staudt
Second Vice President Finance, David Moore
Vice President And General Manager, Cassy Landewee
Vice Chairman, John Moffitt
Chairman, Don Mills
Recording Secretary, Allen Smith
Auditors: WILLIAMS KEEPERS LLC COLUMBIA

LOCATIONS

HQ: MFA INCORPORATED
201 RAY YOUNG DR, COLUMBIA, MO 652013599
Phone: 573 874-5111
Web: WWW.MFA-INC.COM

COMPETITORS

ADM	GROWMARK
Andersons	Heartland Co-op
Cargill	Missouri Farm Bureau
Farm Service	Orscheln Farm and Home
Cooperative	Tennessee Farmers
Farmers Cooperative	Co-op
Company	United Producers

HISTORICAL FINANCIALS

Company Type: Private

Income Statement   FYE: August 31

	REVENUE ($ mil.)	NET INCOME ($ mil.)	NET PROFIT MARGIN	EMPLOYEES
08/18	1,367	6	0.5%	1,393
08/17	1,373	14	1.0%	—
08/16	1,192	4	0.3%	—
08/15	1,434	10	0.8%	—
Annual Growth	(1.6%)	(14.0%)	—	—

MGM HOLDINGS INC.

EXECUTIVES

Ceo, Gary Barber
Pres, Mark Burnett
Manager, Aaron Jackman
Business Analyst, Daniel Trujillo
Is Acquisitions Coordinator, Elizabeth Brouillette
Sales Director, John Ramchandani
Computer Operations Administra, Keith Pennington
Executive Vice President, Kristin Cotich
Senior Vice President, Lori Silfen
Executive Vice President and G, Monty Sarhan
Manager, Stephanie Ho
Auditors: ERNST & YOUNG LLP LOS ANGELES

LOCATIONS

HQ: MGM HOLDINGS INC.
245 N BEVERLY DR, BEVERLY HILLS, CA 902105319
Phone: 310 449-3000
Web: WWW.MGM.COM

HISTORICAL FINANCIALS

Company Type: Private

Income Statement   FYE: December 31

	REVENUE ($ mil.)	NET INCOME ($ mil.)	NET PROFIT MARGIN	EMPLOYEES
12/16	1,184	155	13.1%	4
12/15	1,158	252	21.8%	—
Annual Growth	2.2%	(38.5%)	—	—

MIAMI UNIVERSITY

Not that Miami the other one. Named for the Miami Indian Tribe that inhabited the area now known as the Miami Valley Region of Ohio Miami University emphasizes undergraduate study at its main campus in Oxford (35 miles north of Cincinnati) as well as at commuter campuses in Hamilton Middletown and West Chester Ohio and a European Center in Luxembourg. The school offers bachelors masters and doctoral programs in areas including business administration arts and sciences engineering and education. Its student body includes more than 15000 undergraduates on the Oxford campus; 2500 graduate students; and another 5700 students attending satellite campuses. Miami University was established in 1809.

Financial Performance
Miami University's 2011 revenue increased 3% vs. 2010 due to a correspondingÂ increase in undergraduate tuition on its three campuses and a rising rates for room and board. Net income at the public universityÂ rose 25% over the same period on higher revenue and lower operating expenses due primarily to a reduction in the number of positions and no salary increases. The rise in tuition for Ohio residentsÂ in 2011 was the first in four years. Also investment income rose in 2011 for the second consecutive year.

Company Background
Miami University celebrated its bicentennial in 2009. The school was chartered inÂ February ofÂ 1809 by the State of Ohio but the first classses were not held untilÂ 1824.

EXECUTIVES

Vice President, Beck Parker
Vice President, Brenden Clinton
Chief Information Officer And Vice President Information Technology, Peter Natale
Assistant Vice President For End User Services, Annie Pagura
Senior Vice President Information Technology Programmer, Valerie Garnett
Vice President For Student Affairs, Barbara Jones
Associate Vice President Of Budgeting, David Ellis
Program Associate Vice President Of Finance, Agnes A Shea
Assoc Vice President Finance, Beverly Thomas
Assistant Vice President, Gail Walenga
Assistant Vice President Enterprise Operations Information Technology Services, Troy Travis
Department Chair, Susan Brehm
Miami University 18 Vice President Of Programming, Zach Myers
Vice President Information Technology Technical Support, Carolyn Ledford
Vice President Of Standards, Patrick Harrison
Executive Manager, Susan Clark
Interim Associate Vice President Human Resources, Dawn Fahner
Vice President, John Mcdonnell
Vice President For Information Technology And Chief Officer, David Seidl
Board Member, Phyllis Wykoff
Economics Major Entrepreneurship Minor Theta Chi Treasurer, Michael Beresford
Auditors: MCGLADREY LLP CLEVELAND OHIO

LOCATIONS

HQ: MIAMI UNIVERSITY
501 E HIGH ST, OXFORD, OH 450561846
Phone: 513 529-1809
Web: WWW.MIAMIOH.EDU

HISTORICAL FINANCIALS
Company Type: Private

Income Statement   FYE: June 30

	REVENUE ($ mil.)	NET INCOME ($ mil.)	NET PROFIT MARGIN	EMPLOYEES
06/18	551	184	33.5%	4,925
06/17	544	83	15.4%	—
06/16	522	65	12.5%	—
06/12	440	32	7.5%	—
Annual Growth	3.8%	33.3%	—	—

2018 Year-End Financials
Return on assets: 7.7%   Cash ($ mil.): 85
Return on equity: 15.7%
Current ratio: 6.20

MIAMI VALLEY HOSPITAL

Don't go to Florida looking for this hospital! Miami Valley Hospital (MVH) is an acute care facility serving the residents of Dayton Ohio and surrounding areas through two campuses. MVH and MVH South have roughly 950 beds and offer 50 primary and specialty care practices through its Regional Adult Burn Center the MVH Cancer Center MVH Sports Medicine Center and behavioral health units for outpatient and inpatient chemical dependency therapy and other psychiatric services. MVH also offers Level I trauma services Level III-B NICU adult burn center an air ambulance program and blood marrow and kidney transplant services. The hospital is part of the Premier Health Partners network.

Operations
In addition to MVH the Premier Health Partners network consists of Good Samaritan Hospital (also stationed in Dayton Ohio) Atrium Medical Center in nearby Middletown and Upper Valley Medical Center in Troy. Collectively the multi-hospital health system houses about 1800 inpatient beds and around 65 facilities.

MVH have more than 1100 physicians in more than 70 primary and specialty medical practice areas. It was a 2012 recipient of the HealthGrades Distinguished Hospital Award for Clinical Excellence placing it among the top 5% of hospitals in the US.

In 2012 it had 41555 inpatient admissions; 164140 outpatient visits; 125622 emergency department visits; and oversaw 4000 births.

Financial Performance
Medicare accounted for 40% of the company's 2012 revenues; Medicaid 20%.

Strategy
Over the past few years MVH has focused on upgrading its infrastructure. It has built a $135 million 440000-sq. ft. 11-story heart tower on the south side of the campus and spent $19 million on renovating and expanding its neonatal intensive care unit.

In 2013 it opened its new $6 million 24-hour Emergency Center in Jamestown Ohio to meet the growing demand for emergency care.

In 2013 MVH South opened a $20 million Comprehensive Cancer Center and (in 2012) a new maternity center which includes five labor and delivery suites two surgical suites for c-section deliveries and 16 private after-birthing suites.

Company Background
MVH was formed in 1890.

EXECUTIVES
Pres-Ceo, Bobbie Gerhart
Pres*, Mark Shaker
V Pres*, Makkie Clancy
Cfo*, Lisa Bishop
V Pres-Coo*, Barbara Johnson
Staff, Ed Graham
Coordinator, Carrie Clark
Health Professional, Jon D Girard
Coordinator, Carmen Young
Human Resources, Gretchen Long MBA
Coordinator, Melissa Brook

LOCATIONS
HQ: MIAMI VALLEY HOSPITAL
1 WYOMING ST, DAYTON, OH 454092711
Phone: 937 208-8000
Web: WWW.MIAMIVALLEYHOSPITAL.ORG

PRODUCTS/OPERATIONS

Campus Locations
Miami Valley Hospital - Dayton OH
Miami Valley Hospital South - Centerville Ohio

Selected Services and Specialties
Ablation (Cardiology)
Access and Transfer Center (physicians)
Alcoholism Drug Dependency and Addiction Treatment
Aneurysm (Neurosciences)
Ankle Surgery
Arterial Interventions
Audiology
Bariatrics/Weight Loss Surgery
Behavioral Services
Biotherapy/Targeted Therapy
Blood and Marrow Transplant Program
Brachytherapy
Brain Conditions and Treatments
Brain Injury Rehabilitation
Breast Cancer Navigators
Breast Center
Breast Center
Brethen Center for Surgical Advancement (physicians)
Bull Family Diabetes Center
Burn Center
Cancer Care
Cancer Care (Oncology)
Cardiac Electrophysiology Lab
Cardiac Rehabilitation
Cardiology
Cardiology
Cardiothoracic Surgery
CareFlight - Medical Transportation
Catheterization Lab Procedures
Center for Sleep and Wake Disorders
Chemoembolization
Chemotherapy and Infusion Therapy
Childbirth Education
Colon Cancer
Colorectal Cancer
Complementary Medicine (Cancer)
Comprehensive Outpatient Rehab Program (CORP)
Counseling/Pastoral Care
Craniectomy (Neuroscience)
Craniotomy (Neuroscience)
Cryoablation
CT scan (Imaging)
Dental Center
Depression/Anxiety Treatment
Diabetes
Dialysis Services
Discectomy
Drug Addiction Treatment
Elder Care
Emergency & Trauma Center (ETC)
Foot Surgery
Fractures (Athletes)
Fusion (spinal treatment)
Gastric Bypass
Genetic Testing
Gynecologic Cancer
Gynecology
Hand Therapy
Head and Neck Cancer
Heart Care
Heart Surgery

High Risk Breast Cancer Center
Hip Surgery
Hormone Therapy
Hospitalists/Medical Professionals
Hyperbaric Oxygen Therapy Center
Image Guided Radiation Therapy (IGRT)
Injury Prevention Center
Inpatient Rehabilitation
Intensity Modulated Radiation Therapy (IMRT)
Intensive Care Unit (ICU)
Interventional Radiology
Joint replacements
Kidney Transplant
Knee Surgery
Kyphoplasty
Leukemia
Lung Cancer
Lymphoma
Mammography Screenings
Maternal-Fetal Medicine
Maternity
Maternity
Medical Professionals/Hospitalists
Medical Transportation - CareFlight
Mental Health Services
Minimally Invasive Surgery
Mother and Baby Services
MRI (Imaging)
Nanoknife
Neonatal Intensive Care
Neuro Rehabilitation
NeuroInterventional Center
Neuroscience
Neurosciences
Nutrition Services
OB-GYN
Obstetrics
Occupational Rehabilitation
Occupational Therapy
Oncology
Organ Transplant
Orthopedics
Orthopedics
Outpatient Physical Therapy
Pain Management
Palliative Care
Pancreatic Cancer
Perinatal Intensive Care
PET Scan (Imaging)
Pharmacy
Physiatry
Physical Therapy
Pre-Admission Testing
Premier HeartWorks
Preventive Cardiology
Prostate Cancer
Pulmonary Services
Radiofrequency ablation
Radiology
Radionuclide scan
Rehabilitation
Rehabilitation Institute of Ohio
Respiratory Care
Robotic Surgery
Shoulder Surgery
Shunt (Neuroscience)
Skin Cancer
Sleep Center
Solitaire Revascularization Device (Neurosciences)
Speech-Language Pathology
Spinal decompression surgery
Spinal disc replacement
Spinal fracture treatment
Spinal tumor surgery
Spine and back injuries (Orthopedics)
Spine Conditions and Treatments (Neuroscience)
Sports Medicine
Sports Medicine
Stereotaxis
Stomach Cancer
Stroke Treatments
Surgery Center
Surgical Oncology
Thoracic Surgery
Throat Cancer
Trauma
Ultrasound (Imaging)
Urological Cancer
Urology
Vascular Services
Venous Interventions

Vertebroplasty
Weight Loss Surgery (Bariatrics)
Weight Loss Surgery/Bariatrics
Wheelchair Clinic
Women's Health
Women's Heart Services
Women's Services
Wound Therapy
X-rays (Imaging)
Y-90 Radioembolization

COMPETITORS

Cincinnati Children's Hospital	OhioHealth
Deaconess Associations	The Christ Hospital Corporation
Encompass Health	TriHealth
Good Samaritan Hospital (IN)	UC Health
Kettering Health Network	

HISTORICAL FINANCIALS

Company Type: Private

Income Statement				FYE: December 31
	REVENUE ($ mil.)	NET INCOME ($ mil.)	NET PROFIT MARGIN	EMPLOYEES
12/16	809	35	4.4%	6,000
12/15	827	37	4.5%	—
12/14	785	37	4.8%	—
12/07	622	44	7.1%	—
Annual Growth	3.0%	(2.3%)		

2016 Year-End Financials

Return on assets: 2.3%   Cash ($ mil.): 42
Return on equity: 5.2%
Current ratio: 10.00

MICHIGAN MILK PRODUCERS ASSOCIATION

Ice cream and other dairy products might be missing a major ingredient without Michigan Milk Producers Association (MMPA). The dairy cooperative whichÂ servesÂ more than 2100Â farmers in Michigan Ohio Indiana and Wisconsin produces some 3.9 billion pounds of milk each year. Milk products include sweetened condensed milk instant nonfat milk and dried buttermilk as well as other items the likes of cream cheese butter and ice-cream mixes. With no consumer brands or products MMPA sells its products as ingredients to foodÂ makers whoÂ sell baby formulas candy ice cream and yogurt. Founded in 1916 the co-op operates a pair of Michigan plants and a merchandise facility.

Operations

As part of its business of serving member-farmers MMPA provides themÂ with product quality incentives testing and customized blending as well as protection against loss from disaster.

Geographic Reach

From its headquarters in Novi Michigan MMPA operates solely in the state of Michigan where it has manufacturing plants in the villages of Ovid and Constantine and a merchandise facility in the Michigan city of Saint Louis. Its farmers are located in Michigan Ohio Indiana and Wisconsin.

EXECUTIVES

Vice President, Kris Wardin
Treasurer, Eric Frahm
Auditors: CLIFTONLARSONALLEN LLP

LOCATIONS

HQ: MICHIGAN MILK PRODUCERS ASSOCIATION
41310 BRIDGE ST, NOVI, MI 483751302
Phone: 248 474-6672
Web: WWW.MIMILK.COM

PRODUCTS/OPERATIONS

Selected Products

Condensed skim milk
Condensed whole milk
Dried buttermilk
Dried whole milk
Ice cream mixes
Instant nonfat dry milk
Nonfat dry milk
Standardized cream
Standardized milk
Sweet condensed milk
Sweet cream butter

COMPETITORS

Associated Milk Producers	Land O'Lakes
Dairy Farmers of America	Main Street Ingredients
Dean Foods	Quality Chekd
Foremost Farms	Saputo

HISTORICAL FINANCIALS

Company Type: Private

Income Statement				FYE: September 30
	REVENUE ($ mil.)	NET INCOME ($ mil.)	NET PROFIT MARGIN	EMPLOYEES
09/11	870	6	0.7%	200
09/10	698	6	1.0%	—
09/09	556	6	1.1%	—
Annual Growth	25.1%	3.2%	—	—

2011 Year-End Financials

Return on assets: 3.8%   Cash ($ mil.): 5
Return on equity: 13.4%
Current ratio: 1.50

MICHIGAN STATE UNIVERSITY

Remember the Spartans? You should if you graduated from a land-grant university in the US. Founded in 1855 Michigan State University (MSU) was the model of a land-grant institution made into law in 1862. Today MSU and its 50000 students cover a lot of land in East Lansing. The university offers more than 200 programs of study through 17 colleges. It has extensive programs in core fields including education physics psychology medicine and communications. It is also a leading research university with top-ranked international studies programs. As a highly ranked research university MSU is awarded millions of dollars in research grants each year from public and private entities.

Operations

Each year MSU receives about $600 million in research grants from entities including the National Science Foundation the US Department of Health

and Human Services US Department of Energy and the US Department of Agriculture.

With 5100 faculty and academic staff members and a student-teacher ratio of about 16:1 MSU is noted by U.S. News & World Report for its programs in graduate-level elementary and secondary education nuclear physics and industrial and organizational psychology. It is the only university in the country with three on-campus medical schools graduating allopathic (MD) and osteopathic (DO) physicians as well as veterinarians (DVMs).

Geographic Reach

MSU's 5200-acre main campus is in East Lansing three miles east of Lansing (the capital city of Michigan). The campus includes about 560 buildings (100 of which are academic). The university also has another 20000 acres-some used for animal agricultural and forestry research.

MSU's students hail from all 50 US states as well as more than 130 other countries. It also has one of the largest study abroad programs in the US including about 280 partnerships with international institutions.

Financial Performance

MSU's had budgeted revenues of $1.3 billion in 2017-18. Tuition and fees accounted for about 70% of this and state appropriations about 20%. Higher student tuition and fees have contributed to MSU's revenue growth over the last few years.Academics and related services take about two-thirds of the university's expenditures annually.

Strategy

Expanding facilities is a core growth initiative at MSU. Recent construction projects include a new art museum new science labs and residence halls and a new nursing education building. MSU is also constructing the Facility for Rare Isotope Beams a $680 million center supported by grants from the US Department of Energy to advance understanding of rare nuclear isotopes as well as the evolution of the cosmos. It has also partnered with University of Wisconsin-Madison to establish a $125 million bioenergy research center (also funded by the US Department of Energy).

Company Background

MSU was founded in 1855 a forerunner of the land-grant college concept under the name Agricultural College of the State of Michigan. The Morrill Act which codified land-grant institutions became law in 1862. MSU became a full university in 1955 as Michigan State University of Agriculture and Applied Science. It changed its name to Michigan State University in 1964.

EXECUTIVES

President, Lou Anna K. Simon
Evp For Academic Affairs And Provost, June Youatt
Dean College Of Engineering, Satish Udpa
Dean James Madison College, Sherman W. Garnett
Dean Lyman Briggs College, Elizabeth H. Simmons
Dean College Of Law, Joan W. Howarth
Dean College Of Music, James (Jim) Forger
Dean College Of Natural Science, R. James Kirkpatrick
Dean College Of Osteopathic Medicine, William D. Strampel
Dean Residential College In The Arts And Humanities, Stephen L. (Steve) Esquith
Dean Honors College, Cynthia Jackson-Elmoore
Vp Information Technology And Cio, Joanna Young
Dean College Of Education, Donald E. Heller
Vp Finance And Treasurer, Mark P. Haas
Dean College Of Veterinary Medicine, John Baker

Dean College Of Communication Arts And Sciences, Prabu David
Assistant Vice President For Human Resources, Chris Hanna
Department Chair, Steven Rust
Assistant Vice President Research And Grad Stds Office Of Sponsored Programs, Twila Reighley
Vice President Of Programming, Lisa Thompson
Chairman, Joel I. Ferguson, age 80
Vice Chairman, Mitch Lyons
Wrac Secretary, Diana Shank
Secretary, Nikki Bindschatel
Graduate Secretary, Tammy Spangler
Secretary, Raven Richardson
Graduate Secretary, Logan O'Neil
Treasurer, Raymond Jussame
Auditors: PLANTE AND MORAN PLLC EAST LA

LOCATIONS

HQ: MICHIGAN STATE UNIVERSITY
426 AUDITORIUM RD, EAST LANSING, MI 488242600
Phone: 517 355-1855

PRODUCTS/OPERATIONS

Selected Colleges and Divisions

College of Agriculture and Natural Resources
College of Arts and Letters
College of Communication Arts and Sciences
College of Education
College of Engineering
College of Human Medicine
College of Law (affiliated)
College of Music
College of Natural Science
College of Nursing
College of Osteopathic Medicine
College of Social Science
College of Veterinary Medicine
Eli Broad College of Business and Eli Broad Graduate School of Management
Honors College
James Madison College
Lyman Briggs College
Residential College in the Arts and Humanities
Undergraduate University Division

HISTORICAL FINANCIALS

Company Type: Private

Income Statement				FYE: June 30
	REVENUE ($ mil.)	NET INCOME ($ mil.)	NET PROFIT MARGIN	EMPLOYEES
06/18	1,986	(246)	—	11,100
06/17	1,931	481	25.0%	—
06/16	1,811	71	3.9%	—
06/13	1,578	148	9.4%	—
Annual Growth	4.7%	—	—	—

2018 Year-End Financials

Return on assets: (-3.7%)   Cash ($ mil.): 384
Return on equity: (-10.5%)
Current ratio: 0.50

MID-AMERICA PIPELINE COMPANY, LLC

EXECUTIVES

Mng MBR-Pres, J M Collingsworth
MBR, W Randall Fowler
MBR-Sr V Pres, Michael J Knesek
MBR-Treas, Bryan F Bulawa
MBR-SEC, Raymond P Albrecht
Credit Mgr, Charles Kaufman

Human Resources, Andy Tomasik
Manager, David West

LOCATIONS

HQ: MID-AMERICA PIPELINE COMPANY, LLC
1100 LA ST STE 1000, HOUSTON, TX 77002
Phone: 713 880-6500

HISTORICAL FINANCIALS

Company Type: Private

Income Statement				FYE: December 31
	REVENUE ($ mil.)	NET INCOME ($ mil.)	NET PROFIT MARGIN	EMPLOYEES
12/17	591	361	61.1%	250
12/16	591	366	62.0%	—
Annual Growth	0.0%	(1.4%)	—	—

MID-KANSAS COOPERATIVE ASSOCIATION

EXECUTIVES

Pres, Dave Christiansen
Cfo*, Danny Posch
Coordinator, Hilary Worcester
Manager, Nick Mazouch
Location Manager, Gene Kobylak
Chief Marketing Officer, David Spears
Grain Operations Manager, Lawson Hemberger
Energy Consultant, Brandi Bailey
Energy Consultant, Brent Pelzel
Manager, James Bettenbrock
Controller, Kathy Neufeld
Auditors: LINDBURG VOGEL PIERCE FARIS CE

LOCATIONS

HQ: MID-KANSAS COOPERATIVE ASSOCIATION
307 W COLE ST, MOUNDRIDGE, KS 671077533
Phone: 620 345-6328
Web: WWW.MKCOOP.COM

HISTORICAL FINANCIALS

Company Type: Private

Income Statement				FYE: February 29
	REVENUE ($ mil.)	NET INCOME ($ mil.)	NET PROFIT MARGIN	EMPLOYEES
02/16	458	7	1.7%	250
02/15	403	14	3.7%	—
02/14	120	9	7.6%	—
02/13	125	14	11.1%	—
Annual Growth	53.9%	(17.2%)	—	—

2016 Year-End Financials

Return on assets: 2.3%   Cash ($ mil.): 3
Return on equity: 7.3%
Current ratio: 1.20

MIDCOAST ENERGY PARTNERS, L.P.

Midcoast Energy Partners was formed by Enbridge Energy Partners in 2013 as an investment vehicle to own and grow its natural gas and NGL midstream business. It has minority stakes in Enbridge's network of natural gas and natural gas liquids (NGLs) gathering and transportation systems natural gas processing and treating facilities and NGL fractionation plants in Texas and Oklahoma. Organized as a limited partnership Midcoast Energy Partners is exempt from paying income tax as long as it distributes quarterly dividends to shareholders. It went public in 2013 raising $333 million. In 2017 Enbridge Energy Partners agreed to acquire control of Midcoast Energy Partners.

EXECUTIVES

Pres, Laura Sayavedra
Sr V Pres, Mark A Maki
L.L.C., Gen Ptnr, Midcoast Holdings
Vice President, Stephen J Neyland
Auditors: PRICEWATERHOUSECOOPERS LLP HO

LOCATIONS

HQ: MIDCOAST ENERGY PARTNERS, L.P.
1100 LA ST STE 3300, HOUSTON, TX 77002
Phone: 713 821-2000

COMPETITORS

Buckeye Partners	ONEOK
DCP Midstream Partners	Sunoco Logistics
Duke Energy	TransCanada
Koch Industries Inc.	Williams Companies
Magellan Midstream	
Martin Midstream Partners	

HISTORICAL FINANCIALS

Company Type: Private

Income Statement				FYE: December 31
	REVENUE ($ mil.)	NET INCOME ($ mil.)	NET PROFIT MARGIN	EMPLOYEES
12/16	1,966	(157)	—	11
12/15	2,842	(284)	—	—
12/14	5,894	144	2.4%	—
12/13	5,593	53	1.0%	—
Annual Growth	(29.4%)	—	—	—

2016 Year-End Financials

Return on assets: (-3.2%)   Cash ($ mil.): 7
Return on equity: (-4.2%)
Current ratio: 0.50

MIDWESTERN UNIVERSITY

EXECUTIVES

Pres-Ceo, Kathleen H Goeppinger
Sr V Pres-Cfo*, Gregory J Gaus
V Pres*, Dean Malone
V Pres*, Karen D Johnson
V Pres*, Dean P Malone
V Pres*, Mary Lee

V Pres*, Angela Marty
Sr Exec V Pres*, Arthur G Dobbelaere
Assistant Professor, Reji Mathew
Director, Carol Van Dijk
Program Director, Timothy J Todd
Auditors: ERNST & YOUNG LLP CHICAGO IL

LOCATIONS

HQ: MIDWESTERN UNIVERSITY
555 31ST ST, DOWNERS GROVE, IL 605151235
Phone: 630 515-7300
Web: WWW.MIDWESTERN.EDU

HISTORICAL FINANCIALS

Company Type: Private

Income Statement				FYE: June 30
	REVENUE ($ mil.)	NET INCOME ($ mil.)	NET PROFIT MARGIN	EMPLOYEES
06/18	450	121	27.1%	1,300
06/17	414	118	28.6%	—
06/16	380	69	18.4%	—
06/15	358	86	24.0%	—
Annual Growth	7.9%	12.2%	—	—

2018 Year-End Financials
Return on assets: 8.3%   Cash ($ mil.): 383
Return on equity: 11.8%
Current ratio: 4.40

MILES HEALTH CARE, INC

Miles Health Care provides acute and specialty health care service to the residents of Maine's Lincoln County. The not-for-profit company operates Miles Memorial Hospital — known as LincolnHealth Miles Campus — a rural medical center with about 40 beds and has emergency intensive care surgery and birthing departments. In addition Miles Health Care operates outpatient and specialty practice clinics physician practice offices and home health rehabilitation and hospice programs. It also provides long-term senior care through its nursing assisted and independent living facilities. Miles Health Care is a member of Lincoln County Healthcare (LincolnHealth) which is part of the MaineHealth network.

Change in Company Type

In 2013 parent MaineHealth combined two of its hospitals — Miles Memorial Hospital and St. Andrews Hospital — to form the two-campus LincolnHealth organization. The merger aimed to reduce operating expenses by more than $6 million annually as well as a more than $5 million increase revenue due to the combined organization's new status as a critical access hospital (which leads to higher reimbursements from Medicare and Medicaid plans). The increased earnings will allow the LincolnHealth campuses to reduce the price of services including x-rays laboratory tests and minor surgeries and procedures.

Operations

In addition to the two main hospital campuses LincolnHealth includes physician practices operated by the Lincoln Medical Partners as well as family care and urgent care centers. It also continues to operate nursing home health hospice and assisted-living organizations.

Geographic Reach

The LincolnHealth Miles Campus is located in Lincoln County Maine in the town of Damariscotta (which is north of Portland). The LincolnHealth St. Andrews Campus is located in Boothbay Harbor.

Strategy

Both the Miles and St. Andrews medical centers began using electronic health record (EHR) systems in 2010 which allows doctors to access a patient's past medical and diagnostic experiences to make the best decisions on current treatment plans and avoid duplication. Such EHR systems are part of an initiative to lower the cost of medical care in the US.

Company Background

Miles Health Care was established in 1941. Miles has historically been governed by a board of trustees (the Lincoln County Healthcare Board of Trustees) that also oversee the nearby St. Andrews Hospital; as an independently governed member of MaineHealth Miles has received planning consulting capital and group purchasing benefits. In 2013 St. Andrews Hospital and Miles Memorial Hospital were officially merged to serve as dual campuses of the single LincolnHealth hospital.

EXECUTIVES

Ceo, James Donavan
Administrative Assistant, Dave Phillips
Manager Information Security, Ray Croteau
Lcsw Program Manager Telehealt, Carolyn Suggs
Practice Manager, Andrea Feus

LOCATIONS

HQ: MILES HEALTH CARE, INC
35 MILES ST, DAMARISCOTTA, ME 045434047
Phone: 207 563-1234
Web: WWW.MAINEHEALTH.ORG

PRODUCTS/OPERATIONS

Selected Centers and Services
Chase Point Adult Day Services
Chase Point Assisted Living
Cove's Edge
Emergency Services
Family Support Services
General Surgery
Internal Medicine
Mammography
Miles & St. Andrews Home Health & Hospice
Miles Family Medicine
MMH BabyNet
Obstetrics
Orthopedic Services
Pediatric Services
Schooner Cove
Senior Services
Waldoboro Family Medicine
Wellness and Rehabilitation
Wiscasset Family Medicine
Women's Services

COMPETITORS

Eastern Maine Healthcare Systems	Mercy Health System of Maine
MaineGeneral Health	St. Joseph Healthcare

HISTORICAL FINANCIALS

Company Type: Private

Income Statement				FYE: September 30
	REVENUE ($ mil.)	NET INCOME ($ mil.)	NET PROFIT MARGIN	EMPLOYEES
09/09	1,042	12	1.2%	800
09/08	14	0	3.9%	—
09/06	58	3	5.9%	—
09/05	52	(0)	—	—
Annual Growth	111.6%	—	—	—

2009 Year-End Financials
Return on assets: 112.3%   Cash ($ mil.): —
Return on equity: 494.4%
Current ratio: 1.30

MILLS-PENINSULA HEALTH SERVICES

With health facilities south of San Francisco Mills-Peninsula Health Services provides care to communities in and around Burlingame California. The not-for-profit health care group includes the 240-bed Mills-Peninsula Medical Center an acute-care hospital in Burlingame; Mills Health Center an outpatient diagnostic surgery and rehabilitation facility in San Mateo; and physician practice offices in surrounding areas. The facilities provide specialty services such as cancer care cardiovascular therapy behavioral health radiology respiratory care and senior services. Mills-Peninsula Health Services is part of the Sutter Health network.

Operations

Along with sister company Palo Alto Medical Foundation Mills-Peninsula forms the Peninsula Coastal Region division of Sutter Health. Together the organizations operate collaborative medical clinic and physician practice locations.

Geographic Reach

Mills-Peninsula Health Services operates facilities in Burlingame and San Mateo in California.

Financial Performance

Mills-Peninsula Health Services reported revenues of $611 million (7% of the parent company's net revenues) in 2013.

Its net income in 2013 was $53 million.

Strategy

Through the contribution of donors in 2014 the Mills-Peninsula Women's Center replaced all its digital mammography units with digital breast tomosynthesis allowing it to provide 3D mammography for breast cancer screenings at no extra cost to patients.

The hospital enhanced its surgical capabilities in 2013 with the addition of a da Vinci Si robotic system for surgical procedures.

That year Mills-Peninsula's Dorothy E. Schneider Cancer Center introduced a new cancer treatment Xofigo (Radium-223 dichloride) for patients with advanced-stage prostate cancer that has metastasized to the bones but not other organs.

Company Background

The organization opened the doors on its newly constructed Mills-Peninsula Medical Center in Burlingame in 2011. The $618 million project added a new 240-bed main hospital facility (to replace the aging Peninsula Medical Center facility) with all private patient rooms as well as a 180000 sq. ft. medical office building and a parking garage. The new hospital is compliant with California's new earthquake safety requirements.

The Peninsula facility was founded as a public hospital district in 1954. The two hospitals merged in 1985 and became part of Sutter Health the following year.

Founded in 1908 the Mills hospital was named for philanthropist Elizabeth Mills Reid who helped to fund the medical facility.

Auditors: ERNST & YOUNG US LLP SAN DIEG

LOCATIONS

HQ: MILLS-PENINSULA HEALTH SERVICES
1501 TROUSDALE DR, BURLINGAME, CA 940104506
Phone: 650 696-5400
Web: WWW.MILLS-PENINSULA.ORG

PRODUCTS/OPERATIONS

Selected Services
Arthritis & Osteoporosis
Behavioral Health
Birth Center
Cancer Center
Cardiovascular
Children's Services
Psychiatric Emergency
Senior Services
Obesity Surgery
Orthopedic Surgery
Women's Center

COMPETITORS

Alta Bates Summit Medical Center	John Muir Health
California Pacific Medical Center	Marin General Hospital
Dignity Health	Sequoia Healthcare District
Good Samaritan Hospital (San Jose)	The Palo Alto Medical Foundation
	UCSF Medical

HISTORICAL FINANCIALS

Company Type: Private

Income Statement   FYE: December 31

	REVENUE ($ mil.)	NET INCOME ($ mil.)	NET PROFIT MARGIN	EMPLOYEES
12/13	609	54	8.9%	2,200
12/09	533	56	10.6%	—
12/02	274	18	6.6%	—
12/01	398	0	0.0%	—
Annual Growth	3.6%	172.8%	—	—

2013 Year-End Financials

Return on assets: 12.6%   Cash ($ mil.): 20
Return on equity: 8.9%
Current ratio: 0.10

MILTON HERSHEY SCHOOL & SCHOOL TRUST

EXECUTIVES

Owner, Milton Hershey
Auditors: PRICEWATERHOUSECOOPERS LLP PH

LOCATIONS

HQ: MILTON HERSHEY SCHOOL & SCHOOL TRUST
711 CREST LN, HERSHEY, PA 170338903
Phone: 717 520-1100
Web: WWW.MHSKIDS.ORG

HISTORICAL FINANCIALS

Company Type: Private

Income Statement   FYE: July 31

	REVENUE ($ mil.)	NET INCOME ($ mil.)	NET PROFIT MARGIN	EMPLOYEES
07/17	469	198	42.2%	13
07/12	386	180	46.7%	—
07/10	211	3	1.6%	—
Annual Growth	12.1%	79.2%	—	—

2017 Year-End Financials

Return on assets: 1.4%   Cash ($ mil.): 59
Return on equity: 1.4%
Current ratio: 0.40

MILWAUKEE PUBLIC SCHOOLS (INC)

EXECUTIVES

Supt, Darienne Driver
Cfo*, Gerald Pace
Personnel Dir*, Daniel Chanen
Comptroller*, Lawanda Baldwin
Principal, Deborah Bell
Principal, Martha Wheeler-Fair
Principal, Jewell Riano
Principal, Daniel J Donder
Social Worker, Cathy Klein
Staff, Carmen M Rahming
Lobbyist, Ceasar Stinson
Auditors: BAKER TILLY VIRCHOW KRAUSE LL

LOCATIONS

HQ: MILWAUKEE PUBLIC SCHOOLS (INC)
5225 W VLIET ST, MILWAUKEE, WI 532082698
Phone: 414 475-8393
Web: WWW.MILWAUKEE.K12.WI.US

HISTORICAL FINANCIALS

Company Type: Private

Income Statement   FYE: June 30

	REVENUE ($ mil.)	NET INCOME ($ mil.)	NET PROFIT MARGIN	EMPLOYEES
06/18	1,196	2	0.2%	14,154
06/17	1,182	9	0.8%	—
06/16	1,178	(0)	—	—
06/11	1,292	(2)	—	—
Annual Growth	(1.1%)	—	—	—

MINERS INCORPORATED

Miner's is a family-owned chain of about 30 grocery stores in Michigan North Dakota northern Minnesota and Wisconsin. Most of the company's stores fly the Super One Foods banner but there are a few under the U-Save Foods and Marketplace Foods names. Following the acquisition of seven Jubilee and Festival Foods stores in Minnesota from Plaza Holding Co. Miner's converted the stores to its Super One Foods banner most of which are located in Minnesota. Miner's also has a wholesale grocery operation in Duluth. Miner's was

founded by Anton and Ida Miner who started out selling groceries out of their tavern in Grand Rapids Michigan in the 1930s. In 1943 they built the family's first store Miner's Market.

Geographic Reach
Minnesota is the regional grocery chain's largest market home to 21 of its 31 stores. Wisconsin and Michigan are each home to about five locations. The grocery chain has a single store North Dakota.

Financial Performance
Miner's rang up an estimated $437 million in sales in fiscal 2013 (ended June).

Strategy
Miner's takes a measured approach to growth combining occasional acquisitions with organic growth. Its newest location is a 59000-square-foot Super One Foods store slated to open in 2014 in Superior Wisconsin.

Mergers and Acquisitions
In May 2011 Miner's upped its store count with the acquisition of four family-owned Paulson's Super Valu grocery stores in northern Minnesota and Wisconsin.

Prevented by Minnesota law from selling alcohol in grocery stores the company recently bought two liquor stores in Cloquet and Duluth.

EXECUTIVES

Vice President, Jim Miner
Auditors: RSM US LLP DULUTH MINNESOTA

LOCATIONS

HQ: MINERS INCORPORATED
5065 MILLER TRUNK HWY, HERMANTOWN, MN 558111442
Phone: 218 729-5882
Web: WWW.SUPERONEFOODS.COM

2014 Stores

	No.
Minnesota	21
Michigan	5
Wisconsin	4
North Dakota	1
Total	**31**

PRODUCTS/OPERATIONS

2014 Stores

	No.
Super One Foods	27
U-Save Foods	2
Country Market	1
Marketplace Foods	1
Total	**31**

COMPETITORS

Cub Foods	Roundy's
IGA	SpartanNash
Kroger	Target Corporation
Meijer	Wal-Mart

HISTORICAL FINANCIALS

Company Type: Private

Income Statement   FYE: June 24

	REVENUE ($ mil.)	NET INCOME ($ mil.)	NET PROFIT MARGIN	EMPLOYEES
06/17	548	26	4.8%	2,300
06/12	501	31	6.3%	—
06/11	475	30	6.4%	—
06/10	463	27	5.8%	—
Annual Growth	2.4%	(0.5%)	—	—

2017 Year-End Financials

Return on assets: 10.7%   Cash ($ mil.): 7
Return on equity: 15.4%
Current ratio: 1.80

MINNEAPOLIS PUBLIC SCHOOL DISTRICT

EXECUTIVES

Suptd, Michael Goar
Supt*, Bernadeia Johnson
Payroll Staff, Diane Woolridge
Occupational Specia, Laura Wilcox
Payroll Staff, Stacy Swain
Coordinator, Ben Mulhern
Research Assistant, Eric V Berk
Psychologist, Peggy Wiltse
Coordinator, Matthew Branch
Occupational Specia, Nancy Bradehoft
Teacher, Becky Ramgren
Auditors: BERGAN KDV LTD MINNEAPOLIS

LOCATIONS

HQ: MINNEAPOLIS PUBLIC SCHOOL DISTRICT
1250 W BROADWAY AVE, MINNEAPOLIS, MN
554112533
Phone: 612 668-0200
Web: WWW.MPLS.K12.MN.US

HISTORICAL FINANCIALS
Company Type: Private

Income Statement   FYE: June 30

	REVENUE ($ mil.)	NET INCOME ($ mil.)	NET PROFIT MARGIN	EMPLOYEES
06/16	709	(25)	—	9,000
06/15	685	116	17.1%	—
06/05	441	18	4.2%	—
06/04	632	(42)	—	—
Annual Growth	1.0%	—	—	—

MINNESOTA SOYBEAN PROCESSORS

EXECUTIVES

Chb, Jim Sallstrom
Interim Ceo*, Taryl Enderson
Executive Officer, Rod Smit
Accounting Staff, Ann Schieck-Solomon
Merchandizer, Brian Wiertzema
Coordinator, Korey Stinehart
General Manager, Scott Austin
Maintenance Supervisor, Jeremy Nolte
Director, Tim Graber

LOCATIONS

HQ: MINNESOTA SOYBEAN PROCESSORS
121 ZEH AVE, BREWSTER, MN 561193009
Phone: 507 842-6677
Web: WWW.MNSOY.COM

HISTORICAL FINANCIALS
Company Type: Private

Income Statement   FYE: August 31

	REVENUE ($ mil.)	NET INCOME ($ mil.)	NET PROFIT MARGIN	EMPLOYEES
08/08	515	2	0.4%	80
08/05	207	(5)	—	—
08/04*	199	(2)	—	—
12/02	159	6	4.1%	—
Annual Growth	21.6%	(16.6%)	—	—

*Fiscal year change

2008 Year-End Financials

Return on assets: 1.9%   Cash ($ mil.): —
Return on equity: 4.1%
Current ratio: 1.40

MISSION HEALTH SYSTEM, INC.

EXECUTIVES

Ceo-Pres, Ronald A Paulus
Cmo-Mission Hospital, William R Hathaway
Innovation, Marc B Westle
Operations, Sonya B Greck
Auditors: KPMG LLP CHARLOTTE NORTH CAR

LOCATIONS

HQ: MISSION HEALTH SYSTEM, INC.
425 W NEW ENG AVE STE 300, WINTER PARK, FL
327894228
Phone: 828 213-1111
Web: WWW.MISSIONHEALTH.ORG

HISTORICAL FINANCIALS
Company Type: Private

Income Statement   FYE: September 30

	REVENUE ($ mil.)	NET INCOME ($ mil.)	NET PROFIT MARGIN	EMPLOYEES
09/18	1,799	120	6.7%	12,000
09/17	1,753	161	9.2%	—
09/16	1,632	90	5.5%	—
09/08	17	7	42.3%	—
Annual Growth	59.1%	32.3%	—	—

2018 Year-End Financials

Return on assets: 4.5%   Cash ($ mil.): 149
Return on equity: 6.7%
Current ratio: 2.00

MISSION HOSPITAL REGIONAL MEDICAL CENTER INC

EXECUTIVES

Ceo, Seth Peigen
Financial Executive, Kenn Mc Farland
Manager, Laura Salem
Coordinator, Maryann Hubbard
Cardiac Physician, Michael Miyamoto
Emergency Medicine, Jon Cline
Manager, Jon Greer
Emergency Medicine, Kenneth Kwon
Emergency Medicine, Matthew Kaplan
Icu Ccu Director, Annabelle Braun
Office Manager, Carla Chandler
Auditors: ERNST & YOUNG US LLP SAN DIEG

LOCATIONS

HQ: MISSION HOSPITAL REGIONAL MEDICAL
CENTER INC
27700 MEDICAL CENTER RD, MISSION VIEJO, CA
926916426
Phone: 949 364-1400
Web: WWW.MISSION4HEALTH.COM

HISTORICAL FINANCIALS
Company Type: Private

Income Statement   FYE: June 30

	REVENUE ($ mil.)	NET INCOME ($ mil.)	NET PROFIT MARGIN	EMPLOYEES
06/16	547	28	5.3%	2,600
06/15	516	23	4.5%	—
06/10	500	50	10.1%	—
06/09	355	12	3.5%	—
Annual Growth	6.4%	13.0%	—	—

2016 Year-End Financials

Return on assets: 4.9%   Cash ($ mil.): 38
Return on equity: 10.5%
Current ratio: 1.40

MISSION HOSPITAL, INC.

Its mission is clear and bold: Improve the health of all in western North Carolina. Mission Hospital is a 760-bed regional referral center serving the western quarter of North Carolina and portions of adjoining states. A not-for-profit community hospital system Mission is located in Asheville on two adjoining campuses: Memorial and St. Joseph's. It provides tertiary-level services in neurosciences cardiac care trauma care surgery pediatric medicine and women's services and has a medical staff of more than 540. It also includes the Mission Children's Hospital. Mission Hospital is the flagship hospital of Mission Health System which is being acquired by HCA Healthcare for $1.5 billion.

Change in Company Type

In 2018 hospital operator HCA Healthcare agreed to buy Mission Health System which includes Mission Hospital and six smaller hospitals in Asheville North Carolina for $1.5 billion. As part of the deal HCA will keep all rehab and acute-care hospitals open for at least 10 years. It will also invest several hundreds of millions of dollars in various expenditures.

Geographic Reach

Mission Health System serves patients in western North Carolina.

Strategy

Mission Hospital has been actively expanding and modernizing its facilities in recent years. It built a surgery registration and waiting area to ease patient comfort as they wait to be seen at the Memorial Campus. It also opened a four-story facility to provide more surgery suites and patient beds for Mission Hospital. In order to increase patient satisfaction the hospital opened a new surgery registration and waiting area at its Memorial Campus.

Mission Hospital places great focus on genetic medicine. It has an entire department dedicated to the study of genetics genetic therapy and the study of fetal alcohol spectrum disorders.

Mission Health partnered with Western Carolina University to provide a graduate certification program in Healthcare Innovation Management. The program which began in 2013 is a component of Mission Health's budding Center for Innovation established to foster a spirit of advancement in healthcare throughout western North Carolina. The program consists of four courses over a period of 21 months and is open to all Mission Health employees. Students who complete the program which is fully funded by Mission Health will earn credit towards bachelor's and master's degrees.

Company Background

Mission Hospital was formed in 1996 from the partnership (and eventual merger) of Memorial and St. Joseph's hospitals.

EXECUTIVES

Ceo, Chad Patrick
Pres*, Joseph Damore
Ceo*, Ronald A Paulus
Sr V Pres*, Charles F Ayscue
Human Resources Representative, Teresa McCarthy
Human Resources Representative, Dan McFatter
Chief Staff, Alan S Baumgarten
Business Manager Senior, Cora McPherson
Director, Gordon L Jones

LOCATIONS

HQ: MISSION HOSPITAL, INC.
509 BILTMORE AVE, ASHEVILLE, NC 288014601
Phone: 828 213-1111
Web: WWW.MISSIONHEALTH.ORG

PRODUCTS/OPERATIONS

Surgical Services
General Surgery
Minimally Invasive Surgery
Outpatient Surgery
Prepare for Surgery
Robotic Surgery
Surgery at Mission Hospital
Surgery Guide
Programs of Service
Endoscopy
Genetics
Integrative Healthcare
Mother and Baby
Outpatient Care Centers
Sleep Center
Urology
Weight Management Center
Wound Healing and Hyperbarics
Support Services
Chronic Medical Conditions
Long-Term Acute Care
Laboratory
Pastoral Care Services
Pharmacy
Psychiatric Services
Radiology (Imaging) Services
Rehabilitation Services
Research Institute
Respiratory Therapy

Senior Services and Geriatrics

COMPETITORS

Blue Ridge HealthCare	Haywood Regional
CaroMont	Presbyterian
Carolinas HealthCare System	Healthcare
	UNC Hospitals
Duke University Health System	

HISTORICAL FINANCIALS

Company Type: Private

Income Statement   FYE: September 30

	REVENUE ($ mil.)	NET INCOME ($ mil.)	NET PROFIT MARGIN	EMPLOYEES
09/15	1,019	91	9.0%	10,000
09/14	936	64	6.9%	—
09/13	942	71	7.6%	—
09/12	861	86	10.0%	—
Annual Growth	5.8%	2.0%	—	—

MISSISSIPPI STATE UNIVERSITY

While agriculture is at its roots Mississippi State University's (MSU) is today a four-year university offering approximately 150 undergraduate majors and pre-professional programs as well as master's educational specialist and doctorate degree programs at a dozen colleges and schools. It confers more than 4300 degrees annually and has an enrollment of more than 20870 students at its main campus in Starkville and a regional campus in Meridian. More than three-quarters of its student body hail from Mississippi. MSU was created by the Mississippi Legislature in 1878 as The Agricultural and Mechanical College of the State of Mississippi.

EXECUTIVES

County Secretary, Ste Stephanie

LOCATIONS

HQ: MISSISSIPPI STATE UNIVERSITY
245 BARR AVE MCRTHUR HL MCARTHUR HALL,
MISSISSIPPI STATE, MS 39762
Phone: 662 325-2302
Web: WWW.MSSTATE.EDU

HISTORICAL FINANCIALS

Company Type: Private

Income Statement   FYE: June 30

	REVENUE ($ mil.)	NET INCOME ($ mil.)	NET PROFIT MARGIN	EMPLOYEES
06/17	461	18	4.0%	4,500
06/16	462	48	10.4%	—
06/14	392	64	16.4%	—
06/13	371	25	6.9%	—
Annual Growth	5.6%	(7.9%)	—	—

2017 Year-End Financials

Return on assets: 1.2%   Cash ($ mil.): 113
Return on equity: 3.8%
Current ratio: 2.80

MISSOURI BAPTIST MEDICAL CENTER

EXECUTIVES

Pres, Joan Magruder
V Pres-Cfo*, Gary McLaughlin
Vpres*, Timothy Ranney
Vpres*, Douglas Black
Vpres*, Sandra Young
Vpres*, Tim Mislan
Pricipal*, John Antes
Health Professional, Anshu Jain
Supervisor, Patricia Burns
Diagnostic Radiologist, Geoffrey S Hamill
Director of Mis/Is, Rosa Davila

LOCATIONS

HQ: MISSOURI BAPTIST MEDICAL CENTER
3015 N BALLAS RD, SAINT LOUIS, MO 631312329
Phone: 314 996-5155
Web: WWW.BJC.ORG

HISTORICAL FINANCIALS

Company Type: Private

Income Statement   FYE: December 31

	REVENUE ($ mil.)	NET INCOME ($ mil.)	NET PROFIT MARGIN	EMPLOYEES
12/17	600	18	3.0%	1,670
12/16	570	25	4.5%	—
12/15	511	15	3.0%	—
12/14	472	22	4.8%	—
Annual Growth	8.3%	(7.4%)	—	—

2017 Year-End Financials

Return on assets: 5.0%   Cash ($ mil.): —
Return on equity: 5.3%
Current ratio: 4.40

MMR CONSTRUCTORS, INC.

EXECUTIVES

Pres, James B Rutland
V Pres*, Tom Welborn
SEC-Treas*, Donald Fairbanks
Director of Information Techno, Robert Benoit
Accounting, Alex Smith
Project Manager, Brett Jacob
Human Resources, Christy Trotter
Chief Technology Officer, Jerry Pattterson
Project Engineer, Mike Wilson
Auditors: MADDOX & ASSOCIATES APC BATO

LOCATIONS

HQ: MMR CONSTRUCTORS, INC.
15961 AIRLINE HWY, BATON ROUGE, LA 708177412
Phone: 225 756-5090
Web: WWW.MMRGRP.COM

HISTORICAL FINANCIALS

Company Type: Private

Income Statement				FYE: December 31
	REVENUE ($ mil.)	NET INCOME ($ mil.)	NET PROFIT MARGIN	EMPLOYEES
12/18	775	25	3.3%	4,000
12/17	581	16	2.9%	—
12/16	531	14	2.7%	—
Annual Growth	20.8%	33.1%	—	—

2018 Year-End Financials

Return on assets: 5.5%   Cash ($ mil.): 1
Return on equity: 12.3%
Current ratio: 3.50

MMR GROUP, INC.

That murmur you hear could be the gentle hum of a properly functioning power system. MMG Group provides electrical and instrumentation construction maintenance management and technical services for clients in the oil and gas manufacturing chemical and power generation industries around the world. It also offers services in offshore marine and platform environments. Its Power Solutions division constructs onsite power-generation systems in industrial plants and other facilities. The group primarily operates in the Gulf of New Mexico. Founded in 1990 MMG is 100% management owned and has served such clients as Chevron Shell BP Merck Air Liquide DuPont and 3M.

Operations

MMR Group's provides four main services: electrical and instrumentation contracting safety services panel fabrication and communications.

MMR's electrical and instrumentation contractors work on projects throughout the US and overseas. To ensure its projects are completed on time and within budget its personnel has support and management control systems and emphasizes planning scheduling progress tracking and labor analysis.

The MMR Offshore Safety Services division specializes in disaster prevention and safety helping with navigation fire and gas detection suppression products paging and alarm systems level one cathodic protection inspections and other related services.

For panel fabrication services MMR stages tests and designs control systems that best fit client needs.

The MMR ProCom division is in charge of precommissioning commissioning and start-Up activities for both MMR Group construction projects and for outside clients interested in turning their facilities construction into a safe and reliable operation seamlessly.

Geographic Reach

MMR operates out of some 20 offices spread across North and South America with most of its offices in Texas Louisiana and California. The company works on projects all over the world with foreign affiliate offices in Calgary Canada; Cartagena Colombia; Puerto la Cruz Venezuela; and Port of Spain Trinidad & Tobago.

Sales and Marketing

MMR serves a variety of markets including: alternative energy exploration and production chemical and petrochemical industrial and manufacturing oil and gas power generation and waste and water treatment among others.

Some of the company's panel fabrication clients have included Shell Pipeline Chevron Pipeline Enbridge Pipeline AGI Services Cimitation Engineering ExxonMobil Keystone Engineering W.S. Nelson Engineering and Entergy among others.

Depending on the project and client's preference MMR operates on all types of fixed-price and cost-plus contracts.

Strategy

The company continues to expand its operations to accommodate more projects. In 2014 the company built a 19-office administration building along with a 6000 square-foot warehouse facility to support the influx of new projects going on in the Golden Triangle area between Beaumont TX and Lake Charles LA.

EXECUTIVES

Vice President Marketing, Grady Saucier
Executive Vice President, Thomas Welborn
Auditors: MADDOX & ASSOCIATES APC BATO

LOCATIONS

HQ: MMR GROUP, INC.
15961 AIRLINE HWY, BATON ROUGE, LA 708177412
Phone: 225 756-5090
Web: WWW.MMRGRP.COM

PRODUCTS/OPERATIONS

Selected Services

Instrumentation
Air supply installation
Control room equipment installation
Instrument installation
Process leads
Panel fabrication
Signal wiring
Electrical
Controls
Electrical equipment setting
Grounding
Lighting
Power distribution
Technical
Calibration
Commissioning
Detail design
High voltage testing
Instrument procurement
Loop check
Maintenance
Start up assistance
System analysis

Selected Divisions

MMR Constructors
MMR International
MMR Power Solutions
MMR Offshore Services
MMR Technical Services
Southwestern Power Group

COMPETITORS

Alberici	MYR Group
EMCOR	Matrix Service
Fisk Electric	Turner Industries
Industrial Specialty Contractors	

HISTORICAL FINANCIALS

Company Type: Private

Income Statement				FYE: December 31
	REVENUE ($ mil.)	NET INCOME ($ mil.)	NET PROFIT MARGIN	EMPLOYEES
12/18	786	17	2.2%	4,000
12/17	618	9	1.5%	—
12/16	608	14	2.5%	—
12/15	585	24	4.3%	—
Annual Growth	10.4%	(10.8%)	—	—

2018 Year-End Financials

Return on assets: 3.7%   Cash ($ mil.): 1
Return on equity: 8.4%
Current ratio: 1.90

MODERN WOODMEN OF AMERICA

No need to pitch a tent to have Modern Woodmen in your camp. One of the largest fraternal benefit societies in the US Modern Woodmen of America provides annuities life insurance and other financial savings products to more than 770000 members through some 1600 agents. The group founded in 1883 is organized into "camps" (or chapters) that provide financial social recreational and service benefits to members. Founder Joseph Cullen Root chose the society's name to compare pioneering woodmen clearing forests to men using life insurance to remove the financial burdens their families could face upon their deaths.

Operations

The organization claims some 2400 family and summit chapters and more than 900 youth clubs nationwide. In addition to financial services the chapters also offer social activities and community service opportunities for members and their families. In addition to life insurance and annuities the company offers retirement accounts including IRAs college savings plans investment assistance and other insurance products. Modern Woodmen has more than $36 billion in life insurance in force.

Subsidiary MWA Financial Services offers securities and brokered insurance products. The MWA-Bank (dba Modern Woodmen Bank) division provides retail banking services.

Financial Performance

All told the company has more than $13 billion in assets and roughly $36 billion of life insurance in force. Its 2013 surplus totaled $1.5 billion a 14% increase over 2012.

Strategy

The company enhances its operations by adding new products as well as through marketing efforts for existing products. For instance in 2012 Modern Woodsmen's financial representatives increased promotional efforts for life insurance products leading to a 5% increase in certificates and a 12% rise new policies that year. The increase in life insurance sales was also attributed to the Planning for Life program a system introduced in 2011 to help members understand the role of life insurance in financial planning.

Mergers and Acquisitions

In 2012 Modern Woodmen grew its membership by more than 17000 through the acquisition of Equitable Reserve Association. Through the combination Modern Woodmen assumed the assets liabilities and operations of Equitable Reserve.

Company Background

Although Modern Woodmen's roots are tangled with Woodmen of the World Life Insurance Society the two fraternal benefit societies are not related.

EXECUTIVES

Vice President Of It, Becky Hansen

LOCATIONS

HQ: MODERN WOODMEN OF AMERICA
1701 1ST AVE, ROCK ISLAND, IL 612018779
Phone: 309 793-5537
Web: WWW.MODERNWOODMEN.ORG

PRODUCTS/OPERATIONS

Selected Products

Annuities (fixed immediate and variable; through MWA
   Financial Services)
Banking (MWABank)
   Certificates of Deposit
   Checking and savings accounts
   Credit cards and gift cards
   First mortgage and refinancing home loans
   Home equity loans
Insurance (through MWAGIA)
   Dental and vision insurance
   Disability income insurance
   Group employee benefits
   Group voluntary benefits
   Impaired risk life insurance
   International life and health insurance
   Long-term care insurance
   Major medical insurance
   Medicare supplement insurance
Investment (through MWA Financial Services)
   Brokerage services
   College savings plans
   Mutual funds
   Retirement plans
Life Insurance
   Term life insurance
   Term life insurance for children
   Universal life insurance
   Whole life insurance

COMPETITORS

Allstate	Reliance Standard
MassMutual	Royal Neighbors Of
MetLife	America
Nationwide Financial	State Farm
New York Life	Thrivent Financial
Northwestern Mutual	Woodmen of the World
Prudential	Life Insurance

HISTORICAL FINANCIALS

Company Type: Private

Income Statement   FYE: December 31

	ASSETS ($ mil.)	NET INCOME ($ mil.)	INCOME AS % OF ASSETS	EMPLOYEES
12/07	8,318	96	1.2%	480
12/06	7,928	99	1.3%	—
Annual Growth	4.9%	(2.6%)	—	—

2007 Year-End Financials

Return on assets: 1.2%   Sales ($ mil): 1,065
Return on equity: 8.2%

MONMOUTH MEDICAL CENTER INC.

Monmouth Medical Center is a 530-bed tertiary care teaching hospital providing comprehensive health care to residents of central New Jersey. The not-for-profit medical center offers services ranging from orthopedics diagnostics and obstetric care to surgery dentistry and geriatric services. The medical center campus also includes a children's hospital a cancer center a neuroscience institute an outpatient care clinic and hospice and home health facilities. Monmouth Medical Center is a major teaching affiliate of the Drexel University College of Medicine in Philadelphia. The hospital is an affiliate of the Saint Barnabas Healthcare System.

Operations

Monmouth Medical Center handles 19000 inpatient admissions each year as well as 49000 emergency room visits. Its outpatient clinic handles some 126000 appointments annually. The hospital has 700 doctors representing 60 specialties on its staff.

Geographic Reach

Monmouth Medical Center is located on about 20 acres in Long Branch New Jersey near the Atlantic Ocean. The campus includes the main 16-wing hospital and and about 16 other buildings including resident physician dwellings a day care center a medical education and training facility and a Ronald McDonald House.

The hospital serves a territory consisting of Monmouth Ocean and Middlesex counties with a total of about one million residents. It has outpatient locations in Colts Neck Howell Long Branch Ocean Township and Shrewsbury.

Strategy

The hospital has conducted recent expansion projects including additions of new a new cancer center surgical suites and a family center. In 2013 it opened a new postpartum wing and newborn nursery as well as a larger neonatal ICU. Monmouth Medical Center also extended its pediatric and oncology programs by forming partnerships with other area hospitals in 2012.

Company Background

Monmouth Medical Center was founded in 1887. It has expanded over the years to provide a number of specialist services including high-tech offerings such as robotic surgery.

EXECUTIVES

Vice President Of Patient Care Services, Diann
Johnston
Assistant Vice President Financial Services, James
Alexander
Medical Records Director, Dianna Jankos
Vice President Of Supply Chain, Robert Carretta
Vice President Of Patient Care Services, Sari
Kaplon
Auditors: KPMG LLP NEW YORK NY

LOCATIONS

HQ: MONMOUTH MEDICAL CENTER INC.
   300 2ND AVE, LONG BRANCH, NJ 077406395
Phone: 732 222-5200
Web: WWW.RWJBH.ORG

PRODUCTS/OPERATIONS

Selected Centers and Services
Anesthesiology Services
Behavioral Health Network
Brain Tumor Center (David S. Zocchi)
The Breast Center (Jacqueline M. Wilentz
   Comprehensive)
Burn Center
Cancer Services
Cardiac Services
Cardiac Surgery
Children's Hospital at Monmouth (Pediatrics)
Cleft Palate Center
Cord Blood Banking Program
Cosmetic Surgery
Cranmer Ambulatory Surgery Center
Critical Care Services
Diabetes Education - Center for Diabetes Education
Dental Medicine
Diagnostic Imaging Services
The Eisenberg Family Center
Emergency Services
Epilepsy Monitoring Program
Extracorporeal Membrane Oxygenation Program
   (ECMO)
The Gamma Knife Center
Geriatric Emergency Medicine (GEM) Unit
Geriatric Health Center
Head & Neck Surgery
Hernias Repair Institute for the Treatment of Complex
HIV/AIDS Program
Home Health Care
Home Infusion Care
Hospice
Hyperbaric Oxygen Therapy

Integrative Medicine (Center for)
Joint Replacement and Spine Center
Medical Records
Medical Alert/Lifeline
Medicine (Department of)
Minimally Invasive Surgery
Monmouth Family Health Center
Neonatal Intensive Care Unit (Regional Newborn Center)
Neuroscience Institute
Nutritional Counseling
Obstetrics/Gynecological Services
Occupational Medicine
Orthopaedic Services
Outpatient Services Location
Pain Management Program
Palliative Care
Pastoral Care
Pathology & Laboratory Services
Pediatric Services
Pediatric Subspecialty Center at Toms River The
Pediatric Surgery
Pharmacy Department
Plastic Surgery
Podiatry Services
Pre-Admission Testing Services
Psychiatric Services
Pulmonary Services
Radiation Oncology
Rehabilitation Services
Renal Services
Renal Transplantation
Respiratory Services
Robotic Surgery
Senior Services Program
Sleep Disorders Center
Spine Center
Surgical Services
Total Joint Replacement
Urogynecology
Urology
Valerie Fund Cancer Center (Pediatrics)
Vascular Surgery
The Weight Loss Institute of New Jersey
Wound Treatment Center

COMPETITORS

Atlantic Health	Saint Peter's
Bergen Regional	University Hospital
Medical	Shore Memorial
Capital Health System	Hospital
CentraState Healthcare	St. Joseph's
System	Healthcare System
Hackensack Meridian	Trinitas Regional
Health	Medical Center
Princeton HealthCare	Valley Health System

HISTORICAL FINANCIALS

Company Type: Private

Income Statement   FYE: December 31

	REVENUE ($ mil.)	NET INCOME ($ mil.)	NET PROFIT MARGIN	EMPLOYEES
12/18	546	43	8.0%	2,400
12/17	529	52	10.0%	—
12/16	399	46	11.5%	—
12/14	375	38	10.2%	—
Annual Growth	9.8%	3.4%	—	—

2018 Year-End Financials

Return on assets: 5.7%   Cash ($ mil.): —
Return on equity: 13.3%
Current ratio: 2.80

MONOGRAM FOOD SOLUTIONS, LLC

Monogram Food Solutions is focused on M E A and T. As a manufacturer of meat and meat snack products the company produces beef jerky sausage hot dogs bacon and other processed food items. Its brands include Circle B King Cotton and Trail's Best Meat Snacks. Through several special licensing agreements Monogram Food Solutions also sells Jeff Foxworthy Jerky Products NASCAR Jerky and Steak Strips and Bass Pro Uncle Buck's Licensed Products. The company which distributes its products nationwide operates facilities in Minnesota Indiana and Virginia. Founded in 2004 Monogram Food Solutions was formed through the merger of assets (King Cotton and Circle B) previously owned by Sara Lee Corp.

Geographic Reach

From its headquarters in Memphis Tennessee Monogram Food Solutions directs the operation of additional facilities in (Chandler) Minnesota (Muncie and Bristol) Indiana and (Martinsville) Virginia. The company distributes its products nationwide.

Strategy

Licensing agreements have helped Monogram Food Solutions build a firm foundation for its business. Aside from its deal with Bass Pro Shops and Jeff Foxworthy the company enjoys licensing partnerships with Johnsonville Sausage and Glory Foods. Its alliance with Johnsonville Sausage inked in 2012 gave Monogram Food Solutions the go-ahead to produce and market Johnsonville Deli Bites Bacon Jerky and other meat snacks innovations.

Beginning in 2010 the company began manufacturing and selling meat snacks for the energy drink maker DNA Beverages Corporation under the DNA brand. Geared toward a younger consumer the DNA beef products gives Monogram a larger demographic for its products.

Mergers and Acquisitions

Since its founding the company has quickly built itself up by buying established meat product manufacturers and processing plants. In 2009 it acquired three companies including beef jerky maker Wild Bill's Foods and Al Pete's Meats (and the Pete's Pride brand name). It also acquired the Hannah's Bull's O'Brien's and Dakota meat snack brands from meat processing company American Foods Group.

In late 2012 Monogram Food Solutions purchased Hinsdale Farms of Bristol Indiana. As one of the nation's largest makers of corn dogs Hinsdale also has a hand in serving retail private label customers and co-packing for other manufacturers. The deal added a fourth manufacturing plant for processing meat. As part of the acquisition Monogram Food Solutions is working to integrate the Hinsdale business into its manufacturing and sales systems.

EXECUTIVES

Vice President Operations Fina, George Roden
Senior Vice President Information Technology, Joan Vanness
Management Vice President, Brett Elliott
Vice President General Manager, Richard Foster
Vice President And Product Development, Bill Southard
Vice President Of Operations, Kent Kring
Auditors: MAYER HOFFMAN MCCANN PC MEM

LOCATIONS

HQ: MONOGRAM FOOD SOLUTIONS, LLC
530 OAK COURT DR STE 400, MEMPHIS, TN 381173735
Phone: 901 685-7167
Web: WWW.MONOGRAMFOODS.COM

PRODUCTS/OPERATIONS

Selected Brands
Circle B
Hannah's
King Cotton
O'Brien's Meat Snacks/Sausages
Wild Bill's

COMPETITORS

Bridgford Foods	Hormel
Carl Buddig	Jerky Snack Brands
Clemens Family	Link Snacks
Corporation	Oberto Sausage Company
ConAgra	Weaver Meats

HISTORICAL FINANCIALS

Company Type: Private

Income Statement				FYE: December 29
	REVENUE ($ mil.)	NET INCOME ($ mil.)	NET PROFIT MARGIN	EMPLOYEES
12/18	647	11	1.7%	790
12/17	640	2	0.4%	—
12/16*	565	12	2.2%	—
01/16	419	0	0.2%	—
Annual Growth	15.6%	146.0%	—	—

*Fiscal year change

2018 Year-End Financials

Return on assets: 2.5%
Return on equity: 8.5%
Current ratio: 1.50

Cash ($ mil.): —

MONONGAHELA POWER COMPANY

Electricity flows from Monongahela Power (Mon Power) just like the river the utility was named after. The company services approximately 388000 residential and commercial customers in a service area of 13000 sq. mi. in West Virginia. Mon Power along with West Penn Power and Potomac Edison comprise the Allegheny Power arm of Allegheny Energy which is now part of FirstEnergy. In 2013 Mon Power owned or controlled 3580 MW of generating capacity. The company is contractually obligated to supply Potomac Edison with sufficient power to meet that company's power load obligations in West Virginia.

Operations

Mon Power provides generation transmission and distribution services. Its infrastructure includes 25390 miles of distribution lines and more than 2125 miles of transmission lines.

Geographic Reach

The utility's service area includes Northern Central and Southeastern West Virginia.

Strategy

In 2013 the parent company invested about $131 million in Mon Power and planned to invest about $233 million more in 2014 to help Mon Power expand its operations.

In a transfer of assets within FirstEnergy's West Virginia-based operations to improve efficiencies in 2013 Mon Power sold its 8% share of the Pleasants power plant at its fair market value of $73 million to Allegheny Energy Supply. In return Allegheny Energy Supply sold its 80% stake in the Harrison plant to Mon Power at its book value of $1.2 billion.

To lower carbon emissions in 2012 Mon Power shut down three aging coal-fired power plants in West Virginia: Albright Willow Island and Rivesville.

Company Background

The company is a subsidiary of Allegheny Energy which is owned by FirstEnergy.

Mon Power was incorporated in Ohio in 1924.

EXECUTIVES

Chb-Ceo, Paul J Evanson
V Pres*, Philip L Goulding
Pres*, David E Flitman
Contrl*, Thomas R Gardner
V Pres-SEC*, Hyun Park
Cfo*, Jeffrey David Serkes
Associate Business Analyst, Jane Campbell
General Manager Operations, Mike Haines

LOCATIONS

HQ: MONONGAHELA POWER COMPANY
5001 NASA BLVD, FAIRMONT, WV 265548248
Phone: 800 686-0022
Web: WWW.FIRSTENERGYCORP.COM

COMPETITORS

Appalachian Power	Dominion Transmission
Buckeye Power	Ohio Edison
Dominion Hope	Ohio Valley Electric

HISTORICAL FINANCIALS

Company Type: Private

Income Statement				FYE: December 31
	REVENUE ($ mil.)	NET INCOME ($ mil.)	NET PROFIT MARGIN	EMPLOYEES
12/17	1,619	69	4.3%	4,000
12/16	1,613	66	4.1%	—
Annual Growth	0.3%	4.5%	—	—

2017 Year-End Financials

Return on assets: 1.6%
Return on equity: 5.4%
Current ratio: 1.80

Cash ($ mil.): 76

MONSTER BEVERAGE 1990 CORPORATION

LOCATIONS

HQ: MONSTER BEVERAGE 1990 CORPORATION
1 MONSTER WAY, CORONA, CA 928797101
Phone: 951 739-6200
Web: WWW.MONSTERBEVCORP.COM

COMPETITORS

5-hour ENERGY
Bazi
Campbell Soup
Caribou Coffee
Celsius Holdings
Chiquita Brands
Cinnabon
Clearly Canadian
Coca-Cola
Cott
Del Monte Foods
Dole Food
Dr Pepper Snapple
  Group
Energy Brands
Gatorade
Godiva Chocolatier
Goya
Hornell Brewing
IZZE
Impulse Energy USA
Jones Soda
Mondelez International

Mott's
Naked Juice
National Beverage
National Grape
  Cooperative
Nestle
Ocean Spray
Odwalla
PepsiCo
Red Bull
Reed's
Smucker
South Beach Beverage
Starbucks
Sunny Delight
Suntory Holdings
Tree Top
Tropicana
Unilever
Welch's
Wet Planet Beverages
illy

HISTORICAL FINANCIALS

Company Type: Private

Income Statement

	REVENUE ($ mil.)	NET INCOME ($ mil.)	NET PROFIT MARGIN	EMPLOYEES
12/17	3,369	820	24.4%	2,001
12/16	3,049	712	23.4%	—
12/15	2,722	546	20.1%	—
12/14	2,464	483	19.6%	—
Annual Growth	11.0%	19.3%	—	—

FYE: December 31

2017 Year-End Financials

Return on assets: 17.1%
Return on equity: 21.1%
Current ratio: 3.70

Cash ($ mil.): 528

MONTEFIORE MEDICAL CENTER

The primary teaching hospital of the Albert Einstein College of Medicine Montefiore Medical Center attends to the health care needs of residents of the Bronx and nearby Westchester County. The health system operates four main hospitals with about 1500 beds (and 93000 annual admissions) more than 100 ambulatory care offices a children's hospital and Centers of Excellence in cancer care cardiovascular services transplantation and neurosciences. Additionally it operates a home health care agency as well as outpatient facilities that provide ambulatory and diagnostic services. Montefiore also offers medical education programs in partnership with the Albert Einstein College of Medicine.

Operations

Montefiore provides medical services to more than 2.6 million people in the Bronx and Westchester County. With nearly 300000 visits per year Montefiore's emergency department is one of the busiest in the nation while the home health program provides over 500000 visits annually. As the teaching hospital for Albert Einstein College of Medicine Montefiore provides postgraduate training for nearly 100 accredited residency and fellowship programs at the Children's Hospital at Montefiore Moses Division and Weiler Division and eight residency and fellowship programs sponsored by New York Medical College.

Through Montefiore Care Management the company uses a global prepayment or similar strategies to manage care for 200000 individuals for hospital care rehabilitation outpatient care professional services home care mental health counseling community-based services remote patient monitoring and other programs.

Montefiore and Einstein are among about three dozen academic medical centers nationwide to be awarded the Clinical and Translational Science Award (CTSA) by the National Institutes of Health.

Geographic Reach

Montefiore is made up of four hospitals within three main campuses in the Bronx and more than 100 ambulatory care offices throughout the Bronx and Westchester County (and a total of 140 locations across its entire service area). It has nearly 50 primary care locations throughout the New York metropolitan area.

Strategy

The health center's strategy is to advance its partnership with the Einstein College of Medicine and to improve the health of the communities it serves. Montefiore has grown in scale through acquisitions and mergers in order to diversify its earning potential and increase its bargaining power with drug wholesalers. The system which treats a relatively high percentage of Medicaid patients also stands to benefit by serving a larger volume of patients. Medicaid is shifting to the managed care model which pays a set amount per patient or service. Therefore Montefiore and other providers are seeking growth by caring for more patients in a more efficient manner thereby reducing losses from providing patient care above the government payor's set payment. Additionally the system launched its own insurance coverage for small businesses in early 2015.

The health system is largely involved in the community and is one of the region's hospitals to participate in the Bronx Regional Health Information Organization (Bronx RHIO) a not-for-profit organization established to help the borough's vast number of health care providers share patient information. Participants include hospitals health systems ambulatory care centers individual physician offices long-term care and home care services. Collectively they deliver care to more than 1 million residents including more than 95% of the borough's annual hospital discharges.

Company Background

Founded in 1884 to treat tuberculosis patients Montefiore has a long history of responding to community health crises including lead poisoning and AIDS. In response to rising needs in the community Montefiore opened a community clinic with the aim of vaccinating young women for HPV a sexually transmitted disease that can cause cervical cancer.

EXECUTIVES

Evp Finance And Cfo, Joel A. Perlman
President And Ceo, Steven M. Safyer, age 71
Evp And Coo, Philip O. Ozuah
Svp And Chief Medical Officer, Andrew D. Racine
Chief Development Officer And Vice President, Rachelle Sanders
Director Of Nursing, Maureen Vachna
Medical Director Aids Ctr, Barry Zingman
Secretary, Evette Francis
Secretary, Yvonne Biney
Auditors: ERNST & YOUNG LLP NEW YORK

LOCATIONS

HQ: MONTEFIORE MEDICAL CENTER
  111 E 210TH ST, BRONX, NY 104672401
Phone: 718 920-4321

PRODUCTS/OPERATIONS

Selected Services

Allergy & Immunology
Arthritis & Joint Disease (Rheumatology)
Blood (Hematology)
Bones Muscles & Joints Orthopaedics)
Brain (Neurology)
Centers of Excellence
Dentistry & Oral Surgery
Dermatology
Diabetes Hormones Metabolism (Endocrinology)
Diagnostics & Testing (Pathology)
Digestive & Liver Dieases (Gastroenterology)
Elder Care (Geriatrics)
Emergency Medicine
Eyes (Opthalmology and Visual Sciences)
Family and Social Medicine
General Internal Medicine
Headache Center
HIV/AIDS
Home Care
ICU (Critical Care Medicine)
Infectious Diseases
Internal Medicine
Kidney Disease (Nephrology)
Lungs (Pulmonary Medicine)
Neurosurgery
OB/GYN & Women's Health
Otorhinolaryngology - Head and Neck Surgery
Pain Management & Anesthesiology
Pediatrics
Pharmacy Services
Primary Care
Psychiatry and Behavioral Sciences
Radiology
Rehabilitation Medicine
Sleep-Wake Disorders Center
Surgery
Surgical Services (All)
Urology
Wound Care (Hyperbaric Medicine)

Selected Facilities

Greene Medical Arts Pavilion (outpatient care)
Mercy Community Care (outpatient care)
Montefiore Medical Group (23 Bronx and Westchester locations)
Montefiore Medical Park (outpatient care)
Moses Division Hospital (or Henry and Lucy Moses Division)
  The Children's Hospital at Montefiore
North Division (formerly Our Lady of Mercy Medical Center)
Weiler Division Hospital (or Jack D. Weiler Hospital)

COMPETITORS

Beth Israel Medical
  Center
Bronx-Lebanon Hospital
Brookdale University
  Hospital
Brooklyn Hospital
  Center
Catholic Healthcare
  System
Jamaica Hospital
  Medical Center
Kingsbrook Jewish
  Medical Center

Lenox Hill Hospital
Maimonides Medical
  Center
New York City Health
  and Hospitals
NewYork-Presbyterian
  Healthcare
Northwell Health
Phelps Memorial
  Hospital Center
SUNY Downstate
Winthrop-University
  Hospital

HISTORICAL FINANCIALS

Company Type: Private

Income Statement

	REVENUE ($ mil.)	NET INCOME ($ mil.)	NET PROFIT MARGIN	EMPLOYEES
12/17	3,762	43	1.2%	11,000
12/16	2,690	42	1.6%	—
Annual Growth	39.9%	2.7%	—	—

FYE: December 31

2017 Year-End Financials

Return on assets: 1.2%
Return on equity: 5.1%
Current ratio: 1.70

Cash ($ mil.): 253

MOORE REGIONAL HOSPITAL, INC.

EXECUTIVES

Chb, Walker Morris
SEC*, Judy Cox
Asst SEC*, Charles T Frock
Treas*, Norris L Hodgins Jr
Controller*, Robert T Ward
Data Processing, Bryan Hall
Lab Technician, Lori Ayers

LOCATIONS

HQ: MOORE REGIONAL HOSPITAL, INC.
20 PAGE DR, PINEHURST, NC 283748847
Phone: 910 295-7888

HISTORICAL FINANCIALS

Company Type: Private

Income Statement				FYE: September 30
	REVENUE ($ mil.)	NET INCOME ($ mil.)	NET PROFIT MARGIN	EMPLOYEES
09/15	468	55	11.9%	1,400
09/08	358	31	8.7%	—
09/05	326	45	13.9%	—
Annual Growth	3.7%	2.1%	—	—

2015 Year-End Financials

Return on assets: 5.7%
Return on equity: 8.9%
Current ratio: 2.20
Cash ($ mil.): 25

MORSE OPERATIONS, INC.

Morse Operations (dba Ed Morse Automotive Group) has been selling cars and trucks long enough to know the code of the road. It owns about a dozen new car dealerships across Florida most of them operating under the Ed Morse name. Dealerships house more than 15 franchises and 10 domestic and import car brands including Cadillac Fiat Chevrolet Buick GMC Scion Honda Mazda and Toyota. The company's Bayview Cadillac in Fort Lauderdale is one of the world's largest volume sellers of Cadillacs. Morse Operations also sells used cars provides parts and service and operates a fleet sales division. Founder and auto magnate the late Ed Morse entered the automobile business in 1946 with a 20-car rental fleet.

Operations

Ed Morse Fleet Sales offers vehicles from about 10 different brands including Honda Cadillac Fiat Chevrolet Buick GMC Scion Mazda and Toyota. To date annual fleet sales have reached 100000 vehicles.

Fleet customers include daily rental companies such as National Car Rental Avis and Alamo Rent A Car.

Geographic Reach

The dealership network serves customers throughout Florida along the East and West coasts and in Central Florida.

EXECUTIVES

Pres, Edward J Morse III
V Pres-Cfo*, Carmine Colella
Ceo-Coo*, Dennis M Macinnes
V Pres*, Rany Hoffman
Auditors: CROWE HORWATH LLP FORT LAUDER

LOCATIONS

HQ: MORSE OPERATIONS, INC.
2850 S FEDERAL HWY, DELRAY BEACH, FL 334833216
Phone: 561 276-5000
Web: WWW.EDMORSESAWGRASS.COM

PRODUCTS/OPERATIONS

Selected Dealerships
Brandon Auto Mall
Ed Morse Auto Plaza - Port Richey
Ed Morse Bayview Cadillac
Ed Morse Cadillac - Delray Beach
  Ed Morse C
  Ed Morse C
Ed Morse Delray Toyota/Scion
Ed Morse Honda Blue Heron
  Ed Morse M
Ed Morse Sawgrass

COMPETITORS

AutoNation
Braman Management
Buchanan Automotive
Ferman Automotive
Holman Enterprises
Island Lincoln-Mercury
JM Family Enterprises
Penske Automotive Group
Scott-McRae

HISTORICAL FINANCIALS

Company Type: Private

Income Statement				FYE: December 31
	REVENUE ($ mil.)	NET INCOME ($ mil.)	NET PROFIT MARGIN	EMPLOYEES
12/18	1,125	(0)	—	925
12/17	1,019	4	0.4%	—
12/16	1,334	9	0.7%	—
Annual Growth	(8.2%)	—	—	—

2018 Year-End Financials

Return on assets: (-0.2%)
Return on equity: (-1.1%)
Current ratio: 1.50
Cash ($ mil.): 11

MORTON PLANT HOSPITAL ASSOCIATION, INC.

EXECUTIVES

Pres, Brandon May
V Pres-Oprs-Adm*, Hal Ziecheck
Doctor, Margaret Ann Kelleher
Doctor, Michael Starsiak
Pathologist, Jason Savell
Obstetrician Gynecologist, David D Desper Jr
Physician Director of Er, Stephen I Haire
Facilities Manager, Barbara Przybyszewski
Doctor, Angel Docobo
Doctor, Anup Desai
Internist, Tommie Betancourt

LOCATIONS

HQ: MORTON PLANT HOSPITAL ASSOCIATION, INC.
300 PINELLAS ST, CLEARWATER, FL 337563892
Phone: 727 462-7000

HISTORICAL FINANCIALS

Company Type: Private

Income Statement				FYE: December 31
	REVENUE ($ mil.)	NET INCOME ($ mil.)	NET PROFIT MARGIN	EMPLOYEES
12/16	555	83	14.9%	3,000
12/15	107	(8)	—	—
12/13	598	49	8.3%	—
12/09	517	33	6.5%	—
Annual Growth	1.0%	13.8%	—	—

2016 Year-End Financials

Return on assets: 8.2%
Return on equity: 8.5%
Current ratio: 21.40
Cash ($ mil.): —

MOSAIC LIFE CARE

Heartland Regional Medical Center strives for healthy hearts minds and bodies in the US heartland. The acute care hospital a subsidiary of Heartland Health provides medical services to residents of St. Joseph Missouri and some 20 surrounding counties in northwest Missouri southeast Nebraska and northeast Kansas. Heartland Regional Medical Center encompasses specialty centers for trauma and long-term care acute rehabilitation cancer heart disease and birthing. As part of the services provided by the medical center Heartland Regional Medical Center offers services such as arthritis pain and wound treatments as well as home health and hospice care.

Geographic Reach

Operating in Missouri Heartland Regional Medical Center serves the residents and visitors of its home state as well as those in Nebraska and Kansas. Altogether the medical center caters to a more than 20-county area.

Financial Performance

In fiscal 2012 as compared to 2011 Heartland Regional Medical Center's revenue rose some 8% and its net income saw a 31% boost.

Strategy

As part of its operations Heartland Regional Medical Center partners with several managed care organizations such as Aetna CCN Managed Care Coventry Healthcare and Blue Cross Blue Shield of Kansas City to give its patients payment options for its health services. In 2012 Heartland Regional Medical Center developed an accountable care organization. It's a participant in the Medicare Shared Savings Program and enters into other similar shared savings arrangements with commercial self-insured or other third-party payors.

In recent years the medical facility has been investing in growing its footprint. Heartland Regional Medical Center is funding a $55-million expansion project that includes adding a handful of new operating rooms and renovating 10 more.

EXECUTIVES

Chm, Alfred L Purcell
Ceo*, Mark Laney
SEC*, John Wilson
Project Manager, Chris Bennett
Marketing Staff, Diane R Smith
Director, Karen Baker
Auditors: BLD LLP KANSAS CITY MISSOUR

LOCATIONS

HQ: MOSAIC LIFE CARE
5325 FARAON ST, SAINT JOSEPH, MO 645063488
Phone: 816 271-6000
Web: WWW.MYMOSAICLIFECARE.ORG

PRODUCTS/OPERATIONS

Selected Services

Appendectomy

Cholecystectomy
Colon Resection
Hernia Repair
Nephrectomy
Assisted Vaginal Hysterectomy
Peritoneal Dialysis Catheter Placement
Pyloromyotomy
Tubal Ligation
Abdominal Perineal Resection
Adrenalectomy
Colostomy
Gastric Banding
Gastric Bypass
Gastric Sleeve
Gastrostomy Tube Placement
Laser Lysis of Adhesions/Endometriosis
Nissan Fundoplication
Salpingo-Oophorectomy
Prostatectomy

COMPETITORS

Ascension Health	Shawnee Mission
BJC HealthCare	Medical Center
Catholic Health	Sisters of Charity of
Initiatives	Leavenworth
Children's Mercy	Truman Medical Centers
Hospital	University of Kansas
CoxHealth	Medical Center
Mercy Health	
Saint Luke's Health	
System	

HISTORICAL FINANCIALS
Company Type: Private

Income Statement				FYE: June 30
	REVENUE ($ mil.)	NET INCOME ($ mil.)	NET PROFIT MARGIN	EMPLOYEES
06/18	639	64	10.1%	2,600
06/17	605	26	4.4%	—
06/16	562	(5)	—	—
06/15	563	20	3.7%	—
Annual Growth	4.3%	46.0%	—	—

2018 Year-End Financials

Return on assets: 6.9%   Cash ($ mil.): 22
Return on equity: 10.9%
Current ratio: 1.10

MOTION PICTURE INDUSTRY HEALTH PLAN

EXECUTIVES

Prin, David Wescoe
Assistant Manager, Jose Morales
Auditors: MILLER KAPLAN ARASE LLP NORTH

LOCATIONS

HQ: MOTION PICTURE INDUSTRY HEALTH PLAN
11365 VENTURA BLVD, STUDIO CITY, CA 916043148
Phone: 818 769-0007
Web: WWW.MPIPHP.ORG

HISTORICAL FINANCIALS
Company Type: Private

Income Statement				FYE: December 31
	ASSETS ($ mil.)	NET INCOME ($ mil.)	INCOME AS % OF ASSETS	EMPLOYEES
12/13	856	60	7.1%	17
12/09	543	(75)	—	—
Annual Growth	12.0%	—	—	—

2013 Year-End Financials

Return on assets: 7.1%   Sales ($ mil): 732
Return on equity: 18.7%

MOUNT CARMEL HEALTH PLAN MEDIG

LOCATIONS

HQ: MOUNT CARMEL HEALTH PLAN MEDIG
6150 E BROAD ST, COLUMBUS, OH 432131574
Phone: 614 546-3138
Web: WWW.MEDIGOLD.COM

HISTORICAL FINANCIALS
Company Type: Private

Income Statement				FYE: December 31
	REVENUE ($ mil.)	NET INCOME ($ mil.)	NET PROFIT MARGIN	EMPLOYEES
12/16	571	(20)	—	3
12/13	423	37	8.8%	—
Annual Growth	10.5%	—	—	—

2016 Year-End Financials

Return on assets: (-7.1%)   Cash ($ mil.): 55
Return on equity: (-14.2%)
Current ratio: 3.40

MOUNT CARMEL HEALTH SYSTEM

Mount Carmel Health System cares for the sick in the greater Columbus area and central Ohio. The health care system boasts 1500 physicians at three general hospitals and a specialty surgical hospital offering a comprehensive range of medical and surgical services including cardiovascular care. Mount Carmel Health also operates outpatient centers including primary care and specialty physicians' practices and it offers home health care services. The hospital group is part of Trinity Health one of the largest Catholic health care systems in the US.

Operations

Mount Carmel's facilities include the acute care Mount Carmel East Mount Carmel West and

---

Mount Carmel St. Ann's hospitals as well as the Mount Carmel New Albany a surgical hospital specializing in orthopedic neurological and musculoskeletal treatments. The system also operates several freestanding emergency and surgery centers and other outpatient and community care centers. Its HealthProviders subsidiary manages about two dozen primary care and specialty practices with more than 100 physicians in central Ohio.

In the realm of education Mount Carmel Health operates six medical residency programs for physicians and its Mount Carmel College of Nursing is one of the largest in the state.

Strategy

In 2015 Mount Carmel announced that it was investing more than $700 million in a major expansion. The investment includes big projects at three Mount Carmel campuses: Mount Carmel East Mount Carmel Grove City and Mount Carmel West. Mount Carmel East will begin a $310 million modernization in 2015 to be completed in phases through 2019.

That year the company signed an agreement with HealthSouth to begin construction on a new inpatient rehabilitation hospital in Westerville Ohio. The 60-bed hospital will be a joint venture between HealthSouth and Mount Carmel and will provide specialized rehabilitative care to patients who have experienced stroke trauma brain and orthopedic injuries or other major illnesses or injuries. Construction on the 60000-square-foot hospital is expected to be completed in early 2017. When the new hospital opens Mount Carmel will relocate its existing 24-bed unit at Mount Carmel West to the new facility.

Company Background

In 2012 the company launched a $110 million facilities improvement project (Project GRACE) which includes the renovation of the St. Ann's hospital. Mount Carmel Health plans for the upgraded St. Ann's facility to serve as a regional medical center.

In 2010 Mount Carmel completed construction of a new freestanding emergency center in the town of Canal Winchester through a partnership with Fairfield Medical Center. The center features both general emergency and pediatric urgent care facilities. In time the center might expand into a larger hospital facility.

Mother M. Angela and Sister M. Rufina Dunn of the Congregation of the Sisters of the Holy Cross of Notre Dame founded Mount Carmel in 1886.

EXECUTIVES

Vice President Pfs, Karen Geisler
Vice President Patient Care Services And, Rachel Wright

LOCATIONS

HQ: MOUNT CARMEL HEALTH SYSTEM
6150 E BROAD ST, COLUMBUS, OH 432131574
Phone: 614 234-6000
Web: WWW.MOUNTCARMELHEALTH.COM

PRODUCTS/OPERATIONS

Selected Facilities

Hospitals
Mount Carmel East
Mount Carmel New Albany
Mount Carmel St. Ann's
Mount Carmel West
Other Facilities
Anticoagulation Centers
Atrial Fibrillation Center
Cardiac Rehabilitation
Diley Ridge Medical Center
Mount Carmel Grove City Medical Center
Geriatrics Center
Health Centers
Heart Failure Centers

Home Medical Equipment
Imaging Centers
Mount Carmel Medical Group
Occupational Health Centers
Outpatient Cancer Treatment
Outpatient Labs
Physician Offices
Rehab and Sports Medicine Services
Sleep Medicine
Surgery Centers
Urgent Care Centers
Women's Health Centers
Wound Centers

COMPETITORS

Adena Health System	Nationwide Children's
Fairfield Medical	Hospital
Center	OhioHealth
Genesis HealthCare	Regency Hospital
System (Ohio)	
Licking Memorial	
Health Systems	

HISTORICAL FINANCIALS

Company Type: Private

Income Statement				FYE: June 30
	REVENUE ($ mil.)	NET INCOME ($ mil.)	NET PROFIT MARGIN	EMPLOYEES
06/18	1,911	157	8.2%	8,000
06/15	1,267	131	10.4%	—
06/14	1,223	94	7.7%	—
06/13	1,195	89	7.5%	—
Annual Growth	9.8%	11.9%	—	—

MOUNT CARMEL HEALTH SYSTEM

EXECUTIVES

Ceo, Jay Kasey
Marketing Staff, Steve Dunn
Senior Director, Joyce Bogan
Vice-President, Bruce Lucas
Information Specialist, Mike Croyle
Senior Vice-President, Barbara Hahl
Vice-President, Brian Smith
Vice-President Human Resources, Chris Browning
Internal Medicine Practitioner, John Weiss
Internal Medicine Practitioner, Mark Hackman
Manager, Paul Groh

LOCATIONS

HQ: MOUNT CARMEL HEALTH SYSTEM
793 W STATE ST, COLUMBUS, OH 432221551
Phone: 614 234-5000

HISTORICAL FINANCIALS

Company Type: Private

Income Statement				FYE: June 30
	REVENUE ($ mil.)	NET INCOME ($ mil.)	NET PROFIT MARGIN	EMPLOYEES
06/16	743	33	4.5%	1
06/15	707	47	6.7%	—
Annual Growth	5.1%	(29.5%)	—	—

2016 Year-End Financials

Return on assets: 6.6%   Cash ($ mil.): 39
Return on equity: 7.6%
Current ratio: 3.00

MOUNT SINAI HOSPITALS GROUP, INC.

EXECUTIVES

Pres-Ceo, Kenneth L Davis
Emergency Medicine Specialist, Jacob Isserman
Doctor, Anthony Manasia
Doctor, Bruce Darrow
Doctor, Bryan Markinson
Doctor, Dov Kolker
Doctor, Eric Genden
Director, Albert Siu
Associate Professor, David Muller
Coordinator, Deborah Lehrer
Doctor, James Eisenkraft

LOCATIONS

HQ: MOUNT SINAI HOSPITALS GROUP, INC.
1 GUSTAVE L LEVY PL, NEW YORK, NY 100296504
Phone: 212 241-6500
Web: WWW.MOUNTSINAI.ORG

HISTORICAL FINANCIALS

Company Type: Private

Income Statement				FYE: December 31
	REVENUE ($ mil.)	NET INCOME ($ mil.)	NET PROFIT MARGIN	EMPLOYEES
12/15*	2,025	70	3.5%	12,559
06/15	304	5	1.8%	—
Annual Growth	564.6%	1160.5%	—	—

*Fiscal year change

2015 Year-End Financials

Return on assets: 2.3%   Cash ($ mil.): 194
Return on equity: 5.0%
Current ratio: 2.60

MOUNT SINAI MEDICAL CENTER OF FLORIDA, INC.

Mount Sinai Medical Center of Florida is a not-for-profit acute care teaching hospital providing a wide range of health services to residents of South Florida. The medical center which boasts more than 670 beds provides general medical and surgical care as well as specialty care in cardiology (Mount Sinai Heart Institute) neuroscience oncology orthopedics pulmonology radiology and other fields. It also participates in clinical research studies and drug trials with an emphasis on cancer heart and lung conditions It maintains an inpatient behavioral health unit and houses the Wien Center for Alzheimer's disease and memory disorders diagnosis and research the largest such facililiy in the region.

Operations

Mount Sinai Medical Center of Florida has 26 operating suites and more than 700 physicians. In 2012 it reported more than 63000 emergency visits 22000 patients admissions and 12000 surgeries.

Geographic Reach

Reaching beyond its main South Florida campus the Mount Sinai Medical Center of Florida also op-erates a multi-specialty physicians' clinic emergency care and diagnostic center in nearby Aventura. It also operates physicians' clinics in Key Biscayne and Hialeah and an outpatient center in Coral Gables.

Sales and Marketing

The Center markets its services through TV and radio commercials and via print media.

Financial Performance

The company's revenues grew by 3% to $497 million in 2012 due to higher patient service revenues (net of contractual allowances discounts and other revenue). Medicare accounted for 36% of patient service revenues; Medicaid 7%.

Mount Sinai Medical Center of Florida reported net income of $34 million in 2012 (compared to a net loss in 2011) thanks to the absence of impairment of long-lived assets partially offset by a loss on extinguishment of debt. Net income also improved due to change in the beneficial interest in the net assets of Mount Sinai Medical Center Foundation Inc.

Strategy

The company teams up with larger institutions to expand its reach and skill set. Its medical education programs include a cardiology partnership with Columbia University and resident programs for medical students from the University of Miami Florida International University and Nova Southeastern University. The center's partnership with Columbia University has created the Mount Sinai Heart Institute and the Columbia University Division of Urology at Mount Sinai the only Ivy League affiliated programs in South Florida.

Other programs support students entering such health care professions as nursing pharmacy and therapy.

Enhancing its standing in 2014 Mount Sinai Medical Center of Florida received full accreditation for percutaneous coronary intervention from the Society of Cardiovascular Patient Care an international body dedicated to preventing and treating heart disease.

Company Background

Mount Sinai Medical Center of Florida was founded in 1949 by a group of philanthropists and concerned citizens.

EXECUTIVES

President And Ceo, Steven D. Sonenreich
Evp Operations And Cfo, Alex Mendez
Chief Medical Officer, Robert C. Goldszer
President Medical Staff, Peter Segall
Vice President Patient Services, Karen Hermanson
Assistant Vice President Information Technology, John Wells
Head Nurse, Emelyn Salamorin
Vice President Finance, Wayne Chutkan
Vice President Human Resources, Jennifer Foreman
Assistant Vice President Network Development, Jim Gaton Gomez
Chairman, Michael M. Adler
Medical Secretary, Zocima Gonzalez
Unit Secretary, Allyson Shervington

LOCATIONS

HQ: MOUNT SINAI MEDICAL CENTER OF FLORIDA, INC.
4300 ALTON RD, MIAMI BEACH, FL 331402948
Phone: 305 674-2121
Web: WWW.MSMC.COM

PRODUCTS/OPERATIONS

Florida Locations
MOUNT SINAI MEDICAL CENTER (MAIN CAMPUS): Miami Beach
MOUNT SINAI AVENTURA EMERGENCY ROOM PHYSICIAN OFFICES CANCER CENTER AND DIAGNOSTIC CENTER: Aventura

MOUNT SINAI KEY BISCAYNE PHYSICIAN OFFICES:
Key Biscayne
MOUNT SINAI CORAL GABLES DIAGNOSTIC
CATHETERIZATION LAB: Coral Gables
MOUNT SINAI PRIMARY & SPECIALTY CARE CORAL
GABLES: Coral Gables
MOUNT SINAI HIALEAH: Hialeah

COMPETITORS

Baptist Health South Florida	Miami Children's Hospital
Broward Health	Tenet Healthcare
HCA	University of Miami
Jackson Health System	Hospital

HISTORICAL FINANCIALS

Company Type: Private

Income Statement				FYE: December 31
	REVENUE ($ mil.)	NET INCOME ($ mil.)	NET PROFIT MARGIN	EMPLOYEES
12/16	560	19	3.5%	3,225
12/15	533	38	7.2%	—
12/14	530	17	3.2%	—
12/13	584	42	7.3%	—
Annual Growth	(1.4%)	(22.9%)	—	—

2016 Year-End Financials

Return on assets: 2.8%
Return on equity: 8.7%
Current ratio: 3.30
Cash ($ mil.): 255

MULTICARE HEALTH SYSTEM

MultiCare Health System is a not-for-profit health system that serves the residents of four counties in the southern Puget Sound region and southwestern Washington. Altogether the system's five hospitals have more than 1100 beds. The largest facility Tacoma General boasts about 440 beds and provides specialized cancer cardiac orthopedic and trauma care in addition to general medical and surgical care. Other medical centers include Good Samaritan Hospital (with 286 beds) Allenmore Hospital (130 beds) Auburn Regional Medical Center (195 beds) and Mary Bridge Children's Hospital (82 beds).

Operations

MultiCare has more than 1000 staff physician specialists. In addition to its five hospitals the health system also operates dozens of primary care specialty care and urgent care clinics in the region as well as home health and hospice care agencies. Tacoma General Hospital operates the MultiCare Regional Cancer Center an obstetrics and neonatal intensive care unit the MultiCare Neuroscience Center of Washington orthopedics the MultiCare Surgical Care Center and the MultiCare Regional Heart & Vascular Center. Tacoma General also offers Level II Adult Trauma Center and Level IIIB neonatal intensive care unit. Mary Bridge Children's Hospital & Health Center operates a pediatric intensive care unit a pediatric heart center a Center for Childhood Safety child abuse intervention programs and outpatient specialty clinics.

In 2013 alone the company provided free and subsidized health care services at an estimated cost of $185 million.

In 2013 MultiCare reported 217590 emergency department visits; 47138 admissions; 9616 inpatient surgeries 23502 outpatient surgeries and 5817 live births.

Geographic Reach

MultiCare serves patients in more than 130 locations in Washington's Pierce South King Thurston and Kitsap counties.

Strategy

The company is expanding its infrastructure to keep up with demand.

In 2014 MultiCare opened the 115929-sq.-ft. Rainier Pavilion as part of a $192 million project to expand services for women newborns and children at Tacoma General Hospital and Mary Bridge Children's Hospital. When the final phase is completed in 2015 the project will add 133919 sq. ft. of new space and 144835 sq. ft. of renovated space.

Also that year MultiCare broke ground on a new hospital in Covington improving access to health care services in South King County. The new 24-bed three-story hospital (with the potential to expand to 58 beds) will open in 2016. Other new facilities that broke ground in 2013 and 2014 are a 120-bed psychiatric hospital in Tacoma (for which MultiCare is partnering up with CHI Franciscan Health to build) and a birth center at Tacoma General Hospital.

On the technology front MultiCare uses technologies such as digital mammography CyberKnife Radiosurgery technology and Da Vinci Robotic Surgery to provide better service to the patients. In 2013 MultiCare Auburn Medical Center upgraded its billing processes to an electronic health record system.

EXECUTIVES

Vice President Information Technology, Harold Moscho
Medical Director Sleep Center, Kimberly Mebust
President And Ceo, William G. (Bill) Robertson, age 59
Evp, Florence Chang
President East Pierce Region, Glenn Kasman
President West Pierce Region, Shelly Mullin
Chief Physician Officer, Claire Spain-Remy
Cfo, Anna Loomis
President South King Region, Hugh Kodama
Cio, Robert Biernbaum
Respiratory Therapy Director, Clark Needham
Vice President, Dori Young
Medical Director, John Rieke
Senior Vice President And Cfo, Jim Mcmanus
Vice President Revenue Cycle, Sheri Beekman
Clinical Director, Jodi Gragg
Secretary, Debbie Day
Secretary, Cheryl Wamsley
Auditors: KPMG LLP SEATTLE WA

LOCATIONS

HQ: MULTICARE HEALTH SYSTEM
316 M L KING JR WAY # 314, TACOMA, WA 984054252
Phone: 253 403-1000

PRODUCTS/OPERATIONS

Selected Facilities

Hospitals
Allenmore Hospital (Tacoma)
Auburn Medical Center (Auburn)
Good Samaritan Hospital (Puyallup)
Mary Bridge Children's Hospital and Health Center (Tacoma)
Tacoma General Hospital (Tacoma)
Other facilities
Allenmore Medical Center
Auburn MultiCare Clinic
Covington MultiCare Clinic
Lakewood Urgent Care Clinic
Kent MultiCare Clinic
MultiCare Home Services

Spanaway MultiCare Clinic
Tacoma Family Medicine
University Place Urgent Care Clinic
Westgate Urgent Care Clinic

Selected Services

Adult Day Health
Behavioral Health
Boutique
Breast Health
Cancer Center
Center for Healthy Living
Children's Therapy Unit
Community Programs
CyberKnife Radiosurgery
Diabetes Services
Ear Nose and Throat
Emergency and Urgent Care
Family Birth Centers
Geriatric Psychiatric Center
Health Care Resource Center
Heart Care
Home Health and Hospice
Immunization Clinic
Infusion Center
Institute for Research & Innovation
Laboratories Northwest
Maternal-Fetal Medicine
Medical Imaging
Nephrology
Neonatal Intensive Care Unit
Neurosciences
Nutrition
OB/GYN
Occupational Medicine
Orthopedics
Pain Management
Palliative Medicine
Perinatal Outreach Program
Pharmacy
Physical Therapy
Podiatry
Primary Care Clinics
Pulmonary Care
Pulmonary Rehabilitation
Rehabilitation
Robotic Technology
Senior Services
Sexual Assault Services
Spa
Sports Medicine
Surgical Services
Tobacco Cessation
Transfusion Free Medical and Surgical Program
Urology
Weight Loss and Wellness
Wound Healing Center

COMPETITORS

Catholic Health Initiatives	Providence St. Joseph Health
Franciscan Health System	Seattle Children's Hospital
Harrison Medical Center	Swedish Health Services
Overlake Hospital	Yakima Valley Memorial
PeaceHealth	

HISTORICAL FINANCIALS

Company Type: Private

Income Statement				FYE: December 31
	REVENUE ($ mil.)	NET INCOME ($ mil.)	NET PROFIT MARGIN	EMPLOYEES
12/18	2,922	34	1.2%	6,510
12/17	2,416	347	14.4%	—
12/16	1,927	180	9.4%	—
12/11	1,384	27	2.0%	—
Annual Growth	11.3%	3.2%	—	—

2018 Year-End Financials

Return on assets: 0.8%
Return on equity: 1.3%
Current ratio: 1.90
Cash ($ mil.): 386

MUNICIPAL ELECTRIC AUTHORITY OF GEORGIA

With more juice than a ripe Georgia peach the Municipal Electric Authority of Georgia (MEAG Power) supplies wholesale electric power. The authority has a generating capacity of 2069 MW through its interests in nuclear and fossil-fueled plants. Some 49% of the energy MEAG Power delivered in 2012 came from its nuclear plants. MEAG Power transmits electricity to 48 municipal and one county distribution systems across Georgia that in turn serve some 600000 consumers. It utilizes a transmission network that is co-owned by all the power suppliers in Georgia although it is considering joining a regional transmission organization (RTO) to further defray costs.

Operations

MEAG Power owns more than 1300 miles of high-voltage transmission lines and almost 200 substations. It also provides value-added services including management infrastructure and marketing support to its member municipalities energy marketers and other utilities.

The company generates most of its revenues from Project One (ownership stakes in nine generating units other owned transmission plants and working capital). Higher member billings for operating expenses related to fuel and nuclear operations lifted MEAG Power's revenues and net income in 2010.

Geographic Reach

The company serves 49 communities across Georgia.

Financial Performance

In 2012 MEAG Power's revenues increased by 8% thanks to higher participant billings related to a planned reduction in trust transfers as well as an increase in debt service related to environmental improvements to the coal operations and higher contract energy sales. These gains were partially offset by lower participant billings for maintenance and fuel expenses.

That year the company's net income increased by 351% as the result of higher net sales and decreased operating costs.

Strategy

With Georgia restricted in its natural potential for solar and wind power development MEAG Power is pushing hard for the expansion of nuclear power as a clean energy alternative to coal.

In a major breakthrough in 2012 the Nuclear Regulatory Commission approved a Combined Construction and Operating License for units 3 and 4 of the Vogtle plant (near Waynesboro Georgia) the first such license ever approved for a US nuclear plant and the first federal go-ahead for nuclear plant construction since 1978.

In 2013 MEAG Power completed a basemat of structural concrete for the nuclear island at the Vogtle Unit 4 nuclear expansion site the second of two units under construction at Plant Vogtle.

Company Background

In 2009 the Georgia Public Service Commission gave the go ahead for the expansion of the nuclear-powered Vogtle Electric Generating Plant which is co-owned by MEAG Power and in 2010 MEAP Power sold $2.7 billion in bonds to fund this expansion.

EXECUTIVES

Vice President Finance, Jim Fuller
Treasurer And Senior Portfolio Director, David Coss
Auditors: PRICEWATERHOUSECOOPERS LLP AT

LOCATIONS

HQ: MUNICIPAL ELECTRIC AUTHORITY OF GEORGIA
1470 RIVEREDGE PKWY, ATLANTA, GA 303284640
Phone: 770 563-0300
Web: WWW.MEAGPOWER.ORG

COMPETITORS

AEP	Progress Energy
Dominion Energy	Santee Cooper
Duke Energy	Southern Company
North Carolina	Southern Company Gas
Electric Membership	TVA
Oglethorpe Power	

HISTORICAL FINANCIALS

Company Type: Private

Income Statement

FYE: December 31

	REVENUE ($ mil.)	NET INCOME ($ mil.)	NET PROFIT MARGIN	EMPLOYEES
12/18	681	(4)	—	150
12/17	623	0	—	—
12/16	661	(110)	—	—
12/15	642	(131)	—	—
Annual Growth	2.0%	—	—	—

2018 Year-End Financials

Return on assets: —
Return on equity: —
Current ratio: 1.00

Cash ($ mil.): 651

MUNSON HEALTHCARE

Munson Healthcare is a not-for-profit health care system serving residents in northern Michigan. Its flagship facility is Munson Medical Center in Traverse City a regional referral hospital with about 390 beds offering specialty services including cancer treatment behavioral health cardiac care and orthopedics. Munson Healthcare also has management agreements and other types of affiliations with about a dozen other hospitals in the region. In addition Munson Healthcare operates urgent care and community clinics home health care and hospice agencies an ambulance service and the Northern Michigan Supply Alliance a supply chain management group co-owned with Trinity Health.

Operations

Munson Healthcare is composed of eight hospitals located throughout northern Michigan - Charlevoix Area Hospital (Charlevoix) Kalkaska Memorial Health Center (Kalkaska) Mercy Hospital Cadillac (Cadillac) Mercy Hospital Grayling (Grayling) Munson Medical Center (Traverse City) Otsego Memorial Hospital (Gaylord) Paul Oliver Memorial Hospital (Frankfort) and West Shore Medical Center (Manistee). Services are also available at Munson Community Health Center (Traverse City) and Mercy Community Health Center (Prudenville). Munson Healthcare also works closely with Alpena General Hospital in Alpena and War Memorial Hospital in Sault St. Marie.

In addition to its hospital operations Munson Healthcare also offers in-home care through Munson Home Health and Munson Hospice and Palliative Care. Other specialty services and resources include speech and hearing clinics physical rehabilitation CAT scans magnetic resonance imaging and cardiac catheterization.

Munson Healthcare provides direct access to nearly 800 physicians representing more than 50 specialties.

Eah year the system sees some 22500 admissions performs some 8000 inpatient and 7000 out-patient surgeries and has some 51000 emergency department visits.

Geographic Reach

The health care system offers a continuum of health care services to people in 24 Michigan counties.

Strategy

To better provide services to region residents Munson Healthcare partnered with critical access hospital Mackinac Straits Health System in 2015. The affiliation is focused on improving health care services in rural northern Michigan.

Munson Healthcare is also forming an air ambulance joint venture between its North Flight EMS Air Division and Spectrum Health's Aero Med. The venture to be named North Flight Aero Med will provide critical care air emergency transport services in northern Michigan. It will begin operating in 2016.

Company Background

Munson Healthcare was founded in 1915.

EXECUTIVES

Vice President Facilities And Plant Engineering, Steve Tongue
Director Of Pharmacy, Richard Beckwith
Medical Director, Don Caraccio
Vice President Of Finance, Rob Wilcox
Vice President View Biography, Lorraine Frank-lightfoot
Secretary, Jodi Radtke
Secretary, Robert Sprunk
Department Secretary, Alicia McCurdy
Department Secretary, Carol Saxton
Department Secretary, Melissa Cholger
Vice Chair Kathy Ervin Secretary, Sonja Ganger
Department Secretary, Sue Winowiecki

LOCATIONS

HQ: MUNSON HEALTHCARE
1105 SIXTH ST, TRAVERSE CITY, MI 496842345
Phone: 800 252-2065
Web: WWW.MUNSONHEALTHCARE.ORG

PRODUCTS/OPERATIONS

Selected Michigan Facilities

Charlevoix
Kalkaska M
Mercy Hosp
Mercy Hosp
Munson Community Health Center - Traverse City
Munson Hospice House - Traverse City
Munson Manor Hospitality House - Traverse City
Munson Medical Center - Traverse City
Northwest Michigan Surgery Center - Traverse City
Otsego Mem
Paul Olive
Smith Family Breast Health Center - Traverse City
West Shore
Medical Specialties
Bariatric Surgery
Behavioral Health
Bleeding Disorders Center
Cancer Services
Diabetes
Dialysis
Emergency Services
Hearing Clinic
Heart and Vascular Services
Hospice and Palliative Care
Occupational Health and Medicine
Orthopedics
Senior's Health
Sleep Disorders Center
Stroke Care
Teen's Health
Urgent Care
Urology
Women and Children

COMPETITORS

Borgess Health	McLaren Health Care
Covenant HealthCare	Spectrum Health
Genesys Regional	Trinity Health (Novi)
Medical Center	Zeeland Community
Hurley Medical Center	Hospital

HISTORICAL FINANCIALS

Company Type: Private

Income Statement

FYE: June 30

	REVENUE ($ mil.)	NET INCOME ($ mil.)	NET PROFIT MARGIN	EMPLOYEES
06/18	1,039	142	13.7%	4,000
06/17	940	160	17.1%	—
06/15	8	(7)	—	—
06/13	6	(3)	—	—
Annual Growth	175.3%	—	—	—

2018 Year-End Financials

Return on assets: 10.5%
Return on equity: 16.0%
Current ratio: 2.90

Cash ($ mil.): 106

MUNSON MEDICAL CENTER

EXECUTIVES

Pres-Ceo, Matt Wille
Cfo*, Edward Carlson
Coo*, Derk Pronger
Marketing Manager, Andrea Ludka
Nursing Director, Ann Holmes
Manager, Christopher Layne
Chief Information Officer, Christopher Podges
Neurologist, Cornelius Robens
Other Is It Technology Profess, Daniel Fly
Chief of Pediatrics, David Olson
Network Engineer, David Penne

LOCATIONS

HQ: MUNSON MEDICAL CENTER
1105 SIXTH ST, TRAVERSE CITY, MI 496842386
Phone: 231 935-6000
Web: WWW.MUNSONHEALTHCARE.ORG

HISTORICAL FINANCIALS

Company Type: Private

Income Statement

FYE: June 30

	REVENUE ($ mil.)	NET INCOME ($ mil.)	NET PROFIT MARGIN	EMPLOYEES
06/16	533	67	12.7%	3,100
06/15	509	60	11.9%	—
06/10	441	28	6.4%	—
06/09	394	(0)	—	—
Annual Growth	4.4%	—	—	—

2016 Year-End Financials

Return on assets: 8.4%
Return on equity: 15.5%
Current ratio: 4.30

Cash ($ mil.): 189

MUNSTER MEDICAL RESEARCH FOUNDATION, INC

EXECUTIVES

Pres-Ceo, Donald S Powers
Treas*, George E Watson
Admin*, Edward Robinson
SEC*, Palmer C Singleton
V Pres*, Joseph Morrow
Chm*, Frankie L Fesko
Prin*, James J Richards
SEC*, William A Hasse III
Treas*, David E Wickland
Coordinator, Carol Hernandez
Law Specialist, Cathy Reese
Auditors: ERNST & YOUNG LLP

LOCATIONS

HQ: MUNSTER MEDICAL RESEARCH FOUNDATION, INC
901 MACARTHUR BLVD, MUNSTER, IN 463212901
Phone: 219 836-1600

HISTORICAL FINANCIALS

Company Type: Private

Income Statement

FYE: June 30

	REVENUE ($ mil.)	NET INCOME ($ mil.)	NET PROFIT MARGIN	EMPLOYEES
06/18	548	74	13.5%	2,000
06/16	508	50	9.9%	—
06/15	495	58	11.8%	—
06/14	465	36	7.8%	—
Annual Growth	4.2%	19.5%	—	—

2018 Year-End Financials

Return on assets: 22.9%
Return on equity: 26.4%
Current ratio: 2.90

Cash ($ mil.): —

MV TRANSPORTATION, INC.

Need to supply transportation by bus? MV Transportation will run your bus system so you don't have to. The company operates more than 200 contracts to offer fixed-route and shuttle bus services as well as paratransit (transportation of people with disabilities) and transportation of Medicaid beneficiaries. Its customers consist primarily of transit authorities and other state and local government agencies responsible for public transportation. MV Transportation operates in more than 130 locations spanning 28 US states and in British Columbia Canada and Saudi Arabia; overall the company maintains a fleet of about 7000 vehicles. MV Transportation was founded in 1975.

Geographic Reach

MV Transportation and its subsidiaries joint ventures partnerships and affiliates operate more than 130 locations in 28 states the District of Columbia two Canadian Provinces and Saudi Arabia.

Sales and Marketing

The company provides its transportation services to cities counties municipalities and other jurisdictional entities as well as for private corporations non-profit agencies and community organizations. Some of its customers include Corpus Christi Regional Transportation Authority (B-Line paratransit and shuttle services) Ashland Public Transit (the curb-to-curb demand response transit service) Capital Area Transit System and Ashtabula County Transportation System (paratransit services).

Strategy

The company relies on the signing of year-long contracts and joint ventures for growth. In 2013 MV Transportation received a four-year contract to continue operation of the City of Irvine's iShuttle service; Irvine's iShuttle provides morning and evening peak-hour service along four routes connecting the Irvine Metrolink Station the Tustin Metrolink Station John Wayne Airport Irvine Spectrum and the Irvine Business Complex (IBC).

To expand its presence and experience in Qatar MV Transportation in 2013 opened its newest business venture in Doha Qatar: MV Global Transport Logistics WLL (MVGTL). In addition MVGTL signed an agreement with passenger transportation provider Mowasalat to provide planning scheduling and event management for the numerous events in Doha.

In early 2012 MV Transportation signed its first contract to manage a bus system outside North America when it made a two-year agreement to coordinate an operation of more than 400 buses carrying Saudi Arabian Oil employees in the Middle Eastern kingdom. Striving to extend its international reach even further the company purchased Transportation Management Services UK Limited (TMSUK) a few months later. The deal allowed MV Transportation to enter a niche market as TMSUK designs and operates transportation systems for special events worldwide.

EXECUTIVES

Vice President, Chris Burls
Vice President People, Julie Weber
Vice President Of Customer Service And Operations, Janey Appia
Vice President, Sandra Cunningham
Board Member, John Rogers
Board Member, Carolyn Flowers
Board Member, Scott Letier

LOCATIONS

HQ: MV TRANSPORTATION, INC.
2711 N HASKELL AVE, DALLAS, TX 752042911
Phone: 214 265-3400
Web: WWW.MVTRANSIT.COM

PRODUCTS/OPERATIONS

Selected Services
Bid committee consultation
Emergency evacuation planning
Global mobility and unique technology assets
International transport and logistics solutions
Logistics and security staffing
Paratransit and multimodal transport
Parking management and valet services
Sustainability transport initiatives
Traffic control planning staffing and consultation
Transport planning and operations
VIP fleet services

COMPETITORS

Coach USA	National Express Group
FirstGroup America	Veolia Transportation
LogistiCare	

HISTORICAL FINANCIALS
Company Type: Private

Income Statement
FYE: December 31

	REVENUE ($ mil.)	NET INCOME ($ mil.)	NET PROFIT MARGIN	EMPLOYEES
12/09	706	23	3.3%	224
12/08	645	(2)	—	—
12/07	422	0	—	—
Annual Growth 29.3%	—	—	—	—

2009 Year-End Financials
Return on assets: 12.3%   Cash ($ mil.): 6
Return on equity: 94.1%
Current ratio: 1.50

MVP HEALTH PLAN, INC.

MVP Health Plan also know as MVP Health Care provides health insurance and employee benefits to its more than 700000 members in upstate New York New Hampshire and Vermont. MVP a not-for-profit organization offers a variety of plans including HMO PPO and indemnity coverage as well as dental plans health accounts and Medicare Advantage plans. Subsidiary MVP Select Care provides third-party administration (TPA) services for self-insured employers. MVP Health Care was founded in 1983 as Mohawk Valley Physicians' Health Plan.

Geographic Reach
MVP Health Care operates regional service and support offices across New York Vermont and New Hampshire. New York State is its largest service area. The firm has offices in Binghamton Fishkill Schenectady Syracuse Rochester and Utica New York as well as in Manchester New Hampshire; and Williston Vermont.

The company's provider network includes 19000 doctors in its three-state service territory; the firm also provides its members with access to about 500000 providers in other states through a partnership with CIGNA.

Sales and Marketing
The company uses a direct sales force as well as brokerages and call centers to sell its products. Its customers include individuals Medicare and Medicaid participants and employer groups.

Financial Performance
MVP Health Care revenue increased 18% to $2.9 billion in 2014; that growth was bolstered by the integration of Hudson Health Plan (acquired in 2013) as well as commercial and government membership growth. Medicaid Managed Care membership grew 21% that year.

Despite that growth the company lost a net $13.6 million.

Strategy
In addition to acquiring other area providers MVP Health Care widens its product offerings to attract a diversified customer base adding new non-employer group options (individual and high-deductible plans) and new small employer group products. It is has also launched new financial and preventative care tools including flexible spending accounts and disease management programs. Cutting policy prices has helped boost membership numbers as well.

The company also partners with health care providers to provide better care for its members as well as developing programs to target specific segments of the population.

MVP Health Care utilizes new technologies to cut its own operating costs. Recent initiatives include launching an e-commerce/plan administration platform creating virtual medical records with area health information organizations and supporting the Taconic Health Information Network and Community (an independent physician practice association).

EXECUTIVES

Evp And Medical Affairs Officer, Allen J. Hinkle
Evp Government Programs, Patrick Glavey
President And Ceo, Denise V. Gonick
Evp Networks And Contracting, Karla Austen
Evp And Cfo, Mark Fish
Associate Medical Director, Clifford Elson
Vice President Of Market Innovation, Augusta Martin
Pharmacy Manager, David Stitt
Vice President Legal Affairs And Deputy General Counsel, Dawn Jablonski
Vice President Network Operations, Matt Mackinnon
Vice President And Chief Actuary, Kathleen Fish
Medical Director, Marvin Lederman
Vice Chairwoman, Karen Johnson
Auditors: PRICEWATERHOUSECOOPERS LLP HA

LOCATIONS

HQ: MVP HEALTH PLAN, INC.
625 STATE ST, SCHENECTADY, NY 123052260
Phone: 518 370-4793
Web: WWW.MVPHEALTHCARE.COM

PRODUCTS/OPERATIONS

Selected Products
Alternative Funding Arrangements
Deferred Deductible Plans
Defined Contribution Plans
EPOs and PPOs
Health Spending Accounts
High-Deductible Health Plans
HMOs
Medicare Advantage Plans
Regional Plan Options

COMPETITORS

Affinity Health
Blue Cross and Blue Shield of Vermont
CIGNA
Capital District Physicians' Health Plan
EmblemHealth
Excellus BlueCross BlueShield
Fallon Community Health Plan
Fidelis Care New York
HealthPlus Amerigroup
Healthfirst
Independent Health
Lifetime Healthcare
UnitedHealth Group
healthnow new york inc

HISTORICAL FINANCIALS
Company Type: Private

Income Statement
FYE: December 31

	ASSETS ($ mil.)	NET INCOME ($ mil.)	INCOME AS % OF ASSETS	EMPLOYEES
12/15	589	11	1.9%	1,500
12/14	540	(26)	—	—
Annual Growth 9.2%	—	—	—	—

2015 Year-End Financials
Return on assets: 1.9%   Sales ($ mil): 1,573
Return on equity: 2.7%

MWH GLOBAL, INC.

MWH Global is an environmental engineering construction and management firm that specializes in water-related projects or "wet infrastructure." The company's typical projects include building water treatment or desalination plants water transmission systems or storage facilites. MWH also provides general building services for transportation energy mining ports and waterways and industrial projects. The company is active in some 35 countries and serves governments public utilities and private sector clients. Affiliates of the employee-owned company include software provider Innovyze and business and government relations firm mCapitol. Canadian Engineering firm Stantec acquired MWH Global for $795 million in May 2016.

Geographic Reach
When it comes to projects MWH Global lives up to its name. The Colorado-based firm operates from 180 offices in 35 countries on six continents in the Americas the Asia/Pacific region the Middle East Africa and Europe.

Sales and Marketing
MWH Global seeks projects in five main markets including: the energy and power; water and wastewater; natural resources and mining; ports waterways and coastal; industrial and commercial transportation; and oil and gas markets.

It also does work for local regional and federal governments; US federal clients; public and private utilities; financial institutions; and insurance companies.

Strategy
MWH Global has kept busy in recent years working on a series of high-profile design and construction projects around the globe.

In 2015 the company continued its design-build work on the $7 billion Panama Canal Third Set of Locks project which will double the canal's capacity by the time its completed at the end of the year. The company also continued working with international electricity and gas company National Grid on the largest energy infrastructure program in the UK.

In late-2014 through a joint venture with Costain MWH Global signed on to a Â 200 million ($325 million) contract to provide design and build services for Southern Water's water and wastewater infrastructure and non-infrastructure assets program in Southeast England; part of Southern Waters' Â 3 billion ($5 billion) business plan for 2015-2020. Around the same time MWH Global completed its nearly two-decade-long Huanza Hydroelectric project in the Andes Mountains which now provides 92 Megawatts of electricity to some 90000 households in Peru.

In mid-2014 the South Florida Water Management District awarded MWH Global with a master services agreement to help implement the $880 million Restoration Strategies Regional Water Quality Plan which is part of the state's long-term strategy to restore the Everglades. In 2012 the Qatar Public Works Authority appointed MWH to design a drainage master plan in Qatar which will provide a road map for future investment in water and wastewater treatment and other water-related infrastructure programs over the next 50 years.

EXECUTIVES

Cfo, David G. Barnes, age 56
President Mwh Constructors Mwh Americas, Joseph (Joe) Adams
Chairman And Ceo, Alan J. Krause, age 65
President Innovyze, Paul F. Boulos

President Business Solutions, Dan McConville
President Mwh Constructors, Blair Lavoie
President Europe Africa Government And Infrastructure, Wim Drossaert
President Government And Infrastructure Americas And Asia Pacific, Marshall Davert
Cio, Claire Rutkowski
Managing Director United Kingdom, Catherine Schefer
Chief Strategy Officer, David A. Smith
Vice President Finance, David Harper
Executive Vice President, Donald Smith
Vice President Of Information Technology, Greg Clark
Vice President Client Service Manager, Jonathan Hersey
Vice President Chief Accounting Officer And Corporate Controller, Chad Scherer
Vice President, Sean Searles
Vice President, Kari Shively
Principal Engineer Vice President, Bill Taplin
Vice President Global Human Resources Operations, Shannon Aguilar
Vice President, Geoffrey Carthew
Vice President, Donald A Erpenbeck
Vice President, Jim Stahl
Vice President, Bob Parent
Vice President Location Manager Principal Geotechnical Engineer, Greg Rollins
Vice President, Joe Lauria
Vice President, Vincent Zipparro
Vice President Corporate Communications, Meg Vanderlaan
Senior Vice President, Donal J Bassett
Vice President Finance, Graham Campbell
Vice President, Philip Croessmann
Vice President Business Unit Leader, Beth Knackstedt
Vice President Director Of Business De, Norman Gadzinski
Vice President, Kimberly Kesler-Arnold
Senior Vice President, Mario Finis
Vice President, Jim Brennan
Vice President, Tauseef Choudry
Senior Vice President And Director Of Global Business Development, Paul Dekeyser
Vice President, Edward Cryer
Vice President, Roger Stephenson
Vice President, Jason Hedien
Senior Vice President, James Lindell
Executive Vice President, P Smith
Senior Vice President, Chip Labonte
Auditors: DELOITTE & TOUCHE LLP DENVER

LOCATIONS

HQ: MWH GLOBAL, INC.
370 INTERLOCKEN BLVD # 300, BROOMFIELD, CO 800218009
Phone: 303 533-1900
Web: WWW.STANTEC.COM

PRODUCTS/OPERATIONS

Selected Services

Construction
Airports
General building
Industrial
Highways bridges roads
Marine and port facilities
Engineering and technical services
Facilities development
Government relations
Program management and management consulting
Research and testing
Renewable energy and sustainability
Chemical and soil remediation
Hazardous waste
Hydroelectric power
Non-hydro renewable energy
Power distribution and transmission lines
Thermal power

Risk assessment
Specialized consulting services
Water and environment
Dams and reservoirs
Landfills biosolids
Sanitary/storm sewers conveyance pumping stations
Water resources planning management
Water treatment and desalination plants
Water transmission lines aqueducts
Waste water planning and management

COMPETITORS

AECOM	Peter Kiewit Sons'
Bechtel	Severn Trent
Black & Veatch	Siemens Water
Camp Dresser McKee	Technologies
EA Engineering	Tetra Tech
Engie	Veolia Environnement
Fluor	WS Atkins
Jacobs Engineering	Zachry Inc.
KBR	

HISTORICAL FINANCIALS

Company Type: Private

Income Statement   FYE: January 1

	REVENUE ($ mil.)	NET INCOME ($ mil.)	NET PROFIT MARGIN	EMPLOYEES
01/16*	1,318	35	2.7%	6,700
12/05	946	0	—	—
01/03	975	942	96.6%	—
12/01	774	19	2.6%	—
Annual Growth	3.9%	4.3%	—	—

*Fiscal year change

2016 Year-End Financials

Return on assets: 5.4%   Cash ($ mil.): 68
Return on equity: 19.1%
Current ratio: 1.40

NAES CORPORATION

EXECUTIVES

Pres, Robert E Fishman
Pres-Coo, Tom Bartolomei
Sr V Pres, George Wackerhagen
Sr V Pres, Norman Escover
Sr V Pres, Andrew Gay
Sr V Pres, Glen Canavera
V Pres, Susan George
Plant Manager, Andy Duncan
Senior Recruiter, Christopher Kirk
Administrative Manager, Jennifer Carder
Plant Manager, Michael Salvador
Auditors: PRICEWATERHOUSECOOPERS LLP SE

LOCATIONS

HQ: NAES CORPORATION
1180 NW MAPLE ST STE 200, ISSAQUAH, WA 980278106
Phone: 425 961-4700
Web: WWW.NAES.COM

HISTORICAL FINANCIALS

Company Type: Private

Income Statement   FYE: March 31

	REVENUE ($ mil.)	NET INCOME ($ mil.)	NET PROFIT MARGIN	EMPLOYEES
03/15	514	6	1.2%	2,534
03/14	472	3	0.8%	—
03/13	445	5	1.1%	—
Annual Growth	7.5%	8.7%	—	—

2015 Year-End Financials

Return on assets: 3.8%   Cash ($ mil.): 33
Return on equity: 9.8%
Current ratio: 1.30

NANA DEVELOPMENT CORPORATION

EXECUTIVES

Pres, Helvi Sandvik
Chairman*, Luke Sampson
Chairperson*, Lester Hadley
President*, Sandvik Helvi K
Sr V Pres*, Stan Fleming
V Pres*, Thomas Kevin E
Sr Vice President*, Jacquelyn R Luke
Secretary*, Dood Lincoln
Treasurer*, Henry Horner
Vice President*, Selina Moose
Vice President*, Charles J Greene
Auditors: KPMG LLP ANCHORAGE AK

LOCATIONS

HQ: NANA DEVELOPMENT CORPORATION
909 W 9TH AVE, ANCHORAGE, AK 995013322
Phone: 907 265-4100
Web: WWW.NANA.COM

HISTORICAL FINANCIALS

Company Type: Private

Income Statement   FYE: September 30

	REVENUE ($ mil.)	NET INCOME ($ mil.)	NET PROFIT MARGIN	EMPLOYEES
09/08	1,018	1	0.2%	3,000
09/07	833	7	0.8%	—
09/06	30	31	104.1%	—
09/00	119	0	0.6%	—
Annual Growth	30.7%	11.4%	—	—

2008 Year-End Financials

Return on assets: 0.3%   Cash ($ mil.): 37
Return on equity: 4.0%
Current ratio: 2.10

NANA REGIONAL CORPORATION, INC.,

EXECUTIVES

Prin, Wayne Westlake
Ceo*, Marie Green
Prin*, Kevin Thomas
Coo*, Lori Henry
Information Specialist, Justin Yeoman
Vice President Shareholder Rel, Gia Hanna

LOCATIONS

HQ: NANA REGIONAL CORPORATION, INC.,
3150 C ST STE 150, KOTZEBUE, AK 99752
Phone: 907 442-3301

HISTORICAL FINANCIALS
Company Type: Private

Income Statement — FYE: September 30

	REVENUE ($ mil.)	NET INCOME ($ mil.)	NET PROFIT MARGIN	EMPLOYEES
09/09	1,257	17	1.4%	4,650
09/08	1,175	29	2.5%	—
09/07	975	37	3.8%	—
Annual Growth	13.6%	(32.4%)	—	—

2009 Year-End Financials
Return on assets: 2.3% Cash ($ mil.): 23
Return on equity: 7.0%
Current ratio: 1.60

NAPLES COMMUNITY HOSPITAL INC

EXECUTIVES

Pres-Ceo, Phillip C Dutcher
Cfo*, Rick Wyles
Cso*, Mike Riley
M.D., Cmo*, Frank Astor
Interim Coo*, Jonathan Kling
Buyer, Alan Ipp
Coordinator, Jeanie McCree
Coordinator, Lawrence Lasky
Assistant, Mat Treganza
Chief Operating Officer, Phillip Dutcher
Coordinator, Sandra Danielson

LOCATIONS

HQ: NAPLES COMMUNITY HOSPITAL INC
350 7TH ST N, NAPLES, FL 341025754
Phone: 239 436-5000
Web: WWW.NCHMD.ORG

HISTORICAL FINANCIALS
Company Type: Private

Income Statement — FYE: September 30

	REVENUE ($ mil.)	NET INCOME ($ mil.)	NET PROFIT MARGIN	EMPLOYEES
09/18	472	38	8.2%	3,300
09/17	472	38	8.2%	—
09/15	443	38	8.6%	—
09/14	398	51	12.8%	—
Annual Growth	4.3%	(6.7%)	—	—

2018 Year-End Financials
Return on assets: 4.5% Cash ($ mil.): 68
Return on equity: 6.2%
Current ratio: 1.60

NARRAGANSETT ELECTRIC COMP

LOCATIONS

HQ: NARRAGANSETT ELECTRIC COMP
642 GEORGE WASHINGTON HWY, LINCOLN, RI
028654244
Phone: 401 335-6238

HISTORICAL FINANCIALS
Company Type: Private

Income Statement — FYE: December 31

	REVENUE ($ mil.)	NET INCOME ($ mil.)	NET PROFIT MARGIN	EMPLOYEES
12/17	1,387	121	8.8%	2
12/16	1,269	84	6.7%	
Annual Growth	9.3%	43.0%	—	—

2017 Year-End Financials
Return on assets: 2.6% Cash ($ mil.): 8
Return on equity: 6.1%
Current ratio: 0.70

NASSUA COUNTY INTERIM FINANCE AUTHORITY

EXECUTIVES

Exec Dir, Richard Luke
Executive Director, Evan Cohen

LOCATIONS

HQ: NASSUA COUNTY INTERIM FINANCE AUTHORITY
170 OLD COUNTRY RD # 205, MINEOLA, NY
115014322
Phone: 516 248-2828
Web: WWW.NIFA.NY.GOV

HISTORICAL FINANCIALS
Company Type: Private

Income Statement — FYE: December 31

	REVENUE ($ mil.)	NET INCOME ($ mil.)	NET PROFIT MARGIN	EMPLOYEES
12/18	1,133	(0)	—	6
12/17	1,095	(5)	—	—
12/16	1	140	12831.1%	—
Annual Growth	3122.0%	—	—	—

2018 Year-End Financials
Return on assets: (-0.2%) Cash ($ mil.): —
Return on equity: —
Current ratio: —

NATIONAL ASSOCIATION OF LETTER CARRIERS

EXECUTIVES

Pres, Fredric V Rolando
SEC*, Maria Licalzi
Treas*, Jane E Broendell
Director of Finance, Debra Price
Executive Vice President, Brian Renfroe
Auditors: BOND BEEBE PC BETHESDA MD

LOCATIONS

HQ: NATIONAL ASSOCIATION OF LETTER CARRIERS
100 INDANA AVE NW STE 709, WASHINGTON, DC
20001
Phone: 202 393-4695
Web: WWW.NALC.ORG

HISTORICAL FINANCIALS
Company Type: Private

Income Statement — FYE: March 31

	REVENUE ($ mil.)	NET INCOME ($ mil.)	NET PROFIT MARGIN	EMPLOYEES
03/14*	1,406	97	6.9%	533
12/13	0	0	17.9%	—
12/11	0	0	67.4%	—
03/10	1	0	28.8%	—
Annual Growth	436.7%	275.8%	—	—

*Fiscal year change

2014 Year-End Financials
Return on assets: 10.5% Cash ($ mil.): 245
Return on equity: 20.1%
Current ratio: —

NATIONAL CEMENT COMPANY, INC.

EXECUTIVES

Chb, James E Rotch
Controller, Pragati Kapoor
Director Finance, Denise Taylor
Quality Control Manager, Enrique Hernandez
Location Sales Manager, Puckett Bill
Director, Ken Elkinson

LOCATIONS

HQ: NATIONAL CEMENT COMPANY, INC.
15821 VENTURA BLVD # 475, ENCINO, CA 914362935
Phone: 818 728-5200
Web: WWW.NATIONALCEMENT.COM

HISTORICAL FINANCIALS
Company Type: Private

Income Statement — FYE: December 31

	REVENUE ($ mil.)	NET INCOME ($ mil.)	NET PROFIT MARGIN	EMPLOYEES
12/07	488	47	9.7%	1,100
12/06	529	62	11.8%	—
12/05	455	28	6.3%	—
12/04	364	9	2.7%	—
Annual Growth	10.3%	69.9%	—	—

2007 Year-End Financials
Return on assets: 8.2%   Cash ($ mil.): 6
Return on equity: 12.1%
Current ratio: 2.60

NATIONAL CHRISTIAN CHARITABLE

EXECUTIVES

Prin, Terra Parker
Treasurer, David D Johnson
Vice President, George Cox
Chief Information Officer., Amy Garrett
Vice President., Marsha Walker
Gift Planning Team, Don Etheridge
Director of Giver, Bev Beppler
Chief Information Officer, Dan Brown
Gift Planning Administrator, Julie Shiels
Information Technology Support, Matthew Schulz
Director, Maureen Starr
Auditors: CAPIN CROUSE LLP ATLANTA GE

LOCATIONS

HQ: NATIONAL CHRISTIAN CHARITABLE
11625 RAINWATER DR # 500, ALPHARETTA, GA
300098678
Phone: 404 252-0100
Web: WWW.NCFGIVING.COM

HISTORICAL FINANCIALS

Company Type: Private

Income Statement				FYE: December 31
	REVENUE ($ mil.)	NET INCOME ($ mil.)	NET PROFIT MARGIN	EMPLOYEES
12/16	1,413	306	21.7%	2
12/11	665	141	21.3%	—
12/09	396	50	12.7%	—
Annual Growth	19.9%	29.4%	—	—

2016 Year-End Financials

Return on assets: 14.9%   Cash ($ mil.): 457
Return on equity: 15.1%
Current ratio: —

NATIONAL COLLEGIATE ATHLETIC ASSOCIATION

The National Collegiate Athletic Association (NCAA) supports the intercollegiate sports activities of around 1000 member colleges and universities. A not-for-profit organization the NCAA administers scholarship and grant programs enforces conduct and eligibility rules and works to support and promote the needs of student athletes. The association is known for its lucrative branding and television deals such as those surrounding the popular "March Madness" tournament for Division I men's basketball. Seeking reform of athletics rules and regulations officials from 13 schools formed the Intercollegiate Athletic Association of the United States in 1906. The organization took its current name in 1910.

Financial Performance

NCAA revenue in fiscal 2013 (ended August) was $913 million up 5% versus the prior year most of which came from the rights agreement with CBS Sports and Turner Broadcasting. Indeed about 80% of the NCAA's revenue come from television and marketing rights fees generated primarily from the Division I men's basketball championship. Another 12% comes from championships and NIT tournaments including ticket and merchandise sales.

About 96% of NCAA revenue is distributed directly to the Division I membership or to support championships or programs that benefit student-athletes. The remaining 4% goes for central services such as building operations and salaries not related to particular programs.

Strategy

The NCAA is coming under pressure to modify its rules on how student-athletes are compensated. In 2014 the National Labor Relations Board ruled that a group of Northwestern football players were employees of the univerisity and have the right to form a union and bargain collectively. The organization is also facing challenges regarding compensation for student-athletes whose likenesses are used in video games and broadcasts as well a lawsuits relating to its handling of head injuries.

EXECUTIVES

Vice President, Kevin Lennon
Vice President Of Enforcement, Jonathan Duncan
Vice President For Men's Basketball, Dan Gavitt
Vice President, Daniel Ducher
Board Member, Tom Hosty
Treasurer, Sarah Otey
Auditors: DELOITTE & TOUCHE LLP INDIANA

LOCATIONS

HQ: NATIONAL COLLEGIATE ATHLETIC ASSOCIATION
700 W WASHINGTON ST, INDIANAPOLIS, IN
462042710
Phone: 317 917-6222
Web: WWW.NCAA.ORG

PRODUCTS/OPERATIONS

2013 Revenues

	% of total
Television & marketing rights fees	80
Championships & NIT tournaments	12
Investments	4
Sales & services	3
Contributions facilities & other	1
Total	**100**

HISTORICAL FINANCIALS

Company Type: Private

Income Statement				FYE: August 31
	REVENUE ($ mil.)	NET INCOME ($ mil.)	NET PROFIT MARGIN	EMPLOYEES
08/18	1,064	27	2.5%	508
08/17	1,061	104	9.9%	—
08/16	995	(403)	—	—
08/15	952	43	4.5%	—
Annual Growth	3.8%	(14.5%)	—	—

2018 Year-End Financials

Return on assets: 4.4%   Cash ($ mil.): 14
Return on equity: 6.4%
Current ratio: 0.80

NATIONAL GRAPE CO-OPERATIVE ASSOCIATION, INC.

Well of course grape growers want to hang out in a bunch! The more than 1090 grower/owner-members of the National Grape Cooperative harvest Concord and Niagara grapes from almost 50000 acres of vineyards. The plucked produce supplies the coop's wholly owned subsidiary Welch Foods. Welch Foods makes and sells fruit-based juices jams jellies and spreads under the Welch's and Bama brands in the US and nearly 50 other countries. Offerings include fresh eating grapes distributed by C.H. Robinson Worldwide as well as dried fruit and frozen juice pops. The grape growers own vineyards in Pennsylvania Michigan New York Ohio Washington and Ontario Canada which produce some 300000 tons of grapes annually.

EXECUTIVES

Pres, Randolph Graham
V Pres, Joseph C Falcone
Asst SEC, Vivian S Y Tseng
V Pres, Harold Smith
Dir, Jerry A Czebotar
Dir, Jon Hinkleman
General Manager, Brent Roggie
Executive Administrative Assis, Ivis Edgerton
Auditors: KPMG LLP BOSTON MA

LOCATIONS

HQ: NATIONAL GRAPE CO-OPERATIVE ASSOCIATION, INC.
80 STATE ST, WESTFIELD, NY 14787
Phone: 716 326-5200
Web: WWW.WELCHS.COM

COMPETITORS

B&G Foods	Hornell Brewing
Big Heart Pet Brands	IZZE
Chiquita Brands	Mondelez International
Coca-Cola	Monster Beverage
Constellation Brands	Nestlé USA
Cranberries Limited	Ocean Spray
Dole Food	PepsiCo
Dr Pepper Snapple Group	Procter & Gamble
Fresh Del Monte Produce	Smucker
Goya	Snapple
	Tropicana

HISTORICAL FINANCIALS

Company Type: Private

Income Statement				FYE: August 31
	REVENUE ($ mil.)	NET INCOME ($ mil.)	NET PROFIT MARGIN	EMPLOYEES
08/12	649	74	11.5%	1,325
08/11	640	74	11.6%	—
08/10	658	82	12.6%	—
Annual Growth	(0.7%)	(5.1%)	—	—

2012 Year-End Financials

Return on assets: 19.8%   Cash ($ mil.): 4
Return on equity: 999.9%
Current ratio: 1.50

NATIONAL GRID GENERATION LLC

EXECUTIVES

Pres, John Gregory Cochrane
MBR-Vp*, Robert Teetz
MBR-Sr Vp-Cpo*, Raymond C Schlaff
Mbr-Treasurer*, Malcolm Charles Cooper
Asst SEC*, Alfred C Bereche
Spokesperson, Howard Fichtel
Manager, Steve Trezza
Coordinator, Aaron Womble
Senior Engineer C S, Joseph Schier
Senior Engineer Supervisor, Tony Mattia
Auditors: DELOITTE & TOUCHE LLP NEW YOR

LOCATIONS

HQ: NATIONAL GRID GENERATION LLC
175 E OLD COUNTRY RD, HICKSVILLE, NY
118014257
Phone: 631 755-6650

HISTORICAL FINANCIALS
Company Type: Private

Income Statement — FYE: December 31

	REVENUE ($ mil.)	NET INCOME ($ mil.)	NET PROFIT MARGIN	EMPLOYEES
12/17	471	75	16.0%	200
12/16	463	27	5.9%	—
Annual Growth	1.6%	175.6%	—	—

NATIONWIDE CHILDREN'S HOSPITAL

Buckeye babies toddlers and teens don't have to travel the country to find pediatric care with Nationwide Children's Hospital at their disposal. The Columbus Ohio health care provider is one of the largest pediatric care centers in the US. The hospital has some 430 licensed beds and offers services in areas such as behavioral health cardiology hospice orthopedics and surgery. It has roughly 1100 health care providers on its medical staff and its emergency department treats more than 83000 patients each year. The hospital also operates outpatient and specialty clinics in the area and a research institute which is investigating gene therapy.

Operations
The hospital provides more than $122 million in charity care and community benefit services annually. It had more than 1 million patient visits and had more than 25000 surgery cases in 2014.

Geographic Reach
Nationwide Children's Hospital serves patients from 50 US states and 32 countries. The company is 68 facilities extending out across Ohio and beyond. The company's top ten outpatient visits counties are Franklin Delaware Fairfield Licking Clark Pickaway Madison Union Muskingum and Knox.

Sales and Marketing
Nationwide Children's Hospital payor mix in 2014 included commercial 43%; Medicaid managed care Cap 33%; and Medicaid 13%.

Strategy
In 2015 Nationwide Children's Hospital announced plans to adopt and integrate GenomeNext's genomic sequencing analysis platform for both clinical laboratory services and clinical research initiatives

In 2014 the company outlined numerous details of its $130 million campus expansion project. Its plans include an $85 million outpatient care building and a $45 million building to house faculty offices. The outpatient building called the Livingston Ambulatory Center will house primary care services dental services behavioral health dermatology adolescent medicine sports rehabilitation and various clinics. Both buildings will be six stories tall.

The hospital added helicopter medical transport service in 2013.

Company Background
The health system in 2012 completed a $740 million project to build a new main hospital and add 2 million sq. ft. of clinical research and support space. The expansion added about 100 new beds.

Also in 2012 it opened an ambulatory surgery center in Westerville Ohio and a Close To Home lab and clinic in Springfield. In 2014 it opened the Sharon Woods Primary Care Center in north Columbus.

Nationwide Children's Hospital opened its doors in 1892.

EXECUTIVES

Vice President And Controller, Luke Brown
Chairman The Center For Family Safety And Healing, Abigail S. Wexner
Evp And Cfo, Timothy C. Robinson
President And Coo, Rick Miller
Svp And Chief Nursing Officer, Linda Stoverock
Ceo, Steve Allen
President The Research Institute, John Barnard
President The Center For Family Safety And Healing, Karen Days
Chief Medical Officer, Richard J. Brilli
Surgeon-in-chief, R. Lawrence Moss
Physician-in-chief, J. Philip Saul
Chairman Nationwide Children's Hospital Foundation, Cheryl W. Lucks
Chairman The Research Institute, Donald P. McConnell
Medical Director, Garey Noritz
Vice President Of Perioperative Services, Janet Berry
Pharmd, Kevin Drewes
Medical Director, Desalegn Yacob
Vice President, Pam Edson
Vice President Development Services, Kevin Welch
Vice President, Dennis Minzler
Vice President, Karen Heiser
Senior Vice President Of Planning And Dvlpmt, Patty McClimon
Pharmacy Manager, Kim Novak
Apheresis Medical Director, Erin Meyer
Medical Director, Leena Nahata
Nursing Director Critical Care And Heart Services, Kelly Dials
Chairman, Alex Fischer
Secretary, Lacey Ashenfelter
Secretary, Dawn Friebis
Secretary 2, Trisha Strader
Secretary Ii, Melissa Gallas
Secretary Ii, Marianne starr-Howard
Auditors: ERNST & YOUNG LLP CINCINNATI

LOCATIONS

HQ: NATIONWIDE CHILDREN'S HOSPITAL
700 CHILDRENS DR, COLUMBUS, OH 432052639
Phone: 614 722-2000
Web: WWW.NATIONWIDECHILDRENS.ORG

PRODUCTS/OPERATIONS

Selected Subsidiaries
Nationwide Children's Hospital
Nationwide Children's Behavioral Health
Nationwide Children's Educational Institute
Nationwide Children's Hospital Inc
Nationwide Children's Hospital Homecare
Children's Anesthesia Associates
Nationwide Children's Hospital Foundation
Pediatric Academic Associates
Children's Orthopedic Medical Center
Children's Radiological Institute
Children's Surgical Associates Corp.
The Research Institute at Nationwide Children's Hospital
Pediatric Pathology Associates of Columbus
The Center for Family Safety and Healing at Nationwide Children's Hospital

Selected Departments and Services
Adolescent Congenital Heart Disease
Adolescent Medicine
Adult Congenital Heart Disease
Adult Medicine and Hospital Pediatrics
Allergy/Immunology
Ambulatory Pediatrics
Anatomic Pathology
Anesthesiology & Pain Medicine
Asthma Program
Audiology
Bariatric Surgery
Battelle Center for Mathematical Medicine
Behavioral Health
Blood Conservation Program
Burn Program
Cancer
CAP4Kids
Cardiology
Cardiopulmonary Rehabilitation
Cardiothoracic Surgery
Center for Biobehavioral Health (Research)
Center for Cardiovascular and Pulmonary Research
Center for Childhood Cancer (Research)
Center for Clinical and Translational Research
Center for Colorectal and Pelvic Reconstruction
Center for Gene Therapy (Research)
Center for Healthy Weight and Nutrition
Center for Injury Research and Policy
Center for Innovation in Pediatric Practice
Center for Microbial Pathogenesis (Research)
Center for Molecular and Human Genetics (Research)
Center for Perinatal Research
Center for Vaccines and Immunity (Research)
Central Ohio Poison Center
Cerebral Palsy Program
Chest Wall Clinic
Child Development/Psychology
Child Life Specialists
ChildLab
Cleft Lip and Palate Center
Clinical Nutrition and Lactation
Clinical Services and Care Coordination
Clinical Studies
Clinical Therapies
Close To Home Centers
Community Relations
Connecting Families
Critical Care
Cystic Fibrosis
Dentistry
Dermatology
Developmental/ Behavioral Pediatrics
Diabetes Clinic
Disorders of Sexual Development (DSD)
Ear Nose & Throat Services (Otolaryngology)
Early Childhood Development Program
Education Classes
Emergency Services
Endocrinology Metabolism & Diabetes
Family Advisory Council
Family AIDS Clinic and Educational Services (FACES)
Family Health Information Center
Family Practice
Family Resource Center
Fetal Diagnostics
Financial Matters
Gastroenterology Hepatology and Nutrition
Gender Concerns
General Pediatric Surgery

Genetics (Molecular and Human)
Gift Cards
Gift Shop
Government Relations
Health Info Library
Health Information Management (HIM)
Hearing Program
Heart Center
Hemangioma Vascular Anomalies
Hematology Oncology & BMT
HIV Program
Homecare
Hospice
Immunology
Infectious Diseases
Interdisciplinary Feeding Clinic
International Adoption Clinic
Interventional Radiology
Jeune's Syndrome
Laboratory Medicine/Reference Lab
Massage Therapy
Medical Records
Melanoma & Pigmented Lesion Clinic
Music Therapy
myChildren's
Neonatology
Nephrology
Neurodiagnostics/EEG
Neurology
Neuromuscular Disorders
Neurosciences Center
Neurosurgery
Nuclear Medicine
Nurse-Family Partnership
Occupational Therapy
Ophthalmology/Eye Clinic
Orthopedics
Outpatient Surgery
Pain Service Clinic
Palliative Care
Pastoral Care
Patient and Family Relations
Patient and Visitor Guide
Patient Financial Services
PediaCast: a pediatric podcast for parents
Pediatric and Adolescent Gynecology
Pediatric Psychiatry
Pediatric Psychology
Pharmacy Services (Outpatient)
Physical Medicine & Rehabilitation
Physical Therapy
Physical Therapy - Sports and Orthopedic
Plastic and Reconstructive Surgery
Prader-Willi Syndrome Clinic
Primary Care Centers
Pulmonary Medicine
Radiology
Reach Out and Read
Rehabilitation
Request an Appointment
Research at Children's
Resonance Disorders Program
Rheumatology
Robot-Assisted Surgery
Ronald McDonald House
School Program
Sibling Support (Children's Clubhouse)
Sleep Disorder Center
Social Work
Speech and Language Pathology
Spina Bifida Program
Sports Medicine
Surgical Services
Telehealth
The Center for Family Safety and Healing
Therapeutic Recreation
THRIVE Program (DSD & Complex Urological & Gender Concerns)
Toxicology
Transplant Program
Transport
Trauma
Urgent Care Services
Urology
Velopharyngeal Dysfunction Program
Weight Loss Surgery

COMPETITORS

Akron Children's Hospital
Cincinnati Children's Hospital
Fairfield Medical Center
Genesis HealthCare System (Ohio)
Licking Memorial Health Systems
Mount Carmel Health
OhioHealth
Select Medical
Shriners Hospitals For Children

HISTORICAL FINANCIALS

Company Type: Private

Income Statement — FYE: December 31

	REVENUE ($ mil.)	NET INCOME ($ mil.)	NET PROFIT MARGIN	EMPLOYEES
12/17	2,317	647	27.9%	12,000
12/16	1,385	330	23.9%	—
12/15	1,386	285	20.6%	—
12/14	1,282	332	26.0%	—
Annual Growth	21.8%	24.8%	—	—

2017 Year-End Financials

Return on assets: 14.4%
Return on equity: 19.1%
Current ratio: 1.80
Cash ($ mil.): 315

NATURAL GAS PIPELINE COMPANY OF AMERICA LLC

EXECUTIVES

MBR-Pres, David Devine
Mng MBR*, Richard D Kinder
MBR*, Scott Parker
MBR-Cfo*, Jim Saunders
MBR-Exec V Pres*, Steve Kean
MBR*, Charles Schwager
MBR*, Joseph Listengart
SEC, Tracy Brewer
Plant Manager, William Allison

LOCATIONS

HQ: NATURAL GAS PIPELINE COMPANY OF AMERICA LLC
1001 LOUISIANA ST, HOUSTON, TX 770025089
Phone: 713 369-9000
Web: WWW.KINDERMORGAN.COM

HISTORICAL FINANCIALS

Company Type: Private

Income Statement — FYE: December 31

	REVENUE ($ mil.)	NET INCOME ($ mil.)	NET PROFIT MARGIN	EMPLOYEES
12/17	679	130	19.2%	1,747
12/16	613	121	19.7%	—
Annual Growth	10.8%	8.0%	—	—

2017 Year-End Financials

Return on assets: 6.7%
Return on equity: 9.7%
Current ratio: 1.50
Cash ($ mil.): 15

NAVIGATE AFFORDABLE HOUSING PARTNERS, INC

EXECUTIVES

Prin*, Julie Reynolds
Prin, Lisa McCarroll
Auditors: KASSOUF & CO PC BIRMINGHAM A

LOCATIONS

HQ: NAVIGATE AFFORDABLE HOUSING PARTNERS, INC
1827 1ST AVE N STE 100, BIRMINGHAM, AL 352033137
Phone: 888 466-5572
Web: WWW.NAVIGATEHOUSING.COM

HISTORICAL FINANCIALS

Company Type: Private

Income Statement — FYE: December 31

	REVENUE ($ mil.)	NET INCOME ($ mil.)	NET PROFIT MARGIN	EMPLOYEES
12/17	573	8	1.5%	53
12/16	540	(12)	—	—
12/13	498	(6)	—	—
12/09	407	6	1.7%	—
Annual Growth	4.3%	2.7%	—	—

2017 Year-End Financials

Return on assets: 32.9%
Return on equity: 34.6%
Current ratio: 24.60
Cash ($ mil.): 24

NAVY EXCHANGE SERVICE COMMAND

EXECUTIVES

Ceo, Robert J Bianchi
Coo*, Michael P Good
Cfo*, Laurie P Hasten
Treas*, Thomas McDonald
Controllor*, Gerald Outar
Law Specialist, Nancy Haas
Staff, Cleveland Rogers
Network Manager, Tim Anthony
Coordinator, Charles Early
Law Specialist, Kia Coleman
Law Specialist, Kim Sherman

LOCATIONS

HQ: NAVY EXCHANGE SERVICE COMMAND
3280 VIRGINIA BEACH BLVD, VIRGINIA BEACH, VA 234525799
Phone: 757 631-3696
Web: WWW.MYNAVYEXCHANGE.COM

HISTORICAL FINANCIALS

Company Type: Private

Income Statement

FYE: February 3

	REVENUE ($ mil.)	NET INCOME ($ mil.)	NET PROFIT MARGIN	EMPLOYEES
02/18*	2,617	32	1.2%	14,000
01/17	2,574	45	1.8%	—
01/16	2,635	73	2.8%	—
01/11	2,749	68	2.5%	—
Annual Growth	(0.7%)	(10.3%)	—	—

*Fiscal year change

NCH CORPORATION

NCH has been cleaning up for years and like everyone else it's been using soaps and detergents to do so. The company makes and sells about 450 chemical maintenance repair and supply products including all kinds of cleaners for customers in more than 50 countries throughout the world. NCH markets its products through a direct sales force to companies in the agricultural home-improvement industrial recreational and utility markets. Other products include fasteners welding supplies pet care supplies plumbing parts lubricants and metal-working fluids.

Operations

The company's major areas of focus include producing products for the industrial cleaning and maintenance pet care plumbing specialty industries supply and water treatment and remediation markets.

NCH's cleaning products include hand cleaners industrial cleaners and housekeeping supplies. Specialty chemical products including cleaning and water treatment chemicals deodorizers lubricants paints and paint strippers patching compounds and flooring and carpet treatments account for the majority of sales.

The company's divisions include: Water Treatment Solutions plumbing Pet Care (Simple Solutions® Bags on Board® Vet's Best® and OUT! Pet Care) Specialty Industrial Supplies (operates through Partsmaster) industrial and institutional maintenance oil and gas Parts Washing lubrication and biologicals.

NCH operates more than 40 separate business units. Subsidiary Supply Line Direct offers safety and maintenance products such as janitorial supplies safety signs first aid kits spills kits storage cabinets for hazardous chemicals and protective apparel. Its plumbing products group has plumbing supplies for OEM and retail consumer markets. Other subsidiaries include Pure Solve a parts washing service TERRA Services (which reduces hazardous chemicals used in the hydraulic fracturing process) and X-Chem an oil field services division.

Subsidiary companies in NCH's Chemical Specialties division produce a diverse array of maintenance chemicals that includes cleaners degreasers lubricants grounds care housekeeping and water treatment products. Companies in the Partsmaster group offer a wide variety of items for maintenance and repair including welding supplies and fasteners. The Plumbing Products Group provides plumbing supplies for the do-it-yourself retail consumer and the OEM market. The Retail Products Group markets a wide range of pet supplies.

Geographic Reach

NCH has operations in Asia Europe North America and Latin America. The company has representatives in 30 countries on five continents.

The company's sales and service teams serve customers in North America Latin America Europe Asia Australia and India. NCH has wholly owned subsidiaries in more than 50 countries.

Sales and Marketing

NCH sells its products directly through a number of wholly owned subsidiaries many of which are engaged in the maintenance products business. These include Bags on Board Partsmaster Chemsearch Chem-Aqua and Mantek.

The Plumbing Products group provides supplies for the do-it-yourself consumer and the OEM market. The Retail Products group markets pet supplies. Other subsidiaries include X-Chem an oil field services division and Pure Solve a parts-washing business.

Strategy

NCH continues to seek new opportunities in water treatment oil and gas and in driving innovation to help keep its facilities and equipment running in optimum condition while reducing costs.

Research product development quality control field testing and customized analysis are all part of the ongoing efforts at NCH to deliver market-driven innovative and high-performing products to their customers and this strategy allowed them to remain competitive with larger corporations.

Descendants of founder Milton Levy own the company.

EXECUTIVES

President Nch Asia, Dong Eun Kim
Senior Vice President Sales And Marketing, Mark Ayers
Vice President Corporate Real Estate, Don Moulton
Senior Vice President Sales, Brenda Sanders
Senior Vice President, Roy Levin
Executive Managing Director, Alan Bacon
Vice President General Manager, Gary Whitley
Vice President, Randy Marsh
Vice President Sales (west), Terry Waldo
Vice President, Ann Levy
Vice President Finance And Global Controller, John Currie
Vice President Of Global Logistics, Shayne Mai
Vice President Of Finance, Pete Bocian
Executive Vice President Southwest Regional Manager, Farah Victoria
Vice President Organizational Development And Learning, Jed Davis
Senior Vice President, Frank Pellegrini
Medical Director, Julie Allison
Vice President Information Systems, Bruce Wineberger
Executive Vice President, Lester A Levy
Vice President Sales, Dennis Stein
Senior Vice President, John Larsson
Vice President Sales Brand Manager, Tony Lewis
Vice President Research And Development, John Roheim
Vice President Supply Chain, Walter Adams
Executive Vice President, Joe O'sullivan
Vice President Information Technology, Leonard Brown
Vice President Research And Development, Scott Boyette
Vice President Strategy And Business Development, Mike Howdeshell
Vice President, Andy Leslie
V.p Of Sales, Ron Rashell
Senior Vice President Innovation And Product Development, Michael Schuster
Vice President Sales, Henrik Ingvardsen
Vice President, Garland Edgell
Vice President Engineering And Technology, Allan Browning
Treasurer, Mark Hoesten
Treasurer, Joe Farrier
Auditors: PRICEWATERHOUSECOOPERS LLP DA

LOCATIONS

HQ: NCH CORPORATION
2727 CHEMSEARCH BLVD, IRVING, TX 750626454
Phone: 972 438-0211
Web: WWW.NCH.COM

PRODUCTS/OPERATIONS

Selected Operations and Products

Chemical Specialties
  Cleaning chemicals
  Deodorizers
  Floor and carpet care products
  HVAC products
  Lubricants
  Oil production facility chemicals
  Paint
  Paint removers
  Water-treatment chemicals
Landmark Direct
  First-aid supplies
  Workplace signage and productivity products
Pet Care
Partsmaster Group
  Cutting tools
  Electrical products
  Fasteners
  Welding alloys
Plumbing Products Group
  Plumbing products for new construction
  Plumbing repair and replacement parts
Industrial and Institutional Maintenance
Industrial and commercial cleaning
Industrial Repair and maintenance
Drains Grease Traps and lift stations
Lubrication and coolants
Equipment and supplies
Parts washing
Grounds Care
Personal hygiene
Pet Care
Training pads
Stain and Odor Removers
Cleaners and Disinfectants
Allergy Relief and shed Control
Grooming products
Plumbing
Sinks
Faucets
Tub & Showers
Toilets
Drains
Specialty Industrial Supply
High Performance Cutting Tools
Welding
Abrasives
Compounds
Fasteners
Electrical and Automotive
Shop Supplies
Storage Hardware
Tools
Water Treatment Solutions
Boiler
Cooling Towers
Colsed Recirculation Systems
Biocides and Algaecides
Cleaner/Descalers
Equipment
Wastewater and Bio Remediation

COMPETITORS

Church & Dwight	H.B. Fuller
Cintas	Illinois Tool Works
Clariant	Pioneer Corporation
Danaher	Quaker Chemical
Detrex	Safety-Kleen
Ecolab	WD-40

HISTORICAL FINANCIALS
Company Type: Private

Income Statement   FYE: April 30

	REVENUE ($ mil.)	NET INCOME ($ mil.)	NET PROFIT MARGIN	EMPLOYEES
04/16	996	0	0.0%	8,500
04/12	1,045	6	0.6%	—
04/11	952	6	0.7%	—
Annual Growth	0.9%	(52.6%)	—	—

2016 Year-End Financials
Return on assets: —
Return on equity: 0.2%
Current ratio: 2.40

Cash ($ mil.): 10

NEBRASKA METHODIST HOSPITAL INC

EXECUTIVES

Pres, John M Fraser
V Pres*, Mark A Burmester
Cfo*, Linda K Burt
Prin*, Steven Zuber
Registered Nurse, Carrie Kelseth
Physician, Thomas Brennan
Executive Administrative Assis, Angela Anderson
Administrative Coordinator E, Brooke Walters
Administrative Coordinator E, Gillian Atmore
Team Leader III Food, Jacob Minarich
Magnet Program Director, Jennifer Promes

LOCATIONS

HQ: NEBRASKA METHODIST HOSPITAL INC
8303 DODGE ST, OMAHA, NE 681144108
Phone: 402 354-4540
Web: WWW.BESTCARE.ORG

HISTORICAL FINANCIALS
Company Type: Private

Income Statement   FYE: December 31

	REVENUE ($ mil.)	NET INCOME ($ mil.)	NET PROFIT MARGIN	EMPLOYEES
12/17	520	54	10.4%	2,635
12/16	510	63	12.4%	—
12/15	511	51	10.1%	—
12/14	449	55	12.3%	—
Annual Growth	5.0%	(0.8%)	—	—

2017 Year-End Financials
Return on assets: 6.7%
Return on equity: 11.7%
Current ratio: 2.60

Cash ($ mil.): 48

NEBRASKA PUBLIC POWER DISTRICT

Nebraska Public Power District (NPPD) electrifies the Cornhusker State. The government-owned electric utility the largest in the state provides power in 86 of the state's 93 counties. The firm has a generating capacity of about 3130 MW and operates more than 5200 miles of transmission lines. NPPD distributes electricity to about 89000 retail customers in 81 cities and towns; it also provides power to about 1 million customers through wholesale power contracts with more than 50 towns and 25 public power districts. In addition NPPD purchases electricity from the federally owned Western Area Power Administration and operates a surface water irrigation system.

Operations
The company uses multiple sources including nuclear steam mixed wind hydro and diesel to generate power.

NPPD's revenues comes from wholesale power supply agreements with 50 towns and 25 rural public power districts and rural cooperatives who rely totally or partially on NPPD's electrical system. NPPD also serves about 81 communities at the retail level.

Financial Performance
Revenues for 2013 increased by 2% due mostly to rate increases and sales to other utilities. Net income jumped 30% on the revenue increase and reduced costs. Cash from operations followed suit and rose nearly $100 million.

Strategy
Faced with growing long-term demand for electricity along with pressure to keep prices low NPPD has implemented plans to increase transmission capacity. With a goal of getting of 15% it energy from renewable sources by 2025 the company is exploring alternative fuel sources for future plants. With 45% of NPPD's energy supply coming from coal in 2011 the company was looking to cleaner alternatives such as wind power and biomass in order to meet stricter environmental regulations. In 2014 it signed a deal to purchase wind power from Sempra a move that put it within sight of its goal to have 10% of its power generation come from renewable sources.

Company Background
NPPD was formed in 1970 through the merger of three public utilities: Consumers Public Power District Platte Valley Public Power and Irrigation District and Nebraska Public Power System.

EXECUTIVES

Vice President, Theresa Shank
Vice President, John Wolfe
Vice Chairman, Barry Dekay
Auditors: PRICEWATERHOUSECOOPER LLP ST

LOCATIONS

HQ: NEBRASKA PUBLIC POWER DISTRICT
1414 15TH ST, COLUMBUS, NE 686015226
Phone: 877 275-6773
Web: WWW.NPPD.COM

PRODUCTS/OPERATIONS

2013 Sales

	$ mil.	% of total
Wholesale	584	53
Retail	294	27
Other	227	20
Total	**1,106**	**100**

COMPETITORS

Basin Electric Power	Omaha Public Power
Berkshire Hathaway Energy	Tri-State Generation and Transmission
NorthWestern	

HISTORICAL FINANCIALS
Company Type: Private

Income Statement   FYE: December 31

	REVENUE ($ mil.)	NET INCOME ($ mil.)	NET PROFIT MARGIN	EMPLOYEES
12/18	1,144	82	7.2%	1,900
12/17	1,101	71	6.5%	—
12/16	1,154	82	7.2%	—
12/15	1,097	91	8.3%	—
Annual Growth	1.4%	(3.2%)	—	—

2018 Year-End Financials
Return on assets: 1.7%
Return on equity: 5.3%
Current ratio: 2.40

Cash ($ mil.): 25

NETWORK HEALTH SYSTEM INC

LOCATIONS

HQ: NETWORK HEALTH SYSTEM INC
1165 APPLETON RD, MENASHA, WI 549521905
Phone: 920 831-8920

HISTORICAL FINANCIALS
Company Type: Private

Income Statement   FYE: September 30

	REVENUE ($ mil.)	NET INCOME ($ mil.)	NET PROFIT MARGIN	EMPLOYEES
09/08	461	(17)	—	1,020
09/00	99	(20)	—	—
Annual Growth	21.1%	—	—	—

2008 Year-End Financials
Return on assets: (-14.3%)
Return on equity: (-69.9%)
Current ratio: 0.20

Cash ($ mil.): 2

NEVADA SYSTEM OF HIGHER EDUCATION

You can gamble on a solid academic foundation with The Nevada System of Higher Education (NSHE). The system oversees Nevada's public colleges and institutions. NSHE encompasses eight institutions: the University of Nevada Las Vegas; the University of Nevada Reno; Nevada State College; community colleges Truckee Meadows Great Basin College College of Southern Nevada and Western Nevada College; and environmental research arm Desert Research Institute (DRI). The system which enrolls some 106000 students is governed by the Nevada Board of Regents consisting of 13 members elected for six-year terms.

Financial Performance
Total operating revenue fell 4% in 2012 as an increase in NSHE's largest segment (student tuition and fees) was not enough to offset double-digit declines in federal state and local grants and contracts. The rise in tuition and fees resulted from

an increase in tuition rates to offset an enrollment decrease.

Strategy

In late 2013 NSHE announced a partnership to establish medical schools at the University of Nevada Las Vegas and Reno campuses.

EXECUTIVES

Ceo, Daniel Klaich
Administrative Assistant, Dennis Thieme
Associate Professor, Jeffrey Jablonski
Assistant Professor, Natalie Berman
Acting Pres Wstrnnevadacollege, P Mark Ghan
Editor, Doug Smith
Executive, Emily Dyer
Internal Medicine Practitioner, Jihye Park
Graduate Student Teaching Assi, Armin Saraei
Unlvino Student Manager, Jackie Watson
Network Manager, Chris Gaub
Auditors: GRANT THORNTON LLP RENO NV

LOCATIONS

HQ: NEVADA SYSTEM OF HIGHER EDUCATION
   2601 ENTERPRISE RD, RENO, NV 895121666
Phone: 775 784-4901
Web: WWW.NEVADA.EDU

HISTORICAL FINANCIALS

Company Type: Private

Income Statement				FYE: June 30
	REVENUE ($ mil.)	NET INCOME ($ mil.)	NET PROFIT MARGIN	EMPLOYEES
06/18	953	116	12.2%	8,000
06/17	1,115	140	12.6%	—
06/16	1,055	48	4.6%	—
06/07	685	116	17.0%	—
Annual Growth	3.1%	(0.0%)	—	—

2018 Year-End Financials

Return on assets: 3.0%
Return on equity: 6.5%
Current ratio: 3.10
Cash ($ mil.): 178

NEW ENGLAND PETROLEUM LIMITED PARTNERSHIP

EXECUTIVES

Ptnr, Gary Kaneb
Auditors: PRICEWATERHOUSECOOPERS LLP B

LOCATIONS

HQ: NEW ENGLAND PETROLEUM LIMITED
   PARTNERSHIP
   6 KIMBALL LN STE 400, LYNNFIELD, MA 019402685
Phone: 617 660-7400
Web: WWW.GULFOIL.COM

HISTORICAL FINANCIALS

Company Type: Private

Income Statement				FYE: December 31
	REVENUE ($ mil.)	NET INCOME ($ mil.)	NET PROFIT MARGIN	EMPLOYEES
12/12	1,081	4	0.4%	25
12/11	998	3	0.3%	—
12/10	568	2	0.5%	—
Annual Growth	37.9%	32.5%	—	—

2012 Year-End Financials

Return on assets: 7.7%
Return on equity: 13.5%
Current ratio: 2.40
Cash ($ mil.): 2

NEW JERSEY TRANSPORTATION TRUST FUND AUTHORITY

Auditors: MERCADIEN PC PRINCETON NJ

LOCATIONS

HQ: NEW JERSEY TRANSPORTATION TRUST FUND
   AUTHORITY
   1035 PARKWAY AVE, EWING, NJ 086182309
Phone: 609 530-2035

HISTORICAL FINANCIALS

Company Type: Private

Income Statement				FYE: June 30
	REVENUE ($ mil.)	NET INCOME ($ mil.)	NET PROFIT MARGIN	EMPLOYEES
06/18	1,676	(859)	—	284
06/17	1,338	(532)	—	—
06/16	1,261	(412)	—	—
06/09	934	(1,078)	—	—
Annual Growth	6.7%	—	—	—

2018 Year-End Financials

Return on assets: (-4.2%)
Return on equity: (-157.2%)
Current ratio: 1.00
Cash ($ mil.): 1,417

NEW JERSEY TURNPIKE AUTHORITY INC

The New Jersey Turnpike Authority operates two toll-supported highways the New Jersey Turnpike and the Garden State Parkway. The New Jersey Turnpike runs for 148 miles from the Delaware River Bridge at the southern end of the state to the George Washington Bridge that connects New Jersey with New York. The turnpike includes about 10 rest stops or service areas named for former New Jersey residents such as Alexander Hamilton Vince Lombardi and Walt Whitman. The Garden State Parkway runs for 173 miles and spans the length of New Jersey's Atlantic coastline.

EXECUTIVES

Vice President, John Lewis
Vice Chairman, Ronald Gravino
Treasurer, Michael R Dupont
Secretary To The Authority, Kim Schurman

LOCATIONS

HQ: NEW JERSEY TURNPIKE AUTHORITY INC
   1 TURNPIKE PLZ, WOODBRIDGE, NJ 070955195
Phone: 732 750-5300
Web: WWW.STATE.NJ.US

HISTORICAL FINANCIALS

Company Type: Private

Income Statement				FYE: December 31
	REVENUE ($ mil.)	NET INCOME ($ mil.)	NET PROFIT MARGIN	EMPLOYEES
12/17	1,698	329	19.4%	2,400
12/16	1,689	260	15.4%	—
12/14	1,549	265	17.1%	—
Annual Growth	3.1%	7.5%	—	—

2017 Year-End Financials

Return on assets: 2.2%
Return on equity: 26.4%
Current ratio: 2.00
Cash ($ mil.): 183

NEW PRIME, INC.

Specialized carrier New Prime (which does business simply as Prime) provides refrigerated flatbed tanker and intermodal trucking services throughout North America through more than 10000 remotely monitored temperature-controlled trailers. The company operates in the US and Canada and serves Mexico through arrangements with other carriers. A subsidiary Prime Floral uses the parent company's refrigerated equipment and facilities to serve the flower industry. In addition to its freight-hauling operations Prime provides logistics services including freight brokerage.

Operations

Prime which has a fleet of more than 4700 trucks operates through three divisions.

Prime's liquid bulk fleet (Tanker Division) consists of more than 200 trucks and more than 400 6800-gallon Walker Stainless MC407 trailers with air ride suspensions. The company's Refrigerated Division has a fleet of remotely monitored temperature-controlled trailers and serves businesses whose needs include transportation of fresh produce fresh cut floral produce pharmaceuticals fresh or frozen meats or any other dry or temperature controlled freight. Prime also has a Flatbed Division.

Its affiliates include Amber Aleri Prime Floral Prime Intermodal Prime Logistics and Trailer Skirt.

Geographic Reach

The company serves customers in Canada Mexico and the US. Based in Springfield Missouri Prime operates two US terminals in Pennsylvania and Utah.

Sales and Marketing

Prime has hauled goods for such blue chip consumer goods makers as ConAgra Foods Kraft Foods and General Mills. It markets its products through independent contractors stores and online.

Strategy

Prime is shifting its strategy to align with customer preferences for shortening supply chain mileage and delivery time all of which is intended to offset lower consumer demand and volatile fuel costs.

It is also using technology to enhance its position as an industry leader in the safe cost-effective transport of temperature-sensitive goods. Its Prime Position Tracking software enables the company to locate tractors in real-time within a 600 foot radius at all times. Prime Mapping and Routing provides detailed Rand McNally and PC*Miler directions to driver associates to ensure that loads get to their destination in the quickest safest and most efficient manner.

Company Background

Prime was founded in 1970 by Robert Low who continues to serve as Prime's president.

EXECUTIVES

President And Ceo, Robert E. Low
Manager Of Success Leasing Program, Fred Ege
Director Of Logistics, Rick Gallagher
Director Of Operations, Pat Leonard
Director Of Flatbed And Tanker Operations, Jim Wilkins
Vp Sales And Marketing, Steve Wutke
Director Of Finance, Dean Hoedl
Director Of Technology, Rodney Rader
Manager Of Tanker Division, Brett Vonwiller

LOCATIONS

HQ: NEW PRIME, INC.
 2740 N MAYFAIR AVE, SPRINGFIELD, MO 658035084
Phone: 800 321-4552
Web: WWW.PRIMEINC.COM

COMPETITORS

Boyd Bros. Transportation	Comcar Frozen Food Express
C.H. Robinson Worldwide	KLLM Transport Services
C.R. England	Marten Transport
Central Refrigerated Service	Quality Distribution Stevens Transport

HISTORICAL FINANCIALS

Company Type: Private

Income Statement				FYE: March 31
	REVENUE ($ mil.)	NET INCOME ($ mil.)	NET PROFIT MARGIN	EMPLOYEES
03/17*	1,653	116	7.1%	5,000
04/16	1,598	133	8.3%	—
03/12	1,022	60	6.0%	—
04/11	941	47	5.0%	—
Annual Growth	9.8%	16.2%	—	—

*Fiscal year change

2017 Year-End Financials

Return on assets: 12.7%   Cash ($ mil.): —
Return on equity: 32.2%
Current ratio: 0.40

NEW YORK BLOOD CENTER, INC.

New York Blood Center (NYBC) holds a very literal interpretation of the meaning of life. It is a not-for-profit blood distribution and research organization serving New York City and its environs in New York State and New Jersey as well as parts of Connecticut and Pennsylvania. As one of the largest blood centers in the US NYBC provides nearly 1 million blood components to some 200 hospitals each year. The center's facilities collect blood from more than 2000 donors each day. It also operates the nation's oldest and largest public cord blood bank. In addition its Kimball Research Institute includes more than a dozen research laboratories which study the prevention and treatment of blood-related illnesses.

Operations

Areas of research in the Kimball Research Institute include virology molecular genetics cell biology and signaling viral immunology and infectious disease prevention. It has been responsible for the development and licensing of solvent and detergent technology used to deactivate the potency of viruses in blood and blood products (such as plasma and platelets used in transfusions).

NYBC's clinical services division acts as an adjunct and resource to hospitals throughout its service areas by providing expertise in transfusion medicine as well as delivering more than 8500 specialized procedures each year. In addition the center maintains a bone marrow donor registry for the New York area provides hemophilia services to some 1500 patients and offers screening and education programs for cholesterol high blood pressure and cardiovascular disease.

Geographic Reach

Based in New York NYBC offers its services throughout New York City Long Island the Hudson Valley and in Connecticut New Jersey and Pennsylvania.

Strategy

Seeking greater breadth and financial stability NYBC announced it will combine its operations with Community Blood Center of Greater Kansas City (CBC) to form one of the leading blood centers serving patients and hospitals in the Northeast and Midwest. The combination is expected to be completed in mid-2014. The union of NYBC and CBC is expected to bring synergies in blood and laboratory services medical programs cell therapies and research.

Mergers and Acquisitions

In October 2013 NYBC acquired Coral Blood Services a subsidiary of HemaCare Corp. to advance its mission of providing innovative blood products and medical services to hospitals and patients throughout the Northeast. Coral Blood Services provides more than 2500 therapeutic apheresis procedures annually in New York New Jersey Connecticut and Pennsylvania.

EXECUTIVES

Cio, Michele Scaggiante
Vp And Director Lindsley F. Kimball Research Institute, Mohandas Narla
Director National Cord Blood Program, Pablo Rubinstein
President And Ceo, Christopher D. Hillyer
Head Of The Viral Immunology Laboratory, Shibo Jiang
Svp And Cfo, Elizabeth C. Gibson
Senior Vice President, Paddy C Mullen
Medical Director, Patricia Shi
Vice President And Executive Director Medical Programs And Services, Pascal George
Senior Vice President Strategic Services And Facilities Administration, Jeffrey Jacob
Senior Vice President, Frederick W Hill
Senior Vice President, John R Mullen
Medical Director, Andromachi Scaradavou
Medical Director, Andrew Heaton
Vice President And Executive Director, Elizabeth Mcquail
Vice President Human Resources, Doriane Gloria
Senior Vice President Human Resources, Ollie Cheatham
Vice President Quality And Regulatory Affairs, Betsy Jett
Auditors: KPMG LLP NEW YORK NY

LOCATIONS

HQ: NEW YORK BLOOD CENTER, INC.
 310 E 67TH ST, NEW YORK, NY 100656273
Phone: 212 570-3010
Web: WWW.NYBLOODCENTER.ORG

PRODUCTS/OPERATIONS

Selected Services

Blood products
Clinical services
Hemochromatosis phlebotomy program
Hemophilia services
Laboratory services
Ordertrak
Transfusion medicine services

COMPETITORS

Blood Systems Inc.	Red Cross
CSL Behring	SeraCare Life Sciences
Daxor	

HISTORICAL FINANCIALS

Company Type: Private

Income Statement				FYE: March 31
	REVENUE ($ mil.)	NET INCOME ($ mil.)	NET PROFIT MARGIN	EMPLOYEES
03/18	466	48	10.4%	1,600
03/15	320	(0)		
Annual Growth	13.4%	—	—	—

2018 Year-End Financials

Return on assets: 8.3%   Cash ($ mil.): 42
Return on equity: 10.0%
Current ratio: 6.40

NEW YORK CITY ECONOMIC DEVELOPMENT CORPORATION

EXECUTIVES

Pres-Ceo, Maria Torres-Springer
Chb*, Michael Schlein
Cfo*, Kim Vaccari
Coo*, Euan Robertson
Evp*, Seth Myers
Treas*, Spencer Hobson
Asst Treas*, Fred D'Ascoli
Coordinator, Crissette Maxwell
Project Coordinator, Indira Ori
Vice-President, Harry Singh
Assistant Vice-President, Richard Tom
Auditors: ERNST & YOUNG LLP NEW YORK

LOCATIONS

HQ: NEW YORK CITY ECONOMIC DEVELOPMENT CORPORATION
 1 LIBERTY PLZ, NEW YORK, NY 100061404
Phone: 212 619-5000
Web: WWW.NYCEDC.COM

HISTORICAL FINANCIALS

Company Type: Private

Income Statement				FYE: June 30
	REVENUE ($ mil.)	NET INCOME ($ mil.)	NET PROFIT MARGIN	EMPLOYEES
06/18	761	14	1.9%	438
06/16	908	100	11.1%	—
Annual Growth	(8.5%)	(62.1%)	—	—

2018 Year-End Financials

Return on assets: 1.3%
Return on equity: 3.2%
Current ratio: 2.60

Cash ($ mil.): 92

NEW YORK CITY HEALTH AND HOSPITALS CORPORATION

New York City Health and Hospitals Corporation (NYC H+H) operates health care facilities in all five boroughs of New York City. As one of the largest municipal health service systems in the US HHC serves 1 million New Yorkers including more than 500000 who are uninsured. It operates a network of around 10 acute care hospitals (including Bellevue the nation's oldest public hospital) large diagnostic and treatment centers skilled nursing centers long-term care facilities and a home health care agency. NYC H+H also operates more than 70 community-based clinics and provides medical services to New York City's correctional facilities. In addition it operates MetroPlus a managed health care plan.

Operations

NYC H+H provides health care services including primary and preventive care emergency care long-term care plant-based nutrition guidance school-based health care and services for victims of domestic violence.

Geographic Reach

NYC H+H operates health care facilities in New York's Manhattan Brooklyn Queens Bronx and Staten Island boroughs.

Sales and Marketing

NYC H+H's MetroPlus health plan provides low to no-cost insurance to more than 500000 customers in New York. It insures many New York City government employees.

Financial Performance

NYC H+H's operating revenue fell in fiscal 2017 (ended June) but recovered the following year surpassing that of fiscal 2016. Operating revenue increased 6% to $7.8 billion in 2018 as net patient service revenue and net appropriations from New York City increased. Those gains were partially offset by a decline in grants revenue.

The company has been losing money for years. In fiscal 2018 it had an operating loss of $57.5 million an improvement over the 2017 operating loss of $272.7 million. That improvement was driven by the higher operating revenue plus certain cost-control measures such as lower other-than-personal services and pension expenses. NYC H+H ended fiscal 2018 with a net deficit of $5.5 billion.

Strategy

NYC H+H has been struggling financially facing a projected $1.8 billion budget gap by 2020. In mid-2017 the system cut 476 positions including nearly 400 management positions. It has closed certain clinics and shuttered its Goldwater specialty care hospital and nursing facility. And although the system has received positive care quality reviews from external organizations it is challenged to attract patients with commercial insurance. To further exacerbate matters the health system has a number of older facilities that would benefit from improvements but it has few resources to allocate to those types of projects.

HISTORY

The City of New York in 1929 created a department to manage its hospitals for the poor. During the Depression more than half of the city's residents were eligible for subsidized care and its public hospitals operated at full capacity.

Four new hospitals opened in the 1950s but the city was already having trouble maintaining existing facilities and attracting staff (young doctors preferred private insurance-supported hospitals catering to the middle class). Meanwhile technological advances and increased demand for skilled nurses made hospitals more expensive to operate. The advent of Medicaid in 1965 was a boon for the system because it brought in federal money.

In 1969 the city created the New York City Health and Hospitals Corporation (HHC) to manage its public health care system — and it was hoped to distance it from the political arena. But HHC was still dependent on the city for funds arousing criticism from those who had hoped for more autonomy. A 1973 state report claimed "the people of New York City are not materially better served by the Health and Hospitals Corporation than by its predecessor agencies."

City budget shortfalls in the mid-1970s led to cutbacks at HHC including nearly 20% of staff. Later in the decade several hospitals closed and some services were discontinued. Ed Koch became mayor in 1978 and gained more control over HHC's operations. Struggles between his administration and the system led three HHC presidents to resign by 1981. That year Koch crony Stanley Brezenoff assumed the post and helped transform HHC into a city pseudo-department.

The early 1980s brought greater prosperity to the system. Reimbursement rates and collections procedures improved allowing HHC to upgrade its record-keeping and its ambulatory and psychiatric care programs. In the late 1980s sharp increases in AIDS and crack addiction cases strained the system and a sluggish economy decreased city funding. Criticism mounted in the early 1990s with allegations of wrongful deaths dangerous facilities and lack of Medicaid payment controls. HHC lost patients to managed care providers and revenues plummeted. In 1995 a city panel recommended radically revamping the system.

Faced with declining revenues and criticism from Mayor Rudolph Giuliani that HHC was "a jobs program" the company began cutting jobs and consolidating facilities in 1996. Under Giuliani's direction HHC made plans to sell its Coney Island Elmhurst and Queens hospital centers. In 1997 the New York State Supreme Court struck down Giuliani's privatization efforts saying the city council had a right to review and approve each sale. In 1998 Giuliani continued to seek to restructure HHC and the agency itself contended it was making progress toward its restructuring goals which were aimed at giving HHC more autonomy as well as more fiscal responsibility. In anticipation of a budget shortfall that year the system laid off some 900 support staff employees. In 1999 the state court of appeals ruled HHC could not legally lease or sell its hospitals.

In 2000 HHC launched an effort to improve its physical infrastructure by beginning the rebuilding and renovation of facilities in Brooklyn Manhattan and Queens. The organization also began converting to an electronic (and thus more efficient) clinical information system. In 2001 HHC forged ahead with further restructuring initiatives. It introduced the Open Access plan a cost-cutting measure designed to expedite the processes involved in outpatient visits.

In 2006 Mayor Michael Bloomberg committed $16 million in funds toward the treatment of those affected by exposure to toxic fumes and dust from the 2001 attacks on the World Trade Center. Together with the city HHC established the WTC Environmental Health Center at Bellevue Hospital; treatment was made available at little or no charge to the patient.

EXECUTIVES

President Ceo And Director, Alan D. Aviles
Acting Svp South Manhattan Health Network; Acting Executive Director Bellevue Hospital Center, Lynda D. Curtis
Svp North Bronx Healthcare Network; Executive Director Jacobi Medical Center, William P. Walsh
Svp Finance And Cfo, Marlene Zurack
Executive Director Queens Hospital Center, Antonio Martin
Executive Director Metropolitan Hospital Center, Meryl Weinberg
Executive Director Elmhurst Hospital Center, Chris Constantino
Executive Director And Cfo Gouverneur Healthcare Services, Mendel Hagler
Executive Director And President Metroplus Health Plan, Arnold Saperstein
Executive Director Sea View Hospital Rehabilitation Center And Home, Angelo Mascia
Svp Queens Healthcare Network, Anne Marie Sullivan
Executive Director Hhc Health And Home Care, Ann Frisch
Svp Information Technology And Cio, Norberto (Bert) Robles
Executive Director Dr. Susan Smith Mckinney Nursing And Rehabilitation Center, Michael Tartaglia
Executive Director Coler-goldwater Specialty Hospital And Nursing Facility, Robert K. Hughes
Svp Quality And Corporate Chief Medical Officer, Ross Wilson
Acting Svp Generations Plus Northern Manhattan Healthcare Network; Executive Director Lincoln Medical And Mental Health Center, Denise C. Soares
Executive Director Kings County Hospital Center, Ernest J. Baptiste
Executive Director Queens Hospital Center, Julius Wool
Assistant Vice President Information Technology Services, Michael Keil
Senior Assistant Vice President, Roslyn Weinstein
Senior Assistant Vice President, Caroline Jacobs
Senior Assistant Vice President, Paul Albertson
Senior Vice President, Arthur Wagner
Senior Assistant Vice President, Maxine Katz
Director Of Admissions, Alex Toro
Assistant Vice President Data Science, Vijay Saradhi
Director Of Pharmacy, Danielle Petrocelli
Director Of Health Information, Stephen Natarajan
Vice President Of Finance And Chief Fina, Tim Buit
Chairman, Michael A. Stocker
Vice Chair, Diane E. Lacey
Auditors: KPMG LLP NEW YORK NY

LOCATIONS

HQ: NEW YORK CITY HEALTH AND HOSPITALS
CORPORATION
125 WORTH ST RM 514, NEW YORK, NY 100134006
Phone: 212 788-3321

HHC Networks

Central Brooklyn Family Health Network
  Dr. Susan Smith McKinney Nursing and
  Rehabilitation Center
  East New York Diagnostic & Treatment Center
  Kings County Hospital Center
Generations Plus Northern Manhattan Health Network
  Harlem Hospital Center
  Lincoln Medical and Mental Health Center
  Metropolitan Hospital Center
  Morrisania Diagnostic & Treatment Center
  Renaissance Health Care Network Diagnostic &
  Treatment Center
  Segundo Ruiz Belvis Diagnostic & Treatment Center
North Bronx Healthcare Network
  Jacobi Medical Center
  North Central Bronx Hospital
North Brooklyn Health Network
  Cumberland Diagnostic & Treatment Center
  Woodhull Medical and Mental Health Center
Queens Health Network
  Elmhurst Hospital Center
  Queens Hospital Center
South Brooklyn and Staten Island Health Network
  Coney Island Hospital
  Sea View Hospital Rehabilitation Center & Home
South Manhattan Healthcare Network
  Bellevue Hospital Center
  Gouverneur Healthcare Services

PRODUCTS/OPERATIONS

2018 Sales

	$ mil.	% of total
Net patient services	6,216	80
Net appropriations from City of New York	787	10
Grants	652	9
Other	105	1
Total	**7,761**	**100**

Selected Services

Alcohol and Opioid Use Disorder
Asthma Care
Bariatric Services
Breast Health
Burn Care
Cancer Care
Cardiology
Child Health and Pediatrics
Colon Cancer Screening
Deaf and Hard-of-Hearing
Dental Care
Depression
Diabetes Care
Farmers Market
Flu Vaccination
Geriatric Services
HIV/AIDS Care
HPV Vaccine
Hypertension
Language/Translation Services
LGBTQ Services
Men's Health
Mental Health
Neonatal Intensive Care
Obstetrics & Gynecology
Palliative Care
Parkinson's Disease
Pediatrics
Quit Smoking
Rehab Services
Victims of Domestic Violence
Sexual Response Assault Teams
Sickle Cell Disease
Sleep Disorder Labs
Stroke Prevention and Care
Telehealth Initiatives
Trauma Centers
Vision Care
Women's Health
WTC Environmental Health Center
Youth Health

COMPETITORS

Beth Israel Medical
  Center
Catholic Healthcare
  System
Columbia University
Continuum Health
  Partners
Cornell University
Lenox Hill Hospital
  Memorial
  Sloan-Kettering
Montefiore Medical
NYU
NewYork-Presbyterian
  Healthcare
Northwell Health

HISTORICAL FINANCIALS

Company Type: Private

Income Statement

FYE: June 30

	REVENUE ($ mil.)	NET INCOME ($ mil.)	NET PROFIT MARGIN	EMPLOYEES
06/17	9,550	(193)	—	35,700
06/02	4,285	(118)	—	—
06/01	4,287	(71)	—	—
06/00	4,083	9	0.2%	—
Annual Growth	**5.1%**	**—**	**—**	**—**

2017 Year-End Financials

Return on assets: (-2.8%)   Cash ($ mil.): 1,184
Return on equity: —
Current ratio: 1.00

NEW YORK CITY SCHOOL CONSTRUCTION AUTHORITY

EXECUTIVES

Pres-Ceo, Loraine Grillo
Exec V Pres*, Ross J Holden
Designer, Angelo Liarikos
Computer Technician, Kelvin Pena
Project Leader, Ji W Moy
Manager, Samir Patel
Manager, Carmen Mateo
Senior Manager, Zita Devivo
Manager, Kin Tang
Teacher, Antoine McCoy
Teacher, Daniel Towers
Auditors: PRICEWATERHOUSECOOPER LLP NE

LOCATIONS

HQ: NEW YORK CITY SCHOOL CONSTRUCTION
AUTHORITY
3030 THOMSON AVE FL 3, LONG ISLAND CITY, NY
111013019
Phone: 718 472-8000
Web: WWW.NYCSCA.ORG

HISTORICAL FINANCIALS

Company Type: Private

Income Statement

FYE: June 30

	REVENUE ($ mil.)	NET INCOME ($ mil.)	NET PROFIT MARGIN	EMPLOYEES
06/14	2,190	(410)	—	600
06/13	1,840	(494)	—	—
Annual Growth	**19.0%**	**—**	**—**	**—**

2014 Year-End Financials

Return on assets: (-16.8%)   Cash ($ mil.): 74
Return on equity: (-24.4%)
Current ratio: —

NEW YORK CITY TRANSIT AUTHORITY

New York City Transit Authority has your ticket
to ride in the Big Apple. Known as MTA New York
City Transit it provides subway and bus transportation throughout New York City's five boroughs. It is the primary agency of the MTA and
the largest public transportation system in North
America. Its subway system — which includes more
than 6300 subway cars 468 stations and 660 miles
of track — serves more than 5.5 million passengers
a day day on 238 local six select bus service and
61 express routes in the five boroughs. Its more
than 5700 buses transport some 2.6 million riders
each day. The agency also operates the Staten Island Railway system.

Operations

New York City Subways and Buses is comprised
of two agencies of the MTA regional transportation
network - MTA New York City Transit Transit and
MTA Bus. The regional network also includes MTA
Staten Island Railway (part of NYC Transit's Department of Subways) MTA Long Island Rail Road
MTA Metro-North Railroad MTA Bridges and Tunnels and MTA Capital Construction.

MTA New York City Transit and its subsidiary
Manhattan and Bronx Surface Transit Operating
Authority provide subway and public bus service
within New York City's five boroughs.

In 2013 MTA New York City Transit's total ridership was 2.4 billion up 62 million or 2.7% from
2012. After including 44 million of lost ridership
from Superstorm Sandy in 2012 the company's
2013 ridership increased by 0.8% with a subway
ridership increase of 19 million or 1.1% and no
change in bus ridership.

Geographic Reach

The company serves customers in Brooklyn the
Bronx Manhattan and Queens and Staten Island

Financial Performance

Rebounding from the effects of Superstorm
Sandy on ridership (which resulted in lost revenues
of $52 million) in 2013 MTA New York City Tran-
sit's revenues from fares increased by 9%. In 2014
its operating budget was $10.1 billion.

Strategy

MTA New York City Transit's parent company
the MTA has been plagued by operating losses.
To mitigate its losses the MTA has in recent years
raised fares cut jobs and decreased service on its
buses and subway lines. It has also sought to raise
its non-operating revenues by seeking increased
government funding.

With the help of federal stimulus and other funding MTA New York City Transit has been making
capital improvements to its systems. Projects have
included the construction of the Second Avenue
Subway and renovations at the Fulton Street Transit Center and other stations throughout the system.

In 2013 the company broke ground on a new
MTA Staten Island Railway station. The 27-month
construction project the first such project to include
a parking lot will replace the existing Atlantic and
Nassau Stations in the Tottenville section of the
borough.

Company Background

New York City Transit Authority was formed in
the 1950s by New York's legislature; the city's
transit system dates back to the early 1900s.

EXECUTIVES

Confidential Secretary Ii, Yolanda Gambrell
Auditors: PRICEWATERHOUSECOOPERS LLP ST

NEW YORK POWER AUTHORITY

The hydropower generated by the mighty Niagara Falls is the real authority behind the New York Power Authority (NYPA). More than 70% of the power that NYPA produces is from hydropower resources. The company generates and transmits more than 20% of New York's electricity making it the largest state-owned public power provider in the US. It is also New York's only statewide electricity supplier. NYPA owns hydroelectric and fossil-fueled generating facilities (16 in total) that produce about 5700 MW of electricity and it operates more than 1400 circuit-miles of transmission lines. NYPA is owned by the State of New York.

Geographic Reach

The company serves customers throughout New York State various public corporations in Southeastern New York within the metropolitan area of New York City (SENY Governmental Customers) and certain out-of-state customers.

Sales and Marketing

NYPA services more than 500 businesses and industrial customers including manufacturing companies such as Anchor Glass of Elmira and General Motors of Tonawanda and non-manufacturing companies like GEICO of Amherst and Yahoo! of Lockport and 114 government entities in New York City and Westchester County including New York City government the Metropolitan Transportation Authority The Port Authority of New York and New Jersey the New York City Housing Authority Westchester County government and most Westchester municipalities school districts and other public entities.

The company provides electricity to 51 municipal and cooperative electric systems to sell to their customers.

Financial Performance

In 2014 the company's net revenues increased by 5% to $3.18 billion due to a higher volume of market energy and capacity sales and higher prices on those sales.

Net income grew by 9% due to higher net revenues and an increase in investment income.

In 2014 NYPA's operating cash inflow slightly decreased by 0.2% due to changes in working capital.

Strategy

NYPA receives no state funds or tax credits. Instead it finances new projects through bond sales.

Following its shift from a regulated monopoly to a competitor in an open power market NYPA is aiming to grow by reducing the cost of the energy it provides and by developing electric transportation (such as electric cars) and other energy-efficiency projects including installing emergency power generators in metropolitan buildings. It is also working to improve the state's transmission grid increase its generating capacity and help support the state's directive to get 45% of its power from clean energy sources (including 100 MW of power from solar arrays at buildings across the state). NYPA has been tagged as the lead agency to reduce energy use at state facilities by 20% by 2020.

In 2014 NYPA completed the installation of solar thermal hot water systems at five New York City firehouses in the Rockaways section of Queens. The $550000 investment will reduce operating costs and could lead to the wider use of the clean energy-transfer technology in other city government facilities. The company's energy efficiency projects have saved New Yorkers more than $148 million a year cutting annual oil use by more than 2.7 million barrels and offsetting the release of approximately 890000 tons of greenhouse gases. Its clean transportation program has placed more than 1300 electric-drive vehicles into service.

To improve its delivery of power the company is pursuing the development of a new cross-Hudson transmission line that will connect New York City customers to the PJM Interconnection power grid.

HISTORY

The Power Authority of the State of New York (aka New York Power Authority or NYPA) was established in 1931 by Gov. Franklin Roosevelt to gain public control of New York's hydropower resources. The utility's major power plants came on line with the opening of the St. Lawrence-Franklin D. Roosevelt Power Project (1958) and the Niagara Power Project (1961). The Blenheim-Gilboa Pumped Storage Power Project opened in 1973.

In the mid-1970s NYPA shifted to nuclear power when it opened the James A. FitzPatrick Nuclear Power Plant (1975) and the Indian Point 3 Nuclear Power Plant (1976). The company then opened gas- and oil-powered plants: the Charles Poletti Power Project (1977) and the Richard M. Flynn Power Plant (1994).

In 1998 the authority allocated low-cost electricity to five companies that planned to invest $104 million in business expansions in western New York. The company suffered a loss in 1999 in part from reduced hydro generation and a drop in investment earnings. In 2000 NYPA sold its two nuclear plants (1800 MW of capacity) to utility holding company Entergy for $967 million.

The company completed the installation of 11 gas-powered turbines at various locations in New York City and on Long Island in 2001; the program was initiated to prevent expected energy shortages that summer but it also helped maintain power in areas of the city during the September 11 terrorist attacks.

In 2013 The Village of Lake Placid unveiled a new hybrid-electric shuttle bus that will make commuting on public transportation quieter and cleaner. Financing for the bus was made possible through NYPA's Municipal Electric-Drive Vehicle Program which provides financial assistance to New York municipal utilities to facilitate the replacement of less fuel-efficient vehicles in order to advance the state's clean energy goals. That year

NYPA added seven more hybrids and one more EV to its fleet bringing the total number of electric drive vehicles to 79. It also purchased just over 40000 gallons of B20 biodiesel which earned the Power Authority 17 Alternative Fuel Vehicle credits under the Department of Energy's Energy Policy Act that will be used to purchase additional hybrid and plug-in hybrid vehicles.

EXECUTIVES

Coo, Edward A. (Ed) Welz
President And Ceo, Gil C. Quiniones
Evp And Cfo, Robert F. Lurie
Vice President Technical Compliance, Saul Rojas
Vice President Finance, Scott Tetenman
Vice President Shared Services, Ruth Colon
Senior Vice President Commercial Operations, Jill Anderson
Vice President And Chief Information Security Officer, Kenneth Carnes
Vp Of It, Gina Jackson
Chairman Board Of Trustees, John R. Koelmel
Vice Chair Board Of Trustees, Joanne M. Mahoney
Secretary To Procurement Office, Susan Vertone
Auditors: KPMG LLP NEW YORK NY

LOCATIONS

HQ: NEW YORK POWER AUTHORITY
123 MAIN ST, WHITE PLAINS, NY 106013104
Phone: 914 681-6200
Web: WWW.NYPA.GOV

PRODUCTS/OPERATIONS

2014 Sales

	$ mil.	% of total
Power sales	2,396	76
Wheeling charges	614	19
Transmission charges	165	5
Total	**3,175**	**100**

Selected Operations

Transmission Control Facility
  Frederick R. Clark Energy Center (Oneida County)
Fossil-Fueled Plants
  Charles Poletti Power Project (New York City)
  Richard M. Flynn Power Plant (Suffolk County)
  PowerNow! Turbines (11 units in New York City and Long Island)
Hydropower Plants
  Blenheim-Gilboa Pumped Storage Power Project (Schoharie County)
  Niagara Power Project (Niagara County)
  St. Lawrence-Franklin D. Roosevelt Power Project (St. Lawrence County)
Small Hydropower Plants
  Ashokan Project (Ulster County)
  Crescent Plant (Albany and Saratoga Counties)
  Gregory B. Jarvis Plant (Oneida County)
  Kensico Project (Westchester County)
  Vischer Ferry Plant (Saratoga and Schenectady counties)

COMPETITORS

Avangrid	National Grid USA
CH Energy	Rochester Gas and
Con Edison	Electric
Enbridge	TransCanada
Entergy	

HISTORICAL FINANCIALS

Company Type: Private

Income Statement				FYE: December 31
	REVENUE ($ mil.)	NET INCOME ($ mil.)	NET PROFIT MARGIN	EMPLOYEES
12/17	2,573	119	4.6%	2,237
12/16	2,421	22	0.9%	—
12/15	2,625	74	2.8%	—
12/14	3,175	272	8.6%	—
Annual Growth	(6.8%)	(24.1%)	—	—

NEW YORK PRESBYTERIAN HOSPITAL WEILL CORNELL UNIVERSITY MEDICAL CENTER

2017 Year-End Financials

Return on assets: 1.4%   Cash ($ mil.): 37
Return on equity: 2.5%
Current ratio: 1.60

EXECUTIVES

Prin, Lewis Drusin
Branch/Division/Department Hea, Janet Parisi
Project Leader, Dale Wright
Administrative Assistant, Lynn Reynolds
Administrator, David Weir
Administrator, Harry Sherman
Administrator, Suzan Toro
Research Scientist, Catherine Liu
Security Non Informa, Terre Paul
Vice President, Jolie Singer
Administrative Assistant, Andrea Rivas-Javier

LOCATIONS

HQ: NEW YORK PRESBYTERIAN HOSPITAL WEILL
CORNELL UNIVERSITY MEDICAL CENTER
525 E 68TH ST, NEW YORK, NY 100654870
Phone: 212 746-1754
Web: WWW.MED.CORNELL.EDU

HISTORICAL FINANCIALS

Company Type: Private

Income Statement				FYE: December 31
	REVENUE ($ mil.)	NET INCOME ($ mil.)	NET PROFIT MARGIN	EMPLOYEES
12/15	4,505	265	5.9%	5
12/12	75	21	28.2%	—
Annual Growth	290.4%	131.8%	—	—

2015 Year-End Financials

Return on assets: 3.9%   Cash ($ mil.): 227
Return on equity: 7.6%
Current ratio: 2.20

NEW YORK SOCIETY FOR THE RELIEF OF THE RUPTURED AND CRIPPLED, MAINTAINING THE HOSPITAL FOR

EXECUTIVES

Ceo, Louis Shapiro
Exec V Pres*, Lisa A Goldstein
Exec V Pres*, Stacey L Malakof
Cso*, Lionel B Ivashkiv
Cdo*, Catherine Callagy
Chief Scientific Officer, Steven Goldring
Assistant Administrative Direc, Susan Cardamone
Office Manager, Susan Ngeow
Secretary, Veronica Moran
Human Resources, Yolanda Abreau
Engineer, Andrew Kraszewski

LOCATIONS

HQ: NEW YORK SOCIETY FOR THE RELIEF OF THE
RUPTURED AND CRIPPLED, MAINTAINING THE
HOSPITAL FOR
535 E 70TH ST, NEW YORK, NY 100214823
Phone: 212 606-1000
Web: WWW.HSS.EDU

HISTORICAL FINANCIALS

Company Type: Private

Income Statement				FYE: December 31
	REVENUE ($ mil.)	NET INCOME ($ mil.)	NET PROFIT MARGIN	EMPLOYEES
12/18	1,219	119	9.8%	3,350
12/16	1,038	51	5.0%	—
12/15	811	79	9.8%	—
12/14	996	109	10.9%	—
Annual Growth	5.2%	2.3%	—	—

2018 Year-End Financials

Return on assets: 6.7%   Cash ($ mil.): 122
Return on equity: 11.1%
Current ratio: 4.00

NEW YORK STATE CATHOLIC HEALTH PLAN, INC.

Fidelis Care hopes for always faithful health plan members. The New York State Catholic Health Plan which does business as Fidelis Care serves more than 921000 residents in some 60 counties across the state including the New York City area. The church-sponsored plan's provider network includes more than 63000 physicians hospitals and other health care professionals and facilities. Fidelis Care provides managed Medicaid Medicare and state-sponsored family and children's Health Plus plans as well as long-term care and behavioral health coverage.

Operations

The company boasts an overall statewide member retention rate of more than 78% with a s Child Health Plus retention rate of more than 85%.

Geographic Reach

Fidelis Care's regional offices are located in Rego Park Queens (Greater Metropolitan); Albany (Northeast); Syracuse (Central); and Buffalo (Western) with satellite offices in Poughkeepsie Rochester and Suffern.

Sales and Marketing

The health plan has expanded its membership by seeking new low-income patients who lack coverage. In addition to direct sales efforts Fidelis Care tries to maintain a presence at health centers frequented by its target audience partnering with neighborhood clinics to hold free health screenings and Health Plus enrollment information sessions.

Enroll NY a new website sponsored by not-for-profit organization Hudson Center for Health Equity & Quality is also connecting Fidelis Care and other Medicaid providers with potential customers. In 2013 Fidelis Care began selling through the New York State of Health insurance exchange marketplace.

To bosst membership in 2013 the company ran the "I Want Fidelis Care' campaign (which promoted Fidelis Care as a health care resource) in English and Spanish. TV was added to the media buy in the New York City and Buffalo regions. It also established a social media presence on Facebook Twitter YouTube and Google+.

Financial Performance

Fidelis Care reported gross revenues of $4.1 billion in 2013 up from $3.3 billion in 2012.

Strategy

The company is expanding its office to keep up with demand. In 2014 it opened Ridgewood Community Office; in 2013 it completed of?ce expansion projects in the Albany and Syracuse regional of?ces and the satellite of?ce in Suffern and opened new community of?ces in Flushing (Queens) the Bronx and Bath (Steuben County).

Forecasting substantial growth in 2014 with the enrollment of more than 120000 new members the company announced plans to add more than 75 new information technology jobs at its Buffalo regional office.

In 2013 Fidelis Care moved into 12 new counties with the Medicare Advantage program highlighted by the opportunity to serve residents of western New York for the ?rst time. It also made plans to expand into Seneca Yates and Jefferson counties in 2014 and served additional Managed Long Term Care members as part of the State's phased-in expansion of mandatory enrollment in counties beyond New York City.

Fidelis Care has grown by expanding rapidly into new counties in New York including a number of growth measures in the Medicare marketplace during 2012 and 2013. The health plan's recent activity includes completing construction of Fidelis Care's new operations center and offices in Getzville (Erie County) and the launch of its new provider portal (Provider Access Online). Other growth measures include a 2012 partnership with DentaQuest to promote dental checkups; it also launched a new member portal for members to access benefit information. In 2013 the company gained approval to be a qualified health plan provider on the official New York State of Health marketplace.

Fidelis Care regularly evaluates and broadens its plan offerings. Recent additions include its Fidelis Care at Home managed long-term care offering; the behavioral health and developmental disabilities coverage options; and its fully integrated dual advantage plans (for consumers with both Medicare and Medicaid coverage).

Company Background

The church-sponsored plan was founded in 1993 by the bishops of New York's Roman Catholic dioceses and the Catholic Medical Center of Brooklyn and Queens.

EXECUTIVES

Vice President Network Dev, Pamela Wilkes
Vice President, Carey Shoemaker
Vice President Finance, Dina Soroka
Senior Vice President And Chief Admini, David Thomas
Director Of Government Relations, Colleen Wilson
Vice President, Brian Cummings
Vice President Of Infrastructure, Duncan Ross
Vice President Strategic Planning, James Burnosky
Nursing Director, Margaret Leonard
Vice President Of Information Technology, David Szabad
Medical Director, Camille Pearte
Vice President Product Development And Corporate Innovation Fidelis Care New, Jason Reiser
Assistant Vice President Contract Management, John Place
Senior Medical Secretary, Osvaldo Aquino
Auditors: LB DELOITTE TAX LLP JERICHO

LOCATIONS

HQ: NEW YORK STATE CATHOLIC HEALTH PLAN, INC.
9525 QUEENS BLVD, REGO PARK, NY 113744510
Phone: 888 343-3547
Web: WWW.FIDELISCARE.ORG

PRODUCTS/OPERATIONS

Selected Plans
Child Health Plus
Dual Advantage
Family Health Plus
Fidelis Care at Home (managed long-term care)
Medicaid Advantage Plus (managed long-term care)
Medicaid Managed Care
Medicare Advantage
New York State of Health

COMPETITORS

Aetna
Affinity Health
Anthem
CIGNA
Capital District Physicians' Health Plan
EmblemHealth
Health Net
HealthPlus Amerigroup
Healthfirst
Healthplex
Humana
Independent Health
Lifetime Healthcare
MVP Health Plan
UnitedHealth Group
Vytra Healthcare
healthnow new york inc

HISTORICAL FINANCIALS

Company Type: Private

Income Statement				FYE: December 31
	REVENUE ($ mil.)	NET INCOME ($ mil.)	NET PROFIT MARGIN	EMPLOYEES
12/14	5,304	271	5.1%	1,625
12/10	1,920	51	2.7%	—
12/09	1,435	27	1.9%	—
12/08	1,068	3	0.4%	—
Annual Growth	30.6%	103.1%	—	—

2014 Year-End Financials
Return on assets: 12.4%   Cash ($ mil.): 948
Return on equity: 22.3%
Current ratio: 9.10

NEW YORK STATE ENVIRONMENTAL FACILITIES CORP

EXECUTIVES

President, David Sterman
Accounting Assistant, Shelley Pascuzzi
Head of Environmental Sustaina, Bill Andrews
Auditors: UHY LLP ALBANY NEW YORK

LOCATIONS

HQ: NEW YORK STATE ENVIRONMENTAL FACILITIES CORP
625 BROADWAY, ALBANY, NY 122072942
Phone: 518 486-9267

HISTORICAL FINANCIALS

Company Type: Private

Income Statement				FYE: March 31
	REVENUE ($ mil.)	NET INCOME ($ mil.)	NET PROFIT MARGIN	EMPLOYEES
03/07	528	181	34.4%	10
03/06	498	149	29.9%	—
Annual Growth	6.1%	21.8%	—	—

2007 Year-End Financials
Return on assets: 1.6%   Cash ($ mil.): 23
Return on equity: 4.3%
Current ratio: 2.30

NEW YORK STATE HOUSING FINANCE AGENCY

EXECUTIVES

Pres-Ceo, Stephen J Hunt
Chb*, Judd S Levy
Sr V Pres*, Ralph J Madalena
Sr V Pres*, Bernard H Abramowitz
Sr V Pres*, Robert M Drillings
Sr V Pres*, James Angley
Senior Asset Manager, Roger Harry
Vice President of Information, Jose Dilan
Account Executive, Faith Brenner
Accounts Payable, Patricia Zito-Volynets
Senior Channel Sales Manager, Akello Ragwar
Auditors: DELOITTE & TOUCHE LLP NEW YOR

LOCATIONS

HQ: NEW YORK STATE HOUSING FINANCE AGENCY
641 LEXINGTON AVE FL 4, NEW YORK, NY 100224503
Phone: 212 688-4069
Web: WWW.NYSHCR.ORG

HISTORICAL FINANCIALS

Company Type: Private

Income Statement				FYE: October 31
	REVENUE ($ mil.)	NET INCOME ($ mil.)	NET PROFIT MARGIN	EMPLOYEES
10/18	553	187	33.9%	131
10/17	400	112	28.0%	—
10/16	279	77	27.7%	—
10/09	182	(31)	—	—
Annual Growth	13.1%	—	—	—

2018 Year-End Financials
Return on assets: 1.0%   Cash ($ mil.): 36
Return on equity: 17.5%
Current ratio: 1.70

NEW YORK UNIVERSITY

Higher education is at the core of this Big Apple institution. The setting and heritage of New York University (NYU) make it one of the nation's most popular educational institutions. With more thanÂ 50000 students attending its 18 schools and colleges NYU is among the largest private schools in the US. Its Tisch School of the Arts is well-regarded and its law school and Leonard N. Stern School of Business are among theÂ foremost in the country. NYU occupies five major centers in Manhattan; its Washington Square campus is in the heart of Greenwich Village. The school wasÂ founded in 1831. Notable alumni include former Federal Reserve Chairman Alan Greenspan and film producer Oliver Stone.

Operations

NYU reports its financials in two segments — University and NYU Langone Health. The latter segment is composed of the NYU Langone Health System and NYU School of Medicine.

The University includes nearly 20 colleges and divisions including schools of art and sciences law dentistry business mathematical sciences fine arts professional studies public services social work and engineering. NYU also operates NYU Abu Dhabi and NYU Shanghai a joint venture with East China Normal University. The University segment accounts for some 30% of NYU's total revenue.

NYU Langone Health operates two hospitals Kimmel Pavilion and Tisch Hospital which together have some 850 beds. It also operates the 225-bed NYU Langone Orthopedic Hospital the 450-bed NYU Langone Hospital in Brooklyn and several ambulatory care facilities. The segment brings in some 70% of NYU's total revenue.

NYU alumni and faculty boast several prestigious awards including more than a dozen Nobel and Crafoord prizes and another four Pulitzer prizes.

Geographic Reach

Along with its campuses in New York NYU operates degree-granting campuses in Abu Dhabi and Shanghai. It also has more than 10 global academic centers in Africa Asia Europe and the Americas and research programs in more than 25 countries.

Financial Performance

In fiscal 2018 (ended August) NYU's operating revenue increased 17% to $11.6 billion. Driving that gain was an increase in patient care revenue which rose from $5.6 billion to $7 billion that year.

However the university's excess of operating revenue over expenses fell dramatically from $196.8 million to $11.2 million in fiscal 2018. Salaries and medical and pharmaceutical costs rose as did facilities expenses professional services expenses and all other expenses.

NYU ended fiscal 2018 with $1.5 billion in net cash some $217 million more than what it had at the end of 2017. Operating activities provided $941.1 million in net cash financing activities provided another $580.4 million while investing activities used $1.3 billion.

Strategy

In 2018 NYU School of Medicine offered all students full tuition scholarships regardless of merit or financial need. The move was largely designed to promote the training of primary care physicians which is an area of great need in the US. By removing the heavy debt load that medical students typically face the school hopes to encourage students to pursue careers in lower-paying areas such as primary care.

Later that year NYU announced plans to establish a new medical school on Long Island. That campus will also provide full tuition scholarships to students.

HISTORY

New York University was founded by several prominent New Yorkers in 1831. The school held its first classes the following year in rented rooms on the corner of Beekman and Nassau streets then moved to a building in Washington Square in 1835. It established its law school that year. NYU started its school of medicine in 1841 followed by the school of engineering and science (1854). Postgraduate studies in arts and science (its first coeducational program) began in 1886.

NYU's enrollment jumped from fewer than 2000 in 1900 to 28000 in 1930. After a lull during the Depression and WWII the campus boomed again in the postwar years. During the 1950s the university began focusing on improving academics rather than on increasing enrollment. It created a school of the arts in 1965 and in the early 1970s it completed the Elmer Holmes Bobst Library. However a cash crunch during that decade almost forced the school into bankruptcy.

President Jay Oliva took the reins in 1981 and focused on transforming NYU from a largely commuter college into a global university. The school began a campaign to raise $1 billion in 1984 but earmarked the funds for campus improvements rather than swelling its endowment. During the late 1980s NYU opened several new dormitories and conference spaces. In 1994 British historian and collector Sir Harold Acton bequeathed to the school his Tuscany estate — five art-filled villas overlooking Florence Italy.

In 1996 NYU's Medical Center began talks with Mount Sinai Medical Center aimed at merging their hospitals and medical schools. The talks fell apart in early 1997 but the following year the two sides agreed to merge hospitals and keep their medical schools distinct. Also in 1998 NYU formed NYU On-Line Inc. a for-profit subsidiary to develop and sell specialized Internet courses to other schools training centers and students; the venture was subsequently folded in late 2001. During 1999 contributions to the school approached $250 million. That year however two upper-level school officials were fired following allegations of improper use of university money.

Oliva retired as president in 2002 and was replaced by John Sexton former School of Law dean. In 2004 Sexton announced that NYU would give $1 million to New York City towards renovation of Washington Square Park (the school annually gives some $200000 for the park's ongoing maintenance).

EXECUTIVES

Vp Academic And Health Affairs, Robert (Bob) Berne

Vp Information Technology And Chief Information Technology Officer, Marilyn A. McMillan

Provost, David W. McLaughlin

Evp Finance And Information Technology, Martin S. Dorph

Director Global Institute Of Public Health; Dean Of Global Public Health, Cheryl G. Healton

Dean Libraries, Carol A. Mandel

Herman Robert Fox Dean College Of Dentistry, Charles N. Bertolami

Evp Operations, Alison Leary

Director Institute For The Study Of The Ancient World, Roger Bagnall

Director Courant Institute Of Mathematical Sciences, Gérard Ben Arous

Saul J. Farber Dean Nyu School Of Medicine; Ceo Nyu Hospitals Center, Robert I. Grossman

Dean Gallatin School Of Individualized Study, Susanne L. Wofford

Dean Polytechnic School Of Engineering, Katepalli R. (Sreeni) Sreenivasan

Dean Silver School Of Social Work, Lynn Videka

Dean Liberal Studies, Fred Schwarzbach

Judy And Michael Steinhardt Director Institute Of Fine Arts, Patricia Lee Rubin

Dean Leonard N. Stern School Of Business, Peter B. Henry, age 49

Vice Chancellor New York University Abu Dhabi, Alfred H. Bloom

Vp Global Technology And Chief Global Technology Officer, Thomas A. (Tom) Delaney

Dean For Science Faculty Of Arts And Science, Michael D. Purugganan

President, Andrew Hamilton

Gale And Ira Drukier Dean Steinhardt School For Culture Education And Human Development, Dominic Brewer

Anne And Joel Ehrenkranz Dean Faculty Of Arts And Sciences, Thomas J. Carew

Dean For Humanities Faculty Of Arts And Sciences, Joy Connolly

Harvey J. Stedman Dean School Of Professional Studies, Dennis DiLorenzo

Dean Robert F. Wagner Graduate School Of Public Service, Sherry A. Glied

Dean Tisch School Of The Arts, Allyson Green

Dean For Social Sciences Faculty Of Arts And Science, Michael Laver

Vice Chancellor Nyu Shanghai, Jeffrey S. Lehman

Dean Undergraduate College Leonard N. Stern School Of Business, Geeta Menon

Dean School Of Law, Trevor Morrison

Director Marron Institute Of Urban Management, Paul Romer

Seryl Kushner Dean College Of Arts And Science, G. Gabrielle Starr

Dean College Of Nursing, Eileen Sullivan-Marx

Chancellor Nyu Shanghai, Yu Lizhong

Interim Dean Graduate School Of Arts And Science, Anna L. Harvey

Assistant Vice President, Zoe Ragouzeos

Vice President, Marc Wais

Vice Provost, Carol Morrow

Associate Vice President Student Health, Carlo Ciotoli

Vice President Financial Operations And Treasurer, Stephanie Pianka

Assistant Vice President Employee Relations, Barbara Cardeli-Arroyo

Vice President Finance, Harold T Read

Associate Vice President, Deborah Broderick

Assistant Vice President, Allen Mcfarlane

Vice President, Andrew Gordon

Vice President Of Public Relations, Carolynn Choi

Associate Vice President For Stewardship And Events, Gustave Fleury

Medical Director, Marcy Ferdschneider

Chair Department Of Anthropology, Fred Myers

Associate Vice President Campus Planning And Design, Lori Mazor

Vice President Chief Information Security Officer, Mehdi Idrissi

Assistant Vice President Auxiliary Services, Paul Glimcher

Assistant Vice President, Janet Alperstein

Vice President Human Resources, Robert White

Vice President For Budget And Planning, Anthony Jiga

Nursing Director, Mary Gribbin

Director Of Government Relations, Steve Heuer

Vice President For Enrollment Management, Mj Knoll-finn

Vice President For, Robert Campbell

Vice President Human Resources, Sabrina Ellis

Associate Vice President For Global Technologies, Heather Stewart

Vice President Finance, Pamela Morris

Vice President, Robert Levine

Executive Vice President, Tom Jordan

Executive Vice President Research And Innovation Cross Platform, Lisa Sokolov

Vice President And Special Counsel, Leo L Goldsmith

Vice President, Victoria M Mccoy-cosentino

Vice President Director Engineering, Chris Pak

Vice President Global Security And Crisis Management, Jules Martin

Assistant Vice President External Affairs And Protective Services, Carl Barchus

Vice President, Pallavi Sambasivan

Vice President Finance And Administration, Charice Washington-warner

Vice President Sales, Joe Harris

Vice President Council, John Plecnik

Vice President And Manager Raines Perspectives Raines International, Jessica Deoliveira

Senior Vice President Deputy General Counsel Chief Compliance And Ethics Officer, Genie Gavenchak

Senior Vice President And Deputy General Counsel, Lawrence Bunder

Vice President For Operations Capital Projects, Andy Buonpastore

Vice President, Shaila Dani

Vice President For Capital Projects And Facilities, Linda Chiarelli

Executive Vice President, Mandy Hu

Vice President Facilities Management, Debra Berger

Chairman Board Of Trustees, William R. (Bill) Berkley, age 73

Board Director, Christine Trump

Vice Chair President, Peter Romain

Honorary Board Member, John Tintori

Assistant Treasurer, Elisa Cohen

Medical Secretary, Latia Davis

Secretary, Candice Jarvis

Secretary, Jennifer Neuman

Ward Secretary, Mark Brennan

Ms Global Affairs Candidate Treasurer Energy Policy International Club, Jude Buenaseda

Secretary, Lara Maraziti

Treasurer, Daphne Tso

Secretary, Lewis R Steinberg

Secretary Athletic Development, Raffaela Ianniciello

Secretary And Marketing, August Morar

Secretary I, Kelrick Drake
Secretary, Beverly Wideman
Cab Treasurer, Erin Adams
Secretary, Andy Le
College Of Arts And Sciences History Society
 Treasurer, Samantha Noell
Auditors: PRICEWATERHOUSECOOPERS LLP NE

LOCATIONS

HQ: NEW YORK UNIVERSITY
 70 WASHINGTON SQ S, NEW YORK, NY 100121019
Phone: 212 998-1212

PRODUCTS/OPERATIONS

2018 Sales

	$ mil.	% of total
Patient care	6,981	60
Tuition & fees	1,852	16
Grants & contracts	1,011	9
Auxiliary enterprises	505	4
Hospital affiliations	342	3
Endowment distribution	169	2
Contributions	168	2
Net assets from restrictions	121	1
Insurance premiums earned	115	1
Return on short-term investments	16	-
Programs & other	272	2
Total	**11,556**	**100**

2018 Sales

	$ mil.	% of total
NYU Langone Health	8,298	72
University	3,267	28
Adjustments	(10.3)	-
Total	**11,556**	**100**

Selected Schools and Colleges

College of Arts and Science (founded 1832)
College of Dentistry (1865)
Courant Institute of Mathematical Sciences (1934)
Gallatin School of Individualized Study (1972)
Graduate School of Arts and Science (1886)
Leonard N. Stern School of Business (1900)
Robert F. Wagner Graduate School of Public Service
 (1938)
School of Continuing and Professional Studies (1934)
School of Law (1835)
School of Medicine (1841)
School of Social Work (1960)
Steinhardt School of Culture Education and Human
 Development (1890)
Tisch School of the Arts (1965)

HISTORICAL FINANCIALS
Company Type: Private

Income Statement				FYE: August 31
	REVENUE ($ mil.)	NET INCOME ($ mil.)	NET PROFIT MARGIN	EMPLOYEES
08/16	8,500	177	2.1%	21,000
08/11	5,172	563	10.9%	—
08/06	2,148	195	9.1%	—
Annual Growth	14.7%	(1.0%)	—	—

2016 Year-End Financials
Return on assets: 1.1%   Cash ($ mil.): 1,033
Return on equity: 2.4%
Current ratio: —

NEW YORK UNIVERSITY

EXECUTIVES

Pres, John Sexton
Proj Dir*, Yamilee Bazile
Assistant Professor, Satarupa Dasgupta
Teacher, Stephen Karpiak
Assistant Professor, Cristina Vatulescu
General Practitioner, Emanuela Corielli
General Practitioner, Steven David
Adjunct Instructor, William Hewitt
Associate Professor of Account, Mary Billings
Assistant Training Specialist, Yolanda Fordham
Adjunct Assistant Professor, Alan Barnett
Auditors: PRICEWATERHOUSECOOPERS LLP NE

LOCATIONS

HQ: NEW YORK UNIVERSITY
 433 1ST AVE RM 619, NEW YORK, NY 100104067
Phone: 212 998-5813
Web: WWW.HEARTBREAKDREAMS.COM

HISTORICAL FINANCIALS
Company Type: Private

Income Statement				FYE: August 31
	REVENUE ($ mil.)	NET INCOME ($ mil.)	NET PROFIT MARGIN	EMPLOYEES
08/12	4,016	53	1.3%	30
08/10	3,376	149	4.4%	—
08/09	2,970	(172)	—	—
Annual Growth	10.6%	—	—	—

2012 Year-End Financials
Return on assets: 0.7%   Cash ($ mil.): 982
Return on equity: 1.4%
Current ratio: 0.70

NEW YORK-PRESBYTERIAN FUND INC

EXECUTIVES

Ceo, Phyllis Lantos
Auditors: ERNST & YOUNG US LLP NEW YO

LOCATIONS

HQ: NEW YORK-PRESBYTERIAN FUND INC
 525 E 68TH ST, NEW YORK, NY 100654870
Phone: 212 297-4356

HISTORICAL FINANCIALS
Company Type: Private

Income Statement				FYE: December 31
	REVENUE ($ mil.)	NET INCOME ($ mil.)	NET PROFIT MARGIN	EMPLOYEES
12/17	504	286	56.9%	4
12/09	391	217	55.5%	—
Annual Growth	3.2%	3.5%	—	—

2017 Year-End Financials
Return on assets: 9.9%   Cash ($ mil.): 142
Return on equity: 10.0%
Current ratio: 137.90

NEWARK BETH ISRAEL MEDICAL CENTER INC.

Part of the Saint Barnabas Health Care System Newark Beth Israel Medical Center is a 670-bed acute-care regional referral hospital. The facility servesÂ residents of Newark and surrounding areas in northern New Jersey. The hospital offers services including primary diagnostic emergency surgical and rehabilitative care. It is home to specialized programs such as kidney transplantation cancer care dentistry sleep disordersÂ geriatrics and women's health services. Newark Beth Israel Medical Center also houses the Children's Hospital of New Jersey and the Saint Barnabas Heart Center. The research and teaching hospital has a medical staff of more than 800 physicians.

Operations

Newark Beth Israel Medical Center along with sister hospital Saint Barnabas Medical CenterÂ has a teaching and research affiliation with the New Jersey Medical School (part of the University of Medicine and Dentistry of New Jersey). The hospital also has training programs with other regional schools.

Newark Beth Israel Medical Center handles about 25000 inpatient visits annually while the hospital's outpatient centers see some 300000 patients each year.

EXECUTIVES

Medical Director Cardiologist, Chunguang Chen
Medical Director Center For Asian Health, Su
 Wang
Vice President For Development, Richard J
 Pallamary
Senior Vice President Internal Audit, Anthony
 Palmerio
Senior Vice President Financial Advisor Ubs
 Financial Services, Gil Blitz
Executive Vice President Chief Development
 Officer, Glenn Miller
Executive Vice President Chief Medical And
 Quality Officer, John F Bonamoe
Executive Vice President Office Of Health Care
 Transformation, Joseph Scott
Senior Vice President Business Development,
 Matthew Fulton
Senior Vice President Strategic Marketing And
 Communications, Michael E Knecht
Secretary President Imperial Consultants Inc.,
 Lee Livingston
Auditors: WITHUMSMITHBROWN PC
 MORRISTOW

LOCATIONS

HQ: NEWARK BETH ISRAEL MEDICAL CENTER INC.
 201 LYONS AVE, NEWARK, NJ 071122027
Phone: 973 926-7000
Web: WWW.RWJBH.ORG

PRODUCTS/OPERATIONS

Selected Departments and Centers
Barnabas Health Heart Center
Center for Geriatric Health Care
Center for Women's Health
Children's Hospital of New Jersey
Cohen Comprehensive Cancer and Blood Disorder
 Center
Lung Center
Pacemaker and Defibrillator Center
Palliative Care Program
Regional Perinatal Center
Radiology
Robotic Surgery Center
Renal Transplantation

Sleep Disorders Center

COMPETITORS

AtlantiCare
Atlantic Health
Bergen Regional Medical
CentraState Healthcare System
Children's Specialized Hospital
Chilton Medical Center
East Orange General Hospital
Englewood Hospital and Medical Center
Hackensack Meridian Health
Hackensack University Medical Center
Newton Medical Center
Robert Wood Johnson University Hospital
Robert Wood Johnson University Hospital at Rahway
St. Joseph's Healthcare System
The Valley Hospital
Virtua Health
Winthrop-University Hospital

HISTORICAL FINANCIALS
Company Type: Private

Income Statement				FYE: December 31
	REVENUE ($ mil.)	NET INCOME ($ mil.)	NET PROFIT MARGIN	EMPLOYEES
12/18	645	19	3.1%	3,000
12/17	545	35	6.5%	—
12/16	539	27	5.2%	—
12/15	542	38	7.1%	—
Annual Growth	6.0%	(19.8%)	—	—

2018 Year-End Financials
Return on assets: 3.8%
Return on equity: 9.6%
Current ratio: 4.00
Cash ($ mil.): —

NEWARK CORPORATION

Newark offers all sorts of electronic goods in one place and in places all across the Americas. The company doing business as Newark element14 distributes some 4.4 million electronic components and supplies including semiconductors passive devices electrical equipment connectors wire and cable optoelectronics test and measurement instruments and tools. It is also a source for companies needing parts compliant with the Restrictions of Hazardous Substances order in the European Union. Customers are electronics design engineers maintenance technicians and other electronics buyers. Newark element14 is a subsidiary of Premier Farnell a top UK electronic and industrial parts supplier.

Operations
Newark element14 also offers such services as re-calibration custom panel meters and cable assemblies and re-reeling as well as procurement and stockroom services.

The company stocks more than 500 brands from companies the likes of Analog Devices AVX Cypress Semiconductor Freescale Microchip and Texas Instruments.

Geographic Reach
The company operates in North America.

Sales and Marketing
Like its parent Newark element14 maximizes the Internet for selling and customer service purposes with a growing emphasis on electronics design engineering (EDE). Newark element14's EDE customers can access a website that offers collaborative design tools; the company also maintains a dedicated website just for US federal government customers. In addition to its websites Newark element14 operates a customer contact center has a dedicated sales force and offers a print catalog of its products.

Strategy
As part of its business Newark element14 regularly rolls out new products through partnerships with other companies. In 2014 for instance it launched the MagniV S12ZVML-MINIBRD variable-speed motor-control development kit alongside Freescale as well as the Tektronix TBS1000B Series digital storage oscilloscopes. Newark element14 also introduced three new Fluke Thermal Image cameras to its test and measurement portfolio to help boost a technician's productivity while in the field.

Expanding its distribution agreements also keeps Newark element14 growing. In 2014 the company became an authorized distributor of Wurth Electronics items. Wurth specializes in components circuit boards and intelligent systems.

Company Background
Newark was originally established in 1934 as Newark Electric Company a supplier of radio parts — the name of the Chicago-based company's way of recognizing Newark New Jersey as the home of the the first radio station in the US. Newark Electric first published a catalog of parts in 1948. The company went public in 1960 on the American Stock Exchange (now NYSE MKT) changing its name to Newark Electronics Corporation. In 1968 the company was acquired by Premier Industrial Corporation a Cleveland-based distributor. Premier Industrial merged in 1996 with Farnell Electronics plc to become Premier Farnell. Newark and element14 (another Premier Farnell company) combined in 2011 to create Newark element14.

EXECUTIVES
Vice President Of Marketing Services, David Macaluso

LOCATIONS
HQ: NEWARK CORPORATION
300 S RIVERSIDE PLZ # 2200, CHICAGO, IL 606066765
Phone: 773 784-5100
Web: WWW.PREMIERFARNELL.COM

PRODUCTS/OPERATIONS

Selected Product Categories
Automation and process control
Batteries and chargers
Cable wire and assemblies
Chemicals and adhesives
Circuit protection
Connectors
Crystals and oscillators
Electrical
Enclosures racks and cabinets
Fans heat sinks and HVAC
Fasteners and mechanical
LED technologies
Office and computer
Optoelectronics and displays
Passive components
Power and line protection
Security and audio visual
Semiconductors
Sensors and transducers
Static control and site safety
Switches and relays
Test measurement and inspection
Tools and production supplies
Transformers

COMPETITORS

Arrow Electronics	Future Electronics
Avnet	Rexel Inc.
Davis Instruments	Trek Equipment
EACO	

HISTORICAL FINANCIALS
Company Type: Private

Income Statement				FYE: February 1
	REVENUE ($ mil.)	NET INCOME ($ mil.)	NET PROFIT MARGIN	EMPLOYEES
02/15	543	24	4.5%	834
02/14	541	23	4.4%	—
02/13	580	20	3.5%	—
Annual Growth	(3.2%)	9.6%	—	—

NEWARK ELECTRONICS CORPORATION

EXECUTIVES
Pres, Dan Hill
V Pres, Steven Webb
V Pres-Gen Counsel & SEC, Jospeh R Daprile
Treas & Asst SEC, Paul M Barlak
V Pres, Thomas Mayfield
Sr V Pres, Susan Fischer
Outside Acct Mgr, Brenda Scarbrough

LOCATIONS
HQ: NEWARK ELECTRONICS CORPORATION
300 S RIVERSIDE PLZ, CHICAGO, IL 606066613
Phone: 773 784-5100

HISTORICAL FINANCIALS
Company Type: Private

Income Statement				FYE: January 31
	REVENUE ($ mil.)	NET INCOME ($ mil.)	NET PROFIT MARGIN	EMPLOYEES
01/16*	525	8	1.7%	834
02/15	543	24	4.5%	—
02/14	541	23	4.4%	—
02/13	580	20	3.5%	—
Annual Growth	(3.3%)	(23.9%)	—	—
*Fiscal year change

2016 Year-End Financials
Return on assets: 3.8%
Return on equity: 5.4%
Current ratio: 5.80
Cash ($ mil.): 17

NEWMARK & COMPANY REAL ESTATE, INC.

Whether you're talking cubicle cities or corner offices Newmark & Company Real Estate (dba Newmark Knight Frank or NKF) makes its mark on commercial real estate. As one of the world's top commercial real estate advisory firms it provides property brokerage development and management services to investors corporations and property owners. Newmark also offers facility management services overseeing a portfolio of properties across the globe. Together with its London-based partner Knight Frank NKF operates more than 370 offices across six continents. NKF comprises parent company BGC Partners' Real Estate Services segment which made up 40% of the parent company's total revenue in 2014.

Operations

NKF manages a broad range of properties including headquarters facilities and office space for a wide range of companies. It manages the day-to-day operations and maintenance for urban and suburban commercial properties of most types including office industrial data centers healthcare retail call centers urban towers suburban campuses and landmark buildings.

Property management services include building operations and maintenance leasing vendor and contract negotiation project oversight and value engineering labor relations property inspection/quality control property accounting and financial reporting cash flow analysis financial modeling lease administration due diligence and exit strategies. Newmark's facilities management services also include facility audits and reviews energy management services janitorial services mechanical services bill payment maintenance project management and moving management.

Its affiliates include Cantor Fitzgerald CCRE-Cantor Commercial Real Estate and Cantor Gaming.

Sales and Marketing

NKF serves clients across more than half a dozen sectors including advertising and marketing education healthcare media and entertainment financial services law firms real estate retail and food services and technology and telecom sectors. It counts several big names among its list of clients including AEG Live Apollo Global Management Deutsch CBS Corporation Cornell University and AmTrust Realty Corporation.

Financial Performance

As the Real Estate Services segment of BGC Partners Newmark Knight Frank's revenue jumped 23% to $708.8 million during 2014 thanks to its acquisition of Cornish & Carey stronger broker productivity and favorable trends in sales and leasing in the US commercial real estate market.

Strategy

The company is growing its business by adding new brokers making technological improvements and cultivating the company's relationships with clients in the US and abroad. It has also been growing its geographic reach and business lines by acquiring smaller real estate firms.

Mergers and Acquisitions

In January 2016 NKF bought Memphis-based Steffner Commercial Real Estate which was the "cornerstone" in NKF's plan to grow across the Mid-South region of Tennessee Kentucky Mississippi Alabama Arkansas and Louisiana.

December 2015 the real estate firm boosted its presence in the Midwest after it purchased Cincinnati Commercial Real Estate (CCR) which leases and invests in offices industrial facilities and retail space. The acquisition also added CCR's diversified client base of top Fortune 500 companies institutions and privately owned firms while also supporting growth opportunities for NKF's existing Ohio business in Cleveland and Columbus.

In August 2014 the company bought Cornish & Carey Commercial Inc. the leading full-service commercial real estate services company in the San Francisco Bay area and Silicon Valley. The company believes that this is a key strategic addition for Newmark in the key Northern California market.

In early 2013 it acquired commercial real estate developer Frederick Ross and brokerage Smith Mack.

EXECUTIVES

Managing Principal San Francisco, Michael Brown
Vice President, Alphie Toro
Vice President Director Of Operations, Bart McDade
First Vice President, Paul Graham
Senior Vice President Global Management Services, Joseph Murtha
Sr Vp Newmark Grubb, Doug Schuster

LOCATIONS

HQ: NEWMARK & COMPANY REAL ESTATE, INC.
125 PARK AVE, NEW YORK, NY 100175529
Phone: 212 372-2000
Web: WWW.NGKF.COM

Selected Locations
North America
  US
  Canada
  Mexico
Europe
Asia-Pacific
Africa
Middle East

PRODUCTS/OPERATIONS

Selected Services
Leasing Advisory
Global Corporate Services
Investment Sales and Capital Markets
Retail
Industrial
Consulting
Program and Project Management
Facilities Management
Property Management
Landauer Valuation & Advisory
Residential Construction Services
Specialty Practice Groups
  Data Center Consulting
  Global Gaming Group
  Global Healthcare
  Government
  Hotels
  Law Firm Advisory
  Loan Sale Advisory
  Multi-Housing Group
  Not-For-Profit Advisory
  Retail Occupier Services
  Self Storage Group

COMPETITORS

Breslin Realty Development Corp.	Eastdil Secured
CBRE Group	Greiner-Maltz
Colliers International	Jones Lang LaSalle
Cushman & Wakefield	Lend Lease
	Lincoln Property

HISTORICAL FINANCIALS

Company Type: Private

Income Statement   FYE: December 31

	ASSETS ($ mil.)	NET INCOME ($ mil.)	INCOME AS % OF ASSETS	EMPLOYEES
12/16	860	53	6.3%	2,250
12/15	694	139	20.1%	—
12/14	234	0	—	—
Annual Growth	**91.7%**	—	—	—

2016 Year-End Financials

Return on assets: 6.3%   Sales ($ mil): 1,058
Return on equity: 10.2%

NEWPORT CORPORATION

Newport helps all sorts of customers take a measured approach. The company makes lasers precision components and automated assembly measurement and test equipment. It makes products that are used around the world in such fields as fiber-optic communications health care life sciences military/aerospace scientific research and semiconductor manufacturing. Industrial and scientific components include lenses and other devices for vibration and motion control. Newport also offers automated systems used to make fiber-optic components and photonics. More than 60% of sales come from outside the US. In 2016 Newport was acquired by MKS Instruments.

Change in Company Type

With the acquisition Newport became a part of MKS. The companies expect $1.4 billion combined annual revenue. The $905 million price covered Newport's shares and about $93 million debt. The deal brings together companies with products in adjacent markets. They plan to cross-sell to each others' markets as well as to develop offerings for new customers.

Geographic Reach

Newport operates manufacturing plants stateside and abroad. US plants are located in California Connecticut Massachusetts Montana New York and Utah. Internationally its plants are located in developed and emerging markets in Austria China France Germany Israel and Romania.

The US is its largest single market accounting for about 38% of sales. Europe and Asia each are responsible for about a quarter of sales.

Sales and Marketing

Newport uses a direct sales force as well as an international network of independent distributors and sales representatives. It also uses e-commerce. Customers include OEMs and capital equipment makers.

Financial Performance

Sales for 2015 (ended January 2016) dropped 4% to $603 million from 2014. Photonics its biggest revenue generated managed a 1.5% revenue increase but Lasers and Optics both had less revenue in 2015. In terms of markets both microelectronics and life and health sciences sales were lower in 2015 while scientific research sales rose.

Newport's profit dropped 11% to $31 million in 2015 from 2014. While administrative and R&D costs were lower in 2015 the company recognized losses in selling a facility and software applications it no longer uses. The cost of eliminating some debt also reduced its profit.

Cash flow generated from operations was $52 million in 2015 down from $58 million in 2014.

Strategy

Newport has made several acquisitions to help it shift from a provider of research instruments to one that manufactures both components and integrated systems for research and commercial applications. The company's brands now consist of ILX Lightwave New Focus Newport Ophir Optimet Oriel Instruments Richardson Gratings Spiricon and Spectra-Physics.

The company also divests businesses that are not considered part of its core operations. In late 2013 it announced plans to sell its Micro Robotics Systems advanced packaging business (MRSI) to a private investment group. MRSI makes turn-key die bonding and dispensing systems while Newport is focused on lasers optics and photonics technologies.

EXECUTIVES

President Ceo And Director, Robert J. Phillippy, $529,000 total compensation
Svp Cfo And Treasurer, Charles F. (Chuck) Cargile, $377,577 total compensation
Svp And General Manager Lasers Group, David J. Allen, $300,192 total compensation
Vp Precision Components And Systems Business Photonics And Precision Technologies Division, Dennis L. Werth, $310,192 total compensation
Vp Asia Pacific, Wilson W. Lin
Evp General Counsel Corporate Secretary, Andrew Powell
Vice President Nasso Sales, Jeff Parker
Chairman, Kenneth F. Potashner
Auditors: DELOITTE & TOUCHE LLP COSTA M

LOCATIONS

HQ: NEWPORT CORPORATION
  1791 DEERE AVE, IRVINE, CA 926064814
Phone: 949 863-3144
Web: WWW.NEWPORT.COM

2016 Sales

	$ mil.	% of total
US	231	38
Asia	170	28
Europe	157	26
Other regions	44	8
Total	**602**	**100**

PRODUCTS/OPERATIONS

2016 Sales

	$ mil.	% of total
Photonics & precision technologies	249	41
Lasers	192	32
Optics	160	27
Total	**602**	**100**

COMPETITORS

Adept Technology	Manz
Agilent Technologies	Nikon
Allied Motion	Nordson
Technologies	Oclaro
Anritsu	Palomar Technologies
Carl Zeiss	Parker-Hannifin
Coherent Inc.	Renishaw
Corning	Rockwell Automation
Danaher	Roper Technologies
EXFO	Spectris
HORIBA	TRUMPF
II-VI	Thermo Fisher
IPG Photonics	Scientific
Jenoptik	Viavi Solutions
Kinetic Systems	Zygo

HISTORICAL FINANCIALS

Company Type: Private

Income Statement   FYE: January 3

	REVENUE ($ mil.)	NET INCOME ($ mil.)	NET PROFIT MARGIN	EMPLOYEES
01/15*	605	35	5.8%	2,480
12/13	560	15	2.8%	—
12/12	595	(89)	—	—
Annual Growth	0.8%	—	—	—

*Fiscal year change

2015 Year-End Financials

Return on assets: 6.1%   Cash ($ mil.): 46
Return on equity: 9.9%
Current ratio: 2.90

NEWYORK-PRESBYTERIAN/BROOKLYN METHODIST

New York Methodist Hospital is a not-for-profit acute-care teaching hospital serving Brooklyn residents. Established in 1881 as the Methodist Episcopal Hospital the facility has more than 650 licensed beds. It offers a full range of medical services including primary and emergency care as well as specialty services such as women's health cancer cardiovascular pediatric geriatric and behavioral health. The hospital also operates satellite clinics in surrounding areas. A member of New York-Presbyterian Healthcare System New York Methodist is a teaching hospital affiliated with Cornell University's Weill Medical College.

Operations
New York Methodist Hospital handles about 40000 inpatient admissions and 100000 emergency department visits each year as well as 24000 surgeries and 5000 births. It also processes about 200000 laboratory sample processes annually.

New York Methodist Hospital includes specialty institutes in about 10 fields including pulmonary medicine cancer care and vascular health. In addition to providing inpatient care the organization operates some 10 primary and specialty outpatient centers. It also runs a number of graduate medical programs including programs affiliated with professional training schools in the areas of radiography medical technology radiation therapy and paramedics.

Geographic Reach
New York Methodist Hospital's main campus is in the Park Slope neighborhood of Brooklyn. It has several outpatient centers in other parts of Brooklyn as well.

Strategy
To expand care for area residents New York Methodist is adding new specialist programs and equipment. For instance in 2012 the hospital added a robotic-assisted surgery program for bariatric procedures. It also opened a new wound care and hyperbaric oxygen therapy center for hard-to-heal wounds. In addition in 2013 the hospital moved its sleep disorder center into a new facility.

EXECUTIVES

Senior Vice President, Lauren Yedvab
Auditors: ERNST & YOUNG LLP NEW YORK N

LOCATIONS

HQ: NEWYORK-PRESBYTERIAN/BROOKLYN METHODIST
  506 6TH ST, BROOKLYN, NY 112153609
Phone: 718 780-3000

COMPETITORS

Beth Israel Medical Center	Lutheran HealthCare
Bronx-Lebanon Hospital	Maimonides Medical Center
Brookdale University Hospital	New York City Health and Hospitals
Catholic Healthcare System	Northwell Health
Kingsbrook Jewish Medical Center	SUNY Downstate
	Winthrop-University Hospital

HISTORICAL FINANCIALS

Company Type: Private

Income Statement   FYE: December 31

	REVENUE ($ mil.)	NET INCOME ($ mil.)	NET PROFIT MARGIN	EMPLOYEES
12/17	1,018	139	13.7%	4,929
12/16	788	145	18.5%	—
12/15	732	88	12.1%	—
12/14	687	68	10.0%	—
Annual Growth	14.0%	26.7%	—	—

2017 Year-End Financials

Return on assets: 9.1%   Cash ($ mil.): 137
Return on equity: 20.6%
Current ratio: 3.70

NEWYORK-PRESBYTERIAN/QUEENS

The New York Hospital Medical Center of Queens aims to provide care that's fit for royalty. Better known as the New York Hospital Queens the acute care hospital has about 520 beds and provides both primary and tertiary care. Specialist services include cancer cardiovascular pediatric obstetric surgical and dental care. The medical center also operates about a dozen outpatient clinics and care centers that offer such services as family health kidney dialysis rehabilitation and dental care as well as home health care services. New York Hospital Queens is part of the NewYork-Presbyterian Healthcare System.

EXECUTIVES

Vice President For Human Resources, Helen Lavas
Auditors: ERNST & YOUNG LLP NEW YORK N

LOCATIONS

HQ: NEWYORK-PRESBYTERIAN/QUEENS
  5645 MAIN ST, FLUSHING, NY 113555045
Phone: 718 670-2000

PRODUCTS/OPERATIONS

Selected Services and Centers
Ambulatory Patient Care Facilities
Anesthesiology
Cancer Center
Cardiothoracic Surgery
Center for Dental and Oral Medicine
Children's Health (Pediatrics)
Emergency Medicine
Heart and Vascular Center
Neuroscience Institute
Obstetrics and Gynecology
Orthopaedics and Rehabilitation
Pathology and Laboratories
Primary Care and Specialties
Radiation Oncology
Radiology
Surgery
Women's Health

COMPETITORS

Catholic Healthcare System	NewYork-Presbyterian Hospital
Continuum Health Partners	Nyack Hospital
Jamaica Hospital Medical Center	Southside Hospital
	Winthrop-University Hospital

HISTORICAL FINANCIALS
Company Type: Private

Income Statement				FYE: December 31
	REVENUE ($ mil.)	NET INCOME ($ mil.)	NET PROFIT MARGIN	EMPLOYEES
12/17	846	5	0.6%	2,380
12/14	669	14	2.1%	—
12/05	457	10	2.3%	—
12/03	389	7	1.9%	—
Annual Growth	5.7%	(2.5%)	—	—

2017 Year-End Financials
Return on assets: 0.8%   Cash ($ mil.): 16
Return on equity: 5.8%
Current ratio: 1.80

NFP CORP.

Through a network of subsidiaries and affiliates NFP provides commercial and personal insurance corporate benefits products and wealth management services to businesses and individuals in the US Canada and the UK. The consultancy and brokerage runs three professional advisor organizations: corporate benefits arm Benefits Partners; Partners Financial a network of independent life insurance and financial professionals; and the Retirement Plan Advisory Group (RPAG) which provides due diligence fiduciary compliance business consulting and other services through 2000 retirement plan advisors. NFP a Madison Dearborn Partners portfolio company is one of the largest retirement plan aggregators and privately owned brokers in the US.

Operations
NFP is organized along three business segments. Its Commercial Insurance business covers a range of areas including business income exposure casualty cyber liability domestic and foreign transit and workers' compensation; the company addresses diverse industries including communications chemical construction pharmaceutical and real estate. Corporate Benefits offers employee executive and retirement benefits products and HR consulting services to commercial clients. In addition to life and long-term care insurance Private Client Resources provides estate planning and wealth management to private customers.

Geographic Reach
New York-headquartered NFP has offices throughout the US and Puerto Rico Canada and the UK.

Strategy
NFP's growth strategy is focused heavily on expanding its geographic reach by acquiring regional insurance brokers and consultancies. In early 2019 and late 2018 the company's acquisitions included Ontario-based property and casualty brokers Mass Insurance Brokers and Easyway Insurance Brokers. In Florida the company purchased retirement plan and fiduciary risk firm Fiduciary First property and casualty broker Annette Willis Insurance Agency and financial education company The Participant Effect. The company also bought Louisianan employee benefits brokers Benefit Administration Group and HM Benefits.

Additionally NFP is partnering with and investing in complementary businesses through its NFP Ventures early-stage investment division. In December 2018 the company took minority stakes in Vivante Health and Indio Technologies. Vivante's digestive health management digital platform reduces emergency room and pharmacy costs by expanding digestive health services for clients of NFP's employee benefits offerings. Indio's automated property and casualty insurance data collection software streamlines NFP's underwriting process.

Mergers and Acquisitions
In 2019 NFP acquired Mass Insurance Brokers and Easyway Insurance Brokers. With operations in Ontario and Montreal the companies expand NFP's Canadian property and casualty insurance brokerage business. That year it also bought Independent Bankers Insurance Services a management liability coverage provider for community banks. The deal allows NFP to better serve its financial institution clients by expanding its product and service lineup including default protection and security products.

In late 2018 and early 2019 NFP extended its reach in the southeastern US with its purchases of Florida-headquartered Annette Willis Insurance Agency and Louisiana-based Benefit Administration Group and HM Benefits. Annette Willis is a property and casualty brokerage for businesses and individuals; Benefit Administration and HM Benefits are benefits brokerages with presences in New Orleans.

NFP acquired specialty managing general underwriter group Lenders Risk Services and Lenders Risk Management in November 2018. The Maryland company markets lender's single interest and mortgage impairment products to credit unions and community banks.

Company Background
In 2013 Chicago-based private equity investment firm Madison Dearborn Partners took NFP private in a $1.4 billion deal.

EXECUTIVES

Chairman And Ceo, Jessica M. Bibliowicz, $700,000 total compensation
Evp And Coo, Michael N. Goldman, $325,000 total compensation
Evp General Counsel And Corporate Secretary, Stancil E. (Stan) Barton, $300,000 total compensation
Senior Vice President President Advisor Services Group, James L. Poer
President Corporate Client Group, Edward OÂ'Malley
Executive Vice President Mergers & Acquisitions, Carl Nelson
Senior Vice President Chief Technology Officer, Mark Grosvenor
Evp And General Counsel, Timothy M. Robb
Executive Vice President Chief Financial Officer, Brett Schneider
Cisr Assistant Vice President, Kim Holmes
Senior Vice President Individual Client Group, Robert Hilzenrath
Senior Vice President, Mei Au
Vice President, Elan Sharoni
Vice President Of Sales, Ronald Spencer
Regional Vice President, Sal Lundy
Vice President, Suzanne Jones
Vice President Sales And Marketing, Diane Popiela
Vice President And Corporate Controller, Simon Hoyle
Vice President, Ford STANFORD Darger
Vice President Talent Manageme, Erin Peterson
Vice President, Kim Harvill
Vice President Business Development, Matthew Douglas
Regional Vice President, Joe Kristovich
Senior Vice President Technology, Kevin Witt
Assistant Vice President Business Development, Bob Peckham
Vice President Of Sales, Chris Phillips
Assistant Vice President Product Intelligence, Jeff Driscoll
Assistant Vice President Private Client Group, Stacy Harris
Senior Vice President, Lara Nichols
Executive Vice President, Charlie Nelson
Vice President Of Agency Services, Stacey Scott
Vice President Advanced Sales, Timothy Mcfarland
Vice President Pandc Business, Eric Wright
Assistant Vice President Corporate Benefits, Aleyne Secor
Senior Vice President Retirement, Andrew Prevost

LOCATIONS
HQ: NFP CORP.
340 MADISON AVE FL 21, NEW YORK, NY 101730401
Phone: 212 301-4000
Web: WWW.NFP.COM

COMPETITORS

Aon	Marsh & McLennan
BlackRock	Northwestern Mutual
Brown & Brown	Old Mutual (US)
First Commonwealth Financial	Raymond James Financial
Gallagher	Securities America
Hub International	The Lockton Companies
LPL Financial	USI
M Financial Group	Willis Towers Watson

HISTORICAL FINANCIALS
Company Type: Private

Income Statement				FYE: December 31
	ASSETS ($ mil.)	NET INCOME ($ mil.)	INCOME AS % OF ASSETS	EMPLOYEES
12/11	894	36	4.1%	4,700
12/10	893	42	4.8%	—
12/09	970	(493)	—	—
12/08	1,543	14	1.0%	—
Annual Growth	(16.6%)	35.5%	—	—

2011 Year-End Financials
Return on assets: 4.1%   Sales ($ mil): 1,013
Return on equity: 9.1%

NHK INTERNATIONAL CORPORATION

EXECUTIVES

Pres, Hideto Enomoto
Senior Engineer, Jason Oyler
Sales Associate, Mark Sakata
Administrative Assistant, Cheryl Mason
Information Technology Manager, James Green
Sales Account Manager, Yayoi Akamatsu
Auditors: ERNST & YOUNG LLP LOUISVILLE

LOCATIONS
HQ: NHK INTERNATIONAL CORPORATION
46855 MAGELLAN DR STE 200, NOVI, MI 483772451
Phone: 248 926-0111
Web: WWW.NHKSEATING.COM

HISTORICAL FINANCIALS
Company Type: Private

Income Statement				FYE: March 31
	REVENUE ($ mil.)	NET INCOME ($ mil.)	NET PROFIT MARGIN	EMPLOYEES
03/16	894	12	1.4%	200
03/15	842	(13)	—	—
03/14	739	17	2.4%	—
03/13	688	14	2.1%	—
Annual Growth	9.1%	(4.4%)	—	—

2016 Year-End Financials
Return on assets: 2.8%
Return on equity: 6.1%
Current ratio: 1.00
Cash ($ mil.): 3

NIELSEN HOLDINGS PLC

EXECUTIVES

Ceo, Mitch Barns

LOCATIONS

HQ: NIELSEN HOLDINGS PLC
85 BROAD ST, NEW YORK, NY 100042434
Phone: 646 654-5000

HISTORICAL FINANCIALS
Company Type: Private

Income Statement				FYE: December 31
	REVENUE ($ mil.)	NET INCOME ($ mil.)	NET PROFIT MARGIN	EMPLOYEES
12/15	6,172	575	9.3%	43,061
12/14	6,288	381	6.1%	—
12/13	5,703	736	12.9%	—
12/12	5,612	273	4.9%	—
Annual Growth	3.2%	28.2%	—	—

2015 Year-End Financials
Return on assets: 16.4%
Return on equity: 9.3%
Current ratio: 0.90
Cash ($ mil.): 357

NJMHMC LLC

LOCATIONS

HQ: NJMHMC LLC
55 MEADOWLANDS PKWY, SECAUCUS, NJ
070942977
Phone: 201 392-3100
Web: WWW.MEADOWLANDSHOSPITAL.ORG

HISTORICAL FINANCIALS
Company Type: Private

Income Statement				FYE: December 31
	REVENUE ($ mil.)	NET INCOME ($ mil.)	NET PROFIT MARGIN	EMPLOYEES
12/15	498	2	0.5%	650
12/14	468	2	0.5%	—
Annual Growth	6.6%	(3.1%)	—	—

2015 Year-End Financials
Return on assets: 3.5%
Return on equity: 16.4%
Current ratio: 1.70
Cash ($ mil.): —

NOBLE HOLDING (U.S.) CORPORATION

EXECUTIVES

Prin, David W Williams
Treas, Michael Lamb
Financial Consultant, Juan Munoz
Vice President Marketing, Robert W Eifler
Senior Vice President, Scott W Marks
Auditors: PRICEWATERHOUSECOOPERS LLP H

LOCATIONS

HQ: NOBLE HOLDING (U.S.) CORPORATION
3135 S DAIRY ASHFORD, SUGAR LAND, TX 77478
Phone: 281 276-6100
Web: WWW.NOBLECORP.COM

HISTORICAL FINANCIALS
Company Type: Private

Income Statement				FYE: December 31
	REVENUE ($ mil.)	NET INCOME ($ mil.)	NET PROFIT MARGIN	EMPLOYEES
12/15	3,352	607	18.1%	3,744
12/14	3,232	83	2.6%	—
12/13	4,234	935	22.1%	—
Annual Growth	(11.0%)	(19.4%)	—	—

2015 Year-End Financials
Return on assets: 4.7%
Return on equity: 8.2%
Current ratio: 1.40
Cash ($ mil.): 511

NORTH ADVOCATE SIDE HEALTH NETWORK

EXECUTIVES

Chief Executive, Kenneth J Rojek
Coordinator, San Wilson

LOCATIONS

HQ: NORTH ADVOCATE SIDE HEALTH NETWORK
836 W WELLINGTON AVE, CHICAGO, IL 606575147
Phone: 773 296-5699

HISTORICAL FINANCIALS
Company Type: Private

Income Statement				FYE: December 31
	REVENUE ($ mil.)	NET INCOME ($ mil.)	NET PROFIT MARGIN	EMPLOYEES
12/15	487	97	19.9%	1,600
12/08	317	29	9.3%	—
Annual Growth	6.3%	18.6%	—	—

2015 Year-End Financials
Return on assets: 16.6%
Return on equity: 19.9%
Current ratio: —
Cash ($ mil.): 30

NORTH AMERICAN LIGHTING, INC.

North American Lighting offers travelers a beacon of safety through the fog. The company is an independent manufacturer of vehicle lighting products in North America. Operating through four assembly plants and one technology center the company produces a line-up of headlamps signal lamps and fog lamps. Its forward-lighting products include mercury-free high intensity discharge (HID) headlamps and the Adaptive Front Lighting System (AFS). Among its signal lamps are rear-combo and license plate lamps. Its products are tailored to the designs of large auto makers and local Japanese automakers. Founded in 1983 North American Lighting is a subsidiary of Japan-based KOITO MANUFACTURING.

Geographic Reach

North American Lighting is stationed in Paris Illinois and has four manufacturing plants in Illinois and one in Alabama. Its technology research center resides in Michigan while a tool plan is located in Indiana.

Sales and Marketing

North American Lighting sells its products primarily to vehicle manufacturers in North America. It provides headlights and taillights to Toyota Nissan General Motors and Honda.

Financial Performance

The company generated 16% of its parent's revenue total in 2014. Revenues for the North American segment also skyrocketed by almost 20% in 2014 due to higher demand in the auto sector which resulted in increased automobile production.

Strategy

Like most players in the manufacturing sector North American Lighting's strategy for growth involves the expansion of its manufacturing capacity. It also attracts additional clients through new product launches. In 2013 the company invested $50 million to expand its plant in Edgar County Illinois by building a 200000 sq. ft. addition and purchasing new equipment for added production lines.

In 2014 the company also began production at its North American Lighting Mexico S.A. de C.V. (Mexican manufacturing plant) which was established in 2012 to expand automobile production throughout Mexico.

EXECUTIVES

Ceo, Takashi Ohtake
Pres*, Jun Toyota
V Pres*, Naoshi Misawa
SEC-Treas*, Kirk Gadberry
V Pres*, Kem Cooley
V Pres*, Kishore Ahuja
Asst SEC*, Theodore Cornell
Engineer, Randy Waymack
Engineer, Joel Howell
Program Manager, Keith Blain
Manager, Jim Jamrozek

LOCATIONS

HQ: NORTH AMERICAN LIGHTING, INC.
2275 S MAIN ST, PARIS, IL 619442963
Phone: 217 465-6600
Web: WWW.NAL.COM

COMPETITORS

Delphi Automotive   Robert Bosch
Systems   Valeo
Hella   Visteon

HISTORICAL FINANCIALS

Company Type: Private

Income Statement				FYE: December 31
	REVENUE ($ mil.)	NET INCOME ($ mil.)	NET PROFIT MARGIN	EMPLOYEES
12/17	1,466	111	7.6%	2,200
12/11	297	13	4.4%	—
12/10	297	13	4.4%	—
Annual Growth	25.6%	35.6%	—	—

2017 Year-End Financials

Return on assets: 16.2%   Cash ($ mil.): 77
Return on equity: 22.9%
Current ratio: 2.10

NORTH BROWARD HOSPITAL DISTRICT

North Broward Hospital District which operates as Broward Health takes care of shark bites and more. The taxpayer-supported not-for-profit health system serves the coastal city of Fort Lauderdale and the northern two-thirds of Broward County Florida with four acute care hospitals and a host of community-based centers. Flagship hospital Broward General Medical Center has more than 700 beds and features the Chris Evert Children's Hospital; all of the hospitals together have more than 1500 beds. Broward Health boasts about 30 additional facilities including family health and surgery centers and home health and hospice programs.

Operations

The Broward Health system also includes teaching hospital Broward Health Medical Center facilities such as Broward Health North and Broward Health Imperial Point Broward Health Community Services and Broward Health Physician Group. The company also operates urgent care clinics.

With more than 1200 physicians Broward Health typically sees some 62500 admissions 283000 emergency department visits 267000 outpatient visits and 17000 outpatient clinic visits each year. It also delivers some 6000 babies annually.

Broward Health is controlled by a seven-member board of commissioners appointed by Florida's governor. As a safety-net health provider in its service territory the system's hospitals receive property tax-based funding for the charity care they provide. The rest of Broward County is served by a second public hospital system South Broward Hospital District. (The county's dual structure goes back to the 1950s.)

Geographic Reach

The company has more than 50 locations across Broward County.

Sales and Marketing

Managed care accounts for more than half of Broward Health's net patient revenues; Medicare and Medicaid combined make up more than 20%.

Financial Performance

In fiscal 2014 revenue grew 2% to $971 million due to growth in net patient service revenues. Net income rose 20% that year on higher investment gains and a decline in interest expenses. The system reported an operating cash outflow to $80 million (versus $27 million in 2013) as less cash was generated from third-party payers and patients.

Strategy

Broward Health looks to improve services by adding new or renovating existing facilities in its system. For example in 2014 it opened a new Adult Cancer Infusion Center at Broward Health Medical Center (featuring an outdoor healing garden); it also opened AJ Acker Virtual Hospital with interactive patient simulators at Broward Health North for training purposes. It broke ground on a $70 million renovation of Broward Health North that will add more operating rooms and expand the emergency department. In 2015 it was given approval to expand Broward Health Coral Springs.

EXECUTIVES

Medical Director And Chief Pathologist, William D Williams
Senior Vice President Business Development, Joseph Rogers
Senior Vice President Chief Human Resources Officer, Melanie Hatcher
Director Of Pharmacy, Natalie Trach
Vice President Community Health Services, Jasmin Shirley
Physical Therapy Director, Genevive Cuaboucher
Vice President Of Human Resources Corporate, Xx Wong
Board Member, Ma James-Francis
Vice Chairman, Christopher Ure
Auditors: WARREN AVERETT LLC BIRMINGHA

LOCATIONS

HQ: NORTH BROWARD HOSPITAL DISTRICT
1800 NW 49TH ST, FORT LAUDERDALE, FL 333093092
Phone: 954 473-7010
Web: WWW.BROWARDHEALTH.ORG

PRODUCTS/OPERATIONS

2014 Sales

	$ mil.	% of total
Patient care		
Broward Health Medical Center	432	44
Broward Health North	207	21
Broward Health Imperial Point	100	10
Broward Health Coral Springs	140	15
Other	96	10
Eliminations	(5.9)	7
Total	971	100

Selected Services

Bariatric Surgery
Barrett's Esophagus
Behavioral Health
Broward Health Complete
Cancer Services
Cardiac Services
Children's Diagnostic & Treatment Center
Clinical Trials
Colorectal Services
Concussion Care
Diabetes
Digestive Health
Dysphagia
Emergency Services
Endoscopic Sinus Surgery
Home Health & Hospice Services
International Services
Liver Transplant

Maternity Place
Men's Health
Neurology
Orthopedic Services
Ostomy
Outpatient Services
Pediatric Services
Pharmacy
Primary Care
Senior Services
Sickle Cell Day Unit
Single Incision Laparoscopic Surgery (SILS)

Selected Facilities

Hospitals
  Broward General Medical Center (Fort Lauderdale)
  Coral Springs Medical Center (Coral Springs)
  Imperial Point Medical Center (Fort Lauderdale)
  North Broward Medical Center (Deerfield Beach)
Other Facilities
  Chris Evert Children's Hospital (Fort Lauderdale)
  Broward Health Physician Group (Fort Lauderdale)
  Broward Health Weston (Weston)
  Gold Coast Home Health & Hospice Services (Fort Lauderdale)
  Seventh Avenue Family Health Center (Fort Lauderdale)

COMPETITORS

Baptist Health South   Jupiter Medical Center
 Florida   Larkin Community
Boca Raton Regional   Hospital
 Hospital   Mount Sinai Medical
Continucare   Center of Florida
HCA   South Broward Hospital
Holy Cross Hospital   District
 Fort Lauderdale   University of Miami
Jackson Health System   Hospital

HISTORICAL FINANCIALS

Company Type: Private

Income Statement				FYE: June 30
	REVENUE ($ mil.)	NET INCOME ($ mil.)	NET PROFIT MARGIN	EMPLOYEES
06/18	1,035	120	11.6%	7,000
06/17	1,025	33	3.3%	—
06/16	1,014	(12)	—	—
06/08	1,335	67	5.0%	—
Annual Growth	(2.5%)	6.0%	—	—

2018 Year-End Financials

Return on assets: 7.1%   Cash ($ mil.): 121
Return on equity: 13.3%
Current ratio: 3.60

NORTH CAROLINA BAPTIST HOSPITAL

EXECUTIVES

Ceo, John D McConnell
CIO, Eric Tomlinson
Director Shareholder, Jana Newsome
Programmer Analyst, Jane Henderson
Administrative Assistant, Kathy Clark
Administrative Coordiantor, Margie Troxler
Professor, Nancy Avis
Doctor, Pam Dean
Doctor, Pirouz Daeihagh
Pediatrician, Steven Block
Coordinator, Sylvia Howell

LOCATIONS

HQ: NORTH CAROLINA BAPTIST HOSPITAL
MEDICAL CENTER BLVD, WINSTON SALEM, NC
271570001
Phone: 336 716-2011
Web: WWW.WAKEHEALTH.EDU

HISTORICAL FINANCIALS
Company Type: Private

Income Statement				FYE: June 30
	REVENUE ($ mil.)	NET INCOME ($ mil.)	NET PROFIT MARGIN	EMPLOYEES
06/18	1,633	60	3.7%	12,563
06/11	1,084	195	18.1%	—
Annual Growth	6.0%	(15.4%)	—	—

2018 Year-End Financials
Return on assets: 3.0%   Cash ($ mil.): 43
Return on equity: 5.1%
Current ratio: 1.60

NORTH CAROLINA EASTERN MUNICIPAL POWER AGENCY

EXECUTIVES

Ceo, Jesse C Tilton III
Cfo*, Al Conyers
Manager, Barbera Scheib
Energy Management Eng, Marcus Freeman
Programmer Analyst, Nikki Taylor
Manager Marketing, Robert Tugwell
Engineer, Stuart Britt
Manager Information Technology, Connell Price
Supervisor Library Records Man, Ann Doerrer
Manager, Katherine Horton
CPA, Susan R Ingram
Auditors: CHERRY BEKAERT LLP RALEIGH

LOCATIONS

HQ: NORTH CAROLINA EASTERN MUNICIPAL POWER
AGENCY
1427 MEADOW WOOD BLVD, RALEIGH, NC
276041532
Phone: 919 760-6000
Web: WWW.ELECTRICITIES.COM

HISTORICAL FINANCIALS
Company Type: Private

Income Statement				FYE: December 31
	REVENUE ($ mil.)	NET INCOME ($ mil.)	NET PROFIT MARGIN	EMPLOYEES
12/18	547	(16)	—	100
12/17	531	(13)	—	—
12/16	552	52	9.4%	—
12/12	696	21	3.1%	—
Annual Growth	(3.9%)	—	—	—

NORTH CAROLINA ELECTRIC MEMBERSHIP CORPORATION

It's a cooperative effort: North Carolina Electric Membership CorporationÂ (NCEMC) generates and transmits electricity to the state's 26 electric cooperatives (more than 2.5 million people)Â in 93 of 100 North Carolina counties. The co-op ownsÂ more than 600 MW of generating capacity through four primarilyÂ natural gasÂ peak loadÂ generators plus a 61.5% stake in Catawba Nuclear Station Unit 1 and a 31% stake in the Catawba Nuclear Station in South Carolina. It also buys power from Progress Energy American Electric Power and other for-profit utilities. NCEMC's member cooperatives serve more than 950000 metered businesses and homes in North Carolina. The wholesale co-op also operates an energy operations center.

EXECUTIVES

Vice President Manager Director, Joy Hart
Auditors: DELOITTE TAX LLP ATLANTA GA

LOCATIONS

HQ: NORTH CAROLINA ELECTRIC MEMBERSHIP
CORPORATION
3400 SUMNER BLVD, RALEIGH, NC 276162950
Phone: 919 872-0800
Web: WWW.NCELECTRICCOOPERATIVES.COM

PRODUCTS/OPERATIONS

Subsidiaries
North Carolina Association of Electric Cooperatives
  (NCAEC training programs)
The Tarheel Electric Membership Association Inc.
  (TEMA purchasing and materials supply)
North Carolina Cooperatives
Albemarle Electric Membership Corporation
Blue Ridge Electric Membership Corporation
Brunswick Electric Membership Corporation
Cape Hatteras Electric Cooperative
Carteret-Craven Electric Cooperative
Central Electric Membership Corporation
Edgecombe-Martin County Electric Membership
  Corporation
EnergyUnited
Four County Electric Membership Corporation
French Broad Electric Membership Corporation
Halifax Electric Membership Corporation
Haywood Electric Membership Corporation
Jones-Onslow Electric Membership Corporation
Lumbee River Electric Membership Corporation
Pee Dee Electric Membership Corporation
Piedmont Electric Membership Corporation
Pitt & Greene Electric Membership Corporation
Randolph Electric Membership Corporation
Roanoke Electric Cooperative
Rutherford Electric Membership Corporation
South River Electric Membership Corporation
Surry-Yadkin Electric Membership Corporation
Tideland Electric Membership Corporation
Tri-County Electric Membership Corporation
Union Power Cooperative
Wake Electric Membership Corporation

COMPETITORS

AEP	Progress Energy
Dominion Energy	SCANA
Duke Energy	Santee Cooper
MEAG Power	TVA

HISTORICAL FINANCIALS
Company Type: Private

Income Statement				FYE: December 31
	REVENUE ($ mil.)	NET INCOME ($ mil.)	NET PROFIT MARGIN	EMPLOYEES
12/18	1,188	30	2.5%	150
12/17	1,017	23	2.3%	—
12/16	1,022	25	2.5%	—
12/08	1,006	6	0.6%	—
Annual Growth	1.7%	17.2%	—	—

2018 Year-End Financials
Return on assets: 1.4%   Cash ($ mil.): 163
Return on equity: 11.4%
Current ratio: 2.90

NORTH DAKOTA UNIVERSITY SYSTEM

EXECUTIVES

Administrative Assistant, Marni Morrison
Auditors: ROBERT R PETERSON STATE AUDI

LOCATIONS

HQ: NORTH DAKOTA UNIVERSITY SYSTEM
2000 44TH ST S STE 301, FARGO, ND 581037434
Phone: 701 231-6326
Web: WWW.NDUS.EDU

HISTORICAL FINANCIALS
Company Type: Private

Income Statement				FYE: June 30
	REVENUE ($ mil.)	NET INCOME ($ mil.)	NET PROFIT MARGIN	EMPLOYEES
06/18	713	19	2.8%	14
06/17	702	66	9.5%	—
06/16	695	116	16.8%	—
06/15	676	163	24.1%	—
Annual Growth	1.8%	(50.5%)	—	—

2018 Year-End Financials
Return on assets: 1.0%   Cash ($ mil.): 202
Return on equity: 1.4%
Current ratio: 4.00

NORTH EAST INDEPENDENT SCHOOL DISTRICT

EXECUTIVES

Supt, Brian G Gottardy
Board Pres, Beth Plummer
Board V Pres, Susan Galindo
Board SEC, Sandy Hughey
Occupational Specia, Gayla Aguilar
Corrections Officer, Andres De Leon
Occupational Specia, Katherine Farrimond

Executive of Information Techn, Betsy Williams
Executive of Information Techn, Dawn Gembler
Director of Operations, Juan De Losntos
Accounting Staff, Lori Garrison
Auditors: ABIP PC SAN ANTONIO TEXAS

LOCATIONS

HQ: NORTH EAST INDEPENDENT SCHOOL DISTRICT
8961 TESORO DR, SAN ANTONIO, TX 782176209
Phone: 210 407-0359
Web: WWW.NEISD.NET

HISTORICAL FINANCIALS

Company Type: Private

Income Statement   FYE: June 30

	REVENUE ($ mil.)	NET INCOME ($ mil.)	NET PROFIT MARGIN	EMPLOYEES
06/18	759	23	3.0%	10,000
06/17	747	(2)	—	—
06/16	737	(53)	—	—
06/15	712	(143)	—	—
Annual Growth	2.1%	—	—	—

2018 Year-End Financials

Return on assets: 1.2%   Cash ($ mil.): 251
Return on equity: —
Current ratio: —

NORTH KANSAS CITY HOSPITAL

EXECUTIVES

Ceo, Peggy Schmitt
Cfo*, Henry Seybold
Coo*, Kerri Jenkins
Registered Nurse, Tamara Kettler
Director, Jana Longwith
Director of Manufacturing, Tim Ford
Occupational Therapist, Brenda Ruhnke
Vice President, Dawn Bryant
Case Manager, Dianne Studer
Member To Board of Trustee, James Hake
It Desk Supervisor, Jeff Hearrell
Auditors: BKD LLP KANSAS CITY MISSOUR

LOCATIONS

HQ: NORTH KANSAS CITY HOSPITAL
2800 CLAY EDWARDS DR, NORTH KANSAS CITY, MO
641163220
Phone: 816 691-2000
Web: WWW.NKCH.ORG

HISTORICAL FINANCIALS

Company Type: Private

Income Statement   FYE: June 30

	REVENUE ($ mil.)	NET INCOME ($ mil.)	NET PROFIT MARGIN	EMPLOYEES
06/18	586	6	1.1%	3,100
06/16	484	31	6.6%	—
06/15	462	35	7.6%	—
06/11	419	22	5.3%	—
Annual Growth	4.9%	(16.7%)	—	—

2018 Year-End Financials

Return on assets: 0.8%   Cash ($ mil.): 24
Return on equity: 1.0%
Current ratio: 1.50

NORTH LA COUNTY REGIONAL CENTER INC

EXECUTIVES

Dir, George Stevens
Auditors: LAUTZE & LAUTZE SAN FRANCISCO

LOCATIONS

HQ: NORTH LA COUNTY REGIONAL CENTER INC
15400 SHERMAN WAY STE 170, VAN NUYS, CA
914064272
Phone: 818 778-1900
Web: WWW.NLACRC.ORG

HISTORICAL FINANCIALS

Company Type: Private

Income Statement   FYE: June 30

	REVENUE ($ mil.)	NET INCOME ($ mil.)	NET PROFIT MARGIN	EMPLOYEES
06/18	462	3	0.8%	350
06/17	433	19	4.4%	—
06/16	375	1	0.4%	—
06/15	345	2	0.8%	—
Annual Growth	10.1%	8.1%	—	—

2018 Year-End Financials

Return on assets: 2.3%   Cash ($ mil.): 19
Return on equity: 27.1%
Current ratio: 1.10

NORTH MEMORIAL HEALTH CARE

North Memorial Health Care fights illness in the Twin Cities. Established in 1939 as Victory Hospital the health care network is home to North Memorial Medical Center a 520-bed hospital that features a Level I trauma center and the Humphrey Cancer Center. The hospital also operates specialty centers for cardiovascular care orthopedics pediatrics and women's health as well as an emergency vehicle fleet of more than 125 ambulances and nearly 10 helicopters. The adjacent outpatient center provides oncology radiation and imaging services. North Memorial Health Care also has a network of primary and specialty care clinics in the Twin Cities region and it provides home health and hospice services.

Operations

As a regional trauma center North Memorial Medical Center must maintain a high level of technology resources and recruit skilled emergency room specialists. North Memorial's emergency fleet also adds to the facilities' capabilities as it is one of the largest hospital-based ambulance services in the country with eight helicopters and about 125 ground ambulances. Outpatient facilities include rehabilitation centers sleep diagnostic labs family practice offices imaging centers and mental health facilities.

The system's provider network includes more than 900 physicians including specialists and primary care providers.

Geographic Reach

North Memorial Health Care's primary facility (North Memorial Medical Center) is located in Robbinsdale Minnesota. In partnership with Fairview

Health Services the company operates the 130-bed Maple Grove Hospital in nearby Maple Grove Minnesota. Its ambulance division serves the northwestern Twin Cities area as well other portions of Minnesota and Wisconsin.

Strategy

The health network is expanding its facilities to improve services for area residents. In 2015 it opened walk-in clinics in grocery stores located in the Minnesota cities of New Hope and Oakdale. The clinics offer primary health care services provided by North Memorial physician assistants and nurses.

North Memorial works to stay on top of the latest technological advances to enhance its care offerings. In 2015 North Memorial Medical Center became the first community hospital in Minnesota to use the da Vinci Xi robotic surgical system which provides more precision for minimally invasive procedures. The following year the system provided electronic tablets loaded with software designed to help caregivers calculate appropriate medication dosages for children. The tablets which are used by the company's ambulance EMTs and paramedics allow for first responders to adjust care while out in the field.

EXECUTIVES

Vp Emergency And Enterprise Operations, Mike Parrish
President North Memorial Medical Center, Gayle Mattson
Ceo Maple Grove Hospital, Andy Cochrane
Chief Medical Officer And President Physician Organization, J. Kevin Croston
Vp Patient Care, Tracy Kirby
Chief Information Officer, Pat Taffe
Vp Operations, Jeff Wicklander
Chief Financial Officer, Todd Ostendorf
Vice President Finance, Dave Albright
Treasurer, Ryan Johnson

LOCATIONS

HQ: NORTH MEMORIAL HEALTH CARE
3300 OAKDALE AVE N, MINNEAPOLIS, MN
554222900
Phone: 763 520-5200
Web: WWW.NORTHMEMORIAL.COM

PRODUCTS/OPERATIONS

Selected Locations
Heart & Vascular Center - Maple Grove - Maple Grove Minnesota
Heart & Vascular Clinic - Buffalo - Buffalo Minnesota
Heart & Vascular Clinic - Monticello - Monticello Minnesota
Hope Chest Breast Center - Robbinsdale Minnesota
Humphrey Cancer Center - Robbinsdale Minnesota
Maple Grove Hospital - Maple Grove Minnesota
Maternal Fetal Medicine - Maple Grove - Maple Grove Minnesota
North Memorial Clinic Brooklyn Center - Brooklyn Center Minnesota
North Memorial Clinic Brooklyn Park - Brooklyn Park Minnesota
North Memorial Clinic Camden - Maple Grove - Maple Grove Minnesota
North Memorial Clinic Camden - Minneapolis - Minneapolis Minnesota
North Memorial Clinic Camden - Plymouth - Plymouth Minnesota
North Memorial Clinic Elk River - Elk River Minnesota
North Memorial Clinic Golden Valley - Golden Valley Minnesota
North Memorial Clinic Maple Grove - Maple Grove Minnesota
North Memorial Clinic Minnetonka - Minnetonka Minnesota
North Memorial Clinic Northeast - Minneapolis Minnesota
North Memorial Clinic Plymouth City Center - Plymouth Minnesota

North Memorial Clinic Silver Lake Clinic - St. Anthony - St. Anthony Minnesota
North Memorial Clinic Silver Lake Clinic - Blaine - Blaine Minnesota
North Memorial Medical Center - Robbinsdale Minnesota
North Memorial Urgent Care - Maple Grove - Maple Grove Minnesota
North Memorial Urgent Care - Roseville - Roseville Minnesota
Outpatient Imaging Center - Robbinsdale Minnesota
Outpatient Psychiatric Clinic - Robbinsdale Minnesota
Rehabilitation Services - Robbinsdale Minnesota
Rehabilitation Services - Maple Grove Minnesota
Rehabilitation Services - Elk River Minnesota
Residential Hospice - Brooklyn Center Minnesota
Sleep Health Center - Maple Grove Minnesota
Sleep Health Center - Robbinsdale Minnesota
Urgent Care - Blaine Minnesota

Selected Services

Acupuncture
Acute Concussion Clinic
Acute Inpatient Rehabilitation
Air Care
Ambulance Services
Anterior Hip Replacement
Balance Center
Breast Health
Breast Milk Depot
CACE Unit
Cancer Education & Support
Cancer Treatment
Cardiac Rehabilitation
Cardiology
Cardiology Clinic Services
Complex Heart Procedures and Interventional Services
Computed Tomography - CT
Dermatology
Diabetes Education
Domestic Abuse Victim Advocacy - SafeJourney
Emergency Department
EMS Education
Endovenous Laser Treatment (EVLT) for Varicose Veins
Family Birth Center
Family Medicine
Gastroenterology
General Radiology
Genetics Program
Geriatric Care
Gift Shop
Grief and Loss Support
Group Physical Therapy
Gynecology

COMPETITORS

Allina Hospitals
Bethesda Hospital
Catholic Health Initiatives
CentraCare Health
Children's Hospitals and Clinics of Minnesota
Fairview Health
First Care
HealthEast Care System
Mayo Clinic
Methodist Hospital (MN)
Park Nicollet Health Services
Regions Hospital
SCMC
St. John's Hospital (Minnesota)
St. Luke's Hospital (MN)
University of Minnesota Medical Center

HISTORICAL FINANCIALS
Company Type: Private

Income Statement   FYE: December 31

	REVENUE ($ mil.)	NET INCOME ($ mil.)	NET PROFIT MARGIN	EMPLOYEES
12/17	651	(28)	—	5,180
12/16	721	(0)	—	—
12/13	735	51	7.0%	—
12/12	565	(4)	—	—
Annual Growth	2.8%	—	—	—

2017 Year-End Financials
Return on assets: (-5.0%)   Cash ($ mil.): —
Return on equity: (-8.3%)
Current ratio: 1.30

NORTH MISSISSIPPI HEALTH SERVICES, INC.

North Mississippi Health Services (NMHS) isn't contained by its name: The health system also provides health care to residents of northwestern Alabama. NMHS includes half a dozen community hospitals including its flagship North Mississippi Medical Center in Tupelo. North Mississippi Medical Clinics a regional network of more than 30 primary and specialty clinics; and nursing homes. Combined the facilities have nearly 1000 beds designated for acute long term and nursing care. Specialty services include home health and long-term care inpatient and outpatient behavioral health and treatment centers for cancer and digestive disorders. NMHS also operates outpatient care and wellness clinics in the region.

Operations
During 2014 NMHS handled about 30000 inpatient visits as well as more than 128000 emergency room visits and some 345000 outpatient care visits. It also conducted about 24000 surgeries at its various facilities. Its outpatient centers include more than 30 primary and specialty care clinics in Mississippi and Alabama operated through the North Mississippi Medical Clinics division as well as more than half a dozen wellness centers.

Geographic Reach
In all NMHS serves two dozen counties across the two states. In addition to its main hospital in Tupelo NMHS operates health centers in communities including Eupora Iuka Pontotoc and West Point Mississippi and in Hamilton Alabama. It also manages a center in Calhoun City Mississippi. Its Baldwyn Nursing Facility is located in Baldwyn Mississippi.

Financial Performance
Flagship North Mississippi Medical Center (NNMC)'s revenues increased by 6% due to a growth in net patient revenues. Medicare and Medicaid together accounted for about 50% of net patient revenues; managed care and commercial 25%; Blue Cross 14%; self-pay 10%; and Health Link 1%.

NNMC reported net loss of $14 million in 2014 over net income in 2013 due to pension-related changes.

NNMC's operating cash flow increased by 256% that year.

Mergers and Acquisitions
In 2018 North Mississippi Health Services agreed to buy Gilmore Memorial Hospital out of bankruptcy. It will pay $10.5 million for the Armory Mississippi hospital including the assumption of liabilities and financial commitments.

EXECUTIVES

Medical Director, Ken Harvey
Vice President Of Human Resources, Mark Pittman

LOCATIONS

HQ: NORTH MISSISSIPPI HEALTH SERVICES, INC.
830 S GLOSTER ST, TUPELO, MS 388014934
Phone: 662 377-3000
Web: WWW.NMHS.NET

Selected Locations
Baldwyn Nursing Facility (Baldwyn Mississippi)
Calhoun County Medical Clinic (managed facility; Calhoun Mississippi)
NMMC-Eupora (Eupora Mississippi)
NMMC-Hamilton (Hamilton Alabama)
NMMC-Iuka (Iuka Mississippi)
NMMC-Pontotoc (Pontotoc Mississippi)
NMMC-Tupelo (Tupelo Mississippi)
NMMC-West Point (West Point Mississippi)
North Mississippi Medical Clinics (NMMCI regional)

PRODUCTS/OPERATIONS

Selected Facilities and Services
Acute Stroke Unit
Advanced Wound Center and Hyperbarics
Bariatric Center
Behavioral Health Center
Breast Care Center
Cancer Center
Center for Digestive Health
Community Health
Critical Care Unit
CRNA Program
Diabetes Treatment Center
Emergency Services
Family Medicine Residency Center
Heart Institute
Home Health and Hospice
Hospitalists
Joint Replacement Center
Le Bonheur Specialty Clinics
Medical Imaging
North Mississippi Surgery Center
Outpatient Infusion
Pain Management Center
Pastoral Care
Physician Specialties
Radiology
Rehabilitation Services
Respiratory Therapy
Skilled Nursing Facility
Sleep Disorders Center
Surgical Services
Tupelo Wellness Center
Vein Center
Volunteer Services
Women's Hospital
Women's and Children Services

COMPETITORS

Baptist Memorial Health Care
Community Health Systems
Delta Regional Medical Center
Forrest General Hospital
HCA
Memorial Hospital at Gulfport
Methodist Healthcare
Natchez Regional Medical Center
North Mississippi Medical
Shelby County Health Care
Southwest Mississippi Regional Medical Center

HISTORICAL FINANCIALS
Company Type: Private

Income Statement   FYE: September 30

	REVENUE ($ mil.)	NET INCOME ($ mil.)	NET PROFIT MARGIN	EMPLOYEES
09/17	898	26	3.0%	6,000
09/16	893	30	3.4%	—
09/15	860	19	2.2%	—
09/14	779	(14)	—	—
Annual Growth	4.9%	—	—	—

2017 Year-End Financials
Return on assets: 2.2%   Cash ($ mil.): 36
Return on equity: 3.4%
Current ratio: 4.00

NORTH MISSISSIPPI MEDICAL CENTER, INC.

At North Mississippi Medical Center you might get some Mississippi Mud ice cream after your tonsils are removed. The full-service 650-bed regional referral hospital in Tupelo Mississippi is part of the North Mississippi Health Services system an affiliation of hospitals and clinics serving northern Mississippi northwestern Alabama and parts of Tennessee. It's the largest private not-for-profit hospital in Mississippi and the largest non-metropolitan hospital in America. Specialty services at the medical center include cancer treatment women's health care cardiology and behavioral health care. The hospital also operates a skilled-nursing facility and home health and hospice organizations.

Operations

Besides being a Mississippi State Department of Health-designated Level II trauma center North Mississippi Medical Center offers more than 40 specialties as well as centers for excellence in cardiac surgery cardiology research neurology neurosurgery pulmonology rehabilitation cancer treatment chemical dependency and neonatal programs.

The medical center's Home Health Agency canvases 17 counties in north Mississippi and provides complex and extremely high-tech procedures that can be performed in the home setting. It also operates Baldwyn Nursing Facility.

Geographic Reach

North Mississippi Medical Center serves more than 700000 people across 24 counties in north Mississippi northwestern Alabama and portions of Tennessee.

Strategy

In 2012 North Mississippi Medical Center - Hamilton opened a new pulmonary rehabilitation unit. Also the medical center's Outpatient Rehabilitation Center in 2012 became the first outpatient rehabilitation center in Mississippi to offer Fiberoptic Endoscopic Evaluation of Swallowing (FEES) to assess swallowing function. Awards and Recognition

North Mississippi Medical Center's hospitalist program has been recognized by The American Journal of Medicine for providing cost-effective care to patients in the hospital. The program begun in 1997 serves hospitalized patients who do not have a primary care physician or whose primary care physicians do not have hospital practices.

EXECUTIVES

Secretary, Margaret Lofton

LOCATIONS

HQ: NORTH MISSISSIPPI MEDICAL CENTER, INC.
830 S GLOSTER ST, TUPELO, MS 388014934
Phone: 662 377-3000
Web: WWW.NMHS.NET

Selected Locations
Baldwyn Nursing Facility - Baldwyn Mississippi
NMMC - Eup
NMMC - Ham
NMMC - Iuk
NMMC - Pontotoc - Pontotoc Mississippi
NMMC - Tupelo - Tupelo Mississippi
NMMC - West Point - West Point Mississippi

PRODUCTS/OPERATIONS

Selected Programs & Services
Acute Stroke Unit
Advanced Wound Center and Hyperbarics
Bariatric Center
Behavioral Health Center
Breast Care Center
Cancer Center
Center for Digestive Health
Community Health
Critical Care Unit
CRNA Program
Diabetes Treatment Center
Emergency Services
Family Medicine Residency Center
Gift & Floral Shop
Heart Institute
Home Health and Hospice
Hospitalists
Joint Replacement Center
Le Bonheur Specialty Clinics
Medical Imaging
North Mississippi Surgery Center
Outpatient Infusion
Pain Management Center
Pastoral Care
Physician Specialties
Radiology
Rehabilitation Services
Respiratory Therapy
Skilled Nursing Facility
Sleep Disorders Center
Surgical Services
Tupelo Wellness Center
Vein Center
Volunteer Services
West Bedtower Project
Women's Hospital
Women's and Children Services

COMPETITORS

Community Health Systems
Delta Regional Medical Center
Forrest General Hospital
HCA
Memorial Hospital at Gulfport
Natchez Regional Medical Center
Southwest Mississippi Regional Medical Center

HISTORICAL FINANCIALS
Company Type: Private

Income Statement				FYE: September 30
	REVENUE ($ mil.)	NET INCOME ($ mil.)	NET PROFIT MARGIN	EMPLOYEES
09/15	627	45	7.3%	6,000
09/14	633	52	8.3%	
09/13	537	2	0.5%	
09/12	620	(6)	—	
Annual Growth	0.4%	—	—	—

2015 Year-End Financials
Return on assets: 4.4%   Cash ($ mil.): 18
Return on equity: 6.4%
Current ratio: 2.40

NORTH PACIFIC PAPER COMPANY, LLC

The old adage "all the news fit to print" might not be possible without North Pacific Paper Corporation (NORPAC). The firm a joint venture between Weyerhaeuser and Nippon Paper produces newsprint for newspaper publishers and commercial printers. NORPAC manufactures a variety of paper grades including standard and lightweight newsprint and super- and ultra-lightweight stocks especially for the Japanese market. It produces more than 250000 tons of newsprint annually at its manufacturing facility in Longview Washington.

Its products are sent via truck and train to customers in the western US or are shipped by boat to customers in Japan. Weyerhaeuser is selling its stake in NORPAC to One Rock Capital Partners.

EXECUTIVES

Vice President Supply Chain And Distribution, Nick Karavolos
Vice President Manufacturing, Rob Buckingham

LOCATIONS

HQ: NORTH PACIFIC PAPER COMPANY, LLC
3001 INDUSTRIAL WAY, LONGVIEW, WA 986321057
Phone: 360 636-6400
Web: WWW.NORPACPAPER.COM

COMPETITORS

Brant Industries
Georgia-Pacific
Inland Empire Paper
Company
International Paper

Norske Skog
Oji Holdings
Resolute Forest
Products

HISTORICAL FINANCIALS
Company Type: Private

Income Statement				FYE: December 31
	REVENUE ($ mil.)	NET INCOME ($ mil.)	NET PROFIT MARGIN	EMPLOYEES
12/08	534	22	4.2%	410
12/07	474	(3)	—	
12/06	498	19	3.9%	
Annual Growth	3.5%	7.4%	—	—

NORTH SHORE UNIVERSITY HEALTH SYSTEM

LOCATIONS

HQ: NORTH SHORE UNIVERSITY HEALTH SYSTEM
2650 RIDGE AVE, EVANSTON, IL 602011700
Phone: 847 570-2640
Web: WWW.NORTHSHORE.ORG

HISTORICAL FINANCIALS
Company Type: Private

Income Statement				FYE: September 30
	REVENUE ($ mil.)	NET INCOME ($ mil.)	NET PROFIT MARGIN	EMPLOYEES
09/15	1,419	55	3.9%	3
09/14	1,397	148	10.6%	
09/13	1,815	238	13.1%	
Annual Growth	(11.6%)	(51.7%)	—	—

2015 Year-End Financials
Return on assets: 1.7%   Cash ($ mil.): 62
Return on equity: 3.0%
Current ratio: 0.60

NORTH SHORE UNIVERSITY HOSPITAL

North Shore University Hospital (NSUH) knows you shouldn't have to leave the island for quality health care. The Long Island hospital has more than 800 beds devoted to adult and pediatric medicine rehabilitation stroke care women's health orthopedics urology wound healing dentistry and trauma emergency services among other areas. The hospital is home to specialist institutes for cancer care and cardiology. It also serves as a campus for the Hofstra Northwell Shool of Medicine. NSUH is part of Northwell Health.

Operations

The not-for-profit NSUH operates numerous satellite community health centers that provide primary surgery psychiatric dental and specialty care including the Schwartz Ambulatory Surgery Center. Its Stern Family Center for Extend Care and Rehabilitation has about 250 beds; NSUH also includes a Katz Women's Hospital (one of two in the system). The hospital provides comprehensive care in all health care specialties including organ transplant services. In addition the hospital operates mobile health vehicles and conducts educational and wellness programs for area residents.

NSUH has a staff of more than 6000 specialist and subspecialist physicians nurses and other medical workers. It handles about 50000 inpatient visits 90000 emergency room visits 20000 surgeries and 6000 births each year.

NSUH has medical health professional and nursing school affiliations with about 15 colleges and universities. Programs include residencies postgraduate training and fellowships.

Geographic Reach

Strategy

NSUH and the larger Northwell Health system tend to grow through the acquisitions of smaller campuses and mergers with other systems. This allows the hospital to gain operating efficiency through vertical integration bargaining power with vendors and a more diversified revenue stream.

In 2017 NSUH opened the Sandra Atlas Bass Heart Hospital for advanced cardiac care. The facility will be the first on Long Island to offer heart transplants and the sixth in New York State (which has a very high number of transplant candidates on its waiting list).

As part of its efforts to bring cutting-edge health care to the community it serves the hospital began offering 3D-printed titanium spinal implants in 2017.These synthetic implants approved in the US in 2016 are made with titanium powder rather than from a donor or from the patient's own body and manufactured using a 3D-printing process.

EXECUTIVES

Executive Vice President Chief Financial Officer, Robert S. (Bob) Shapiro
President North Shore-long Island Jewish Health System, Ralph A. Nappi
Senior Vice President Strategy And Business Informatics, Jeffrey A. Kraut
Executive Vice President Chief Operating Officer, Mark J. Solazzo
Regional Executive Director, Dennis Dowling
Executive Vice President And Physician-in-chief, Lawrence G. Smith
Executive Director, Susan Somerville
Director Of Radiology, Edward S Wind
Vice President, Dorothy Feldman
Senior Vice President Consolidated Business Services, Donna Drummond

Director Of Him, Elizabeth Heller
Chief Procurement Officer And Vice President, Phyllis McCready
Vice President Of Marketing, Don Simon
Vice President And Chief Talent Officer, Elaine Page
Assistant Vice President Clinical Applications, Chris Petillo
Vice President Finance, Patricia Drolet
Secretary Department, Linda Muscarella
Vice Chairman Department Of Family Medicine, Martin P Edelstein

LOCATIONS

HQ: NORTH SHORE UNIVERSITY HOSPITAL
 300 COMMUNITY DR, MANHASSET, NY 110303876
Phone: 516 562-0100

PRODUCTS/OPERATIONS

Selected Centers and Services
Bariatric Services
Cancer Institute
Cardiovascular and Thoracic Services
Colorectal Surgery
Emergency Department / Trauma Services
Fertility and Reproductive Services
Geriatric and Palliative Medicine
Infectious Diseases / AIDS Research
Kidney Transplantation
Laparoendoscopic Single-Site Surgery
Military/Veterans Services
Minimally Invasive Robotic Surgery
Neuroscience
Obstetrics and Gynecology
Orthopaedics
Pain Management
Pediatric Services
Radiation Medicine
Travel Immunization
Urology Services
Wound Care

COMPETITORS

Brookhaven Memorial Hospital Medical Center
 Catholic Health Services of Long Island
 Catholic Healthcare System
 Long Island College Hospital
 Maimonides Medical Center
 New York City Health and Hospitals
 NewYork-Presbyterian Healthcare
 Winthrop-University Hospital

HISTORICAL FINANCIALS

Company Type: Private

Income Statement				FYE: December 31
	REVENUE ($ mil.)	NET INCOME ($ mil.)	NET PROFIT MARGIN	EMPLOYEES
12/17	1,826	191	10.5%	5,000
12/16	1,795	171	9.6%	—
12/15	1,617	37	2.3%	—
12/14	1,495	84	5.7%	—
Annual Growth	6.9%	31.1%	—	—

2017 Year-End Financials

Return on assets: 8.6%   Cash ($ mil.): 64
Return on equity: 15.9%
Current ratio: 3.80

NORTH SHORE-LONG ISLAND JEWISH HEALTH CARE

EXECUTIVES

Prin, Filippo Petti
Director, Edward Bochynski
Information Technology/Interne, Phil Leonardi
Project Manager, Cathlyn Fagan
Director Health Sciences Libra, Debra Eisenberg
Director, James Abberton
Supervisor Admin Office, Karen Taylor

LOCATIONS

HQ: NORTH SHORE-LONG ISLAND JEWISH HEALTH CARE
 972 BRUSH HOLLOW RD 5TH, WESTBURY, NY 115901740
Phone: 516 876-6611

HISTORICAL FINANCIALS

Company Type: Private

Income Statement				FYE: December 31
	REVENUE ($ mil.)	NET INCOME ($ mil.)	NET PROFIT MARGIN	EMPLOYEES
12/14	719	(34)	—	2
12/13	633	(33)	—	—
12/09	351	(2)	—	—
Annual Growth 15.4%		—	—	—

2014 Year-End Financials

Return on assets: (-1.9%)   Cash ($ mil.): 74
Return on equity: (-7.7%)
Current ratio: 0.50

NORTH TEXAS MUNICIPAL WATER DISTRICT

EXECUTIVES

Pres, Darwin Whiteside
V Pres*, Joe Joplin
SEC*, Terry Sam Anderson
Exec Dir*, Tom Kula
Scientist, Rachel Blakey
Information Specialist, Shaya Hamilton
Program Inspector, Manual Rivas
Program Inspector, Richard Welsh
Lims Administrator, Edward Howland
Wastewater Program Manager, Bret Ellis
Administrative Technician, Jennifer Simpson
Auditors: WEAVER AND TIDWELL LLP DA

LOCATIONS

HQ: NORTH TEXAS MUNICIPAL WATER DISTRICT
 501 E BROWN ST, WYLIE, TX 750984406
Phone: 972 442-5405
Web: WWW.NTMWD.COM

HISTORICAL FINANCIALS

Company Type: Private

Income Statement
FYE: September 30

	REVENUE ($ mil.)	NET INCOME ($ mil.)	NET PROFIT MARGIN	EMPLOYEES
09/18	484	117	24.3%	670
09/17	439	129	29.4%	—
09/16	398	125	31.6%	—
09/15	338	86	25.7%	—
Annual Growth	12.7%	10.7%	—	—

2018 Year-End Financials

Return on assets: 2.5%
Return on equity: 8.1%
Current ratio: 6.70
Cash ($ mil.): 74

NORTHBAY HEALTHCARE GROUP

EXECUTIVES

Ceo, Deborah Sugiyama
Internal Medicine Practitioner, Olexander Barchan
Training and Direc, Becky Lessler
Chief of Medicine, Tracy Johnson
Urology Specialist, Kevin Rycyna
Physician Director of Er, Fredric Gough
Internist, Ali Hassani
Internist, Jayanth K Madderla
Registered Nurse, Nancy Wright
Chief Nursing Officer, Traci Duncan
Buyer, June Holstrom

LOCATIONS

HQ: NORTHBAY HEALTHCARE GROUP
1200 B GALE WILSON BLVD, FAIRFIELD, CA
945333552
Phone: 707 646-5000
Web: WWW.NORTHBAY.ORG

HISTORICAL FINANCIALS

Company Type: Private

Income Statement
FYE: December 31

	REVENUE ($ mil.)	NET INCOME ($ mil.)	NET PROFIT MARGIN	EMPLOYEES
12/17	530	(4)	—	1,200
12/16	557	44	7.9%	—
12/15	460	15	3.3%	—
12/14	441	47	10.9%	—
Annual Growth	6.4%	—	—	—

2017 Year-End Financials

Return on assets: (-0.6%)
Return on equity: (-1.6%)
Current ratio: 1.70
Cash ($ mil.): 9

NORTHEAST GEORGIA MEDICAL CENTER, INC.

EXECUTIVES

Ceo, Carol Burrell
V Pres*, Tracy Vardeman
V Pres*, Anthony Williamson
V Pres*, Paul Vervalin
Cfo*, Anthony M Herdener
Oncology, Jack T Griffeth
Director, Lawana Bryan
Director, Deven Mattheus
Internal Medicine Practitioner, Ernest T Kamara
Coordinator, Jason Grady
Internal Medicine Practitioner, Franklin Fontem

LOCATIONS

HQ: NORTHEAST GEORGIA MEDICAL CENTER, INC.
743 SPRING ST NE, GAINESVILLE, GA 305013715
Phone: 770 219-9000
Web: WWW.NGHSCAREERS.COM

HISTORICAL FINANCIALS

Company Type: Private

Income Statement
FYE: September 30

	REVENUE ($ mil.)	NET INCOME ($ mil.)	NET PROFIT MARGIN	EMPLOYEES
09/17	1,152	7	0.7%	3,053
09/16	1,024	45	4.5%	—
09/15	892	51	5.8%	—
09/14	819	110	13.5%	—
Annual Growth	12.0%	(58.8%)	—	—

2017 Year-End Financials

Return on assets: 0.4%
Return on equity: 1.1%
Current ratio: 1.40
Cash ($ mil.): 23

NORTHEASTERN UNIVERSITY

Since 1898 Northeastern University has been educating students in Boston and beyond. The school enrolls roughly 24000 students and employs 1600 faculty members. Its nine colleges offer 100 undergraduate programs and 160 graduate programs in areas such as the arts business engineering and law. Northeastern has a student-to-teacher ratio of about 13:1. Its highly-regarded experiential education program integrates classroom learning with real-world experience; students typically alternate between school and paid full-time work and leave with up to two years of professional experience. Northeastern started out as a night school housed in a YMCA facility.

Operations

Roughly 90% of Northeastern's students participate in its cooperative learning program which is conducted over four or five years and can include overseas study programs. The idea behind the teaching strategy is to give students some professional experience before graduation putting them a step ahead of peers. Sectors include the arts and humanities (think Boston Symphony Orchestra) finance and insurance (Goldman Sachs in the UK) and communications (the White House offers a co-op opportunity in its media affairs office).

The school also boasts extensive research centers and institutes. Northeastern receives research funding from a number of outside sources that include the National Institutes of Health the Department of Energy and the Department of Defense and the Department of Homeland Security. Funded research areas include heart disease the link between preterm births and environmental contaminants new ways to detect explosives and renewable energy sources.

Geographic Reach

Northeastern's students hail from all 50 states and about 90 countries. The university has study abroad programs in locations including Argentina Costa Rica France China Germany and the UK (among many others).

In addition to its main campus in Boston Northeastern has satellite graduate schools in Charlotte North Carolina Seattle California and Toronto.

Financial Performance

Northeastern reported revenue of $1.16 billion in 2017 which was about the same as 2016. Tuition and fees account for about 98% of the university's revenue. Tuition and fees totaled $1.14 billion in 2017 from about $1 billion in 2016. The university paid about $316 million in financial aid in 2017 an increase from about $292 million the year before.

EXECUTIVES

Senior Vice President Administration And Finance, John McCarthy
Svp And Ceo Northeastern University Global Network, Philomena V. Mantella
Senior Vice President For External Affairs External Affairs, Michael Armini
President, Joseph E. Aoun
Svp Academinc Affairs And Provost, James C. Bean
Vp And Chief Marketing Officer, Brian Sullivan
Senior Vice President For University Advancement, Diane Macgillivray
Vice President, Kathy Spiegelman
Vice President Enrollment Management, Jane Brown
Vice President Facilities, Nancy May
Vice President For Government Relations, Tim Leshan
Vice President, Michael J Power
Vice President For Communications, Renata Nyul
Assistant Vice President Student Affairs, Madeleine Estabrook
Special Assistant To The Senior Vice President, Maria Galarza
Vice President Student Affairs, Edward Klotzbier
Vice Provost Undergraduate Education, Malcolm Hill
Office Of The Senior Vice President University Advancement, Sarah Balal
Assistant Vice President Student Affairs Residential Life, Marina Macomber
Vice President Academic Affairs, John Griffith
Vice President Of Student Services, Steve Smith
Associate Vice President, Paul Zernicke
Vice President Cio, Bob Weir
Vice President, Jarvis Chen
Medical Director, Gairy Hall
Associate Vice President Corporate And Foundation Rela, Robert Silk
Vice President Of External Affairs Bmes, Rachel Shaffer
Vice President Of Media And Membership, Vijayeta Singh
Vice President Online Experiential Learning, Chris Mallett
Vp Finance, Abhishek Garg
First Vice President, Heather L Seligman
Director Of Admissions, Jackson Dan
Vice President, Norton Julie
Executive Vice President, Angela Antoniello

Vice President, Harry Brodsky
Vice President Of Alumnae Relations, Sarah Nesti
Associate Vice President University Advancement, Bob Dietrich
Director Of Clinical Services, Sievert Jules Rochiell
Associate Vice President, Mallik Sundharam
Vice President, Doug Landry
Vice President For Government Relations, Michael Sarno
Secretary Receptionist Health Services, Debra Smith

Board Member, Mary Florentine
Assistant Treasurer, Alysa Gerlach
Auditors: PRICEWATERHOUSECOOPERS LLP B

LOCATIONS

HQ: NORTHEASTERN UNIVERSITY
360 HUNTINGTON AVE, BOSTON, MA 021155000
Phone: 617 373-2000
Web: WWW.NORTHEASTERN.EDU

PRODUCTS/OPERATIONS

Selected Schools & Colleges
Bouvé College of Health Sciences
College of Arts Media and Design
College of Computer and Information Science
College of Engineering
College of Professional Studies
College of Science
College of Social Sciences and Humanities
D'Amore-McKim School of Business
School of Law

HISTORICAL FINANCIALS
Company Type: Private

Income Statement   FYE: June 30

	REVENUE ($ mil.)	NET INCOME ($ mil.)	NET PROFIT MARGIN	EMPLOYEES
06/18	1,306	163	12.5%	4,175
06/17	1,161	169	14.6%	—
06/16	1,106	3	0.3%	—
06/13	947	147	15.6%	—
Annual Growth	6.6%	2.0%	—	—

2018 Year-End Financials

Return on assets: 5.5%   Cash ($ mil.): 239
Return on equity: 9.1%
Current ratio: —

NORTHERN INDIANA PUBLIC SERVICE COMPANY

Northern Indiana Public Service Company (NIPSCO) can shine a little light on the topic of Hoosiers. The largest subsidiary of utility holding company NiSource NIPSCO has more than 457000 electricity customers and more than 786000 natural gas customers. The utility has three coal-fired power plants with 2540 MW of generating capacity. On the power side of the business NIPSCO generates transmits and distributes electricity to the northern part of Indiana and engages in electric wholesale and transmission transactions. The company operates approximately 13000 miles of electric transmission and distribution lines and 16000 miles of gas mains.

Operations

NIPSCO's three operating power facilities have a net capability of 2540 MW. It also owns and operates Sugar Creek a combined cycle gas turbine plant with a 535 MW capacity four gas-fired generating units with a net capability of 206 MW and two hydroelectric generating plants with a net capability of 10 MW. During 2012 NIPSCO generated 74.1% and purchased 25.9% of its electric requirements.

Geographic Reach

NIPSCO Gas is the largest natural gas distribution company in Indiana and NIPSCO Electric which serves customers in 20 counties is the state's #2 power distribution company behind Duke Energy Indiana.

Strategy

NIPSCO is promoting incentive plans to help customers save money through energy efficiency programs including appliance rebates for the installation of more energy efficient water heaters and other electric appliances and for automated air-conditioning cycling (cutting use for limited periods during peak loads). Other incentives are available for weatherizing energy audits and green construction projects.

In 2011 the company increased residential customer rates by 5%. The rate increase was in part a way to compensate for a decline in usage and revenues as a result of the global recession.

In 2011 NiSource companies Northern Indiana Fuel & Light and Kokomo Gas were consolidated with and into NIPSCO in order to improve operating efficiencies.

EXECUTIVES

Vice President Of Finance, William Omalley
Senior Vice President, Dan Douglas
Vice President, Dave Walter
Vice President, Paul Kelly
Vice President, Jim Zucal
Senior Vice President, Mike Hooper

LOCATIONS

HQ: NORTHERN INDIANA PUBLIC SERVICE COMPANY
801 E 86TH AVE, MERRILLVILLE, IN 464106271
Phone: 800 464-7726
Web: WWW.NIPSCO.COM

PRODUCTS/OPERATIONS

Selected Services
Call 811 Before You Dig
Commercial and Industrial Services
DependaBill
Dusk to Dawn Streetlights
Extra Service Protection
Green Power
IN-Charge Electric Vehicle Program
Meter Reading
NIPSCO Choice Program
NIPSCO Connect
Price Protection Service
Residential Builder and Developer Services
Selling Your Clean Energy
Smart Grid Technology
Start or Stop Gas and Electric Services
Trees and Power Lines
Wood Stove Changeout Program

COMPETITORS

AEP
Citizens Energy
Dominion Energy
Duke Energy Indiana

IPALCO Enterprises
Indiana Michigan Power
Vectren

HISTORICAL FINANCIALS
Company Type: Private

Income Statement   FYE: December 31

	REVENUE ($ mil.)	NET INCOME ($ mil.)	NET PROFIT MARGIN	EMPLOYEES
12/17	2,418	226	9.3%	3,096
12/16	2,252	178	7.9%	—
/ 0	0	—	—	—
Annual Growth	—	—	—	—

2017 Year-End Financials

Return on assets: 3.2%   Cash ($ mil.): 7
Return on equity: 9.0%
Current ratio: 0.50

NORTHERN NATURAL GAS COMPANY

Northern Natural Gas (NNG) keeps the pipes gassed up. The company operates 14700 miles of natural gas pipeline (6300 miles of transmission line and 8400 miles of branch and lateral lines) stretching from the Permian Basin in Texas to the Great Lakes in the Midwest. It also provides transportation and storage services to almost 80 utilities and a number of other customers in the Upper Midwest. The company has a 5.5 billion cu. ft. per day market area peak capacity and its five natural gas storage facilities have a total capacity of 73 billion cu. ft. including 4 billion cu. ft. of liquefied natural gas (LNG). NNG which was formed in 1930 is an indirect subsidiary of Berkshire Hathaway Energy.

Operations

The company provides cross-haul and grid transportation between other interstate and intrastate pipelines in the Permian Anadarko Hugoton and Midwest areas.

Geographic Reach

NNG accesses natural gas supply in the Mid-Continent Rocky Mountain and Western Canadian basins. Its northern service unit (Market Area) delivers gas supply to customers in Illinois Iowa Michigan Minnesota Nebraska South Dakota and Wisconsin. Its southern system (Field Area) delivers to locations in Kansas New Mexico Oklahoma and Texas.

Sales and Marketing

The company offers its products for utilities municipalities gas marketing companies industrial and commercial users and other end-users.

In 2014 Northern Natural Gas had three customers including MidAmerican Energy that each accounted for greater than 10% of its transportation and storage revenue and its ten largest customers accounted for 63% of its system-wide transportation and storage revenue.

Financial Performance

The company's revenues increased by 22% due to higher gas & liquid and transportation sales.

NNG's net income was flat as the result of higher revenues being offset by higher operating cost and lower other income.

The company's operating cash flow increased by 12% due to a change in accounts payable and other accrued liabilities and a decline in cash used by accounts receivable and other assets.

Strategy

Growing its storage capacity since 2006 NNG has added 14 billion cu. ft. of storage cycle capacity through expansions and upgrades at its Cunningham Kansas and Redfield Iowa storage locations. In 2014 the company began working on a plan to add new pipelines compressor stations and meter stations between Nebraska and Iowa.

Company Background
NNG was established in 1930 in Omaha to serve 44 communities in Iowa Kansas and Nebraska. Its more recent history includes a takeover by Dynegy in 2002 from the pipeline unit's former parent bankrupt energy giant Enron. The deal was part of Dynegy's proposed acquisition of Enron which was subsequently called off. To strengthen its own balance sheet Dynegy ended up selling NNG to MidAmerican Energy (which later became Berkshire Hathaway Energy) that year.

In 2011 NNG brought in 13 billion cu. ft. of new gas supply to its northern system from tight sand formations in Oklahoma and Texas.

EXECUTIVES

President Ceo, Mark A. Hewett
Vp Operations, Royce Ramsay
Vp Information Technology, Paul Maakestad
Vp Marketing, Adam Wright

LOCATIONS

HQ: NORTHERN NATURAL GAS COMPANY
1111 S 103RD ST, OMAHA, NE 681241072
Phone: 877 654-0646
Web: WWW.NORTHERNNATURALGAS.COM

COMPETITORS

Enbridge	ONEOK Partners
Kinder Morgan Energy	TransCanada
Partners	Williams Companies

HISTORICAL FINANCIALS
Company Type: Private

Income Statement				FYE: December 31
	REVENUE ($ mil.)	NET INCOME ($ mil.)	NET PROFIT MARGIN	EMPLOYEES
12/17	693	170	24.6%	1,055
12/16	636	159	25.0%	—
12/07	663	161	24.3%	—
12/06	633	142	22.5%	—
Annual Growth	0.8%	1.7%	—	—

2017 Year-End Financials
Return on assets: 4.6%
Return on equity: 10.8%
Current ratio: 1.00
Cash ($ mil.): 20

NORTHERN VIRGINIA ELECTRIC COOPERATIVE

NOVEC is no novice when it comes to electricity distribution. Northern Virginia Electric Cooperative (NOVEC) is a member-owned not-for profit utility that serves more than 150000 residential commercial industrial and government customers in a 651-sq. ml. service area in northern Virginia. NOVEC which has more than 6790 miles of power lines receives its power supply from the PJM Interconnection marketplace. The company also markets natural gas to retail customers in Virginia and Maryland through its NOVEC Energy Solutions unit. Subsidiary NOVEC Solutions sells gas and electric water heaters and other energy appliances and provides optical data networking service for large businesses and government agencies.

Geographic Reach
NOVEC distributes power to customers in Clarke Fairfax Fauquier Loudoun Prince William and Stafford counties and the City of Manassas Park.

Sales and Marketing
The utility company's large commercial customers include AT&T Doane Food Products Potomac Mills Outlet Mall NOAA's Mount Weather Facility and Vulcan Materials Company. NOVEC Energy Solutions supplies natural gas service to 20000 primarily residential customers.

Financial Performance
Due to the lower costs of generating power because of low natural gas prices NOVEC cut rates in 2011 and implemented a power cost adjustment credit in 2012 reducing the amount that customers paid for NOVEC-supplied power. Revenues decreased by 14% in 2012; net margin by 49%.

Strategy
In 2012 NOVEC received $10 million from the Department of Energy as a part of Smart Grid Investment Grant program. The company uses the proceeds to automate of 38 of its 53 substations; replaced 19 outdated line-protective devices; install 164 capacitor banks with automatic switching devices; and install 14 remote-controlled motor-operated switches to isolate problems and help restore power quickly.

Company Background
NOVEC was formed in 1983 through the merger of Prince William Electric Cooperative and Tri-County Electric Cooperative.

EXECUTIVES

Senior Vice President Finance, Wilber Rollin
Vice Pres, Gilbert Jaramillo
Vice President Business Development And Energy Services, Mike Dailey

LOCATIONS

HQ: NORTHERN VIRGINIA ELECTRIC COOPERATIVE
10323 LOMOND DR, MANASSAS, VA 201093113
Phone: 703 335-0500
Web: WWW.NOVEC.COM

Northern Virginia Electric Cooperative operates in rural areas in Clarke Fairfax Fauquier Loudoun Prince William and Stafford counties as well as in the Town of Clifton and the City of Manassas Park in northern Virginia.

PRODUCTS/OPERATIONS

Subsidiaries and Affiliates
NOVEC Energy Solutions (formerly America's Energy Alliance retail gas marketing)
NOVEC Solutions (formerly NOVASTAR energy products and services)

COMPETITORS

AEP	FirstEnergy
Chesapeake Utilities	NiSource
Constellation Energy	Pepco Holdings
Group	Southern Company Gas
Delmarva Power	WGL Holdings
Dominion Energy	

HISTORICAL FINANCIALS
Company Type: Private

Income Statement				FYE: December 31
	REVENUE ($ mil.)	NET INCOME ($ mil.)	NET PROFIT MARGIN	EMPLOYEES
12/15	471	20	4.3%	275
12/14	433	20	4.7%	—
12/13	396	23	6.0%	—
12/09	419	50	12.2%	—
Annual Growth	2.0%	(14.2%)	—	—

2015 Year-End Financials
Return on assets: 2.4%
Return on equity: 3.1%
Current ratio: 4.90
Cash ($ mil.): 45

NORTHSHORE UNIVERSITY HEALTHSYSTEM

NorthShore University HealthSystem provides care to residents of Chicago's north side and its suburbs. The health system operates four hospitals a home care organization and a Medical Group with some 970 primary and specialty care physicians. With about 355 beds the organization's flagship Evanston Hospital has teaching and research programs as well as capabilities for trauma cancer and cardiology. The system also includes Glenbrook Hospital (about 175 beds) Highland Park Hospital (140 beds) and Skokie Hospital (more than 120 beds). The health care system is affiliated with the University of Chicago Pritzker School of Medicine.

Operations
Each of NorthShore's hospitals is known for a certain specialty. Evanston for example specializes in cancer and cardiac care; Glenbrook Hospital is known for advanced technology for the treatment of gastrointestinal disorders; Highland Park Hospital is the site of the first open heart surgery in the region; and Skokie Hospital is known for its expertise in cardiac care and orthopedics.Each year the hospitals see some 128000 emergency room visits and some 63000 hospital admissions.

The Center for Personalized Medicine at NorthShore is a comprehensive precision medicine organization utilizing genetic testing to help inform patients' care including disease prevention and treatment.

The system also operates a not-for-profit home and hospice services agency.

Geographic Reach
Based in Evanston Illinois NorthShore has some 130 medical offices across the region.

Financial Performance
NorthShore has annual revenues of approximately $2.1 billion.

Strategy
NorthShore's health facility network has grown over the years through acquisitions and through organic measures. The system regularly conducts expansion and remodeling projects at its facilities and it has stepped up recruiting efforts to attract high-skill doctors. In 2018 it announced plans to spend between $50 million and $60 million to open 50 immediate care centers by late 2020. (At the time of the announcement it operated six immedi-

ate care centers.) That strategy should bring more patients to the system overall as some 20% of its immediate care center patients are new to NorthShore.

The organization has also been working to expand its medical group to broaden its offering of specialized health care services. In 2017 it began offering genetic testing as part of patients' annual checkups through its Center for Personalized Medicine.

Fortunately for NorthShore it thrives in an area where the population is young and poverty is limited. While the health system receives a good amount of revenue from Medicare and Medicaid it also receives income from commercial insurance payers with a low level of charity care despite economic turmoil in the US. This patient mix has allowed the company to maintain revenue and income growth as well as plenty of cash on hand to fund its expansion initiatives.

In 2017 Northshore scrapped plans to merge with Advocate Health Care to create Advocate NorthShore Health Partners (ANHP). The combination would have created the largest integrated health care delivery system in Illinois (serving 3 million patients a year) and the 11th largest not-for-profit health care system in the US. The merger was blocked by the FTC which claimed that the deal would harm consumers by raising prices and lowering health care quality.

EXECUTIVES

President Northshore University Healthsystem Medical Group, Joseph Golbus
President Northshore Evanston Hospital, Douglas M. Silverstein
President Northshore Skokie Hospital, Kristen Murtos
Chief Investment Officer, Thomas H. Hodges
Chief Nursing Officer, Nancy Semerdjian
Cio, Steven Smith
President Highland Park Hopital, Jesse Peterson Hall
Evp Finance And Cfo, Gary E. Weiss
Chief Scientific Officer Northshore Research Institute, Michael S. Caplan
President Northshore Glenbrook Hospital, Sean OÂ'Grady
President And Ceo, Gerald (J.P.) Gallagher
Executive Director Northshore Foundation, Murray T. Ancell
Avp Application Services Health Information Technology, Kate Steele
Medical Director, Harry J Jaffe
Assistant Vice President, Kevin Katz
Vice President Perioperative Services, Beverly Beine
Svp Marketing And Corporate Communications, Carol Franczek
Chairman, Mark R. Neaman
Unit Secretary, Sumbul Tahir
Vice Chairman Northshore Orthopaedic Institute And Division Head Of Hand And Upper Extremity Department Of Orthopaedic Surgery, Leon Benson

LOCATIONS

HQ: NORTHSHORE UNIVERSITY HEALTHSYSTEM
1301 CENTRAL ST, EVANSTON, IL 602011613
Phone: 847 570-5295
Web: WWW.NORTHSHORE.ORG

COMPETITORS

Advocate Health Care	MetroSouth Medical
Central DuPage Hospital	Northwest Community Healthcare
Children's Hopsital of Chicago	Northwestern Memorial HealthCare
Community Health Systems	Rockford Health System
Mercy Hospital and Medical Center	Rush System for Health
	University of Chicago Medical Center

HISTORICAL FINANCIALS
Company Type: Private

Income Statement   FYE: September 30

	REVENUE ($ mil.)	NET INCOME ($ mil.)	NET PROFIT MARGIN	EMPLOYEES
09/18	2,153	197	9.2%	9,000
09/09	1,085	(71)	—	—
09/08	26	0	0.4%	—
09/05	1,061	64	6.0%	—
Annual Growth	5.6%	9.1%	—	—

2018 Year-End Financials
Return on assets: 5.0%   Cash ($ mil.): 52
Return on equity: 7.0%
Current ratio: 1.00

NORTHSIDE HOSPITAL, INC.

Northside Hospital is no one-trick pony — it actually operates three hospitals serving Atlanta and surrounding areas. Also known as the Northside Healthcare Delivery System the Northside Hospital network includes some 840 licensed beds and more than 2500 physicians on multiple campuses with a host of outpatient health facilities including physician office parks and specialized cancer centers. All of Northside's hospitals are full-service acute-care facilities that provide specialty care including cancer care surgery radiology and women's health. Northside Hospital which opened in 1970 is merging with Gwinnett Health System.

Operations
In addition to its 537-bed hospital in Sandy Springs Northside has hospitals in Cherokee and Forsyth counties as well as more than 120 outpatient centers across Georgia.

Northside Hospital handles about 700000 patient visits annually at its facilities. The organization's cancer treatment division partners with the Cancer Support Community of Atlanta to provide mental health social and educational services to cancer patients and survivors as well as family members and friends.

Geographic Reach
Northside Hospital's three campuses are located in Atlanta Forsyth and Cherokee Georgia. It also operate about 40 outpatient clinics and physician practices scattered across the northern Atlanta metropolitan area.

Strategy
Northside Hospital is conducting expansion and renovation efforts to meet the needs of area residents. It recently completed an expansion and relocation of its Cherokee County Spine & Pain Center (near the Cherokee hospital campus). In 2015 it expanded its radiology offerings with a new outpatient imaging center in Jasper.

After two years of talks with fellow Georgia-based hospital system Gwinnett Health Northside and Gwinnett have agreed to merge operations. The combined system will have nearly 3500 physicians and 1480 beds.

EXECUTIVES

Cfo, Peggy Gatliff
Vp Administration And Ceo Northside Hospital-forsyth, Robert Putnam
Ceo Northside Hospital-cherokee, William (Billy) Hayes
Chair Department Of Obstetrics And Gynecology, Ceana Nezhat
Ceo Northside Hospital-forsyth, Skip Putnam
Coo, Peter Kennedy
Vice President Purchasing, Chuck Dalton
Director Of Pharmacy Supervisor, Mike Tate
Director Of Radiology Services, Mary Shepherd
Vice President Marketing And Communications, Lee Echols
Pharmacy Manager, Lorenzo Bethea
Director Of Pharmacy, Rae Benton
Senior Vice President, Stephanie Hamner
Vp Of Finance And Administration, Katherine Boelte
Secretary, Beth Keivani
Secretary, Gordon Azar

LOCATIONS

HQ: NORTHSIDE HOSPITAL, INC.
1000 JOHNSON FERRY RD, ATLANTA, GA 303421611
Phone: 404 851-8000
Web: WWW.NORTHSIDE.COM

Selected Locations
Alpharetta Medical Campus
Dunwoody Cancer Center
Imaging at Peachtree Dunwoody
Medlock Bridge Imaging
Meridian Park Plaza
Northside Hospital Doctors Center
Northside Hospital-Atlanta
Northside Hospital-Cherokee
Northside Hospital-Forsyth
Northside-Forsyth Outpatient Surgery Center
Northside Sugar Hill Imaging (Buford)
Pediatric Center at Northside/Alpharetta
Roswell Cancer Center
Townelake Medical Office/Riverstone Imaging

COMPETITORS

Children's Healthcare of Atlanta	Piedmont Healthcare
DeKalb Medical	Regency Hospital
Emory Healthcare	Shepherd Center
Grady Health System	SunLink Health Systems
Gwinnett Health System	The Fulton-DeKalb Hospital Authority
Northeast Georgia Health System	WellStar Health System

HISTORICAL FINANCIALS
Company Type: Private

Income Statement   FYE: September 30

	REVENUE ($ mil.)	NET INCOME ($ mil.)	NET PROFIT MARGIN	EMPLOYEES
09/17	2,002	301	15.0%	8,000
09/16	1,897	157	8.3%	—
09/15	1,733	223	12.9%	—
09/13	1,253	109	8.7%	—
Annual Growth	12.4%	28.9%	—	—

2017 Year-End Financials
Return on assets: 13.5%   Cash ($ mil.): 427
Return on equity: 19.6%
Current ratio: 4.90

NORTHSIDE INDEPENDENT SCHOOL DISTRICT

EXECUTIVES

Supt, John Folks
Supt*, Brian T Woods
Pres*, Robert Blount Jr
V Pres*, Katie N Reed
SEC*, Bennie L Cole
Principal, Ellen Sutton
General, Lora Mathison
Manager, Joe Delgadillo
Teacher, John Moran
Assistant Director, Ernest Vasquez
Director of Information Techno, Kellye Halpern
Auditors: RSM US LLP SAN ANTONIO TEXAS

LOCATIONS

HQ: NORTHSIDE INDEPENDENT SCHOOL DISTRICT
5900 EVERS RD, SAN ANTONIO, TX 782381606
Phone: 210 397-8770
Web: WWW.NISD.NET

HISTORICAL FINANCIALS

Company Type: Private

Income Statement   FYE: August 31

	REVENUE ($ mil.)	NET INCOME ($ mil.)	NET PROFIT MARGIN	EMPLOYEES
08/18	1,203	57	4.8%	13,698
08/17	1,152	75	6.5%	—
08/16	1,119	16	1.5%	—
08/15	1,057	64	6.1%	—
Annual Growth	4.4%	(3.5%)	—	—

2018 Year-End Financials

Return on assets: 1.9%   Cash ($ mil.): 691
Return on equity: —
Current ratio: —

NORTHWEST DAIRY ASSOCIATION

Northwest Dairy Association (NDA) members milk a lot of cows. The dairy cooperative's 550-plus member/farmers ship 7.2 billion pounds of milk annually which is processed by the co-op's subsidiary Darigold and packaged and sold under the Darigold label. NDA produces fluid and cultured dairy products including milk butter cottage cheese sour cream and yogurt that altogether generate some $2 billion in sales. It also makes bulk butter and cheese milk powder and whey products. The co-op caters to several sectors nationwide. Its customers include food retailers and wholesalers as well as foodservice and food-manufacturing companies. The association's membership spans half a dozen US states.

EXECUTIVES

Ceo, Jim Werkhoven
Pres, James Wegner
V Pres, Steve Rowe
SEC-Treas, Randy Lindley

Corporate Health, Erin Allen
Quality Control Manager, Geoff Campbell
Corporate Counsel, Kristi Keene
Senior Director, Marie-Claude Milot
Asstchief Engineer, Paul Lord

LOCATIONS

HQ: NORTHWEST DAIRY ASSOCIATION
5601 6TH AVE S STE 300, SEATTLE, WA 981082544
Phone: 206 284-7220
Web: WWW.DARIGOLD.COM

PRODUCTS/OPERATIONS

Selected Products

Consumer
Butter
Buttermilk
Cottage cheese
Cream
Half and half
Milk
Sour cream
Whipping cream
Yogurt
Ingredients
Bleached sweet dry whey
Colored cheddar cheese
Cultured skim milk powder
Milk protein concentrate
Monterey Jack cheese
Nonfat dry milk
Salted sweet cream butter
Skim milk powder
Sweet cream buttermilk powder
Unsalted butter
Whey protein concentrate

COMPETITORS

Associated Milk
 Producers
Berkeley Farms
California Dairies
 Inc.
Dairy Farmers of
 America

Dean Foods
Humboldt Creamery
Land O'Lakes
Straus Family Creamery
Tillamook County
 Creamery Association

HISTORICAL FINANCIALS

Company Type: Private

Income Statement   FYE: March 31

	REVENUE ($ mil.)	NET INCOME ($ mil.)	NET PROFIT MARGIN	EMPLOYEES
03/08	2,207	87	4.0%	1,300
03/07	1,450	12	0.9%	—
03/04	1,297	(6)	—	—
03/03	1,140	2	0.2%	—
Annual Growth	14.1%	107.0%		—

2008 Year-End Financials

Return on assets: 17.7%   Cash ($ mil.): 10
Return on equity: 41.5%
Current ratio: 1.80

NORTHWEST FARM CREDIT SERVICES

Customer-owned financial cooperative Northwest Farm Credit Services is an agricultural lender that provides financial services to farmers ranchers agribusinesses commercial fishermen timber producers and rural home owners in Alaska Idaho Montana Oregon and Washington. The company has a network of around 45 branches and offers a broad range of flexible loan programs to meet the needs of people in the agriculture business. Northwest Farm Credit also provides leasing services appraisal services and life mortgage disability and crop insurance as well as legal advocacy and assistance to customers in need. It is part of the Farm Credit System a network of lenders serving the US agriculture industry.

Operations
The credit union provides financing and related services to farmers ranchers agribusinesses commercial fishermen timber producers rural homeowners and crop insurance customers. Northwest Farm Credit provides $10.3 billion in loans. Farm Credit System a nationwide network of borrower-owned lending institutions of which it is part provides $205 billion in loans to rural America.

Geographic Reach
Northwest Farm Credit serves customers through 45 offices located in Idaho Alaska Montana Oregon and Washington.

Sales and Marketing
Northwest Farm Credit finances farmers ranchers agribusinesses commercial fishermen timber producers and rural homeowners as well as farm-related businesses agricultural cooperatives and rural utilities.

Financial Performance
In 2015 the company's net revenue increased by 5% due to higher net interest income driven by increased loan volume.
Northwest Farm Credit's net income rose by 12% due to higher net revenues and a decrease in income tax expense.
In 2015 the company's operating cash inflow increased by 19%.

Strategy
The company plans to continue to fund lending operations primarily through its borrowing relationship with CoBank (a fellow Farm Credit System member) and from retained earnings.

Mergers and Acquisitions
In 2014 the company expanded its operations in Montana by buying Culbertson State Agency's crop insurance portfolio.

Company Background
The US Congress created the Farm Credit System in 1916 to meet the financial needs of farmers ranchers and cooperatives who invest as well as borrow from the institutions within the system. All Farm Credit System members are regulated by the Farm Credit Administration.

EXECUTIVES

Evp Financial Services, Fred (Fred) DePell
Evp And General Counsel, Thomas (Tom) Tracy
Evp Corporate Administration And Secretary, Joan E. Haynes
Evp Cfo And Cio, Tom Nakano
Relationship Manager Vice President, Kurt Wittman
Vice President Human Resources, Alice Hardin
Vice President, Carol L Sobson
Vice President Appraisal Services, Joe Moore
Chairman, Drew Eggers
Vice Chairman, Kevin Riel
Auditors: PRICEWATERHOUSECOOPERS LLP S

LOCATIONS

HQ: NORTHWEST FARM CREDIT SERVICES
2001 S FLINT RD, SPOKANE, WA 992249198
Phone: 509 838-2429
Web: WWW.NORTHWESTFCS.COM

PRODUCTS/OPERATIONS

2015 Sales

	$ mil.	% of total
Interest Income	412	82
Patronage income	52	11
Financially Related Services	19	4
loans and other fee	6	1
Other non-interest income	11	2
Total	**502**	**100**

COMPETITORS

Bank of America	U.S. Bancorp
First Interstate	Wells Fargo
Idaho Independent Bank	Zions Bancorporation
KeyCorp	
Northwest Bancorporation	

HISTORICAL FINANCIALS

Company Type: Private

Income Statement

FYE: December 31

	ASSETS ($ mil.)	NET INCOME ($ mil.)	INCOME AS % OF ASSETS	EMPLOYEES
12/14	10,252	228	2.2%	500
12/13	9,604	236	2.5%	—
12/12	9,471	187	2.0%	—
12/11	8,696	159	1.8%	—
Annual Growth	**5.6%**	**12.7%**	**—**	**—**

2014 Year-End Financials

Return on assets: 2.2%   Sales ($ mil): 476
Return on equity: 12.0%

NORTHWESTERN MEMORIAL HOSPITAL

EXECUTIVES

Ceo, Dean Harrison
Pres, Richard J Gannotta
Cfo, Peter McCanna
Chb, William J Brodsky
Associate Professor of Medicin, Gary Noskin
Health Consultant, Hattie Johnson
Resource Coordinator, Larry Klowden
Human Resources Program Direct, Maria Lin
Interim Director Radiology, Michael Manka
Neurologist, Alan G Shepard
Urology, William Catalona

LOCATIONS

HQ: NORTHWESTERN MEMORIAL HOSPITAL
251 E HURON ST, CHICAGO, IL 606113055
Phone: 312 926-2000
Web: WWW.NM.ORG

HISTORICAL FINANCIALS

Company Type: Private

Income Statement

FYE: August 31

	REVENUE ($ mil.)	NET INCOME ($ mil.)	NET PROFIT MARGIN	EMPLOYEES
08/16	1,499	237	15.8%	5,800
08/15	1,337	198	14.8%	—
08/10	1,380	64	4.7%	—
08/09	1,304	4	0.3%	—
Annual Growth	**2.0%**	**76.0%**	**—**	**—**

NORTHWESTERN UNIVERSITY

With its main campus in the Chicago suburb of Evanston Northwestern University (NU) serves its 21000 students through about a dozen schools and colleges such as the Medill School of Journalism and the McCormick School of Engineering and Applied Sciences. Its Chicago campus houses the schools of law and medicine as well as several hospitals of the McGaw Medical Center. With a faculty of more than 3300 the school has a student-to-teacher ratio of about 6:1. NU is home to several research centers and community outreach programs; it also has a branch in Qatar. It is the only private member of the Big 10 conference; varsity sports include baseball football basketball and fencing.

Operations

Among NU's top-ranked programs are its law school medical school and its engineering program. Its Kellogg Graduate School of Management consistently ranks among the nation's top five business schools by Business Week and U.S. News & World Report. Its prestigious journalism and drama programs produced such alumni as Charlton Heston Gary Marshall and Julia Louis-Dreyfus. Retired US Supreme Court Justice John Paul Stevens is also a former Wildcat.

NU spends its $1.6 billion research budget (including about $620 million in sponsored funds) performing research at 24 university research centers (and nearly 100 other centers) in areas such as materials science biomedical engineering African studies performance studies and marketing. The school has earned recognition for its research in genetic medicine nanotechnology biochemistry neuroscience cancer research and materials sciences. NU partners have included the Argonne National Laboratory Fermilab and local universities.

Geographic Reach

NU's main campus in Chicago encompasses about 240 acres in Evanston. The university operates another 25-acre campus in Chicago as well as its education center in Qatar. NU was founded to serve the Northwest region of the US which includes parts or all of the states of Illinois Indiana Michigan Minnesota Ohio and Wisconsin.

Financial Performance

NU reported a 6% decrease in revenues to $2.1 billion in fiscal 2015 (ended August) a drop that was primarily driven by a decline in private gifts. Net income plummeted 91% to $192 million that year and operating cash outflow totaled $91.4 million.

HISTORY

Northwestern University's Methodist founders met in 1850 to create an institution of higher learning serving the original Northwest Territory. The university was chartered in 1851 and two years later it acquired 379 acres of property north of Chicago on Lake Michigan. The town of Evanston was later named after John Evans one of the school's founders.

Classes began in the fall of 1855 with two professors and 10 students. By 1869 Northwestern had more than 100 students and began to admit women. In 1870 Northwestern signed an affiliation agreement with the Chicago Medical College (founded 1859) and three years later it joined with the original University of Chicago (no relation to the current institution) to create the Union College of Law. When the University of Chicago closed in

1886 due to financial difficulties Northwestern took control of the law school. The university reorganized in 1891 consolidating its affiliated professional schools (dentistry law medicine and pharmacy) into the university.

By 1900 Northwestern had become the third-largest university in the US (after Harvard and Michigan) with an enrollment of 2700. During the 1920s the university created the Medill School of Journalism named for Joseph Medill founder of the Chicago Tribune. In 1924 the school's athletic teams adopted the nickname Wildcats and two years later the university completed the primary buildings that form its Chicago campus. Northwestern suffered a drop in enrollment during the Depression but after WWII it saw student numbers swell as veterans took advantage of the GI Bill. Expansion continued throughout the 1960s and 1970s.

In 1985 the school and the City of Evanston began developing a research center to attract more high-tech industries to the area. The university's graduate school of business achieved national prominence in 1988 after it was ranked #1 in the US by Business Week. In 1995 Northwestern's football team forever the doormat of the Big 10 achieved national fame when it won the conference championship.

In 1998 faculty member Professor John Pople won the Nobel Prize in Chemistry the first Nobel Prize awarded to a faculty member while teaching at the university.

Northwestern won a significant legal battle in 1998 when a judge ruled that the university was not obligated to pay a faculty member simply because he had been granted tenure.

The university's dental school closed its doors in 2001 citing the difficulties posed for private schools in providing a competitive dental education.

EXECUTIVES

Vp Finance Operations And Treasurer, Ingrid S. Stafford, age 66
Vp Information Technology And Cio, Sean B. Reynolds
Dean Kellogg School Of Management, Sally E. Blount
Vp And Chief Investment Officer, William H. (Will) McLean
Dean School Of Communication, Barbara J. O'Keefe
Evp, Nim Chinniah
Provost, Daniel I. Linzer, age 66
Dean Libraries, Sarah M. Pritchard
President, Morton O. Shapiro
Vp Global Marketing And Cfhief Marketing Officer, Mary L. Baglivo
Dean Northwestern University In Qatar, Everette E. Dennis
Dean School Of Professional Studies, Thomas F. Gibbons
Dean Medill School Of Journalism Media And Integrated Marketing Communications, Bradley Hamm
Dean Graduate School, Dwight A. McBride
Dean Bienen School Of Music, Toni-Marie Montgomery
Dean Feinberg School Of Medicine, Eric G. Neilson
Dean School Of Education And Social Policy, Penelope L. Peterson
Dean Weinberg College Of Arts And Sciences, Adrian W. B. Randolph
Dean Mccormick School Of Engineering And Applied Science, Julio M. Ottino
Dean Pritzker School Of Law, Daniel B. Rodriguez
Vice President Student Affairs, William Banis
Physical Therapy And Human Movement Sc, Julius Dewald

Vp Of It, Mylowe Wooley
Associate Vice President For Research, Fruma
  Yehiely
Vice President For Student Affairs, Margaret
  Sullivan
**Assistant Vice President Marketing And
  Communications,** Natasha DiPrima
**Associate Vice President Alumni Relations And
  Development,** David Lively
Associate Vice President And Executive Director,
  Alicia Loffler
Medical Director, Linda Guthrie
Vice President For International Relations,
  Devora Grynspan
Assistant Vice President, Christopher Watson
**Vice President Of Marketing And Product
  Management,** Mark Crandon
Assistant Vice President For Research, Meg
  McDonald
Vice President, Jeffrey Kopin
**Vice President For Research Professor Of
  Biomedical Engineering,** Jay Walsh
**Senior Vice President Global Human Resources
  Executive,** Mikenzie Steffens
Associate Vice President And Dean Of Students,
  Todd Adams
Associate Vice President Administrative Systems,
  Kristine O'Brien
**Director Of Health Safety Security And
  Environment,** Michael McDonough
Assistant Vice President Of Program Review,
  Megan Blackwelder
**Director Of Admissions Evening And Weekend
  Mba Program Kellogg School Of Management,**
  Emily Haydon
Vice President Information Technology, Jane Erb
Associate Vice President Human Resources, Dana
  Bradley
Director Of Clinical Services, David Shor
**Executive Vice President Executive Director
  Senior Vice President Managing Director General
  Manager Vice President,** Mike Null Monahan
Medical Director, Matthew Kippenhan
Vp Compliance And Governance, Betty Mcphillimy
Vice President Information Technology, Meghan
  Monaghan
Chairman, William A. Osborn, age 71
Assistant Treasurer, Richard Emrich
Secretary, Debbie Robert
**Vice Chair For Research Department Of Medical
  Social Sciences,** Richard Gershon
Secretary 1, Sheila Hodges
Board Member, Virginia Delancey
Board Member, Angela Y Lee
Treasurer, Spencer Carlson
Division Secretary, Kelly Thompson
Board Member, Leon Platanias
Treasurer And Membership, Jack Snarr
Auditors: PRICEWATERHOUSECOOPERS LLP

LOCATIONS

HQ: NORTHWESTERN UNIVERSITY
  633 CLARK ST, EVANSTON, IL 602080001
Phone: 847 491-3741

PRODUCTS/OPERATIONS

Selected Programs
Continuing and Professional Programs
Graduate Programs
Pre-Collegiate Programs
Undergraduate Programs

Selected Schools and Colleges
Bienen School of Music
Feinberg School of Medicine
The Graduate School
Kellogg School of Management
McCormick School of Engineering and Applied Science
Medill School of Journalism Media Integrated Marketing
  Communications
Northwestern in Qatar

School of Communication
School of Continuing Studies
School of Education and Social Policy
School of Law
Weinberg College of Arts and Science

HISTORICAL FINANCIALS
Company Type: Private

Income Statement   FYE: August 31

	REVENUE ($ mil.)	NET INCOME ($ mil.)	NET PROFIT MARGIN	EMPLOYEES
08/18	2,464	560	22.7%	5,954
08/17	2,309	668	29.0%	
Annual Growth	6.7%	(16.2%)	—	—

2018 Year-End Financials
Return on assets: 3.6%   Cash ($ mil.): 185
Return on equity: 4.6%
Current ratio: —

NORTON HOSPITALS, INC

EXECUTIVES

Pres, Steven A Williams
SEC*, Robert B Azar
Treas*, Michael W Gough
V Pres*, Russell F Cox
SEC*, Theodore T Myre Jr
Internal Medicine Practitioner, Deep Ajmani
Manager of Management Informat, Joy Karrer
Human Resources Director, Judy Settle
Human Resources Director, Kevin Guthrie
Internal Medicine Practitioner, Sergio Cardinali
Chaplain, Kerry Wentworth

LOCATIONS

HQ: NORTON HOSPITALS, INC
  200 E CHESTNUT ST, LOUISVILLE, KY 402021831
Phone: 502 629-8000
Web: WWW.NORTONHEALTHCARE.COM

HISTORICAL FINANCIALS
Company Type: Private

Income Statement   FYE: December 31

	REVENUE ($ mil.)	NET INCOME ($ mil.)	NET PROFIT MARGIN	EMPLOYEES
12/15	1,712	137	8.0%	1,500
12/14	1,577	187	11.9%	
Annual Growth	8.6%	(26.7%)	—	—

2015 Year-End Financials
Return on assets: 8.0%   Cash ($ mil.): —
Return on equity: 8.6%
Current ratio: 2.20

NOVA SOUTHEASTERN UNIVERSITY, INC.

Nova Southeastern University (NSU) gives a whole new meaning to "school of sharks." NSU whose mascot is the deep sea predator has an enrollment of more than 27000 students and offers a variety of undergraduate graduate and professional academic programs. NSU offers degrees in several medical disciplines (osteopathic medicine pharmacy optometry nursing) marine biology business law education and computer sciences. The not-for-profit independent school operates four campuses in the Miami-Fort Lauderdale area several health centers and an oceanographic center. Founded in 1964 Nova University merged with Southeastern University of the Health Sciences in 1994 to become Nova Southeastern University.

Operations

In addition to its undergraduate and graduate programs NSU also operates The University School a pre-K through 12th grade college preparatory day school that draws part of its staff from NSU's School of Education and Human services. The university's Mailman Segal Institute for Early Childhood Studies serves the local community with programming for parents and educators.

Geographic Reach

NSU is a distance education pioneer (it was the first US university to offer graduate programs online) offering classes on the Internet as well as at six regional centers in Florida and Puerto Rico.

Financial Performance

Continuing a trend of earnings growth over the last five years from organic growth measures NSU reported a 4% rise in revenues in 2014 to some $640 million. The growth was attributed to increased tuition and fee income as well as revenues from auxiliary enterprises and government grants.

Strategy

As universities do NSU regularly invests in facility upgrades to meet the growing needs of its students. In 2014 it broke ground on the NSU Center for Collaborative Research (CCR) that will house an IBM supercomputer a tech incubator one of the state's largest wet labs and space for guest researchers. Other CCR facilities will include cancer and neuro-immune institutes an incubator for security businesses and an entire floor for the US Geological Survey which will partner with the university on research into Everglades restoration projects.

EXECUTIVES

**Vice President Community And Government
  Affairs Professor,** Larry Calderon
Chancellor Health Professions Division, Frederick
  Lippman
Ceo President And Trustee, George L. Hanbury
Vp Finance, W. David Heron
Dean Student Affairs, Brad Williams
**Director Alvin Sherman Library Research And
  Information Technology Center,** Harriett
  MacDougall
Dean Shepard Broad Law Center, Athornia Steele
University Provost And Evp Academic Affairs,
  Frank DePiano
Dean University School, Jerome Chermak
Dean College Of Health Care Sciences, Richard E.
  Davis
Dean Oceanographic Center, Richard E. Dodge
Dean Center For Psychological Studies, Karen
  Grosby
Dean College Of Medical Sciences, Harold E.
  Laubach

Dean Mailman Segal Institute For Early Childhood Studies, Roni Leiderman
Dean College Of Optometry, David S. Loshin
Dean College Of Pharmacy, Andrés Malavé
Dean Farquhar College Of Arts And Sciences, Don Rosenblum
Dean College Of Osteopathic Medicine, Anthony J. Silvagni
Dean Fischler School Of Education, H. Wells Singleton
Dean College Of Dental Medicine, Robert A. Uchin
Dean Graduate School Of Humanities And Social Sciences, Honggang Yang
Evp And Coo, Jacqueline A. Travisano
Senior Executive Assistant President Manager, Shirley Naidoo
Ceo Health Clinics, Robert S. Oller
Vp Information Technology And Cio, Tom West
Executive Assistant Vice President, Katharine Perren
Pharmacy Manager, Todd Schmidt
Vice President Human Resources, Robert Pietrykowski
Senior Human Resources Advisor To Vice President Of Development, Roxana Ross
Vice President For Legal Affairs, Joel Berman
Executive Vice President, Catalina Gonzalez
Vice President, Heather Ruff
Vice President Finance, Noel Oliveras
Director Of Admissions, Bridget Varisco
Vice President Marketing, Kyle Fisher
Department Chair, Wilma Robles
Phi Lambda Sigma Vice President, Meredith Brook
Evp And Coo, Harry Moon
Vice President, Jim Parrish
Chair, Ronald G. Assaf
Vice Chair, Barry J. Silverman
Auditors: LB KPMG LLP GREENSBORO NC

LOCATIONS

HQ: NOVA SOUTHEASTERN UNIVERSITY, INC.
3301 COLLEGE AVE, DAVIE, FL 333147796
Phone: 954 262-7300
Web: WWW.NOVA.EDU

COMPETITORS

Florida Atlantic University
Florida International University
University of Florida

HISTORICAL FINANCIALS

Company Type: Private

Income Statement				FYE: June 30
	REVENUE ($ mil.)	NET INCOME ($ mil.)	NET PROFIT MARGIN	EMPLOYEES
06/15	678	45	6.7%	2,500
06/12	689	48	7.1%	—
06/10	612	22	3.7%	—
Annual Growth	2.1%	15.2%	—	—

2015 Year-End Financials
Return on assets: 3.5%   Cash ($ mil.): 35
Return on equity: 6.6%
Current ratio: 0.20

NOVANT HEALTH, INC.

With 14 hospitals and about 2600 beds Novant Health certainly has what it takes to keep denizens along the Eastern Seaboard in tip-top condition. The not-for-profit health system provides medical care to residents in more than 30 counties throughout North and South Carolina Georgia and Virginia. Its largest facilities include the 920-bed Forsyth Medical Center in Winston-Salem North Carolina and the 600-bed Presbyterian Hospital in Charlotte North Carolina. It also operates about 340 physician clinics outpatient surgery and diagnostic imaging centers. Additionally Novant is home to nursing homes rehabilitation and community outreach programs and philanthropic foundations.

Operations

In addition to owning and operating an array of health care facilities Novant provides management services for hospitals including information technology and managed care efficiency. The health care network has been expanding its services in the region through partnerships and acquisitions.

The system performs some 120000 surgeries each year.

Geographic Reach

Novant Health has dual headquarters in Winston-Salem and Charlotte North Carolina; it provides health care services to more than 500 locations.

Financial Performance

Novant reported a 7% increase in revenue for 2014 from $3.5 billion to $3.8 billion due largely to a 5% increase in patient revenue. Net income dropped from $395 million in 2013 to $106 million in 2014. This was primarily driven by a drop in investment earnings and charges related to defined benefit plans.

Cash flow from operations rose 6% to $319 million that year.

Strategy

Novant's five foundations — Presbyterian Hospital Foundation Forsyth Medical Center Foundation Thomasville Medical Center Foundation Rowan Regional Medical Center Foundation and Prince William Health System Foundation — help the organization fund its various methods of growth be they acquisitions or organic growth. They also aid the medical provider in establishing and running its various community outreach programs. Novant provides community education and screenings and supports health clinics that care for the uninsured.

In 2014 the system continued to expand its services and it geographic footprint. It opened a new medical center in Clemmons North Carolina and added a new $19 million geriatric psychiatric facility to its Franklin Medical Center. Novant also began the process of converting all its facilities to electronic health records per a government requirement and opening clinics inside some Charlotte Target store locations.

Company Background

Novant Health was formed in 1997 by a merger of Carolina Medicorp Presbyterian Healthcare and Thomasville Medical Center.

EXECUTIVES

President Novant, Paul M. Wiles
Evp And Chief Clinical Officer, Sallye A. Liner
President And Ceo, Carl S. Armato
Evp And Chief Medical Officer, Stephen L. Wallenhaupt
President Forsyth Medical Center, Denise Mihal
Evp And Cfo, Fred M. Hargett
Evp And Coo, Jeff Lindsay
Evp And Chief Administrative Officer, Jacqueline R. Daniels
Evp And Chief Consumer Officer, Jesse Cureton
President Tml Copiers Xerox Company, Michael Hoover
Coo, Richard Belden
Chairman Department Of Ob/gyn At The Novant Health Matthews Medical Center, Gregory Reynolds

Vp Operational Design And Improvement, Andrew Piersol
Vice President Business Development And, Derek Goldin
Executive Vice President And Chief Human Resources Officer, Janet Smith-Hill
Vice President Human Resources, Marilyn Gilliam
Pharmacy Manager, Ron Lyerly
Vice President Finance, Melanie Shipek
Associate Vice President Treasury, Mitchell Clark
Vice President, Heather Bogan
Chairman, Michael B. Baughan
Vice Chairman, Robert H. Stolz
Board Member, Melissa Ward
Advisory Board Member, Neil Desmond

LOCATIONS

HQ: NOVANT HEALTH, INC.
2085 FRONTIS PLAZA BLVD, WINSTON SALEM, NC 271035614
Phone: 336 277-1404

PRODUCTS/OPERATIONS

Selected Health Facilities
Brunswick Community Hospital (Supply North Carolina)
Forsyth Medical Center (Winston-Salem North Carolina)
Franklin Regional Medical Center (Louisburg North Carolina)
Kerner's Medical Center (Kernersville North Carolina)
Medical Park Hospital (Winston-Salem North Carolina)
The Oaks at Forsyth (residental long-term care; Winston-Salem North Carolina)
Presbyterian Hospital (Charlotte North Carolina)
Presbyterian Hemby Children's Hospital
Presbyterian Hospital Huntersville (Huntersville North Carolina)
Presbyterian Hospital Matthews (Charlotte North Carolina)
Presbyterian Orthopaedic Hospital (Charlotte North Carolina)
Rowan Regional Medical Center (Salisbury North Carolina)
Springwood Care Center (residental long-term care; Winston-Salem North Carolina)
Thomasville Medical Center (Thomasville North Carolina)
Upstate Carolina Medical Center (Gaffney South Carolina)

Selected Services
Assisted living
Behavioral health
Blood services
Breast health
Cancer
Children's services
Clinical research
Corporate health & wellness
Critical care
Diabetes
Emergency
Employer services
Heart & vascular
Hospice
Imaging
Infusion services
Inpatient services
Laboratory services
Orthopedics
Pain management
Pastoral care
Pharmacy
Rehabilitation
Respiratory services
Sickle cell
Sleep health
Sports medicine
Stroke & neurosciences
Supportive care
Surgery
Urgent and express care
Weight loss services
Wellness programs and services
Women's health
Women's heart health
Wound care

COMPETITORS

Alamance Regional Medical Center	High Point Regional Health System
Bon Secours Health	New Hanover Regional Medical Center
Carilion Clinic	
CaroMont	Rex Healthcare
Carolinas HealthCare System	Riverside Health System (Virginia)
Carolinas Medical Center-NorthEast	Rowan Regional Medical Center
Cone Health	Sentara Healthcare
Davis Regional Medical Center	UNC Hospitals
	Upstate Affiliate
Duke University Health System	Vidant Health
	WakeMed
HCA	

HISTORICAL FINANCIALS

Company Type: Private

Income Statement   FYE: December 31

	REVENUE ($ mil.)	NET INCOME ($ mil.)	NET PROFIT MARGIN	EMPLOYEES
12/18	4,985	109	2.2%	13,800
12/17	167	(142)	—	—
12/16	4,340	559	12.9%	—
12/14	0	0	—	—
Annual Growth	—	—	—	—

2018 Year-End Financials

Return on assets: 1.7%   Cash ($ mil.): 228
Return on equity: 2.7%
Current ratio: 1.50

NOVARTIS PHARMACEUTICALS CORPORATION

EXECUTIVES

Pres, Marie-France Tschudin
Sr V-Pres-Cmo*, Nancy Lurker
Pres*, Andre Wyss
V Pres*, Yves Teirlynck
V Pres*, Julie Kane
Coo*, Alex Gorsky
V-Pres-Cfo*, Gary E Rosenthal
Cfo*, Helen Boudreau
Vice-President Corporate Commu, Anna Frable
Scientist, Katherine Chan
Manager, Debra Bloodgood
Auditors: PRICEWATERHOUSECOOPERS LLP-BR

LOCATIONS

HQ: NOVARTIS PHARMACEUTICALS CORPORATION
 1 HEALTH PLZ, EAST HANOVER, NJ 079361016
Phone: 862 778-8300
Web: WWW.NOVARTIS.COM

HISTORICAL FINANCIALS

Company Type: Private

Income Statement   FYE: December 31

	REVENUE ($ mil.)	NET INCOME ($ mil.)	NET PROFIT MARGIN	EMPLOYEES
12/16	49,436	6,698	13.5%	7,000
12/15	49,440	17,794	36.0%	—
12/13	58,831	9,292	15.8%	—
Annual Growth	(5.6%)	(10.3%)	—	—

2016 Year-End Financials

Return on assets: 5.1%   Cash ($ mil.): 7,007
Return on equity: 8.9%
Current ratio: 1.10

NOVO CONSTRUCTION, INC.

EXECUTIVES

Ceo, James C Fowler
Pres*, Jim Fowler
SEC*, Robert Williamson
Project Manager, Scott Plummer
Superintendent, Dave Fournier
Superintendent, Todd Freeman
Executive Officer, Colin Stoner
Director, Brian Cronin
Project Manager, Kevin Ho
Project Manager, Ryan Smith
Project Executive, Doug Ballou

LOCATIONS

HQ: NOVO CONSTRUCTION, INC.
 1460 OBRIEN DR, MENLO PARK, CA 940251432
Phone: 650 701-1500
Web: WWW.NOVOCONSTRUCTION.COM

HISTORICAL FINANCIALS

Company Type: Private

Income Statement   FYE: October 31

	REVENUE ($ mil.)	NET INCOME ($ mil.)	NET PROFIT MARGIN	EMPLOYEES
10/18	684	7	1.1%	155
10/17	603	5	0.9%	—
10/16	577	6	1.1%	—
10/15	553	5	1.0%	—
Annual Growth	7.3%	12.0%	—	—

2018 Year-End Financials

Return on assets: 3.1%   Cash ($ mil.): 40
Return on equity: 88.1%
Current ratio: 1.00

NPC RESTAURANT HOLDINGS, LLC

NPC International is the prince of pepperoni in a pizza empire. The world's largest franchisee of Pizza Hut restaurants NPC owns and operates more than 1275 pizza restaurants and delivery kitchens in about 30 states. The quick-service eateries located mostly in such southern states as Alabama Florida Georgia and Tennessee serve a variety of pizza styles as well as such items as buffalo wings and pasta. The pizza parlors are franchised from YUM! Brands the world's largest fast-food restaurant company. NPC was founded in 1962 by former chairman Gene Bicknell who was one of the first Pizza Hut franchisees. The company was acquired by private equity group NPC International Holdings in late 2011.

Operations

NPC runs more than 20 Wendys restaurants in addition to its large stable of pizza places. As a franchisee NPC gets the benefit of operating restaurants under a popular and well known name. It pays YUM! Brands royalties and fees in exchange for the right to use the Pizza Hut brand and other intellectual property. Typically local operators are also held to certain standards regarding food and service quality.

Strategy

NPC has grown to such a large size primarily through a series of acquisitions mostly corporate-run locations. In 2012 it snapped up 36 Pizza Hut units located primarily in Florida for roughly $19 million from Pizza Hut Inc. The deal enabled NPC to strengthen its position in its largest geographical market.

While NPC doesn't own the Pizza Hut chain as its largest franchisee the company can exert a certain amount of influence in how the fast-food business operates. It called upon YUM! Brands to improve its Pizza Hut marketing strategy while sales were slumping amid the economic downturn. The company spends 6% of its revenue on national and local advertising demonstrating its commitment to Pizza Hut operations and advertising strategy.

NPC's revenue improved in 2010 and 2011 partly as a result of promoting its value-priced menu items as a way to gain market share from competing chains including Domino's and Papa John's. (Within its local markets NPC competes against #1 Domino's franchisee RPM Pizza and Papa John's operator PJ United.)

EXECUTIVES

Chb-Pres-Coo, James K Schwartz
Exec V Pres Fin-Cfo, Troy D Cook
Sr V Pres-Head of Oprs, D Blayne Vaughn
Sr V Pres Mktg, Linda L Sheedy
Cao, Jason P Poenitske
Territory Vice President-South, Thomas D White
Territory Vice President-West, Tracy A Armentrout
Auditors: KPMG LLP KANSAS CITY MISSOUR

LOCATIONS

HQ: NPC RESTAURANT HOLDINGS, LLC
 7300 W 129TH ST, OVERLAND PARK, KS 662132631
Phone: 913 327-5555
Web: WWW.NPCINTERNATIONAL.COM

COMPETITORS

Boddie-Noell	PJ United
Burger King	Papa John's
Captain D's	RPM Pizza
Carrols	Sbarro
Chick-fil-A	Sonic Corp.
Domino's	Subway
Hardee's	Tacala
Interfoods	United States Beef
K-MAC	Valenti Management
Krystal	Wendy's
Little Caesar's	West Quality Foods
McDonald's	

HISTORICAL FINANCIALS

Company Type: Private

Income Statement   FYE: December 27

	REVENUE ($ mil.)	NET INCOME ($ mil.)	NET PROFIT MARGIN	EMPLOYEES
12/16	1,236	8	0.7%	29,000
12/15	1,223	6	0.5%	—
12/14	1,179	1	0.1%	—
12/13	1,094	29	2.7%	—
Annual Growth	4.2%	(33.5%)	—	—

Return on assets: 0.7%   Cash ($ mil.): 13
Return on equity: 3.1%
Current ratio: 0.40

NTG INVESTMENT PARTNERS, INC

EXECUTIVES

Ceo, Kevin Nolan
President, Harold Baron
Cfo, Tyler Garell
Coo, Blake Malone
Operations Manager, Danny Sparks
Executive Officer, Harris Rainbow
Account Manager, Eli Weiner
Senior Account Manager, Steve Ngt
Account Manager, Weston Verner
Chief Financial Officer, Fritz Owens
National Account Manager, Jonathan Osorio
Auditors: BARNETT & STEGALL LLC

LOCATIONS

HQ: NTG INVESTMENT PARTNERS, INC
365 NORTHRIDGE RD STE 100, ATLANTA, GA
303506100
Phone: 770 509-9611
Web: WWW.NTGFREIGHT.COM

HISTORICAL FINANCIALS

Company Type: Private

Income Statement				FYE: December 31
	REVENUE ($ mil.)	NET INCOME ($ mil.)	NET PROFIT MARGIN	EMPLOYEES
12/17*	468	2	0.4%	881
09/16	199	(0)	—	—
12/14	114	0	0.4%	—
12/13	49	0	0.5%	—
Annual Growth	75.7%	66.6%	—	—

*Fiscal year change

2017 Year-End Financials

Return on assets: 2.6%   Cash ($ mil.): 2
Return on equity: 37.1%
Current ratio: 1.40

OAKLAND UNIFIED SCHOOL DISTRICT

EXECUTIVES

Coordinator, Sailaja Suresh
Computer Technician, Fred Guss
Executive Secretary, Beulah John
Director, Jerome Gourdine
Office Manager, Kechette Walls
Coordinator, Marcus Silvi
Executive Assistant, Wendy Green
Coordinator, Barbara McClung
Manager, Byron Huey
Coordinator, Adimu Madyun
Teacher, Barbara Cone

LOCATIONS

HQ: OAKLAND UNIFIED SCHOOL DISTRICT
1000 BROADWAY FL 4, OAKLAND, CA 946074099
Phone: 510 434-7790
Web: WWW.OUSD.ORG

HISTORICAL FINANCIALS

Company Type: Private

Income Statement				FYE: June 30
	REVENUE ($ mil.)	NET INCOME ($ mil.)	NET PROFIT MARGIN	EMPLOYEES
06/18	677	(45)	—	7,200
06/17	658	(2)	—	—
06/06*	0	0	—	—
12/05	0	0	—	—
Annual Growth	—	—	—	—

*Fiscal year change

OCEAN BEAUTY SEAFOODS LLC

Prefer your piscatory purchase to be fresh frozen or canned? Ocean Beauty Seafoods has it covered. Doing no fishing of its own the company buys seafood from commercial fishermen and then processes sells and distributes its seafood products in Alaska and across the continental US. Founded in 1910 the company also exports seafood to Mexico Europe Asia Africa and the Middle East. Ocean Beauty's specialty products include smoked salmon smoked salmon spreads pickled and marinated herring shrimp cocktail caviar and lobster p té. Nonprofit Bristol Bay Economic Development Corporation owns 50% of Ocean Beauty; individual investors own the rest.

Operations

Boasting offices or plants in eight US states plus overseas in Japan Ocean Beauty operates its own fleet of seafood delivery trucks across the Western US. The fleet makes regular stops at the seafood company's distribution facilities located in Oregon Idaho Texas Montana Utah and Washington. The company operates six production sites in Alaska in Alitak Cordova Excursion Inlet Kodiak Naknek and Petersburg as well as a pair of production sites in Seattle and Monroe Washington. Sales and administration offices are located in Seattle and Tokyo. Ocean Beauty exports its products to Mexico Europe Asia Africa and the Middle East.

Geographic Reach

Based in Washington Ocean Beauty enjoys a global reach.

Sales and Marketing

Ocean Beauty sells its fresh and frozen seafood products to both retail and foodservice customers. The company maintains sales offices in the states in Seattle and overseas in Tokyo.

Strategy

Ocean Beauty claims to be the first company to vacuum pack Alaskan seafood (in 1954). The company's products are primarily caught in the waters of the Pacific Northwest but Ocean Beauty also purchases fish from harvesters worldwide. Its major manufacturing facilities are certified against the British Retail Consortium Audit Standards.

Ocean Beauty also voluntarily participates in the US Department of Commerce's Hazard Actions Critical Control Points (HACCP) Seafood Inspection Program for added assurance that its products are safe wholesome and properly labeled. The company's production and distribution operations are conducted in compliance with the US Food and Drug Administration's HACCP regulations.

EXECUTIVES

Vice President Sales, Wayne Kvasnikoff

LOCATIONS

HQ: OCEAN BEAUTY SEAFOODS LLC
1100 W EWING ST, SEATTLE, WA 981191321
Phone: 206 285-6800
Web: WWW.OCEANBEAUTY.COM

PRODUCTS/OPERATIONS

Selected Brands

CircleSea

Commander
Deep Sea
Echo Falls
Icy Point
LASCCO
McGovern
Nathan's
Neptune
Ocean Beauty
Ocean Bonita
Pillar Rock
Pink Beauty
Pirate
Port Clyde
RITE
Royal Alaska
Sea Choice
Searchlight
Sound Beauty
St. Andrews
Surf King
Three Star
Tribe

Selected Products
Imported finfish
  Mahi mahi
  Sea Bass
  Shark
  Swordfish
  Tuna
North Pacific finfish
  Cod
  Farm-raised
  Flounder
  Halibut
  Perch
  Pollock
  Rockfish
  Salmon
  Sole
  Sturgeon
  Whiting
Shellfish
  Coldwater shrimp meat
  Clams
  Crab
  Mussels
  Oysters
  Prawns
Other products
  Milt
  Pickled herring
  Roe
  Surimi

COMPETITORS

Alaska Sausage	Maruha Nichiro
Alaska Seafood company	Orca Bay Seafoods
Alaskan Leader	Pacific Seafood Group
Fisheries	Peter Pan Seafoods
Arrowac Fisheries	Princes Limited
Banner Smoked Fish	Red Chamber Co.
Bumble Bee Foods	Salmolux
Chicken of the Sea	Santa's Smokehouse
Gorton's	Seafood Sales
High Liner Foods	StarKist
Icelandic Group	Trident Seafoods
Icicle Seafoods	

HISTORICAL FINANCIALS
Company Type: Private

Income Statement
FYE: December 31

	REVENUE ($ mil.)	NET INCOME ($ mil.)	NET PROFIT MARGIN	EMPLOYEES
12/16*	453	(27)	—	2,500
01/16	437	(4)	—	—
01/15	439	4	1.1%	—
12/13	425	11	2.6%	—
Annual Growth	2.1%	—	—	—

*Fiscal year change

2016 Year-End Financials
Return on assets: (-15.7%) Cash ($ mil.): 2
Return on equity: (-85.7%)
Current ratio: 1.40

OCEAN SPRAY CRANBERRIES, INC.

Ocean Spray Cranberries has transformed that ubiquitous Thanksgiving side dish into a big business with beverages cereals and snacks. Known for its blue-and-white wave logo Ocean Spray is a top US maker of canned bottled and shelf-stable juice drinks. Structured as a cooperative Ocean Spray is owned by more than 700 cranberry and grapefruit growers in North America. It produces juice drinks by blending cranberries with other fruits typically ranging from apples to blueberries at around 20 processing facilities. Its other products include fresh and dried cranberries sauces and trail mixes along with fresh citrus fruits. Ocean Spray sells its products through food retailers foodservice providers and food makers worldwide.

Geographic Reach
Headquartered in Massachusetts Ocean Spray boasts a global business. It supplies cranberry products to food and beverage manufacturers worldwide. The company serves customers in North America the Caribbean Central America South America Africa Asia/Pacific Europe and the Middle East.

It has juice bottling facilities in Nevada Wisconsin Pennsylvania and Texas and dried cranberries and concentrate facilities in Washington Massachusetts and Wisconsin as well as Chile and Canada. All cranberry sauce is produced in Kenosha Wisconsin which Ocean Spray touts as The Home of Cranberry Sauce.

Mergers and Acquisitions
In 2018 Ocean Spray acquired Atoka Cranberries a Quebec based cranberry grower from The Bieler Group. Ocean Spray will invest in Atoka's operations to increase efficiency and improve yield.

HISTORY

Ocean Spray Cranberries traces its roots to Marcus Urann president of the Cape Cod Cranberry Company. In 1912 Urann who became known as the "Cranberry King" began marketing a cranberry sauce that was packaged in tins and could be served year-round. Inspired by the sea spray that drifted off the Atlantic and over his cranberry bogs Urann dubbed his concoction Ocean Spray Cape Cod Cranberry Sauce.

It didn't take long for other cranberry growers to make their own sauces and rather than compete the Cranberry King consolidated. In 1930 Urann merged his company with A.D. Makepeace Company and with Cranberry Products forming a national cooperative called Cranberry Canners. During the 1940s it added growers in Wisconsin Oregon and Washington and to reflect its new scope changed its name to National Cranberry Association.

Canadian growers were added to the fold in 1950. Urann retired in 1955 and two years later the co-op introduced its first frozen products. To take advantage of the popular Ocean Spray brand name in 1959 the company changed its name to Ocean Spray Cranberries.

EXECUTIVES

Assistant Vice President Internal Audit, Phil Parks
Vice President, Earl Larson
Vice President, Jane Borkowski
Svp Cooperative Dev't., Peter Wyman
Senior Vice President North America, Larry Martin
Senior Vice President Chief Operating Officer, Brian Schiegg
Vice President Cooperative Development General Counsel And Secretary, Rich Stamm
Vice President Marketing Services, Yash Sikand
Treas, Richard A Lees
Auditors: PRICEWATERHOUSECOOPERS LLP BO

LOCATIONS

HQ: OCEAN SPRAY CRANBERRIES, INC.
  1 OCEAN SPRAY DR, MIDDLEBORO, MA 023490001
Phone: 508 946-1000
Web: WWW.OCEANSPRAY.COM

PRODUCTS/OPERATIONS

Selected Brands & Products
Dried fruit
  Craisins Blueberry Juice Infused Dried Cranberries
  Craisins Cherry Juice Infused Dried Cranberries
  Craisins Original Dried Cranberries
  Craisins Pomegranate Juice Infused Dried Cranberries
  Craisins Snack Packs
  Craisins Trail Mix - Cranberry & Chocolate
  Craisins Trail Mix - Cranberry Fruit & Nut
Fresh Produce
  Clementines
  Cranberries
  Grapefruit
  Lemons
  Limes
  Oranges
  Tangerines
Instant oatmeal
  Cranberry
  Cranberry Honey Multigrain
  Cranberry Orange Muffin
  Cranberry Pomegranate
Juice
100% Juice Blends
  Blueberry Juice Drinks
  Cran•Energy Energy Juice Drinks
  Cranberry Juice Cocktails
  Cranberry Juice Drink Blends
  Diet Juice Drinks
  Fruit & Veggie Juice
  Fruit & Veggie Juice Drinks
  Grapefruit Juice
  Grapefruit Juice Drinks
  Juice Drinks
  Light Juice Drinks
  On the Go Juice
  On the Go Juice Drinks
  Sugar-Free Drink Mixes
  White Cranberry Juice Drinks
Sauces
  Jellied cranberry sauce
  Whole berry cranberry sauce

COMPETITORS

A. Duda & Sons	Freshco
Arcade Industries	Jugos del Valle USA
Cherry Central	Mariani Packing
Cooperative Inc.	Meridian Nut Growers
Chiquita Brands	Naked Juice
Citrus World	National Grape
Coca-Cola	Cooperative
Coloma Frozen Foods	Nestlé USA
Cranberries Limited	Odwalla
Dole Food	Shoreline Fruit
Dundee Citrus Growers	Sunsweet Growers
Edinburg Citrus	Tampico Beverages
Fresh Del Monte	Tropicana
Produce	Wonderful Company

HISTORICAL FINANCIALS
Company Type: Private

Income Statement
FYE: August 31

	REVENUE ($ mil.)	NET INCOME ($ mil.)	NET PROFIT MARGIN	EMPLOYEES
08/15	1,719	317	18.5%	2,000
08/14	1,655	289	17.5%	—
08/13	1,658	389	23.5%	—
08/12	1,662	338	20.4%	—
Annual Growth	1.1%	(2.2%)	—	—

2015 Year-End Financials
Return on assets: 18.6% Cash ($ mil.): 38
Return on equity: 104.4%
Current ratio: 2.10

OCHSNER CLINIC FOUNDATION

EXECUTIVES

Ceo-Pres, Patrick J Quinlan
Exec V Pres-Dir of Fin, B C Brannon
MD, Elizabeth Lapeyre
Supervisor, Jacob Olivares
Project Consultant, Sandy Warren
Endocrinology, Anita Richard
Assistant Vice President, Ann Lockhart
Executive Vice President, Bobby Brannon
Information Technology Manager, Bryan Clark
Senior Executive Assistant, Carol Villafana
Infectious Diseases, Cheryl Balot
Auditors: ERNST & YOUNG US LLP AUSTIN

LOCATIONS

HQ: OCHSNER CLINIC FOUNDATION
  1514 JEFFERSON HWY, NEW ORLEANS, LA 701212483
Phone: 504 842-3000
Web: WWW.OCHSNER.ORG

HISTORICAL FINANCIALS
Company Type: Private

Income Statement   FYE: December 31

	REVENUE ($ mil.)	NET INCOME ($ mil.)	NET PROFIT MARGIN	EMPLOYEES
12/17	8,405	128	1.5%	10,500
12/14	2,196	(16)	—	—
12/13	5,550	52	0.9%	—
12/12	4,829	12	0.3%	—
Annual Growth	11.7%	60.1%	—	—

2017 Year-End Financials
Return on assets: 4.9%   Cash ($ mil.): 306
Return on equity: 13.3%
Current ratio: 0.60

OCHSNER HEALTH SYSTEM

EXECUTIVES

Ceo, Fernis Leblanc
Dir, Pedro Cazabon M D
Dir, F Ralph Dauterive
Dir, William H Hines
Dir, R Paker Lecorgne
Accountant, Jessica George
Coordinator, John Cbet
Coordinator, Lee Carrigan
Coordinator, Ann Conger
Coordinator, Ashley Powell
Assistant Vice-President, Jennifer Bollinger
Auditors: ERNST & YOUNG LLP NEW ORLEANS

LOCATIONS

HQ: OCHSNER HEALTH SYSTEM
1516 JEFFERSON HWY, NEW ORLEANS, LA
701212429
Phone: 504 842-3483
Web: WWW.OCHSNER.ORG

HISTORICAL FINANCIALS
Company Type: Private

Income Statement   FYE: December 31

	REVENUE ($ mil.)	NET INCOME ($ mil.)	NET PROFIT MARGIN	EMPLOYEES
12/16	2,812	55	2.0%	19,000
12/15	2,592	63	2.5%	—
Annual Growth	8.5%	(13.2%)	—	—

2016 Year-End Financials
Return on assets: 2.4%   Cash ($ mil.): 121
Return on equity: 7.8%
Current ratio: 1.40

OHIO EDISON COMPANY

Ohio Edison has taken a shine to the folks in the Buckeye state. The company distributes electricity to a population of about 2.3 million (more than 1 million customers) in a 7000 sq. ml. area of central and northeastern Ohio. Ohio Edison a unit of FirstEnergy also has 5955 MW of generat-ing capacity from interests in primarily fossil-fueled and nuclear generation facilities and it sells excess power to wholesale customers. The utility's power plants are operated by sister companies FirstEnergy Nuclear and FirstEnergy Generation. Subsidiary Pennsylvania Power Company provides electric service to communities in a 1100 sq. ml. area of western Pennsylvania which has a population of approximately 400000.

Operations
Ohio Edison and Pennsylvania Power provide regulated electric distribution services and procure of generation services. Ohio Edison operates more than 30460 miles of distribution lines and 500 miles of transmission lines.

Geographic Reach
Ohio Edison and Pennsylvania Power conduct business in portions of Ohio and Pennsylvania.

Financial Performance
Revenues decreased by 11% in 2011 due to lower retail generation revenues partially offset by higher distribution and wholesale generation revenues. Retail generation revenues decreased primarily due to a drop in energy sales caused from an increase in customers shopping for alternative power providers and lower average prices across all customer classes.

Ohio Edison's net income decreased by 17% in 2011 due to lower revenues partially offset by lower purchased power costs.

Strategy
In 2011 parent FirstEnergy acquired Allegheny Energy in a $8.5 billion deal that grew FirstEnergy's generation capacity and dramatically boosted the company's position as a leading regional energy provider.

Company Background
FirstEnergy and Ohio Edison reached a settlement in 2005 with the federal government to reduce harmful emissions from its Ohio power generating plants; in addition to fines Ohio Edison has been mandated to pledge $25 million for wind power biomass and other alternative energy sources. In 2009 Ohio Edison began retrofitting two units at its Shadyside Ohio power plant to burn wood and other biomass materials in order to lower its greenhouse gas output.

EXECUTIVES

Pres, Charles E Jones Jr
Sr V Pres-Cfo*, James F Pearson
V Pres-Controller*, Harvey L Wagner
Director of Operations Support, Tracy Mayse
Engineer, Gregory Macmaster
Supervisor Reg Operations Line, Darren Puffinburger
Supervisor Reg Operations Line, Harvey Pelfrey
Board Member, Paul Addison
Supervisor Reg Operations Line, Richard Kaszowski
Executive Assistant, Robin Micco
Adv Administrative Assistant, Tina Martin
Auditors: PRICEWATERHOUSECOOPES LP CLEV

LOCATIONS

HQ: OHIO EDISON COMPANY
76 S MAIN ST BSMT, AKRON, OH 443081817
Phone: 800 736-3402
Web: WWW.FIRSTENERGYCORP.COM

COMPETITORS

Columbia Gas of Ohio	Ohio Power
DPL	Vectren Energy
Dominion East Ohio	Delivery of Ohio
Duke Energy Ohio	

HISTORICAL FINANCIALS
Company Type: Private

Income Statement   FYE: December 31

	REVENUE ($ mil.)	NET INCOME ($ mil.)	NET PROFIT MARGIN	EMPLOYEES
12/16	1,394	150	10.8%	1,190
12/11	1,633	128	7.8%	—
12/10	1,836	157	8.6%	—
12/09	2,516	122	4.9%	—
Annual Growth	(8.1%)	3.0%	—	—

OHIOHEALTH CORPORATION

Operating throughout the central part of the state OhioHealth aims to keep Buckeyes healthy. The not-for-profit system runs eight acute care hospitals and is affiliated with another 11 community hospitals and area health systems. All told OhioHealth has about 2000 staffed beds in and around Columbus. Additional facilities offer urgent care physical rehabilitation diagnostic imaging and sleep diagnostics services. Subsidiary HomeReach provides home health care and hospice care. Its WorkHealth program offers workers' compensation care management and occupational rehabilitation services. OhioHealth Group OhioHealth's joint venture with The Medical Group of Ohio operates the HealthReach PPO.

Operations
In addition to offering patient care OhioHealth also operates the The OhioHealth Research & Innovation Institute which coordinates research throughout the health system including conducting clinical trials of new drugs and medical devices. The system also operates The Center for Medical Education and Innovation a medical training facility that among other technologies offers human patient simulators on which medical professionals can practice new procedures in various clinical situations.

OhioHealth has some 28000 associates physicians and volunteers. Every year it facilitates approximately 2 million outpatient visits 95000 admissions 346000 emergency department visits 60000 surgeries and 13000 births.

Geographic Reach
OhioHealth operates in the Ohio communities of Athens Columbus Delaware Dublin Kenton Mansfield and Shelby.

Strategy
The company is focused on expanding geographically and capitalizing on opportunities due to population growth in the area. In 2013 it completed the construction of a new patient tower at its Riverside Methodist Hospital; the tower houses much of the company's Neuroscience Institute.

OhioHealth is now building an outpatient facility in Nelsonville which is expected to open sometime in 2017.

The system struck up a partnership with Berger Health System another Ohio-based health care network in 2014. The partners will explore ways to improve health care for the communities they serve.

Mergers and Acquisitions
In 2014 OhioHealth acquired O'Bleness Health System expanding its presence in southeastern Ohio. It also acquired MedCentral Health System.

Company Background

The health system traces its roots back to 1892 when Protestant Hospital (now known as Riverside Methodist Hospital) opened. The system initially organized as U.S. Health Corporation in 1984 later took on the OhioHealth name in 1997.

EXECUTIVES

Senior Vice President And Chief Communications Officer, Sue Jablonski
President And Ceo, David P. Blom, age 65
Evp And Coo, Michael W. (Mike) Louge
Coo Riverside Methodist Hospital, Bruce Hagen
President Riverside Methodist Hospital, Brian D. Jepson
Chief Medical Officer, Bruce Vanderhoff
Svp And Cio, Michael Krouse
Svp External Affairs; President Ohiohealth Foundation, Karen Morrison
President Doctors Hospital, Mike Reichfield
President Ohiohealth Physician Group, Hugh Thornhill
President Ohiohealth Home Care, James P. Newbrough
President O'bleness Hospital, Mark Seckinger
President Mansfield Hospital And Shelby Hospital, Jean Halpin
Svp And Cfo, Vinson M. Yates
President Grant Medical Center, Michael Lawson
Svp And Chief Nursing Executive, Donna Hanly
President Dublin Methodist Hospital And Grady Memorial Hospital, Steve Bunyard
Medical Director Trauma And Acute Care Surgery, Shay O'mara
Medical Director Of Hospital Medicine Services, Laura Burelli
Vice President System Service Line Support, Casey Liddy
Vice Chairman, John P. McConnell, age 65
Chairman, Steve Rasmussen
Auditors: PLANTE & MORAN PLLC COLUMBUS

LOCATIONS

HQ: OHIOHEALTH CORPORATION
3430 OHHALTH PKWY FL 5 FLR 5, COLUMBUS, OH 43202
Phone: 614 788-8860

PRODUCTS/OPERATIONS

Selected Facilities

Owned
Doctors Hospital (Columbus)
Doctors Hospital Nelsonville (Nelsonville)
Dublin Methodist Hospital (Dublin)
Grady Memorial Hospital (Delaware)
Grant Medical Center (Columbus)
Hardin Memorial Hospital (Kenton)
Marion General Hospital (Marion)
O'Bleness Memorial Hospital (Athens)
Riverside Methodist Hospital (Columbus)
Affiliated
Blanchard Valley Medical Center
Galion Community Hospital (Galion)
Genesis Healthcare System (Zanesville)
Knox Community Hospital
Morrow County Hospital (Mt. Gilead)
Samaritan Regional Health System (Ashland)
Southern Ohio Medical Center (Portsmouth)

COMPETITORS

Adena Health System
Fairfield Medical Center
Licking Memorial Health Systems
Mount Carmel Health
Nationwide Children's Hospital
Regency Hospital
Select Medical

HISTORICAL FINANCIALS

Company Type: Private

Income Statement — FYE: June 30

	REVENUE ($ mil.)	NET INCOME ($ mil.)	NET PROFIT MARGIN	EMPLOYEES
06/18	4,045	519	12.8%	15,000
06/17	3,792	631	16.6%	—
06/14	2,179	354	16.3%	—
06/11	2,328	412	17.7%	—
Annual Growth	8.2%	3.3%	—	—

2018 Year-End Financials

Return on assets: 7.6%
Return on equity: 10.4%
Current ratio: 0.90
Cash ($ mil.): 121

OHIOHEALTH RIVERSIDE METHODIST HOSPITAL

EXECUTIVES

Pres-Ceo, Brian D Jepson
Sr V Pres*, Steve Markovitch
Physician, Mark Brownell
Director of Information Techno, Vandhana V Veerni
Information Specialist, Anne Rhodes
Information Specialist, Elizabeth Queen
Information Specialist, Jeanne Walker
Chief of Medicine, Mark Davis
Network Engineer, Jack Krider
Emergency Medicine Specialist, Timothy J Kirkpatrick
Technical Manager, James Lowder

LOCATIONS

HQ: OHIOHEALTH RIVERSIDE METHODIST HOSPITAL
3535 OLENTANGY RIVER RD, COLUMBUS, OH 432143908
Phone: 614 566-5000
Web: WWW.RIVERSIDERAD.COM

HISTORICAL FINANCIALS

Company Type: Private

Income Statement — FYE: June 30

	REVENUE ($ mil.)	NET INCOME ($ mil.)	NET PROFIT MARGIN	EMPLOYEES
06/16	1,207	190	15.8%	944
06/15*	19	0	2.3%	—
12/01	49	(1)	—	—
12/00	0	0	—	—
Annual Growth	—	—	—	—

*Fiscal year change

2016 Year-End Financials

Return on assets: 28.3%
Return on equity: —
Current ratio: 0.50
Cash ($ mil.): —

OKLAHOMA STATE UNIVERSITY

Oooooklahoma where the... students come to learn! Oklahoma State University is the flagship campus of its namesake (OSU) system which also includes OSU-Tulsa OSU-Oklahoma City OSU-Okmulgee the OSU Center for Health Sciences in Tulsa the OSU College of Veterinary Medicine and the Oklahoma Agricultural Experiment Station. OSU offers courses in a variety of disciplines and confers undergraduate graduate doctoral and professional degrees in everything from agriculture and the arts to business and engineering. Altogether the system boasts an enrollment of about 36000 students across its five campuses; its student-teacher ratio is about 17:1.

EXECUTIVES

Assoc Vice President Academic Affairs, Gail Gates
Vice President For Univ Relations, Gary C Clark
Vice President For Rsch Technology, Stephen W Mckeever
Vice President For Research And Technology, Linda Goodwin
Vice President Administration And Finance, David Bosserman
Vice President, Cem Diniz
Vice President, Adeanya Hunt
Vice President, Tony Johnson
Managing Director Anethesia Or, Brad White
Vice President Of Fiscal Services, Jim Smith
Vice President, Autumn James
Avp For Research Compliance, Dawn Underwood
Treasurer, Tian Lin
Board Member, Kerry Morton
Auditors: GRANT THORNTON LLP OKLAHOMA

LOCATIONS

HQ: OKLAHOMA STATE UNIVERSITY
401 WHITEHURST HALL, STILLWATER, OK 740781030
Phone: 405 744-5000
Web: WWW.OKSTATE.COM

PRODUCTS/OPERATIONS

Selected Colleges
Agricultural Sciences and Natural Resources
Arts and Sciences
Education
Engineering Architecture and Technology
Human Sciences
Spears School of Business
Center for Veterinary Health Sciences
Graduate College
Honors College

HISTORICAL FINANCIALS

Company Type: Private

Income Statement — FYE: June 30

	REVENUE ($ mil.)	NET INCOME ($ mil.)	NET PROFIT MARGIN	EMPLOYEES
06/18	802	8	1.1%	8,882
06/17	815	40	5.0%	—
Annual Growth	(1.5%)	(77.8%)	—	—

2018 Year-End Financials

Return on assets: 0.4%
Return on equity: 1.0%
Current ratio: 2.40
Cash ($ mil.): 106

OMAHA PUBLIC POWER DISTRICT

Thirteen's the lucky number for Omaha Public Power District (OPPD). A subdivision of the Nebraska state government OPPD generates and distributes electricity to residents and businesses in 13 counties in southeastern Nebraska. It operates and maintains its facilities without tax revenues and raises money for major construction through bonds. OPPD serves more than 356000 customers in an area covering 5000 sq. mi. The utility has a generating capacity of more than 3235 MW which is powered by primarily nuclear coal oil and natural gas sources. It sells wholesale power to other utilities and offers energy consulting and management services.

Operations

OPPD is the 12th-largest publicly owned electric system in the US in terms of numbers of customers served. The power district provides retail service to about 50 towns and wholesale to five. OPPD operates more than 15500 miles of electric line.

The majority of OPPD's power comes from three baseload power plants: North Omaha Station and Nebraska City Station (both coal-fired) and the Fort Calhoun Station nuclear power plant.

Financial Performance

In 2013 OPPD's revenues grew by 4% primarily due to a jump in retail sales as the result of higher energy prices and an increase in the adjustment for the under-recovery of fuel and purchased power expenses. Retail sales growth was partially offset by a decrease in off-system sales and other electric sales.

The company's net income grew by 1% that year due to higher revenues.

In 2013 OPPD's operating cash inflow increased to $168.71 million (from $151.73 million in 2012) due to higher net income and a change in working capital as a result of an increase in cash received from retail customers and insurance companies. This was partially offset by higher cash paid to off-system parties for additional wind energy.

Strategy

Like other utilities OPPD is pushing conservation and green energy initiates to reduce carbon emissions with its customers as a service to help them control costs.

In 2015 OPPD approved the future generation resource plan created in June 2014 calling for the retirement of three of the district's oldest coal generation units and additional environmental controls. The plan includes a mixture of new programs and expansion of some existing programs aimed at reducing power demand.

The company is pursuing a goal of getting 30% of its retail energy from renewable sources. In 2013 it announced a wind farm deal (located northeast of O'Neill Nebraska). The 20-year agreement the largest wind power purchase to date for OPPD will increase its renewable energy generation capacity to 817 MW.

Company Background

It 2011 the utility announced that it was studying how to support both the auto industry and customers regarding the larger numbers of electric cars being introduced into its service region.

OPPD was organized as a self-supporting subdivision of the State of Nebraska in 1946 although state power operations date back to 1917.

EXECUTIVES

President And Ceo, W. Gary Gates, age 68
Coo, Timothy J. (Tim) Burke
Vp And Cfo, Edward E. Easterlin
Vp Operations, Dale Widoe
Vice President, John Imig
Vice President Marketing, Tracy Boston
Vice President Information Technology, Kathleen Brown
Vice Chair, Anne L. McGuire
Vice Chair, Michael A. (Mick) Mines
Division Secretary, Renee Oltman
Division Secretary, Pamela Price
Department Secretary, Tammy Collinson
Treasurer, Craig Moody

LOCATIONS

HQ: OMAHA PUBLIC POWER DISTRICT
444 S 16TH ST, OMAHA, NE 681022247
Phone: 402 636-2000
Web: WWW.OPPD.COM

COMPETITORS

Basin Electric Power   Tri-State Generation
NorthWestern   and Transmission
Preferred Energy
Services

HISTORICAL FINANCIALS

Company Type: Private

Income Statement				FYE: December 31
	REVENUE ($ mil.)	NET INCOME ($ mil.)	NET PROFIT MARGIN	EMPLOYEES
12/17	1,104	77	7.0%	2,300
12/16	1,126	(933)	—	—
12/15*	1,131	34	3.1%	—
06/15	1,096	16	1.5%	—
Annual Growth	0.2%	67.4%	—	—

*Fiscal year change

2017 Year-End Financials

Return on assets: 1.4%   Cash ($ mil.): 10
Return on equity: 7.1%
Current ratio: 2.00

OMAHA PUBLIC SCHOOLS

EXECUTIVES

Supt, Cheryl Logan
Controller, Dr Liz Standish
Assist Superintendent, Dr Dennis Pool
Coordinator, Suann Witt
Assistant, Jennifer Schlapia
Health Professional, Kari Caddell
Technology/Computer Coordinato, Brandon Spore
Project Coordinator, Lesley Dean
Coordinator, Lisa Thompson
Coordinator, Sherri McNair
Special Education, Aaron Brooker
Auditors: SEIM JOHNSON LLP OMAHA NEBR

LOCATIONS

HQ: OMAHA PUBLIC SCHOOLS
3215 CUMING ST, OMAHA, NE 681312000
Phone: 402 557-2120
Web: WWW.OPS.ORG

HISTORICAL FINANCIALS

Company Type: Private

Income Statement				FYE: August 31
	REVENUE ($ mil.)	NET INCOME ($ mil.)	NET PROFIT MARGIN	EMPLOYEES
08/18	763	20	2.7%	8,000
08/17	720	33	4.7%	—
08/16	693	(41)	—	—
08/15	626	126	20.3%	—
Annual Growth	6.9%	(45.4%)	—	—

2018 Year-End Financials

Return on assets: 1.4%   Cash ($ mil.): 305
Return on equity: —
Current ratio: —

ONEAMERICA FINANCIAL PARTNERS, INC.

EXECUTIVES

Chb-Pres-Ceo, J Scott Davison
Exec V Pres-Cfo, Jeffrey D Holley
Exec V Pres, Mark Roller
Exec V Pres-Sr Clo-SEC, Thomas M Zurek
Sr V Pres-CIO, Gene P Berry
Sr V Pres-Chief Hr Officer, Karin Sarratt
Pres Individual Insurance, Patrick M Foley
Vice President, Angela Trefethen
Consultant, Bartholomew Brown
Manager Public Relations Tax, Christina Cozzolino
Analyst, Christy Wieringa

LOCATIONS

HQ: ONEAMERICA FINANCIAL PARTNERS, INC.
1 AMERICAN SQ, INDIANAPOLIS, IN 462820020
Phone: 317 285-1877
Web: WWW.ONEAMERICA.COM

HISTORICAL FINANCIALS

Company Type: Private

Income Statement				FYE: December 31
	ASSETS ($ mil.)	NET INCOME ($ mil.)	INCOME AS % OF ASSETS	EMPLOYEES
12/16	19,921	88	0.4%	9,875
12/15	18,491	67	0.4%	—
12/14	0	0	—	—
12/04	15,028	56	0.4%	—
Annual Growth	2.4%	3.8%	—	—

2016 Year-End Financials

Return on assets: 0.4%   Sales ($ mil): 1,103
Return on equity: 6.7%

ONEOK PARTNERS, L.P.

For ONEOK Partners it's OK to have three businesses: natural gas pipelines; gas gathering and processing; and natural gas liquids (NGLs). Its pipelines include Midwestern Gas Transmission

Guardian Pipeline Viking Gas Transmission and OkTex Pipeline. The ONEOK affiliate operates 17100 miles of gas-gathering pipeline and 7600 miles of transportation pipeline as well as gas processing plants and storage facilities (with 52 billion cu. ft. of capacity). It also owns one of the US's top natural NGL systems (more than 7200 miles of pipeline). In 2017 41%-owner ONEOK agreed to buy the stock of ONEOK Partners that it did not already own for $9.3 billion in a stock deal. Operations ONEOK Partners operates in three business segments: natural gas gathering and processing; natural gas pipelines; and natural gas liquids. Geographic Reach The company gathers and processes natural gas in the Mid-Continent region which includes the NGL-rich Cana-Woodford Shale and Granite Wash formations the Mississippian Lime formation of Oklahoma and Kansas and the Hugoton and Central Kansas Uplift Basins of Kansas. The Natural Gas Pipelines segment owns and operates regulated natural gas transmission pipelines natural gas storage facilities and natural gas gathering systems for nonprocessed gas. It also provide interstate natural gas transportation and storage service. The company's interstate natural gas pipeline assets transport natural gas through pipelines in North Dakota Minnesota Wisconsin Illinois Indiana Kentucky Tennessee Oklahoma Texas and New Mexico. Its Natural gas liquids assets provide nondiscretionary services to producers that consist of facilities that gather fractionate and treat NGLs and store NGL products primarily in Oklahoma Kansas and Texas. It also owns or has stakes in natural gas liquids gathering and distribution pipelines in Oklahoma Kansas Texas Wyoming and Colorado and terminal and storage facilities in Missouri Nebraska Iowa and Illinois. In addition it owns natural gas liquids distribution and refined petroleum products pipelines in Kansas Missouri Nebraska Iowa Illinois and Indiana that connect the company's Mid-Continent assets with Midwest markets including Chicago.

Financial Performance

Revenues decreased by 10% in 2012 due to lower net realized natural gas and NGL product prices offset partially by higher natural gas and NGL sales volumes from completed capital projects. The increase in natural gas supply resulting from the development of nonconventional resource areas in North America and a warmer than normal winter caused natural gas prices to drop. NGL prices particularly ethane and propane also decreased in 2012 due primarily to increased NGL production and an increase in available supply. Propane prices also were affected by a warmer than normal winter.

ONEOK Partners' net income grew by 7% in 2012 thanks to lower costs of sales and fuels and lower interest expenses.

Strategy

The company pursues a strategy of building up its fee-based earnings coupled with organic growth and complementary acquisitions in both conventional oil and gas and unconventional (shale plays).

It is looking to increase NGL volumes gathered and fractionated in its NGL segment and natural gas volumes processed in its natural gas gathering and processing segment as producers continue to develop NGL-rich resource plays in the Mid-Continent and Rocky Mountain areas.

In 2012 ONEOK Partners announced plans to invest up to $360 million to grow its projects in the Woodford Shale formation.

Company Background

ONEOK Partners was formed in 2006 when ONEOK spun off its gathering and processing NGLs pipelines and storage businesses for $3 billion following that company's acquisition of Northern Border Partners (which was founded in 1993). Building out its assets in 2007 the company acquired an interstate pipeline system from Kinder Morgan Energy Partners for $300 million.

EXECUTIVES

Pres-Ceo, Terry K Spencer
Evp-Cfo, Walter S Hulse III
Svp,naturalgasgathering&procce, Michael A Fitzgibbons
Executive Vice President Opera, Robert F Martinovich

LOCATIONS

HQ: ONEOK PARTNERS, L.P.
100 W 5TH ST STE LL, TULSA, OK 741034298
Phone: 918 588-7000
Web: WWW.ONEOKPARTNERS.COM

PRODUCTS/OPERATIONS

Natural Gas Pipelines

Midwestern Gas Transmission Company
Viking Gas Transmission Company
Guardian Pipeline
OkTex Pipeline Company
ONEOK Gas Transportation
ONEOK Gas Gathering
ONEOK Gas Storage
ONEOK WesTex Transmission
ONEOK Texas Gas Storage
Mid Continent Market Center
ONEOK Transmission Company
Natural Gas Gathering & Processing
Crestone Energy Ventures
ONEOK Field Services
ONEOK Rockies Midstream

COMPETITORS

Enbridge
Kinder Morgan Energy Partners

Panhandle Eastern Pipe Line
TransCanada

HISTORICAL FINANCIALS

Company Type: Private

Income Statement				FYE: December 31
	REVENUE ($ mil.)	NET INCOME ($ mil.)	NET PROFIT MARGIN	EMPLOYEES
12/16	8,918	1,072	12.0%	2,364
12/15	7,761	597	7.7%	—
12/14	12,191	911	7.5%	—
Annual Growth	(14.5%)	8.5%	—	—

2016 Year-End Financials

Return on assets: 6.9%
Return on equity: 17.4%
Current ratio: 0.40
Cash ($ mil.): —

ORANGE AND ROCKLAND UTILITIES INC

Orange and Rockland Utilities (O&R) operates under the auspices of its big city cousin holding company Consolidated Edison (Con Edison). O&R's subsidiaries Rockland Electric and Pike County Power & Light operate in southeastern New York and adjacent portions of New Jersey and Pennsylvania. The utilities distribute electricity to more than 301800 customers in about 100 communities in those three states and deliver natural gas more than to 128000 customers in New York and Pennsylvania. O&R's transmission and distribution facilities include 5550 miles of overhead and underground power distribution lines 560 miles of transmission lines and more than 1850 miles of gas pipeline.

EXECUTIVES

Pres, John McAvoy
Pres*, William G Longhi
V Pres*, Francis Peverly
Senior Engineer, Anthony Rainone

LOCATIONS

HQ: ORANGE AND ROCKLAND UTILITIES INC
1 BLUE HILL PLZ STE 20, PEARL RIVER, NY 109653100
Phone: 845 352-6000
Web: WWW.ORU.COM

PRODUCTS/OPERATIONS

2011 Sales

	$ mil.	% of total
Electric	641	75
Gas	214	25
Total	**855**	**100**

Subsidiaries

Subsidiaries
Pike County Light & Power Company
Rockland Electric Company

COMPETITORS

Avangrid
Delmarva Power
Enbridge
National Fuel Gas
New Jersey Resources

Niagara Mohawk
PPL Corporation
Public Service
Enterprise Group

HISTORICAL FINANCIALS

Company Type: Private

Income Statement				FYE: December 31
	REVENUE ($ mil.)	NET INCOME ($ mil.)	NET PROFIT MARGIN	EMPLOYEES
12/16	653	59	9.1%	1,060
12/05	824	50	6.1%	—
12/04	703	46	6.5%	—
12/03	727	45	6.2%	—
Annual Growth	(0.8%)	2.1%	—	—

2016 Year-End Financials

Return on assets: 2.1%
Return on equity: 9.2%
Current ratio: 0.50
Cash ($ mil.): —

ORANGE COUNTY HEALTH AUTHORITY, A PUBLIC AGENCY

EXECUTIVES

Ceo, Richard Chambers
Ceo, Michael Schrader
Chief Medical Officer, Richard Helmer
Chief Operating Officer, Ladan Khamseh
Chief Counsel, Gary Crockett
Chief Administrative Officer, Kim Cunningham
General Counsel, George L Root
Telecommunications Admi, Chris Williams

Coordinator, Barbara Collins
Information Specialist, Faye Heidari
Information Specialist, Patrick Maez

LOCATIONS

HQ: ORANGE COUNTY HEALTH AUTHORITY, A
PUBLIC AGENCY
505 CITY PKWY W, ORANGE, CA 928682924
Phone: 714 246-8500
Web: WWW.CALOPTIMA.ORG

HISTORICAL FINANCIALS

Company Type: Private

Income Statement				FYE: June 30
	REVENUE ($ mil.)	NET INCOME ($ mil.)	NET PROFIT MARGIN	EMPLOYEES
06/09	1,078	(17)	—	432
06/05	812	(24)	—	—
06/04	0	0	—	—
06/03	756	1	0.2%	—
Annual Growth	6.1%	—	—	—

2009 Year-End Financials

Return on assets: (-5.2%)   Cash ($ mil.): 81
Return on equity: (-13.3%)
Current ratio: 1.00

ORANGE COUNTY TRANSPORTATION AUTHORITY

Public transportation in sunny Orange County California is overseen by the Orange County Transportation Authority (OCTA). The OCTA is the main provider of bus services in its 800-sq.-mi. territory which is home to more than 3 million people. In cooperation with the Southern California Regional Rail Authority the OCTA oversees Metrolink commuter rail service in Orange County. The agency also operates a 10-mile toll road and issues permits to taxi operators. Revenue from a half-cent local sales tax allows the agency to pay for road improvement and mass transit projects.

Operations

OCTA builds designs operates plans maintains and regulates the robust transportation network within Orange County. In addition to the four modes of transportation (transit driving bicycling and walking) OCTA oversees paratransit services taxi services light rail commuter rail and high?occupancy managed lanes.

It operates rail service for OCTA centers on Metrolink Southern California's commuter rail system linking residential communities to employment and activity centers. Metrolink is operated by the Southern California Regional Rail Authority- a joint powers authority of five member agencies representing the counties of Los Angeles Orange Riverside San Bernardino and Ventura. OCTA is one of the five member agencies that administers Orange County Metrolink activities.

The 91 Express Lanes is a four-lane 10-mile toll road built in the median of California's Riverside Freeway (SR-91) between the Orange/Riverside County line and the SR-55.

Geographic Reach

The company is located in Southern California - south of Los Angeles County north of San Diego County and west of Riverside and San Bernardino counties.

Financial Performance

OCTA's rail budget for fiscal year 2015-16 consists of both operating and capital expenses. Operating expenses in FY 2015-16 are budgeted at $31.6 million while capital expenditures are anticipated to reach $100.4 million. The FY 2015-16 rail capital projects. The organization saw a decline in its budget for FY 2015-16 due to drop in passenger fares and state assistance federal capital assistance grants.

(OCTA uses its revenue primarily in salaries and benefits professional services and capital expenditure).

Strategy

The 2014 - 2019 OCTA Strategic Plan takes a comprehensive forward-looking approach to address Orange County's transportation needs during the next five years.(OCTA maintains a Long-Range Transportation Plan updated every four years to account for new planning efforts as well as changes in demographics economic conditions and available sources of transportation funding).

In the FY 2015-16 budget $6.9 million of Measure M funds deposited in the General Fund are being used to fund the final work on the West County Connectors project.

After four years in the making OCTA marked the completion of the $297 million West County Connector project in 2014 which will bring congestion relief where three major freeways (Interstate 405 Interstate 605 and State Route 22) converge.

In 2014 OCTA purchased 400 new buses for fixed-route and ACCESS services. This purchase combined with the in-process repainting of the existing fleet presents a cost-effective opportunity to explore new branding concepts for Orange County bus services.

Company Background

OCTA was formed in 1991 in a consolidation of seven transportation agencies.

EXECUTIVES

Senior Secretary, Annie Mendoza
Auditors: VAVRINEK TRINE DAY & CO LL

LOCATIONS

HQ: ORANGE COUNTY TRANSPORTATION AUTHORITY
550 S MAIN ST, ORANGE, CA 928684506
Phone: 714 636-7433
Web: WWW.OCTA.NET

PRODUCTS/OPERATIONS

2014 Sales

	$ mil.	% of total
Sales taxes	451	93
Unrestricted investment earning	18	4
Property taxes	12	3
Other	0	-
Total	**482**	**100**

Selected Services

91 Express Lanes toll facility
Bus transit service
Freeway improvements funding
Freeway Service Patrol
Long-range planning
Measure M2 administration
Metrolink rail service
Rideshare options
Street and road improvements grants
Taxi administration program
Vanpool subsidies

HISTORICAL FINANCIALS

Company Type: Private

Income Statement				FYE: June 30
	REVENUE ($ mil.)	NET INCOME ($ mil.)	NET PROFIT MARGIN	EMPLOYEES
06/18	634	(53)	—	1,050
06/17	611	54	9.0%	—
06/16	600	67	11.2%	—
06/15	607	43	7.2%	—
Annual Growth	1.5%	—	—	—

OREGON HEALTH & SCIENCE UNIVERSITY

Oregon Health & Science University (OHSU) is the state's sole institution providing doctoral degrees in medicine dentistry and nursing. Its other two schools are science and engineering and in partnership with Oregon State University pharmacy. OHSU has about 2900 students. The university is also home to two hospitals (one a children's hospital) as well as specialty and primary care clinics research and interdisciplinary centers and community service programs. OHSU traces its roots to 1867 when members of the medical department at Willamette University began the first formal medical education program in Oregon.

Operations

OHSU's medical school has a small student-teacher ratio at just 4:1. The organization is renowned for its research initiatives. It has about 3000 active research projects and produced about 130 inventions in 2014. OHSU receives about $370 million in research funding each year. The school engages in an array of multidisciplinary research projects including diseases of the central nervous system weight regulation cancer rare genetic disorders and infectious disease.

Much of the university's medical research is performed at or in concert with clinical care operations at the University Hospital the Doernbecher Children's Hospital and other family care and specialty centers. The medical centers care for some 260000 patients each year.

Researchers at OHSU's Stem Cell Center worked with the Oregon National Primate Research Center to pioneer the first successful cloned nonhuman primate embryonic stem cells. Such cells could help stem cell research gain acceptance as the human element that causes such controversy has been removed.

Geographic Reach

OHSU's main campus includes about 40 buildings on 120 acres on Marquam Hill (overlooking downtown Portland). OHSU also operates two smaller research locations: The Schnitzer Campus in Portland and the West Campus in Hillsboro.

Financial Performance

The university's revenue totaled $2.5 billion in 2015 (versus less than $2 billion in 2012). The earnings primarily came from patient service revenue gifts grants and contracts. Net income increased 49% that year to $320 million thanks to the growing revenues.

OHSU has an operating budget of some $2.4 billion.

Strategy

OHSU completed construction of its collaborative life sciences building on the Schnitzer Campus in 2014. The 650000-sq.-ft. building features lecture halls classrooms specialty research centers offices simulation centers and serves as home to the School of Dentistry; it was built on land donated by the Schnitzer family in 2004. OHSU has purchased additional parcels of land in the area for future expansion efforts.

Also in 2014 OHSU partnered with the small hospital Mid-Columbia Medical Center (MCMC) to recruit medical professionals. Recruits will be employees of OHSU and their services will be leased to MCMC.

The system is working with Adventist Health Kaiser Permanente and Legacy Health to open up the Portland area's first comprehensive behavioral health center (to be named the Unity Center for Behavioral Health). It is expected to open in late 2016.

EXECUTIVES

Executive Vice President Chief Financial Officer, Lawrence J. Furnstahl
Evp And Executive Director Ohsu Hospitals And Clinics, Peter F. Rapp
President And Director, Joseph (Joe) Robertson
Dean School Of Medicine, Mark Richardson
Executive Vice President And Provost, Jeanette Mladenovic
Senior Vice President, Constance French
Regional Vice President, Tom Wang
Vice President And Chief Integrity Officer, Jennifer Ruocco
Associate Vice President, Donald Lollar
Vice President Technology And Services, Nancy Goldschmidt
Medical Director, Zane Horowitz
Department Head Professor, Antonio Baptista
Medical Director, Karen Deibert
Vice President Of Network Operations, Mark Enger
Vice President Technology Transfer And Business Development, Brendan Rauw
Medical Director, Jim Chesnutt
Vice President Of Medical Affairs, Mariah Null Mason
Executive Vice President, Elena Andresen
Medical Director, Tyler Weaver
Medical Director, Scott Naugler
Medical Director, Don Spight
Senior Vice President Of Human Resources, E F Keeling
Chairman, Charles A. Wilhoite
Vice Chairman, Jay Waldron
Treasurer, Thomas Hilton
Secretary, Diana Gernhart
Diplomate American Board Of Orthodontics, Ross Kaplan
Treasurer, Diane Price
Auditors: KPMG LLP PORTLAND OR

LOCATIONS

HQ: OREGON HEALTH & SCIENCE UNIVERSITY
3181 SW SAM JACKSON PK RD, PORTLAND, OR 972393011
Phone: 503 494-8311
Web: WWW.OHSU.EDU

PRODUCTS/OPERATIONS

Selected schools
School of Dentistry
School of Medicine
School of Nursing
School of Pharmacy (with Oregon State University)
School of Science & Engineering

HISTORICAL FINANCIALS
Company Type: Private

Income Statement   FYE: June 30

	REVENUE ($ mil.)	NET INCOME ($ mil.)	NET PROFIT MARGIN	EMPLOYEES
06/18	3,050	259	8.5%	19,500
06/17	2,846	222	7.8%	—
06/13	2,169	221	10.2%	—
06/12	1,975	78	4.0%	—
Annual Growth	7.5%	22.0%	—	—

2018 Year-End Financials
Return on assets: 4.7%   Cash ($ mil.): 52
Return on equity: 7.7%
Current ratio: 2.20

OREGON STATE LOTTERY

The Oregon State Lottery operates the Beaver State's lottery and other state-run games of chance. It offers traditional lotto numbers games and instant-win tickets and it operates video lottery and video poker machines. Oregon also takes part in the multistate Powerball drawing. About 65% of the lottery's profits are channeled into public education programs while the rest is used to fund economic development projects state parks and other government programs. Oregon created its lottery in 1984.

EXECUTIVES

Comm, Chris Telfer
Comm*, Elisa Dozono
Comm*, Mary Wheat
Comm*, Raul Valdivia
Comm*, Liz Carle
Dir*, Barry Pack
Coordinator, Sharon Ingram
Coordinator, James B Scheppke
Manager, Eric White
Senior Quality Assurance Analy, Gavin Araki
Contracts Officer, Angela Schneider

LOCATIONS

HQ: OREGON STATE LOTTERY
500 AIRPORT RD SE, SALEM, OR 973015068
Phone: 503 540-1000
Web: WWW.OREGONLOTTERY.ORG

COMPETITORS

California State Lottery	Washington State Lottery
Multi-State Lottery	

HISTORICAL FINANCIALS
Company Type: Private

Income Statement   FYE: June 30

	REVENUE ($ mil.)	NET INCOME ($ mil.)	NET PROFIT MARGIN	EMPLOYEES
06/18	1,302	(14)	—	420
06/16	1,230	61	5.0%	—
Annual Growth	2.9%	—	—	—

2018 Year-End Financials
Return on assets: (-1.8%)   Cash ($ mil.): 328
Return on equity: (-5.3%)
Current ratio: 1.40

OREGON UNIVERSITY SYSTEM

Auditors: CLIFTONLARSONALLEN LLP GREENW

LOCATIONS

HQ: OREGON UNIVERSITY SYSTEM
, EUGENE, OR 97403
Phone: 541 737-0827
Web: WWW.OUS.EDU

HISTORICAL FINANCIALS
Company Type: Private

Income Statement   FYE: June 30

	REVENUE ($ mil.)	NET INCOME ($ mil.)	NET PROFIT MARGIN	EMPLOYEES
06/14	1,782	83	4.7%	26,000
06/13	1,701	14	0.8%	—
06/12	1,657	10	0.6%	—
06/08	1,251	80	6.4%	—
Annual Growth	6.1%	0.6%	—	—

2014 Year-End Financials
Return on assets: 9.8%   Cash ($ mil.): 456
Return on equity: 4.7%
Current ratio: 1.30

ORLANDO HEALTH, INC.

It's not Disney World but for Floridians needing health care it is a prime destination. Orlando Health is a not-for-profit organization with a network of community and specialty hospitals with nearly 2300 beds in Central Florida. Its flagship facility the Orlando Regional Medical Center features a Level 1 trauma center and provides comprehensive acute care services in a range of specialties. Orlando Health also operates several community hospitals. Its specialty hospitals include the Arnold Palmer Hospital for Children and the Winnie Palmer Hospital for Women and Babies. It also operates the renowned M. D. Anderson Cancer Center Orlando (the first affiliate of Houston-based M. D. Anderson center).

Operations

In addition to the Orlando Regional Medical Center and three fully owned community hospitals the company operates two medical centers through partnerships. It holds a 50% stake in the South Lake Hospital and a 20% stake in the St. Cloud Regional Medical Center. It also operates physician practice associations and an emergency air transport service (Air Care).

Across its facilities Orlando Health has about 2000 affiliated physicians who provide a full spectrum of health care services. Areas of clinical excellence include heart and vascular care cancer care obstetrics and gynecology neonatology neurosciences surgery pediatric orthopedics and sports medicine. Annually Orlando Health serves more than 2 million residents of central Florida and 4500 international patients. The organization also provides between $250 and $300 million in community health programs each year.

As a statutory teaching hospital system Orlando Health also engages in medical training programs through affiliation agreements with the University of Central Florida College of Medicine and other institutions. Orlando Health offers a number of medical residency and fellowship programs; its seven residencies are offered to 250 participants and include programs in emergency medicine internal medicine OB-GYN orthopedic surgery pathology and pediatrics. The organization also conducts research studies and clinical trials through partnerships with educational and commercial organizations.

Geographic Reach

Orlando Health operates throughout Orlando and in neighboring Clermont Longwood Ocoee and St. Cloud Florida.

Financial Performance

The company's revenues increased by 9% in 2014 due to higher net patient service revenues and other revenues. Medicare accounted for 23% of the net patient revenues; Medicaid 19%.

Orlando Health's net income grew by 349% due to higher revenues and investment income.

Operating cash flow increased by 235% in 2014.

Strategy

Orlando Health is working to improve its operating model by improving the quality of patient outcomes; enhancing collaboration between physicians medical professionals hospitals research centers and other institutions; and increasing clinical integration of various disciplines to share resources and skills.

As an example of its collaborative and quality enhancement efforts Orlando Health is involved in the formation of a regional health information exchange to connect its electronic health record (EHR) systems with other Central Florida health providers and the public health department. The program aims to improve quality of care by eliminating redundant tests and other repeated efforts as well as by providing hospitals swift access to patient data.

Orlando Health is also focused on making improvements to its Orlando Regional Medical Center through a multi-year $297-million renovation project. In 2015 the company opened its new 245-bed 10-story 345000-square-foot North Tower's front entrance and its existing Orlando Regional Medical Center building now will be referred to as Orlando Regional Medical Center South Tower. The North Tower is part of the hospital's redesign and renovation project and includes an expanded emergency department cardiovascular service areas operating suites and other ancillary services located inside Orlando Regional Medical CenterSouth Tower. The South Tower expansion is expected to was completed in 2015. That year the Orlando Regional Medical Center redesign and renovation project continued with its Surgical Services expansion and renovation. The 28000-square-foot addition includes 10 new operating rooms a new Post Anesthesia Care Unit area with 24 patient bays.

Other planned projects include the expansion of the neonatal intensive care unit at Winnie Palmer Hospital for Women and Babies.

In 2015 Orlando Health Physician Associates officially opened its doors in the Lake Nona area.

That year the West Orange Healthcare District awarded a $13.8 million grant to Health Central Hospital to expand. The grant was the second largest in the history of the district and funded 75 percent of the total expansion costs. Orlando Health funded the remaining 25 percent. Upon completion the expansion project will add 40 rooms to Health Central Hospital increasing its bed count from 171 to 211 and enabling the further development of specialized care.

Mergers and Acquisitions

In 2015 Orlando Health Physician Associates acquired Pediatric Associates of Orlando. Founded in 1939 it was one of the first pediatric practices in Central Florida.

Company Background

In 2012 Arnold Palmer Hospital added an outpatient rehabilitation center.

The health system expanded its network in 2012 by acquiring the 170-bed Health Central Hospital and its associated facilities in Ocoee Florida for $181 million. Orlando Health further expanded through the purchase of Physician Associates a professional practice organization in 2013.

Orlando Health was founded in 1918.

EXECUTIVES

Vp And Cio, Rick Schooler
President And Ceo, David W. Strong
Svp; President Arnold Palmer Medical Center Orlando Health Foundation And Arnold Palmer Medical Center Foundation, John Bozard
President Adult Hospitals Group, Shannon Elswick
President South Seminole Hospital, Steve Glazier
Cfo, Bernadette Spong
Vp; Executive Director Orlando Health Foundation, Karen Jensen
Vp; President Dr. P. Phillips Hospital, Mark A. Jones
Coo, Jessica Wertman
Medical Director, Muhammad Jawad
Vice President And Senior Development Officer, Lee Ann Fleming
Chairman, Dianna Morgan
Auditors: GRANT THORNTON LLP ORLANDO F

LOCATIONS

HQ: ORLANDO HEALTH, INC.
52 W UNDERWOOD ST, ORLANDO, FL 328061110
Phone: 407 841-5111

PRODUCTS/OPERATIONS

2014 Sales

	$ mil.	% of total
Net patient service revenue less provision for bad debts	2,010	95
Other revenue	103	5
Net assets released from restrictions	4	-
Total	**2,118**	**100**

Selected Facilities

Arnold Palmer Hospital for Children (Orlando)
Dr. P. Phillips Hospital (formerly Orlando Regional Sand Lake Hospital Orlando)
Health Central Hospital (Ocoee)
Lucerne Pavilion (Orlando)
M. D. Anderson Cancer Center Orlando
Orlando Health Heart Institute
Orlando Health Rehabilitation Institute
Orlando Regional Medical Center
South Lake Hospital (50% affiliate Clermont)
South Seminole Hospital (Longwood)
St. Cloud Regional Medical Center (20% affiliate)
Winnie Palmer Hospital for Women & Babies (Orlando)

Selected Specialties

Cancer care (at M. D. Anderson Cancer Center Orlando)
Emergency and trauma care
Heart and vascular
Neurosciences
Oncology/hematology
Orthopedic and sports medicine
Surgery
Women's services

Selected Services

Anesthesiology
Brain Injury Rehabilitation Center (BIRC)
Endocrinology (diabetes)
Endoscopy
Epilepsy care
Home health care
Infectious diseases
Internal medicine
Laboratory and pathology Services
Mammography
Memory Disorder Center
MRI
Multiple sclerosis treatment

Nephrology
Nuclear medicine
Ophthalmology
Otolaryngology (Ears Nose Throat)
Pain management
Patient and family counseling
Pediatric outpatient surgery
Pulmonary medicine
Radiology and diagnostic imaging
Rehabilitation and physical therapy

COMPETITORS

Adventist Health System Sunbelt Healthcare
All Children's Hospital
Baptist Health South Florida
Baptist Health System
Community Health Systems
Florida Hospital Heartland
Florida Hospital Waterman
HCA
Health First
Holmes Regional Medical Center
Mayo Clinic Jacksonville
Mount Sinai Medical Center of Florida
Munroe Regional Health System
Nemours Foundation
Ocala Regional Medical Center
Osceola Regional Medical Center
St. Vincent's Health System
UF&Shands

HISTORICAL FINANCIALS

Company Type: Private

Income Statement				FYE: September 30
	REVENUE ($ mil.)	NET INCOME ($ mil.)	NET PROFIT MARGIN	EMPLOYEES
09/14	1,663	231	13.9%	23,000
09/13	1,576	115	7.3%	—
09/10	1,700	91	5.4%	—
Annual Growth	(0.6%)	26.1%	—	—

2014 Year-End Financials

Return on assets: 9.8%
Return on equity: 20.5%
Current ratio: 2.30

Cash ($ mil.): 65

ORLEANS INTERNATIONAL, INC.

EXECUTIVES

Ceo, Earl Tushman
SEC-Treas, Lawrence Tushman
V Pres, Larry Tushman
V Pres, Reed Tushman
V Pres, Marc Tushman
V Pres, Steve Sanger
Chief Financial Officer, Jerry Castellano
Coordinator, Andrea Thilmany
Executive Officer, Tim Stuart
Controller, Debbie Trimboli
Controller, Beth Ehrlich
Auditors: UHY LLP FARMINGTON HILLS MIC

LOCATIONS

HQ: ORLEANS INTERNATIONAL, INC.
30600 NORTHWESTERN HWY # 300, FARMINGTON HILLS, MI 483343172
Phone: 248 855-5556
Web: WWW.ORLEANSINTL.COM

OSF HEALTHCARE SYSTEM

OSF Healthcare helps patients who are feeling oh-so-frail in northern Illinois and southwestern Michigan. OSF Healthcare system includes 11 acute care hospitals and one long-term care facility that combined are home to more than 1500 beds and offer a full spectrum of inpatient and outpatient medical and surgical services. The system's primary care physician network consists of about 650 physicians at more than 105 locations throughout its service area. Subsidiary OSF Home Care provides hospice home visit and equipment services and OSF Saint Francis provides ambulance pharmacy and health care management services. The not-for-profit system is a subsidiary of the Sisters of The Third Order of St. Francis.

Operations

Along with its various acute care hospitals OSF Healthcare provides urgent care through its OSF PromptCare locations. PromptCare administers a range of services including labs MRI ultrasound and primary and specialty care.

The company also has two colleges of nursing — Saint Francis Medical Center College of Nursing in Peoria Illinois; and the Saint Anthony College of Nursing in Rockford Illinois.

The system had some 58000 inpatient admissions; 1.3 million outpatient visits; and 254000 emergency department visits in 2014.

Financial Performance

In 2014 gross patient services revenue totaled $6.9 billion.

Strategy

OSF Healthcare has an incubation collaboration with the University of Illinois College of Medicine at Peoria. The venture dubbed Jump Trading Simulation and Education Center was established in 2013 to focus on advances in education research and innovation. It has been involved in such activities as funding 3-D printing for surgical procedures and exposing high school students to medical training experiences.

EXECUTIVES

Ceo, Robert Sehring
Ceo Northern Region, Carol Friesen
Consultant, Dick Brooks
Executive Officer, Judith Duva
Staff, Marc Matulis
Corporate Office Site Director, Mike Redd
Executive Officer, Ruth Clift
Auditors: KPMG LLP CHICAGO ILLINOIS

LOCATIONS

HQ: OSF HEALTHCARE SYSTEM
800 NE GLEN OAK AVE, PEORIA, IL 616033200
Phone: 309 655-2850
Web: WWW.OSFHEALTHCARE.ORG

PRODUCTS/OPERATIONS

Selected Clinical Services
Cancer Care
Diabetes & Endocrinology
Emergency Services
Heart & Vascular
Home Health
Hospice
Neurosciences
Pediatrics
Primary Care
Rehabilitation
Surgery
Transplant Services
Weight Loss Management
Women's Health

Selected Support Services
Advance Care Planning
Clinical Research
Equipment Technology Services
Home Infusion Pharmacy
Home Medical Equipment
Mobile Medical Systems
OSF Life Flight
Retail Services
Skilled Nursing Network
System Laboratory
Telehealth

Selected Facilities
OSF Holy Family Medical Center (Monmouth IL)
OSF Saint Anthony Medical Center (Rockford IL)
OSF Saint Clare Home (Peoria Heights IL)
OSF Saint Elizabeth Medical Center (formerly Ottowa Regional Hospital Ottowa IL)
OSF Saint Francis Medical Center (Peoria IL)
OSF Saint James - John W. Albrecht Medical Center (Pontiac IL)
OSF St. Mary Medical Center (Galesburg IL)
OSF St. Francis Hospital (Escanaba MI)
OSF St. Joseph Medical Center (Bloomington IL)

COMPETITORS

Advocate BroMenn	Rush-Copley Medical
Centegra Health System	Center
Central DuPage	SwedishAmerican Health
Hospital	System
Covenant HealthCare	University of Chicago
Genesis Health System	Medical Center
McDonough District	University of Michigan
Hospital	Health System
Memorial Health System	Wheaton Franciscan
Northwestern Memorial	Services
HealthCare	

OUR LADY OF THE LAKE HOSPITAL, INC.

Our Lady of the Lake Regional Medical Center reaches out to Baton Rouge residents with a helping hand. Participating in teaching programs for LSU and Tulane medical schools the medical center has some 800 inpatient beds and includes trauma emergency surgery general medical and specialty care centers for conditions including heart disease cancer orthopedics and ENT (ear nose and throat) disorders. Our Lady of the Lake also includes a Children's Hospital two nursing homes and an independent-living facility and it offers outpatient services at its main campus and at satellite facilities throughout the greater Baton Rouge area.

Operations

The hospital's family of services include an 800-bed Regional Medical Center; a dedicated Children's Hospital; a 350-provider Physician Group primary care network free-standing emergency room in Livingston Parish; an outpatient imaging and surgery centers; Assumption Community Hospital; a network of urgent care clinics; and Our Lady of the Lake College.

Our Lady of the Lake is a primary teaching site for graduate medical education programs and serves 45000 inpatients and 350000 outpatients a year.

The company has more than 850 doctors. Some 70% of its physicians and other professional medical staff members are board certified and in nearly one-third of the hospital system's medical specialty areas 100% of the physicians and other professionals are board certified.

Strategy

As a major facility in the Baton Rouge area Our Lady of the Lake has been expanding its services in the region in recent years. In 2015 Our Lady of the Lake Children's Hospital opened its first pediatric specialty clinic outside of the Baton Rouge area offering specialized outpatient care for pediatric gastroenterology patients.

In 2014 the company opened a new children's emergency room and expanded its adult emergency department.

Company Background

In 2012 the hospital constructed a freestanding emergency room facility in the suburban community of Livingston Louisiana. It is also building a new nine-story patient tower to the main hospital campus; the tower will house the heart and vascular center as well as an expanded ER and a new level 1 regional trauma center and will be completed in late 2013.

Our Lady of the Lake has also expanded its education programs. For instance it added a pediatric residency program in 2010. The hospital also moved to extend its relationship with LSU that year by agreeing to become the primary clinical site for the LSU medical school. The agreement came as LSU considered whether to build a replacement hospital for its aging teaching facility and coincides with the Our Lady of the Lake expansion projects. The partnership launched a new psychiatric residency program in 2012.

Our Lady of the Lake was founded in 1923 by the Franciscan Missionaries of Our Lady.

EXECUTIVES

Vice Chair, William E Balhoff
Secretary, Yolanda Dixon

LOCATIONS

HQ: OUR LADY OF THE LAKE HOSPITAL, INC.
7777 HENNESSY BLVD, BATON ROUGE, LA
708084300
Phone: 225 765-6565
Web: WWW.OLOLRMC.COM

PRODUCTS/OPERATIONS

Selected Services
Advanced Wound and Ostomy Clinic
Cancer
Children's Hospital
Critical Care
Diabetes & Nutrition Center
Emergency Services
Endoscopy Center
Hearing and Balance Center
Heart & Vascular Institute
Imaging Services
Laboratory and Diagnostics
Lake Express Check-In
LSU Health Baton Rouge
Mental and Behavioral Health
Neurology Neurosurgery and Stroke
Orthopedics
Palliative Care
Pharmacy
Rehabilitation Center
Respiratory Care
Senior Services
St. Anthony's Home
Surgery
Trauma Center
Urgent Care
Voice Center
Weight Loss

COMPETITORS

CHRISTUS St. Frances
  Cabrini Hospital
Dynacq Healthcare
General Health System
Lane Regional Medical
  Center

Our Lady of Lourdes
  River Parishes
  Hospital
Woman's Hospital

HISTORICAL FINANCIALS

Company Type: Private

Income Statement				FYE: June 30
	REVENUE ($ mil.)	NET INCOME ($ mil.)	NET PROFIT MARGIN	EMPLOYEES
06/18	1,254	103	8.2%	1,800
06/16	895	(89)	—	—
06/15	984	21	2.1%	—
06/14	946	56	6.0%	—
Annual Growth	7.3%	16.0%	—	—

2018 Year-End Financials
Return on assets: 5.1%
Return on equity: 9.5%
Current ratio: 1.80
Cash ($ mil.): 118

OVERLAKE HOSPITAL ASSOCIATION

EXECUTIVES

Prin, Diane Sperry
Coordinator, Lisa Sato
Nurse Manager, Jody Burnell
Coordinator, Jennifer Fischer
Registered Nurse, Nancy Corbridge
Registered Nurse, Anastasia Samsonov
Admitting Manager, Jill Salsbury

Nurse, Pamela Johnson
Therapist, Svetlana Young
Emergency Medicine Specialist, David Bronstein
Director Care Management, Dee Aust
Auditors: KPMG LLP SEATTLE WA

LOCATIONS

HQ: OVERLAKE HOSPITAL ASSOCIATION
1035 116TH AVE NE, BELLEVUE, WA 980044604
Phone: 425 688-5000
Web: WWW.OVERLAKEHOSPITAL.ORG

HISTORICAL FINANCIALS

Company Type: Private

Income Statement				FYE: June 30
	REVENUE ($ mil.)	NET INCOME ($ mil.)	NET PROFIT MARGIN	EMPLOYEES
06/18	559	41	7.4%	198
06/17	513	58	11.3%	—
06/16	511	8	1.6%	—
06/15	490	20	4.1%	—
Annual Growth	4.5%	27.3%	—	—

2018 Year-End Financials
Return on assets: 4.2%
Return on equity: 7.4%
Current ratio: 1.30
Cash ($ mil.): 29

OVERLAKE HOSPITAL MEDICAL CENTER

Over the lake and through the sound to Overlake Hospital Medical Center we go! The not-for-profit hospital provides health care services to residents of Bellevue Washington in the Puget Sound region. The nearly 350-bed facility provides comprehensive inpatient and outpatient services ranging from cancer care and surgery to specialized senior care. Overlake also operates a number of outpatient clinics providing primary care urgent care and specialty care such as weight loss surgery. The organization also provides patients with health and wellness programs addressing issues like women's and children's health.

Operations
The medical center has more than 1000 physicians on staff and runs Centers of Excellence in cardiac care cancer care surgical services women's and infants' care and emergency and Level III trauma care. The facility is home to a 24-hour urgent care clinic an anticoagulation clinic and a breast screening center. Overlake also operates numerous outpatient clinics providing primary care urgent care and specialty care.

Geographic Reach
Overlake provides health care services to residents of Bellevue Washington and the entire Puget Sound region. It operates clinics on its main campus in Bellevue as well as in Redmond and in Issaquah and on Mercer Island.

Sales and Marketing
In 2014 Medicare payments accounted for 27% of net patient revenues followed by group health organizations (17%) Premera (13%) and Regence (12%).

Financial Performance
Overlake's revenues increased by 2% to $433 million in 2014 as the result of higher net patient revenues and contribution revenues.

Net income rose 50% to $60 million that year primarily due to income from change in net unrealized gains on investments. Cash flow from operations fell 3% to $47 million as more cash was used in net clinic accounts receivable pledges receivable prepaid expenses and other long-term receivables.

Strategy
Increasing demand in the region has led the hospital to invest in expansions and equipment upgrades that include more emergency treatment capabilities and an on-campus helistop for trauma patients being airlifted to the area.

Along with its expansion and construction projects Overlake is investing in new technology to keep the health system in line with its competitors and to improve patient care. It is adding endoscopic video towers to its operating rooms to facilitate improved views of surgical procedures and is also moving to digitize all of its facilities with electronic health records.

In 2013 it opened the new $17.4 million David and Shelley Hovind Heart & Vascular center. The new 19200-sq.-ft. facility brings cardiac and vascular services together in one location.

Overlake has also focused on adding new primary care clinics and expanding its physician network to serve patients in locations closer to where they live and work.

Company Background
Overlake founded in 1960 is led by CEO Craig Hendrickson a veteran health care executive.

EXECUTIVES

Vice President Human Resources, Lisa Brock
Medical Director Ed, Steve Marshall
Vice President Strategy And Marketing, Caitlin Hillary
Vice President Of It, Jolene Lim
Treasurer, Julie Sun
Auditors: KPMG LLP SEATTLE WA

LOCATIONS

HQ: OVERLAKE HOSPITAL MEDICAL CENTER
1035 116TH AVE NE, BELLEVUE, WA 980044687
Phone: 425 688-5000
Web: WWW.OVERLAKEHOSPITAL.ORG

Selected Locations
Outpatient Rehabilitation Services
Outpatient Surgery (park in the West Garage; Outpatient Surgery is located on the first floor of the West Garage.)
Overlake Bellevue Campus and Overlake Medical Clinics Medical Tower
Overlake Medical Clinics Downtown Bellevue
Overlake Medical Clinics Issaquah
Overlake Medical Clinics Kirkland
Overlake Medical Clinics Redmond
Urgent Care Clinic in Issaquah
Urgent Care Clinic in Redmond

PRODUCTS/OPERATIONS

2014 Sales

	$ mil.	% of total
Net patient service revenue	419	97
Other operating revenue	11	3
Contribution revenue	2	-
Total	433	100

Selected Medical Services
Breast Health Services
Cancer Center at Overlake
Cardiac Center at Overlake
Clinical Trials
Emergency & Trauma Center
Medical Imaging
Overlake Medical Clinics
Surgical Services
Weight Loss Surgery
Women's & Infants' Center

HISTORICAL FINANCIALS

Company Type: Private

Income Statement   FYE: June 30

	REVENUE ($ mil.)	NET INCOME ($ mil.)	NET PROFIT MARGIN	EMPLOYEES
06/18	555	39	7.1%	2,450
06/16	502	21	4.3%	—
06/15	485	16	3.5%	—
06/14	450	59	13.3%	—
Annual Growth	5.4%	(10.0%)	—	—

2018 Year-End Financials

Return on assets: 4.1%   Cash ($ mil.): 28
Return on equity: 7.2%
Current ratio: 1.30

OXBOW SULPHUR INC.

EXECUTIVES

Pres, Mark Whittemore
Auditors: GRANT THORNTON LLP HOUSTON T

LOCATIONS

HQ: OXBOW SULPHUR INC.
   1450 LAKE ROBBINS DR # 500, THE WOODLANDS,
   TX 773803258
Phone: 281 907-9500

HISTORICAL FINANCIALS

Company Type: Private

Income Statement   FYE: December 31

	REVENUE ($ mil.)	NET INCOME ($ mil.)	NET PROFIT MARGIN	EMPLOYEES
12/08	878	26	3.0%	60
12/07	273	4	1.5%	—
12/05	170	(0)	—	—
Annual Growth	72.8%	—	—	—

2008 Year-End Financials

Return on assets: 17.3%   Cash ($ mil.): 19
Return on equity: 75.7%
Current ratio: 1.40

PACIFIC COAST PRODUCERS

Fruits seafood sauces and organic tomato puree — rather than movies — are the creative output of this particular group of Pacific Coast Producers. The cooperative markets the apricots grapes peaches pears and tomatoes grown by its approximately 160 California-based members. It turns the produce into private-label canned fruit sauces and juices and sells them to the retail and foodservice industries. Pacific Coast Producers typically serves retailers the likes of Albertson's Aldi Kroger Safeway SUPERVALU Whole Foods and Wal-Mart as well as the US Department of Agriculture. The company founded in 1971 operates three production sites and one distribution center in California.

Operations

The cooperative boasts three food-processing facilities in California as well as distribution centers in California and Washington.

Geographic Reach

From its base in Lodi California Pacific Coast Producers grows its fruits in California and sells them nationwide.

Sales and Marketing

Pacific Coast Producers sells the products it grows and processes to retailers and foodservice operators nationwide as well as to the US Department of Agriculture.

Financial Performance

As one of California's premier private label packers Pacific Coast Producers has logged annual sales in excess of $535 million plus $100 million in alliance income.

Strategy

Pacific Coast Producers has expanded its warehouse space in Lodi to improve efficiency and boost capacity. The move cost the company $23 million. It expanded its distribution center by 50% to meet rising demand for canned food.

The cooperative serves tomato processor Morning Star through a sales and marketing alliance it formed with the company in 2009. As part of the collaboration Pacific Coast Producers provides canned tomatoes to the retail and foodservice industries.

EXECUTIVES

Vice President Finance Chief Financial Officer, Mark Wahlman
Vice President General Counsel, Mona Schulman
Vice President Human Resources, Richard Ehrler
Vice President Operations, Dan Sroufe
Auditors: KPMG LLP SACRAMENTO CALIFOR

LOCATIONS

HQ: PACIFIC COAST PRODUCERS
   631 N CLUFF AVE, LODI, CA 952400756
Phone: 209 367-8800
Web: WWW.PACIFICCOASTPRODUCERS.COM

PRODUCTS/OPERATIONS

Selected Products

Apricots

Catsup
Chili Sauces
Chunky Mixed Fruit
Concentrated Crushed Tomatoes
Diced Style Tomatoes
Extra Heavy Concentrated Crushed Round Tomato Puree
Formulated Pizza Sauces
Fruit Cocktail
Fruit for Salad
Fruit Mix
Ground Tomatoes
Marinara Sauces
Non-Formulated Pizza Sauce
Organic Tomatoes
Peaches
Pears
Random Cut / Strip Style Tomatoes
Seafood Sauces
Stewed Style Tomatoes
Tomato Juice
Whole Peeled Tomatoes

HISTORICAL FINANCIALS

Company Type: Private

Income Statement   FYE: May 31

	REVENUE ($ mil.)	NET INCOME ($ mil.)	NET PROFIT MARGIN	EMPLOYEES
05/18	668	22	3.4%	1,000
05/17	607	26	4.4%	—
05/16	630	30	4.8%	—
05/15	623	30	4.9%	—
Annual Growth	2.3%	(9.4%)	—	—

2018 Year-End Financials

Return on assets: 4.3%   Cash ($ mil.): 1
Return on equity: 10.0%
Current ratio: 2.00

PACIFIC PREMIER BANK

EXECUTIVES

Pres-Ceo, Steven R Gardner
Chb*, Jeff C Jones
Sr V Pres-Cfo*, Kent Smith
Sr Exec Vpres-Cfo*, Ronald J Nicolas Jr
Cro*, Michael Karr
Evp-Cco*, Donn Jakosky
Evp-Chief Acctg Officer*, Lori Wright
Customer Representativ, Leticia Rodriguez
Senior Vice President Director, Thomas Galindo
Vice President, Flo Jenkins
Senior Vice President, Douglas Wolfe

LOCATIONS

HQ: PACIFIC PREMIER BANK
   17901 VON KARMAN AVE, IRVINE, CA 926146297
Phone: 714 431-4000
Web: WWW.PPBI.COM

HISTORICAL FINANCIALS

Company Type: Private

Income Statement   FYE: December 31

	ASSETS ($ mil.)	NET INCOME ($ mil.)	INCOME AS % OF ASSETS	EMPLOYEES
12/17	8,022	68	0.9%	104
12/16	4,035	44	1.1%	—
12/15	2,782	29	1.1%	—
12/14	2,033	18	0.9%	—
Annual Growth	58.0%	54.0%	—	—

2017 Year-End Financials

Return on assets: 0.9%   Sales ($ mil): 298
Return on equity: 5.1%

PAN AMERICAN HEALTH ORGANIZATION INC

EXECUTIVES

Dir, Carissa Etienne
Pres, Mirta Periago
Cfo, Esteban Alzamora
Information Specialist, Claudia Ortiz
Information Specialist, Douglas Alvarado
Coordinator, Farida Kerouani
Human Resources, Paul De La
Coordinator, Alessandra Senisse
Coordinator, Fatima W Marinho
Information Specialist, Manuel A Mijango
Human Resources, Eduardo Curaca

LOCATIONS

HQ: PAN AMERICAN HEALTH ORGANIZATION INC
525 23RD ST NW, WASHINGTON, DC 200372825
Phone: 202 974-3000
Web: WWW.PAHO.ORG

HISTORICAL FINANCIALS

Company Type: Private

Income Statement | | | | FYE: December 31

	REVENUE ($ mil.)	NET INCOME ($ mil.)	NET PROFIT MARGIN	EMPLOYEES
12/09	1,268	101	8.0%	1,500
12/06	541	84	15.7%	—
Annual Growth	32.9%	6.2%	—	—

2009 Year-End Financials

Return on assets: 0.9%   Cash ($ mil.): 351
Return on equity: 8.0%
Current ratio: 14.00

PANDUIT CORP.

Panduit's got your cables covered connected and enclosed. The company's electrical components tie together the communications computing power and security systems of a building or physical location. Products include cabling connectors copper wire fiber-optic components cabinets and racks grounding systems outlets terminals and other electrical components. It also offers software used to integrate and manage separate building functions. Panduit's products are used in data centers office buildings industrial plants processing lines and other settings. The privately held company has customers in more than 100 countries. Among its customers are Noosa Yogurt Iveco and Purdue University.

Financial Performance

Panduit claims to generate more than $1 billion in annual revenue.

Strategy

As companies have built out data centers Panduit has been in the thick of it supplying cables cabinets and rack enclosures. Most of the new products the company has introduced in recent years have concerned infrastructure that routes and connects miles of cable in data centers.

Panduit runs a robust research arm employing more than 200 R&D personnel working in about 20 laboratories. The company's research has netted about 2000 global patents. Panduit works with partners like Cisco Systems and Rockwell Automation and in 2019 the three companies opened a

manufacturing technology center in Mexico City to showcase their products.

The company expanded its capability to provide audio/visual technologies with its acquisition of Atlona in 2019. With Atlona's networked AV signal distribution wireless collaboration and AV system automation offerings Panduit provides products for the increasing convergence of AV onto the network.

Some of Panduit's rivals have more revenue and resources to develop and market new products. Competitors include Amphenol TE Connectivity Molex and Corning all of which generate 10-times more annual revenue than Panduit.

Mergers and Acquisitions

Panduit makes acquisitions to expand its product line and reach new customers.

In 2019 Panduit acquired Atlona a maker of audio-visual equipment based in San Jose California. The deal helps Panduit round out its offerings with Atlona's networked AV signal distribution wireless collaboration and AV system automation technologies. Atlona became part of Atlona's enterprise group.

Company Background

Panduit was established in 1955 by Jack Caveney Sr.Its first product was the Panduct Wiring Duct.

EXECUTIVES

Ceo, John E. (Jack) Caveney
Vp Global Sales And Marketing, Ronald K. (Ron) Partridge
Cto, Jack Tison
President, Thomas C. (Tom) Donovan
Senior Vice President Global Supply Chain, William Ernest
Vice President Oem Business, Bob Krisel
Vice President Sls And Marketing, Bernard Westapher
Vp Of Information Technology, Joanne Tyree
Vice President Marketing, Chad Reynolds
Vice President, Rina Lim
Group Vice President, Mark Acklin
Vp Quality, Glenn Henning
National Account Manager, Michael Taylor
Vice President, Vincent Walsh
Regional Vice President, Hank Smith
Vice President Business Operations, Joergen Schuetze
Svp Strategic Programs, Randall Woods
Vice President Contractor Development, Jeff Miller
Senior Vice President Human Resources, Tim Dee
Group Vp Of It, Jim Hall
Vice President Information Technology, Janet Derwinski
Vice President Of Finance, Gerald Lange
Vice President Business Development, Dave Mack
Auditors: GRANT THORNTON

LOCATIONS

HQ: PANDUIT CORP.
18900 PANDUIT DR, TINLEY PARK, IL 604873600
Phone: 708 532-1800

PRODUCTS/OPERATIONS

PRODUCTS

Cabinets Thermal Management Racks and Enclosures
Cable and Wire Bundling
Cable Routing and Pathways
Copper Systems
Fiber Systems
Grounding
Identification
Japan Market Only Products
Power Distribution and Environmental Monitoring
Product Promotions
Safety and Security
Software and Hardware
Tools
Wire Routing Protection and Insulation

Wire Termination
SOFTWARE/INTELLIGENCE
DCIM
6 Zone™ Methodology
Data Center Management
Enterprise Management
Intelligent Hardware
Intelligent Software
SmartZone Overview
PROFESSIONAL SERVICES
Case Studies
Industrial Automation Services
Safety Services

COMPETITORS

Amphenol	Ortronics
Avaya	RiT Technologies
CommScope	Schneider Electric
Corning	Siemens AG
Molex	TE Connectivity
Optical Cable	

HISTORICAL FINANCIALS

Company Type: Private

Income Statement | | | | FYE: December 31

	REVENUE ($ mil.)	NET INCOME ($ mil.)	NET PROFIT MARGIN	EMPLOYEES
12/16	937	0	—	5,110
12/15	924	0	—	—
12/14	973	0	—	—
Annual Growth	(1.9%)	—	—	—

PAREXEL INTERNATIONAL CORPORATION

PAREXEL International excels in pharmaceutical development services. A top contract research organization (CRO) the firm counts among its clients some of the world's largest drug biotech diagnostics and medical device firms. Its core Clinical Research Services (CRS) segment provides clinical trial and data management study design patient recruitment biostatistical analysis clinical pharmacology and industry training and publishing. Its PAREXEL Consulting Services (PC) segment handles the non-clinical aspects of drug development regulatory affairs and new product launches. Finally the PAREXEL Informatics (PI) segment offers patient technology solutions and regulatory and clinical solutions. PAREXEL was taken private by Pamplona Capital Management for $4.5 billion in 2017.

Change in Company Type

In late 2017 PAREXEL was acquired by Pamplona Capital Management for some $4.5 billion. The deal was announced after pressure was placed on the company to sell itself due to lower-than-expected profit margins. The deal also followed a trend of consolidation in the CRO market.

Operations

PAREXEL's largest segment Clinical Research Services (CRS) accounts for more than half of total sales. Its core development business covers all phases of drug and device development from discovery research through clinical trials and post-marketing studies. The division has benefited from the market trend of increased R&D outsourcing by pharmaceutical and biotech drug companies particularly in the areas of Phase II Phase III and Early Phase development.

The PAREXEL Informatics (PI) segment's Perceptive Informatics and other units offer information technology systems and services that help manage clinical trials.

The PAREXEL Consulting Services (PC) segment provides product development and strategic compliance consulting as well as regulatory outsourcing services.

Geographic Reach

PAREXEL has some 85 facilities in more than 40 countries in Europe the Asia/Pacific region the Middle East North America South America and Africa. More than half of PAREXEL's sales are generated outside of the Americas partly because of its core client base of large multinational corporations.

Sales and Marketing

PAREXEL's sales force directs custom marketing efforts towards niche market segments to match the appropriate services with each customer's needs. Its overall goal is to help clients reduce costs and risks related to product development and commercialization.

Strategy

PAREXEL stands to benefit from such industry factors as the virtualization of biopharmaceutical firms the trend to conduct smaller but more complex trials and advances in information technology. To best take advantage of these opportunities the company continues to serve its multinational clients while also expanding its offerings for small and mid-sized developers.

The company has a number of major customers such as Pfizer which has brought in more than 10% of total sales. PAREXEL is somewhat vulnerable to the loss of major customers which could occur due to a number of reasons ranging from budgetary concerns to corporate mergers to the completion of product launches. Losing a big customer could significantly impact the firm's sales.

Additionally the CRO market is very competitive with pharmaceuticals providing their own research in-house universities and teaching hospitals entering the fray and marketing and consulting firms providing product development advisory services. To stay competitive PAREXEL looks to establish and maintain long-term alliances with pharmaceutical companies.

In early 2019 the company established a division dedicated to serving the needs of emerging biotech companies. The unit offers customers expertise in operating in China's growing market genomic medicine services and other programs tailored to the sector. The timing coincides with rapid growth in the biotech sphere.

Mergers and Acquisitions

In early 2017 PAREXEL acquired The Medical Affairs Company which provides outsourced medical affairs services including consulting communications support and medical science liaison services to pharmaceutical biotech and medical device clients.

Company Background

Founders Josef von Rickenbach a health care and international products specialist and Anne Sayigh a chemist and regulatory affairs specialist started PAREXEL in 1982 to provide regulatory consulting services to pharmaceutical firms. Its name referred to 16th-century Swiss physician Theophrastus Bombastus von Hohenheim — better known as Paracelsus the father of empirical chemistry.

Through a series of acquisitions PAREXEL entered new markets including biostatistics and data management medical marketing and health consulting.

The company went public in 1995 and was taken private again in 2017.

HISTORY

Founders Josef von Rickenbach a health care and international products specialist and Anne Sayigh a chemist and regulatory affairs specialist started PAREXEL in 1982 to provide regulatory consulting services to pharmaceutical firms. Its name referred to 16th-century Swiss physician Theophrastus Bombastus von Hohenheim — better known as Paracelsus the father of empirical chemistry.

In 1988 PAREXEL bought Consulting Statisticians and moved into the biostatistics and data management market. The next year it went international with the purchase of the biostatistics and data management division of McDonnell Douglas Information Systems. In 1991 PAREXEL augmented its European operations with the acquisition of German contract researcher AFB Arzneimittelforschung — a move that paid off in rising sales.

PAREXEL went public in 1995. In the following two years it bought six health consulting firms including State and Federal Associates and medical marketing firm Rescon with the intention of boosting its ability to get its clients' products on the market. The company continued its acquisition spree in 1998; this time European marketing and research companies were on the shopping list. Competitor Covance was set to buy PAREXEL in 1999 then called off the deal when investors balked.

The company announced in 2000 that it would lay off more than 400 workers after Novartis cancelled a major contract. That year the company formed new alliances with such companies as NeuroRecovery Research Phenome Sciences and Prevention Concepts. PAREXEL also bought a full-service clinical pharmacology unit in the UK from GlaxoWellcome (now GlaxoSmithKline) as well as a majority stake in FARMOVS a clinical pharmacology research business and laboratory in South Africa.

In 2001 the company formed Perceptive Informatics a subsidiary focused on developing Internet-based information management systems. To strengthen its clinical trial management services PAREXEL bought software developer FW Pharma Systems in 2003. In 2006 it purchased US-based Behavioral and Medical Research LLC for $69 million to expand its research services.

EXECUTIVES

Chairman And Ceo, Josef H. von Rickenbach, $966,874 total compensation
President And Coo, Mark A. Goldberg, $622,263 total compensation
President Perceptive Informatics, Xavier Flinois
Svp And Cfo, Simon N. R. Harford
Svp And Worldwide Head Parexel Access, Joshua Schultz
Svp General Counsel And Secretary, Douglas A. Batt, $415,860 total compensation
Svp Clinical Research Services, Gadi Saarony, $455,051 total compensation
Vp And Worldwide Head Early Phase, Sy Pretorius
Vice President, Paul Bridges
Vice President Of Human Resources, Michael Brandt
Senior Medical Director, Karla Kanis
Vp Clinical Science, Roland Andersson
Vice President, Conal Burgess
Vice President Worldwide Head Of Medcom, Susan Kammerman
Medical Director, Regina Sohn
Vice President Worldwide Head Business Development Clinical Pharmacology, Yves Grenon
Corporate Vice President, Janet Edwards
Vice President, Frank Panaccio

Global Privacy Officer And Vice Presiden, Uwe Fiedler
Medical Director, Lynn McRoy
Vice President Human Resources, Carl Weaver
Medical Director, Wayne Dankner
Vice President Human Resource Operations, Guy Schiller
Senior Vice President, Mary Bareilles
Vice President Technical, Tony Warchut
It Vice President Process Qm, Deborah Wade
Vice President Marketing, Ronald Kraus
Associate Medical Director, Claire Chehrazi
Medical Director, Marina Bussel
Corporate Vice President Strategic Account Leader, Jim Anthony
Corporate Vp Compensation Benefits And Hr Mergers And Acquisitions, Michele Fournier
Vice President Corporate Communications, Mark Stephenson
Corporate Vice President Head Global Medical Services, Dana Washburn
Vice President And Chief Scientific Officer For Medical Imaging, Peter Steiger
Vice President, Ubavka Denoble
Vice President Global Monitoring Operations, Dennis Joseph
Vice President Of Tax, John Benoit
Evp And Cfo, Greg Rush
Corporate Vp Commercial Growth, Frederick Lemoine
Vp Regulatory Consulting Service, Amy Mckee
Senior Medical Director, Rohit Sood
Vp Production Services Studio Operations, Shana Zarcufsky
Vp Access Consulting, Thom Schoenwaelder
Auditors: ERNST & YOUNG LLP BOSTON MAS

LOCATIONS

HQ: PAREXEL INTERNATIONAL CORPORATION
195 WEST ST, WALTHAM, MA 024511146
Phone: 781 487-9900
Web: WWW.PAREXEL.COM

COMPETITORS

Albany Molecular Research
BioClinica
Charles River Laboratories
Covance
DATATRAK International
ICON
INC Research
IQVIA
PharmaNet Development Group
Pharmaceutical Product Development
ReSearch Pharmaceutical Services
WuXi PharmaTech
eResearchTechnology
inVentiv Health

HISTORICAL FINANCIALS

Company Type: Private

Income Statement				FYE: June 30
	REVENUE ($ mil.)	NET INCOME ($ mil.)	NET PROFIT MARGIN	EMPLOYEES
06/17	2,441	107	4.4%	18,900
06/16	2,426	154	6.4%	—
06/15	2,330	147	6.3%	—
06/14	2,266	129	5.7%	—
Annual Growth	2.5%	(6.0%)	—	—

2017 Year-End Financials

Return on assets: 4.6%   Cash ($ mil.): 302
Return on equity: 16.9%
Current ratio: 1.50

PARK NICOLLET METHODIST HOSPITAL

Park Nicollet Methodist Hospital helps keep residents swimmingly healthy in the City of Lakes. Operating as Methodist Hospital the acute care facility serves the greater Minneapolis area. It has some 430 beds and provides such specialized care programs as cancer treatment cardiovascular health emergency care obstetrics therapy for eating disorders and neurological rehabilitation. The facility is home to the Struthers Parkinson's Center which is devoted to helping patients with Parkinson's disease and their families to cope with the disease. Methodist Hospital is owned by Minnesota-based not-for-profit health care organization HealthPartners.

Operations
Methodist Hospital along with parent Health-Partners works with local government agencies schools and not-for-profit groups to establish innovative programs addressing community health needs.

Strategy
To keep pace with growing community care needs Methodist Hospital has embarked on a $150 million expansion and renovation project. In 2016 it opened two new inpatient floors with some 50 private rooms and expanded its surgery center adding eight new operating rooms. With expansions complete renovations (including energy efficiency upgrades) are in order for the next couple of years.

EXECUTIVES

Cfo Park Nicollet Health Services, David J. Cooke
Coo Park Nicollet Health Services, Michael B. Kaupa
President Park Nicollet Foundation, Christa Getchell
President And Ceo, David J. Abelson
Vice President Marketing And Communications And Chief Marketing Officer, Melissa Schoenherr
Auditors: DELOITTE TAX LLP MINNEAPOLIS

LOCATIONS

HQ: PARK NICOLLET METHODIST HOSPITAL
6500 EXCELSIOR BLVD, SAINT LOUIS PARK, MN 554264702
Phone: 952 993-5000

COMPETITORS

Abbott Northwestern Hospital
Allina Hospitals
CentraCare Health
Children's Hospitals and Clinics of Minnesota
Fairview Health
Mayo Clinic Rochester
North Memorial Health Care
Rainy Lake Medical
SCMC
University of Minnesota Medical Center

HISTORICAL FINANCIALS
Company Type: Private

Income Statement · FYE: December 31

	REVENUE ($ mil.)	NET INCOME ($ mil.)	NET PROFIT MARGIN	EMPLOYEES
12/14*	489	47	9.6%	2,503
06/05	1	0	55.1%	—
12/02	301	11	3.8%	—
12/01	734	0	0.0%	—
Annual Growth	(3.1%)	150.8%	—	—

*Fiscal year change

2014 Year-End Financials
Return on assets: 1.4%   Cash ($ mil.): —
Return on equity: 9.6%
Current ratio: 1.60

PARKLAND COMMUNITY HEALTH PLAN, INC., A PROGRAM OF DALLAS COUNTY HOSPITAL

EXECUTIVES

Ceo, Rob Smith
Pharmacy Manager, Nneka Okpalla
Director of Provider Relations, Patricia Carney
Vice President of Operations, Jill Hassmann
Officer, Cindy Scott
Accounting Manager Affiliate, Marsha Beasley
Auditors: BRUCE E BERNSTEIN & ASSOC PC

LOCATIONS

HQ: PARKLAND COMMUNITY HEALTH PLAN, INC., A PROGRAM OF DALLAS COUNTY HOSPITAL
1341 W MOCKINGBIRD LN 1150E, DALLAS, TX 752474974
Phone: 214 266-2100

HISTORICAL FINANCIALS
Company Type: Private

Income Statement · FYE: December 31

	REVENUE ($ mil.)	NET INCOME ($ mil.)	NET PROFIT MARGIN	EMPLOYEES
12/17	541	17	3.3%	2
12/15	527	(32)	—	—
12/13	519	27	5.2%	—
12/12	515	24	4.7%	—
Annual Growth	1.0%	(6.0%)	—	—

2017 Year-End Financials
Return on assets: 12.3%   Cash ($ mil.): 136
Return on equity: 17.9%
Current ratio: 3.20

PARSONS ENVIRONMENT & INFRASTRUCTURE GROUP INC.

A unit of Parsons Corporation Parsons Commercial Technology Group (PARCOMM) provides project management engineeringÅ construction design maintenance and related services for industrial and commercialÅ projects.Å The company'sÅ clients include firms inÅ the telecommunications health care manufacturing defense petroleum and chemical industries. PARCOMM also completesÅ projects for schools colleges and government entities.Å Specialized services include industrial environmental remediation factory modernization and developing state vehicle inspection and compliance programs. PARCOMM operates throughout the US and the world.

EXECUTIVES

Vice President Human Resources, Debra Fiori

LOCATIONS

HQ: PARSONS ENVIRONMENT & INFRASTRUCTURE GROUP INC.
4701 HEDGEMORE DR, CHARLOTTE, NC 282093281
Phone: 704 529-6246
Web: WWW.PARSONS.COM

COMPETITORS

Bechtel   Halliburton
Fluor   Jacobs Engineering

HISTORICAL FINANCIALS
Company Type: Private

Income Statement · FYE: July 29

	REVENUE ($ mil.)	NET INCOME ($ mil.)	NET PROFIT MARGIN	EMPLOYEES
07/14*	684	(12)	—	1,205
12/12	684	(12)	—	—
12/11	443	(57)	—	—
Annual Growth	15.6%	—	—	—

*Fiscal year change

2014 Year-End Financials
Return on assets: (-1.9%)   Cash ($ mil.): 24
Return on equity: (-3.1%)
Current ratio: 1.30

PARTNERS HEALTHCARE SYSTEM, INC.

Partners HealthCare operates two large acute-care medical centers — Brigham and Women's Hospital and Massachusetts General Hospital — and about 15 community hospitals in Boston and surrounding communities. The not-for-profit system also provides primary and specialty care through clinics physician offices rehabilitation centers long-term care facilities and home health and hospice agencies. Subsidiary MassHealth provides medical insurance to state residents. Partners HealthCare also provides medical training and research through an affiliation with Harvard. The organization has additional partnerships with health research and educational organizations around the globe.

Financial Performance

Partners Healthcare reported $13.3 billion in revenue in 2018 a less than 1% decline from 2017 results. Patient service revenue which accounts for about 70% of sales increased 10% but insurance premium revenue (10% of sales) decreased 43% due to membership declines (related to the transition of customers from managed care to accountable care programs). Academic and research revenue (15% of sales) increased 4%.

Excess of revenue over expenses increased 25% to $826.6 million due to lower operating costs related to the insurance business.

The organization ended 2018 with $398.4 million in cash down $340.7 million from 2017. Operating activities contributed $899 million while investing activities used $1.4 billion (mostly for acquisitions property and equipment) and financing activities contributed $140.8 million via long-term debt proceeds and investment income.

Strategy

Partners HealthCare has expanded its operations through a stream of acquisitions and construction efforts. It completed construction of a replacement facility for the Nantucket Cottage Hospital in 2018. The company is also adding three new outpatient care buildings (containing primary women's cancer diagnostic orthopedic physical therapy and surgery care centers) to its Wentworth-Douglass Hospital campus.

Partners HealthCare is investing in new IT tools to improve efficiencies enhance quality and lower the cost of care. The company has installed an electronic health record (EHR) system across all of its facilities; it is also adding a digital imaging platform and a centralized credentialing system.

In addition the company regularly updates medical equipment at its facilities to keep pace with medical innovations. For instance it has added a minimally invasive spine surgery program at Brigham and Women's Faulkner Hospital and robotic surgery centers at two of its community hospitals in recent years.

Mergers and Acquisitions

Partners HealthCare has had two failed efforts to expand beyond Massachusetts. The company's agreement to acquire Care New England was canceled in 2019 after Rhode Island's governor objected to the deal. Partners and Care New England had approached Rhode Island-based Lifespan to also join forces in 2018 but that proposal was subsequently dropped. The organization did successfully acquire specialty hospital Massachusetts Eye and Ear in 2018.

Company Background

Partners HealthCare was founded in 1994 through the merger of Brigham and Women's Hospital and Massachusetts General Hospital.

EXECUTIVES

Vice President Public Affairs Partners Community Benefit Programs, Lee Chelminiak
Vice President Of Finance, David Mcguire
Evp Administration And Finance Cfo And Treasurer, Peter K. Markell, age 63
President And Ceo Massachusetts General Hospital, Peter L. Slavin
Cio, James W. (Jim) Noga
President And Ceo North Shore Medical Center, Robert G. (Bob) Norton, age 69
President And Ceo Neighborhood Health Plan, Deborah C. Enos

President And Ceo Partners Continuing Care, David E. Storto
President And Ceo Brigham And Women's Hospital, Elizabeth G. (Betsy) Nabel
President And Chief Executive Officer, David F. Torchiana
President Of Partners Community, Thomas H. Lee
President And Ceo Spaulding Rehabilitation Network, Maureen Banks
President Mclean Hospital, Scott L. Rauch
President And Ceo Brigham And Women's Physicians Organization, Allen L. Smith
President And Ceo Martha's Vineyard Hospital, Timothy J. Walsh
President And Ceo Mgh Institute Of Health Professions, Janis P. Bellack
President And Ceo, David Torchiana
President And Ceo Nantucket Cottage Hospital, Margot Hartmann
President And Ceo Partners Healthcare At Home, Rod Carnifax
Medical Director, Jane Erb
Vice President Government Affairs, Joseph D Alviani
Medical Director Breast Care Center, Katherina Zabicki
Director Of Nursing, Deborah Morrissey
Medical Director For Population Health Management, Namita Mohta
Nursing Director, Michelle Anastasi
Nursing Director, Lauren Willard
Medical Director Of The Breast And Ovarian Cancer, Paula Ryan
Nursing Director, Elizabeth Mcgrath
Medical Director, David Chen
Clinical Director, Karon Konner
Nursing Director, Janet Quigley
Nursing Director, Mary Sylvia-Reardon
Medical Director, William Holgerson
Senior Vice President Of Clinical Services, David Mccready
Medical Director, Richard Kaufman
Project Manager To Senior Vice President Research, Angela Vail
Medical Director, Sharon Bober
Nursing Director, Michele Ohara
Clinical Director, Martha Kane
Clinical Director Department Of Pt Ot; Clinical Content Lead Partners Ecare, James Zachazewski
Vice President Of Operations, Hofmann Erika
Nursing Director, Peggy Settle
Director Of Medical Records, Doherty Linda
Nursing Director, Lisa Wichmann
Vice President Of Systems, Meg Costello
Nursing Director, Dorothy Parker
Clinical Director, Scott Waugh
Nursing Director, Donna Crown
Senior Vice President Of Clinical Services, Julia Sinclair
Vice President, Anne Fitzgerald
Assistant Vice President Regional Consultant, Viscomi Rudy
Nursing Director, Jennifer Sargent
Vice President Innovation, Chris Coburn
Rsvp Team Leader, Jessica Grajeda
Vice President Of Information Technology, Karl Fitch
Medical Director, Renee Sorrentino
Medical Director, Angelo Volandes
Senior Vice President For Research, Harry Orf
Vice President, Shelly Anderson
Medical Director Emergency Medicine, Patricia Henwood
Clinical Director, Keilty Colleen
Senior Vice President Of Communication And Public Affairs, Erin Mcdonough
Corporate Vice President Clinical Operations And Chief Nursing Officer, Maclaughlin Ellen
Senior Vice President Payer Solution Sales, Wilson Caryn

Vice President Of Operations, Ricci Elisabeth
Senior Vice President Research, Richard Bringhurst
Medical Director, Robert Gottlieb
Vice President Operations Mumbai, Prue Stewart
Nursing Director, Kathryn Hall
Senior Vice President, Estrela Rui
Senior Vice President Of Finance And Treasurer, Karen Lavoie
Vice President, Eileen Flaherty
Pharmacy Manager, James Blackwell
Associate Medical Director, R Nicholas Nace Md
Physical Therapy, Tom Rossignoll
Chairman, Edward P. Lawrence, age 77
Secretary, Maria Sanchez
Secretary, Ruth Valdez
Board Member, Warren Foote
Treasurer, Xandra Breakefield
Vice Chair For Radiology Education, Shank Erik
Board Member, Martha Pitman
Secretary Pathology, Mary Niederberger
Department Secretary, Theresa Crotty
Secretary, Evan David
Secretary, Estimable Jerry
Department Secretary, Julie Baratta
Amb. Practice Secretary I, Bertha Taylor
Treasurer, Susanne Churchill
Board Member, Michael Jerosch-herold

LOCATIONS

HQ: PARTNERS HEALTHCARE SYSTEM, INC.
800 BOYLSTON ST STE 1150, BOSTON, MA 021998123
Phone: 617 278-1000

PRODUCTS/OPERATIONS

2014 Sales

	$ mil.	% of total
Net patient service revenue	7,042	65
Premium revenue	1,622	15
Direct academic and research	1,225	11
Indirect academic and research	353	3
Other revenue	662	6
Total	**10,906**	**100**

COMPETITORS

Baystate Health	Milford Regional
Boston Medical Center	Medical Center
Cambridge Health	Northeast Health
Alliance	System
Cape Cod Healthcare	Southcoast Hospitals
Cape Cod Hospital	Group
Care New England	Steward Health Care
CareGroup	Universal Health
Children's Hospital	Services
Boston	

HISTORICAL FINANCIALS

Company Type: Private

Income Statement
FYE: September 30

	REVENUE ($ mil.)	NET INCOME ($ mil.)	NET PROFIT MARGIN	EMPLOYEES
09/15	11,665	(916)	—	67,000
09/10	8	(0)	—	—
09/08	551	(44)	—	—
Annual Growth	54.7%	—	—	—

2015 Year-End Financials

Return on assets: (-6.1%)   Cash ($ mil.): 621
Return on equity: (-15.1%)
Current ratio: 2.30

PARTNERSHIP FOR SUPPLY CHAIN MANAGEMENT, INC.

EXECUTIVES

Exec Dir, Richard C Owens Jr
CIO*, Charles Davenport
Dir*, Wesley Kreft
Dir*, Clinton De Souza
Cfo*, Erin Seidner
General Ledger Acct, Elvira Shagimuratova
Director, Richard Owens
Regional Administrator, Harrigan Mike
Senior Contracts Officer, Ross Douthard
Deputy Director, Michael McGunnigle

LOCATIONS

HQ: PARTNERSHIP FOR SUPPLY CHAIN
MANAGEMENT, INC.
2733 CRYSTAL DR FL 4, ARLINGTON, VA 222023584
Phone: 571 227-8600
Web: WWW.PFSCM.ORG

HISTORICAL FINANCIALS

Company Type: Private

Income Statement   FYE: September 30

	REVENUE ($ mil.)	NET INCOME ($ mil.)	NET PROFIT MARGIN	EMPLOYEES
09/11	517	(2)	—	140
09/10	389	1	0.4%	—
09/09	294	1	0.5%	—
Annual Growth	32.6%	—	—	—

2011 Year-End Financials

Return on assets: (-2.0%)   Cash ($ mil.): 61
Return on equity: (-84.2%)
Current ratio: 1.00

PASADENA HOSPITAL ASSOCIATION, LTD.

No need to hunt for medical care if you're near Huntington Hospital. The not-for-profit Pasadena Hospital Association which does business as Huntington Hospital provides health care to residents of the San Gabriel Valley in Southern California. The hospital boasts some 625 beds and offers acute medical and surgical care and community services in a number of specialties including cardiology gastroenterology women's and children's health orthopedics and neurology. It engages in clinical cancer research (as well as diagnosis and treatment) through the Huntington Cancer Center. The hospital is also a teaching facility for the University of Southern California (USC) Keck School of Medicine.

Operations

As part of its operations the California hospital runs The Stroke Center Heart and Vascular Center Huntington Hospital Cancer Center Regional Neonatal Intensive Care Unit Prenatal High Risk Unit and Pediatric Intensive Care Unit. The hospital is the only level II trauma center and level III NICU in the San Gabriel Valley.

Through its partnership with USC Huntington Hospital offers graduate medical education in areas such as general surgery and internal medicine. Its Huntington Cancer Center partners with area physicians (including some affiliated with USC and UCLA) and the City of Hope medical center to provide comprehensive oncology services and research potential new cancer treatments.

The hospital has 900 physicians and more than 1200 nurses. In 2013 it had about 26000 inpatient admissions more than 216000 outpatient visits and helped deliver more than 3300 babies. Huntington Hospital provided a $92.9 million in community benefits that year.

Geographic Reach

Huntington Hospital serves the health care needs of those who reside in and around Southern California's San Gabriel Valley.

Sales and Marketing

The medical center is working to upgrade its information technology systems including the addition of an electronic health record (EHR) system.

Financial Performance

Huntington Hospital's revenues rose by 3% in 2013 thanks to an increase in patient services and revenues.

The hospital recorded a net loss of $10 million that year due to higher expenses (including salaries employees benefits and other costs).

Strategy

The company is pursuing infrastructure and services expansion and innovation to keep up with demand.

In 2014 Huntington Hospital collaborated with Anthem Blue Cross and six of its fellow leading hospitals in Los Angeles and Orange counties to form Anthem Blue Cross Vivity a new insurance entity.

In 2013 the hospital signed a deal with Shriners Hospitals for Children- Southern California to provide inpatient surgical services for its pediatric patients.

Huntington Hospital completed renovating its existing emergency facility in 2013. The project to increase patient capacity up to 80000 and increase diagnostic facilities came about in response to growing levels of ER visits.

Company Background

Huntington Hospital broke ground several years ago on an $80-million expansion effort to double the size of its emergency department. The project has included building a new portion that was completed in 2012.

Upgrading its technology to increase efficiency in 2012 Huntington Hospital launched a multi-year project to replace and upgrade its computer information system with new system (Huntington Access Network Knowledge) to manage the hospital's clinical and financial software.

In a medical innovation in 2012 the hospital became the first hospital in Southern California to offer an Ekso Bionics' technology enabling patients with lower-extremity paralysis or weakness to stand and walk.

Huntington Hospital was founded in 1892.

EXECUTIVES

Medical Director Of Radiology, Christopher G Hedley
Pharm D Operations Coordinator, Leslie Berina
Auditors: ERNST & YOUNG US LLP IRVINE

LOCATIONS

HQ: PASADENA HOSPITAL ASSOCIATION, LTD.
100 W CALIFORNIA BLVD, PASADENA, CA 911053010
Phone: 626 397-5000

PRODUCTS/OPERATIONS

Selected Services

Ambulatory Care/Dispensary
Angiography
Anticoagulation Clinic
Asthma Education and Management
Bariatric Surgery
Breast Cancer Program
Cardiac Catheterization Lab
Cardiac Electrophysiology (EP)
Cardiac Rehabilitation
Cardiac Screening and Diagnostics
Cardiothoracic Surgery
Community Outreach
CT Scanning (Type 2) Diabetes Prevention and Management
Epilepsy and Brain Mapping
Gastroenterology
Genetic Counseling
Geriatric Assessment Clinic
Gynecological Cancer Program
Heart and Vascular Services
Neurophysiology
Neuroradiology
Neurosciences
Neurosurgery
Obstetrics
Orthopedics
Ostomy Clinic
Pediatric Obesity Prevention
Prenatal High Risk Unit
Prostate Cancer Program
Radiation Oncology
Urology
Uterine Artery Embolization (UAE)

COMPETITORS

Adventist Health System West	Dignity Health
Cedars-Sinai Medical Center	Glendale Adventist Medical Center
Citrus Valley Health Partners	Memorial Health Services
	Tenet Healthcare

HISTORICAL FINANCIALS

Company Type: Private

Income Statement   FYE: December 31

	REVENUE ($ mil.)	NET INCOME ($ mil.)	NET PROFIT MARGIN	EMPLOYEES
12/17	654	15	2.3%	2,800
12/16	695	8	1.2%	—
12/15	593	0	0.0%	—
Annual Growth	5.0%	678.3%	—	—

2017 Year-End Financials

Return on assets: 1.7%   Cash ($ mil.): 11
Return on equity: 2.6%
Current ratio: 3.30

PASADENA INDEPENDENT SCHOOL DISTRICT

EXECUTIVES

Pres, Mariselle Quijano-Lerma
Supt*, Dr Kirk Lewis
V Pres*, Vickie Morgan
SEC*, Fred Roberts
Teacher, Annie Sargent
Administrative Secretary, Aurora Espinoza

Office Manager, Bibi Nunez-Mejia
Teacher, Brandon Ware
Administrator, Charlyn Jannasch
School Counselor, Cindy Resendez
Librarian, Dana Dimarco
Auditors: WHITLEY PENN LLP TEXAS CITY

LOCATIONS

HQ: PASADENA INDEPENDENT SCHOOL DISTRICT
1515 CHERRYBROOK LN, PASADENA, TX 775024099
Phone: 713 740-0000
Web: WWW.PASADENAISD.ORG

HISTORICAL FINANCIALS

Company Type: Private

Income Statement | | | | FYE: August 31

	REVENUE ($ mil.)	NET INCOME ($ mil.)	NET PROFIT MARGIN	EMPLOYEES
08/18	680	99	14.7%	5,000
08/17	606	(93)	—	—
08/16	611	(32)	—	—
08/13	522	98	18.9%	—
Annual Growth	5.5%	0.3%	—	—

2018 Year-End Financials

Return on assets: 7.0%   Cash ($ mil.): 14
Return on equity: 128.1%
Current ratio: —

PATERSON PUBLIC SCHOOL DISTRICT

EXECUTIVES

Supt, Jacqueline Jones
Supt*, Donnie W Evans
Transportation Director, Gisela Aultmon
Research Director, Annalesa Barker
Supervisor of School Improveme, Irene Delrosso
Supervisor, Alicia Pavone
Supervisor of Mathematics, Brian Rawlins
Supervisor, Cheryl Chadderton
School Secretary, Denise Williams
Data Management Analyst, Elizabeth Gonzalez-Flores
Coordinator of Information Man, Jason Lockley
Auditors: LERCH VINCI & HIGGINS LLP F

LOCATIONS

HQ: PATERSON PUBLIC SCHOOL DISTRICT
90 DELAWARE AVE, PATERSON, NJ 075031804
Phone: 973 321-0980
Web: WWW.PATERSON.K12.NJ.US

HISTORICAL FINANCIALS

Company Type: Private

Income Statement | | | | FYE: June 30

	REVENUE ($ mil.)	NET INCOME ($ mil.)	NET PROFIT MARGIN	EMPLOYEES
06/18	602	(4)	—	3,055
06/17	601	1	0.3%	—
06/11	541	7	1.3%	—
06/05	0	0	—	—
Annual Growth	—	—	—	—

2018 Year-End Financials

Return on assets: (-1.0%)   Cash ($ mil.): 14
Return on equity: (-3.0%)
Current ratio: —

PATIENT ACCESS NETWORK FOUNDATION

EXECUTIVES

Dir of Ops, Svelana Durkovic
Prin, Julia E Reynes
Marketing Staff, Megan Crout
Chief Operating Officer, Randy Crout
Manager, Divya Sriram
Business Consultant, Ali Chegini
Director of Patient Advocacy, Amy Niles
Marketing, Liz Eckert
Auditors: CHERRY BEKAERT LLP CHARLOTTE

LOCATIONS

HQ: PATIENT ACCESS NETWORK FOUNDATION
805 15TH ST NW STE 500, WASHINGTON, DC
200052207
Phone: 202 347-9274
Web: WWW.PANFOUNDATION.ORG

HISTORICAL FINANCIALS

Company Type: Private

Income Statement | | | | FYE: December 31

	REVENUE ($ mil.)	NET INCOME ($ mil.)	NET PROFIT MARGIN	EMPLOYEES
12/17	532	171	32.2%	3
12/16	577	(243)	—	—
12/14	673	161	24.0%	—
Annual Growth	(7.5%)	1.9%	—	—

2017 Year-End Financials

Return on assets: 43.8%   Cash ($ mil.): 91
Return on equity: 67.7%
Current ratio: —

PCL CONSTRUCTION ENTERPRISES, INC.

PCL Construction Enterprises is the contractor to call on for commercial and civil construction concerns. The company serves as the parent to half a dozen US construction companies: PCL Construction Services PCL Civil Constructors PCL Construction PCL Industrial Services PCL Industrial Construction and Nordic PCL Construction. The companies serve as the operating entities for PCL one of Canada's largest general contracting groups. Having completed projects in nearly every US state PCL Construction Enterprises is active in the commercial institutional multi-family residential heavy industrial and civil construction sectors. PCL first entered the US construction market in 1975.

Operations

PCL Construction Enterprises and its subsidiaries work on a variety of projects. PCL Construction Enterprises has completed bridges water and wastewater systems manufacturing plants office buildings and restaurants nationwide.

Like many construction companies PCL was hit by the economic recession. Backlogs were lacking and new projects became tougher to win due to an increase in competition. Contracts with water wastewater and renewable energy projects and universities have helped PCL Construction Enterprises through the downturn.

Geographic Reach

Denver-based PCL Construction Enterprises through its half a dozen operating units concentrates on commercial civil and industrial construction projects located in the US.

Its parent's work spans the US Canada the Caribbean and Australia.

Sales and Marketing

PCL caters to customers in three primary sectors: commercial buildings civil infrastructure and heavy industrial construction. Clients have included the Alaska Railroad Corporation US Army Corps of Engineers Shaw Constructors and OUC-The Reliable One.

Its markets span big cities in Alaska Georgia California North Carolina Texas Colorado Hawaii Minnesota Florida Arizona and Washington.

EXECUTIVES

Vice President And District Manager, Dave Yount
Vice President, Keith Sandlin
Vice President Of Health Safety And Environment, Jim Barry

LOCATIONS

HQ: PCL CONSTRUCTION ENTERPRISES, INC.
2000 S COLORADO BLVD 2-500, DENVER, CO
802227908
Phone: 303 365-6500
Web: WWW.PCL.COM

PRODUCTS/OPERATIONS

Selected Operating Companies

Nordic PCL Construction Inc.
PCL Civil Constructors Inc.
PCL Construction Inc.
PCL Construction Services Inc.
PCL Industrial Construction Co.
PCL Industrial Services Inc.

COMPETITORS

Adolfson & Peterson Inc.	M. B. Kahn
Andersen Construction	Skanska USA Civil
Brasfield & Gorrie	Suffolk Construction
C.W. Driver	TIC Holdings
Dimeo Construction	Torix General Contractors
FCI Constructors	Turner Corporation
Fluor	
Gilbane Building Company	

HISTORICAL FINANCIALS

Company Type: Private

Income Statement | | | | FYE: October 31

	REVENUE ($ mil.)	NET INCOME ($ mil.)	NET PROFIT MARGIN	EMPLOYEES
10/10	1,616	23	1.5%	3,300
10/09	2,182	52	2.4%	—
10/08	2,315	84	3.7%	—
Annual Growth	(16.4%)	(47.2%)	—	—

2010 Year-End Financials

Return on assets: 4.2%   Cash ($ mil.): 95
Return on equity: 17.6%
Current ratio: 1.20

PEACEHEALTH

PeaceHealth provides patients with a tranquil place to recover. Make that several tranquil places to recover. PeaceHealth serves residents in southeastern Alaska coastal regions of Washington and central portions of Oregon. Its medical centers include PeaceHealth Ketchikan Medical Center PeaceHealth St. Joseph Medical Center PeaceHealth St. John Medical Center Sacred Heart Medical Center (two campuses) Cottage Grove Community Hospital Peace Harbor Hospital PeaceHealth Peace Island Medical Center and PeaceHealth Southwest Medical Center. Other operations include physician practices community clinics hospices chemical dependency rehabilitation clinics and other outpatient facilities and services.

Operations
In all PeaceHealth has about 16000 acute beds and 30 nursing home beds. It has some 16000 caregivers and a multi-specialty medical group practice with more than 800 physicians. It also has 10 medical centers in both rural and urban communities throughout the Northwest.

In 2014 the system reported more than 72000 inpatient admissions and nearly 746000 outpatient registrations as well as 1.2 million patient encounters with its medical group. It had more than 8000 infant births and more than 302000 emergency department visits that year.

Sales and Marketing
Commercial and other payers accounted for about half of Peacehealth's net patient revenue while Medicare accounts for about a third%.

Mergers and Acquisitions
In late 2018 Peacehealth agreed to buy telemedicine specialist ZOOM+Care. Formed in 2006 ZOOM+Care provides urgent care primary care specialty care and mental health care services. The purchase will further broaden the services Peacehealth provides in its communities.

Company Background
PeaceHealth was formed in 1923 by the Sisters of St. Joseph of Peace who opened the Little Flower Hospital in Ketchikan named after Saint Teresa. The Sisters of St. Joseph of Peace had previously opened St. Joseph Hospital in Bellingham in 1891.

PeaceHealth and Southwest Washington Health System merged in early 2011 boosting PeaceHealth's hospital holdings from six to eight with the addition of the two-campus Southwest Washington Medical Center in Vancouver Washington.

Under terms of the affiliation Southwest Washington Health System became part of PeaceHealth allowing Southwest to benefit from its larger peer's medical and financial resources. The move allows both health systems to increase the scope of services they offer in Washington State where Southwest Washington Health System also operates clinics a medical group and a foundation through which it conducts fundraising efforts.

EXECUTIVES

Ceo, Liz Dunne
President Peacehealth Medical Group, Michael Metcalf
Evp And Chief Administrative Officer, Carol Aaron
Chief Executive Columbia Network, Sean J. Gregory
Chief Executive Northwest Network, Dale Zender
Svp And Chief Nursing Officer, Victoria King
Svp And Cio, Dan Hein
President Hospital Services Oregon, Rand O'Leary
Evp Strategy And Community Health, Michael Dwyer
Evp And Cfo, Kimberly Hodgkinson
Evp And General Counsel, Ron Saxton
System Vice President Supply Chain, Eddie Sharp
Director Of Clinical Services, Merry Keane
Senior Vice President, Mark Hallett
Chairman, Andrea Nenzel

LOCATIONS

HQ: PEACEHEALTH
1115 SE 164TH AVE # 328, VANCOUVER, WA 986838003
Phone: 360 788-6841
Web: WWW.PEACEHEALTH.ORG

PRODUCTS/OPERATIONS

2013 Sales

	$ mil.	% of total
Patient service revenue	1,984	92
Premium revenue	93	4
Other operating revenue	94	4
Total	**2,171**	**100**

Selected Hospitals
PeaceHealth Ketchikan Medical Center (Ketchikan Alaska)
Cottage Grove Community Hospital (Cottage Grove Oregon)
Peace Harbor Hospital (Florence Oregon)
PeaceHealth Peace Island Medical Center (Friday Harbor Washington)
PeaceHealth Southwest Medical Center (Vancouver Washington)
PeaceHealth St. John Medical Center (Longview Washington)
PeaceHealth St. Joseph Medical Center (Bellingham Washington)
Sacred Heart Medical Center at RiverBend (Springfield Oregon)
Sacred Heart Medical Center University District (Eugene Oregon)
Other Operations
PeaceHealth Laboratories (locations throughout Oregon and Washington)
PeaceHealth Medical Group (operates in Alaska Oregon and Washington)

COMPETITORS

Alaska Native Tribal Health Consortium	Providence St. Joseph Health
Franciscan Health System	Seattle Children's Hospital
HCA	South Peninsula Hospital
Harrison Medical Center	Swedish Health Services
Immediate Care	Tenet Healthcare
MultiCare Health System	Yakima Valley Memorial
Overlake Hospital	

HISTORICAL FINANCIALS
Company Type: Private

Income Statement
FYE: June 30

	REVENUE ($ mil.)	NET INCOME ($ mil.)	NET PROFIT MARGIN	EMPLOYEES
06/14	2,249	114	5.1%	6,690
06/09	1,372	(88)	—	—
06/06	1,048	103	9.8%	—
Annual Growth	**10.0%**	**1.3%**	**—**	**—**

2014 Year-End Financials
Return on assets: 3.3%   Cash ($ mil.): 549
Return on equity: 6.5%
Current ratio: 0.70

PEDERNALES ELECTRIC COOPERATIVE, INC.

Created by Texas ranchers and business owners Pedernales Electric Cooperative provides electricity services in the Texas Hill Country. The company the largest electric cooperative in the US purchases its electricity from wholesale providers primarily the Lower Colorado River Authority (LCRA) and transmits and distributes it to about 209350 cooperative members (or more than 247810 individual customer meters). Pedernales Electric Cooperative operates more than 17450 miles of power line and maintains 290000 wooden utility poles in its service area.

Geographic Reach
The cooperative serves a customer base spread across 24 counties in Central Texas (8100 sq. miles an area larger than the state of Massachusetts).

Financial Performance
In 2012 the company's revenues decreased by 3% as the result of unfavorable weather conditions weakening demand for power (despite an increase of 5500 new customers). Net income decreased 24% driven by lower net sales.

Strategy
A member of the American Wind Energy Association Pedernales Electric Cooperative is committed to move toward conservation and cleaner energy (to meet clean air standards) and has a renewable energy goal of 30% of energy from renewable sources by 2020. The coop contracts with AEP Energy Partners to buy wind power produced at the South Trent Wind Farm near Sweetwater Texas. In all the wind-power purchase is expected to power up 22000 to 27000 homes.

In 2013 company upgraded the electric system in the Canyon Lake area manually converting more than 1900 transformers to accept higher voltage to better serve the growing energy needs of nearly 2600 coop members in the Clear Water Estates Tamarack Shores Scenic Terrace Linda Ledges Hancock Oak Hills and Rocky Creek Ranch subdivisions.

Company Background
As part of reforming its operations following a financial scandal in 2009 Pedernales Electric Cooperative became one of the first electric distribution cooperatives in the US to broadcast its Board meetings live on the Internet. In 2009 the cooperative ratified the first member advisory panel (on energy conservation and renewable energy use) in Pedernales Electric Cooperative's history.

Pedernales Electric Cooperative was founded in 1938 with the help of local landowner (and later US president) Lyndon Johnson.

EXECUTIVES

Vice President Sales Andamp; Marketing, Larry Landaker
Seinor Vice President And General Manager, Frank Chavez
Vice President, Richard Arellano
Vice President Markets, David Thompson
Secretary, Wendy Gloor
Auditors: BKD LLP HOUSTON TX

LOCATIONS

HQ: PEDERNALES ELECTRIC COOPERATIVE, INC.
201 S AVENUE F, JOHNSON CITY, TX 786364827
Phone: 830 868-7155
Web: WWW.PEC.COOP

HISTORICAL FINANCIALS
Company Type: Private

Income Statement
FYE: December 31

	REVENUE ($ mil.)	NET INCOME ($ mil.)	NET PROFIT MARGIN	EMPLOYEES
12/11	589	6	1.1%	741
12/10	550	53	9.8%	—
12/09	578	57	10.0%	—
Annual Growth	0.9%	(66.5%)	—	—

2011 Year-End Financials
Return on assets: 0.5% Cash ($ mil.): 27
Return on equity: 1.6%
Current ratio: 0.20

PENNSYLVANIA - AMERICAN WATER COMPANY

Pennsylvania-American Water distributes water and provides wastewater services to a population of more than 2 million people in some 390 communities across Pennsylvania. The company serves 635000 water customers and 17500 wastewater customers. It operates about 35 water treatment plants six wastewater facilities and 9800 miles of pipeline. Pennsylvania-American Water's service territory covers some three dozen Pennsylvania counties. The utility the largest regulated water and wastewater service provider in Pennsylvania is a subsidiary ofÂ New Jersey-based American Water Works.

Operations
Pennsylvania-American Water also has 85 well stations and treats and delivers about 216 millions of gallons of water each day. In addition itÂ operates 70 groundwater treatment facilities which process water sourced from more than 100 groundwater wells and maintains 250 treated water storage facilities 280 pumping stations and 60 dams.

Geographic Reach
The utility's primarily service areas include Mechanicsburg Mon Valley Norristown Pittsburgh Scranton Washington and Wilkes-Barre.

Financial Performance
Pennsylvania-American Water represents about a fifth of its parent company's sales; in 2011 it reported $516 million in revenue from Pennsylvania.

Mergers and Acquisitions
The utility expands its reach in Pennsylvania by picking up smaller water systems; in 2012 it completed six such acquisitions including a Monroe County system serving the Fernwood Resort and a Pike County system serving about 100 residents.

EXECUTIVES
Pres, Kathy Pape
V Pres, William C Kelvinton
SEC, Velma A Redmond
Treas, Stephen F Analdo
Support Manager, James P Oehling
Manager, David Derr
Director of Mis/Is, David Jerpe
Domino Administrator, Jill Breneman
Senior Developer, Richard Watts
Counsel, Susan Simms
Senior Financial Analyst, Jim Alexander

LOCATIONS
HQ: PENNSYLVANIA - AMERICAN WATER COMPANY
800 W HERSHEY PARK DR, HERSHEY, PA 170332400
Phone: 717 533-5000

COMPETITORS
Aqua America   Utilities Inc.
United Water Inc.

HISTORICAL FINANCIALS
Company Type: Private

Income Statement
FYE: December 31

	REVENUE ($ mil.)	NET INCOME ($ mil.)	NET PROFIT MARGIN	EMPLOYEES
12/17*	661	160	24.3%	1,007
06/14	589	127	21.7%	—
03/14	584	128	22.0%	—
12/13	571	122	21.4%	—
Annual Growth	3.7%	7.1%	—	—

*Fiscal year change

2017 Year-End Financials
Return on assets: 3.5% Cash ($ mil.): 3
Return on equity: 5.6%
Current ratio: 0.20

PENNSYLVANIA ELECTRIC COMPANY

Pennsylvania Electric (Penelec) has elected to provide power to the people of the Keystone State. The company distributes power to a population of 1.6 million in a 17600-square-mile portion of northern western and south-central Pennsylvania. The utility operatesÂ more thanÂ 20170 miles of distribution and more than 2700Â transmission lines. The Waverly Electric Light & Power Company a subsidiary of Penelec provides electric services to a population of about 8400 in Waverly New York. Penelec is an operatingÂ subsidiary of regional utilityÂ power player FirstEnergy.

EXECUTIVES
Pres-Ceo, Charles E Jones
Exec V Pres-Cfo*, Mark T Clark
Exec V Pres-Gen Counsel, Leila L Vespoli
V Pres-Controller-Cao, Harvey L Wagner
V Pres-Treas, James F Pearson
Director Generation and Fes In, Gunther Hehn
Vice President Human Resources, Josh Martin
Auditors: PRICEWATERHOUSECOOPERS LLP CL

LOCATIONS
HQ: PENNSYLVANIA ELECTRIC COMPANY
76 S MAIN ST BSMT, AKRON, OH 443081817
Phone: 800 545-7741
Web: WWW.FIRSTENERGYCORP.COM

COMPETITORS
Columbia Gas of   PECO Energy
  Pennsylvania   PPL Electric
Direct Energy   Peoples Natural Gas

HISTORICAL FINANCIALS
Company Type: Private

Income Statement
FYE: December 31

	REVENUE ($ mil.)	NET INCOME ($ mil.)	NET PROFIT MARGIN	EMPLOYEES
12/17	893	95	10.7%	896
12/16	904	88	9.8%	—
12/10	1,539	59	3.9%	—
12/09	1,448	65	4.5%	—
Annual Growth	(5.9%)	4.9%	—	—

2017 Year-End Financials
Return on assets: 2.2% Cash ($ mil.): —
Return on equity: 7.8%
Current ratio: 1.20

PENNSYLVANIA HOUSING FINANCE AGENCY

Pennsylvania Housing Finance Agency (PHFA) helps residents of the Keystone State obtain keys to their dream homes. The government-owned agency provides financing for low-income homebuyers including the elderly and disabled and participates in rental housing development initiatives. It generates funding from state and federal grants interest earned on investments and loans and the sale of its own securities to private investors.Â The agencyÂ is run by a board which includes Pennsylvania's secretary of banking secretary of community and economic development secretary of public welfare and the state treasurer. The PHFA has funded more than 130000 houses and 54000 apartment units since its founding in 1972.

EXECUTIVES
Vice President Of Information Technology, Kristy Provost

LOCATIONS
HQ: PENNSYLVANIA HOUSING FINANCE AGENCY
211 N FRONT ST, HARRISBURG, PA 171011406
Phone: 717 780-3800
Web: WWW.PHFA.ORG

HISTORICAL FINANCIALS
Company Type: Private

Income Statement
FYE: June 30

	ASSETS ($ mil.)	NET INCOME ($ mil.)	INCOME AS % OF ASSETS	EMPLOYEES
06/18	4,366	20	0.5%	250
06/12	5,593	10	0.2%	—
06/11	6,051	39	0.7%	—
06/10	6,265	24	0.4%	—
Annual Growth	(4.4%)	(2.2%)	—	—

2018 Year-End Financials
Return on assets: 0.5% Sales ($ mil): 192
Return on equity: 2.7%

PEPPER CONSTRUCTION COMPANY

EXECUTIVES

Ceo, J David Pepper
President, Kenneth Egidi
Exec Pres, James A Nissen
Cfo, Chris Averill
Manager, Atul Raj
Safety Manager, Justin Teague
Project Manager, Michael Burkholder
Project Manager, Chuck Hutton
Director of Quality Management, Corey Zussman
Safety Coordinator, Danny Torres
Senior Project Manager, Jenny Spence
Auditors: BDD LLP OAKBROOK TERRACE IL

LOCATIONS

HQ: PEPPER CONSTRUCTION COMPANY
  643 N ORLEANS ST, CHICAGO, IL 606543690
Phone: 312 266-4700
Web: WWW.PEPPERCONSTRUCTION.COM

HISTORICAL FINANCIALS

Company Type: Private

Income Statement   FYE: September 30

	REVENUE ($ mil.)	NET INCOME ($ mil.)	NET PROFIT MARGIN	EMPLOYEES
09/17	704	14	2.1%	900
09/16	805	20	2.5%	—
09/15	709	10	1.5%	—
09/11	668	4	0.6%	—
Annual Growth	0.9%	23.3%	—	—

2017 Year-End Financials

Return on assets: 6.7%   Cash ($ mil.): 21
Return on equity: 37.7%
Current ratio: 1.20

PEPPER CONSTRUCTION GROUP, LLC

Pepper Construction GroupÂ spices up the construction business with a little of this and a pinch of that.Â The company provides general contracting and construction management services for commercial office education entertainmentÂ health care and institutional clients as well as waterworks projects.Â (Health care projects account for about 50% of Pepper's revenue.) ItsÂ client list includes UBS Northwestern University University of Notre DameÂ Texas Heart Institute Loyola University Medical CenterÂ and NASA. Pepper Construction Group has divisions in Illinois Indiana Ohio and Texas.Â Stanley F. Pepper founded the company in Chicago in 1927. The group is owned by his family and employees of the firm.

Operations

The company's Pepper Environmental Technologies unitÂ provides environmental services. Green building has become a large part of Pepper Construction's operations. Its Green Team of certified professionals have helped construct more than 2.9 million sq. ft. of eco-friendly space. The GreenÂ Team has built the Apple Computer flagship store HSBC Chicago North and Kohl's Children's Museum.

The firm's Pepper-Lawson Waterworks groupÂ constructs water purification plants for municipal clients including Houston and Missouri City Texas.

Geographic Reach

Chicago-based Pepper Construction comprises four geographic divisions: Illinois; Indiana; Ohio; and Texas. Overall the company is active in about 20 states mostly in the central and northeastern states.

EXECUTIVES

Chm, Dave Pepper
V Pres-Assist SEC*, Stephanie Vitner
Sr V Pres-Gen Counselor-Sec*, Timothy F Sullivan
Evp-Cfo*, Chris Averill
Senior Business Unit Accountan, Kelly Hampton
Project Manager, Zach Gaines
Senior Administrative, Kate Holstein
Director of Business Developme, Scott Nemshick
Senior Project Accountant, Stacy Briggs
Auditors: BKD LLP OAKBROOK TERRACE IL

LOCATIONS

HQ: PEPPER CONSTRUCTION GROUP, LLC
  643 N ORLEANS ST, CHICAGO, IL 606543690
Phone: 312 266-4700
Web: WWW.PEPPERCONSTRUCTION.COM

PRODUCTS/OPERATIONS

Selected Operations

Pepper Construction Group LLC (Chicago Illinois)
Pepper Construction Co. (Chicago Illinois)
Pepper Construction Co. of Indiana (Indianapolis Indiana)
Pepper Construction Co. of Ohio LLC (Dublin Ohio)
Pepper Environmental Technologies Inc. (Barrington Illinois)
Pepper-Lawson Construction LP (Houston Texas)
Pepper-Lawson Waterworks LLC (Houston Texas)

COMPETITORS

Barton Malow	Graycor
Bulley & Andrews	M. A. Mortenson
C. G. Schmidt	McCarthy Building
Charles Pankow Builders	Power Construction
Clark Enterprises	Turner Corporation
Gilbane	Walbridge Aldinger
	Walsh Group

HISTORICAL FINANCIALS

Company Type: Private

Income Statement   FYE: September 30

	REVENUE ($ mil.)	NET INCOME ($ mil.)	NET PROFIT MARGIN	EMPLOYEES
09/17	1,119	21	1.9%	1,100
09/16	1,179	23	2.0%	—
09/15	1,110	9	0.9%	—
09/11	911	15	1.7%	—
Annual Growth	3.5%	5.2%	—	—

2017 Year-End Financials

Return on assets: 6.8%   Cash ($ mil.): 36
Return on equity: 37.6%
Current ratio: 1.20

PEREZ TRADING COMPANY, INC.

No matter how you say it paper or el papel Perez Trading has it. From its Miami warehouse the company distributes more than 15000 tons of paper and paperboard inventory including corrugated box equipment napkin paper printing paper and other printing and shipping equipment and supplies. Customers include commercial printers converters distributors and packaging manufacturers. Perez Trading imports and exports to nearly 30 countries encompassing the Caribbean Islands Central and South America MexicoÂ and the US. Perez Trading has been family owned and operated since 1947.

EXECUTIVES

National Sales Manager, Gisel Martin
Vice President Marketing, Roberta Perez
Vice President, Jaime Escudero

LOCATIONS

HQ: PEREZ TRADING COMPANY, INC.
  3490 NW 125TH ST, MIAMI, FL 331672412
Phone: 305 769-0761
Web: WWW.PEREZTRADING.COM

COMPETITORS

Georgia-Pacific	International Paper

HISTORICAL FINANCIALS

Company Type: Private

Income Statement   FYE: December 31

	REVENUE ($ mil.)	NET INCOME ($ mil.)	NET PROFIT MARGIN	EMPLOYEES
12/14	514	11	2.1%	140
12/13	526	16	3.2%	—
12/12	570	20	3.6%	—
Annual Growth	(5.1%)	(26.3%)	—	—

2014 Year-End Financials

Return on assets: 5.1%   Cash ($ mil.): —
Return on equity: 10.0%
Current ratio: 2.00

PERISHABLE DISTRIBUTORS OF IOWA, LTD.

EXECUTIVES

Pres, Dan Wampler
Exec V Pres*, Linda Sharp
Executive of Information Techn, Gary Churchill
Human Resources Executive, Janel Jones
Maintenance Supervisor, Glen Sievers
Engineer, Trent Maring
Human Resources Director, Leigh Walters
Director, Mark Kloberdanz
Manager, Scott Hamilton
Manager, Mark Choate
Freight Coordinator, Jeff Wood

LOCATIONS

HQ: PERISHABLE DISTRIBUTORS OF IOWA, LTD.
2741 SE PDI PL, ANKENY, IA 500213958
Phone: 515 965-6300
Web: WWW.CONTACTPDI.COM

HISTORICAL FINANCIALS

Company Type: Private

Income Statement				FYE: September 30
	REVENUE ($ mil.)	NET INCOME ($ mil.)	NET PROFIT MARGIN	EMPLOYEES
09/18*	1,346	38	2.9%	687
10/17	1,343	35	2.6%	—
10/16	1,307	33	2.6%	—
09/15	1,248	31	2.5%	—
Annual Growth	2.5%	7.3%	—	—

*Fiscal year change

2018 Year-End Financials

Return on assets: 25.9%
Return on equity: 55.2%
Current ratio: 1.30
Cash ($ mil.): 15

PERMANENT UNIVERSITY FUND

LOCATIONS

HQ: PERMANENT UNIVERSITY FUND
221 W 6TH ST STE 1700, AUSTIN, TX 787013400
Phone: 512 225-1600

HISTORICAL FINANCIALS

Company Type: Private

Income Statement				FYE: August 31
	REVENUE ($ mil.)	NET INCOME ($ mil.)	NET PROFIT MARGIN	EMPLOYEES
08/18	1,906	1,964	103.0%	2
08/17	2,888	2,032	70.4%	—
Annual Growth	(34.0%)	(3.4%)	—	—

PETER KIEWIT SONS', INC.

A heavyweight in the heavy construction industry Kiewit is one of North America's largest construction and engineering firms. The company is active in building industrial mining oil gas chemicals power transportation water and wastewater. It builds everything from roads and dams to highrise office towers and power plants. The company focuses on projects located throughout the US Canada and Mexico. Affiliate Kiewit Mining owns or manages coal mines in Texas and Wyoming and manages a phosphate operation in southeast Idaho. Founded in 1884 Kiewit is owned by employees and Kiewit family members.

Operations

Kiewit's operations are diversified across seven segments: Building; Industrial; Mining; Oil Gas & Chemical; Power; Transportation; and Water/Wastewater.

Kiewit's Transportation segment constructs airport runways bridges marine and port projects rail lines mass transit roads and tunnels. Transportation has completed about 1000 projects which provided nearly $30 billion in revenue over the last 10 years. Kiewit's Power unit is active in gas coal retrofit power delivery renewables nuclear energy and engineering. Over the last 10 years Power has generated almost $20 billion.

Generating $7.5 billion through more than 1100 projects in the last 10 years the company's Building segment builds offices; industrial complexes; education and sports facilities; hotels; hospitals; transportation terminals; science and technology facilities; manufacturing retail and special-use facilities; interior construction; and tenant improvements. Kiewit conducts general construction construction management design-build and -assist and turnkey project development.

The Mining segment (which has generated nearly $3 billion over more than 100 mining projects in the last 10 years) carries out contract mining mine infrastructure ore processing and owned operations. Kiewit's Oil Gas & Chemical business includes offshore construction oil sands gas processing compressor and pump stations pipelines and terminals liquefied natural gas and refining.

Through its Industrial division the company processes minerals; builds cement plants; treats water; provides engineering procurement and construction for the ferrous and non-ferrous metal industries; installs paper production and packaging machines; and constructs food plants and related structures. Water/Wastewater manages dam water supply and wastewater projects.

Kiewit operates a number of subsidiaries. Kiewit Offshore Services fabricates complex offshore oil production platforms at a facility in Texas. Another subsidiary Kiewit Energy US refines petroleum. Kiewit's TIC subsidiary is a heavy industrial construction and engineering firm based in Colorado.

Geographic Reach

Based in Omaha Nebraska Kiewit operates across the US (more than 80 locations) Canada (more than 10 locations) and Mexico (1 location).

Sales and Marketing

Kiewit's clients include various public and private entities.

Financial Performance

Kiewit doesn't publish financial data but the firm garnered revenue of $8.7 billion in 2017.

Strategy

Kiewit has completed nearly 6000 projects in the last 15 years. Recent major projects include the Air Force Weather Agency headquarters ? a $27 million data center and office building spanning 188000 square feet ? and the National Park Services Regional Headquarters in Omaha Nebraska. The National Park Services Regional Headquarters is a 68000-square-foot mixed private and public office building with exhibits a book store a library and public meeting rooms.

Company Background

The sons of Dutch immigrants Peter and Andrew Kiewit founded masonry contractor Kiewit Brothers in 1884 in Omaha Nebraska. Following the dissolution of the partnership in 1904 Peter continued as the company's sole proprietor. In 1931 ? 17 years after Peter's death ? his son Peter reorganized the business as Peter Kiewit Sons'.

HISTORY

Born to Dutch immigrants Peter Kiewit and brother Andrew founded Kiewit Brothers a brickyard in 1884 in Omaha Nebraska. By 1912 two of Peter's sons worked at the yard which was named Peter Kiewit & Sons. When Peter Kiewit died in

1914 his son Ralph took over and the firm took the name Peter Kiewit Sons'. Another son Peter joined Ralph at the helm in 1924 after dropping out of Dartmouth and later took over.

During the Depression Kiewit managed huge federal public works projects and in the 1940s it focused on war-related emergency construction projects.

One of the firm's most difficult projects was top-secret Thule Air Force Base in Greenland above the Arctic Circle. For more than two years 5000 men worked around the clock beginning in 1951; the site was in development for 15 years. In 1952 the company won a contract to build a $1.2 billion gas diffusion plant in Portsmouth Ohio. It also became a contractor for the US interstate highway system (begun in 1956).

Peter Kiewit died in 1979 after stipulating that the largely employee-owned company should remain under employee control and that no one employee could own more than 10%. His 40% stake when returned to the company transformed many employees into millionaires. Walter Scott Jr. whose father had been the first graduate engineer to work for Kiewit took charge. Scott made his mark by parlaying money from construction into successful investments.

When the construction industry slumped Kiewit began looking for other investment opportunities and in 1984 it acquired packaging company Continental Can Co. (selling off noncore insurance energy and timber assets). Continental was saddled with a 1983 class action lawsuit alleging that it had plotted to close plants and lay off workers before they were qualified for pensions. In 1991 Kiewit agreed to pay $415 million to settle the lawsuit. In the face of a consolidating packaging industry the company sold Continental in the early 1990s.

In 1986 Kiewit loaned money to a business group to build a fiber-optic loop in Chicago; by 1987 it had launched MFS Communications to build local fiber loops in downtown districts. In 1992 Kiewit split its business into two pieces: the construction group which was strictly employee-owned; and a diversified group to which it added a controlling stake in phone and cable TV company C-TEC in 1993. That year Kiewit took MFS public; by 1995 it had sold all its shares and the next year MFS was bought by telecom giant WorldCom.

In 1996 Kiewit assisted CalEnergy (now Mid-American Energy) in a hostile $1.3 billion takeover of the UK's Northern Electric. Kiewit got stock in CalEnergy and a 30% stake in the UK electric company all of which it sold to CalEnergy in 1998.

That year Kiewit spun off its telecom and computer services holdings into Level 3 Communications. Scott who had been hospitalized the year before for a blood clot in his lung stepped down as CEO and Ken Stinson CEO of Kiewit Construction Group took over Peter Kiewit Sons'.

In 1999 Kiewit acquired a majority interest in Pacific Rock Products a construction materials firm in Canada. Kiewit spun off its asphalt concrete and aggregates operations in 2000 as Kiewit Materials. Also that year the company created Kiewit Offshore Services to focus on construction for the offshore drilling industry. In 2001 the company acquired marine construction firm General Construction Company (GCC). The next year it expanded its offshore business further by buying a Canadian subsidiary from oil and gas equipment services company Friede Goldman Halter which was trying to emerge from bankruptcy.

Kiewit made history in 2002 for the fastest completion of a project of its type when it completed the rebuilding of Webbers Falls I-40 Bridge in Oklahoma at the end of July. (The bridge had collapsed in May after being hit by a pair of barges resulting in 14 fatalities.)

In 2004 Kiewit greatly increased its coal sales and reserves with the acquisition of the Buckskin Mine in Wyoming from Arch Coal.

Kiewit underwent a changing of the guard at the end of 2004 when 22-year veteran Bruce Grewcock took the reins as the company's fourth CEO since its founding. Stinson stayed on as the company's chairman.

In 2008 the group acquired TIC Holdings a heavy industrial construction and engineering firm.

Through its Kiewit Power Engineers Co. the company was contracted by Plutonic Energy Corporation and GE Energy Financial Services to work on the 235 MW hydroelectric Toba Montrose project one of British Columbia's largest renewable energy projects (completed around 2011).

In 2013 Kiewit entered the Australian market through a joint venture agreement that involves as $247 million engineer-procure-construct contract for a wet front end and ore wash plant situated at the Cloudbreak Mine in Northwest Australia. Fortescue Metals Group is the previous owner of Cloudbreak prior to the handover in early 2013.

EXECUTIVES

Svp And Cfo, Michael J. Piechoski, $236,600 total compensation
Chairman President And Ceo, Bruce E. Grewcock, $750,000 total compensation
Evp Energy, Thomas S. Shelby
Cio, Kris Lappala
Vice President For Development, Gerald Pfeffer
Vice President And General Counsel, Sam Gilmore
Vice President Healthcare Services, AJ Klebba
Vice President Finance Canada, Leonardo Morabito
Executive Vice President Operations, Jay Steinmetz
Treasurer, Stephen Thomas
Secretary, Matthew Michler
Auditors: KPMG LLP OMAHA NEBRASKA

LOCATIONS

HQ: PETER KIEWIT SONS', INC.
3555 FARNAM ST STE 1000, OMAHA, NE 681313374
Phone: 402 342-2052
Web: WWW.KIEWIT.COM

Selected Locations

US
   Alaska
   Arizona
   Arkansas
   California
   Colorado
   Florida
   Georgia
   Hawaii
   Idaho
   Illinois
   Iowa
   Kansas
   Louisiana
   Maryland
   Massachusetts
   Minnesota
   Nebraska
   Nevada
   New Jersey
   New York
   North Carolina
   Oregon
   Tennessee
   Texas
   Utah
   Virginia
   Washington
   Wyoming
Australia
   Western Australia
Canada

   Alberta
   British Columbia
   Manitoba
   Newfoundland
   New Brunswick
   Ontario
   Quebec
   Saskatchewan

PRODUCTS/OPERATIONS

Selected Locations

US
Alaska
Arizona
California
Colorado
Florida
Georgia
Hawaii
Illinois
Iowa
Kansas
Maryland
Massachusetts
Minnesota
Nebraska
Nevada
New Jersey
New York
North Carolina
Oregon
Texas
Utah
Virginia
Washington
Wyoming
Canada
Alberta
British Columbia
Newfoundland
Ontario
Quebec
Mexico
Mexico City

Selected Subsidiaries and Affiliates

Aero Automatic Sprinkler
Cherne Contracting Corporation
Continental Fire Sprinkler Company
Kiewit Australia
Kiewit Bridge & Marine
Kiewit Building Group
Kiewit Energy Company.
Kiewit Engineering Group Inc.
Kiewit Infrastructure Co.
Kiewit Infrastructure South Co.
Kiewit Infrastructure West Co.
Kiewit Mining Group
Dry Valley/No. Rassmussen Ridge Mines
Buckskin Mining Company
San Miguel Mine
Walnut Creek Mining Company
Kiewit Offshore Services Ltd..
Kiewit Power Constructors Co.
Kiewit Power Engineers
Kiewit Texas Construction L.P.

COMPETITORS

ABB	Lane Construction
Ames Construction	PCL Constructors
Balfour Beatty	Parsons Corporation
Infrastructure	Raytheon
Bechtel	Rio Tinto plc
Black & Veatch	Skanska USA Civil
Fluor	Turner Corporation
Granite Construction	Tutor Perini
Halliburton	Walsh Group
Hubbard Group	Whiting-Turner
Jacobs Engineering	Williams Companies
KBR	

HISTORICAL FINANCIALS

Company Type: Private

Income Statement				FYE: December 29
	REVENUE ($ mil.)	NET INCOME ($ mil.)	NET PROFIT MARGIN	EMPLOYEES
12/12	11,220	515	4.6%	14,700
12/11	10,381	790	7.6%	—
12/10	9,938	789	7.9%	—
Annual Growth	6.3%	(19.2%)	—	—

2012 Year-End Financials

Return on assets: 7.6%   Cash ($ mil.): 1,447
Return on equity: 13.2%
Current ratio: 1.90

PETRO STAR INC.

Petro Star is an oil refining and fuel marketing shining star that brings heating fuel and energy (diesel gasoline and aviation and marine fuel)s to the citizens of the communities in the vast cold and lonely expanses of the US' largest state Alaska. It operates refineries at North Pole and Valdez and distributes fuels and lubricants throughout Interior Alaska Dutch Harbor Kodiak and Valdez. Started in 1984 by a group of petroleum industry veterans the company built its first refinery operations along the Trans-Alaska Pipeline at North Pole Alaska. Petro Star is a subsidiary of Arctic Slope Regional Corp..

Operations

The company's divisions are Refining; Retail; Lubricants; Marine Fuel; Heating Fuel; and Aviation.

Refining operates two refineries: the 60000 barrel-per-day Petro Star Valdez refinery which produces jet fuel JP-8 JP-5 marine diesel heating fuel and turbine fuel; and the North Pole refinery a 22000-barrel-per-day facility producing heating fuel kerosene diesel and jet fuels.

Its retail division is engaged in retail stores selling its products (North Pacific Fuel and Sourdough Fuel).

Petro Star Lubricants is a bulk lube repackaging company offering several product lines and provide technical services for all of the company's product lines.

Marine offers marine fueling as well as supplies such as pumps hoses and nozzles.

Heating Fuel distributes locally produced heating and diesel fuel directly from the company's refineries in North Pole and Valdez to locations throughout Alaska.

Aviation is a supplier of jet fuel for the Ted Stevens International Airport for both commercial and corporate aircraft.

Sales and Marketing

The company operates several gas stations and convenience stores throughout the state offering fuel food groceries and propane sales.

The company's customers include residential commercial industrial and military customers.

Company Background

The company has expanded through acquisitions including fuel distribution firm Sourdough Fuel (in 1986) as well as the 1991 purchase of Alaska Lube and Fuel (now Petro Star Lubricants). Kodiak Sales (in 1997) and North Pacific Fuel (in 1998).

In 2008 Petro Star secured a $158.7 million aviation fuel contract from the Defense Logistics Agency.

EXECUTIVES

Vp Heating Fuel And Marine, Don Castle
Director North Pacific Fuel Operations, Mark Hughes

LOCATIONS

HQ: PETRO STAR INC.
3900 C ST STE 802, ANCHORAGE, AK 995035963
Phone: 907 339-6600
Web: WWW.PETROSTAR.COM

COMPETITORS

Exxon Mobil   Valero Energy
Tesoro

HISTORICAL FINANCIALS

Company Type: Private

Income Statement   FYE: December 31

	REVENUE ($ mil.)	NET INCOME ($ mil.)	NET PROFIT MARGIN	EMPLOYEES
12/08	992	0	—	300
12/03	291	3	1.2%	—
12/02	267	1	0.7%	—
12/01	279	3	1.1%	—
Annual Growth	19.9%	—	—	—

2008 Year-End Financials

Return on assets: —   Cash ($ mil.): 106
Return on equity: —
Current ratio: 1.90

PETROCARD, INC.

EXECUTIVES

Ceo-Pres, Laura Yellig
Chm*, Joseph Chythlook
V Pres*, Jack Mowreader
Treas*, Andrew Rewolinski
Senior Financial Analyst, Rebecca Benson
Chief Information Officer, Roger Hall
Fuel Consultant, Jim Anderson
Consultant, Jim Hester
Information Technology Team ME, Andrew McAllister
Branch Manager, David Harris
Fuel Consultant, Ryan McShane

LOCATIONS

HQ: PETROCARD, INC.
730 CENTRAL AVE S, KENT, WA 980326109
Phone: 253 852-7801
Web: WWW.PETROCARD.COM

HISTORICAL FINANCIALS

Company Type: Private

Income Statement   FYE: March 31

	REVENUE ($ mil.)	NET INCOME ($ mil.)	NET PROFIT MARGIN	EMPLOYEES
03/12	1,173	0	0.1%	190
03/11	948	3	0.4%	—
03/10	791	3	0.4%	—
Annual Growth	21.7%	(50.7%)	—	—

2012 Year-End Financials

Return on assets: 0.6%   Cash ($ mil.): 1
Return on equity: 1.7%
Current ratio: 1.00

PETROLEUM TRADERS CORPORATION

Petroleum Traders Corporation barters with fuel. The company provides wholesale gasoline diesel fuel and heating oil to fuel distributors government agencies and other large consumers of fuel such as businesses with vehicle fleets. The largest pure wholesale fuel distributor in the country Petroleum Traders operates and trades in 44 US states. It supplies #1 and #2 low sulfur diesel fuels biodiesel high sulfur heating oil and kerosene and conventional ethanol and reformulated blends of gasoline in regular midgrade and premium octane ratings.

Operations

Petroleum Traders focuses on supplying wholesale diesel and gasoline exclusively in the US offering a range of turnkey wholesale diesel fuel and wholesale gasoline fuel services.

Sales and Marketing

The company provides discount fuel to commercial government and wholesale customers. In the commercial space it services the trucking construction railroad mining and manufacturing industries as well as utilities and private fleets.

Strategy

Petroleum Traders parlays its hedging experience into fuel cost management for its customers via firm pricing cap programs collars and fuel swaps.

Company Background

The company was founded in 1979.

EXECUTIVES

Vice President, Vicki Himes
Vice President, L Himesvicki
Auditors: BADEN GAGE & SCHROEDER LLC

LOCATIONS

HQ: PETROLEUM TRADERS CORPORATION
7120 POINTE INVERNESS WAY, FORT WAYNE, IN 468047928
Phone: 260 432-6622
Web: WWW.PETROLEUMTRADERS.COM

COMPETITORS

George Warren   Petro Holdings
Gulf Oil   Sun Coast Resources
Martin Resource Management

HISTORICAL FINANCIALS

Company Type: Private

Income Statement   FYE: June 30

	REVENUE ($ mil.)	NET INCOME ($ mil.)	NET PROFIT MARGIN	EMPLOYEES
06/18	1,815	11	0.6%	150
06/17	1,606	19	1.2%	—
06/16	1,667	38	2.3%	—
06/15	2,128	64	3.0%	—
Annual Growth	(5.2%)	(43.6%)	—	—

2018 Year-End Financials

Return on assets: 5.9%   Cash ($ mil.): 45
Return on equity: 9.8%
Current ratio: 2.20

PGA TOUR, INC.

It takes the ferocity of a Tiger to get to the top of this membership organization. The PGA TOUR which includes Tiger Woods and golf's other top players puts on more than 100 official events per year that offer more than $350 million in prize money. Its major championships are the Masters US Open British Open and PGA Championship. The group also oversees the Champions Tour for players 50 and older and the Nationwide Tour for emerging players. The PGA TOUR is separate from the PGA of America which consists mostly of club pros although most tour players maintain membership in both groups. The PGA TOUR was formed in 1968 by a splinter faction of the PGA of America.

Geographic Reach

The PGA TOUR holds events in the US and the UK. Its sponsors and players hail from around the world.

Sales and Marketing

Like other sporting organizations and leagues the TOUR depends heavily on sponsorships and fees from broadcasters to generate revenue. The recession and the financial crisis have put pressure on the sports world as many of the major sponsors have either reined in spending or been forced to pull out of sponsoring events altogether.

Strategy

Golf however continues to be supported by advertisers and broadcasters thanks to the popularity of the sport with fans. The PGA TOUR also benefits from licensing agreements with more than 50 golf equipment makers. The PGA TOUR has been expanding its digital footprint through various websites and mobile apps.

EXECUTIVES

Senior Vice President Human Resources, Tom Perry
Executive Vice President And Chief Legal Officer, Richard Anderson
Commissioner, Timothy W. (Tim) Finchem
Commissioner, Jay Monahan
Vp And Managing Director Pga Tour Japan, Masashi Ishii
Senior Vice President Treasury, Andrea King
Senior Vice President Customer Relations, Sheila Mclenaghan
Vice President, Ronald E Price
Vice President Of Business Development, Jim Wasson
Vice President, Peter Kent
Vice President Business Development, Dan Glod
Vice President Of Field Operations, Roger Stevenson
Vice President Digital Operations, Luis Goicouria
Senior Vice President New Media, David Logue
Vice President Of Competition, Tyler Dennis
Vice President Of Tournament Business Affairs, Tom Alter
Vice President Of Information Systems, Steve Evans
Senior Vice President Of Human Resources, Thomas Perry
Vice President Marketing, Tom Kuhn
Vice President Client Management, Mcmanu Christin
Treasurer, Bodney Alex
Treasurer, Bobelis Vita
Auditors: PRICEWATERHOUSECOOPERS LLP JA

LOCATIONS

HQ: PGA TOUR, INC.
100 PGA TOUR BLVD, PONTE VEDRA BEACH, FL
320823046
Phone: 904 285-3700
Web: WWW.GOLFEXPERIENCES.COM

COMPETITORS

FIFA
LPGA
Major League Baseball
Major League Soccer
NBA
NFL

PGA
Professional Bowlers
Association
USTA
WTA Tour

HISTORICAL FINANCIALS

Company Type: Private

Income Statement   FYE: December 31

	REVENUE ($ mil.)	NET INCOME ($ mil.)	NET PROFIT MARGIN	EMPLOYEES
12/13	1,075	34	3.2%	3,563
12/06	894	3	0.3%	—
12/05	875	4	0.5%	—
12/04	802	3	0.4%	—
Annual Growth	3.3%	29.4%	—	—

2013 Year-End Financials

Return on assets: 1.6%   Cash ($ mil.): 149
Return on equity: 3.7%
Current ratio: —

PHILADELPHIA CONSOLIDATED HOLDING CORP.

Because each industry has its own unique set of risks Philadelphia Insurance Companies and its subsidiaries specialize in designing and underwriting commercial property/casualty insurance. Its niche clients include rental car companies (for that insurance they always want to sell you at the counter) not-for-profits health and fitness centers and day-care facilities. Its specialty lines include loss-control policies and liability coverage for such professionals as lawyers doctors accountants dog groomers and even insurance claims adjusters. Philadelphia Insurance Companies is a subsidiary of Tokio Marine Holdings.

Geographic Reach

Philadelphia Insurance Companies' operating subsidiaries Philadelphia Insurance and Philadelphia Indemnity Insurance sell and service policies through a network of independent agents and about 50 regional offices that stretch across the US. With its new-found backing from Tokio Marine the insurer has access to broader distribution avenues in the US and overseas.

Sales and Marketing

In addition to commercial property and casualty insurance the company also sells personal coverage for collectible cars and homeowners flood insurance.

Strategy

Philadelphia Insurance Companies has been enhancing its information technology systems. The firm is working to upgrade its back-office infrastructure for more efficient handling of billing claims accounting and data management functions.

EXECUTIVES

Regional Vice President, Brent Kruse
Senior Vice President Marketing, Brian O'Reilly
Vice President Assistant Treasurer, Michael Kelly
Vice President Operations, Deborah Sutton
Assistant Vice President, Michael Henk
Vp Marketing, Mike Ricca
Assistant Vice President Human Resources, Laura Boylan
Vice President And Product Manager, Paul Siragusa
Senior Vice President, John Doyle
Regional Vice President, Bill Misita
Assistant Vice President, Liney Kevin
Vice President Commerical Underwriting, Mark Plousis
Avp Contract Surety, Rick Morgan
Vp Accident And Health Division, Michael Flood
Vice President, Robert Morgan
Regional Vice President, Daniel Shea
Assistant Vice President Chief Information Security Officer (ciso), Mark Viola
Vice President, Jon Peeples

LOCATIONS

HQ: PHILADELPHIA CONSOLIDATED HOLDING CORP.
1 BALA PLZ STE 100, BALA CYNWYD, PA 190041401
Phone: 610 617-7900
Web: WWW.PHLY.COM

PRODUCTS/OPERATIONS

Selected Products
Commercial and Personal Property/Casualty Insurance
Adoption agencies
Adult day care
Amateur sports
Antique collector car
Apartments
Auto leasing/rental program
Boat dealers
Bowling centers
Builder's exchange
Builders' risk
Business auto fleet
Camp operators
Child care centers
Consulting foresters
Contractor environmental coverage
Crime protection plus
Entertainment
Environmental
Fairs and fairgrounds
Festivals
Film production
Flood
Golf and country clubs
Health fitness and wellness
Home health care
Homeowners association
Hospice
Hotels
Life and business coaches
Loss control
Medical facilities and hospitals
Motorsports
Museums
Non-profit and social service organizations
Nursing homes
Office parks
Outdoor recreation
Performing arts
Pest control services
Professional sports
Public entities
Real rstate dchedules
Religious organizations
RV parks and campgrounds
Schools
Security services (The Guardian)
Shopping centers
Special events
Substance abuse rehabilitation facilities
Temporary staffing agencies
Volunteer fire department
Zoos

Liability
Accountants professional liability
Allied Health professional liability
Business owners
Cyber security liability
Employed lawyers professional liability
Employment practices stand alone
Excess liability
Miscellaneous professional liability (Affinity Pro)

COMPETITORS

AIG
American Financial
Group
CNA Financial
Hagerty Insurance
Hanover Insurance

Liberty Mutual
Markel
North Pointe
RLI
State Farm
Travelers Companies

HISTORICAL FINANCIALS

Company Type: Private

Income Statement   FYE: December 31

	ASSETS ($ mil.)	NET INCOME ($ mil.)	INCOME AS % OF ASSETS	EMPLOYEES
12/16	9,719	347	3.6%	1,374
12/15	9,047	323	3.6%	—
Annual Growth	7.4%	7.5%	—	—

PHOEBE PUTNEY MEMORIAL HOSPITAL, INC.

Phoebe Putney Memorial Hospital provides health care services to residents of southwest Georgia. With more than 650 beds and some 300 physicians the acute-care hospital provides emergency and inpatient services as well as cardiology oncology psychiatric women's health and pediatric specialty care. It's one of Georgia's largest comprehensive regional medical centers. Founded in 1911 it is part of the Phoebe Putney Health System which also includes the 25-bed Phoebe Worth Medical Center and several satellite community health centers that provide outpatient primary health laboratory and surgical services. The health system is governed by the Albany-Dougherty County Hospital Authority.

Operations

As part of its operations Phoebe Putney Memorial Hospital runs an ambulatory infusion center Carlton Breast Health Center and surgical weight loss/wellness center. Inpatient admissions average more than 21000 a year while clinic visits typically run about 711000 annually. With some 3800 employees payroll at Phoebe Putney Memorial Hospital is about $180 million on average.

Geographic Reach

The hospital serves a growing group of residents in 35 counties across southwest Georgia.

Sales and Marketing

Third-party payors accounted for 42% of net patient service revenues in 2014; Medicare and Medicaid accounted for 29% and 13% respectively.

Financial Performance

In 2014 revenue fell 5% to $488 million as net patient service revenues slipped. However the system returned to the black that year reporting $13 million in net income due to an absence of loss on impairment of goodwill. Cash flow from operation rose to $29 million (versus $9000 in 2013) due to changes in receivables supplies and estimated settlements. A decline in cash used for payments and expenses also contributed to the increase.

Strategy

To ensure that it can meet current and future demand for health care services Phoebe Putney Memorial Hospital has been focusing on building up its physician network.

EXECUTIVES

Vice President Surgical Services, Maureen Jackson
President Ceo And Director, Joel Wernick
Svp And Cfo, Kerry Loudermilk
Vp Information Systems Clinical Informatics, Jesse Diaz
Evp And Coo, Joe Austin
Vp Strategy And Marketing, Jackie Ryan
Director Of Radiology, Lorenzo Carson
Vice President Internal Audits, Brad Hallford
Vice President Chief Compliance Officer, Audrey Pike
Svp And Chief Nursing Officer Phoebe Putney Memorial Hospital, Evelyn Olenick
Vice Chairman, Mary H. Dykes
Chairman, John Culbreath

LOCATIONS

HQ: PHOEBE PUTNEY MEMORIAL HOSPITAL, INC.
417 W 3RD AVE, ALBANY, GA 317011943
Phone: 229 312-1000

PRODUCTS/OPERATIONS

Selected Services
Ambulatory Infusion Center
Bariatric Surgery
Behavioral Health
Cardiac Rehabilitation
Carlton Breast Health Center
Corporate Health Services
Corporate Onsite Services
Da Vinci Robotic Surgery
Endoscopy Department
Hematology/Oncology
Hospice and Palliative Care
Hyperbaric Oxygen Therapy
Neurodiagnostics
Orthopedics
Pediatrics
Prostate Brachytherapy
Radiation Oncology
Rheumatology
Sickle Cell Clinic
Speech Therapy
Sports Medicine
Surgical Weight Loss/Wellness Center
Wound Care

COMPETITORS

Central Georgia Health Systems	Regency Hospital
HCA	WellStar Health System
Oconee Regional Health Systems	

HISTORICAL FINANCIALS

Company Type: Private

Income Statement				FYE: July 31
	REVENUE ($ mil.)	NET INCOME ($ mil.)	NET PROFIT MARGIN	EMPLOYEES
07/16	498	(13)	—	3,000
07/15	490	32	6.6%	—
07/09	513	19	3.8%	—
07/08	500	15	3.0%	—
Annual Growth	(0.0%)	—	—	—

2016 Year-End Financials
Return on assets: (-2.2%) Cash ($ mil.): 49
Return on equity: (-14.8%)
Current ratio: 4.60

PHOEBE PUTNEY MEMORIAL HOSPITAL, INC.

EXECUTIVES

BR Mgr, Judy Clay
Analyst, Carol Pressley
Vice President, Richard Bowe
Nurse Recruiter, Tim Davis
Chief Operations Officer, Joe Austin
Director, Lori Jenkins
Compensation Analyst, Misty Jones

LOCATIONS

HQ: PHOEBE PUTNEY MEMORIAL HOSPITAL, INC.
2000 PALMYRA RD, ALBANY, GA 317011528
Phone: 229 434-2000
Web: WWW.PPMH.ORG

HISTORICAL FINANCIALS

Company Type: Private

Income Statement				FYE: July 31
	REVENUE ($ mil.)	NET INCOME ($ mil.)	NET PROFIT MARGIN	EMPLOYEES
07/15	490	32	6.6%	1
07/13	515	(4)	—	—
Annual Growth	(2.5%)	—	—	—

2015 Year-End Financials
Return on assets: 5.5% Cash ($ mil.): 49
Return on equity: 23.7%
Current ratio: 3.70

PHOENIX CHILDREN'S HOSPITAL, INC.

Phoenix Children's Hospital (PCH) invests in the health of the next generation. Founded in 1983 the hospital provides a comprehensive range of medical services specifically for children and adolescents in the greater Phoenix area. The hospital has about 385 beds and provides care in a number of pediatric sub-specialties including childhood cancers hematology neuroscience heart disease trauma and orthopedics. It also operates a newborn intensive care unit (NICU) at its main campus. PCH has several pediatric outpatient care centers in surrounding Phoenix suburbs.

Operations

The hospital has nearly 1000 pediatric specialists providing inpatient outpatient emergency and trauma care across more than 75 pediatric subspecialties. Each year PCH has some 18800 inpatient admissions 81000 emergency department visits 238000 outpatient visits and 16000 surgical cases.

PCH has clinical and non-clinical research collaborations with other institutions to make advances in pediatric care such as Mayo Clinic Translational Genomics Institute and the Children's Oncology Group.

Subsidiary Cambridge Arizona Insurance Company provides captive insurance coverage to the hospital and its affiliates.

Geographic Reach

The system operates satellites in Mesa Scottsdale the Northwest Valley Avondale Yuma and

Sales and Marketing

State Medicaid payments account for more than half of net patient revenues followed by contracted health care agreements (38%). The remainder comes from patients and other payors.

Financial Performance

The hospital's revenue increased by 11% to $724 million in fiscal 2014 on 10% higher net patient service earnings and a 74% jump in other operating income. However net income decreased 59% to $39 million on lower non-operating income more employee compensation paid and more cash used towards supplies and professional services. Operating cash flow totaled $66 million that year.

Strategy

To meet population growth levels in the region PCH is working to expand its medical center facilities. In 2015 it broke ground on a $40 million project to build a new emergency department and pediatric trauma center tripling the number of exam rooms at the hospital. This and other expansion efforts allow PCH to accommodate patients from other areas of Arizona and surrounding states in the Southwest.

In 2014 the hospital invested in a partnership with Obstetrix Medical Group of Phoenix to establish Arizona Pediatric Cardiology and Phoenix Children's Cardiology Diagnostics (which manages the PCH's cardiology product lines). PCH owns 25% of the pediatric cardiology unit and 63% of the diagnostics unit.

Also that year PCH opened a 22-bed pediatric inpatient unit on the campus of Dignity Health Mercy Gilbert Medical Center.

EXECUTIVES

President And Ceo, Robert L. Meyer
Vp And Chief Medical Officer, Murray M. Pollack
Evp And Cfo, Douglas T. Myers
Evp Phoenix Childrenâ's Medical Group And Surgeon-in-chief, Dennis P. Lund
Evp And Coo, Betsy Kuzas
Svp And Chief Information Officer, David Higginson
Svp Patient Care And Chief Nursing Officer, Pamela J. Carlson
Vp And Chief Medical Information Officer, Vinay Vaidya
Svp And Chief Administrative Officer Phoenix Childrenâ's Medical Group, Roger Logan
President Phoenix Children's Medical Staff, Jeffrey P. Morray
Chairman Phoenix Children's Hospital Foundation Board Of Directors, Brian Swartz
Medical Director, Janice Piatt
Medical Director Of Laboratories, Paul Dickman
Senior Vice President Chief Sales Officer, Bob Campbell
Vice President Finance, James Champlin
Vice President Human Resources, Tom Diederich
Medical Director, Karen Gerber-Vecsey
Vice President Perioperative Services, Barbara Pankratz
Vice President Operations, Casey Osborne
Vice President Talent Acquisition, Kip Welch
Medical Director Department Of Pathology And Laboratory Medicine, Daphne Demello
Vice President Individual Giving, Terri Burkel
Medical Director Antimicrobial Stewardship Program, Wassim Ballan
Senior Vice President Strategic Planning, Rich Lehmuth
Senior Vice President Of Research And Chief Research Officer, Terrence L Stull
Senior Vice President Human Resources, Page Bachman
Executive Vice President, Nenad Robert

Chairman, Mark B. Bonsall
Vice Chairman, Jon Hulburd
Board Member, ELIZABETH ZORN

LOCATIONS

HQ: PHOENIX CHILDREN'S HOSPITAL, INC.
1919 E THOMAS RD, PHOENIX, AZ 850167710
Phone: 602 546-1000
Web: WWW.PHOENIXCHILDRENS.ORG

PRODUCTS/OPERATIONS

2014 Sales

	$ mil.	% of total
Net patient service revenue	691	95
Net assets released from restrictions used for operations	10	2
Donations gifts & contributions	8	1
Other operating revenue	15	2
Total	**725**	**100**

Selected Center of Excellence

Barrow Neurological Institute at Phoenix Children's
  Hospital
Center for Cancer and Blood Disorders
Center for Pediatric Orthopaedics
Level One Pediatric Trauma Center
Neonatal Intensive Care
Phoenix Children's Heart Center

COMPETITORS

Banner Health
Dignity Health
Flagstaff Medical
  Center
John C. Lincoln Health
  Network
Northern Arizona
  Healthcare

Scottsdale Healthcare
Shriners Hospitals For
  Children
University of Arizona
  Health Network

HISTORICAL FINANCIALS
Company Type: Private

Income Statement				FYE: December 31
	REVENUE ($ mil.)	NET INCOME ($ mil.)	NET PROFIT MARGIN	EMPLOYEES
12/14	661	26	4.1%	3,000
12/13	655	31	4.9%	—
12/11	498	(5)	—	—
12/09	408	106	26.1%	—
Annual Growth	**10.1%**	**(24.1%)**	**—**	**—**

2014 Year-End Financials
Return on assets: 2.4%   Cash ($ mil.): 130
Return on equity: 8.8%
Current ratio: 4.50

PIEDMONT HOSPITAL, INC.

Those feeling ill in Atlanta can count on Piedmont Healthcare for help. Founded in 1905 the not-for-profit organization's flagship facility is Piedmont Atlanta an acute care hospital with more than 485 beds. Piedmont Atlanta provides general and advanced medical-surgical care including open-heart surgery organ transplantation and neurosurgery. Also part of the Piedmont family are Piedmont Fayette Hospital with more than 170 beds; Piedmont Mountainside Hospital a 52-bed community hospital north of Atlanta; and the Piedmont Physicians Group a network of more than 150 primary care physicians operating in dozens of offices throughout metropolitan Atlanta.

Operations

Piedmont Healthcare also operates Piedmont Newnan Hospital a community hospital in Coweta County Georgia and the acute care community hospital Piedmont Henry Hospital.

Each year the system serves around 2 million patients performing some 44000 surgeries completing more than 200 organ transplants and handling more than 250000 emergency department visits. It also sees some 472000 outpatients and around 8000 infant deliveries annually.

Sales and Marketing

Medicare and Medicaid payments combined account for more than 40% of Piedmont's total net patient service revenue.

Financial Performance

Revenue increased 4% to $1.7 billion in fiscal 2014 (ended June) on higher net patient service revenues and other revenues. However net income fell 27% to $104.2 million as operating expenses and pension adjustments increased.

Cash flow from operations rose 66% to $150.1 million that year due primarily to a change in working capital.

Strategy

The health care system expands its offerings through investment and renovation as well as partnerships and acquisitions. In 2014 it partnered with WellStreet to launch Piedmont Urgent Care by WellStreet a network of urgent care centers offering extended-hour walk-in treatment for non-life threatening illnesses and injuries.

EXECUTIVES

Radiology Director, Louis H Jacobs
Ceo Piedmont Physicians, Sid Kirschner
Chief Medical Officer, Leigh S. Hamby
Vice Chair, Harry M. McFarling
Coo, Gregory A. (Greg) Hurst
Chief Nurse Executive, Denise Ray
President And Ceo, Kevin Brown
Chief Strategy & Performance Improvement Officer, Michelle Fisher
Chief Consumer Officer, Matt Gove
Cfo, Michael McAnder
Cio, Geoff Brown
Vice President Financial Planning And Analysis, Scott Connor
Director Of Health Information Management, Pamela Marshall
Executive Assistant To Mark Cohen Medical Director Vpma, Kathie Alhadeff
Vice President Of Supply Chain, Joe Colonna
Medical Director Radiation Oncology, Fred Schwaibold
Senior Business Intelligence Developer, Brianna Boylston
Vp Corporate Finance Treasurer, Marie Gaffney
Executive Vice President, Alan Laughridge
Executive Vice President, Edward Lovern
Chair, Janine Brown
Medical Secretary, Karin Jackson
Medical Secretary, Jane Kelly
Department Secretary, Lucy Curtis
Medical Secretary, Susan Scott

LOCATIONS

HQ: PIEDMONT HOSPITAL, INC.
1968 PEACHTREE RD NW, ATLANTA, GA 303091285
Phone: 404 605-5000
Web: WWW.PIEDMONT.ORG

PRODUCTS/OPERATIONS

2014 Sales

	$ mil.	% of total
Net patient service revenue	1,595	96
Other revenue	62	4
Total	**1,657**	**100**

Selected Operations
Piedmont Atlanta
Piedmont Fayette Hospital (Fayetteville)
Piedmont Henry Hospital (Stockbridge)
Piedmont Mountainside Hospital (Jasper)
Piedmont Newnan Hospital (Newnan)
Piedmont Physicians Group (metropolitan Atlanta)

COMPETITORS

Children's Healthcare
  of Atlanta
DeKalb Medical
Emory Healthcare
Grady Health System

Northside Hospital
Shepherd Center
Tenet Healthcare
Universal Health
  Services

HISTORICAL FINANCIALS
Company Type: Private

Income Statement				FYE: June 30
	REVENUE ($ mil.)	NET INCOME ($ mil.)	NET PROFIT MARGIN	EMPLOYEES
06/16	918	60	6.5%	6,419
06/15	857	66	7.8%	—
06/10*	689	75	11.0%	—
12/09	1	(0)	—	—
Annual Growth	**199.4%**	**—**	**—**	**—**

*Fiscal year change

2016 Year-End Financials
Return on assets: 6.1%   Cash ($ mil.): 25
Return on equity: 17.0%
Current ratio: 2.40

PIGGLY WIGGLY ALABAMA DISTRIBUTING CO., INC.

EXECUTIVES

Branch Manager, Dennis T Stewart
Auditors: DENT BAKER & COMPANY LLP BI

LOCATIONS

HQ: PIGGLY WIGGLY ALABAMA DISTRIBUTING CO., INC.
2400 J TERRELL WOOTEN DR, BESSEMER, AL 350202272
Phone: 205 481-2300
Web: WWW.PWADC.NET

HISTORICAL FINANCIALS
Company Type: Private

Income Statement				FYE: July 29
	REVENUE ($ mil.)	NET INCOME ($ mil.)	NET PROFIT MARGIN	EMPLOYEES
07/11	772	0	0.1%	500
07/10	837	0	0.0%	—
07/09	830	0	0.0%	—
Annual Growth	**(3.5%)**	**85.6%**	**—**	**—**

2011 Year-End Financials
Return on assets: 0.5%   Cash ($ mil.): 4
Return on equity: 1.7%
Current ratio: 1.70

PIH HEALTH HOSPITAL - WHITTIER

EXECUTIVES

Ceo, James R West
Cfo, Anita Chou
Cno, Ramona Pratt
Doctor, John R Hamilton
Dentist, Sue Ponce
Social Worker, Dan Ogletree
MD, Bill Kim
MD, Brent Gray
MD, Davis Lee
Chief Financial Officer, Greg Williams
Manager, Guillermo Vicencio

LOCATIONS

HQ: PIH HEALTH HOSPITAL - WHITTIER
12401 WASHINGTON BLVD, WHITTIER, CA
906021006
Phone: 562 698-0811
Web: WWW.PIHHEALTH.ORG

HISTORICAL FINANCIALS
Company Type: Private

Income Statement				FYE: September 30
	REVENUE ($ mil.)	NET INCOME ($ mil.)	NET PROFIT MARGIN	EMPLOYEES
09/14	495	18	3.8%	3,150
09/13	491	81	16.7%	—
09/12	419	69	16.6%	—
Annual Growth	8.7%	(48.0%)	—	—

2014 Year-End Financials
Return on assets: 1.6%   Cash ($ mil.): —
Return on equity: 3.4%
Current ratio: 3.50

PIKEVILLE MEDICAL CENTER, INC.

Taking a nasty fall while hiking the rugged Appalachians will likely land you at Pikeville Medical Center (PMC). Serving patients in eastern Kentucky the hospital boasts more than 260 beds and provides a full range of inpatient outpatient and surgical services. PMC's centers and departments handle a number of specialties such as diagnostic imaging echocardiogram neurosurgery cancer care and bariatric surgery. Employing some 350 physicians PMC also operates a rehabilitation hospital a home health agency and outpatient family practice and specialty clinics as well as a physician residency program. PMC first opened on Christmas Day in 1924.

Operations
Pikeville Kentucky-based PMC offers more than 400 services.

Strategy
PMC is rapidly expanding its services and facilities to keep pace with the needs of area residents. In recent years it has added such new services as pulmonary rehabilitation plastic surgery and orthopedic trauma. In addition the hospital launched a $150 million expansion project that will add an 11-story outpatient center (including physician practices and surgery suites) and a 10-story park-

ing garage. Additional expansion efforts have included opening new outpatient cancer diagnostic pain management and primary care clinics.

An active participant in clinical trials and studies PMC works to expand its research opportunities for patients and physicians. In 2013 the hospital began new treatment for patients with Paroxysmal Atrial Fibrillation (Afib) using Medtronic's Arctic Front Advance Cardiac Cryoballoon System.

Since 2012 when it inked a Medicaid contract with Coventry PMC has contracts with all three providers: Coventry Wellcare and Kentucky Spirit. PMC become member of the Mayo Clinic Care Network in 2013. The agreement gives PMC providers access to Mayo Clinic resources including its online point-of-care information system and its electronic consulting process that connects physicians with Mayo Clinic specialists on questions of diagnosis therapy or care management.

EXECUTIVES

Ceo-Pres, Walter E May
V Pres*, Ronald Burchett
SEC-Treas*, Joe Dean Anderson
Vp*, Michelle Hagy
Chief Operating Officer*, Debbie Puckett
Vp*, Peggy Rasnick Justice
Coo*, Juanita Deskins
Cfo*, Michelle Hagey
Occupational Specia, Alisa Bowers
Scientist, Sharon Weddington
Chief of Medicine, Ihari Malempati
Auditors: PERSHING YOAKLEY & ASSOCIATES

LOCATIONS

HQ: PIKEVILLE MEDICAL CENTER, INC.
911 BYPASS RD, PIKEVILLE, KY 415011689
Phone: 606 218-3500
Web: WWW.PIKEVILLEHOSPITAL.ORG

PRODUCTS/OPERATIONS

Selected Services
Bariatric Surgery
Breast Care Center
Critical Care
Diagnostics
Diabetes Education
Ear Nose & Throat (Otolaryngology)
Emergency
Endocrinology
Family Practice
Gastroenterology
Gynecology/Obstetrics
Family Practice Clinic
Heart Institute
Heart Failure/Coumadin Clinic
Home Health
Home Medical Equipment
Inpatient
Infectious Disease
Laboratory Services
Leonard Lawson Cancer Center
Neonatology
Nephrology
Neurosurgery
Ophthalmology
Other Patient Services
Orthopedic Surgery
Palliative Care
Pediatrics
Pharmacy
Plastic & Reconstructive Surgery
Pulmonary Clinic
Radiology
Rehabilitation
Residency Program
Rheumatology
Sleep
Urology
Women and Childrens' Services
Wound Care Center

COMPETITORS

Appalachian Regional Healthcare
Clinch Valley Medical Center
Community Health Systems
Highlands Health
Norton Community Hospital
Norton Healthcare
Russell County Medical Center
University of Kentucky Chandler Hospital

HISTORICAL FINANCIALS
Company Type: Private

Income Statement				FYE: September 30
	REVENUE ($ mil.)	NET INCOME ($ mil.)	NET PROFIT MARGIN	EMPLOYEES
09/18	524	(14)	—	2,527
09/16	489	29	5.9%	—
09/15	381	9	2.5%	—
09/14	367	8	2.4%	—
Annual Growth	9.3%	—	—	—

2018 Year-End Financials
Return on assets: (-2.6%)   Cash ($ mil.): 148
Return on equity: (-5.2%)
Current ratio: 3.80

PILKINGTON NORTH AMERICA, INC.

Pilkington North America has a clear view of the US glass market.The company manufactures and markets glass and glazing products primarily for the automotive and building industries. Benefits of its glass include fire protection noise control solar heat control and thermal insulation. A majority of its sales come from automotive glass sold to the original equipment and replacement markets. More than a quarter of sales are made from building glass geared at homeowners and architects. A small but growing part of its business focuses on specialty glass used in solar energy conversion. Pilkington North America is a subsidiary of Pilkington plc which operates as part of Japanese glass giant Nippon Sheet Glass.

Geographic Reach
Pilkington North America manages six float glass lines in the US (where molten glass is poured on a bed of molten tin to ensure flat surface and uniform thickness) more than half a dozen automotive glass fabrication facilities in the US Canada and Mexico and a network of more than 100 US wholesale centers that distribute automotive replacement glass products.

Its six float glass lines including Rossford Ohio (2); Laurinburg North Carolina (2); Ottawa Illinois (1); Lathrop California (1). Products are shipped from its distribution centers in Columbus Ohio and Phoenix Arizona to external retailers and wholesale customers.

Sales and Marketing
The company provides glass products and glazing systems to automotive original equipment manufacturers of light vehicles buses trucks and specialized and utility vehicles; and glass products and accessories for replacing and repairing windshields and other glass parts to automotive glass replacement aftermarket sectors. Pilkington North America also serves homeowners architects and other window manufacturers and offers its products to retailers and wholesalers.

Automotive products (57% OEMs and 43% for automotive glass replacement) account for 70% of total sales; architectural products account for the remaining 30%. Products are shipped from its distribution centers in Phoenix and Columbus Ohio to external retailers and wholesale customers.

Strategy

In line with its parent's strategy a key focus for Pilkington North America's future is expanding its solar energy portfolio within its building products segment. The company anticipates an increase in volumes and that sales of solar energy glass will contribute a significant portion of those higher volumes. Although some of its float glass production lines were suspended during the economic crisis some have since been converted into solar energy lines and are coming back on stream to support its expansion particularly in photovoltaics.

Product introductions are also a key part of Pilkington North America's growth strategy. In 2014 it introduced Pilkington MirroView 50/50 which enhances the standard MirroView's visual performance for a brightly lit environment such as a store or showroom and Pilkington OptiView Pro a non-conductive anti-reflection coating especially designed for touch screen applications. In 2013 the company introduced Optiwhite which widens the color choice.

EXECUTIVES

Vp Human Resources, Spencer Harris

LOCATIONS

HQ: PILKINGTON NORTH AMERICA, INC.
811 MADISON AVE FL 3, TOLEDO, OH 436045688
Phone: 419 247-3731
Web: WWW.PILKINGTON.COM

PRODUCTS/OPERATIONS

Selected Products and Brands

Decoration
Texture glass (18 pattern designs)
Fire protection
Pyrodur (fire-resistant and radiant heat-protected glass)
Pyrostop (fire-resistant insulating glass)
Glass systems
Planar (structural glass system for architects)
Profilit (exterior glazing glass)
Noise control
Optiphon (laminated glass with high sound insulation)
Self-cleaning
Activ Clear (clear float glass with self-cleaning properties)
Solar control
Arctic Blue (tinted glass)
Eclipse Advantage (solar control and thermal insulation glass)
EverGreen (tinted glass)
Solar-E (solar control and thermal insulation glass)
SuperGrey (gray-colored solar control float glass)
Solar energy
NSG TEC (coated glass for photovoltaic technologies)
Sunplus (extra clear patterned glass for solar energy conversion)
Optiwhite (extra clear float glass for solar energy conversion)
Special applications
Mirropane (interior glass to create "infinity" mirror effects)
TEC Glass (electrically conductive glass for flat panel displays heated glass and oven doors)
Thermal insulation
Energy Advantage (energy-efficient window glass)
OptiFloat (float glass)
Spacia (medium thermal insulation glass)

COMPETITORS

Apogee Enterprises	Saint-Gobain
Asahi Glass	Schott Corporation
Cardinal Glass	Taylor Made Group
Guardian Glass	Viracon
PPG Industries	

HISTORICAL FINANCIALS

Company Type: Private

Income Statement   FYE: March 31

	REVENUE ($ mil.)	NET INCOME ($ mil.)	NET PROFIT MARGIN	EMPLOYEES
03/08	967	(11)	—	3,747
03/07	913	(17)	—	
03/04	931	31	3.4%	
Annual Growth	1.0%	—	—	—

2008 Year-End Financials

Return on assets: 12.3%   Cash ($ mil.): —
Return on equity: (-1.2%)
Current ratio: 0.50

PIMA COUNTY

EXECUTIVES

Admin, Chuck Huckelberry
Information Specialist, Ed Sander
Customer Staff, Dana Moore
Coordinator, Anastasia Olander
Coordinator, Len Altieri
Coordinator, Monica Dennis
Coordinator, Sydne Meyers
Deputy Director, Ana Olivares
Child Care Health Consultant, Belinda Davis
Computer Technician, Jeff May-Stahl
Administration, Jennifer Coyle
Auditors: STATE OF ARIZONA-DEBBIE DAVENP

LOCATIONS

HQ: PIMA COUNTY
201 N STONE AVE FL 9, TUCSON, AZ 857011215
Phone: 520 243-4600
Web: WWW.PIMA.GOV

HISTORICAL FINANCIALS

Company Type: Private

Income Statement   FYE: June 30

	REVENUE ($ mil.)	NET INCOME ($ mil.)	NET PROFIT MARGIN	EMPLOYEES
06/17	873	17	2.0%	7,500
06/16	863	2	0.3%	
06/13	789	(13)	—	
Annual Growth	2.6%	—	—	—

2017 Year-End Financials

Return on assets: 0.4%   Cash ($ mil.): 521
Return on equity: 0.9%
Current ratio: —

PINNACLE HEALTH HOSPITAL

EXECUTIVES

Ceo, Roger Longenderfer
Sr V Pres-Treas-Cfo*, William Pugh
Administrator*, Philip Guarneschelli
Director, Betsy Kopp
Information Technology/Interne, Chris Reisinger
Nurse, Laurie Whitmyer
Law Specialist, John Warner
Business Manager, Kimberly Snow
Surgeon, Ronald G Barsanti
Surgeon, Timothy Leone
Coordinator, Amy Hench
Auditors: BAKER TILLY VIRCHOW KRAUSE LLP

LOCATIONS

HQ: PINNACLE HEALTH HOSPITAL
4300 LONDONDERRY RD, HARRISBURG, PA
171095317
Phone: 717 782-3131
Web: WWW.PINNACLEHEALTH.ORG

HISTORICAL FINANCIALS

Company Type: Private

Income Statement   FYE: June 30

	REVENUE ($ mil.)	NET INCOME ($ mil.)	NET PROFIT MARGIN	EMPLOYEES
06/14	759	94	12.5%	4,800
06/13	733	105	14.4%	
06/08	0	0	14.6%	
06/05	0	0	—	
Annual Growth	—	—	—	—

2014 Year-End Financials

Return on assets: 10.0%   Cash ($ mil.): 1
Return on equity: 25.5%
Current ratio: 0.30

PITT COUNTY MEMORIAL HOSPITAL, INCORPORATED

Vidant Medical Center is an acute health services facility that serves the vibrant community of Greenville North Carolina and surrounding areas. The 909-bed regional referral hospital's specialty divisions include Vidant Children's Hospital East Carolina Heart Institute a rehabilitation center and the outpatient Vidant SurgiCenter. Other services include oncology transplant women's health orthopedic behavioral care and home health and hospice care units. The center also serves as a teaching facility for East Carolina University's Brody School of Medicine. Vidant Medical Center (formerly Pitt County Memorial Hospital) is a member of University Health Systems of Eastern Carolina (dba Vidant Health).

Operations

In addition to serving as a primary teaching facility for the Brody School of Medicine Vidant Medical Center provides clinical training for East Carolina University's allied health and nursing programs. About 2000 students complete clinical programs at the medical center and its affiliated Vidant Health facilities each year.

Its subsidiary PMI Inc. offers property management services.

Altogether Vidant Medical Center serves more than 1.4 million people across its 29-county service area. Boasting a clinical staff of more than 500 physicians and 1200 nurses the medical center in 2013 tended to more than 46000 inpatients and more than 275000 outpatients. Its emergency department visits reached 121000-plus in 2013.

Geographic Reach
Vidant Medical Center provides care to patients in a 29-county service territory in eastern North Carolina. It operates as a regional referral center for smaller community hospitals in the area taking on complex care cases in its specialized fields of medicine.

Strategy
To enhance its service offerings to area residents the Vidant Health organization regularly updates its facilities through capital improvement projects. In addition to basic equipment and infrastructure upgrades in 2011 the hospital completed phase one of an expansion project at the Vidant Medical Center that aims to improve the hospital's pediatric and cancer care capabilities.

To signify its mission to enhance the quality of life in its service territories in 2012 University Health Systems of Eastern Carolina began operating as Vidant Health and the Pitt County Memorial Hospital was renamed as Vidant Memorial Hospital.

EXECUTIVES

Svp, Van Smith
Vice President Financial Services Supply Chain Management, Preston Comeaux
Senior Vice President Operations Vmg, Daniel Drake
Vice President Strategic Marketing, Daniel Stevens
Vice President Human Resources, Charlene Wilson
Vice President Director Of Information Technology Risk Management, Robin Watson
Auditors: RSM US LLP MINNEAPOLIS MINNE

LOCATIONS

HQ: PITT COUNTY MEMORIAL HOSPITAL, INCORPORATED
2100 STANTONSBURG RD, GREENVILLE, NC 278342832
Phone: 252 847-4100
Web: WWW.VIDANTHEALTH.COM

PRODUCTS/OPERATIONS

Selected Services
Asthma Program (Pediatric)
Audiology
Behavioral & Mental Health
Cancer Care
Child Life
Children's Care
Children's Emergency Department
Children's Hospital
Community Health Programs
CyberKnife
Diagnostic Imaging
Diabetes
Emergency Services
Endoscopy Services
Gamma Knife

COMPETITORS

Adventist Health System Sunbelt Healthcare
Bon Secours Health
Carolinas HealthCare System
Duke University Health System
Novant Health
Sentara Healthcare
Tenet Healthcare
UNC Hospitals
Upstate Affiliate

HISTORICAL FINANCIALS
Company Type: Private

Income Statement				FYE: September 30
	REVENUE ($ mil.)	NET INCOME ($ mil.)	NET PROFIT MARGIN	EMPLOYEES
09/18	1,201	131	10.9%	15,000
09/15	1,066	79	7.5%	—
09/14	1,025	79	7.8%	—
09/13	1,031	91	8.9%	—
Annual Growth	3.1%	7.4%	—	—

2018 Year-End Financials

Return on assets: 8.3%   Cash ($ mil.): 10
Return on equity: 10.7%
Current ratio: 2.70

PITTSBURGH SCHOOL DISTRICT

EXECUTIVES

Supt, Linda Lane
Auditors: MAHER DUESSEL PITTSBURGH PEN

LOCATIONS

HQ: PITTSBURGH SCHOOL DISTRICT
341 S BELLEFIELD AVE, PITTSBURGH, PA 152133552
Phone: 412 622-3500
Web: WWW.PGHSCHOOLS.ORG

HISTORICAL FINANCIALS
Company Type: Private

Income Statement				FYE: December 31
	REVENUE ($ mil.)	NET INCOME ($ mil.)	NET PROFIT MARGIN	EMPLOYEES
12/17	674	(4)	—	5,707
12/16	735	(2)	—	—
12/15	639	15	2.5%	—
Annual Growth	2.7%			

2017 Year-End Financials

Return on assets: (-0.5%)   Cash ($ mil.): 67
Return on equity: —
Current ratio: 1.60

PLACID HOLDING COMPANY

EXECUTIVES

Pres, Dan Robinson
V Pres, Larry Doty
V Pres, Ron Hurst
Manager, Eric Belvaux
Auditors: HEIN & ASSOCIATES LLP DALLAS

LOCATIONS

HQ: PLACID HOLDING COMPANY
1601 ELM ST STE 3900, DALLAS, TX 752014708
Phone: 214 880-8479

HISTORICAL FINANCIALS
Company Type: Private

Income Statement				FYE: December 31
	REVENUE ($ mil.)	NET INCOME ($ mil.)	NET PROFIT MARGIN	EMPLOYEES
12/13	4,929	47	1.0%	2
12/02	532	3	0.6%	—
12/01	579	18	3.1%	—
12/00	564	5	1.0%	—
Annual Growth	18.1%	17.5%	—	—

2013 Year-End Financials

Return on assets: 7.5%   Cash ($ mil.): 51
Return on equity: 12.8%
Current ratio: 1.40

PLACID REFINING COMPANY LLC

A calm presence in the volatile oil and gas industry Placid Refining owns and operates the Port Allen refinery in Louisiana which converts crude oil into a number of petroleum products including diesel ethanol gasoline liquid petroleum gas jet fuel and fuel oils. Placid Refining's refinery has the capacity to process 80000 barrels of crude oil per day. The company is one of the largest employers and taxpayers in West Baton Rouge Parish. Placid Refining which is controlled by Petro-Hunt distribute fuels across a dozen states in the southeastern US from Texas to Virginia and is a major supplier of jet fuel to the US military.

EXECUTIVES

Treasurer, Barry Joffrion
Auditors: HEIN & ASSOCIATES LLP DALLAS

LOCATIONS

HQ: PLACID REFINING COMPANY LLC
2101 CEDAR SPRINGS RD # 600, DALLAS, TX 752012104
Phone: 214 880-8479
Web: WWW.PLACIDREFINING.COM

COMPETITORS

CITGO Refining and Chemicals   United Refining
NuStar Energy   Valero Energy

HISTORICAL FINANCIALS
Company Type: Private

Income Statement   FYE: December 31

	REVENUE ($ mil.)	NET INCOME ($ mil.)	NET PROFIT MARGIN	EMPLOYEES
12/13	4,929	47	1.0%	200
12/11	4,699	4	0.1%	—
12/10	3,686	39	1.1%	—
12/06	2,925	128	4.4%	—
Annual Growth	7.7%	(13.1%)	—	—

2013 Year-End Financials
Return on assets: 4.2%   Cash ($ mil.): 42
Return on equity: 1.0%
Current ratio: 1.10

PLAINS COTTON COOPERATIVE ASSOCIATION

Plainly speaking most of the US cotton used by textile mills worldwide starts with the Plains Cotton Cooperative Association (PCCA). The farmer-owned co-op markets millions of bales annually for members in Oklahoma Kansas and Texas. To obtain a competitive price for their cotton PCCA takes advantage of Telmark LP's access to The Seam an online cotton marketplace that continually updates cotton prices buyer data and more. The co-op operates cotton warehouses in Texas Oklahoma and Kansas. PCCA sold its textile and apparel operations in 2014 to focus exclusively on cotton marketing and warehousing. Formed in 1953 PCCA's customers include Replay Urban Outfitters and Abercrombie & Fitch.

EXECUTIVES

Pres-Ceo, Kevin Brinkley
Chm, Eddie Smith
Exec V Pres-Fin & Treas, Sam Hill
Auditors: CROWE HORWATH LLP DALLAS TEX

LOCATIONS

HQ: PLAINS COTTON COOPERATIVE ASSOCIATION
3301 E 50TH ST, LUBBOCK, TX 794044331
Phone: 806 763-8011
Web: WWW.PCCA.COM

PRODUCTS/OPERATIONS

Selected Sales and Services
Buying cotton
Cotton gins
  Gin bookkeeping
  Gin patronage
  Marketing and invoicing
  Scale ticket software
  Support and training
  Technology solutions
Cotton producers
  Agent gins
  Cash marketing
  marketing contracts
  Pool marketing
Warehousing

COMPETITORS

Alabama Farmers   Cooperative
Calcot
Dunavant Enterprises
Greenwood Mills
International Cotton   Marketing

J.G. Boswell Co.
Parkdale Mills
Staplcotn
Weil Brothers Cotton

HISTORICAL FINANCIALS
Company Type: Private

Income Statement   FYE: June 30

	REVENUE ($ mil.)	NET INCOME ($ mil.)	NET PROFIT MARGIN	EMPLOYEES
06/17	1,373	45	3.3%	170
06/16	892	23	2.7%	—
06/15	975	25	2.6%	—
06/14	947	(36)	—	—
Annual Growth	13.2%	—	—	—

PLAINS PIPELINE, L.P.

EXECUTIVES

Ceo, Greg L Armstrong
V Pres, Harry N Pefanis
Exec V Pres, Al Swanson
Assistant Division Manager, Roddy Hughes
Board Member, Everardo Goyanes
Board Member, Taft Symonds
Manager, Charles Manis
Board Member, Gary Petersen

LOCATIONS

HQ: PLAINS PIPELINE, L.P.
333 CLAY ST STE 1600, HOUSTON, TX 770024101
Phone: 713 646-4100
Web: WWW.PLAINSALLAMERICAN.COM

HISTORICAL FINANCIALS
Company Type: Private

Income Statement   FYE: December 31

	REVENUE ($ mil.)	NET INCOME ($ mil.)	NET PROFIT MARGIN	EMPLOYEES
12/17	935	783	83.7%	200
12/16	780	621	79.6%	—
Annual Growth	19.9%	26.1%	—	—

2017 Year-End Financials
Return on assets: 8.9%   Cash ($ mil.): 8
Return on equity: 17.4%
Current ratio: 0.40

PLAN INTERNATIONAL, INC.

EXECUTIVES

Ceo, Rose Caldwell
Zone Coordinator Kissidougou P, Michel Kamano
Finance Director, Olli Jahnsson
Business Manager, Ryan Lander

Ict Manager Plan, Abdoulaye Ndiaye
Ict Manager Plan, Ben Amoussou
Director, Brittney Rocourt
Administrative Officer Plan In, Carlos Barros
Auditors: DYL & PERILLO INC PROVIDENCE

LOCATIONS

HQ: PLAN INTERNATIONAL, INC.
155 PLAN WAY STE A, WARWICK, RI 028861099
Phone: 401 294-3693
Web: WWW.PLAN-INTERNATIONAL.ORG

HISTORICAL FINANCIALS
Company Type: Private

Income Statement   FYE: June 30

	REVENUE ($ mil.)	NET INCOME ($ mil.)	NET PROFIT MARGIN	EMPLOYEES
06/15	684	(5)	—	7
06/14	657	(5)	—	—
06/12	601	29	4.9%	—
06/10	531	93	17.6%	—
Annual Growth	5.2%	—	—	—

2015 Year-End Financials
Return on assets: (-2.2%)   Cash ($ mil.): 185
Return on equity: (-3.1%)
Current ratio: 6.60

PLANO INDEPENDENT SCHOOL DISTRICT

EXECUTIVES

Exec Dir, Mark Allen
Spdt, Richard Matkin
Deputy Supt, Jeff Bailey
Assoc Supt, Jim Hirsch
Accounting Staff, Brenda Lagerlef
Assistant, Mark De Hertogh
Coordinator, Suzana Spina
High School English Teacher, Adam Dyer
Elementary Teacher, Alyson Esch
Librarian, Andrea Doerr
Student Dean, Andrea Wigginton
Auditors: WEAVER AND TIDWELL LLP DA

LOCATIONS

HQ: PLANO INDEPENDENT SCHOOL DISTRICT
2700 W 15TH ST, PLANO, TX 750757524
Phone: 469 752-8100
Web: WWW.PISD.EDU

HISTORICAL FINANCIALS
Company Type: Private

Income Statement   FYE: June 30

	REVENUE ($ mil.)	NET INCOME ($ mil.)	NET PROFIT MARGIN	EMPLOYEES
06/18	840	34	4.1%	5,610
06/17	775	288	37.2%	—
06/16	712	19	2.8%	—
06/15	669	(18)	—	—
Annual Growth	7.9%			

PLY GEM HOLDINGS, INC.

Ply Gem brings out a new side of homes. The company makes and supplies exterior building materials used in home construction and renovation primarily in the US. Its products — vinyl siding aluminum windows and doors stone veneer and fencing — are supplied to home center retailers distributors construction companies and contractors in North America. Subsidiaries include Variform (vinyl siding) Napco (vinyl and metal exterior siding and trim) Kroy Building Products (vinyl fencing) and Great Lakes Window (energy-efficient vinyl windows and patio doors). Ply Gem Holdings was founded in 2004; it was acquired by Clayton Dubilier & Rice in 2018.

Change in Company Type

In April 2018 building products manufacturer Clayton Dubilier & Rice (CD&R) completed the acquisition of Ply Gem for $2.4 billion along with another company Atrium Windows & Doors. The combined Ply Gem and Atrium companies are now a privately-held exterior products subsidiary of CD&R under the Ply Gem name. The new Ply Gem will continue to be headquartered in Cary NC.

Operations

Ply Gem divides its business into two segments: windows and doors; and siding fencing and stone.

The windows and doors segment which generates nearly 55% of the company's revenue sells its products under the Ply Gem Windows Simonton Windows Great Lakes Window and Ply Gem Canada brands.

The siding fencing and stone segment which accounts for more than 45% of total revenue sells siding and accessories (under brands such as Variform Napco and Mastic) vinyl fencing and railing and stone veneer products. The company also sells cellular PVC trim engineered slate and shake roofing and gutter protection products.

Geographic Reach

North Carolina-based Ply Gem maintains manufacturing operations in the US and Canada. The company operates about 90 facilities across both countries. The US accounts for nearly 90% of revenue with Canada and other foreign countries accounting for the remaining 10%.

Sales and Marketing

Ply Gem has a multi-channel distribution network that serves both the new construction and the home repair and remodeling sectors. The company sells its products to specialty and wholesale distributors and directly to independent building material dealers regional and national lumberyard chains retail home centers independent home improvement dealers and big box retail outlets. Its top ten customers account for more than 45% of the company's net sales. ABC Supply Co. Inc. the company's largest customer accounts for more than 10%.

Financial Performance

Ply Gem's net revenues have seen a steady increase in the past five years. Sales increased more than 7% to $2.0 billion in 2017 compared with the previous year. In the windows and doors segment a 6% increase was the result of improved market conditions in the US and Canada especially in the new construction business. Net sales for the siding fencing and stone segment saw a 9% increase with contributing factors being— higher demand for its products new business wins and higher average selling prices.

Net income fell by 9% to $68.3 million in 2017 mainly as a result of increased product costs and higher operating expenses. A 30% decrease in operating cash ($102 million compared with $145 million in 2016) was driven by higher working capital levels rising commodity costs and the company's early pay discount practices.

Strategy

Going forward Ply Gem aims to capitalize on the continued improvement in the new construction and home repair and remodeling markets. Current strategic initiatives include increasing brand equity with digital marketing initiatives and improving profitability.

With housing starts recovering and the current underinvestment in homes in the US Ply Gem believes there is significant opportunity for growth. It will focus on products targeting energy efficiency and potential cost savings for the customer.

The company has invested recently in digital marketing capabilities such as improved search engine optimization lead generation and website user experience in order to build brand equity and increase market penetration.

To boost profits Ply Gem launched a new profitability initiative entitled "2x20" during 2017 aimed at increasing net sales by at least $40 million by 2020. 2x20 activities include lean manufacturing vertical integration in its manufacturing facilities and consolidating purchases of key raw materials supplies and services. It has also centralized many back-office functions into its corporate office in Cary NC and has implemented more automation in its manufacturing processes.

EXECUTIVES

Chairman President And Ceo, Gary E. Robinette, age 70, $825,000 total compensation

Evp And Coo, John C. Wayne, age 57, $527,875 total compensation

Evp And Cfo, Shawn K. Poe, age 57, $420,000 total compensation

Svp Human Resources, David N. Schmoll, age 60, $285,700 total compensation

President U.s. Window And Door Group, Arthur W. (Art) Steinhafel, age 50

President Siding Fencing And Stone Group, John L. Buckley, age 54, $337,840 total compensation

National Sales Manager, Rick Rinshed

Vice President Sales (window Group), Steve Gore

Vice President Corporate Controller, Brian Boyle

Vice President Financial Planning And Analysis, Jennifer Ward

National Accounts Manager, Jim Ross

Senior Vice President Human Resources, Dave Schmoll

National Account Manager, John Wolma

Vice President Finance, Chris Schaefer

Auditors: KPMG LLP RALEIGH NORTH CAROL

LOCATIONS

HQ: PLY GEM HOLDINGS, INC.
5020 WESTON PKWY STE 400, CARY, NC 275132322
Phone: 919 677-3900
Web: WWW.PLYGEM.COM

2017 Sales

	$ mil.	% of total
United States	1,849	90
Canada	202	10
Other foreign countries	3	-
Total	**2,056**	**100**

PRODUCTS/OPERATIONS

2017 Sales

	$ mil.	% of total
Windows & Doors	1,086	53
Sliding Fencing & Stone	970	47
Total	**2,056**	**100**

Selected Brands

Variform Siding
Napco Siding
Mastic Siding
Mitten Siding
Performance Siding
Georgia-Pacific
Canyon Stone
Simonton Windows
Great Lakes Window
Durabuilt
Leaf Relief
Leaf Relief Snap Tight
Leaf Smart
Leaf Logic
Ply Gem Shutters & Accents
Ply Gem Fence & Rail
Ply Gem Gutters
Ply Gem Roofing
Ply Gem Stone
Ply Gem Trim & Moulding
Ply Gem Windows & Doors

Selected Products

Fence & Rail
Gutters
Siding
Steel Siding
Stone Veneer
Trim
Windows and Doors

COMPETITORS

Alsco	Louisiana-Pacific
Andersen Corporation	MI Windows and Doors
Arconic	Masco
Armstrong World Industries	Owens Corning
	Pella
Associated Materials	Royal Group
Atrium	Simonton Windows Inc.
CertainTeed	Therma-Tru
Harvey Industries	Trex Company
JELD-WEN	

HISTORICAL FINANCIALS

Company Type: Private

Income Statement				FYE: December 31
	REVENUE ($ mil.)	NET INCOME ($ mil.)	NET PROFIT MARGIN	EMPLOYEES
12/17	2,056	68	3.3%	9,000
12/16	1,911	75	3.9%	—
12/15	1,839	32	1.8%	—
12/14	1,566	(31)	—	—
Annual Growth	9.5%	—	—	—

2017 Year-End Financials

Return on assets: 5.2%   Cash ($ mil.): 71
Return on equity: 83.4%
Current ratio: 1.70

POLK COUNTY SCHOOL DISTRICT

EXECUTIVES

Spdt, Jacqueline Byrd
Occupational Specia, Amy Radano
Teacher Personnel Director, Brian Warren
Associate Superintendent, Michael Perrone Jr
Facilities Specialist, Traci Allen
Administrative Secretary, Yvette Vega
Senior Director, Carolyn Bridges
Teacher, Jane Martinez
Counselor, Lavieria Nottage
Purchasing Agent, Susan Kelley
Director of Charter Schools, Melissa Brady
Auditors: CHERRY BEKAERT LLP ORLANDO F

LOCATIONS

HQ: POLK COUNTY SCHOOL DISTRICT
1915 S FLORAL AVE, BARTOW, FL 338307124
Phone: 863 534-0500
Web: WWW.POLKSCHOOLSFL.COM

HISTORICAL FINANCIALS

Company Type: Private

Income Statement				FYE: June 30
	REVENUE ($ mil.)	NET INCOME ($ mil.)	NET PROFIT MARGIN	EMPLOYEES
06/14	871	(5)	—	3,362
06/13	827	(40)	—	—
06/12	821	(42)	—	—
Annual Growth	3.0%	—	—	—

2014 Year-End Financials

Return on assets: (-0.4%)   Cash ($ mil.): 69
Return on equity: (-0.6%)
Current ratio: —

POPULATION SERVICES INTERNATIONAL

Population Services International (PSI) goes far beyond the scope of its name. Founded in 1970 to promote global family planning PSI has established social programs thatÂ use local networks in low-income regions to distribute such lifelinesÂ as insecticide-treated mosquito nets iodized salt snake boots and insect repellent along with condoms contraceptives and pregnancy test kits. The group prides itself on using business principals to confront health issues in more than 65 countries worldwide. It reportedly has averted 4.2 millionÂ unintended pregnancies someÂ 29 million malaria cases and providedÂ 1.8-plus million clients withÂ of HIVÂ testing and counseling. PSI is also active ensuring safe water supplies.

EXECUTIVES

Vice President, Douglas Call
Vice President, Krishna Jafa
Vice President Of Finance, Marusya Lazo
Executive Vice President, Peter Clancy
Senior Vice President And Chief Operating Officer, Christine Sow
Senior Vice President Chief Strategy And Resources Officer, Michael Holscher
Managing Director Deputy, Odette Hekster

LOCATIONS

HQ: POPULATION SERVICES INTERNATIONAL
1120 19TH ST NW STE 600, WASHINGTON, DC
200363605
Phone: 202 785-0072
Web: WWW.PSI.ORG

HISTORICAL FINANCIALS

Company Type: Private

Income Statement				FYE: December 31
	REVENUE ($ mil.)	NET INCOME ($ mil.)	NET PROFIT MARGIN	EMPLOYEES
12/13	584	4	0.8%	417
12/01	121	(0)	—	—
12/00	96	3	3.4%	—
Annual Growth	14.8%	2.9%	—	—

2013 Year-End Financials

Return on assets: 10.1%   Cash ($ mil.): 210
Return on equity: 0.8%
Current ratio: 0.60

PORT OF LOS ANGELES

EXECUTIVES

Exec Dir, Gene Seroka
Environmental Manager, Lisa Cloud Ochsner
Port Police Sergeant, David Clements
Port Police Officer III, William Yocham
Auditors: MACIAS GINI & O'CONNELL LLP L

LOCATIONS

HQ: PORT OF LOS ANGELES
425 S PALOS VERDES ST, SAN PEDRO, CA
907313309
Phone: 310 732-3508
Web: WWW.PORTOFLOSANGELES.ORG

HISTORICAL FINANCIALS

Company Type: Private

Income Statement				FYE: June 30
	REVENUE ($ mil.)	NET INCOME ($ mil.)	NET PROFIT MARGIN	EMPLOYEES
06/18	490	93	19.0%	51
06/17	474	103	21.8%	—
06/16	441	99	22.4%	—
Annual Growth	5.5%	(2.9%)	—	—

2018 Year-End Financials

Return on assets: 2.0%   Cash ($ mil.): 672
Return on equity: 2.8%
Current ratio: 4.50

PORT OF SEATTLE

The Port of Seattle oversees both an airport (Seattle-Tacoma International also known as Sea-Tac) and a seaport. The agency's aviation division sees more than 33.2 million passengers a year. The seaport division serves more than 18 container steamship lines that import and export containerized and bulk cargo. It also handles calls from cruise ships. In addition the seaport division oversees commercial fishing marinas and portside commercial properties. Most of the agency's revenue comes from airport operations. The Port of Seattle is run by a five-member commission elected by King County voters.

Operations

One of the top landholders in King County the Port owns parks and public access areas cargo and container terminals and Sea-Tac airport. It also owns conference facilities at the airport and on the waterfront recreational boating marinas piers office space and storage and warehouse facilities.

Financial Performance

Operating revenues for fiscal 2013 were budgeted at $550.6 million 6% up on 2012 . Aeronautical revenues were $249.3 million (up 6%). Other operating revenues were budget for $301.3 million (7% higher than the 2012 budget) mainly due to Terminal 18 special bond refunding and higher concessions.

Strategy

Going forward the Port's projects are broadly aimed at preserving traffic to the Midwest via Seattle which other global gateways (the Panama and Suez canals and Prince Rupert's port British Columbia) threaten to divert. To this end it is pursuing cooperative opportunities between rail and highway infrastructure agencies. Concurrently the Port of Seattle is evaluating Sea-Tac airport's capacity needs. Its subsidy of Fisherman's Terminal which sustains jobs as well as the seaport's history and culture is on the table too given the cost to renovate and terminal's declining fish life. Most significant the Port is determined to continue to distinguish itself as the Green Gateway with the goal of minimizing the environmental consequences of its activities.

Company Background

In 2011 the Port marked its centennial year for moving people and cargo in and out of the Pacific Northwest.

EXECUTIVES

Cfo And Administrative Officer, Dan Thomas
Interim Ceo, Dave Soike
Managing Director Aviation Division, Lance Lyttle
Managing Director Economic Development Division, David McFadden
Managing Director Maritime Division, Lindsay Pulsifer
Vice President Of Internal Audit, Debbie Browning
Government Relations Director, Pearse Edwards
Auditors: MOSS ADAMS LLP SEATTLE WASHI

LOCATIONS

HQ: PORT OF SEATTLE
2711 ALASKAN WAY PIER 69, SEATTLE, WA
981211107
Phone: 206 728-3000
Web: WWW.PORTSEATTLE.ORG

HISTORICAL FINANCIALS

Company Type: Private

Income Statement				FYE: December 31
	REVENUE ($ mil.)	NET INCOME ($ mil.)	NET PROFIT MARGIN	EMPLOYEES
12/17	632	199	31.6%	1,515
12/16	598	41	6.9%	—
12/15	558	19	3.6%	—
12/14	534	131	24.5%	—
Annual Growth	5.7%	15.1%	—	—

2017 Year-End Financials

Return on assets: 2.7%   Cash ($ mil.): 39
Return on equity: 6.0%
Current ratio: 1.30

PORTLAND GENERAL ELECTRIC COMP

EXECUTIVES

Plant Manager, Nicholas Loos

LOCATIONS

HQ: PORTLAND GENERAL ELECTRIC COMP
33831 SE FARADAY RD, ESTACADA, OR 970238432
Phone: 503 630-6821

HISTORICAL FINANCIALS
Company Type: Private

Income Statement				FYE: December 31
	REVENUE ($ mil.)	NET INCOME ($ mil.)	NET PROFIT MARGIN	EMPLOYEES
12/17	2,009	187	9.3%	3
12/16	1,923	193	10.0%	
Annual Growth	4.5%	(3.1%)	—	—

2017 Year-End Financials
Return on assets: 2.4% Cash ($ mil.): 39
Return on equity: 7.7%
Current ratio: 1.20

PORTLAND PUBLIC SCHOOLS

EXECUTIVES

Superintendent, Carole Smith
Interim Chief of Staff, Alexander Perrins
Chief Academic Officer, Yvonne Curtis
Facilities, Adam Napier
Supervisor, Alicia Fecker
Administrative Assistant, Andrea Atherton
Teacher, Andrea Pepitone
Program Director, Andrew Johnson
Program Director Title VI Indi, Angela Morrill
George Teacher, Ben Keefer
Special Education Teacher, Beth Brod
Auditors: TALBOT KORVOLA & WARWICK LLP

LOCATIONS

HQ: PORTLAND PUBLIC SCHOOLS
501 N DIXON ST, PORTLAND, OR 972271876
Phone: 503 916-2000
Web: WWW.PPS.NET

HISTORICAL FINANCIALS
Company Type: Private

Income Statement				FYE: June 30
	REVENUE ($ mil.)	NET INCOME ($ mil.)	NET PROFIT MARGIN	EMPLOYEES
06/18	882	336	38.1%	5,244
06/17	770	(127)	—	—
06/16	744	(109)	—	—
06/15	691	255	36.9%	—
Annual Growth	8.5%	9.5%	—	—

2018 Year-End Financials
Return on assets: 22.6% Cash ($ mil.): 111
Return on equity: —
Current ratio: —

POUDRE VALLEY HEALTH CARE, INC.

Providing health care is what this Poudre Valley is all about. The not-for-profit Poudre Valley Health System (PVHS) cares for residents of Colorado western Nebraska and southern Wyoming through the Poudre Valley Hospital and the Medical Center of the Rockies. With a total of about 440 beds the two hospitals offer general medical and surgical services and trauma care. They also offer treatment centers for specialties including cancer heart brain and spine disorders. PVHS is home to the Mountain Crest Behavioral Healthcare Center which administers mental health and substance abuse treatment. PVHS is part of the Health District of Northern Larimer County; it is also part of University of Colorado Health.

Operations
The Poudre Valley Hospital features 270 patient beds while the Medical Center of the Rockies has a capacity of about 170 beds. Beyond its primary hospital campuses the health system also operates several outpatient clinics and a family medicine center that hosts a rural medicine residency program. Altogether PVHS has more than 550 physicians practicing in more than 40 specialty fields.

In addition to its joint operating agreement with the University of Colorado Hospital PVHS has formed collaborative care partnerships with local organizations including a local laser eye surgery center numerous outpatient centers for rehabilitation surgery and infusion therapy as well as home health care and home supply companies.

Geographic Reach
PVHS serves residents of Estes Park Fort Collins Greeley and Loveland Colorado as well as Larimer and Weld Counties. The system also serves customers from Cheyenne and Laramie Wyoming and Scottsbluff Nebraska.

Strategy
The organization has held a long tradition of partnering with numerous local organizations to expand its service offerings. To create a broader health organization for the Rocky Mountain region PVHS formed a joint operating agreement with University of Colorado Hospital in 2012. Together the systems are known as University of Colorado Health and are governed by a single board of directors. The hospitals continue to operate under their existing names.

Other growth efforts include the construction of a new $14.5 million emergency care center in 2012 and the opening of a new 12-bed women's and children's unit at Medical Center of the Rockies in 2013.

In 2013 it also opened the 36000-sq.-ft. Indian Peaks Medical Center in Frederick at an estimated cost of $20 million to $30 million. It includes cardiology and diagnostics departments.

Company Background
The organization was founded in 1925. Since 1995 when PVHS reorganized as a private not-for-profit health care organization local property taxes that used to go straight to PVHS have been paid to the Health District of Northern Larimer County which then uses them to fund PVHS' various activities.

EXECUTIVES

Dpt Ocs Faaompt Physical Therapy Specialist, Anthony Kinney
Director Of Him, Kendra Adams
Treasurer, Daniel Wilson

LOCATIONS

HQ: POUDRE VALLEY HEALTH CARE, INC.
2315 E HARMONY RD STE 200, FORT COLLINS, CO 805288620
Phone: 970 495-7000

PRODUCTS/OPERATIONS

Selected Services
Back Neck and Spine Care
Cancer Care
Diabetes and Endocrinology
Hyperbaric Medicine
Imaging and Radiology
Laboratory Services
Orthopedics
Pain Care and Management
Seniors' Health
Weight and Metabolism
Women's Health
Wound Care

COMPETITORS

Catholic Health Initiatives
Centura Health
Denver Health and Hospital Authority
Exempla Healthcare
HealthONE
Memorial Health System (Colorado)
North Colorado Medical Center
University of Colorado Hospital
Valley View Hospital
Wyoming Medical Center

HISTORICAL FINANCIALS
Company Type: Private

Income Statement				FYE: June 30
	REVENUE ($ mil.)	NET INCOME ($ mil.)	NET PROFIT MARGIN	EMPLOYEES
06/16	523	92	17.7%	2,800
06/15	480	98	20.6%	—
06/14	478	38	8.0%	—
Annual Growth	4.7%	56.2%	—	—

2016 Year-End Financials
Return on assets: 7.7% Cash ($ mil.): 25
Return on equity: 10.7%
Current ratio: 0.70

POWER ENGINEERS, INCORPORATED

EXECUTIVES

Chb, Ron Carrington
Corporate Governance Departmen, Rachel Moore
Treasurer, Jan James
Evp*, William Hansen
Evp, Gerry Murray
Evp*, Timothy Ostermeier
Cao-Evp*, Jim Haynes
Vp-Cfo, Chuck Kemp
Vp-Chro, Mark Mary
Svp, Holger Peller
Auditors: DELOITTE & TOUCHE LLP BOISE

LOCATIONS

HQ: POWER ENGINEERS, INCORPORATED
3940 GLENBROOK DR, HAILEY, ID 833338446
Phone: 208 788-3456
Web: WWW.POWERENG.COM

HISTORICAL FINANCIALS
Company Type: Private

Income Statement				FYE: December 31
	REVENUE ($ mil.)	NET INCOME ($ mil.)	NET PROFIT MARGIN	EMPLOYEES
12/18	466	21	4.5%	2,551
12/17	460	32	7.1%	—
12/16	398	15	3.9%	—
Annual Growth	8.1%	17.2%	—	—

Return on assets: 9.5%   Cash ($ mil.): 25
Return on equity: 18.9%
Current ratio: 2.60

POWERSOUTH ENERGY COOPERATIVE

Several hundred thousand Alabamans and Floridians get their electric power courtesy of the work of PowerSouth Energy Cooperative which provides wholesale power to its member-owners (16 electric cooperatives and four municipal distribution utilities). Its distribution members provide electric services to almost 417200 customer meters in central and southern Alabama and western Florida. PowerSouth operates a more than 2200-mile power transmission system and has more than 2000 MW of generating capacity from interests in six fossil-fueled and hydroelectric power plants.

Geographic Reach

PowerSouth serves customers in Alabama (39 counties) and Florida (10 counties).

Operations

The company owns and operates six generation facilities and holds ownership interest in an additional facility. Its diverse generating fuel mix includes natural gas coal and water (hydro). It also has compressed air energy storage technology and a disciplined fuel supply hedging program that minimizes the impact of fuel cost increases. In addition PowerSouth maintains long-term purchased power agreements to ensure economic and reliable power supply for its members.

PowerSouth serves the wholesale energy needs of electric cooperatives and municipal electric systems in Alabama and northwest Florida who in turn serve more than a million consumers. PowerSouth is dedicated to providing reliable energy at the lowest possible cost to its members.

Financial Performance

The company's revenues increased by 3% in 2013 primarily due to an increase in member revenues as a result of an increase in energy sales. The remaining increase was due to the surcharges added to the excess demand rate during 2013.

That year PowerSouth's net income decreased by 6% as the result of increased operating costs caused by higher distribution costs and administration and general expenses.

Its operating cash inflow increased to $63.5 million in 2013 (compared to $38.3 million in 2012) due to a rise in account receivables and inventories.

Strategy

To meet future demand and tightening environmental regulations the company is looking to diversify and expand its power production assets with an emphasis on cleaner energy plants. PowerSouth's long-term energy plans include a 20-year contract for 125 MW of nuclear power from two Vogtle Units being built by the Municipal Energy Authority of Georgia near Augusta and due to come onstream in 2016 and 2017. The company is also investing in wind power and biomass-to-energy initiatives.

Company Background

PowersSouth is owned and managed by it 20 distribution members.

The company once provided propane but sold its Cooperative Propane unit in 2011 to focus on its core power businesses.

In 2008 Alabama Electric Cooperative changed its name to PowerSouth Energy Cooperative to better reflect its service territory (Alabama and Florida) and its opportunities for future growth.

Founded in 1941 as Alabama Electric Cooperative the coop promotes a strong economic development program aimed at bringing industry into both Alabama and Florida.

EXECUTIVES

Vice President Corporate Affairs, Beth Woodard
Vice President Information Technology, Lewis Jeffers
Vice President Administration, Elizabeth Woodard
Department Secretary, Angela Kelly
Auditors: BKD LLP OKLAHOMA CITY OKLAH

LOCATIONS

HQ: POWERSOUTH ENERGY COOPERATIVE
2027 E THREE NOTCH ST, ANDALUSIA, AL 364212427
Phone: 334 427-3000
Web: WWW.POWERSOUTH.COM

PRODUCTS/OPERATIONS

View Archived What Charts | Edit 2013 Sales

	% of total
Electric	
Cooperatives	93
Municipalities	6
Other	1
Total	**100**

HISTORICAL FINANCIALS

Company Type: Private

Income Statement				FYE: December 31
	REVENUE ($ mil.)	NET INCOME ($ mil.)	NET PROFIT MARGIN	EMPLOYEES
12/17	588	9	1.6%	640
12/16	596	13	2.2%	—
12/15	622	17	2.7%	—
12/14	675	16	2.5%	—
Annual Growth	(4.5%)	(17.0%)	—	—

2017 Year-End Financials

Return on assets: 0.6%   Cash ($ mil.): 49
Return on equity: 2.8%
Current ratio: 1.40

PRAIRIE FARMS DAIRY, INC.

Prairie Farms Dairy is very cooperative. With some 700 dairy farmer/members the cooperative offers a full line of retail and food service dairy products. It turns raw milk into fresh fluid cultured and frozen dairy products under the Prairie Farms label. It also makes juices and ice cream novelties. The company's customers include food drug and convenience stores mass merchandisers schools restaurants and other food service operators. Located in Carlinville Illinois it is the managing partner for joint ventures with smaller regional dairies. It makes its products at 24 Prairie Farms-owned plants and 13 joint-venture plants which are located throughout the midwestern and southern areas of the US.

Operations

From its 700 member farms Prairie Farms sources milk products for its array of food products. It produces all varieties of milk butter cottage cheese cream ice cream yogurt and other diary-based products. It also goes outside its core to produce and sell teas juices and iced coffee

To get its dairy products to market the co-op relies on subsidiaries Hawthorne-Mellody Distributors in Chicago and Tom David & Sons in Detroit.

In addition to manufacturing diary foods co-packing is a big part of Prairie Farms' operation. Approximately 50% of the co-operative's sales come from packing non-Prairie Farm brands. The co-op's PFD Supply and GMS Transportation non-dairy subsidiaries distribute products for fast-food chains including McDonald's Dairy Queen and Church's Chicken.

Geographic Reach

Prairie Farms and its subsidiaries manufacture dairy products at 24 co-op-owned plants as 13 joint venture plants in Arkansas Illinois Indiana Iowa Kansas Kentucky Michigan Mississippi Missouri Nebraska Oklahoma Ohio Tennessee and Wisconsin.

Sales and Marketing

Prairie Farms' products are for sale through a variety of retail grocery store foodservice drug store mass merchandiser and school locations in the same states in which it has production facilities. It sells about half of its product under the Prairie Farms brand name and the co-op also sells products through partners Central Hiland Dairy Foods Ice Cream Specialties Turner and Muller.

Company Background

The cooperative dates back to 1932 when Illinois farmers formed a statewide organization Illinois Producers Creameries to market and sell cream. In 1938 it became Prairie Farms Dairy.

EXECUTIVES

Director Information Services, Mark Harris
Ceo, Fletcher Gourley
National Accounts Manager, Chad Moss
Vice President Procurement, Lee Gary
Auditors: BKD LLP ST LOUIS MO

LOCATIONS

HQ: PRAIRIE FARMS DAIRY, INC.
3744 STAUNTON RD, EDWARDSVILLE, IL 620256936
Phone: 618 659-5700
Web: WWW.PRAIRIEFARMS.COM

Selected Areas of Distribution
Arkansas
Illinois
Indiana
Iowa
Kansas
Kentucky
Michigan
Mississippi
Missouri
Nebraska
Ohio
Oklahoma
Tennessee
Wisconsin

PRODUCTS/OPERATIONS

Branded Partners
Hiland Dairy Foods Company
Ice Cream Specialties
Madison Farms Butter
Muller-Pinehurst Dairy
Turner Dairy

Selected Products
Butter
Cultured dairy products
  Cottage cheese (regular low fat and fat-free; small and large curd)
  Dips
  Sour cream

Yogurt (regular low fat and fat-free)
Fluid milk products
   Buttermilk
   Cream
   Egg nog (seasonal)
   Milk (regular low fat and fat-free)
   Flavored milk
Frozen desserts
   Frozen yogurt
   Ice cream (regular low fat and fat-free)
   Novelties
   Sherbet
Juices drinks and iced tea

COMPETITORS

Associated Milk	Foremost Farms
Producers	Friendly's Ice Cream
Dairy Farmers of	HP Hood
America	Land O'Lakes
Darigold Inc.	Quality Chekd
Dean Foods	Rockview Dairies
Dreyer's	Wells' Dairy
Farmland Dairies	

HISTORICAL FINANCIALS

Company Type: Private

Income Statement				FYE: September 30
	REVENUE ($ mil.)	NET INCOME ($ mil.)	NET PROFIT MARGIN	EMPLOYEES
09/13	1,721	14	0.8%	1,965
09/12	1,649	38	2.4%	—
09/11	1,607	28	1.7%	—
Annual Growth	3.5%	(28.9%)	—	—

2013 Year-End Financials

Return on assets: 1.9%   Cash ($ mil.): 12
Return on equity: 3.4%
Current ratio: 1.20

PRATT CORRUGATED HOLDINGS, INC.

LOCATIONS

HQ: PRATT CORRUGATED HOLDINGS, INC.
1800 SARASOT BUS PKWY NE C, CONYERS, GA
300135775
Phone: 770 918-5678

HISTORICAL FINANCIALS

Company Type: Private

Income Statement				FYE: June 30
	REVENUE ($ mil.)	NET INCOME ($ mil.)	NET PROFIT MARGIN	EMPLOYEES
06/18	2,518	87	3.5%	116
06/17	2,360	65	2.8%	
Annual Growth	6.7%	33.4%	—	—

2018 Year-End Financials

Return on assets: 9.3%   Cash ($ mil.): 86
Return on equity: 18.8%
Current ratio: 1.30

PRECISION CASTPARTS CORP.

Precision Castparts Corp. (PCC) is a maker of investment castings and forged and airframe products that have applications in industries from aerospace and energy to machinery and medical implants. Products include metal components for aircraft engines industrial gas turbines (IGT) medical implants unmanned aerial vehicles (UAVs) and other industrial applications. The company also makes metal forgings including seamless pipe used in power plants downhole casings and tubing pipe for oil and gas production and aerospace and defense applications. PCC is also a leading manufacturer of fasteners and fastening systems used in the aerospace construction automotive machinery and energy industries. The aerospace sector accounts for most of PCC's sales. The company is a subsidiary of Berkshire Hathaway.

HISTORY

The history of Precision Castparts Corp. (PCC) is not as precise as its castings. The Oregon Saw Company was founded in 1949 and sold in 1953; its buyer wanted neither the future PCC nor a power tools unit so the two became Omark Industries. In 1956 a buyer purchased the power tool business but wasn't interested in castings; that operation was spun off as Precision Castparts Corp.

In the early 1950s a group of Oregon Saw's casting employees developed a process for producing parts as large as 60 inches by use of investment casting making products that rivaled the strength of forged and machined parts at a fraction of the cost. After a two-year search they landed their first aerospace customer — Air Research Corp. — with many to follow. The higher operating temperatures generated by aircraft engines led the company to buy a vacuum furnace in 1959 to fabricate parts that could tolerate greater heat; two more vacuum furnaces were added and sales vaulted toward $10 million by 1967. PCC went public in 1968 and continued to grow. In 1976 the company acquired Centaur Cast Alloys (small investment castings UK) to make parts for the European aerospace industry. By that time General Electric (GE) and Pratt & Whitney accounted for most of PCC's business. Edward Cooley who had masterminded the company's growth since incorporation forged ahead with plans to double production capacity.

In 1980 the airline industry crashed but PCC's sales held at about $90 million. Structural airplane products soon picked up and in 1984 the company bought two titanium foundries in France. To diversify it added TRW's cast airfoils (used in aircraft engines and industrial gas turbines) division in 1986. That acquisition renamed PCC Airfoils increased PCC's annual sales by about 80%; sales reached $443 million by 1989.

The company broadened its offerings again in 1991 when it acquired Advanced Forming Technology which made small complex metal-injection molded parts used in everything from adding machines to military ordnance. The early 1990s recession hit the airline industry and sales dropped. Cooley retired as chairman in 1994 and GE veteran William McCormick replaced him. The next year PCC acquired Quamco Inc. (industrial tools and machines). In 1996 PCC flowed into the fluid management market with the acquisition of NEWFLO for about $300 million.

In 1997 PCC spent $437 million to acquire seven more companies that helped boost sales

75% from 1996 levels. The next year it purchased four metalworking companies that served industries other than aerospace. Having reduced dependence on sales to the aerospace industry to just over 50% PCC began consolidating operations and closing plants to reduce costs.

The company continued to diversify through acquisitions in 1999 but it also expanded its aerospace operations with the purchase of Wyman-Gordon a leading maker of advanced metal forgings for the aerospace market. PCC's 2000 acquisitions included the aerospace division of United Engineering Forgings and Germany-based Convey Engineering (heavy-duty valves). The next year the company bought the assets of Netherlands-based Wouter Witzel and the US's Drop Dies and Forgings Company (renamed Wyman-Gordon Cleveland). In 2002 PCC bought the rest of Western Australian Specialty Alloys (casting and forging alloys) for $27.6 million in cash and PCC shares.

In 2003 Precision Castparts' PCC Structurals unit reached a $400 million agreement with Rolls-Royce to supply large titanium and steel castings. That year the company acquired SPS Technologies a producer of fasteners and other metal components for the aerospace automotive and industrial markets. In 2004 subsidiary SPS Aerospace Fasteners signed a four-year deal with Airbus worth about $72 million to supply collars nuts studs and titanium pins to Airbus plants across Europe.

PCC acquired Air Industries Corporation in early 2005. In 2006 PCC bought Special Metals Corporation (SMC) a maker of nickel alloys and super alloys for $295 million in cash and the assumption of $245 million in SMC debt. PCC intended to use SMC's product as raw materials for its own aircraft engine components. SMC also served the automotive chemical and power generation industries.

Later in 2006 PCC bought Shur-Lok Corporation a manufacturer of aerospace fasteners for about $110 million. The acquisition combined with the 2005 purchase of Air Industries Corporation helped to further PCC's desire to grow its airframe fasteners business.

Early in 2007 PCC completed the purchase of GSC a leading maker of aluminum and steel structural investment casting for the aerospace energy and medical markets. It also acquired Cherry Aerospace which expanded its fastener products portfolio.

In 2009 the company acquired Carlton Forge Works which makes aircraft engines for Boeing and Airbus; California-based Arcturus Manufacturing (hammer forging operations) was included in the transaction. PCC also picked up Airdrome Holdings (fluid fittings) Fatigue Technology (cold expansion technology) and Hackney Ladish (forged pipe fittings) in 2009.

In late summer 2011 PPC purchased Primus International a maker of complex metal industrial parts and assemblies. Its products (machined aluminum and titanium components used in aircraft wings fuselages and engine-related assemblies) cater to Boeing Airbus and other aerospace OEMs. The $900 million deal furthered the company's commitment to the global aerospace industry. In a similar vein the company obtained Unison Engine Components (operating as Tru-Form Rings) from GE Aviation in mid-2011. Tru-Form made flash-welded and cold-rolled rings with jet engine as well as gas turbine applications.

PCC also acquired RathGibson which makes tubing for the oil and gas chemical/petrochemical power-generation and other markets in 2012.

To expand both its Fasteners and Forged Products segments PCC acquired the aerostructures and industrial products businesses of Héroux-Devtek for about CAD$300 million (about $295.5 million) in 2012. Among other benefits the acquisition expanded the company's product line for such OEMs as Lockheed Bombardier and Gulf-stream. PCC also inked a deal to purchase the Synchronous Aerospace Group business of private investment firm Littlejohn & Co. in late 2012.

EXECUTIVES

Evp And Cfo, Shawn R. Hagel, $687,500 total compensation
Chairman And Ceo, Mark Donegan, $1,585,000 total compensation
Svp And President Airframe Products, Alan J. (Al) Power
Evp And President Wyman-gordon, Andrew V. Masterman, $592,500 total compensation
Vp And Cio, Byron J. Gaddis
Evp, Steven G. (Steve) Hackett, $708,750 total compensation
Svp And General Counsel, Ruth A. Beyer, $569,000 total compensation
President Aerostructures Products, Joseph I. Snowden, $356,347 total compensation
Svp And President Pcc Airfoils, John P. O'Neill
Svp And President Timet And Special Metals, James R. Pieron
Vice President, Mark Ellis
Vice President, Geoffrey Hawkes
Senior Vice President, Ross Lienhart
Secretary, Russell Pattee
Auditors: DELOITTE & TOUCHE LLP PORTLAN

LOCATIONS

HQ: PRECISION CASTPARTS CORP.
4650 SW MCDAM AVE STE 300, PORTLAND, OR 97239
Phone: 503 946-4800
Web: WWW.PRECAST.COM

PRODUCTS/OPERATIONS

Selected Products and Services

Fasteners
Advanced forming technology
E/One (for the disposal of residential sanitary waste)
J&L fiber services (for pulp and paper industry)
PCC Precision Tool Group
SPS aerospace fasteners (for commercial/military aircraft)
SPS engineered fasteners (high strength for automotive and construction applications)
Forged products
Special Metals Corporation
Wyman-Gordon Forgings
Investment Cast Products
PCC Airfoils (high-temperature blades and vanes)
PCC Structurals (structural investment castings)
Specialty materials and alloys (alloys waxes and metal processing for investment casting)

COMPETITORS

ATI Ladish	Hitachi Metals
Allegheny Technologies	Kennametal
Arconic	LISI
Carpenter Technology	Mettis Aerospace
Chicago Rivet	SOURIAU PA&E
Crane Co.	Swagelok
Curtiss-Wright	Teleflex
ESCO	ThyssenKrupp
Farwest Steel Corporation	United Technologies
Federal Screw Works	Universal Stainless
Georg Fischer	V & M Tubes (USA)
Haynes International	Volvo Aero

HISTORICAL FINANCIALS

Company Type: Private

Income Statement   FYE: January 3

	REVENUE ($ mil.)	NET INCOME ($ mil.)	NET PROFIT MARGIN	EMPLOYEES
01/16*	7,002	817	11.7%	30,100
03/15	10,005	1,533	15.3%	—
03/14	9,616	1,784	18.6%	—
03/13	8,377	1,429	17.1%	—
Annual Growth	(5.8%)	(17.0%)		

*Fiscal year change

2016 Year-End Financials

Return on assets: 4.0%   Cash ($ mil.): 343
Return on equity: 7.0%
Current ratio: 3.90

PREMIER HEALTHCARE ALLIANCE, L.P.

EXECUTIVES

MBR-Ceo, Susan Devore
MBR-Chb*, Glenn Steel Jr
MBR-V Chb*, Dennis Vonderfecht
Coo*, Michael Alkire
Cfo*, Craig McKasson
Ceo*, Richard A Norling
Sr V Pres*, Ann D Rhoads
Vice-President Information Ser, Larry D Grandia
Lawson Edi Administrat, Rory Flood
Business Continuity and Disast, David A Shimberg
Data Specialist/Membership Gro, Joseph Lawrence

LOCATIONS

HQ: PREMIER HEALTHCARE ALLIANCE, L.P.
13034 BALNTYN CORP PL, CHARLOTTE, NC 282771498
Phone: 704 357-0022
Web: WWW.PREMIERINC.COM

HISTORICAL FINANCIALS

Company Type: Private

Income Statement   FYE: June 30

	REVENUE ($ mil.)	NET INCOME ($ mil.)	NET PROFIT MARGIN	EMPLOYEES
06/12	590	326	55.3%	199
06/11	679	311	45.8%	—
06/09	1,830	0	—	—
Annual Growth	—18233.3%		—	—

2012 Year-End Financials

Return on assets: 72.7%   Cash ($ mil.): 129
Return on equity: 92.9%
Current ratio: 5.30

PREMISE HEALTH HOLDING CORP.

EXECUTIVES

Ceo, Edward Stuart Clark
Coo, Trent Riley
Cfo, Shannon Farrington
Pres, Jami Doucette
Chief Information Officer, Haden McWhorter
Chief Human Resources Officer, Elizebeth Reimer
Chief Compliance Officer, Dana Fields
Chief Information Security Off, Joey Johnson
Exec V Pres, Peter Vasquez
Exec V Pres, Ed McNamara
Operations, Beth Ratliff
Auditors: RSM US LLP CHICAGO ILLINOIS

LOCATIONS

HQ: PREMISE HEALTH HOLDING CORP.
5500 MARYLAND WAY STE 200, BRENTWOOD, TN 370274973
Phone: 615 468-6562
Web: WWW.PREMISEHEALTH.COM

HISTORICAL FINANCIALS

Company Type: Private

Income Statement   FYE: December 31

	REVENUE ($ mil.)	NET INCOME ($ mil.)	NET PROFIT MARGIN	EMPLOYEES
12/17	685	7	1.0%	4,500
12/16	630	(2)	—	—
12/15	581	0	0.0%	—
12/14	303	(14)	—	—
Annual Growth	31.2%	—	—	—

2017 Year-End Financials

Return on assets: 2.1%   Cash ($ mil.): 37
Return on equity: 6.4%
Current ratio: 2.20

PRESBYTERIAN HOSPITAL

EXECUTIVES

Ceo, Carl Armato
Pres*, Lynn Bodgs
Coordinator, Jacqueline Vaughn
Coordinator, Rachel Karo
Administrative Assistant, Clarissa Price
Transcription Supervisor, Debra O Hara
Supervisor, Cynthia Jackson
Registered Nurse, Suzanne Smith
Registered Nurse, Melanie Martin
Auditor, Monique Huntley
Registered Nurse Anesthetist, Jason Driggers

LOCATIONS

HQ: PRESBYTERIAN HOSPITAL
200 HAWTHORNE LN, CHARLOTTE, NC 282042528
Phone: 704 384-4000
Web: WWW.NOVANTHEALTHIMAGING.COM

HISTORICAL FINANCIALS
Company Type: Private

Income Statement				FYE: December 31
	REVENUE ($ mil.)	NET INCOME ($ mil.)	NET PROFIT MARGIN	EMPLOYEES
12/09	688	68	10.0%	3,100
12/08	500	18	3.7%	—
Annual Growth	37.6%	270.7%	—	—

2009 Year-End Financials

Return on assets: —
Return on equity: 10.0%
Current ratio: —

Cash ($ mil.): —

PRESBYTERIAN MEDICAL CENTER OF THE UNIVERSITY OF PENNSYLVANIA HEALTH SYSTEM

EXECUTIVES

Exec Dir, Michele Volpe
Program Director, Jeanmarie Perch
Operations Manager, Bob Russell
Executive Director Nurse, Diane Maccarone
Operations Manager, Karen Greenfield
Associate Professor of Clinica, Martin Bohnenkamp
Clinical Assistant Professor O, Michael Colucciello
Staff Nurse, Rasheda Peoples
Internist, Andrew W Maier
PA C, Dawn Carson
Assistant Professor, Dennis L Sprecher

LOCATIONS

HQ: PRESBYTERIAN MEDICAL CENTER OF THE UNIVERSITY OF PENNSYLVANIA HEALTH SYSTEM
51 N 39TH ST, PHILADELPHIA, PA 191042692
Phone: 215 662-8000
Web: WWW.PENNMEDICINE.ORG

HISTORICAL FINANCIALS
Company Type: Private

Income Statement				FYE: June 30
	REVENUE ($ mil.)	NET INCOME ($ mil.)	NET PROFIT MARGIN	EMPLOYEES
06/15	546	(0)	—	1,370
06/14	445	21	4.7%	—
06/13	429	7	1.7%	—
06/05	301	(1)	—	—
Annual Growth	6.2%	—	—	—

PRESSURE VESSEL SERVICE, INC.

EXECUTIVES

Pres, James B Nicholson
V Pres, James M Nicholson
V Pres, Allan Schlumberger
V Pres, David A Nicholson
V Pres-Cfo, Candee M Saferian
Minibulk Account Representativ, Bill Rivers
Business Director, Jeff Stein
Manager, Pete Becker
Director, Beth Bania
Sales Staff, Becky Robb
Payroll Staff, Sonya Dotson

LOCATIONS

HQ: PRESSURE VESSEL SERVICE, INC.
10900 HARPER AVE, DETROIT, MI 482133364
Phone: 313 921-1200
Web: WWW.PVSCHEMICALS.COM

HISTORICAL FINANCIALS
Company Type: Private

Income Statement				FYE: December 31
	REVENUE ($ mil.)	NET INCOME ($ mil.)	NET PROFIT MARGIN	EMPLOYEES
12/15	497	6	1.4%	800
12/12	566	21	3.8%	—
12/11	461	12	2.6%	—
12/10	356	10	2.8%	—
Annual Growth	6.9%	(7.5%)	—	—

PRINCE GEORGE'S COUNTY PUBLIC SCHOOLS

EXECUTIVES

Ceo, Kevin Maxwell
Assoc Supt Budget & Fin, Dr Kenneth Brown
Health Professional, William Kurtz
Security Staff, Clifford Mack
Staff, Georgene Arneson
Teacher, Charla Gillespie
Analyst, Patrick Miller
Human Resources Coordinator, Kellee Christian
Secretary, Lisa Huff
Administrative Assistant, Theresa Long
Teacher, Andrew Hoffman
Auditors: CLIFTONLARSONALLEN LLP BALTIM

LOCATIONS

HQ: PRINCE GEORGE'S COUNTY PUBLIC SCHOOLS
14201 SCHOOL LN, UPPER MARLBORO, MD 207722866
Phone: 301 952-6000
Web: WWW.PERRYWOODPTA.COM

HISTORICAL FINANCIALS
Company Type: Private

Income Statement				FYE: June 30
	REVENUE ($ mil.)	NET INCOME ($ mil.)	NET PROFIT MARGIN	EMPLOYEES
06/14	1,932	(6)	—	22,000
06/13	1,966	43	2.2%	—
06/11	1,855	3	0.2%	—
06/07	1,627	13	0.8%	—
Annual Growth	2.5%	—	—	—

PRINCE WILLIAM COUNTY PUBLIC SCHOOLS

EXECUTIVES

Supt, Steven Walts
Assistant Superintendent, J Keith Johnson
Safety/Security Director, Ronald Crowe
Staff, Sandy Reuse
Tech Prep Coordinator, Douglas Wright
Coordinator, Neil Bagnell
Facilities, Pat Hill
Bookkeeper, Barbara Boyd
Supervisor, Ben Swecker
Teacher, Jeannie Brumagim
Teacher, Kristina Nelson
Auditors: CHERRY BEKAERT LLP TYSONS COR

LOCATIONS

HQ: PRINCE WILLIAM COUNTY PUBLIC SCHOOLS
14715 BRISTOW RD, MANASSAS, VA 201123945
Phone: 703 791-7200
Web: WWW.PWCS.EDU

HISTORICAL FINANCIALS
Company Type: Private

Income Statement				FYE: June 30
	REVENUE ($ mil.)	NET INCOME ($ mil.)	NET PROFIT MARGIN	EMPLOYEES
06/13	1,048	23	2.3%	8,907
06/12	968	(18)	—	—
06/11	887	(66)	—	—
Annual Growth	8.7%	—	—	—

PRISMA HEALTH-UPSTATE

From education and research to primary care and surgery Upstate Affiliate Organization (dba Prisma Health-Upstate formerly Greenville Hospital System) is out to keep residents of the "Golden Strip" (the corridor connecting Charlotte North Carolina and Atlanta) healthy. Originally founded in 1912 the system encompasses eight inpatient hospitals and more than 100 outpatient facilities. Its flagship facility is Prisma Health Greenville Memorial Hospital a referral and academic medical center with more than 800 beds; other facilities include several smaller community hospitals a nursing home and a long-term acute care hospital. Greenville Hospital System merged with Palmetto Health in 2017; the combined system rebranded as Prisma Health in early 2019.

Operations

Prisma Health-Upstate offers a full range of services including a primary care physician network outpatient services and home health care.

The system has teaching affiliations with Medical University of South Carolina and University of South Carolina Medical School and nursing school affiliations with Clemson University and Bob Jones University. Prisma Health-Upstate offers residency programs in about a dozen specialties including internal medicine OB-GYN and vascular surgery. It also performs extensive medical research in partnership with pharmaceutical companies in areas including oncology pediatric oncology women's health cardiology and vascular disease.

Prisma Cancer Institute (formerly GHS Cancer Institute) a regional leader in cancer care offers cancer treatment and prevention trials through the Community Clinical Oncology Program. It also offers Phase 1 clinical trials genetic counseling a blood and marrow transplant program and a number of patient-specific programs.

Strategy

In an effort to reduce unnecessary trips to the emergency room Prisma Health-Upstate has been opening several MD360 urgent care clinics. By diverting patients away from the ER for after-hours and non-emergency health problems GHS hopes to reduce health care costs and increase access to medical care.

Mergers and Acquisitions

In 2017 Greenville Hospital System joined forces with Palmetto Health to create South Carolina's largest health care system. The combined company rebranded itself as Prisma Health in early 2019. Greenville Hospital System became Prisma Health-Upstate.

EXECUTIVES

Vp Information Services And Cio, Rich Rogers
President And Ceo, Michael C. Riordan
Evp And Coo, Gregory J. Rusnak
Evp Medical And Academic Affairs; Dean University Of South Carolina School Of Medicine Greenville, Jerry R. Youkey
Vp Chief Of Staff; System Chief Learning Officer, Tod N. Tappert
Vp Financial Services And Cfo, Terri T. Newsom
Vp Clinical Integration And Chief Medical Officer, Angelo Sinopoli
Vp Physician Engagement And Chief Academic Officer; President Ghs Clinical University, Spence M. Taylor
Vp Patient Care Services And Chief Nursing Officer, Michelle Taylor Smith
President University Medical Group, William Schmidt
Director Of Pharmacy, Fred Bender
Pharmacy Manager, Richard Capps
Director Of Nursing, Cynthia Trout
Senior Vice President Human Resources, Mary Martin
Director Of Clinical Services And Operations, Julie Martin
Vice President Information Services And Cio, Richard Rogers
Vice President, Bruce Cantrell
Medical Director, Lynn Teague
Medical Director, Parampal Bhullar
Director Of Nursing, Henry Stubbs
Medical Director, Meenu Jindal
Pharmd Bcps Title: Clinical Assistant Professor, John Howard

Medical Director, Zachary George
Medical Director Of Business Health, Sandra Hardee
Vice Chairman, Margaret L. Jenkins
Chairman, William M. Webster
Secretary, Nancy Owings
Unit Secretary, Jessica Mcmahan
Secretary, Leah Belle
Board Member, Meg Jewell
Unit Secretary, Kinetra Ware
Unit Secretary, Shanna Childs

LOCATIONS

HQ: PRISMA HEALTH-UPSTATE
 701 GROVE RD, GREENVILLE, SC 296054210
Phone: 864 455-7000
Web: WWW.GHS.ORG

PRODUCTS/OPERATIONS

2015 Sales

	$ mil.	% of total
Net patient services	1,973	96
Other operating revenues	82	4
Total	**2,056**	**100**

Selected Operations

Baptist Easley Hospital (with Palmetto Health Easley)
Greenville Memorial Hospital (tertiary academic and referral medical center)
Greer Memorial Hospital (Greer acute care hospital)
Hillcrest Memorial Hospital (Simpsonville general acute care hospital)
Laurens County Memorial Hospital (Clinton)
North Greenville Hospital (long-term acute care hospital)
Oconee Memorial Hospital (Seneca inpatient and outpatient services)
Patewood Memorial Hospital (Greenville inpatient elective hospital and outpatient center)

Selected Services

Behavioral Health
Cancer Institute
Children's Hospital
Heart & Vascular Institute
Medicine
Orthopaedics & Neurosurgery
Radiology
Rehabilitation
Surgery
Women's Health

COMPETITORS

AnMed Health	MCG Health
Blue Ridge HealthCare	Novant Health
Bon Secours Health	Piedmont Athens
CaroMont	Regional
Doctors Hospital of Augusta	Spartanburg Regional Healthcare System
Grace Hospital	St. Mary's Health Care
Gwinnett Health System	Walton Rehabilitation
Laurens County Hospital	Hospital

HISTORICAL FINANCIALS

Company Type: Private

Income Statement — FYE: September 30

	REVENUE ($ mil.)	NET INCOME ($ mil.)	NET PROFIT MARGIN	EMPLOYEES
09/13	1,001	80	8.1%	7,200
09/05	789	21	2.7%	—
09/04	789	21	2.7%	—
09/03	754	52	7.0%	—
Annual Growth	2.9%	4.4%	—	—

2013 Year-End Financials

Return on assets: —
Return on equity: 8.1%
Current ratio: —
Cash ($ mil.): —

PRO PETROLEUM, INC.

EXECUTIVES

Pres, Marcus Griffin
Treas-Cfo, Don Hayden
Stkhldr, B R Griffin
Marketing Assistant, Tammy Snyder
Manager, Wayne Barron
Auditors: GARRETT AND SWANN LLP LUBBOC

LOCATIONS

HQ: PRO PETROLEUM, INC.
 4710 4TH ST, LUBBOCK, TX 794164900
Phone: 806 795-8785
Web: WWW.PROPETROLEUM.COM

HISTORICAL FINANCIALS

Company Type: Private

Income Statement — FYE: December 31

	REVENUE ($ mil.)	NET INCOME ($ mil.)	NET PROFIT MARGIN	EMPLOYEES
12/17	1,075	17	1.6%	150
12/15	1,063	5	0.5%	—
12/14	1,701	4	0.3%	—
12/13	1,815	12	0.7%	—
Annual Growth	(12.3%)	9.4%	—	—

2017 Year-End Financials

Return on assets: 10.6%
Return on equity: 29.1%
Current ratio: 1.30
Cash ($ mil.): 21

PRODUCTION TECHNOLOGIES, INC.

EXECUTIVES

Chm, John Maclennon
Ceo, Mark Utley
V Pres, Michael Lundequam
Sales and Marketing Staff, Martha Timmers
Manager, Martha Smith

LOCATIONS

HQ: PRODUCTION TECHNOLOGIES, INC.
 7651 WASHINGTON AVE S, EDINA, MN 554392417
Phone: 952 944-1076
Web: WWW.PTIMN.COM

HISTORICAL FINANCIALS

Company Type: Private

Income Statement — FYE: December 31

	REVENUE ($ mil.)	NET INCOME ($ mil.)	NET PROFIT MARGIN	EMPLOYEES
12/16	3,289	580	17.6%	25
12/15	3,488	719	20.6%	—
12/14	3,880	348	9.0%	—
12/11	4	0	9.8%	—
Annual Growth	280.1%	327.2%	—	—

PROVIDENCE HEALTH & SERVICES

EXECUTIVES

Ceo, Rod Hochman
Pres- Chief Dev Officer, Laurie Kelley
Exec V Pres-Cfo, Todd Hofheins
Technology, Henry Morgan
Program Manager, Mark Sizemore
Officer, Matt Price
Director of Operations, Ruth M Arevalo
Administrative Assistant, Alexander Jackson
Coordinator, Mayra Graves
Senior, Alitha Jenkins
Security Engineering Consultan, Diana Bullion
Auditors: KPMG LLP SEATTLE WA

LOCATIONS

HQ: PROVIDENCE HEALTH & SERVICES
1801 LIND AVE SW, RENTON, WA 980573368
Phone: 425 525-3355
Web: WWW.PROVIDENCE.ORG

HISTORICAL FINANCIALS
Company Type: Private

Income Statement				FYE: December 31
	REVENUE ($ mil.)	NET INCOME ($ mil.)	NET PROFIT MARGIN	EMPLOYEES
12/15	14,433	49	0.3%	9,700
12/12	280	14	5.3%	—
12/08	7,026	(156)	—	—
12/07	6,348	434	6.8%	—
Annual Growth	10.8%	(23.8%)	—	—

2015 Year-End Financials

Return on assets: 0.3%   Cash ($ mil.): 729
Return on equity: 0.6%
Current ratio: 1.40

PROVIDENCE HEALTH & SERVICES - OREGON

EXECUTIVES

Pres-Ceo, John Koster
Sr V Pres-Cfo, Mike Butler
Pres, Rodney Hochman
SEC, Cindy Strauss
Treas, Todd Hofheins
Proj Coordinator, Jeanette Staley
Coordinator, Sandy Tingley
Regional Manager, Tamar Sarid
Analyst Senior Epic Access, Kecia Atchley
Regional Coding Supervisor, Teresa Benson
Access Supervisor, Schmidt Susan
Auditors: CLARK NUBER PS BELLEVUE WA

LOCATIONS

HQ: PROVIDENCE HEALTH & SERVICES - OREGON
1801 LIND AVE SW, RENTON, WA 980573368
Phone: 425 525-3355
Web: WWW.PROVIDENCE.ORG

HISTORICAL FINANCIALS
Company Type: Private

Income Statement				FYE: December 31
	REVENUE ($ mil.)	NET INCOME ($ mil.)	NET PROFIT MARGIN	EMPLOYEES
12/17	3,479	781	22.5%	8,511
12/09	2,057	57	2.8%	—
12/08	73	7	10.5%	—
Annual Growth	53.6%	67.2%		

2017 Year-End Financials

Return on assets: 24.4%   Cash ($ mil.): 327
Return on equity: 29.7%
Current ratio: 3.00

PROVIDENCE HEALTH & SERVICES-WASHINGTON

EXECUTIVES

Pres-Ceo, Michael Butler
Treas*, Jo Ann Escasa-Haigh
Corp SEC*, Cindy Strauss
Asst Corp SEC*, John Whipple
Asst SEC*, Shannon Dwyer
Asst SEC For Enrollment*, Donald Anderson Jr
Asst Corp SEC*, Tammy Teodosio
Real Estate Manager, Teresa Peterson
Auditors: CLARK NUBER PS BELLEVUE WA

LOCATIONS

HQ: PROVIDENCE HEALTH & SERVICES-WASHINGTON
1801 LIND AVE SW 9016, RENTON, WA 980573368
Phone: 425 525-3355
Web: WWW.2.PROVIDENCE.ORG

HISTORICAL FINANCIALS
Company Type: Private

Income Statement				FYE: December 31
	REVENUE ($ mil.)	NET INCOME ($ mil.)	NET PROFIT MARGIN	EMPLOYEES
12/09	3,178	(37)	—	9,700
12/08	26	(0)	—	—
12/07	6,348	434	6.8%	—
12/06	2,055	113	5.5%	—
Annual Growth	15.6%	—	—	—

2009 Year-End Financials

Return on assets: (-0.8%)   Cash ($ mil.): 314
Return on equity: (-2.4%)
Current ratio: —

PROVIDENCE HEALTH AND SERVICES

EXECUTIVES

Pres, Rodney Hochman
SEC, Cindy Strauss
SEC, Tammy Teodosio
SEC, John Whipple
Treas, Todd Hofheins
Cfo, Thomas Risse
Chief Exec, Jim Leonard
Manager, Craig Arneson
Records Director, Janelle Duncan
Infection Control Manager, Lou Hilken
Emergency Medicine, Sarah Wurster

LOCATIONS

HQ: PROVIDENCE HEALTH AND SERVICES
413 LILLY RD NE, OLYMPIA, WA 985065133
Phone: 360 491-9480
Web: WWW.PROVIDENCE.ORG

HISTORICAL FINANCIALS
Company Type: Private

Income Statement				FYE: December 31
	REVENUE ($ mil.)	NET INCOME ($ mil.)	NET PROFIT MARGIN	EMPLOYEES
12/16	458	10	2.3%	2,400
12/05	3	0	7.5%	—
12/02	211	5	2.6%	—
12/01	910	0	—	—
Annual Growth	—	95.6%	—	—

2016 Year-End Financials

Return on assets: 4.2%   Cash ($ mil.): —
Return on equity: 7.5%
Current ratio: 1.50

PSCU INCORPORATED

Credit unions turn to PSCU to provide key card services. As one of the nation's largest credit union service organizations PSCU (short for Payment Systems for Credit Unions) provides credit debit ATM and prepaid card servicing as well as electronic banking bill payment risk management specialized marketing and contact center services to credit unions across the US. The not-for-profit cooperative serves more than 1300 institutions nationwide which combined represent more than 18 million cardholder accounts and one million online bill payment subscribers. PSCU is owned by about 800 member credit unions.

Operations

The centers perform new member enrollment automated lending collections cardholder support cross-selling and customer service. Its four contact centers handle more than 18 million inquiries a year.

Geographic Reach

PSCU operates four Contact Centers covering three major US regions: the Eastern US with one center located in St. Petersburg Florida; the Western US with one center in Phoenix Arizona; and the Midwest with two centers in Detroit Michigan.

Sales and Marketing

PSCU's clients have included: Redwood Credit Union State Department Federal Credit Union Corporate One Federal Credit Union Advantis Credit Union and the Indiana Credit Union League.

Strategy

PSCU has taken a string of steps to help its partnering credit unions adopt newer safer digital payment technologies in recent years. In early 2015 for example it helped its clients Redwood Credit Union and State Department Federal Credit Union implement access to the smartphone-based Apple Pay platform so their cardholders could make digital payments using their iPhones and iPads. In 2013 the company expanded its Phoenix site to house its PSCU technology-based services and developed six new mobile apps to help clients' members interact with their core deposit prepaid credit card and rewards accounts via smart phone technology. It also introduced the CardLock solution (which works in tandem with PSCU's fraud detection and prevention platform) to enable cardholders to block and unblock authorizations on cards they register with the service. In 2012 the company became the first to issue VISA Prepaid EMV (Europay MasterCard and Visa) cards in the US.

PSCU also continues to lock in its long-term contracts with existing and new clients to keep business growing. In late 2014 the company signed a five-year renewal agreement with the $4.2 billion Corporate One Federal Credit Union to continue providing its credit and debit processing services. In mid-2014 PSCU signed a two new long-term contracts including: a five-year agreement with the $1.1 billion Advantis Credit Union in Portland and secured another long-term agreement with the Indiana Credit Union League.

Company Background
PSCU was formed in 1977 by leaders from Pinellas County Teachers Credit Union and the federal credit unions of GTE Publix Employees Suncoast Schools and Railroad and Industrial.

EXECUTIVES

Senior Vice President Chief Risk Officer, Steve Ruwe
Executive Vice President, Steve Salzer
President And Ceo, Michael J. (Mike) Kelly
Evp Credit Debit Prepaid Ecommerce Contact Center And Information Technology, Tom Gandre
Evp Credit Union Experience, Fredda McDonald
Evp Human Resources, Lynn Heckler
Executive Vice President & Chief Financial Officer, Brian Caldarelli
Chief Information Officer, Sam Esfahani
Senior Vice President & Chief Marketing Officer, Dan Csont
Senior Vice President, Brandi Quinn
Vice President Account Management, Joe Poulliott
Area Vice President, Scott Mullendore
Vice President, Ron Metsker
National Executive Director Executive Vice President Account Management, Charles Fagan
Vice President Workforce And Strategic Operations, Randy Kahlich
Senior Vice President Process And Program Excellence, Dan Rosen
Chairman, Craig Esrael
Vice Chairman, Mike Valentine
Board Member, David Doss
Treasurer, Frank Weidner
Secretary, Andrew Rosen
Board Member, Cathy Pace
Board Member, Rob Stuart
Auditors: PRICEWATERHOUSECOOPERS LLP TA

LOCATIONS

HQ: PSCU INCORPORATED
560 CARILLON PKWY, SAINT PETERSBURG, FL 337161294
Phone: 727 572-8822
Web: WWW.PSCU.COM

PRODUCTS/OPERATIONS

Selected Services
Advisors Plus
Credit Solutions
Debit Solutions
eCommerce Solutions
EMV
Prepaid Solutions
Risk Management Solutions
Total Member Care
Technology Tools

PSCU Partnerships/Sponsorships
Credit Union Cherry Blossom Run
Credit Union Student Choice
Filene Research Institute
Financial Service Center Cooperatives (FSCC)
Ongoing Operations
The Colonial Williamsburg Foundation

COMPETITORS

CUSO Financial Services	LPL Financial
Fidelity National Information Services	Raymond James Financial
	U.S. Central

HISTORICAL FINANCIALS
Company Type: Private

Income Statement FYE: September 30

	REVENUE ($ mil.)	NET INCOME ($ mil.)	NET PROFIT MARGIN	EMPLOYEES
09/18	481	11	2.4%	1,850
09/16*	458	28	6.1%	—
12/12	377	38	10.2%	—
12/11	425	29	6.9%	—
Annual Growth	1.8%	(12.7%)	—	—

*Fiscal year change

2018 Year-End Financials
Return on assets: 1.6%
Return on equity: 4.8%
Current ratio: 1.10
Cash ($ mil.): 141

PUBLIC BROADCASTING SERVICE

You might say these shows get a lot of public support. Public Broadcasting Service (PBS) is a non-profit organization that provides educational and public interest programming to more than 350 member public TV stations in the US. In addition to such programs as NOVA This Old House and Downton Abbey it provides related services such as distribution fundraising support and technology development. PBS gets its revenue from underwriting membership dues federal funding (including grants from the not-for-profit Corporation for Public Broadcasting) royalties license fees and product sales. The organization was founded in 1969 to provide cultural and educational programming.

Operations
PBS operates through more than 350 member public TV stations across the US.

Geographic Reach
PBS reaches almost 200 million people through television and nearly 28 million people online each month.

Strategy
While PBS — and its federal funding — regularly finds itself caught in the crossfire between liberal and conservative political groups supporters of the non-profit trumpet the benefits of publicly-funded television programming created to serve groups often overlooked by commercial broadcasters.

PBS' children's programming and news shows such as Frontline and PBS NewsHour (formerly The NewsHour with Jim Lehrer) are often touted as examples of how public broadcasting can fill voids left by the major networks.

The organization has also been looking to capitalize on new distribution channels to get its programming to the public. PBS sells its programs on

DVD and through Apple's iTunes store. It has also ramped up its online video efforts.

EXECUTIVES

Svp And Cfo, Barbara L. Landes
Coo, Jonathan Barzilay
Svp And General Manager Pbs Digital, Ira Rubenstein
President Ceo And Director, Paula A. Kerger
Executive Director Pbs Foundation, Brian J. Reddington
Cto, Mario Vecchi
Chief Programming Executive And General Manager General Audience Programming, Beth Hoppe
Svp Marketing And Communications; General Manager Children's Programming, Lesli Rotenberg
Senior Vice President System Leadership, Juan Sepulveda
Senior Vice President Strategy And Operations, Jayme Swain
Vice President Digital Marketing And Services, Don Wilcox
Executive Vice President, Karla Aikens-allen
Executive Vice President, Wayne Luippold
Vice President Education, Sara Schapiro
Vice President Fundraising Programming, Joe Campbell
Vice President News And Public Affairs Pbs, Marie Nelson
Senior Vice President Programming And Business Affairs, Mike Kelley
Chairman, Donald A. (Don) Baer
Director, Tom Axtell
Auditors: BDO USA LLP BETHESDA MD

LOCATIONS

HQ: PUBLIC BROADCASTING SERVICE
2100 CRYSTAL DR STE 100, ARLINGTON, VA 222023784
Phone: 703 739-5000
Web: WWW.PBS.ORG

PRODUCTS/OPERATIONS

Selected Programming
Antiques Roadshow
Austin City Limits
Barney
Downton Abbey
Frontline
Juila Child: Lessons with Master Chefs
Live from Lincoln Center
Masterpiece Theatre
Mister Rogers' Neighborhood
MotorWeek
Mystery!
Nature
NOVA
NOW
P.O.V.
PBS NewsHour
Reading Rainbow
Sesame Street
Teletubbies
This Old House
Victory Garden
Washington Week
ZOOM

COMPETITORS

ABC Cable Networks	Discovery
ABC Inc.	HBO
AMC Networks	MTV Networks
BBC Worldwide	NBC
CBS	Scripps Networks
Current Media	Turner Broadcasting

HISTORICAL FINANCIALS

Company Type: Private

Income Statement				FYE: June 30
	REVENUE ($ mil.)	NET INCOME ($ mil.)	NET PROFIT MARGIN	EMPLOYEES
06/15	473	(46)	—	507
06/14	539	89	16.7%	—
06/10	505	28	5.6%	—
06/09	502	(80)	—	—
Annual Growth	(1.0%)	—	—	—

2015 Year-End Financials

Return on assets: (-9.7%)
Return on equity: (-13.9%)
Current ratio: 0.80
Cash ($ mil.): 39

PUBLIC HEALTH TRUST OF MIAMI DADE COUNTY

Jackson Memorial Hospital is the flagship facility of the Jackson Health System (JHS). It has roughly 2450 beds and offers a wide variety of services including burn treatment trauma pediatrics rehabilitation obstetrics and transplants. It is also a teaching facility for the University of Miami School of Medicine. JHS also operates Holtz Children's Hospital a rehabilitation hospital a mental health hospital primary and specialty care centers two long-term care nursing facilities six corrections health clinics and two community hospitals. Jackson Memorial Hospital and JHS are overseen by The Public Health Trust of Miami-Dade County.

Operations

Jackson Memorial Hospital's Ryder Trauma Center is Miami-Dade County's only adult and pediatric Level 1 trauma center.

JHS is its region's primary provider of charity care spending some $700 million annually to administer health care to Florida's uninsured and underinsured populations. Along with Jackson Memorial Hospital JHS delivers medical care to Floridians through the Jackson South Community Hospital (226 beds) and the Jackson North Medical Center (382 beds) which also serves as a teaching hospital for the Florida International University College of Medicine. Holtz Children's Hospital is one of the largest children's hospitals in the state and one of three in the US that specializes in pediatric multi-organ transplants.

Strategy

The system has acquired a site to build a new campus (Jackson West) that will include a children's outpatient center and a free-standing emergency department. JHS is also adding a new walk-in facility on South Beach. The company has invested in bringing new lab equipment and software to its facilities.

Other initiatives have included adjusting prices to be more competitive doing business with HMOs and drawing in more affluent patients through first-class offerings.

Company Background

The Public Health Trust was created in 1973 by the Board of County Commissioners as an independent governing body to provide leadership for joint planning between Jackson Health System the University of Miami Miller School of Medicine Miami-Dade County and other private and community organizations. Today the Public Health Trust is considered the hospital system's governing board picking its CEO and overseeing the system's operations.

EXECUTIVES

President And Ceo Jackson Health System, Carlos A. Migoya
Evp And Coo Jackson Health System, David R. Small
Chief Administrative Officer Jackson Memorial Hospital And Jackson Rehabilitation Hospital, Alex Contreras-Soto
Chief Administrative Officer Jackson Behavioral Health Hospital, R. John Repique
Associate Vice President For Communications, Christine Morris
Medical Director, Nicolette Schreiber
Vice President Government Relations, Jeanette Nunez
Department Head, Walter Bradley
Medical Director, Diana Cardenas
Medical Director, Pablo Calzada
Medical Director, Shashi Razdan
Unit Secretary, Cristal Lozada

LOCATIONS

HQ: PUBLIC HEALTH TRUST OF MIAMI DADE COUNTY
1611 NW 12TH AVE, MIAMI, FL 331361005
Phone: 305 585-1111

COMPETITORS

Baptist Health South Florida
Broward Health
Continucare
Encompass Health
HCA
Larkin Community Hospital
MJHHA
Miami Children's Hospital
Mount Sinai Medical Center of Florida
NCH Healthcare
Plantation General
South Broward Hospital District
South Miami Hospital
University of Miami Hospital

HISTORICAL FINANCIALS

Company Type: Private

Income Statement				FYE: September 30
	REVENUE ($ mil.)	NET INCOME ($ mil.)	NET PROFIT MARGIN	EMPLOYEES
09/17	1,160	184	15.9%	11,000
09/15*	883	200	22.7%	—
06/05	0	0	—	—
09/03	960	(26)	—	—
Annual Growth	1.4%	—	—	—
*Fiscal year change

2017 Year-End Financials

Return on assets: 8.7%
Return on equity: 35.4%
Current ratio: 1.20
Cash ($ mil.): 304

PUBLIC HOSPITAL DISTRICT 1 OF KING COUNTY

EXECUTIVES

Admin-Ceo, Richard D Roodman
Cfo*, Michael Bernstein
Comm*, Carole Anderson
Coo*, Paul Hayes
Doctor, Olga V Khait-Palant
Doctor, Daniel Letinsky
Doctor, Shreeketa M Mehta
Internal Medicine Practitioner, Amit Joshi
Anesthesiology, Andrew O Smith
Doctor, Joyce V Gauthier
Anesthesiology, Sidney W Postma
Auditors: KPMG LLP SEATTLE WASHINGTON

LOCATIONS

HQ: PUBLIC HOSPITAL DISTRICT 1 OF KING COUNTY
400 S 43RD ST, RENTON, WA 980555714
Phone: 425 228-3440
Web: WWW.VALLEYMED.ORG

HISTORICAL FINANCIALS

Company Type: Private

Income Statement				FYE: June 30
	REVENUE ($ mil.)	NET INCOME ($ mil.)	NET PROFIT MARGIN	EMPLOYEES
06/18	653	40	6.2%	2,700
06/16*	519	11	2.2%	—
12/07	327	25	7.8%	—
Annual Growth	7.1%	4.7%	—	—
*Fiscal year change

2018 Year-End Financials

Return on assets: 5.7%
Return on equity: 15.5%
Current ratio: 1.90
Cash ($ mil.): 48

PUBLIC UTILITY DISTRICT 1 OF CLARK COUNTY

There are no "we're No 1" signs waving at this publicly minded company's head office. Public Utility District No. 1 of Clark County (Clark Public Utilities) provides utility services to residents and businesses in Clark County Washington. Clark Public Utilities transmits and distributes electricity toÂ more than 184100 customers; the companyÂ operates aÂ 250-MW gas-fired power plantÂ but purchasesÂ the bulk of its power from the Bonneville Power Administration. Clark Public Utilities also distributes water toÂ more thanÂ 30640 customers and collects and treats wastewater for the City of La Center Washington.

EXECUTIVES

Secretary, Jim Malinowski
Auditors: MOSS ADAMS LLP PORTLAND ORE

LOCATIONS

HQ: PUBLIC UTILITY DISTRICT 1 OF CLARK COUNTY
1200 FORT VANCOUVER WAY, VANCOUVER, WA
986633527
Phone: 360 992-3000
Web: WWW.CLARKPUBLICUTILITIES.COM

COMPETITORS

PacifiCorp
Portland General
  Electric
Puget Energy

HISTORICAL FINANCIALS
Company Type: Private

Income Statement				FYE: December 31
	REVENUE ($ mil.)	NET INCOME ($ mil.)	NET PROFIT MARGIN	EMPLOYEES
12/18	481	38	7.9%	325
12/17	502	45	9.1%	—
12/16	486	35	7.3%	—
12/05	463	2	0.5%	—
Annual Growth	0.3%	23.6%	—	—

2018 Year-End Financials

Return on assets: 3.3%
Return on equity: 8.0%
Current ratio: 3.40

Cash ($ mil.): 324

PUBLIC UTILITY DISTRICT 1 OF SNOHOMISH COUNTY

Keeping its customers satisfied is priority No. 1 at Public Utility District No. 1 of Snohomish County Washington (Snohomish County PUD) which distributes electricity to 332516 commercial industrial and residential customers in Washington State. The utility the largest PUD in the state with a 2200 sq. ml. service area purchases most of its power supply from third parties (Bonneville Power Administration and other producers. It operates hydroelectric and fossil-fueled power plants and participates in wholesale power transactions to balance its supply load. Snohomish County PUD also serves more than 20000 water utility customers in a 205 sq. ml. service territory via about 375 miles of pipe.

Operations

Snohomish County PUD's operations consist of three systems: the Electric System the Generation System and the Water System.

The Electric System is made up of electric transmission and distribution system.

The Generation System is composed of the company's Jackson Hydroelectric Project and two smaller hydroelectric projects.

The Water System is made up of water distribution system.

Sales and Marketing

The PUD serves three categories of customers: Residential (301639) Commercial (30524) Industrial (76) and other (street lighting temporary lighting etc. - 277).

The company offers a wide range of energy-efficiency solutions for business customers.

Financial Performance

In 2014 the PUD's revenues grew by 3% due to an increase in retail sales as a result of a general and a power contract pass-through rate increase in 2013 and wholesale sales driven by a rise in Megawatt-Hours sold.

The company's net income decreased by 19% due to an increase in operating expenses driven by higher volume of power purchases from the wholesale power market and increased operations expenses due to higher transmission and ancillary costs and costs related to the PUD's effort to implement a new enterprise resource planning system.

In fiscal 2014 the company's operating cash inflow decreased by 10% due to lower net income and changes in working capital.

Strategy

To meet federal and state goals for reducing greenhouse gases the utility is exploring a range of green energy options conservation measures and new power generation activities including geothermal tidal wind and solar power.

In 2015 the PUD's solar program increased its total contribution to 3.7 MW an almost 150% increase over the previous year.

In 2014 the company spent $110 million on electric system capital expenditures up from $94 million in 2013. The company increased the capital programs over the past two years to maintain expand and enhance its electric distribution system.

Company Background

In 2013 solar energy capacity stood at two MW enough to serve 170 homes. More than 350 PUD customers cover part of their electricity needs through their own solar energy units. The PUD's Solar Express program offers financial incentives and technical assistance for solar photovoltaic and solar hot water systems.

In 2012 the company amended a power contract with Hampton Lumber (a fuel supplier since 2007) that will boost the level of biomass energy the utility will receive from the lumber company's Darrington plant. The new agreement will allow Snohomish County PUD to receive up to 2.5 MW of energy from Hampton Lumber enough energy to power about 2000 homes.

Supported by $15.8 million in matching federal stimulus dollars in 2011 Snohomish County PUD completed its first major project as part of a long-term upgrade of its electric grid with smart grid technology. The upgrade includes the installation of more than 160 miles of fiber optic cable and connecting them to 62 substations two radio sites and other utility buildings.

The company began providing water utility service to parts of Snohomish County in 1946. Public Utility District No. 1 of Snohomish County began operating as power utility in 1949 providing publicly owned electric and water utility service to the residents of Snohomish County and Camano Island.

EXECUTIVES

President Send An, Toni Olson
General Manager, Steve Klein
Assistant General Manager Water Resources Division, Kim Moore
Chief Information Officer, Benjamin Beberness
President Board Of Commissioners, Kathleen (Kathy) Vaughn
Auditors: BAKER TILLY MADISON WI

LOCATIONS

HQ: PUBLIC UTILITY DISTRICT 1 OF SNOHOMISH COUNTY
2320 CALIFORNIA ST, EVERETT, WA 982013750
Phone: 425 257-9288
Web: WWW.SNOPUD.COM

PRODUCTS/OPERATIONS

2014 Sales

	$ mil.	% of total
Retail sales	554	86
Wholesale sales	59	9
Other	30	5
Total	**645**	**100**

COMPETITORS

Avista
  Chelan County PUD
  Grant County Public Utility District
  Public Utility District No. 1 of Clark County
  Puget Energy
  Tacoma Public Utilities

HISTORICAL FINANCIALS
Company Type: Private

Income Statement				FYE: December 31
	REVENUE ($ mil.)	NET INCOME ($ mil.)	NET PROFIT MARGIN	EMPLOYEES
12/18	695	80	11.5%	879
12/17	686	75	11.1%	—
12/16	657	60	9.2%	—
12/15	626	52	8.3%	—
Annual Growth	3.5%	15.5%	—	—

2018 Year-End Financials

Return on assets: 3.6%
Return on equity: 5.6%
Current ratio: 2.10

Cash ($ mil.): 93

PUBLIX SUPER MARKETS, INC.

Publix Super Markets tops the list of privately owned grocery operators in the US. By emphasizing service and a family-friendly image over price Publix has outgrown and outperformed its regional rivals. Some two-thirds of its nearly 1200 stores are in Florida but it also operates in half a dozen other southeastern states. Publix makes some of its own bakery deli dairy goods and fresh prepared foods at its own manufacturing plants in Florida and Georgia. Many stores also house pharmacies and banks. Founder George Jenkins began offering stock to Publix employees in 1930; employees own more than a quarter of the company.

Operations

Publix stores sell grocery products (dairy produce deli baker meat and seafood) health and beauty care products general merchandise pharmacy products flowers and other products and services. Grocery activities account for some 85% of sales.

Geographic Reach

Publix has nearly 1200 supermarkets in Florida (about two-thirds of total) and Georgia (more than 15% of total) as well as Alabama South Carolina Tennessee North Carolina and Virginia.

It restocks store shelves from nine distribution centers — seven in Florida and one each in Georgia and Alabama. The grocer also operates half a dozen dairy bakery and deli facilities four in Florida and two in Georgia.

Financial Performance

Publix has shown solid sales growth over the past five years as it continues to expand and open new stores across the Southeast. Its revenue has risen some 20% since 2013. With profit margins higher than many (if not all) of its grocery competitors the company has also seen increases in its net income in recent years.

In 2017 Publix reported revenue of $34.8 billion up about 1.5% from the prior year. New store openings powered the growth along with a 1.7% increase in comparable-store sales which was helped by customers' stocking up and replenishing before and after Hurricane Irma hit Florida. This was more than enough to offset an additional week of operation in 2016 which was a 53-week fiscal year.

As the dominant grocer in its primary market Florida Publix regularly reports net profit margins of between 5.5%-6% much higher than other super market chains (Kroger for example is in the 1.5%-2% range). In 2017 it had net earnings of $2.3 billion up from $2 billion in 2016. In addition to the increased revenue net earnings were boosted some $224 million by the Tax Cut and Jobs Act of 2017.

Cash at the end of 2017 was $580 million an increase of about $140 million from the prior year. Cash from operations contributed $3.6 billion to the coffers while investing and financing activities used some $3.45 million mainly for expenditures used in new and remodeled stores and for dividends and stock buybacks.

Strategy

Publix's growth strategy is based on investing in its stores and enhancing its customer service.

It plans to spend more than $1.5 billion in 2018 to open new stores remodel existing stores and increase ownership of its store portfolio. The company opened 44 stores in 2017 including its first locations in Virginia. At year's end it had about 35 stores under construction. In addition Publix remodeled more than 130 locations in 2017. It also continues to invest in its real estate portfolio. At the end of 2017 the company owned nearly a third of its stores up from 29% in 2016 and 11% in 2007.

Publix is also focused on keeping up with customer demand for delivery and other advanced services. It began working with grocery delivery firm Instacart in 2016 and currently offers home delivery in more than 90% of its operating area. The company is also testing curbside pickup and its online ordering platform has been expanded with smokehouse meats fried chicken and other items. It has also enhanced its pharmacy offerings through a partnership with BayCare Health System and serves pharmacy patients with new web and mobile applications.

Lastly Publix has announced plans to relaunch its GreenWise Market concept in select locations in 2018. GreenWise Market targets the health-conscious consumer with specialty natural and organic selections.

EXECUTIVES

Evp And Cfo, David P. Phillips, age 59, $1,051,090 total compensation
General Counsel And Secretary, John A. Attaway, age 60, $690,310 total compensation
Svp, David E. Bornmann, age 61, $488,300 total compensation
President Ceo And Director, Randall T. (Todd) Jones, age 56, $1,688,750 total compensation
Svp And Cio, Laurie Z. Douglas, age 55, $890,255 total compensation
Manager Government Relations, Shane Kunze
Pharmacy Manager, Larry Jones
Vice Chairman, Hoyt R. (Barney) Barnett, age 76
President And Director, William E. (Ed) Crenshaw, age 68

LOCATIONS

HQ: PUBLIX SUPER MARKETS, INC.
3300 PUBLIX CORP PKWY, LAKELAND, FL 338113311
Phone: 863 688-1188
Web: WWW.PUBLIX.COM

2017 Supermarkets

	No.
Florida	779
Georgia	186
Alabama	65
South Carolina	58
Tennessee	41
North Carolina	30
Virginia	8
Total	**1,167**

PRODUCTS/OPERATIONS

2017 Sales

	% of total
Grocery	84
Other	16
Total	**100**

Selected Supermarket Departments
Bakery
Dairy
Deli
Floral
Groceries
Health and beauty care
Meat
Pharmacy
Produce
Seafood
Foods Processed
Baked goods
Dairy products
Deli items

COMPETITORS

ALDI	Kroger
CVS	Rite Aid
Costco Wholesale	Sedano's
Food Lion	Southeastern Grocers
IGA	Wal-Mart
Ingles Markets	Walgreen
Kmart	Whole Foods

HISTORICAL FINANCIALS
Company Type: Private

Income Statement				FYE: December 31
	REVENUE ($ mil.)	NET INCOME ($ mil.)	NET PROFIT MARGIN	EMPLOYEES
12/16	34,274	2,025	5.9%	193,000
12/15	32,618	1,965	6.0%	—
12/14	30,802	1,735	5.6%	—
12/12	27,706	1,552	5.6%	—
Annual Growth	5.5%	6.9%	—	—

2016 Year-End Financials
Return on assets: 11.6%
Return on equity: 19.4%
Current ratio: 1.60
Cash ($ mil.): 438

PURCHASING POWER, LLC

EXECUTIVES

Ceo, Joseph Loughran
Coo, Elizabeth Halkos

Cfo, Wade Pierce
Cto, Prakash Muthukrishnan
Clo, Greg Birge
Cpo, Racquel Roberts
Cdo-Cmo, Bryon Colby
Regional Vice-President, Lynette Stevens
Vp-Financial Planning & Analys, Melissa Manley
Senior Accountant, Shauna Stanback
Vp Supply Chain, Timo Kirschner
Auditors: PRICEWATERHOUSECOOPERS LLP AT

LOCATIONS

HQ: PURCHASING POWER, LLC
1349 W PEACHTREE ST NW # 1100, ATLANTA, GA 303092956
Phone: 404 609-5100

HISTORICAL FINANCIALS
Company Type: Private

Income Statement				FYE: December 31
	REVENUE ($ mil.)	NET INCOME ($ mil.)	NET PROFIT MARGIN	EMPLOYEES
12/18	478	6	1.4%	250
12/17	425	(6)	—	—
Annual Growth	—	—	—	—

2018 Year-End Financials
Return on assets: 1.1%
Return on equity: 2.7%
Current ratio: 2.60
Cash ($ mil.): 33

QUALITY OIL COMPANY, LLC

With more services than your average oil company Quality Oil helps its customers get fueled up cooled off and well rested. And they can smoke if they want to. The company distributes fuel oil and propane to customers in the Winston-Salem area of North Carolina. Quality Oil provides air conditioning and heating equipment service operates 47 convenience stores (Quality Marts) and about 20 service stations and owns hotels in five southern states. In addition the company operates 60 Quality Plus locations at which drivers can buy cigarettes at discount prices. The company also provides Right-a-Way oil change services at many of its gas stations.

Operations

In addition the company's real estate unit (Quality Oil Real Estate) operates a diverse portfolio of retail and hotel sites industrial units residential subdivision developments and a shopping center. Quality Marts and Quality Plus also provide heating and cooling and fleet fueling services.

Geographic Reach

Quality Oil owns and operates four Hampton Inns two Hampton Inn & Suites and one Homewood Suites in the Carolinas Florida Georgia and Virginia. Affiliate Reliable Tank Line LLC transports petroleum products and provides fleet fueling services at 10 locations in North Carolina northern South Carolina eastern Virginia and eastern Tennessee. Quality Oil Heating-Cooling has assets throughout North Carolina and parts of South Carolina Virginia Florida and Tennessee and serves Forsyth County Stokes County Davie County Davidson County Yadkin County Rowan County and Iredell County.

Sales and Marketing

The company markets Shell oil products.

Strategy

To sharpen its competitive edge in 2013 Quality Oil created a new department — Retail Technology — to maintain PDI Pricebook and POS Systems and test and implement future technological developments.

To increase operational efficiency in 2012 Quality Oil installed Professional Datasolutions Inc. (PDI) scanning software at all of its retail outlets.

Mergers and Acquisitions

To complement its existing oil and propane business in 2012 Quality Oil acquired regional gas station and convenience store operator Horn Oil Co. in Mocksville North Carolina.

Company Background

Expanding its store network in 2011 the company opened Quality Mart locations #46 and #47 in Kernersville and Morrisville.

Quality Oil was founded in 1929 by Joe Glenn and Bert Bennett as a Shell oil products distributor and is still owned and operated by descendants of the founders.

EXECUTIVES

Pres, Graham F Bennett
MBR*, Don McIver
Sr V Pres*, Ernie Rhymer
Sr V Pres*, Buddy Jenkins
Sr V Pres*, Tim Lowman
Sr V Pres*, Andy Sayles
Director of Sales, Kimberly Campbell
Sales Manager, Lisa Mann
General Manager, Chelsea Baines
Auditors: BUTLER & BURKE LLP WINSTON-S

LOCATIONS

HQ: QUALITY OIL COMPANY, LLC
1540 SILAS CREEK PKWY, WINSTON SALEM, NC 271273705
Phone: 336 722-3441
Web: WWW.QUALITYOILNC.COM

PRODUCTS/OPERATIONS

Selected Brands

Hampton Inn
Quality Heating and Air Conditioning
Quality Mart
Quality Oil Appliance Sales and Service
Quality Oil Commercial Heating and On-Site Fueling
Quality Oil Fuel Oil
Quality Oil Gas Logs and Heaters
Quality Oil Propane
Quality Plus
Reliable Tank Line
Shell Oil products

Selected Mergers and Acquisitions

COMPETITORS

Cumberland Farms	Marriott
E-Z Mart Stores	Racetrac Petroleum
Hyatt	WilcoHess

HISTORICAL FINANCIALS

Company Type: Private

Income Statement				FYE: December 31
	REVENUE ($ mil.)	NET INCOME ($ mil.)	NET PROFIT MARGIN	EMPLOYEES
12/09	634	11	1.9%	1,000
12/08	806	27	3.4%	—
12/07	619	10	1.8%	—
12/06	542	15	2.8%	—
Annual Growth	5.4%	(8.1%)	—	—

2009 Year-End Financials

Return on assets: 9.9%
Return on equity: 13.1%
Current ratio: 0.90
Cash ($ mil.): 11

R. DIRECTIONAL DRILLING & UNDERGROUND TECHNOLOGY, INC.

EXECUTIVES

Pres-Ceo, Jose M Ruiz
V Pres of Oprs*, Aurelio Ruiz
Vice President of Sales*, Derek Reeve
Auditors: KEN DUSSEAU PC

LOCATIONS

HQ: R. DIRECTIONAL DRILLING & UNDERGROUND TECHNOLOGY, INC.
8560 N 77TH DR, PEORIA, AZ 853457969
Phone: 602 374-3173

HISTORICAL FINANCIALS

Company Type: Private

Income Statement				FYE: December 31
	REVENUE ($ mil.)	NET INCOME ($ mil.)	NET PROFIT MARGIN	EMPLOYEES
12/12	7,667	(1,040)	—	61
12/11*	7	2	29.9%	—
09/10	2	0	27.4%	—
Annual Growth	5174.7%	—	—	—

*Fiscal year change

2012 Year-End Financials

Return on assets: (-24.4%)
Return on equity: (-48.7%)
Current ratio: 1.30
Cash ($ mil.): 416

R. E. MICHEL COMPANY, LLC

Blowing hot and cold is good for R.E. Michel. The company is one of the nation's largest wholesale distributors of heating air-conditioning and refrigeration (HVAC-R) equipment parts and supplies. The family-owned and operated firm offers more than 16000 items through about 2 sales offices located across the Southern Mid-Atlantic and Northeastern regions of the country. R.E. Michel ships more than 20000 items each day from its 900000-sq.-ft. distribution center in Maryland. Its Exclusive Supplier Partnership (ESP) program offers customers inventory control advertising and marketing support. R.E. Michel was founded in 1935 as a supplier to the home heating oil burner industry.

Geographic Reach

The HVAC wholesaler maintains a handful of offices to cater to customers located in the Southern US as well as in the Mid-Atlantic and Northeastern regions. Most recently opened offices reside in Ohio California Virginia Florida South Carolina Arizona and Tennessee.

Sales and Marketing

R.E. Michel uses up to 50 trailers to ship its more than 10000 items each day. To this end the company also ships more than 3200 items via the

United Parcel Service each week. As part of its business it publishes a 1300 page catalog that includes 20000 catalog line items.

EXECUTIVES

Vice President Of Operations, Gene Winters
Exec Vp, Ronald Miller
Auditors: CLIFTONLARSONALLEN LLP BALTIM

LOCATIONS

HQ: R. E. MICHEL COMPANY, LLC
1 RE MICHEL DR, GLEN BURNIE, MD 210606408
Phone: 410 760-4000
Web: WWW.REMICHEL.COM

PRODUCTS/OPERATIONS

Selected Products & Services

Air conditioning & heating
Indoor air quality
Boilers
Water heating equipment
Hydronic & steam systems
Valves
Pipe & fittings
Fuel oil systems
Gas systems
Chemicals
Refrigeration equipment & supplies
Controls
Electrical supplies
Motors
Air handling products
Venting products
Duct registers & grilles
Tools & test instruments
O.E.M. Parts

COMPETITORS

Emco Corporation	Lowe's
Ferguson Enterprises	MSC Industrial Direct
Gensco	W.W. Grainger
HD Supply	WinWholesale

HISTORICAL FINANCIALS

Company Type: Private

Income Statement				FYE: December 31
	REVENUE ($ mil.)	NET INCOME ($ mil.)	NET PROFIT MARGIN	EMPLOYEES
12/13	685	31	4.6%	1,960
12/12	611	3	0.6%	—
12/11	606	8	1.4%	—
12/10	593	11	1.9%	—
Annual Growth	4.9%	41.2%	—	—

2013 Year-End Financials

Return on assets: 12.2%
Return on equity: 4.6%
Current ratio: 0.60
Cash ($ mil.): —

R. M. PARKS, INC.

EXECUTIVES

Pres, R M Parks
V Pres, Tim Callison
SEC-Treas, Marilyn Callison
Offc Mgr, Jason Patterson
Sales Team Member, Bobby Rogers
Accounting Manager, Sherrill Morris
Auditors: GUMBINER SAVETT INC SANTA MO

LOCATIONS

HQ: R. M. PARKS, INC.
 1061 N MAIN ST, PORTERVILLE, CA 932571686
Phone: 559 784-2384
Web: WWW.RMPARKSINC.COM

HISTORICAL FINANCIALS

Company Type: Private

Income Statement				FYE: October 31
	REVENUE ($ mil.)	NET INCOME ($ mil.)	NET PROFIT MARGIN	EMPLOYEES
10/18	571	0	0.0%	4
10/17	477	(0)	—	—
10/16	448	0	0.2%	—
10/15	534	0	0.2%	—
Annual Growth	2.3%	(73.9%)	—	—

2018 Year-End Financials

Return on assets: 0.1%   Cash ($ mil.): —
Return on equity: 0.2%
Current ratio: 1.30

R.C. WILLEY HOME FURNISHINGS

R.C. Willey Home Furnishings does its best to be top dog. The company drives traffic by giving away some 600000 hot dogs a year at about a dozen stores in Utah Nevada California and Idaho. Despite Sunday store closures and operations in only four states R.C. Willey is one of the nation's largest furniture retailers. It sells furniture (La-Z-Boy Flexsteel) appliances (GE Maytag) electronics (Sony Panasonic) and flooring. The company also sells mattresses (Serta Spring Air Simmons). In 1932 Rufus Call (R.C.) Willey sold appliances door-to-door; today the company he founded is run by his son-in-law chairman Bill Child and grandsons. Berkshire Hathaway purchased the company in 1995.

Operations

R.C. Willey is part of Berkshire Hathaway's home furnishings business alongside Nebraska Furniture Mart Star Furniture and Jordan's Furniture.

The Salt Lake City Utah-based company boasts some 1.7 million sq. ft. of retail space across its nearly a dozen retail stores a pair of retail clearance facilities and three distribution centers to support its entire operation. R.C. Willey is known for its large selection and reliable brand names. It carries General Electric Whirlpool LG Maytag Amana KitchenAid Broyhill Flexsteel Lane Natuzzi AICO Pluaski Schnadi Sony Mitsubishi Toshiba Samsung Serta Spring Air Simmons and Tempur Sealy.

Geographic Reach

R.C. Willey operates its furniture business nationwide primarily in a handful of states.

Sales and Marketing

A plus to R.C. Willey Home Furnishings customers the company offers financing through its R.C. Willey Credit Card.

EXECUTIVES

President, Jeffrey S. (Jeff) Child
Cfo, Curtis Child
Vice President Of Marketing, Jack De Mill
Chairman, William H. (Bill) Child

LOCATIONS

HQ: R.C. WILLEY HOME FURNISHINGS
 2301 S 300 W, SALT LAKE CITY, UT 841152516
Phone: 801 461-3900
Web: WWW.RCWILLEY.COM

PRODUCTS/OPERATIONS

Selected Products

Appliances
Electronics
Fitness
Flooring
Furniture
Mattresses

COMPETITORS

Abbey Carpet	J. C. Penney Company
Best Buy	La-Z-Boy
Costco Wholesale	Lowe's
Ethan Allen	Pier 1 Imports
Fry's Electronics	RadioShack
Home Depot	Williams-Sonoma

HISTORICAL FINANCIALS

Company Type: Private

Income Statement				FYE: December 31
	REVENUE ($ mil.)	NET INCOME ($ mil.)	NET PROFIT MARGIN	EMPLOYEES
12/17	807	19	2.4%	2,700
12/16	800	26	3.3%	—
12/14	712	17	2.4%	—
12/13	664	15	2.3%	—
Annual Growth	5.0%	6.3%	—	—

2017 Year-End Financials

Return on assets: 2.1%   Cash ($ mil.): 62
Return on equity: 2.5%
Current ratio: 4.10

RADY CHILDREN'S HOSPITAL AND HEALTH CENTER

EXECUTIVES

Pres-Ceo, Donald B Kearns
Cmo*, Irvin A Kaufman
Exec V Pres*, Margareta E Norton
Sr V Pres-Cfo*, Roger G Roux
Coo*, Nicholas Holmes
Network Administrator, Jim Ward
Analyst, Benjelyn Barrera
Coordinator, Giuseppe Principato
Scientist, Andrea Hazen
Supervisor, Ruth Felix
Coordinator, Carrie Arii
Auditors: LB KPMG LLP LOS ANGELES CA

LOCATIONS

HQ: RADY CHILDREN'S HOSPITAL AND HEALTH CENTER
 3020 CHILDRENS WAY, SAN DIEGO, CA 921234223
Phone: 858 576-1700
Web: WWW.RCHSD.ORG

HISTORICAL FINANCIALS

Company Type: Private

Income Statement				FYE: June 30
	REVENUE ($ mil.)	NET INCOME ($ mil.)	NET PROFIT MARGIN	EMPLOYEES
06/18	1,243	205	16.5%	4,033
06/17	1,092	220	20.2%	—
06/15	13	13	98.7%	—
06/14	3	2	87.7%	—
Annual Growth	338.9%	189.2%	—	—

2018 Year-End Financials

Return on assets: 9.3%   Cash ($ mil.): 44
Return on equity: 13.9%
Current ratio: 6.30

RADY CHILDREN'S HOSPITAL-SAN DIEGO

Rady Children's Hospital-San Diego handles the big injuries of pint-sized patients. Serving as the region's only pediatric trauma center the nonprofit hospital boasts more than 520 beds. As part of its services Rady Children's Hospital-San Diego offers comprehensive pediatric care including surgical services convalescent care a neonatal intensive care unit and orthopedic services. Across its service area the hospital also operates about 25 satellite centers that provide such primary and specialized care services as physical therapy and hearing diagnostics. Rady Children's Hospital a teaching hospital affiliated with the University of California San Diego Medical School was founded in 1954.

Operations

Rady Children's operates its own 36-bed emergency department — The Sam S. and Rose Stein Emergency Care Center — that each day sees up to 300 patients. It is the only regional emergency center solely dedicated and equipped to care for children. The hospital also operates California's only pediatric skilled nursing facility — The Helen Bernardy Center — to provide 24-hour care to disabled and medically fragile children in a homelike environment.

For treating non-life-or-limb-threatening injuries and illnesses the hospital operates neighborhood urgent care centers in Escondido La Mesa Oceanside and San Diego.

Through its medical school affiliation Rady Children's engages in nearly 500 clinical trials in all pediatric specialties. It collaborates with University of California San Diego the Sanford-Burnham Medical Research Institute The Scripps Research Institute the Salk Institute for Biological Studies and St. Jude Children's Research Hospital. Specialized research facilities on campus include the Autism Discovery Institute the Blair L. Sadler Center for Quality and the Child and Adolescent Services Research Center.

The hospital operates a LEED-certified Acute Care Pavilion which holds a neonatal intensive care unit the Peckham Center for Cancer and Blood Disorders and the Warren Family Surgical Center. It serves those suffering from eating disorders through its inpatient center to allow for intensive psychiatric therapy for patients with anorexia and bulimia and to aid families with home care.

In 2014 the hospital had 18782 inpatient admissions 230383 outpatient visits nearly 85000 emergency department visits and more than 54000 urgent care visits. It performed about 20000 surgeries.

Geographic Reach

Rady Children's Hospital serves as the pediatric medical center that caters to the California region of San Diego Imperial and southern Riverside counties. It has more than 30 offices throughout San Diego and southern Riverside counties with satellite locations in Chula Vista El Centro Encinitas Escondido La Jolla La Mesa Murrieta Oceanside San Diego and Solana Beach.

EXECUTIVES

Chairman Rady Pediatric Genomics And Systems Medicine Institute, David F. Hale, age 70
President And Ceo Rady Pediatric Genomics And Systems Medicine Institute, Stephen Kingsmore
Evp And Chief Administrative Officer, Margareta E. (Meg) Norton
President And Ceo, Donald Kearns
Vp And Cio, Albert Oriol
Vp And Chief Nursing Executive, Mary Fagan
Chief Medical Officer, Irvin A. Kaufman
Svp And Coo, Nicholas Holmes
Executive Director Rady Childrenâ's Hospital Foundation And Svp Rady Childrenâ's Hospital, Stephen Jennings
Physician-in-chief And Chief Scientific Officer And Chairman Of Pediatrics Uc San Diego, Gabriel G. Haddad
Svp Rady Childrenâ's Specialists Of San Diego, Herb Kimmons
Respiratory Therapy Director, Toni Popien
Medical Director, Sretenka Dokich
Clinical Director, Carolina Schaber
Senior Vice President Major Gifts, Lauren Bergquist
Vice Chairman, Michael P. (Mike) Peckham
Chairman, Theodore D. (Ted) Roth, age 68

LOCATIONS

HQ: RADY CHILDREN'S HOSPITAL-SAN DIEGO
3020 CHILDRENS WAY, SAN DIEGO, CA 921234223
Phone: 858 576-1700
Web: WWW.RCHSD.ORG

Selected Satellite Locations
Chula Vista
El Centro
Encinitas
Escondido
La Jolla
La Mesa
Murrieta
Oceanside
San Diego
Solana Beach

PRODUCTS/OPERATIONS

Selected Services

Allergy/Immunology
Attention Deficit Hyperactivity Disorder
Audiology/Hearing
Autism Discovery Institute
Behavioral Health
Brachial Plexus Clinic
Cancer & Blood Disorders
Cardiology
Cardiovascular Surgery
Celiac Disease Clinic
Center for Healthier Communities
Cerebral Palsy Center
Chadwick Center For Children & Families
Child & Adolescent Psychiatry Services (CAPS)
Child & Adolescent Services Research Center (CASRC)
Child Life Services
Children's Care Connection (C3)
Children's Hospital Emergency Transport (CHET)
Cleft Palate Clinic
Craniofacial Disorders
Critical Care

Cystic Fibrosis Center
Dental Surgery
Dermatology
Developmental Evaluation Clinic
Developmental-Behavioral Pediatrics
Developmental Screening & Enhancement Program (DSEP)
Developmental Services
Down Syndrome Center
Eating Disorders/
Medical-Behavioral Disorders Unit
Emergency Medicine
Endocrinology/Diabetes
Fatty Liver Clinic
Feeding Team
Gastroenterology Hepatology & Nutrition
Genetics/Dysmorphology
Heart Institute
Helen Bernardy Center for Medically Fragile Children
Hematology/Oncology
HomeCare
Hospice
Infectious Diseases
Kawasaki Disease Clinic
Kidney/Liver Tranplant Program
Kidney Disease
Laboratory Services/Pathology
Liver Disease
Liver Transplant
Muscle Disease Clinic
Metabolic Medicine
Neonatology
Nephrology
Neurology
Neurosurgery
Newborn Screening Program
Nutrition Clinic
Occupational Therapy
Ophthalmology
Orthopedics
Otolaryngology/ENT
Pain Services
Palliative Care
Pediatric Surgery
Pediatrics & Hospital Medicine
Pharmacy Services
Physical Therapy
Prader-Willi Syndrome Clinic
Psychiatry
Pulmonary/Respiratory Medicine
Radiology
Rehabilitation Medicine
Rheumatology
Sleep Center
Speech/Language Pathology
Spiritual Care
Sports Medicine
Surgery
Toddler School (Alexa's PLAYC)
Trauma Center
Urgent Care
Urology
Weight & Wellness Center

COMPETITORS

All Children's Hospital
Children's Health System
Children's Hospital & Research Center at Oakland
Children's Hospital of Orange County
Children's Hospital of Philadelphia
Children's Hospital of Richmond
Children's Specialized Hospital
Childrens Hospital Los Angeles
Cook Children's Health Care System
Dell Children's Medical Center
Nationwide Children's Hospital
Palomar Health
Scripps Health
Seattle Children's Hospital
Sharp HealthCare
Shriners Hospitals For Children
St. Jude Children's Research Hospital
Sutter Health
Tri-City Healthcare District
UCSF Medical

HISTORICAL FINANCIALS
Company Type: Private

Income Statement				FYE: June 30
	REVENUE ($ mil.)	NET INCOME ($ mil.)	NET PROFIT MARGIN	EMPLOYEES
06/15	522	104	20.1%	2,313
06/14	838	82	9.8%	—
06/10	619	42	6.9%	—
06/09	490	(56)	—	—
Annual Growth	1.0%	—	—	—

2015 Year-End Financials
Return on assets: 7.0%   Cash ($ mil.): 75
Return on equity: 12.2%
Current ratio: 6.20

RALEY'S

Raley's has to stock plenty of fresh fruit and great wines — it sells to the people that produce them. The company operates about 130 supermarkets and superstores in California and Nevada. In addition to about 80 flagship Raley's Superstores the company operates about 20 Bel Air Markets (in the Sacramento area) and Nob Hill Foods (an upscale Bay Area chain with some 20 locations). Raley's stores typically offer groceries natural foods and liquor as well as in-store pharmacies. Founded during the Depression by Thomas Porter Raley the company is still owned and run by the Raley family.

Operations

In addition to Raley's Bel Air and Nob Hill supermarkets Raley's operates nearly 10 discount warehouse stores under the Food Source banner in Northern California and Nevada and one Market 5-ONE-5 neighborhood market in downtown Sacramento. The company offers online shopping and delivery in some markets.

Geographic Reach

Raley's approximately 130 stores are located primarily in Central and Northern California with a cluster around its headquarters city of Sacramento. It has about 20 locations in Nevada.

Strategy

Raley's strategy is centered around providing health fresh food at affordable prices. To that end in late 2018 it divested its Aisle 1 fuel stations which are adjacent to Raley's supermarkets to focus on core operations. It has also launched new products to appeal to changing tastes for healthy natural foods and prepared meals including a line of chef-created fresh meal kits vegetable sides (introduced in late 2018). Earlier in 2018 the company removed soda and candy from its check-out stands reducing its overall sugar offerings by 25%.

Raley's has also invested in technology to better serve customers and in 2018 launched a new website and campaign to promote online shopping and introduced a pharmacy mobile app.

Company Background

Raley's traces its roots to Placerville California and the 1935 opening of a grocery store by Tom Raley. The company has grown organically and through acquisitions; it acquired Bel Air Markets in 1992 and Nob Hill Foods in 1998. It remains family-owned.

EXECUTIVES

Ceo, Michael J. (Mike) Teel
Svp Store Operations, Kevin Konkel

Svp Merchandising And Supply Chain, Kevin Curry
Cfo And Controller, Ken Mueller
Svp Marketing, Deirdre A. Zimmermann
President And Coo, Keith Knopf
Board Of Directors, Dale Henley

LOCATIONS

HQ: RALEY'S
500 W CAPITOL AVE, WEST SACRAMENTO, CA 956052696
Phone: 916 373-3333
Web: WWW.RALEYS.COM

2018 Stores

	No.
California	110
Northern Nevada	18
Total	**128**

PRODUCTS/OPERATIONS

2018 Stores

	No.
Supermarkets	
Raley's	78
Nob Hill	20
Bel Air	20
Food Source	8
Other	2
Total	**128**

COMPETITORS

Andronico's Market	Safeway
Costco Wholesale	Save Mart
Food 4 Less Holdings	Trader Joe's
Grocery Outlet	Wal-Mart
Kroger	Whole Foods
Lunardi's Super Market	WinCo Foods
Ralphs Grocery	

HISTORICAL FINANCIALS

Company Type: Private

Income Statement				FYE: June 30
	REVENUE ($ mil.)	NET INCOME ($ mil.)	NET PROFIT MARGIN	EMPLOYEES
06/12	3,162	(1)	—	14,000
06/10	3,064	0	—	—
06/09	0	0	—	—
Annual Growth	—	—	—	—

2012 Year-End Financials

Return on assets: (-0.2%)   Cash ($ mil.): 26
Return on equity: (-0.6%)
Current ratio: 0.90

RAPID CITY REGIONAL HOSPITAL, INC.

Mt. Rushmore sightseers bikers and locals alike can seek medical care at Rapid City Regional Hospital. The medical facility is a general and psychiatric hospital with some 330 acute care beds and 50 psychiatric beds located in the Black Hills region of western South Dakota. In addition to emergency and acute care the not-for-profit hospital also offers a behavioral health center a rehabilitation facility a cancer care institute and women's and children's departments. Rapid City Regional Hospital is part of Regional Health a network of regional hospitals medical clinics and senior care centers.

Operations

Regional Health is comprised of five hospitals 24 clinic locations and employs nearly 5000 physicians and caregivers. In addition to Rapid City Regional Hospital the Regional Health group includes the Custer Regional Lead-Deadwood Regional Spearfish Regional and Sturgis Regional hospitals. It also operates area clinics and doctors' offices including a family medicine clinic that manages a physician residency program as well as retirement communities and nursing homes. Altogether Regional Health has a total of about 40 facilities in South Dakota's Black Hills region.

Sales and Marketing

Rapid City Regional Hospital provides health care services to the 360000 people who live in the Black Hills of South Dakota and the surrounding region as well as thousands of visitors each year.

Company Background

The hospital was established in 1973.

EXECUTIVES

Ceo, Charles Hart
V Pres, Michael Keegan
Treas, Jim Sorensen
Doctor, Byran Den Hartog
General, Dick Latushie
Vp Affairs, Robert Allen Jr
Information Specialist, Brian Crown
Human Resources Information MA, Jeremy Weaver
Projects Coordinator, Erin Jarvis
Vp Strategic Marketing, Robin Zebroski
Blood Bank Manager, Danielle Highbear

LOCATIONS

HQ: RAPID CITY REGIONAL HOSPITAL, INC.
353 FAIRMONT BLVD, RAPID CITY, SD 577017393
Phone: 605 719-1000

PRODUCTS/OPERATIONS

Selected Services

Bariatrics and Weight Management
Behavioral Health
Bones Muscles and Joints
Brain and Spine
Cancer Care
Clinics (Primary and Speciality)
Diabetes
Heart and Vascular Care
Home Care
Home Medical Equipment
Hospice Care
Hospitalist
Hyperbaric Oxygen Therapy
Infusion Services
Intensive Care
Laboratory Services
Labor and Delivery
Lactation Services
Medical Imaging
Digital Mammography
Neonatal Care
Neurology
Nutrition Services
Pain Management
Pediatrics
Physical Therapy and Rehabilitation
Regional Health Research
Senior Care
Sepsis
Sports Medicine
Stroke Care
Telemedicine
Wound Care

COMPETITORS

Avera Health	St. Alexius Medical
Mayo Clinic	Center
Sanford	St. Mary's Healthcare
Health-MeritCare	

HISTORICAL FINANCIALS

Company Type: Private

Income Statement				FYE: June 30
	REVENUE ($ mil.)	NET INCOME ($ mil.)	NET PROFIT MARGIN	EMPLOYEES
06/16	467	28	6.1%	4,200
06/15	437	39	9.0%	—
06/14	517	56	10.9%	—
06/13	489	49	10.2%	—
Annual Growth	(1.6%)	(17.2%)	—	—

2016 Year-End Financials

Return on assets: 3.1%   Cash ($ mil.): 17
Return on equity: 4.5%
Current ratio: 1.20

RAYMOND JAMES & ASSOCIATES INC

Does everybody love Raymond James & Associates (RJA)? Raymond James Financial hopes so. RJA is that company's primary subsidiary and one of the largest retail brokerages in the US. The unit provides brokerage financial planning investments and related services to consumers. It performs equity and fixed income sales trading and research for institutional clients in North America and Europe. Its investment banking group provides corporate and public finance debt underwriting and mergers and acquisitions advice. RJA also makes markets for approximately 1000 stocks including thinly traded issues. Planning Corporation of America a wholly-owned subsidiary of RJA sells insurance and annuities.

Operations

RJA is engaged in most aspects of securities distribution and investment banking.

Geographic Reach

The company has more than 200 branches and satellite offices concentrated in the Mid-Atlantic Midwest Southeast and Southwest portions of the US in addition to ten institutional sales offices in Europe.

Sales and Marketing

RJA has many big name clients across dozens of industries. In 2013 Titan Medical announced that it has retained RJA to provide advisory services and present options which could include a possible sale.

Strategy

In 2012 the company's parent completed its acquisition of Morgan Keegan & Co. and MK Holding Inc. from Regions Financial Corporation. Some of the equity capital markets and fixed income operations of were integrated into RJA.

EXECUTIVES

Vice President, Scott Cutliff
Vice President Investments Financial Advisor, Aamsa Zuniga
Auditors: KPMG LLP TAMPA FL

LOCATIONS

HQ: RAYMOND JAMES & ASSOCIATES INC
880 CARILLON PKWY, SAINT PETERSBURG, FL 337161100
Phone: 727 567-1000
Web: WWW.RAYMONDJAMES.COM

COMPETITORS

Ameriprise	Janney Montgomery
Charles Schwab	Scott
E*TRADE Financial	Merrill Lynch
Edward D. Jones	Scottrade
Edward Jones	TD Ameritrade
FMR	Wells Fargo Advisors

HISTORICAL FINANCIALS
Company Type: Private

Income Statement   FYE: September 30

	ASSETS ($ mil.)	NET INCOME ($ mil.)	INCOME AS % OF ASSETS	EMPLOYEES
09/17	9,917	198	2.0%	10,000
09/16	10,689	145	1.4%	—
09/15	7,893	167	2.1%	—
09/14	6,955	182	2.6%	—
Annual Growth	12.6%	2.8%	—	—

2017 Year-End Financials
Return on assets: 2.0%
Return on equity: 7.8%
Sales ($ mil): 3,255

RAYMOURS FURNITURE COMPANY, INC.

Raymours Furniture is heating up the oft-chilly Northeast doing business as Raymour & Flanigan. The company operates in several states through 94 retail stores including nearly a dozen clearance centers. It sells furniture for just about every room in the house (bedroom dining room home office living room) offering such pieces as bookcases entertainment centers headboards mattresses nightstands recliners sofas and tables. Brands such as Broyhill La-Z-Boy Natuzzi and Tempur Sealy are represented. Raymours is run by founding Goldberg family.

Operations
The company boasts 94 full-line showrooms about a dozen clearance centers 15 customer service centers and four distribution centers in New York New Jersey Pennsylvania Connecticut Massachusetts Delaware and Rhode Island. Raymours also operates more than a dozen customer distribution centers. Its one warehouse property is located in Quakertown Pennsylvania.

Geographic Reach
Based in New York Raymours has become the largest furniture retailer in the Northeast. Through a contractor it provides furniture delivery across the continental US.

Sales and Marketing
Raymours sells its furniture and accessories through its retail stores and online.

Strategy
Following significant expansion in 2008 Raymours has focused in recent years on expanding its presence on the Internet to entice more customers to shop. It added rugs and home decor items such as lamps throw pillows wall art and silk florals to its online furniture catalog. It also extended its furniture delivery area to all states within the continental US through a partnership with a contracted delivery service.

Raymours also expanded its existing partnership with Kathy Ireland Worldwide (led by its namesake model-actress) by adding 10 upholstered pieces to its Kathy Ireland Home furniture collection. The Kathy Ireland pieces are sold exclusively through Raymours.

The company has been expanding its New York distribution center in Rockland County spending some $46 million to purchase and renovate the 839000-sq.-ft. facility which will serve as its primary regional warehouse and distribution hub for the New York New Jersey and Connecticut areas.

In 2015 Raymours purchased the North Oaks Shopping Plaza. The majority of the complex located at 1345 Route 1 South in North Brunswick had been vacant for years. Raymours will become the plaza's new anchor.

Since 2013 Raymours has been prudently adding furniture showrooms in New York one in Brooklyn in 2013 on Fulton Street and another in 2014 in Queens which spans 22000 sq. ft. on multiple levels.

Company Background
Founded in 1947 by brothers Arnold and Bernard Goldberg Raymour & Flanigan is run by president and CEO Neil Goldberg and EVPs Michael and Steven.

EXECUTIVES
Chb, Neil Goldberg
Exec V Pres*, Michael Goldberg
Exec V Pres*, Steven Goldberg
Cfo*, James Poole
Consultant, John Burke
Coordinator, Marcelino Berrios
Customer Representativ, Phillip Barnett
Manager, Alan Copeland
Home Furnishings Consultant, Linda Sheppard
Inventory Control Manager, Corin McManus
Home Furnishings Consultant, Brian Brown
Auditors: GREEN & SEIFTER SYRACUSE NEW

LOCATIONS
HQ: RAYMOURS FURNITURE COMPANY, INC.
7248 MORGAN RD, LIVERPOOL, NY 130904535
Phone: 315 453-2500
Web: WWW.RAYMOURFLANIGAN.COM

PRODUCTS/OPERATIONS

Selected Products

Accents
Area Rugs
Bedrooms
Dining Rooms
Entertainment
Home Decor
Home Office
Living Rooms
Mattresses
Youth Bedrooms

Selected Brands
Berkline
Bernhardt
Broyhill
Cindy Crawford Home
Kathy Ireland Home
La-Z-Boy
Natuzzi
Rowe
Sealy
Stanley Furniture
Stearns & Foster
Tempur-Pedic

COMPETITORS
ABC Home Furnishings
American Signature
Bassett Furniture
Bob's Discount Furniture Bob's Discount Furnitu
Crawford Furniture
Dillard's
Ethan Allen
Euromarket Designs
Jennifer Convertibles
La-Z-Boy
Room & Board
Rooms To Go
Williams-Sonoma

HISTORICAL FINANCIALS
Company Type: Private

Income Statement   FYE: December 29

	REVENUE ($ mil.)	NET INCOME ($ mil.)	NET PROFIT MARGIN	EMPLOYEES
12/07	881	30	3.4%	4,400
12/06	780	23	3.0%	—
12/05	655	21	3.2%	—
Annual Growth	16.0%	20.2%	—	—

2007 Year-End Financials
Return on assets: 13.5%
Return on equity: 38.1%
Current ratio: 1.50
Cash ($ mil.): —

READING HOSPITAL

No it's not a square on the game of Monopoly but The Reading Hospital and Medical Center does treat patients in Berks County Pennsylvania and the surrounding area. Operating as Reading Health System the not-for-profit 735-bed medical center provides acute care and rehabilitation programs as well as behavioral and occupational health services. Specialty units include cancer cardiovascular weight management diabetes orthopedic trauma (level II) and women's health centers. In addition to the main hospital the Reading Health System includes Reading Health Rehabilitation Hospital and medical centers in nearby communities as well as laboratory imaging and outpatient centers throughout its region.

Operations
The system also delivers academic clinical training through its School of Health Sciences and Residency programs and operates the 113-acre Highlands at Wyomissing retirement community.

Altogether Reading Health System operates more than 45 locations with roughly 800 combined beds including primary and specialty care centers operated by Reading Health Physician Partners Reading Health Medical Services and the Quick Care and Urgent Care organizations. It employs some 1000 physicians and serves a population of more than 750000 residents. The Reading Health System served about 124400 emergency room patients during 2014; it also handled more than 31000 inpatient discharges and 19000 surgeries.

More than 90% of the company's revenues come from patient care services while residential (rehabilitation) and other services account for the rest.

Geographic Reach
Reading Health System's main hospital campus is located on a 22-building campus on 36 acres in West Reading Pennsylvania.

The system serves Berks County and the surrounding area.

Financial Performance

Reading Health System reported revenues of $901.1 million in fiscal 2014 (ended June) with net income of $62.8 million. Cash flow from operations totaled $30.2 million.

Strategy

Like most other hospitals Reading Health System sees its fair share of uninsured or underinsured patients seeking care at the ER for problems that are often not emergencies which can put a strain on hospital finances. Reading works to divert these patients to its Quick Care and Urgent Care Centers to help reduce some of that burden. The organization is also working to increase the size of its primary care network.

Within the main hospital Reading Health System is working to add new specialists such as interventional neuroradiologists and pediatric hospitalists as well as physicians who specialize in cardiac revascularization and robotic surgery procedures. It is also working to modernize technologies build new facilities and expand partnerships with area health care organizations. For example in 2013 it implemented its Reading HealthConnect electronic health record (EHR) system.

In addition the network broke ground on a $354 million expansion at the main West Reading hospital campus. The facility which is expected to open in 2016 will include new surgery and emergency treatment capacity and will add 150 private patient rooms; the project also includes conversion of existing rooms to private status. In 2015 Reading Health System opened a new family health care center; a new medical facility (featuring primary care physicians' offices imaging services and a laboratory) in Douglassville is also in the works.

Company Background

The Reading Hospital and Medical Center was founded in 1868 as The Reading Dispensary.

EXECUTIVES

Pres, Clint Matthews
Ceo*, David Clint Matthews
V Pres*, Theresa Sucher
Assistant To Human Resources M, Lori Fiddler
Coordinator, Lynn Burkett
Coordinator, Patti Luckenbill
Staff, Brian Le
Registered Nurse, Kristen Warrell
Assistant Manager, Michelle Gallen
Director of Perioperative Serv, Julie Schlappich
Gynecologist, Stephen H Fehnel
Auditors: PRICEWATERHOUSECOOPERS LLP PH

LOCATIONS

HQ: READING HOSPITAL
420 S 5TH AVE, READING, PA 196112143
Phone: 484 628-8000

Selected Pennsylvania Operations

The Reading Health Dispensary (Reading)
The Reading Hospital (West Reading)
Reading Health Medical Services
Reading Health Medical Services at Muhlenberg (Reading)
Reading Health Medical Services at Northern Berks (Hamburg)
Reading Health Medical Services at Spring Ridge (Wyomissing)
Reading Health Medical Services at Wyomissing (Wyomissing)
Reading Health Medical Services at Wyomissing Plaza (Reading)
Reading Health Physicians
Reading Health Rehabilitation Hospital (Wyomissing)
QuickCare Centers (regional)
Urgent Care Centers (regional)

Selected Services

Audiology
Behavioral Health Services
Behavioral Medicine Pain Management
Center for Public Health
Chaplaincy Services
Chest Pain Center
Cleft Palate Clinic
Cochlear Implant Program
da Vinci Surgical System
Diabetes Center
Emergency Services
Epilepsy Monitoring Unit
Family Risk Assessment Program (FRAP)
HelpLine
Hospitalist Program
Infusion Center
Interventional Radiology
Laboratory Services
Library Services
Mammography Services
Nutrition Services
Occupational Health Services
Occupational Therapy
Pain Management
Palliative Care Program
Pediatrics - St' Chris Care
PET/CT Imaging
Physical Therapy
QuickCare -Reading Health Physician Network
Radiology Services
Rehabilitation Services
Respiratory Care
Senior Assessment Program
Sleep Center
Social Service
Speech and Hearing Center
Stroke Center
The Reading Hospital Home Care
Tobacco-Free Wellness Program
Travel Immunization Service
Women's Health Services
Wound Healing and Hyperbaric Medicine Center

COMPETITORS

Ascension Health
Doylestown Hospital
LVHN
Lancaster General
Main Line Health System
Moses Taylor Hospital
Sacred Heart Hospital of Allentown
St. Luke's University Health Network
Universal Health Services
University of Pennsylvania Health System
Wyoming Valley Health Care System

HISTORICAL FINANCIALS

Company Type: Private

Income Statement — FYE: June 30

	REVENUE ($ mil.)	NET INCOME ($ mil.)	NET PROFIT MARGIN	EMPLOYEES
06/09	675	42	6.2%	5,500
06/08	640	50	7.8%	—
06/06	783	0	—	—
Annual Growth	—	—	—	—

2009 Year-End Financials

Return on assets: 5.4%
Return on equity: 103.7%
Current ratio: 1.80
Cash ($ mil.): 43

RECKSON OPERATING PARTNERSHIP, L.P.

EXECUTIVES

Pres-Ceo, Marc Holliday
Cfo-Cao-Treas, Matthew J Diliberto
Gen Ptnr, Wyoming Acquisition GP LLC

LOCATIONS

HQ: RECKSON OPERATING PARTNERSHIP, L.P.
420 LEXINGTON AVE, NEW YORK, NY 101700002
Phone: 212 594-2700
Web: WWW.SLGREEN.COM

HISTORICAL FINANCIALS

Company Type: Private

Income Statement — FYE: December 31

	ASSETS ($ mil.)	NET INCOME ($ mil.)	INCOME AS % OF ASSETS	EMPLOYEES
12/18	7,009	199	2.8%	279
12/17	8,541	198	2.3%	—
12/16	8,754	313	3.6%	—
12/15	8,858	362	4.1%	—
Annual Growth	(7.5%)	(18.1%)	—	—

2018 Year-End Financials

Return on assets: 2.8%
Return on equity: 3.2%
Sales ($ mil): 816

RECTOR & VISITORS OF THE UNIVERSITY OF VIRGINIA

The nation's third president Thomas Jefferson founded the University of Virginia in 1819. Named Rector and Visitors of the University of Virginia the university is known as UVa today. It is said to be Jefferson's proudest achievement and boasts an enrollment of more than 22000 students throughout its 12 graduate and undergraduate schools. One of the most prestigious public universities in the US the school has been noted for its law program English department and its more than 160-year-old student-enforced conduct code (the Honor System). The school also includes the University of Virginia Health System which trains future doctors and other health care workers at its Medical Center hospital.

Operations

UVa is an agency of the Commonwealth of Virginia governed by the university's Board of Visitors. The university comprises three divisions: the Academic Division the University of Virginia's College at Wise and the Medical Center Division. Its College at Wise focuses on the humanities arts science and professional disciplines concentrating on instruction research and public service. The Medical Center Division offers both routine and ancillary patient services via its full-service hospital and clinics and brings in around half of the university's revenue.

The university which has a 16:1 student-faculty ratio employs some 2800 full-time faculty and research staff supported by 10500 full-time staff members. It offers about 50 bachelor's degrees in nearly 50 fields some 85 master's degrees in about 70 fields half a dozen specialist degrees a pair (law and medicine) of first professional degrees and nearly 60 doctoral degrees in 55 fields. The university has about 16000 undergraduates and about 6500 graduate students.

Geographic Reach

The University of Virginia operates its 12 schools and medical center in Charlottesville while its College at Wise is in the Southwest Virginia town of Wise.

Financial Performance

In fiscal 2017 (ended June 30) UVa's revenue increased 5% to $2.7 billion amid increased in student tuition and fees patient services and sponsored programs. Student tuition and fees rose thanks to higher rates new programs and enrollment growth. Patient services revenue increased on the back of higher patient collections after write-offs due to outpatient volume growth. Non-operating revenue also grew steeply due to a much improved performance from its investments growing from a loss of $113 million to a gain of $729 million.

EXECUTIVES

Vp And Cio, James L. Hilton
Dean Darden School Of Business, Robert F. Bruner
Dean Mcintire School Of Commerce, Carl P. Zeithaml
Dean School Of Engineering And Applied Science, James H. Aylor
Dean College And Graduate School Of Arts And Sciences, Meredith J. E. Woo
Dean School Of Nursing, Dorrie K. Fontaine
Dean School Of Law, Paul G. Mahoney
Dean Curry School Of Education, Robert C. Pianta
Dean School Of Medicine, Steven T. (Steve) DeKosky
Evp And Provost, Thomas C. Katsouleas
President, Teresa A. Sullivan
Dean Frank Batten School Of Leadership And Public Policy, Harry Harding
Dean School Of Architecture, Kim Tanzer
Dean School Of Continuing And Professional Studies, Billy K. Cannaday
Dean Undergraduate Admission, Gregory W. Roberts
Chancellor College At Wise, Donna Price Henry
Evp And Coo, Patrick D. Hogan
Senior Vice President, Don Detmer
Vice President, Gertrude Fraser
Associate Vice President And Dean Of Students, Allen Groves
Vice President Professional Responsibilities, Malcolm Bell
Communication Assistant To The Assistant Vice President For Public Affairs, Charles M Mccance
Vice President, Steve Thornton
Vice Presient Information Technology, Ronald Hutchins
Assistant Vice President Financial Planning And Analysis, Nicole Ferretti
Assistant Vice President Financial Operations, Gerald Burke
Assistant Vice President Enterprise Infrastructure, Clayton Lockhart
Assistant Vice President Clery Act Compliance, Gabriel Gates
Assistant Vice President Department, Jeffrey Legro
Rector, Helen E. Dragas
Vice Rector, George K. Martin
Auditors: WALTER J KUTCHARSKI RICHMOND

LOCATIONS

HQ: RECTOR & VISITORS OF THE UNIVERSITY OF VIRGINIA
1001 EMMET ST N, CHARLOTTESVILLE, VA 229034833
Phone: 434 924-0311
Web: WWW.VIRGINIA.EDU

PRODUCTS/OPERATIONS

Selected Schools

College and Graduate School of Arts & Sciences
Curry School of Education
Darden Graduate School of Business Administration
McIntire School of Commerce
School of Architecture
School of Continuing & Professional Studies
School of Engineering and Applied Science
School of Law
School of Medicine
School of Nursing

HISTORICAL FINANCIALS

Company Type: Private

Income Statement

FYE: June 30

	REVENUE ($ mil.)	NET INCOME ($ mil.)	NET PROFIT MARGIN	EMPLOYEES
06/11	1,909	909	47.6%	13,300
06/10	524	97	18.6%	—
06/08	2,181	312	14.3%	—
06/07	2,121	1,114	52.5%	—
Annual Growth	(2.6%)	(5.0%)	—	—

2011 Year-End Financials

Return on assets: 11.4%
Return on equity: 14.5%
Current ratio: 1.40
Cash ($ mil.): 324

REDNER'S MARKETS, INC.

Redner's Markets operates about 45 warehouse club-style supermarkets under the Redner's Warehouse Markets banner and more than a dozen Quick Shoppe convenience stores. Most of the company's stores are located in eastern Pennsylvania but the regional grocer also operates several locations in Maryland and Delaware having closed its one New York supermarket. Redner's Warehouse Markets house bakery deli meat produce and seafood departments as well as in-store banks. The employee-owned company was founded by namesake Earl Redner in 1970. It is still operated by the Redner family including chairman and CEO Richard and COO Ryan Redner.

Financial Performance

Redner's Markets rang up an estimated $865 million in sales in fiscal 2012 (ends September) up from about $859 million in sales the previous year.

Strategy

Redner's has been tinkering with its store portfolio shuttering underperforming locations including several in its core Pennsylvania market while building new stores in existing and new markets. The regional chain has grown to four stores each in Delaware and Maryland since entering those markets in 2008 and 2005 respectively. Redner's is also growing its Web presence doubling its on-line traffic in the first year of a digiral shopper marketing program conducted in partnership with Google Shopping Network.

EXECUTIVES

Vice President Retail And Perishable Operations, Gary O'Brien
Vice President Human Resource, Bob Mcdonough
Vice President Human Resources, Robert McDonough
Vice President Purchasing, Dan Eberhart
Vice President And General Counsel, Jason Hopp
Vice President Perishable Operations, Gary Obrien
Auditors: RKL LLP WYOMISSING PENNSYLV

LOCATIONS

HQ: REDNER'S MARKETS, INC.
3 QUARRY RD, READING, PA 196059787
Phone: 610 926-3700
Web: WWW.REDNERSMARKETS.COM

2012 Warehouse Market Stores

	No.
Pennsylvania	36
Delaware	4
Maryland	4
Total	**44**

PRODUCTS/OPERATIONS

2012 Stores

	No.
Redner's Warehouse Market	44
Quick Shoppe	14
Total	**58**

COMPETITORS

7-Eleven
A&P
Cumberland Farms
Giant Food Stores
Sheetz
Wal-Mart
Wawa Inc.
Wegmans
Weis Markets

HISTORICAL FINANCIALS

Company Type: Private

Income Statement

FYE: October 1

	REVENUE ($ mil.)	NET INCOME ($ mil.)	NET PROFIT MARGIN	EMPLOYEES
10/16*	864	4	0.6%	4,800
09/15	884	6	0.7%	—
09/14	902	1	0.2%	—
09/13	892	4	0.5%	—
Annual Growth	(1.1%)	1.8%	—	—

*Fiscal year change

2016 Year-End Financials

Return on assets: 3.0%
Return on equity: 4.0%
Current ratio: 3.40
Cash ($ mil.): 56

REDWOOD CREDIT UNION

EXECUTIVES

Pres-Ceo, Brett Martinez
Programmer, Sky Walker
Consultant, Carrie Bruce
Assistant Manager, Earl Chavez
Manager, Stephen Hazard
Information Specialist, Jonathan Busch
Assistant Manager, Amy Murphy
Coordinator, Crickett Green
Accountant, Catharine Lyne
Business Manager, Jana Beatty
Senior Web Developer, David Gindy
Auditors: CLIFTONLARSONALLEN LLP PHOENI

LOCATIONS

HQ: REDWOOD CREDIT UNION
3033 CLEVELAND AVE # 100, SANTA ROSA, CA 954032126
Phone: 707 545-4000
Web: WWW.REDWOODCU.ORG

HISTORICAL FINANCIALS

Company Type: Private

Income Statement

	ASSETS ($ mil.)	NET INCOME ($ mil.)	INCOME AS % OF ASSETS	EMPLOYEES
12/17	4,046	67	1.7%	390
12/16	3,287	57	1.7%	—
12/14	2,468	47	1.9%	—
12/13	2,271	48	2.1%	—
Annual Growth	15.5%	8.6%	—	—

FYE: December 31

2017 Year-End Financials

Return on assets: 1.7%
Return on equity: 14.9%
Sales ($ mil): 126

REGAL ENTERTAINMENT GROUP

Regal Entertainment Group hopes to create loyal subjects out of fickle movie-goers. The largest theater owner and exhibitor in the US has around 560 theaters with some 7300 screens in 40-plus states through its Regal Cinemas Edwards Theatres United Artists Theatre Company Great Escapes Theatres and Hollywood Theatres brands. Its theaters house an average of 12.9 screens and more than 75% of its screens are in theaters with stadium seating. Regal Entertainment co-owns National CineMedia a joint venture that sells in-theater ads and operates a video network that distributes digital content to theaters. Regal Entertainment Group was formed in 2002. It was acquired by UK-based Cineworld in a $3.6 billion reverse takeover in 2018.

Change in Company Type

Regal Entertainment was acquired by UK-based cinema chain Cineworld in a $3.4 billion reverse takeover. The deal which closed in spring 2018 makes Cineworld the second-largest cinema chain globally after AMC.

Operations

Regal Entertainment manages its business under one reportable segment: theater exhibition operations.

Geographic Reach

Tennessee-based Regal Entertainment operates in around 45 US states the District of Columbia Guam Saipan and American Samoa. The chain targets midsized metropolitan markets and suburban growth areas of larger cities. It has a large number of theaters in California Florida and New York; those three states together account for nearly a third of Regal Entertainment's locations.

Sales and Marketing

Regal Entertainment employs an interactive marketing program for specific films and concession items to increase attendance and consumption. Its Regal Crown Club loyalty program rewards frequent moviegoers with deals of concessions and more.

The company uses the internet mobile and social media print and multimedia advertising to promote its service. Regal Entertainment conducts special interactive marketing programs for specific films and concessions items.

Regal Entertainment spends $1.1 billion on film rental and advertising costs annually.

Financial Performance

Regal Entertainment's revenue has been growing slowly and unevenly over the last five years.

In fiscal 2017 sales decreased 1% to $3.2 billion amid a 2-3% decline across the industry in the US. Revenue from concessions was unchanged as the impact of lower attendance was mostly offset by higher revenue per customer thanks to higher beverage and popcorn sales and selective price increases. Regal's other revenue streams recorded a net 10% uptick which include sales from its vendor marketing programs internet ticketing surcharges theater access fees paid by National CineMedia and gift card and bulk-ticket purchase programs.

Net income fell 34% to $112.3 million due to lower revenue a higher cost of concessions and an increase in loss on disposals and asset impairments.

Cash from operations in 2017 was unchanged at $410 million.

Strategy

A major part of Regal Entertainment's strategy to get customers out of the living room (where they are more inclined to watch DVDs from fancy home theater systems) and into the movie theater is through digital cinema. The company has most of its screens outfitted with digital projection systems and stadium seating. The theater chain completed its 3D deployment a couple of years ago.

Regal announced a new pricing strategy in 2018 based on peaks and troughs in demand. This means customers will pay more to see popular films at peak times and less for unpopular films at awkward hours. The company hopes the strategy will maximize revenue from customers desperate to see tentpole releases such as Star Wars and Marvel films on their opening weekends while drawing more customers in for cheaper mid-week showings of less popular pictures.

EXECUTIVES

Vice President Human Resources, Jackie McClure
Chairman And Ceo, Amy E. Miles, $1,024,850 total compensation
Evp General Counsel And Secretary, Peter B. Brandow, $504,700 total compensation
President And Coo, Gregory W. (Greg) Dunn, $612,850 total compensation
Evp Cfo And Treasurer, David H. Ownby, $566,500 total compensation
Vice President Film Systems And Administration, Kelly Palmer
Vice President Of Technical Services, Matt Basford
Vp Senior Film Buyer, Bob Mccormick
Vice President, Alan Davy
Senior Vice President And Human Resources Counsel, Randy Smith
Vice President Real Estate, Jerry Grewe
Senior Vice President Of Real Estate, John Roper
Vice President, John Curry
Vice President Film Marketing, Ken Foreman
Executive Vice President Business Development, Raymond Nutt
Vice President Of Theater Equipment, Ray Dunlap
Auditors: KPMG LLP KNOXVILLE TENNESSEE

LOCATIONS

HQ: REGAL ENTERTAINMENT GROUP
101 E BLOUNT AVE STE 100, KNOXVILLE, TN 379201605
Phone: 865 922-1123
Web: WWW.REGMOVIES.COM

PRODUCTS/OPERATIONS

2017 Sales

	$ mil.	% of total
Admissions	2,008	64
Concessions	930	29
Other	224	7
Total	**3,163**	**100**

Selected Operations

Cinemas
  Edwards Theatres
  Regal Cinemas
  United Artists Theatre Company
Theater advertising
  National CineMedia (20%)

COMPETITORS

AMC Entertainment	Marcus Corporation
Alamo Drafthouse	National Amusements
Carmike Cinemas	Netflix
Cinemark	Pacific Theatres
Cineplex	Reading International
Landmark Theatres	Redbox

HISTORICAL FINANCIALS

Company Type: Private

Income Statement

	REVENUE ($ mil.)	NET INCOME ($ mil.)	NET PROFIT MARGIN	EMPLOYEES
12/17	3,163	112	3.6%	25,359
12/16	3,197	170	5.3%	—
12/15*	3,127	153	4.9%	—
01/15	2,990	105	3.5%	—
Annual Growth	1.9%	2.2%	—	—

FYE: December 31
*Fiscal year change

2017 Year-End Financials

Return on assets: 999.9%
Return on equity: —
Current ratio: 0.80
Cash ($ mil.): —

REGENT SEVEN SEAS CRUISES, INC.

EXECUTIVES

Ceo, Frank Del Rio
Pres*, Kunal S Kamlani
Sr V Pres of Finance*, Harry Sommer
V Pres*, James H Peterson
Exec V Pres*, Randall Soy
Cfo*, Jason Montague
Treas*, Lisa Wilson
Coordinator, Joslyn Symmonds
Business Manager, Marie Merlo
Consultant, Tara Miller
Retail Sales, Anthony Vazquez
Auditors: PRICEWATERHOUSECOOPERS LLP MI

LOCATIONS

HQ: REGENT SEVEN SEAS CRUISES, INC.
7665 CORPORATE CENTER DR, MIAMI, FL 331261201
Phone: 844 863-8275
Web: WWW.RSSC.COM

HISTORICAL FINANCIALS

Company Type: Private

Income Statement

	REVENUE ($ mil.)	NET INCOME ($ mil.)	NET PROFIT MARGIN	EMPLOYEES
12/12	529	2	0.6%	217
12/11	485	11	2.4%	—
Annual Growth	8.9%	(73.9%)		

FYE: December 31

Return on assets: 0.2%   Cash ($ mil.): 99
Return on equity: 0.5%
Current ratio: 0.60

REGENTS OF THE UNIVERSITY OF MICHIGAN

Ranking among the top US public universities Regents of the University of Michigan (or simply University of Michigan) boasts more than 60000 students and about 8000 faculty members in southeast Michigan. Its three campuses in Ann Arbor Dearborn and Flint offer more than 260 undergraduate and graduate degree programs in fields including architecture education law medicine music and social work. The university has a student to faculty ratio of 15:1. The vast University of Michigan Health System which includes four hospitals and numerous outpatient centers provides about half of annual revenue. The university is supported by an $11.9 billion endowment.

Financial Performance

University of Michigan's revenue for operating activities was $8.7 billion for the 2018-2019 year. Operating revenue was $7.5 billion in fiscal 2018 (ending June 30) up 5% from 2017. Patient care revenue increased 6% tuition and fees rose 7% and federal grants and contracts grew 4%.

The university ended 2018 with $133.4 million in cash up $28.2 million from 2017. Operating activities used $411.1 million while investing activities contributed $299.3 million (from investment proceeds).

Strategy

University of Michigan strives to maintain national standards for academics research and health care. The university also works to recruit qualified faculty and health care staff and to attract high-performing students. Recent investments include expanding educational and health facilities and conducting enterprise-wide IT system upgrades. It completed construction of the Brighton Center for Specialty Care and launched construction of a new robotics engineering research and teaching facility in 2018.

University of Michigan has been conducting cost-cutting and productivity enhancement programs to combat the effects of reduced state educational appropriations and rising health care and facility costs.

EXECUTIVES

Vp Government Relations, Cynthia H. Wilbanks
Vp Development, Jerry A. May
Chancellor University Of Michigan-dearborn, Daniel Little
Evp And Cfo, Kevin P. Hegarty, age 63
Chairman Victors For Michigan, Stephen M. Ross
President, Mark S. Schlissel
Dean School Of Public Health, Martin Philbert
Vp Information Technology And Cio, Kelli Trosvig
Dean Stamps School Of Art And Design, Gunalan Nadarajan
Dean School Of Dentistry, Laurie McCauley
Dean Law School, Mark D. West
Chancellor University Of Michigan-flint, Susan E. Borrego

Interim Provost And Evp Academic Affairs, Paul N. Courant
Evp Medical Affairs; Dean Medical School; Ceo Michigan Medicine, Marschall S. Runge
Vp And General Counsel, Timothy G. Lynch
Vp Research, S. Jack Hu
Interim Dean Taubman College Of Architecture And Urban Planning, Robert Fishman
Edward J. Frey Dean Ross School Of Business, Scott DeRue
Dean School Of Education, Elizabeth Birr Moje
Dean School Of Engineering, Alec D. Gallimore
Dean School Of Information, Thomas A. Finholt
Dean School Of Kinesiology, Lori Ploutz-Snyder
Dean College Of Literature Science And The Arts, Andrew D. Martin
Dean College Of Music Theatre And Dance, Aaron Dworkin
Interim Dean School Of Natural Resources And Environment, Dan Brown
Dean School Of Nursing, Patricia D. Hurn
Dean College Of Pharmacy, James T. Dalton
Dean School Of Social Work, Lynn Videka
Dean Rackham Graduate School; Vice Provost Academic Affairs Graduate Studies, Carol A. Fierke
Assoc Vice President Development, Dondi Cupp
Assoc Vice President For Human Rscs, Laurita Thomas
Associate Vice President And Executive Director For Research Administration, Marvin Parnes
Associate Vice President Development, Julie Sparkman
Vice President Marketing, Rachelle Caoagas
Assistant Vice President Estate, Diane Tracy
Vice President Research, Stephen Forrest
Associate Vice President For Research Douvan Collegiate Professor Of Psychology Research Professor, Toni Antonucci
Vp Finance, Elizabeth Bills
Vice President Technology, Jamila Power
Vice President Technology, Mehra Rohit
Vice President Of Finance, Ruohao Li
Vice President Of Administration, Andy White
Vice President Student Government Budget Allocations Committee, Mackenzie Swart
Director Of Admissions And Orientation, Deb Peffer
Vice President Of Sales, Bill Bobrowsky
Vice President Finance Technology, William Hausman
Int Assistant Vice President Academic Human Resources, Donna Lartigue
Interim Vp Information Technology And Cio, Andrew Rosenberg
Vice President Of Resource Development Chief Fundrasing Officer, Darci Hoag
Director Of Clinical Services And Research; Assistant Professor Of Psychiatry, Renee Hoste
Office Of The Vice President For Student Affairs Student Aid, Michael Chrzan
Interim Vice President For Communications, Kate Michael
Vice President Of Finance, Morgan Slaff
Uofm Emba Vice President, Eric James Forster
Dance Student Assembly Vice President, Kelli Yapp
Vice President, Mohammed Islam
Vice President Finance, Dennis Diebolt
Vice President Of Projects Net Impact Advanced Fellow, Charlene Franke
Vice President Corporate Relations, Brandon Meloche
Vice President, Olivia Herron
Vice President And Corporate Counsel, Gael Tisack
Vice President, Shiuh Lee
Vice President, Beatrice Thaman
Vp Of Women In Mathematics, Vijita Kamath
Executive Vice President, David Witters

Vice Chairman, Michael J. Behm
Chairman, Mark J. Bernstein
Program Secretary, Frances Liao
Secretary Senior, Dawn Schulz
Senior Business Analyst Treasurers Office Department, Kristopher Covietz
Secretary Iv Law School Department, LauraA Shiltz
Secretary Iii Department Of Family Medicine Department, SophiaS Scoma
Board Member, Shary Balius
Board Member, Neil Elkin
Secretary Office Of Early Childhood Education And Family Services, Martin Stroud
Secretary, Mary Burton
Secretary Iii, Qiana London
Secretary Iv Pediatrics Ambulatory Care Pgm Department, CynthiaLynn Ellis
Treasurer, Eleonore Edgell
Senior Secretary, Andrew Mcintyre
Treasurer, Nahiyan Bakr
Treasurer, Alex Darr
Secretary B Temp Flint Ecdc, Kristina Russo
Secretary Of The University Office Of, Roberta Ruth Palmer
Lead Secretary, Amber French
Board Member, Ellen Toronto
Assistant Secretary Of The University, Erin Katz
Secretary Office Of The Vice President For Government Relations, Jill Crane
Auditors: PRICEWATERHOUSECOOPERS LLP DE

LOCATIONS

HQ: REGENTS OF THE UNIVERSITY OF MICHIGAN 503 THOMPSON ST, ANN ARBOR, MI 481091340
Phone: 734 764-1817
Web: WWW.UMICH.EDU

PRODUCTS/OPERATIONS

Selected Academic Units

Architecture and urban planning
Art and design
Business administration
Dentistry
Education
Engineering
Kinesiology
Law
Literature science and the arts
Medicine
Music
Natural resources and environment
Nursing
Pharmacy
Public health
Public policy
Social work

HISTORICAL FINANCIALS

Company Type: Private

Income Statement				FYE: June 30
	REVENUE ($ mil.)	NET INCOME ($ mil.)	NET PROFIT MARGIN	EMPLOYEES
06/18	7,466	920	12.3%	34,624
06/17	7,079	1,275	18.0%	—
06/16	6,278	(294)	—	—
06/14	5,534	1,574	28.5%	—
Annual Growth	7.8%	(12.6%)	—	—

2018 Year-End Financials

Return on assets: 4.2%   Cash ($ mil.): 163
Return on equity: 6.4%
Current ratio: 1.50

REGIONAL HEALTH, INC.

EXECUTIVES

Chm, Tom Morrison
Ceo, Charles E Hart
Exec V Pres, Joseph Sluka
Treas, Roy Dishman
Coo, Timothy Sughrue
Prin, Dennis Nesbit
Information, Bill Stockmann
Staff, Clinton Oyler
Staff, Teresa Lemmer
Compliance Staff, Sabine Colton
Manager, Trina Allen

LOCATIONS

HQ: REGIONAL HEALTH, INC.
353 FAIRMONT BLVD, RAPID CITY, SD 577017375
Phone: 605 755-1000
Web: WWW.REGIONALHEALTH.ORG

HISTORICAL FINANCIALS

Company Type: Private

Income Statement   FYE: June 30

	REVENUE ($ mil.)	NET INCOME ($ mil.)	NET PROFIT MARGIN	EMPLOYEES
06/18	689	22	3.2%	4,258
06/09	0	0	—	—
Annual Growth 114.9%		—	—	—

2018 Year-End Financials

Return on assets: 1.9%   Cash ($ mil.): 26
Return on equity: 2.9%
Current ratio: 3.30

REGIONAL TRANSPORTATION AUTHORITY

EXECUTIVES

Exec Dir, Richard J Bacigalupo
Chb, Thomas J McCraken Jr
Dep Exec Dir-Cfo, Joseph G Costello
Treas, Allan Sharkey
Prin, Julie Gomez
Prin, Carole Brown
Manager, Roxann Galvan
Manager, Michael Vandekreke
Senior Financial Analyst, Alejandro Montero
Project Manager, Fluturi Demirovski
Receptionist, Rochelle Holmes
Auditors: RSM US LLP CHICAGO ILLINOIS

LOCATIONS

HQ: REGIONAL TRANSPORTATION AUTHORITY
175 W JACKSON BLVD # 1650, CHICAGO, IL
606042711
Phone: 312 913-3200
Web: WWW.RTACHICAGO.ORG

HISTORICAL FINANCIALS

Company Type: Private

Income Statement   FYE: December 31

	REVENUE ($ mil.)	NET INCOME ($ mil.)	NET PROFIT MARGIN	EMPLOYEES
12/16	637	(99)	—	80
12/15	805	(77)	—	—
12/14	755	(3)	—	—
12/13	934	(102)	—	—
Annual Growth (12.0%)		—	—	—

2016 Year-End Financials

Return on assets: (-12.4%)   Cash ($ mil.): 109
Return on equity: —
Current ratio: 2.20

REGIONS HOSPITAL

EXECUTIVES

Manager, Jason Mahlman
Human Resources, Diane Collins
Database Administrator, Eswaramoorthy Kaliappan
Manager, Janette Schull
Director, Kay Schmitt
Physician Recruiter, Sandy Lachman
Human Resources, Sherri Shultheis
Vice-President, Tobi Tanzer
Information Specialist, William Rush
Counsel, Nancy Evert
Manager, Phil Traeger
Auditors: KPMG LLP MINNEAPOLIS MN

LOCATIONS

HQ: REGIONS HOSPITAL
8170 33RD AVE S, MINNEAPOLIS, MN 554254516
Phone: 952 883-6280
Web: WWW.HEALTHPARTNERS.COM

HISTORICAL FINANCIALS

Company Type: Private

Income Statement   FYE: December 31

	REVENUE ($ mil.)	NET INCOME ($ mil.)	NET PROFIT MARGIN	EMPLOYEES
12/17	790	47	6.0%	43
12/14	691	40	5.9%	—
12/09	515	17	3.4%	—
Annual Growth	5.5%	13.0%	—	—

2017 Year-End Financials

Return on assets: 5.7%   Cash ($ mil.): 124
Return on equity: 8.9%
Current ratio: 0.80

REGIONS HOSPITAL FOUNDATION

If you live around the Twin Cities Regions Hospital can help with your medical needs. The not-for-profit hospital has more than 450 beds and provides acute medical and emergency care services as well as specialty programs in areas including behavioral health rehabilitation burn care cancer cardiovascular orthopedic pediatrics and women's care. Regions Hospital is one of a handful of level I trauma centers in Minnesota and is also a teaching and residency center for the University of Minnesota Medical School. Regions Hospital is part of HealthPartners which operates a network of medical centers and a health plan in the Twin Cities area.

Operations

In 2012 Regions Hospital operated at a 78% occupancy rate with some 25000 inpatient visits. It also handled 78000 emergency center visits 13000 surgeries and some 2500 births. It has about 650 physicians on its staff plus another 800 affiliated doctors who are members of the HealthPartners Medical Group physician practice organization.

The hospital provided some $56 million in community benefits during 2012 including charity care and outreach programs.

Geographic Reach

Regions Hospital serves the St. Paul Minnesota metropolitan area as well as patients from other areas across Minnesota and in western Wisconsin. It also sees visitors from other Midwest states.

Strategy

The hospital has expanded its facilities in recent years to meet the demands of a growing Twin Cities population and address certain underserved community health needs. For instance in 2012 Regions Hospital completed construction of a new $36 million eight-story inpatient mental health center with about 100 beds designed to replace its aging mental health facility. In addition in 2009 the hospital wrapped up a $180 million expansion and renovation project that gave it a new 10-story patient tower with 20 new operating rooms more than 35 private patient beds and shell space for further expansion in the future.

In addition the hospital looks to enhance services through new equipment and procedural offerings as well as through partnerships with other area providers.

Company Background

Established in 1872 Regions Hospital became part of the HealthPartners network in 1993.

EXECUTIVES

Pres, Brock Nelson
Cfo*, Greg Klugherz
Psychiatrist, Scott Oakman

LOCATIONS

HQ: REGIONS HOSPITAL FOUNDATION
640 JACKSON ST, SAINT PAUL, MN 551012595
Phone: 651 254-3456
Web: WWW.HEALTHPARTNERS.COM

PRODUCTS/OPERATIONS

Selected Specialties and Divisions
Behavioral Health
Birth Center
Breast Health Center
Burn Center
Cancer Care Center
Center for Dementia and Alzheimer's Care
Digestive Care Center
Emergency Center
Heart Center
Level I Trauma Center
Level I Pediatric Trauma Center
Neurosciences
Orthopedics
Palliative Care Unit
Rehabilitation Institute
Spine Center
Stroke Center
Surgery Center

COMPETITORS

Allina Hospitals
 Amery Regional Medical Center
Catholic Health Initiatives
CentraCare Health
Children's Hospitals and Clinics of Minnesota
Fairview Health
Gillette Children's
HealthEast Care System
Mayo Clinic
North Memorial Health Care
Olmsted Medical
Paynesville Area Healthcare System

HISTORICAL FINANCIALS

Company Type: Private

Income Statement				FYE: December 31
	REVENUE ($ mil.)	NET INCOME ($ mil.)	NET PROFIT MARGIN	EMPLOYEES
12/12	581	36	6.3%	3,000
12/06	413	4	1.0%	—
12/05	430	12	2.8%	—
12/04	7	0	0.0%	—
Annual Growth	71.3%	320.5%	—	—

2012 Year-End Financials

Return on assets: 6.2%
Return on equity: 6.3%
Current ratio: 1.70

Cash ($ mil.): 64

RENAISSANCE CHARITABLE FOUNDATION INC.

EXECUTIVES

President, Greg Baker
Treasurer, Steven R Ko
Secretary, Douglas Cox
Executive Director, Susie McEuen

LOCATIONS

HQ: RENAISSANCE CHARITABLE FOUNDATION INC.
 8910 PURDUE RD STE 550, INDIANAPOLIS, IN
 462686117
Phone: 317 843-5400
Web: WWW.RCGF.ORG

HISTORICAL FINANCIALS

Company Type: Private

Income Statement				FYE: December 31
	REVENUE ($ mil.)	NET INCOME ($ mil.)	NET PROFIT MARGIN	EMPLOYEES
12/17	489	273	55.9%	3
12/13*	164	91	55.8%	—
11/09	81	42	52.2%	—
12/08	81	42	52.2%	—
Annual Growth	22.0%	22.9%	—	—

*Fiscal year change

2017 Year-End Financials

Return on assets: 18.9%
Return on equity: 19.0%
Current ratio: —

Cash ($ mil.): 170

RENESAS ELECTRONICS AMERICA INC.

Intersil makes transfer of power an orderly process at least in electronics. Its line of semiconductor devices for power management include power regulators converters and controllers power modules amplifiers and buffers proximity and light sensors data converters video decoders and interfaces. Its products are components in data centers computers smartphones autos and a range of other applications. Almost three-quarters of its sales are to customers in Asia. In 2017 Intersil was bought by Renesas Electronics for $3.2 billion.

Change in Company Type

Intersil's products should fit nicely with the microcontroller business of Renesas. Having Intersil technology on board should help Renesas further its penetration of the automotive market a growing area for semiconductor companies. Intersil became a wholly owned subsidiary of Renesas after the transaction closed in early 2017.

Operations

Intersil's industrial and infrastructure division which addresses power automotive aerospace and broad-line industrial applications accounted for 64% of sales in 2014. Products in the company's computing division 21% of sales provide power management functions for personal computers including ultrabooks notebooks and desktops. The consumer division 15% makes devices for gaming consoles and systems.

Geographic Reach

As a region Asia accounts for 73% of Intersil's sales. China by itself makes up 50% of sales. The next highest country is the US with about 18%. Countries in Europe generate about 8% of sales.

Based in Milpitas California Intersil has sales and design operations around the world. It has a manufacturing plant in Florida where it makes about 13% of its products. The rest of production is handled by contract manufacturers including Global Foundries Taiwan Semiconductor Manufacturing Company and United Microelectronics Corporation.

Sales and Marketing

About 60% of revenue comes through distributors and value-added resellers. Avnet Inc. accounted for about 18% of revenue and WPG Holdings Ltd. for just more than 10% in 2014.

Financial Performance

Intersil's revenue fell by about 2% to $562.5 million in 2014 from 2013. Sales in its industrial and infrastructure division rose 6% (nearly $19 million) in 2014 from 2013 but sales were off 1% ($1.2 million) in computing. Intersil's de-emphasis of lower-margin products in its consumer division was reflected in the 26% ($30 million) drop in sales the unit posted in 2014.

The company's net income on the other hand rocketed 1800% higher to $55 million in 2014 from $2.8 million in 2013. The main reason was that Intersil didn't carry the burden of a $28 million restructuring charge it took in 2013. Reductions in head count and other factors also reduced expenses in 2014. Cash flow from operations fell to $73 million in 2014 from about $107 million the year before.

Strategy

Intersil has made power management its focus shedding most of its connectors business. The restructuring began in 2013 and was largely completed by 2015.

The main focus of the refocusing is toward the company's industrial and infrastructure applications for growing markets such with power management needs. They include data centers communications infrastructure and industrial applications with a desire for better energy efficiency.

Another area is automotive and aerospace markets. For automotive the company makes video circuits for the growing use of cameras in autos and power products for the increasing demands of monitoring and managing power in hybrid and electric vehicles. For aerospace applications the company makes components for satellites bombarded by high radiation as they sail through space.

In 2014 Intersil expanded its line of radiation hardened (rad hard) devices to include the ISL71091SEH10 20 33 and 40. The product offers stable output voltage noise and a reference voltage providing better precision in data acquisition signal processing and power management.

The company introduced a Single-Chip Display Power and LED driver for smartphones in 2014. It incorporates display power and backlight LED driver functions in a single chip which improves efficiency and increases battery life.

A product that could improve efficiency for product such as battery powered drills are Intersil's First Half and Full-Bridge Drivers for multi-cell lithium-ion battery devices. They provide a safety feature that prevents voltage kickback a leading cause of damage and deterioration of lithium-ion batteries.

The company made no acquisitions in 2014 but maintains the possibility to do so in order to add to its power management product line.

EXECUTIVES

Cfo, Richard D. (Rick) Crowley
Svp Infrastructure Power Products, Mark A. Downing
Vp Corporate Marketing, Susan J. Hardman, $362,151 total compensation
Svp Worldwide Operations And Technology, Gerry Edwards
Svp Mobile Power Products, Andrew M. Cowell, $338,511 total compensation
Evp Renesas Electronics And President And Ceo Intersil, Necip Sayiner
Vp Precision Products, Philip Chesley
Vice President Of Sales For The Asia Pacific Region, Clifton Ho
Senior Vice President Worldwide Sales, Roger Wendelken
Vice President Product Development, Diwakar Vishakhadatta
Vice President, Noel Lister
Executive Vice President, Ryan Roderick
Senior Vice President Worldwide Operations, Sunny Gupta
Senior Vice President Of Information Technology, Stephen Brickles
Senior Vice President And Chief, Rick Crowley
Assistant Treasurer, Carol Hackney
Auditors: KPMG LLP SANTA CLARA CALIFOR

LOCATIONS

HQ: RENESAS ELECTRONICS AMERICA INC.
 1001 MURPHY RANCH RD, MILPITAS, CA 950357912
Phone: 408 432-8888
Web: WWW.RENESAS.COM

2012 Sales

	% of total
Asia/Pacific	78
North America	15
Europe & other	7
Total	**100**

PRODUCTS/OPERATIONS

2012 Sales

	% of total
Industrial & infrastructure	57
Personal computing	23
Consumer	20
Total	**100**

Selected Products

Amplifiers
Audio integrated circuits (ICs)
Automotive ICs
Bridge driver power management products
Broadband and hot plug power management products
Buffers
Core power devices (computers)
Data converters
Display ICs
High speed converters
Interface ICs
Line driver
Military-qualified analog ICs
Modulator/demodulators
Multiplexers
Operational amplifiers
Optical sensors
Optical storage devices
Potentiometers
Power amplifiers
Power converters
Power management ICs
Power modules
Signal integrity
Switches
Timing circuits
Video ICs
Voltage references

COMPETITORS

ANADIGICS	Monolithic Power
Advanced Analogic	Systems
Technologies	NXP Semiconductors
Alpha and Omega	ON Semiconductor
Analog Devices	Qualcomm Atheros
Fairchild	STMicroelectronics
Semiconductor	Semtech
Maxim Integrated	Siliconix
Products	Texas Instruments
Microchip Technology	

HISTORICAL FINANCIALS

Company Type: Private

Income Statement   FYE: January 1

	REVENUE ($ mil.)	NET INCOME ($ mil.)	NET PROFIT MARGIN	EMPLOYEES
01/16	521	7	1.4%	1,027
01/15	562	54	9.7%	—
01/14	575	2	0.5%	—
Annual Growth	(4.8%)	58.7%	—	—

2016 Year-End Financials

Return on assets: 0.6%
Return on equity: 0.8%
Current ratio: 2.20

Cash ($ mil.): 247

RESEARCH TRIANGLE INSTITUTE INC

The scientists at Research Triangle Institute address the problems of a sphere (the planet). Operating mainly under its trade name RTI International (RTI) the not-for-profit enterprise conducts research in such areas as advanced technologies environmental resources and medicine. It provides such services as certification and materials testing as well as software used in laboratories and research projects. Serving the US federal government other governments nonprofits and for-profit companies RTI offers analytical perspectives on public policy and has researchers working in offices around the world.

Operations

The company offers analytical perspectives on public policy. Its staff members represent more than 80 nationalities and speak nearly 90 languages enabling RTI to communicate and collaborate effectively with peer researchers clients and stakeholders around the world.

Geographic Reach

RTI serves clients in more than 75 countries. It has eight US offices and offices in China El Salvador India Indonesia Kenya Spain Sweden the UAE and the UK.

Sales and Marketing

The organization works with clients in government industry academia and public service. RTI's main clients are the Department of Health and Human Services and the US Agency for International Development. RTI's private sector clients have included 3M Chevron Cisco Systems GE and Sanofi-Aventis.

Financial Performance

The institute reinvests its net income in programs facilities and new capabilities.

EXECUTIVES

Evp And Coo, James J. (Jim) Gibson
Evp Rti Health Solutions, Allen W. Mangel
President And Ceo, E. Wayne Holden
Evp International Development Group, Aaron S. Williams
Evp Social Statistical And Environmental Sciences, Timothy J. (Tim) Gabel
Evp And Cfo, Michael H. (Mike) Kaelin
Chair Fellow Program And Distinguished Fellow Early Childhood Development, Don Bailey
Unit Vice President, John Mitchell
Vice President Contracts, Mary Reiss
Vp Business Strategy And Communications, Nicole Barnes
Vice President, Chris Buchholtz
Vice President Research Services, Howard Speizer
Executive Vice President International Development, Paul Weisenfeld
Vice President And Head Of Corporate Development, Matt Jenkins
Vice President Division For Research On Healthcare Value Equity And The Lifespan, Robin Weinick
Senior Vice President Education And Workforce Development, Kimberly Omalley
Vice President, Justin Eiler
Vice President, Sam Field
Svp Global Hr Business Partnering, Jeff Frederick
Vice Chairman, Peter M. Scott
Chairman, William M. Moore
Auditors: DELOITTE & TOUCHE LLP RALEIGH

LOCATIONS

HQ: RESEARCH TRIANGLE INSTITUTE INC
3040 CORNWALLIS RD, DURHAM, NC 277090155
Phone: 919 541-6000
Web: WWW.RTI.ORG

PRODUCTS/OPERATIONS

Selected Research Areas

Advanced technology research and development
Drug discovery and development
Economic and social
Education and training
Energy
Environmental
Health
International development
Laboratory and chemistry
Statistics
Survey

COMPETITORS

Battelle Memorial	Urban Institute
QSS Group	
Sandford Burnham	
Institute	

HISTORICAL FINANCIALS

Company Type: Private

Income Statement   FYE: September 30

	REVENUE ($ mil.)	NET INCOME ($ mil.)	NET PROFIT MARGIN	EMPLOYEES
09/17	972	22	2.4%	3,117
09/16	884	15	1.8%	—
09/15	831	40	4.9%	—
09/14	788	31	4.0%	—
Annual Growth	7.2%	(10.4%)	—	—

2017 Year-End Financials

Return on assets: 3.3%
Return on equity: 5.5%
Current ratio: 2.10

Cash ($ mil.): 29

REX HEALTHCARE, INC.

Part of the UNC HealthCare System UNC REX Healthcare is a not-for-profit health care provider that serves residents of Raleigh and the rest of Wake County North Carolina. Founded in 1894 UNC REX Healthcare includes the more than 430-bed acute-care Rex Hospital and two nursing homes with nearly 230 beds as well as primary and specialty care clinics throughout the area. Specialty centers and clinics provide services such as birthing cancer treatment same-day surgery heart and vascular care pain management and sleep disorder therapy. UNC REX also provides home health and mobile emergency medical services. UNC HealthCare also includes affiliate UNC Hospitals.

Operations

The health care system employs a medical staff of more than 1100 physicians and 1700 nurses. Its operations consist of an acute care hospital five wellness centers a pair of skilled nursing facilities (for rehabilitation and long-term nursing care) six suburban campuses and freestanding outpatient diagnostic urgent care and surgery centers.

Each year Rex has approximately 34000 in-patient visits 6000 births 30000 surgeries and 58000 emergency room visits.

Geographic Reach

UNC REX operates facilities in Wake County North Carolina in the cities of Apex Cary Garner Holly Springs Knightdale Wakefield and Raleigh.

Financial Performance

In 2015 net patient service revenue increased 14% to $814 million largely due to higher amounts of cardiovascular and oncology care provided. Operating income rose to $42 million and net income totaled $4 million.

Strategy

The company's venture capital investment fund REX Health Ventures was established to invest in researchers entrepreneurs and inventors and to support start-up companies.

In late 2014 UNC REX began construction on its new $200 million eight-story cardiac care tower. The following year it opened a new breast surgery clinic; it plans to open a new vascular disease center as well.

EXECUTIVES

Vice President Physician, Bob Ricker
Coo, Susan Sandberg
Svp Cfo And Interim Cio, Bernadette Spong
Vp Rex Healthcare Foundation, Sylvia Hackett
President, Steve Burriss
Vp Surgical Services, Jane Byrd
Vp Medical Affairs Chief Medical Officer And Chief Medical Information Officer, Linda Butler
Cfo, Andrew Zukowski
Vp Patient Care Services And Chief Nursing Officer, Joel Ray
Director Of Pharmacy, Jane Green
Medical Director Respiratory Therapy Program, Rohit Ahuja
Medical Director Of Bariatric Surgery, Lindsey Sharp
Chairman, A. Dale Jenkins
Unit Secretary, Annette Laster
Unit Secretary, Melody Adams
Secretary, Dorvetta Ford
Auditors: CLIFTON LARSON ALLEN LLP CHAR

LOCATIONS

HQ: REX HEALTHCARE, INC.
4420 LAKE BOONE TRL, RALEIGH, NC 276077505
Phone: 919 784-3100
Web: WWW.REXHEALTH.COM

PRODUCTS/OPERATIONS

Selected Specialty Services

Oncology
Heart and vascular
Surgical Services: Bariatric Heartburn and GI
Orthopedic Neuro and Spine
Rehabilitation
Emergency and Urgent Care
Women's Services
Wound Healing

COMPETITORS

Carolinas HealthCare System
Cone Health
Cumberland County Hospital System
Danville Regional Medical Center
Duke University Health System
FirstHealth of the Carolinas
Morehead Memorial Hospital
Novant Health
Vidant Health
WakeMed

HISTORICAL FINANCIALS
Company Type: Private

Income Statement				FYE: June 30
	REVENUE ($ mil.)	NET INCOME ($ mil.)	NET PROFIT MARGIN	EMPLOYEES
06/13	731	8	1.2%	5,500
06/12	719	34	4.8%	—
06/11	628	69	11.0%	—
Annual Growth	7.9%	(64.1%)	—	—

2013 Year-End Financials
Return on assets: 1.2%
Return on equity: 1.9%
Current ratio: 1.40
Cash ($ mil.): 74

REX HOSPITAL, INC.

EXECUTIVES

Pres, Steve Burriss
Vp Legal Affairs, Tate Bombard
Vp Medical Affairs/ Cmo, Linda Butler
Vp/Rex Healthcare Foundation, Sylvia Hackett
Vp Patient Care Services / Cno, Joel Ray
Vp Physician Services, Bob Ricker
Vp Heart & Vascular Services, Kirsten Riggs
Ccmo, Lisa Schiller
Vp, Tammie Stanton
Vp Regional Hospitalist Servic, Sean Tehrani
Vp Ambulatory Services, Tom Williams

LOCATIONS

HQ: REX HOSPITAL, INC.
4420 LAKE BOONE TRL, RALEIGH, NC 276076599
Phone: 919 784-3100
Web: WWW.REXHEALTH.COM

HISTORICAL FINANCIALS
Company Type: Private

Income Statement				FYE: June 30
	REVENUE ($ mil.)	NET INCOME ($ mil.)	NET PROFIT MARGIN	EMPLOYEES
06/16	904	106	11.8%	3,500
06/15	813	4	0.5%	—
06/14	724	25	3.6%	—
06/13	701	7	1.0%	—
Annual Growth	8.9%	145.0%	—	—

2016 Year-End Financials
Return on assets: 10.9%
Return on equity: 25.0%
Current ratio: 1.50
Cash ($ mil.): 91

RHODE ISLAND HOSPITAL

EXECUTIVES

Ceo, Margaret Van Bree
Director of Laboratory, Marilyn McAllister
Audiologist, Heather Taylor
Associate Director, Nicholas Ward
Doctor, Andrew Maslow
Doctor, Ronald A Delellis
Coordinator, Ann Roberto
Doctor, James M Klinger
Chief of Medicine, John Murphy
Coordinator, Marna Jones
Doctor, Andrew Cohen

LOCATIONS

HQ: RHODE ISLAND HOSPITAL
593 EDDY ST, PROVIDENCE, RI 029034923
Phone: 401 444-4000
Web: WWW.HASBROCHILDRENSHOSPITAL.ORG

HISTORICAL FINANCIALS
Company Type: Private

Income Statement				FYE: September 30
	REVENUE ($ mil.)	NET INCOME ($ mil.)	NET PROFIT MARGIN	EMPLOYEES
09/14	1,016	(5)	—	6,400
09/13	1,048	49	4.7%	—
09/07	918	110	12.0%	—
Annual Growth	1.5%	—	—	—

2014 Year-End Financials
Return on assets: (-0.5%)
Return on equity: (-1.2%)
Current ratio: 1.70
Cash ($ mil.): 32

RICELAND FOODS, INC.

Handling more than 125 million bushels of grain a year Riceland Foods is ingrained in its business. The agricultural cooperative processes and markets the rice soybeans and wheat grown by its 9000 member/owners who farm in Arkansas Louisiana Mississippi Missouri and Texas. One of the world's largest rice millers it sells white and brown rice plus flavored rices and meal kits under the Riceland and private-label brands. The co-op sells to food retailers and food service and food manufacturing companies worldwide. Riceland also makes cooking oils and processes soybeans bran and lecithin and offers rice bran and hulls to pet food makers and livestock farmers as feed and bedding.

Operations
Riceland's Research and Technical Center (Stuttgart Arkansas) is staffed by scientists and technicians with experience in rice edible oil and lecithin chemistry applications and process engineering.

The facility houses separate soybean and rice research laboratories to conduct product development product and process improvement and customer support. Riceland's business lines are supported by on-site analytical food applications and regulatory compliance labs consumer and food-service test kitchens and a well-equipped pilot plant. An ongoing research program reinforces Riceland's position as a premier supplier of rice edible oils and lecithin.

In addition to being a leader in rice milling the cooperative is a major soybean processor. Indeed its soybean processing plant in Stuttgart provides high-protein soybean meal and soybean mill run to poultry catfish and other livestock producers in the Mississippi Delta region and southwestern US.

Geographic Reach
Arkansas-based Riceland provides marketing services to farmers in its home state as well as Louisiana Mississippi Missouri and Texas.

Riceland markets rice products under the Riceland label private labels as ingredients and in bulk. Riceland's products are sold across the US and in more than 75 foreign destinations.

Sales and Marketing
A major rice exporter and edible oil producer Riceland markets its rice and oil products under the Riceland and Chefway (vegetable oil and shortening) labels. Its products are sold nationwide and to more than 75 foreign destinations.

Rice and oil products are supplied to many of America's leading restaurants fast-food chains cafeterias and military installations. Packaged and flavored rice products are marketed under the

Riceland brand. Vegetable oil and shortening products are sold under Riceland and private label brands. Wheat is exported to Mexico and Egypt. Soybeans are sold to US buyers. Rough rice is sold to Mexico and Central America.

Financial Performance

In 2014 Riceland Foods' revenues topped more than $1 billion for the seventh consecutive year. However its net sales for the year were down about 12% due to a decline in prices for rice and soybeans.

Strategy

A key business objective for Riceland is to increase the number of value-added products (such as Riceland Rice 'N Easy flavored rice mixes Riceland Turkey Fry Oil and Fish Fry Oil) and the level of its value added marketing. In 2014 a new riceland.com website went online allowing Riceland customers worldwide access to product information and sales personnel. The website brings consumers face-to-face with some Riceland farmer-members discussing their farming operations. It also includes cooking videos by Georgia Pellegrini a celebrity chef and author of 'Modern Pioneering.' The website

In 2015 Sage V Foods of Boulder Colorado has sold its interest in an instant rice production facility in Little Rock to Best Rice LLC which is jointly owned by Riceland Foods and Producers Rice Mill both based in Stuttgart.

EXECUTIVES

Ceo, Danny Kennedy
Auditors: BKD LLP LITTLE ROCK ARKANSA

LOCATIONS

HQ: RICELAND FOODS, INC.
2120 S PARK AVE, STUTTGART, AR 721606822
Phone: 870 673-5500
Web: WWW.RICELAND.COM

PRODUCTS/OPERATIONS

Selected Products

Consumer
Saffron Yellow Rice Mix
Rice N Easy Mix Wild Rice
Long Grain & Wild Mix Rice N Easy Mix
Broccoli & Cheese Rice N Easy Mix
Spanish Rice Mix Rice N Easy Mix
Chicken Rice Mix Rice N Easy Mix
Long Grain Rice Riceland Extra Long Grain Rice
Riceland GOLD Perfected Rice
Riceland Jasmine Rice
Riceland Natural Brown Rice
Riceland Plump & Tender Medium Grain Rice
Food Service
Oil
Rice
Food Ingredients
Long grain milled rice
Long grain brown rice
Medium grain milled rice
Parboiled rice
Broken grains

COMPETITORS

AarhusKarlshamn	Goya
American Rice	JFC International
CHS	Lotus Foods
Cereal Byproducts	Louis Dreyfus Group
Connell Company	Producers Rice Mill
Ebro Foods	Riviana Foods
Farmers Rice Milling	Specialty Rice
Farmers' Rice Cooperative	

HISTORICAL FINANCIALS
Company Type: Private

Income Statement   FYE: July 31

	REVENUE ($ mil.)	NET INCOME ($ mil.)	NET PROFIT MARGIN	EMPLOYEES
07/17	941	0	0.0%	1,646
07/16	1,007	5	0.6%	—
07/15	1,122	9	0.9%	—
07/14	1,148	2	0.2%	—
Annual Growth	(6.4%)	(54.4%)	—	—

2017 Year-End Financials

Return on assets: —
Return on equity: 0.1%
Current ratio: 3.10

Cash ($ mil.): 2

RICH PRODUCTS CORPORATION

Starting in 1945 with "the miracle cream from the soya bean" Rich Products has grown from a niche maker of soy-based whipped toppings and frozen desserts to a leading global US frozen foods maker. The family-owned business has developed other products such as toppings and icings and Coffee Rich (nondairy coffee creamer). It has expanded its product line to include frozen bakery and pizza doughs and ingredients for the food service and in-store bakery markets plus appetizers and snacks (Farm Rich) baked goods frozen ice cream cakes (Carvel) seafood (SeaPak) meatballs and barbecue meat. Rich Products markets more than 4000 food items that are sold in more than 100 countries; it has operations around the world on six continents.

Financial Performance
Rich Products boasts $3.7 billion in annual sales and more than 10000 employees worldwide.

Strategy
Rich Products is looking to Europe for growth and is making changes to better position itself in the region. In 2019 the company consolidated three UK production plants into one new 15-acre facility in Andover which will allow the plant to increase production respond quickly to market trends and serve as an international hub.

The company is developing new products aimed at meeting the changing needs of consumers who are seeking more convenient and ready-to-eat items. Recent products have included its portable SeaPak on-the-go Shimp and Cocktail Sauce pack Farm Rich Grilled Cheese Sticks and Farm Rich Bean Dip Bites. Rich Products has expressed interest in acquisitions in the refrigerated value-added seafood space to better diversify into different temperature states since most of its SeaPak products are frozen. The company has also partnered with brands such as beer maker Budweiser for a new line of beer-battered seafood.

One of Rich Products' biggest customers is Walmart. To better serve the retailing giant the company operates a plant in Texas largely dedicated to making products for Walmart. The company has also partnered with Walmart to create custom products such as ready-to-eat cobblers and bread puddings and has offered the retailer exclusive access to certain new product launches.

EXECUTIVES

Vice President Finance, Mary Kiener

President And Ceo, William G. (Bill) Gisel
Evp Sales And Marketing, Kevin R. Malchoff
President Rich's Entertainment Group, Melinda R. (Mindy) Rich
Executive Vp Chief Financial Officer, James R. (Jim) Deuschle
Executive Vp Chief Operating Officer, Richard M. Ferranti
Vice President Corporate Relations, Howard Rich
Vice President Of National Account Sales, Paul J Rich
Executive Vice President, Dwight Gram
Senior Vice President Of Operations, Dave Konst
Executive Vice President, Edward Moore
Senior Vice President, Paul Klein
National Account Manager, Tony Murphy
National Sales Manager, Susan Duran
National Account Manager, Tamara Boyer
Senior Vice President Global Supply Chain, David Cowperthwait
Vice President Of Finance, Eric Eynon
National Account Manager, Brandon Janesz
Assistant To Thomas R Greco Executive Vice President And Cco Pepsi, Sharon Delozier
Vice President Of Strategic Technology, Joel Cristall
Vice President, Matthew Wilson
Chairman, Robert E. (Bob) Rich

LOCATIONS

HQ: RICH PRODUCTS CORPORATION
1 ROBERT RICH WAY, BUFFALO, NY 142131701
Phone: 716 878-8000

PRODUCTS/OPERATIONS

Selected Product Categories
Appetizers and snacks
Bakery products
BBQ
Breads and rolls
Cakes & desserts
Cooking creams
Gluten-free and all-natural
Meatballs and pasta
Pizza
Shrimp and seafood
Syrups and soaked cakes
Toppings and icings

Selected Consumer Brands
Byron's
Carvel
Casa
Coffee Rich
Farm Rich
Freal
French Meadow Bakery
Rich's
SeaPak

COMPETITORS

BakeMark	Gorton's
Campbell Soup	Heinz
Canada Bread Company	Hom/Ade Foods
ConAgra	Nestlé
Dawn Food Products	Pinnacle Foods
Dean Foods	Schwan's
General Mills	Windsor Foods
Gonnella Baking	

HISTORICAL FINANCIALS
Company Type: Private

Income Statement   FYE: December 31

	REVENUE ($ mil.)	NET INCOME ($ mil.)	NET PROFIT MARGIN	EMPLOYEES
12/12	2,858	0	—	10,536
12/11	2,736	0	—	—
12/10	2,465	0	—	—
Annual Growth	7.7%	—	—	—

RIVER CITY PETROLEUM, INC.

EXECUTIVES

Ceo, Jeanne Haskell
Cfo*, Kurt Schmidl
Customer Staff, Lydia Castellanos
Coordinator, Jeremy Bautista
Marketing Manager, Brian Rosser
Information Technology, Chris Gaither
General Manager, Brad Folkins
Assistant, Kreidler John
Assistant Staff Accountant, Macie Wightman
Auditors: BFBA LLP SACRAMENTO CALIFOR

LOCATIONS

HQ: RIVER CITY PETROLEUM, INC.
3775 N FREEWAY BLVD # 101, SACRAMENTO, CA
958341959
Phone: 916 371-4960
Web: WWW.RCPFUEL.COM

HISTORICAL FINANCIALS

Company Type: Private

Income Statement   FYE: December 31

	REVENUE ($ mil.)	NET INCOME ($ mil.)	NET PROFIT MARGIN	EMPLOYEES
12/14	589	2	0.4%	55
12/13	655	1	0.2%	—
12/12	579	1	0.2%	—
12/11	656	2	0.4%	—
Annual Growth	(3.5%)	0.4%	—	—

2014 Year-End Financials

Return on assets: 6.9%   Cash ($ mil.): 7
Return on equity: 12.5%
Current ratio: 1.70

RIVERSIDE HEALTHCARE ASSOCIATION, INC.

Extra! Extra! Read all about it! Residents of Newport News (and about a dozen other cities in Eastern Virginia) Turn to Riverside Health for Medical Care. The not-for-profit health care provider administers general emergency and specialty medical services from five hospitals Riverside Regional Medical Center Riverside Walter Reed Hospital Riverside Tappahannock Hospital and Riverside Shore Memorial Hospital and Riverside Doctors Hospital as well as a psychiatric hospital a physical rehabilitation facility and retirement communities. Riverside also operates physician offices and medical training facilities. Specialty centers provide home and hospice care cancer treatment and dialysis.

Operations

Combined Riverside's hospitals (including rehabilitation and psychiatric) are home to nearly 1000 beds. Its major hospitals include Riverside Regional Medical Center (450-bed flagship hospital); Riverside Walter Reed Hospital (67-bed acute care facility); Riverside Tappahannock Hospital (67-bed serving the Northern Neck rural area); Riverside Shore Memorial Hospital (143-bed facility); and Riverside Doctors' Hospital Williamsburg (40 private rooms). It also operates specialty medical facilities including a psychiatric hospital a physical rehabilitation facility and retirement communities.

Geographic Reach

It serves Eastern Virginia including cities of Gloucester Hampton Newport News Poquoson Richmond Tappahannock West Point Williamsburg and Yorktown; Eastern Shore Area of Virginia; Counties of Essex Gloucester Isle of Wight James City King and Queen King William Lancaster Mathews Middlesex New Kent Northumberland Richmond and Surry.

Strategy

To keep up with demand Riverside Health has been upgrading its older facilities and building new ones.

In 2013 the company opened a new hospital the Doctors Hospital in Williamsburg. The 40 room hospital provides acute and emergency care as well as specialty services including cardiology neurology and pulmonary care.

That year Riverside broke ground on the new Riverside Shore Memorial Hospital in Onley which is expected to be completed in late 2015. It will have 57 private inpatient rooms with the ability to add 12 more in the future.

In 2012 Riverside Walter Reed Hospital opened a new intensive care unit.

It is also investing in technology physician expertise and patient services. In 2013 Riverside Shore Medical Center at Metompkin converted to digital mammography equipment offering patients a superior diagnostic tool to film mammograms.

Company Background

The original charter for Riverside dates back to 1915 when the company began as one hospital founded by the community. In 1962 the hospital was relocated to the present site in central Newport News.

EXECUTIVES

Vice President And Chief Pharmacy Officer, Cindy Williams
Director Of Nursing, Gaynor Callis
Director Of Physical Therapy, Chris Mchose
Auditors: ERNST & YOUNG LLP RICHMOND V

LOCATIONS

HQ: RIVERSIDE HEALTHCARE ASSOCIATION, INC.
701 TOWN CENTER DR # 1000, NEWPORT NEWS, VA
236064283
Phone: 757 534-7000
Web: WWW.RIVERSIDEONLINE.COM

Selected Facilities – Virginia

HOSPITALS
Riverside Behavioral Health Center (Hampton)
Riverside Doctors' Hospital (Williamsburg)
Riverside Regional Medical Center (Newport News)
Riverside Rehabilitation Institute (Williamsburg)
Riverside Tappahannock Hospital (Tappahannock)
Riverside Shore Memorial Hospital (Nassawadox)
Riverside Walter Reed Hospital (Gloucester)
RETIREMENT COMMUNITIES
Patriots Colony (Williamsburg)
Sanders (Gloucester)
Warwick Forest (Newport News)
SURGERY CENTERS
Doctors Surgery Center (Williamsburg)
Peninsula Surgery Center (Newport News)
Riverside Hampton Surgery Center (Hampton)

COMPETITORS

Alleghany Regional Hospital	Franklin Hospital Corp.
Bon Secours Health	Novant Health
Carilion Clinic	Sentara Healthcare
Centra Health Inc.	
Children's Hospital of The King's Daughters	

HISTORICAL FINANCIALS

Company Type: Private

Income Statement   FYE: December 31

	REVENUE ($ mil.)	NET INCOME ($ mil.)	NET PROFIT MARGIN	EMPLOYEES
12/15	1,149	21	1.8%	8,000
12/14	1,059	(86)	—	—
12/13	1,017	101	10.0%	—
12/12	948	41	4.4%	—
Annual Growth	6.6%	(20.3%)	—	—

2015 Year-End Financials

Return on assets: 1.5%   Cash ($ mil.): 1
Return on equity: 2.9%
Current ratio: 1.50

RIVERSIDE HOSPITAL, INC.

Riverside Hospital operates as Riverside Regional Medical Center a 450-bed acute-care facility that serves the residents of Newport News Virginia. Founded in 1916 the hospital moved to its current 72-acre campus in 1963 providing more than 30 medical specialties including cancer treatment cardiology birthing and diagnostic imaging. It specializes in cardiovascular and neurological surgeries and provides radiosurgery (radiation surgery) through a partnership with the University of Virginia Health System. Its emergency department is a 42-room Level II Trauma Center that treats more than 57000 patients each year. Riverside Hospital is part of the Riverside Health System.

Operations

As part of its operations Riverside Hospital operates a heart center neonatal center 18-bed neonatal intensive care unit cancer care center and radiosurgery center through a partnership with Chesapeake Regional and the University of Virginia Health System. Riverside Hospital works to prevent diagnose and treat diseases of the stomach intestines esophagus pancreas gall bladder liver and biliary tract through its Peninsula Gastroenterology & Riverside Endoscopy Center.

Geographic Reach

Riverside Hospital serves the health care needs of those who reside in and around Newport News Virginia.

EXECUTIVES

Ceo-Pres, William B Downey
SEC*, Wade D Broughman
V Pres*, Mike J Doucette
Treas*, Walter W Austin Jr
Coordinator, Holly Hicks
Internal Medicine Practitioner, Camelia Pana
Manager, Kitty Williams
Surgeon, Laura Cordes
Lab Director, David Smith
Surgeon, Jeffrey Morrison
Nurse Educator, Kimberly Lamm
Auditors: ERNST YOUNG RICHMOND VA

LOCATIONS

HQ: RIVERSIDE HOSPITAL, INC.
500 J CLYDE MORRIS BLVD, NEWPORT NEWS, VA
236011929
Phone: 757 594-2000
Web: WWW.RIVERSIDEONLINE.COM

PRODUCTS/OPERATIONS

Selected Services
Diagnostic Services
  Cardiac testing
  CT
  Digital mammography
  Electrocardiography
  Magnetic resonance imaging
  Nuclear medicine
  PET
  Ultrasound
Nutrition Services
  Radiosurgery Center
  Leksell Gamma Knife Synergy S Radiosurgery
  Gastroenterology Procedures
  Colonoscopy and polypectomy
  Flexible sigmoidoscopy
  Upper endoscopic exams and therapy
  Endoscopic retrograde cholangiopancreatography (ERCP)
  Percutaneous endoscopic gastrostomy (PEG)
  Capsule/Cam (M2A) study of the small intestine
  Esophageal dilation
  Esophageal and anal manometry
  BRAVO pH study of the esophagus
Pulmonary Rehabilitation
Surgical Services

COMPETITORS

Alleghany Regional Hospital	Franklin Hospital Corp.
Bon Secours Health	Novant Health
Carilion Clinic	Sentara Healthcare
Centra Health Inc.	
Children's Hospital of The King's Daughters	

HISTORICAL FINANCIALS
Company Type: Private

Income Statement   FYE: December 31

	REVENUE ($ mil.)	NET INCOME ($ mil.)	NET PROFIT MARGIN	EMPLOYEES
12/17	611	57	9.4%	8,000
12/16	636	65	10.3%	—
12/11	466	36	7.8%	—
12/10	429	20	4.9%	—
Annual Growth	5.2%	15.5%	—	—

RIVERSIDE MIDDLE PENINSULA HOSPITAL, INC.

EXECUTIVES

Pres, William Downey
Pharmacist, Jennifer Edwards
Sales Associate, Brian Billings
Technology, Elizabeth Martin
Auditors: ERNEST YOUNG RICHMOND VA

LOCATIONS

HQ: RIVERSIDE MIDDLE PENINSULA HOSPITAL, INC.
  7519 HOSPITAL DR, GLOUCESTER, VA 230614178
Phone: 757 875-7545
Web: WWW.RIVERSIDEONLINE.COM

HISTORICAL FINANCIALS
Company Type: Private

Income Statement   FYE: December 31

	REVENUE ($ mil.)	NET INCOME ($ mil.)	NET PROFIT MARGIN	EMPLOYEES
12/12	948	41	4.4%	50
12/11	59	10	17.3%	—
12/10	53	8	16.1%	—
12/09	53	10	19.8%	—
Annual Growth	160.1%	57.6%	—	—

2012 Year-End Financials

Return on assets: 3.4%   Cash ($ mil.): 53
Return on equity: 6.0%
Current ratio: 1.50

RIVERSIDE REGIONAL MEDIAL CENTER

EXECUTIVES

Principal, Debbie Davis
Vp of Ambulatory Care, Susan Mc Andrews

LOCATIONS

HQ: RIVERSIDE REGIONAL MEDIAL CENTER
  500 J CLYDE MORRIS BLVD, NEWPORT NEWS, VA 236011929
Phone: 757 856-7030
Web: WWW.RIVERSIDEONLINE.COM

HISTORICAL FINANCIALS
Company Type: Private

Income Statement   FYE: December 31

	REVENUE ($ mil.)	NET INCOME ($ mil.)	NET PROFIT MARGIN	EMPLOYEES
12/14	544	73	13.5%	1
12/08	301	0	0.2%	—
Annual Growth	10.4%	123.6%	—	—

RIVERSIDE UNIFIED SCHOOL DISTRICT

EXECUTIVES

Supt, Dr David Hansen
Supt*, Michael H Fine
Pres*, Lynn Carmen Day
V Pres*, Charles L Beaty PHD
Staff, Brian Caldwell
Analyst, Don Kramer
Teacher, Annabelle Porter
Psychologist, Linda Albright
Executive Assistant, Cheryl Anderson
Analyst, Alberto Isaac
Science Teacher, Carlo Rozzi
Auditors: NIGRO & NIGRO PC MURRIETA C

LOCATIONS

HQ: RIVERSIDE UNIFIED SCHOOL DISTRICT
  3380 14TH ST, RIVERSIDE, CA 925013810
Phone: 951 788-7135
Web: WWW.RIVERSIDEUNIFIED.ORG

HISTORICAL FINANCIALS
Company Type: Private

Income Statement   FYE: June 30

	REVENUE ($ mil.)	NET INCOME ($ mil.)	NET PROFIT MARGIN	EMPLOYEES
06/18	540	(8)	—	3,740
06/17	513	75	14.7%	—
06/16	499	18	3.6%	—
06/15	428	11	2.6%	—
Annual Growth	8.0%	—	—	—

2018 Year-End Financials

Return on assets: (-0.8%)   Cash ($ mil.): 290
Return on equity: (-5.3%)
Current ratio: —

ROBERT BOSCH LLC

Robert Bosch LLC is your one-stop shop for German-engineered auto parts appliances and power tools. The North American subsidiary of German giant Robert Bosch GmbH Bosch LLC makes and markets automotive original equipment and aftermarket products industrial drive and control technology packaging technology power tools home appliances security and communication systems thermotechnology and software solutions. Robert Bosch LLC's biggest area Mobility Solutions makes products aimed at the next generation of automobiles particularly around connectivity automation and electrification. Active since 1906 Bosch LLC has grown to around 70 primary North American locations.

Operations

Robert Bosch LLC comprises four reporting segments Mobility Solutions Industrial Technology Consumer Goods and Energy and Building Technology.

The Mobility Solutions segment represents two-thirds of sales and is active in injection technology and powertrain peripherals for internal-combustion engines powertrain electrification steering systems safety and driver-assistance systems car multimedia vehicle-to-vehicle and vehicle-to-infrastructure communication repair-shop concepts and technology and services.

The Industrial Control segment produces drive and control products and packaging technology and generates around 10% of sales. The Consumer Goods segment accounts for around a fifth of sales and consists of Robert Bosch's US power tools home appliances business. Energy and Building Technology segment (5% of sales) outfits buildings with heating ventilation and lighting infrastructure.

Geographic Reach

Robert Bosch LLC accounts for 15% of global sales. It has around 70 primary facilities in the US Canada and Mexico

Financial Performance

Robert Bosch LLC's sales grew 6% to $14.5 billion in 2018.

Strategy

One of Robert Bosch's major markets North America continues to receive substantial investment. It has expanded Mobility Solutions plants in Charleston and Anderson South Carolina and a dishwasher factory and central distribution center in New Bern North Carolina. It has also broke earth in the construction of a $120 million plant in Celaya Mexico. The 225000 sq. ft. factory will produce electronic control units which are used in connected mobility for the American market. Most recently Bosch opened a technology and innovation hub in Guadalajara Mexico.

EXECUTIVES

President Bosch Security Systems Inc., Christopher P. Gerace

Cfo; Evp Controlling Finance And Administration, Maximiliane Straub

President And Ceo Bosch Rexroth Corporation, Berend Bracht

Regional President Gasoline Systems North America, Sujit Jain

Regional President Chassis Systems Control, D. Scott Winchip

Evp Original Equipment Sales Chrysler, Juergen Peters

Evp Original Equipment Sales Ford, Manfred Mueller

President And Ceo Bsh Home Appliances Corporation, Michael Traub

Regional President Automotive Electronics North America, Timothy (Tim) Frasier

Regional President Diesel Systems North America, Bernd Boisten

President, Mike Mansuetti

Regional President Robert Bosch Automotive Aftermarket Division, Odd Joergenrud

Evp Original Equipment Sales General Motors, Clesio Honma

Regional President Electrical Drives, Peter Denk

Regional President Starter Motors And Generators North America, Pres Lawhon

Regional President Bosch Engineering Group North America, Wayne (Keith) Andrews

President Robert Bosch Healthcare Systems Inc., Micha Kirchhoff

Vp Original Equipment Sales Chrysler, Paul Thomas

Vice President Business Development, Michael Barhaug

Vice President Purchasing, Scott Schafer

Vice President, Tim Williams

Vp Human Resources, Michael Mckenna

Vice President, Christine Zimmerman

Executive Vice President Finance And Administ, Cara Reynolds

Senior Vice President, Martin Kueper

Vice President, Heiko Weller

Vice President Of Sales, Doug Arnold

Vice President Automotive Aftermarket, Karen Folger

Vice President Of Information Technology, James Puttick

National Sales Manager, Robert Dono

Vice President Operations, Scott Langston

Vice President Of Sales, Rajesh Darji

Vice President Operations, Charles Miklich

Vice President Marketing And Business Strategy, Andreas Sambel

Vice President Sales Marketing And Aftermarket, Ross Long

Vice President Mergers And Acquisitions, Marcia Medendorp

Chairman, Werner Struth

LOCATIONS

HQ: ROBERT BOSCH LLC
2800 S 25TH AVE, BROADVIEW, IL 601554532
Phone: 248 876-1000
Web: WWW.BOSCHTECHINFO.COM

PRODUCTS/OPERATIONS

2019 Sales

	% of total
Mobility Solutions	66
Consumer Goods	18
Industrial Technology	10
Energy and Building Technology	6
Other	3
Total	**100**

Selected Products

Automotive Technology
  Aftermarket
  Alternators
  Brake pads
  Car audio products
  Diesel parts
  Filters
  Fuel pumps
  Ignition products
  Oxygen sensors
  Spark plugs
  Spark plug wire sets
  Starters
  Wiper blades
  Original equipment
  Actuators
  Braking and chassis systems
  Car multimedia
  Electrical systems
  Electronic systems
  Powertrain systems - diesel
  Powertrain systems - gasoline
Consumer Goods and Building Technology
  Household appliances
  Cooktops
  Dishwashers
  Ovens
  Washers and dryers
  Power tools
  Angle grinders
  Belt sanders
  Circular saws
  Drill bits
  Drills
  Drywall drivers
  Impact wrenches
  Jigsaws
  Orbit sanders/polishers
  Planers
  Reciprocating saws
  Rotary hammers
  Routers
  Screwdriver bits and accessories
  Wet/dry vacuums
  Security Systems
  Access control
  Communications
  Fire detection
  Security management
  Video surveillance
  Thermotechnology
  Indoor climate control (heating and cooling and hot water production)
Industrial Technology
  Drive and control
  Assembly
  Electric drives and controls
  Gears
  Hydraulics
  Linear motion
  Pneumatics
  Packaging
  Confectionary cosmetics and chemicals
  Packaging machines
  Packaging services
  Pharmaceuticals
  Production tools
  Air assembly tools
  Cordless assembly tools
  DC electric assembly tools
  Electric assembly tools
  Solar Energy
  Crystalline PV modules
  Solar cells
  Thin-film modules
  Wafers

COMPETITORS

AISIN World Corp.	LG Electronics
Advanced Security & Controls	Makita
DENSO America	Molins
Dana	Motorcar Parts
Delphi Automotive Systems	NGK Spark Plugs
GE	Neaton Auto Products
Hitachi Automotive Systems Americas	Stanley Black and Decker
	Visteon
	Whirlpool

HISTORICAL FINANCIALS

Company Type: Private

Income Statement

FYE: December 31

	REVENUE ($ mil.)	NET INCOME ($ mil.)	NET PROFIT MARGIN	EMPLOYEES
12/14	10,474	181	1.7%	12,986
12/10	6,810	326	4.8%	—
12/09	5,464	59	1.1%	—
Annual Growth	13.9%	25.1%	—	—

2014 Year-End Financials

Return on assets: 2.7%   Cash ($ mil.): 832
Return on equity: 13.0%
Current ratio: 0.90

ROBERT W. BAIRD & CO. INCORPORATED

Employee-owned Robert W. Baird & Co. bringsÂ midwestern sensibility to the high-flying world of investment banking. The company offers brokerage asset management and investment banking services to middle-market corporations institutional clients and wealthy individuals and families.Â Its investment banking activities include underwriting and distributing corporate securities mergers and acquisition advisory and institutional sales and trading. The company also conducts equity research on more than 600 US firms.Â Baird manages more than $97 billion in client assets.

Operations

The companyÂ manages aboutÂ 10 bond and equity mutual funds: Baird Advisors manages fixed income investments while Baird Investment Management handles the equities side. Baird also invests in private equity and venture capital.

Geographic Reach

The firm has more than 100Â officesÂ in North America Asia and Europe where it ownsÂ 48% of Baird UK. More than half of Baird's locations areÂ wealth management offices in the US.

Sales and Marketing

Baird is the marketing name for Robert W. Baird & Co. Incorporated and its subsidiaries and affiliates worldwide.

Financial Performance

The company's revenues increased by 9% in 2011 and net incomeÂ grew by 2%.

Strategy

The driving forces for the company's growth have been its wealth management and investment banking operations. Unlike many financial services firms Baird has been adding staff and opening new offices in the US.

The company has also turned to the East for its fortunes. Its private equity group recently has an office in Shanghai hoping to capitalize on China's increasingly business-friendly environment.Â The outpost focuses on small high-growth businesses that have been overlooked by other venture capitalists. Baird has also expanded its investment banking operations in the region.

In 2012 Baird formed a strategic alliance with Axis Capital the investment banking subsidiary of Axis Bank with an initial focus on cross-border mergers and acquisitions between India and Europe and India and the US.

Company Background

Founded in 1919 Baird had been majority-owned by Northwestern Mutual since 1982. However employees bought back the company's stock in a series of purchases that culminated in 2004.

EXECUTIVES

Coo, Russell P. (Russ) Schwei
Chief Investment Officer, Mary Ellen Stanek
Cfo, Terrance P. (Terry) Maxwell
President Private Wealth Management, Michael J. (Mike) Schroeder
Director Fixed Income Capital Markets, Patrick S. (Pat) Lawton
Managing Director And Director Institutional Equity Services, William W. (Bill) Mahler
Co-head Global Investment Banking, Brian S. Doyal
President And Ceo, Steven G. (Steve) Booth
Co-head Global Investment Banking, Brian McDonagh
Director Risk Management, Mark A. Roble
Managing Partner Baird Capital, Gordon G. Pan
Head Global Equities And Director Equity Research, Jon A. Langenfeld
Cio, Timothy (Tim) Byrne
Senior Vice President, Jay Schwister
Vice President, Mark Zalewski
Vice President, Peter Klode
Vice President Vice President Administration, Thomas Seidcheck
Vice President, Joseph G Verdi
Senior Vice President, Dustin Hutter
Vice President, Florian Stoeger
Senior Vice President, Karen Heintz
Vice President Technology Product Manager, Lesley Augustine
Vice President, Tom Coburn
Senior Vice President Of Wealth Management Office, Paul McWane
Senior Vice President Supervisory Analyst, Keith Dorris
Vice President Information Technology Architect, Jim Cornelius
Vice President, Charles Galarza
Vice President, Robert Ferriman
Senior Vice President, Peter Hammond
Vice President, Tim Duchow
Vice President, John W Diemer
Vice President Financial Analyst, Lori Jackson
Vp, Owen Wrassman
Senior Vice President Investments, Cory Davis
Senior Vice President, Jayson C Bales
Senior Vice President And Senior Portfolio Manager, Daniel Tranchita
Senior Vice President, Michael Chorley
Vice President, Janet Holsclaw
Vice President, Marla Regan
First Vice President Purchase And Sales, Dean Markofski
Vice President, Charles Narmi
Vice President, Dalena Welkomer
Vice President, Adrianne Limjoco
Vice President, Ryan Unthank
Assistant Vice President, Tonia G Morris
Senior Vice President, Richard Palm
Vice President, Dale Rudow
Assistant Vice President Compliance Officer, Heidi Mclemore
Senior Vice President, Mark Kindler

Assistant Vice President Private Asset Management, Robert Filetti
Vice President, Mike Monfeli
Vice President Financial Advisor, Dan Koth
Vice President Private Wealth Management, Rebecca Ross
Senior Vice President Private Wealth Management, Matthew H Schmitt
Senior Vice President, Shawn B Smith
Senior Vice President Public Relations, Angela Pittman Taylor
Assistant Vice President, Dominic Burrescia
Vice President, Abhishek Pulakanti
Senior Vice President, Douglas Stencel
First Vice President Tech And Systems, Dennis Weishan
Vice President Financial Advisor, Jeff Pedersen
First Vice President, Guy Sawyer
Vice President And Art Director, Virginia Sunu
Vice President, Mike Malone
Vice President Wealth Management, Theresa Rynaski
Vice President Transition Process Manager, Denise Renner
Vice President Information Technology Project Services, Jim Whittet
Senior Vice President, Chuck Cairns
Vice President, Frank Downey
Vice President, Dawn Decicco
Vice President Financial Advisor, Blaine Gibson
Assistant Vice President And Marketing Specialist, Karen Sweeney
First Vice President, Bryan Fiene
Vice President, Mary E Levar
Vice President, Michael Halloran
Assistant Vice President, Genise Brandt
Private Equity Finance Manager Vice President, Erin Jelenchick
Senior Vice President, Rob Zwiebel
Assistant Vice President, Heather Melzer
Assistant Vice President, Kathy Cobb
Vice President Cash Management, Stephanie Raykuczynski
Senior Vice President Private Wealth Management, Bryan Sampson
Senior Vice President Internal Audit Director, David Cook
Vice President Investments, Thomas Olson
Senior Vice President Director Of Application Development, Jason Montague
Vice President Investment Banking, Christopher Hildreth
Vice President, Alex Ballantine
Vice President Portfolio Analyst, Aaron Benson
Vice President, Suzanne King
Vice President, John P Campbell
Senior Vice President, Gail Bivens-rose
Vice President, Jessica Stamm
First Vice President, Terry Lineberger
Vice President And Financial Advisor, Jon Bolton
Vice President, Rich Nigro
Senior Vice President Investments, Ronald Christian
Vice President, Marcy Finley
Senior Vice President, Mike Parrott
Vice President Equity Research, Mircea Dobre
Senior Vice President, David Schwarz
Vice President, Greg Pauly
Vice President Senior Research Associate, Luke Junk
Senior Vice President, Mark Falci
Vice President, Chase Hinderstein
Vice President, Joe Vruwink
Vice President, Brian Ellenbecker
Assistant Vice President, Stacey Leigh
Assistant Vice President, Deanne Soetenga
Vice President, Frederick Jetter
Vice President Private Wealth Management, Robert King
Assistant Vice President, Bernadette Ross

Vice President Investment Banking, Matthew Tingler
Vice President, Ryan Cox
Senior Vice President, Douglas Crandall
Senior Vice President, Timothy Butler
Vice President, Randall McLaughlin
Vice President, Richard Roesch
Senior Vice President, Orlando C Montesino
First Vice President Research, Ron Freisleben
Vice President Private Wealth Management, Phyllis Lovrien
Vice President Investment Banking, John Sun
Vice President, Brian Kelso
Vice President, Justin Albert
Assistant Vice President Andamp; Administrative Office M, Sandra Gary
Vice President Investments, John Barnefield
Senior Vice President, Andy Roed
Vice President, Gavin Amato
Vice President Private Wealth Management, Larry Magid
Vice President Senior Estate Planner, Rick Holman
Assistant Vice President, Brian Hanrahan
Vice President, Dawn Mattrisch
Vice President, Alex Lawhorn
Vice President Investments, Frances D Bobbie
Assistant Vice President, Ginny Moye
Vice President, Peter Philpott
Senior Vice President, Mary Howard
Vice President, James Cain
Vice President Private Wealth Management, Wes Oliver
Assistant Vice President, Dale Jacques
Senior Vice President, Gerald Jarzabek
Senior Vice President, Jan Bayle
Assistant Vice President, Mary Zavaglia
Assistant Vice President, Judie Meriweather
Vice President Pwm, Clay Ryan
Assistant Vice President, Mary Walters
First Vice President, Thomas Hayden
Senior Vice President And Associate General Counsel, Andrew Ketter
Vice President Resources Consultant Business Partner Human Capital, Lynn Rudolph
Senior Vice President Investments, Lewis Krinsky
Assistant Vice President, Michelle Hernandez
Vice President, Alice Ambrowiak

LOCATIONS

HQ: ROBERT W. BAIRD & CO. INCORPORATED
777 E WISCONSIN AVE FL 29, MILWAUKEE, WI 532025391
Phone: 414 765-3500
Web: WWW.RWBAIRD.COM

PRODUCTS/OPERATIONS

Business Groups
Asset Management
Equity Capital Markets
Fixed Income Capital Markets
Private Equity
Private Wealth Management

COMPETITORS

Citigroup Global Markets	Piper Jaffray
Cowen Group	Raymond James Financial
Goldman Sachs	Stephens
Greenhill	Stifel Financial
Jefferies Group	Thomas Weisel Partners
Morgan Stanley	William Blair

HISTORICAL FINANCIALS

Company Type: Private

Income Statement

	ASSETS ($ mil.)	NET INCOME ($ mil.)	INCOME AS % OF ASSETS	EMPLOYEES
12/09	2,063	41	2.0%	5,215
12/08	1,080	36	3.4%	—
12/07	1,712	50	2.9%	—
Annual Growth	9.8%	(8.6%)	—	—

FYE: December 31

2009 Year-End Financials

Return on assets: 2.0% Sales ($ mil): 699
Return on equity: 11.2%

ROBERT WOOD JOHNSON UNIVERSITY HOSPITAL, INC.

Robert Wood Johnson University Hospital (RWJUH) is the flagship facility of the Robert Wood Johnson Health System and Network. The medical center offers patients acute and tertiary care including cardiovascular services organ and tissue transplantation pediatric care (at The Bristol-Myers Squibb Children's Hospital) Level I trauma care cancer treatment (at the Cancer Hospital of New Jersey) women's health and emergency medicine. Founded in 1884 the 965-bed facility serves as a teaching center for the Robert Wood Johnson Medical School (RWJMS). The Robert Wood Johnson Health System plans to merge with fellow New Jersey hospital system Barnabas Health.

Operations

More than 1300 physicians affiliated with RWJUH treat some 200000 patients each year. The hospital handles some 17000 inpatient admissions each year as well as 48000 emergency visits. The hospital's cancer unit is the flagship partner of the Cancer Institute of New Jersey a research and treatment center located adjacent to RWJUH that is the only National Cancer Institute-designated cancer center in New Jersey. In addition the Bristol-Myers Squibb Children's Hospital works in tandem with the Child Health Institute of New Jersey (also located on the integrated medical campus).

Its RWJMS-partnered educational programs include residency programs for some 300 to 400 students. The hospital's nursing program covers 500 students and is affiliated with five schools; RWJUH also offers allied health professional training programs in fields including pharmacy; radiology; dental technology; dietary health; emergency medicine; and physical occupational speech/hearing and respiratory therapy.

Other members of the Robert Wood Johnson Health System include Robert Wood Johnson University Hospital Rahway Robert Wood Johnson University Hospital Hamilton and the Children's Specialized Hospital. The Robert Wood Johnson Health Network is an affiliated group of health care providers including hospitals nursing homes and health clinics which are located throughout New Jersey.

Geographic Reach

RWJUH has locations in New Brunswick Hamilton Rahway and Somerville New Jersey.

Sales and Marketing

Third-party commercial payors account for about two-thirds of the hospital's net patient service revenue; government payors account for around one third.

Financial Performance

In fiscal 2014 revenue increased 24% to $1.04 billion primarily due to an increase in net patient service earnings. Net income fell 28% to $78 million as investment returns declined. A sizable sum was also paid towards the recently established Robert Wood Johnson Physician Enterprise a for-profit professional association further cutting into net income.

Cash flow from operations increased 4% to $80 million due to such factors as an increase in accounts payable.

Strategy

To expand operations the company has merged with existing hospitals and opened new satellite locations. In 2014 Somerset Medical Center was merged into RWJUH adding more than 300 beds and providing RWJUH entry into the Somerset community.

Mergers and Acquisitions

In mid-2015 Barnabas Health and the Robert Wood Johnson Health System agreed to join forces in a merger that will create the largest hospital system in New Jersey. The combined entity will operate under the name RWJ Barnabas Health and will include 11 hospitals. The deal is just one of a series of consolidation deals that have been taking place in New Jersey as companies work to remain competitive in the wake of the passing of the Affordable Care Act.

EXECUTIVES

President, John Gantner
President Somerset, Anthony V. Cava
Vice President Human Resources, Martin Everhart
Director Of Nursing, Billie Bellamy
Head Nurse, Jennifer Mackown
Vice President Critical Care, Julie Arsenault
Nursing Director Pediatric Critical Care Pediatric Transport Program Pediatric Oncology And Pacct, Linda Palkoski
Vice President Is, Robert Irwin
Assistant Vice President Finance, Geri Swenarton
Director Of Radiology, Barbara Richardson
Head Nurse, Laura Viggiano
Vice President Foundation And Development, Mark Hanichak
Secretary, Ivy Mccord
Auditors: KPMG LLP NEW YORK NY

LOCATIONS

HQ: ROBERT WOOD JOHNSON UNIVERSITY HOSPITAL, INC.
1 ROBERT WOOD JOHNSON PL, NEW BRUNSWICK, NJ 089011928
Phone: 732 828-3000
Web: WWW.RWJBH.ORG

PRODUCTS/OPERATIONS

Selected Services

Bariatric Surgery
Bloodless Surgery
Cardiothoracic Surgery
Colorectal Surgery
Comprehensive Sleep Disorders Center
Diabetes
Digestive Disorders
Emergency Department
Executive Health Program
Heart Transplantation
Injury Prevention
Kidney and Pancreas Transplantation
Lab Services (blood work and blood collection)
Level 1 Trauma Center
Neurosciences
  Clinical Neurosciences Center

Deep Brain Stimulation for Movement Disorders
Laser Ablation for Brain Tumor Treatment
Neurosurgery
New Jersey Brain Aneurysm & AVM Program
Parkinson's Disease Information and Referral Center
Stroke Center
The Gamma Knife Center: Advanced Treatment for Brain and Spine
New Jersey Pain Institute at RWJUH
Orthopedic Surgery
Outpatient Radiology: University Radiology at Robert Wood Johnson
Palliative Care Program
Pastoral Care
Pelvic Floor and Incontinence Program
Physical and Occupational Therapy
Prostate Cancer Surgery
Radiation Oncology
  Gynecologic Brachytherapy
  Prostate Brachytherapy
  TomoTherapy
  Total Skin Electron Beam Therapy
Radiology (including CT MRI and ultrasound)
Speech and Hearing Program
The Center for Wound Healing
The Limb Preservation Program
Therapeutic Apheresis
Thoracic Surgery
Vascular Surgery

COMPETITORS

Bergen Regional Medical	Saint Peter's University Hospital
Capital Health System	St. Joseph's Healthcare System
Princeton HealthCare	
Raritan Bay Medical Center	

HISTORICAL FINANCIALS

Company Type: Private

Income Statement

	REVENUE ($ mil.)	NET INCOME ($ mil.)	NET PROFIT MARGIN	EMPLOYEES
12/18	1,337	(3)	—	4,674
12/17	1,249	(59)	—	—
Annual Growth	—	—	—	—

FYE: December 31

2018 Year-End Financials

Return on assets: (-0.2%) Cash ($ mil.): 1
Return on equity: (-0.3%)
Current ratio: 4.50

ROCHESTER CITY SCHOOL DISTRICT

EXECUTIVES

Supt, Jean C Brizard
Supt*, Bolgen Vargas
RES*, Malik Evans
V-Pres*, Jose Cruz
V Pres*, Van Henri White
MBR-Board of Edu*, Mary Adams
MBR-Board of Edu*, Melisza Campos
MBR-Board of Edu*, Cynthia Elliot
Mgr-Board of Edu*, Willa Powell
Human Resources Secretary II, Annette Ramos
Executive Director of Health, Carlos Cotto
Auditors: FREEDMAXICK CPAS PC ROCHES

LOCATIONS

HQ: ROCHESTER CITY SCHOOL DISTRICT
131 W BROAD ST, ROCHESTER, NY 146141103
Phone: 585 262-8100
Web: WWW.RCSDK12.ORG

HISTORICAL FINANCIALS

Company Type: Private

Income Statement				FYE: June 30
	REVENUE ($ mil.)	NET INCOME ($ mil.)	NET PROFIT MARGIN	EMPLOYEES
06/13	708	74	10.6%	5,470
06/11	681	(19)	—	—
Annual Growth	1.9%	—	—	—

2013 Year-End Financials

Return on assets: 8.7% Cash ($ mil.): 315
Return on equity: 123.6%
Current ratio: —

ROCHESTER GAS AND ELECTRIC CORPORATION

Upstate New York residents count on Rochester Gas and Electric (RG&E) to keep the lights turned on. The regulated utility provides electricity to about 370000 customers and natural gas to 306000 customers. RG&E operates 22500 miles of power transmission and distribution lines and has a generating capacity of approximately 400 MW from interests in fossil-fueled and hydroelectric power plants. RG&E and sister utility company New York State Electric & Gas (NYSEG) are subsidiaries of regional power and gas distribution player Avangrid).

Change in Company Type
In 2012 ultimate parent company IBERDROLA reorganized consolidating Iberdrola Renewables Holdings and IBERDROLA USA under a new Avangrid holding company. Intermediate holding company Iberdrola USA Networks was then created to hold all of IBERDROLA's regulated US electric and gas utilities including RG&E.

Geographic Reach
RG&E's service territory contains a substantial suburban area and a large agricultural area in parts of nine counties including and surrounding the city of Rochester New York with a population of 1 million.

Financial Performance
The company operates under the Network business of IBERDROLA. The Network business accounted for 25% of IBERDROLA's 2013 revenues; some 28% of Network sales came from US operations. IBERDROLA generated 10% of its total revenues from the US in 2013.

Strategy
To reduce its carbon emissions RG&E along with affiliate NYSEG is pushing green energy options including a wind energy power program whereby residents can choose to have their power supply from wind generated sources.

In 2013 the company announced plans to retire its 18-MW Rochester 9 natural gas-fired combustion turbine as it would be too expensive to repair the equipment failures that forced the unit offline that year.

Company Background
Between 2008 and the end of 2010 NYSEG or RG&E interconnected six landfill gas plants with a total of 26MW of generating capacity three wind farms with 209 wind turbines (381 MW of generating capacity) in Wyoming and Steuben counties a new 30 MW combined heat and power facility for Cornell University and a lithium-ion battery energy storage facility for AES Corporation.

EXECUTIVES

Vice President General Manager, Jeff Masters
Auditors: KPMG LLP NEW YORK NEW YORK

LOCATIONS

HQ: ROCHESTER GAS AND ELECTRIC CORPORATION
89 EAST AVE, ROCHESTER, NY 146490002
Phone: 800 295-7323

COMPETITORS

CH Energy	New York Power
Con Edison	Authority
National Fuel Gas	Niagara Mohawk

HISTORICAL FINANCIALS

Company Type: Private

Income Statement				FYE: December 31
	REVENUE ($ mil.)	NET INCOME ($ mil.)	NET PROFIT MARGIN	EMPLOYEES
12/17	850	83	9.8%	865
12/16	1,042	80	7.7%	—
12/10	982	54	5.5%	—
Annual Growth	(2.0%)	6.3%	—	—

2017 Year-End Financials

Return on assets: 2.3% Cash ($ mil.): —
Return on equity: 8.8%
Current ratio: 1.20

ROCHESTER GENERAL HOSPITAL INC

EXECUTIVES

Ceo, Mark Clement
Cfo*, Robert Nesselbush
Clinical Director, Timothy Van Vassem
Information Specialist, Emily Wishart
Information Specialist, Heidi Mix
Coordinator, Nancy Latacki
Coordinator, Rank James
Accounting Staff, Stephanie Beiter
Talent Acquisition Coordinator, Brandi Holloway
Dermatologist, Brett Shulman
Center For Pain Management, Calvin Chiang

LOCATIONS

HQ: ROCHESTER GENERAL HOSPITAL INC
1425 PORTLAND AVE BLDG 3, ROCHESTER, NY 146213095
Phone: 585 922-4101
Web: WWW.ROCHESTERREGIONAL.ORG

HISTORICAL FINANCIALS

Company Type: Private

Income Statement				FYE: December 31
	REVENUE ($ mil.)	NET INCOME ($ mil.)	NET PROFIT MARGIN	EMPLOYEES
12/17	899	32	3.6%	3,100
12/16	858	24	2.9%	—
12/15	847	27	3.3%	—
12/14	810	32	4.0%	—
Annual Growth	3.5%	(0.6%)	—	—

2017 Year-End Financials

Return on assets: 2.9% Cash ($ mil.): 36
Return on equity: 7.2%
Current ratio: 1.50

ROCHESTER INSTITUTE OF TECHNOLOGY (INC)

The Rochester Institute of Technology (RIT) is a privately endowed university with nine colleges focused on providing career-oriented education to about 18600 students. The school which has a student-faculty ratio of about 14:1 offers more than 90 bachelor's degree programs in art and design business engineering science and hotel management. RIT also confers master's and doctorate degrees. The university's National Technical Institute for the Deaf is the first and largest technological college for learners who suffer from hearing loss. RIT which traces its roots back to 1829 counts among its alumni the CEOs of Kodak and The Associated Press.

Operations
Spanning some 1300 acres in Rochester New York RIT's campus serves 15400 undergraduate and 3200 graduate students with help from its faculty and staff of more than 3850. Approximately 1300 deaf and hard-of-hearing students live study and work alongside hearing students on the RIT campus. Tuition runs nearly $33000 for general students and more than $12000 for deaf and hard-of-hearing students.

RIT operates a campus in Dubai's Silicon Oasis a government-owned high tech complex. The campus serves the university's goal of growing its reputation worldwide and expanding international opportunities for students. RIT Dubai offers undergraduate and graduate degree programs in engineering business information technology and leadership.

Geographic Reach
RIT is based in Rochester New York; it has locations abroad in Eastern Europe the Middle East and Asia.

Sales and Marketing
The university's students come from all 50 states and more than 100 nations around the world.

Financial Performance
Net revenue increased 4% to $523.9 million in fiscal 2015 as the school generated more income from tuition and fees auxiliary services and government grants and contracts. However net income dropped 79% to $18.5 million largely due to a drop in investment earnings as well as higher operating expenses including salaries and benefits.

Cash flow from operations remained flat that year dropping 1% to $35.9 million mainly due to changes in working capital.

Strategy

To boost investment returns the university has adjusted its asset allocation to include more equities and alternative investments.

EXECUTIVES

Svp Finance And Administration, James H. Watters
Dean Kate Gleason College Of Engineering, Harvey Palmer
President, William W. (Bill) Destler
Dean College Of Applied Science And Technology, H. Fred Walker
Svp Academic Affairs And Provost, Jeremy A. Haefner
Vp And Dean Institute Of Health Sciences And Technology, Daniel B. Ornt
Dean College Of Imaging Arts & Sciences, Lorraine Justice
Dean College Of Liberal Arts, James J. Winebrake
Dean College Of Science, Sophia Maggelakis
Dean And President National Technical Institute For The Deaf, Gerard J. Buckley
Svp Enrollment Management And Career Services, James Miller
Dean B. Thomas Golisano College Of Computing And Information Sciences, Anne Haake
Dean Saunders College Of Business, Jacqueline Mozrall
Dean Graduate Studies, Hector Flores
Svp Student Affairs, Sandra Johnson
Secretary Of The Institute And Chief Of Staff, Karen Barrows
President Kosovo Campus, Sharon Y. Hart
Vice President Government And Community Relations, Deborah Stendardi
Student Affiars Vice Presidents Office, Kathy Routly
Assistant Vice President For Facilities Management Services, John Moore
Department Head, Risa Robinson
Academic Affiars Vice President S Office, Lynne Mazadoorian
Associate Vice President For Academic Affairs, Stephen Aldersley
Assistant Vice President Human Resources, Judy Bender
Assistant Vice President For Student Affairs, David Bagley
Student Affiars Vice President S Office, Nicole Boulais
Assistant Vice President Registrar, Joseph Loffredo
Associate Vice President Of Academic Affairs And Registrar, Joe Loffredo
Vice President, Dawn Lucas
Assistant Vice President For Finance And Administration, James Fisher
Assistant Vice President For Institutional Research, Richard Dirmyer
Vice President Of The Association Of Computing, Vicki Hanson
Associate Vice President And Director Of Financial Aid, Larry Chambers
Associate Vice President For Student Health, Wendy Gelbard
Department Chair, Rebecca Edwards
Department Chair And Associate Professor, Shal Khazanchi
Vice President, Bao Ha
Board Member, Thomas Kausch
Board Of Directors Secretary, Tori Budgeon Baker
Scheduling Secretary, Jan Firpo
Eboard Treasurer, David Anthony
Eboard Secretary, Marcela Lopez
Auditors: PRICEWATERHOUSECOOPERS LLP RO

LOCATIONS

HQ: ROCHESTER INSTITUTE OF TECHNOLOGY (INC)
1 LOMB MEMORIAL DR, ROCHESTER, NY 146235698
Phone: 585 475-2411
Web: WWW.RIT.EDU

PRODUCTS/OPERATIONS

Selected Colleges
College of Applied Science and Technology
  School of Engineering Technology
  School of International Hospitality and Service Innovation
E. Philip Saunders College of Business
B. Thomas Golisano College of Computing and Information Sciences
Kate Gleason College of Engineering
College of Health Sciences and Technology
College of Imaging Arts and Sciences
  School for American Crafts
  School of Art
  School of Design
  School of Film and Animation
  School of Media Sciences
  School of Photographic Arts and Sciences
College of Liberal Arts
National Technical Institute for the Deaf
College of Science

Selected Graduate & Undergraduate Programs
Accounting
Applied Networking & Systems Administration
Applied Statistics
Biochemistry
Business
Civil Engineering Technology
Clinical Chemistry
Computer Integrated Machining Technology
Computer Science
Digital Imaging & Publishing Technology
Electrical/Mechanical Engineering Technology
Environmental Science
Finance
Glass & Glass Sculpture
Health Systems Administration
Healthcare Billing & Coding Technology
Imaging Arts: Photography
Industrial & Systems Engineering
Instruction Technology
Management
Medical Illustration
Metals/Jewelry Design
Ophthalmic Optical Finishing Technology
Print Media
Psychology
Service Leadership and Innovation
Voice Communication
Woodworking and Furniture Design

HISTORICAL FINANCIALS

Company Type: Private

Income Statement				FYE: June 30
	REVENUE ($ mil.)	NET INCOME ($ mil.)	NET PROFIT MARGIN	EMPLOYEES
06/18	579	203	35.2%	3,300
06/17	560	74	13.2%	—
06/12	490	16	3.4%	—
06/06	370	45	12.2%	—
Annual Growth	3.8%	13.4%	—	—

2018 Year-End Financials

Return on assets: 10.4%   Cash ($ mil.): 62
Return on equity: 14.2%
Current ratio: —

ROCKFORD, BOARD OF EDUCATION

EXECUTIVES

Supt, Dr Ehren Jarrett
Pres*, Harmon Mitchell
V Pres*, Jude Makulec
SEC*, Lisa Jackson
Supt*, Linda Hernandez
Coordinator, Veronica Montoya
Teacher, Amanda Janitzky
School Social Worker, Carlee Siggeman
Teacher, Jenner Irvin
Administrator, Maureen Schoenemann
Teacher, Michelle Keffer
Auditors: SIKICH LLP ROCK ILLINOIS

LOCATIONS

HQ: ROCKFORD, BOARD OF EDUCATION
501 7TH ST, ROCKFORD, IL 611041242
Phone: 815 966-3000
Web: WWW.RPS205.COM

HISTORICAL FINANCIALS

Company Type: Private

Income Statement				FYE: June 30
	REVENUE ($ mil.)	NET INCOME ($ mil.)	NET PROFIT MARGIN	EMPLOYEES
06/17	509	(23)	—	4,304
06/16	445	(15)	—	—
06/15	446	19	4.4%	—
06/14	398	(54)	—	—
Annual Growth	8.5%	—	—	—

ROCKIES EXPRESS PIPELINE LLC

EXECUTIVES

Director, Doug Griffin
Operations Supervisor, Gene Thim
Coordinator, Jacqui Hayes
Senior, Jason Nonnemaker
Director, Jay Meyers
Information Technology, Jeb Saylor
Associate Administrat, Jennifer Schendel
Facilities Supervisor, Katie Gravilla
Technical Supervisor, Robert Baures

LOCATIONS

HQ: ROCKIES EXPRESS PIPELINE LLC
370 VAN GORDON ST # 4000, LAKEWOOD, CO 802281526
Phone: 877 546-5877

HISTORICAL FINANCIALS

Company Type: Private

Income Statement				FYE: December 31
	REVENUE ($ mil.)	NET INCOME ($ mil.)	NET PROFIT MARGIN	EMPLOYEES
12/18	967	487	50.4%	37
12/17	893	298	33.4%	—
12/16	730	178	24.5%	—
Annual Growth	15.1%	65.2%	—	—

ROTARY INTERNATIONAL

The rotary phone may be a thing of the past but Rotary International (founded in 1905 and now with more than 1.2 million members) is still going strong. The service organization with a motto of Service Above Self comprises 34000-plus clubs in more than 200 countries and territories. Rotary service projects are intended to alleviate problems such as hunger illiteracy poverty and violence. Grants from the Rotary Foundation support its efforts. Along with its service projects Rotary aims to promote high ethical standards in the workplace. Membership in Rotary clubs is by invitation. Each club strives to include representatives from major businesses professions and institutions in its community.

Operations

Rotary (whose name arose from the early practice of rotating meetings among members' offices) boasts more than 34000 clubs globally with a membership of 1.2-plus million. In 2014 the organization had $24 million in its endowment fund.

Rotary began admitting women to its clubs in 1989. In 2014 women accounted for more than 16% of its global membership.

Geographic Reach

From its headquarters in Evanston Illinois Rotary operates in more than 200 countries.

Financial Performance

Rotary's revenues increased by 20% in 2014 due to a rise in contributions membership dues and net investment returns.

Net income increased by 29% that year as the result of higher revenues and a decline in grant expenses.

Strategy

As part of its Future Vision plan Rotary is working to partner with established organizations with expertise in any of Rotary's six areas of focus: peace and conflict prevention/resolution disease prevention and treatment water and sanitation maternal and child health basic education and literacy and economic and community development.

In its second century of operations Rotary has chosen the eradication of polio as one of its top priorities. Helping the organization meet these goals the Bill & Melinda Gates Foundation's initial grant of $100 million spurred a challenge grant with an additional $225 million. Rotary's working to raise an extra $200 million in grant funds. Other goals include expanding internationally and increasing the diversity of the organization's membership.

In 2014 the organization received a $70 million 2-to-1 match from the Bill & Melinda Gates Foundation by meeting its obligation to commit $35 million from the PolioPlus Fund toward the Global Polio Eradication Initiative.

In 2014 the Peace Corps and Rotary signed a letter of collaboration strengthening the organizations' cooperation to promote global development and volunteer service.

HISTORY

On February 23 1905 lawyer Paul Harris met with three friends in an office in Chicago's Unity Building. Inspired by the fellowship and tolerance of his boyhood home in Wallingford Vermont Harris proposed organizing a men's club to meet periodically for the purpose of camaraderie and making business contacts. The new endeavor was organized as the Rotary Club of Chicago and had 30 members by the end of the year.

As additional clubs followed the organization assumed its role as a civic and service organization (the installation of public comfort stations in Chicago's City Hall was one of its first projects). At the first convention of the National Association of Rotary Clubs in 1910 Harris was elected president. International clubs soon followed and by 1921 there were Rotary clubs on six continents.

In 1932 while struggling to revive a company with financial difficulties Rotarian Herbert Taylor devised a statement of business ethics that later became the Rotarian mantra. Taylor's "4-Way Test" consisted of the following questions: "Is it the truth? Is it fair to all concerned? Will it build goodwill and better friendships? Will it be beneficial to all concerned?"

During WWII Rotary clubs promoted war relief and peace fund efforts. Following WWII the clubs assisted in efforts to aid refugees and prisoners of war. The extent of Rotarian involvement in international issues became clear when 49 members assisted in drafting the United Nations Charter in 1945.

The first significant contributions to The Rotary Foundation followed Harris' death in 1947. These funds formed the bedrock for the foundation's programs and in 1965 the foundation created its Matching Grants and Group Study Exchange programs. Rotary International also welcomed younger members in the 1960s by creating its Interact and Rotaract clubs in 1962 and 1968 respectively.

The largest meeting of Rotarians occurred in 1978 when almost 40000 members attended the organization's Tokyo convention. But controversy was fast approaching the male-only organization. In 1978 a California Rotary club defied the male-only requirement and admitted two women. Claiming that the club had violated the organization's constitution Rotary International revoked the club's charter. A lengthy court battle ensued and a series of appeals landed the issue on the docket of the US Supreme Court. In 1987 the court ruled that the all-male requirement was discriminatory. Two years later Rotary International officially did away with its all-male status.

In the 1990s membership in Rotary clubs grew but at a slower pace than in the organization's past. Mary Wolfenberger was appointed the organization's first female CFO in 1993 (resigned 1997). In 1998 Rotary International joined with the United Nations to launch a series of humanitarian service projects in developing areas. In 1999 the organization spearheaded events to help flood victims in North Carolina and refugees in the Balkans. In 2000 the group created a program specializing in peace and conflict resolution. Rotary International established its first Internet-based Rotary club in early 2002. Also that year the group founded the Rotary Centers for International Studies which selects 70 scholars a year to participate in a master's-level peace studies program.

In addition to celebrating its 100th anniversary in 2005 the organization awarded grants in Sudan and Indonesia to stop polio and assist victims of the tsunami that struck Southeast Asia at the end of the year.

EXECUTIVES

Member Board Of Directors, Lori Carlson
Auditors: DELOITTE & TOUCHE LLP CHICAG

LOCATIONS

HQ: ROTARY INTERNATIONAL
1 ROTARY CTR, EVANSTON, IL 602014422
Phone: 847 866-3000
Web: WWW.ROTARY.ORG

PRODUCTS/OPERATIONS

2014 Sales

	$ mil.	% of total
Contributions	254	54
Net investment return	124	26
Dues	63	14
Other activities	29	6
Total	**471**	**100**

HISTORICAL FINANCIALS
Company Type: Private

Income Statement   FYE: June 30

	REVENUE ($ mil.)	NET INCOME ($ mil.)	NET PROFIT MARGIN	EMPLOYEES
06/18	503	71	14.3%	800
06/16	355	(17)	—	—
06/12	90	(1)	—	—
06/11	433	168	38.9%	—
Annual Growth	2.2%	(11.5%)	—	—

2018 Year-End Financials

Return on assets: 5.0%   Cash ($ mil.): 57
Return on equity: 5.7%
Current ratio: —

ROUND ROCK INDEPENDENT SCHOOL DISTRICT (INC)

EXECUTIVES

Supt, Dr Jess H Chvez
Prin*, Georgia Mill
Supt*, Dr Steven Flores
Executive Assistant, Lisa Ramirez
Education Specialist, Candy Squilla
Information Specialist, Debby Acevedo
Programmer Analyst, Mick Bull
Information Technology/Interne, Steve Burpee
Coordinator, Nicole Shannon
Executive Assistant, Starla Taylor
Information Technology/Interne, Brent Engelhardt
Auditors: MAXWELL LOCKE & RITTER LLP AU

LOCATIONS

HQ: ROUND ROCK INDEPENDENT SCHOOL DISTRICT (INC)
1311 ROUND ROCK AVE, ROUND ROCK, TX 786814941
Phone: 512 464-5000
Web: WWW.ROUNDROCKISD.ORG

HISTORICAL FINANCIALS
Company Type: Private

Income Statement   FYE: June 30

	REVENUE ($ mil.)	NET INCOME ($ mil.)	NET PROFIT MARGIN	EMPLOYEES
06/18	546	(70)	—	4,500
06/17	533	(65)	—	—
06/16	523	64	12.3%	—
06/15	491	126	25.7%	—
Annual Growth	3.6%	—	—	—

ROUSE'S ENTERPRISES, L.L.C.

EXECUTIVES

MBR, Anthony J Rouse Sr
MBR*, Donald J Rouse
MBR*, Thomas B Rouse
Offc Mgr, Penny Thibodaux
Manager, Patrick Morris
Facilities Manager, Bob Bixenman
Director, Michael O'Shell
Purchasing Director, Dantre Blanchard
Auditors: TS KEARNS & CO THIBODAUX

LOCATIONS

HQ: ROUSE'S ENTERPRISES, L.L.C.
1301 SAINT MARY ST, THIBODAUX, LA 703016527
Phone: 985 447-5998
Web: WWW.ROUSES.COM

HISTORICAL FINANCIALS
Company Type: Private

Income Statement				FYE: December 29
	REVENUE ($ mil.)	**NET INCOME** ($ mil.)	**NET PROFIT MARGIN**	**EMPLOYEES**
12/10	691	24	3.5%	5,200
12/09	689	21	3.1%	—
12/06	247	11	4.8%	—
Annual Growth	29.4%	19.7%	—	—

2010 Year-End Financials

Return on assets: 15.7%   Cash ($ mil.): 8
Return on equity: 25.8%
Current ratio: 2.00

ROYAL TEN CATE (USA), INC.

EXECUTIVES

Ceo, Loek De Vries
Vice Pres-Cfo*, Joseph W Averette
SEC*, Henry Hope
Director, David Clarke
Extrusion Manager, Tony Pilgrim

LOCATIONS

HQ: ROYAL TEN CATE (USA), INC.
365 S HOLLAND DR, PENDERGRASS, GA 305674625
Phone: 706 693-2226
Web: WWW.TENCATEGEO.US

HISTORICAL FINANCIALS
Company Type: Private

Income Statement				FYE: December 31
	REVENUE ($ mil.)	**NET INCOME** ($ mil.)	**NET PROFIT MARGIN**	**EMPLOYEES**
12/14	640	0	—	1,500
12/13	613	0	—	—
12/12	626	0	—	—
12/11	178	0	—	—
Annual Growth	53.0%	—	—	—

2014 Year-End Financials

Return on assets: —   Cash ($ mil.): 18
Return on equity: —
Current ratio: 3.00

RUDOLPH AND SLETTEN, INC.

Rudolph and Sletten ... the little-known tenth reindeer? More like the elves who built Santa's workshop. The firm is a mainstay of the California construction scene especially Silicon Valley. It has built corporate campuses for Apple Microsoft and Wells Fargo as well as Lucasfilm's Skywalker Ranch production facility. Rudolph and Sletten is one of the US' largest general building contractors with site selection design/build and construction management capabilities. Key projects also include biotech labs hospitals and schools. Onslow "Rudy" Rudolph founded the company in 1959 and was joined by partner Kenneth Sletten in 1962. Rudolph and Sletten is a subsidiary of Tutor Perini Corporation .

Geographic Reach

Redwood City California-based Rudolph and Sletten has regional offices in San Francisco Sacramento Irvine San Diego and Stockton California. The firm is licensed to build in California Arizona Nevada Washington Colorado Idaho Oregon Oklahoma and Texas.

Sales and Marketing

Big name clients have included a number of prestigious institutions such as Childrens Hospital Los Angeles The University of Southern California Genentech and the Monterey Bay Aquarium. The company reports that more than 95% of its business comes from repeat customers.

Financial Performance

California is Rudolph and Slatten's largest market representing an estimated $666 million in revenue in 2013.

Strategy

To capitalize on San Francisco's building boom the firm hired several San Francisco construction veterans in early 2014 to expand its operations there. Rudolph and Sletten is currently working on projects in Mission Bay and the Financial District.

The firm is renowned for its green building practices with nearly half the staff Leadership in Energy and Environmental Design (LEED)-accredited; it aims for 100% accreditation by 2013. Its own corporate headquarters was Gold LEED-certified based on its use of recycled materials energy and water efficiency and sustainable site. Other sustainable projects undertaken by Rudolph and Sletten include the Lawrence Berkeley National Laboratory and the NOAA Fisheries Services Southwest Science Center.

EXECUTIVES

Vice President Operations, Rene Olivo
Vice President Preconstruction Services, Mike Mohrman
Sr. Vice President, Jon Foad
Auditors: DELOITTE & TOUCHE LLP LOS AN

LOCATIONS

HQ: RUDOLPH AND SLETTEN, INC.
2 CIRCLE STAR WAY FL 4, SAN CARLOS, CA 940706200
Phone: 650 216-3600

PRODUCTS/OPERATIONS

Major Markets

Biotechnology/pharmaceutical
Commercial office and corporate campuses
Education
Gaming and hospitality
Government
Health care
Industrial
Justice
Sports and entertainment
Technology

Selected Services
Estimating
Scheduling
Value engineering
Constructibility review
Building Information Modeling (BIM)
Construction
Construction management
Project management
Quality control
Disruption management
Commissioning
Self performed work
Sustainable cpnstruction
Safety

COMPETITORS

Charles Pankow Builders	Kitchell
Clark Construction Group	McCarthy Building
	PCL Constructors
DPR Construction	Summit Builders
Devcon Construction	Swinerton
Hathaway Dinwiddie Construction	Turner Construction
	Webcor Builders
Hensel Phelps Construction	Whiting-Turner

HISTORICAL FINANCIALS
Company Type: Private

Income Statement				FYE: December 31
	REVENUE ($ mil.)	**NET INCOME** ($ mil.)	**NET PROFIT MARGIN**	**EMPLOYEES**
12/16	1,307	14	1.1%	700
12/15	940	7	0.7%	—
12/14	637	3	0.5%	—
12/13	665	(0)	—	—
Annual Growth	25.2%	—	—	—

RUSAL AMERICA CORP.

EXECUTIVES

Ceo, Sergey Bubnov
V Pres, Susan Scarinci
SEC/Treas, Sergei Korshun
Accounting Manager, Deana Brewster

2018 Year-End Financials

Return on assets: (-5.7%)   Cash ($ mil.): 364
Return on equity: (-75.6%)
Current ratio: 6.20

Executive Officer, Albert Avetikov
Executive Officer, Nailya Akalaeva
Executive Officer, Alexandra Mazurova
Senior Vice President, Kurochkina Vera
Senior Process Engineer, Mamadou Balde
Head of Caustic Soda Departmen, Aleksey Tarasov
Head of Alloys Unit, Alexandra Denizli

LOCATIONS

HQ: RUSAL AMERICA CORP.
 800 WESTCHESTER AVE S308, RYE BROOK, NY
 105731330
Phone: 914 670-5771

HISTORICAL FINANCIALS

Company Type: Private

Income Statement				FYE: December 31
	REVENUE ($ mil.)	NET INCOME ($ mil.)	NET PROFIT MARGIN	EMPLOYEES
12/14	539	0	0.1%	11
12/11	611	0	0.1%	—
12/10	525	0	0.1%	—
Annual Growth	0.6%	13.3%	—	—

2014 Year-End Financials

Return on assets: 11.0%   Cash ($ mil.): 3
Return on equity: 0.1%
Current ratio: 0.10

RUSH UNIVERSITY MEDICAL CENTER

EXECUTIVES

Ceo-Cmo, Omar Lateef
Pres, Michael J Dandorph
Manager, Cindy Quiles
Chief of Medicine, David Amsell
Accounting Staff, Donna Ameismeier
General, Fred A Cbet
Doctor, George Katsoyannis
Coordinator, Janie Voyles
Staff, John S Weitzner
Doctor, Juan-Miguel Mosquera
Director of Security, Lauris Freidenfelds

LOCATIONS

HQ: RUSH UNIVERSITY MEDICAL CENTER
 1653 W CONGRESS PKWY, CHICAGO, IL 606123833
Phone: 312 942-5000
Web: WWW.RUSH.EDU

HISTORICAL FINANCIALS

Company Type: Private

Income Statement				FYE: June 30
	REVENUE ($ mil.)	NET INCOME ($ mil.)	NET PROFIT MARGIN	EMPLOYEES
06/17	2,267	302	13.3%	8,000
06/16	1,502	83	5.6%	—
06/15	1,408	(22)	—	—
06/14	1,969	208	10.6%	—
Annual Growth	4.8%	13.2%	—	—

2017 Year-End Financials

Return on assets: 7.9%   Cash ($ mil.): 99
Return on equity: 13.7%
Current ratio: 0.90

RUSSELL SIGLER, INC.

Russell Sigler has built a business providing a rather cool service in a hot region. Through about 30 offices located primarily in California and Arizona (but also in Idaho Nevada New Mexico and Texas) the company provides commercial and residential air conditioning contractors with equipment parts supplies and technical support. Its brands include Carrier Bryant and Payne. Russell Sigler has distributed Carrier products for more than 60 years. As part of its business the company also operates a residential and commercial distribution joint venture with industry giant Carrier. Russell Sigler owns a 60% stake while Carrier holds 40%.

Geographic Reach

Based in Tolleson Arizona Russell Sigler has branch locations in Arizona California Idaho Nevada New Mexico and Texas.

Sales and Marketing

Russell Sigler provides its products to retail stores and to dealers.

EXECUTIVES

Pres, John J Sigler
Chm-Dir, Russell Sigler
Cfo-Dir-Treas, Robert D Osborne
SEC, Lee Lanning Sigler
Accounting Staff, Monica Streeter
Sales Staff, Brian Pollard
Warehouse Manager, Steve McClendon
Sales Staff, Jorge Felix
Engineer of Sales, Joseph Alday
Accounting Staff, Andrea Nease
Customer Representativ, Clayton Schultz
Auditors: MCGLADREY LLP PHOENIX ARIZON

LOCATIONS

HQ: RUSSELL SIGLER, INC.
 9702 W TONTO ST, TOLLESON, AZ 853539703
Phone: 623 388-5100
Web: WWW.SIGLERS.COM

Selected Locations

California

Arizona

Texas

Idaho
New Mexico
Nevada

COMPETITORS

Chas Roberts Air Conditioning	Johnstone Supply
Ferguson Enterprises	US Airconditioning Distributors
Gustave A. Larson Company	Watsco
HD Supply	WinWholesale

HISTORICAL FINANCIALS

Company Type: Private

Income Statement				FYE: December 31
	REVENUE ($ mil.)	NET INCOME ($ mil.)	NET PROFIT MARGIN	EMPLOYEES
12/14	513	10	2.0%	550
12/13	488	6	1.3%	—
12/09	140	(0)	—	—
12/08	176	1	0.8%	—
Annual Growth	19.4%	38.4%	—	—

2014 Year-End Financials

Return on assets: 5.2%   Cash ($ mil.): —
Return on equity: 20.6%
Current ratio: 2.80

RYMAN HOSPITALITY PROPERTIES, INC.

Ryman Hospitality Properties (formerly Gaylord Entertainment) may be hollerin' for attention in the hospitality game but it's no corporate hayseed. Its properties consist of resort hotels tethered closely to attractions that appeal to the meetings and conventions market. They include the Gaylord Opryland Resort & Convention Center in Nashville the Gaylord Palms Resort in Florida (close to Disney World) the Gaylord Texan Resort near Dallas and the Gaylord National Resort and Convention Center in the Washington DC area. Ryman's hotels are managed by hotel giant Marriott. In 2012 the company changed its name convered to a REIT and sold its hotel brand and management business to Marriott.

HISTORY

The origins of Gaylord Entertainment can be traced back to the Oklahoma Publishing Co. a newspaper publishing company founded by Edward K. Gaylord Ray Dickinson and Roy McClintock in 1903. The publisher of The Daily Oklahoman Oklahoma Publishing branched into radio in 1928 with the purchase of Oklahoma City radio station WKY. With its 1949 creation of Oklahoma City television station WKY-TV Oklahoma Publishing made the leap into television.

Edward K. Gaylord died in 1974 at the age of 101 and his son Edward L. Gaylord was appointed CEO. Under his leadership the company purchased Opryland USA in 1983 — an acquisition that netted it the Grand Ole Opry Opryland Themepark and the Opryland Hotel. Opryland USA also launched country music cable network The Nashville Network that year.

In 1991 the increasingly diverse Oklahoma Publishing spun off its entertainment and broadcast holdings in the form of public company Gaylord Entertainment which established its headquarters in Nashville Tennessee. Gaylord Entertainment acquired a majority interest in cable music network Country Music Television (CMT) the same year. It later expanded CMT into Latin America Asia and the Pacific Rim. CMT also made a brief foray into Europe but that initiative was ended in 1998.

Facing a consolidating entertainment and media landscape Gaylord sold The Nashville Network and the US operations of CMT to Westinghouse (now CBS) in 1997. It also sold television station KSTW that year. The company expanded its reach into Christian music with the purchase of Word Entertainment and its 1997 acquisition of Blanton Harrell Entertainment gave Gaylord a presence in artist management. Terry London was appointed CEO in 1997.

The company closed its Opryland theme park in 1998 in the face of declining attendance and broke ground at the same site for the Opry Mills entertainment shopping and restaurant complex (opened 2000). Gaylord also purchased a Nashville Ramada Inn in 1998 (later renaming it Radisson Hotel at Opryland). With its 1998 acquisition of Paris-based Pandora Investment Gaylord branched into film distribution.

In 1999 the company formed Opryland Hospitality Group to oversee expansion of the Opryland hotel concept across the US. It also sold its last television station KTVT in Dallas/Fort Worth to CBS. Edward K. Gaylord II succeeded his father as chairman in 1999. That year the company launched its Internet division GETdigitalmedia (later renamed Gaylord Digital) and moved online with the purchase of Christian Web sites Musicforce.com and Lightsource.com. Later the same year the company expanded its Internet presence with the purchase of Songs.com a music Web site focused on independent artists. But in late 2000 the company announced it would close its Internet unit. Also in 2000 the company bought Corporate Magic a firm focused on producing entertainment events for corporate audiences.

At the end of 2000 Gaylord sold Musicforce.com to Christian Book Distributors. Following that sale it sold Lightsource.com to LifeAudio.com in early 2001. That year the company sold its film and television production units and announced a restructuring in order to cut costs. It also renamed Opryland Hotels to Gaylord Opryland while expanding into Texas and Florida. Colin Reed was appointed CEO in 2001.

Between 2001 and 2003 Gaylord Entertainment sold Word Entertainment to Warner Music Group the Opry Mills shopping and restaurant complex to The Mills Corporation the Acuff-Rose Music Publishing business to Sony/ATV two of its Nashville radio stations to Cumulus Media and its majority interest in the Oklahoma City Redhawks minor league baseball team.

Edward L. Gaylord officially retired from the company in 2003 at age 83. Also that year the company significantly expanded its hospitality business with the purchase of ResortQuest a vacation and condominium property management firm. In 2004 the Gaylord family sold more than half its shares in the company making Gabelli Funds the majority owner.

In 2005 Gaylord acquired 50% of Corporate Magic a Dallas-based provider of production support for corporate meetings and events. It did so to support its meeting and convention facilities.

The company unloaded its minority interest in minor league hockey team the Nashville Predators in 2005. Two years later it sold ResortQuest to a subsidiary of Leucadia National Corp. for $35 million. Also in 2007 it sold its interest in sporting goods store operator Bass Pro Group. In 2008 the company opened the Gaylord National Resort and Convention Center in the Washington DC area. The property has some 2000 rooms and approximately 450000 square feet of meeting space.

Also in 2008 Gaylord terminated plans to acquire the Westin La Cantera Resort in San Antonio for about $253 million citing a tough economic environment. In addition the 2008 sale of its ResortQuest subsidiary an online booking service in vacation rentals property management and resort real estate sales fit the company's strategy of selling off assets that aren't related to its Grand Ole Opry or its operations in the meetings and convention market.

In 2009 the company responded to weak earnings by cutting approximately 500 jobs across all areas of the business. Gaylord reported steep dip in profits in 2010 primarily due to harsh flooding in Nashville when the Cumberland River rose to historic levels flowing over protective levees. The flood resulted in property damage and temporary closures at its properties in Nashville causing lost revenues and an increase in expenses. Also in 2010 Gaylord sold its 50% stake in Corporate Magic back to that company's CEO.

The company changed its name to Ryman Hospitality Properties in 2012. It also converted to an REIT and sold the Gaylord brand to Marriott which now manages Ryman's hotel properties and certain other entertainment holdings.

EXECUTIVES

Evp Ryman Hospitality Properties; President Opry Entertainment Group, Stephen G. (Steve) Buchanan
Chairman And Ceo, Colin V. Reed, age 71, $782,830 total compensation
Svp Investments Design And Construction, Bennett D. Westbrook, age 52, $318,447 total compensation
President And Cfo, Mark Fioravanti, age 57, $469,407 total compensation
Svp Asset Management, Patrick Chaffin, age 45, $274,975 total compensation
Svp General Counsel And Secretary, Scott J. Lynn, age 45, $364,876 total compensation
Senior Vice President And Corporate Controller, Jennifer Hutcheson
Vice President Information Technology, Sharon Asmus
Vice President, James Chamblin
Vice President Human Resources, Shawn Smith
Svp Of Marketing, Laura Hollingsworth
Board Member, Michael J Bender
Member Board Of Directors, Fazal Merchant
Auditors: ERNST & YOUNG LLP NASHVILLE

LOCATIONS

HQ: RYMAN HOSPITALITY PROPERTIES, INC.
1 GAYLORD DR, NASHVILLE, TN 372141207
Phone: 615 316-6000
Web: WWW.RYMANHP.COM

PRODUCTS/OPERATIONS

2015 Sales

	$ mil.	% of total
Hospitality	994	91
Entertainment (previously Opry and Attractions)	97	9
Total	**1,092**	**100**

2015 Sales

	$ mil.	% of total
Food and beverage	461	42
Rooms	404	37
Other hotel revenue	129	12
Entertainment (previously Opry and Attractions)	97	9
Total	**1,092**	**100**

Select Operations

Hospitality
 Gaylord Opryland Resort & Convention Center (Tennessee)
 Gaylord Palms Resort & Convention Center (Florida)
 Gaylord Texan Resort & Convention Center
 Radisson Hotel at Opryland (Tennessee)
Attractions
 Gaylord Springs Golf Links (golf club Tennessee)
 General Jackson Showboat
 Grand Ole Opry
 Ryman Auditorium
 Wildhorse Saloon
 WSM-AM

COMPETITORS

CKX
 Caesars Entertainment
 Disney Parks & Resorts
 Elvis Presley Enterprises
 Herschend Entertainment
 Hershey Entertainment
 Hilton Worldwide
 Kennywood
 Las Vegas Sands
 Live Nation Entertainment
 MGM Resorts
 Marriott
 New York Convention Center Operating Corporation
 SeaWorld
 Welk Group

HISTORICAL FINANCIALS

Company Type: Private

Income Statement				FYE: December 31
	ASSETS ($ mil.)	NET INCOME ($ mil.)	INCOME AS % OF ASSETS	EMPLOYEES
12/16	2,405	159	6.6%	1,000
12/15	2,331	111	4.8%	—
12/14	2,413	126	5.2%	—
12/13	2,424	113	4.7%	—
Annual Growth	(0.3%)	12.0%	—	—

2016 Year-End Financials

Return on assets: 6.6%   Sales ($ mil): 1,149
Return on equity: 43.3%

S & B ENGINEERS AND CONSTRUCTORS, LTD.

S & B Engineers and Constructors makes it possible for others to burn the midnight oil. The employee-owned company specializes in engineering procurement and construction of process plants in the chemical petrochemical refining power generation infrastructure and pulp and paper industries. S&B also flexes its engineering muscle on transportation waste and wastewater and environmental and telecommunications projects for public sector clients. Founded in 1967 by James Slaughter and William Brookshire to serve refineries and other process plants along the Texas and Louisiana gulf coasts the company has expanded services globally with two offices in India.

Operations

The company has divisions that focus on specific geographic areas and services. S&B's Engineers and Constructors division provides engineering procurement and construction services for combustion turbine combined and simple cycle projects as well as environmental AQCS retrofit projects for existing coal plants.

Ford Bacon & Davis (acquired in 1996) does much of its business in the southern US where it takes on engineering and design projects for oil gas and chemical companies. It not only constructs new plants but is often hired to rebuild facilities that have been damaged by fires or explosions.

The firm's Plant Services division provides small capital construction supplemental maintenance turnaround professional services asset management and other plant services including productivity studies and specialty training. S&B Infrastructure caters to private and government clients — ranging from federal to state to local authorities — while its private sector services extend from land development to industrial to pipeline client needs.

S&B India services its parent company's US clients as well as clients in India and other countries.

Geographic Reach

Houston-based S & B Engineers and Constructors boasts about a dozen offices throughout Texas (including four in Houston) a handful of offices in Louisiana and a single office in Greenville South Carolina. S&B India (established in 2000) has engineering centers in Bangalore and New Delhi.

Sales and Marketing

The company primarily serves the refining and chemical/petrochemical industry which alone accounts for more than half of its projects. About 25% of its projects are in the Midstream industry while remaining business comes from the Cogen and industrial power alternative energy and other industries.

Financial Performance
Its projects generate roughly $5 billion a year.

Strategy
S & B continues to grow its reputation with each project completed which in turn should lead to more business opportunities.

As an example S&B inked a deal with Chevron Phillips Chemical Company back in 2012 to engineer and build a plant that leverages the energy company's 2nd-generation on-purpose 1-hexene technology — which would be the world's largest on-purpose 1-hexene plant capable of producing up to 250000 metric tons (551000000 lbs) per year at the energy firm's Cedar Bayou Chemical Complex in Baytown Texas. In late 2014 not long after the completion of the project the company was recognized for the 1-Hexene plant as it received the top Excellence in Construction award in the heavy industrial category and first runner up for the "Best of Houston" award by the Associated Builders and Contractors (ABC) of Greater Houston.

EXECUTIVES

Senior Vice President Of Sales, Rich Akin
President, James G. Slaughter
Svp Engineering, Charles R. Reid
Svp Construction, Tommy H. Collins
Vice President Construction Home Office, Randy Walker
Vice President Business Development, Terry A Doyle
Vice President Procurement, Kent Malone
Vice President, James Harrod
Vice President Process Technology, Guy Suffridge
Legal Secretary, Raymond Harper
Vice President Business Development, Harvey Hensley
Vice President Business Development, Greg Hafer
Vice President Project Services, Sandy Lee
Vice President Construction Services, Kirk Morrow
Vice President Human Resources, Ralph Morales
Vice President Field Operations Manager, David Taylor
Vice President Business Development, Blane Vincent
Co-founder And Chairman, William A. Brookshire
Auditors: ERNST & YOUNG LLP HOUSTON TX

LOCATIONS

HQ: S & B ENGINEERS AND CONSTRUCTORS, LTD.
7825 PARK PLACE BLVD, HOUSTON, TX 770874697
Phone: 713 645-4141
Web: WWW.SBEC.COM

Selected Locations

US
Austin TX
Baton Roug
El Paso TX
Fort Worth TX
Freeport TX
Greenville SC
Houston
Longview TX
McAllen TX
Monroe LA
New Orleans
San Antonio
India
Bangalore
New Delhi

PRODUCTS/OPERATIONS

Selected Projects
Sulfur Tailgas Treating Unit Blaine WA
Crude Upgrade Project El Segundo CA

Pipeline Terminal Project Los Angeles CA
Refinery Revamp Project Bakersfield CA
Fractionation Expansion Project Billings MT
Gas Plant Project Meeker CO
SMR Project Port Arthur TX
ABF Program BP Refinery Texas City
Low Sulfur Gasoline & Diesel Projects Houston TX
Fine Paper Machine Project Kingsport TN

Selected Services
Construction
Engineering
Modules and skids
Plant services
Procurement
Project management

Selected Divisions
Ford Bacon & Davis
S&B India
S&B Infrastructure
S&B Plant Services
S&B Power Division

COMPETITORS

Bechtel	KBR Building Group
Fluor	Parsons Corporation
Jacobs Engineering	Turner Industries
KBR	Zachry Inc.

HISTORICAL FINANCIALS
Company Type: Private

Income Statement				FYE: December 31
	REVENUE ($ mil.)	NET INCOME ($ mil.)	NET PROFIT MARGIN	EMPLOYEES
12/18	679	0	—	2,400
12/17	679	0	—	
12/16	950	0	—	
12/13	0	0	—	
Annual Growth	—	—	—	—

2018 Year-End Financials
Return on assets: —
Return on equity: —
Current ratio: 1.50
Cash ($ mil.): 59

SACRAMENTO CITY UNIFIED SCHOOL DISTRICT

EXECUTIVES

Supt, Jose Banda
Cfo*, Tom Barrinson
C-Level Human Resources, Robert Garcia
Academic Advisor, Jeff Weiss
Auditors: CROWE LLP SACRAMENTO CALIFOR

LOCATIONS

HQ: SACRAMENTO CITY UNIFIED SCHOOL DISTRICT
5735 47TH AVE, SACRAMENTO, CA 958244528
Phone: 916 643-7400
Web: WWW.SCUSD.EDU

HISTORICAL FINANCIALS
Company Type: Private

Income Statement				FYE: June 30
	REVENUE ($ mil.)	NET INCOME ($ mil.)	NET PROFIT MARGIN	EMPLOYEES
06/17	625	71	11.5%	6,500
06/16	656	47	7.2%	
06/11	509	(0)	—	
06/06	434	0	—	
Annual Growth	3.4%	—	—	—

SACRAMENTO MUNICIPAL UTILITY DISTRICT

The Sacramento Municipal Utility District (SMUD) doesn't want its name to be mud. One of the largest locally owned electric utilities in the US SMUD serves more than 624770 residential and commercial customer meters (a service area population of 1.4 million) in California's Sacramento and Placer counties. The utility generates about 70% of its electricity (its 1300-MW capacity is derived primarily from hydroelectric and cogeneration power plants) and buys the rest. SMUD also sells power to wholesale customers andhas one of the largest solar energy distribution systems in the US.

Operations
The utility operates more than 10470 miles of transmission and distribution lines across its 900-sq.-mi. service area. It gets power from varied sources including hydropower natural-gas-fired generators renewable energy (such as solar and wind power) and purchases power on the wholesale market.

The company has installed 600000 smart meters at customer locations across its entire service area.

Geographic Reach
SMUD generates transmits and distributes electricity to a territory that includes Sacramento Sacramento County and a small portion of Placer County.

Financial Performance
In fiscal 2015 SMUD's net revenue decreased by 4% due to lower wholesale revenues as the result of lower surplus gas sales driven by a decrease in gas prices and less gas sold and lower energy prices and sales.

The company's net income decreased by 23% due to lower net sales and an increase in administrative general and customer and maintenance expenses.

In fiscal 2015 SMUD's operating cash inflow decreased by 15%.

Strategy
In response to market deregulation and the nationwide push for carbon emission reduction SMUD has increased its generation capacity placing a priority on renewable energy sources. As part of this green energy push the company has a 15-year deal with Shell Energy (which expires in 2024) to buy landfill gas from sites in Texas. SMUD has installed more than 600000 smart meters to help customers to better control their power use.

In 2015 the company invested $3.3 billion in electric utility plant assets and construction work in progress.

The utility even works with local dairies to install anaerobic digesters to turn manure into renewable energy.

Company Background

In 2012 SMUD announced that it is the leading utility in the US in terms of new homes which had solar panels installed during construction. The utility commenced the SMUD Solar Smart Homes program in 2006 and had constructed more than 1000 homes with solar panels by 2012.

The company has been delivering power to customers in the region since 1946 but its history goes back to 1923 when citizens voted to create SMUD as a community-owned electric service. However years of engineering studies political battles and legal wrangling delayed SMUD's purchase of PG&E' s local electrical system.

In March 1946 the California Supreme Court denied PG&E's final petition to halt the sale and nine months later SMUD finally began operations.

EXECUTIVES

Director Business Planning And Budget And Chief Risk Officer, James A. (Jim) Tracy
Ceo And General Manager, Arlen Orchard
Assistant General Manager Power Supply And Grid Operations, Paul Lau
Board Vice President, Rob Kerth
Vice President, Brad Gacke
President Board Of Directors, Nancy Bui-Thompson
Assistant Treasurer, Tim Ryan
Senior Staff Secretary To Bd Off Conf, Suzanne Rodriguez
Assistant Treasurer, Larry Stark
Treasurer, Noreen Roche-Carter
Treasurer, Dale Johnson
Auditors: BAKER TILLY VIRCHOW KRAUSE L

LOCATIONS

HQ: SACRAMENTO MUNICIPAL UTILITY DISTRICT
6201 S ST, SACRAMENTO, CA 958171818
Phone: 916 452-3211
Web: WWW.SMUD.ORG

PRODUCTS/OPERATIONS

2015 Sales

	% of total
Commercial & industrial	47
Residential	42
Wholesale power	6
Street lighting & other	5
Total	**100**

Selected Products and Services

Conservation programs
Customer billing programs
Diagnostic services
Electric vehicle charging stations
Energy assistance programs
Energy-efficient appliances and equipment
Energy management
Green energy programs
Power quality and environmental services
Security lighting
Shade trees for customers
Solar water heating
Surge protection
Tree trimming

COMPETITORS

AES	Los Angeles Water and
Avista	Power
Duke Energy	PG&E Corporation
Edison International	Sempra Energy

Income Statement — FYE: December 31

	REVENUE ($ mil.)	NET INCOME ($ mil.)	NET PROFIT MARGIN	EMPLOYEES
12/18	1,595	209	13.1%	2,213
12/17	1,559	181	11.6%	—
12/16	1,494	195	13.1%	—
12/15	1,474	128	8.7%	—
Annual Growth	**2.7%**	**17.5%**		

2018 Year-End Financials

Return on assets: 3.2%
Return on equity: 12.2%
Current ratio: 1.20

Cash ($ mil.): 211

SADDLE BUTTE PIPELINE LLC

Auditors: HEIN & ASSOCIATES LLP DENVER

LOCATIONS

HQ: SADDLE BUTTE PIPELINE LLC
858 MAIN AVE UNIT 301, DURANGO, CO 813015496
Phone: 970 375-3150
Web: WWW.SBPIPELINE.COM

HISTORICAL FINANCIALS

Company Type: Private

Income Statement — FYE: December 31

	REVENUE ($ mil.)	NET INCOME ($ mil.)	NET PROFIT MARGIN	EMPLOYEES
12/12	689	656	95.2%	30
12/11	69	(10)	—	—
12/10	68	0	0.0%	—
Annual Growth	**218.1%**	**199**	**13.8%**	—

2012 Year-End Financials

Return on assets: 425.5%
Return on equity: 433.6%
Current ratio: 50.40

Cash ($ mil.): 144

SAINT AGNES MEDICAL CENTER

Protecting and caring for the vulnerable Saint Agnes continues to ward off death for the patients at Saint Agnes Medical Center. The medical center provides health care to Valley residents of Fresno California through a 436-bed acute care hospital. Along with general surgery the hospital offers a variety of services including asthma management bariatric surgery (for which it has scored statewide accolades) cardiac rehabilitation hospice care and home care. The facility also runs an internal medicine physician residency and a nurses' residency program. Saint Agnes is part of Trinity Health one of the largest Catholic health care systems in the US.

Operations

Saint Agnes Medical Center is a 436-bed medical campus that has some 2600 staff members. The system typically logs more than 200 emergency department visits per day.

Geographic Reach

Saint Agnes Medical Center provides care to residents of California's Fresno Madera Kings and Tulare counties.

Financial Performance

In fiscal 2017 (ended June) Saint Agnes Medical Center had operating revenues of $483 million.

Strategy

In 2017 Saint Agnes Medical Center established a graduate medical education program which offers residency programs for internal medicine physicians and for nurses. As a teaching hospital the facility is better positioned to attract physicians to its growing community as well as training new ones who may stick around. Other programs in the works include family practice and emergency medicine physician residencies.

Company Background

The hospital system was established in 1929 by nine Holy Cross Sisters.

Saint Agnes Medical Center sponsors a number of community outreach programs throughout the Valley including adult day care senior activity programs health care clinics for the uninsured and services for poor and homeless women.

EXECUTIVES

Coo, Mark T. Bateman
Chief Medical Officer, Stephen Soldo
Cfo, Phil Robinson
Chief Nursing Officer, Debi Pasley
President And Ceo, Jim Leonard
Evp And, Rick OConnell
Pharm D, Tai Kosiyangkakul
Vice President Of Information Technology, Richard Blanks
Medical Director, Hector Ramos
Medical Director, Lesley Hanes
Vice President, Teri Amerine
Director Of Radiology, Joseph E Burns
Vice President Management, Amy Schneider
Vice President Mission Integration, Frank Beazley
Chairman, Michael Martinez

LOCATIONS

HQ: SAINT AGNES MEDICAL CENTER
1303 E HERNDON AVE, FRESNO, CA 937203309
Phone: 559 450-3000
Web: WWW.SAMC.COM

PRODUCTS/OPERATIONS

Selected Programs and Services

Cancer Services
Emergency Services
Endoscopy
Heart & Vascular
Home Health Care
Hospice
Imaging Services
Laboratory Services
Neuroscience
Occupational Health Center
Orthopaedics
Surgery
Palliative Care
Pulmonary Rehabilitation
Women's Services
Wound Care Hyperbaric Medicine and Amputation Prevention

Selected Facilities

Breast Center
Cancer Center
The California Eye Institute at Saint Agnes
Child Development Center
Home Health and Hospice
Medical Library

Occupational Health Center
Outpatient Surgery North
Satellite Labs
Wound Care Hyperbaric Medicine and Amputation
Prevention

COMPETITORS

Community Medical Centers	Memorial Hospitals Association
Dignity Health	Northern Inyo Hospital
HCA	Tenet Healthcare

HISTORICAL FINANCIALS

Company Type: Private

Income Statement   FYE: June 30

	REVENUE ($ mil.)	NET INCOME ($ mil.)	NET PROFIT MARGIN	EMPLOYEES
06/18	513	35	6.9%	2,400
06/16	486	11	2.3%	—
06/15	478	24	5.1%	—
06/13	503	19	3.8%	—
Annual Growth	0.4%	13.3%	—	—

2018 Year-End Financials

Return on assets: 4.6%   Cash ($ mil.): 75
Return on equity: 6.0%
Current ratio: 2.80

SAINT ALPHONSUS REGIONAL MEDICAL CENTER INC.

EXECUTIVES

Pres-Ceo, Sally Jeffcoat
Director, Sarah Berg
Director, Robin Navert
Emergency Medicine Specialist, Brian Boesiger
Staff Coordinator, Kimberly Ehlert
Family Practitioner, Kristi Clukey
Human Resources Business Partn, Kyle Stevenson
Chief of Pharmacy, Larry L Munkelt

LOCATIONS

HQ: SAINT ALPHONSUS REGIONAL MEDICAL CENTER INC.
1055 N CURTIS RD, BOISE, ID 837061309
Phone: 208 367-6899
Web: WWW.SAINTALPHONSUS.ORG

HISTORICAL FINANCIALS

Company Type: Private

Income Statement   FYE: June 30

	REVENUE ($ mil.)	NET INCOME ($ mil.)	NET PROFIT MARGIN	EMPLOYEES
06/18	937	50	5.4%	40
06/15	37	(5)	—	—
06/14	29	(5)	—	—
06/11	0	(0)	—	—
Annual Growth	—	—	—	—

2018 Year-End Financials

Return on assets: 4.5%   Cash ($ mil.): 208
Return on equity: 6.8%
Current ratio: 3.40

SAINT ALPHONSUS REGIONAL MEDICAL CENTER, INC.

Saint Alphonsus Regional Medical Center makes medical care its primary mission. The 384-bed hospital provides Boise Idaho and the surrounding region (including eastern Oregon and northern Nevada) with general acute and specialized health care services. Its facilities and operations include a level II trauma center an orthopedic spinal care unit an air transport service and a home health and hospice division. Saint Alphonsus Regional Medical Center is part of Trinity Health's four-hospital Saint Alphonsus Health System which serves Boise and Nampa in Idaho and Ontario and Baker City in Oregon. The Sisters of the Holy Cross founded the hospital in 1894.

Operations

Saint Alphonsus Regional Medical Center provides outpatient services through the 70 affiliated physician practices that make up the Saint Alphonsus Medical Group. It also operates the Saint Alphonsus Health Plaza which provides urgent care and outpatient surgery laboratory rehabilitation and primary care services.

The hospital also offers rural or homebound patients telemedicine services through which remote physician visits are conducted using audio or video.

Geographic Reach

Saint Alphonsus Regional Medical Center serves a territory that includes portions of southwestern Idaho northern Nevada and eastern Oregon.

Strategy

Saint Alphonsus Regional Medical Center expands its facilities to improve medical care in its service territory. In 2014 it opened its newly expanded and renovated emergency department which included a 30% increase in square footage. Also that year it became the first hospital in the region to utilize the EndoWrist Stapler technology on the da Vinci robotic system for minimally invasive surgeries.

EXECUTIVES

Vice President Quality Services, James Robert Polk
Vice President System Philanthropy Marketing Communications Advocacy Saint Alphonsus Health System, Linda Smith
Medical Director Of Physician Relations, Patrice Burgess
Medical Director, Rick Turner
Vice President Corporate Development Marketing, Jean Basom
Director Of Pharmacy, Mark T Phillips
Vice President Finance, Lannie Checketts
Assistant Vice President, Tom Reinhardt
Treasurer, Richard Presnell

LOCATIONS

HQ: SAINT ALPHONSUS REGIONAL MEDICAL CENTER, INC.
1055 N CURTIS RD, BOISE, ID 837061309
Phone: 208 367-2121
Web: WWW.SAINTALPHONSUS.ORG

COMPETITORS

Ascension Health	St. Luke's Health System
HCA	
Intermountain Health Care	

HISTORICAL FINANCIALS

Company Type: Private

Income Statement   FYE: June 30

	REVENUE ($ mil.)	NET INCOME ($ mil.)	NET PROFIT MARGIN	EMPLOYEES
06/15	556	40	7.3%	3,500
06/14	572	46	8.0%	—
06/13	545	43	7.9%	—
06/10	449	13	3.1%	—
Annual Growth	4.3%	24.1%	—	—

2015 Year-End Financials

Return on assets: 5.4%   Cash ($ mil.): 267
Return on equity: 8.8%
Current ratio: 4.80

SAINT ELIZABETH MEDICAL CENTER, INC.

ItÂ doesn't have much to do with the Holy TrinityÂ except for the fact thatÂ St. Elizabeth Medical Center (operating as St. Elizabeth Healthcare)Â does businessÂ inÂ a trinity of states. The system provides health care services to residentsÂ in Kentucky Ohio and West Virginia.Â St. Elizabeth Healthcare's programs includeÂ stroke and cardiac care hospice servicesÂ and neurosurgery.Â The systemÂ isÂ home toÂ six hospitals with about 1200 beds and dozens of primary care offices. St. Elizabeth Healthcare was formedÂ through aÂ merger between St. Elizabeth Medical and nearby St. Luke Hospitals.Â The organization has one board of directors and one management structure and is sponsored by the Catholic Diocese of Covington.

EXECUTIVES

President, Garren Colvin
Evp And Coo, Gary Blank
Cfo, Lori Ritchey-Baldwin
Assistant Vice President Of Planning And Marketing, Rosanne Nields
Vice President Business Development, Julie Siemer
Vice President Of Foundation, Larry Warkoczeski
Assistant Vice President, Vera Hall
Director Of Pharmacy, R Frey
Vice President Of Sales, Cynthia Glass
Vice President Oncologist, Jack Basil
Senior Vice President Facilities, Harry Watson
Secretary To Director, Lisa Robinson

LOCATIONS

HQ: SAINT ELIZABETH MEDICAL CENTER, INC.
1 MEDICAL VILLAGE DR, EDGEWOOD, KY 410173403
Phone: 859 301-2000
Web: WWW.STELIZABETH.COM

Selected locations
St. Elizabeth Covington (Covington Kentucky)
St. Elizabeth Edgewood (Edgewood Kentucky)
St. Elizabeth Grant (Williamstown Kentucky)
St. Elizabeth Ft. Thomas (St. Thomas Kentucky)
St. Elizabeth Florence (Florence Kentucky)
St. Elizabeth Falmouth (Falmouth Kentucky)

Adventist Health System Sunbelt Healthcare
Bethesda North
Catholic Health Initiatives
Cincinnati Children's Hospital
Deaconess Associations
HCA
Kettering Health Network
Mount Carmel Health
OhioHealth
Regency Hospital
Tenet Healthcare
The Christ Hospital Corporation
TriHealth
UC Health
Universal Health Services

HISTORICAL FINANCIALS

Company Type: Private

Income Statement				FYE: December 31
	REVENUE ($ mil.)	NET INCOME ($ mil.)	NET PROFIT MARGIN	EMPLOYEES
12/14	633	45	7.1%	6,227
12/13	984	124	12.7%	—
12/08	623	(32)	—	—
12/06	483	49	10.2%	—
Annual Growth	3.4%	(1.0%)	—	—

2014 Year-End Financials

Return on assets: 3.9%
Return on equity: 6.1%
Current ratio: 1.40
Cash ($ mil.): 22

SAINT EUGENE MEDICAL CENTER

EXECUTIVES

Pres, Donald Sandoval
Scientist, Jenny McDaniel

LOCATIONS

HQ: SAINT EUGENE MEDICAL CENTER
301 E JACKSON ST, DILLON, SC 295362509
Phone: 843 774-4111

HISTORICAL FINANCIALS

Company Type: Private

Income Statement				FYE: September 30
	REVENUE ($ mil.)	NET INCOME ($ mil.)	NET PROFIT MARGIN	EMPLOYEES
09/12	514	152	29.6%	300
09/00	26	1	5.9%	—
09/99	20	1	8.1%	—
09/98	20	1	8.1%	—
Annual Growth	25.9%	38.0%	—	—

2012 Year-End Financials

Return on assets: 12.4%
Return on equity: 17.3%
Current ratio: 3.60
Cash ($ mil.): 54

SAINT FRANCIS HOSPITAL AND MEDICAL CENTER FOUNDATION, INC.

Saint Francis takes care of the hearts of Hartford Connecticut. The Saint Francis Hospital and Medical Center is a not-for-profit regional medical center with some 620 beds and 65 bassinets. The hospital specializes in cardiology oncology neurology orthopedics and women's and children's health services. It also offers behavioral health weight management trauma care and injury rehabilitation programs. Saint Francis serves as a teaching hospital affiliated with the University of Connecticut Schools of Medicine and Dentistry. It also operates laboratories a home health and hospice agency and other entities. Saint Francis is part of Catholic health care system Trinity Health.

Operations

Saint Francis' on-campus specialty centers include the Hoffman Heart and Vascular Institute which specializes in open-heart surgeries and catheterization procedures.

Strategy

Saint Francis has initiated a number of internal cost-reduction efforts to keep its operations and finances healthy. It is also improving its internal information management systems to increase efficiencies at its facilities. Trinity Health which acquired Saint Francis in 2015 is investing at least $275 million through 2020 towards capital projects and programmatic investments in the hospital's region. Recently introduced programs include the Center for Diabetes and Metabolic Care's Inpatient Glycemic Initiative.

Company Background

Saint Francis joined the Trinity Health Network in 2015.

EXECUTIVES

President, John Rodis
Vp Finance, Jennifer S. Schneider
Vp Facilities Support Services And Construction, Robert J. (Bob) Falaguerra
Vp And Chief Development Officer Saint Francis Foundation, Lynn Rossini
Vp Operations, Thomas M. Burke
Vp Professional Nursing Practice And Quality; Chief Nursing Officer, Denise M. Peterson
Physical Therapy, Dan Henck
Vice President, Diane Bertrand
Vice President Human Resources, Dennis Sparks

LOCATIONS

HQ: SAINT FRANCIS HOSPITAL AND MEDICAL CENTER FOUNDATION, INC.
114 WOODLAND ST, HARTFORD, CT 061051208
Phone: 860 714-4006

COMPETITORS

Bristol Hospital
Connecticut Children's Medical Center
Griffin Health
Hartford Health Care
Hospital of Central Connecticut
Lawrence & Memorial Hospital
MidState Medical Center
Stamford Health
University of Connecticut Health Center
Yale New Haven Health System

HISTORICAL FINANCIALS

Company Type: Private

Income Statement				FYE: September 30
	REVENUE ($ mil.)	NET INCOME ($ mil.)	NET PROFIT MARGIN	EMPLOYEES
09/17	769	52	6.8%	3,270
09/14	670	17	2.6%	—
09/10	651	(10)	—	—
09/09	1,321	0	—	—
Annual Growth	—	314.7%	—	—

2017 Year-End Financials

Return on assets: 7.3%
Return on equity: 37.0%
Current ratio: 2.80
Cash ($ mil.): 16

SAINT FRANCIS HOSPITAL, INC.

EXECUTIVES

Ceo, Jake Henry
Human Resources, Brenda Garner
Director, Carl Bogler
Director, Karen Cochran
Vice-President, Marcus McKinney
Senior Vice-President, Pete Aran
Director, Philip Marcus
Director, Tiffani Fagan
V Chm, Peter C Boylan
Vice-President Engineering, Mike Wilson
Coordinator, April M Borg

LOCATIONS

HQ: SAINT FRANCIS HOSPITAL, INC.
6161 S YALE AVE, TULSA, OK 741361992
Phone: 918 502-2050
Web: WWW.SAINTFRANCIS.COM

HISTORICAL FINANCIALS

Company Type: Private

Income Statement				FYE: June 30
	REVENUE ($ mil.)	NET INCOME ($ mil.)	NET PROFIT MARGIN	EMPLOYEES
06/16	913	128	14.0%	4,000
06/15	877	171	19.6%	—
06/13	910	190	21.0%	—
06/12	838	157	18.7%	—
Annual Growth	2.2%	(5.0%)	—	—

2016 Year-End Financials

Return on assets: 5.6%
Return on equity: 6.5%
Current ratio: 8.90
Cash ($ mil.): 312

SAINT JOSEPH HOSPITAL, INC

The goal of Saint Joseph Hospital (formerly Exempla Saint Joseph Hospital) is to give residents of the Mile High City exemplary care. The Denver acute care facility has nearly 400 licensed beds and specializes in areas including cardiovascular disease cancer orthopedics pediatrics neurology diagnostics and high-risk labor and delivery. The Catholic not-for-profit hospital sees about 50000 emergency department visits annually and employs more than 1300 physicians. The hospital also offers residency programs in family practice internal medicine obstetrics and gynecology and general surgery. Catholic-sponsored Saint Joseph is part of SCL Health - Front Range.

Operations

Saint Joseph is one of the largest hospitals in the region. The medical center is a regional provider of critical cardiac care neonatal ICU orthopedic and radiation oncology services. Its pediatric ward is a satellite facility of the Children's Hospital Colorado. The Saint Joseph campus also includes three outpatient care clinics that offer charity care and the hospital conducts outreach programs in neighboring communities.

Altogether the hospital admits some 20000 inpatients per year and handles some 150000 outpatient visits more than 6875 inpatients and 6330 outpatient surgeries. As a not-for-profit entity Saint Joseph contributes more than 10% of annual revenues to charity care and community service efforts.

Sales and Marketing

Saint Joseph maintains contracts with most Denver-area health plans and is a major admitting hospital for Kaiser Health Plan of Colorado.

Strategy

Saint Joseph has constructed a replacement facility for its aging hospital facilities. The new $623 million medical center includes 365 beds (primarily in private patient rooms) as well as improved surgery emergency and diagnostic centers. The facility provides 826143 square feet of new diagnostic treatment and patient care spaces. The new facility specializes in heart and vascular care cancer treatment labor and delivery respiratory health orthopedics and emergency care. The hospital was completed in the second half of 2014 with occupancy commencing in early 2015.

In 2013 Saint Joseph announced its intention to form a joint operating agreement with National Jewish Health. Together the entities plan to collaborate on patient-centered health care methods as well as education and research programs. The clinical operations of each organization would be jointly managed through the agreement though the organizations will retain their respective assets.

The hospital is also involved in a federal pilot program designed to decrease the amount of unnecessary testing and treatments that can occur at hospitals by bundling service fees paid by Medicare; the program is managed by the Centers for Medicare and Medicaid Services. Such measures are part of the overall goal of the US health care industry to reduce medical spending.

Company Background

Saint Joseph Hospital merged with Lutheran Medical Center and Exempla Medical Group in 1997 to form Exempla Healthcare. The health network was co-sponsored by the Catholic-based Sisters of Charity of Leavenworth Health System (SCL Health System) and the Lutheran-sponsored Community First Foundation (CFF) until 2012 when SCL Health System acquired CFF's interest in the venture in a deal worth some $275 million. SCLHS had already gained operational oversight of all of the system's hospitals in late 2009.

Saint Joseph Hospital was founded in 1873 by SCL Health System. It was the first private hospital established in Colorado.

EXECUTIVES

Pres, Bain Farris
Pres, Bain J Farris
Chb, William Jessee
V Pres, Mary Shepler
V Pres, Barb Jahn
V Pres, Shawn Dufford
V Pres, Brad Ludford
Cmo, Travis Sewalls
Staff Pharmacist, Lesa Mc Kenzie
Dir Materials Mgmt/Purchasing, Peter Mc Guire
Staff Pharmacist, Carol De Lucia

LOCATIONS

HQ: SAINT JOSEPH HOSPITAL, INC
   1375 E 19TH AVE, DENVER, CO 802181114
Phone: 303 812-2000
Web: WWW.SCLHEALTH.ORG

PRODUCTS/OPERATIONS

Selected Services

Breast Care Center
Comprehensive Cancer Center
Community Outreach
Construction updates for exempla Saint Joseph Hospital
Electronic Medical Records
Emergency Care
Exemplea's Your Safety+Satisfaction
Family Medicine/Bruner Clinic
Heart Care
Home When Ready
Imaging Center
Intensive Care Unit
Medical Residency Programs
Midwife Practice
NICU-Neonatal Intensive Care Unit
                                        Outpatient
Pediatric Care
Plastic and Reconstructive Surgery
Saint Christopher Inn
The Blood Donor Center
Weight Loss Surgery Center
Women's and Children's Services

COMPETITORS

Catholic Health Initiatives	Porter Adventist Hospital
Centura Health	Rose Medical Center
Denver Health and Hospital Authority	University of Colorado Hospital
HealthONE	Valley View Hospital

HISTORICAL FINANCIALS

Company Type: Private

Income Statement   FYE: December 31

	REVENUE ($ mil.)	NET INCOME ($ mil.)	NET PROFIT MARGIN	EMPLOYEES
12/14	465	25	5.5%	2,300
12/13	490	51	10.5%	—
Annual Growth	(4.9%)	(50.2%)	—	—

2014 Year-End Financials

Return on assets: 3.1%   Cash ($ mil.): 1
Return on equity: 4.9%
Current ratio: 2.00

SAINT LOUIS UNIVERSITY

This university gives students a SLU of opportunities. Saint Louis University (SLU) is a Jesuit Catholic school offering about 90 undergraduate 100 graduate and a host of professional degree programs through about a dozen schools and colleges including a school of medicine and a campus in Madrid Spain. Most programs require core classes in philosophy and theology. SLU has an enrollment of more than 8200 undergraduate and more than 4600 graduate and professional students. Its student-teacher ratio is 9:1. Saint Louis University was founded in 1818 by Reverend Louis William Du Bourg Catholic Bishop of Louisiana.

Operations

In addition to its extensive educational programs SLU's students and staff are involved in a number of research projects in areas including cancer molecular biology cardiovascular disease biodefense and neurology and aging.

SLU also operates primary and specialty medical care clinics (some through its SLU Physicians organization) on its medical school campus. The medical campus also includes the SLU Hospital which is owned by Tenet Healthcare but which serves as a primary teaching facility for the university.

Geographic Reach

SLU's students hail from all 50 US states and about 80 countries. In addition to its main campus in St. Louis Missouri the university operates a campus in Madrid Spain.

Financial Performance

SLU is supported by an endowment of about $1.1 billion. About two-thirds of the university's revenues come from educational activities (including student tuition and fees) while another third comes from patient care at the medical center campus. It also receives about $45 million in research funding from external partners including government agencies (like the National Institutes of Health) and private foundations.

Strategy

Beyond its educational goals SLU contributes more than $715 million in annual economic impact to the region and supports more than 6800 jobs in the St. Louis metropolitan area.

EXECUTIVES

Treasurer And Chief Investment Officer, Gary L. Whitworth
President, Fred P. Pestello
Vp Medical Affairs, Philip O. Alderson
Vp And Cfo, David Heimburger
Vp And Cio, David Hakanson
Director Of Admissions, Alice Dickherber
Assistant Vice President, Jill Carnaghi
Assistant Vice President Alumni Donor Engagement, Tony Minor
Vice President Diversity And Community Engagement, Jonathan Smith
Assistant Vice President Public Safety, James Moran
Academic Department Chair, Sara Den
Director Of Admissions, Heidi Buffington
Associate Vice President For Facilities Services, Michael Lucido
Assistant Vice President University Development, Ted Cox
Vice President Facilities Services, Antoinette Dean
Director Of Government Relations, Marc Scheessele
Chairman, J. Joe Adorjan
Vice Chairman, Patrick J. Sly
Secretary Administrative, Sheryl Smith
Secretary Medical, Mary Streif
Secretary Medical, Nola Johnsen
Secretary Medical, Jan Heizer
Secretary Medical, Georgene Menshouse
Secretary Administrative, Megan Osborn
Secretary Administrative, Ruth Hartsell
Secretary Administrative, Vicki Shipp
Secretary Medical, Loletta Zasaretti
Secretary Medical, Angie Kaestner

LOCATIONS

HQ: SAINT LOUIS UNIVERSITY
1 N GRAND BLVD, SAINT LOUIS, MO 631032006
Phone: 314 977-2500
Web: WWW.SLU.EDU

PRODUCTS/OPERATIONS

Colleges Schools and Degree Granting Centers
Advanced Dental Education Center for (CADE)
Arts and Sciences College of
Business John Cook School of
Education and Public Service College of
Engineering Aviation and Technology Parks College of
Health Care Ethics Albert Gnaegi Center for
Health Sciences Doisy College of
Law School of
Madrid Spain Campus
Medicine School of
Nursing School of
Outcomes Research Center for (SLUCOR)
Philosophy and Letters College of
Professional Studies School for
Public Health School of
Social Work School of

HISTORICAL FINANCIALS

Company Type: Private

Income Statement   FYE: June 30

	REVENUE ($ mil.)	NET INCOME ($ mil.)	NET PROFIT MARGIN	EMPLOYEES
06/10	750	28	3.8%	7,500
06/09	697	0	—	—
06/08	633	(54)	—	—
Annual Growth	8.9%	—	—	—

2010 Year-End Financials
Return on assets: 1.7%   Cash ($ mil.): 141
Return on equity: 2.3%
Current ratio: —

SAINT LUKE'S HEALTH SYSTEM, INC.

Caring for the residents of Missouri's largest city is no mean feat but Saint Luke's Health System manages it through 10 area hospitals and a host of clinics located throughout Kansas City. The not-for-profit system's flagship facility is Saint Luke's Hospital which offers a Level I trauma center and internationally recognized cardiac and stroke care. Its Crittenton Children's Center is a behavioral health center serving children and their families on an inpatient and outpatient basis. Saint Luke's Health System is a network of almost 320 doctors providing primary and specialty care through clinics and other locations. The system is affiliated with the University of Missouri- Kansas City School of Medicine.

Operations
The health system offers a heart transplant program treatment for complex brain and spinal cord diseases advanced surgical care liver and kidney transplantation programs and a Level III neonatal intensive care unit. Other specialized services include women's health cancer treatment rehabilitation and home care.

Saint Luke Health System also engages extensively in medical research; its more than 330 researchers conduct more than 430 studies each

year. Its activities have drawn funding and sponsorship from the National Institutes of Health the American Heart Association and the Saint Luke's Hospital Foundation.

Saint Luke's Health System BJC HealthCare of St. Louis CoxHealth of Springfield (Missouri) and Memorial Health System of Springfield Illinois make up The BJC Collaborative. Through economies of scale and the sharing of resources the multi-system Collaborative seeks to achieve higher quality care for the patients served by these independent not-for-profit health care organizations.

While remaining independent Collaborative members have more than 4820 hospital beds in Missouri Illinois and Kansas and combined annual revenues of almost $7 billion allowing the members of the BJC Collaborative to focus on achieving savings; deploying clinical programs and services to improve access to quality of health care for patients; lowering health care costs; and creating additional efficiencies.

Geographic Reach
In addition to the Kansas City metropolitan area (some 2 million people) Saint Luke's Health System's service area spans 67 counties in Missouri and Kansas.

Strategy
To expand its market penetration the system will open two Convenient Care clinics — one in Kansas and another in Missouri — during 2016. Additionally Saint Luke's has broken ground on a specialty clinic in Mission Farms in Kansas. That project is expected to be complete in 2017. Also in 2017 a specialty clinic will be opened in Blue Springs Missouri.

Company Background
The predecessor to Saint Luke's Hospital was founded in 1882 by Episcopal priest Henry David Jardine.

EXECUTIVES

Ceo Saint Luke's South, Julie L. Quirin
Vp And Chief Nursing Officer Saint Luke's South, Katherine A. (Kathy) Howell
Ceo Saint Lukeâ's Hospital Of Kansas City, Jani L. Johnson
Svp Finance And Administration And Cfo, Chuck Robb
President And Ceo, Melinda L. Estes
Svp And Chief Physician Executive, Leonardo J. Lozada
Medical Director, Tim Pluard

LOCATIONS

HQ: SAINT LUKE'S HEALTH SYSTEM, INC.
901 E 104TH ST, KANSAS CITY, MO 641314517
Phone: 816 932-2000

PRODUCTS/OPERATIONS

2015 Sales

	$ mil.	% of total
Hospital	1,501	61
Other university	962	39
Total	**2,463**	**100**

Selected facilities
Anderson County Hospital (Garnett Kansas)
Crittenton Children's Center (Kansas City Missouri)
Hedrick Medical Center (Chillicothe Missouri)
Saint Luke's Cushing Hospital (Leavenworth Kansas)
Saint Luke's East (Lee's Summit Missouri)
Saint Luke's Hospital (Kansas City Missouri)
Saint Luke's Northland Hospital (Kansas City Missouri)
Saint Luke's Northland Hospital (Smithville Missouri)
Saint Luke's South (Overland Park Kansas)
Wright Memorial Hospital (Trenton Missouri)

Selected Services
Cancer services
Heart and vascular

Home care and hospice
Neuroscience
Surgical services
Transplant services
Women's and maternity services

COMPETITORS

Ascension Health
Children's Mercy Hospital
CoxHealth
Heartland Regional Medical
Shawnee Mission Medical Center

Truman Medical Centers
University of Kansas Medical Center
Via Christi Health System

HISTORICAL FINANCIALS

Company Type: Private

Income Statement   FYE: December 31

	REVENUE ($ mil.)	NET INCOME ($ mil.)	NET PROFIT MARGIN	EMPLOYEES
12/18	1,901	42	2.2%	5,111
12/17	1,721	88	5.2%	—
12/15	155	(3)	—	—
12/14	140	(0)	—	—
Annual Growth	91.8%	—	—	—

2018 Year-End Financials
Return on assets: 1.7%   Cash ($ mil.): 262
Return on equity: 3.0%
Current ratio: 2.90

SAINT LUKE'S HOSPITAL OF BETHLEHEM, PENNSYLVANIA

EXECUTIVES

Pres, Richard A Anderson
Sr V-Pres Finance*, Thomas P Lichtenwalner
Human Resources Director, Andrew Seidel
Gynecology/Obstetrics, Christopher B Gilbert
Security Staff, William Paslawsky
Senior Director, Jared King
Coordinator, Lisa Johnson
Orthopedic Surgeon, William Delong Jr
Manager, Scott Siegfried
Accounting Staff, Zoraida Zeno
Administrator, Brian Repetz
Auditors: WITHUMSMITHBROWN PC MORRISTOW

LOCATIONS

HQ: SAINT LUKE'S HOSPITAL OF BETHLEHEM, PENNSYLVANIA
801 OSTRUM ST, BETHLEHEM, PA 180151000
Phone: 484 526-4000
Web: WWW.SLHN.ORG

HISTORICAL FINANCIALS

Company Type: Private

Income Statement   FYE: June 30

	REVENUE ($ mil.)	NET INCOME ($ mil.)	NET PROFIT MARGIN	EMPLOYEES
06/18	890	126	14.2%	9,604
06/15	660	31	4.8%	—
06/14	629	36	5.8%	—
Annual Growth	9.1%	36.3%	—	—

2018 Year-End Financials

Return on assets: 6.9%   Cash ($ mil.): 91
Return on equity: 17.4%
Current ratio: 1.70

SAINT LUKE'S HOSPITAL OF KANSAS CITY

EXECUTIVES

Ceo, Jani L Johnson
V Pres-Cno*, Debbie Wilson
Coo*, Jane Peck
Cfo*, Amy Nachtigal
Chief of Medicine, George A Pagels
Optometrists, Terry D Anderson
Executive of Information Techn, Denise Kintigh
Coordinator, Denise Mogg
Doctor, Richard Hill
Internal Medicine Practitioner, Amit Sharma
Internal Medicine Practitioner, Chernet Teklemichael

LOCATIONS

HQ: SAINT LUKE'S HOSPITAL OF KANSAS CITY
4401 WORNALL RD, KANSAS CITY, MO 641113241
Phone: 816 932-2000
Web: WWW.SAINTLUKESKC.ORG

HISTORICAL FINANCIALS

Company Type: Private

Income Statement   FYE: December 31

	REVENUE ($ mil.)	NET INCOME ($ mil.)	NET PROFIT MARGIN	EMPLOYEES
12/18	803	4	0.5%	5,000
12/17	699	63	9.1%	—
12/16	641	26	4.1%	—
12/15	561	0	0.0%	—
Annual Growth	12.7%	198.0%	—	—

2018 Year-End Financials

Return on assets: 0.3%   Cash ($ mil.): 33
Return on equity: 0.5%
Current ratio: 3.10

SAINT MARYS HOSPITAL

EXECUTIVES

Pres, Robert R Waller
Director, Cindy Molko
Clinical Director, Joyce Dube
Chief of Radiology, Bernard F King
Admissions Director, Cydni Smith
Chief Marketing Officer, Kathy Zarling
Diagnostic Radiologist, Sanjay Misra
Physician Director of Er, Thomas Hellmich

LOCATIONS

HQ: SAINT MARYS HOSPITAL
1216 2ND ST SW, ROCHESTER, MN 559021970
Phone: 507 255-5123
Web: WWW.MAYOCLINIC.ORG

HISTORICAL FINANCIALS

Company Type: Private

Income Statement   FYE: December 31

	REVENUE ($ mil.)	NET INCOME ($ mil.)	NET PROFIT MARGIN	EMPLOYEES
12/16	2,091	556	26.6%	3,250
12/15	1,963	503	25.6%	—
Annual Growth	6.6%	10.6%	—	—

2016 Year-End Financials

Return on assets: 27.3%   Cash ($ mil.): —
Return on equity: 33.4%
Current ratio: 4.10

SAINT TAMMANY PARISH SCHOOL BOARD

EXECUTIVES

Pres, Stephen Loup
Supt*, Gayle Sloan
Deputy-Supt*, William Folse
Prin*, Cheryl Arabie
Pres*, Elizabeth B Heintz
V Pres*, Robert R Womack
General Manager, Kim Taylor
Secretary, Janet Jackson
Director of Payroll, Ron Randolph
Reading, Chris Robert
Vice President, Elizabeth Heintz
Auditors: LA PORTE APAC COVINGTON LA

LOCATIONS

HQ: SAINT TAMMANY PARISH SCHOOL BOARD
321 N THEARD ST, COVINGTON, LA 704332835
Phone: 985 892-2276
Web: WWW.STPSB.ORG

HISTORICAL FINANCIALS

Company Type: Private

Income Statement   FYE: June 30

	REVENUE ($ mil.)	NET INCOME ($ mil.)	NET PROFIT MARGIN	EMPLOYEES
06/18	504	38	7.7%	4,400
06/17	501	5	1.1%	—
06/16	505	(21)	—	—
06/15	475	49	10.4%	—
Annual Growth	2.0%	(7.9%)	—	—

2018 Year-End Financials

Return on assets: 4.4%   Cash ($ mil.): 153
Return on equity: —
Current ratio: —

SAINT THOMAS HOSPITAL

EXECUTIVES

Ceo, Tom Beeman
Chief Staff, E Dale Batchelor
Chief Technology Officer, David Van Hooser
Auditors: DELOITTE TAX LLP CINCINNATI

LOCATIONS

HQ: SAINT THOMAS HOSPITAL
4220 HARDING PIKE, NASHVILLE, TN 372052095
Phone: 615 222-5976
Web: STHEALTH.COM/LOCATIONS/SAINT-THOMAS-WEST-HOSPITAL

HISTORICAL FINANCIALS

Company Type: Private

Income Statement   FYE: June 30

	REVENUE ($ mil.)	NET INCOME ($ mil.)	NET PROFIT MARGIN	EMPLOYEES
06/11	493	60	12.2%	99
06/10	455	60	13.3%	—
Annual Growth	8.4%	(0.2%)	—	—

2011 Year-End Financials

Return on assets: 7.5%   Cash ($ mil.): 35
Return on equity: 11.1%
Current ratio: 2.30

SALEM-KEIZER SCHOOL DISTRICT 24J

EXECUTIVES

Supt, Thirsty Perry
Supt*, Kay Baker
Supt*, Paula Radich
Safety/Security Director, John Van Dreal
Teacher, John Robinson
Information Technology Manager, Kathi Etchemendy
Assistant, Martina Mangan
Bus Finance Purchasing Directo, Susan Dodd
Office Manager, Sara Downie
Auditors: GROVE MUELLER & SWANK PC

LOCATIONS

HQ: SALEM-KEIZER SCHOOL DISTRICT 24J
2450 LANCASTER DR NE # 100, SALEM, OR 973051200
Phone: 503 399-3000
Web: WWW.SALKEIZ.K12.OR.US

HISTORICAL FINANCIALS

Company Type: Private

Income Statement   FYE: June 30

	REVENUE ($ mil.)	NET INCOME ($ mil.)	NET PROFIT MARGIN	EMPLOYEES
06/17	519	(13)	—	4,000
06/16	516	(15)	—	—
06/06	319	8	2.7%	—
06/04	319	8	2.7%	—
Annual Growth	3.8%	—	—	—

SALINAS VALLEY MEMORIAL HEALTHCARE SYSTEMS

The primary facility of the Salinas Valley Memorial Healthcare System (a public hospital district) is Salinas Valley Memorial Hospital which opened in 1953 and has some 270 acute-care beds. The medical center includes a comprehensive cancer center joint replacement clinic regional heart and spine centers a level III neonatal intensive care unit and a women's and children's unit. Salinas Valley Memorial Healthcare System also operates the Summerville Harden Ranch an 80-bed assisted-living facility and a network of outpatient care clinics. The system has collaborative relationships with other area care providers as well as a partnership with NASA that allows earthbound physicians to assist astronauts with medical emergencies in space.

Operations

The system has some 300 board-certified physicians across a range of specialties and partners with affiliates throughout the region. Its other programs include the Harden Memorial Heart Program a wound healing center diagnostics and sleep medicine. Its emergency department sees more than 44000 patients each year.

Financial Performance

In 2014 revenue increased 1% to $351 million as net patient service revenues rose. Net income fell 3% to $26 million though as operating expenses including salaries and benefits increased. Cash flow from operations slipped 16% that year to $38 million.

Strategy

Salinas Valley Memorial Healthcare System partnered with MedAssist in late 2013 to expand its regional care services. The partners provide personalized assistance to help consumers enroll in the state's Health Insurance Exchange.

EXECUTIVES

Senior Vice President And Patient Care And Cardiovascular Services, Irene Neumeister
Vp Systems, James Brennan
Medical Records Director, Shereen Martin
Department Secretary, Noelle Griffin
Assistant Treasurer, Carissa Purnell
Treasurer, Alfred Diaz-infante
Auditors: MOSS ADAMS LLP SAN FRANCISCO

LOCATIONS

HQ: SALINAS VALLEY MEMORIAL HEALTHCARE SYSTEMS
450 E ROMIE LN, SALINAS, CA 939014029
Phone: 831 757-4333
Web: WWW.SVMH.COM

PRODUCTS/OPERATIONS

2014 Sales

	$ mil.	% of total
Net patient revenue	345	98
Other revenue	6	2
Total	**351**	**100**

Selected Services

Anesthesiology
Angiography
Art & Music Therapy
Gynecology
Health Education
Health Promotion
Heart Health
Palliative Medicine
Pediatrics
Pharmacy
Physical Therapy
Plastic & Reconstructive Surgery
Positron Emission Tomography (PET)
Pre-Surgery Orientation
Tele-Care
Treadmill Stress Test
Vascular Care

COMPETITORS

Community Hospital of the Monterey Peninsula
Dignity Health
John Muir Health
Sequoia Healthcare District
Stanford Health Care
Sutter Health
UCSF Medical

HISTORICAL FINANCIALS

Company Type: Private

Income Statement   FYE: June 30

	REVENUE ($ mil.)	NET INCOME ($ mil.)	NET PROFIT MARGIN	EMPLOYEES
06/17	494	50	10.1%	1,800
06/16	366	44	12.0%	—
06/15	344	37	10.9%	—
06/05	284	14	5.0%	—
Annual Growth	**4.7%**	**11.1%**	**—**	**—**

2017 Year-End Financials

Return on assets: 7.5%   Cash ($ mil.): 103
Return on equity: 10.3%
Current ratio: 2.30

SALT RIVER PROJECT AGRICULTURAL IMPROVEMENT AND POWER DISTRICT

One of the US's largest government-owned utilities Salt River Project (SRP) provides Phoenix with two types of currents: electric and water. Electricity comes from the Salt River Project Agricultural Improvement and Power District a political subdivision of the State of Arizona that has a generating capacity of about 8300 MW and distributes power to more than 984000 homes and businesses. The district sells excess power to wholesale customers. Water comes from the Salt River Valley Water Users' Association a private firm that delivers 1 million acre-feet of water per year to residents and agricultural irrigators; the association also operates dams canals reservoirs and wells in its service area.

Operations

Staying true to its mission of providing water and electricity to SRP customers the company owns or has stakes in a dozen major power generating plants fueled by diverse sources including nuclear hydro coal biomass and natural gas.

Geographic Reach

It serves residential commercial industrial and agricultural power customers in a 2900-square-mile service territory spanning parts of Maricopa Gila and Pinal counties in Arizona. In addition the enterprise has mining loads in an adjacent 2400-square-mile area in Gila and Pinal counties. SRP is the region's top water supplier delivers about 800000 acre-feet of water annually with a service area of more than 375 square miles and with management responsibilities for a watershed covering 13000 square miles.

The Association provides the water supply for an area of 248200 acres within the major portions of the cities of Phoenix Avondale Glendale Mesa Tempe Chandler Peoria Scottsdale and Tolleson; the Town of Gilbert; and the Gila River Indian Community.

Financial Performance

The company's net revenues increased by 6% in 2014 primarily due to higher wholesale revenues.

The increase in wholesale revenues was primarily due to an increase in kWh sold and higher wholesale power prices as well as a $38.6 million higher gain realized from fair value adjustments on wholesale positions.

Strategy

SRP is aiming to get 20% of its power from renewable sources by 2020 in order to meet tightening environmental regulations. In fiscal 2012 renewables (primarily hydroelectric power and including some purchased green power from third parties) accounted for more than 9% of its total generating capacity. In addition to hydropower the company is investing in wind geothermal landfill gas and solar power generation technologies. Initiatives include the Dry Lake Wind Project (the first commercial wind farm in Arizona) and an incentive program that rewards customers for installing solar panels at their homes and businesses.

It is also pushing conservation measures and installed about 1 million smart meters (efficient automated systems that allow customers to monitor and reduce energy use) by the end 2013.

In order to upgrade its older coal plants and to build additional generation transmission distribution and irrigation assets&SRP has earmarked $5.6 billion in capital improvements by 2015.

Mergers and Acquisitions

In 2015 SRP acquired Los Angeles Department of Water and Power's share of the Navajo Generating Station. SRP is looking to significantly reduce emissions from the plant by 2020 to meet EPA requirements.

In 2013 it acquired a 625 MW gas-fired power plant from Sempra U.S. Gas & Power.

Company Background

SRP was founded in 1903 under the Natural Reclamation Act.

EXECUTIVES

Ceo And General Manager, Mark B. Bonsall
Associate General Manager And Ceo Power System, Mike Hummel
Associate General Manager And Chief Financial Executive, Aidan McSheffrey
President, David Rousseau
Vice President, John R. Hoopes
Auditors: PRICEWATERHOUSECOOPERS LLP PH

LOCATIONS

HQ: SALT RIVER PROJECT AGRICULTURAL IMPROVEMENT AND POWER DISTRICT
1500 N MILL AVE, TEMPE, AZ 852811252
Phone: 602 236-5900
Web: WWW.SRPNET.COM

PRODUCTS/OPERATIONS

2016 Sales

	$ mil.	% of total
Retail electric	2,749	90
Water	15	1
Other	282	9
Total	**3,047**	**100**

Selected Subsidiaries

Salt River Project Agricultural Improvement and Power District (electric utility)
New West Energy Corporation (energy support services)
Papago Park Center Inc. (real estate facility management)
SRP Captive Risk Solutions Ltd. (domestic captive property boiler and machinery insurer)
Salt River Valley Water Users' Association

COMPETITORS

American States Water	PacifiCorp
American Water	Pinnacle West
Calpine	Sempra Energy
NV Energy	Southwest Gas
PG&E Corporation	UNS Energy
PNM Resources	Xcel Energy

HISTORICAL FINANCIALS

Company Type: Private

Income Statement   FYE: April 30

	REVENUE ($ mil.)	NET INCOME ($ mil.)	NET PROFIT MARGIN	EMPLOYEES
04/17*	3,084	247	8.0%	4,336
01/10	2,217	517	23.3%	—
Annual Growth	**4.8%**	**(10.0%)**	**—**	**—**

*Fiscal year change

2017 Year-End Financials

Return on assets: 2.0%
Return on equity: 4.9%
Current ratio: 1.40
Cash ($ mil.): 313

SAMARITAN HEALTH SERVICES, INC.

EXECUTIVES

Ceo, Doug Boysen
Gynecology/Obstetrics, Jodell J Boyle
Administrative Assistant, Barbara Croney
Chief of Medicine, Darrell Prins
Chief of Cardiology, Bob Vanderford
Doctor, David Eason
Director of Laboratory, Harlan Akers
Doctor, Jodell Boyle
Coordinator, Lisa Ely
Executive Officer, Pat Zeller
Chief of Medicine, Paul Daskalos

LOCATIONS

HQ: SAMARITAN HEALTH SERVICES, INC.
3600 NW SAMARITAN DR, CORVALLIS, OR 973303737
Phone: 541 757-5111
Web: WWW.SAMHEALTH.ORG

HISTORICAL FINANCIALS

Company Type: Private

Income Statement   FYE: December 31

	REVENUE ($ mil.)	NET INCOME ($ mil.)	NET PROFIT MARGIN	EMPLOYEES
12/18	1,168	9	0.8%	4,550
12/17	1,101	26	2.4%	—
12/08	1	0	—	—
12/04	65	(1)	—	—
Annual Growth	**22.9%**	**—**	**—**	**—**

2018 Year-End Financials

Return on assets: 1.1%
Return on equity: 2.4%
Current ratio: 1.80
Cash ($ mil.): 144

SAMARITAN'S PURSE

EXECUTIVES

Chb-Ceo, Franklin Graham
V Pres, Phyllis Payne
South Sudan Country Direc, Phil Ewert
Director, Eugene Jesel
Surgeon, Warren Cooper
Facilities Director, Ray Halle
Information Specialist, Paula Woodring
Administrative Assistant, Amber Light
Broadcast Engineering Manager, Ben Cranor
Deputy Director, Matt Olson
Director Proj, Edward Densham
Auditors: DIXON HUGHES GOODMAN LLP CHAR

LOCATIONS

HQ: SAMARITAN'S PURSE
801 BAMBOO RD, BOONE, NC 286078721
Phone: 828 262-1980
Web: WWW.SAMARITANSPURSE.ORG

HISTORICAL FINANCIALS

Company Type: Private

Income Statement   FYE: December 31

	REVENUE ($ mil.)	NET INCOME ($ mil.)	NET PROFIT MARGIN	EMPLOYEES
12/17	800	189	23.7%	525
12/16	634	51	8.0%	—
12/15	599	82	13.7%	—
12/14	520	31	6.0%	—
Annual Growth	**15.5%**	**82.8%**	**—**	**—**

2017 Year-End Financials

Return on assets: 28.0%
Return on equity: 30.3%
Current ratio: 15.80
Cash ($ mil.): 230

SAN ANTONIO INDEPENDENT SCHOOL DISTRICT FAC

EXECUTIVES

Supt, Dr Sylvester Syl Perez
Pres*, Ed Garza
V Pres*, Olga M Hernandez
SEC*, Arthur V Valdez
Information Specialist, Mark McRae
Law Specialist, Andrea Tena
Federal Program Director, Barbara Rodriguez
Child Nutrition Coordinator, Olga Perez
Inservice Training Director, Theresa Salinas
Web Administrator, Brad Wehring
Assistant Athletic Director, Brian Clancy
Auditors: GARZA/GONZALEZ & ASSOCIATES S

LOCATIONS

HQ: SAN ANTONIO INDEPENDENT SCHOOL DISTRICT FAC
141 LAVACA ST, SAN ANTONIO, TX 782101039
Phone: 210 554-2200
Web: WWW.SAISD.NET

HISTORICAL FINANCIALS

Company Type: Private

Income Statement   FYE: June 30

	REVENUE ($ mil.)	NET INCOME ($ mil.)	NET PROFIT MARGIN	EMPLOYEES
06/16	659	43	6.5%	7,600
06/15	624	(14)	—	—
06/14*	600	(110)	—	—
08/09	549	6	1.2%	—
Annual Growth	**2.6%**	**30.2%**	**—**	**—**

*Fiscal year change

2016 Year-End Financials

Return on assets: 3.0%
Return on equity: 10.6%
Current ratio: —
Cash ($ mil.): 189

SAN ANTONIO WATER SYSTEM

Wasting water is a sore point in drought-prone South Texas and San Antonio Water System (SAWS) seeks to husband this precious resource the best it can. The company serves about 460000 water and 411000 wastewater customers or about 1.6 million people in the San Antonio metropolitan area (including most of the city of San Antonio several suburban municipalities and adjacent parts of Bexar County). In addition to serving its own retail customers SAWS provides wholesale water supplies to several smaller utility systems in its service area. The utility is owned by the City of San Antonio.

Operations
SAWS oversees more than 10400 miles of water and sewer mains.

Geographic Reach
The company serves Texas customers in Bexar County as well as parts of Medina and Atascosa counties.

Sales and Marketing

The company serves retail customers and also provides wholesale water supplies to several smaller utility systems.

Financial Performance

In 2014 SAWS' net revenue increased by 8% due to an average power rate increase of 5.1% a 3.9% increase in metered water usage and average customer growth of 1.8%.

The company's net income increased by 57% due to higher net revenues and a decline in salaries and fringe benefits related to retirement incentive program and efficiency improvements implemented and synergies associated with integrating the operations of Bexar Metropolitan Water District with the company.

In 2014 SAWS' operating cash inflow increased by 14%.

Strategy

The water and wastewater utility expects its population base to increase from 1 million in 2006 to 2.2 million by 2050 and its water demand to double during the same time period. Faced with a regional long term drought scenario SAWS is pushing conservation measures.

To avoid costly federal litigation over alleged Clean Water Act violations in 2013 SAWS agreed to invest an additional $492 million in infrastructure and maintenance to reduce sewer spills in San Antonio under a settlement with the EPA and the Texas Commission on Environmental Quality.

The company focuses on integration pipeline and pump station and brackish groundwater desalination (designed to produce 13440 acre-feet of water per year) and the expanded Carrizo project which is projected to produce 21000 acre-feet of water from the Carrizo aquifer in southeast Bexar by 2027.

Company Background

SAWS and a neighboring water authority the Lower Colorado River Authority signed an agreement in 2002 to study the feasibility of drawing water from the lower Colorado River basin for use by San Antonio. The LCRA reported in 2009 that it had found that there was not a sufficient amount of extra water available to build a proposed reservoir. SAWS sued LCRA for $1.2 billion over the results of the study but the suit was tossed out by a state district judge.

SAWS was formed in 1992 through a merger of three entities: the City Water Board the City Wastewater Department and the Alamo Water Conservation and Reuse District.

EXECUTIVES

Senior Vice President And Chief Operating Officer, Steve Clouse
Svp And Coo, Steven (Steve) Clouse
Svp And Cfo, Douglas (Doug) Evanson
Vp Distribution And Collection Operations, Mike Brinkmann
President And Ceo, Robert R. Puente
Senior Director Sewer System Improvements, Jeff Haby
Chief Information Systems, Joe Samples
Vp Water Resources And Conservation, Charles E. Ahrens
Vice President Of Communications And External Affairs, Gavino Ramos
Auditors: BAKER TILLY VIRCHOW KRAUSE

LOCATIONS

HQ: SAN ANTONIO WATER SYSTEM
2800 US HIGHWAY 281 N, SAN ANTONIO, TX 782123106
Phone: 210 704-7297
Web: WWW.SAWS.ORG

PRODUCTS/OPERATIONS

2014 Sales

	$ mil.	% of total
Operating revenues		
Wastewater system	210	42
Water supply system	150	30
Water delivery system	127	25
Chilled water and steam system	11	2
Non-operating revenues	5	1
Total	**505**	**100**

HISTORICAL FINANCIALS
Company Type: Private

Income Statement   FYE: December 31

	REVENUE ($ mil.)	NET INCOME ($ mil.)	NET PROFIT MARGIN	EMPLOYEES
12/17	666	240	36.1%	1,700
12/16	622	213	34.3%	—
12/12	0	0	—	—
Annual Growth	—	—	—	—

2017 Year-End Financials

Return on assets: 3.9%   Cash ($ mil.): 36
Return on equity: 8.4%
Current ratio: 3.00

SAN BERNARDINO CITY UNIFIED SCHOOL DISTRICT

EXECUTIVES

Spdt, Dale Marsden
Staff, Susie Sellas
It Security, Rita Munoz
Coordinator, Terry Comnick
Director, Adriane Robles
On Assignment, Kenneth Martinez
Administrative Assistant Email, Sylvia Ross
School Counselor, Michael Bennie
Buyer, Selene Tirado

LOCATIONS

HQ: SAN BERNARDINO CITY UNIFIED SCHOOL DISTRICT
777 N F ST, SAN BERNARDINO, CA 924103017
Phone: 909 381-1100
Web: WWW.SBCUSD.K12.CA.US

HISTORICAL FINANCIALS
Company Type: Private

Income Statement   FYE: June 30

	REVENUE ($ mil.)	NET INCOME ($ mil.)	NET PROFIT MARGIN	EMPLOYEES
06/18	712	27	3.8%	6,000
06/08	759	97	12.8%	—
06/05	0	0	—	—
06/02	409	11	2.8%	—
Annual Growth	3.5%	5.5%	—	—

SAN FRANCISCO BAY AREA RAPID TRANSIT DISTRICT

If you're going to San Francisco — from Oakland Berkeley or another Bay Area community — San Francisco Bay Area Rapid Transit District (BART) can take you there. BART's trains carry about 365000 daily weekday riders from more than 45 stations over more than 100 miles of track including the 3.6 mile Transbay Tube under the San Francisco Bay that links the City by the Bay with Oakland and other East Bay communities. Directors elected from nine districts in Alameda Contra Costa and San Francisco counties oversee BART which operates with an annual budget of about $480 million. Construction on the rail system began in 1964 and BART carried its first passengers in 1972.

Operations

BART which has the oldest fleet in the US has awarded Bombardier about $896 million to design and make more than 400 train cars that may be ready for use by 2017. The contract represents the first phase of a $2.5 billion project to replace BART's fleet of some 670 cars with a larger fleet of more than 770 new cars. Three-fourths of the project's cost is being paid by the federal government with the remainder coming from BART.

Another major project is the $1.3 billion Earthquake Safety Program which is almost finished and scheduled for completion in 2016. The program includes bolting 2.5-inch steel plates on the concrete wall of the Transbay Tube — which carries about half of BART's daily weekday riders — and similar strengthening measures for more than 30 stations more than 20 miles of elevated track and other facilities.

Geographic Reach

BART serves the Bay Area through its 45 stations spanning the four counties of Alameda Contra Costa San Francisco and San Mateo.

Financial Performance

In 2014 the company's revenue increased by 4% to $463 million due to a spike in passenger fares along with higher parking rates implemented in 2014 at several stations. BART was also helped by an increase in advertising revenue and a rise in ground lease revenue resulting from the reassignment of its original ground lease at West Dublin Station to a new lessee. In addition its net income increased by 8% in 2014 due to the increase in revenues along with lower transportation expenses.

EXECUTIVES

Vice President Information Technology, William Longstaff
Auditors: MACIAS GINI & O'CONNELL LLP O

LOCATIONS

HQ: SAN FRANCISCO BAY AREA RAPID TRANSIT DISTRICT
300 LAKESIDE DR, OAKLAND, CA 94604
Phone: 510 464-6000
Web: WWW.BART.GOV

HISTORICAL FINANCIALS

Company Type: Private

Income Statement

	REVENUE ($ mil.)	NET INCOME ($ mil.)	NET PROFIT MARGIN	EMPLOYEES
06/18	605	212	35.2%	3,347
06/16	545	331	60.8%	
06/06	275	(2)	—	—
06/05	0	0	—	—
Annual Growth	—	—	—	—

FYE: June 30

2018 Year-End Financials

Return on assets: 2.1% Cash ($ mil.): 415
Return on equity: 3.1%
Current ratio: 4.20

SAN JUAN UNIFIED SCHOOL DISTRICT

EXECUTIVES

Supt, Pat Jaurequi
Supt*, Glynn Thompson
Assistant Superintendent, Rick Messer
Information Technology/Interne, Bart Hubbard
Teacher, Michelle Lavery
Teacher, Brent Fanchar
Teacher, Carla Elkins
Teacher, Deb House
Teacher, Herbert Larsh
Teacher, Richele Bridges
Teacher, Allen Kiksman
Auditors: CROWE HORWATH LLP SACRAMENTO

LOCATIONS

HQ: SAN JUAN UNIFIED SCHOOL DISTRICT
3738 WALNUT AVE, CARMICHAEL, CA 956083099
Phone: 916 971-7700
Web: WWW.SANJUAN.EDU

HISTORICAL FINANCIALS

Company Type: Private

Income Statement

	REVENUE ($ mil.)	NET INCOME ($ mil.)	NET PROFIT MARGIN	EMPLOYEES
06/18	620	(38)	—	4,200
06/17	577	104	18.2%	—
06/16	576	(6)	—	—
06/08	0	0	—	—
Annual Growth	—	—	—	—

FYE: June 30

SANFORD

Sanford is one of the largest not-for-profit integrated health care systems in the US. It primarily serves rural areas through its network of more than 40 regional and community hospitals in nine states including the Dakotas Iowa Minnesota and Nebraska. The organization operating as Sanford Health also operates local clinics and long-term care centers. In addition to primary care and general hospital services Sanford's medical centers and specialty outpatient practices provide care in fields including senior living cancer cardiology vascular health neurology orthopedics pediatrics virology and women's health. In early 2019 Sanford merged with Good Samaritan Society which specializes in senior care.

Operations

In addition to its 40-plus hospitals Sanford's network includes about 200 senior living facilities (long-term care assisted-living and independent living centers) and 140 clinics. Altogether the facilities in the Sanford Health network handle some 50000 inpatient admissions and about 1.35 million outpatient visits each year. The network's 1400 physicians provide care in more than 80 specialist fields.

Along with its health care facilities Sanford Health also operates Sanford Laboratories based in Sioux Falls and Rapid City South Dakota. The system maintains Sanford Research a not-for-profit research organization that draws upon the physicians of Sanford Health and researchers at the University of South Dakota. Sanford Research conducts some $100 million in research projects each year. Finally the Sanford Health Plan is a not-for-profit health plan that serves individuals and employers across the system's region.

Geographic Reach

Sanford Health has locations in more than 125 communities in nine states including California Iowa Minnesota Nebraska North Dakota Oklahoma Oregon and South Dakota. It also has clinical affiliates in locations including Ghana Africa; Karmiel Israel; and Baja Mexico.

Strategy

Growth plans for Sanford include the construction of hospital and clinic facilities in Minnesota and North Dakota and new health care and research facilities in South Dakota. A $700 million gift from local philanthropist T. Denny Sanford is enabling the establishment of several new facilities. That contribution is also supporting the organization's research programs in children's health and initiatives to find cures for conditions including breast cancer and type 1 diabetes.

In addition Sanford Health expands by acquiring small community medical centers. The system is also growing by striking partnerships with small regional health care providers.

In 2018 the system merged with long-time collaborator Neuropsychiatric Research Institute. That transaction expanded Sanford's research activities; Sanford ultimately hopes to establish a major research center in its hometown of Fargo North Dakota.

Mergers and Acquisitions

In early 2019 Sanford merged with senior health services provider The Evangelical Lutheran Good Samaritan Society. The transaction combined Sanford's hospital system with Good Samaritan's senior living facilities creating an integrated health care research and insurance entity.

In 2018 Sanford Research absorbed Neuropsychiatric Research Institute which focuses on eating disorders and obesity. With that acquisition Sanford intends to establish a major research program in Fargo North Dakota.

Company Background

Sanford was created from the 2009 merger of two Dakota health care legends: South Dakota's Sanford Health and North Dakota's MeritCare Health System. Both date back to the 1890s. Following the merger the two units briefly kept their separate identities but in 2010 organized under the Sanford Health-MeritCare name. The operating name was later shortened to Sanford Health.

EXECUTIVES

Medical Director, Julie Blehm
Director Of Clinical Services, Ann Mays
Vice President Of Research Sanford Health, David Pearce
Physical Therapy, Kris Naig
Vice President Major Initiatives, Brian Bonde
Director Of Nursing, Kellee Johnk
Vice President Marketing, Karoliina Slack
Vice President Marketing Fargo Region, Jennifer Cresap
Managing Director, Barbara Bentz
Medical Director, William Klava
Nursing Director, Jeri Schons
Occupational Therapy Dir, MELISSA GREWE
Vice President, Misty Anderson
Auditors: DELOITTE & TOUCHE LLP MINNEAP

LOCATIONS

HQ: SANFORD
801 BROADWAY N, FARGO, ND 581023641
Phone: 701 234-6000
Web: WWW.SANFORDHEALTH.ORG

PRODUCTS/OPERATIONS

Selected Major Regional Medical Centers
Sanford Bemidji Medical Center (Bemidji Minnesota)
Sanford Medical Center Bismarck (Bismarck North Dakota)
Sanford Medical Center Fargo (Fargo North Dakota)
Sanford USD Medical Center Sioux Falls (Sioux Falls South Dakota)

COMPETITORS

Altru Health	Rapid City Regional
Avera Health	Hospital
Catholic Health	St. Alexius Medical
Initiatives	Center
Mayo Clinic	St. Mary's Healthcare
North Memorial Health	Wellmark
Care	

HISTORICAL FINANCIALS

Company Type: Private

Income Statement

	REVENUE ($ mil.)	NET INCOME ($ mil.)	NET PROFIT MARGIN	EMPLOYEES
06/18	4,639	117	2.5%	50,000
06/17	4,411	175	4.0%	—
06/16	4,231	108	2.6%	—
06/14	3	(11)	—	—
Annual Growth	486.1%	—	—	—

FYE: June 30

2018 Year-End Financials

Return on assets: 2.7% Cash ($ mil.): 185
Return on equity: 4.6%
Current ratio: 1.60

SANFORD HEALTH

EXECUTIVES

Pres, Kelby K Krabbenhoft
Sr V Pres-Coo, Becky Nelson
Pres-Clinic, Dan Blue
Pres-Regional Health Services, Ed Weiland
Pres-Foundation, Brian Mortensen
Pres-Health Plan, Ruth Krystopolski
Ex V Pres, Dave Link
Cfo, Michelle Bruhn
Director of Public Affairs, Warren Larson
Point of Contact, Ronda Hinsch
Emergency Room Coordinator, Maria Botker
Auditors: DELOITTE & TOUCHE LLP MINNEA

LOCATIONS

HQ: SANFORD HEALTH
 1305 W 18TH ST, SIOUX FALLS, SD 571050401
Phone: 605 333-1720
Web: WWW.SANFORDHEALTH.ORG

HISTORICAL FINANCIALS

Company Type: Private

Income Statement				FYE: December 31
	REVENUE ($ mil.)	NET INCOME ($ mil.)	NET PROFIT MARGIN	EMPLOYEES
12/18*	4,819	141	2.9%	2,939
06/17	4,411	175	4.0%	—
06/16	4,231	114	2.7%	—
06/12	2,516	72	2.9%	—
Annual Growth	9.7%	10.1%	—	—

*Fiscal year change

2018 Year-End Financials

Return on assets: 3.3%   Cash ($ mil.): 109
Return on equity: 5.3%
Current ratio: 1.80

SANFORD HEALTH

Auditors: DELOITTE TAX LLP MINNEAPOLIS

LOCATIONS

HQ: SANFORD HEALTH
 1305 W 18TH ST, SIOUX FALLS, SD 571050401
Phone: 605 333-1000

HISTORICAL FINANCIALS

Company Type: Private

Income Statement				FYE: June 30
	REVENUE ($ mil.)	NET INCOME ($ mil.)	NET PROFIT MARGIN	EMPLOYEES
06/17	3,741	138	3.7%	2
06/10	1,038	35	3.4%	—
Annual Growth	20.1%	21.4%	—	—

2017 Year-End Financials

Return on assets: 5.0%   Cash ($ mil.): 78
Return on equity: 11.9%
Current ratio: —

SANFORD NORTH

EXECUTIVES

Prin, Roger L Gilbertson
Cfo*, Lisa Carlson
Coordinator, Pammie Dohman
Pediatrician, Brenda Thurlow

LOCATIONS

HQ: SANFORD NORTH
 801 BROADWAY N, FARGO, ND 581023641
Phone: 701 234-2000
Web: WWW.SANFORDHEALTH.ORG

HISTORICAL FINANCIALS

Company Type: Private

Income Statement				FYE: June 30
	REVENUE ($ mil.)	NET INCOME ($ mil.)	NET PROFIT MARGIN	EMPLOYEES
06/10	677	(15)	—	7,200
06/08	112	2	2.0%	—
Annual Growth	145.1%			

2010 Year-End Financials

Return on assets: (-10.8%)   Cash ($ mil.): —
Return on equity: (-24.5%)
Current ratio: 1.40

SANTA BARBARA COTTAGE HOSPITAL

EXECUTIVES

Ceo, Ronald C Werft
Exec V Pres*, Steven Fellows
Cfo*, Brett Tande
Chief of Medicine, Robert S Wright
Coordinator, Ruben Orozco
Executive Assistant, Teresa Guzman-Petter
Director Neurovascular, Alois Zauner
Vice President Information TEC, Bill Worthington
Rn, Carol Prager
Registered Nurse, Cat Demourkas
Clinical Pharmacist, Chris Ray

LOCATIONS

HQ: SANTA BARBARA COTTAGE HOSPITAL
 400 W PUEBLO ST, SANTA BARBARA, CA 931054353
Phone: 805 682-7111

HISTORICAL FINANCIALS

Company Type: Private

Income Statement				FYE: December 31
	REVENUE ($ mil.)	NET INCOME ($ mil.)	NET PROFIT MARGIN	EMPLOYEES
12/17	646	178	27.6%	1,786
12/16	603	42	7.0%	—
12/15	610	(15)	—	—
12/14	38	32	83.3%	—
Annual Growth	156.0%	77.2%	—	—

2017 Year-End Financials

Return on assets: 10.6%   Cash ($ mil.): 13
Return on equity: 17.3%
Current ratio: 1.90

SANTA CLARA VALLEY MEDICAL CENTER

EXECUTIVES

Ceo, Paul E Lorenz
Human Resources Director, Dave Manson
Internal Medicine Practitioner, Susan X Zhao
Pathologist, Wendy Wu
Coordinator, Cindy Stewart
Pathologist, Sharmila Pramanik
Director of Planning, Joy Alexiou
Nurse Practitioner Family, Leslyn Watson
Facility Manager, Alex Gallego
Chief of Nephrology, Amul Jobalia
Director, Daniela Cohen

LOCATIONS

HQ: SANTA CLARA VALLEY MEDICAL CENTER
 751 S BASCOM AVE, SAN JOSE, CA 951282699
Phone: 408 885-5000

HISTORICAL FINANCIALS

Company Type: Private

Income Statement				FYE: June 30
	REVENUE ($ mil.)	NET INCOME ($ mil.)	NET PROFIT MARGIN	EMPLOYEES
06/16	490	61	12.4%	19
06/15	417	21	5.1%	—
Annual Growth	17.5%	187.4%	—	—

2016 Year-End Financials

Return on assets: 3.0%   Cash ($ mil.): 439
Return on equity: 5.7%
Current ratio: 1.90

SANTA ROSA MEMORIAL HOSPITAL INC

EXECUTIVES

Ceo, Todd Salnas
V Pres*, Gary Greensweig
Cfo*, Mich Riccioni
Chief Nursing Officer*, Kathrine Hardin
Manager*, Jennifer Triplitt
Facilities Manager, Michael Fink
Internal Medicine Practitioner, John P Hurwitz
Anesthesiologist, Margaret A Fanucchi
Neurologist, Zachary R Lewton
Hematologist Oncologist, Hyun C Kang
Maintenance Director, Kevin Fitzgerald

LOCATIONS

HQ: SANTA ROSA MEMORIAL HOSPITAL INC
 1165 MONTGOMERY DR, SANTA ROSA, CA
 954054897
Phone: 707 546-3210

HISTORICAL FINANCIALS

Company Type: Private

Income Statement				FYE: June 30
	REVENUE ($ mil.)	NET INCOME ($ mil.)	NET PROFIT MARGIN	EMPLOYEES
06/17	518	55	10.7%	2,100
06/16	509	49	9.7%	—
06/15	489	64	13.1%	—
06/14	387	47	12.2%	—
Annual Growth	10.1%	5.4%	—	—

2017 Year-End Financials

Return on assets: 11.6%   Cash ($ mil.): —
Return on equity: 20.6%
Current ratio: 1.60

SAPP BROS., INC.

Need air in those 18 wheels? Sapp BrosÂ Travel Centers (formerly Sapp Bros Truck Stops) has the usual air gas food but also offers human conveniences such as laundry rooms mailbox rentals private showers and TV lounges. The company operates a chain ofÂ some 15 truck stops — readily identifiable by the giant red-and-white coffeepot logo — along interstate highways from Utah to Pennsylvania; with a concentration in Nebraska. Half of the locations also operate service centers offering oil changes new tires and safety checks. Its sister company Sapp Bros Petroleum distributes fuels and lubricants to more than 200 retailers. TheÂ firm is run by CEO Bill Sapp one of the four founding Sapp brothers.

Geographic Reach
Omaha-based Sapp Bros. has travel centers in eight states: Nebraska Iowa Utah Colorado Wyoming Kansas Illinois and Pennsylvania.

Strategy
To raise its profile and rev up its business Sapp Bros. in 2013 joined the roster of VP Racing Fuels's retail brand partners. The benefits of the affiliation include association with an attractive retail image competitive credit card rates and the ability to source unbranded fuel for its travel centers.

EXECUTIVES

Board Of Directors, Allen Marsh
Auditors: KPMG LLP OMAHA NEBRASKA

LOCATIONS

HQ: SAPP BROS., INC.
  9915 S 148TH ST, OMAHA, NE 681383876
Phone: 402 895-7038
Web: WWW.SAPPBROS.NET

2012 Locations

	No.
Nebraska	8
Iowa	2
Colorado	1
Illinois	1
Kansas	1
Pennsylvania	1
Utah	1
Wyoming	1
Total	**16**

COMPETITORS

Exxon Mobil	Stuckey's
Love's Country Stores	TravelCenters of
Pilot Flying J	America

HISTORICAL FINANCIALS
Company Type: Private

Income Statement   FYE: September 30

	REVENUE ($ mil.)	NET INCOME ($ mil.)	NET PROFIT MARGIN	EMPLOYEES
09/18	1,259	11	0.9%	1,700
09/17	990	11	1.2%	—
09/16	802	18	2.3%	—
09/15	1,128	20	1.8%	—
Annual Growth	**3.7%**	**(17.5%)**	**—**	**—**

2018 Year-End Financials
Return on assets: 6.8%   Cash ($ mil.): 4
Return on equity: 17.4%
Current ratio: 1.30

SARASOTA COUNTY PUBLIC HOSPITAL DISTRICT

Sarasota County Public Hospital Board which does business as the Sarasota Memorial Health Care System is a publicly owned hospital system serving residents in and around Sarasota on Florida's western coast. It operates Sarasota Memorial Hospital a not-for-profit acute-care facility with more than 800 beds (and more than 900 doctors) that provides general medical and surgical care as well as specialized care in areas such as heart disease cancer and neuroscience. The system also features a skilled nursing facility walk-in medical centers an outpatient surgical center and home health care operations. Additionally the hospital conducts clinical trials and has an educational affiliation with Florida State University.

Operations
Sarasota Memorial has the only obstetrics program and neonatal intensive care unit in the county and its Bayside Center includes one of the county's only inpatient behavioral health facilities. The health care system's Charter Health Plan program offers group health insurance to local business owners.

Sarasota Memorial receives some 32000 inpatient visits and 950000 outpatient and physician visits each year.

Geographic Reach
Sarasota Memorial serves Florida's Sarasota County.

Sales and Marketing
Medicare and Medicaid combined account for some 60% of Sarasota Memorial's net patient service revenue. Self-pay and managed care make up the remainder.

Financial Performance
Sarasota's total revenues increased by 9% in fiscal 2016 (ended September) due to a 9% increase in net patient revenue due to higher volume. The company reported $107 million in excess revenues over expenses that year a 13% decline versus the prior year. Operating expenses including salaries fringe benefits and supplies costs all increased in 2016.

Cash flow from operations increased 38% to $85.8 million thanks to an increase in cash received from patient care services.

Strategy
Sarasota Memorial seeks to improve its financial performance by pursuing profitable inpatient and outpatient growth through an aggressive focus on physician alignment and integration and capturing new patients residing in high growth areas. The system has also been opening new facilities to boost patient service revenues. In 2016 it opened its sixth urgent care center. The following year it opened a 74000-sq.-ft. Rehabilitation Pavilion the only site of its kind in Sarasota County to offer comprehensive inpatient and outpatient rehabilitation services.

The system also introduced its nurse residency program and an internal medicine residency program in 2017.

Company Background
Sarasota Memorial was founded as a community hospital in 1925.

EXECUTIVES

Vp And Cio, Denis Baker
Cfo Sarasota Memorial Health Care System, David Verinder, age 52
Chief Nursing Officer, Jan Mauck
Cfo, William Woeltjen
Chief Of Medical Operations, R. Stephen Taylor
Medical Director Research, Ricardo Yaryura
Medical Records Director, Diane Settle
Director Of Nursing Resources Picc Team, Janet Steves
Medical Director Of All Children, Jennifer Mayer
Radiology Director, Debbie Bohanon
Medical Director Hospitalist Program, John Moritz
Vice President And Chief Legal Officer, Carol Kalish
Board Secretary, Donna Desisto
First Vice Chairman, Gregory Carter
Second Vice Chairwoman, Marguerite G. Malone
Second Vice Chairman, Alex Miller

LOCATIONS

HQ: SARASOTA COUNTY PUBLIC HOSPITAL DISTRICT
  1700 S TAMIAMI TRL, SARASOTA, FL 342393509
Phone: 941 917-9000
Web: WWW.SMH.COM

PRODUCTS/OPERATIONS

2016 Sales

	% of total
County Public Hospital District	
Sarasota Memorial Hospital	59
Corporate Division	2
Nursing & Rehabilitation Center	1
Charter Plan	-
SMH Health Care Inc.	33
Physician Services Inc.	5
Total	**100**

COMPETITORS

All Children's	HCA
Hospital	St. Joseph's-Baptist
Bayfront Health	Health Care
Encompass Health	Tampa General Hospital
Florida Hospital Tampa	
Bay Division	

HISTORICAL FINANCIALS
Company Type: Private

Income Statement   FYE: September 30

	REVENUE ($ mil.)	NET INCOME ($ mil.)	NET PROFIT MARGIN	EMPLOYEES
09/17	793	99	12.6%	4,200
09/16	12	0	4.0%	—
09/15	590	131	22.3%	—
09/14	524	92	17.6%	—
Annual Growth	**14.8%**	**2.6%**	**—**	**—**

2017 Year-End Financials
Return on assets: 6.0%   Cash ($ mil.): 27
Return on equity: 9.7%
Current ratio: 1.00

SAVANNAH HEALTH SERVICES, LLC

Memorial Health University Medical Center wants to provide memorable health care to residents of Savannah Georgia and surrounding areas.

An affiliate of Mercer University School of Medicine the tertiary care facility provides such services as cardiac and trauma care and rehabilitation. Also known as Memorial University Medical Center (MUMC) the hospital has some 620 beds and includes the MUMC Children's Hospital. It also operates specialty cancer care and women's health centers as well as research programs. Founded in 1955 MUMC is the flagship facility in a broader system of entities known as Memorial Health which includes affiliated primary and specialty care clinics in the region.

Operations

MUMC's cancer center the Curtis and Elizabeth Anderson Cancer Institute provides cancer treatment and surgical procedures; it also conducts research efforts to discover and develop new cancer therapies. The Women's Health Institute offers obstetrics gynecology and neonatology. MUMC also includes a level I trauma center and a Heart and Vascular Institute as well as programs in orthopedics neurology gastroenterology urology and pulmonary care. The affiliated Memorial Health University Physicians (MHUP) group operates primary and specialty care offices in the area.

Geographic Reach

MUMC serves a 35-county region in southeastern Georgia and southern South Carolina. The medical center serves as a regional referral center for several smaller community hospitals in the area. Affiliates include Bacon County Hospital Evans Memorial Hospital and Liberty Regional Medical Center.

Strategy

In 2012 Memorial Health formed an affiliation with Novant Health. The partnership will help the MUMC organization cut costs provide for future growth opportunities and improve its operational infrastructure. By joining the Novant Health Shared Services group MUMC will gain access to a larger base of supply chain clinical engineering information technology and best practices resources.

EXECUTIVES

Pres-Ceo, Magaret Gill
SEC*, Helen Dean Downing
Treas*, J Harry Haslam Jr
Coo*, Mary Chatman
Senior Vice-President, David Byck

LOCATIONS

HQ: SAVANNAH HEALTH SERVICES, LLC
4700 WATERS AVE, SAVANNAH, GA 314046220
Phone: 912 350-8000
Web: WWW.MEMORIALHEALTH.COM

COMPETITORS

Appling	St. Joseph's/Candler
Beaufort Memorial	Health System
Hospital	Tift Regional Medical
Doctors Hospital of	Center
Augusta	Universal Health
Liberty Regional	Services
Medical Center	University Health
Redmond Regional	Services
Medical Center	Walton Rehabilitation
South Georgia Medical	Hospital
Center	

HISTORICAL FINANCIALS

Company Type: Private

Income Statement   FYE: December 31

	REVENUE ($ mil.)	NET INCOME ($ mil.)	NET PROFIT MARGIN	EMPLOYEES
12/15	466	9	2.1%	4,700
12/14	469	32	6.9%	—
12/13	547	38	7.1%	—
12/08	453	(29)	—	—
Annual Growth	0.4%	—	—	—

2015 Year-End Financials

Return on assets: 2.1%   Cash ($ mil.): 15
Return on equity: 11.3%
Current ratio: 1.50

SAVANNAH-CHATHAM COUNTY BOARD OF EDUCATION

EXECUTIVES

Pres, Jolene Byrne
Executive of Information Techn, Cathy Mc Culloch
Kindergarten Teacher, Leslie Ducey
Auditors: KRT CPAS PC SAVANNAH GEOR

LOCATIONS

HQ: SAVANNAH-CHATHAM COUNTY BOARD OF EDUCATION
208 BULL ST, SAVANNAH, GA 314013843
Phone: 912 395-5534
Web: WWW.MASSIEHERITAGECENTER.WORDPRESS.COM

HISTORICAL FINANCIALS

Company Type: Private

Income Statement   FYE: June 30

	REVENUE ($ mil.)	NET INCOME ($ mil.)	NET PROFIT MARGIN	EMPLOYEES
06/18	525	41	7.8%	4,800
06/17	500	(30)	—	—
06/16	493	21	4.3%	—
06/07	373	20	5.4%	—
Annual Growth	3.2%	6.6%	—	—

SAVE THE CHILDREN FEDERATION, INC.

Save the Children helps poor and malnourished children in some 15 US states and nearly 120 countries focusing on such areas as health and nutrition economic development education child protection and HIV/AIDS. The humanitarian organization also participates in international disaster relief efforts focusing on children and their families. Save the Children spends about 90% of its budget on program services with the rest allocated to administration and fundraising. The group was founded in 1932 inspired by the international children's rights movement begun in the UK in 1919 by Eglantyne Jebb founder of the British Save the Children Fund. It is a member of the International Save the Children Alliance.

Operations

Some 43% of the humanitarian organization's work is centered in Asia with 34% in Africa. Save the Children spends the rest of its time in the US Latin America and the Middle East.

In 2012 alone Save the Children helped 125 million girls and boys worldwide.

Geographic Reach

Save the Children operates programs in some 120 countries including the US. It comprises 29 member organizations worldwide.

Financial Performance

The global aid organization's revenue declined by 3.5% in 2012 versus 2011 due largely to a 12% drop in private gifts grants and contributions which account for nearly half of its total revenue. Save the Children directed 89% of its expenses to programs which benefit children and allow the humanitarian organization to keep private costs (includes fundraising and management and general) at about 10% — one of the best ratios for nonprofit organizations.

Strategy

With about 28% of its program services devoted to emergencies and 20% to education Save the Children in 2014 partnered with The Malala Fund to help vulnerable Syrian and Jordanian children return to school. As part of the partnership Save the Children is launching a pair of education projects. Another large portion of Save the Children's program services are focused on Health and Nutrition (25%) and Hunger & Livelihoods (10%).

EXECUTIVES

Vice President Policy And Humanitarian Response, Michael Klosson
Vice President, Gary Shaye
Associate Vice President Foundations And, Taussig Nancy
Vice President, Robert Clay
Associate Vice President, Anna Schowengerdt
Associate Vice President Individual Philanthropy, Lucy Roche
Associate Vice President, John Farden
Auditors: KPMG LLP NEW YORK NY

LOCATIONS

HQ: SAVE THE CHILDREN FEDERATION, INC.
501 KINGS HWY E STE 400, FAIRFIELD, CT 068254861
Phone: 203 221-4000
Web: WWW.SAVETHECHILDREN.ORG

Selected Countries of Operation

Australia
Brazil
Canada
Denmark
Dominican Republic
Fiji
Finland
Germany
Guatemala
Honduras
Hong Kong
Iceland
India
Italy
Japan
Jordan
Korea
Lithuania
Mexico
Netherlands
New Zealand
Norway
Romania

South Africa
Spain
Swaziland
Sweden
Switzerland
United Kingdom
United States

HISTORICAL FINANCIALS
Company Type: Private

Income Statement				FYE: December 31
	REVENUE ($ mil.)	NET INCOME ($ mil.)	NET PROFIT MARGIN	EMPLOYEES
12/16	652	(7)	—	3,000
12/15	678	(10)	—	—
Annual Growth	(3.9%)	—	—	—

2016 Year-End Financials

Return on assets: (-2.8%)   Cash ($ mil.): 46
Return on equity: (-4.1%)
Current ratio: 1.50

SCAI HOLDINGS, LLC

SCAI Holdings (dba SCA or Surgical Care Affiliates) can stitch 'em up and move 'em out. The company operates one of the largest networks of outpatient surgery centers in the US. (Also known as ambulatory surgical centers or ASCs these facilities charge less than hospitals to perform routine surgeries.) SCA operates more than 200 surgery centers and surgical hospitals in about 35 states. The centers offer non-emergency day surgeries in orthopedics ophthalmology gastroenterology pain management otolaryngology (ear nose and throat) urology and gynecology. The company went public in 2013 but was acquired by insurance giant UnitedHealth in 2017 for some $2.3 billion.

Change in Company Type
In early 2017 Surgical Care Affiliates agreed to be acquired by UnitedHealth for some $2.3 billion. The renamed SCAI joined UnitedHealth's OptumHealth division which itself operates hundreds of health care facilities.

Operations
SCA's outpatient surgery centers are operated in partnership with more than 40 health care systems such as Indiana University Health Sutter Health Texas Health Resources and MemorialCare. It has approximately 3000 physician partners.

Geographic Reach
SCA's facilities are located in 34 states across the US. Its largest markets are Texas California and North Carolina which respectively accounted for 14% 14% and 13% of net patient revenues in 2014. Other large markets include Alabama Connecticut Florida and Idaho.

Sales and Marketing
SCA's sales and marketing efforts are directed at physicians who are responsible for referring patients to its facilities. It also directly negotiates agreements with insurance companies and Medicare. Outpatient surgery centers which perform procedures that don't require an overnight stay are able to charge less than full service hospitals. This 'day surgery' model can be attractive to both patients and insurance companies looking to keep costs down.

As such SCA sees a lot of opportunity in building up its portfolio of outpatient surgery centers. The company estimates there are approximately 5400 Medicare-certified centers in the US and still plenty of opportunity to invest and partner in new facilities.

Payments from non-governmental third-party payors represented more than 60% of the firm's net patient revenues in 2014; Medicare payments accounted for 20%.

Financial Performance
SCA has seen solid revenue growth for the past four years. In 2014 revenue increased 9% to $897.3 million on higher net patient revenue a result of both higher admission numbers and the addition of more facilities. Management fee revenues also rose that year (again thanks to acquisitions).

After four years of reporting losses the company became profitable in 2014 with net income of $32 million. This was driven by the higher revenue as well as the absence of loss from extinguishment of debt and a decline in interest expenses. At the end of 2014 the company's accumulated deficit totaled $176 million.

Cash flow from operations has been on the rise as of late. In 2014 it increased 27% to $210.6 million.

Strategy
In order to expand its network of facilities SCA strives to buy existing surgical facilities and develop new facilities in partnership with area physicians and health care systems. During 2014 it acquired controlling stakes in 28 consolidated facilities. It also added three affiliated facilities with three new health system partners.

Mergers and Acquisitions
In 2014 Surgical Care Affiliates acquired a controlling interest in 15 ASCs for $138.1 million. Other purchases that year included a 51% stake in an ASC in California and a 59% stake in an ASC in Maryland.

Company Background
SCA is the former outpatient surgery unit of HealthSouth. HealthSouth sold the division to private equity firm TPG in 2007.

EXECUTIVES

Evp And Cfo, Peter Clemens
President And Ceo, Andrew P. Hayek
Evp And Chief Development Officer, Joseph T. (Joe) Clark
Evp And Coo, Michael Rucker
Svp Sales And Market Development, Winborne Macphail
Svp Perioperative Services, Gerry Biala
Svp Clinical Services And Training, Linda Lansing
Evp And General Counsel, Rich Sharff
Director Of Clinical Services, Lisa Berus
Vice President Sales And Market Development Surgical Care Affiliates, Matt Stewart
Vice President Business Offfice Operations, Linda Funston
Executive Vice President, Joe Clark
Vice President, Ali Reza
Group Vice President Operations, Chip Zahn
Regional Vice President Of Operations, Diana Shi
Vice President Finance And Investor Relations, Leslie Wachsman
Group Vice President, Jack Pocorobba
Vp Midwest Region Operations, Cory Kruger
Senior Vice President Of Development, Mark Langston
Senior Vice President Development, Tim Buono
Vice President Of Anesthesia Services Surgical Care Affiliates, James Martin
Vp Strategy And Payer Engagement, Bryan Breen
Vice President Operations, David Cutter
Vice President Of Operations, Rena Courtay
Vice President Operations, Thomas Lally
Vp Financial Quality Assurance, Nick Fees
Senior Vice President Operations, Paul Davis
Senior Vice President, Marie Edler
Vice President Of Operations, Carol Crump

Vice President Total Rewards And Hris, Dale Moyer
Rvp, Robert Harmon
Group Vice President, Nicole Semeraro
Group Vice President, Nick Laperriere
Chairman, Todd B. Sisitsky
Auditors: PRICEWATERHOUSECOOPERS LLP BI

LOCATIONS

HQ: SCAI HOLDINGS, LLC
510 LAKE COOK RD STE 400, DEERFIELD, IL 600154971
Phone: 847 236-0921
Web: WWW.SCASURGERY.COM

PRODUCTS/OPERATIONS

2014 Sales by Payor

	% of total
Managed care & other discount plans	62
Medicare	20
Workers' compensation	10
Patients & other third-party payors	5
Medicaid	3
Total	**100**

2014 Sales

	$ mil.	% of total
Net patient revenues	788	91
Management fee revenue	58	7
Other revenues	17	2
Total	**864**	**100**

COMPETITORS

HCA	United Surgical
Novamed Inc.	Partners
Symbion	Universal Health
Tenet Healthcare	Services

HISTORICAL FINANCIALS
Company Type: Private

Income Statement				FYE: December 31
	REVENUE ($ mil.)	NET INCOME ($ mil.)	NET PROFIT MARGIN	EMPLOYEES
12/16	1,281	226	17.7%	5,248
12/15	1,051	273	26.0%	—
12/14	864	157	18.2%	—
12/13	802	52	6.6%	—
Annual Growth	16.9%	62.5%	—	—

2016 Year-End Financials

Return on assets: 8.5%   Cash ($ mil.): 131
Return on equity: 19.6%
Current ratio: 1.30

SCHAUMBOND GROUP, INC.

EXECUTIVES

Pres-Ceo, Baohua Zheng
CPA, Kevin Hsu

LOCATIONS

HQ: SCHAUMBOND GROUP, INC.
225 S LAKE AVE STE 300, PASADENA, CA 911013009
Phone: 626 215-4998

HISTORICAL FINANCIALS
Company Type: Private

Income Statement				FYE: December 31
	ASSETS ($ mil.)	NET INCOME ($ mil.)	INCOME AS % OF ASSETS	EMPLOYEES
12/07	65	4	7.5%	550
12/06	50	4	9.6%	—
Annual Growth	28.2%	(0.0%)	—	—

2007 Year-End Financials
Return on assets: 7.5%   Sales ($ mil): 2,200
Return on equity: 8.0%

SCHOOL BOARD OF BREVARD COUNTY

EXECUTIVES

Chairperson, Andy Ziegler
Chairperson*, Amy Kneessy
Budget Specialist, Joseph Strohfus
Coordinator, Jason Faulds
Coordinator, Diane McAlister
Auditors: MOORE STEPHENS LOVELACE PA

LOCATIONS

HQ: SCHOOL BOARD OF BREVARD COUNTY
2700 JDGE FRAN JMESON WAY, VIERA, FL
329406699
Phone: 321 633-1000
Web: WWW.OLDMELHI.COM

HISTORICAL FINANCIALS
Company Type: Private

Income Statement				FYE: June 30
	REVENUE ($ mil.)	NET INCOME ($ mil.)	NET PROFIT MARGIN	EMPLOYEES
06/14	626	7	1.2%	9,031
06/09	613	(19)	—	—
06/06	628	100	15.9%	—
06/05	564	43	7.8%	—
Annual Growth	1.2%	(18.0%)	—	—

2014 Year-End Financials
Return on assets: 0.7%   Cash ($ mil.): 64
Return on equity: 1.9%
Current ratio: 2.40

SCHOOL BOARD OF BROWARD COUNTY, THE (INC)

EXECUTIVES

Chair, Nora Rupert
V Chair*, Heather Brinkworth
Asst Contrl, Lauris N Hazelwood
Accounting Staff, Darla Timmons

Staff, Carol Burton
Coordinator, Bernadette Lohrer
Accounting Staff, Chanda Peoples
Coordinator, Jennifer Austin
Acting Director, Lori Canning
Coordinator, Rachael Garafola
Purchasing Agent, Debra Swain
Auditors: MOORE STEPHENS LOVELACE PA O

LOCATIONS

HQ: SCHOOL BOARD OF BROWARD COUNTY, THE
(INC)
600 SE 3RD AVE, FORT LAUDERDALE, FL 333013125
Phone: 754 321-0000
Web: WWW.BROWARDSCHOOLS.COM

HISTORICAL FINANCIALS
Company Type: Private

Income Statement				FYE: June 30
	REVENUE ($ mil.)	NET INCOME ($ mil.)	NET PROFIT MARGIN	EMPLOYEES
06/18	2,806	(65)	—	4,265
06/17	2,738	5	0.2%	—
06/09	2,548	(274)	—	—
06/08	2,811	75	2.7%	—
Annual Growth	(0.0%)	—	—	—

2018 Year-End Financials
Return on assets: (-1.5%)   Cash ($ mil.): 782
Return on equity: (-14.5%)
Current ratio: 1.90

SCHOOL BOARD OF ORANGE COUNTY FLORIDA

EXECUTIVES

Chairperson, Bill Sublette
Supt*, Barbara M Jenkins
Cfo*, Toni Greene
Executive of Information Techn, Jim Wolf
Occupational Specia, Yesenia Rivera
Staff, Beth McCaules
Coordinator, Frenchie Porter
Athletic Director, Julie Sanford
Assistant, Mabel Rios
Assistant Director, Peter Berry
Assistant, Robert Ryner
Auditors: CHERRY BEKAERT LLP ORLANDO F

LOCATIONS

HQ: SCHOOL BOARD OF ORANGE COUNTY FLORIDA
445 W AMELIA ST LBBY, ORLANDO, FL 328011153
Phone: 407 317-3200
Web: WWW.ORANGECOUNTYFL.NET

HISTORICAL FINANCIALS
Company Type: Private

Income Statement				FYE: June 30
	REVENUE ($ mil.)	NET INCOME ($ mil.)	NET PROFIT MARGIN	EMPLOYEES
06/12	1,823	30	1.7%	25,000
06/11	1,895	24	1.3%	—
Annual Growth	(3.8%)	26.1%	—	—

2012 Year-End Financials
Return on assets: 0.6%   Cash ($ mil.): 194
Return on equity: 1.0%
Current ratio: —

SCHOOL BOARD OF PALM BEACH COUNTY

EXECUTIVES

Chmn, Chuck Shaw
Human Resources Administrator, Elaine Gallagher
Administrative Secretary, Barbie Rosero
Teacher, Jamie Mowery
Manager, Jetawn Shannon
Teacher, Lakisha Robinson
Resource Teacher, Christine Ferlita
Specialist, Heidi Schwab
Information Technology, Mickey Ryan
Director of Assessment, Paul Houchens
Photographer Editor, Gary Russ

LOCATIONS

HQ: SCHOOL BOARD OF PALM BEACH COUNTY
3300 FOREST HILL BLVD C316, WEST PALM BEACH,
FL 334065813
Phone: 561 434-8000
Web: WWW.PALMBEACHSCHOOLS.ORG

HISTORICAL FINANCIALS
Company Type: Private

Income Statement				FYE: June 30
	REVENUE ($ mil.)	NET INCOME ($ mil.)	NET PROFIT MARGIN	EMPLOYEES
06/08	2,093	(68)	—	21,000
06/07	2,010	501	24.9%	—
06/05	1,657	(121)	—	—
06/04	1,290	61	4.8%	—
Annual Growth	12.9%	—	—	—

2008 Year-End Financials
Return on assets: (-1.4%)   Cash ($ mil.): 1,290
Return on equity: (-3.4%)
Current ratio: —

SCHOOL DISTRICT NO. 1 IN THE CITY AND COUNTY OF DENVER AND THE STATE OF COLORADO

EXECUTIVES

Spdt, Tom Boasberg
Pres*, Carrie Olson
Principal, Emillo Esquibel
Director of Total Rewards, Adam Barnett

Second Grade, Amy Duncan
Purchasing Agent, Candi Davidson
Dean of Students, Faase Jennifer
Executive Director, Julie Nichols
Teacher Secondary Middle, Leslie Aguilar
Dance Director, Alicia Karczewski
Accountant, Amar Vaanchig
Auditors: CLIFTONLARSONALLEN LLP GREENW

LOCATIONS

HQ: SCHOOL DISTRICT NO. 1 IN THE CITY AND
COUNTY OF DENVER AND THE STATE OF
COLORADO
1860 N LINCOLN ST, DENVER, CO 802037301
Phone: 720 423-3200
Web: WWW.DPSK12.ORG

HISTORICAL FINANCIALS

Company Type: Private

Income Statement   FYE: June 30

	REVENUE ($ mil.)	NET INCOME ($ mil.)	NET PROFIT MARGIN	EMPLOYEES
06/12*	916	(100)	—	99
12/08	0	(0)	—	—
06/08	790	(38)	—	—
Annual Growth	3.8%	—	—	—

*Fiscal year change

2012 Year-End Financials

Return on assets: (-7.5%)   Cash ($ mil.): 348
Return on equity: —
Current ratio: —

SCHWAB CHARITABLE FUND

EXECUTIVES

Exec Dir, Susan Heldman
Pres, Kim Laughton
Chb*, Carrie Schwab-Pomerantz
Dir, Brooks Walker
Mgr, Margae Diamond
Offc Mgr, Michael Smithwick
Auditors: DELOITTE & TOUCHE LLP SAN FRA

LOCATIONS

HQ: SCHWAB CHARITABLE FUND
211 MAIN ST, SAN FRANCISCO, CA 941051905
Phone: 415 667-9131
Web: WWW.SCHWABCHARITABLE.ORG

HISTORICAL FINANCIALS

Company Type: Private

Income Statement   FYE: June 30

	REVENUE ($ mil.)	NET INCOME ($ mil.)	NET PROFIT MARGIN	EMPLOYEES
06/18	3,465	1,549	44.7%	26
06/17	3,147	1,551	49.3%	—
06/16	2,018	819	40.6%	—
06/12	722	172	23.9%	—
Annual Growth	29.9%	44.1%	—	—

2018 Year-End Financials

Return on assets: 12.0%   Cash ($ mil.): 12
Return on equity: 12.0%
Current ratio: 1.50

SCL HEALTH - FRONT RANGE, INC.

Exempla aims to provide exemplary health care to residents in the Denver area. The Exempla medical network operating as Exempla Healthcare includes three hospitals: Exempla Saint Joseph Hospital (570 beds) Exempla Lutheran Medical Center (400 beds) and Good Samaritan Medical Center (more than 230 beds). It also operates the Exempla Physician Network a chain of primary care clinics. The company employs more than 2100 physicians. Among its specialties are cardiovascular services and surgeries rehabilitation cancer care orthopedics and women's and children's services. Exempla Healthcare is sponsored by the Catholic faith-based Sisters of Charity of Leavenworth Health System (SCL Health System).

Strategy

Exempla is investing in expansion of the facilities at Lutheran Medical Center. It is also constructing a new building for Saint Joseph Hospital that is set to open in 2015.

Company Background

Exempla Healthcare was formed in 1998 when Saint Joseph Hospital and Lutheran Medical Center combined.

EXECUTIVES

Vice President Finance, Judy Boller
211947989431 Vice President Strategy Business Development Elmc, Jennifer Wrona
Senior Vice President And Chief Communications And Marketing Officer, Christine Woolsey
Vice President Operations, Barb Jahn
Vice President Human Resources, Darren Walker
Vice President Ethics And Theology, Ken Homan
Vice President Strategic Financial Plan, Robert Fries
Director Of Pharmacy, Carstens Kelly
Auditors: ERNST & YOUNG US LLP PHOENIX

LOCATIONS

HQ: SCL HEALTH - FRONT RANGE, INC.
8300 W 38TH AVE, WHEAT RIDGE, CO 800336005
Phone: 303 813-5000
Web: WWW.SCLHEALTH.ORG

PRODUCTS/OPERATIONS

2009 Revenues

	$ mil.	% of total
Exempla Saint Joseph Hospital	377	40
Exempla Lutheran Medical Center	302	32
Exempla Good Samaritan Medical Center	217	23
Exempla Physician Network	22	2
Colorado Lutheran Home & Exempla West Pines Behavioral Health	22	2
Exempla Lutheran Collier Hospice	6	1
Total	948	100

COMPETITORS

Catholic Health Initiatives
Centura Health
Denver Health and Hospital Authority
HealthONE
Porter Adventist Hospital
Presbyterian/St. Luke's Medical Center
Rose Medical Center
University of Colorado Hospital

HISTORICAL FINANCIALS

Company Type: Private

Income Statement   FYE: December 31

	REVENUE ($ mil.)	NET INCOME ($ mil.)	NET PROFIT MARGIN	EMPLOYEES
12/09	597	7	1.3%	5,300
12/05	472	30	6.5%	—
12/04	335	37	11.2%	—
12/02	267	27	10.1%	—
Annual Growth	12.2%	(16.2%)	—	—

2009 Year-End Financials

Return on assets: 0.9%   Cash ($ mil.): 53
Return on equity: 2.2%
Current ratio: 0.40

SCOTT & WHITE HEALTH PLAN

The Scott & White Health Plan (SWHP)Â works to keep its members Safe & Well. The not-for-profit company provides health insurance plans and related services to more than 200000 members across some 50Â countiesÂ in and aroundÂ Central Texas. OwnedÂ by the Scott & White network of hospitals and clinics SWHPÂ hasÂ employer-sponsored plans (including HMO PPO andÂ consumerÂ choiceÂ options)Â as well as several choices for individuals and families. It also offers COBRA state-administered continuation plansÂ the Young Texan Health Plan for children MedicareÂ and dental and vision benefits. The company began offering its services in 1982. Owner Scott & White is exploring a merger with Baylor Health Care System.

EXECUTIVES

Vice President Information Systems, Troy Stillwagon
Vice President Of Planning And Corporate Development, Donna Wright
Vice President Facilities And Constructon, Scott Liles
Vice President Quality And Patient Safety, Terry Long
System Vice President Human Resources Strategic And Business Services, Queen Greene
Associate Vice President, Susan Bradshaw
Secretary, Deborah Kennedy
Auditors: ERNST & YOUNG US LLP INDIANAP

LOCATIONS

HQ: SCOTT & WHITE HEALTH PLAN
1206 WEST CAMPUS DR, TEMPLE, TX 765027124
Phone: 254 298-3000
Web: WWW.SWHP.ORG

PRODUCTS/OPERATIONS

Selected Products
Employer plans
Individual and family plans
Medicare plans
Vital Care programs

COMPETITORS

Aetna
Blue Cross and Blue Shield of Texas
CIGNA
Centene

Humana
Texas Health Resources
USHEALTH Group
UnitedHealth Group

HISTORICAL FINANCIALS

Company Type: Private

Income Statement

	REVENUE ($ mil.)	NET INCOME ($ mil.)	NET PROFIT MARGIN	EMPLOYEES
12/09	660	13	2.0%	426
12/08	621	(4)	—	
12/07	586	8	1.4%	
12/06	557	3	0.7%	
Annual Growth	5.8%	54.1%	—	—

FYE: December 31

2009 Year-End Financials

Return on assets: 8.5% Cash ($ mil.): 8
Return on equity: 18.4%
Current ratio: 1.50

SCOTT & WHITE MEMORIAL HOSPITAL

EXECUTIVES

Ceo, Robert Pryor
Pres*, Shahin Motakef
Coo*, Donny Sequin
Cfo*, Ken Johnson
Accounting Staff, Bud Watson
Senior Director, Stephen Bush
Doctor, Amanda Hudson
Director, Christy Gregory
Cardiac Physician, Daniel Larsen
Communications Coordinator, Donna Dunn
Physician Assistant, Jaime Caro

LOCATIONS

HQ: SCOTT & WHITE MEMORIAL HOSPITAL
  2401 S 31ST ST, TEMPLE, TX 765080001
Phone: 254 724-2111
Web: WWW.BSWHEALTH.COM

COMPETITORS

Baylor Health
  Community Health
  Systems
Cook Children's Health
  Care System
Dell Children's
  Medical Center
HCSC
Hill Country
Seton Healthcare
  Network

Shriners Hospitals For
  Children
St. David's Health
  Care
St. David's Round Rock
  Medical Center
Texas Children's
  Hospital

HISTORICAL FINANCIALS

Company Type: Private

Income Statement

	ASSETS ($ mil.)	NET INCOME ($ mil.)	INCOME AS % OF ASSETS	EMPLOYEES
06/14*	1,251	87	7.0%	8,000
08/13	1,060	76	7.2%	
08/10	1,402	41	3.0%	
Annual Growth	(2.8%)	20.3%	—	—

FYE: June 30
*Fiscal year change

2014 Year-End Financials

Return on assets: 7.0% Sales ($ mil): 832
Return on equity: 8.1%

SCOTTSDALE HEALTHCARE CORP.

Scottsdale Healthcare a not-for-profit organization serves the health care needs of central Arizona residents. Its operations include three acute care hospitals that combined boast some 900 beds. Scottsdale Healthcare also operates other campuses that offer physician offices a cancer center home health and other health care services. It conducts clinical research through the Scottsdale Healthcare Research Institute. The group's Essential Touch Wellness Center and Boutique provides spa-like stress-reduction therapies. With nearly 2000 medical and surgical staff members the company offers some 35 medical specialties. Scottsdale Healthcare is an affiliate of Scottsdale Lincoln Health Network along with John C. Lincoln Health Network.

Operations

The group's hospitals are Scottsdale Healthcare Osborn Medical Center (trauma orthopedics neurosurgery cardiovascular and critical care) Scottsdale Healthcare Shea Medical Center (full-service hospital including emergency medical and surgical critical care cardiovascular and oncology services) and Scottsdale Healthcare Thompson Peak (patient-family centered medical/surgical hospital). Additionally Scottsdale Healthcare operates five Urgent Care Plus clinics the Piper Outpatient Surgery Center at the Shea Medical Center the Greenbaum Surgical Specialty Hospital at Osborn Medical center and the Scottsdale Healthcare Primary Care network of primary care physicians.

Geographic Reach

Scottsdale Healthcare serves central Arizona specifically in an around the entire Northeast Valley as well as the area north of Loop 101.

Strategy

Since 2012 the health care network has been expanding into Northeast Phoenix to deepen its relationships with community physicians and diversify beyond its three-hospital Scottsdale campuses. To this end it opened new Scottsdale Healthcare Primary Care physician offices in 2013 — one each in Phoenix and Tempe — to join existing locations in Arcadia Scottsdale and Grayhawk.

What makes Scottsdale Healthcare stand out is its military training program the only one of its kind in the country. Its Readiness Skill Sustainment Training Program gives National Guard Air Force Reserve and nearby Air Force base personnel 12 days of training in treating trauma burns and other wounds they might encounter when deployed in a war zone. Participants also work in intensive care ride along with EMS personnel and get orthopedics and operating room practice. It has since expanded the program to include a $1.6-million military trauma training center which serves military medical personnel with classroom and simulation training and trains civilian paramedics and firefighters.

The organization performs clinical research through the Scottsdale Healthcare Research Institute. Through the institute the organization conducts clinical trials in a range of disciplines including cancer and other complex diseases.

In 2014 Scottsdale Healthcare formed an affiliation with John C. Lincoln Health Network. The combined networks operating under the moniker Scottsdale Lincoln Health Network include five hospitals with some 3700 affiliated physicians and an extensive outpatient services network.

The group opened a new 28-bed unit at its Scottsdale Healthcare Thompson Peak Hospital in 2013. The unit provides care to orthopedic and spine surgery patients.

Company Background

Scottsdale Healthcare was established in 1962 as City Hospital of Scottsdale.

EXECUTIVES

Vp And Cio, James R. (Jim) Cramer
Svp And Coo, Thomas J. (Tom) Sadvary
Svp And Chief Medical Officer, James F. Burke
Svp And Chief Clinical Officer, Peggy J. Reiley
Evp Healthcare Operations, Gary E. Baker
President Scottsdale, John N. Ferree
Svp And Cfo, Todd LaPorte
Vp And Administrator Thompson Peak Hospital, Kim Post
Chief Medical Officer; Vp Physician Alignment, Richard Silver
Evp, Laura R. Grafman
Chief Operating Officer, Bruce Pearson
Assistant Vice President Supply Chain Consolidated Services, Michael Hildebrandt
Associate Vice President Of Laboratory Services, Marybeth Hess
Vice President, Alan Kelly
Radiology Director, Julie Hughes
Associate Vice President Nursing Practice, Kathy Zarubi
Medical Director Critical Care, Jack Applefeld
Vice President Major And Planned Gifts, Janice Miller
Vice President Finance, Brian Steines
Medical Director, Robin Blackstone
Assistant Vice President Project Management Office, Amy Clay
Medical Records Director, Apollonia Seianna
Assoc. Vp Workplace And Public Safety, Todd Larson
Associate Vp Enterprise Pmo, Eric Zuhlke
Associate Vice President Care Management, Pamela Foster
Vice President Procurement And Supply Chain, Tim Miller
Associate Vp Supply Chain Operations, Ryan Kirane
Chairman, Steven M. (Steve) Wheeler, age 71
Vice Chairman, Brad A. Gazaway
Treasurer, Drew Brown
Auditors: ERNST & YOUNG US LLP PHOENIX

LOCATIONS

HQ: SCOTTSDALE HEALTHCARE CORP.
  8125 N HAYDEN RD, SCOTTSDALE, AZ 852582463
Phone: 480 882-4000
Web: WWW.HONORHEALTH.COM

PRODUCTS/OPERATIONS

Selected Services

Bariatric Weight Loss Surgery
Cancer Care
Community Health
Corporate Health
Diabetes Management
Diagnostic Imaging Services
Digestive Health
Emergency Services
Heart & Vascular
Home Health Services
Infusion & Treatment Services
Minimally Invasive Surgery
Neurosciences
Nutrition Services
Orthopedic Services
Outpatient Therapy Services
Pediatrics
Sleep Disorders Center
Trauma Center
Wound Management
Urgent Care Plus
Urology Services

Banner Health
Community Health Systems
Dignity Health
Flagstaff Medical Center
Mayo Clinic
Phoenix Children's Hospital
Sun Health
Universal Health Services
University of Arizona Health Network
Yuma Regional Medical Center

HISTORICAL FINANCIALS
Company Type: Private

Income Statement · FYE: December 31

	REVENUE ($ mil.)	NET INCOME ($ mil.)	NET PROFIT MARGIN	EMPLOYEES
12/18	1,967	77	3.9%	17,000
12/17	1,763	104	6.0%	—
12/16	1,716	92	5.4%	—
12/14	88	9	11.2%	—
Annual Growth	117.3%	67.2%	—	—

2018 Year-End Financials
Return on assets: 3.1%   Cash ($ mil.): 217
Return on equity: 5.4%
Current ratio: 5.30

SCOTTSDALE HEALTHCARE HOSPITALS

EXECUTIVES
Ceo, Todd Laporte
Chb*, Robert C Johnson
V Chb*, Gary J Goodman
Pres*, Max Poll
SEC*, Julian L Fruhling
Exec V Pres*, Gary Baker
Sr V Pres*, James F Burke
Sr V Pres*, Alan B Kelly
Treas*, F Michael Geddes
Member*, Jennifer Miller
Prin*, Justin Caltabiano
Auditors: LB ERNST & YOUNG US LLP PHOEN

LOCATIONS
HQ: SCOTTSDALE HEALTHCARE HOSPITALS
8125 N HAYDEN RD, SCOTTSDALE, AZ 852582463
Phone: 480 324-7215
Web: WWW.DESERTMISSION.COM

HISTORICAL FINANCIALS
Company Type: Private

Income Statement · FYE: December 31

	REVENUE ($ mil.)	NET INCOME ($ mil.)	NET PROFIT MARGIN	EMPLOYEES
12/17	1,817	44	2.5%	14,000
12/14*	900	25	2.9%	—
09/09	847	4	0.5%	—
09/08	812	(17)	—	—
Annual Growth	9.4%	—	—	—

*Fiscal year change

2017 Year-End Financials
Return on assets: 2.1%   Cash ($ mil.): 96
Return on equity: 3.9%
Current ratio: —

SCRIPPS HEALTH

Scripps Health houses many a script-writing physician in its hospitals. The not-for-profit health system serves the San Diego area through five acute-care hospitals. Altogether the health system is home to approximately 1700 inpatient beds and a network of outpatient clinics. The system also offers home health care and operates community outreach programs. Its hospitals along with several outpatient Scripps Clinic and Scripps Coastal Medical Center locations employ some 3000 affiliated general practice and specialty physicians.

Operations

Scripps Health's facilities include the 700-bed Scripps Mercy Hospital which has a main campus in San Diego and a satellite campus in Chula Vista as well as Scripps Green Hospital (173 beds in La Jolla) Scripps Memorial Hospital Encinitas (138 beds) and Scripps Memorial Hospital La Jolla (444 beds). The system's network also includes the new Prebys Cardiovascular Institute (168 beds) about a dozen coastal medical centers two wellness centers and about 20 specialty centers.

In 2016 the system had more than 445000 hospital outpatient visits 21500 surgeries and 1.2 million medical office visits.

Scripps Health is the official health care provider for the San Diego Padres baseball team.

Financial Performance

Scripps Health had $2.9 billion in revenues in fiscal 2016 (ended September). Some $2.2 billion of that revenue came from net patient service income while $0.5 billion came from capitation premiums. After operating expenses the system had $292.3 million in excess of revenues over expenses attributable to controlling interests.

Strategy

Scripps Health's overall strategy is to remain on the cutting edge of technology in order to treat patients more effectively therefore reporting better patient outcomes (which in turns makes it eligible for certain government incentives). It also aims to make itself the destination of choice for patients — both locally and globally — for cardiac cancer and other types of specialty care. For example it partners with renowned oncology center MD Anderson to operate the Scripps MD Anderson Cancer Center slated to open in mid-2018.

As a major provider in the larger San Diego area Scripps Health is constantly evaluating its scope of services to meet the ever-increasing demand for health care. The company is building several outpatient clinics including cancer treatment and cardiac care centers. It is also expanding and upgrading its hospitals. In addition Scripps Health has launched an initiative to increase the number of clinical trials conducted at its facilities.

However after missing its budget for the first time in more than a dozen years Scripps Health announced plans to lower operating costs through restructuring efforts. It ultimately aims to rely more heavily on outpatient care and wellness services to reduce hospital visits. Layoffs are part of the restructuring plans: For example the system eliminated the CEO positions at its five hospitals. The hospitals are now led by chief operations executives reporting to regional (North and South) CEOs. Additionally Scripps Health shut down its loss-making hospice operations in 2017.

EXECUTIVES
Svp And Chief Executive Scripps Green Hospital, Robin B. Brown
Svp And Chief Executive Scripps Memorial Hospital La Jolla, Gary G. Fybel
Svp And Chief Executive Scripps Mercy Hospital, Tom Gammiere
Corporate Evp And Cfo, Richard K. Rothberger
Svp And Chief Executive Scripps Memorial Hospital Encinitas, Carl J. Etter
President And Ceo, Christopher D. Van Gorder
Corporate Svp And Chief Medical Officer, James LaBelle
Svp And Chief Executive Scripps Medical Foundation, Shiraz M. Fagan
Corporate Svp And Cio, Andy Crowder
Assistant Vice President Supply Chain Management, Cecile Hozouri
Assistant Vice President Information Services, Clark Kegley
Vice President Finance, June Komar
Corporate Senior Vice President, Barbara Price
Senior Vice President Human Resources Interim Employee Training Devel, Vic Buzachero
Medical Director, Martin Charlat
Vice President Managed Care, Karri Rodgers
Corporate Vice President And Chief Audit And Compliance Executive, Gerry Soderstrom
Medical Director Of Respiratory Care, Bao Q Luu
Medical Director Scripps Md Anderson Cancer Center, Thomas Buchholz
Vice President For Nursing Operations, Mary E Doyle
Vice Chairman, Mark Sherman
Secretary, Nancy Bernardy

LOCATIONS
HQ: SCRIPPS HEALTH
10140 CAMPUS POINT DR AX415, SAN DIEGO, CA 921211520
Phone: 800 727-4777

Selected Facilities
Scripps Clinic (outpatient centers)
Scripps Coastal Medical Center (outpatient centers)
Scripps Green Hospital (La Jolla)
Scripps Memorial Hospital Encinitas
Scripps Memorial Hospital La Jolla
Scripps Mercy Hospital (San Diego)
Scripps Mercy Hospital Chula Vista

COMPETITORS
Adventist Health System West
Cedars-Sinai Medical Center
Community Health Systems
Dignity Health
Grossmont Hospital
HCA
Palomar Health
Paradise Valley Hospital
Prospect Medical
Rady Children's Hospital
Sharp HealthCare
Tenet Healthcare

HISTORICAL FINANCIALS
Company Type: Private

Income Statement · FYE: September 30

	REVENUE ($ mil.)	NET INCOME ($ mil.)	NET PROFIT MARGIN	EMPLOYEES
09/15	2,943	371	12.6%	13,445
09/08	1,953	18	0.9%	—
09/07	1,781	223	12.6%	—
Annual Growth	6.5%	6.5%	—	—

2015 Year-End Financials
Return on assets: 8.3%   Cash ($ mil.): 464
Return on equity: 12.0%
Current ratio: 0.80

SCRIPPS NETWORKS INTERACTIVE, INC.

Lifestyle TV is a livelihood for this company. Scripps Networks Interactive operates six lifestyle cable networks including Home & Garden Television (home building and decoration) the Food Network (culinary programs) DIY - Do It Yourself Network (home repair and improvement) the Cooking Channel (culinary how-to programming) and the Travel Channel (travel and tourism). The company additionally owns music channel Great American Country and has minority interests in Asian Food Channel and regional sports network FOX Sports Net South. It also owns a 50% stake in UKTV. Trusts for the Scripps family own majority control of the company.In 2017 Discovery Communications agreed to buy Scripps Networks in a $14.6 billion deal.

Operations

Scripps Networks has two reportable segments: US networks and International Networks. Its US network segment accounts for almost 85% of total revenue.

Geographic Reach

Scripps Networks is based in Knoxville Tennessee. The company has additional offices located in Atlanta Chicago Dallas Detroit Los Angeles New York City San Francisco Miami Chevy Chase Maryland and Washington DC. Scripps Networks maintains international offices in London Milan S o Paulo Sydney the Philippines and Singapore.

The company's Cooking Channel is available in Canada. HGTV is available in the Asia-Pacific region the Middle East North Africa and New Zealand. Scripps Networks has also expanded Food Network across Latin America and Australia.

Sales and Marketing

Cable programmers such as Scripps Networks generate most of their revenue through advertising and carriage fees paid by cable system operators and satellite TV service providers. To help keep viewer loyalty and ratings high the company targets its channels toward specific interests rather than airing programming for a general audience.

The company advertises its products through broadcast television networks online and mobile outlets radio programming and print media. Scripps Networks spent $161.1 million on advertising and promotions in fiscal 2016.

Financial Performance

Scripps Networks reported about $3.4 billion in revenue for fiscal 2016. That was an increase of more than $400 million compared to the $3 billion the company reported for revenue the previous fiscal year. The increase was due to increased advertising sales and affiliate fee revenues.

Scripps Networks' net income was $673 million in fiscal 2016. That was an increase of about $67 million compared to the prior fiscal period when the company claimed a net income of $606 million primarily as a result of an increase in total revenue.

The company ended fiscal 2016 with $948 million in cash from operating activities which was an increase compared to fiscal 2015 when Scripps Networks ended the year with $814 million in cash from operations.

Strategy

Scripps Networks is focused on growing advertising revenues by increasing video plays and attracting more unique visitors to its websites through site enhancements and adding more video. Its strategy also includes trying to attract a broader audience through programming on national video streaming sites developing new sources of revenue that capitalize on traffic growth at the company's own websites and capitalizing on the movement of advertising dollars to mobile platforms.

The growth of the company's international business continues to be a strategic priority. Scripps Networks has expanded in Asia Europe and Latin America in recent years.

EXECUTIVES

Chairman President And Ceo, Kenneth W. (Ken) Lowe, age 69, $1,683,858 total compensation
Coo, Burton F. Jablin, age 60, $1,110,000 total compensation
Evp Operations And Cto, Mark S. Hale, age 60, $600,000 total compensation
Head Of International Lifestyle Channels, Derek Chang, age 51
President International And Interim President Tvn, Jim Samples
Evp Finance, Lori A. Hickok, age 55, $775,000 total compensation
President Ad Sales And Marketing And Branded Entertainment, Steven J. (Steve) Gigliotti
Cio, Bob Baskerville, age 55
President Content Distribution And Marketing, Henry Ahn
President Hgtv And Diy Network, Kathleen Finch
Evp Digital Sales, Beth Lawrence
Evp Digital, Tamara Franklin
Evp Corporate Giving And Community Relations, James B. (Jim) Clayton
Evp Legal, Cynthia L. Gibson, age 55, $680,000 total compensation
President National Ad Sales And Marketing, Jon Steinlauf
Evp And Chief Communications Officer, Dylan P. Jones
Svp Culinary, Katherine Alford
Evp And Chief Human Resources Officer, Nello-John (NJ) Pesci, age 57
Senior Vice President Engineering And Distribution Technologies, Mike Donovan
Vice President Programming And Production, John Feld
Senior Vice President Program Planning And Strategy U.s. Networks, Julie Taylor
Vice President Production Operations, Johanna Hammond Hoover
Vice President Corporate Finance, Peter Feret
Vice President Advertising Sales, John Dailey
Vice President Human Resources Operations, Cassie Brown
Senior Vice President Ad Sales Food Network And Cooking Channel, Karen Grinthal
Vice President Legal Affairs, Erik Hestnes
Senior Vice President And Head Legal International, Timon Marshall
Senior Vice President Ad Sales Hgtv And Diy Network, Donna Stephens
Vp Media And Content Delivery, Chuck Hurst
Vice President Affiliate Accounting, Twuanna Munroe
Senior Vice President Internal Audit, Andy Broyles
Vice President Programming And Development Food Network Cooking Channel And Travel Channel, Lynn Sadofsky
Senior Vice President Business And Legal Affairs, Sue Underwald
Vice President Engineering And Distribution Technologies, Bart Palmer
Vice President Human Resources, Laura A Schmidt
Vice President Operations And Data Strategy, Jeff Kissinger
Auditors: DELOITTE & TOUCHE LLP CINCIN

LOCATIONS

HQ: SCRIPPS NETWORKS INTERACTIVE, INC.
9721 SHERRILL BLVD, KNOXVILLE, TN 379323330
Phone: 865 694-2700
Web: WWW.DISCOVERY.COM

2016

	$ mil.	% of total
United States	2,884	85
Poland	443	13
Other International	73	2
Total	**3,401**	**100**

PRODUCTS/OPERATIONS

2016 sales

	$ mil.	% of total
operating revenue		
U.S Networks	2,871	84
International Networks	557	16
Total	**3,428**	**100**

2016 sales

	$ mil.	% of total
Advertising	2,416	71
Distribution	894	26
other	90	3
Total	**3,401**	**100**

Selected Operations

Lifestyle media
  Cooking Channel
  DIY Network
  Food Network (75%)
  Fox Sports Net South (7%)
  Great American Country
  HGTV (Home & Garden Television)
  Travel Channel (65%)
  UKTV (50%)
  Asian Food Channel (100%)
Interactive Services
  CookingChanneltv.com
  DIYNetwork.com
  FoodNetwork.com
  GACTV.com
  HGTV.com
  TravelChannel.com

COMPETITORS

A&E Networks	NBCUniversal
ABC Cable Networks	PBS
AMC Networks	Turner Broadcasting
MTV Networks	

HISTORICAL FINANCIALS

Company Type: Private

Income Statement				FYE: December 31
	REVENUE ($ mil.)	NET INCOME ($ mil.)	NET PROFIT MARGIN	EMPLOYEES
12/17	3,561	814	22.9%	3,500
12/16	3,401	847	24.9%	—
12/15	3,018	778	25.8%	—
12/14	2,665	726	27.3%	—
Annual Growth	10.1%	3.9%	—	—

2017 Year-End Financials

Return on assets: 12.5%   Cash ($ mil.): 130
Return on equity: 26.2%
Current ratio: 3.10

SEATTLE PUBLIC SCHOOLS

EXECUTIVES

Supt, Raj Manhas
Dir*, Carol Johnson
Dir of Fin*, Sephen Nielson
Customer Staff, Alma Clark
Coordinator, Bernardo Ruiz
Facilities, Silas Potter
Reading Specialist, Anne Presecan
Teacher, Alia Delacour
Teacher, Amy Carroll
Teacher, Amy Ferguson
Planning Staff, Anita Demahy

LOCATIONS

HQ: SEATTLE PUBLIC SCHOOLS
2445 3RD AVE S, SEATTLE, WA 981341923
Phone: 206 252-0000
Web: WWW.SEATTLESCHOOLS.ORG

HISTORICAL FINANCIALS

Company Type: Private

Income Statement				FYE: August 31
	REVENUE ($ mil.)	NET INCOME ($ mil.)	NET PROFIT MARGIN	EMPLOYEES
08/18	1,042	39	3.8%	4,650
08/06	553	4	0.8%	—
08/05	429	10	2.4%	—
Annual Growth	7.1%	11.0%	—	—

2018 Year-End Financials
Return on assets: 8.2%
Return on equity: 24.0%
Current ratio: —
Cash ($ mil.): 271

SECURITIES INVESTOR PROTECTION CORPORATION

Securities Investor Protection Corporation (SIPC) is an industry-financed insurance plan that protects clients of most broker-dealers registered with the US Securities and Exchange Commission (SEC). SIPC insures customers' securities (up to $500000 per account) against losses due to the financial failure of brokerage firms. Losses caused by fluctuations in market value are not protected. The not-for-profit membership corporation was mandated by the Securities Investor Protection Act and has more than 6000 members. Its board is appointed by the US president the treasury secretary and the Federal Reserve Board. Assessments from members and investments in government securities provide money for the SIPC Fund.

EXECUTIVES

Vice President Operations, Karen Saperstein
Auditors: GRANT THORNTON MCLEAN VA

LOCATIONS

HQ: SECURITIES INVESTOR PROTECTION CORPORATION
1667 K ST NW STE 1000, WASHINGTON, DC 200061620
Phone: 202 371-8300
Web: WWW.SIPC.ORG

HISTORICAL FINANCIALS

Company Type: Private

Income Statement				FYE: December 31
	ASSETS ($ mil.)	NET INCOME ($ mil.)	INCOME AS % OF ASSETS	EMPLOYEES
12/16	2,944	362	12.3%	39
12/15	2,652	169	6.4%	—
12/14	2,362	307	13.0%	—
12/11	1,606	131	8.2%	—
Annual Growth	12.9%	22.4%	—	—

2016 Year-End Financials
Return on assets: 12.3%
Return on equity: 18.2%
Sales ($ mil): 486

SECURITY FINANCE CORPORATION OF SPARTANBURG

Folks looking for a little financial security just might turn to Security Finance Corporation of Spartanburg. Founded in 1955 the consumer loan company provides personal loans typically ranging from $100 to $600 (some states however allow loan amounts as high as $3000). Customers can also turn to Security Finance for credit reports and tax preparation services. The company operates approximately 900 offices in more than 15 states that are marketed under the Security Finance Sunbelt Credit and PFS banner names. A subsidiary of Security Group the financial institution also has locations operating as Security Financial Services in North Carolina and Longhorn Finance in Texas.

Operations
Security Finance boasts some 900 offices nationwide that operate under the Security Finance Sunbelt Credit and PFS names. The company specializes in offering consumers loans to individuals. It also provides consumer credit reports and assistance as well as tax preparation services.

Geographic Reach
From its headquarters in South Carolina Security Finance boasts offices in more than 15 states nationwide.

Company Background
Security Finance exited Colorado in 2010 after the state's attorney general general office filed a compliant that the company had been refinancing some consumer loans more than three times a year (the limit under Colorado law). The company agreed to repay acquisition fees that it had charged the customers for refinancing the loans.

EXECUTIVES

Vice President Of Talent Management, Sal Calvio
Auditors: ELLIOTT DAVIS DECOSIMO LLC G

LOCATIONS

HQ: SECURITY FINANCE CORPORATION OF SPARTANBURG
181 SECURITY PL, SPARTANBURG, SC 293075450
Phone: 864 582-8193
Web: WWW.SECURITY-FINANCE.COM

Selected Locations
Alabama
Florida
Georgia
Idaho
Illinois
Louisiana
Missouri
Nevada
New Mexico
North Carolina
Oklahoma
South Carolina
Tennessee
Texas
Utah
Wisconsin

PRODUCTS/OPERATIONS

Selected Banners
Longhorn Finance (Texas)
PFS
Security Finance
Security Financial Services (North Carolina)
Sunbelt Credit

COMPETITORS

1st Franklin Financial	DFC Global
ACE Cash Express	EZCORP
Advance America	FirstCash
Bank of America	OneMain
Capital One	OneMain Financial
Cash Plus	Value Financial
Community Choice	Services
Financial	World Acceptance

HISTORICAL FINANCIALS

Company Type: Private

Income Statement				FYE: December 31
	ASSETS ($ mil.)	NET INCOME ($ mil.)	INCOME AS % OF ASSETS	EMPLOYEES
12/16	625	70	11.3%	2,500
12/15	651	78	12.1%	—
12/14	648	83	12.8%	—
12/13	616	62	10.2%	—
Annual Growth	0.5%	4.1%	—	—

2016 Year-End Financials
Return on assets: 11.3%
Return on equity: 20.6%
Sales ($ mil): 558

SECURITY GROUP, INC.

EXECUTIVES

Chb, Susan A Bridges
V Chb*, Clarence Edwards
Pres, Ray Biggs
V Pres-Fin, A Greg Williams
Treas, Beadie H Townsel
Information Technology Manager, Stacy Jordon
Sr Treasury Accountant, Ann Craine
Senior Database Administrator, Glenn Shepherd
Senior Vice President, Lisa Burroughs
Site Manager, Yhonis Frint
Auditors: ELLIOTT DAVIS DECOSIMO LLC G

HQ: SECURITY GROUP, INC.
181 SECURITY PL, SPARTANBURG, SC 293075450
Phone: 864 582-8193
Web: WWW.SECURITY-FINANCE.COM

HISTORICAL FINANCIALS

Company Type: Private

Income Statement				FYE: December 31
	ASSETS ($ mil.)	NET INCOME ($ mil.)	INCOME AS % OF ASSETS	EMPLOYEES
12/16	1,002	87	8.8%	2,500
12/15	1,020	97	9.6%	—
12/14	1,040	135	13.0%	—
12/13	1,263	107	8.5%	—
Annual Growth	(7.4%)	(6.4%)	—	—

2016 Year-End Financials

Return on assets: 8.8%　　　Sales ($ mil): 635
Return on equity: 12.7%

SECURITY HEALTH PLAN OF WISCONSIN, INC.

Security Health Plan of Wisconsin provides health insurance coverage and related services to some 200000 members in more than 35 Wisconsin counties. Its managed network of providers includes more than 4000 physicians 40 hospitals and health care facilities as well 55000 pharmacies across the US. Security Health Plan provides policies for groups and individuals. Its products include HMO coverage plans and supplemental Medicare plans as well as prescription drug and equipment coverage disease management programs and administration services for self-funded plans. Established in 1986 the company is the managed healthcare arm of Marshfield Clinic which operates medical practices across the state.

Operations

Since it is affiliated with a medical care provider Security Health Plan's coverage decisions are directly impacted by the practicing physician. The company's provider network consists of independent physician locations and parent Marshfield Clinic's more than 50 locations in Wisconsin.

In addition to HMO plans the firm's comprehensive medical coverage plans include POS (point of service) and high-deductible offerings. Security Health Plan offers health care reimbursement accounts through third-party provider agreements with Employee Benefits Corporation and Diversified Benefits Services. In addition the company provides community education and wellness programs.

Geographic Reach

Headquartered in the town of Marshfield Security Health Plan serves the counties of Adams Ashland Barron Bayfield Burnett Chippewa Clark Columbia Dane Douglas Dunn Eau Claire Forest Iron Jackson Juneau Langlade Lincoln Marathon Marquette Monroe Oneida Pepin Portage Price Rusk Sauk Sawyer Shawano Taylor Trempealeau Vilas Washburn Waupaca Waushara and Wood.

Sales and Marketing

Security Health Plan serves individuals families and small to large employer groups.

Strategy

Originally started in 1986 as an offshoot of the Greater Marshfield Community Health Plan Security Health Plan's service territory has grown over the years. For instance in 2012 the company extended its Advocare Medicare Advantage plan offering into several new counties. Security Health Plan also regularly adds primary care and specialty providers to its network to provide a broader range of accessible care services to its members as well as to strengthen its operations in underserved regions. The company is also looking to enhance its IT systems to allow for greater information access communication methods and collaboration among its providers and members.

EXECUTIVES

Medical Director, Dharmesh Babaria
Auditors: KPMG LLP MINNEAPOLIS MN

LOCATIONS

HQ: SECURITY HEALTH PLAN OF WISCONSIN, INC.
1515 N SAINT JOSEPH AVE, MARSHFIELD, WI 544491343
Phone: 715 221-9555
Web: WWW.SECURITYHEALTH.ORG

COMPETITORS

Aetna
Blue Cross Blue Shield of Wisconsin
CIGNA
Centene
Dean Health Plan
Group Health Cooperative
Gundersen Lutheran
Humana
UnitedHealth Group
Unity Health Plans Insurance
WEA Trust
Wisconsin Physicians Service Insurance Corporation

HISTORICAL FINANCIALS

Company Type: Private

Income Statement				FYE: December 31
	REVENUE ($ mil.)	NET INCOME ($ mil.)	NET PROFIT MARGIN	EMPLOYEES
12/17	1,234	9	0.8%	1,006
12/09	814	27	3.4%	—
12/05	385	0	—	—
12/04	369	17	4.7%	—
Annual Growth	9.7%	(4.4%)	—	—

2017 Year-End Financials

Return on assets: 2.8%　　　Cash ($ mil.): 159
Return on equity: 5.7%
Current ratio: 1.10

SEFCU SERVICES, LLC

EXECUTIVES

Mng MBR, Michelle Raymond
MBR*, Robert Maclasco
Loan Officer, Donn Luthanen
Senior Manager, Ellyn Bolduc
Loan Officer Assistant, Alexandra Agnos
Manager, Erin Buckley
Senior Consultant, Joanne Lashin
Loan Officer, Linda Deluke
Senior Loan Officer, Mary Duhamel
Assistant Manager Loan Servici, Monique Haller
Vice President, Nancy Brown

LOCATIONS

HQ: SEFCU SERVICES, LLC
700 PATROON CREEK BLVD, ALBANY, NY 122061067
Phone: 518 783-1234
Web: WWW.SEFCUMORTGAGESERVICES.COM

HISTORICAL FINANCIALS

Company Type: Private

Income Statement				FYE: December 31
	ASSETS ($ mil.)	NET INCOME ($ mil.)	INCOME AS % OF ASSETS	EMPLOYEES
12/17	3,555	21	0.6%	102
12/16	3,328	18	0.6%	—
Annual Growth	6.8%	16.0%	—	—

2017 Year-End Financials

Return on assets: 0.6%　　　Sales ($ mil): 110
Return on equity: 8.3%

SELECT ENERGY SERVICES, LLC

EXECUTIVES

Mng MBR, John Schmitz
MBR*, SES Holdings LLC
V Pres - Human Resources, J Brady Crouch
Erp Manager, Amy Washek
Data Entry, Carlos Santana
Recruiter, Crystal Davis
Operator, Hermenegildo Ramos
Laredo Office Manager, Imelda Moreno
Treasury Controller, Cheryl Rohmer
Soil Cement Manager, James Veal
Senior Director, Joshua Teahen

LOCATIONS

HQ: SELECT ENERGY SERVICES, LLC
1820 N I 35, GAINESVILLE, TX 762402179
Phone: 940 668-1818
Web: WWW.SELECTENERGYSERVICES.COM

HISTORICAL FINANCIALS

Company Type: Private

Income Statement				FYE: December 31
	REVENUE ($ mil.)	NET INCOME ($ mil.)	NET PROFIT MARGIN	EMPLOYEES
12/10	502	55	11.0%	1,600
12/09	115	11	10.4%	—
Annual Growth	336.8%	364.4%	—	—

2010 Year-End Financials

Return on assets: 11.5%　　　Cash ($ mil.): 22
Return on equity: 19.9%
Current ratio: 2.00

SEMCO ENERGY, INC.

Alaska and Michigan have more in common than a cold climate. SEMCO ENERGY serves approximately 423000 natural gas consumers in both states. The company's main subsidiary is utility SEMCO ENERGY Gas which distributes gas to more than 290000 customers in 24 Michigan counties. SEMCO's ENSTAR Natural Gas unit distributes gas to more than 133000 customers in and around Anchorage Alaska. The company's unregulated operations include propane distribution in Michigan and Wisconsin; pipeline and storage facility operation; and information technology outsourcing. In 2012 SEMCO ENERGY was acquired by AltaGas.

EXECUTIVES

Vice President Manager Director, Tracy Vincent
Vice President Employee Services, Ann Forster
Vice President, Steven Warsinske
Auditors: ERNST & YOUNG LLP DETROIT MI

LOCATIONS

HQ: SEMCO ENERGY, INC.
1411 3RD ST STE A, PORT HURON, MI 480605480
Phone: 810 987-2200
Web: WWW.SEMCOENERGYGAS.COM

COMPETITORS

AEP	Halliburton
ARB	Southwest Gas
Chugach Electric	Tengasco
Consumers Energy	WEC Energy
DTE Electric	

HISTORICAL FINANCIALS

Company Type: Private

Income Statement				FYE: December 31
	REVENUE ($ mil.)	NET INCOME ($ mil.)	NET PROFIT MARGIN	EMPLOYEES
12/16	575	51	9.0%	500
12/14	674	51	7.6%	—
12/13	608	48	8.0%	—
12/12	582	41	7.2%	—
Annual Growth	(0.3%)	5.5%	—	—

2016 Year-End Financials

Return on assets: 3.2%   Cash ($ mil.): 4
Return on equity: 9.0%
Current ratio: 1.20

SEMINOLE ELECTRIC COOPERATIVE, INC.

This Seminole is not only a native Floridian but it has also provided electricity in the state since 1948. Seminole Electric Cooperative generates and transmits electricity for 10 member distribution cooperatives that serve 1.4 million residential and business customers in 42 Florida counties. Seminole Electric has more than 3350 MW of primarily coal-fired generating capacity. The cooperative also buys electricity from other utilities and independent power producers and it owns 350 miles of transmission lines. Some 90% of its power load uses the transmission systems of other utilities through long-term contracts.

Operations

Seminole Electric's primary resources include the 1300 MW Seminole Generating Station and the 810 MW Richard J. Midulla Generating Station. The coop's renewable energy resources include waste-to-energy facilities landfill gas-to-energy facilities and a biomass facility. It also buys power as needed on the market.

Seminole Electric has more than 350 miles of transmission line.

Geographic Reach

The company serves customers in 45 counties in northeast south central and southeast Florida.

Financial Performance

In 2013 the coop's revenues declined by 1% due to lower rates and as well as a reduction in Member energy requirements and lower volumes sold to Non-Members.

Seminole Electric's net income increased by 48% in 2013 thanks to lower operating costs as a result of the absence of asset impairment costs and a drop in interest expenses.

The company's operating cash inflow increased to $86.05 million in 2013 (from $34.81 million in 2012) primarily due to improved net income and a change in working capital.

Strategy

The coop is seeking to respond to the State of Florida's push to get more power generation from renewable sources. In 2014 the company generating about 58% of its electricity from coal 35% from natural gas and 7% from green energy sources (up from 5.5% in 2011 making Seminole Electric one of the largest green energy providers in Florida).

Company Background

In 2012 it also made major environmental improvements to its main power plant the coal-fired Seminole Generating Station. In 2011 Seminole Electric boosted its portfolio of purchased green energy to more than 140 MW (including 113 MW from waste-to-energy facilities).

Seminole Electric was formed in 1948 to aggregate the power demands of its members and is governed by a board of trustees representing the 10 member utilities. The cooperative built its first power plant in the 1970s.

EXECUTIVES

Vp Administration, Al Garcia
Vice President Of Power Production, Charles W Huguenard
Auditors: PRICEWATERHOUSECOOPERS LLP TA

LOCATIONS

HQ: SEMINOLE ELECTRIC COOPERATIVE, INC.
16313 N DALE MABRY HWY, TAMPA, FL 336181427
Phone: 813 963-0994
Web: WWW.SEMINOLE-ELECTRIC.COM

PRODUCTS/OPERATIONS

Members

Central Florida Electric Cooperative
Clay Electric Cooperative
Glades Electric Cooperative
Lee County Electric Cooperative
Peace River Electric Cooperative
Sumter Electric Cooperative
Suwannee Valley Electric Cooperative
Talquin Electric Cooperative
Tri-County Electric Cooperative
Withlacoochee River Electric Cooperative

COMPETITORS

Duke Energy	NextEra Energy
Florida Power & Light	Progress Energy
Florida Public Utilities	Southern Company
JEA	TECO Energy

HISTORICAL FINANCIALS

Company Type: Private

Income Statement				FYE: December 31
	REVENUE ($ mil.)	NET INCOME ($ mil.)	NET PROFIT MARGIN	EMPLOYEES
12/18	1,083	21	1.9%	528
12/17*	1,067	23	2.2%	—
03/17	1,052	33	3.2%	—
12/16	1,067	20	1.9%	—
Annual Growth	0.7%	2.1%	—	—

*Fiscal year change

2018 Year-End Financials

Return on assets: 1.1%   Cash ($ mil.): 35
Return on equity: 5.4%
Current ratio: 1.10

SENTARA HEALTHCARE

Sentara Healthcare is not-for-profit operator of more than 300 health facilities in Virginia and North Carolina. The system includes a dozen acute care hospitals housing a total of more than 2000 beds including Sentara Norfolk Sentara RMH and Sentara Virginia Beach. Several of its hospitals contain specialist facilities such as the Sentara Heart Hospital the Hospital for Extended Recovery and two orthopedic hospitals. In addition the company operates medical practices urgent care clinics imaging centers rehab facilities nursing homes hospice and home health agencies and ambulance providers. Its Optima Health unit provides HMO PPO and other health insurance products to about 450000 Virginians.

Financial Performance

Sentara Healthcare reports more than $5 billion in annual revenue. About three-fourths of earnings come from patient services (mostly from inpatient care); insurance premiums and capitation revenue make up most of the rest.

The company spends more than $350 million annually on community benefits primarily for uncompensated care of uninsured patients. It also supports community education and screening programs as well as professional education programs at the Eastern Virginia Medical School.

Strategy

While it is already one of the largest health care organizations in the state Sentara Healthcare continues to grow through acquisitions construction efforts (both expansions and new buildings) and mergers.

In 2018 the company broke ground on its new $93.5 million Sentara Cancer Center in Norfolk VA. The facility scheduled for completion in 2020 will bring together medical teams from Sentara Medical Group and affiliates Virginia Oncology Associates and Eastern Virginia Medical School. The company is also building a new 20-bed hospital in Suffolk Virginia at the Sentara BelleHarbour outpatient campus.

As the health care industry shifts towards less-expensive outpatient settings Sentara is working to upgrade some ambulatory care facilities to provide more convenient care options for patients.

The company has worked to stay ahead of information technology trends that help improve operational efficiencies and quality of care. It has invested in fields such as population health management telehealth (Sentara MDLIVE) advanced patient monitoring (Sentara eICU) and workflow productivity and healthcare analytics (in partnership with Medstreaming).

Company Background

Sentara Healthcare was founded in 1888 as Norfolk's 25-bed Retreat for the Sick. Norfolk General and Leigh Memorial merged in 1972.

Additional hospitals were acquired over the years including Hampton General Hospital (1988) Bayside Hospital (1991) Virginia Beach General Hospital (1998) Williamsburg Community Hospital (2002) Obici Hospital (2006) Potomac Hospital (2009) RMH Healthcare (2011) Martha Jefferson Hospital (2011) and Halifax Regional Health System (2013). Construction of the Sentara Princess Anne Hospital was completed in 2011.

In 2014 it acquired the assets and operations of Albemarle Hospital Albemarle Physician Services and Regional Medical Services through a 30-year capital lease agreement with Pasquotank County and Albemarle Hospital Authority. The businesses were combined into newly formed subsidiary SAMC.

EXECUTIVES

Vice President Human Resources, Michael Taylor
Ceo, Howard P. Kern
Svp And Cio, Bertram S. (Bert) Reese
Svp And Cfo, Robert A. (Rob) Broerman
Svp; President Sentara Health Plans And Optima Health, Michael M. Dudley
President Sentara Leigh Hospital, Teresa L. (Terrie) Edwards
President Sentara Careplex Hospital, Debra A. Flores
Corporate Vp Sentara Norfolk General Hospital Sentara Careplex Hospital And Sentara Williamsburg Regional Medical Center, Mary L. Blunt
President Sentara Martha Jefferson Hospital, Jonathan S. Davis
President Sentara Virginia Beach General Hospital, Elwood B. (Bernie) Boone
Chief Nursing Officer, Genemarie McGee
Svp And Chief Medical Officer, Terry Gilliland
President Sentara Williamsburg Regional Medical Center, David J. (Dave) Masterson
President Sentara Norfolk General Hospital, Kurt Hofelich
President Sentara Life Care Corporation, Bruce Robertson
President Sentara Princess Anne Hospital, Thomas B. Thames
Corporate Vp; President Sentara Rmh Medical Center, Jim Krauss
Corporate Vp; President Sentara Medical Group, Robert (Doug) Culling
Corporate Vp, Michael Gentry
President Sentara Enterprises, Linda R. Huffer
President Sentara Obici Hospital, Steve Julian
President Sentara Halifax Regional Hospital, Chris A. Lumsden
Corporate Vp; President Sentara Northern Virginia Medical Center, Stephen D. Porter
President Sentara Albemarle Medical Center, Coleen Santa Ana
Medical Director, Frank Barch
Vice President Finance, Lester Eljaiek
Director Of Pharmacy, Betsy Early
Medical Director, Carl Hartman
Vice President Operations, Robert Firestone
Vice President Operations, Valerie Keane
Vice President And Chief Information Security Officer, Daniel Bowden
Vice President Government Relations And Health Policy, Paul Speidell
Vice President For Clinical Informatics And Transformation, David Mohr
Vice President Patient Care Nurse Executive, Peggy Braun
Medical Director, Steve Fisher

Vice President Information Technology, Kris Clickner
Vice President Of Medical Affairs, Dennis Szurkus
Vice President Operations, Allura Kemick
Vice President Medical Affairs, Michael Ashby
Vp Clinical Services Optima, Karen Bray
Vice President Hospital Finance, Leo Deleon
Chairman, Bob Fort
Vice Chairman, Henry (Sandy) Harris
Auditors: KPMG LLP NORFOLK VIRGINIA

LOCATIONS

HQ: SENTARA HEALTHCARE
6015 POPLAR HALL DR, NORFOLK, VA 235023819
Phone: 800 736-8272
Web: WWW.SENTARA.COM

PRODUCTS/OPERATIONS

Selected Hospitals

Charlottesville
Martha Jefferson Hospital
MJH Outpatient Care Center
Health Services at Proffit Road
Health Services at Spring Creek
Sentara Home Care Services
Optima Health
Hampton Roads
Sentara CarePlex Hospital
Sentara Heart Hospital
Sentara Leigh Hospital
Sentara Norfolk General Hospital
Sentara Obici Hospital
Sentara Princess Anne Hospital
Sentara Virginia Beach General Hospital
Sentara Williamsburg Regional Medical Center
Orthopaedic Hospital at Sentara CarePlex
Sentara Northern Virginia Medical Center
Martha Jefferson Hospital
RMH Healthcare
Harrisonburg
RMH Healthcare
Optima Health
Northern Virginia
Sentara Northern Virginia Medical Center
Sentara Lake Ridge
Sentara Medical Group physicians
Sentara Home Care Services
Sentara Heart and Vascular Center
Optima Health

Selected Services

Cancer
Cardiac (Heart)
Digestive (Colorectal)
Home Care
Imaging
Maternity
Neurosciences
Rehabilitation
Seniors
Thoracic
Transplant
Trauma/Emergency Services
Urology
Vascular
Weight Loss Surgery
Women's

COMPETITORS

Aetna
Anthem Health Plans of Virginia
Bon Secours Health
CIGNA
Carilion Clinic
Centra Health Inc.
Children's Hospital of The King's Daughters
Franklin Hospital Corp.
HCA Capital Division
Humana
Inova
Kaiser Foundation Health Plan of the Mid-Atlantic
Norton Community Hospital
Novant Health
Riverside Health System (Virginia)
Twin County Regional Healthcare
UnitedHealth Group

HISTORICAL FINANCIALS

Company Type: Private

Income Statement				FYE: December 31
	REVENUE ($ mil.)	NET INCOME ($ mil.)	NET PROFIT MARGIN	EMPLOYEES
12/17	5,297	580	11.0%	28,000
12/16	5,083	329	6.5%	—
12/15	4,833	139	2.9%	—
12/14	4,694	359	7.7%	—
Annual Growth	4.1%	17.3%	—	—

2017 Year-End Financials

Return on assets: 7.8%   Cash ($ mil.): 704
Return on equity: 12.1%
Current ratio: 1.70

SENTARA HOSPITALS - NORFOLK

EXECUTIVES

Ceo, David L Bernd
Pres, Howard Kern
SEC, Jeffrey King
Cfo, Robert A Broermann
Pres-Cfo, Kern Howard P
Vice-President, Peggy Evans
Cardiac Physician, Gary Zeevi
Nurse, Brenda Smith
Lab Safety Officer, Dan Scungio
Otolaryngologist, Joseph Han
Team Coordinator, Viswanathan Venkataraman
Auditors: KPMG LLP NORFOLK VIRGINIA

LOCATIONS

HQ: SENTARA HOSPITALS - NORFOLK
600 GRESHAM DR, NORFOLK, VA 235071904
Phone: 757 388-3000
Web: WWW.SENTARA.COM

HISTORICAL FINANCIALS

Company Type: Private

Income Statement				FYE: December 31
	REVENUE ($ mil.)	NET INCOME ($ mil.)	NET PROFIT MARGIN	EMPLOYEES
12/17	877	63	7.2%	167
12/16	831	100	12.1%	—
12/15	791	92	11.7%	—
12/14	748	76	10.2%	—
Annual Growth	5.5%	(6.2%)	—	—

SERVCO PACIFIC INC.

Servco Pacific's business flows through an ocean's worth of enterprises. The company sells passenger vehicles (including Toyota Subaru Suzuki and Chevrolet models) and commercial trucks through dealerships in Hawaii and Australia. In addition Servco Home & Appliance wholesales kitchen and bath products to building professionals throughout the South Pacific; Servco Raynor Overhead Doors installs residential and commercial garage doors; Servco Insurance Services offers insurance coverage for businesses and individuals; and Servco School & Office Furniture outfits educational institutions and government agencies with desks seating and other furnishings. Servco Pacific was founded by Peter Fukunaga in 1919.

Operations

The diversified firm sells insurance through Servco Insurance Services (SIS) in Washington state. It clients are in the fishing shipping and cargo industries in several states including Alaska. SIS also operates in Hawaii where sister chains Servco Home & Appliance Servco Forklift & Industrial Equipment and Servco Automotive also operate. Sercvo Tire Company sells tires on Maui and in Honolulu.

Geographic Reach

Honolulu-based Servco Pacific has insurance offices in Seattle and Tacoma Washington. Its other businesses operate in Hawaii (Kauai Maui Oahu and the Big Island); and Australia (New South Wales Queensland).

Financial Performance

The private company reports revenue of approximately $800 million annually.

Strategy

Servco Pacific through its Australian subsidiary has been expanding its Toyota dealer operations in recent years. During 2010 the company acquired majority stakes in Sunshine Toyota of Queensland and Dubbo City Toyota of New South Wales. It also purchased Pacific Toyota in Cairns in 2009. The deals have significantly grown Servco Pacific's business in Australia part of a bid to strengthen its international presence; altogether Servco Pacific owns five dealerships in the country. The firm started operating in Australia in late 2007 with the acquisition of a Toyota dealership in Brisbane. Closer to home Servco is acquiring dealerships in Hawaii amid a influx of off-island businesses including Lithia Motors to Hawaii.

Mergers and Acquisitions

In February 2014 Servco acquired the assets of Maui's Island Subaru dealership in Kahului. The newly-acquired dealership will operate as Servco Subaru.

EXECUTIVES

Senior Vice President, Glenn Inouye
Senior Vice President, Brian Horikami
Group Vice President Cio, John Harris
Vice President Finance, Craig Mishina
Senior Vice President Human Resources, Peter Hirano
Vice President And Corporate Tax Director, John Lee
Executive Vice President, Peter Dames
Vice President Director If Parts, Beverly Sato
Senior Vice President, Thor Toma
Senior Vice President, Peter Dooher

LOCATIONS

HQ: SERVCO PACIFIC INC.
2850 PUKOLOA ST STE 300, HONOLULU, HI 968194475
Phone: 808 564-1300
Web: WWW.SERVCO.COM

PRODUCTS/OPERATIONS

Selected Operations

Automotive
Rex Tire and Supply
Scion Dealers of Hawaii
Subaru Dealers of Hawaii
Suzuki Dealers of Hawaii
Servco Australia
Servco Chevy
Servco Lexus
Servco Truck & Commercial
Toyota Dealers of Hawaii
Servco Home and Appliance Distribution
Servco Insurance Services
Servco Raynor Overhead Doors
Servco School and Office Furniture

COMPETITORS

AutoNation	HD Supply
Citigroup	Inchcape
Fletcher Jones	Lithia Motors

HISTORICAL FINANCIALS
Company Type: Private

Income Statement   FYE: December 31

	REVENUE ($ mil.)	NET INCOME ($ mil.)	NET PROFIT MARGIN	EMPLOYEES
12/17	1,629	26	1.6%	925
12/16	1,435	29	2.1%	—
12/12	923	15	1.7%	—
12/11	429	5	1.2%	—
Annual Growth	24.9%	30.7%	—	—

2017 Year-End Financials
Return on assets: 3.3%   Cash ($ mil.): 30
Return on equity: 11.5%
Current ratio: 1.20

SES HOLDINGS, LLC

EXECUTIVES

Pres, Kelly Stanley
V Pres*, Faye McCarrell
Cfo*, Eric Mattson
Principal, John D Schmitz
Auditors: KPMG LLP DALLAS TX

LOCATIONS

HQ: SES HOLDINGS, LLC
1820 N INTERSTATE 35, GAINESVILLE, TX 762402179
Phone: 940 668-1818
Web: WWW.SELECTENERGYSERVICES.COM

HISTORICAL FINANCIALS
Company Type: Private

Income Statement   FYE: December 31

	ASSETS ($ mil.)	NET INCOME ($ mil.)	INCOME AS % OF ASSETS	EMPLOYEES
12/12	941	2	0.3%	1,700
12/11	1,019	131	12.9%	—
12/10	617	57	9.3%	—
Annual Growth	23.5%	(78.7%)		

2012 Year-End Financials
Return on assets: 0.3%   Sales ($ mil): 945
Return on equity: 0.6%

SEVENTY SEVEN ENERGY LLC

Seventy Seven Energy (formerly Chesapeake Oilfield Services) is a company that was spun off from Chesapeake Energy one of the top onshore energy companies in the US. Chesapeake Energy reorganized six of its oilfield services subsidiaries into then Chesapeake Oilfield Services to create a new publicly traded entity that offers drilling hydraulic fracturing and trucking services as well as renting tools and manufacturing natural gas compressor equipment. It operates in onshore plays in the US. The company filed for Chapter 11 bankruptcy protection in 2016. In 2017 the company was bought by Patterson-UTI in a $1.76 billion stock deal including debt.

Operations

The company conducts business through three operating segments: Hydraulic Fracturing Drilling and Oilfield Rentals.

The hydraulic fracturing segment (51% of Seventy Seven Energy's total revenues in 2015) operates through Performance Technologies and provides high-pressure hydraulic fracturing services and other well stimulation services. This unit owns 11 hydraulic fracturing fleets with an aggregate of 440000 horsepower and six of these fleets are contracted in the Anadarko Basin and the Eagle Ford and Utica Shales. The fracturing process consists of pumping a fracturing fluid into a well at sufficient pressure to fracture the formation.

The drilling segment (38%) operates through Nomac Drilling and provides land drilling services for oil and natural gas E&P activities.

The oilfield rentals segment (11%) operates through Great Plains Oilfield Rental and provides premium rental tools and specialized services for land-based oil and natural gas drilling completion and workover activities. It offers an extensive line of rental tools including a full line of tubular products specifically designed for horizontal drilling and completion with high-torque premium-connection drill pipe drill collars and tubing.

Geographic Reach

Seventy Seven Energy operates in the Anadarko and Permian Basins and the Eagle Ford Haynesville Marcellus Niobrara and Utica Shales.

Sales and Marketing

The company got 70% of its revenues from Chesapeake Energy (CHK) and its affiliates in 2015.

Financial Performance

In 2015 Seventy Seven Energy's net revenues decreased by 46%.

Drilling revenues decreased due to lower revenue days driven by a drop in demand by non-CHK customers.

Hydraulic fracturing revenues declined due to a decrease in revenue per stage driven by market pricing pressure.

Oilfield rental revenues decreased due to a decline in utilization and pricing pressure.

In 2015 Seventy Seven Energy's net loss grew by 2675% due to lower revenues loss on sale of a business loss on sales of property and equipment net and impairment of goodwill.

Cash from operating activities increased by 7% due to the changes in the timing of collection of accounts receivable and the decline in overall operational activity.

Strategy

Chesapeake Energy decided to spin off its oilfield services in order to keep that activity separate from exploration and production. With exploration production and oilfield services under one umbrella the company only had one customer - itself. By separating the oilfield services unit Chesapeake Energy reduces its risk should exploration and production slow down much as it did with natural gas drilling and the shift to natural gas liquids.

Nomac Drilling continued to upgrade its rig fleet in 2015 making 80% of its rig fleet capable of drilling on multi well pads. As one of the most active drillers in the United States Nomac also continues to diversify its customer base serving more than 20 different operators.

Seventy Seven Energy expects to spend $100 million in aggregate growth and maintenance capital expenditures in 2016. It also intends to explore opportunistic complementary acquisitions particularly within the hydraulic fracturing segment.

In 2015 the company completed the previously disclosed sale of Hodges Trucking Company L.L.C. to a wholly-owned subsidiary of Aveda Transportation and Energy Services Inc. for $42 million.

Company Background

The company was formed in October 2011 and filed to go public in April 2012 in an initial public offering seeking up to $862.5 million. It completed the spinoff in July 2014 and renamed the company Seventy Seven Energy.

EXECUTIVES

Svp Corporate Development Cfo And Treasurer, John E. Vollmer, age 63

President And Ceo, William A. (Andy) Hendricks, age 54

Vice President Operations, Jerry Townley

Auditors: PRICEWATERHOUSECOOPERS LLP OK

LOCATIONS

HQ: SEVENTY SEVEN ENERGY LLC
777 NW 63RD ST, OKLAHOMA CITY, OK 731167601
Phone: 405 608-7777
Web: WWW.PATENERGY.COM

PRODUCTS/OPERATIONS

SERVICES
Drilling
Pumping
Rentals

Selected Subsidiaries
Compass Manufacturing L.L.C. (maufatures natural gas compression equipment)
Great Plains Oilfield Rental L.L.C. (tool and equipment rental)
Hodges Trucking Company L.L.C. (trucking services)
Nomac Drilling L.L.C. (drilling services)
Oilfield Trucking Solutions L.L.C. (trucking services)
Performance Technologies L.L.C. (hydraulic fracturing)

2015 Sales

$ mil.		% of total
Drilling	436.4	38
Hydraulic fracturing	575.4	51
Oilfield rentals	76.5	7
Oilfield trucking	42.7	4
other operations	0.2	-
Total	**1131.2**	**100**

COMPETITORS

Baker Hughes	Parker Drilling
Basic Energy	Patterson-UTI Energy
FTS International	Precision Drilling
Halliburton	RPC
Helmerich & Payne	Schlumberger
Key Energy	Superior Energy
Nabors Industries	Trinidad Drilling
Oil States	Weatherford
International	International

HISTORICAL FINANCIALS
Company Type: Private

Income Statement   FYE: December 31

	REVENUE ($ mil.)	NET INCOME ($ mil.)	NET PROFIT MARGIN	EMPLOYEES
12/15	1,131	(221)	—	1,700
12/14	2,080	(7)	—	
Annual Growth	(45.6%)	—	—	—

2015 Year-End Financials

Return on assets: (-11.6%)   Cash ($ mil.): 130
Return on equity: (-186.3%)
Current ratio: 2.10

SEYFARTH SHAW LLP

Every day is labor day at law firm Seyfarth Shaw which specializes in handling employment-related matters for its clients. The firm divides its numerous practices into four main areas: business services employee benefits labor and employment and litigation. Overall Seyfarth Shaw has about 800 attorneys in 14 offices — ten spread throughout the US plus four international outposts. Seyfarth Shaw draws clients from industries such as financial services life sciences and telecommunications. Henry Seyfarth Lee Shaw and Owen Fairweather founded the firm in 1945.

Geographic Reach

The firm maintains offices in Atlanta Boston Chicago Houston London Los Angeles Melbourne New York Sacramento San Francisco Shanghai Sydney and Washington DC. It extends its offerings through alliances with other firms in leading business centers around the world.

Sales and Marketing

Seyfarth's clients have included more than 300 companies from the FORTUNE 500 .

Strategy

The firm has been expanding its real estate practice.

EXECUTIVES

Chairman Intellectual Property Practice Group, Brian L. Michaelis

Co-managing Partner New York, John P. Napoli

Office Managing Partner Chicago, David J. Rowland

National Chairman Real Estate Department, Paul P. Mattingly

National Chairman Seyfarth's Labor & Employment Department, Lisa J. Damon

Managing Partner San Francisco, Nick C. Geannacopulos

Chairman National Wage And Hour Litigation Practice Group, Richard L. Alfred

Chairman And Managing Partner, Peter C. Miller

Managing Partner Houston And Chair Of The Business Services Group, Mark W. Coffin

Managing Partner Washington D.c., Robert L. Bodansky

Managing Partner Boston, Russell B. Swapp

Cio, Andrew D. Jurczyk

Managing Director Seyfarth Shaw At Work, Philippe Weiss

Ceo Seyfarth Lean Consulting, Robert Saccone

Co-managing Partner New York, Lorie E. Almon

Managing Partner Atlanta, Steven L. Kennedy

Managing Partner Los Angeles - Century City, Laura Wilson Shelby

Co-managing Partner Los Angeles - Downtown, Aaron R. Lubeley

Co-managing Partner Los Angeles - Downtown, Richard Mendelson

Cfo, Kate Kohn

Legal Secretary, Beverly Maxwell
Legal Secretary, Nancy Davilla
Legal Secretary, Venessa Brown
Legal Secretary, Karen Rodrigues
Legal Secretary, Barb Havenga
Legal Secretary, Heather Paras
Legal Secretary, Carol Alaniz
Legal Secretary, Margaret Chan
Legal Secretary, Jenny Willingter
Legal Secretary, Kimberly Freshour
Legal Secretary, Carol Cameron
Legal Secretary, Siobhan Gilvarry
Legal Secretary, Jolynn Simon
Legal Secretary, Ernest Bacon
Secretary, Linda Milbourn
Secretary, Rebecca Ortega
Secretary, Margaret Brueck
Secretary, Eloisa Flores
Secretary, Deborah Hodgson
Litigation Secretary, Karen Wooten
Secretary, Georgie Marino
Secretary, Tiffany Urena
Secretary, Patricia Stumpf
Litigation Secretary, Marsha Herring
Secretary, Rosie Mercado
Secretary, Anne Foley

LOCATIONS

HQ: SEYFARTH SHAW LLP
233 S WACKER DR STE 8000, CHICAGO, IL 606066448
Phone: 312 460-5000
Web: WWW.SEYFARTH.COM

PRODUCTS/OPERATIONS

Selected Practice Areas
Bankruptcy workouts and business reorganization
Commercial class action defense
Commercial litigation
Construction
Corporate
E-discovery
Employee benefits and executive compensation
Environmental safety and toxic torts
Government contracts
Intellectual property
International
Labor and employment
Product liability
Real estate
Securities and financial litigation
Tax
Trade secrets computer fraud and non-competes

Selected Industries Served
Financial services
Health care
Hospitality
Insurance

Life sciences: pharmaceuticals biotechnology and
  medical devices
Media
Professional services
Retail
Technology
Telecommunications
Trusts and estates

COMPETITORS

Baker & McKenzie	McDermott Will & Emery
Baker Botts	Ogletree Deakins
Hinshaw & Culbertson	Paul Hastings
Jones Day	Proskauer Rose
Kirkland & Ellis	Sidley Austin
Littler Mendelson	Skadden Arps
Mayer Brown	Winston & Strawn

HISTORICAL FINANCIALS

Company Type: Private

Income Statement				FYE: December 31
	REVENUE ($ mil.)	NET INCOME ($ mil.)	NET PROFIT MARGIN	EMPLOYEES
12/08	462	146	31.7%	1,608
12/07	431	141	32.9%	—
12/06	385	136	35.3%	—
12/05	332	124	37.4%	—
Annual Growth	11.7%	5.8%	—	—

2008 Year-End Financials

Return on assets: 139.9%   Cash ($ mil.): 41
Return on equity: 158.7%
Current ratio: 7.90

SGT, LLC

Like its acronym name suggests SGT (aka Stinger Ghaffarian Technologies) is used to taking military orders; in this case very specific technical ones. An engineering services firm SGT provides aerospace engineering project management IT systems development and related services to NASA the US Navy the US Air Force and other primarily military-related government entities through contracts. The company also offers science-related services such as earth climate and planetary modeling and analysis. SGT's facilities are located near airfields and other military facilities.

Geographic Reach
SGT operates a more than dozen offices including in Houston Cleveland and Los Angeles White Sands (New Mexico) and Wallops Island (Virginia).

Sales and Marketing
The company serves the aerospace and aeronautics sectors in addition to civilian agencies and national security entities.

Strategy
SGT grows by signing contracts and working with other partners. In early 2017 it won a $45 million contract to support the National Oceanic and Atmospheric Administration (NOAA). Under the contract SGT will support the National Mesonet Program which brings non-federal meteorological data sources to NOAA for use in operations at weather forecast offices and numerical modeling information at the National Centers for Environmental Protection. To achieve this SGT is working in partnership with Earth Networks Weather Telematics WeatherFlow Synoptic Data Corp. Sonoma Technology Inc. Panasonic Avionics Corp. and the University of Oklahoma.

Company Background
SGT was founded in 1994 by Harold Stinger and Kam Ghaffarian.

EXECUTIVES

Evp Business Development, Charlie Goorevich
President And Ceo, Kam Ghaffarian
Cfo, Joe Morway
Coo, Dave Wolt
Svp Civil Defense Business, Wayne Friedman
Vice President Sales Marketing, Ron Marinzel
Vice President Finance Chief F, Mike Gigliotti
Vice President Business Development, Mary Armstrong
Chairman, Harold Stinger
Auditors: GRANT THORNTON LLP MCLEAN VI

LOCATIONS

HQ: SGT, LLC
  7701 GREENBELT RD STE 400, GREENBELT, MD 207706521
Phone: 301 614-8600
Web: WWW.SGT-INC.COM

COMPETITORS

Ball Aerospace	QSS Group
CACI International	Sierra Nevada Corp
CDI Government Services	Techshot
Digital Fusion	United Space Alliance
Lockheed Martin Space Systems	

HISTORICAL FINANCIALS

Company Type: Private

Income Statement				FYE: September 30
	REVENUE ($ mil.)	NET INCOME ($ mil.)	NET PROFIT MARGIN	EMPLOYEES
09/15	570	23	4.2%	2,300
09/13	416	15	3.7%	—
09/12	374	9	2.4%	—
09/08	292	8	2.8%	—
Annual Growth	10.0%	16.3%	—	—

2015 Year-End Financials

Return on assets: 20.1%   Cash ($ mil.): —
Return on equity: 69.0%
Current ratio: 1.40

SHAMROCK FOODS COMPANY

Shamrock Foods Company is one of the nation's leading foodservice distributors with a strong presence in the western US. It primarily serves restaurants healthcare facilities and hospitality customers by providing everyday staples such as meats produce dry goods beverages and supplies as well as ethnic foods and artisanal gourmet and other specialty foods. Proprietary brands include Gold Canyon Markon Jensen Foods and Ridegline. Through Shamrock Farms the company is also one of the largest family-owned and -operated dairies in the country. Founded in 1922 as a mom-and-pop dairy Shamrock Foods Company is still owned and operated by the founding McClelland family.

Strategy
Shamrock Farms is focused on strengthening its position in the western US and upgrading its facilities to ensure it continues to meet the needs of customers. In 2019 the company acquired the Boise Idaho operations of Food Services of America extending its reach in the West. Also that year

it purchased land in Aurora Colorado for a new distribution facility.

EXECUTIVES

President Shamrock Farms Company, Norman McClelland
National Sales Manager, Paul Hohmann
Svp Cfo Secretary And Treasurer, F. Phillips (Phil) Giltner
President, Kent McClelland
Vp & Cio, Rob Baxter
Vice President Eastern Operations, Jack West
National Sales Manager, Tamara Jampo Clarke
Vp Human Resources, Vince Daniels
Vice President Marketing, Andy Johnston
National Accounts Manager, Darryl Cooper
Vice President Farms Div, Jim Whitehurst

LOCATIONS

HQ: SHAMROCK FOODS COMPANY
  3900 E CAMELBACK RD # 300, PHOENIX, AZ 850182615
Phone: 602 477-2500
Web: WWW.SHAMROCKFOODSERVICE.COM

PRODUCTS/OPERATIONS

Selected Products

Beverages
Center of the plate (meats)
Dairy
Cleaning supplies
Dry goods and groceries
Ethnic foods
Frozen foods
Paper and disposable products
Produce
Specialty
Supplies and equipment

COMPETITORS

Blue Bell	Performance Food Group
C&S Wholesale	Services Group of America
California Dairies Inc.	Stonyfield Farm
Dairy Farmers of America	Sysco
Dean Foods	US Foods
Land O'Lakes	United Dairymen of Arizona
McLane	Wells' Dairy
Meadowbrook Meat Company	

HISTORICAL FINANCIALS

Company Type: Private

Income Statement				FYE: September 30
	REVENUE ($ mil.)	NET INCOME ($ mil.)	NET PROFIT MARGIN	EMPLOYEES
09/18	3,900	0	—	4,000
09/17	3,447	0	—	—
/	0	0	—	—
Annual Growth	—	—	—	—

2018 Year-End Financials

Return on assets: —   Cash ($ mil.): 46
Return on equity: —
Current ratio: 1.50

SHANDS JACKSONVILLE HEALTHCARE, INC.

EXECUTIVES

Pres, Susan Brownie
Information Specialist, Phil Lambert
Internal Medicine Practitioner, Robert Kim
Cardiac Physician, Theodore Bass
Internal Medicine Practitioner, Hammad Bhatti
Internal Medicine Practitioner, Myint Thway
Internal Medicine Practitioner, Mohammad Shahid
Internal Medicine Practitioner, Tifinni Romero
Director, Jessica Schacht
Director of Professional Pract, Joan Sacerio
Vice President Managed Care An, Michael Lawton

LOCATIONS

HQ: SHANDS JACKSONVILLE HEALTHCARE, INC.
655 W 8TH ST, JACKSONVILLE, FL 322096511
Phone: 904 244-0411
Web: WWW.UFHEALTHJAX.ORG

HISTORICAL FINANCIALS
Company Type: Private

Income Statement			FYE: June 30	
	REVENUE ($ mil.)	NET INCOME ($ mil.)	NET PROFIT MARGIN	EMPLOYEES
06/16	665	22	3.3%	3,000
06/13	522	(5)	—	—
06/12	515	(22)	—	—
Annual Growth	6.6%	—	—	—

2016 Year-End Financials
Return on assets: 3.8%   Cash ($ mil.): 73
Return on equity: 11.6%
Current ratio: 2.40

SHANDS JACKSONVILLE MEDICAL CENTER, INC.

Close to the shifting sands of the northern Florida coast Shands Jacksonville Medical Center (doing business as UF Health Jacksonville) offers a range of services to the 19 counties it serves in Florida and southern Georgia. The 695-bed hospital includes a cardiovascular center Level III neonatal intensive care unit and a Level I trauma center. It also operates primary and specialty clinics in the Jacksonville area. The medical center is affiliated with the University of Florida and is the largest of seven hospitals in the Shands HealthCare family.

Operations
UF Health Jacksonville operates about 40 outpatient care centers. Overall its facilities handle some 34000 inpatient visits and 600000 outpatient visits per year. The hospital's affiliation with the University of Florida (UF) includes collaborative treatment and research programs in areas including cancer cardiovascular neurology orthopedic and pediatric care.

Together with its UF colleagues and affiliates UF Health Jacksonville provides a wide range of health care services across the continuum of care on an inpatient and outpatient basis. Backed by a team of more than 400 faculty physicians it offers nearly 100 specialty services.

Geographic Reach
UF Health Jacksonville's facilities are located in Jacksonville Florida and surrounding areas of northeastern Florida and southeastern Georgia.

Financial Performance
The company's revenues increased by 3% in 2014 due to growth in net patient service revenues as a result of a growth in inpatient and outpatient volumes. Medicare accounted for 25% net patient revenues; Medicaid 31%.

UF Health Jacksonville reported net income of $3 million in 2014 over a net loss in 2013 due to higher interest and a loss on the disposal of capital assets.

Operating cash flow in 2014 decreased by 8% due to higher payments to suppliers and vendors.

Strategy
UF Health Jacksonville has plans to build a second campus on the north side of Jacksonville to meet the needs of a growing community. It's also exploring ways to increase clinical efficiencies such as implementing an electronic health record (EHR) system (with help from federal stimulus funding); it also is looking to maximize funding opportunities for its research programs.

The company is looking to develop a Health Science Center Medical Education on Jacksonville Regional Campus including undergraduate graduate and health-related professions.

It also plans to build a 92-bed hospital wing for the North Campus which will provide greater access to more health care services for the center's residents as well as those living in surrounding communities. Construction is scheduled to begin in 2015 with completion in 2017.

In 2015 UF Health North opened the six-story 210000-square-foot outpatient medical complex in North Jacksonville which includes a 28-bed emergency room advanced imaging a midwife-led birth center rehabilitation services and more than 20 specialty services.

Company Background
Founded in 1870 as the Duval Hospital and Asylum UF Health Jacksonville started the first cancer program in Florida in 1948.

EXECUTIVES

Director Of Nursing, Angel Mills
Medical Director Fl Poison Information Center Jacksonville, Tom Kunisaki
Medical Director, Eric Stewart
Medical Records Director, Amy Connell
Auditors: CROWE LLP FORT LAUDERDALE

LOCATIONS

HQ: SHANDS JACKSONVILLE MEDICAL CENTER, INC.
655 W 8TH ST, JACKSONVILLE, FL 322096511
Phone: 904 244-5576

PRODUCTS/OPERATIONS

Selected Services
Cancer services
Cardiovascular services
Neuroscience services
Orthopaedic services
Pediatrics
Poison Center
Trauma and critical care services
Women and families

COMPETITORS

Baptist Health System	Ocala Regional Medical
Bay Medical Center	Center
Brooks Rehabilitation	Orange Park Medical
Florida Hospital Tampa	Orlando Health
Bay Division	Palms West Hospital
Mayo Clinic	St. Vincent's Health
Jacksonville	System
Nemours Foundation	
North Florida Regional	
Medical Center	

HISTORICAL FINANCIALS
Company Type: Private

Income Statement				FYE: June 30
	REVENUE ($ mil.)	NET INCOME ($ mil.)	NET PROFIT MARGIN	EMPLOYEES
06/16	663	23	3.6%	3,000
06/15	480	10	2.2%	—
06/10	592	19	3.2%	—
06/09	591	7	1.2%	—
Annual Growth	1.6%	18.8%	—	—

2016 Year-End Financials
Return on assets: 4.0%   Cash ($ mil.): 68
Return on equity: 12.3%
Current ratio: 2.50

SHANDS TEACHING HOSPITAL AND CLINICS, INC.

While its full name is Shands Teaching Hospital and Clinics most people call it UF&Shands. The network affiliated with the University of Florida Health Science Center provides health care services to patients in north-central and northeast Florida. The company is made up of seven not-for-profit acute care community and specialty hospitals as well as more than 80 physician practices and outpatient rehabilitation centers. It also operates a home health care agency. The Shands network has some 1700 licensed beds and about 1000 affiliated University of Florida doctors. Specialty services include oncology pediatrics cardiovascular transplants and neurological care.

Operations
In 2013 the organization along with the University of Florida launched the UF Health brand for their combined operations.

UF&Shands consists of the main teaching hospital at the University of Florida; it includes UF Health Shands Cancer Hospital UF Health Shands Psychiatric Hospital UF Health Shands Rehab Hospital as well as outpatient rehabilitation centers and a home health care agency. UF Health Jacksonville has some 700 beds and 400 full-time faculty members.

The hospital has a 40% stake in Community Health Systems which operates three rural community hospitals in Lake City Starke and Live Oak Florida.

Geographic Reach
UF&Shands operates hospitals in Gainesville and Jacksonville Florida.

Financial Performance
Revenues increased 3% to $1.2 billion in 2014 as net patient revenues and other operating rev-

enues rose. Net income fell by 7% though to $66 million that year as a result of rising non-operating costs such as interest expenses and net losses on disposal of assets.

Cash flow from operations declined 7% to $127 million in 2014 as a result of increased salary and benefit expenses as well as supplier and vendor payments.

Strategy

UF&Shands operates with the goal of improving the diversity of its academic health center and engagement within its communities. It focuses on patient care education and research. Its Gainesville campus is getting an expansion gaining a new building that will include 216 beds and 20 operating rooms. In 2015 it was announced that its neonatal intensive care unit on the same campus will get a $20.7 million renovation and expansion; that project is expected to be completed in 2017.

EXECUTIVES

Svp And Cfo, William J. (Bill) Robinson
Interim Ceo, Ed Jimenez
Vp Nursing And Patient Services, Irene Alexaitis
Svp And Cio, Kari Cassel
Evp Regional And Governmental Affairs, Timothy M. Goldfarb
President And Svp Health Affairs, David S. Guzick

LOCATIONS

HQ: SHANDS TEACHING HOSPITAL AND CLINICS, INC.
1600 SW ARCHER RD, GAINESVILLE, FL 326103003
Phone: 352 265-0111
Web: WWW.SHANDS.UFL.EDU

PRODUCTS/OPERATIONS

Selected Hospitals

UF Health Jacksonville (Jacksonville)
UF Health Physicians (Gainesville and Jacksonville)
UF Health Shands HomeCare and Shands Jacksonville Home Health (Gainesville and Jacksonville)
UF Health Shands Hospital (Gainesville)
UF Health Shands Psychiatric Hospital (Gainesville)
UF Health Shands Rehab Centers (Gainesville)
UF Health Shands Rehab Hospital (Gainesville

COMPETITORS

Baptist Health System
Bay Medical Center
Brooks Rehabilitation
Florida Hospital Tampa Bay Division
Florida Hospital Waterman
Lawnwood Medical Center

Mayo Clinic Jacksonville
North Florida Regional Medical Center
Orlando Health
Palms West Hospital
St. Vincent's Health System

HISTORICAL FINANCIALS

Company Type: Private

Income Statement				FYE: June 30
	REVENUE ($ mil.)	NET INCOME ($ mil.)	NET PROFIT MARGIN	EMPLOYEES
06/15	1,242	81	6.6%	3,071
06/14	1,243	66	5.3%	—
06/10	1,040	(67)	—	—
06/09	1,735	(183)	—	—
Annual Growth	(5.4%)	—	—	—

2015 Year-End Financials

Return on assets: 8.9%   Cash ($ mil.): —
Return on equity: 11.3%
Current ratio: 1.30

SHARP HEALTHCARE

Sharp HealthCare stands on the cutting edge of health care delivery in Southern California. The system of not-for-profit hospitals and health care facilities is the largest in the San Diego area. The network includes four acute-care hospitals (Sharp Chula Vista Sharp Coronado Sharp Grossmont and Sharp Memorial) as well as three specialty hospitals for women's care psychiatry and chemical dependence. It also operates two physician medical groups and a number of urgent care and outpatient facilities and clinics. With some 2100 beds and about 2600 physicians Sharp HealthCare offers cancer and cardiac care fertility and maternity services surgical procedures and hospice care.

Operations

Altogether the Sharp HealthCare facilities handle 1600 surgeries each year. In addition to medical services the organization operates its own health plan; the Sharp Health Plan is a not-for-profit HMO serving tens of thousands of members in and around San Diego.

The Sharp Grossmont hospital which serves eastern San Diego County is run by Grossmont Hospital Corporation a subsidiary holding a 30-year lease to manage the facility. One of the system's specialty operations Sharp Mary Birch Hospital for Women & Newborns claims to deliver more babies than any other hospital in California. Sharp's two medical groups are Sharp Community and Sharp Rees-Stealy which between them comprise more than 1100 doctors providing both primary and specialty care.

Geographic Reach

In addition to its operating bases in San Diego Sharp HealthCare has California facilities in Carmel Valley Chula Vista El Cajon La Mesa Mira Mesa Otay Ranch Point Loma Rancho Bernado San Diego Scripps Ranch Serra Mesa and Sorrento Mesa.

Financial Performance

Sharp's net revenues have trended upward in recent years. The company's revenues grew by $100 million in 2014 due to increase in net patient revenue and premiums. Revenues from the Medicare and Medi-Cal programs accounted for 30% and 24% respectively of Sharp's gross patient charges.

The company's net income decreased by 4% due to pension-related changes other than net periodic pension cost and increase in employee benefits and medical fees expenses.

Sharp's operating cash flow decreased by 48% in 2014.

Strategy

Sharp HealthCare improves its services to area residents through facility upgrades.

In 2015 the company launched Sharp Health News an online news site featuring engaging and original stories about medical breakthroughs new technology and health and wellness.

In 2014 Sharp HospiceCare opened its newest hospice residence BonitaView the first facility of its kind in the South Bay area of San Diego County for end-of-life care designed around the needs of patients and their families.

The organization installed new imaging equipment at the Sharp Memorial Outpatient Pavilion in 2013 and a opened the new Sharp Rees-Stealy center in Del Mar in 2014.

Company Background

In 2011 the system doubled the capacity of Sharp Chula Vista Medical Center's emergency department at a cost of $12 million and in 2012 the Chula Vista hospital opened a new cancer center.

The system began as a single hospital in 1955 named for a local pilot who died in WWII.

EXECUTIVES

Senior Vice President Human Resources, Ky Lewis
President And Ceo, Michael W. (Mike) Murphy
Evp Hospital Operations, Daniel L. (Dan) Gross
Svp And Ceo Sharp Healthcare Foundation, Bill Littlejohn
Svp And Cio, Ken Lawonn
President And Ceo Sharp Health Plan, Melissa Hayden-Cook
Svp And Ceo Sharp Memorial Hospital, Tim Smith
Svp And Ceo Sharp Chula Vista Medical Center, Pablo Velez
Svp And Ceo Sharp Coronado Hospital, Susan Stone
Ceo Sharp Rees-stealy Medical Group, Stacey Hrountas
Svp And Ceo Sharp Mary Birch Hospital For Women & Newborns, Trisha Khaleghi
Svp Marketing And Communications, Diane Gage Lofgren
Svp And Ceo Sharp Grossmont Hospital, Scott Evans
Svp And Cfo, Staci Dickerson
Ceo Sharp Community Medical Group, Paul Durr
Legal Secretary, Jenna Haynes
Vice President Business Development, Mary Keithgiordano
Director Of Nursing And Patient Care Services, Maryjo Webb
Vice President Business Development, Donna Thompson
Vice President Of Compensation And Benefits, Anne Stephenson
Vice President Corporate Compliance, Paul Belton
Vice President Government Relations, Sara Steinhoffer
Director Of Pharmacy, Kenneth Schell
Vice President Of Finance, Donna Serpico
Vice President And Chief Business Development Officer, Michael Byrd
Vice President, Mehra Li
Vice President Information Services, Kara Marx
Vice President, Harry Henderson
Vice President Clinical Operations, Anthony Damico
Vice President Patient Care Information Systems, Sandra Mccullough
Vice President, Jacqueline Schwoerke
Medical Director, Mark Jabro
Senior Vice President Sharp Healthcare, Amy Adome
Vice President Quality, Patricia J Atkins
Vice President Patient Care Gh, Louise White
Medical Director, Lloyd Kuritsky
Medical Director, Jim Lyon
Vice President Philanthropy, Beth Morgante
Chair, Richard Freeman
Vice Chair, Lori Moore
Department Secretary, Aileen Carr
Department Secretary, Denise Long
Board Member, Henry Garcia
Department Secretary, Donna Whitehouse
Department Secretary, Irma Samudio
Department Secretary, Lacie Paige
Department Secretary, Gloria Rivera
Department Secretary, Sandra Powers
Department Secretary, Carmen Ramirez
Secretary, Nancy Earl
Board Member, Sharlee Middlebrook
Auditors: ERNST & YOUNG LLP SAN DIEGO

LOCATIONS

HQ: SHARP HEALTHCARE
8695 SPECTRUM CENTER BLVD, SAN DIEGO, CA 921231489
Phone: 858 499-4000

PRODUCTS/OPERATIONS

2014 Sales

	$ mil.	% of total
Net patient revenue	1,806	62
Premium	1,024	35
Other	97	3
Total	**2,928**	**100**

Selected Programs and Services

Alcohol and drug dependency
Bloodless medicine
Cancer treatment
Complimentary and alternative medicine
Diabetes
Ear nose and throat
Eating disorders
Emergency and trauma
Endoscopy
Executive health
Eye care
Flu care
Health and wellness
Heart and vascular care
   Heart valve surgery
Home care
Hospice
Integrative and complementary medicine
International patient services
Laboratory services
Men's health
Mental health
Neurology
Nutrition
Occupational health
Orthopedics
Pediatrics
Pregnancy and childbirth
Primary care and family health
Radiology and diagnostic imaging
Rehabilitation and physical therapy
Robotic surgery
Safety and injury prevention
Senior care and services
Skilled nursing
Sleep disorders
Stroke and neurology
Transplant
Travel medicine
Urgent care
Weight loss
   Weight management support
   Weight-loss surgery (bariatric)
Women's care
Worksite wellness
Wound care and hyperbaric medicine

Selected Facilities

Sharp Chula Vista Medical Center (340 beds)
Sharp Coronado Hospital (180 beds)
Sharp Grossmont Hospital (540 beds La Mesa)
Sharp Mary Birch Hospital for Women & Newborns (170 beds San Diego)
Sharp McDonald Center (20 beds San Diego)
Sharp Memorial Hospital (675 beds San Diego)
Sharp Mesa Vista Hospital (150 beds San Diego)

COMPETITORS

Adventist Health System West
Dignity Health
HCA
Palomar Health
Paradise Valley Hospital
Rady Children's Hospital
Scripps Health
Sutter Health
Tenet Healthcare
Tri-City Healthcare District

HISTORICAL FINANCIALS

Company Type: Private

Income Statement

FYE: September 30

	REVENUE ($ mil.)	NET INCOME ($ mil.)	NET PROFIT MARGIN	EMPLOYEES
09/15	3,396	355	10.5%	14,000
09/14	1,234	(12)	—	—
09/13	1,158	(11)	—	—
09/09	897	(0)	—	—
Annual Growth	**24.8%**	—	—	—

2015 Year-End Financials

Return on assets: 9.1%
Return on equity: 13.7%
Current ratio: 1.90

Cash ($ mil.): 305

SHARP MEMORIAL HOSPITAL

The docs and the scalpels are sharp at Sharp Memorial Hospital. The flagship facility of Sharp HealthCare the not-for-profit hospital has roughly 675 beds and is a designated trauma center for San Diego County. Specialties include cardiac care women's health multi-organ transplantation and cancer treatment. It also provides skilled nursing home health and hospice services. Sharp Memorial Hospital first opened in 1955. Sharp HealthCare completed reconstruction efforts on the Sharp Memorial facility in 2009; the new hospital has improved inpatient surgery emergency trauma and intensive care facilities.

Operations

Along with a full range of inpatient services Sharp Memorial's Outpatient Pavilion provides patients with cancer care women's imaging and endoscopy services. The center also conducts outpatient surgery procedures ranging from LASIK to orthopedic surgeries. More and more hospitals are adding outpatient services to their roster because they tend to be reimbursed at higher rates. The facility also provides patient education services such as community health classes.

Sharp Memorial which provides some $199 million in community benefits (including charity care and outreach efforts) each year is affiliated with a number of other hospitals clinics and physician groups through its parent organization.

EXECUTIVES

Senior Vice President Of Business Development Sharp Healthcare, Alison J Fleury
Vp Operations, Robert Wherry
Pharmacy Manager, Kim Allen
Senior Vice President And Chief Information Officer, Ken Lawonn
Department Secretary, Lawanda Martin
Department Secretary, Marianne Branson

LOCATIONS

HQ: SHARP MEMORIAL HOSPITAL
7901 FROST ST, SAN DIEGO, CA 921232701
Phone: 858 939-3636

COMPETITORS

Adventist Health System West
Grossmont Hospital
Palomar Health
Rady Children's Hospital
Scripps Health
Tenet Healthcare
Tri-City Healthcare District

HISTORICAL FINANCIALS

Company Type: Private

Income Statement

FYE: September 30

	REVENUE ($ mil.)	NET INCOME ($ mil.)	NET PROFIT MARGIN	EMPLOYEES
09/17	1,158	237	20.5%	3,500
09/16	1,200	290	24.2%	—
09/15	1,195	240	20.1%	—
09/14	1,042	227	21.9%	—
Annual Growth	**3.6%**	**1.3%**	—	—

2017 Year-End Financials

Return on assets: 9.1%
Return on equity: 11.0%
Current ratio: 23.20

Cash ($ mil.): 1

SHAWMUT WOODWORKING & SUPPLY, INC.

Shawmut Woodworking & Supply which does business as Shawmut Design and Construction provides beginning-to-end construction services from preconstruction planning to post-construction quality assurance checks. The $860 million national construction management firm has experience building retail hotel gaming spa sports restaurant education banking healthcare and life science facilities. It also handles corporate interiors and high-end residential construction and boasts expertise in cultural and historical preservation projects. Founded in 1982 by Jim Ansara the employee-owned company serves clients nationwide from offices in a handful of US states.

Operations

Shawmut's operations are divided into several groups including the design and construction of Academic Projects; Commercial Projects; Corporate Interiors Projects; Cultural and Historic Projects; Gaming Projects; Healthcare and Science Projects; Hotel Projects; Restaurant Projects; Retail Projects; Spas and Health Clubs Projects; and Sports Venues Projects.

Geographic Reach

Shawmut Woodworking & Supply operates from offices in Boston; New York; Los Angeles; Las Vegas; Providence Rhode Island; New Haven Connecticut; Miami Florida; and West Springfield Massachusetts.

Sales and Marketing

Shawmut Woodworking & Supply serves a range of markets with varying needs with projects involving corporate interiors cultural and historic structures healthcare and science restaurants retail spas and health clubs sports venues and universities.

Its clients have included Harvard University Massachusetts Institute of Technology Babson College Bank of America Accenture Mercantile Bank Cisco Systems the Nantucket Whaling Museum Harry

Winston Hard Rock Cafe and Ruth's Hospitality Group.

Strategy

Shawmut Woodworking & Supply has been busy taking on high-value projects over the past few years. In early 2015 it completed its work on Boston's $115-million Dudley Municipal Building. In 2014 Shawmut's growing Healthcare and Life Sciences division started two new projects for two top clients. This included the renovation of clinical and support spaces in the health center a new wellness center and construction for additional examination rooms for Beth Israel Deaconess Medical Center; and a 35000-square-foot addition to a building at the Boston Medical Center.

The company has also been building high-end retail stores for top name clients in New York and elsewhere in recent years. Projects have included boutiques for Gucci Chanel and Juicy Couture.

To keep its business growing in more areas Shawmut Woodworking & Supply has extended its operations across the US in recent years. In 2013 the firm added new offices on both US coasts with an office in Los Angeles and another in West Springfield Massachusetts.

EXECUTIVES

Ceo, Les Hiscoe
Vp And Cfo, Roger C. Tougas
Vp Chief Legal Officer And Cio, Doug Lareau
Vice President, Ron Simoneau
Vice President Field Operations, Paul Doherty
Vice President Retail, William Pisani

LOCATIONS

HQ: SHAWMUT WOODWORKING & SUPPLY, INC.
560 HARRISON AVE STE 200, BOSTON, MA 021182632
Phone: 617 622-7000
Web: WWW.SHAWMUT.COM

PRODUCTS/OPERATIONS

Selected Markets
Academic
Commercial
Corporate interiors
Cultural and historic
Gaming
Healthcare and science
Restaurants
Retail
Spas and healthclubs
Sports venues

Selected Services

Services
Pre-Construction
Master planning services
Master project scheduling
Lease review
Value engineering
Feasibility studies
Green design services
Drawing reviews
Facilities audits and campus assessments
Collaborative approach with architect/design team
Comprehensive conceptual estimating
BIM and virtual construction
In-house M/E/P expertise
Bid packages
Constructability reviews
Due diligence and site surveys
Pre-qualification of subcontractors
Management of permitting and approvals
Development of specific phasing schedules and delivery methods
Open book subcontractor bidding
Logistics planning
National purchasing power
Construction
Master project scheduling
Weekly project team meetings
Sites monitored by a Safety Manager

Zero-tolerance safety program
BIM and virtual construction services
LEED documentation certification and green building techniques
Permitting services
Design/build services
Communication with surrounding community
Coordination of owner-supplied items and vendors
Procurement solutions
Schedule and budget controls
24-hour/7 days-a-week emergency services
Specialized services for program clients
Indoor air quality management
Construction and demolition waste recycling
Customized waterproofing details
Post-Construction
Commissioning and close-out services
O&M manuals and training
Project services division
1-year warranty walkthrough

COMPETITORS

Andrew Velez Construction	Conti Enterprises
BBL Construction Services	E.W. Howell
	Skanska USA Building
Barr & Barr	Structure Tone
	Turner Corporation

HISTORICAL FINANCIALS

Company Type: Private

Income Statement   FYE: November 30

	REVENUE ($ mil.)	NET INCOME ($ mil.)	NET PROFIT MARGIN	EMPLOYEES
11/14	957	7	0.7%	1,476
11/11	662	3	0.6%	—
11/09*	618	(21)	—	—
12/05	440	3	0.7%	—
Annual Growth	9.0%	9.9%	—	—

*Fiscal year change

2014 Year-End Financials

Return on assets: 2.4%   Cash ($ mil.): 74
Return on equity: 14.5%
Current ratio: 1.20

SHAWNEE MISSION MEDICAL CENTER, INC.

Shawnee Mission Medical Center (SMMC) cares for Kansas City residents primarily on the Kansas-side. The health care facility located in the city's southwest suburbs has some 500 inpatient beds. It also offers outpatient surgery and other health services in areas such as pediatrics rehabilitation oncology and radiology. The medical center's emergency department receives some 50000 visits each year. SMMC also operates satellite facilities including the Shawnee Mission Outpatient Pavilion in nearby Lenexa which offers emergency and outpatient diagnostic general practice and surgical care. SMMC is part of Adventist Health System.

Operations

SMMC handles some 20000 inpatient admissions each year as well as some 200000 outpatient visits. Its staff includes about 700 physicians who specialize in about 50 fields of medicine. Specialist care centers include a Chest Pain Emergency Center and the Center for Women's Health. The hospital also provides primary and specialty care through the Shawnee Mission Physicians Group including after-hours clinical care and cardiology and reproductive medicine services. SMMC delivers

more babies per year than any other hospital in the metropolitan area.

Geographic Reach

SMMC is located on a more than 50-acre campus in Shawnee Mission (near Kansas City) in Johnson County Kansas and serves the surrounding area. The main hospital campus includes a free-standing surgery center six physician practice buildings a child-care center for associates and a community health center.

Strategy

The SMMC organization looks at community needs to determine where it should grow. In 2013 the hospital opened a $44 million new birthing center to meet the growing need for obstetric services in the Kansas City area. The expansion effort tripled the size of the medical center's labor and delivery and postpartum rooms allowing it to accommodate up to 5000 births annually and added a level III neonatal intensive care unit.

The facility is also adding to its technological abilities to better serve the community. In late 2014 it deployed the eMediTrack platform to help document and analyze data for compliance and accreditation readiness.

Company Background

SMMC is part of a network of more than 500 health care facilities sponsored by the Seventh-day Adventist Church.

EXECUTIVES

Medical Records Director, Charlene Scott
Vice President Taxation, Maxine Grassinger
Medical Director, Lolitta Aznaurova
Executive Vice President And Chief Finan, Karsten Randolph
Respiratory Therapy Director, Jane Burdolski
Senior Management (senior Vice President General Manager Director), Jack Wagner
Director Physician Recruitment, Rob Diennen
Executive Vice President Human, Brad Hoffman
Vice President, Andrew Weston
Radiology Director, Johnathon Myers
Director Of Radiology, Janelle Paul
Secretary, Gregg Amos
Secretary, Jana Duckworth

LOCATIONS

HQ: SHAWNEE MISSION MEDICAL CENTER, INC.
9100 W 74TH ST, SHAWNEE MISSION, KS 662044004
Phone: 913 676-2000
Web: WWW.ADVENTHEALTH.COM

PRODUCTS/OPERATIONS

Selected Centers and Services
Bariatric Surgery
Behavioral Health
Britain Center (Cancer)
Center for Pain Medicine
CorporateCare
Diabetes
Emergency Services
Express Care
GI Services
Hand Specialty Center
HEALTHaware
Heart and Vascular Center
Home Health Care
Maternity
Holistic Care
Men's Health Program
Neurology
Nutrition and Weight Loss
Orthopedics
Plastic Surgery
Radiology
Rehabilitation Services
Reproductive Medicine
Robotic Surgery
Sleep Disorders Center
SM Outpatient Pavilion
SportsCare

Support Groups
Surgical Services
TherapyPlus
Transfer Center Urgent Care
Weight Loss Surgery
Women's Health
Wound Care Center

COMPETITORS

Ascension Health
Children's Mercy
  Hospital
CoxHealth
HCA
Heartland Health
Mercy Health
Saint Luke's Health
  System

Sisters of Charity of
  Leavenworth
Truman Medical Centers
University of Kansas
  Medical Center
Via Christi Health
  System

HISTORICAL FINANCIALS

Company Type: Private

Income Statement				FYE: December 31
	REVENUE ($ mil.)	NET INCOME ($ mil.)	NET PROFIT MARGIN	EMPLOYEES
12/17	491	55	11.3%	1,850
12/16	454	54	12.0%	—
12/15	435	38	8.7%	—
12/14	385	25	6.6%	—
Annual Growth	8.4%	29.6%	—	—

2017 Year-End Financials

Return on assets: 7.4%
Return on equity: 10.2%
Current ratio: —

Cash ($ mil.): 303

SHEA HOMES LIMITED PARTNERSHIP, A CALIFORNIA LIMITED PARTNERSHIP

EXECUTIVES

Ptnr, Jim Shontere
Ptnr, John F Shea LP
Treasurer, Robert Odell
Chief Information Officer, Bruce Verker
Sales Director, Janet Benavidez
Customer Manager, Chip Pennington
Sales Executive, Adam Heib
Technology/Computer Coordinato, Bert Selva
Sales Executive, Eric Snider
Sales Executive, Heather Stevenson
Sales Executive, Ken Peterson
Auditors: ERNST & YOUNG LLP LOS ANGELES

LOCATIONS

HQ: SHEA HOMES LIMITED PARTNERSHIP, A
  CALIFORNIA LIMITED PARTNERSHIP
  655 BREA CANYON RD, WALNUT, CA 917893078
Phone: 909 594-9500
Web: WWW.JFSHEA.COM

HISTORICAL FINANCIALS

Company Type: Private

Income Statement				FYE: December 31
	REVENUE ($ mil.)	NET INCOME ($ mil.)	NET PROFIT MARGIN	EMPLOYEES
12/14	1,140	133	11.7%	1,200
12/13	930	125	13.5%	—
12/12	680	29	4.3%	—
12/99	1,793	184	10.3%	—
Annual Growth	(3.0%)	(2.1%)	—	—

2014 Year-End Financials

Return on assets: 8.0%
Return on equity: 24.0%
Current ratio: 1.40

Cash ($ mil.): 236

SHELL MEDICAL PLAN

Auditors: PNCEWATERHOUSECOOPERS LLP PIT

LOCATIONS

HQ: SHELL MEDICAL PLAN
  , PHOENIX, AZ 85072
Phone: 800 352-3705

HISTORICAL FINANCIALS

Company Type: Private

Income Statement				FYE: December 31
	REVENUE ($ mil.)	NET INCOME ($ mil.)	NET PROFIT MARGIN	EMPLOYEES
12/16	617	5	1.0%	2
12/15	571	(40)	—	—
12/13	536	6	1.2%	—
Annual Growth	4.8%	(1.6%)	—	—

2016 Year-End Financials

Return on assets: 10.1%
Return on equity: 10.1%
Current ratio: —

Cash ($ mil.): 58

SHI INTERNATIONAL CORP.

Businesses that need more than boxes of hardware and software can call SHI International. The company distributes scores of computer hardware and software products from suppliers such as Adobe Cisco Microsoft VMware Symantec and Lenovo. It resells PCs networking products data storage systems printers software and keyboards among other items. SHI offers a range of professional services including software licensing asset management managed desktop services systems integration and vocational training. The company serves corporate government and health care customers from more than 30 offices across the US Canada the UK Germany France and Hong Kong. SHI was founded in 1989 by Chairman Koguan Leo.

Operations

SHI serves several sectors and verticals. The company specializes in software and hardware pro-

curement deployment planning configuration data center optimization IT asset management and cloud computing as well as custom IT solutions.

Geographic Reach

Based in Somerset New Jersey SHI has a global reach through its 30-plus offices located across the US Canada the UK Germany France and Hong Kong. In the US the company operates primarily in Texas and California but also in Arizona Colorado Florida Georgia Illinois Indiana Kansas Massachusetts Michigan Minnesota Missouri New Jersey New York Pennsylvania Virginia and Washington. Specifically its cloud briefing center is housed in New York City and its corporate call center runs from Austin Texas. The company's 420000-sq.-ft. headquarters operates beside its 305000-sq.-ft. Integration Center in Somerset New Jersey.

Financial Performance

SHI International rang up $6.8 billion in sales in 2015 a 14% increase versus the prior year. SHI's Strategic Enterprise Commercial Enterprise Corporate and Public Sector divisions contributed nearly equally to the revenue total for the year and growth outside the U.S. was steady with SHI's Canada U.K. and France divisions each posting double-digit growth. In addition SHI recognized over $1 billion in revenue from cloud products and solutions.

The seller of IT products and services boasts a 99% annual customer retention rate.

Strategy

The company has transformed itself from a $1 million regional reseller of software to a $5 billion global provider of information technology products and services.To this end SHI has invested some $20 million in a new data center that provides cloud services specifically what the company terms infrastructure-as-a-service (IaaS). The data center is one of six in the US that houses virtual machines for IT professionals to provide services such as application deployment disaster recovery software-as-a-service (SaaS). It also offers on-demand burst computing services where customers use the additional bandwidth to handle peaks in demand.

SHI's professional services unit already provides some cloud services and data center consulting. SHI sees IaaS as a logical extension of the software asset management (SAM) service it already provides. Under the SAM program SHI handles software deployment licensing compliance and inventories across a business.

SHI partners with Omaha Nebraska-based information security software specialist Solutionary to manage data security services using its ActiveGuard software product to block computer network security breaches as data center security is one of the biggest concerns for businesses in a cloud computing environment. Awards and Recognition

SHI is the largest minority and women-owned Business Enterprise (MWBE) in the US. The company's ranked 13th on CRN's 2015 Solution Provider 500 list of the largest IT solution providers in North America.

EXECUTIVES

President And Co-ceo, Thai Lee, age 62
Vp And General Manager, Hal Jagger
Vice President Internal Audit And Finance
  Operations, Kevin Boyles
Vice President, Melissa Graham
Chairman, Koguan Leo
Auditors: COHNREZNICK LLP NEW YORK NEW

LOCATIONS

HQ: SHI INTERNATIONAL CORP.
  290 DAVIDSON AVE, SOMERSET, NJ 088734145
Phone: 732 764-8888

PRODUCTS/OPERATIONS

Selected Products
Accessories
Peripherals
Hardware
Memory
Software

Selected Services
Cloud services
Computer vocational training services
Data center services
Events
Hardware services
Networking
POLARIS Software asset management
Storage
Strategic consulting
Webinars

COMPETITORS

ASI Computer Technologies	Computacenter
Agilysys	Ingram Micro
Arrow Electronics	Insight Enterprises
Avnet	PC Mall
CDW	Softchoice
CompuCom	Tech Data

HISTORICAL FINANCIALS

Company Type: Private

Income Statement — FYE: December 31

	REVENUE ($ mil.)	NET INCOME ($ mil.)	NET PROFIT MARGIN	EMPLOYEES
12/18	9,767	245	2.5%	4,500
12/17	8,243	197	2.4%	—
12/16	7,268	104	1.4%	—
12/15	6,540	69	1.1%	—
Annual Growth	14.3%	52.1%	—	—

2018 Year-End Financials
Return on assets: 11.0%   Cash ($ mil.): 29
Return on equity: 45.7%
Current ratio: 1.30

SIERRA NEVADA CORPORATION

Sierra Nevada Corporation (SNC) believes that military agility isn't just about how fast a soldier completes the obstacle course in basic training. It's also about employing technology to support the soldier. The company provides defense electronics engineering manufacturing and integration services. Its operates in three overall areas: Space Systems Commercial Solutions and National Security and Defense. SNC's Dream Chaser space vehicle was selected by NASA to provide service to the International Space Station.

Operations

SNC offers technology products in a range of industries including aerospace avionics electronics communications systems micro-satellite propulsion solar energy and space.Its divisions are Dream Chaser Space Habitats Spacecraft & Satellite Solutions Rocket Engines & Propulsion Environmental Systems and Space Technologies & Subsystems.

Geographic Reach

SNC operates from more than 30 offices in 17 states across the US and at customer sites around the world.It has offices in Germany and Turkey.

Sales and Marketing

SNC counts US Department of Defense and NASA among its key clients.

Strategy

SNC focuses on the commercial sector through internal advancements in dual-use applications and outside acquisitions including the emerging markets of renewable energy telemedicine nanotechnology cyber and net-centric operations.

The company also teams up with strategic partners to fuel growth and add technology to its portfolio.In 2018 SNC renewed its teaming agreement with Textron to develop fixed-wing utility aircraft.

Company Background

SNC has been named the Top Woman-Owned Federal Contractor in the US. The company was founded in 1963.

EXECUTIVES

Ceo, Fatih Ozmen
Chairman And President, Eren Ozmen
Vice President Of Business Development, David Klingler
Vice President Technology, Charlie Leber
Corporate Vice President, Bill Shaver
Vice President, Jennifer Jensen
Vice President, Lev Sadovnik
Vice President Engineering And Technology, Kirk Slenker
Vice President Of Operations, Jason Priebe
Vice President Of Strategic Planning, Mike Meermans
Executive Vice President Operations, Gerald Harvey
Senior Vice President Business Operations, Patrick Garman
Vice President Business Development, Gregory Cox
Corporate Vice President, Joel Madison
Vice President Of International Programs, Ali Dian
Senior Vice President, Fred Rost
Vice President For Integrated Tactical Solutions, Taco Gilbert
Vice President Cns Atm Business Development, Dutch Neilson
Vice President Procurement, Ed Mills
Vp Human Resources, Anne Bruce
Vice President Aviation Systems, Robert Horky
Vp International Business, S Sita Sonty
Vice President And Director Business Development, Stephen Stearns
Vice President Training And Operations Support, Ed Topps
Auditors: DELOITTE & TOUCHE LLP PHOENIX

LOCATIONS

HQ: SIERRA NEVADA CORPORATION
444 SALOMON CIR, SPARKS, NV 894349651
Phone: 775 331-0222
Web: WWW.SNCORP.COM

PRODUCTS/OPERATIONS

Selected Products
Advanced Technology
Enhanced Flight Vision Systems
Mobile ATC Towers
Navigation and Landing Systems
Network/Communications
Business Units
Dream Chaser
Integrated ISR Solutions
Aircraft Design Modification and Support
Rotary-Wing Integration & Remanufacturing
Space Habitats
Cyber Security
Navigation Guidance & Landing
Spacecraft & Satellite Solutions

Electronic Warfare Systems

COMPETITORS

Argon ST	L3 Technologies
BAE SYSTEMS	Lockheed Martin
DRS Technologies	Northrop Grumman
Exelis	Raytheon
General Dynamics	United Technologies
Honeywell International	

HISTORICAL FINANCIALS

Company Type: Private

Income Statement — FYE: December 31

	REVENUE ($ mil.)	NET INCOME ($ mil.)	NET PROFIT MARGIN	EMPLOYEES
12/14	1,481	0	—	3,063
12/13	1,623	0	—	—
12/12	1,400	0	—	—
Annual Growth	2.9%	—	—	—

2014 Year-End Financials
Return on assets: —   Cash ($ mil.): 22
Return on equity: —
Current ratio: 1.50

SIGNATURE FINANCIAL LLC

EXECUTIVES

Ceo-MBR, Joseph J Depaolo
MBR, Eric Howell
Senior Vice President, Ann Buzzo
Senior Vice President, Anne Doligale
Senior Vice President, Lisa Wente
Senior Vice President, Marietta Mullane
Executive Sales Officer, Stephen Port

LOCATIONS

HQ: SIGNATURE FINANCIAL LLC
565 5TH AVE AT46TH, NEW YORK, NY 100172413
Phone: 646 865-0767
Web: WWW.SIGNATUREBANK.BANK

HISTORICAL FINANCIALS

Company Type: Private

Income Statement — FYE: December 31

	ASSETS ($ mil.)	NET INCOME ($ mil.)	INCOME AS % OF ASSETS	EMPLOYEES
12/17	43,119	387	0.9%	11
12/16	39,047	396	1.0%	—
12/15	33,450	373	1.1%	—
Annual Growth	13.5%	1.9%	—	—

2017 Year-End Financials
Return on assets: 0.9%   Sales ($ mil): 1,502
Return on equity: 9.6%

SILICON GRAPHICS INTERNATIONAL CORP.

Silicon Graphics International (SGI) handles computing on a large scale. The company provides high-performance computer servers that are based on the Linux operating system and designed for large-scale data center deployments. SGI also offers data storage servers as well as modular data center systems sold under the ICE brand. Its equipment is tailored to quickly access analyze process manage visualize and store large amounts of data. SGI targets the IT Internet financial services government and electronics sectors as well as scientific community. Clients have included Amazon.com (18% of sales in 2014) Microsoft Yahoo! and Deutsche Bank. In November 2016 SGI was acquired by Hewlett-Packard Enterprise.

Change in Company Type

HPE closed on the $275 million deal for SGI in November 2016. HPE plans to deploy SGI's supercomputing capabilities to beef up HPE's enterprise offerings to provide faster and higher capacity analytics to customers. The deal is expected to close in early 2017.

Operations

About 74% of SGI's sales come from of its product business and the other 26% was generated by the services unit.

The product segment contains products from both High Performance Computing (HPC) and High Performance Data Analytics (HPDA) operating segments as well as compute solutions which include scale-out computing scale-up computing software and cloud/web products.

The service segment focuses on technical services such as hardware and software maintenance system installation and configuration. The division also offers consulting systems design and support as well as on-site staffing for customers.

Geographic Reach

About 46% of SGI's revenue comes from customers outside the US. Overall North America and South America accounted for 54% of SGI's sales followed by Asia/Pacific at 24% of revenue and Europe at 20%.

SGI is based in Milpitas California and conducts assembly and testing at a plant in Chippewa Falls Wisconsin. SGI's offices in Japan France Germany and the UK are used for sales services research and development and administration.

Sales and Marketing

SGI has more than 6500 customers who it reaches through a direct sales force in nearly 20 countries and a network of resellers and distributors.

Government agencies generate about 45% of SGI's revenue. Government customers include education and research institutions. A portion of those sales are made through system integrators.

Financial Performance

SGI reported its 2016 (ended June) financial results before the HP Enterprise deal.

In 2016 SGI had a bit of a bounce in revenue with a 2% increase to about $524 million. A 5% rise in product sales came from large strategic project wins in Europe and Asia. Services sales notched down 2% for the year.

The sales rise helped reduce SGI's net loss to $11 million in 2016 from $48 million in 2015. A reduction in headcount helped reduce the loss.

Cash flow from operations popped into positive territory at $27 million on decreases in accounts receivable and inventory compared to a negative $97 million in 2015.

Strategy

SGI is moving away from it older cloud computing business and directing its attention and resources to areas that should bring higher margins. Those areas include High Performance Computing High Performance Data Analytics storage and services. The company will expand its business in several vertical markets including weather and climate; physical sciences; life sciences; energy aerospace and automotive; financial services; internet; and media and entertainment.

Those changes set the company in good stead for its acquisition by HP Enterprise particularly in the data analytics area.

Company Background

The company took its pre-HP form when Rackable Systems bought the assets of high-performance computer pioneer Silicon Graphics Inc. (SGI) for $42.5 million in cash in 2009. Rackable expanded its product line customer base and geographic reach with the acquisition and the company adopted the better-known SGI brand in an effort to tap a larger global market. Uniquely for a computer maker the company performs all of its manufacturing assembly and testing at a facility in the US.

EXECUTIVES

President And Ceo, Jorge L. Titinger, $585,000 total compensation
Svp And Cto, Eng Lim Goh
Evp And Coo, Cassio Conceicao, $376,250 total compensation
Svp And Cfo, Mack Asrat
Chairman, Ronald D. Verdoorn
Auditors: DELOITTE & TOUCHE LLP SAN JOS

LOCATIONS

HQ: SILICON GRAPHICS INTERNATIONAL CORP.
940 N MCCARTHY BLVD, MILPITAS, CA 950355128
Phone: 669 900-8000
Web: WWW.HPE.COM

2016 Sales

	$ mil.	% of total
Americas	295	56
Asia Pacific	130	24
Europe Middle East & Africa	107	20
Total	**532**	**100**

PRODUCTS/OPERATIONS

2016 Sales

	$ mil.	% of total
Product	394	74
Service	138	26
Total	**532**	**100**

Selected Products

Modular data center infrastructure (ICE Cube)
Servers
  Blade (Scale Out)
  Half-depth rack-mount
  Standard depth rack-mount
Software
Storage
  Arrays (OmniStor)
  Massive array of idle disks (MAID platform)
  Servers and clusters (Altix)
  Storage (InfiniteStorage)
  Visualization systesm (Virtu)

COMPETITORS

Cirrascale	Microsoft
Cray	NEC
Dell	NetApp
EMC	Quantum Corporation
Egenera	Super Micro Computer
Fujitsu	Symantec
HP	Toshiba
Hitachi Data Systems	Unisys
IBM	

HISTORICAL FINANCIALS

Company Type: Private

Income Statement

FYE: June 24

	REVENUE ($ mil.)	NET INCOME ($ mil.)	NET PROFIT MARGIN	EMPLOYEES
06/16	532	(11)	—	1,100
06/15	521	(39)	—	—
06/14	529	(52)	—	—
06/13	767	(2)	—	—
Annual Growth (11.4%)		—	—	—

2016 Year-End Financials

Return on assets: (-3.1%)   Cash ($ mil.): 92
Return on equity: (-20.3%)
Current ratio: 1.60

SINAI HOSPITAL OF BALTIMORE, INC.

Sinai Hospital of Baltimore part of the LifeBridge Health network provides medical care in northwestern Baltimore. The 470-bedÂ hospital isÂ a not-for-profit medical centerÂ that includesÂ such facilities as a heart center a children's hospital a cancer institute and a rehab center. Other specialties include orthopedics neurology and women's care. Medical students from Johns Hopkins University and the University of Maryland do some of their training at the hospital. Sinai Hospital of Baltimore was founded in 1866 as the Hebrew Hospital and Asylum and becameÂ a subsidiaryÂ of LifeBridge when it merged with other area providers in 1998.

Operations

The Sinai Hospital of Baltimore handles about 26000 inpatient admissions and some 75000 emergency room visits per year. It also conducts about 20000 inpatient and outpatient surgeries annually.

The medical center conducts a number of education and training programs including residencies and fellowships for about 400 medical students each year. It is a designated training site for the Johns Hopkins University's ambulatory and internal medicine clerkships.

Strategy

Sinai Hospital of Baltimore has completed several expansion efforts in recent years. In 2012 it opened a new dedicated inpatient hospice unit as well as a new center for geriatric surgery.Â In addition the 20-bed Friedman Neurological Rehabilitation CenterÂ was completedÂ that year.

EXECUTIVES

Ceo, Neil Meltzer
Chief Medical Officer*, Daniel C Silverman
Chm*, Brian L Moffet
Treas*, Barry F Levin
SEC*, Nancy Hackerman
Staff, Roger Sheets
Coordinator, Ndubuisi Mbah
Occupational Specia, Amy Herman
Manager, Sakinah Abdullah
Laboratory Information, John Wall

LOCATIONS

HQ: SINAI HOSPITAL OF BALTIMORE, INC.
2401 W BELVEDERE AVE, BALTIMORE, MD
212155270
Phone: 410 601-5678
Web: WWW.SSCSI.COM

PRODUCTS/OPERATIONS

Selected Centers

Alvin & Lois Lapidus Cancer Institute at LifeBridge
  Health
Center for Joint Preservation and Replacement
Children's Hospital at Sinai
ER-7 Emergency Center
Heart Center at Sinai
International Center for Limb Lengthening
Krieger Eye Institute
Louis and Phyllis Friedman Neurological Rehabilitation
  Center
Rubin Institute for Advanced Orthopedics
Sandra and Malcolm Berman Brain & Spine Institute
Sinai Rehabilitation Center
The Spine Center at Sinai

Selected Services

Allergy and Immunology
Anesthesia
Cardiology
Cancer/Medical Oncology
Dermatology
Dialysis
Emergency Medicine
Endocrinology and Metabolism
Family Medicine
Gastroenterology
General Internal Medicine
Geriatric Medicine
Infectious Diseases
Nephrology (kidneys)
Pulmonary and Critical Care Medicine
Rheumatology (joints tendons)
Neurology
Neurosurgery
Obstetrics and Gynecology
Ophthalmology (eye care)
Oral and Maxillofacial Surgery and Dentistry
Orthopedic Surgery
Otolaryngology (ear nose & throat)
Pathology
Pediatrics
Pharmacy
Physical Medicine and Rehabilitation
Psychiatry
Radiation Oncology
Radiology
Surgery
Urology

COMPETITORS

Anne Arundel Medical
  Center
Ascension Health
Bon Secours Health
Franklin Square
  Hospital Center
GBMC

Johns Hopkins Health
  System
MedStar Health
Meritus Health
University of Maryland
  Medical System

HISTORICAL FINANCIALS

Company Type: Private

Income Statement   FYE: June 30

	REVENUE ($ mil.)	NET INCOME ($ mil.)	NET PROFIT MARGIN	EMPLOYEES
06/17	769	63	8.2%	4,497
06/16	690	26	3.9%	—
06/15	677	45	6.7%	—
06/14	714	41	5.8%	—
Annual Growth	2.5%	14.9%	—	—

2017 Year-End Financials

Return on assets: 8.8%
Return on equity: 24.3%
Current ratio: 2.30

Cash ($ mil.): 66

SKANSKA USA CIVIL INC.

Skanska USA Civil builds some of the world's largest cable-stayed bridges. Part of the US operations of Swedish engineering and construction giant Skanska Skanska USA Civil focuses on infrastructure projects throughout the country. Along with sister firm Skanska USA Building it is a market leader in the New York area where it has worked on the Brooklyn Bridge the AirTrain light-rail system and the Roosevelt Island Bridge. It builds roads tunnels and rail systems in addition to bridges and industrial and marine facilities such as power and water filtration plants gas-treatment plants and dry docks.

Operations

Parent-company Skanska USA operates Skanska USA Civil and three sister business units with different specialties such as Skanska USA Building Infrastructure Development USA and Commercial Development USA. The parent boasts a staff of nearly 11000 US employees (as of mid-2016).

Among Skanska USA Civil's divisions is Bayshore Concrete which produces precast concrete components for tunnel bridge dock and pier construction. Bayshore Concrete's plant in Virginia focuses on East Coast shipments. Skanska Koch which is based in New Jersey has built or worked on some of the country's most recognizable structures such as Yankee Stadium and the Brooklyn Bridge.

Another division Underpinning & Foundation Skanska is a heavy foundation contractor based in New York. It offers underpinning and pile-driving services for private and public projects that range from single-story buildings to skyscrapers.

Geographic Reach

While the firm's largest market is in its home state of New York it serves the US from offices in California Washington Arizona and Florida. Parent Skanska USA has 31 offices across the US and works on projects in nearly all 50 states the District of Columbia and Puerto Rico (as of mid-2016). The US is Skanska AB's largest market accounting for 37% of its global revenue during 2015.

Sales and Marketing

Skanska USA Civil provides public and private clients with construction services in the civil mechanical industrial marine foundation and environmental sectors.

Financial Performance

Parent-company Skanska USA's revenue has been growing in recent years and reached $7.1 billion in 2015.

Strategy

Parent Skanska USA ranked the third-largest building/manufacturing contractor by revenue and the third-largest heavy contractor by revenue on Engineering News-Record's rankings in 2015. The Skanska USA Civil division in particular has built a dominating presence on the East Coast since completing major projects such as the Meadowlands Football Stadium and Boston's Central Artery.

Skanska USA Civil in 2015 secured a contract with Competitive Power Ventures Holdings (CPV) to build the CPV Valley Energy Center in Wawayanda New York with an order value of SEK 2.1 billion ($250 million); a new contract with MTA New York City Transit to rebuild three rail stations in Brooklyn with an order value of SEK 670 million ($80 million); and a new joint-venture contract in California to improve State Route 58 near Hink-

ley with Skanska USA's share of the order value worth SEK 640 million ($76 million).

Sister division Skanska USA Building in 2015 secured a SEK 750 million ($89 million) contract from existing customer Tahoma School District to construct a new high school and learning center in Maple Valley Washington. That year the division also won a SEK 730 million ($87 million) contract to build Boeing's Commercial Airplane Decorative Paint Facility in Charleston South Carolina.

Company Background

Civil construction which is often publicly funded was less affected by the economic downturn that hindered other construction segments such as home building. However Skanska is looking to diversify its business and become less dependent on public projects. In 2011 the company acquired US-based Industrial Contractors for $135 million. Industrial Contractors (integrated into Skanska US Civil) works on power and energy commercial and light industrial and heavy industrial projects.

EXECUTIVES

Vice President, Michael Dipaolo
Auditors: KPMG LLP NEW YORK NY

LOCATIONS

HQ: SKANSKA USA CIVIL INC.
7520 ASTORIA BLVD STE 200, EAST ELMHURST, NY
113701135
Phone: 718 340-0777
Web: WWW.USA.SKANSKA.COM

PRODUCTS/OPERATIONS

Selected Services

Commercial development
Construction management
Design-build
Financial services
Pharmaceutical validation
Pre-construction
Public-private validation
Self-performance
Operating Units
Bayshore Concrete Products
Industrial Construction Skanska
PCI Skanska
Skanska Koch
Underpinning & Foundation Skanska

COMPETITORS

A & L
American Civil Constructors Holdings
American Infrastructure
Balfour Beatty Infrastructure
Bechtel
Flatiron Construction
Fluor
Granite Construction
J.L. Patterson & Associates
Jones Bros.
Lane Construction
Parsons Brinckerhoff
Parsons Corporation
Peter Kiewit Sons'
RailWorks
Ruscilli Construction
Tutor Perini
Vecellio Group

HISTORICAL FINANCIALS

Company Type: Private

Income Statement   FYE: December 31

	REVENUE ($ mil.)	NET INCOME ($ mil.)	NET PROFIT MARGIN	EMPLOYEES
12/08	1,753	54	3.1%	5,200
12/07	1,611	52	3.2%	—
Annual Growth	8.8%	5.2%	—	—

Return on assets: 6.1%   Cash ($ mil.): 172
Return on equity: 13.6%
Current ratio: 1.50

SKANSKA USA CIVIL NORTHEAST INC.

EXECUTIVES

Ceo, Richard Cavallaro
Sr V Pres*, Ralph Russo
Contracts Director, Barry Nosowitz
Project Manager, Alper Ayar
Engineer, Patrick Bifone
Compliance Officer, Suzanne Miritello
Chief Engineer, Alfredas Daugiala
Design Build Manager, David Tullis
Chief Estimator, Fabio Liscidini
Project Manager, James Sartorio
Project Engineer, Stephen Vick

LOCATIONS

HQ: SKANSKA USA CIVIL NORTHEAST INC.
  7520 ASTORIA BLVD STE 200, EAST ELMHURST, NY
  113701135
Phone: 718 340-0777
Web: WWW.SKANSKA.COM

HISTORICAL FINANCIALS
Company Type: Private

Income Statement   FYE: December 31

	REVENUE ($ mil.)	NET INCOME ($ mil.)	NET PROFIT MARGIN	EMPLOYEES
12/08	816	51	6.3%	1,500
12/07	622	27	4.5%	—
12/06	467	17	3.7%	—
12/05	487	12	2.6%	—
Annual Growth	18.8%	59.9%	—	—

2008 Year-End Financials

Return on assets: 12.0%   Cash ($ mil.): 121
Return on equity: 25.1%
Current ratio: 1.70

SKF USA INC.

SKF USA is a subsidiary of Swedish ball bearing giant AB SKF and a global supplier of bearings seals lubricants linear motion components and condition monitoring systems. It also specializes in related services from repair and rebuilding to consulting logistics and training. Its repair stations also provide bearing inspection repair and overhaul services. With hundreds of manufacturing sales and authorized distribution locations across the US SKF USA's offerings are geared at a wide range of industries including aerospace automotive construction machine tooling and alternative energy. Brand names include Alemite Lincoln Reelcraft and S2M.

Operations

SKF USA groups its technologies across five platforms: bearings and units seals lubrication systems mechatronics (combining mechanics and electronics into intelligent systems) and services.

Although bearings and seals are core product lines the company isn't just focused on traditional hardware. It is increasingly launching performance-based products that help to extend the life-cycle of those bearings and seals. Recent products include a portable user-friendly technology for performing bearing grease condition assessments directly in the field. It offers a hydraulic-driven lubricator that eliminates the need for manual lubrication of construction and off-highway equipment attachments. And the product line perhaps showing the most promising growth is its "smart" condition monitoring systems which consist of hardware and software and in some cases sensors that work together to collect store and analyze data.

Geographic Reach

The company has almost 30 manufacturing sites in the US where it provides customized application engineering services through factories in Houston and Cleveland. The company additionally operates a technical Center in Plymouth Michigan that provides a range of engineering and testing services.

Sales and Marketing

SKF USA sells thousands of products and services through a network of over 4000 US-based authorized distributors. For the auto industry it serves the aftermarket for cars and commercial vehicles.

Strategy

SKF USA markets its condition monitoring systems particularly to alternative energy customers in the US a market that is experiencing good growth as a result of tightening environmental regulations.

However following several fiscal quarters of declining sales amid a slow industrial market the company's Sweden-based parent SKF throughout 2016 began consolidating several North American facilities including closing its sites in San Diego and Baltimore. Outside the US SKF also closed its Y-Bearing and Units production channels in Puebla Mexico which served North American agriculture customers.

EXECUTIVES

Treasurer, Brian J. Duffy
President Skf North America, Poul Jeppesen
National Account Manager, Lakshmi Yalamanchili
Vice President Operations, Colin Deis
National Account Manager, Jeffrey Zuziak
National Account Manager, Bob Young
Vice President, Gunilla Nilsson
Vice President Corporate Accounts, Mark Keaveny
Vp Strategic Hr Business Partner Industrial Sales North America, Mary-beth Depaolo
Vice President, Filippo Zingariello

LOCATIONS

HQ: SKF USA INC.
  890 FORTY FOOT RD, LANSDALE, PA 194464303
Phone: 267 436-6000
Web: WWW.SKF.COM

PRODUCTS/OPERATIONS

PRODUCTS
Actuation systems
Bearings units & housings
Condition monitoring
Coupling systems
Linear motion
Lubrication solutions
Magnetic systems
Maintenance products
Power transmission
Seals
Test & measurement equipment
Vehicle aftermarket
SERVICES
Asset management services
Business consulting

Customer training
Engineering consultancy
Logistics
Mechanical maintenance
Remanufacturing & maintenance services
Service contracts

COMPETITORS

A. Stucki Company   NN Inc.
Accuride International NSK
EnPro   NTN Bearing Corp. of
FAG Kugelfischer   America
Hoover Precision   Nippon Bearing
  Products   RBC Bearings
JTEKT   Schaeffler
Kaydon   Timken
MinebeaMitsumi   Waukesha Bearings

HISTORICAL FINANCIALS
Company Type: Private

Income Statement   FYE: December 31

	REVENUE ($ mil.)	NET INCOME ($ mil.)	NET PROFIT MARGIN	EMPLOYEES
12/14	3,138	155	5.0%	4,000
12/13	2,554	95	3.7%	—
12/12	2,397	138	5.8%	—
Annual Growth	14.4%	6.0%	—	—

2014 Year-End Financials

Return on assets: 3.8%   Cash ($ mil.): 29
Return on equity: 16.4%
Current ratio: 2.40

SMDC MEDICAL CENTER

EXECUTIVES

Ceo, Peter Person
Ceo*, John Smylie
Gen Counsel*, James N Abelsen
Director, Donna Van Kessel
Scientist, Stephen Waring
Director of Radiology, Andrew Tritz
Clinical Informatics Analyst, Linda Rhodenbaugh

LOCATIONS

HQ: SMDC MEDICAL CENTER
  502 E 2ND ST, DULUTH, MN 558051913
Phone: 218 726-4000

HISTORICAL FINANCIALS
Company Type: Private

Income Statement   FYE: June 30

	REVENUE ($ mil.)	NET INCOME ($ mil.)	NET PROFIT MARGIN	EMPLOYEES
06/17	504	0	0.0%	750
06/16	500	16	3.4%	—
06/15	502	19	4.0%	—
06/14	475	11	2.4%	—
Annual Growth	2.0%	(79.3%)	—	—

2017 Year-End Financials

Return on assets: —   Cash ($ mil.): 63
Return on equity: 0.1%
Current ratio: 4.30

SMITHSONIAN INSTITUTION

The Smithsonian Institution has many hats from the one worn by Harrison Ford in the Indiana Jones movies to the one worn by Abraham Lincoln the night he was assassinated. One of the world's leading cultural institutions the Smithsonian houses some 155 million objects in 19 museums and galleries most of which are on the National Mall in Washington DC. Roughly 30 million people visit every year to view the Smithsonian's exhibits on art music TV and film science history and other subjects. Admission to all but one of the Smithsonian's facilities is free; only the Cooper-Hewitt National Design Museum in New York charges admission.

Operations

A board of regents that includes the vice president and the chief justice of the US six members of Congress and nine private citizens leads the institution. The Smithsonian's exhibits display items such as the Declaration of Independence the ruby slippers worn by Judy Garland in The Wizard of Oz and the Wright brothers' first airplane. Along with its museums and galleries the Smithsonian also operates the National Zoo and nine research facilities and publishes magazines and books.

Among its museums are the African American Museum Archives of American Art Natural History Museum and the Smithsonian Castle.

Geographic Reach

The Smithsonian Institution is located in Washington DC. The world's largest museum and research complex averages about 30 million visitors per year.

Financial Performance

With operating revenue in 2016 of $1.5 billion (up about 20% from the prior year) the Smithsonian receives nearly 55% of its funding from federal appropriations. Contributions and private grants account for nearly 20% and business activities brought in more than 10%. The Institution's net assets have grown steadily over the past five years from $3 billion in 2012 to $3.8 billion in 2016.

Strategy

Recent initiatives at the Institution include the grand opening of the National Museum of African American History and Culture in late 2016 as well as plans for a $900 million overhaul of the Air and Space Museum (scheduled to start in 2018) and a $2 billion upgrade and expansion of its South Mall Campus (scheduled to start in 2022).

The institution aims to expand the Smithsonian's global relevance in the 21st century. As part of this strategy it released a strategic plan that focuses on four priorities or "grand challenges" as they are called. They include unlocking the mysteries on the universe understanding and sustaining a biodiverse planet valuing world cultures and understanding the American experience.

HISTORY

English chemist James Smithson wrote a proviso to his will in 1826 that would lead to the creation of the Smithsonian Institution. When he died in 1829 he left his estate to his nephew Henry James Hungerford with the stipulation that if Hungerford died without heirs the estate would go to the US to create "an Establishment for the increase and diffusion of knowledge among men." Hungerford died in 1835 without any heirs and the US government inherited more than $500000 in gold.

Congress squandered the money after it was received in 1838 but perhaps feeling pangs of guilt covered the loss. The Smithsonian was finally created in 1846 and Princeton physicist Joseph Henry was named its first secretary. That year it established the Museum of Natural History the Museum of History and Technology and the National Gallery of Art. The Smithsonian's National Museum was developed around the collection of the US Patent Office in 1858. The Smithsonian continued to expand adding the National Zoological Park in 1889 and the Smithsonian Astrophysical Observatory in 1890.

The Freer Gallery a gift of industrialist Charles Freer opened in 1923. The National Gallery was renamed the National Collection of Fine Arts in 1937 and a new National Gallery created with Andrew Mellon's gift of his art collection and a building opened in 1941. The Air and Space Museum was established in 1946.

More museums were added in the 1960s including the National Portrait Gallery in 1962 and the Anacostia Museum (exhibits and materials on African-American history) in 1967. The Kennedy Center for the Performing Arts was opened in 1971. The Collection of Fine Arts was renamed the National Museum of American Art and the Museum of History and Technology was renamed the National Museum of American History in 1980.

The Smithsonian placed its first-ever contribution boxes in four of its museums in 1993.

A planned exhibit featuring the Enola Gay — the plane that dropped the atomic bomb on Hiroshima — created a firestorm in 1994 with critics charging that the exhibit downplayed Japanese aggression and US casualties in WWII. The original exhibit was canceled in 1995 the director of the Air and Space Museum resigned and a scaled-down version of the exhibit premiered. In 2004 the exhibit attracted more protestors prompting Smithsonian officials to evacuate and temporarily close the museum.

Large contributions from private donors continued in the 1990s; the Mashantucket Pequot tribe gave $10 million from its casino operations in 1994 for the Smithsonian's planned American Indian museum and prolific electronics inventor Jerome Lemelson donated $10.4 million in 1995. The museum celebrated its sesquicentennial in 1996 amid news that $500 million in repairs were needed over the next 10 years.

California real estate developer Kenneth Behring gave the largest cash donation ever to the museum in 1997 — $20 million for the National Museum of Natural History. Short of funds the Smithsonian had to cut back on its 150th-anniversary traveling exhibit that year. The Smithsonian announced a $26 million renovation for the National Museum of Natural History in 1998. Two years later Behring quadrupled his record-breaking 1997 donation of $20 million by giving $80 million to the National Museum of American History. Catherine Reynolds withdrew most of her $38 million gift in 2002 after the Smithsonian Institution refused to implement her ideas for an exhibit at the National Museum of American History.

The National Museum of the American Indian opened on the National Mall in 2004.

Secretary Lawrence Small resigned under pressure in March 2007 amid criticism of his spending practices. Cristi n Samper director of the Smithsonian's National Museum of Natural History was named acting secretary. A report on the matter issued by the Smithsonian in June said its Board of Regents failed to provide the oversight that might have prevented Small's extravagant spending.

In July 2008 Wayne Clough became the 12th secretary of the Smithsonian.

EXECUTIVES

John And Adrienne Mars Director National Air And Space Museum, John R. (Jack) Dailey
Director Government Relations, Penelope (Nell) Payne, age 62
Director External Affairs, Virginia B. (Ginny) Clark
Secretary, David J. Skorton
Director National Postal Museum, Allen R. Kane
Director National Museum Of African American History And Culture, Lonnie G. Bunch, age 64
Director Equal Employment And Minority Affairs, Era L. Marshall
Director Smithsonian Marine Station At Fort Pierce, Valerie J. Paul
Director Smithsonian Affiliations, Harold A. Closter
Director Smithsonian Institution Libraries, Nancy E. Gwinn
Ombudsman, Chandra P. Heilman
Director Smithsonian Center For Education And Museum Studies, Stephanie L. Norby
Acting Assistant Secretary Communications And External Affairs And Deputy Under Secretary Finance And Administration, John K. Lapiana
Director Smithsonian Environmental Research Center, Anson (Tuck) Hines
Director Smithsonian Institution Archives, Anne Van Camp
Acting Under Secretary For History Art And Culture, Richard Kurin
Director National Museum Of African Art, Johnnetta B. Cole
Director Smithsonian Tropical Research Center, Matthew Larsen
Acting Under Secretary Science, Scott Miller
General Counsel, Judith E. Leonard
Director Harvard-smithsonian Center For Astrophysics, Charles R. Alcock
Director Smithsonian Latino Center, Eduardo D az
Director Smithsonian Museum Conservation Institute, Robert J. Koestler
Acting Director Cooper-hewitt National Design Museum, Caroline Baumann
Director National Zoological Park, Dennis Kelly
Director Consortia For The Humanities, Michelle Anne Delaney
Director Office Of Facilities Engineering And Operations, Nancy Bechtol
President Smithsonian Enterprises, Christopher Liedel
Inspector General, Cathy Helm
Director Smithsonian Exhibits, Susan Ades
Cio, Deron Burba
Editor-in-chief Smithsonian Magazine, Michael Caruso
Director Finance And Accounting, Jean Garvin
Director Office Of Planning Management And Budget, David Voyles
Acting Director Office Of Policy And Analysis, Whitney Watriss
Director Office Of Fellowships And Internships, Eric Woodard
Director The Smithsonian Associates, Fredie Adelman
Director Smithsonian American Art Museum And The Renwick Gallery, Elizabeth (Betsy) Broun
Director Hirshhorn Museum And Sculpture Garden, Melissa Chiu
Director National Museum Of American History Behring Center, John Gray
Director Archives Of American Art, Kate Haw
Director National Museum Of Natural History, Kirk Johnson
Director Smithsonianâ's Center For Folklife And Cultural Heritage, Michael Atwood Mason
Director Freer Gallery Of Art And Arthur M. Sackler Gallery, Julian Raby
Director National Portrait Gallery, Kim Sajet

Interim Director Smithsonian Institution Traveling Exhibition Service, Myriam Springuel
Director Consortia For Science, Pierre Comizzoli
Chancellor Board Of Regents, John G. Roberts, age 65
Auditors: KPMG LLP WASHINGTON DC

LOCATIONS

HQ: SMITHSONIAN INSTITUTION
1000 JEFFERSON DR SW, WASHINGTON, DC 205600009
Phone: 202 633-1000
Web: WWW.SI.EDU

PRODUCTS/OPERATIONS

2016 Operating Revenue

	% of total
Federal appropriations	53
Contributions & private grants	18
Business activities	11
Government grants & contracts	8
Endowment	5
Other	5
Total	**100**

Selected Museums and Research Centers

Anacostia Community Museum
Arthur M. Sackler Gallery
Arts and Industries Building
Center for Folklife and Cultural Heritage
Conservation and Research Center
Cooper-Hewitt National Design Museum (New York)
Freer Gallery of Art
Hirshhorn Museum and Sculpture Garden
National Air and Space Museum
National Museum of African Art
National Museum of American History
National Museum of Natural History
National Museum of the American Indian
National Museum of the American Indian - George
  Gustav Heye Center (New York)
National Science Research Center
National Portrait Gallery
National Postal Museum
National Zoological Park
Smithsonian American Art Museum
Smithsonian Astrophysical Observatory
Smithsonian Center for Latino Initiatives
Smithsonian Center for Materials Research and
  Education
Smithsonian Environmental Research Center (SERC)
Smithsonian Institution Building (The Castle)
Smithsonian Museum Conservation Institute
Smithsonian Tropical Research Institute

HISTORICAL FINANCIALS

Company Type: Private

Income Statement				FYE: September 30
	REVENUE ($ mil.)	NET INCOME ($ mil.)	NET PROFIT MARGIN	EMPLOYEES
09/18	1,563	177	11.3%	6,100
09/17	1,514	153	10.1%	—
09/16	1,541	192	12.5%	—
09/15	1,412	50	3.6%	—
Annual Growth	**3.4%**	**51.8%**	**—**	**—**

2018 Year-End Financials

Return on assets: 3.4%
Return on equity: 4.3%
Current ratio: 1.00
Cash ($ mil.): 634

SMMH PRACTICE PLAN, INC.

Auditors: KPMG LLP PITTSBURGH PA

LOCATIONS

HQ: SMMH PRACTICE PLAN, INC.
7175 SALTSBURG RD, PITTSBURGH, PA 152352252
Phone: 412 795-6069

HISTORICAL FINANCIALS

Company Type: Private

Income Statement				FYE: June 30
	REVENUE ($ mil.)	NET INCOME ($ mil.)	NET PROFIT MARGIN	EMPLOYEES
06/15	2,060	27	1.3%	26
06/14	2,005	570	28.4%	—
06/13	1,985	402	20.3%	—
06/12	1,976	(90)	—	—
Annual Growth	**1.4%**	**—**	**—**	**—**

2015 Year-End Financials

Return on assets: 4.8%
Return on equity: 1.3%
Current ratio: 0.60
Cash ($ mil.): 49

SMO, INCORPORATED

EXECUTIVES

Ceo, Julian B Wills III
V Pres, Mark Samuels
Asst SEC, Kenneth Halperin

LOCATIONS

HQ: SMO, INCORPORATED
6355 CRAIN HWY, LA PLATA, MD 206464267
Phone: 301 932-3600
Web: WWW.SMOENERGY.COM

HISTORICAL FINANCIALS

Company Type: Private

Income Statement				FYE: September 30
	REVENUE ($ mil.)	NET INCOME ($ mil.)	NET PROFIT MARGIN	EMPLOYEES
09/10	496	6	1.3%	450
09/09	395	8	2.1%	—
09/06	0	0	—	—
09/05	0	0	—	—
Annual Growth	**—**	**—**	**—**	**—**

2010 Year-End Financials

Return on assets: 5.8%
Return on equity: 8.8%
Current ratio: 2.40
Cash ($ mil.): 6

SNAKE RIVER SUGAR COMPANY

EXECUTIVES

Prin, Duane Grant
Pres*, Vic Jaro
Exec Dir*, Terry L Ketterling
SEC*, John McCreedy
Cfo*, Wayne Neely
Information Technology Manager, Ano Sundara
Information Technology Directo, Dennis Costesso
Technical, Jerry Wagner
Auditors: EIDEBAILLY LLP BOISE IDAHO

LOCATIONS

HQ: SNAKE RIVER SUGAR COMPANY
1951 S SATURN WAY STE 100, BOISE, ID 837092924
Phone: 208 383-6500
Web: WWW.SRCOOP.COM

HISTORICAL FINANCIALS

Company Type: Private

Income Statement				FYE: August 31
	REVENUE ($ mil.)	NET INCOME ($ mil.)	NET PROFIT MARGIN	EMPLOYEES
08/11	876	13	1.5%	2,500
08/10	839	18	2.2%	—
08/09	658	22	3.4%	—
Annual Growth	**15.3%**	**(23.8%)**	**—**	**—**

2011 Year-End Financials

Return on assets: 1.9%
Return on equity: 4.8%
Current ratio: 0.80
Cash ($ mil.): 17

SNYDER'S-LANCE, INC.

If you're familiar with the munchies named Toastchee Nip Chee and Captain's Wafers Snyder's-Lance (formerly Lance) has undoubtedly helped you satisfy a snack attack. The company produces single-serve multi-pack and family-sized packages of bakery products and sweet and savory snack foods including cookies crackers nuts potato chips and pretzels. Its snacks are sold under the Lance Cape Cod Tom's Archway and Snyder's brands at food retailers mass merchants and convenience and club stores in the US. International brands include Kettle Chips and Metcalfe's popcorn. The company also makes private-label and branded snacks for food makers. Snyder's-Lance agreed to its acquisition by The Campbell Soup company in 2017 in a $4.9 billion deal.

Change in Company Type

In late 2017 Snyder's-Lance agreed to its acquisition by The Campbell Soup Company which is looking to boost its snack foods division. The deal is expected to close for around $4.9 billion.

Operations

Snyder's-Lance manufactures pretzels sandwich crackers kettle cooked chips pretzel crackers cookies potato chips tortilla chips restaurant style crackers popcorn nuts and other salty snacks. It generates around 80% of its sales from its owned branded products with the remainder coming from third-party branded products and other branded products.

The company has R&D facilities in Hanover Pennsylvania and Salem Oregon.

Geographic Reach

Based in North Carolina Snyder's-Lance operates manufacturing facilities in the US in California North Carolina Oregon Pennsylvania Iowa Indiana Georgia Arizona Massachusetts Florida Ohio and Wisconsin as well as in the UK.

Sales and Marketing

The snack food giant sells its products to mass merchandisers club stores discount stores convenience stores foodservice operators and other retailers the likes of drug stores the military schools and government facilities. Wal-Mart its largest customer represents nearly 15% of the company's revenues.

The company distributes snack food products nationwide using a large direct-store-delivery (DSD) network consisting of some 3000 distribution routes served mostly by Independent Business Owners (IBOs) and others that are company-owned.

Financial Performance

After a few years of sluggish growth in fiscal 2016 Snyder's-Lance's sales jumped 27% to $2.1 billion thanks to the acquisitions of Diamond Foods in February and Metcalfe in September of that year. The company also grew its core business particularly its Lance sandwich crackers Snack Factory pretzel crisps Cape Cod chips and the Late July brand.

Net income fell $35.2 million to $14.9 million due to acquisition expenses higher advertising spend and impairment charges relating to changes in manufacturing operations.

Cash from operations increased 79% to $261.2 million due to lower income tax as the company used net operating losses acquired in the Diamond Foods transaction to offset taxes payable.

Strategy

Snyder's-Lance seeking revenue growth abroad through acquisitions. In 2016 it acquired Diamond Foods which does a roaring trade for its Kettle Chips brand in the UK as well as the US; and Metcalfe which makes the UK's best-selling upmarket ready-to-eat popcorn. The two acquisitions also play into Snyder's-Lance's strategy of growing its "better-for-you" product segment.

Mergers and Acquisitions

In early 2016 the company acquired Diamond Foods makers of Diamond and Emerald nuts for about $1.3 billion. The move added snack brands as well as UK and US distribution might to Snyder's-Lance. Later in 2016 to maintain focus on its core products the company sold its Diamond of California culinary nut business to private equity firm Blue Road Capital. Diamond of California had been one of four Diamond Foods brands at the time of Snyder's-Lance's acquisition.

Also in 2016 it acquired all of Metcalfe's Skinny Limited (it previously owned a 26% stake) the maker of the UK's leading upmarket popcorn brand as well as a range of corn and rice cake products.

EXECUTIVES

President Ceo And Director, Brian J. Driscoll, age 61

Svp And Chief Supply Chain Officer, Patrick S. McInerney, $379,950 total compensation

Svp And Chief Marketing And Innovation Officer, Rodrigo F. Troni Pena, age 52, $338,250 total compensation

Evp And Cfo, Alexander W. Pease, age 47, $90,538 total compensation

President Dsd Division, Francis B. (Frank) Schuster, age 52, $341,813 total compensation

President Direct Division, John T. Maples

President Clearview Division, Peter L. Michaud

Managing Director Kettle Foods Limited (uk), Ashley Hicks

Division Vp And General Manager Growth And Developing Markets, Matthew T. Insolia

Vice President Of Human Resources Operations, Emily Berwager

Vice President Of Engineering, Rob Miller

Vice President Information Technology Global Thermal Equipment And Services, Robert F Foster

Vice President National Account Strategy, John McGinn

Vice President Of Strategic Innovation, Tim Old

Chairman, James W. Johnston, age 72

Auditors: PRICEWATERHOUSECOOPERS LLP CH

LOCATIONS

HQ: SNYDER'S-LANCE, INC.
13515 BALNTYN CORP PL, CHARLOTTE, NC 282772706
Phone: 704 554-1421
Web: WWW.SNYDERSLANCE.COM

PRODUCTS/OPERATIONS

2015 Revenue

	$ mil.	% of total
Branded products	1,155	70
Private brands	335	20
Other	165	10
Total	**1,656**	**100**

Selected Brands

Archway
Brent
Bugles
Cape Cod Potato Chips
Captain's Wafers
Choc-o-Lunch
Delicious
Diamond of California
Don Pablo's
EatSmart
Emerald
Grande
Jays
Kettle brand
KETTLE
Krunchers!
Lance
Nekot
Nipchee
Pop Secret
Pretzel Crisps
Sam's
Salerno
Snyder's of Hanover
Stella D'oro
Texas Pete
Thunder
Toastchee
Toasty
Tom's
Van-o-Lunch
Vista

COMPETITORS

American Pop Corn	Kettle Foods
Beer Nuts	King Nut Companies
Bridgford Foods	Legacy Bakehouse
Campbell Soup	McKee Foods
Chattanooga Bakery	Mondelez International
ConAgra	Old Dutch Foods
Evans Food Products	Otis Spunkmeyer
Flowers Foods	Pepperidge Farm
Frito-Lay	Poindexter Nut
General Mills	Pretzels Inc.
Golden Enterprises	Procter & Gamble
Inventure foods	Snappy Popcorn
John Sanfilippo & Son	Weaver Popcorn Company
Kellogg U.S. Snacks	

HISTORICAL FINANCIALS

Company Type: Private

Income Statement — FYE: December 30

	REVENUE ($ mil.)	NET INCOME ($ mil.)	NET PROFIT MARGIN	EMPLOYEES
12/17	2,226	149	6.7%	5,900
12/16*	2,109	14	0.7%	—
01/15	1,620	192	11.9%	—
12/13	1,761	79	4.5%	—
Annual Growth	**6.0%**	**17.2%**	**—**	**—**

*Fiscal year change

2017 Year-End Financials

Return on assets: 4.1%
Return on equity: 7.4%
Current ratio: 1.60
Cash ($ mil.): 18

SOCORRO INDEPENDENT SCHOOL DISTRICT

EXECUTIVES

Supt, Jose Espinoza
Supt*, Charles Fighs
Cfo*, Tony Reza
Staff, Philip A Acosta
Coordinator, Susie Godina
Chief Operating Officer, Thomas Eyeington
Project Coordinator, Zaide Cabezuela
Staff Accountant, Adriana Aguirre
Network Administrator, Oscar Dominguez
Admin Specialist I, Adriana Balandran
Nurse, Ramona Garcia
Auditors: GIBSON RUDDOCK PATTERSON LLC

LOCATIONS

HQ: SOCORRO INDEPENDENT SCHOOL DISTRICT
12440 ROJAS DR, EL PASO, TX 799285261
Phone: 915 937-0100
Web: WWW.SISD.NET

HISTORICAL FINANCIALS

Company Type: Private

Income Statement — FYE: June 30

	REVENUE ($ mil.)	NET INCOME ($ mil.)	NET PROFIT MARGIN	EMPLOYEES
06/18	470	168	35.8%	6,000
06/17	453	200	44.1%	—
06/16	443	(4)	—	—
Annual Growth	**3.0%**	**—**	**—**	**—**

2018 Year-End Financials

Return on assets: 14.6%
Return on equity: 224.2%
Current ratio: —
Cash ($ mil.): 371

SOLSTICE HOLDINGS INC.

EXECUTIVES

Pres, Mr Doug L Devos
Chm, Stephen Van Andel
Exec V Pres-Cfo, Russ Evans
Exec V Pres-Coo, Alvin Koop
V Pres, Mr Michael Mohr
Cntrl, Mr Craig V Witcher

LOCATIONS

HQ: SOLSTICE HOLDINGS INC.
7575 FULTON ST E, ADA, MI 493550001
Phone: 616 787-1000

HISTORICAL FINANCIALS

Company Type: Private

Income Statement   FYE: December 31

	REVENUE ($ mil.)	NET INCOME ($ mil.)	NET PROFIT MARGIN	EMPLOYEES
12/08	8,235	0	—	14,000
12/07	7,168	0	—	—
12/06	6,387	0	—	—
Annual Growth 13.5%		—	—	—

2008 Year-End Financials

Return on assets: —   Cash ($ mil.): 1,072
Return on equity: —
Current ratio: 1.10

SOUTH BROWARD HOSPITAL DISTRICT

South Broward Hospital District (dba Memorial Healthcare System) is a community-owned health services network that provides health service to residents of Florida's Broward Dade and Palm Beach counties. The system's major hospitals include Memorial Regional Hospital Memorial Hospital Pembroke Memorial Hospital West and Memorial Hospital Miramar. The hospitals have a combined capacity of roughly 1900 licensed beds and provide services including diagnostic emergency surgical and rehabilitative care. Memorial also operates a pediatric hospital cardiac and vascular medicine institute a cancer treatment center and a center for women's health as well as nursing home facilities (120 beds) and community clinics.

Operations

The system's hospitals include Memorial Regional Memorial Regional South Joe DiMaggio Children's Memorial West Memorial Miramar Memorial Pembroke and the Memorial Manor nursing home.

Memorial Regional offers a cardiac and vascular institute a cancer institute and a neuroscience center.

Geographic Reach

Memorial Healthcare System operates health care facilities in Florida and Washington.

Financial Performance

In 2015 revenue increased 12% to $1.8 billion as net patient service earnings rose primarily due to an increase in surgical procedures given. Net income rose 89% to $191.4 million that year due

to the higher revenue and a decrease in depreciation and amortization. Operating cash flow also increased rising 68% to $292.4 million.

Strategy

Memorial Healthcare System provides care in a number of ways including through home health services and health care plans. It is adding two additional health plans in 2016 to reach a goal of managing more than 100000 lives in the network.

During 2016 the company entered into a partnership with Holy Cross Physician Partners creating the Atlantic Coast Health Network. The new network represents some 1400 physicians.

EXECUTIVES

President And Ceo, Frank V. Sacco
Svp And Cfo, Matthew J. Muhart
Svp And Chief Medical Officer, Stanley W. Marks
Evp And Coo, Aurelio M. Fernandez
Pharmacy Manager, Margaretta Kearson
Director Physician Recruitment, Ken Bolis
Vice President Of Property Management, David Schlemmer
Vice President Marketing Communications, S S Khan
Vice President Of Managed Care, Sandra Dilts
Respiratory Therapy Director, Sandy Santoro
Respiratory Therapy Director, Darlene Moretti
Vice President Finance North Mississippi Health Services, Lynn Holland
Director Of Nursing, Barbara Bertot
Medical Director, Dexter Sereda
Chairman, Jose Basulto
Vice Chairman, Vic Narang
Secretary, Debbie Delotta
Secretary, Ruth Marcus
Department Secretary, Tracy Kalinowski
Unit Secretary, Sandra Baptiste
Auditors: ERNST & YOUNG LLP MIAMI FL

LOCATIONS

HQ: SOUTH BROWARD HOSPITAL DISTRICT
3501 JOHNSON ST, HOLLYWOOD, FL 330215421
Phone: 954 987-2000
Web: WWW.MHS.NET

PRODUCTS/OPERATIONS

2015 Sales

	$ mil.	% of total
Net patient service	1,630	92
Disproportionate share distribution	83	5
Other operating revenue	49	3
Total	**1,764**	**100**

Selected Facilities

Esther L. Grossman Women's Health & Resource Center
Memorial Cancer Institute
Memorial Hospital Miramar
Memorial Hospital Pembroke
Memorial Hospital West
Memorial Manor
Memorial Outpatient Center
Memorial Primary Care Center - Dania Beach
Memorial Primary Care Center - Hollywood
Memorial Primary Care Center - Miramar
Memorial Primary Care Center - West Hollywood
Memorial Regional Hospital
  Joe DiMaggio Children's Hospital
Memorial Regional Hospital South
Memorial Regional Hospital Fitness & Rehabilitation Center
Memorial Same Day Surgery Center
Memorial Urgent Care Center
Same Day Surgery Center at Memorial Hospital West

COMPETITORS

Baptist Health South Florida	Florida Hospital Heartland
Boca Raton Regional Hospital	HCA
Broward Health	Jackson Health System
Continucare	MJHHA
	South Miami Hospital

HISTORICAL FINANCIALS

Company Type: Private

Income Statement   FYE: April 30

	REVENUE ($ mil.)	NET INCOME ($ mil.)	NET PROFIT MARGIN	EMPLOYEES
04/18	2,014	64	3.2%	9,200
04/17	1,937	134	6.9%	—
04/16	1,897	188	9.9%	—
04/15	854	(649)	—	—
Annual Growth 33.1%		—	—	—

2018 Year-End Financials

Return on assets: 1.9%   Cash ($ mil.): 526
Return on equity: 3.1%
Current ratio: 6.10

SOUTH CAROLINA PUBLIC SERVICE AUTHORITY (INC)

This company turns the lights on in South Carolina. South Carolina Public Service Authority known as Santee Cooper (after two interconnected river systems) provides wholesale electricity to 20 cooperatives and two municipalities that serve more than 2 million customers in South Carolina. It directly retails electricity to more than 174000 customers. One of the largest US state-owned utilities Santee Cooper operates in all 46 counties in South Carolina and has stakes in power plants (fossil-fueled nuclear hydro and renewable) that give it more than 5180 MW of generating capacity. Its Santee Cooper Regional Water System also distributes water to customers in its service area.

Operations

Santee Cooper operates 5029 miles of transmission lines and more than 2841 miles of distribution lines. It also operates 105 transmission stations and 54 distribution substations. The company is the leading renewable energy producer in South Carolina.

Geographic Reach

In addition to supplying power to 20 cooperatives in all 46 counties in South Carolina Santee Cooper also supplies power directly to 29 large industrial customers in 10 counties Charleston Air Force Base the town of Bamberg and the City of Georgetown.

Sales and Marketing

The company serves more than 2 million customers in South Carolina. It directly retails electricity to more than 174000 customers.

Financial Performance

In 2015 Santee Cooper's net revenues decreased by 6% to $1.9 billion compared due to lower kilowatt-hour sales (down 3%) and demand usage (down 2%).

The company's net income decreased by 73% to $34.4 million as the result of lower net revenues and higher electric maintenance expenses.

In 2015 Santee Cooper's operating cash inflow decreased by 77% to $237.6 million.

Strategy

With a eye toward getting 40% of its power from non-carbon emitting sources and conservation by 2020 the company has begun to invest heavily in nuclear solar wind and other renewable energy sources.

In 2015 the company agreed to changes in its agreement with Westinghouse Electric which acquired assets of a second partner in the V.C. Summer Nuclear Station plant construction consortium giving Westinghouse more control over the project.

In 2014 Santee Cooper in collaboration with Central Electric Power Cooperative and the state's electric cooperatives agreed to buy the total energy output of Colleton Solar Farm a utility-scale solar power farm being built by TIG Sun Energy a subsidiary of the North Charleston-based InterTech Group. The solar array consists of 10010 photovoltaic panels. Some panels are fixed while other panels follow the direction of the sun to maximize the production of solar energy.

South Carolina Resources Santee Cooper Central Electric Power Cooperative and the state's electric cooperatives agreed in 2013 to build Colleton Solar Farm the largest solar farm in the state (3000 kilowatts of electricity).

Mergers and Acquisitions

In 2014 South Carolina Electric & Gas Company (SCE&G) principal subsidiary of SCANA Corporation and Santee Cooper announced an agreement for SCE&G to acquire from Santee Cooper a 5% ownership interest in the two new nuclear units which are under construction at V.C. Summer Nuclear Station in Jenkinsville. Under the ownership agreement SCE&G owns 55%; Santee Cooper 45%. The 5% ownership interest would be acquired in three stages with 1% to be acquired at the commercial operation date of the first new nuclear unit (late 2017 or the first quarter of 2018); an additional 2% to be acquired no later than the first anniversary of such commercial operation date; and the final 2% to be acquired no later than the second anniversary date of such commercial operation date.

Company Background

Santee Cooper is a government-owned entity.

Historically the $48.2 million Santee Cooper project (55% federal loan and 45% federal grant) which connected the Santee and Cooper rivers and established hydroelectric dams and a transmission grid began to generate electricity for the first time in 1942. It was founded in 1934.

EXECUTIVES

Vice President Human Resource Management, W Brown
President And Ceo, Lonnie N. Carter
Svp And Cfo, Jeff Armfield
Svp Nuclear Energy, Michael Crosby
Evp Competitive Markets And Generation, Marc R. Tye
Svp And Cio, Dom Maddalone
Svp Power Delivery, Arnold R. Singleton
2nd Vice Chairman, Barry Wynn
Chairman, W. Leighton Lord
1st Vice Chairman, William A. Finn
Auditors: CHERRY BEKAERT LLP RALEIGH N

LOCATIONS

HQ: SOUTH CAROLINA PUBLIC SERVICE AUTHORITY (INC)
1 RIVERWOOD DR, MONCKS CORNER, SC 294612998
Phone: 843 761-4121
Web: WWW.SANTEECOOPER.COM

PRODUCTS/OPERATIONS

2015 Sales

	$ mil.	% of total
Electricity	1,856	99
Water	8	-
Other	15	1
Total	**1,879**	**100**

COMPETITORS

Delmarva Power	PS Energy
Dominion Energy	Progress Energy
Duke Energy	SCANA
Florida Public Utilities	TVA Utilities Inc.
MLGW	
North Carolina Electric Membership	

HISTORICAL FINANCIALS

Company Type: Private

Income Statement — FYE: December 31

	REVENUE ($ mil.)	NET INCOME ($ mil.)	NET PROFIT MARGIN	EMPLOYEES
12/17	1,756	90	5.2%	1,748
12/15	1,879	34	1.8%	—
12/13	1,816	65	3.6%	—
12/12	1,887	84	4.5%	—
Annual Growth	(1.4%)	1.4%	—	—

2017 Year-End Financials

Return on assets: 0.7%
Return on equity: 4.3%
Current ratio: 3.00
Cash ($ mil.): 731

SOUTH FLORIDA WATER MANAGEMENT DISTRICT LEASING CORP.

EXECUTIVES

Chb, Daniel O'Keefe
V Cbb*, Kevin Powers
MBR*, Lennart Lindahl
V Pres*, Mitch Hutchcraft
Scientist, Patricia Robertshaw
Coordinator, Guangliang Liu
Compliance Staff, Jay Floyd
Coordinator, Peter Harlem
Executive Assistant, Haley Koptak
Mechanic, Kevin Jarvis
Chief Operator, Luis Bianchi

LOCATIONS

HQ: SOUTH FLORIDA WATER MANAGEMENT DISTRICT LEASING CORP.
3301 GUN CLUB RD, WEST PALM BEACH, FL 334063007
Phone: 561 686-8800
Web: WWW.SFWMD.GOV

HISTORICAL FINANCIALS

Company Type: Private

Income Statement — FYE: September 30

	REVENUE ($ mil.)	NET INCOME ($ mil.)	NET PROFIT MARGIN	EMPLOYEES
09/10	595	(42)	—	1,200
09/08	910	(64)	—	—
09/06	947	51	5.4%	—
Annual Growth	(11.0%)	—	—	—

SOUTH MIAMI HOSPITAL, INC.

South Miami Hospital offers primary and tertiary health care services to the residents living near the University of Miami. The hospital has about 470 beds and is one of the largest members of Baptist Health South Florida a top regional health system. Specialty services include emergency care cardiovascular services oncology neurology women's health metabolic care and rehabilitation. It operates an addiction treatment residential facility provides home health care and provides child development diagnostic and early intervention services. South Miami Hospital was founded in 1960.

Operations

South Miami Hospital handles 15000 inpatient admissions each year as well as 30000 emergency room visits 5000 outpatient surgeries and 4000 births. It has about 1300 physicians on its medical staff.

As part of the broader Baptist Health South Florida system South Miami Hospital benefits from shared resources including procurement administration and technology the coordination of which helps the member facilities control costs during times of economic trouble and rising medical care expenses in the US.

Strategy

The Baptist Health system facilities including South Miami Hospital are installing electronic health record (EHR) systems to manage patient records across the system. Such EHR systems are designed to improve quality and lower expenses by facilitating communication between care providers and increasing patient involvement in condition management.

In addition South Miami Hospital has improved its services through expansion and renovation projects. It has added specialty units for robotic surgery birthing heart care and neonatal intensive care. In addition it completed an $80 million two-story construction in 2013 that enhanced the medical center's emergency surgery and imaging departments.

EXECUTIVES

Ceo, Lincoln S Mendez
Pres*, Javier Hermandev-Lichto
SEC*, Domingo C Rodriguez
Tres*, George M Corrigan
Staff Coordinator, Christine Stiltner Angulo
Chief of Ob/Gyn, Rene A Paez
Chief of Emergency, Tracey C Patricoff
Chief of Medicine, Jorge Murillo
Staff Coordinator, Maria Cabrera
Health Professional, Ghassan Haddad

LOCATIONS

HQ: SOUTH MIAMI HOSPITAL, INC.
6200 SW 73RD ST, SOUTH MIAMI, FL 331434679
Phone: 786 662-4000

COMPETITORS

Adventist Health System Sunbelt Healthcare
Broward Health
H. Lee Moffitt Cancer Center & Research Institute
HCA
Jackson Health System
Larkin Community Hospital
Miami Children's Hospital
Mount Sinai Medical Center of Florida
South Broward Hospital District
UF&Shands
University of Miami Hospital

HISTORICAL FINANCIALS
Company Type: Private

Income Statement				FYE: September 30
	REVENUE ($ mil.)	NET INCOME ($ mil.)	NET PROFIT MARGIN	EMPLOYEES
09/17	484	6	1.4%	2,205
09/16	492	3	0.7%	—
09/15	495	40	8.2%	—
09/14	505	53	10.6%	—
Annual Growth	(1.4%)	(50.0%)	—	—

2017 Year-End Financials
Return on assets: 2.1%   Cash ($ mil.): —
Return on equity: 10.0%
Current ratio: 0.80

SOUTH NASSAU COMMUNITIES HOSPITAL INC

EXECUTIVES
Ceo, Richard J Murphy
Svp-Cfo*, John A Pohlman
Chief Officer, Daniel McAluey
Health Professional, Carol Cannella
Vice-President Engineering, Lori Allocca
Information Specialist, Michael Tsymbalyuk
Chief Financial Officer, Gerard Haas
Director, Barbara Guy
Executive, Stephen Bello
Manager, Suhas Kavthekar

LOCATIONS
HQ: SOUTH NASSAU COMMUNITIES HOSPITAL INC
  1 HEALTHY WAY, OCEANSIDE, NY 115721551
Phone: 516 632-3000
Web: WWW.SOUTHNASSAU.ORG

HISTORICAL FINANCIALS
Company Type: Private

Income Statement				FYE: December 31
	REVENUE ($ mil.)	NET INCOME ($ mil.)	NET PROFIT MARGIN	EMPLOYEES
12/17	451	(47)	—	2,800
12/16	437	(33)	—	—
12/15	423	(3)	—	—
12/14	434	13	3.0%	—
Annual Growth	1.3%	—	—	—

2017 Year-End Financials
Return on assets: (-6.8%)   Cash ($ mil.): 20
Return on equity: (-17.4%)
Current ratio: 1.60

SOUTH SHORE HOSPITAL, INC.

EXECUTIVES
Ceo, Gene E Green
Pres*, Pamela Daley Whelton
Cfo-Sr V Pres*, Michael Cullen
Sr V Pres*, Margaret Holda
Sr V Pres*, Christopher J Oconnor
Coo*, Joseph Cahill
V Pres Clinical*, Edward Liao
Pres Acute Care Oprs*, Timothy Quigley
Medical Staff, Joseph Jiang
Medical Staff, A K Elamine
Registered Nurse, Kim Noble

LOCATIONS
HQ: SOUTH SHORE HOSPITAL, INC.
  55 FOGG RD, SOUTH WEYMOUTH, MA 021902455
Phone: 781 624-8000
Web: WWW.SOUTHSHOREHEALTH.ORG

HISTORICAL FINANCIALS
Company Type: Private

Income Statement				FYE: September 30
	REVENUE ($ mil.)	NET INCOME ($ mil.)	NET PROFIT MARGIN	EMPLOYEES
09/17	563	9	1.7%	2,375
09/16	558	17	3.1%	—
09/15	522	50	9.6%	—
09/14	495	30	6.1%	—
Annual Growth	4.4%	(31.5%)	—	—

2017 Year-End Financials
Return on assets: 1.4%   Cash ($ mil.): 40
Return on equity: 3.3%
Current ratio: 1.50

SOUTH TEXAS ELECTRIC COOPERATIVE, INC.

EXECUTIVES
Pres, Barbara Miller
V Pres*, Ron Hughes
SEC-Treas*, Paul Brysch
Asst SEC/ Treas*, Larry Huesser
Vice-President Information Ser, Darryl Klinitchek
Compliance Staff, Travis Chrest
Fleet Manager Lead Mechanic, Hank Stall
Marketing Director, Norm Walters
Corportate Risk Officer, Amy Pratka
Manager, John A Packard
Security, Pete Masiel
Auditors: BUMGARDNER MORRISON AND COMPA

LOCATIONS
HQ: SOUTH TEXAS ELECTRIC COOPERATIVE, INC.
  2849 FM 447, VICTORIA, TX 77905
Phone: 361 575-6491
Web: WWW.STEC.ORG

HISTORICAL FINANCIALS
Company Type: Private

Income Statement				FYE: December 31
	REVENUE ($ mil.)	NET INCOME ($ mil.)	NET PROFIT MARGIN	EMPLOYEES
12/18	522	32	6.2%	253
12/17	495	26	5.4%	—
12/16	451	24	5.4%	—
12/15	416	31	7.5%	—
Annual Growth	7.9%	1.5%	—	—

2018 Year-End Financials
Return on assets: 2.3%   Cash ($ mil.): 68
Return on equity: 9.9%
Current ratio: 1.50

SOUTHCOAST HOSPITALS GROUP, INC.

When you feel more than a little physically washed up get to one of the Southcoast Hospitals Group facilities. The not-for-profit company provides medical services in the southeastern corner of Massachusetts and in Rhode Island. Its primary facilities in Massachusetts are the Charlton Memorial Hospital (with about 330 beds) in Fall River St. Luke's Hospital (420 beds) in New Bedford and Tobey Hospital (65 beds) in Wareham which provide acute medical care and specialty services including cardiology neurology orthopedics and women's care. Southcoast Hospitals Group also operates about 20 ancillary facilities including nursing and assisted-living facilities and home health and hospice agencies.

Auditors: DELOITTE TAX LLP JERICHO NY

LOCATIONS
HQ: SOUTHCOAST HOSPITALS GROUP, INC.
  363 HIGHLAND AVE, FALL RIVER, MA 027203703
Phone: 508 679-3131
Web: WWW.SOUTHCOAST.ORG

COMPETITORS
Baystate Health	Partners HealthCare
Boston Medical Center	Roger Williams Medical
Care New England	Center
CareGroup	Steward Health Care
Hallmark Health	Yale New Haven Health
Lifespan Corporation	System
McLean Hospital	
Memorial Hospital of	
Rhode Island	

HISTORICAL FINANCIALS
Company Type: Private

Income Statement				FYE: September 30
	REVENUE ($ mil.)	NET INCOME ($ mil.)	NET PROFIT MARGIN	EMPLOYEES
09/13	687	22	3.3%	3,853
09/12	704	49	7.0%	—
09/06	506	14	2.8%	—
09/04	445	13	3.1%	—
Annual Growth	4.9%	5.4%	—	—

2013 Year-End Financials
Return on assets: 6.9%   Cash ($ mil.): 6
Return on equity: 3.3%
Current ratio: 0.60

SOUTHEAST PETRO DISTRIBUTORS, INC.

EXECUTIVES

Pres, Mahesh Shah
V Pres-SEC, Rashmi Shah
V Pres, Shah Summit
Director of Operations, Lori Lemay
Vice President Principle, Summit Shah
Auditors: JAMES MOORE & CO PL GAINE

LOCATIONS

HQ: SOUTHEAST PETRO DISTRIBUTORS, INC.
402 HIGH POINT DR STE A, COCOA, FL 329266600
Phone: 321 631-0245
Web: WWW.SOUTHEASTPETRO.COM

HISTORICAL FINANCIALS

Company Type: Private

Income Statement				FYE: December 31
	REVENUE ($ mil.)	NET INCOME ($ mil.)	NET PROFIT MARGIN	EMPLOYEES
12/11	553	5	1.0%	12
12/10	416	5	1.3%	—
12/09	331	4	1.5%	—
12/02	57	0	0.9%	—
Annual Growth	28.6%	29.8%	—	—

2011 Year-End Financials

Return on assets: 13.1%   Cash ($ mil.): 8
Return on equity: 35.4%
Current ratio: 1.20

SOUTHEASTERN PENNSYLVANIA TRANSPORTATION AUTHORITY

The Southeastern Pennsylvania Transportation Authority known as SEPTA provides passenger transportation services in the Philadelphia area. The agency's operations include buses subways and elevated trains trolleys and light rail and commuter rail lines. All together SEPTA maintains more than 300 stations and bus terminals chiefly in five Pennsylvania counties (Bucks Chester Delaware Montgomery and Philadelphia) and in the neighboring states of Delaware and New Jersey. Its territory spans some 2200 sq. mi. The Pennsylvania legislature established SEPTA in 1964 and over the years the agency has acquired the assets of several for-profit transportation companies that operated in the region.

Geographic Reach

The company serves the Bucks Chester Delaware Montgomery and Philadelphia counties.

Financial Performance

SEPTA's passenger revenues increased almost 7% from $443 million in 2013 to $473 million in 2014 primarily due to a fare increase effective July 2013. This growth was partially offset by a 2% decrease in ridership impacted by the severe winter weather.

Strategy

SEPTA has launched dozens of development projects to improve its system's infrastructure. The projects include refurbishing subway stations renovating regional rail stations and installing new track and signals.

EXECUTIVES

Cfo And Treasurer, Joseph M. (Joe) Casey
Cfo And Treasurer, Richard G. Burnfield
Chairman, Pasquale T. (Pat) Deon
Board Member, Thomas E. Babcock
Auditors: ZELENKOFSKE AXELROD LLC HARRI

LOCATIONS

HQ: SOUTHEASTERN PENNSYLVANIA TRANSPORTATION AUTHORITY
1234 MARKET ST FL 4, PHILADELPHIA, PA 191073701
Phone: 215 580-7800
Web: WWW.SEPTA.ORG

PRODUCTS/OPERATIONS

2014 Sales

		% ofotal
Passenger fare	473	90
State shared ride program	15	3
Advertising	13	2
Route Guarantees	2	1
Area agency on aging	1	-
Other contract revenue	0	-
Miscellaneous	19	4
Total	**525**	**100**

HISTORICAL FINANCIALS

Company Type: Private

Income Statement				FYE: June 30
	REVENUE ($ mil.)	NET INCOME ($ mil.)	NET PROFIT MARGIN	EMPLOYEES
06/18	525	120	22.9%	9,000
06/16	528	0	0.0%	—
Annual Growth	(0.3%)	3659.6%	—	—

2018 Year-End Financials

Return on assets: 2.3%   Cash ($ mil.): 32
Return on equity: 10.7%
Current ratio: 0.90

SOUTHERN BAPTIST HOSPITAL OF FLORIDA INC.

EXECUTIVES

Pres, Hugh Greene
Oo*, John Wilbanks
Chmn*, M C Harden
V Pres*, Harvey Granger
V Pres*, John Wilbanks
SEC-Treas*, Richard L Sisisky
Health Professional, Christopher Carroll
Coordinator, John Polisknowski
Facilities Manager, Larry Peterson
Director, Shannon Baum
Manager, Robert Mitarotonda
Auditors: ERNST & YOUNG LLP JACKSONVIL

LOCATIONS

HQ: SOUTHERN BAPTIST HOSPITAL OF FLORIDA INC.
800 PRUDENTIAL DR, JACKSONVILLE, FL 322078202
Phone: 904 202-2000
Web: WWW.BAPTISTJAX.COM

HISTORICAL FINANCIALS

Company Type: Private

Income Statement				FYE: September 30
	REVENUE ($ mil.)	NET INCOME ($ mil.)	NET PROFIT MARGIN	EMPLOYEES
09/18	1,234	209	17.0%	4,000
09/17	1,151	296	25.8%	—
09/16	1,129	205	18.2%	—
09/09	793	(21)	—	—
Annual Growth	5.0%	—	—	—

2018 Year-End Financials

Return on assets: 7.3%   Cash ($ mil.): —
Return on equity: 10.9%
Current ratio: 1.00

SOUTHERN CAL SCHOOLS VOL EMP BENEFITS ASSOC

EXECUTIVES

Prin, George McGregor
Auditors: ROSNER BROWN TOUCHSTONE & KELL

LOCATIONS

HQ: SOUTHERN CAL SCHOOLS VOL EMP BENEFITS ASSOC
8885 RIO SAN DIEGO DR # 327, SAN DIEGO, CA 921081624
Phone: 619 278-0021
Web: WWW.VEBAONLINE.COM

HISTORICAL FINANCIALS

Company Type: Private

Income Statement				FYE: December 31
	REVENUE ($ mil.)	NET INCOME ($ mil.)	NET PROFIT MARGIN	EMPLOYEES
12/14	598	4	0.7%	8
12/13	551	5	1.0%	—
Annual Growth	8.6%	(29.1%)	—	—

2014 Year-End Financials

Return on assets: 6.6%   Cash ($ mil.): 38
Return on equity: 19.6%
Current ratio: 2.30

SOUTHERN ILLINOIS HEALTHCARE E

Auditors: MCGLADREY LLP SPRINGFIELD IL

LOCATIONS

HQ: SOUTHERN ILLINOIS HEALTHCARE E
2370 N MCROY DR, CARBONDALE, IL 629015629
Phone: 618 457-5200
Web: WWW.SIH.NET

HISTORICAL FINANCIALS
Company Type: Private

Income Statement   FYE: March 31

	REVENUE ($ mil.)	NET INCOME ($ mil.)	NET PROFIT MARGIN	EMPLOYEES
03/15	528	36	6.8%	14
03/14	1	0	44.8%	—
Annual Growth	34279.8%	5154.4%	—	—

2015 Year-End Financials

Return on assets: 4.4%   Cash ($ mil.): 12
Return on equity: 6.9%
Current ratio: 1.60

SOUTHERN ILLINOIS HEALTHCARE ENTERPRISES, INC.

Southern Illinois Healthcare a nonprofit health care system operates the flagship 145-bed tertiary-care Memorial Hospital of Carbondale as well as Herrin Hospital (with 114 beds) and St. Joseph Memorial Hospital (with 25 beds). The hospitals serve residents of across southern Illinois. The nearly 280-bed system provides services such as birthing cardiac cancer and emergency care as well as surgery and rehabilitation. Its cardiac care is offered through an affiliation with the Prairie Heart Institute at St. John's Hospital in Springfield Illinois. The medical school at Southern Illinois University conducts its Family Practice Residency Program at Memorial Hospital of Carbondale.

Operations
Across its health system Southern Illinois Healthcare employs more than 3000 people. Physicians at its primary hospital Memorial Hospital of Carbondale represent nearly 40 medical specialties. It maintains the only dedicated pediatric unit in the region as well as the largest birthing center with Level II Plus Special Care Nursery.

St. Joseph Memorial Hospital is a full-service critical access hospital.

In addition to the patient hospitals the system includes two clinics two physician professional buildings an urgent care clinic and dedicated neurology cancer heart sleep and rehabilitation centers.

Geographic Reach
Most of Memorial Hospital of Carbondale's inpatient and outpatient visits come from residents of seven Illinois counties (Jackson Franklin Williamson Perry Johnson Union and Saline). St.

Joseph Memorial Hospital serves the Murphysboro community.

Strategy
Teaming up to provide better care independent not-for-profit health care organizations BJC HealthCare of St. Louis CoxHealth of Springfield Missouri Memorial Health System of Springfield Illinois. and Saint Luke's Health System of Kansas City Missouri created The BJC Collaborative L.L.C. (in 2012). Blessing Health System of Quincy and Southern Illinois Healthcare joined the Collaborative in 2013.

Company Background
During 2012 Southern Illinois Healthcare collaborated with community partners to conduct a Community Health Needs Assessment to spotlight health and quality of life issues in the communities served by Southern Illinois Healthcare.

Southern Illinois Healthcare was first established by four doctors in 1946 as the Southern Illinois Hospital Corporation.

EXECUTIVES

Vice President Quality And Risk, Shelly Pierce
Medical Director, Naresh Ahuja
Auditors: RSM US LLP SPRINGFIELD ILLIN

LOCATIONS

HQ: SOUTHERN ILLINOIS HEALTHCARE ENTERPRISES, INC.
1239 E MAIN ST STE C, CARBONDALE, IL 629013176
Phone: 618 457-5200

PRODUCTS/OPERATIONS

Selected Facilities
Herrin Hospital
Memorial Hospital of Carbondale
St. Joseph Memorial Hospital

Selected Services
Birthing Center
Cancer
Senior Renewal
Heart
Infusion Therapy
Neurosciences
Occupational Health
Pediatrics
Rehabilitation
Robotic-assisted Surgery
Sleep Medicine
Stroke
Surgical Services
Weight Loss Surgery
Wound Healing

COMPETITORS

Community Health Systems	Saint Francis Medical Center
Heartland Health Memorial Hospital (Illinois)	St. John's Hospital (Illinois)

HISTORICAL FINANCIALS
Company Type: Private

Income Statement   FYE: March 31

	REVENUE ($ mil.)	NET INCOME ($ mil.)	NET PROFIT MARGIN	EMPLOYEES
03/18	624	30	4.9%	3,493
03/17	1	0	41.4%	—
03/16	1	0	29.6%	—
03/14	1	0	44.8%	—
Annual Growth	349.1%	157.9%	—	—

2018 Year-End Financials

Return on assets: 2.9%   Cash ($ mil.): 18
Return on equity: 4.9%
Current ratio: 1.70

SOUTHERN ILLINOIS UNIVERSITY INC

Southern Illinois University (SIU) helps to train future doctors dentists and other other professionals. The university enrolls some 32000 students at its two institutions — Southern Illinois University at Carbondale (SIUC which includes medical and law schools) and Southern Illinois University at Edwardsville (SIUE which houses education dental and nursing schools) — as well as smaller satellite centers. SIU offers associate baccalaureate master's doctoral and professional degrees. It also boasts a number of study abroad partnerships with international universities. Tracing its roots back to 1869 SIU is known for its extensive research programs.

Operations
Students across SIU's institutions hail from all 50 states and more than 100 countries. Combined the campuses have some 2600 faculty members and an annual budget of $870 million.

The Carbondale campus was chartered in 1869 as a teachers college while the Edwardsville campus was founded in 1957. Most of the university's doctoral programs are housed at the SIUC campus which conducts residencies through the School of Medicine. A majority of the institutions master's degrees are conferred at the SIUE campus.

Undergraduate and research programs are conducted at both primary SIU campuses. Students and faculty members participate in research programs in a number of fields including biology biodiversity and molecular science. The university receives $78.5 million in research grants annually.

Geographic Reach
From its flagship campus in Carbondale Illinois SIU reaches to Edwardsville and to other parts of Southern Illinois including Springfield through satellite campus locations. Its satellite schools include SIU School of Medicine SIU School of Dental Medicine and SIU School of Nursing.

Financial Performance
SIU logged increases of 2% in fiscal 2012 as compared to 2011 pointing to a rise in student tuition and fees private grants and contracts and sales and services for the gains. Net income for the same reporting period rose 17% due to a boost in non-operating revenues attributable to increases in gifts and contributions investment income and payments on behalf of the university.

Strategy
As part of its focus SIU is working to strengthen its undergraduate graduate and professional education. It's also concentrating on streamlining its administrative process while expanding its intercampus and intra-campus collaboration through degree programs international distributed learning fundraising and research opportunities for both students and faculty. SIU is also establishing partnerships with public and private sector groups.

EXECUTIVES

Pres, Randy J Dunn
Sr V Pres*, Duane Stucky
Staff, John Massie
Assistant Professor, William Eichfeld
Automotive Parts Manager Asa, Cynthia Gerlock
Director, Michelle Richerson
Assistant Professor Asa School, Linda Preece
Administrative Aide, Jane Meuth
Chief Academic Adviser College, Tamora Workman
Accountant, Judy Wright
Assistant Professor, Reza Habib

LOCATIONS

HQ: SOUTHERN ILLINOIS UNIVERSITY INC
1400 DOUGLAS DR, CARBONDALE, IL 629014332
Phone: 618 536-3475
Web: WWW.SIUMED.EDU

HISTORICAL FINANCIALS

Company Type: Private

Income Statement				FYE: June 30
	REVENUE ($ mil.)	NET INCOME ($ mil.)	NET PROFIT MARGIN	EMPLOYEES
06/18	584	139	23.9%	9,576
06/17	601	(59)	—	—
06/16	740	(104)	—	—
06/15	597	27	4.6%	—
Annual Growth	(0.7%)	72.2%	—	—

2018 Year-End Financials

Return on assets: 11.5%   Cash ($ mil.): 53
Return on equity: 24.6%
Current ratio: 2.20

SOUTHERN INDIANA GAS & ELECTRIC COMPANY

EXECUTIVES

Ceo, Carl L Chapman
Ceo*, Niel C Ellerbrook
Exec V Pres-Cfo*, Jerome A Benkert Jr
Sr V Pres*, Ronald E Christian
V Pres-Treas*, Robert Goocher
V Pres-Controller*, M Susan Hardwick
Pres*, William S Doty
V Pres*, Daniel Bugher
V Pres*, Ellis S Redd
V Pres*, Eric J Schach
Human Resources, Andrea McClure

LOCATIONS

HQ: SOUTHERN INDIANA GAS & ELECTRIC COMPANY
1 VECTREN SQ, EVANSVILLE, IN 477081209
Phone: 812 424-6411
Web: WWW.VECTREN.COM

HISTORICAL FINANCIALS

Company Type: Private

Income Statement				FYE: December 31
	REVENUE ($ mil.)	NET INCOME ($ mil.)	NET PROFIT MARGIN	EMPLOYEES
12/17	661	86	13.1%	779
12/16	692	95	13.9%	—
12/03	438	48	11.1%	—
12/02	693	59	8.6%	—
Annual Growth	(0.3%)	2.6%	—	—

2017 Year-End Financials

Return on assets: 3.8%   Cash ($ mil.): 2
Return on equity: 9.7%
Current ratio: 1.80

SOUTHERN METHODIST UNIVERSITY INC

What do former first lady Laura Bush actress Kathy Bates and NFL Hall-of-Famer Doak Walker have in common? They're all graduates of Southern Methodist University (SMU). Founded in 1911 by what is now The United Methodist Church SMU is a nonsectarian private institution offering undergraduate graduate and professional degrees in arts business engineering humanities law science and theology through seven schools. It'sÂ one of a handful of schools nationwide to offer an academic major in human rights.Â Some 11000 students attend the university which has a student-faculty ratio of 11:1. About 85% of the 700-member full-time faculty hold the doctorate or highest degree in their fields.

Operations
The university offers more than 120 undergraduate degrees and about 130 graduate degrees through seven schools.Â SMU also offers more than two dozen doctorates. Most of theÂ its degrees are conferred in the humanities and sciences and business.

Geographic Reach
SMU is housed in more than 75 buildings. The Texas university operates through a main campus located in University Park within Dallas County. Also in Texas it maintains propertyÂ inÂ Dallas (19 acres) Highland Park (2 acres) and Plano (25 acres). In Taos New Mexico SMU holds 423 acres.

Sales and Marketing
SMU's enrollment includesÂ international students from 90 countries. The largest numbers of students in descending order are from India China Saudi Arabia Mexico Korea Taiwan (Province of China) Guatemala Thailand Iran and Canada.

Financial Performance
Endowment gifts from donors reached $14.9 million in 2012. The private university's revenue decreased by 9% in 2012 as compared to 2011 due to dips in tuition and fees net realized and unrealized gains grants and contracts. Net income also decreased by 44% during the same reporting period. Revenue declines and increases in program expenses contributed to the net income woes.

EXECUTIVES

Vice President Of Sales, Lori White
President, R. Gerald Turner, age 73
Dean Edwin L. Cox School Of Business, Albert W. Niemi, age 76
Dean Dedman School Of Law, John B. Attanasio
Dean And Director Central University Libraries, Gillian M. McCombs
Provost And Vp Academic Affairs, Paul W. Ludden
Vp Business And Finance, Christine (Chris) Regis
Dean Meadows School Of The Arts, José A. Bowen
Dean Annette Caldwell Simmons School Of Education And Human Development, David Chard
Dean Perkins School Of Theology, William B. Lawrence
Dean Research And Graduate Studies, James E. Quick
Cio, Joe Gargiulo
Chief Investment Officer And Treasurer, Michael A. Condon
Dean Dedman College Of Humanities And Sciences, William M. Tsutsui
Dean Lyle School Of Engineering, Marc P. Christensen
President Smu Student Body, Alexander Mace
President Smu Faculty Senate, Jose L. Lage

Vice President Executive Affairs, Thomas E Barry
Vice President, Andrea Smith
Department Chair Fire And Ems Technology, Mattie Eiland
Vice President For Development, Dominique Sims
Department Chair, Robert Gregory
Associate Vice President Information Technology Services, George Chrisman
Vice President, Cchea Nugent
Senior Vice President, James Gallegos
Radiology Director, Astria Smith
Provost And Vice President For Academic Affairs, Steven Currall
Assistant Vice President Developer, Robert Bucker
Vice President, Vishal Goel
Vice President Academic Excellence, Olivia Waidmann
Vice President And Treasurer, Andrew Hornung
Associate Vice President, Barry Ernie
Vice President Of Programming, William Hagens
Provost And Vice President Academic Affairs, Tom Tunks
Vice President Finances, Lizzie Ranshaw
Avp Of Marketing And Communications At Smu, Regina Moldovan
Vice President For Policy Research, Alison Griffin
Vice President Engineering, Stephen Smith
Assistant Vice President, Paula Voyles
Chair, Caren Prothro
Ward Secretary, Julio Lopez
Department Secretary, Tiffany Powell
Secretary, Suzanne Nelsen
Vice President Legal Affairs And Government Relations Secretary And General Counsel, Leon S Bennett
Theater Secretary, Dylan Guerra
Ward Secretary, Dan Howard
Secretary, Scott Kingsley
Treasurer, Marcia Felts
Treasurer, Cole Bildstein
Treasurer, Tim Clifford
Auditors: KPMG LLP DALLAS TX

LOCATIONS

HQ: SOUTHERN METHODIST UNIVERSITY INC
6425 BOAZ LN, DALLAS, TX 75205
Phone: 214 768-2000
Web: WWW.SMU.EDU

PRODUCTS/OPERATIONS

Selected Schools and Divisions
Annette Caldwell Simmons School of Education and Human Development
Bobby B. Lyle School of Engineering
Cox School of Business
Dedman College of Humanities and Sciences
Dedman School of Law
Meadows School of the Arts
Perkins School of Theology

HISTORICAL FINANCIALS

Company Type: Private

Income Statement				FYE: May 31
	REVENUE ($ mil.)	NET INCOME ($ mil.)	NET PROFIT MARGIN	EMPLOYEES
05/18	652	96	14.7%	2,200
05/17	580	56	9.8%	—
05/13	563	115	20.5%	—
05/11	602	58	9.6%	—
Annual Growth	1.1%	7.4%	—	—

2018 Year-End Financials

Return on assets: 2.9%   Cash ($ mil.): 183
Return on equity: 4.6%
Current ratio: —

SOUTHERN NATURAL GAS COMPANY, L.L.C.

Now here's a company that pipes in the goods that keep the South fueled naturally. Southern Natural Gas operates an 7600-mile long natural gas pipeline (SNG System) which serves major markets across the southeastern US.Â ThisÂ system transportsÂ more than 3Â billion cu. ft. of natural gas per day. The SNG pipeline system hasÂ about 60 billion cu. ft.Â of underground working natural gas storage capacity. MajorÂ customers includeÂ Atlanta Gas Light Company Alabama Gas Southern Company and SCANA .Â Southern Natural Gas is a unit of El Paso Pipeline Partners.

EXECUTIVES

Pres-Ceo, Norman G Holmes
Exec V Pres-Cfo, John R Sult
V Pres-Controller-Cao, Rosa P Jackson
Senior Vp, Larry E Powell

LOCATIONS

HQ: SOUTHERN NATURAL GAS COMPANY, L.L.C.
 1001 LOUISIANA ST, HOUSTON, TX 770025089
Phone: 713 420-2600
Web: WWW.KINDERMORGAN.COM

COMPETITORS

Alagasco
 American Midstream
 Partners
Bridgeline
Crestwood Midstream
 Partners LP

Gulf South Pipeline
Panhandle Eastern Pipe
 Line
Piedmont Natural Gas
U.S. Transmission

HISTORICAL FINANCIALS

Company Type: Private

Income Statement   FYE: December 31

	REVENUE ($ mil.)	NET INCOME ($ mil.)	NET PROFIT MARGIN	EMPLOYEES
12/17	606	143	23.7%	3
12/16	609	169	27.8%	—
Annual Growth	(0.6%)	(15.2%)	—	—

2017 Year-End Financials

Return on assets: 5.2%   Cash ($ mil.): 3
Return on equity: 10.8%
Current ratio: 0.90

SOUTHERN NUCLEAR OPERATING COMPANY, INC.

The night the lights went out in Georgia they should have called Southern Nuclear Operating Company. The company a subsidiary of Southern Company since 1990 operates six nuclear powerÂ units at three plantÂ locations which combined provide about 20% of the electricity used in Alabama and Georgia. Southern Nuclear's Joseph M. Farley Nuclear Plant began commercial operation in 1977. The Edwin I. Hatch Nuclear Plant and

the Alvin W. Vogtle Electric Generating Plant areÂ jointly owned by Southern Company's Georgia Power (50%) Oglethorpe Power (30%) the Municipal Electrical Authority of Georgia (18%) and the city of Dalton.

EXECUTIVES

Ceo, Thomas A Fanning
Chairman*, Barnie Beasley
V Pres*, J W Averett
V Pres*, J O Meier
Contrl*, Kathleen King
Exec Asst*, Herry Mitchell
Vp-Fleet Operations Support, Bradley J Adam
Coordinator, Malinda Jenkins
Designer, John Lockhart
Project Engineer, Denver Atwood
Human Resources Business Consu, Amy Self

LOCATIONS

HQ: SOUTHERN NUCLEAR OPERATING COMPANY, INC.
 42 INVERNESS CENTER PKWY, BIRMINGHAM, AL 352424809
Phone: 205 992-5000

COMPETITORS

Duke Energy
 NextEra Energy

Progress Energy

HISTORICAL FINANCIALS

Company Type: Private

Income Statement   FYE: December 31

	REVENUE ($ mil.)	NET INCOME ($ mil.)	NET PROFIT MARGIN	EMPLOYEES
12/16	922	0	0.0%	2,960
12/04	479	0	—	—
12/03	441	0	—	—
12/02	455	0	—	—
Annual Growth	5.2%	—	—	—

2016 Year-End Financials

Return on assets: —   Cash ($ mil.): 14
Return on equity: 0.1%
Current ratio: 1.00

SOUTHERN PIPE & SUPPLY COMPANY, INC.

Southern Pipe and Supply Co. sells pipes and anything that connects to them. Serving everyone from contractors and homeowners to commercial real estate property owners Southern Pipe sells plumbing heating and air-conditioning supplies through more than 90 stores located throughout seven southeastern states. The company operates a central distribution center and a handful of Southern Bath & Kitchen showrooms that feature various products for homeowners. Southern Pipe's vendors include dozens of supply companies and manufacturers such as MOEN Kohler and Amana Heating and Air Conditioning. Southern Pipe and Supply Co. was founded in 1938.

EXECUTIVES

Pres, Jay Davidson
Chb, Martin D Davidson
V Pres, Mark Roebuck
Sec-Treas-Cfo, Marc Ransier
Outside Sales, Adam McMinn

Inside Sales, Brandon Beckworth
Assistant Credit Manager, Jeffrey Rhett
Human Resources Director, Ronald Black
Operations Manager, Tim Ballard
Operations, Bruce Haberman
Counter Sales, Nolan Crawford
Auditors: HORNE CPA LLP

LOCATIONS

HQ: SOUTHERN PIPE & SUPPLY COMPANY, INC.
 4330 HIGHWAY 39 N, MERIDIAN, MS 393011082
Phone: 601 693-2911
Web: WWW.SOUTHERNPIPE.COM

Selected Locations

	No.
Mississippi	26
Alabama	17
Louisiana	16
Georgia	14
Arkansas	10
Florida	4
Tennessee	3
Total	**90**

PRODUCTS/OPERATIONS

Selected Products
Heating & cooling equipment
Kitchen & bath fixtures
Plumbing
Residential & commercial pipe valves & fittings
Tools & safety equipment
Water metering fire hydrants & fittings
Waterworks

COMPETITORS

Baker Distributing
 Ferguson Enterprises
HD Supply
Lowe's

Stuart C. Irby
WinWholesale
Wolverine Tube

HISTORICAL FINANCIALS

Company Type: Private

Income Statement   FYE: December 31

	REVENUE ($ mil.)	NET INCOME ($ mil.)	NET PROFIT MARGIN	EMPLOYEES
12/16	451	19	4.2%	767
12/15	436	19	4.6%	—
Annual Growth	3.6%	(4.5%)	—	—

SOUTHFRESH AQUACULTURE, LLC

EXECUTIVES

Member, Mark Lamb
MBR-Asst Treas*, Andrea Boles
MBR-Cfo*, Justin Funk

LOCATIONS

HQ: SOUTHFRESH AQUACULTURE, LLC
 505 ENERGY CENTER BLVD # 605, NORTHPORT, AL 354732795
Phone: 205 247-4490
Web: WWW.SOUTHFRESH.COM

HISTORICAL FINANCIALS

Company Type: Private

Income Statement   FYE: July 31

	REVENUE ($ mil.)	NET INCOME ($ mil.)	NET PROFIT MARGIN	EMPLOYEES
07/11*	450	9	2.0%	250
12/08	0	0	—	
05/03	54	1	2.4%	
05/02	52	0	1.5%	
Annual Growth	27.0%	31.3%	—	—

*Fiscal year change

2011 Year-End Financials

Return on assets: 3.9%   Cash ($ mil.): 13
Return on equity: 8.3%
Current ratio: 1.60

SOUTHWEST RESEARCH INSTITUTE INC

If you're looking for research at an institute in the Southwest look no further. Founded in 1947 by oilman and rancher Thomas Slick Jr. Southwest Research Institute (SwRI) is an independent not-for-profit research and development institution that contracts to explore subjects in areas including automation and data systems applied physics space science and engineering and chemistry. SwRI has about 2700 scientists engineers and support staff at some 40 laboratories and offices in the US China and the UK. Customers include the private sector and government agencies. SwRI's Signature Science subsidiary researches national security environmental management and biotechnology.

Operations

SwRI provides contract research and development services to industrial and government clients. It keeps the scope of its work confidential and assigns patent rights arising from its sponsored research to the client. SwRI generally retains rights to Institute-funded advancements and holds more than 900 patents awarded to staff members.

The company operates through nearly a dozen technical divisions including Aerospace Electronics; Systems Engineering & Training; Applied Physics Chemistry & Chemical Engineering; Engine Emissions & Vehicl; Research; Geosciences & Engineering; Mechanical Engineering; and Space Science & Engineering.

Geographic Reach

The company is based in San Antonio Texas and the Institute has technical offices and laboratories in Ann Arbor Michigan.; Beijing China; Boulder Colorade; Hill Air Force Base (Ogden) Utah; Hanover and Rockville Maryland.; Minneapolis Minnesota; Oklahoma City Oklahoma.; Warner Robins Georgia; and Durham New Hampshire.

Strategy

SwRI's current projects include cooperative research focusing on safe reliable cost-effective energy storage systems for electric and hybrid-electric vehicle applications. In addition it has formed a consortium to conduct research and code development and apply advanced ROS (Robot Operating System)software to industrial applications.

EXECUTIVES

Associate Vice President, Scott Bolton
Treasurer, Linda Boehme
Senior Secretary, Julie Bowles

Treasurer, Debra Streeter
Secretary, Melody Cherry
Senior Secretary Cap Om, Sylvia Rodriguez
Senior Secretary, Eva Gonzalez
Secretary, Sheri Baetz
Secretary, Dorothea Martinez
Senior Secretary, Chun-mei Yu
Auditors: RSM US LLP AUSTIN TEXAS

LOCATIONS

HQ: SOUTHWEST RESEARCH INSTITUTE INC
  6220 CULEBRA RD, SAN ANTONIO, TX 782385100
Phone: 210 684-5111
Web: WWW.SWRI.ORG

PRODUCTS/OPERATIONS

Selected Technical Divisions

Aerospace Electronics and Information Technology
Applied Physics
Applied Power
Automation and Data Systems
Chemistry and Chemical Engineering
Engine Emissions and Vehicle Research
Fuels and Lubricants Research
Geosciences and Engineering
Mechanical Engineering
Signal Exploitation and Geolocation
Space Science and Engineering
Training Simulation and Performance Improvement

COMPETITORS

Battelle Memorial	QinetiQ
Berkeley Lab	Southern Research
Brookhaven Lab	Institute
Lawrence Livermore Lab	

HISTORICAL FINANCIALS

Company Type: Private

Income Statement   FYE: September 28

	REVENUE ($ mil.)	NET INCOME ($ mil.)	NET PROFIT MARGIN	EMPLOYEES
09/18	583	38	6.6%	2,754
09/17	498	11	2.3%	
09/16	559	6	1.2%	
09/15	592	23	4.0%	
Annual Growth	(0.5%)	17.3%	—	—

2018 Year-End Financials

Return on assets: 5.3%   Cash ($ mil.): 16
Return on equity: 6.9%
Current ratio: 3.40

SOUTHWEST WASHINGTON HEALTH SYSTEM

EXECUTIVES

Pres-Ceo, Joe Kortum
Hr Provider Recruitment Coordi, Amanda Moss
Information Technology Informa, Mary Paeth
Senior Marketing Specialist, Sarah Schemmel
Director Information I, Tony Wente

LOCATIONS

HQ: SOUTHWEST WASHINGTON HEALTH SYSTEM
  400 NE MOTHER JOSEPH PL, VANCOUVER, WA
  986643200
Phone: 360 514-2000
Web: WWW.PEACEHEALTH.ORG

HISTORICAL FINANCIALS

Company Type: Private

Income Statement   FYE: December 31

	REVENUE ($ mil.)	NET INCOME ($ mil.)	NET PROFIT MARGIN	EMPLOYEES
12/09	601	9	1.5%	3,500
12/08*	110	(38)	—	
09/08	10	(0)	—	
Annual Growth	5757.2%	—	—	—

*Fiscal year change

2009 Year-End Financials

Return on assets: 1.4%   Cash ($ mil.): 13
Return on equity: 2.9%
Current ratio: 1.40

SPARROW HEALTH SYSTEM

Ailing residents of central Michigan fly to Sparrow Health System for care. The not-for-profit network's hospitals include the flagship Sparrow Hospital Sparrow Clinton Memorial Hospital Sparrow Specialty Hospital and Carson City Hospital. The health system also operates dozens of satellite clinics a long-term-care center a hospice care provider medical equipment rental unit and athletic club. Through affiliate Physicians Health Plan Sparrow Health provides health plan coverage to some 70000 Michigan residents. Its Sparrow Physicians Health Network includes some 1000 physicians in the region. The system traces its roots back to 1896.

Operations

The Sparrow Health System is a not-for-profit community-governed organization. Its flagship facility Sparrow Hospital is a 700-bed regional referral hospital providing a range of general and specialty services. Community service is important to Sparrow Health as the organization provides millions of dollars worth of charity care underfunded services and community outreach services each year.

Geographic Reach

Sparrow Health's hospitals are located in Lansing St. John's Ionia and Carson City Michigan. It also has dozens of satellite care sites throughout central Michigan.

Strategy

Over the years Sparrow Health System has expanded its services and geographic reach through a series of affiliations. It is part the Mayo Clinic Care Network which allows it to improve the care it provides its patients. In 2016 Sparrow formalized its long-time affiliation with Hayes Green Beach Memorial Hospital which will become an official affiliate by 2019. That hospital is now undergoing a renovation and expansion.

To provide health care to a more sizable population the system regularly opens new health care facilities and expands its physicians care network; it has also been investing in modernizing itself through technological advances. Its Sparrow Care Network a physician-led clinically integrated organization has grown to include more than 650 physicians. In 2016 the system opened additional retail clinics (dubbed "Fast Care" sites) within area grocery stores. And in 2017 the system opened its Herbert-Herman Cancer Center and Plaza.

Sparrow has also been growing its mobile health clinics in partnership with local agencies and organizations.

One of Sparrow's hospitals Sparrow Carson Hospital has come under fire for infection-control issues. In 2018 it was dropped from its Medicare contract after an audit showed it wasn't in compliance with sterilization procedures. The accusations are serious as hospital-based infections are the third leading cause of deaths in the US.

Sparrow closed its St. Lawrence emergency department in mid-2018. It added about a dozen beds to its primary hospital to make up for the closure. It also opened a new urgent care center giving patients a choice of health care based on the severity of their ailments.

Company Background

Sparrow Health got its start in 1896 when a group of women set out with $400 a house on Ottawa Street (in Lansing Michigan) and a mission to care for the sick.

EXECUTIVES

Coo, Dennis Swan
President Php, Scott Wilkerson
Vp And Cio, Thomas A. (Tom) Bres
Cfo, Paula Reichle
Vp Sparrow Medical Group, Peter Graham
President Sparrow Clinton Hospital, Ed Bruun
President And Ceo Sparrow Ionia Hospital, William Roeser
Ceo Sparrow Specialty Hospital, Kira Carter-Robertson
Coo And Chief Nursing Officer, Barbara (Barb) McQuillan
Vp Strategic Planning And Marketing, Melissa Sears
Senior Vice President Chief Administrative Officer And Chief Information Officer, Tom Bres
Medical Director Pediatric Emergency Services, Pamela Coffey
Vice President Marketing Communications, Ilene Cantor
Vice President Sparrow Medical Group, Douglas Edema
Vice President Of Finance, William Howe
Chair, Barbara Given
Secretary, Teressia Green
Secretary, Bobbi Bongiovanni
Auditors: PLANTE & MORAN LLC GRAND RAP

LOCATIONS

HQ: SPARROW HEALTH SYSTEM
1215 E MICHIGAN AVE, LANSING, MI 489121811
Phone: 517 364-1000
Web: WWW.SPARROW.ORG

PRODUCTS/OPERATIONS

Selected Services
Emergency room/Urgent Care
Laboratory
Medical Supply
Outpatient Rehabilitation
Pharmacy
Radiology

COMPETITORS

Bronson Battle Creek	Hurley Medical Center
Covenant HealthCare	McLaren Health Care
Crittenton Hospital	Munson Healthcare
Detroit Medical Center	Sheridan Community
Genesys Health System	Hospital
Genesys Regional	St. John Health
Medical Center	Trinity Health (Novi)
Henry Ford Health	
System	

HISTORICAL FINANCIALS

Company Type: Private

Income Statement   FYE: December 31

	REVENUE ($ mil.)	NET INCOME ($ mil.)	NET PROFIT MARGIN	EMPLOYEES
12/18	1,281	(57)	—	3,400
12/17	1,259	49	3.9%	—
12/16	1,286	63	5.0%	—
12/14	1,156	(53)	—	—
Annual Growth	2.6%	—	—	—

2018 Year-End Financials

Return on assets: (-3.4%)   Cash ($ mil.): 96
Return on equity: (-6.7%)
Current ratio: 2.50

SPAW GLASS HOLDING, L.P.

Deep in the heart of Texas SpawGlass Holding is busy providing general building and construction management services for commercial and institutional projects through its SpawGlass Construction and SpawGlass Contractors subsidiaries. The group also offers design/build delivery and tenant finish-out services. Among its landmark projects is the interior restoration of the Texas State Capitol. It also worked on the NASA Shuttle Flight Training Facility near Houston and the University of Texas Health Science Center at San Antonio. Louis Spaw and Frank Glass formed SpawGlass in 1953. The company now employee-owned has offices in Austin Houston San Antonio and the Rio Grande Valley in Texas.

EXECUTIVES

Ceo-Chm, Joel Stone
Cfo, Bobby Friedel
Coo, Michael Emmons
Project Manager, Chris Schwertner
Accounting Manager, Clayton Carroll
Project Manager, Thompson Cory
Assistant Project Manager, Clare Wilmore
Superintendent, Eddie Rodriguez
Superintendent, Juan Murillo
Project Manager, Matias Maldonado
Assistant Superintendent, Matt Bearden

LOCATIONS

HQ: SPAW GLASS HOLDING, L.P.
9331 CORPORATE DR, SELMA, TX 781541250
Phone: 210 651-9000
Web: WWW.SPAWGLASS.COM

COMPETITORS

Beck Group	Structure Tone
Cadence McShane	Southwest
Harvey Builders	Tellepsen Builders
Linbeck	Turner Corporation
Manhattan Construction	W.S. Bellows
Satterfield & Pontikes	

HISTORICAL FINANCIALS

Company Type: Private

Income Statement   FYE: December 31

	REVENUE ($ mil.)	NET INCOME ($ mil.)	NET PROFIT MARGIN	EMPLOYEES
12/09	460	8	1.9%	650
12/07	336	5	1.8%	—
12/06	1,879	0	—	—
Annual Growth (37.4%)		—	—	—

2009 Year-End Financials

Return on assets: 5.7%   Cash ($ mil.): 41
Return on equity: 31.2%
Current ratio: 1.20

SPECIAL SCHOOL DISTRICT OF ST. LOUIS COUNTY

EXECUTIVES

Supt, Donald Bohannon
Occupational Specia, Carmen Bolt
Human Resources Manager, Darlene Deloach
Coordinator, Jeff Ferguson
Bus/Finance/Purchasing Directo, Kelly Alexander
Manager of Management Informat, Rob Emerson
Teacher, Gale Wagoner
Administrator, John Cary
Director, John Mueller
Coordinator, Amy Blumenfeld
Assistant Superintendent, Carla Addoh
Auditors: SCHOWALTER & JABOURI PC ST

LOCATIONS

HQ: SPECIAL SCHOOL DISTRICT OF ST. LOUIS COUNTY
12110 CLAYTON RD, SAINT LOUIS, MO 631312599
Phone: 314 989-8100
Web: WWW.SSDMO.ORG

HISTORICAL FINANCIALS

Company Type: Private

Income Statement   FYE: June 30

	REVENUE ($ mil.)	NET INCOME ($ mil.)	NET PROFIT MARGIN	EMPLOYEES
06/18	452	25	5.7%	5,204
06/17	433	16	3.9%	—
06/16	425	23	5.5%	—
06/13	366	3	0.9%	—
Annual Growth	4.3%	50.3%	—	—

SPECTRA ENERGY CORP

Spectra Energy covers the spectrum of natural gas activities — gathering processing transmission storage and distribution. The company now part of Enbridge operates more than 15400 miles of transmission pipeline and has 305 billion cu. ft. of storage capacity in the US and Canada. Units include U.S. Gas Transmission Texas Eastern Transmission Natural Gas Liquids Division and Market Hub Partners. It also has stakes in DCP Midstream Maritimes & Northeast Pipeline Gulfstream Natural Gas System Spectra Energy Income Fund and 75% of Spectra Energy Partners. Its Union Gas unit distributes gas to 1.5 million Ontario customers. In 2017 Spectra merged with Enbridge creating the largest energy infrastructure company in North America.

Change in Company Type

In 2017 Enbridge acquired Spectra Energy for $28 billion. The combination of the two companies created the largest energy infrastructure company in North America with a pro-forma enterprise value of about $127 billion. Enbridge shareholders owned 57% of the combined company (Enbridge) and Spectra Energy shareholders 43%.

Operations

Spectra Energy has managed its businesses in four reportable segments: Spectra Energy Partners Distribution Western Canada Transmission & Processing and Field Services.

Spectra Energy Partners provides transmission storage and gathering of natural gas for customers in various regions of the Midwestern northeastern and southeastern US and operates a crude oil pipeline system that connects Canadian and U.S. producers to refineries in the U.S. Rocky Mountain and Midwest regions. Spectra Energy Partners has accounted for about 50% of the company's revenue.

Distribution about 30% of revenue provides retail natural gas distribution service (its Union Gas unit distributes gas to 1.5 million customers in 400 communities in Ontario). It also provides natural gas transportation and storage services to other utilities and energy market customers.

Western Canada Transmission & Processing about 20% of revenue provides its customers with transportation services to move natural gas natural gas gathering and processing services and NGL extraction fractionation transportation storage and marketing services.

Field Services gathers processes treats compresses transports and stores natural gas; it also fractionates transports gathers processes stores markets and trades NGLs. Its DCP Midstream joint venture is 50% owned by Phillips 66. DCP operates in 17 US states.

Transportation storage and processing of natural gas have accounted for about two-thirds of Spectra Energy's revenue.

Geographic Reach

Spectra Energy's Spectra Energy Partners operates in northeastern and southeastern US and operates a crude oil pipeline system that connects Canadian and US producers to refineries in the Rocky Mountains and the Midwest. The Distribution segment serves natural gas customers in Ontario Canada. Western Canada Transmission & Processing serves customers in western Canada and the northern US. Field Services gathers natural gas from the Mid-Continent Rocky Mountain East Texas-North Louisiana Barnett Shale Gulf Coast South Texas Central Texas Antrim Shale and Permian Basin.

All told Spectra Energy has more than 100 facilities across North America.

Sales and Marketing

Spectra Energy's customers (end-users) purchase gas directly from suppliers or marketers as well as through retail and wholesale outlets.

Financial Performance

Spectra Energy reported a 6% decline in revenue in 2016 to $4.9 billion from 2015. Each segment posted lower revenue for 2016. Lower energy prices were passed on to customers and warmer weather meant they used less energy. Revenue also was hurt by a weaker Canadian dollar. The Distribution segment did see some growth with additional customers and the Dawn Parkway Expansion Project.

The company's net income jump some 250% to $693 million in 2016 from 2015 mostly because of charges and costs the company had in 2015 but not 2016.

Spectra has cash flow from operations of about $2 billion in 2016 down from about $2.2 billion in 2015. The difference was driven by non-cash goodwill impairments in 2015 offset by higher earnings.

Company Background

In 2012 Spectra Energy acquired one-third of DCP Sand Hills Pipeline and DCP Southern Hills Pipeline (NGL pipelines) from DCP Midstream for $459 million.

In 2012 Spectra Energy opened a new natural gas processing plant in Dawson Creek British Columbia part of its $1.5 billion investment strategy in infrastructure. That year it also signed a deal with BG Group to develop a pipeline from northeast British Columbia to serve BG Group's potential LNG export facility in Prince Rupert on the northwest coast of the province.

To raise cash in 2012 it sold a 38.76% interest in Maritimes & Northeast Pipeline to Spectra Energy Partners for $375 million.

In a move to boost its Gulf Coast natural gas storage position in 2010 Spectra Energy acquired the Bobcat Gas Storage asset from Haddington Energy Partners and GE Energy Financial Service for about $540 million.

The company was founded in 2006.

EXECUTIVES

Cfo, J. Patrick (Pat) Reddy, $634,900 total compensation
Vice President Of It, Mark Wyatt
Vice President, John Bremner
Chief Administrative Officer, Dorothy M. Ables, $475,488 total compensation
Chairman President And Ceo, Gregory L. (Greg) Ebel, $1,133,000 total compensation
President Spectra Energy Transmission West And Canadian Lng, R. Mark Fiedorek
President Us Transmission And Storage, William T. (Bill) Yardley, $409,500 total compensation
President Union Gas, Stephen W. (Steve) Baker
General Counsel, Reginald D. (Reggie) Hedgebeth, $568,033 total compensation
Chief Development Officer, Guy G. Buckley, $438,333 total compensation
Vice President, Gregory Rizzo
Senior Vice President, Carlo V Dechiro
Auditors: DELOITTE & TOUCHE LLP HOUSTON

LOCATIONS

HQ: SPECTRA ENERGY CORP
5400 WESTHEIMER CT, HOUSTON, TX 770565353
Phone: 713 627-5400
Web: WWW.ENBRIDGE.COM

2016 Sales

	$ mil.	% of total
U.S.	2,461	50
Canada	2,455	50
Total	**4,916**	**100**

PRODUCTS/OPERATIONS

2016 Sales

	$ mil.	% of total
Spectra Energy Partners	2,533	52
Distribution	1,370	28
Western Canada Transmission & Processing	1,005	20
Others	8	-
Total	**4,916**	**100**

2016 Sales

	$ mil.	% of total
Transportation storage and processing of natural gas	3,251	66
Distribution of natural gas	1,144	23
Transportation of crude oil	359	7
Sales of natural gas liquids	68	2
Other	94	2
Total	**4,916**	**100**

Selected Mergers and Acquisitions

COMPETITORS

Entergy	Piedmont Natural Gas
Enterprise Products	TransMontaigne
Kinder Morgan	Williams Companies
Koch Industries Inc.	

HISTORICAL FINANCIALS

Company Type: Private

Income Statement

FYE: December 31

	REVENUE ($ mil.)	NET INCOME ($ mil.)	NET PROFIT MARGIN	EMPLOYEES
12/16	4,916	1,020	20.7%	8,700
12/15	5,234	460	8.8%	—
Annual Growth	(6.1%)	121.7%	—	—

SPECTRUM HEALTH HOSPITALS

EXECUTIVES

Pres, Kevin R Splaine
V Pres*, Joseph J Fifer
Pres*, David M Krhovsky
V Pres, William L Bush
Cardiology Director, Duane Berkompas
Physician, Peter Vasiu
Public Relations Director, Paula Mackenzie
Doctor of Medicine, Bruce H Murray
Doctor of Medicine, David Pennes
Manager, Ginger Boogerd
Chief of Obstetrics Gynecology, Rodman Taber

LOCATIONS

HQ: SPECTRUM HEALTH HOSPITALS
100 MICHIGAN ST NE MC-498, GRAND RAPIDS, MI 495032560
Phone: 616 391-1774
Web: WWW.SPECTRUMHEALTH.ORG

HISTORICAL FINANCIALS

Company Type: Private

Income Statement				FYE: June 30
	REVENUE ($ mil.)	NET INCOME ($ mil.)	NET PROFIT MARGIN	EMPLOYEES
06/16	1,905	196	10.3%	11,000
06/15	1,764	196	11.1%	—
06/08	2,595	(21)	—	—
06/06	1,013	77	7.6%	—
Annual Growth	6.5%	9.8%		

2016 Year-End Financials

Return on assets: 7.9% Cash ($ mil.): 206
Return on equity: 22.0%
Current ratio: 1.90

SPECTRUM HEALTH SYSTEM

EXECUTIVES

Pres, Richard C Breon
Svp-Cfo, Matthew Cox
Coordinator, Josh Miller
Administrative Director, Larry Genzink
Director, Cynthia Pollock
Fleet Staff, Greg Elderkin
Administrator, Jodi Scully
Director, Alan Kranzo
Project Manager, Amy Robertson
Software Developer, Brett Vanderhaar
Neurologist, Jason Umfleet

LOCATIONS

HQ: SPECTRUM HEALTH SYSTEM
100 MICHIGAN ST NE, GRAND RAPIDS, MI
495032560
Phone: 616 391-1774
Web: WWW.SPECTRUMHEALTH.ORG

COMPETITORS

Ascension Health	HealthPlus of Michigan
Blue Cross Blue Shield of Michigan	McLaren Bay
Borgess Health	McLaren Health Care
Bronson Battle Creek	Mercy Health Hackley
Bronson Health Care	Munson Healthcare
CareSource	OmniCare Health Plan
Covenant HealthCare	Sheridan Community Hospital
Great Lakes Health Plan	Total Health Care
Hayes Green Beach Memorial Hospital	Zeeland Community Hospital
Health Alliance Plan of Michigan	

HISTORICAL FINANCIALS

Company Type: Private

Income Statement				FYE: June 30
	REVENUE ($ mil.)	NET INCOME ($ mil.)	NET PROFIT MARGIN	EMPLOYEES
06/18	6,004	332	5.5%	16,996
06/17	5,681	357	6.3%	—
06/10	1,446	142	9.9%	—
06/09	1,266	0	—	—
Annual Growth	18.9%	—	—	—

2018 Year-End Financials

Return on assets: 5.7% Cash ($ mil.): 707
Return on equity: 9.5%
Current ratio: 1.40

SPIRE ALABAMA INC.

With all the gas a customer could possibly need Alagasco is THE gas co. in Alabama. A unit of Spire (formerly The Laclede Group) in 2015 utility Alabama Gas Corporation (Alagasco) distributed natural gas to 425000 commercial and industrial customers in about half of the counties in the state. The utility also provides gas transportation services to large end users who purchase wholesale gas from suppliers. Alagasco has seven operating districts: Anniston Birmingham Gadsden Montgomery Opelika Selma and Tuscaloosa. The Alagasco distribution system includes 11230 miles of mains and more than 12000 miles of service lines.

Change in Company Type

Seeking to increase its customer base in 2014 The Laclede Group (now Spire) bought Alagasco from Energen for about $1.6 billion.

Operations

The company distributes natural gas to residential commercial and industrial customers in about half of the counties in Alabama. Alagasco purchases natural gas through interstate and intrastate suppliers and distributes the purchased gas to residential commercial and industrial customers and other natural gas end users. The company also provides transportation services to large industrial and commercial customers on its distribution system.

Alagasco's distribution system is connected to two major interstate natural gas pipeline systems Southern Natural Gas and Transcontinental Gas Pipe Line. It is also connected to two intrastate natural gas pipeline systems and to Alagasco's two liquefied natural gas (LNG) facilities.

In 2015 Alagasco purchased natural gas from 15 different suppliers to meet current gas sales storage injection and LNG liquefaction requirements of which six are under long-term supply agreements.

Alagasco also has 13 operation centers and two business centers.

Geographic Reach

Alagasco serves customers in more than 170 cities towns and other communities in 28 Alabama counties.

Financial Performance

The company is part of Spire's Gas Utility segment which contributed 96% to the parent company's total net sales in 2015. Alagasco's residential commercial and small industrial markets represented 79% of Spire's 2015 operating revenues.

Strategy

Recognizing the need for green energy options to reduce carbon emissions and dependence on foreign oil the company has a fleet of natural gas vehicles (NGVs) designed to run only on natural gas and bi-fuel NGVs which have two separate fueling systems natural gas and conventional fuel (gasoline or diesel).

Company Background

Alagasco dates back to 1852 when the Montgomery City Council passed an ordinance authorizing the Montgomery Gas Light Company to provide gas lighting for that city. Following a series of mergers and expansions the company became the

---

Alabama Gas Corporation (Alagasco) a publicly traded entity in 1953. In 1979 it was acquired by Energen in a corporate reorganization.

EXECUTIVES

President And Coo, Dudley C. Reynolds, $310,000 total compensation
Vp System Integrity, Kenneth A. (Ken) Smith
Vp Rates And Regulations, Amy E. Watson

LOCATIONS

HQ: SPIRE ALABAMA INC.
2101 6TH AVE N STE 210, BIRMINGHAM, AL
352032761
Phone: 205 326-8100
Web: WWW.SPIREENERGY.COM

COMPETITORS

Alabama Power	Ferrellgas Partners
Duke Energy	Sempra Energy

HISTORICAL FINANCIALS

Company Type: Private

Income Statement				FYE: September 30
	REVENUE ($ mil.)	NET INCOME ($ mil.)	NET PROFIT MARGIN	EMPLOYEES
09/18	500	1	0.3%	819
09/17	400	58	14.5%	—
09/16	368	53	14.4%	—
09/15	479	48	10.0%	—
Annual Growth	1.5%	(70.0%)	—	—

SPIRE MISSOURI INC.

EXECUTIVES

Pres-Ceo, Steven L Lindsey
Chb*, Suzanne Sitherwood
Cfo*, Steven P Rasche
Asst V Pres-Reg Admin, R Lawrence Sherwin

LOCATIONS

HQ: SPIRE MISSOURI INC.
700 MARKET ST, SAINT LOUIS, MO 631011829
Phone: 314 342-0500
Web: WWW.SPIREENERGY.COM

HISTORICAL FINANCIALS

Company Type: Private

Income Statement				FYE: September 30
	REVENUE ($ mil.)	NET INCOME ($ mil.)	NET PROFIT MARGIN	EMPLOYEES
09/18	1,285	129	10.1%	2,271
09/17	1,171	113	9.6%	—
09/16	1,087	105	9.7%	—
09/15	1,416	105	7.4%	—
Annual Growth	(3.2%)	7.1%	—	—

2018 Year-End Financials

Return on assets: 3.5% Cash ($ mil.): 2
Return on equity: 6.2%
Current ratio: 0.50

SPIRIT REALTY CAPITAL, INC.

EXECUTIVES

Pres-Ceo, Jackson Hsieh
Exec V Pres-Cfo, Phillip D Joseph Jr
Exec V Pres-Chief Acquisitions, Boyd Messmann
Exec V Pres Asset Management, Mark L Manheimer
Sr V Pres-Chief Hr Officer, Michelle M Greenstreet
Sr V Pres-Cao, Prakash J Parag
Chb, Richard I Gilchrist
Evp-Cfo, Michael Hughes
Asset Management Analyst, Charlie Bernet
Accounts Payable Specialist, Carina Cabalitasan
Information Technology Directo, Colin Lane
Auditors: ERNST & YOUNG LLP DALLAS TEX

LOCATIONS

HQ: SPIRIT REALTY CAPITAL, INC.
2727 N HARWOOD ST STE 300, DALLAS, TX 752012407
Phone: 480 606-0820
Web: WWW.SPIRITREALTY.COM

HISTORICAL FINANCIALS

Company Type: Private

Income Statement				FYE: December 31
	ASSETS ($ mil.)	NET INCOME ($ mil.)	INCOME AS % OF ASSETS	EMPLOYEES
12/17	7,263	77	1.1%	71
12/16	7,677	97	1.3%	—
12/14	8,017	(33)	—	—
12/13	7,231	1	0.0%	—
Annual Growth	0.1%	160.4%	—	—

2017 Year-End Financials

Return on assets: 1.1%   Sales ($ mil): 668
Return on equity: 2.3%

SPOKANE PUBLIC SCHOOLS

EXECUTIVES

Spdt, Shelley Redinger
V Pres*, Susan Chapin
Principal, Chase Middle School, John Andes
Before/After School Coordinato, Lorna Spear
Director, Doug Wordell
Business Manager, Pam Austin
Staff, Michele Adams
Education Assistant, Rebecca Oestreich
Manager, Christine Wilson
Assistant Secretary, Tracy Van Halderen
Manager, Alana Christensen
Auditors: PAT MCCARTHY-STATE AUDITOR OL

LOCATIONS

HQ: SPOKANE PUBLIC SCHOOLS
200 N BERNARD ST, SPOKANE, WA 992010206
Phone: 509 354-5900
Web: WWW.SPOKANESCHOOLS.ORG

HISTORICAL FINANCIALS

Company Type: Private

Income Statement				FYE: August 31
	REVENUE ($ mil.)	NET INCOME ($ mil.)	NET PROFIT MARGIN	EMPLOYEES
08/18	458	20	4.4%	3,226
08/17	437	(32)	—	—
08/16	414	31	7.6%	—
08/15	403	6	1.7%	—
Annual Growth	4.3%	43.9%	—	—

2018 Year-End Financials

Return on assets: 2.5%   Cash ($ mil.): 135
Return on equity: —
Current ratio: —

SPORTS, INC.

EXECUTIVES

Pres, Tony Cardinal
Pres-Dir*, Barry Cory
V Pres*, Chad Wyffels
V Pres & Asst SEC-Treas*, Nancy Wilson
Dir*, Mark Daniels
Dir*, John Phillips
Executive Officer, Frances Hines
Accounting Staff, Shannon Peterschick
Marketing Manager, Andy Eames
Marketing Staff, Corry Arntzen
Member Representat, Angela Ehlert
Auditors: JUNKERMIER CLARK CAMPANELLA

LOCATIONS

HQ: SPORTS, INC.
333 2ND AVE N, LEWISTOWN, MT 594572700
Phone: 406 538-3496
Web: WWW.SPORTSINC2.COM

HISTORICAL FINANCIALS

Company Type: Private

Income Statement				FYE: December 31
	REVENUE ($ mil.)	NET INCOME ($ mil.)	NET PROFIT MARGIN	EMPLOYEES
12/18	960	0	0.0%	38
12/17	913	0	0.0%	—
12/16	963	0	0.0%	—
12/15	841	0	0.0%	—
Annual Growth	4.5%	21.9%	—	—

2018 Year-End Financials

Return on assets: 0.1%   Cash ($ mil.): —
Return on equity: 1.4%
Current ratio: 1.10

SPRING BRANCH INDEPENDENT SCHOOL DISTRICT (INC)

EXECUTIVES

Supt, Scott R Muri
Transportation Director, Sherri Lawson
Elementary Assistant, Sherrie Folger
Administrative Assistant, Betty Head
Payroll Specialist, Evelyn Medrano
Director, Jessica M Hughes
Field Supervisor, Jessica Jackowski
Manager, Jorge Lopez
Production Specialist, Kristen Cain
Purchasing Clerk, Martha Cantu
Assistant Director, Michael Francis
Auditors: WHITLEY PENN HOUSTON TEXAS

LOCATIONS

HQ: SPRING BRANCH INDEPENDENT SCHOOL DISTRICT (INC)
955 CAMPBELL RD, HOUSTON, TX 770242803
Phone: 713 464-1511
Web: WWW.FROSTWOODPTA.COM

HISTORICAL FINANCIALS

Company Type: Private

Income Statement				FYE: June 30
	REVENUE ($ mil.)	NET INCOME ($ mil.)	NET PROFIT MARGIN	EMPLOYEES
06/18	513	135	26.4%	4,484
06/17	500	(4)	—	—
06/16	451	(38)	—	—
06/13	353	(67)	—	—
Annual Growth	7.8%	—	—	—

SRC HOLDINGS CORPORATION

EXECUTIVES

Pres, John P Stack
V Pres, Dennis Sheppard
Treas, Laura Ruzicka
Evp, Vaughn Henson
Mgr, William D Sheppard
Vice President Business Develo, Don Ross
Officer, William Sheppard
Executive Assistant, Amanda Koch
Director of Sales, Darin Bridges
Deputy General Counsel, Don Chenevert
Corporate Administrative Assis, Rebecca Darrow
Auditors: KPM CPAS PC SPRINGFIELD MIS

LOCATIONS

HQ: SRC HOLDINGS CORPORATION
531 S UNION AVE, SPRINGFIELD, MO 658022659
Phone: 417 862-2337
Web: WWW.SRCHOLDINGS.COM

HISTORICAL FINANCIALS

Company Type: Private

Income Statement				FYE: January 27
	REVENUE ($ mil.)	NET INCOME ($ mil.)	NET PROFIT MARGIN	EMPLOYEES
01/19	453	32	7.2%	1,500
01/18	390	25	6.4%	—
01/17	381	19	5.2%	—
01/16	403	17	4.4%	—
Annual Growth	4.0%	23.0%	—	—

2019 Year-End Financials

Return on assets: 13.1%   Cash ($ mil.): 22
Return on equity: 20.1%
Current ratio: 2.40

SRCTEC, LLC

EXECUTIVES

Pres, Drew James
Treas*, Deborah Sabella
SEC*, Mary Pat Hartnett
Scientist, Laura Morlacci
Manufacturing Engineer, Tom Chappini
Director, Stephen Winslow
Senior Financial Analyst, Andrea Emery
Director, Bill Kramer
Senior Quality Engineer, Bill Laveck
Manager, Dan Aird
Manager of Financial Planning, Deb E Sabella

LOCATIONS

HQ: SRCTEC, LLC
   5801 E TAFT RD STE 6, SYRACUSE, NY 132123275
Phone: 315 452-8700
Web: WWW.SRCINC.COM

HISTORICAL FINANCIALS

Company Type: Private

Income Statement				FYE: September 30
	REVENUE ($ mil.)	NET INCOME ($ mil.)	NET PROFIT MARGIN	EMPLOYEES
09/10	583	42	7.3%	150
09/09	365	19	5.4%	—
Annual Growth	59.7%	115.0%	—	—

2010 Year-End Financials

Return on assets: 14.3%   Cash ($ mil.): 44
Return on equity: 7.3%
Current ratio: 1.30

SSM HEALTH CARE CORPORATION

The mission of SSM Health began with five nuns who fled religious persecution in Germany in 1872 only to arrive in St. Louis in the midst of a smallpox epidemic. They formed their first hospital there in 1877. Today the Midwest-based not-not-for-profit system sponsored by the Franciscan Sisters of Mary owns some 25 acute care hospitals with about 4500 licensed beds; it also has management or affiliation agreements with a number of other area hospitals. Additionally the company offers more than 300 outpatient facilities including physicians' practices home care and hospice services post-acute facilities and an insurance company.

Operations

In southern Wisconsin SSM Health facilities include St. Clare Hospital in Baraboo St. Mary's Janesville Hospital in Janesville and St. Mary's Hospital in Madison. Southern Illinois locations include St. Mary's Good Samaritan Hospital in Mount Vernon and St. Mary's Hospital in Centralia. The company owns and operates about 10 hospitals in Missouri; these include Cardinal Glennon Children's Hospital and DePaul Hospital. Oklahoma hospitals include St. Anthony Hospital in Oklahoma City and St. Anthony Shawnee Hospital in Shawnee.

SSM Health has some 9500 physicians on its staff. The system has some 176000 inpatient admissions and some 1.6 million outpatient visits each year.

The system participates in a Medicare Accountable Care Organization (ACO). It also has a pharmacy benefit arm.

Geographic Reach

SSM Health's facilities are located in Illinois Missouri Oklahoma and Wisconsin.

Sales and Marketing

Managed care payments account for about half of SSM Health's net patient revenue before provision for uncollectible accounts; Medicare accounts for about 30% and Medicaid accounts for about 15%.

The system spent $20666 on advertising on 2016 up from $17956 in 2015.

Financial Performance

SSM Health's operating revenue increased 12% to $6.1 billion due largely to a rise in net patient service revenues and an increase in other revenue. Premiums earned and investment income also rose that year.

However operating expenses increased across most areas and the system reported a decrease in excess of revenues over expenses which fell 52% to $99.4 million. Similarly operating cash flow fell 51% to $220.4 million in 2016. Factors contributing to that drop included an increase in pension-related changes and in provisions for uncollectible accounts and bad debts.

Strategy

SSM Health often partners with other care providers which helps it expand without having to invest in new facilities from the ground up.

Like most health systems SSM has been challenged with lower government reimbursement rates. It is implementing a financial improvement initiative which includes some company layoffs.

Mergers and Acquisitions

SSM Health has been making a number of acquisitions to expand its network. For example in 2016 it doubled its stake in St. Clare Surgical Center to 60% and acquired the rest of Physicians Surgery Center at DePaul it didn't already own. SSM also took over the operations of about 25 health clinics located in Walgreens stores in Greater St. Louis.

In early 2018 the system acquired Agnesian HealthCare and Monroe Clinic (both based in Wisconsin) adding four hospitals eight post-acute facilities and several outpatient facilities.

EXECUTIVES

President And Ceo, William P. Thompson
Svp Finance, Kris A. Zimmer
President Hospital Operations, Chris Howard
Evp; President Health Care Delivery Finance And Integration, Gaurov Dayal
Svp Strategy Communications And Marketing, Paula J. Friedman
President Ssm St. Joseph Health Center, Mike Bowers
Evp; President Physician And Ambulatory Operations, Shane Peng
Chief Nursing Officer, Maggie Fowler
Svp And Cio, Phillip Loftus
President St. Marya's Hospital, Jon Rozenfeld
President Ssm Health At Home, Alison Ruehl
Auditors: DELOITTE & TOUCHE LLP ST LOU

LOCATIONS

HQ: SSM HEALTH CARE CORPORATION
   10101 WOODFIELD LN # 100, SAINT LOUIS, MO 631322944
Phone: 314 994-7800
Web: WWW.SSMHEALTH.COM

PRODUCTS/OPERATIONS

Selected Facilities

Illinois
   St. Mary's Good Samaritan (joint sponsorship with Felician Services two hospitals in Mt. Vernon and Centralia)
Missouri
   St. Francis Hospital & Health Services (Maryville)
   St. Mary's Health Center (Jefferson City)
   SSM Cardinal Glennon Children's Medical Center (St. Louis)
   SSM DePaul Health Center (Bridgeton)
   SSM St. Clare Health Center (St. Louis)
   SSM St. Joseph Health Center (St. Charles)
   SSM St. Joseph Health Center (Wentzville)
   SSM St. Joseph Hospital West (Lake St. Louis)
   SSM St. Mary's Health Center (Richmond Heights)
Oklahoma
   Bone & Joint Hospital (Oklahoma City)
   Shawnee Medical Center Clinic (Shawnee)
   St. Anthony Hospital (Oklahoma City)
   Unity Health Center (Shawnee)
Wisconsin
   Boscobel Area Health Care (managed hospital and clinics Boscobel)
   Columbus Community Hospital (affiliate Columbus)
   Edgerton Hospital and Health Services (Edgerton)
   St. Clare Hospital (Baraboo)
   St. Clare Meadows Care Center (nursing home Madison)
   St. Mary's Care Center (nursing home Madison)
   St. Mary's Hospital (Madison)
   St. Mary's Janesville Hospital (Janesville)
   Stoughton Hospital (affiliate Stoughton)
   Uplands Hill Health (affiliate hospital and nursing care Dodgeville)

COMPETITORS

Adventist Health System Sunbelt Healthcare
Advocate Health Care
Allina Hospitals
Ascension Health
BJC HealthCare
Carle Physician Group
Community Health Systems
HCA
Hospital Sisters Health System
Mayo Clinic
Mercy Health
Meriter Health Services
MetroSouth Medical
Rush System for Health
Tenet Healthcare
University of Wisconsin Hospital and Clinics
VITAS Healthcare

HISTORICAL FINANCIALS
Company Type: Private

Income Statement   FYE: December 31

	REVENUE ($ mil.)	NET INCOME ($ mil.)	NET PROFIT MARGIN	EMPLOYEES
12/17	6,497	245	3.8%	24,230
12/16	6,109	(30)	—	
12/13	1,177	32	2.8%	—
Annual Growth	53.3%	65.9%		

2017 Year-End Financials
Return on assets: 3.3%   Cash ($ mil.): 126
Return on equity: 10.5%
Current ratio: 0.80

SSM HEALTH CARE OF OKLAHOMA, INC.

EXECUTIVES

Ceo, Joe Hodges
V Pres of Fin*, Shasta Manuel
V Pres*, Cynthia Brundige
V Pres*, Kersey Winfree
Regional Cfo*, Garrick Muller
Admin Asst of Pres, Donna Retter
Physician, Blake Parsons
Chief of Psychiatric, Brent Bell

LOCATIONS

HQ: SSM HEALTH CARE OF OKLAHOMA, INC.
   1000 N LEE AVE, OKLAHOMA CITY, OK 731021036
Phone: 405 272-7000
Web: WWW.SSMHEALTH.COM

HISTORICAL FINANCIALS
Company Type: Private

Income Statement   FYE: December 31

	REVENUE ($ mil.)	NET INCOME ($ mil.)	NET PROFIT MARGIN	EMPLOYEES
12/17	507	15	3.0%	3,000
12/16	454	13	3.0%	—
12/14	444	9	2.1%	—
12/01	196	(11)	—	—
Annual Growth	6.1%	—	—	—

2017 Year-End Financials
Return on assets: 4.5%   Cash ($ mil.): 44
Return on equity: 4.5%
Current ratio: 97.40

ST BARNABAS MEDICAL CENTER (INC)

Part of the Saint Barnabas Health Care System Saint Barnabas Medical Center is a 600-bed acute-care hospital that provides a full range of health services to residents of Livingston New Jersey and surrounding areas. The not-for-profit medical center provides general inpatient and outpatient care programs as well as burn and perinatal care. It also houses units specializing in organ transplant stroke care cardiac surgery and comprehensive cancer treatment. Its Institute for Reproductive Medicine and Science provides assisted reproductive technology services. Saint Barnabas Medical Center treats some 35000 inpatients and more than 85000 emergency-room patients each year.

Operations

In combination with its satellite Saint Barnabas Ambulatory Care Center the medical center serves about 300000 outpatients per year. Saint Barnabas Medical Center is also a teaching affiliate of several regional schools includingÂ the University of Medicine and Dentistry of New Jersey and Drexel University College of Medicine.

Company Background

New Jersey's first hospital Saint Barnabas Medical Center was founded in 1865 in a private home.

EXECUTIVES

Senior Vice President, Robert Iannaccone
Vice President Human Resources, Arnie Manzo
Medical Director, Adrian L Connolly
System Vice President Cancer Service, Robert Braun
Assistant Vice President Legal Affairs, Margaret H Campbell
Auditors: KPMG LLP NEW YORK NY

LOCATIONS

HQ: ST BARNABAS MEDICAL CENTER (INC)
   94 OLD SHORT HILLS RD # 1, LIVINGSTON, NJ 070395668
Phone: 973 322-5000
Web: WWW.RWJBH.ORG

COMPETITORS

Atlantic Health
 Children's Specialized Hospital
 Chilton Medical Center
 East Orange General Hospital
 Hackensack Meridian Health
 Hackensack University Medical Center
 JFK Medical Center
 Newark Beth Israel Medical Center
 Raritan Bay Medical Center
 Robert Wood Johnson University Hospital
 Robert Wood Johnson University Hospital at Rahway
 Saint Peter's University Hospital
 St. Joseph's Healthcare System
 Trinitas Regional Medical Center
 Virtua Health

HISTORICAL FINANCIALS
Company Type: Private

Income Statement   FYE: December 31

	REVENUE ($ mil.)	NET INCOME ($ mil.)	NET PROFIT MARGIN	EMPLOYEES
12/18	818	113	13.9%	4,000
12/17	818	113	13.9%	—
12/16	760	84	11.1%	—
12/15	728	87	12.0%	—
Annual Growth	4.0%	9.0%	—	—

2018 Year-End Financials
Return on assets: 7.5%   Cash ($ mil.): —
Return on equity: 11.3%
Current ratio: 9.20

ST LOUIS CHILDREN'S HOSPITAL

EXECUTIVES

Act Pres, Peggy Gordin
Sr V Pres*, Michael Dehaven
V Pres*, David Aplington
Pres*, Joan Magruder
Coordinator, Karen Rieker
Distribution/Shipping/Transpor, Lynne Andreski
It Manager, Cindy Derby
General Manager, Ellie Glenn
Manager of Child Life, Jill Malan
Director of Is, John Barenkamp
Bereavement Coordinator, Mary Lucido

LOCATIONS

HQ: ST LOUIS CHILDREN'S HOSPITAL
   1 CHILDRENS PL, SAINT LOUIS, MO 631101081
Phone: 314 454-6000
Web: WWW.STLOUISCHILDRENS.ORG

HISTORICAL FINANCIALS
Company Type: Private

Income Statement   FYE: December 31

	REVENUE ($ mil.)	NET INCOME ($ mil.)	NET PROFIT MARGIN	EMPLOYEES
12/17	609	62	10.2%	2,959
12/16	563	58	10.3%	—
12/15	527	50	9.5%	—
12/14	513	36	7.1%	—
Annual Growth	5.9%	19.6%	—	—

2017 Year-End Financials
Return on assets: 11.5%   Cash ($ mil.): —
Return on equity: 14.2%
Current ratio: 1.60

ST LUKE'S HOSPITAL & HEALTH NETWORK INC

EXECUTIVES

Pres, Richard A Anderson
Sr V Pres, Rthomas P Lichtenwalner
Media Specialist, Anne Kemp
Coordinator, Kathleen Hedges
Administrator, Brian Repetz
Administrator, Crystal Corredera
Chief Information Offi, Marc Portner
Supervisor, Michael Sanchez
Analyst, Angela Koch
Doctor, Christopher Gilbert
Manager, David Finkelstein

LOCATIONS

HQ: ST LUKE'S HOSPITAL & HEALTH NETWORK INC
   801 OSTRUM ST, BETHLEHEM, PA 180151000
Phone: 484 526-4000
Web: WWW.SLHN.ORG

HISTORICAL FINANCIALS
Company Type: Private

Income Statement   FYE: June 30

	REVENUE ($ mil.)	NET INCOME ($ mil.)	NET PROFIT MARGIN	EMPLOYEES
06/16	648	47	7.4%	75
06/15	602	38	6.4%	—
Annual Growth	7.6%	24.9%	—	—

2016 Year-End Financials
Return on assets: 5.1%   Cash ($ mil.): 43
Return on equity: 130.2%
Current ratio: 1.30

ST LUKE'S HOSPITAL OF KANSAS CITY

LOCATIONS
HQ: ST LUKE'S HOSPITAL OF KANSAS CITY
4401 WORNALL RD, KANSAS CITY, MO 641113220
Phone: 816 932-2000
Web: WWW.SAINTLUKESHEALTHSYSTEM.ORG

HISTORICAL FINANCIALS
Company Type: Private

Income Statement   FYE: December 31

	REVENUE ($ mil.)	NET INCOME ($ mil.)	NET PROFIT MARGIN	EMPLOYEES
12/13	647	11	1.8%	4
12/09	479	13	2.7%	—
Annual Growth	7.8%	(2.8%)	—	—

2013 Year-End Financials
Return on assets: 1.0%   Cash ($ mil.): 34
Return on equity: 1.4%
Current ratio: 0.40

ST LUKE'S-ROOSEVELT HOSPITAL CENTER

EXECUTIVES
Pres, Frank Cracolici
Sr V Pres*, Robert Catalano
Research Manager*, Anthony Grillo
Scientist, Emilia Sordillo
Manager, Jeff Horvath
Infectious Disease Specialist, Luz Lugo
Administrator, Sheila Monroe
Editor, Carolyn Waldron
Coordinator, Christella Watts
Social Worker, Yvette Washington
Assistant Professor, Preetika Mukherjee
Auditors: ERNST & YOUNG US LLP INDIANAP

LOCATIONS
HQ: ST LUKE'S-ROOSEVELT HOSPITAL CENTER
1111 AMSTERDAM AVE, NEW YORK, NY 100251716
Phone: 212 523-4000
Web: WWW.MOUNTSINAI.ORG

HISTORICAL FINANCIALS
Company Type: Private

Income Statement   FYE: December 31

	REVENUE ($ mil.)	NET INCOME ($ mil.)	NET PROFIT MARGIN	EMPLOYEES
12/16	901	53	5.9%	6,000
12/15	859	61	7.1%	—
12/14	1,160	(17)	—	—
Annual Growth	(11.9%)		—	—

2016 Year-End Financials
Return on assets: 6.0%   Cash ($ mil.): 39
Return on equity: —
Current ratio: 0.80

ST. BERNARDS HEALTHCARE

EXECUTIVES
Pres, Ben Owens
Prin*, Chris Barber
Prin*, Harry Hutchison
Prin*, Charles Pigg
Dir*, Sister Miriam Burns
Information Specialist, Tim Miller
Project Leader, Chris Parrish
Director of Operaton, Brad Bauer
Director, Brian Reed
Auditors: BKD LLP LITTLE ROCK AR

LOCATIONS
HQ: ST. BERNARDS HEALTHCARE
225 E JACKSON AVE, JONESBORO, AR 724013119
Phone: 870 897-2052
Web: WWW.STBERNARDS.INFO

HISTORICAL FINANCIALS
Company Type: Private

Income Statement   FYE: September 30

	REVENUE ($ mil.)	NET INCOME ($ mil.)	NET PROFIT MARGIN	EMPLOYEES
09/18	475	8	1.8%	2,000
09/17	20	0	—	—
09/15	20	0	4.9%	—
09/14	19	0	0.2%	—
Annual Growth	123.7%	291.2%	—	—

2018 Year-End Financials
Return on assets: 2.5%   Cash ($ mil.): 53
Return on equity: 3.5%
Current ratio: 1.90

ST. CHARLES HEALTH SYSTEM, INC.

EXECUTIVES
Pres-Ceo, Joe Sluka
Coordinator, Sue Takemoto
Manager, Alan Burke
Operating Room Dir, Carla Stevens
Certified Assistant, Christine Williams
Rn, Dana Peters
Licensed Clinical Social Worke, John Walkenhorst
Human Resources Specialist, Kristi Durr
Point of Care Coordinator, Lura Wilhelm
Director Community Hea, Robert Ross
Survivorship, Wendy Rudy

LOCATIONS
HQ: ST. CHARLES HEALTH SYSTEM, INC.
2500 NE NEFF RD, BEND, OR 977016015
Phone: 541 382-4321
Web: WWW.STCHARLESHEALTHCARE.ORG

HISTORICAL FINANCIALS
Company Type: Private

Income Statement   FYE: December 31

	REVENUE ($ mil.)	NET INCOME ($ mil.)	NET PROFIT MARGIN	EMPLOYEES
12/17	809	41	5.1%	3,200
12/13	631	40	6.4%	—
12/07	367	8	2.4%	—
12/06	173	0	—	—
Annual Growth	15.0%		—	—

2017 Year-End Financials
Return on assets: 3.9%   Cash ($ mil.): 57
Return on equity: 6.4%
Current ratio: 0.50

ST. DOMINIC-JACKSON MEMORIAL HOSPITAL

EXECUTIVES
Pres, Claude W Harbarger
SEC-Treas*, Sister Mary Trinita
Pres*, Lester Diamond
Project Manager, Craig Church
Surgeon, James Grady
Engineer, Justin Huff
Officer, Renee Beckum
Surgeon, William Harris
Accounts Payable Coordinator, Adam Washington
Physician, Claude Harbager
Auditors: I BKD LLP JACKSON MS

LOCATIONS
HQ: ST. DOMINIC-JACKSON MEMORIAL HOSPITAL
969 LAKELAND DR, JACKSON, MS 392164606
Phone: 601 200-6776
Web: WWW.STDOM.COM

HISTORICAL FINANCIALS
Company Type: Private

Income Statement   FYE: December 31

	REVENUE ($ mil.)	NET INCOME ($ mil.)	NET PROFIT MARGIN	EMPLOYEES
12/15	478	(0)	—	2,400
12/14	418	16	4.1%	—
12/13	0	0	—	—
12/08	337	(51)	—	—
Annual Growth	5.1%	—	—	—

2015 Year-End Financials
Return on assets: (-0.1%)   Cash ($ mil.): 51
Return on equity: (-0.1%)
Current ratio: 4.10

ST. FRANCIS HOSPITAL, ROSLYN, NEW YORK

Sure St. Francis Hospital can handle yourÂ gall bladderÂ and sinus difficulties butÂ it's really on top of your heart problems. The hospital's Heart CenterÂ — New York State's only specially designated cardiac center — providesÂ surgicalÂ diagnostic and treatment services.Â The 365-bed St. Francis Hospital also has centers for ENT (ear nose and throat) orthopedic vascular prostate cancer gastrointestinal and general surgery services. As part of Catholic Health Services of Long Island St. Francis opened its doors in 1954 to children and adults. It was originally established as St. Francis Hospital and Sanatorium for Cardiac Children in 1936.

Operations
St. Francis Hospital's Heart Center performsÂ about 8000 cardiac catheterizationsÂ 3000 coronary angioplasties andÂ about 1500 open-heart operations every year.Â The center'sÂ DeMatteis Center for Cardiac Research and Education works to developÂ improved techniques for heart disease diagnosis including conducting clinical trials throughÂ partnerships with device and equipment makersÂ and provides patient education and fitness programs.

Geographic Reach
St. Francis Hospital is located in Roslyn New York. In addition it has satellite New YorkÂ locations in Greenvale (DeMatteis Center for Cardiac Research and Education) West Islip (South Bay Cardiovascular Center) and Hicksville (Bishop McHugh Health Center) as well as administrative offices in Port Washington.

Strategy
St. Francis HospitalÂ has expanded in recent years to keep up with growing patient demand. It opened the Bishop McHugh Health Center to provide outpatient primary care services for uninsured and underinsured patients in 2012.

The hospital completed its largest expansion project to date in 2009 with the construction of theÂ $190 million Nancy and Frederick DeMatteis Pavilion; the projectÂ increased the hospital's clinical space by about 40% and added 85 beds.

EXECUTIVES

Pres-Ceo, Alan Guerci
Sr V Pres-Cfo, William C Arms
Sr Vp-Coo, Martin A Bieber
Vp-Development & Public Relati, Linda Cavallo-Miller
R.N., Sr V Pres, Ann Cella Rn
Vp-Human Resources, Betty Anson
Exec V Pres, Ruth Hennessey
Sr V Pres, Jack Soterakis
PH 516 705-1925, Jenny Mitchell
Chief Anesthesiology, H Sinan Berkay
Director of Discharge Planning, Mary Anne Highland
Auditors: PRICEWATERHOUSECOOPERS LLP NE

LOCATIONS

HQ: ST. FRANCIS HOSPITAL, ROSLYN, NEW YORK
100 PORT WASHINGTON BLVD, ROSLYN, NY 115761347
Phone: 516 562-2000

PRODUCTS/OPERATIONS

Selected Services

Anesthesiology
Breast Surgery

Cardiology
Cardiothoracic Surgery
Diabetes Care Center
Emergency Medicine
Gastroenterology
General Surgery
Hematology/Oncology
Nephrology
Neurology
Orthopedic Surgery
Otolaryngology
Podiatry
Psychiatry
Pulmonary Medicine
Radiology
Rehabilitation
Urology
Vascular Services
Women's Center

COMPETITORS

Bronx-Lebanon Hospital
Brookhaven Memorial Hospital Medical Center
Calvary Hospital
Continuum Health Partners
Franklin Hospital
Huntington Hospital
Mather Memorial Hospital
MediSys Health Network
Memorial Sloan-Kettering
New York City Health and Hospitals
NewYork-Presbyterian Healthcare
Northwell Health
NuHealth

HISTORICAL FINANCIALS
Company Type: Private

Income Statement				FYE: December 31
	REVENUE ($ mil.)	NET INCOME ($ mil.)	NET PROFIT MARGIN	EMPLOYEES
12/15	614	37	6.2%	2,184
12/08	385	28	7.4%	—
12/04	366	47	12.9%	—
12/02	828	0	—	—
Annual Growth	—	152.0%	—	—

2015 Year-End Financials

Return on assets: 3.9% Cash ($ mil.): 34
Return on equity: 5.5%
Current ratio: —

ST. FRANCIS MEDICAL CENTER

EXECUTIVES

Ceo, Richard Adcock
Ceo*, Gerald Kozai
Office Coordinator, Marianne Metzger
Environmental Manager, Keith Scurfield
Manager Respiratory Care, Benjamin Hardy
Chief Technology Officer, Eileen Williams
MD, Arturo Pelayo
Food Director, Bianca Peyvan
Admissions Director, Catherine Naiman
Supervisor, Harold Handshuh
Pastoral Care Director, Richard Hirbe

LOCATIONS

HQ: ST. FRANCIS MEDICAL CENTER
3630 E IMPERIAL HWY, LYNWOOD, CA 902622609
Phone: 310 900-8900
Web: WWW.VERITY.ORG

HISTORICAL FINANCIALS
Company Type: Private

Income Statement				FYE: June 30
	REVENUE ($ mil.)	NET INCOME ($ mil.)	NET PROFIT MARGIN	EMPLOYEES
06/16	451	28	6.4%	172
06/15	500	70	14.1%	—
06/14	407	21	5.3%	—
Annual Growth	5.2%	15.7%	—	—

2016 Year-End Financials

Return on assets: 5.8% Cash ($ mil.): 21
Return on equity: 11.1%
Current ratio: 6.00

ST. JOHN HEALTH SYSTEM, INC.

St. John Health SystemÂ aims to bringÂ healthÂ into the lives of the ill. The not-for-profit system provides health care services to residents of Tulsa and surrounding areas inÂ northeastern Oklahoma and southern Kansas. In addition toÂ flagship facilityÂ St. John Medical CenterÂ it owns or manages eight other community hospitals as well asÂ urgent care and long-term care facilities. St. John Health SystemÂ provides primary and specialty medical care through OMNI Medical Group and offers health insurance through CommunityCare health plan. Established in 1926 by the Sisters of the Sorrowful Mother the health system isÂ part of Marian Health.

Operations
Facilities owned managed or sponsored by St. John Health SystemÂ include hospitals Oklahoma State University Medical Center St. John Sapulpa St. John Owasso St. John Broken Arrow Pawhuska City Hospital Sedan City Hospital Nowata Hospital andÂ Jane Phillips Medical Center.Â The company'sÂ senior living facilities include Franciscan Villa Frances Streitel Villa Heartsworth House and Rosewood Terrace.

Strategy
St. John Health System will periodically add services to its offerings toÂ meet community demand. In early 2011 St. John HealthÂ opened the St. John Weight Management Institute to offer its patients weight loss options including bariatric surgery. The health system's newest hospital St. John Broken Arrow near Tulsa was constructed in 2009.

In 2012 Marian Health entered talks with another Catholic health system operator Ascension Health over the possibility of merging St. John Health System and other Marian organizations into the Ascension organization.

EXECUTIVES

Vice President, Ann Paul
Pharmacy Manager, Cornell Nathan
Secretary Iv, Julie Anderson

LOCATIONS

HQ: ST. JOHN HEALTH SYSTEM, INC.
1923 S UTICA AVE, TULSA, OK 741046520
Phone: 918 744-2180
Web: WWW.STJOHNHEALTHSYSTEM.COM

PRODUCTS/OPERATIONS

Selected Facilities and Operations – Oklahoma
CommunityCare (health plan)
Jane Phillips Medical Center (Bartlesville)
Nowata Hospital
Oklahoma State University Medical Center (managed facility in Tulsa)
OMNI Medical Group (physicians group)
Pawhuska City Hospital
Regional Medical Laboratory (clinical lab testing)
Sedan City Hospital
St. John Broken Arrow Hospital
St. John Medical Center (Tulsa)
St. John Owasso Hospital
St. John Physicians
St. John Sapulpa Hospital

COMPETITORS

Anthem	INTEGRIS Health
Ardent Health Services	Kindred Healthcare
CIGNA	Marian Health System
Catholic Health Initiatives	Norman Regional Health Presbyterian
Community Health Systems	Healthcare Services
	SSM Health Care
Deaconess Health Care	Saint Francis Health
HCA	System
Hillcrest Medical Center	UnitedHealth Group

HISTORICAL FINANCIALS

Company Type: Private

Income Statement				FYE: June 30
	REVENUE ($ mil.)	NET INCOME ($ mil.)	NET PROFIT MARGIN	EMPLOYEES
06/14*	1,056	79	7.5%	4,011
09/12	977	74	7.7%	—
09/11	895	17	2.0%	—
Annual Growth	5.7%	64.9%	—	—

*Fiscal year change

2014 Year-End Financials

Return on assets: 5.2%
Return on equity: 9.9%
Current ratio: 1.70
Cash ($ mil.): 44

ST. JOHN HOSPITAL AND MEDICAL CENTER

St. John Hospital & Medical Center is part of the larger Detroit area-based St. John Health regional health care system. Besides providing acute and trauma care the 770-bed teaching hospital operates specialized cancer and pediatric centers a hip and knee center an inpatient mental health unit and a Parkinson's Disease clinic. It also operates the only emergency trauma center on Detroit's East Side. The hospital was established in 1952 and has grown to include a 200-physician medical team that specializes in more than 50 medical and surgical fields. It boasts 34000 admissions; 14500 surgical visits; and more than 126500 emergency center visits each year.

Operations
Its emergency center is a Level II Trauma Center that boasts Chest Pain Center and Heart Failure Center accreditations. St. John Hospital also operates a large inpatient pediatric unit PICU and Level III NICU or Level II Special Care Nursery. The hospital runs the Van Elslander Cancer Center.

Strategy
St. John Hospital expanded its operations by opening the Elaine E. Blatt Endoscopy Department and a new pediatric burn treatment room both in 2012. It also expanded its mammography service capabilities with the purchase of Lakeshore Mammograph giving it more than a dozen new mammography sites across southeastern Michigan. In addition St. John Hospital opened a new cardiac catheterization lab that brought new diagnostic options to patients in the Michigan Blue Water Area.

EXECUTIVES

Ceo, Mark Taylor
Obstetrician, Nathan V Wagstaff
Internal Medicine Practitioner, Jason M Donaghue
Senior Manager, Corey Kennard
Internal Medicine Practitioner, Victoria Dufour
Information Specialist, Meghan McGinn
Coordinator, Nancy Derita
Registered Nurse, Susan Wollenzin
Physician Assistant, Jill Wells
Infection Control Manager, Riad Khatib

LOCATIONS

HQ: ST. JOHN HOSPITAL AND MEDICAL CENTER
28000 DEQUINDRE RD, WARREN, MI 480922468
Phone: 313 343-4000
Web: WWW.ASCENSION.ORG

PRODUCTS/OPERATIONS

Selected Services and Operations
Alternative Health
Breast Care
Breast Feeding (Lactation) Consultation
Cracchiolo Inpatient Rehabilitation Center
Diabetes Education and Care
Diagnostic and Imaging Services
Echocardiogram
Emergency
Heart and Vascular Care
Hip and Knee Center
Minimally Invasive Surgery
Minor Emergency
Neonatal Intensive Care Unit (NICU)
Obstetrics
Oncology (cancer)
Parkinson's Movement Disorder Clinic
Pediatrics
Physical Therapy
Spine Center
TravelCare
Urgent Care
Wound Care

COMPETITORS

Beaumont Health System	Mount Clemens Regional
Crittenton Hospital	Medical Center
Detroit Medical Center	Trinity Health (Novi)
Henry Ford Health System	

HISTORICAL FINANCIALS

Company Type: Private

Income Statement				FYE: June 30
	REVENUE ($ mil.)	NET INCOME ($ mil.)	NET PROFIT MARGIN	EMPLOYEES
06/15	753	36	4.8%	5,000
06/09	638	1	0.3%	—
06/05	0	0	—	—
06/03	1,642	9	0.6%	—
Annual Growth	(6.3%)	12.0%	—	—

2015 Year-End Financials

Return on assets: 3.0%
Return on equity: 6.1%
Current ratio: 2.20
Cash ($ mil.): 1

ST. JOHN'S HOSPITAL OF THE HOSPITAL SISTERS OF THE THIRD ORDER OF ST. FRANCIS

Truck-struck Homer Simpson might use his last gasp trying to blurt out "St. John's Hospital of the Hospital Sisters of the Third Order of St. Francis-Springfield" to his ambulance driver but he might be better off using the hospital's more common name St. John's. D'oh! The 440-bed St. John's Hospital serves residents of central and southern Illinois with general and specialized health care services. The teaching hospital affiliated with Southern Illinois University's School of Medicine has centers devoted to women and children's health trauma cardiac care cancer orthopedics and neurology. It also operates area health clinics. Founded in 1875 St. John's is part of the Hospital Sisters Health System.

Operations
The facility is Hospital Sisters Health System's flagship hospital. It has grown to boast about 700 physicians podiatrists and dentists from more than 30 specialties. In addition to educating medical students through Southern Illinois University's School of Medicine St. Johns also supports those working on careers in nursing through its own nursing school St. John's College. It also offers courses in pharmacy pathology respiratory therapy and electroneurodiagnostics (brain disorder diagnostics) professions.

St. John's physicians perform more than 15000 surgical procedures each year. It also receives some 54000 emergency department visits and helps deliver about 2000 babies annually.

Financial Performance
In 2014 revenue fell 26% to $450 million; this was primarily due to an 89% decline in contributions investments and foundation assets.

Strategy
The hospital has been expanding its offerings to provide more specialized services to area residents. Recent additions include 3-D mammographies and expanded children's surgical services. St. John's is also focused on improving access to health care through technology such as telemedicine. In 2014 it partnered with Greenville Regional Hospital to provide advanced treatment to stroke patients at their home hospital through STAT Stroke TeleMedicine.

Other strategic initiatives at the hospital include increasing doctor and nurse retention rates growing nursing school enrollment rates and increasing patient satisfaction scores. Part of its efforts to reach more patients has led St. John's to open new outpatient health centers in areas near the main hospital facility. The hospital has also renovated its main buildings including the revamp of its day surgery and intermediate care departments.

EXECUTIVES

Ceo, Charles Lucore
Cfo*, Larry Ragel
Coo*, Dave Olejniczak
Doctor, Nestor A Ramirez Lopez
Telecommunications Staff, Bonnie Williams
Vice-President Legal, Amy Bulpitt
Manager, Denise Rice
Pharmacist, Diane Martin
Chief Perfusionist, Elizabeth Kabrick

Director, Harold Jones
Pathologist, Lena Scherba
Auditors: CROWE HORWATH LLP CHICAGO IL

LOCATIONS

HQ: ST. JOHN'S HOSPITAL OF THE HOSPITAL
SISTERS OF THE THIRD ORDER OF ST. FRANCIS
800 E CARPENTER ST, SPRINGFIELD, IL 627690002
Phone: 217 544-6464
Web: WWW.ST-JOHNS.ORG

PRODUCTS/OPERATIONS

2014 Sales

	$ mil.	% of total
Amount generated for taking care patients excluding provision	427	95
Other contributions	20	5
Other	1	-
Total	**449**	**100**

Selected Services

AthletiCare
Behavioral Health Services
Birth Center
Cancer Institute
Center for Living
Children's Hospital
Connect
Emergency/Trauma Care
Gastroenterology
Health Centers | Priority Care
Home Health
Hospice
Intensive Care Unit
Lab
Neurosciences Institute
Orthopedics
Pain Management Center
Prairie Heart Institute
Radiology
Regional Wound Care Center
Sleep Center
Stroke Treatment
Surgery | daVinci
TherapyCare | Rehab
Third Age Living
Women's Services

COMPETITORS

Advocate Health Care	Memorial Health System
Blessing Hospital	Memorial Hospital
Community Health	(Illinois)
Systems	Southern Illinois
Decatur Memorial	Healthcare
Hospital	

HISTORICAL FINANCIALS

Company Type: Private

Income Statement				FYE: June 30
	REVENUE ($ mil.)	NET INCOME ($ mil.)	NET PROFIT MARGIN	EMPLOYEES
06/16	494	3	0.7%	3,000
06/15	501	3	0.8%	—
06/14	500	10	2.1%	—
06/08	393	(8)	—	—
Annual Growth	2.9%	—	—	—

2016 Year-End Financials

Return on assets: 0.5%   Cash ($ mil.): 3
Return on equity: 1.2%
Current ratio: —

ST. JOHN'S UNIVERSITY

EXECUTIVES

Assistant Professor, Elizabeth Albert
Assistant Professor, Robert Eschenauer
Assistant Professor, Judith McVarish
Assistant Professor, Senshang Lin
Assistant Professor, Susan Horning
Assistant Professor, Thomas Avery
Scientist, Ales Vancura
Assistant Professor, Alla Baeva
Security Staff, Kevin Mikalonis
Assistant Professor, Monica Wagner
Assistant Professor, Paula Lazrus
Auditors: KPMG LLP NEW YORK NY

LOCATIONS

HQ: ST. JOHN'S UNIVERSITY
8000 UTOPIA PKWY, JAMAICA, NY 114399000
Phone: 718 990-2000
Web: WWW.STJOHNS.EDU

HISTORICAL FINANCIALS

Company Type: Private

Income Statement				FYE: May 31
	REVENUE ($ mil.)	NET INCOME ($ mil.)	NET PROFIT MARGIN	EMPLOYEES
05/13	473	64	13.5%	466
05/12	652	30	4.7%	—
Annual Growth	(27.4%)	107.4%	—	—

2013 Year-End Financials

Return on assets: —   Cash ($ mil.): 7
Return on equity: 13.5%
Current ratio: —

ST. JOSEPH HEALTH SYSTEM

EXECUTIVES

Ceo-Pres, Richard Afable
Pres-Strat, Annette M Walker
Exec V Pres-Gen Counsel, Shannon Dwyer
Exec V Pres-Cfo, Jo Ann Escasa-Halgh
Reg-Exec V Pres, Kevin Klockenga
Event Coordinator and Developm, Katie Gozzarino
Manager, Vanessa De Gier
Chief Information Officer, Benjamin R Williams
Coordinator, Hala Abduljalil
Coordinator, Kimberly Reynolds
Ecis Application Manager, Jake Chan
Auditors: ERNST & YOUNG LLP IRVINE CA

LOCATIONS

HQ: ST. JOSEPH HEALTH SYSTEM
3345 MICHELSON DR STE 100, IRVINE, CA
926120693
Phone: 949 381-4000

COMPETITORS

Adventist Health	Loma Linda University
Arrowhead Medical	Medical Center
Center	Los Angeles County
Banner Health	Health Department
Catholic Health	Memorial Health
Initiatives	Services
Cedars-Sinai Medical	Pasadena Hospital
Center	Association
Citrus Valley Health	Prospect Medical
Partners	Scripps health
City of Hope	Sutter Health
Dignity Health	Tenet Healthcare
HCA	Western Medical Center
Kaiser Permanente	- Santa Ana

HISTORICAL FINANCIALS

Company Type: Private

Income Statement				FYE: June 30
	REVENUE ($ mil.)	NET INCOME ($ mil.)	NET PROFIT MARGIN	EMPLOYEES
06/13	4,955	2,082	42.0%	5,000
06/10	4,268	268	6.3%	—
Annual Growth	5.1%	98.1%	—	—

2013 Year-End Financials

Return on assets: 3.6%   Cash ($ mil.): 329
Return on equity: 42.0%
Current ratio: 0.80

ST. JOSEPH HOSPITAL OF ORANGE

If you're feeling green or blue in Orange County St. Joseph Hospital of Orange is there to help get back to feeling pink and rosy. The California hospital provides general medical and surgical services as well as specialty care such as women's health mental health services oncology cardiology and physical rehabilitation. Part of the St. Joseph Health System the hospital provides primary care and specialty outpatient services through a network of affiliated physician practices. It also operates low-income and mobile clinics. The hospital has about 468 beds and a medical staff of some 1000.

Operations

In addition to physician group affiliates St. Joseph Hospital Affiliated Physicians and St. Joseph Heritage Medical Group the hospital also partners with the Childrens Hospital of Orange County to help expand pediatric care throughout the region. The hospital has more than 20100 inpatient discharges and about 290400 outpatient visits a year.

Geographic Reach

St. Joseph Hospital serves Orange County California and the greater Los Angeles metropolitan area.

Strategy

St. Joseph Hospital has been working to expand its community outreach programs related to cancer through a number of projects including offering improved access to clinical trials; providing better overall access to cancer care; and implementing measures to garner support for the implementation of cancer electronic health records. St. Joseph Hospital is using stimulus money and about a $3 million award from the National Cancer Institute Community Cancer Centers Program to help fund its various projects.

Company Background
The company was founded in 1929 by the Sisters of St. Joseph of Orange.

EXECUTIVES

Director Of Nursing, Linda Simon
Vice President Management, Terry Alvarez
Executive Medical Director, Lawrence D Wagman
Vice President Performance Improvement, Mary Ann Vincent
Vice President Site Administrator Sj Wayne Hospital, Daniel Kline
Unit Secretary, Connie Antis
Unit Secretary, Joanne Dour
Board Member, Aa Jewel Box

LOCATIONS

HQ: ST. JOSEPH HOSPITAL OF ORANGE
1100 W STEWART DR, ORANGE, CA 928683891
Phone: 714 633-9111
Web: WWW.SJO.ORG

PRODUCTS/OPERATIONS

Selected Services
Bariatric Surgery
Behavioral Health
Cancer
Nasal & Sinus Center
Heart & Vascular Center
Kidney Dialysis Center
Maternity
Orthopedic Services
Sleep Disorders Center

COMPETITORS

Anaheim Regional
  Medical Center
Children's Hospital of
  Orange County
Citrus Valley Health
  Partners
Hoag Memorial Hospital
  Memorial Health
  Services
Pasadena Hospital
  Association

Providence St. Joseph
  Health
Southwest Healthcare
Sutter Health
Tenet Healthcare
Torrance Memorial
  Medical Center
Trinity Health (Novi)
Western Medical Center
  - Santa Ana

HISTORICAL FINANCIALS

Company Type: Private

Income Statement				FYE: June 30
	REVENUE ($ mil.)	NET INCOME ($ mil.)	NET PROFIT MARGIN	EMPLOYEES
06/17	655	29	4.5%	3,300
06/16	599	11	2.0%	—
06/15	567	2	0.5%	—
06/14	566	(5)	—	—
Annual Growth	4.9%	—	—	—

2017 Year-End Financials

Return on assets: 4.0%   Cash ($ mil.): 14
Return on equity: 8.2%
Current ratio: 1.00

ST. JOSEPH HOSPITAL, INC.

EXECUTIVES

Ceo, Bain J Farris
Prin*, Barb Jahn
Internal Medicine Practitioner, Thomas Perille
Manager of Accounting, Edna Palmer
Executive Assistant, Judy Holbrook
Neurologist, Patricia G Soffer
Registration Manager, Tricia Fox
or Materials Manager, Clarke McDonald
Director, Kelli Lewis

LOCATIONS

HQ: ST. JOSEPH HOSPITAL, INC.
1375 E 19TH AVE, DENVER, CO 802181114
Phone: 303 837-7111
Web: SCLHEALTH.ORG/LOCATIONS/SAINT-JOSEPH-HOSPITAL/

HISTORICAL FINANCIALS

Company Type: Private

Income Statement				FYE: December 31
	REVENUE ($ mil.)	NET INCOME ($ mil.)	NET PROFIT MARGIN	EMPLOYEES
12/16	530	(49)	—	2,400
12/15	498	37	7.5%	—
Annual Growth	6.5%	—	—	—

2016 Year-End Financials

Return on assets: (-6.4%)   Cash ($ mil.): —
Return on equity: (-9.8%)
Current ratio: 2.60

ST. JOSEPH'S HOSPITAL HEALTH CENTER

With about 450 inpatient beds St. Joseph's Hospital Health Center serves the residents of 16 central New York counties. The not-for-profit hospital system provides general emergency and surgical care as well as specialty services in areas such as obstetrics cardiology dialysis and wound care. In addition to its inpatient facilities the organization operates a home health agency a nursing school medical and dental residency programs and several outpatient care centers. Its Franciscan Companies affiliate offers some ancillary services including the provision of medical supplies home health equipment and senior services. St. Joseph's Hospital Health Center was founded in 1869 and became part of Trinity Health in 2015.

Geographic Reach
St. Joseph's Hospital Health Center's service territory includes the New York counties of Broome Cayuga Chenango Cortland Delaware Herkimer Jefferson Lewis Madison Oneida Onondaga Oswego Otsego St. Lawrence Tioga and Tompkins.

EXECUTIVES

Vice President Chief Integrity, Jennifer Reschke Bolster

LOCATIONS

HQ: ST. JOSEPH'S HOSPITAL HEALTH CENTER
301 PROSPECT AVE, SYRACUSE, NY 132031899
Phone: 315 448-5882
Web: WWW.SJHSYR.ORG

PRODUCTS/OPERATIONS

Selected Services
Centers of Excellence
  Cardiac Services
  The Center for Orthopedic and Spine Care
  Vascular Services
  Women and Children's Services
  Wound Care
  Home Care
  Dialysis
  Bariatric (Weight Loss) Services
Other Services and Centers
  Aesthetic Services
  Behavioral Health
  da Vinci Robotic Surgery
  Emergency Services
  Imaging
  Infusion (CPEPCNY)
  Interventional Radiology
  Medical Equipment
  Obstetric Services
  Palliative Care
  Pharmacy
  Physical Medicine & Rehabilitation
  Pulmonary Services
  Sleep Laboratory
  Social Adult Day Care
  Surgical Services
  Urology Services
Outpatient Services
  Dental Services
  Family Medicine Center
  Obstetrics and Gynecology
  Pediatric Office
  Physician Health
  Primary Care
  Westside Family Health Center

COMPETITORS

Catholic Health System
  Ellis Hospital
  Kaleida Health
  Lifetime Health
Oneida Healthcare
  Center

SUNY Upstate Medical
  University
United Health Services
  Hospitals

HISTORICAL FINANCIALS

Company Type: Private

Income Statement				FYE: December 31
	REVENUE ($ mil.)	NET INCOME ($ mil.)	NET PROFIT MARGIN	EMPLOYEES
12/15	542	(2)	—	3,300
12/14	523	0	0.1%	—
12/09	436	5	1.2%	—
12/08	399	6	1.6%	—
Annual Growth	4.5%	—	—	—

2015 Year-End Financials

Return on assets: (-0.6%)   Cash ($ mil.): 36
Return on equity: (-3.9%)
Current ratio: 1.80

ST. JOSEPH'S HOSPITAL, INC.

EXECUTIVES

Pres, Lorraine Lutton
Pres*, Isaac Mallah
Cfo*, Cathy Yoder
V Pres-Fin*, Tommy Inzina
Pres*, Kimberly Guy
Pres*, Paula McGuiness
Cmo*, Peter Charvat
C-Level Human Resources, Craig Brethauer
Executive of Information Techn, Brenda Pingle
Director, Betsy Mead
Facilities Manager, Janet Wells

LOCATIONS

HQ: ST. JOSEPH'S HOSPITAL, INC.
3001 W DR MRTN LTHR KNG B MARTIN LUTHER,
TAMPA, FL 33607
Phone: 813 554-8500
Web: WWW.SJHFOUNDATION.ORG

HISTORICAL FINANCIALS

Company Type: Private

Income Statement				FYE: December 31
	REVENUE ($ mil.)	NET INCOME ($ mil.)	NET PROFIT MARGIN	EMPLOYEES
12/14	872	141	16.2%	300
12/09	719	75	10.4%	—
12/08	663	29	4.5%	—
12/06	565	63	11.2%	—
Annual Growth	5.6%	10.6%	—	—

2014 Year-End Financials

Return on assets: 11.0%
Return on equity: 12.5%
Current ratio: 5.40
Cash ($ mil.): —

ST. JOSEPH'S UNIVERSITY MEDICAL CENTER INC

EXECUTIVES

Pres-Ceo, Kevin Slavin
Cfo*, Dennis Roemer
Chm*, Patricia Thiele
Coo*, Lisa Brady
Chief of Neonatology, Adel M Zauk
Administrative Assistant To Vp, Christine Strangeway
Director of Environmental Svs, John Di' Giovani
Chief of Pulmonary Medicine, M Aness Khan
Doctor, Aldo Khoury
Vice President Human Resources, John P Bruno
Chief of Medicine, Robert C Amoruso

LOCATIONS

HQ: ST. JOSEPH'S UNIVERSITY MEDICAL CENTER
INC
703 MAIN ST, PATERSON, NJ 075032621
Phone: 973 754-2000
Web: WWW.STJOSEPHSHEALTH.ORG

HISTORICAL FINANCIALS

Company Type: Private

Income Statement				FYE: December 31
	REVENUE ($ mil.)	NET INCOME ($ mil.)	NET PROFIT MARGIN	EMPLOYEES
12/16	763	(12)	—	6,000
12/15	752	60	8.0%	
12/08	472	(41)	—	
12/06	437	17	3.9%	
Annual Growth	5.7%	—	—	

2016 Year-End Financials

Return on assets: (-1.5%)
Return on equity: (-6.5%)
Current ratio: 3.60
Cash ($ mil.): 132

ST. JOSEPHS MEDICAL CENTER INC

EXECUTIVES

Pres, Donald J Wiley
V Pres Bus Dev't & Strategy*, Kathy Tohrnan
V Pres Hr*, Nancy Vargas
V Pres Medical Affirs*, Dr Susan McDonald
Vice President of Nursing Svs*, Rae Charos
V Pres Support Srvces*, Terry Spring
Customer Source Liaison, Esther Basilio
Director Physician Recruitment, Doug O' Ryan
Chief Staff, Prafad Dighe
Coordinator of Risk Management, Robin Kelly
Health Professional, Yazeed Arikat

LOCATIONS

HQ: ST. JOSEPHS MEDICAL CENTER INC
1800 N CALIFORNIA ST, STOCKTON, CA 952046019
Phone: 209 943-2000

HISTORICAL FINANCIALS

Company Type: Private

Income Statement				FYE: June 30
	REVENUE ($ mil.)	NET INCOME ($ mil.)	NET PROFIT MARGIN	EMPLOYEES
06/16	478	23	5.0%	150
06/15*	482	48	10.1%	—
12/05	0	0	—	—
Annual Growth	—	—	—	—

*Fiscal year change

2016 Year-End Financials

Return on assets: 5.5%
Return on equity: 9.7%
Current ratio: 2.80
Cash ($ mil.): 16

ST. JUDE HOSPITAL

St. Jude Medical Center gets sickly Southern Californians on their feet again. The faith-based not-for-profit acute care facility with some 385 beds serves the residents of Orange County. The medical center provides an onsite cancer center (the Virginia K. Crosson Cancer Center) and a heart institute that offers cardiac surgeries and re-habilitation programs. It also provides inpatient and outpatient physical rehabilitation services and a variety of community outreach programs. Established by the Sisters of St. Joseph of Orange religious order in the 1950s St. Jude Medical Center is part of the St. Joseph Health System.

Operations

Beyond the medical center's campus St. Jude operates its Heritage Medical Group with outpatient locations throughout its region. The medical group includes specialists in plastic surgery rheumatology and gastroenterology. Altogether St. Jude employs some 700 physicians. It handles more than 17000 inpatient admissions each year as well as 13000 surgeries 2000 births and 54000 emergency room visits.

The organization spends some $47 million in community benefits including outreach and charity care. Its mobile and fixed-site community clinics offer medical dental and preventative care services for low-income residents.

Geographic Reach

St. Jude serves residents in communities in California's Orange County including Brea Buena Park Fullerton La Habra Placentia and Yorba Linda.

Strategy

St. Jude is expanding its facilities through the construction of a new $312 million patient tower schedule to open in late 2014. The Northwest Tower will feature private patient rooms as well as enhanced surgical and data management capabilities. Other improvement measures include technology upgrades such as a new neurovascular surgical system added in 2012.

In October 2011 St. Jude Medical Center closed its 12-bed pediatric unit and redirected patients younger than 16 to nearby Children's Hospital of Orange County. St. Jude's NICU (neonatal intensive care unit) remains open and the hospital continues to provide emergency and outpatient services to children.

EXECUTIVES

Medical Records Director, Pamela Frey
Director Icu Coronary Care Uni, Claudia Skinner
Occupational Medicine, Robert Maurer
Vice President Human Resources, Lisa Schoening
Director Of Pharmacy, Don Miller

LOCATIONS

HQ: ST. JUDE HOSPITAL
101 E VALENCIA MESA DR, FULLERTON, CA
928353875
Phone: 714 871-3280
Web: WWW.STJUDEMEDICALCENTER.ORG

COMPETITORS

Anaheim Regional Medical Center	Memorial Health Services
Children's Hospital of Orange County	Western Medical Center - Santa Ana
Hoag Memorial Hospital	

HISTORICAL FINANCIALS

Company Type: Private

Income Statement				FYE: June 30
	REVENUE ($ mil.)	NET INCOME ($ mil.)	NET PROFIT MARGIN	EMPLOYEES
06/17	544	45	8.3%	2,600
06/16	490	4	0.9%	—
06/15	458	8	2.0%	—
06/14	477	51	10.8%	—
Annual Growth	4.4%	(4.4%)	—	—

ST. LUKE'S EPISCOPAL-PRESBYTERIAN HOSPITALS

St. Luke's Episcopal-Presbyterian Hospital doing business as St. Luke's Hospital provides health care services to St. Louis residents and surrounding areas of eastern Missouri. The medical center houses more than 490 beds and offers general medical and surgical care as well as specialty services in areas such as heart disease cancer neuroscience orthopedics pediatrics and women's health. St. Luke's also operates half a dozen urgent care clinics in St. Louis and St. Charles counties providing treatment for minor emergencies such as cuts and animal bites as well as a skilled-nursing facility rehabilitation hospital and several diagnostic imaging centers. The not-for-profit hospital was founded in 1866.

Operations
In 2014 St. Luke's Hospital had more than 18000 inpatients and 315000 outpatients performed some 17500 surgeries facilitated 1800 births and had more than 30000 emergency department visits.

Financial Performance
In fiscal 2014 (ended June) operating revenue in excess of expense totaled $20.4 million. Total operating revenue grew 4% to $478 million that year.

Strategy
St. Luke's Hospital continues to grow via expansion projects. In 2013 the medical center renovated its neonatal special care nursery adding six private rooms and areas for twins and other multiples to stay together. The following year it opened a new urgent care center and a new facility with the state's only Open Upright MRI scanner. Other urgent care centers and physicians' offices are in the works. In 2015 the hospital broke ground on a $40 million outpatient building on its campus; it is expected to open in late 2016.

The company also grows by adding physicians to its network. During 2014 it added 34 new physicians to its staff with specializations in the areas of primary care neurology oncology cardiovascular orthopedics and others. In all the medical staff has more than 60 specialties.

EXECUTIVES

Vice President, Jan Hess
Secretary, Russell Jokerst
Auditors: KPMG LLP OKLAHOMA CITY OK

LOCATIONS

HQ: ST. LUKE'S EPISCOPAL-PRESBYTERIAN HOSPITALS
232 S WOODS MILL RD, CHESTERFIELD, MO 630173406
Phone: 314 434-1500
Web: WWW.STLUKES-STL.COM

PRODUCTS/OPERATIONS

Selected Services
Brain and spine
Cardiac
Orthopedic
Pulmonary
Sleep medicine
Women's services

COMPETITORS

Barnes-Jewish Hospital
CHRISTUS Health
Mercy Health
SSM Health Care
St. Anthony's Medical Center
Tenet Healthcare

HISTORICAL FINANCIALS
Company Type: Private

Income Statement
FYE: June 30

	REVENUE ($ mil.)	NET INCOME ($ mil.)	NET PROFIT MARGIN	EMPLOYEES
06/15	470	49	10.6%	3,000
06/04	274	11	4.1%	—
06/03	263	9	3.5%	—
06/02	1,170	0	—	—
Annual Growth	—	148.2%	—	—

2015 Year-End Financials
Return on assets: 8.6%
Return on equity: 11.9%
Current ratio: 1.00
Cash ($ mil.): 68

ST. LUKE'S HEALTH NETWORK, INC.

St. Luke's University Hospital (formerly St. Luke's Hospital - Bethlehem Campus)Â serves residents of Pennsylvania's Lehigh Valley with primary specialtyÂ and emergency care services. The not-for-profit teaching hospital has about 480 acute-careÂ beds.Â ItsÂ medical specialties include trauma oncology cardiology orthopedics neurology open-heart surgery radiology and robotic surgery. The medical center also operates outpatient surgery centers and general physicianÂ care clinics and it operates home health and community wellnessÂ programs. St. Luke'sÂ University HospitalÂ was founded in 1872 and is part of the St. Luke'sÂ University Health Network.

EXECUTIVES

Medical Director Emergency Medicine, Christopher Stromski
Vp Finance, Carl Alberto
Auditors: WITHUMSMITHBROWN PC MORRISTOW

LOCATIONS

HQ: ST. LUKE'S HEALTH NETWORK, INC.
801 OSTRUM ST, BETHLEHEM, PA 180151000
Phone: 610 954-4000
Web: WWW.STLUKESPAWILDMED.COM

PRODUCTS/OPERATIONS

Selected Services
Cancer Center
Children's health
Diagnostic and Treatment Centers
Emergency
Heart Center
Neuroscience
Orthopaedics
Radiology/Imaging
Regional Breast Center (Center Valley)
Urgent Care Centers
Women's Imaging & Health Centers

COMPETITORS

Ascension Health
Evangelical Community Hospital
LVHN
Moses Taylor Hospital
Reading Hospital and Medical Center
Sacred Heart Hospital of Allentown
Wyoming Valley Health Care System

HISTORICAL FINANCIALS
Company Type: Private

Income Statement
FYE: June 30

	REVENUE ($ mil.)	NET INCOME ($ mil.)	NET PROFIT MARGIN	EMPLOYEES
06/18	1,844	159	8.6%	2,958
06/17	1,521	121	8.0%	—
06/15	0	0	—	—
06/14	67	0	—	—
Annual Growth	128.7%	—	—	—

2018 Year-End Financials
Return on assets: 7.3%
Return on equity: 19.1%
Current ratio: 1.40
Cash ($ mil.): 106

ST. LUKE'S HEALTH SYSTEM, LTD.

To Catholics St. Luke is also known as the "beloved physician" and St. Luke's Health System strives to live up to its namesake. The regional not-for-profit health system provides a range of health services to residents of Idaho eastern Oregon and northern Nevada. St. Luke's is home to six general acute care hospitals with a total of about 860 beds. Its flagship facility is the 400-bed St. Luke's Boise Medical Center which also includes a full-service children's hospital. St. Luke's also runs a network of cancer care sites under the name Mountain States Tumor Institute as well as a number of urgent care family practice and specialty health centers.

Operations
St. Luke's hospitals handle about 50000 inpatient visits 35000 surgeries and 8000 births each year. The network also sees about 700000 outpatients annually through its urgent care family health and specialty care centers. The company's diagnostic care operations include about five imaging centers and eight breast cancer detection clinics. Overall St. Luke's employs about 1000 physicians.

The Boise campus is home to its tertiary care services - cancer heart and the Children's Hospital - meaning the most acute cases from the region are brought there for the most specialized care. St. Luke's Children's Hospital sees 85000 patient visits a year has Idaho's first and only Pediatric Intensive Care Unit and has the state's largest and most experienced Level III Newborn Intensive Care Unit. Its Boise campus is also the base of St. Luke's Mountain States Tumor Institute (MSTI which cares for about 820 cancer patients a day) and St. Luke's Heart services one of the top 50 cardiovascular programs in the US.

Geographic Reach
St. Luke's has Idaho operations in Boise Caldwell Eagle Fruitland Jerome Ketchum McCall Meridian Mountain Home Nampa and Twin Falls.

Strategy

The growing need for care from each of these leading service lines is a significant part of the Integrated Care Model that has guided the company's Master Plan. St. Luke's has been investing a significant amount of money to upgrade and expand its facilities in recent years.

In 2014 the federal courts ordered St. Luke's to divest Saltzer Medical Group (Idaho's state's largest independent multi-specialty physician practice) after concluding that St. Luke's 2012 acquisition of Saltzer violated Section 7 of the Clayton Act and the Idaho Competition Act.

Company Background

In 2011 St. Luke's completed a $130 million project to rebuild the St. Luke's Magic Valley Medical Center. The new hospital building had about 190 beds and expanded emergency cancer and cardiac centers. The health system was also working to expand its Boise Medical Center's heart and vascular and pediatric departments as well as its system-wide MSTI facilities.

The health system has also expanded its outpatient network to include new family practice emergency care and urgent care clinics in recent years. The network opened a St. Luke's Nampa emergency care clinic and medical complex in 2012. In addition to updating its facilities the St. Luke's Health System was working to upgrade its information technology assets.

St. Luke's added its fifth and sixth acute care hospitals in 2010 and 2011 when the 15-bed St. Luke's McCall (formerly McCall Memorial Hospital) and 25-bed St. Luke's Jerome (formerly St. Benedicts Medical Center) hospitals joined the health network through affiliation and merger agreements.

The health system was formed in 2006 when the three hospitals of the old St. Luke's Regional Medical Center network (Boise Meridian and Wood River) merged with Magic Valley Regional Medical Center a former county facility in Twin Falls Idaho.

EXECUTIVES

President Ceo And Director, David C. Pate
Nursing Director, Katie Schimmelpfennig
Medical Director Mountain States Tumor Institute, Thomas Beck
Chairman, Jon Miller
Auditors: DELOITTE & TOUCHE LLP BOISE

LOCATIONS

HQ: ST. LUKE'S HEALTH SYSTEM, LTD.
190 E BANNOCK ST, BOISE, ID 837126241
Phone: 208 381-2222
Web: WWW.STLUKESONLINE.ORG

PRODUCTS/OPERATIONS

Selected Idaho Facilities
St. Luke's Boise Medical Center (Boise)
St. Luke's Children's Hospital
St. Luke's Clinics (multiple locations)
St. Luke's Eagle Urgent Care (Eagle)
St. Luke's Jerome Medical Center (Jerome)
St. Luke's Magic Valley Medical Center (Twin Falls)
St. Luke's McCall Memorial Hospital (McCall)
St. Luke's Meridian Medical Center (Meridian)
St. Luke's Mountain States Tumor Institute (multiple locations)
St. Luke's Wood River Medical Center (Hailey/Ketchum)

COMPETITORS

Ascension Health
Benedictine Health System
HCA
Intermountain Health Care
Saint Alphonsus Regional Medical Center
Trinity Health (Novi)

HISTORICAL FINANCIALS

Company Type: Private

Income Statement   FYE: September 30

	REVENUE ($ mil.)	NET INCOME ($ mil.)	NET PROFIT MARGIN	EMPLOYEES
09/18	2,602	34	1.3%	7,891
09/17	2,327	10	0.4%	—
09/16	1,937	48	2.5%	—
09/09	49	0	—	—
Annual Growth 55.5%		—	—	—

2018 Year-End Financials

Return on assets: 1.4%   Cash ($ mil.): 121
Return on equity: 3.2%
Current ratio: 1.20

ST. LUKE'S HOSPITAL OF DULUTH

St. Luke's cares for colds cancers and other conditions in the chilly northern US. St. Luke's Hospital provides a variety of health care services to patients in northeastern Minnesota northwestern Wisconsin and parts of Michigan. The medical center has some 270 beds and a staff of about 370 physicians. Services include cardiology emergency medicine pediatrics oncology rehabilitation and vascular surgery. In addition to acute care services the organization offers primary and specialty health care services through a network of outpatient clinics.

Operations

The medical system consists of two hospitals (St. Luke's Hospital and Lake View Hospital) 14 primary care clinics 24 specialty clinics and two pharmacies.

St. Luke's handles about 11000 inpatient visits per year as well as 900 births 10300 surgeries and 73600 emergency room or urgent care visits. Its emergency room serves as a regional trauma center. St. Luke's also sees about 485000 patients annually at its primary and specialty care clinics. Its outpatient service divisions include Q Care (express medical clinic) St. Luke's Orthopedics and St. Luke's Infusion Therapy Clinic. The hospital conducts medical studies through a partnership with the Whiteside Institute for Clinical Research; it also has collaborative care relationships with the Pavilion Surgery Center and the Lake View Memorial Hospital.

Geographic Reach

St. Luke's serves a 17-county region in three states — encompassing northeastern Minnesota northwestern Wisconsin and the western Upper Peninsula of Michigan — through its acute care hospital in Duluth Minnesota and about 40 outpatient clinics providing primary and specialty care services.

Financial Performance

St. Luke's reported $823.5 million in patient services revenue in 2013. After contractual deductions and other obligations total revenues were reported at about $355 million.

Strategy

In 2013 St. Luke's Laurentian Medical Clinic completed a $2 million dollar expansion increasing its size by 60% allowing it to become an ambulatory care center. The clinic offers primary care visiting specialists urgent care and imaging services

including low dose CT ultrasound MRI scans and mobile echocardiography.

To expand its services for area residents in 2012 St. Luke's completed construction of a new medical office building which is located adjacent to the main hospital facilities and will include centers for sports medicine pediatrics neurosurgery and plastic surgery. Also that year St. Luke's opened its da Vinci Si surgical system suite which allows surgeons to conduct minimally invasive surgical procedures using the robotic system.

St. Luke's launched its iPad Project in the Birthing Center allowing new mothers and families can check out an iPad for the duration of their stay. The $100000 project was funded by St. Luke's Foundation's annual Circle of Light event and individual donors.

In 2012 the health system added two urgent care clinics: The Northland Obstetrics & Gynecology Lake View Pharmacy opened as part of the Lake View campus in Two Harbors; St. Luke's Campus Building A opened expanding patient access to specialty care.

Company Background

In 2011 St. Luke's formed a new maternal child health department to improve its birthing services; the new unit provides labor and delivery nursery and pediatric services.

St. Luke's Hospital was founded in 1881. What was established as a typhoid response clinic became the city of Duluth's first hospital.

EXECUTIVES

Treasurer, Barbara Hayden Haugen
Vice Chair, Jeff Borling

LOCATIONS

HQ: ST. LUKE'S HOSPITAL OF DULUTH
915 E 1ST ST, DULUTH, MN 558052193
Phone: 218 726-5555
Web: WWW.SLHDULUTH.COM

Selected Services Centers and Affiliates
Birthing Center
Breast Center
Cardiac Care
Cancer Care
Diagnostic Imaging
Emergency Care
Family Medicine
Laboratory Services
Lake View Pharmacy
Lake View Memorial Hospital
Northland Pharmacy
Pavilion Outpatient Surgery Center
Physical Rehabilitation Services
Sleep Center
St. Luke's Center for Diagnostic Imaging
St. Luke's Foundation
Surgery
Urgent Care
Whiteside Institute for Clinical Research

COMPETITORS

Allina Hospitals
CentraCare Health
First Care
Gillette Children's
Howard Young Health Care
North Memorial Health Care
Sanford Bemidji
Spectrum Health

HISTORICAL FINANCIALS

Company Type: Private

Income Statement				FYE: December 31
	REVENUE ($ mil.)	NET INCOME ($ mil.)	NET PROFIT MARGIN	EMPLOYEES
12/17	471	22	4.7%	2,200
12/16	434	9	2.1%	—
12/13	377	2	0.8%	—
12/09	307	8	2.6%	—
Annual Growth	5.5%	13.5%	—	—

2017 Year-End Financials

Return on assets: 7.3%
Return on equity: 25.8%
Current ratio: 3.00

Cash ($ mil.): 83

ST. LUKE'S REGIONAL MEDICAL CENTER, LTD.

EXECUTIVES

Pres, Edwin Dahlberg
V Pres*, Gary Fletcher
V Pres-Fin*, Clarence Pumeroy
General Manager, Mike Jones
Diagnostic Radiologist, Amaya Basta
Health Professional, Colleen Walker-Vamos
Pediatrician, Elizabeth Kleweno
Health Professional, Elizabeth Olberding
Neurology Specialist, James Whiteside
Pediatrician, Kathryn Beattie
Emergency Medicine Specialist, Kendall Rader

LOCATIONS

HQ: ST. LUKE'S REGIONAL MEDICAL CENTER, LTD.
190 E BANNOCK ST, BOISE, ID 837126241
Phone: 208 381-5500
Web: WWW.STLUKESONLINE.ORG

HISTORICAL FINANCIALS

Company Type: Private

Income Statement				FYE: September 30
	REVENUE ($ mil.)	NET INCOME ($ mil.)	NET PROFIT MARGIN	EMPLOYEES
09/14	1,255	31	2.5%	4,500
09/13	1,121	(19)	—	—
09/08	898	44	4.9%	—
Annual Growth	5.7%	(5.5%)	—	—

2014 Year-End Financials

Return on assets: 1.7%
Return on equity: 4.6%
Current ratio: 5.60

Cash ($ mil.): 258

ST. MARY MEDICAL CENTER

EXECUTIVES

Chb, Ron Gigliotti
Pres*, Greg Wozniak
Cmo*, Charles K Anderson
Cfd, Sharon Prosera
Clinical Coordinator, Jeanette M Bernacki
Outpatient Pharmacy Manager, Jack O' Brien
Cardiology, George Heyrich
Coordinator, Nicole Lattanzio
Personnel Manager, Laura James
Coordinator, Sheilagh Volz
Director of Volunteer, Lil Schonewolf

LOCATIONS

HQ: ST. MARY MEDICAL CENTER
1201 LANGHORNE NEWTOWN RD, LANGHORNE, PA 190471295
Phone: 215 710-2000
Web: WWW.STMARYHEALTHCARE.ORG

HISTORICAL FINANCIALS

Company Type: Private

Income Statement				FYE: June 30
	REVENUE ($ mil.)	NET INCOME ($ mil.)	NET PROFIT MARGIN	EMPLOYEES
06/18	539	50	9.4%	2,400
06/16	419	26	6.3%	—
06/15	443	64	14.5%	—
Annual Growth	6.7%	(7.7%)	—	—

ST. MARY'S HEALTH, INC.

St. Mary's Medical Center of Evansville is a 433-bed hospital serving Indiana's River City. It is the primary facility in regional St. Mary's Health System which is in turn part of Ascension Health. The Evansville hospital provides emergency trauma diagnostic surgical and rehabilitative services as well as specialized cancer cardiac orthopedic and neurological services. With a total of some 750 physicians St. Mary's Health System also includes St. Mary's Hospital for Women & Children (100 beds adjacent to the main hospital) and St. Mary's Warrick (a 25-bed hospital in Boonville Indiana) as well as specialty outpatient surgical cancer and home health units in surrounding areas of southern Indiana.

Operations

St. Mary's Medical Center of Evansville admits some 17000 inpatients annually. It also handles around 64000 emergency room visits and performs approximately 4700 inpatient and 18000 outpatient surgeries each year.

Company Background

St. Mary's Medical Center of Evansville was originally a Marine Hospital built by the US government. When the government shuttered its doors city business leaders bought the building in 1872 and partnered with the Daughters of Charity to operate a community hospital.

EXECUTIVES

Board Member, Anthony Stephens
Auditors: DELOITTE TAX LLP INDIANAPOLIS

LOCATIONS

HQ: ST. MARY'S HEALTH, INC.
3700 WASHINGTON AVE, EVANSVILLE, IN 477140541
Phone: 812 485-4000
Web: WWW.STVINCENT.ORG

PRODUCTS/OPERATIONS

Selected Services

Breast Center
Cancer Care Services
Children's Health Care Services and Programs
Community Outreach Services
Convenient Care Centers
Diabetic Foot Clinic
Diabetes Services
Emergency Services Department
Endoscopy Suite
Foundation
Heart Services
Home Health Services
Hospitalists
Imaging/Radiology
Infusion Center
Laboratory Services
LifeFlight
Medical Equipment
Mental Health Services
Neurosciences & Stroke Care
Occupational Medicine Services
Orthopedic Healthcare
Palliative Care
Pastoral Care
Quality and Patient Safety
Rehabilitation Services
Respiratory Care
Senior Services
Sleep Disorders Center
Surgical Services
Trauma Services
Volunteers & Auxiliary
Weight Management Center
Women's Services and Programs
Women's Wellness Center

COMPETITORS

Ball Memorial Hospital
Community Health Network
Daviess Community Hospital
Deaconess Health System
Good Samaritan Hospital (IN)
Henry County Memorial Hospital
Kosciusko Community Hospital
Memorial Hospital (Logansport)

HISTORICAL FINANCIALS

Company Type: Private

Income Statement				FYE: June 30
	REVENUE ($ mil.)	NET INCOME ($ mil.)	NET PROFIT MARGIN	EMPLOYEES
06/16	495	66	13.3%	3,500
06/15	574	52	9.2%	—
06/13	468	48	10.4%	—
06/11	0	0	—	—
Annual Growth	—	—	—	—

2016 Year-End Financials

Return on assets: 7.7%
Return on equity: 10.2%
Current ratio: 0.60

Cash ($ mil.): 11

ST. MARY'S HEALTH, INC.

LOCATIONS

HQ: ST. MARY'S HEALTH, INC.
3700 WASHINGTON AVE, EVANSVILLE, IN 477140541
Phone: 812 485-7623

HISTORICAL FINANCIALS

Company Type: Private

Income Statement				FYE: June 30
	REVENUE ($ mil.)	NET INCOME ($ mil.)	NET PROFIT MARGIN	EMPLOYEES
06/15	487	71	14.7%	5
06/11	20	4	22.9%	—
06/10	19	2	15.0%	—
Annual Growth	89.4%	88.8%	—	—

2015 Year-End Financials

Return on assets: 8.7%   Cash ($ mil.): 12
Return on equity: 12.5%
Current ratio: 0.50

ST. MARY'S HOSPITAL & MEDICAL CENTER, INC.

EXECUTIVES

Pres, Brian Davidson
V Pres*, Sister Barbara Aldrich
V Pres*, Dan Prinster
Cfo*, Terri Chinn
Coo*, Bryan Johnson
Controller, Thad Ritter
Network Engineer, Allan Worley
Care Manager, Bryan Newman
Surgeon, Charles Breaux
Director Med Rec, Elaine Barnett
Payroll Specialist, Robin Sutton

LOCATIONS

HQ: ST. MARY'S HOSPITAL & MEDICAL CENTER, INC.
2635 N 7TH ST, GRAND JUNCTION, CO 815018209
Phone: 970 298-2273

HISTORICAL FINANCIALS

Company Type: Private

Income Statement				FYE: December 31
	REVENUE ($ mil.)	NET INCOME ($ mil.)	NET PROFIT MARGIN	EMPLOYEES
12/16	450	37	8.2%	2,000
12/15	436	54	12.4%	—
12/14	410	45	11.1%	—
12/09	360	50	13.9%	—
Annual Growth	3.3%	(4.2%)	—	—

2016 Year-End Financials

Return on assets: 5.4%   Cash ($ mil.): 2
Return on equity: 5.6%
Current ratio: 8.40

ST. PETER'S HEALTH CARE SERVICES

Auditors: DELOITTE & TOUCHE LLP ROCHEST

LOCATIONS

HQ: ST. PETER'S HEALTH CARE SERVICES
315 S MANNING BLVD, ALBANY, NY 122081707
Phone: 518 525-1550
Web: WWW.SPHCS.ORG

HISTORICAL FINANCIALS

Company Type: Private

Income Statement				FYE: June 30
	REVENUE ($ mil.)	NET INCOME ($ mil.)	NET PROFIT MARGIN	EMPLOYEES
06/17	1,327	37	2.9%	6,000
06/16	552	39	7.1%	—
06/15	527	44	8.5%	—
06/14	509	21	4.1%	—
Annual Growth	37.6%	21.7%	—	—

2017 Year-End Financials

Return on assets: 2.7%   Cash ($ mil.): 124
Return on equity: 4.4%
Current ratio: 2.60

ST. VINCENT HEALTHCARE

EXECUTIVES

Pres-Ceo, Steve Loveless
Coo*, Jack Bell
Administrative Assistant, Brett Close
Supervisor, Karen Broeder
Director, Annette Hoffman
Internal Medicine Practitioner, Benson Babu
Emergency Medicine Specialist, Douglas Parker
Family Practitioner, Edwin Rodriguez
Internal Medicine Practitioner, Katherine Dietrich
Nephrology Specialist, Marjorie Tevlin
Gastroenterologist, Mary Compton

LOCATIONS

HQ: ST. VINCENT HEALTHCARE
1233 N 30TH ST, BILLINGS, MT 591010127
Phone: 406 657-7000
Web: WWW.SCLHEALTH.ORG

HISTORICAL FINANCIALS

Company Type: Private

Income Statement				FYE: December 31
	REVENUE ($ mil.)	NET INCOME ($ mil.)	NET PROFIT MARGIN	EMPLOYEES
12/17	471	55	11.8%	1,800
12/16	428	15	3.7%	—
12/15	439	58	13.3%	—
12/14	440	40	9.2%	—
Annual Growth	2.3%	11.4%	—	—

2017 Year-End Financials

Return on assets: 8.3%   Cash ($ mil.): —
Return on equity: 8.9%
Current ratio: 12.70

ST. VINCENT HOSPITAL OF THE HOSPITAL SISTERS OF THE THIRD ORDER OF ST. FRANCIS

EXECUTIVES

Chb-Pres, Mary Beth Culnan
Ceo*, Theresa Shuck
V Pres*, Joseph J Neidenbach
Information Specialist, Nikki Vieau
Director, Bobbi Giles
Plant Manager, Rocky Compton
Program Manager, Doreen Kluth
Auditors: CROWE HORWATH LLP CHICAGO IL

LOCATIONS

HQ: ST. VINCENT HOSPITAL OF THE HOSPITAL
SISTERS OF THE THIRD ORDER OF ST. FRANCIS
835 S VAN BUREN ST, GREEN BAY, WI 543013575
Phone: 920 433-0111
Web: WWW.STVINCENTHOSPITAL.ORG

HISTORICAL FINANCIALS

Company Type: Private

Income Statement				FYE: June 30
	REVENUE ($ mil.)	NET INCOME ($ mil.)	NET PROFIT MARGIN	EMPLOYEES
06/16	505	(35)	—	2,360
06/15	480	29	6.0%	—
06/11	424	26	6.3%	—
06/10	376	16	4.4%	—
Annual Growth	5.0%	—	—	—

2016 Year-End Financials

Return on assets: (-5.3%)   Cash ($ mil.): 13
Return on equity: (-8.0%)
Current ratio: 1.90

ST. VINCENT'S MEDICAL CENTER, INC

EXECUTIVES

Pres, Moody Chisolm
Pres*, Blain Claypool
V Pres*, Sean Fitzpatrick
V Pres*, Ann Carey
Coo*, Gene Miyamoto
Coo*, Donnie Romine
Coordinator, Rebecca Timberlake
Trainer Administrative Assista, Candace C Logan
Auditors: DELOITTE TAX LLP CINCINNATI

LOCATIONS

HQ: ST. VINCENT'S MEDICAL CENTER, INC
4205 BELFORT RD STE 4030, JACKSONVILLE, FL
322161475
Phone: 904 308-7300
Web: WWW.JAXHEALTH.COM

HISTORICAL FINANCIALS

Company Type: Private

Income Statement — FYE: June 30

	REVENUE ($ mil.)	NET INCOME ($ mil.)	NET PROFIT MARGIN	EMPLOYEES
06/15	452	32	7.3%	3,535
06/14	445	33	7.4%	—
06/10	448	34	7.7%	—
06/09	377	(32)	—	—
Annual Growth	3.1%	—	—	—

2015 Year-End Financials

Return on assets: 9.9%
Return on equity: 28.2%
Current ratio: 2.60

Cash ($ mil.): 2

STAN BOYETT & SON, INC.

EXECUTIVES

Pres, Dale Boyett
V Pres*, Scott Castle
Accounting Staff, Laverne Couch
Account Executive, Kristine Katz
Manager, David Zellman
District Manager, James Martin
Coordinator, Martha Garcia
Sales, Samantha Falk
Manager, Benjamin Frizzell
Account Executive, Kristine Freitag
Marketing, Michelle Gill

LOCATIONS

HQ: STAN BOYETT & SON, INC.
601 MCHENRY AVE, MODESTO, CA 953505411
Phone: 209 577-6000
Web: WWW.BOYETT.NET

HISTORICAL FINANCIALS

Company Type: Private

Income Statement — FYE: December 31

	REVENUE ($ mil.)	NET INCOME ($ mil.)	NET PROFIT MARGIN	EMPLOYEES
12/08	656	0	0.1%	170
12/07	559	0	0.0%	—
12/06	475	0	0.1%	—
12/05	416	0	0.1%	—
Annual Growth	16.4%	28.4%	—	—

2008 Year-End Financials

Return on assets: 3.3%
Return on equity: 17.6%
Current ratio: 1.00

Cash ($ mil.): 2

STANFORD HEALTH CARE

Doctors patients medical students and researchers gather at Stanford Health Care (formerly Stanford Hospital and Clinics). As Stanford University's primary medical teaching facility the more than 600-bed Stanford Hospital specializes in such areas as cardiac care cancer treatment neurology surgery and organ transplant. The affiliated Stanford Clinics is a physician group practice organization that represents more than 100 specialized fields of medicine. Stanford Health Care is part of the Stanford Medicine organization which also includes the nearby Stanford University School of Medicine and the 310-bed Lucile Packard Children's Hospital (named for the wife of Hewlett-Packard co-founder David Packard).

Operations

Stanford Health Care handles some 25000 inpatient admissions each year more than 50000 emergency room visits and about 425000 outpatient encounters. The organization boasts such specialized clinics as the Byers Eye Institute the Stanford Comprehensive Cancer Center the Stanford Center for Marfan Syndrome and Aortic Disorders and the California VitreoRetinal Center. It also operates centers for orthopedic brain blood and marrow transplant and other specialist procedures.

Educational programs include medical and graduate student training as well as residency and fellowship programs. The organization also conducts research in medical and biological fields.

Additionally the system owns stakes in physician network University HealthCare Alliance radiation therapy facility Stanford Emanuel Radiation Oncology Center health care advocacy firm Care-Counsel and HMO plan University HealthCare Advantage.

Geographic Reach

Stanford Health Care operates in more than 15 locations in the San Francisco Bay Area.

Sales and Marketing

Stanford Health Care receives 70% of its revenues from managed care (commercial insurance) providers. Another 20% of patient service income is sourced to Medicare and Medicaid programs.

Financial Performance

Revenue increased 10% to $3 billion in fiscal 2014 (ended August) due to higher net patient service revenues primarily from managed care and Medicare fee increases. However net income dropped 22% to $432.2 million that year as operating costs rose and the system reported losses on investments.

Cash flow from operations grew 8% to $366.5 million in fiscal 2014 largely due to a change in working capital items.

Strategy

To remain at the forefront of medicine and technology the hospital is constructing a new $2 billion 600-bed facility next to its existing building. Local high-tech firms including Apple Hewlett-Packard and Intel are kicking in $15 million and technology partnerships to support the project. As corporate partners the firms will help to develop and integrate state-of-the-art information technology for the new facility.

Other growth projects include the construction of a new outpatient cancer clinic in San Jose. The center opened in 2014.

Also in 2014 the system changed its name from Stanford Hospitals and Clinics to Stanford Health Care. That change signified the broader scope of its operations which go beyond inpatient and outpatient facilities to include affiliated physician practices and health plans.

In fiscal 2015 Stanford Health Care engineers developed and launched a new MyHealth mobile application for the iPhone. The app connects with Epic electronic health records and Apple's HealthKit enabling patients to monitor their health data. MyHealth provides consumers with such capabilities as telehealth (video) physician visits appointment scheduling online payments and the ability to manage prescriptions and access test results.

EXECUTIVES

President And Ceo, David Entwistle
Vp And Chief Marketing Officer, Deborah Italiano
Chief Risk Officer, Jeff Driver
Vp Clinical Cancer Center And Cardiovascular Health, Sridhar Seshadri
Chief Medical Officer, Norman W. Rizk
Coo, Quinn L. McKenna
Cio, Pravene Nath
Coo, James Hereford
Interim Cfo, David Connor
Chief Quality Officer, Raj Behal
Chief Medical Information Officer, Christopher (Topher) Sharp
Director Of Respiratory Therap, Robert Shields
Ambulatory Services Dir, Catherine Krna
Department Head, Craig Burkhart
Vice President, Jaclyn Tandler
Ambulatory Services Dir, Sue Hoopes
Auditors: PRICEWATERHOUSECOOPERS LLP SA

LOCATIONS

HQ: STANFORD HEALTH CARE
300 PASTEUR DR, STANFORD, CA 943052200
Phone: 650 723-4000

PRODUCTS/OPERATIONS

2014 Sales

	$ mil.	% of total
Net patient service revenue	2,839	95
Premium revenue	60	2
Other revenue	98	3
Total	**2,998**	**100**

Selected Services

Heart Center
Neurosciences
Orthopaedics
Sports Medicine
Stanford Cancer Center
Surgical Services
Transplant

COMPETITORS

Dignity Health	Sutter Health
Sequoia Capital	UCSF Medical

HISTORICAL FINANCIALS

Company Type: Private

Income Statement — FYE: August 31

	REVENUE ($ mil.)	NET INCOME ($ mil.)	NET PROFIT MARGIN	EMPLOYEES
08/18	4,910	456	9.3%	5,045
08/17	4,454	450	10.1%	—
08/15	3,570	372	10.4%	—
08/10	2,141	186	8.7%	—
Annual Growth	10.9%	11.9%	—	—

2018 Year-End Financials

Return on assets: 6.3%
Return on equity: 11.5%
Current ratio: 0.50

Cash ($ mil.): 652

STANFORD HEALTH SERVICES

LOCATIONS

HQ: STANFORD HEALTH SERVICES
  300 PASTEUR DR, STANFORD, CA 943052200
Phone: 650 723-4000
Web: WWW.STANFORDCHILDRENS.ORG

HISTORICAL FINANCIALS

Company Type: Private

Income Statement   FYE: August 31

	REVENUE ($ mil.)	NET INCOME ($ mil.)	NET PROFIT MARGIN	EMPLOYEES
08/11	2,510	415	16.6%	4
08/10	2,141	186	8.7%	—
Annual Growth	17.2%	123.2%	—	—

2011 Year-End Financials

Return on assets: —   Cash ($ mil.): 395
Return on equity: 16.6%
Current ratio: 0.50

STAPLE COTTON COOPERATIVE ASSOCIATION

Referred to as Staplcotn the Staple Cotton Co-operative has been a staple of its member-producers' business lives since 1921. One of the oldest and largest cotton marketing co-ops in the US it provides domestic and export marketing cotton warehousing and agricultural financing to some 9730 members in 47 states. As of 2011 the co-op handles nearly 14000 farm accounts in 10 states. Staplcotn's inventory is consigned by member-producers and averages from 2.5 million to 3 million bales of cotton a year. The co-op operates though 15 warehouses serving the mid-south and south-eastern US to supply more than 25% of the cotton consumed by the US textile industry as well as the needs of textile mills overseas.

EXECUTIVES

Vp Sales Operations, David Camp
Vice President, Shane Stephens
Vp Human Resources, Russell Robertson
Vice President Customer Service And Support,
  Sterling Jones

LOCATIONS

HQ: STAPLE COTTON COOPERATIVE ASSOCIATION
  214 W MARKET ST, GREENWOOD, MS 389304329
Phone: 662 453-6231
Web: WWW.STAPLCOTN.COM

PRODUCTS/OPERATIONS

Selected Services
Cotton services
  Loans
  Mill Sales Program
Marketing
Stapldiscount
Warehouse

COMPETITORS

Alabama Farmers Cooperative	King Ranch
Calcot	Louis Dreyfus Group
Cargill	Noble Group
Dunavant Enterprises	Olam
International Cotton Marketing	Plains Cotton
J.G. Boswell Co.	Southern States
JB Cotton	Tennessee Farmers Co-op
	Weil Brothers Cotton

HISTORICAL FINANCIALS

Company Type: Private

Income Statement   FYE: August 31

	REVENUE ($ mil.)	NET INCOME ($ mil.)	NET PROFIT MARGIN	EMPLOYEES
08/13	1,138	5	0.5%	187
08/12	1,236	8	0.7%	—
08/11	963	875	90.8%	—
Annual Growth	8.7%	(91.7%)	—	—

2013 Year-End Financials

Return on assets: 2.5%   Cash ($ mil.): 33
Return on equity: 5.3%
Current ratio: 1.80

STATE BOARD FOR COMMUNITY COLLEGES AND OCCUPATIONAL EDUCATIONAL SYSTEM

EXECUTIVES

Pres, Nancy McCallin
V Pres, Cliff Richardson
Administrative Assistant, Daniel Baniszewski
Coordinator, Stacy Roe
Education Specialist, Terry Reeves
Director, Karen Funston
Cognos Administrator, Douglas Stormont
Project Manager Business Proce, Krystal Dilka
Benefits Specialist Colorado C, Teresa Murphy
Senior Linux Admin Colorado Co, Carlos Naranjo
Vice President, Geri Anderson
Auditors: KPMG LLP DENVER COLORADO

LOCATIONS

HQ: STATE BOARD FOR COMMUNITY COLLEGES AND
  OCCUPATIONAL EDUCATIONAL SYSTEM
  9101 E LOWRY PL, DENVER, CO 802306011
Phone: 303 595-1552
Web: WWW.SANDRACLARKFINEART.COM

HISTORICAL FINANCIALS

Company Type: Private

Income Statement   FYE: June 30

	REVENUE ($ mil.)	NET INCOME ($ mil.)	NET PROFIT MARGIN	EMPLOYEES
06/18	471	(365)	—	2,658
06/16	460	(9)	—	—
06/15	412	2	0.5%	—
06/13	0	0	3.0%	—
Annual Growth	327.3%		—	—

2018 Year-End Financials

Return on assets: (-29.9%)   Cash ($ mil.): 288
Return on equity: —
Current ratio: 4.50

STATE OF CALIFORNIA

EXECUTIVES

Governor, Gavin Newsom
Lt. Governor*, Eleni Kounalakis
Consultant, A Kirk McKenzie
Chief Licensing/Information Te, Brian Desmarais
Chief Information Security Off, Carol Kelly
Budgets and Fiscal STA, Caroline McNeil
Computer Support Staff Represe, Cheryl Drefs
Budgets and Fiscal STA, Diane Herteg
Chief Technology Support Servi, Jim Rengstorff
AG Technician II, Jose Antonio Diaz
Analyst, Karen Bianchi Walsh
Auditors: JOHN F COLLINS II CPA DEPUTY

LOCATIONS

HQ: STATE OF CALIFORNIA
  STATE CAPITAL, SACRAMENTO, CA 95814
Phone: 916 445-2864
Web: WWW.CA.GOV

HISTORICAL FINANCIALS

Company Type: Private

Income Statement   FYE: June 30

	REVENUE ($ mil.)	NET INCOME ($ mil.)	NET PROFIT MARGIN	EMPLOYEES
06/16	255,725	4,798	1.9%	208,580
06/15	249,923	6,252	2.5%	—
06/14	219,871	8,082	3.7%	—
06/13	204	8	3.9%	—
Annual Growth	976.7%	742.3%	—	—

STATE OF NEW YORK MORTGAGE AGENCY

The State of New York Mortgage Agency (SONYMA pronounced "Sony Mae") is a public benefit corporation of the State of New York that makes homebuying more affordable for low- and moderate-income residents of the state. SONYMA has two program divisions: Its single-family programs and financing division provides low-interest rate mortgages to first-time homebuyers with low and moderate incomes through the issuance of mortgage revenue bonds while its mortgage insurance fund provides mortgage insurance and credit support for multi-family affordable residential projects and special care facilities throughout the state.

EXECUTIVES

Vice President, Daniel Murphy
Assistant Vice President, Robert Rosado
Vice President Special Projects, Mark Flescher
Vice President Internal Audit, Stephen Chopey
Senior Vice President, Michael Friedman
Vice President, Michael Esposito
Assistant Vice President, Olivia Jervis

Avp Originations Project Set Aside Director,
Marie Cammarata
Auditors: ERNST & YOUNG LLP NEW YORK N

LOCATIONS

HQ: STATE OF NEW YORK MORTGAGE AGENCY
641 LEXINGTON AVE FL 4, NEW YORK, NY
100224503
Phone: 212 688-4000
Web: WWW.NYSHCR.ORG

HISTORICAL FINANCIALS

Company Type: Private

Income Statement				FYE: October 31
	ASSETS ($ mil.)	NET INCOME ($ mil.)	INCOME AS % OF ASSETS	EMPLOYEES
10/18	5,324	147	2.8%	221
10/17	5,228	34	0.7%	—
10/16	5,187	63	1.2%	—
10/09	5,225	162	3.1%	—
Annual Growth	0.2%	(1.0%)	—	—

STATE OF OKLAHOMA

EXECUTIVES

Governor, Kevin Stitt
Lt Gov*, Todd Lamb
General Counsel-Sec*, James Williamson
Sec, Science and Innovation, Kayse Shrum
Sec, Health and Mental Health, Jerome Loughridge
Contracting Andamp, Kathy Hallum
Sales Representative, Amanda Porter
Coordinator Mark, Barbara Charlet
Personnel Director, Barbara Jones
Assistant Professor, Blaine Mooers
Senior Vice President, Brian Maddy
Auditors: GARY A JONES CPA CFE OKLAH

LOCATIONS

HQ: STATE OF OKLAHOMA
421 NW 13TH ST STE 220, OKLAHOMA CITY, OK
731033784
Phone: 405 521-2342
Web: WWW.OK.GOV

HISTORICAL FINANCIALS

Company Type: Private

Income Statement				FYE: June 30
	REVENUE ($ mil.)	NET INCOME ($ mil.)	NET PROFIT MARGIN	EMPLOYEES
06/18	17,805	602	3.4%	37,613
06/17	17,175	48	0.3%	—
06/16	16,789	(1,025)	—	—
06/15	17,331	314	1.8%	—
Annual Growth	0.9%	24.2%	—	—

2018 Year-End Financials

Return on assets: 1.4%   Cash ($ mil.): 6,680
Return on equity: 2.2%
Current ratio: 2.80

STATE OF RHODE ISLAND AND PROVIDENCE PLANTATIONS

EXECUTIVES

Gov, Gina M Raimondo
Lt Gov, Daniel J McKee
State Controller, Lawrence C Franklin Jr
Research Scientist, Adam Miller
Grant Manager, Andrea Creach
Control Administrator, Arthur Sheridan
Research Technician, Caitlin Oconnor
Human Resources Manager, Cecille Antonelli
Associate Director, Cheryl Burrell
Human Resources Rep, Crystine Marandola
Manager, David Salvatore
Auditors: DENNIS E HOYLE CPA-OFFICE OF

LOCATIONS

HQ: STATE OF RHODE ISLAND AND PROVIDENCE PLANTATIONS
82 SMITH ST STE 102, PROVIDENCE, RI 029031121
Phone: 401 222-2080
Web: WWW.GOPROVIDENCE.COM

HISTORICAL FINANCIALS

Company Type: Private

Income Statement				FYE: June 30
	REVENUE ($ mil.)	NET INCOME ($ mil.)	NET PROFIT MARGIN	EMPLOYEES
06/17	7,012	215	3.1%	13,535
06/16	6,860	(10)	—	—
06/15	6,787	160	2.4%	—
06/14	6,282	(46)	—	—
Annual Growth	3.7%	—	—	—

2017 Year-End Financials

Return on assets: 1.4%   Cash ($ mil.): 1,215
Return on equity: 8.7%
Current ratio: 2.10

STATE OF TEXAS

EXECUTIVES

Governor, Greg Abbott
Chief of Staff*, Luis Saenz
Deputy Chief of Staff*, David Whitley
Chief Operating Officer*, Reed Clay
Deputy Chief of Staff*, Jordan Hale
Senior Adviser For State Opera, Steven Albright
Texas District Attorney, Andria Bender
Senior Adviser, Sarah Hicks
Deputy Director, Aimee Snoddy
Regional Manager, Alan Piller
Computer Operator, Allan Bagby
Auditors: JOHN KENT CPA AUSTIN TEXAS

LOCATIONS

HQ: STATE OF TEXAS
CAPI BLDG 1100 N CONG AVE, AUSTIN, TX 78701
Phone: 512 463-2000

HISTORICAL FINANCIALS

Company Type: Private

Income Statement				FYE: August 31
	REVENUE ($ mil.)	NET INCOME ($ mil.)	NET PROFIT MARGIN	EMPLOYEES
08/17	115,336	1,882	1.6%	144,175
08/15	107,350	1,993	1.9%	—
08/14	109,860	8,184	7.4%	—
08/13	0	0	—	—
Annual Growth	—	—	—	—

2017 Year-End Financials

Return on assets: 0.6%   Cash ($ mil.): 29,217
Return on equity: 1.1%
Current ratio: 1.90

STATE UNIVERSITY OF NEW YORK

SUNY days are ahead for many New Yorkers seeking higher education. With an enrollment of more than 460000 students The State University of New York (SUNY) is vying with California State University System for the title of largest university system in the US. Most students are residents of New York State. Students come from all 50 states as well as 160 countries. SUNY maintains 64 campuses around the state including four university centers about two dozen university colleges 30 community colleges and a handful of technical colleges as well as medical centers. The system has a student-teacher ratio of about 16:1.

Operations

The school offers more than 7500 undergraduate programs of study — including engineering business literature medicine agriculture performing arts and human services. SUNY also offers about 400 study abroad programs.

EXECUTIVES

Pres, Havidan Rodriguez
Chb, Merryl H Tisch
Acting Pres, James Stellar
Pres, Tina Good
Prin, John B King Jr
Interim Chancellor, John B Clark
Cfo - V Chancellor, Kimberly R Cline
Provost - V Chancellor - Acade, Peter D Salins
V Chancellor - SEC of The Univ, John O'Connor
V Chancellor - Business & Indu, R Wayne Diesel
Auditors: KPMG LLP ALBANY NY

LOCATIONS

HQ: STATE UNIVERSITY OF NEW YORK
353 BROADWAY, ALBANY, NY 122462915
Phone: 518 320-1100
Web: WWW.SUNY.EDU

HISTORICAL FINANCIALS

Company Type: Private

Income Statement				FYE: June 30
	REVENUE ($ mil.)	NET INCOME ($ mil.)	NET PROFIT MARGIN	EMPLOYEES
06/12	5,961	(374)	—	88,024
06/06*	4	(2)	—	—
10/05	0	0	—	—
Annual Growth	—	—	—	—
*Fiscal year change				

Return on assets: (-2.5%)   Cash ($ mil.): 1,642
Return on equity: —
Current ratio: 1.50

STATEN ISLAND UNIVERSITY HOSPITAL

Staten Island University Hospital (SIUH) ferries health care services to residents of New York City's fastest growing borough and surrounding areas at its two medical campuses. Established in 1861 SIUH maintains about 715 beds and is a teaching affiliate of the State University of New York's Brooklyn Health Science Center. Its larger north campus includes units specializing in cardiology pathology cancer blood-related diseases burn treatment trauma and women's health. The south campus site offers specialty programs such as sleep medicine geriatric psychiatry and substance abuse services. A member of Northwell Health SIUH employs approximately 1200 physicians.

Operations

SIUH's Heart Institute of Staten Island located on the north campus is a joint venture between the hospital and Richmond University Medical Center. The Heart Institute specializes in cardiac diagnostics and "beating heart" surgeries.

The hospital operates several general physician practice and specialty health clinics on Staten Island. It also provides a home visit program and hospital-based hospice services.

SIUH is an affiliate of the SUNY Health Science Center at Brooklyn; its campuses serve as clinics for the Hofstra North Shore-LIJ School of Medicine which SIUH owns in partnership with Hofstra University.

In 2013 SIUH had nearly 3000 births nearly 45000 hospital discharges about 126000 emergency department visits and more than 16000 ambulatory surgeries.

EXECUTIVES

Pres, Anthony C Ferreri
Exec V Pres*, Robin Wittenstein
V Pres-Fin-Controller*, John Steiger
Cfo*, Thomas Reca
Exec V Pres*, Nicholas Caruselle
Sr V Pres*, Margaret Dialto
V Pres*, John P Demoleas
SEC*, Arthur Fried
Exec Dir*, Donna Proske
Staff, Vincent Logatto
Sr Hr Rep, Jenie Grodowski

LOCATIONS

HQ: STATEN ISLAND UNIVERSITY HOSPITAL
475 SEAVIEW AVE, STATEN ISLAND, NY 103053436
Phone: 718 226-9000

PRODUCTS/OPERATIONS

Selected Services

Behavioral Health
Cancer Services
Cardiac Services
Cardiovascular and Thoracic Surgery
Medical Services including Endocrinology
Gastroenterology Nephrology and Pulmonary
Neuroscience and Spine Services
Orthopedic Services
Pediatrics
Rehabilitation Medicine

Surgical Services including General Surgery Colorectal Head & Neck and Urology
Trauma and Burn Services
Women's Health

Selected Centers of Care

Center for Bariatric Surgery
Comprehensive Breast Center
Heart Institute
Institute of Sleep Medicine
Level III Perinatal Center
New York Head & Neck Institute at Staten Island University Hospital
Regional Burn Center
Stroke Center
The Elizabeth A. Connelly Emergency and Trauma Center
The Sanford R. Nalitt Institute for Cancer and Blood Related Diseases; Children's Cancer Center

COMPETITORS

Bronx-Lebanon Hospital
Catholic Healthcare System
CenterLight Health System Inc.
Continuum Health Partners
Eger Health Care
Kingsbrook Jewish Medical Center
Maimonides Medical Center
MediSys Health Network
New York City Health and Hospitals
NewYork-Presbyterian Healthcare

HISTORICAL FINANCIALS

Company Type: Private

Income Statement				FYE: December 31
	REVENUE ($ mil.)	NET INCOME ($ mil.)	NET PROFIT MARGIN	EMPLOYEES
12/17	891	69	7.8%	5,700
12/16	871	57	6.6%	—
12/15	850	41	4.9%	—
12/14	811	51	6.4%	—
Annual Growth	3.2%	10.2%	—	—

2017 Year-End Financials

Return on assets: 6.5%   Cash ($ mil.): 5
Return on equity: 12.0%
Current ratio: 3.60

STEPHEN GOULD CORPORATION

Others can worry about what's inside — Stephen Gould Corporation concentrates on the package. The company provides a full range of packaging-related design and printing services for customers worldwide. Its products include gift packaging point-of-purchase displays product merchandising and retail and industrial packaging. Stephen Gould Corporation also provides graphic design and package-engineering services as well as assembly and fulfillment. The company was originally founded in 1939 by Stephen Gould David Golden and Leonard Beckerman.

Geographic Reach

Stephen Gould Corporation operates from about 40 facilities; branches are located primarily in the US (more than 20 states) but also in China Ireland Malaysia and Mexico.

EXECUTIVES

Executive Vice President Operations, John Golden

LOCATIONS

HQ: STEPHEN GOULD CORPORATION
35 S JEFFERSON RD, WHIPPANY, NJ 079811043
Phone: 973 428-1500
Web: WWW.GOULDNY.COM

PRODUCTS/OPERATIONS

Selected Products and Services

Products
Aerospace reusable cases
Corrugated containers
Gift packaging
Industrial packaging
Point of sale packaging
Protective packaging
Services
Creative services
Logistics & facilities
Package design & engineering

COMPETITORS

Consolidated Carqueville
Focus Packaging & Display group
Fort Dearborn
Gibraltar Packaging
Metro Packaging and Imaging
R.R. Donnelley
WS Packaging Group

HISTORICAL FINANCIALS

Company Type: Private

Income Statement				FYE: December 31
	REVENUE ($ mil.)	NET INCOME ($ mil.)	NET PROFIT MARGIN	EMPLOYEES
12/17	678	7	1.1%	325
12/16	665	11	1.8%	—
12/13	526	3	0.7%	—
12/12	526	3	0.7%	—
Annual Growth	5.2%	14.7%	—	—

2017 Year-End Financials

Return on assets: 2.9%   Cash ($ mil.): 7
Return on equity: 9.3%
Current ratio: 1.90

STEVENS TRANSPORT, INC.

Staying cool is a must for Stevens Transport. An irregular-route refrigerated truckload carrier (or reefer) Stevens hauls temperature-controlled cargo throughout the US covering the 48 contiguous states. Through alliances Stevens also covers every province in Canada and every state in Mexico. The company operates a fleet of about 2000 Kenworth and Peterbuilt tractors and 3500 Thermo King refrigerated trailers from a network of more than a dozen service centers. Partnerships with railroads allow Stevens to arrange intermodal transport of temperature-controlled cargo. The company also provides third-party logistics services. Stevens Transport was founded in 1980.

Operations

The company owns 49% of B2B Transport which provides an array of transportation related services to large mid-sized and small companies throughout North America.

Geographic Reach

Stevens Transport maintains its operations across Canada Mexico and the US through its partnerships with BNSF Norfolk Southern CSX and

Union Pacific. It has 13 logistics offices located in Canada and throughout the US.

Sales and Marketing

Stevens has provided refrigerated shipping services for such big names as General Mills Kraft Foods M&M Mars Procter & Gamble and Wal-Mart.

Strategy

Even in a US economy ripe with unpredictable fuel costs and a decline in consumer confidence one thing has always worked in Stevens' favor: people will always need their food. The company has managed to maintain a steady growth rate by keeping costs down updating the technology of its trucking equipment and maintaining an efficient operating structure. Along these lines in 2012 it implemented new mobile computing platforms across its fleet of tractors to enhance its customer services and optimize productivity.

EXECUTIVES

Vice President Risk Management, William Tallent
Executive Vice President, Mike Richey
National Accounts Manager, Brandon Bogusch
Vice Chairman, Todd Aaron
Auditors: SADDOCK & CO PLLC DALLAS T

LOCATIONS

HQ: STEVENS TRANSPORT, INC.
9757 MILITARY PKWY, DALLAS, TX 752274805
Phone: 972 216-9000
Web: WWW.STEVENSTRANSPORT.COM

PRODUCTS/OPERATIONS

Selected Services

Intermodal

International

Logistics

Truckload

COMPETITORS

C.R. England	Marten Transport
Central Refrigerated Service	Navajo Shippers
	Prime Inc.
Comcar	Southern Refrigerated
Covenant Transportation	Transport
	TransAm Trucking
Frozen Food Express	Watkins Associated
Henderson Trucking	Industries
Jim Palmer Trucking	Willis Shaw Express
KLLM Transport Services	

HISTORICAL FINANCIALS

Company Type: Private

Income Statement				FYE: December 31
	REVENUE ($ mil.)	NET INCOME ($ mil.)	NET PROFIT MARGIN	EMPLOYEES
12/15	668	87	13.0%	2,100
12/12	607	85	14.0%	—
12/11	566	76	13.5%	—
12/08	550	0	0.0%	—
Annual Growth	2.8%	505.7%	—	—

2015 Year-End Financials

Return on assets: 13.0%
Return on equity: 16.3%
Current ratio: 4.60
Cash ($ mil.): 152

STEWARD HEALTH CARE SYSTEM LLC

Steward Health Care System is a steward of its patients' good health. With a total of some 7300 beds Steward Health operates 36 hospitals in 10 states including Holy Family Hospital Norwood Hospital St. Elizabeth's Medical Center The Medical Center of Southeast Texas and Pikes Peak Regional Hospital. Several of the hospitals are affiliated with Boston-area medical schools. The company also has managed operations in Arizona Utah and Massachusetts. Steward Health also includes a physician practice organization an outpatient clinic network and a home care and hospice agency. Steward which is owned by Cerberus Capital Management merged with IASIS Healthcare in 2017 to become the US' largest private for-profit hospital operator.

Operations

Steward Health is a community-based care organization that offers a full range of health care services. Its operations include integrated network physicians 36 hospital campuses more than 25 affiliated urgent care providers more than 40 preferred skilled nursing facilities and other services.

The three main components of the system are: Steward Medical Group (which has more than 1400 providers and has more than 1 million patient encounters per year in 10 states); Steward Health Care Network (a fully integrated care management company with some 4800 providers and 2 million patient encounters per year); and Steward Hospitals.

Other operations include Steward Home Care and Hospice Steward Urgent Care and Steward Insurance Plans

Strategy

Steward Health provides care for patients across the care spectrum. By providing health care services in a coordinated and more efficient manner the system is able to control costs and improve quality eliminate care fragmentation and reduce duplication of services in the delivery of health care.In 2016 sold its hospitals to Medical Properties Trust in a sale-leaseback transaction that provided capital to pay down debt make improvements at its facilities and pursue geographic expansion.

Among the company's initiatives has been to expand beyond its base in Massachusetts as evidenced by its 2017 acquisition of IASIS Healthcare (which added 18 hospitals to its network). It made a sale-leaseback arrangement with Medical Properties Trust for 10 hospitals gained in the IASIS transaction.

The largest private hospital operator in the US Steward Health is very secretive with its financial statements.

Mergers and Acquisitions

In 2017 Steward Health completed a major acquisition when it bought eight hospitals from Community Health Systems for $304 million. The hospitals located in Ohio Pennsylvania and Florida were the company's first outside of New England. The deal added some 1800 beds to its operations.

Later that year the company made an even bigger smash when it merged with IASIS Healthcare to create a system with 36 hospitals (with some 7500 beds) in 10 states as well as managed care operations in three states.

Company Background

The company changed its name from Caritas Christi to Steward Health after being acquired by Cerberus Capital Management in 2010; it had pre-viously been operated by the Catholic Archdiocese of Boston. The acquisition by Cerberus was worth some $895 million and provided operational funding and capital for hospital improvement projects; it also helped pay down debt obligations. As a result of the transaction Steward Health became a for-profit corporation; however a stipulation of the deal mandated that the health system's hospitals retain their pastoral and charitable care policies. The sale to Cerberus was not the first attempt by the Archdiocese of Boston to sell the ailing Caritas Christi system which had been suffering from financial troubles for several years prior to the deal.

EXECUTIVES

Senior Vice President Chief Marketing Officer, Brian Carty
Coo, Joshua S. Putter
President Steward Medical Network, Mark Girard
Chairman And Ceo, Ralph de la Torre
Evp And General Counsel, Joseph Maher
Cfo, Mark Rich
Evp, Robert E. (Bob) Guyon
President - Steward Medical Group, Michael G. Callum
Chief Information Officer, Drexel DeFord
President, Craig A. Jesiolowski
Executive Vice President Network Insurance And Physician Operations, John Polanowicz
Vp Hr, Patrick Lombardo

LOCATIONS

HQ: STEWARD HEALTH CARE SYSTEM LLC
1900 N PEARL ST STE 2400, DALLAS, TX 752012470
Phone: 469 341-8800
Web: WWW.STEWARD.ORG

Services

Behavioral Health Services
Centers for Cancer Care
Center for Advanced Cardiac Surgery
Centers for Cardiac and Vascular Care
Centers for Weight Control
Home Care and Hospice
MAKOplasty®; Services
Maternity Services

Selected Hospitals

Arizona
Mountain Vista Medical Center (Mesa)
St. Luke's Medical Center (Phoenix)
Tempe St. Luke's Hospital
Arkansas
Wadley Regional Medical Center at Hope
Colorado
Pikes Peak Regional Hospital & Surgery Center (Woodland Park)
Florida
Rockledge Regional Medical Center
Sebastian River Medical Center
Louisiana
Glenwood Regional Medical Center (West Monroe)
Massachusetts
Carney Hospital (Dorchester)
Good Samaritan Medical Center (Brockton)
Holy Family Hospital (Methuen)
Morton Hospital (Taunton)
Nashoba Valley Medical Center (Ayer)
New England Sinai Hospital (Stoughton)
Norwood Hospital
Quincy Community Care Network
Saint Anne's Hospital (Fall River)
St. Elizabeth's Medical Center (Brighton)
Ohio
Northside Regional Medical Center (Youngstown)
Trumbull Regional Medical Center (Warren)
Pennsylvania
Easton Hospital
Sharon Regional Medical Center
Texas
Southwest General Hospital (San Antonio)
The Medical Center of Southeast Texas (Port Arthur)
The Medical Center of Southeast Texas — Victory Campus (Beaumont)
Utah
Davis Hospital and Medical Center (Layton)

Jordan Valley Medical Center (West Jordan)
Mountain Point Medical Center (Lehi)

COMPETITORS

Adventist Health System Sunbelt Healthcare
Berkshire Health Systems
Boston Medical Center
Cambridge Health Alliance
Cape Cod Healthcare
Care New England
CareGroup
Children's Hospital Boston
Emerson Hospital
Hallmark Health
John C. Lincoln Health Network
New England Alliance for Health
Northeast Health System
Partners HealthCare
Southcoast Hospitals Group
University of Utah Hospitals & Clinics
Winchester Healthcare

HISTORICAL FINANCIALS
Company Type: Private

Income Statement				FYE: September 30
	REVENUE ($ mil.)	NET INCOME ($ mil.)	NET PROFIT MARGIN	EMPLOYEES
09/07	1,240	30	2.5%	37,000
09/06	1,220	47	3.9%	—
09/05	27	2	8.0%	—
Annual Growth	572.6%	272.9%	—	—

2007 Year-End Financials
Return on assets: 3.6%   Cash ($ mil.): 73
Return on equity: 10.8%
Current ratio: 1.10

STEWART'S SHOPS CORP.

I scream you scream we all scream for Stewart's ice cream — especially if we live in upstate New York or Vermont home to some 330 Stewart's Shops. The chain of convenience stores sells more than 3000 products across 30-plus counties. They include dairy items groceries food to go (soup sandwiches hot entrees) beer coffee gasoline and of course ice cream. In addition to its retail business the company owns about 100 rental properties including banks hair salons and apartments near its stores. Stewart's Shops formerly known as Stewart's Ice Cream Company was established in 1945. The founding Dake family owns about two-thirds of the company; employee compensation plans own the rest.

Operations

The convenience store chain which spans New York and Vermont offers consumers milk ice creams coffee to-go foods beer gasoline and groceries. As part of its business Stewart's Shops also acquires and develops (preferably adjacent) properties the likes of shops banks hair salons and apartments that it then leases or sells.

Stewart's Shops makes its own dairy products including its own ice cream in more than 50 flavors that are hand-dipped and packaged. Recognized for its quality products the company relies on a group of about 45 farmers in New York to supply its milk.

The vertically-integrated company which makes about 75% of the items it sells also offers private-label goods and national brands in its stores. Its private-label brands extend far beyond dairy products to include soda chips bread and juices.

Geographic Reach

Based in New York Stewart's Shops operates a chain of convenience stores across upstate New York and in Vermont.

Sales and Marketing

Stewart's Shops serves consumers through its New York and Vermont shops; two-thirds of its stores sell gas.

Strategy

The convenience store operator regularly extends its reach. In 2014 it's focused on Syracuse New York following several store openings in 2013 in Keeseville Herkimer Rotterdam and Heuvelton New York. The latter shops boast an expanded cooler walk-in beer cave and seating.

The company is also investing in environmentally friendly facilities. In 2013 for instance it had 2400 solar panels installed at its manufacturing and distribution center. Stewart's Shops anticipates that the effort will save nearly $40000 a year in energy costs at the plant after about a 5-year period.

It enlisted the help of Paragon Software in 2014 to automate the planning of daily and seasonal deliveries. In turn Stewart's Shops aims to lower mileage reduce fuel usage and improve truckload efficiencies.

EXECUTIVES

Pres, Gary C Dake
Chm*, William P Dake
V Pres*, Nancy Trimbur
Asst Treas*, David Farr
Treas*, Michael Cocca
SEC*, Matthew Gutch
Distribution/Shipping/Transpor, Chris Burby
Information Technology Manager, Lisa Vanslyke
Merchandizer, Carrie Niciu
Real Estate Conultant, Chuck Marshall
Project Coordinator, Mike Cannizzo
Auditors: SAXBST LLP ALBANY NEW YORK

LOCATIONS

HQ: STEWART'S SHOPS CORP.
2907 STATE ROUTE 9, BALLSTON SPA, NY
120204201
Phone: 518 581-1201
Web: WWW.STEWARTSSHOPS.COM

PRODUCTS/OPERATIONS

Selected Products

Beverages

Coffee
Ice Cream
Food to go
Gasoline
Groceries
Milk

COMPETITORS

7-Eleven   Hannaford Bros.
Ben & Jerry's   Kroger
Carvel   McDonald's
Cumberland Farms   Sunoco
Exxon Mobil   TravelCenters of
Friendly's Ice Cream   America
Golub

HISTORICAL FINANCIALS
Company Type: Private

Income Statement				FYE: December 31
	REVENUE ($ mil.)	NET INCOME ($ mil.)	NET PROFIT MARGIN	EMPLOYEES
12/17	1,542	92	6.0%	3,800
12/16	1,405	80	5.7%	—
12/14	1,610	59	3.7%	—
12/13	1,577	73	4.7%	—
Annual Growth	(0.6%)	5.9%	—	—

2017 Year-End Financials
Return on assets: 12.7%   Cash ($ mil.): 50
Return on equity: 16.1%
Current ratio: 3.10

STILLWATER MINING COMPANY

EXECUTIVES

Pres-Ceo, Michael J McMullen
Cfo*, Christopher M Bateman
V Pres Safety Health & Hr*, Kristen K Koss
V Pres Mine Oprs*, Dee L Bray
Foreman/Supervisor, Dave Crabtree
Accounting Team Member, Luttschwager Yvonne
Production Shifter, Blaise Gubler
Production Superviser, Jason Sironen
Senior Site Accountant, Joyce Weber
Manager of Materials, Wayne Gransbery
Raisebore, Jeff Branson
Auditors: KPMG LLP BILLINGS MONTANA

LOCATIONS

HQ: STILLWATER MINING COMPANY
26 W DRY CREEK CIR # 400, LITTLETON, CO
801204475
Phone: 406 373-8700
Web: WWW.STILLWATERMINING.COM

COMPETITORS

Anglo American   Impala Platinum
  Platinum   Lonmin
Aquarius Platinum   North American
Diadem Resources   Palladium
Franco-Nevada   Vale Limited

HISTORICAL FINANCIALS
Company Type: Private

Income Statement				FYE: December 31
	REVENUE ($ mil.)	NET INCOME ($ mil.)	NET PROFIT MARGIN	EMPLOYEES
12/16	711	9	1.3%	1,432
12/15	726	(23)	—	—
12/14	943	68	7.3%	—
12/13	1,039	(302)	—	—
Annual Growth	(11.9%)	—	—	—

2016 Year-End Financials
Return on assets: 0.7%   Cash ($ mil.): 123
Return on equity: 1.0%
Current ratio: 7.00

STOCKTON UNIFIED SCHOOL DISTRICT

EXECUTIVES

Supt, Dr Steve Lowder
Pres*, Sara L Cazares
Vice Pres*, Gloria Allen
Psychologist, Scott Runion
Research/Development Director, Mong Thi Nguyen
Mechanical Division Manager, Tabatha Hoak
Senior Personnel Technician, Alicia Cabrera
Kindergarten Teacher, Tracey Gray
Counselor, Alejandro Duran
Program Coordinator, Bernadette Bettencourt
Executive Assistant II, Carmen Jimenez

LOCATIONS

HQ: STOCKTON UNIFIED SCHOOL DISTRICT
701 N MADISON ST, STOCKTON, CA 952021634
Phone: 209 933-7000
Web: WWW.STOCKTONUSD.NET

HISTORICAL FINANCIALS
Company Type: Private

Income Statement   FYE: June 30

	REVENUE ($ mil.)	NET INCOME ($ mil.)	NET PROFIT MARGIN	EMPLOYEES
06/18	536	(24)	—	3,000
06/17	557	36	6.6%	—
06/16	527	98	18.6%	—
06/11	354	(1)	—	—
Annual Growth	6.1%	—	—	—

STORMONT-VAIL HEALTHCARE, INC.

EXECUTIVES

Ceo, Randall Peterson
Ceo*, Randy Peterson
Vice Pres*, Tracy O'Rourke
Sr V Pres-Medi Dir, Kent Palmberg
V Pres-Medi Svc Div*, Deb Yocum
V Pres-Chf Info Offc*, Janet Stanek
V Pres-Patient Care Svcs*, Carol Perry
V Pres-Fclty Mgmt*, David Cuningham
V Pres-Hr*, Bernard Becker
Cfo*, Kevin Han
Svp-Gen Counsel-Chief Complian*, Kevin Steck
Auditors: RSM US LLP DAVENPORT IOWA

LOCATIONS

HQ: STORMONT-VAIL HEALTHCARE, INC.
1500 SW 10TH AVE, TOPEKA, KS 666041301
Phone: 785 354-6000
Web: WWW.STORMONTVAIL.ORG

HISTORICAL FINANCIALS
Company Type: Private

Income Statement   FYE: September 30

	REVENUE ($ mil.)	NET INCOME ($ mil.)	NET PROFIT MARGIN	EMPLOYEES
09/18	719	88	12.4%	4,500
09/17	654	70	10.8%	—
09/16	634	30	4.8%	—
09/15	582	(9)	—	—
Annual Growth	7.3%	—	—	—

2018 Year-End Financials
Return on assets: 11.0%   Cash ($ mil.): 101
Return on equity: 18.3%
Current ratio: 2.50

STRACK AND VAN TIL SUPER MARKET INC.

One of Chicagoland's leading grocery chains Strack & Van Til operates more than 35 supermarkets in and around Chicago and northern Indiana. Stores operate under the banners of Strack & Van Til Town & Country Food Market and Ultra Foods. The regional grocery chain offers fresh and packaged foods and has delicatessen and bakery divisions in each of its stores. Its websites offer weekly circulars and coupons as well as feature recipes cooking videos meal planners and food-related articles. The company is owned by Chicago-based grocery distributor Central Grocers which also operates supermarkets under the Berkot's and Key Market banners.In 2017 Central Grocers filed for Chapter 11 bankruptcy protection and put Strack & Van Til up for sale as part of the filing.

Strategy

Strack & Van Til and its regional rivals are facing increased competition from national chains including Wal-Mart and Trader Joe's moving into the market while taking advantage of the woes of smaller ones. Rather than retreat the grocery chain is pursuing a growth strategy acquiring seven stores in its market area in late 2012. (With Safeway-owned Dominick's Supermarkets on the block its stores are in play.) It is also investing in its existing stores and stocking more organic foods to compete with the likes of Whole Foods. The company is revamping supermarkets in Valpariso Hobart and Chesterton was well as an Ultra Foods store in Highland Strack's supermarkets in Munster and Schereville and an Ultra in Lansing are slated for upgrades as well.

Wal-Mart which had been expanding aggressively in the Chicago suburbs has begun opening supercenters and smaller Walmart Express stores within the city limits. Its arrival has sparked fierce price competition among area grocers. Other relative newcomers to the Illinois grocery market include Roundy's and non-traditional grocery chains such as SuperTarget stores and limited-assortment ALDI. To take on nationwide retailers Strack & Van Til bands together with other independent stores as members of the Central Grocers cooperative. The combined buying power helps the stores to offer competitive pricing and product selection.

In late 2013 the grocery chain launched a new marketing campaign I'm a Strack & Van Til Shopper to appeal to a wide audience while maintaining the company's value proposition.

Mergers and Acquisitions

In December 2012 Strack & Van Til acquired seven grocery stores from Indiana-based WiseWay Supermarkets. Four of the stores were converted to the Strack & Van Til banner while three became Ultra Foods stores. Like Strack & Van Til Wise-Way was also supplied by Central Grocers.

EXECUTIVES

Pres, David Wilkinson
V Pres*, Andrew Raab
V Pres*, Jeff Strack
Cfo*, Keith Bruxvoort
V Pres*, Robert Wasiuta
V Pres*, Rex Mudge
V Pres*, Joe Kolavo
SEC*, Jim Denges
Executive Assistant, Danielle Ramirez
Director, Mike Mulle
Field Supervisor, Gale Mote
Auditors: MCGLADREY & PULLEN LLP CHICAG

LOCATIONS

HQ: STRACK AND VAN TIL SUPER MARKET INC.
2244 45TH ST, HIGHLAND, IN 463222629
Phone: 219 924-7588

COMPETITORS

ALDI	Target Corporation
Jewel Osco	Trader Joe's
Kmart	Wal-Mart
Meijer	Whole Foods
Roundy's	

HISTORICAL FINANCIALS
Company Type: Private

Income Statement   FYE: August 1

	REVENUE ($ mil.)	NET INCOME ($ mil.)	NET PROFIT MARGIN	EMPLOYEES
08/10	961	15	1.7%	2,000
08/09	995	13	1.4%	—
Annual Growth	(3.4%)	16.1%	—	—

2010 Year-End Financials
Return on assets: 7.7%   Cash ($ mil.): 10
Return on equity: 12.9%
Current ratio: 1.40

SUASIN CANCER CARE INC.

Auditors: ERNST & YOUNG US LLP SAN DIEG

LOCATIONS

HQ: SUASIN CANCER CARE INC.
1301 PUNCHBOWL ST, HONOLULU, HI 968132402
Phone: 512 583-0205

HISTORICAL FINANCIALS
Company Type: Private

Income Statement   FYE: June 30

	REVENUE ($ mil.)	NET INCOME ($ mil.)	NET PROFIT MARGIN	EMPLOYEES
06/15	1,003	50	5.0%	4
06/14	851	31	3.7%	—
06/13	856	109	12.8%	—
Annual Growth	8.2%	(32.4%)	—	—

Return on assets: 3.4%   Cash ($ mil.): 29
Return on equity: 7.9%
Current ratio: 0.30

SUFFOLK CONSTRUCTION COMPANY, INC.

Suffolk Construction Company provides construction services from top to bottom. The company kicks off the building process with pre-construction services and follows through with design/build general contracting and construction management. Suffolk Construction builds for both the public and private organizations in the science and technology health care education government and commercial sectors operating in the Northeast Mid-Atlantic Southeast and West Coast regions of the US. Founded in 1982 the privately-held firm is owned by president and CEO John Fish whose family has been in construction for four generations.

Geographic Reach

The Boston-based construction firm operates nationwide across the Northeast Mid-Atlantic Southeast and West Coast regions. Its offices are located Boston; Miami; Los Angeles; San Diego; San Francisco; Tarrytown New York; and Estero Florida.

Sales and Marketing

Suffolk Construction offers its services for projects in the assisted living aviation and transportation commercial education entertainment government healthcare hospitality non-profit residential retail and science and technology sectors.

The company has also worked on projects for federal and local governments. In the past Suffolk has built for the Army Corps of Engineers the US Marine Corps and US Navy.

Strategy

Suffolk reemphasized its "Build Smart" approach in 2015 which is designed to boost productivity and cut costs in the construction management process on every project. Before the company breaks ground at a job site it uses technologies such as virtual models and Building Information Modeling (BIM) to build projects virtually. The practice minimizes risk lessens design conflicts and issues and lowers costs for Suffolk Construction clients.

Suffolk Construction serves several sectors to keep the company thriving even in challenging times. The firm extended its reach into the growing health care sector by launching National Healthcare Group which specializes in building health care projects nationwide.

Company Background

Already a successful builder in the New England area Suffolk Construction has expanded nationally in the past through acquisitions. In 2009 it bought Massachusetts-based William A. Berry & Son creating Suffolk's Berry Division which specializes in health care and biomedical projects.

Suffolk Construction also acquired The Dietze Construction Group based in Ashburn Virginia in 2010. The deal strengthened Suffolk's position in the Mid-Atlantic region and expanded its ability to serve the government health care education science/technology and commercial sectors. Giving

the company a boost in the West Suffolk Construction acquired Southern California-based ROEL Construction in 2011.

EXECUTIVES

Chairman And Ceo, John F. Fish
President West Region, Andrew J. (Andy) Ball
Evp And Cfo, Michael (Mike) Azarela
President And General Manager Northeast Region, Mark L. DiNapoli
President & General Manager Southeast Region, Rex B. Kirby
General Manager San Diego, Wayne Hickey
Chief Operating Officer San Francisco Office, Michael (Mike) DiNapoli
Executive Vice President Work Acquisition Northeast Region, Peter Welsh
President Healthcare/science And Technology & Chief Innovation Officer, Peter Campot
Vice President And Chief Information Officer, Corren Collura
Evp And General Manager Mid-atlantic Region, Stephen Skinner
Vice President & Chief Operating Officer Commercial Education And Government Northeast Region, Angus Leary
Executive Vice President Of National Business Development, Christopher Woods
Senior Vice President Chief Information Officer, Kevin McDonough
Executive Vice President And General Manager, Jeffrey Gouveia
Vice President Retail, Mike DiNapoli
Executive Vice President And Chief Innovation Officer, Chris Mayer
Vice President Customer Soluti, Chris Gedrich
Vice President Preconstruction, David Slomsky
Vice President, Christopher Debruin
Treas, Mike Lindblom

LOCATIONS

HQ: SUFFOLK CONSTRUCTION COMPANY, INC.
65 ALLERTON ST, BOSTON, MA 021192923
Phone: 617 445-3500
Web: WWW.SUFFOLK.COM

PRODUCTS/OPERATIONS

Selected Services
Building information modeling
Construction management
Design/build
General contracting
Preconstruction
Sustainable building

COMPETITORS

Balfour Beatty Construction	Pepper Construction
Clark Enterprises	Swinerton
DooleyMack	Turner Corporation
Kraus-Anderson	Tutor Perini
McCarthy Building	Walsh Group
	Whiting-Turner

HISTORICAL FINANCIALS
Company Type: Private

Income Statement				FYE: August 31
	REVENUE ($ mil.)	NET INCOME ($ mil.)	NET PROFIT MARGIN	EMPLOYEES
08/15	2,500	0	—	1,150
08/14	1,761	0	—	—
08/13	1,825	0	—	—
Annual Growth	17.0%	—	—	—

2015 Year-End Financials
Return on assets: —   Cash ($ mil.): 126
Return on equity: —
Current ratio: 1.10

SUMMIT HEALTH

EXECUTIVES

Pres-Ceo, Norman P Epstein
Prin*, Patrick O'Donnell
Assistant Controller, Lori Leedy
Engineer, Roger Shadle
Administrative Assistant, Audra Price
Human Resources, Margie Gyurisin
Buyer, Sara Johnson
Project Manager, Karen Lison
Director, Charles Rickard
Doctor, Jane Rice
Cardiology Director, Arshad Safi
Auditors: SMITH ELLIOTT KEARNS & COMPANY

LOCATIONS

HQ: SUMMIT HEALTH
112 N 7TH ST, CHAMBERSBURG, PA 172011720
Phone: 717 267-3000
Web: WWW.SUMMITHEALTH.ORG

HISTORICAL FINANCIALS
Company Type: Private

Income Statement				FYE: June 30
	REVENUE ($ mil.)	NET INCOME ($ mil.)	NET PROFIT MARGIN	EMPLOYEES
06/18	539	33	6.3%	2,968
06/17	520	85	16.4%	—
06/16	480	(37)	—	—
06/15	445	9	2.2%	—
Annual Growth	6.6%	50.5%	—	—

2018 Year-End Financials
Return on assets: 4.5%   Cash ($ mil.): 36
Return on equity: 6.9%
Current ratio: 1.50

SUN COAST RESOURCES, INC.

Breaking the glass ceiling with large containers of Texas tea woman-owned Sun Coast Resources buys refined oil and sells it to more than 10000 third-party customers such airlines and construction educational energy industrial and retail companies in about 40 states. The company has an extensive truck fleet (more than 1000 vehicles) and delivers gasoline and diesel fuels marine and aviation fuels and lubricants. It also provides oilfield transportation and services onsite and fleet fueling petroleum tanks and generator fueling services. Sun Coast was founded in 1985 by president and CEO Kathy Lehne with $2000 in start-up capital.

Operations

Sun Coast carries a full line of Chevron oils and lubricants and is one of Chevron's largest lubricant distributors in the US. Other Sun Coast services include additive packages bulk storage and warehousing a computerized fleet tracking system and customized schedule and deliveries. The company has 1.5 million gallons of bulk fuel storage more than 10000 fuel and lubricant tanks including skid tanks aviation certified tanks emergency ISO tanks and others. Its truck fleet includes bobtails lowboys lube trucks pick-ups roll-backs and vacuum trucks.

Its transport trucks are capable of hauling 7500 gallons of diesel fuel and 8600 gallons of gasoline. Its bobtails are used for orders of less than 4500 gallons. Sun Coast's lubricant trucks are capable of hauling 2000 gallons of bulk lubricants as well as drums totes and other packaged products.

The company's products include aviation gasoline (avgas) gasoline jet fuel kerosene marine diesel ultra-low sulfur diesel fuel and Chevron Conoco Mystik Phillips 66 and TOTAL lubrication products. It also offers services card lock service filtration and fluid purification fleet fueling and mobile on-site fueling spill response and other services.

Sun Coast's crude/condensate segment serves more than 300 well sites and numerous gathering facilities and transports more 37000 barrels per day (more than 10 million barrels a year).

Geographic Reach

Sun Coast owns and operates 17 offices in Arkansas New Mexico Mississippi Oklahoma Texas and Louisiana. It also has more than of 350000 sq. ft. of office and warehouse space in nine facilities in Texas. It markets its products in 39 US states. Sun Coast also provides equipment and services in fast-growing shale plays including the Eagle Ford Eagle Ford Bryan Permian Haynesville Cline Woodford and Marcellus.

Sales and Marketing

Sun Coast provides fuel supply services and related equipment to communication companies delivery services firms government entities utilities and other fleet operators.

Financial Performance

Hurt by lower oil prices in 2014 Sun Coast's revenues declined to $1.8 billion down slightly on 2013.

Strategy

The company pursues a strategy of organic growth supplemented by complementary acquisitions in its core geographic markets.

In 2015 Chevron selected Sun Coast to be the sole provider of Chevron ISOClean products and services in Texas and surrounding areas. The ISO-CLEAN Program is a first of its kind national program that offers a solution to particle contamination through products and in-plant services designed to assist customers in maximizing the life of their equipment by meeting stringent quality control standards set by original equipment manufacturers.

Company Background

It expanded into Louisiana in 2012 with the purchase of St. Martin Oil and Gas which operated a small fleet of fuel transportation trucks from two bulk storage facilities in St. Martinville and Denham Springs.

Further expanding its portfolio in 2012 the company acquired assets from bankrupt SMF Energy including its wholly owned affiliate H&W Petroleum Co. Properties included more than 100 fuel trucks and support vehicles previously used by SMF's mobile refueling operations outside of Texas and about 100 fuel and chemical transportation and support vehicles from H&W its Lufkin blending facility and fuel storage tanks across Texas.

That year Sun Coast further expanded its branded and unbranded fuel and lubricant distribution business by buying Houston-based ADA Resources.

In 2011 the company bought the commercial fuel and disaster response businesses of Cypress Texas-based Roy Moffitt Customized Fueling.

EXECUTIVES

President And Ceo, Kathy Lehne
Vp Sales And Marketing, Kyle Lehne
Director Information Technology, Bryan Frazier
President And Cfo, Sheila Kahanek
Operations Manager, Larry Bothmann

LOCATIONS

HQ: SUN COAST RESOURCES, INC.
6405 CAVALCADE ST BLDG 1, HOUSTON, TX 770264315
Phone: 713 844-9600
Web: WWW.SUNCOASTRESOURCES.COM

PRODUCTS/OPERATIONS

Selected Products
Petroleum Products
  Aviation gasoline
  High sulfur diesel fuel
  Jet fuel
  Kerosene
  Lubricants
  Marine fuels
  Mid-grade fuel
  Low sulfur diesel fuel
  Premium low sulfur diesel fuel
  Premium unleaded gasoline
  Unleaded gasoline
Oils and Lubricants
  Automatic transmission fluid
  Chain oils
  Food-grade oils
  Fuel Additives
  Gear oils
  Greases
  Heat transfer oils
  Hydraulic oils
  Metal-working oils
  Motor oils
  Refrigeration oils
  Solvents and chemicals

Selected Mergers and Acquisitions

COMPETITORS

George Warren
  Global Partners
  Gulf Oil
  J.A.M. Distributing

Martin Resource
  Management
Mercury Air Group

HISTORICAL FINANCIALS
Company Type: Private

Income Statement				FYE: December 31
	REVENUE ($ mil.)	NET INCOME ($ mil.)	NET PROFIT MARGIN	EMPLOYEES
12/07	1,064	2	0.3%	1,649
12/06	864	7	0.8%	—
12/05	867	13	1.6%	—
12/04	697	3	0.4%	—
Annual Growth	15.1%	(2.7%)	—	—

2007 Year-End Financials

Return on assets: 2.3%   Cash ($ mil.): —
Return on equity: 13.4%
Current ratio: 3.30

SUN MAR MANAGEMENT SERVICES

EXECUTIVES

Ceo, Frank Johnson
Cfo, Bill Presnell
Offc Mgr, Deloris Toney
Data Processing Staff, Angelo D Jesus
Director, Susanne Dean
Executive Vice-President, Kelly Iasparro

LOCATIONS

HQ: SUN MAR MANAGEMENT SERVICES
3050 SATURN ST STE 201, BREA, CA 928216278
Phone: 714 577-3880
Web: WWW.SUN-MAR.COM

HISTORICAL FINANCIALS
Company Type: Private

Income Statement				FYE: March 31
	REVENUE ($ mil.)	NET INCOME ($ mil.)	NET PROFIT MARGIN	EMPLOYEES
03/09*	742	0	0.1%	500
12/08	6	(0)	—	—
Annual Growth	**********%	—	—	—

*Fiscal year change

SUNBELT SUPPLY L.P.

EXECUTIVES

Ceo-Pres, Scott Jackson
S Vp of Fin, Joao Vaz
Sr V Pres-Gen Counsel, Suzanne Mailes-Dineff
Senior Vice President of Busin, Dan Sisney
Manager, Anthony James

LOCATIONS

HQ: SUNBELT SUPPLY L.P.
3750 HWY 225, PASADENA, TX 77503
Phone: 713 672-2222
Web: WWW.FLOWORKSPVF.COM

HISTORICAL FINANCIALS
Company Type: Private

Income Statement				FYE: January 31
	REVENUE ($ mil.)	NET INCOME ($ mil.)	NET PROFIT MARGIN	EMPLOYEES
01/14	657	24	3.8%	573
01/13	668	28	4.3%	—
Annual Growth	(1.6%)	(14.5%)	—	—

SUNDT CONSTRUCTION, INC.

EXECUTIVES

Ceo-Pres, G Michael Hoover
Svp-Gen Counsel*, Ronald Stuff
Svp/Cfo/Treas*, Kevin M Burnett
Payroll Staff, Karolyn Comstock
Vice-President Business Develo, Cade Rowly
Staff, Patrick Comiskey
Coordinator, Kimberly Evans
Pres-Industrial Group, Richard Keil
Contractor, Dave Fleming
Project Director, Hal Hardister
Operations Manager, Jim Pullen
Auditors: MAYER HOFFMAN & MCCANN

HISTORICAL FINANCIALS

Company Type: Private

Income Statement
FYE: September 30

	REVENUE ($ mil.)	NET INCOME ($ mil.)	NET PROFIT MARGIN	EMPLOYEES
09/18	1,432	0	—	1,000
09/17	1,134	0	—	—
09/16	813	0	—	—
09/13	895	0	—	—
Annual Growth	9.8%	—	—	—

2018 Year-End Financials

Return on assets: —
Return on equity: —
Current ratio: 1.70
Cash ($ mil.): 140

SUNKIST GROWERS, INC.

Sunkist Growers is one business that is least susceptible to an outbreak of scurvy among its employees. America's oldest continually operating citrus cooperative the company is owned by California and Arizona citrus growers who farm some 300000 acres of citrus trees. Sunkist offers traditional and organic fresh oranges lemons limes grapefruit and tangerines worldwide. The co-op which operates some 20 packing facilities also makes juice and cut fruit packaged in jars. Fruit that doesn't meet fresh market standards is turned into oils and peels for use in food products made by other manufacturers. Sunkist's customers include food retailers and manufacturers and food-service providers worldwide.

Operations

The cooperative's seasonal citrus includes Meyer lemons mandarin oranges Clementine oranges blood oranges and tangelos. Sunkist is one of the most recognized brand names in the world.

Through some 40 licensing agreements the Sunkist name appears on more than 600 beverages and other products — from vitamins to candy to soda to pistachios. It offers Sunkist Fruit Gems (gummie candies) made for the company by the Jelly Belly Candy Company.

Some 45% of Sunkist's fresh fruit sales revenues come from markets outside the US as well as more than 20% of its processed products revenues. To maintain its reach abroad Sunkist works with the US government and the governments of foreign countries to open new markets that are off limits to Western citrus growers.

Geographic Reach

California-based Sunkist operates in the Americas Europe the Middle East and Asia Pacific.

Sales and Marketing

Sunkist regularly advertises worldwide to encourage use of its citrus products and build its brand. Additionally the company leverages television to get its name out such as its alliance with the NBC motivational weight loss competition The Biggest Loser .

Sunkist which has operated a centralized sales organization since 2009 sells its products primarily to food retailers and manufacturers as well as to foodservice providers worldwide. The company is the largest marketing cooperative in the global fruit and vegetable industry.

Financial Performance

Gross annual sales of Sunkist-brand products exceed $1.2 billion worldwide.

Strategy

The company has been focused on market and portfolio expansion and getting the most from its citrus juice and oils and for-profit businesses. It is working to extend its reach to new markets such as India the Middle East and Eastern Europe where its core product has not historically been traded. To reach beyond citrus and expand its products portfolio Sunkist is concentrating on table grapes. Through a pilot program with its existing citrus growers the company markets Sunkist-branded California table grapes grown by them.

It also worked in recent years to improve the productivity of its Tipton juice processing plant. To this end Sunkist in 2012 entered a 50:50 joint venture agreement with fellow juice processor Ventura Coastal. Under the name Ventura Coastal LLC the entity operates the Ventura Coastal plant in Visalia and the Sunkist plant in Tipton. Beginning in 2013 Sunkist also partnered with Greene River Marketing to sell its Florida citrus in promising domestic and export markets.

The 2011-2012 growing season got off to a late start thanks to slow maturing fruit. Its navel orange crop grew to a manageable 88 million cartons as compared to a challenging 93-million-carton crop the previous year. Lemons started slowly as well but both demand and price picked up. Protected groves fared well during the year while unprotected ones — those outside the traditional growing areas — did not. More susceptible to the cold mandarins crops have suffered.

EXECUTIVES

Managing Director Of Global Licensing, Mark Madden
Coo And Vp, Christian Harris

LOCATIONS

HQ: SUNKIST GROWERS, INC.
27770 ENTERTAINMENT DR, VALENCIA, CA 913551092
Phone: 661 290-8900
Web: WWW.SUNKIST.COM

PRODUCTS/OPERATIONS

Selected Products

Fresh fruit
  Grapefruit
  Melo Golds
  Oro Blancos
  Pummelos
  Sweeties
  Texas Rio Star
  Western
  Lemons
  Eurkea/Lisbon
  Meyer
  Limes
  Key
  Persian
  Mandarins
  Clementine
  Honey
  Royal
  Satsuma
  Shasta Gold
W. Murcott
  Oranges
  Cara Cara
  Moro
  Navel
  Valencia
  Tangelos
  Minneola
  Orlando
  Tangerines
  Dancy
  Fairchild
  Pixie

Packaged fruit
  Beverage concentrates
  Carbonated beverages (under license)
  Chilled fruit jellies (under license)
  Fruit juice
  Fruit juice drinks
  Fruit snacks (under license)
  Powdered fruit drinks
  Vitamins (under license)

COMPETITORS

Alico Inc.	Lionel Hitchen
Big Heart Pet Brands	Louis Dreyfus Group
Chiquita Brands	M&B Products
Citrus World	Old Orchard
Coca-Cola	Orchard House Foods
Dole Food	R & Z Ventures
Dundee Citrus Growers	Silver Springs
Edinburg Citrus	Southern Gardens
Fresh Del Monte Produce	Citrus
Freshco	Sunny Delight
Great Western Juice	Tropicana
King Ranch	U.S. Sugar
Lake Placid Groves	Wonderful Company

HISTORICAL FINANCIALS

Company Type: Private

Income Statement
FYE: October 31

	REVENUE ($ mil.)	NET INCOME ($ mil.)	NET PROFIT MARGIN	EMPLOYEES
10/18	1,359	2	0.2%	500
10/17	1,299	9	0.7%	—
10/16	1,207	7	0.6%	—
10/15	1,150	5	0.5%	—
Annual Growth	5.7%	(20.9%)	—	—

2018 Year-End Financials

Return on assets: 1.2%
Return on equity: 2.0%
Current ratio: 1.40
Cash ($ mil.): 31

SUNOCO PIPELINE L.P.

LOCATIONS

HQ: SUNOCO PIPELINE L.P.
4041 MARKET ST, UPPER CHICHESTER, PA 190143121
Phone: 610 859-5700

HISTORICAL FINANCIALS

Company Type: Private

Income Statement
FYE: December 31

	REVENUE ($ mil.)	NET INCOME ($ mil.)	NET PROFIT MARGIN	EMPLOYEES
12/17	804	1,419	176.6%	3
12/16	1,070	796	74.4%	—
Annual Growth	(24.9%)	78.2%	—	—

SUNTORY INTERNATIONAL CORP.

Suntory USA established in the 1960s on the other side of the globe from its parent Japanese trading giant Suntory Holdings Limited imports Suntory products to the US market from its New York headquarters. Well-known offerings include wine beer and distilled spirits such as Yamazaki Single Malt Whisky and Zen Green Tea and Midori Melon liqueurs. Other operations handled by Suntory USA include a soft drink bottling business (Pepsi Bottling Ventures) a winery various restaurants and its parent's bottled water division Suntory Water Group once the second-largest bottled water producer in the US. Altogether Suntory USA comprises 17 companies contributing 4% of its parent's 2013 revenue.

EXECUTIVES

Pres, Tsuyoshi Nishizaki
Exec V Pres, Yoshihiko Kunimoto
Cfo, Tsutomu Santoki
Treas, Yoshito Shihara
SEC, Masaru Ijima
Agent, David L Hayutin
Sales Manager, Mauro Vidale
Auditors: PRICEWATERHOUSECOOPERS LLP NE

LOCATIONS

HQ: SUNTORY INTERNATIONAL CORP.
4141 PARKLAKE AVE STE 600, RALEIGH, NC 276122380
Phone: 917 756-2747

PRODUCTS/OPERATIONS

Selected Products & Brands
Beer & Happoshu
 Diet Draft Happoshu
 Hop's Draft Happoshu
 Jokki Beer
 Kinmugi Beer
 Magnum Dry Happoshu
 Malt's Beer
 The Premium Malt's Beer
Cocktails
 Calori
 Cocktail Bar
 Cocktail Calori
 Ginza Cocktail
 Super Chu-hi
Distilled Spirits
 Barley Shochu Wanko
 Daijuhyo Ko-rui Shochu
 HAKUSHU Blended Whiskey
 Hanauta Shochu Nanco
 HIBIKI Blended Whiskey
 KAKUGBIN Whiskey
 Ko-otsu Blended Shochu
 Kyogetsu GREEN
 Midori Melon liqueur
 Otsu-rui Sochu
 Suntory Shirofuda Whiskey
 Sweet Potato Shochu Wanco
 YAMAZAKI Single Malt Whiskey
 Zen Green Tea liqueur
Wine
 Akadama Sweet Wine
 Delica Maison Delicious Wine
 Sankaboshizai Mutenka Wine
 Tomi no oka Wine
 Tomi Wine
 Yukisaibai Budo no Oishii Wine

COMPETITORS

Anheuser-Busch	Heineken
Aquaterra Corporation	Kirin Holdings Company
Asahi Breweries	Kokubu
Coca-Cola	Kyowa Hakko Kirin
Coca-Cola Bottling	Naked Juice
Consolidated	Nestlé Waters
Coca-Cola Refreshments	Odwalla
Coke United	PepsiCo
Danone Water	SABMiller
Diageo	Sapporo
Dr Pepper Snapple	Takara
Group	

HISTORICAL FINANCIALS
Company Type: Private

Income Statement				FYE: December 31
	REVENUE ($ mil.)	NET INCOME ($ mil.)	NET PROFIT MARGIN	EMPLOYEES
12/10	790	60	7.7%	2,199
12/09	13	5	42.0%	—
Annual Growth	5928.4%	1002.2%	—	—

2010 Year-End Financials
Return on assets: 8.1%
Return on equity: 13.8%
Current ratio: 1.50
Cash ($ mil.): 60

SUPERIOR COMMUNICATIONS, INC.

EXECUTIVES

Chb, Solomon Chen
Pres, Jeffrey Banks
Sr V Pres, Robert Chen
Cfo, Keith Kam
Legal Counsel, Jennifer Ju
Stckhldr, Michael Cavanah
Coo, Mike Cost
Dir of Credit & Payables Recei, Ava Cheung
Cmo, Scott Shanks
Purchasing Director, Armando Jara
Procurement Manager, Caroline Chin
Auditors: PRICEWATERHOUSECOOPERS LLP IR

LOCATIONS

HQ: SUPERIOR COMMUNICATIONS, INC.
5027 IRWINDALE AVE # 900, IRWINDALE, CA 917062187
Phone: 877 522-4727
Web: WWW.SUPERIORCOMMUNICATIONS.COM

HISTORICAL FINANCIALS
Company Type: Private

Income Statement				FYE: December 31
	REVENUE ($ mil.)	NET INCOME ($ mil.)	NET PROFIT MARGIN	EMPLOYEES
12/14*	734	6	0.9%	273
06/13	296	2	0.7%	—
12/12	1,365	0	—	—
Annual Growth	(26.7%)	177565.4%	—	—

*Fiscal year change

2014 Year-End Financials
Return on assets: 2.2%
Return on equity: 73.8%
Current ratio: 1.10
Cash ($ mil.): 25

SUTTER BAY HOSPITALS

Sutter West Bay Hospitals (doing business as California Pacific Medical Center or CPMC) is a health care complex located in the heart of hospital-heavy San Francisco. The private not-for-profit center's four area campuses (California Davies Pacific and St. Luke's) offer acute and specialty care including obstetrics and gynecology cardiovascular services pediatrics neurosciences orthopedics and organ transplantation. With more than 1300 beds between its campuses the center also conducts professional education and biomedical clinical and behavioral research. CPMC is part of the West Bay Region division of the Sutter Health hospital system.

Operations

CPMC's Sutter Health West Bay Region also includes Novato Community Hospital Sutter Lakeside Hospital and Sutter Medical Center of Santa Rosa. In addition to acute medical services CPMC also provides outpatient services at clinics in the San Francisco area operates home health and hospice organizations and conducts health education and charity care programs.

In 2011 CPMC's Research Institute conducted more than 200 clinical trials including studies on aging cancers epilepsy diabetes cardiovascular disease osteoporosis organ transplantation and more. That year CPMC's Kidney and Pancreas Transplant Program performed the first ever single-hospital five-way kidney swap transplant in California. CPMC's Joint Replacement Center is one of the leading joint replacement centers in the Bay Area performing roughly 1200 hip knee shoulder and elbow procedures per year. It has 1859 CPMC Medical Staff (including St. Luke's) and 109 medical residents and fellows.

That year the healthcare system reported about 619400 outpatient visits and 30300 inpatient cases.

Geographic Reach

CPMC serves patients from San Francisco Marin San Mateo Oakland Berkeley Palo Alto Santa Rosa San Jose. and the Bay Area.

Strategy

In order to meet California's seismic construction standards CPMC plans to renovate or rebuild most of its hospital campuses which are among the oldest medical centers in the San Francisco area. Its $2.5 billion reorganization plan includes the construction of a new 550-bed Cathedral Hill Campus that will include a full acute care hospital plus specialized women's and children's departments. CPMC also plans to rebuild and downsize the St. Luke's campus and convert the Pacific and California campuses into ambulatory care clinics. Reconstruction efforts at the Davies campus will include a new patient pavilion and a new Davies Neurosciences Institute for expanded neurological care. Major construction projects began in 2011 and will extend through 2015.

In 2010 the company sold its outpatient kidney dialysis operations to DaVita to focus on core operations.

Company Background

In 2007 parent Sutter Health merged St. Luke's Hospital into California Pacific to help keep the ailing St. Luke's afloat; St. Luke's provides care to many of San Francisco's low-income patients. CPMC had announced plans to turn St. Luke's into an outpatient facility in 2007; however the company rescinded those plans after San Franciscans objected to the proposal.

EXECUTIVES

Board Member, Steven Cummings
Auditors: ERNST & YOUNG US LLP SAN DIEG

LOCATIONS

HQ: SUTTER BAY HOSPITALS
633 FOLSOM ST FL 5, SAN FRANCISCO, CA
941073623
Phone: 415 600-6000
Web: WWW.SUTTERHEALTH.ORG

PRODUCTS/OPERATIONS

Selected Hospitals

California Campus (aka Children's Hospital of San Francisco)
Davies Campus (aka Davies Medical Center or Franklin Hospital)
Pacific Campus (aka Presbyterian Medical Center)
St. Luke's Campus (aka St. Luke's Hospital)

COMPETITORS

Children's Hospital & Research Center at Oakland
Dignity Health
HCA
John Muir Health
Stanford Health Care
Tenet Healthcare
UCSF Medical
ValleyCare Health System

HISTORICAL FINANCIALS

Company Type: Private

Income Statement   FYE: December 31

	REVENUE ($ mil.)	NET INCOME ($ mil.)	NET PROFIT MARGIN	EMPLOYEES
12/11	1,616	67	4.1%	3,597
12/09	1,245	159	12.8%	—
12/08	830	168	20.3%	—
Annual Growth	24.9%	(26.5%)	—	—

2011 Year-End Financials

Return on assets: 4.3%   Cash ($ mil.): 76
Return on equity: 6.6%
Current ratio: 1.20

SUTTER HEALTH

Whether you drink too much in Wine Country hit some rough waters off the Marin Headlands or trip during a hike through the redwood forest it's likely Sutter Health is just a stone's throw away. The Northern California not-for-profit health care system is one of the nation's largest with more than 4250 acute care beds. After being formed through the merger of Sutter Health and California Healthcare System Sutter Health now caters to residents of more than 100 communities from the California Bay Area to the beaches of Hawaii. Its services are provided through affiliated doctors from a host of health care facilities including acute care hospitals home health networks and skilled nursing facilities.

Operations

Sutter Health affiliates provide acute care services health education home health care hospice care adult day care prenatal clinics immunization services and other specialized health care services.

The system's health plan network includes about 25 hospitals and campuses and dozens of other facilities with more than 5000 providers serving some 40000 members throughout Northern California.

In 2017 the system reported more than 11 million outpatient visits; more than 190000 discharges; and some 870000 emergency room visits.

Sutter reports its revenue in four categories: patient service revenue (more than 85% of total) premium revenue (around 10%) contributions and other (combined less than 5%)

Geographic Reach

Sutter Health structures its governance into two geographic regions across Northern California: the Bay Area (which also includes Hawaii) and the Valley.

Sales and Marketing

Sutter Health earns its revenue through patient care with payers including health insurers and government programs.

Financial Performance

In 2018 Sutter Health reported $12.7 billion in operating revenue a 2% increase over the prior year. However operating expenses increased and investment income fell 44% to $187 million that year. The company reported a $198 million net loss versus income of $893 million in 2017.

Sutter ended 2018 with $362 million in net cash $33 million less than it had at the end of 2017. Operating activities provided $758 million and financing activities provided another $574 million but investing activities used $1.4 billion.

Strategy

As a not-for-profit system Sutter Health reinvests its earnings into the communities it serves. For example it recently built the new two-campus California Pacific Medical Center in San Francisco; the facilities opened their doors in 2018. It also has construction projects to expand its network of clinics.

Like most other health care organizations across the country Sutter Health is using technology to improve the quality of care given to patients. In 2019 it began a partnership with digital scribe firm Suki to pilot an AI-powered digital assistant for doctors. The voice-enabled tool will integrate with Sutter's existing electronic health records system allowing doctors to spend more quality time with their patients and giving patients access to updated care data. Suki will learn each doctor's preference and clinical practice guidelines and ultimately will be able to create an actionable plan of care.

Company Background

Although it traces its roots back to the 1800s Sutter Health was officially formed through the 1996 merger of Sacramento's Sutter Health and the Bay Area's California Healthcare System.

EXECUTIVES

Ceo Sutter Health Sacramento-sierra Region, Sarah Krevans, age 60
Svp And Cfo, Robert D. (Bob) Reed, age 67
President Sutter Health Central Valley Region, David P. Benn
President Sutter Health East Bay Region, David Bradley
Svp And Cio, Jonathan (Jon) Manis
Svp; Executive Officer Sutter Medical Network, Jeffrey Burnich
President Sutter Health West Bay Region, Mike Cohill
President Sutter Health Sacramento Sierra Region, James E. Conforti
President Sutter Health Peninsula Coastal Region, Jeff Gerard
Ceo Sutter Solano Medical Center, Abhishek Dosi
Vice President Finance And Treasurer, Svend Ryge
Vice President, Theresa Frei
Vice President Of Construction, Melinda Dow
Vice President And Medical Director, Joan Etzell
Vice President Is Corporation Client Services, Jennifer Sierras

Senior Vice President And General Counse, Florence Di Benedetto
Vice President Total Rewards, Diane Schnabel
Vice President Legal Operations, Pamela Marino
Vice President Strategy And Business Development Sutter Health Medical And Markets Network, Todd Smith
Vice President, Tom Hart
Regional Vice President, Jodi Davis
Vice President Talent And Change Management, Christopher Henry
Medical Director, Jeff Jenkins
Medical Director, Gina Bell
Vice President Chief Nursing Informatics Officer, Donna Woelfel
Vice President Managed Care, Karrie Abe
Vice President Clinical Informatics And Electronic Health Records, Howard Landa
Chair, Geraldine R. Brinton
Board Member, Portia Diwa
Unit Secretary, Vicki Pugh
Unit Secretary, Alicia Marzan-goble

LOCATIONS

HQ: SUTTER HEALTH
2200 RIVER PLAZA DR, SACRAMENTO, CA
958334134
Phone: 916 733-8800
Web: WWW.SUTTERHEALTH.ORG

Selected Hospitals

Alta Bates Summit Medical Center (Berkeley Oakland)
California Pacific Medical Center (San Francisco)
Eden Medical Center (Castro Valley)
Kahi Mohala (Ewa HI)
Marin General Hospital (Greenbrae)
Memorial Hospital Los Banos (Los Banos)
Memorial Medical Center (Modesto)
Menlo Park Surgical Hospital
Mills-Peninsula Health Services (Burlingame)
Novato Community Hospital (Novato)
Sutter Amador Hospital (Jackson)
Sutter Auburn Faith Hospital (Auburn)
Sutter Coast Hospital (Crescent City)
Sutter Davis Hospital (Davis)
Sutter Delta Medical Center (Antioch)
Sutter Lakeside Hospital (Lakeport)
Sutter Maternity & Surgery Center of Santa Cruz
Sutter Medical Center (Sacramento)
Sutter Medical Center of Santa Rosa
Sutter Roseville Medical Center
Sutter Solano Medical Center (Vallejo)
Sutter Tracy Community Hospital (Tracy)

PRODUCTS/OPERATIONS

2018 Sales

	$ mil.	% of total
Patient service revenue	10,957	86
Premium revenue	1,383	11
Contributions	6	-
Other	351	3
Total	**12,697**	**100**

Selected Services

Allergy Care
Alzheimer's and Brain Health
Arthritis and Rheumatology
Asthma Care
Back and Spine Services
Behavioral Health Care
Bioethics Services
Cancer Services
Cosmetic Surgery
Dermatology Services
Diabetes Services
Ear Nose and Throat Services
Emergency Services
Endocrinology
Fertility Services
Gastroenterology
Gynecology and Women's Health
Health Education
Heart and Vascular Services
Holistic and Integrative Medicine
Home Health and Hospice Care
Imaging

Kidney Disease and Nephrology
Lab and Pathology
Liver Care
Neuroscience
Occupational Health
Orthopedic Services
Palliative Care and Advanced Illness Management
Pediatric Services
Physical Therapy and Rehabilitation
Podiatric Services
Pregnancy and Childbirth Services
Primary Care
Pulmonary Care
Reconstructive Plastic Surgery
Senior Services and Geriatric Care
Surgical Services
Transplant Services
Urgent Care
Urology
Vision Care
Weight Loss Services
Long-Term Care Centers
Irene Swindells Alzheimer's Residential Care Center San
    Francisco
Sutter Oaks Nursing Center Sacramento
Sutter Senior Care PACE Program Sacramento
Cancer Centers
Alta Bates Summit Comprehensive Cancer Center
    Berkeley and Oakland
California Pacific Medical Center San Francisco
Dorothy E. Schneider Cancer Center at Mills-Peninsula
    Health Services Burlingame
Eden Medical Center Castro Valley
Memorial Regional Cancer Center Modesto
Sutter Auburn Faith Hospital Auburn
Sutter Cancer Center Sutter Medical Center Sacramento
Sutter Cancer Center Sutter Roseville Medical Center
    Roseville
Sutter Solano Cancer Center Vallejo
Programs listed above are approved by the American
    College of Surgeons' Commission on Cancer.
Research Institutes
California Pacific Medical Center San Francisco
Palo Alto Medical Foundation Research Institute Palo
    Alto
Sutter Health Institute for Research and Education San
    Francisco
Sutter Institute for Medical Research Sacramento
Home Health and Hospice Services
Coming Home Hospice
Cohen Cormier Home Attendant & Care Management
Sutter Auburn Faith VNA & Hospice
Sutter Care at Home
Sutter Coast Home Care
Sutter Infusion & Pharmacy Services / Emeryville and
    Sacramento
Sutter Lakeside Home Medical Services
Sutter Lifeline / Sacramento
Sutter North Home Health Agency
VNA of the Central Valley
VNA of Santa Cruz County
Express Medical Clinics
Sutter Express Care (Three locations in Sacramento &
    Placer counties)

COMPETITORS

Adventist Health System West
 Alta Bates Summit Medical Center
Ascension Health
Children's Hospital & Research Center at Oakland
HCA
Hawai'i Pacific Health
Kuakini Health System
Providence St. Joseph Health
Rehabilitation Hospital of the Pacific
Stanford Health Care
Tenet Healthcare
UCSF Medical

HISTORICAL FINANCIALS
Company Type: Private

Income Statement   FYE: December 31

	REVENUE ($ mil.)	NET INCOME ($ mil.)	NET PROFIT MARGIN	EMPLOYEES
12/18	12,697	(447)	—	48,000
12/17	12,444	1,060	8.5%	—
12/16	11,873	422	3.6%	—
12/15	10,998	84	0.8%	—
Annual Growth	4.9%	—	—	—

2018 Year-End Financials
Return on assets: (-2.6%)   Cash ($ mil.): 362
Return on equity: (-4.9%)
Current ratio: 3.40

SUTTER HEALTH SACRAMENTO SIERRA REGION

EXECUTIVES

Ceo, Patrick E Fry
Sr Staff Pres, Darling Lones
Coordinator, Sue Hawley
Orthopedic Surgeon, Philip Orisek
Auditors: ERNST & YOUNG US LLP SAN DIEG

LOCATIONS

HQ: SUTTER HEALTH SACRAMENTO SIERRA REGION
    2200 RIVER PLAZA DR, SACRAMENTO, CA
    958334134
Phone: 916 733-8800
Web: WWW.SUTTERHEALTH.ORG

HISTORICAL FINANCIALS
Company Type: Private

Income Statement   FYE: December 31

	REVENUE ($ mil.)	NET INCOME ($ mil.)	NET PROFIT MARGIN	EMPLOYEES
12/13	1,884	148	7.9%	4,000
12/11	1,752	(16)	—	—
12/09	1,453	154	10.6%	—
12/02	4,634	322	6.9%	—
Annual Growth	(7.9%)	(6.8%)	—	—

2013 Year-End Financials
Return on assets: 8.6%   Cash ($ mil.): 69
Return on equity: 30.8%
Current ratio: 0.30

SUTTER ROSEVILLE MEDICAL CENTER

EXECUTIVES

Ceo, Patrick Brady
Pharmacist, Charles Elliot
Human Resources Manager, Julie Fralick

Case Manager, Mary Nourot
Hematology Supervisor, Alex Alba
Senior Officer, Rebecca Thompson
MD, Napoleon Bernardo
Emergency Medicine Specialist, John Dutton
Senior Officer, Susan Willson
General Surgeon, Yona Barash
Executive Assistant, Leslie Shane

LOCATIONS

HQ: SUTTER ROSEVILLE MEDICAL CENTER
    1 MEDICAL PLAZA DR, ROSEVILLE, CA 956613037
Phone: 916 781-1000
Web: WWW.SUTTERHEALTH.ORG

HISTORICAL FINANCIALS
Company Type: Private

Income Statement   FYE: December 31

	REVENUE ($ mil.)	NET INCOME ($ mil.)	NET PROFIT MARGIN	EMPLOYEES
12/17	669	126	18.9%	1,700
12/16	628	121	19.3%	—
12/15	558	74	13.3%	—
12/12	484	95	19.6%	—
Annual Growth	6.7%	5.9%	—	—

2017 Year-End Financials
Return on assets: 35.4%   Cash ($ mil.): —
Return on equity: 129.3%
Current ratio: 3.70

SUTTER VALLEY MEDICAL FOUNDATION

EXECUTIVES

Ceo, Tom Blinn
Manager, Tom Stoffregen
Project Coordinator, Dalena Spahr
Coordinator, Rebeca Colom
Coordinator, Vincent Fung
Project Manager, Tanya Hughes
Regional Director Nutrition, Jack Breezee
Director, Debbie Sandberg
Project Manager III, Mark Hajny
Coordinator, Sherri Reese
Manager Human Resources, Christine Dupont
Auditors: ERNST & YOUNG LLP ROSEVILLE

LOCATIONS

HQ: SUTTER VALLEY MEDICAL FOUNDATION
    2700 GATEWAY OAKS DR, SACRAMENTO, CA
    958334337
Phone: 916 887-7122
Web: WWW.SUTTERHEALTH.ORG

HISTORICAL FINANCIALS
Company Type: Private

Income Statement   FYE: December 31

	REVENUE ($ mil.)	NET INCOME ($ mil.)	NET PROFIT MARGIN	EMPLOYEES
12/09	505	(21)	—	700
12/02	111	(7)	—	—
12/01	189	(10)	—	—
Annual Growth	13.1%	—	—	—

Return on assets: (-6.5%)   Cash ($ mil.): 30
Return on equity: (-9.1%)
Current ratio: 0.90

SWEDISH HEALTH SERVICES

Swedish Health Services doing business as Swedish Medical Center is the largest not-for-profit health provider in the greater Seattle area. Swedish Medical operates five acute care hospitals; it also runs two ambulatory care centers and the Swedish Medical Group physician practice organization which has more than 100 primary and specialty care offices in the greater Puget Sound region. Swedish Medical is affiliated with Providence St. Joseph Health a Catholic not-for-profit organization with 50 hospitals in seven states.

Operations

Swedish Medical has more than 2800 physicians and its hospitals are home to more than 1500 beds. The network's facilities see over 57000 in-patients per year as well as 175000 emergency room visits more than 9000 births and about 39000 surgeries. Swedish Medical operates numerous institutes across its campuses including its Cancer Institute Heart and Vascular Institute Neuroscience Institute and Orthopedic Institute. Other medical specialties include transplants pediatrics and women's health.

Swedish Medical also conducts clinical research programs with as many as 700 trials being conducted at one time making it one of the largest clinical trial sites in the US. The network's research programs are supported by government and commercial partners.

Geographic Reach

Swedish Medical has three hospital locations in Seattle as well as hospitals in Edmonds and Issaquah Washington. Its ambulatory centers (with emergency and specialty facilities) are located in Redmond and Everett Washington.

Financial Performance

In 2013 the system reported $2 billion in revenue (96% of which came from patient care services) and $59 million in net operating income.

Strategy

The company grows both organically and through partnerships. Through its affiliation with Providence St. Joseph Health Swedish Medical combined with Providence's Washington facilities under a new not-for-profit holding company. The two health systems retain their independent identities but share clinical and IT resources to work towards reducing medical costs and increasing the quality of care in the region.

The company announced a $63.5 million expansion to its Swedish Edmonds hospital campus in 2014. The two-story expansion will include a new emergency department and an outpatient diagnostic imaging center.

Also in 2014 Swedish Medical launched a hematologic malignancies program to research and treat blood-based cancers such as leukemia multiple myeloma and lymphoma.

To balance the costs of growth Swedish Medical occasionally exits underperforming businesses. In 2012 for instance the company ceased operations of its Swedish Visiting Nurse Services program which provide home health care hospice and therapy services. The unit had incurred continuous losses since 2009.

Company Background

Not-for-profit Swedish Medical began in 1910 as a single hospital with 24 beds.

EXECUTIVES

Interim Chief Executive Swedish Medical Group, Jon Younger, age 65
Chief Operating And Administrative Officer, June Altaras
Ceo, R. Guy Hudson
Interim Chief Medical Officer, Charles Watts
President And Chief Development Officer Swedish Medical Center Foundation, Harold A. (Jay) Vogelsang
Vice President Of Patient Care Services Chief Nursing Officer, Nancy Wood
Respiratory Therapy Director, Jim Kumpula
Medical Director Swedish Cardiac Surgery, Glenn Barnhart
Nursing Director, Margo Bykoned
Chairman, Teresa Bigelow

LOCATIONS

HQ: SWEDISH HEALTH SERVICES
747 BROADWAY, SEATTLE, WA 981224379
Phone: 206 386-6000

PRODUCTS/OPERATIONS

Selected Washington Facilities

Ballard Campus (Seattle)
Cherry Hill Campus (Seattle)
Edmonds Campus (Edmonds)
First Hill Campus (Seattle)
Issaquah Campus (Issaquah)
Mill Creek Campus (ambulatory center in Everett)
Redmond Campus (ambulatory center in Redmond)

Selected Institutes and Services

Cancer Institute
Emergency Services
Heart and Vascular Institute
Neuroscience Institute
Orthopedic Institute
Pediatric Specialty Care
Primary Care
Pregnancy and Childbirth
Surgical Services
Transplant Program
Women's Health

COMPETITORS

Franciscan Health System	Seattle Children's Hospital
Harrison Medical Center	University of Washington
MultiCare Health System	Wenatchee Valley Medical Center
Overlake Hospital	Yakima Valley Memorial
PeaceHealth	

HISTORICAL FINANCIALS

Company Type: Private

Income Statement   FYE: December 31

	REVENUE ($ mil.)	NET INCOME ($ mil.)	NET PROFIT MARGIN	EMPLOYEES
12/17	2,438	(9)	—	9,700
12/16	1,278	(2)	—	—
12/15	1,240	56	4.6%	—
12/14	1,127	79	7.1%	—
Annual Growth	29.3%	—	—	—

2017 Year-End Financials

Return on assets: (-0.3%)   Cash ($ mil.): 51
Return on equity: (-1.2%)
Current ratio: —

SWEDISHAMERICAN HOSPITAL

EXECUTIVES

Ceo, Bill Gorski
V Pres-Oprs*, Michael F Richter
Cfo*, Don Haring
Exec V Pres*, John R Mecklenburg
SEC*, David R Rydell
Information Specialist, Amira Christiansen
Coordinator, Dick Robinson
Information Specialist, Nathan Sweeney
Coordinator, Patricia R Yocum
Security Staff, Matthew Bartsch
Coordinator, Julie Gadow

LOCATIONS

HQ: SWEDISHAMERICAN HOSPITAL
1401 E STATE ST, ROCKFORD, IL 611042315
Phone: 815 968-4400
Web: WWW.SWEDISHAMERICAN.ORG

HISTORICAL FINANCIALS

Company Type: Private

Income Statement   FYE: June 30

	REVENUE ($ mil.)	NET INCOME ($ mil.)	NET PROFIT MARGIN	EMPLOYEES
06/18	527	31	6.0%	1,599
06/17	495	16	3.4%	—
Annual Growth	6.3%	87.0%		

2018 Year-End Financials

Return on assets: 4.1%   Cash ($ mil.): 62
Return on equity: 6.4%
Current ratio: 1.20

SWEETWATER UNION HIGH SCHOOL DISTRICT

EXECUTIVES

Supt, Karen Janney
Senior Buyer, Don Prince
Marketing Strategist, Gamez Cezar
School Psychologist, Rosa Ruiz
Staff, Edna Espinoza
Planning Project Manager, Frank Mendoza
Credentials Specialist, Anna Hurtado
Senior Administrative Assistan, Erika Gonzales
School Secretary, Manuela Aragon
Auditors: CHRISTYWHITE ACCOUNTANCY CORPO

LOCATIONS

HQ: SWEETWATER UNION HIGH SCHOOL DISTRICT
1130 FIFTH AVE, CHULA VISTA, CA 919112812
Phone: 619 691-5500
Web: WWW.SWEETWATERSCHOOLS.ORG

Income Statement   FYE: June 30

	REVENUE ($ mil.)	NET INCOME ($ mil.)	NET PROFIT MARGIN	EMPLOYEES
06/18	553	(17)	—	3,521
06/17	546	(48)	—	—
06/16	525	77	14.8%	—
06/09	0	0	—	—
Annual Growth	147.3%	—	—	—

SWINERTON BUILDERS

Swinerton Builders a subsidiary of Swinerton focuses on commercial and sustainable construction and renovation projects. Operating primarily in the western US its interiors group offers interior tenant finishes and remodeling working on such projects as high-tech and lab renovations hospitals retail facilities and seismic upgrades. The employee-owned company's building group focuses on new construction and retrofitting for such projects as the San Francisco Museum of Modern Art a Lockheed Martin launch vehicle assembly plant in Colorado and the Bay Bridge toll operations building in San Francisco. Swinerton Builders operates from offices in California Colorado Hawaii Texas New Mexico and Washington.

Operations
As part of its business Swinerton Builders is involved in high-tech and lab renovations hospitals retail facilities and seismic upgrades as well as new construction and retrofitting projects.

Swinerton Builders also constructs many buildings to meet environmental standards. Green projects have ranged from fire stations and retail outlets to college facilities and hotels. Swinertons' own corporate offices in California are solar powered.

Geographic Reach
The building arm of Swinerton serves the western US through offices in California Colorado Hawaii Texas Oregon and Washington. Its offices are located across California as well as in Austin Texas; Denver Colorado; Portland Oregon; Seattle Washington; and Honolulu Hawaii.

Sales and Marketing
Swinerton Builders serves a variety of sectors involving: critical facilities education government healthcare hospitality interiors multi-family residential native American and renewable energy projects. Its clients have included NASA the Federal Aviation Administration Bureau of Indian Affairs and several military and governmental entities including the US Air Force US Army US Department of Agriculture US Department of Homeland Security and the US National Park Service.

Strategy
Swinerton Builders continues to work on high-value projects around the country. In 2015 after being selected from a two-phase best value selection process the company secured a contract to lead the design-build construction project of a $46 million parking building (with some 1795 parking spaces) at the Denver International Airport (DIA) in Colorado.

The company's Swinerton Renewable Energy unit which builds and offers services to the solar utility industry expanded its capabilities in 2013 by adding comprehensive operations and mainte-

nance (O&M) services for any solar facility across North America. The unit also launched a monitoring platform named SOLV to manage all the operational needs of customers with solar utility plants.

EXECUTIVES

Vice President, John Capener
Auditors: CLIFTONLARSONALLEN WALNUT CRE

LOCATIONS

HQ: SWINERTON BUILDERS
260 TOWNSEND ST, SAN FRANCISCO, CA 941071761
Phone: 415 421-2980

PRODUCTS/OPERATIONS

Selected Services

BIM/VD&C
Corporate Services
Critical Facilities
General Contracting
Government Construction
Management & Consulting
Preconstruction
Renewable Energy
Sustainable Construction/LEED

COMPETITORS

Andersen Construction
Charles Pankow
  Builders
Clark Builders Group
Cordoba
DPR Construction
Devcon Construction
Gilbane Building
  Company
Hathaway Dinwiddie
  Construction

Hensel Phelps
  Construction
J.F. Shea
Jaynes Companies
Kitchell
Torix General
  Contractors
Turner Corporation
W. L. Butler
Webcor Builders
Whiting-Turner

HISTORICAL FINANCIALS
Company Type: Private

Income Statement   FYE: December 31

	REVENUE ($ mil.)	NET INCOME ($ mil.)	NET PROFIT MARGIN	EMPLOYEES
12/18	3,541	38	1.1%	900
12/17	3,306	39	1.2%	—
12/16	3,664	53	1.5%	—
12/15	2,826	28	1.0%	—
Annual Growth	7.8%	9.5%	—	—

2018 Year-End Financials

Return on assets: 2.9%   Cash ($ mil.): 211
Return on equity: 14.0%
Current ratio: 1.30

SWINERTON INCORPORATED

Swinerton is building up the West just as it helped rebuild San Francisco after the 1906 earthquake. One of the largest contractors in California the construction group builds commercial industrial and government facilities including resorts subsidized housing public schools soundstages hospitals and airport terminals. Through its subsidiaries (including Swinerton Builders) Swinerton offers general contracting and design/build services as well as construction and program management. The firm also provides property manage-

ment for conventional subsidized and assisted living residences and is active in the renewable energy sector. The 100% employee-owned company traces its roots to 1888.

Operations
Swinerton has a special renewable energy division (Swinerton Renewable Energy) focused on solar and wind projects.

For North American solar power facilities the company also offers comprehensive operations and maintenance (O&M) services which include performance monitoring and alerting parts management service ticketing reporting preventive and corrective maintenance warranty administration and site maintenance (including vegetation mitigation and module washing).

Swinerton also has a special division to handle government construction projects delivering large-scale complex design and construction services for government agencies. Through the division Swinerton has worked on federal courthouses and administrative buildings training centers VA hospitals and military housing projects.

Geographic Reach
San Francisco-based Swinerton has more than a dozen offices throughout California Colorado Hawaii Texas Oregon and Washington.

Financial Performance
With the California construction market experiencing some of the strongest growth the industry has seen since 2008 Swinerton posted nearly $1.8 billion in revenue in 2013 about $1.4 billion of which was rung up in California.

Strategy
Swinerton's renewable energy division has been busy with a series of projects and new services coming to the fold in recent years. In 2014 Duke Energy awarded Swinerton a contract to develop a pair of 20-megawatt solar farms called the Pumpjack and Wildwood solar power projects which will power some 10000 households in central California once they're completed. In 2013 the company began offering comprehensive operations and maintenance (O&M) services for any North American solar facility.

The company also continues to work on other projects in recent years. In 2014 it started building the five-story 117000-square-foot building on behalf of the developer Breevast which secured a 12-year lease agreement on the building with file-sharing service provider Dropbox. In 2013 it started work on Telecom Real Estate Services' Block Data Center in Las Vegas with the goal of turning an existing warehouse facility into a Tier III modular data center. That year it also began construction on Chevron's 340000 square-foot office complex and campus in Midland Texas.

As one of the top waste-reducing companies in California Swinerton employs green building construction and design practices to conserve resources reduce waste and create healthier environments. The company's own headquarters building in San Francisco received Gold LEED-EB (Leadership in Energy & Environmental Design for Existing Buildings) — a top certification from the U.S. Green Building Council. Swinerton also built the LEED platinum rated NASA Ames Research Center Sustainability Base the greenest government building in history.

EXECUTIVES

Vice President Corporate Manager Of Proj, Michael Murphy
Vice President Manager Director, Seva Vaysband
Vice President Operations Manager, Gerald Mejia
Asst Sec, Lisa Telles
Auditors: CLIFTONLARSONALLEN LLP WALNU

LOCATIONS

HQ: SWINERTON INCORPORATED
260 TOWNSEND ST, SAN FRANCISCO, CA 941071761
Phone: 415 421-2980
Web: WWW.SWINERTONRENEWABLE.COM

PRODUCTS/OPERATIONS

Selected Companies and Divisions
Cameron Swinerton
Harbison-Mahony-Higgins Builders Inc. (HMH general contracting)
Swinerton Builders (general contracting)
Swinerton Government Services
Swinerton Management & Consulting (property assessment)
Swinerton Property Services (property management)
William P. Young Construction (engineering and civil construction)

Selected Projects
100 Montgomery
AECOM
Agilent Technologies
Andaz Wailea Resort & Villas
Avaya Research & Development
Bank of New York Mellon Newport Beach
Bank of New York Mellon San Francisco
Bright Horizons Colorado
Bright Horizons South Lake Union
Bruceville | 19.15 MWdc
Cache Creek Casino Resort
CalSTRS Office Headquarters
Caltech Solar Project | 1.10 MWdc
Cathedral of the Blessed Sacrament
Christopher High School
Cinépolis Del Mar
City Center Plaza and Entry Upgrades
City Target at the Metreon
CNET Headquarters
Columbia 3 | 11.06 MWdc Columbia Sportswear
de Young Museum
Delta Airlines Sky Club
Dillard | 12.03 MWdc

COMPETITORS

A.G. Spanos	J.F. Shea
Bechtel	JCM Partners
Beck Group	Kitchell
Charles Pankow Builders	McCarthy Building
Clark Construction Group	Menas Realty
	PCL Construction Enterprises
Cordoba	Rudolph & Sletten
DPR Construction	Skanska USA Building
Devcon Construction	Sundt
Gilbane	Turner Corporation
Hathaway Dinwiddie Construction	Tutor-Saliba
	Webcor Builders
Hensel Phelps Construction	Western National Group
	Whiting-Turner

HISTORICAL FINANCIALS

Company Type: Private

Income Statement				FYE: December 31
	REVENUE ($ mil.)	NET INCOME ($ mil.)	NET PROFIT MARGIN	EMPLOYEES
12/18	3,631	36	1.0%	900
12/17	3,365	31	0.9%	—
12/16	0	0	—	—
12/15	2,827	21	0.8%	—
Annual Growth	8.7%	18.9%	—	—

2018 Year-End Financials

Return on assets: 2.5%   Cash ($ mil.): 230
Return on equity: 14.3%
Current ratio: 1.30

SYRACUSE CITY SCHOOL DISTRICT

EXECUTIVES

Spdt, Jaime Alicea
Spdt, Sharon Contrerasn
Teacher, Lacey Dowd
Teacher, Jason Short
Coordinator, Susan Centore
Analyst Designer, Jonathan Mason
Psychologist, Nancy Sudmyer
Teacher, Rashaan Listenbee
Teaching Assistant, Sharon Mitchell
Administrator, Chris Hodge
Teacher, Christopher Constantino
Auditors: BONADIO & CO LLP SYRACUSE

LOCATIONS

HQ: SYRACUSE CITY SCHOOL DISTRICT
725 HARRISON ST, SYRACUSE, NY 132102395
Phone: 315 435-4499
Web: WWW.SYRACUSECITYSCHOOLS.COM

HISTORICAL FINANCIALS

Company Type: Private

Income Statement				FYE: June 30
	REVENUE ($ mil.)	NET INCOME ($ mil.)	NET PROFIT MARGIN	EMPLOYEES
06/17	489	4	1.0%	4,361
06/16	464	(12)		
Annual Growth	5.3%	—	—	—

2017 Year-End Financials

Return on assets: 0.8%   Cash ($ mil.): 33
Return on equity: —
Current ratio: —

T. D. WILLIAMSON, INC.

Keeping onshore and offshore pipelines operating safely flowing freely is what T. D. Williamson is all about. A leading global pipeline equipment and services provider the company designs manufactures and maintains oil field machinery and systems including pipeline pigging (scraping) gas leak detection pipeline inspection plugging tapping valve and clamp and cathodic protection equipment. The company also offers general pipeline training turnkey and repair services. T. D. Williamson operates a global network of sales offices and representatives.

Operations

T.D. Williamson provides pipeline equipment and services for onshore and offshore applications including geometry and magnetic flux leakage inspection hot tapping and plugging pig technology services pigging and non-tethered plugging and pipeline cleaning. Its major operating subsidiary is TDW Offshore Services.

Geographic Reach

Serving oil and gas companies in every major oil patch the company has strategically located international service centers and/or manufacturing plants worldwide including in Belgium India Mexico Singapore South Africa the UAE the UK the US and Venezuela.

Strategy

T.D. Williamson leverages its leading market position by offering a broad spectrum of technical experience and a continuously refined portfolio of customized services and state-of-the-art equipment. Its support personnel includes engineers project managers and technicians who are accessible to clients on a 24/7 basis.

Growing its operations in the Middle East in 2014 the company opened a new maintenance center in Abu Dhabi to complement its existing hot tap and STOPPLE plugging service center. The expansion is in keeping with T.D. Williamson's plans to strengthen its inspection business in the Gulf region and to provide turnkey facilities and back-up for the preparation maintenance and mobilization of inline inspection equipment.

Expanding its geographic network in 2013 T.D. Williamson opened a service center in Abu Dhabi and in 2012 an office in Kazakhstan.

The company puts a strong emphasis on innovation and product development.

In 2013 TDW Offshore Services signed a deal with Centrica Storage Limited to provide pipeline isolation services using its SmartPlug Technology. The tool makes allows operators to gain significant benefits in the form of reduced downtime and associated costs by safely isolating pressure in an active pipeline and maintaining production while maintenance is carried out.

Company Background

It conducted a successful pipeline intervention in 2012 using the SmartPlug pressure isolation tool. Carried out for Talisman Malaysia Limited the operation allowed the safe replacement of a shutdown valve on a key section of a gas export pipeline without having to bleed down the line.

In 2012 the company developed and deployed a new proprietary inline inspection reporting software — Interactive Report 2013 — a data visualization tool that makes it easy for users to filter and view their pipeline inspection data.

That year the company unveiled its Subsea 1200RC Tapping Machine a compact remote-controlled subsea machine that allows hot tapping (tying in to a pressurized system while under full operating conditions) to be carried out with increased safety from a diving support vessel.

Growing its project contract portfolio in 2012 T.D. Williamson signed a three-year global pipeline intervention and isolation services contract with BP (one of only four such contracts awarded worldwide by BP).

T.D. Williamson has expanded internationally in the last two decades. With opening of service centers in Dubai Jamnagar (India) Moscow Rayong (Thailand) and Warsaw in 2007 it had locations in every continent except Antarctica. It opened a facility in India in 2010 in order to respond to the growing pipeline business in that country (which is expected to double from 25000 km. by 2015).

In 2011 it created the Global Pipeline Integrity Center in Salt Lake City Utah to combine the TDW inline inspection engineering manufacturing operations service center and data analysis functions in one location.

The company was founded by T.D. Williamson Sr. in 1920 as The Petroleum Electric Company an electrical contracting firm to supply electric motors for gas booster stations oil well drilling equipment and electric generator stations used by the local oil and gas industry in the US. It adopted the T.D. Williamson name in 1933.

EXECUTIVES

Vice President General Counsel, Jay Dalton
Auditors: PRICEWATERHOUSECOOPERS LLP TU

LOCATIONS

HQ: T. D. WILLIAMSON, INC.
6120 S YALE AVE STE 1700, TULSA, OK 741364235
Phone: 918 493-9494
Web: WWW.TDWILLIAMSON.COM

PRODUCTS/OPERATIONS

TDW ProductsCathodic Protection EquipmentGas Leak DetectionPipeline Drilling and Hot Tapping MachinesPipeline FittingsPigging Products and AccessoriesPipeline Plugging EquipmentPipeline Rehabilitation ProductsPipeline ValvesServicesGas Leak DetectionHot

COMPETITORS

Cameron International	Oil States
Cypress Energy	International
Partners	Schlumberger
Halliburton	T3 Energy Services
J-W Operating	Weatherford
National Oilwell Varco	International

HISTORICAL FINANCIALS

Company Type: Private

Income Statement   FYE: December 31

	REVENUE ($ mil.)	NET INCOME ($ mil.)	NET PROFIT MARGIN	EMPLOYEES
12/15	539	0	—	1,425
12/02	116	1	1.5%	—
12/01	106	2	2.4%	—
12/00	91	2	2.5%	—
Annual Growth	12.6%	—	—	—

2015 Year-End Financials

Return on assets: —
Return on equity: —   Cash ($ mil.): 30
Current ratio: 3.60

TA CHEN INTERNATIONAL, INC.

EXECUTIVES

Ceo, Johnny Hsieh
V Pres, James Chang
V Pres, John Hellighausen
Cfo, Andrew Chang
Manager, Matt Joyner
Software Engineer, Chin Wang
Auditors: CHEN & FAN ACCOUNTANCY COPR

LOCATIONS

HQ: TA CHEN INTERNATIONAL, INC.
  5855 OBISPO AVE, LONG BEACH, CA 908053715
Phone: 562 808-8000
Web: WWW.TACHEN.COM

HISTORICAL FINANCIALS

Company Type: Private

Income Statement   FYE: December 31

	REVENUE ($ mil.)	NET INCOME ($ mil.)	NET PROFIT MARGIN	EMPLOYEES
12/17	1,257	32	2.6%	500
12/14	1,178	27	2.3%	—
12/13	904	8	1.0%	—
Annual Growth	8.6%	38.0%	—	—

2017 Year-End Financials

Return on assets: 3.2%
Return on equity: 7.8%   Cash ($ mil.): 3
Current ratio: 6.10

TACOMA PUBLIC SCHOOLS

EXECUTIVES

Supt, Carla Fantorno
Pres*, Debbie Winskill
V Pres*, Kurt Miller
Coo*, Christopher Williams
Coordinator, Deana Siegel
Teacher, Karen Vialle
Accounting Staff, Dee Kirkevold
Athletic Director, Jennifer Kubista
Payroll Staff, Maggie Thomas
Coordinator, Norma Maldonado
Technology/Computer Coord, Shaun Taylor

LOCATIONS

HQ: TACOMA PUBLIC SCHOOLS
  601 S 8TH ST, TACOMA, WA 984054614
Phone: 253 571-1000
Web: WWW.TACOMASCHOOLS.ORG

HISTORICAL FINANCIALS

Company Type: Private

Income Statement   FYE: August 31

	REVENUE ($ mil.)	NET INCOME ($ mil.)	NET PROFIT MARGIN	EMPLOYEES
08/18	495	(50)	—	3,700
08/17	469	3	0.8%	—
08/06	41	(2)	—	—
08/05	41	(2)	—	—
Annual Growth	21.0%	—	—	—

2018 Year-End Financials

Return on assets: (-3.7%)
Return on equity: (-15.3%)   Cash ($ mil.): 11
Current ratio: —

TALEN ENERGY SUPPLY, LLC

EXECUTIVES

Svp And Chief Administrative Officer, James E. (Jim) Schinski
Svp And Chief Commercial Officer, Clarence J. (Joe) Hopf
President And Ceo, Paul A Farr
Svp Cfo And Chief Accounting Officer, Jeremy R. McGuire
Svp And Chief Nuclear Officer, Timothy S. Rausch
Auditors: ERNST & YOUNG LLP PHILADELPHI

LOCATIONS

HQ: TALEN ENERGY SUPPLY, LLC
  600 HAMILTON ST STE 600 # 600, ALLENTOWN, PA 181012130
Phone: 888 211-6011
Web: WWW.TALENENERGY.COM

HISTORICAL FINANCIALS

Company Type: Private

Income Statement   FYE: December 31

	REVENUE ($ mil.)	NET INCOME ($ mil.)	NET PROFIT MARGIN	EMPLOYEES
12/18	2,714	(37)	—	4,981
12/16	3,913	(352)	—	—
12/15	4,481	(341)	—	—
12/14	3,736	410	11.0%	—
Annual Growth	(7.7%)	—	—	—

2018 Year-End Financials

Return on assets: (-0.4%)
Return on equity: (-1.6%)   Cash ($ mil.): 22
Current ratio: 1.10

TALLAHASSEE MEMORIAL HEALTHCARE, INC.

Tallahassee Memorial HealthCare (TMH) aims to take the hassle out of health care. The community health system serves residents of Florida's state capital and its surrounding communities. The system is anchored by Tallahassee Memorial Hospital a not-for-profit facility with more than 770 beds and about 560 physicians on staff who represent some 50 different specialties. TMH provides general medical and surgical care as well as specialty care in areas such as oncology rehabilitation women's and children's health obesity and diabetes. TMH also has a trauma center offers a family practice residency program and provides primary medical care through a handful of regional clinics.

Operations

TMH is Florida's eighth-largest hospital boasting more than 24000 inpatient admissions per year. As part of its operations TMH has a 60-bed psychiatric hospital and offers adult day care and home health care services. It operates the only Level II trauma center in the region which benefits from newly added telemedicine equipment that includes videoconferencing. Trauma centers are specially trained and equipped to handle severe injuries and all such patients in the area are routed to trauma certified facilities.

The system partners with the H. Lee Moffitt Cancer Center & Research Institute in Tampa to allow cancer patients to participate in clinical trials and other experimental and research opportunities.

The system offers a range of cardiovascular services from diagnostic procedures to open-heart surgery a designated acute brain and spinal cord injury center and a 110000-sq.-ft. childbirth facility — the region's only Level Three Neonatal Intensive Care Unit.

In 2014 the hospital had 122100 emergency and urgent care visits and 29586 general admissions.

Geographic Reach

TMH serves 17 counties across North Florida and South Georgia.

Financial Performance

In 2014 TMH's net revenues increased by 7% due to higher net patient service revenues (net of contractual allowances and discounts).

The company's net income rose by 15% due to higher net revenues and a decrease in interest.

TMH's operating cash inflow in 2014 increased by 16%.

Strategy

The medical facility operates the Tallahassee Memorial Transition Center created in partnership with Capital Health Plan and Florida State University College of Medicine. The center was designed to improve wellness through new approaches and collaborative research. Looking to position itself as a regional center for healthcare Tallahassee Memorial has plans to roll out more new services and add physicians.

In 2015 the hospital and Apalachee Center expanded their agreement to include administrative management of Tallahassee Memorial behavioral health services by Apalachee Center to improve behavioral health services in the community. As part of an earlier agreement the company will continue to provide some psychiatric medical coverage for Apalachee Center's inpatient services as well as providing all psychiatric medical services at the Tallahassee Memorial Behavioral Health Center.

In 2014 TMH and Doctors' Memorial Hospital signed an agreement to create an equal governance partnership between the two institutions that will ultimately enhance services to Doctors' Memorial Hospital and expand its role in Taylor County's health care system.

To expand its capabilities TMH opened the Tallahassee Memorial Emergency Center - Northeast in mid-2013 and broke ground in 2013 on a new surgery and adult intensive care facility that's anticipated to cost as much as $175 million.

Company Background

TMH was founded in 1948.

EXECUTIVES

Vp And Cfo, William (Bill) Giudice
Vp And Coo, Jason Moore
Vp And Cio, Don Lindsey
President Tmh Foundation, Paula Fortunas
Associate Chief Medical Officer, Dean Watson
Administrator Behavioral Health Center, Carl Mahler
Director Premier Health And Fitness Center, Len Harvey
Administrator Orthopedic And Neurological Services, Judy Greenwald
Administrator Surgery Services, David Thompson
President And Ceo, G. Mark OÂ'Bryant
Vp And Chief Nursing Officer, Barbara Alford
Administrator Cancer Center, Matt Sherer
Interim Administrator Emergency Medicine Services, Eric Hartigan
Administrator Heart And Vascular Center, Terri McDonald
Administrator Regional Development Population Health And Telemedicine, Lauren Faison
Administrator Womenâ's Pavilion And Childrenâ's Center, Connie Styons
Vice President, Stephanie Derzypolski
Medical Records Director, Gail Robinson
Chairman, Glenda Thornton
Unit Secretary, Tracy Blue
Unit Secretary, Jureen Lamb
Department Secretary, Shirley Heuring
Department Secretary, Cindy Allen
Unit Secretary In Surgery, Doris Chester
Md Secretary, Carlos Campo

LOCATIONS

HQ: TALLAHASSEE MEMORIAL HEALTHCARE, INC.
1300 MICCOSUKEE RD, TALLAHASSEE, FL 323085054
Phone: 850 431-1155
Web: WWW.TMH.ORG

PRODUCTS/OPERATIONS

2014 sales

	% of total
Hospitals	97
TMHV	1
Medicus	2
Total	**100**

Selected Services

Behavioral Health Center
Rehabilitation Center
Cancer Center
Bixler Emergency Center
Heart & Vascular Center
Diabetes Center
Orthopedic Center
NeuroScience Center
Surgical Services
Women's Pavilion
Home Health Care
Clinical Genetics Center
Bariatric Center
Chronic Pain Management
Lipid Center

COMPETITORS

Adventist Health System Sunbelt Healthcare
Baptist Health System
Bay Medical Center
H. Lee Moffitt Cancer Center & Research Institute
HCA
Jackson County Hospital of Florida
Munroe Regional Health System
Sacred Heart Health System
UF&Shands

HISTORICAL FINANCIALS

Company Type: Private

Income Statement				FYE: September 30
	REVENUE ($ mil.)	NET INCOME ($ mil.)	NET PROFIT MARGIN	EMPLOYEES
09/15	589	38	6.5%	6,430
09/14	532	33	6.2%	—
09/13	566	31	5.6%	—
09/12	479	40	8.4%	—
Annual Growth	7.1%	(1.4%)	—	—

2015 Year-End Financials

Return on assets: 6.3%   Cash ($ mil.): 227
Return on equity: 14.0%
Current ratio: 3.60

TARRANT COUNTY HOSPITAL DISTRICT

If Fort Worth residents are searching for health care they need look no further than Tarrant County Hospital District (dba JPS Health Network). Founded in 1906 in Fort Worth Texas the network's flagship facility John Peter Smith Hospital has approximately 540 beds and provides specialty services including orthopedics cardiology and women's health. JPS Health Network also includes behavioral health treatment center Trinity Springs Pavilion and the JPS Diagnostic & Surgery Hospital of Arlington. The company provides family medical dental and specialty care through dozens of health care centers in northern Texas.

Operations

JPS Hospital is a member of the Council of Teaching Hospitals and Health Systems (COTH).

Sales and Marketing

The health system carries a Level 1 Trauma designation across the spectrum of health care specialties meaning it is the referral hospital of choice for patients who are terribly injured.

Strategy

The health system works to improve the health of Tarrant County as a whole by training health care workers and physicians about working outside the hospital walls and within the community. The institution sponsors programs that are accredited through the Accreditation Council for Graduate Medical Education (ACGME) American Osteopathic Association (AOA) and the Council on Podiatric Medical Education (CPME).

JPS Health Network opened JPS Medical Home Southeast Tarrant a primary and specialty care facility in 2014. The following year the system relocated its Pain Management Clinic to a renovated site in Fort Worth.

EXECUTIVES

Vice President Operations, Kathleen Whelan
Cfo, David Salsberry
Executive Vice President Chief Medical Officer, Gary Floyd
Coo, Bill Whitman
Vice President, Scott Rule
Md;senior Vice President Population Health, Elizabeth Carter
Senior Vice President Of Human Resources And Learning, Nikki Sumpter
Vice President Of Support Services, Charles Williams
Vice President Communications And Community Affairs, Taffee Becker
Department Chairman, Kellie Flood-Shaffer
Manager, Scott W. Fisher
Manager, Trent Petty

LOCATIONS

HQ: TARRANT COUNTY HOSPITAL DISTRICT
1500 S MAIN ST. FORT WORTH, TX 761044917
Phone: 817 921-3431
Web: WWW.JPSHEALTHNET.ORG

Primary Locations – Texas

Ambulatory Surgery Center (Fort Worth)
Cardiology Center (Fort Worth)
Enrollment & Eligibility Center (Fort Worth)
Family Medicine & Surgical Specialty Center (Fort Worth)
Healing Wings AIDS Center (Fort Worth)
John Peter for Cancer Care (Fort Worth)
JPS Urgent Care Center (Fort Worth)
Lifespan Family Medicine & Pediatrics (Fort Worth)
Patient Care Pavilion (Fort Worth)
Professional Building-Medicine Clinic (Fort Worth)
Trinity Springs Pavilion for Psychiatric Services (Fort Worth)

PRODUCTS/OPERATIONS

Selected Services

Behavioral Services
Cancer
Cardiology
Dental
Geriatrics
Healing Wings HIV/AIDS Center
Orthopedics and Sports Medicine
Robotic Surgery
School-Based Health Centers
Sexual Assault Nurse Examiner Program
    Stroke / N
Surgical Services
Trauma Services
Women's Services

COMPETITORS

Baylor University
  Medical Center
CHRISTUS Health
Community Health
  Systems
Cook Children's Health
  Care System
HCA
Harris Methodist Fort
  Worth Hospital
Parkland Health &
  Hospital System

Presbyterian Hospital
  of Dallas
Southwestern Medical
  Center
Tenet Healthcare
Texas Health Resources
The Methodist Health
  System
Universal Health
  Services

HISTORICAL FINANCIALS

Company Type: Private

Income Statement				FYE: September 30
	REVENUE ($ mil.)	NET INCOME ($ mil.)	NET PROFIT MARGIN	EMPLOYEES
09/18	632	(3)	—	3,000
09/16	576	18	3.2%	—
09/15	557	48	8.7%	—
09/14	285	48	16.9%	—
Annual Growth	22.0%	—	—	—

2018 Year-End Financials

Return on assets: (-0.3%)
Return on equity: (-0.4%)
Current ratio: 4.30

Cash ($ mil.): 161

TATA AMERICA INTERNATIONAL CORPORATION

Tata America International is the North American holding company for Indian conglomerate Tata Group. In the US the company has about a dozen subsidiaries including offices for Tata Communications IT services firm Tata Consultancy Services (with more than 20 locations) and engineering consultancy Tata Technologies. In the industrial sector Tata America owns steel manufacturing plants in Ohio and Pennsylvania and General Chemical Industrial Products a soda ash plant in Wyoming. Other holdings include hotels (The Pierre in New York the Taj Boston and the Taj Campton Place in San Francisco) and sales offices for its beverage brands Eight O'Clock Coffee Good Earth and Tetley.

EXECUTIVES

President, Surya Kant
Vp Marketing And Communications, John Lenzen
Cfo, S. Mahalingam
Auditors: DELOITTE HASKINS & SELLS LLP

LOCATIONS

HQ: TATA AMERICA INTERNATIONAL CORPORATION
  101 PARK AVE RM 2603, NEW YORK, NY 101782604
Phone: 212 557-8038
Web: WWW.TCS.COM

PRODUCTS/OPERATIONS

Selected Subsidiaries
IT Services
  Tata Business Support Services
  Tata Communications
  Tata Consultancy Services

Tata Elxsi
Tata Interactive Systems
Tata Technologies
Engineering
  Tata AutoComp Systems
Services
  Campton Place
  Taj Boston
  The Pierre
Consumer Products
  Eight O'Clock Coffee
  Good Earth
  Tanishq
  Tata Tea Inc.
  Tetley
Chemicals
  General Chemical

COMPETITORS

Accenture
Atos North America
CIBER
Capgemini North
  America
Cognizant Tech
  Solutions
Computer Sciences
  Corp.
Fujitsu America

HCL Technologies
HP Enterprise Services
IBM Global Services
ICP Inc.
Infosys
NTT Data
Syntel
Unisys
Wipro Technologies
Zensar Technologies

HISTORICAL FINANCIALS

Company Type: Private

Income Statement				FYE: March 31
	REVENUE ($ mil.)	NET INCOME ($ mil.)	NET PROFIT MARGIN	EMPLOYEES
03/18	8,197	121	1.5%	1,700
03/17	845	168	19.9%	—
03/16	755	118	15.7%	—
03/15	6,800	111	1.6%	—
Annual Growth	6.4%	3.0%	—	—

2018 Year-End Financials

Return on assets: 6.8%
Return on equity: 25.1%
Current ratio: 1.30

Cash ($ mil.): 15

TAUBER OIL COMPANY

No liquid petrochemical product is taboo for oil refiner and marketer Tauber Oil. The family owned company markets refined petroleum products carbon black feedstocks liquefied petroleum gases chemicals and petrochemicals (including benzene styrene monomer and methanol). Tauber Oil is one of the US's leading suppliers of feedstocks for reforming and olefin cracking. It also has oil and gas exploration and production operations. Subsidiary Tauber Petrochemical was created in 1997 to beef up the company's international petrochemical business. Tauber Oil which is owned by David and Richard Tauber maintains a fleet of more than 500 rail cars to supply its customers.

Operations

Tauber Oil's blending group works with refineries and producers to create a market for by-product/co-product streams. It also supplies liquid petroleum products to marine diesel customers fuel to power generators cutters for bunker blending clients and a number of other fuel applications.

The company's natural gas liquids department works with producers and consumers to create a market; the refined products department trades refined products with refiners traders distributors and other customers.

Tauber Petrochemical markets a range of products including alkylate benzene C9 aromatics ethyl benzene pyrolysis gasoline styrene monomer toluene and xylene.

Geographic Reach

The company's rail and barge fleet moves products from inland to Gulf Coast markets. It gathers blends and distributes out of tankage in Houston Texas City and on the Mississippi River. Tauber Oil's has oil and gas exploration and production operations in the East Texas South Texas the Gulf Coast of Texas Southern Louisiana and Oklahoma. (Additionally Tauber participates in 3-D seismic projects lease acquisitions and funding for geological and geophysical projects). Its Canadian Crude group works with heavy crude oil producers.

Sales and Marketing

The company transports its products via ship barge tank truck and rail car. It maintains a fleet of more than 500 rail cars to supply on-time delivery requirements to customers.

Strategy

Unlike most other oil and gas suppliers Tauber Oil does not rely on a financial speculation strategy (the buying and selling of contracts for petroleum products). The company primarily plays the role of the middleman and more than 90% of the company's businesses involve the actual delivery of petroleum products and gas liquids.

Price volatility goes with Tauber Oil's territory and the company relies on its track record of reliable service and long-term relationships with customers to weather downturns in the market.

In order to develop and grow new operations the company enters into partnerships collaborations joint ventures and acquisition arrangements. Tauber Oil is partnered with Rio Energy International to provide adequate storage tank capacity at multiple terminals which helps it to maintain low cost train operations from Western Canada to the US Gulf Coast.

Company Background

To strengthen its finances and to focus on its core oil chemical and petrochemical businesses in 2012 the company merged its natural gas division with Interconn Resources Inc. to form Interconn Resources LLC. Interconn Resources specializes in delivering competitively priced natural gas to municipal industrial retail and governmental customers across the southeastern US.

Tauber Oil was founded in 1953 by O. J. Tauber Sr. He gained his oil and petroleum products trading experience working for a small Houston refinery called Eastern States Refining.

His son (and company executive) Richard Tauber is also the president of a small affiliated oil company Tauber Exploration and Production.

EXECUTIVES

Vice President, Steven Elliott
Vp Credit Finance, Stephen E. Hamlin
Owner And Principal, David W. Tauber
Owner And Principal, Richard E. Tauber
Vice President Public Relation, Connie Kubiak
Vice President Residual Fuels, Ed Naspinski
Vice President Refined Products, Blake Hale
Vice President, Bob Mackenzie
Vice President Finance And Corporate Development, Matthew Crotts
Vice President Crude Oil Marketing, Jacqueline Taton
Auditors: MOHLE ADAMS HOUSTON TEXAS

LOCATIONS

HQ: TAUBER OIL COMPANY
  55 WAUGH DR STE 700, HOUSTON, TX 770075837
Phone: 713 869-8700
Web: WWW.TAUBEROIL.COM

PRODUCTS/OPERATIONS

Selected Products:
Natural Gas Liquids
  Butane
  Ethane
  Isobutane
  Propane
Petrochemicals
  Benzene
  Methanol
  MTBE
  Styrene monomer
  Toluene
  Xylene
Refined
  Aviation jet fuel
  Kerosene
  Low sulfur diesel
  No. 2 fuel oil

COMPETITORS

Cabot Oil & Gas   Marathon Oil
Devon Energy   Occidental Petroleum
Exxon Mobil   Tesoro
George Warren   Valero Energy
Global Partners

HISTORICAL FINANCIALS

Company Type: Private

Income Statement   FYE: December 31

	REVENUE ($ mil.)	NET INCOME ($ mil.)	NET PROFIT MARGIN	EMPLOYEES
12/14	4,831	10	0.2%	135
12/13	4,769	16	0.3%	—
12/12	5,088	21	0.4%	—
Annual Growth	(2.6%)	(29.0%)	—	—

2014 Year-End Financials
Return on assets: 2.7%   Cash ($ mil.): 15
Return on equity: 6.9%
Current ratio: 1.50

TECHNIP USA, INC.

EXECUTIVES

V Pres, Matthew Seinsheimer
Pres, Deanna Goodwin
Designer, Allan Salvador
Coordinator, Christopher Bennett
Procurement Staff, Sam Daik
Buyer Onshore, Joshua Connelly
Manager, Natalie Michulka
Project Manager, Qiang Zeng
Associate Engineer, Tanner Powell
Project Engineering Manager, Bachar Mourad
Subcontracts Manager Procureme, Dwayne Nedbalek

LOCATIONS

HQ: TECHNIP USA, INC.
  11740 KATY FWY STE 100, HOUSTON, TX 770791254
Phone: 281 870-1111
Web: WWW.TECHNIPFMC.COM

HISTORICAL FINANCIALS

Company Type: Private

Income Statement   FYE: December 31

	REVENUE ($ mil.)	NET INCOME ($ mil.)	NET PROFIT MARGIN	EMPLOYEES
12/08	1,377	111	8.1%	4,346
12/04	609	(1)	—	—
12/97	225,116	0	0.0%	—
Annual Growth	(37.1%)	79.2%	—	—

2008 Year-End Financials
Return on assets: 10.7%   Cash ($ mil.): 205
Return on equity: 26.5%
Current ratio: 1.20

TECUMSEH PRODUCTS COMPANY LLC

Named for the legendary Shawnee chief Tecumseh Products makes a line of hermetically sealed compressors and heat pumps for residential and commercial refrigerators and freezers water coolers air conditioners dehumidifiers and vending machines. The company's line of scroll compressor models are suited for demanding commercial refrigeration applications and consist primarily of reciprocating and rotary designs. Tecumseh sells its products to OEMs and aftermarket distributors in more than 100 countries worldwide with more than 80% of its sales generated outside of the US. In mid-2015 Tecumseh agreed to be acquired by affiliates of Mueller Industries and Atlas Holdings for $123 million.

Geographic Reach
Tecumseh's products are manufactured in about a dozen plants in the US Brazil France (five facilities) and India (two facilities); assembly plants are located in Canada Malaysia and Mexico. Some of the company's facilities are made possible through joint ventures; one such venture is Song Jiang in China.

Sales and Marketing
The company serves 1600 customers including Whirlpool and Electrolux which together generate about 12% of the company's business. In 2014 almost 45% of the sales from its Brazilian location were made to its three largest customers. The company sells its products in 97 countries primarily through its own sales staff as well as independent sales representatives and authorized wholesale distributors. It markets its products under brand names that include Celseon Tecumseh Wintsys Masterflux Silensys and Vector.

Financial Performance
Tecumseh has suffered four straight years of declining revenues and two straight years of net losses. Revenues fell 12% from $824 million in 2013 to $724 million in 2014 as the company posted a net loss of $33 million in 2014.

The decrease in revenue for 2014 was primarily due to a 8% drop in sales of compressors used in commercial refrigeration and aftermarket applications a 23% decrease in sales of compressors for air conditioning applications and a 13% drop in sales for compressors used in household refrigeration and freezer applications. Tecumseh was also negatively affected by a competitive pricing environment in Brazil and soft market conditions in North America throughout 2014.

Strategy
Focused on growing internationally Tecumseh has invested in research and development engineering laboratories in North America Europe South America and India. It also partners with R&D facilities at universities throughout the globe to provide life science research on how its products interface with the environment.

HISTORY

Master toolmakers Ray Herrick (friend and advisor to Henry Ford and Thomas Edison) and Bill Sage founded the Michigan-based company in 1930 as Hillsdale Machine & Tool. Its first products included small tools toys and car and refrigerator parts. By 1933 Herrick controlled the company. The next year the company bought a facility in Tecumseh Michigan where it began mass-producing car and refrigerator parts. The company changed its name to Tecumseh Products in 1934 and went public in 1937.

By the end of the 1930s Tecumseh was a major producer of hermetic compressors. In 1941 its focus shifted to WWII efforts and it began making anti-aircraft projectile casings and aircraft engine parts. Herrick's son Kenneth began working for Tecumseh in 1945. Two years later a company-made compressor was used in the first home window air-conditioning unit.

Tecumseh bought two Ohio companies in 1950 and 1952 and introduced an AC compressor for cars in 1953. Two years later the company bought compressor designer Tresco and hired Joseph Layton as Tecumseh's president and CEO. Tecumseh gained entry into the gasoline engine market with the purchase of Wisconsin's Lauson Engine (1956) and Power Products (1957). Acquisitions in the 1960s allowed Tecumseh to tap into the power-train market.

EXECUTIVES

Ceo-Pres, Harold M Karp
Evp-Cfo-Treas, Janice E Stipp
Cbd&ro, Igor Popov
Evp, Jerry L Mosingo
Pres Compressor Business Unit, Eric L Stolzenberg
Pres Elec Comp Business Unit, Ronald E Pratt
Global Engineering, Ryan Burns
Global Human Resources, Roger Jackson
Coordinator, Trina Higgins
Coordinator, Debra Hodge
Regional Sales Manager, Jeff Horne

LOCATIONS

HQ: TECUMSEH PRODUCTS COMPANY LLC
  5683 HINES DR, ANN ARBOR, MI 481087901
Phone: 734 585-9500
Web: WWW.TECUMSEH.COM

2014 Sales

	$ mil.	% of total
Europe	191	26
South America		
Brazil	182	25
Other countries	45	6
North America		
US	125	18
Other countries	15	2
Asia		
India	105	14
China	13	2
Other countries	5	1
Middle East & Africa	39	6
Total	724	100

PRODUCTS/OPERATIONS

2014 Sales

	% of total
Commercial refrigeration	62
Household refrigerator & freezer	19
Residential & specialty air conditioning	19
Total	**100**

Selected Products

Compressors (all hermetically sealed)
 Reciprocating (for air conditioning and commercial refrigeration)
 Rotary (for room and mobile air conditioning)
 Scroll (especially designed for demanding commercial refrigeration applications)
 Highlighted Products
 A Legend Reborn
 Tecumseh "K” Kits

COMPETITORS

Brasmotor	Mitsubishi Electric
Bristol Compressors	Panasonic Corp
Daikin	SANYO
Danfoss Turbocor	Sullair
Emerson Electric	Trane Inc.
LG Electronics	WEG Electric
Lennox	

HISTORICAL FINANCIALS

Company Type: Private

Income Statement				FYE: December 31
	REVENUE ($ mil.)	NET INCOME ($ mil.)	NET PROFIT MARGIN	EMPLOYEES
12/14	724	(32)	—	5,800
12/13	823	(37)	—	—
12/12	854	22	2.6%	—
Annual Growth	(7.9%)	—	—	—

2014 Year-End Financials

Return on assets: (-8.3%)   Cash ($ mil.): 42
Return on equity: (-21.8%)
Current ratio: 1.40

TEKNOR APEX COMPANY

Teknor Apex offers a wide-ranging portfolio of chemicals and synthetic polymers. The company's six business divisions provide colorants (through its Teknor Color unit) vinyl compounds thermoplastic elastomers engineering thermoplastics chemicals for the polyvinyl chloride (PVC) plasticizer market and garden hoses. The company's compounds are used for building and construction consumer products industrial manufacturing electrical and electronic devices medical tools packaging and vehicular components. Founded in 1924 by Alfred A. Fain and his son-in-law Albert Pilavin Teknor invented the first plasticized (flexible) PVC.

Operations

Teknor Apex operates via six business segments.

The company's Teknor Color unit offers standard and custom colorants for polymers including olefins styrenics polyethylene terephthalate (PET) engineering thermoplastics and thermoplastic elastomers.

Teknor's vinyl products include flexible and rigid polyvinyl chloride (PVC) fire-resistant plenum PVC PVC elastomers PVC blends (including rigid blends) chlorinated PVC PVC film and halogen-free flame retardant.

The company's thermoplastic elastomers lineup comprises styrenic block copolymer (SBC) com-

pounds polyolefin blends thermoplastic vulcanizates polyurethane compounds and other specialty blends.

Through its Engineering Thermoplastics business Teknor markets three nylon-based compounds that are used in outdoor power equipment hinges furniture and cars ? including chassis exterior and interior parts and engine components.

The company's Chemicals segment produces esters for the PVC plasticizer market under its TruVis brand. Its offerings include adipate low-viscosity trimellitate high-viscosity trimellitate and polyol esters. The chemicals are used as base stocks and additives for automotive and industrial applications metalworking fluid and grease.

Teknor also sells hoses under brands like ZeroG Neverkink Flexalloy and Apex for gardens professional landscaping farms and ranches RVs and marine vehicles industrial and construction applications and food and services.

Geographic Reach

Pawtucket Rhode Island-based Teknor Apex has nine US manufacturing plants (including one manufacturing plant and sales office) in California Kentucky Massachusetts the Carolinas Rhode Island Tennessee Texas and Vermont; one plant in each of Belgium Germany and China; one sales office in each of Germany the Netherlands and Taiwan; two sales offices in China; and a plant and sales office in Singapore.

Sales and Marketing

Teknor Apex serves a diverse client base including building and construction firms consumer goods producers electrical and electronics companies industrial manufacturers healthcare providers packaging companies and vehicle fabricators.

Strategy

Teknor Apex is expanding its geographic footprint and product lineup through organic growth and acquisitions.

In 2018 the firm launched its Chemlon 500 Series recycled polyamide compounds in Europe. The engineering thermoplastics based on polyamide 66 are used for automotive components office furniture and other products. Two years prior the company made available its Apex 1583 Series flexible polyvinyl chloride (PVC) compounds which are used in automotive drain tubing to diverts water from sunroofs and roof ditch moldings to vehicle wheel wells).

Company Background

The company was founded in 1924 as a tire distributor and retreader by Alfred Fain in 1924. Fain's grandson now leads the privately held company.

EXECUTIVES

Vice President Human Resources, Laurie Meisner
President, Jonathan D. Fain
Evp, Bertram M. Lederer
President, William J. (Bill) Murray
Cio, Peter Matteo
Vice President Of Information Technology, Craig White
Vice President General Manager Chem Polymer, Scott Fleming
Vice President Business Development, Robert Brookman
Senior Vice President Of Manufacturing, Bill Murray
National Accounts Manager, John Mcdermott
National Account Manager, Chris Bates
Vice President Technology, Ryszard Brzoskowski
Auditors: PICCERELLI GOLSTEIN & COMPANY

LOCATIONS

HQ: TEKNOR APEX COMPANY
 505 CENTRAL AVE, PAWTUCKET, RI 028611900
Phone: 401 725-8000
Web: WWW.TEKNORAPEX.COM

PRODUCTS/OPERATIONS

Selected Products and Services

Vinyl
FLEXIBLE PVC COMPOUNDS
Apex Flexible PVC
FireGuard LS FR PVC
Flexalloy PVC Elastomers
Apex PVC Blends
RIGID PVC COMPOUNDS
Apex Rigid PVC
AquaGuard CPVC
Apex Rigid PVC Blends
CALENDERED PVC FILM
Apex Calendered PVC Film
Thermoplastic Elastomers (TPE)
TPS TPV TPO AND TPU COMPOUNDS
Medalist Medical TPEs
Monprene
Sarlink
Elexar
Engineering Thermoplastics
POLYAMIDES
Chemlon
Creamid
Polyolefins
HalGuard LS HFFR Compounds

Colorants

Teknor Color
Color Store
Esters
TruVis Esters
Garden Hose

COMPETITORS

GLS	RB Rubber
NatureWorks	Synthomer
PMC Global	Tekni-Plex
PolyOne	Vulcan International

HISTORICAL FINANCIALS

Company Type: Private

Income Statement				FYE: July 31
	REVENUE ($ mil.)	NET INCOME ($ mil.)	NET PROFIT MARGIN	EMPLOYEES
07/14	996	50	5.0%	2,500
07/05	574	0	—	—
Annual Growth	6.3%	—	—	—

2014 Year-End Financials

Return on assets: 6.8%   Cash ($ mil.): 74
Return on equity: 5.0%
Current ratio: 2.40

TEKSYSTEMS, INC.

TEKsystems a subsidiary of staffing giant Allegis provides IT consulting and staffing services from locations in North America and Europe. Considered one of the nation's largest IT staffing firms the company places more than 80000 technical professionals each year who work in a variety of fields including biotechnology telecommunications and construction and engineering. TEKsystems has 100 offices serving about 6000 clients. In addition the company runs the thingamajob.com website which is an online job board for technical staff. Spinning off of fellow Allegis unit Aerotek TEKsystems was formed in 1994 to focus on the IT needs of clients.

Geographic Reach

The company has more than 100 locations throughout North America Europe and Asia.

Sales and Marketing

TEKsystems works to help its clients control cost mitigate risk and deliver quality product outcomes.

Strategy

The company has used strategic partnerships to grow its business.

EXECUTIVES

President, Keith Bozeman
Vice President Finance, Paul Oldham
Regional Vice President, Dustin Hunt
Auditors: PRICEWATERHOUSECOOPERS LLP BA

LOCATIONS

HQ: TEKSYSTEMS, INC.
7437 RACE RD, HANOVER, MD 210761112
Phone: 410 540-7700

PRODUCTS/OPERATIONS

SELECTED SERVICES

IT STAFFING SOLUTIONS
Communications Staffing Services
Digital Services
End User Services
IT Applications Staffing Services
IT Direct Placement Services
Network Infrastructure Staffing Services
TEKsystems Staffing Quality Process
Time and Expense
IT SERVICES
Applications Services
Education Services
Global Delivery Network
Infrastructure Services
Project Governance
IT TALENT MANAGEMENT EXPERTISE
Local Market

Selected Markets Served

Communications
Financial services
Government
Information technology
Expertise

COMPETITORS

Acro Service	Info Technologies
Adecco	Kelly Services
CDI	ManpowerGroup
CorSource Technology	Prosum
Group	Robert Half

HISTORICAL FINANCIALS

Company Type: Private

Income Statement				FYE: December 31
	REVENUE ($ mil.)	NET INCOME ($ mil.)	NET PROFIT MARGIN	EMPLOYEES
12/17	4,350	0	—	2,900
12/16	4,132	0	—	—
12/14	3,618	0	—	—
12/13	3,551	0	—	—
Annual Growth	5.2%	—	—	—

2017 Year-End Financials

Return on assets: —   Cash ($ mil.): 41
Return on equity: —
Current ratio: 3.00

TEMPLE UNIVERSITY HEALTH SYSTEM, INC.

Temple University Health System (TUHS) is a network of academic and community hospitals associated with the Temple University School of Medicine. It provides primary secondary and tertiary care to residents in the Philadelphia County (Pennsylvania) area. The system includes 722-bed Temple University Hospital (a Level 1 trauma center) and a pair of community-based hospitals that provide acute and emergency care as well as the Jeanes Hospital and TUH-Episcopal Campus (home to a 120-bed behavioral health unit). TUHS supports programs in pediatric and adult cardiology organ transplantation oncology and pulmonary disease. TUHS also includes a community-wide network of primary care physicians.

Operations

The $1.4-billion academic health system comprises Temple University Hospital TUH-Episcopal Campus TUH-Northern Campus Fox Chase Cancer Center Jeanes Hospital Temple Transport Team and Temple Physicians. It's affiliated with Temple University School of Medicine. Bermuda-based TUHS Insurance Company Ltd. is a captive insurance company established to reinsure the professional liability claims of TUHS subsidiaries.

It offers everything from specialized cardiac care and spinal rehabilitation to a lung care center a burn center and stroke treatments.

Medicare and Medicaid account for 65% of net patient revenues.

Geographic Reach

Temple University Health System serves the residents of Philadelphia.

Sales and Marketing

TUHS markets itself through TV commercials and print and billboard advertising.

Financial Performance

In fiscal 2012 revenue rose by 37% to $1.35 billion vs. 2011. It attributes the double-digit gains to increases in net patient service revenue research revenue and other revenue. The system logged $107 million in net income during the reporting period as compared to a net loss in 2011.

Strategy

TUHS concentrates on adding services and expanding its geographic reach. It added Fox Chase Cancer Center in 2012; opened the women's care center in Elkins Park Pennsylvania in 2012; opened a third urgent care facility in Jenkintown Pennsylvania in 2013; and expanded into new markets by opening the Temple Health Center City facility.

EXECUTIVES

Pres*, Richard M Englert
Vp For Public Affairs*, William T Bergman
Auditors: DELOITTE & TOUCHE LLP PHILADE

LOCATIONS

HQ: TEMPLE UNIVERSITY HEALTH SYSTEM, INC.
2450 W HUNTING PARK AVE, PHILADELPHIA, PA 191291302
Phone: 215 707-2000
Web: WWW.TEMPLEHEALTH.ORG

COMPETITORS

Albert Einstein Healthcare Network
Aria Health
Children's Hospital of Philadelphia
Community Health Systems
Crozer-Keystone Health System
Doylestown Hospital
Jefferson Health
Main Line Health System
Mercy Health System
North Philadelphia Health System
Northwestern Human Services
Our Lady of Lourdes Medical Center
Pennsylvania Hospital
The Magee Memorial Hospital for Convalescents
University of Pennsylvania Health System

HISTORICAL FINANCIALS

Company Type: Private

Income Statement				FYE: June 30
	REVENUE ($ mil.)	NET INCOME ($ mil.)	NET PROFIT MARGIN	EMPLOYEES
06/12	1,004	(48)	—	7,573
06/11	994	45	4.6%	—
06/09	0	(0)	—	—
Annual Growth	1819.9%	—	—	—

2012 Year-End Financials

Return on assets: (-5.1%)   Cash ($ mil.): 103
Return on equity: (-22.0%)
Current ratio: 2.30

TEMPLE UNIVERSITY-OF THE COMMONWEALTH SYSTEM OF HIGHER EDUCATION

Temple University's owl mascot reflects its start as a night school but the owl's sagacity also points to the school's educational credentials. More than 38000 students are enrolled in its 320 academic programs across the Philadephia university's 17 schools. Its Health Sciences Center includes Temple University Hospital and schools that teach medicine and dentistry. Part of Pennsylvania's Commonwealth System of Higher Education Temple has six different campuses in the Philadelphia area as well campuses in Tokyo and Rome and educational programs in China Greece France Israel and the UK. The system has a student-teacher ratio of about 15:1. Dr. Russell Conwell founded the university in 1884; it was incorporated as Temple University in 1907.

Operations

Temple's campus in suburban Ambler Pennsylvania offers programs in community and regional planning horticulture and landscape architecture. Together all of its campuses offer a combined total of about 140 bachelor's 125 master's 60 doctoral and nearly 10 professional degrees. Students can obtain professional degrees in dentistry law medicine pharmacy and podiatric medicine among others.

Financial Performance

In 2017 (ended June 30) Temple's revenue increased 6% to $3.3 billiondue to higher tuition patient care income.

EXECUTIVES

Senior Vice President Gov, Kenneth Lawrence
Dean Fox School Of Business And Management, M. Moshe Porat
Vp Computer And Information Services, Timothy C. O'Rourke
Dean Katz School Of Medicine, Larry R. Kaiser
Provost And Svp Academic Affairs, Hai-Lung Dai
Dean Boyer College Of Music And Dance, Robert T. Stroker
Vp Cfo And Treasurer, Ken Kaiser
President, Neil D. Theobald
Dean Of Students, Stephanie Ives
Interim Dean Tyler School Of Art, Hester Stinnett
Dean Kornberg School Of Dentistry, Amid I. Ismail
Dean College Of Education, Gregory Anderson
Dean Beasley School Of Law, JoAnne A. Epps
Dean School Of Media And Communication, David Boardman
Dean School Of Pharmacy, Peter Doukas
Dean School Of Podiatric Medicine, John A. Mattiacci
Dean College Of Public Health, Laura A. Siminoff
Dean College Of Science And Technology, Michael L. Klein
Assistant Vice President Human Resources Operations, Karen Ward
Assistant Vice President Benefits, Jennifer Silvestri
Associate Vice President And Controller, Frank Annunziato
Department Chair, Alice Hausman
Vice President, Michael Guglielmo
Associate Vice President Care, Steven Carson
Vice President Of Information Services, Raymond Johnson
Associate Vice President, Larry Brandolph
Associate Vice President, Dozie Ibeh
Assistant Vice President, Shawn Kleitz
Vice President, Ryan Olson
Assistant Vice President Government Affairs, George Kenney
Associate Vice President, Timm Rinehart
Vice President Of Operations, William Bergman
Associate Vice President University Relations, George Ingram
Associate Vice President Budget And Planning, Rick Chant
Vice President, Robert Salomon
Vice President, Deanna Geddes
Assoicate Vice President Human Resources, Kim Sakil
Vice President Finance, Lee Shirley
First Vice President, Kelsey Boyd
Assoc Vice President Acad Computing Service, Sheri Stahler
Assistant Vice President, Adam Ferrero
Assistant Vice President, Kathryn Dangelo
Associate Vice President For Finance And Administration, Joe De Jesus
Assistant Vice President For Community Relations And Economic Development, Beverly Coleman
Assistant Vice President Government Rltns, Dennis Lynch
Associate Vice President Finance And Administration, William J Wilkinson
Director Of Admissions, Brian F Hahn
Assistant Vice President Comp Service, Michael Taylor
Associate Vice President Bus Services, Rich Rumer
Director Of Admissions, Karin West
Assistant Vice President, Lisa Zimmaro
Vice President Student, Ariel Pierre
Vice President Of Services, Kayla Martin
Vice President Finance(treasurer), Ramesh Narasimhan
Chairman, Patrick J. (Pat) O'Connor

Vice Chairman, Anthony J. Scirica
Secretary, Mary Vesey
Secretary, Rosa Grier
Assistant Secretary, Janet Carruth
Executive Board Member, Camillia Keach
Secretary, Ruby Hammond
Secretary, Valentina Cleary
Secretary, Myrla Barksdale
Secretary, Cynthia Grabusic
Surgery Secretary, Devonna Smith
Financial Secretary Rachel Miller Secretary, Jenny Moon
Head Secretary, Helen Kim
Graduate Secretary, Patricia Mcfadden
Secretary, Patrick Aragon
Auditors: DELOITTE & TOUCHE LLP PHILADE

LOCATIONS

HQ: TEMPLE UNIVERSITY-OF THE COMMONWEALTH SYSTEM OF HIGHER EDUCATION
1801 N BROAD ST, PHILADELPHIA, PA 191226003
Phone: 215 204-1380
Web: WWW.TEMPLE.EDU

Selected Campuses

Philadelphia
 Ambler
 Center City
 Fort Washington
 Harrisburg
 Main
 Podiatric Medicine
 Health Sciences Center
International
 Japan
 Rome Italy

HISTORICAL FINANCIALS

Company Type: Private

Income Statement				FYE: June 30
	REVENUE ($ mil.)	NET INCOME ($ mil.)	NET PROFIT MARGIN	EMPLOYEES
06/13	2,635	192	7.3%	9,061
06/12	2,254	(37)	—	—
06/08	2,034	228	11.2%	—
Annual Growth	5.3%	(3.4%)	—	—

2013 Year-End Financials
Return on assets: 4.7%   Cash ($ mil.): 241
Return on equity: 9.7%
Current ratio: 3.10

TENASKA ENERGY, INC.

EXECUTIVES

Chb-Ceo, Howard L Hawks
Pres-Dir*, Jerry K Crouse
Dir*, Thomas E Hendricks
Exec V Pres*, Michael C Lebens
SEC*, Ronald N Quinn
Director, Scott Harwell
Director, Jay Hoellen
Administrator, Rich Hurlbut
Vice President, Terry Clarke
Senior Director, Kevin Kohlscheen
Assistant Controller, Lisa Jones

LOCATIONS

HQ: TENASKA ENERGY, INC.
14302 FNB PKWY, OMAHA, NE 681544446
Phone: 402 691-9500
Web: WWW.TENASKA.COM

HISTORICAL FINANCIALS

Company Type: Private

Income Statement				FYE: December 31
	REVENUE ($ mil.)	NET INCOME ($ mil.)	NET PROFIT MARGIN	EMPLOYEES
12/07	654	0	—	300
12/05	10,020	0	—	—
Annual Growth	(74.4%)	—	—	—

2007 Year-End Financials
Return on assets: —   Cash ($ mil.): 142
Return on equity: —
Current ratio: 1.70

TENASKA MARKETING VENTURES

EXECUTIVES

Chm, Howard L Hawks
Pres, Fred R Hunzeker
V Pres, David N Schettler
Mgr-Dir, Janet Corritore
Mgr-V Pres, Mike Metzler
Sr V Pres, Terry K Cameron
Sr V Pres, Lori A Bruck
Mgr-V Pres, John Obermiller
Mgr-V Pres, Martin E Titus
Mrg-Dir, John G Hall
V Pres, Terry Clarke

LOCATIONS

HQ: TENASKA MARKETING VENTURES
14302 FNB PKWY, OMAHA, NE 681544446
Phone: 402 691-9500
Web: WWW.TENASKA.COM

HISTORICAL FINANCIALS

Company Type: Private

Income Statement				FYE: December 31
	REVENUE ($ mil.)	NET INCOME ($ mil.)	NET PROFIT MARGIN	EMPLOYEES
12/07	10,309	0	—	91
12/05	9,470	0	—	—
12/04	0	0	—	—
12/03	4,940	0	—	—
Annual Growth	20.2%	—	—	—

TESLA ENERGY OPERATIONS, INC.

Ready to get off the grid? SolarCity can help. The company sells installs finances and monitors turnkey solar energy systems that convert sunlight into electricity. Its systems either mounted on a building's roof or the ground are used by residential commercial and government customers such as eBay Intel Wal-Mart and Homeland Security. SolarCity doesn't manufacture its systems but uses solar panels from Trina Solar Yingli Green Energy and Kyocera Solar and inverters from Power-One SMA Solar Technology and Schneider Electric. In late 2016 SolarCity was acquired by Tesla Motors in a deal worth $2.6 billion.

Change in Company Type

SolarCity was acquired by Tesla Motors for $2.6 billion in late 2016. Both companies will be led by Elon Musk and expect to achieve cost synergies of $150 million in the first full year after closing. By combining Tesla's new electric vehicles with SolarCity's newest solar products the companies expect to lower hardware costs reduce installation costs and improve their manufacturing efficiency.

Operations

SolarCity's main selling point is that it offers renewable energy for less than traditional utility companies. While customers feel good about choosing an alternative energy source they're also usually saving money. Much of the costs associated with new installation and monthly fees are offset by SolarCity's investment funds. To date the company has formed more than 20 investment funds and raised more than $1.5 billion from banks and other companies such as Credit Suisse Google PG&E Corporation and U.S. Bancorp. (Two funds however are being audited by the IRS.) SolarCity also depends on federal and state tax rebates and credits to lower costs and create incentives for fund investors. For example the federal government offers a tax credit of 30% to install solar power through 2016. (After 2016 the tax credit will fall to 10%.)

Electricity is sold under long-term contracts; generally customers agree to a 20-year term. Customers are either signed up as leases or power purchase agreements. Lease customers pay a fixed monthly rate while the rate for power purchase agreement customers depends on the amount of electricity the solar energy system produces. The vast majority of its customers (some 90%) "rent" the solar installations instead of buying them outright in order to keep SolarCity in charge of the product warranty.

Geographic Reach

California-based SolarCity serves customers in 16 states and the District of Columbia. Its offices and warehouses reside in Arizona California Colorado Connecticut Hawaii Maryland Massachusetts Nevada New Jersey New York Oregon Texas Canada and China. The company earned over 75% of its revenue collectively from California Arizona Colorado Hawaii and New York.

Sales and Marketing

The company's client list includes residential customers commercial entities such as Wal-Mart eBay Intel and Safeway and government entities such as the U.S. Military. SolarCity sells its products and services through a direct outside sales force from 64 sales offices in 16 states and Washington DC. (Most states have one sales office but its home state of California has 12.) It also has a call center.

Financial Performance

Fast-growing SolarCity is posting impressive revenue gains but no profits yet. Indeed the solar services company reported $255 million in sales in 2014 an increase of 56% versus 2013. The company credited the double-digit gain for 2014 to a major increase in the installation and operation of solar energy systems under lease and power purchase agreements in new and existing markets along with an increase in sales of solar energy systems and components. SolarCity's net loss for 2014 was fueled by an increase in sales and marketing costs and interest expenses.

Strategy

SolarCity installs about one of every four solar energy systems in the US but is still hungry for more. The company's products and services are available through home-improvement-retail-giant The Home Depot. Also in 2014 the company partnered with electronics retailer Best Buy to offer its products and services through some 60 Best Buy stores in California Arizona Hawaii New York and Oregon. SolarCity also partners with more than 100 homebuilders including Pulte and Del Webb. Other channel partners include Tesla Motors Viridian Energy Honda Acura and BMW.

While residential customers are important to the company going forward SolarCity is seeking to install larger solar energy systems for businesses and government customers. The company is also growing its business through acquisitions.

Mergers and Acquisitions

In mid-2014 SolarCity acquired Silevo a solar panel technology and manufacturing company. The acquisition helped to manage the company's supply chain and control the design and manufacturing of solar cells and photovoltaic panels that are a key component of its solar energy systems. The deal also enabled SolarCity to utilize and combine Silevo's technology with economies of scale to achieve significant cost reductions.

Company Background

SolarCity was founded in 2006 by CEO Lyndon Rive and his brother COO and CTO Peter Rive. The Rives are cousins of non-executive chairman Elon Musk a notable entrepreneur who co-founded PayPal and also heads Tesla Motors and SpaceX.

EXECUTIVES

Ceo, Lyndon R. Rive, $275,000 total compensation
Cto, Peter J. Rive, $275,000 total compensation
Evp General Counsel And Secretary, Seth R. Weissman, $270,000 total compensation
Evp Strategy And Global Markets, Marco Krapels
Evp Customer Operations, Brendon Merkley
Cfo, J. Radford Small
President Global Sales And Customer Experience, Toby Corey
Vice President Customer Account Management Group, Paul Brandt
Vice President Supply Chain, Vinayak Gupta
Vice President Regional Sales, Courtney Reynolds
Senior Vice President Of Product Engineering, Jiunn Heng
Vice President Of Sc Direct, John Frampton
Vice President Talent Acquisition And Analytics, Raj Dev
Vice President Inside Sales, Paul Bajus
Chairman, Elon Musk
Board Member, Antonio Gracias
Auditors: ERNST & YOUNG LLP LOS ANGELES

LOCATIONS

HQ: TESLA ENERGY OPERATIONS, INC.
3055 CLEARVIEW WAY, SAN MATEO, CA 944023709
Phone: 888 765-2489

PRODUCTS/OPERATIONS

2013 Sales

	$ mil.	% of total
Operating leases	82	51
Solar energy system	81	49
Total	**163**	**100**

Selected Products and Services

Products
Solar energy systems (panels inverters and mounting racks)

Services

Energy efficiency upgrades
Home energy evaluations

COMPETITORS

AEE Solar	Real Goods Solar
Ameresco	SolarCraft Services
Chevron	SunEdison
Conergy Inc.	SunPower
First Solar	Sunvalley Solar
REC Solar	

HISTORICAL FINANCIALS

Company Type: Private

Income Statement				FYE: December 31
	REVENUE ($ mil.)	NET INCOME ($ mil.)	NET PROFIT MARGIN	EMPLOYEES
12/16	730	(820)	—	12,000
12/15	399	(768)	—	
12/14	255	(375)	—	
12/13	163	(151)	—	
Annual Growth 64.6%		—	—	—

2016 Year-End Financials

Return on assets: (-9.0%)   Cash ($ mil.): 290
Return on equity: (-42.5%)
Current ratio: 0.50

TEXAS AROMATICS, LP

EXECUTIVES

Pres, Melbern G Glasscock
V Pres, Trenton L Kelley
Sales Executive, Staci Voll
Accounting Team Member, Vivian Mursuli
Vice President, Edwin Echols
Business Manager, Randy Suhl
Senior Accountant, Nadine Boyle
Scheduler, Natalie Pappas
Distribution Coordinator, Tiffany Buck
Auditors: WEAVER AND TIDWELL LLP HOUST

LOCATIONS

HQ: TEXAS AROMATICS, LP
3555 TIMMONS LN STE 700, HOUSTON, TX
770276450
Phone: 713 520-2900
Web: WWW.TEXASAROMATICS.COM

HISTORICAL FINANCIALS

Company Type: Private

Income Statement				FYE: December 31
	REVENUE ($ mil.)	NET INCOME ($ mil.)	NET PROFIT MARGIN	EMPLOYEES
12/17	470	9	2.0%	20
12/16	449	11	2.6%	—
12/15	531	10	2.0%	—
12/14	961	10	1.1%	—
Annual Growth (21.2%)		(2.7%)	—	—

2017 Year-End Financials

Return on assets: 10.9%   Cash ($ mil.): 36
Return on equity: 19.0%
Current ratio: 2.30

TEXAS CHILDREN'S HOSPITAL

Texas Children's Hospital (TCH) is the flagship facility of Texas Children's Hospital Integrated Delivery System. Founded in 1954 the not-for-profit hospital provides full-service medical care for children conducts extensive research and trains pediatric medical professionals. Part of the Texas Medical Center complex it has clinical facilities for every ailment ranging from psychological troubles to surgery and physical rehabilitation as well as specialized heart cancer and neurological care. TCH is the primary pediatric training facility for Baylor College of Medicine.

Operations
TCH comprises a 491-bed tertiary care pediatric facility a 115-bed obstetrics and gynecological care facility focusing on high-risk births (both located on the Texas Medical Center campus) and a 44-bed full-service pediatric facility in west Houston. The hospital includes the Jan and Dan Duncan Neurological Research Institute and the Feigin Center for pediatric research.

The hospital's staff includes more than 1500 primary physicians and other medical specialists as well as some 6000 nurses. The hospital has satellite facilities in and around Houston and it operates the Texas Children's Pediatric Associates primary care network of more than 170 physicians. The company also runs the Texas Children's Health Plan which offers Medicaid and Texas CHIP (Children's Health Insurance Plan) programs.

TCH's International coordinates care for sick children who come to Texas Children's Hospital from abroad. The international segment also sends out medical teams to care for critically ill children throughout Latin America the Middle East Europe Africa and Asia. For instance it has established a number of AIDS clinics in African countries.

The hospital performs more than 25000 surgeries annually. It has some 1.9 million patient encounters some 31000 admissions and about 117000 emergency department visits each year.

Geographic Reach
TCH includes four main facilities — its main hospital and Texas Children's Pavilion for Women at the Medical Center Texas Children's West Campus in the Houston suburb of Katy and Texas Children's The Woodlands in that suburb (opening in 2017).

Financial Performance
Though most of its revenue comes from patient care fees TCH relies heavily on donations and federal funding to supplement its operations. For instance the hospital and Baylor College of Medicine represent one of the most active and well-funded pediatric research programs in the US with more than 800 basic research and clinical studies backed by more than $100 million in annual grants.

Increased patient revenue and premiums led to a 9% rise in revenue for 2014 from $2.3 billion to $2.5 billion. Net income fell 29% to $257 million due to a decline in investment returns and increased operating expenses including salaries and benefits supplies and pharmaceuticals. Cash flow from operations rose 63% to $257 million as a result of higher accounts payable.

Strategy
TCH has been opening new facilities some in suburban locations and expanding others to reach additional patients. In 2013 it introduced the da Vinci robotic system and expanded its children's hematology center to include a dozen exam rooms and four acute care rooms. It also opened its oculoplastic clinic for pediatric patients.

In 2014 the hospital opened its in vitro fertilization lab the first in Houston to utilize the EmbryoScope embryo monitoring system. It is also building an eight-bed isolation unit at its west campus.

EXECUTIVES

Senior Vice President Human Resources And Organizational Development, Linda Aldred
Vice President Strategic Capital Projects, Robert McCleskey
President And Ceo, Mark A. Wallace, age 67
Physician-in-chief, Mark W. Kline
Evp And Cfo, Benjamin (Ben) Melson
Obstetrician/gynecologist-in-chief, Michael A. Belfort
President Texas Children's Hospital The Woodlands, Michelle Riley-Brown
President Texas Children's Hospital West Campus, Chanda Cashen Chac n
Cio, Myra Davis
Vice President Business Operations, Carlos Rodriguez
Senior Vice President For Development, John Scales
Respiratory Therapy Director, Lee Evey
Vice President, Tabitha Rice
Assistant Vice President Facilities Operations, Bert Gumeringer
Nursing Director, Tangula Taylor
Vice President Of Public Affairs, Claire M Bassett
Vice President And General Counsel, Lance Lightfoot
Medical Director, Silvana Lawrence
Nursing Director, Gail M Parazynski
Medical Director, Edward Mason
Assistant Vice President Of Communications, Lori Williams
Vice President, Rachel Shupe
Vice President, Maria Javallana
Vice President For Public Affairs, Shawn Davis
Assistant Vice President For Finance, Kimberly Cotner
Senior Vice President, David Holcomb
Senior Vice President, Linda Waldred
Vice President, Debra Kahanek
Medical Director Blue Bird Circle Multiple Sclerosis Clinic, Timothy Lotze
Vice President, Debra Ward
Medical Director, Brandie Nichols
Medical Director, Angie Medellin
Vice President Marketing, Jenny Dudley
Vice President Of Purchasing, Sabrina Cowans
Vice President, Dan DiPrisco
Assistant Vice President, Sara Montenegro
Medical Director, Joseph Coselli
Vice President Marketing, Bobby Alford
Senior Vice President Technology, Samuel Wu
Vice President Audit Services, Randy Langenderfer
Treasurer, Dorine Mascari
Unit Secretary, Maya Cross
Secretary, Susan Boykin

LOCATIONS

HQ: TEXAS CHILDREN'S HOSPITAL
6621 FANNIN ST, HOUSTON, TX 770302399
Phone: 832 824-1000

PRODUCTS/OPERATIONS

2014 Sales

	$ mil.	% of total
Net patient revenue	1,530	60
Premium revenue	876	34
Medicaid & other supplemental reimbursement	59	2
Net assets released from restrictions for operations	28	1
Grants	21	1
Other income	41	2
Total	**2,558**	**100**

2014 Net Patient Revenue

	% of total
Managed care	61
Medicaid managed care	15
Medicaid	13
Self-pay	6
Commercial	5
Total	**100**

Selected Serives

Bariatric/weight control services
Certified trauma center
Chemotherapy
Dental services
Heart catheterization—diagnostic (child)
Genetic testing/counseling
HIV-AIDS services
Heart catheterization—treatment (child)
Kidney dialysis
Chemotherapy
Physical rehabilitation
Psychiatric services (Child/adolescent services Consultation and Outpatient care)
Sleep center
Sports medicine
Urgent-care center
Women's health center
Wound management services

COMPETITORS

CHRISTUS Health
Children's Hospital of Philadelphia
Children's Medical Center of Dallas
Cook Children's Health Care System
Dell Children's Medical Center
Mayo Clinic
Memorial Hermann Healthcare

Methodist Hospital System
Shriners Hospitals For Children
St. Jude Children's Research Hospital
St. Luke's Episcopal Hospital
Tenet Healthcare

HISTORICAL FINANCIALS
Company Type: Private

Income Statement				FYE: September 30
	REVENUE ($ mil.)	NET INCOME ($ mil.)	NET PROFIT MARGIN	EMPLOYEES
09/15	1,546	96	6.3%	6,000
09/14	1,383	70	5.1%	—
09/13	1,229	78	6.4%	—
09/12	2,043	289	14.2%	—
Annual Growth	(8.9%)	(30.6%)	—	—

2015 Year-End Financials

Return on assets: 2.1%   Cash ($ mil.): 93
Return on equity: 3.0%
Current ratio: 1.10

TEXAS CHRISTIAN UNIVERSITY INC

Home of the Horned Frogs (the school mascot) Texas Christian University (TCU) offers bachelor's master's and doctorate degrees in more than 200 fields of study. Almost 10400 undergraduate and graduate students attend the university's nine colleges and schools the cover fields of study ranging from liberal arts to engineering to business. TCU has 630 full-time faculty members and a student-to-faculty ratio of 13:1. It also has one of the NCAA's top football programs. TCU is affiliated with the Disciples of Christ a Protestant denomination.

Operations

The TCU academic programs are organized under nine schools in fields including liberal arts communication education fine arts science and engineering nursing and health and business. It offers 119 bachelors 53 masters and 28 doctoral degrees.

Tuition fees room and board and books cost about $55630 per year.

Geographic Reach

TCU's campus takes up about 280 acres about five miles from downtown Fort Worth.

Financial Performance

The university reported a 2015-2016 annual budget of $646 million. It had total investments (as at June 30 2016) of $1.5 billion.

Strategy

TCU is investing in facility upgrades and enhancement efforts as part of its strategic plan entitled Academy of Tomorrow. Over the past few years the school has upgraded academic administrative recreational and residence facilities including the construction of a new commons building on the eastern end of its campus. In 2015 it completed a $32.8 million upgrade of its main library.

Company Background

Brothers Addison and Randolph Clark established the school in 1873 as Addran Male and Female College (the school changed its name to Texas Christian University in 1902).

EXECUTIVES

Chancellor, Victor J. Boschini
Vice Chancellor Academic Affairs And Provost, R. Nowell Donovan
Vice Chancellor Finance And Administration, Brian G. Gutierrez
Chief Investment Officer, James R. Hille
Cto, Bryan Lucas
Dean Addran College Of Liberal Arts, F. Andrew Schoolmaster
Dean Neeley School Of Business, O. Homer Erekson
Vice Chancellor Marketing And Communication, Tracy Syler-Jones
Dean College Of Science And Engineering, Philip S. (Phil) Hartman
Vice Chancellor For Human Resources, Yohna Chambers
Dean Harris College Of Nursing & Health Sciences Professor And Executive Director Of The Health Innovation Institute, Susan Weeks
Dean Of The Bob Schieffer College Of Communication, Kris Bunton
Dean College Of Fine Arts, Anne Helmreich
Director Of Admissions, Sandra Mackey
Vice President Of Membership Development, Gillian Hogan
Panhellenic Vice President Of Community Involvement, Katie Hamilton
Vice President Of External Affairs, Jake Neal
Financial Vice President Of Delta Sigma Pi, Julie Brandenburg
Panhellenic Vice President Recruitment, Simone Elices
Neeley Fellows Program Executive Vice President, Jimmy Etti-williams
Sigma Phi Epsilon Vice President Of Communications, Dillon Smith
Vice President Finance, Carol Campbell
Student Body Vice President For External Affairs, Hillary Shepheard
Executive Vice President, Nancy Ramsay
Student Body Vice President, Ryker Thompson
Vice President Public Relations, Morgan Relyea
Ama Vice President Of Licensing, Jacky Meacham
Vice President Of Service Honors Ambassador Program, Adam Bartek
Collegiate Scholars Vice President, Natalie Shelton

Vice President Of Communication, Alexandra Peters
Vice President Of Membership, Blake Brumley
Vice President, John Hillman
Vice President, Alex Noetzel
Vp Of Operations, Kat Nestor
Vice President Public Relations, Madison Benveniste
Chairman, Clarence Scharbauer
Chairman, Mark L. Johnson
Vice Chair, Kit Tennison Moncrief
Executive Board Member, Sophie Anderson
Auditors: PRICEWATERHOUSECOOPERS LLC FO

LOCATIONS

HQ: TEXAS CHRISTIAN UNIVERSITY INC
2800 S UNIVERSITY DR, FORT WORTH, TX 761290001
Phone: 817 257-7000
Web: WWW.TCU.EDU

PRODUCTS/OPERATIONS

Selected Colleges and Schools

AddRan College of Liberal Arts
College of Communication
College of Education
College of Fine Arts
College of Science and Engineering
Harris College of Nursing and Health Sciences
John V. Roach Honors College
Neeley School of Business
Relationship with Brite Divinity School

HISTORICAL FINANCIALS

Company Type: Private

Income Statement			FYE: May 31
	REVENUE ($ mil.)	NET INCOME ($ mil.)	NET PROFIT MARGIN	EMPLOYEES
05/18	521	185	35.6%	3,400
05/17	499	123	24.7%	—
05/14	637	154	24.2%	—
05/12	441	(4)	—	—
Annual Growth	2.8%	—	—	—

2018 Year-End Financials

Return on assets: 5.8%   Cash ($ mil.): 11
Return on equity: 7.8%
Current ratio: —

TEXAS COUNTY AND DISTRICT RETIREMENT SYSTEM

EXECUTIVES

Exec Dir, Gene Glass
Cao*, Ray Smith
Deputy Dir*, Amy Bishop
Staff, Brad Eddins
Network Analyst, Brad Watkins
Contrl, Vincent Prendergast
Manager of Human Resources, David Redd
Director, Kim Kizer
General Counsel, Ann McGeehan
Hedge Associate, Derek Bergquist
Benefits Team Leader, Gina Pax
Auditors: KPMG LLP AUSTIN TX

LOCATIONS

HQ: TEXAS COUNTY AND DISTRICT RETIREMENT SYSTEM
901 S MO PAC EXPY IV500, AUSTIN, TX 787465776
Phone: 512 328-8889
Web: WWW.TCDRS.ORG

HISTORICAL FINANCIALS

Company Type: Private

Income Statement				FYE: December 31
	ASSETS ($ mil.)	NET INCOME ($ mil.)	INCOME AS % OF ASSETS	EMPLOYEES
12/16	26,387	1,761	6.7%	108
12/15	24,654	(182)	—	—
12/14	24,832	0	—	—
12/10	18,116	2,178	12.0%	—
Annual Growth	6.5%	(3.5%)	—	—

2016 Year-End Financials

Return on assets: 6.7%   Sales ($ mil): 3,030
Return on equity: 6.7%

TEXAS EASTERN TRANSMISSION, LP

EXECUTIVES

Pres-Ceo-Ptnr, Martha B Wyrsch
Manager, Wayne Thibodeaux
Director, Joe Carvelli
Chief Communications Officer, Julie Dill
Vp Regulatory, Richard Kruse
Administrative Asst III, Deanna Cordova
Legal Secretary, Felecia Lee
GM, Leah Moss
Administrative Assistant, Nancy Price
Auditors: DELOITTE & TOUCHE LLP HOUSTO

LOCATIONS

HQ: TEXAS EASTERN TRANSMISSION, LP
5400 WESTHEIMER CT, HOUSTON, TX 770565353
Phone: 713 627-5400
Web: WWW.SPECTRAENERGYPARTNERS.COM

HISTORICAL FINANCIALS

Company Type: Private

Income Statement				FYE: December 31
	REVENUE ($ mil.)	NET INCOME ($ mil.)	NET PROFIT MARGIN	EMPLOYEES
12/17	1,389	347	25.0%	700
12/16	1,350	329	24.4%	—
12/12	956	406	42.5%	—
Annual Growth	7.8%	(3.1%)	—	—

TEXAS HEALTH HARRIS METHODIST HOSPITAL FORT WORTH

Harris Methodist Fort Worth Hospital is the largest and busiest hospital in Fort Worth. It is a private not-for-profit almost 730-bed tertiary care hospital serving the residents of Tarrant County and nearby communities in Texas. Harris Methodist provides both inpatient and outpatient care through its main medical center and on-site health clinics. Specialized services include emergency medicine trauma care orthopedics occupational health women's health oncology and rehabilitation. Its Harris Methodist Heart Center has about 100 beds. The hospital is the flagship facility of the Texas Health Resources hospitals system.

Operations

Harris Methodist also known as Texas Health Harris Methodist Hospital Fort Worth serves as a regional referral center. The hospital employs a medical staff of about 1000 physicians.

Sales and Marketing

To promote its services to area residents Harris Methodist uses a range of marketing avenues including print television online radio and outdoor advertising.

Strategy

To meet the growing needs of Fort Worth area residents in 2012 Harris Methodist launched a $58 million construction project to add a new emergency care center adjacent to the medical center campus. The 75000-sq. ft. center scheduled for completion in 2014 will increase the hospital's emergency room capacity from about 60 beds to 90 beds. A sky bridge will connect the new emergency care center to the main hospital.

Mergers and Acquisitions

To further expand outpatient services in 2012 Harris Methodist acquired the Clear Fork Surgery Center (now named Texas Health Outpatient Surgery Center Fort Worth). The ambulatory surgery center is located on the Harris Methodist hospital campus and was previously operated through a venture with Symbion and a group of physicians. The center performs about 10000 procedures per year.

Company Background

The organization opened its doors in 1930 the leadership of Dr. Charles Harris and the Methodist Church.

EXECUTIVES

President, Lillie Biggins
Chief Medical Officer*, Joseph Prosser
Chief Nursing Officer*, Elaine Nelson
Sr Asst, Elizabeth Goenn
Staff, Carla A Castaneda
Purchasing Coordinator, Chris Benson
Assistant Vice President Marke, Pam Marecki
Supervisor, Tommy Jackson
Evs Manager, Angela Jackson
Hospitalist, Cynthia Dockins
Senior Administrative Assistan, Roshonda Helm

LOCATIONS

HQ: TEXAS HEALTH HARRIS METHODIST HOSPITAL FORT WORTH
1301 PENNSYLVANIA AVE. FORT WORTH, TX 761042122
Phone: 817 250-2000

PRODUCTS/OPERATIONS

Selected Centers and Services
Breast Center
Breastfeeding Resource Center
Business Health Services
Cancer
Complementary or Alternative Medicine
Diabetes
Emergency Trauma Services
Executive Health Program
Fitness Center
Heart and Vascular
Gastroenterology
Home Health
Hospitalist Program
Imaging
Infertility
Mobile Health Unit
Neurosciences
Occupational Health
Orthopedics
Outpatient Physical Therapy
Respiratory
Weight Loss
Texas Health Physician Offices Saginaw
Palliative Care
Rehabilitation
Sports Medicine
Primary Stroke Center
Surgery
Texas Health Physician Offices Keller
Vascular and Interventional Radiology
Women and Infants
Wound Care

COMPETITORS

Baylor University Medical Center	JPS Health Network
Cook Children's Health Care System	Parkland Health & Hospital System
Encompass Health	Tenet Healthcare
HCA	The Methodist Health System

HISTORICAL FINANCIALS

Company Type: Private

Income Statement   FYE: December 31

	REVENUE ($ mil.)	NET INCOME ($ mil.)	NET PROFIT MARGIN	EMPLOYEES
12/17	843	55	6.5%	3,500
12/15	770	55	7.1%	—
Annual Growth	4.6%	0.1%	—	—

TEXAS HEALTH RESOURCES

Texas Health Resources (THR) provides care of the Dallas/Fort Worth and North Texas region. The not-for-profit system includes about 30 acute care and short-stay hospitals including owned managed and joint venture facilities. THR also operates outpatient and surgical centers and physicians' offices and it maintains affiliations with imaging diagnostic rehabilitation facilities and home health agencies. THR's network includes more than 5500 doctors and more than 3800 licensed beds. Its Research and Education Institute for Texas Health Resources provides clinical studies management medical device testing and medical training services.

Operations

THR's hospitals operate under names including Texas Health Presbyterian Texas Health Arlington Memorial Texas Health Harris Methodist and Texas Health Huguley. The company operates 20 outpatient facilities and it coordinates general practice care through its physician practice groups. Its Texas Health MedSynergies unit provides office management services for doctors' offices.

Geographic Reach

THR's primary service territory includes about 25 counties in north-central Texas. It has locations in towns including Allen Alliance Arlington Azle Burleson Cleburne Craig Ranch Dallas Denton Flower Mound Fort Worth Huguley Kaufman Plano Richardson Rockwall Southlake Stephenville and Sherman.

Sales and Marketing

The organization promotes its medical services through print television outdoor online and radio advertising.

Strategy

In order to keep up with the growing population of North Texas in 2007 THR launched a $1.5 billion initiative to expand its facilities over a 10-year period. Project efforts thus far have included establishing a joint venture hospital in Flower Mound and the expansion of existing facilities. For instance in 2015 it opened a 70000 sq. ft. cancer center at Presbyterian Hospital Dallas. In 2017 it completed an expansion at its Texas Health Alliance facility which included adding 24 private beds; the same facility will also expand its emergency department. THR has also opened a number of outpatient surgery imaging wellness and specialist centers and it is now building a new 74-bed hospital campus in Frisco Texas.

In 2016 the system established a joint venture with emergency room operator Adeptus Health through which Adeptus' 27 North Texas First Choice Emergency Rooms as well as its First Texas Hospital in Carrollton became part of THR. The move helped THR as it works to expand its access points to emergency health care (an area it has struggled with).

Other expansion moves include the 2016 purchase of Forest Park Medical Center Fort Worth for $141 million and the creation of a jointly owned health plan with health insurer Aetna.

THR has also built up its information technology networks including the implementation of electronic health record (EHR) systems. In addition the organization is adding new medical professional training programs.

Company Background

THR was formed in 1997 by the merger of Harris Methodist Health System Presbyterian Healthcare System and Arlington Memorial Hospital Foundation. In 2008 the organization rebranded its hospitals unifying them all under the Texas Health Resources name.

THR had originally been the minority shareholder in a venture with Triad Hospitals to own Presbyterian Hospital of Denton. However THR grew dissatisfied when Triad was acquired by Community Health Systems in 2007. After a long legal tussle THR paid $100 million to acquire the hospital outright in 2009 and changed its name to Texas Health Presbyterian Hospital Denton. Texas Health Presbyterian found itself the focus of international media attention in 2014 when it treated the first case of Ebola on US soil.

EXECUTIVES

Evp People And Culture, Bonnie Bell
Evp Southeast Zone Operations Leader, Oscar L. Amparan
Sevp And Chief Clinical Officer, Daniel W. Varga
Evp And Cfo, Ronald R. (Ron) Long
Evp North Zone Operations Leader, Brett S. McClung
Sevp And Coo, Barclay E. Berdan
Svp And Chief Nurse Executive, Joan S. Clark

Executive Vice President And Southwest Zone Operations Leader, Kirk King
Sevp And Coo, Jeffrey L. Canose
Evp Southwest Zone Clinical Leader, Harold Berenzweig
Evp Southeast Zone Clinical Leader, Mark C. Lester
Evp North Zone Clinical Leader, Elizabeth Ransom
Evp Population Health; President Texas Health Population Health Education And Innovation Center, Tricia Nguyen
President Texas Health Physicians Group, Shawn D. Parsley
Vice President Of Information Systems, Joe Hodge
Senior Vice President Of Brand Experience, Paul Szablowski
Vice President Chief Nursing Officer, Rosemarie Aznavorian
Senior Vice President Of Care Continuum And Collaborations, Krystal Mims
Services Cmrp Senior Vice President Supply Chain Management, Shaun Clinton
Vice President Chief Learning Officer, Daniel Gandarilla
Vice President Human Resources, Janelle Browne
Vice President, John Wilson
Director Of Radiology Services, Tammy Ormuz
Radiology Medical Director, David Robinson
Medical Director Of Adolescent Services, Robert Harden
Vice President Corporate Controller, David Jackson
Vice President Applications And Ehr, Cynda Grimes
Senior Vice President Legal Counsel, Ken Kramer
Vice President Supply Chain Management, Becky Daniel
Director Of Nursing, Michelle Pecenka
Director Of Nursing, Vickie Turner
Physical Therapy Tech, Lanandra Hamilton
Vice President Financial Planning, Luke Gorman
Director Of Nursing, Jennifer Mayhan
Director Of Radiology, Kevin Stone
Director Of Radiology, Dung Pham
Vp Director Of Other It Is Department, Willie Johnson
Director Of Radiology And Women's Imaging Services, Darlene Rodriguez
Ache Member Vice President Strategy And Business, Virginia Rose
Chairman, John R. Ferguson
Vice Chairman, Wesley R. Turner
Secretary, Stacey Mcjunkin
Unit Secretary, Tina Sosebee
Secretary, Bernadina Richey
Unit Secretary, Claudia Love
Unit Secretary, Mary Kinman
Unit Secretary, Monica Dillard
Unit Secretary, Muzzet Davis
Secretary, Shandlyn Hearn
Unit Secretary, Maureen Yamada
Unit Secretary, Karessa Griggs
Auditors: KMPG LLP DALLAS TEXAS

LOCATIONS

HQ: TEXAS HEALTH RESOURCES
612 E LAMAR BLVD STE 400, ARLINGTON, TX 760114125
Phone: 682 236-7900

PRODUCTS/OPERATIONS

Selected Facilities and Affiliates
Acute Care and Specialty Hospitals
Texas Health Arlington Memorial
Texas Health Harris Methodist Hospital Fort Worth
Texas Health Huguley Hospital Fort Worth South
Texas Health Presbyterian Hospital Dallas
Texas Health Presbyterian Hospital Flower Mound
Texas Health Presbyterian Hospital Rockwall
Texas Health Center for Diagnostics & Surgery Plano
Texas Heath Heart & Vascular Hospital Arlington

USMD Hospital at Arlington
USMD Hospital at Fort Worth
Affiliates
Envision Imaging of North Fort Worth
Texas Rehabilitation Partners
Two Forest Imaging Dallas
Southwest Diagnostic Imaging Center

COMPETITORS

Community Health Systems
Cook Children's Health Care System
HCA
JPS Health Network
Parkland Health & Hospital System
Southwestern Medical Center
Tenet Healthcare
The Methodist Health System

HISTORICAL FINANCIALS
Company Type: Private

Income Statement   FYE: December 31

	REVENUE ($ mil.)	NET INCOME ($ mil.)	NET PROFIT MARGIN	EMPLOYEES
12/17	4,688	869	18.6%	21,277
12/13	718	285	39.8%	—
12/09	334	2	0.9%	—
12/06	2,287	2,299	100.5%	—
Annual Growth	6.7%	(8.5%)	—	—

2017 Year-End Financials
Return on assets: 9.8%   Cash ($ mil.): 435
Return on equity: 14.2%
Current ratio: 1.60

TEXAS PERMANENT SCHOOL FUND MANAGEMENT COMPANY, INC.

EXECUTIVES

Prin, Elizabeth Jones
Senior Real Estate Portfolio M, Nick Tramontana
Auditors: LISA R COLLIER CPA CFE CID

LOCATIONS

HQ: TEXAS PERMANENT SCHOOL FUND MANAGEMENT COMPANY, INC.
1701 CONGRESS AVE, AUSTIN, TX 787011402
Phone: 512 463-1814
Web: WWW.TEA.TEXAS.GOV

HISTORICAL FINANCIALS
Company Type: Private

Income Statement   FYE: August 31

	ASSETS ($ mil.)	NET INCOME ($ mil.)	INCOME AS % OF ASSETS	EMPLOYEES
08/17	44,517	4,154	9.3%	4
08/16	38,820	1,519	3.9%	—
Annual Growth	14.7%	173.4%	—	—

2017 Year-End Financials
Return on assets: 9.3%   Sales ($ mil): 5,375
Return on equity: 10.0%

TEXAS STATE UNIVERSITY

Texas State University-San Marcos has about 38800 students pursuing degrees in about 100 undergraduate programs 90 graduate programs and a dozen doctoral programs. Comprising eight colleges as well as a graduate school Texas State University-San Marcos is the largest school in the Texas State University system which includes Angelo State University Lamar University Sam Houston State University and Sul Ross State University. It also offers bachelor's and graduate-level courses at a campus in Round Rock. The school has 209 buildings on its San Marcos cmapus.

Geographic Reach
Texas State's main campus in the Central Texas community of San Marcos consists of some 490 acres. The university also operates some 5000 acres of recreational and instruction properties in the area.

Strategy
As Texas State is ranked among the top US colleges for awarding degrees to bachelor's degrees to Hispanic students the university targets a portion of its marketing efforts towards minority students. About 50% of its student body is composed of ethnic minorities. Texas State also enrolls students through international efforts.

To accommodate its growing student base Texas State has been expanding its campus facilities. It opened the Angelina and San Gabriel residence halls in 2016 and the Performing Arts Center in 2014.

Also in 2014 the school became a member of the American Academic Research Institute in Iraq (TAARII) which promotes scholarly research on Iraq and ancient Mesopotamia by providing graduate and post-graduate fellowships for Americans and Iraqis. Other TAARII members include Columbia University Georgetown University and Harvard.

Company Background
The former Southwest Texas State University (the name was changed in 2003) was originally a teacher's college founded by the state legislature in 1903.

EXECUTIVES

Assistant Vice President Finance Support Services Plng, Nancy Nusbaum
President, Denise M. Trauth
Vp Student Affairs, Joanne Smith
Provost And Vp Academic Affairs, Eugene J. (Gene) Bourgeois
Vp University Advancement, Barbara Breier
Vp Finance And Support Services, Eric Algoe
Vp Information Technology, Ken Pierce
Presidential Fellow, Lisa Kay Lloyd
Dean College Of Applied Arts, Jaime Chahin
Dean Mccoy College Of Business Administration, Denise T. Smart
Dean College Of Education, Stan Carpenter
Dean College Of Fine Arts And Communication, John Fleming
Dean College Of Health Professions, Ruth B. Welborn
Dean Honors College, Heather C. Galloway
Dean College Of Liberal Arts, Michael J. Hennessy
Interim Dean College Of Science And Engineering, Robert Habingreither
Dean University College, Daniel A. Brown
Dean The Graduate College, Andrea Golato
Assistant Vice President Technology Resources, Mark Hughes

Associate Vp Financial Se, Darryl Borgonah
Associate Vice President For Enrollment
  Management And Marketing, Michael Heintze
Assistant Vice President Enrollmt Management
  Undgrad Admis, Stephanie J Anderson
Vice President Information Technology, Kenneth
  Pierce
Assistant Vice President, Dan Perry
Vice President For Research, Greg Snodgrass
External Vice President Alex Cooper, Ryan
  Goodrum
Vice President Sigma Phi Lambda, Amanda
  Weaver
Vice President, Cathy Fleuriet
Vice President, Marianne Reese
Vice President Chapter Promotion, Stephanie
  Feliciano
Board Of Directors, Lydia Blanchard
Treasurer, Valarie Van Vlack
Board Member, Jane Saunders
Secretary, Kerry Craig
Y.o.u Treasurer, Keeasha Shaw
Secretary, Kassandra Banda
Txst Secretary, Jason Kraus
Treasurer, Maurice Johnson

LOCATIONS

HQ: TEXAS STATE UNIVERSITY
  601 UNIVERSITY DR, SAN MARCOS, TX 786664684
Phone: 512 245-2111
Web: WWW.TXSTATE.EDU

PRODUCTS/OPERATIONS

Schools and Colleges
College of Applied Arts
College of Education
College of Fine Arts and Communication
College of Health Professions
College of Liberal Arts
College of Science
The Graduate College
McCoy College of Business Administration
University College (general studies)

HISTORICAL FINANCIALS

Company Type: Private

Income Statement				FYE: August 31
	REVENUE ($ mil.)	NET INCOME ($ mil.)	NET PROFIT MARGIN	EMPLOYEES
08/18	459	27	5.9%	3,156
08/16	436	34	7.9%	—
08/15	404	25	6.2%	—
08/14	377	73	19.4%	—
Annual Growth	5.0%	(21.9%)	—	—

2018 Year-End Financials

Return on assets: 1.5%   Cash ($ mil.): 328
Return on equity: 1.8%
Current ratio: 2.00

TEXAS STATE UNIVERSITY SYSTEM

EXECUTIVES

Chancellor, Brian McCall
Vice Chancellor For Finance, Claire Jackson
Director, Scott Cupp
Abroad Coordinator Follow, Josh Andrews
Assistant Director of Admissio, Joshua Hector
Assistant Professor of Dance, Joshua Manculich

Professor, Paul Corder
General Counsel, Randall Sarosdy
Security Coordinator, Renee Starns
Director Email, Rusti Wade
Manager, David W Shirley

LOCATIONS

HQ: TEXAS STATE UNIVERSITY SYSTEM
  601 COLORADO ST, AUSTIN, TX 787012904
Phone: 512 463-1808
Web: WWW.TSUS.EDU

HISTORICAL FINANCIALS

Company Type: Private

Income Statement				FYE: August 31
	REVENUE ($ mil.)	NET INCOME ($ mil.)	NET PROFIT MARGIN	EMPLOYEES
08/18	862	190	22.0%	3,196
08/17	854	145	17.1%	—
08/16	846	126	14.9%	—
08/15	6	71	1147.5%	—
Annual Growth	418.2%	38.8%	—	—

2018 Year-End Financials

Return on assets: 5.3%   Cash ($ mil.): 522
Return on equity: 13.1%
Current ratio: 1.50

TEXAS TECH UNIVERSITY HEALTH SCIENCES CENTER

EXECUTIVES

Exec V Pres*, Elmo M Cavin Jr
Assistant Professor, Eric Maclaughlin
Assistant Professor, Jannette Dufour
Associate Professor, John C Fowler
Assistant Professor, John M Mackay
Assistant Professor, Juan Figueroa
Assistant Professor, Mark Hall
Assistant Professor, Morgan House
Assistant Professor, Raj Rishi
Assistant Professor, Rhonda Fleming
Assistant Professor, Sid Obryant

LOCATIONS

HQ: TEXAS TECH UNIVERSITY HEALTH SCIENCES
  CENTER
  3601 4TH ST, LUBBOCK, TX 794300002
Phone: 806 743-1000
Web: WWW.TTUHSC.EDU

HISTORICAL FINANCIALS

Company Type: Private

Income Statement				FYE: August 31
	REVENUE ($ mil.)	NET INCOME ($ mil.)	NET PROFIT MARGIN	EMPLOYEES
08/18	475	67	14.2%	5,017
08/11	452	52	11.6%	—
08/08	0	0	—	—
08/05	0	0	—	—
Annual Growth		—	—	—

2018 Year-End Financials

Return on assets: 7.6%   Cash ($ mil.): 126
Return on equity: 8.7%
Current ratio: 2.90

TEXLA ENERGY MANAGEMENT, INC.

EXECUTIVES

Pres, Lacy H Williams II
Cfo-V Pres, Randy Miller
Vice President Business Develo, David Musgrove
Vice President Crude Oil Marke, Gary Moore
Trade Analyst, Nathan Offers
Vice President, Scott Beasley
Auditors: MOHLE ADAMS LLP HOUSTON TEXA

LOCATIONS

HQ: TEXLA ENERGY MANAGEMENT, INC.
  1100 LA ST STE 4700, HOUSTON, TX 77002
Phone: 713 655-9900
Web: WWW.TEXLAENERGY.COM

HISTORICAL FINANCIALS

Company Type: Private

Income Statement				FYE: December 31
	REVENUE ($ mil.)	NET INCOME ($ mil.)	NET PROFIT MARGIN	EMPLOYEES
12/17	1,291	3	0.3%	19
12/04	949	2	0.3%	—
12/03	596	1	0.2%	—
12/02	271	2	0.9%	—
Annual Growth	11.0%	1.8%	—	—

2017 Year-End Financials

Return on assets: 2.8%   Cash ($ mil.): 7
Return on equity: 15.1%
Current ratio: 1.30

THE ADMINISTRATORS OF THE TULANE EDUCATIONAL FUND

EXECUTIVES

Vice President For Development, Luann Dozier
Assistant Vice President Of University Financial
  Aid, Georgia Whiddon
Vice President For Finance, JP Gooderham
Assistant Vice President For Student Affairs,
  Brian Johnson
Tsba Vice President, Lynne Firmin
Avp Information Security And Ciso, Robert Fink
Secretary To The Associate Dean, Linda Civello
Secretary, Mildred Freemon
Auditors: DELOITTE & TOUCHE LLP NEW ORL

LOCATIONS

HQ: THE ADMINISTRATORS OF THE TULANE
EDUCATIONAL FUND
6823 SAINT CHARLES AVE, NEW ORLEANS, LA
701185665
Phone: 504 865-5000
Web: WWW.TULANE.EDU

Selected Campuses

Tulane University main uptown campus
The F. Edward Hebert Research Center (Louisiana)
The School of Continuing Studies (Louisiana and
Mississippi)
The Health Sciences downtown campus
School of Medicine
School of Public Health and Tropical Medicine
Tulane Medical Center and Technology Services
The North Shore campus
Tulane National Primate Research Center (Louisiana)
The A.B. Freeman School of Business (Texas)

PRODUCTS/OPERATIONS

Selected Schools and Colleges

A.B. Freeman School of Business
Faculty of Liberal Arts and Sciences
Graduate School
Law School
Newcomb College
School of Architecture
School of Engineering
School of Medicine
School of Public Health and Tropical Medicine
School of Social Work
Tulane College
University College

HISTORICAL FINANCIALS

Company Type: Private

Income Statement — FYE: June 30

	REVENUE ($ mil.)	NET INCOME ($ mil.)	NET PROFIT MARGIN	EMPLOYEES
06/16	924	(63)	—	5,500
06/15	1,054	40	3.9%	—
06/10	738	48	6.5%	—
06/09	737	0	—	—
Annual Growth	3.3%	—	—	—

2016 Year-End Financials

Return on assets: (-2.7%) Cash ($ mil.): 22
Return on equity: (-4.5%)
Current ratio: —

THE AEROSPACE CORPORATION

A not-for-profit company The Aerospace Corporation provides space-related research development and advisory services primarily for US government programs. Its chief sponsor is the US Air Force and its main customers have included the Space and Missile Systems Center of Air Force Space Command and the National Reconnaissance Office. Other clients have included NASA and the National Oceanic and Atmospheric Administration as well as commercial enterprises universities and international organizations. Areas of expertise include launch certification process implementation systems engineering and technology application. The Aerospace Corporation was established in 1960 and operates through about 20 offices.

Operations

Officially The Aerospace Corporation operates a federally funded research and development cen-

ter or FFRDC for the Air Force. The Aerospace FFRDC is one of more than 40 established to help government agencies with tasks related to aviation defense energy health and human services space and tax administration.

Geographic Reach

The US relies on space systems for intelligence communications navigation and weather making Aerospace's mission assurance and systems engineering services vital to national security.

Strategy

Among the company's projects are work on the next generation of satellites including the Global Positioning System IIF Space Based Space Surveillance Advanced Extremely High Frequency Wideband Global Satcom and Space Based Infrared System programs. These new satellites will provide new capabilities and replace systems from the 1970s and 1980s.

Scientists at The Aerospace Corporation also have been developing a nanosatellite to test high-efficiency solar cells under space conditions. Solar cells made by Spectrolab (a subsidiary of Boeing Space and Intelligence Systems) and EMCORE convert sunlight into electricity. The nanosatellite only 14 pounds is one of many such small satellites pioneered by Aerospace. Compared to larger satellites nanosatellites are less expensive to launch and operate.

EXECUTIVES

Senior Vice President General Counsel Secretary, Gordon Louttit
Evp, David J. Gorney
Vp And Cio, William C. (Willie) Krenz
Vp Vaeros, Edward M. (Ed) Swallow
Svp National Systems Group, Catherine J. Steele
Acting Principal Director Finance Directorate Assistant Cfo And Assistant Treasurer, Ellen M. Beatty
Svp Operations And Support Group, Wayne H. Goodman
President And Ceo, Steven J. (Steve) Isakowitz
Vp Space Launch Operations, Randolph L. (Randy) Kendall
Vp Space Program Operations, Malina M Hills
Vice President Space Launch Operations, Ray F Johnson
Executive Vice President, Glenn E Peterson
Vice President Technology, Sherrie Zacharius
Vice President Program Assessments, Howard Mitchell
Vice President Space Program Operations, Stephen E Burrin
Executive Vice President, Michael Daugherty
Vice President Director Manager, Jeanne Campanella
Vice President, George Paulikas
Vice President Director Manager, James Jusko
Vice President, Shirley Dohzen
Vice President Technology, Lawrence Greenberg
Vice President, Ed Swallow
Vice President Chief Human Resources Officer, Heather Laychak
Vice President, Jamie Morin
Senior Vice President Systems Planning, Rand Fisher
Vice President, Ed Serhal
Chairman, Barbara M. Barrett, age 67
Vice Chairman, Michael B. Donley
Board Member, Kathryn Brenan
Auditors: DELOITTE & TOUCHE LLP LOS ANG

LOCATIONS

HQ: THE AEROSPACE CORPORATION
2310 E EL SEGUNDO BLVD, EL SEGUNDO, CA
902454609
Phone: 310 336-5000
Web: WWW.AEROSPACE.ORG

PRODUCTS/OPERATIONS

Selected Services

Civil and Commercial
CORDS
Cyber Security
Labs
Launch Support
Mission Assurance
Systems Engineering
Technical Resources

COMPETITORS

AKKA Technologies   QinetiQ
Orbital Research

HISTORICAL FINANCIALS

Company Type: Private

Income Statement — FYE: September 30

	REVENUE ($ mil.)	NET INCOME ($ mil.)	NET PROFIT MARGIN	EMPLOYEES
09/15	916	(15)	—	3,920
09/14	881	5	0.6%	—
09/13	868	0	0.0%	—
09/12	903	4	0.5%	—
Annual Growth	0.5%	—	—	—

2015 Year-End Financials

Return on assets: (-2.3%) Cash ($ mil.): 23
Return on equity: —
Current ratio: 1.10

THE AMALGAMATED SUGAR COMPANY LLC

The Amalgamated Sugar Company with roots reaching back to 1915 turns beets into sweets. It's the second-largest US sugar producer processing sugar beets grown on about 180000 acres in Idaho Oregon and Washington. The company manufactures granulated coarse powdered and brown consumer sugar products marketed under the brand White Satin. It also makes products for retail grocery chains under private labels. The sugar company produces beet pulp molasses and other beet by-products for use by food and animal-feed manufacturers. Since 1997 Amalgamated Sugar has been owned by the Snake River Sugar Company a cooperative that comprises sugar beet growers in Idaho Oregon and Washington.

Operations

The Amalgamated Sugar Company processes up to 1.6 billion pounds of sugar each year. Along with processing the cooperative's crops the company provides its owner-farmers with agronomy advice and services runs workshops and seminars operates a co-op store and sells used equipment.

The company's key management team is employed on a contract basis. A seven-member Management Committee oversees the management team. The committee comprises members of the cooperative's board of directors.

Geographic Reach

The Idaho-based company's sugar beets which are grown in Idaho Oregon and Washington are processed through the three sugar processing facilities it operates in Idaho. The Amalgamated Sugar Company's warehouses and bulk transfer stations are strategically located from the Midwest to the West Coast.

Sales and Marketing

The Amalgamated Sugar Company markets its sugar primarily in the nation's North Central Intermountain and Northwest regions. The company competes with not only cane sugar refiners but also manufacturers of other forms of sweeteners such as regular and high fructose corn syrup (HFCS) and non-nutritive high intensity sweeteners the likes of aspartame.

Financial Performance

The Amalgamated Sugar Company generates some 90% of its annual sales through the sale of refined sugar. The balance of its revenue comes from animal feed derived from beet pulp and molasses and other by-products as a result of sugar beet processing.

Strategy

The industry's return to the use of real sugar in soft drinks and other beverages has become a boon for The Amalgamated Sugar Company. To this end Pepsi Bottling Ventures has tapped the sugar beet processor to supply the bottler with granulated sugar. During the past few decades more beverage makers have moved to using lesser-expensive high fructose corn syrup (HFCS) to sweeten their beverages as a way to cut costs and boost profits but the shift spurred by consumers to return to sugar-sweetened drinks has become profitable for sugar processors the likes of The Amalgamated Sugar Company.

EXECUTIVES

Pres-Ceo, John McCreedy
V Pres-Coo, Joe Huff
V Pres, Pat Laubacher
V Pres-Fins, Craig Hanks
V Pres-SEC, Scott Blickenstaff
Human Resource Coordinator, Lori Orisio
Manager, Troy Lentell
Auditors: EIDE BAILLY LLP BOISE IDAHO

LOCATIONS

HQ: THE AMALGAMATED SUGAR COMPANY LLC
1951 S SATURN WAY STE 100, BOISE, ID 837092924
Phone: 208 383-6500

PRODUCTS/OPERATIONS

Selected Products
Bakers' special sugar
Brown sugar
Dark brown sugar
Extra-fine granulated sugar
Fine granulated sugar
Gel gran granulated sugar
Industrial coarse sugar
Powdered sugar 10x and 12x
Sugar packets
Sugar standards
Type 50 medium invert sugar
Type O liquid sucrose (66.5 brix)
Type O liquid sucrose (67.5 brix)

COMPETITORS

Alico Inc.
American Crystal Sugar
Associated British Foods
C&H Sugar
Cosun
Cumberland Packing
Eurosugar
Florida Crystals
Imperial Sugar
Ingredion
M. A. Patout
Merisant
Michigan Sugar Company
Minn-Dak Co-op
Nippon Beet Sugar
Nordzucker
NutraSweet
SMBSC
Sterling Sugars
Sugar Cane Growers Cooperative of Florida
S dzucker
U.S. Sugar
Western Sugar Cooperative

HISTORICAL FINANCIALS

Company Type: Private

Income Statement				FYE: December 31
	REVENUE ($ mil.)	NET INCOME ($ mil.)	NET PROFIT MARGIN	EMPLOYEES
12/13	953	62	6.6%	1,500
12/12	907	14	1.6%	—
12/11	886	46	5.3%	—
Annual Growth	3.7%	16.0%	—	—

2013 Year-End Financials
Return on assets: 8.0%   Cash ($ mil.): 1
Return on equity: 54.7%
Current ratio: 0.90

THE AMERICAN ENDOWMENT FOUNDATION

EXECUTIVES

Grants Administrator, Angela Barak
Administrator, Dawn Davis
Executive Vice President, John Farren
Administrator, Kristin Wilcoxson
Grants Administrator, Anne Wise
Treasurer, Gail Tobin
Grant Administrator, Elyse Smith
Associate, Alex Jeffries
Account Administrator, Cindi Ferris
Vp Marketing, Eric Kinaitis
Associate, Laura Landreth
Auditors: MALONEY NOVOTNY LLC CANTON O

LOCATIONS

HQ: THE AMERICAN ENDOWMENT FOUNDATION
5700 DARROW RD STE 118, HUDSON, OH 442365026
Phone: 330 655-7552
Web: WWW.AEFONLINE.ORG

HISTORICAL FINANCIALS

Company Type: Private

Income Statement				FYE: December 31
	REVENUE ($ mil.)	NET INCOME ($ mil.)	NET PROFIT MARGIN	EMPLOYEES
12/16	848	349	41.2%	5
12/15	640	335	52.3%	—
12/12	133	86	64.7%	—
12/11	68	42	61.6%	—
Annual Growth	65.4%	52.6%	—	—

2016 Year-End Financials
Return on assets: 23.9%   Cash ($ mil.): 70
Return on equity: 24.3%
Current ratio: 21.30

THE ASSOCIATED PRESS

This just in: The Associated Press (AP) is reporting tonight and every night wherever news is breaking. AP is one of the world's largest news gathering organizations with news bureaus in about 100 countries. It provides news photos graphics and audiovisual services that reach people daily through print radio TV and the Web. It also offers advertising management and distribution services. The not-for-profit cooperative is owned by 1500 US daily newspaper members. A group of New York newspapers founded the AP in 1846 in order to chronicle the US-Mexican War more efficiently. Founding papers include The New York Sun The Journal of Commerce The Courier and Enquirer The New York Herald and The Express.

Operations

The AP has about 3200 employees globally working around 280 locations worldwide.

Geographic Reach

The Associated Press is headquartered in New York City. The AP serves 1700 newspapers and 5000 radio and television outlets in the US many of which are members.

Financial Performance

In fiscal 2014 the AP's total annual revenue increased by 1% to $604 million compared to $595 million in fiscal 2013. The company's net income increased dramatically to $140 million in fiscal 2014 compared to $3.26 million in fiscal 2013 mainly due to increased gross revenue and interest income.

Strategy

In recent years the AP has shifted its focus away from providing content to newspapers and towards serving online media sources; some of the company's biggest customers now include media outlets such as Google MSN and Yahoo!. It has also focused on developing AP Direct its live video news agency service. It sells its back catalog of video through AP Video Archives.

To cope with the decline in print readership the news co-op is continuing to invest in digital initiatives. It is currently undergoing a multimillion-dollar upgrade of its newsgathering infrastructure to increase its video coverage of global events. It is also pushing to increase its high definition footage to broadcast and digital markets and ensure that its video and images integrate seamlessly with new digital workflows to drive value for customers.

HISTORY

The Associated Press traces its roots to 1846 when New York Sun publisher Moses Yale Beach agreed to share news arriving by telegraph about the Mexican-American War with four other New York newspapers. The cooperative news gathering effort was later established as the AP which began selling wire reports to other papers and started creating regional associations. Adapting to changing technologies and public interests AP began covering sports financial and public interest stories in the 1920s and was selling news reports to radio stations in the 1940s. Advancements during WWII included using transatlantic cable and radio-teletype circuits to deliver news and photos.

In the late 1960s AP and Dow Jones introduced services to improve business and financial reporting. AP improved photo delivery reception and storage in the 1970s with the advent of Laserphoto and the Electronic Darkroom. It began transmitting news by satellite and offering color photographs to newspapers in the 1980s. In 1985 Louis Boccardi took over the job as president and CEO of AP.

AP adjusted to the media-heavy culture of the 1990s by launching the APTV international news video service and the All News Radio network in 1994. It then moved onto the Internet with The WIRE in 1996 and began offering online access to its Photo Archive in 1997. It bought Worldwide Television News in 1998 combining it with APTV to form AP Television News Limited (APTN). The following year it purchased the radio news contracts of UPI after the rival organization announced it was getting out of broadcast news.

In 2000 AP created an Internet division AP Digital to focus on marketing news to online providers. The cooperative continued its Internet focus the following year launching AP Online en Español (news for Spanish-language websites) and AP Entertainment Online (multimedia entertainment news for websites). Also that year AP bought the Newspaper Industry Communication Center from the Newspaper Association of America.

In 2002 the company launched an expanded editorial partnership with Dow Jones Newswires increasing the amount of financial news distributed on AP wires. Later that year it acquired Capitolwire a provider of state government news. Boccardi stepped down as CEO in 2003 handing the reins to former USA TODAY publisher Tom Curley.

AP relocated in 2004 from Rockefeller Plaza (its home for 65 years) to a new headquarters on the west side of Manhattan that features a 105000-sq.-ft. newsroom and serves as a central hub of digital news streams.

The organization moved to strengthen its sports information coverage in 2005 merging its AP MegaSports operation with News Corporation's STATS Inc. to form STATS LLC a 50-50 joint venture that provides sports-related information content and statistical analysis.

The following year AP launched The Online Video Network (OVN) service to provide news video to AP member and customer websites. The co-op responded to the harsh economy by cutting costs in 2008 with consolidation of its print broadcast and digital sales and marketing units. It continued its cost-cutting efforts in 2009 when it cut some 90 jobs instituted a hiring freeze and bought out about 100 employees.

EXECUTIVES

President & Ceo, Gary B. Pruitt, age 61
Svp And Executive Editor, Kathleen Carroll
Svp And Cio, Lorraine Cichowski
Svp And Cfo, Ken Dale
Svp And Cto, Gianluca D'Aniello
First Vice President, Justin Casson
Senior Vice President, Timothy Sheehan
Senior Vice President And Deputy General Counsel, Chuck Gerber

Vice President, Tom Duke
Director, Mary E. Junck, age 72
Auditors: ERNST & YOUNG LLP NEW YORK N

LOCATIONS

HQ: THE ASSOCIATED PRESS
200 LIBERTY ST FL 19, NEW YORK, NY 102812102
Phone: 212 621-1500
Web: WWW.AP.ORG

PRODUCTS/OPERATIONS

Selected Products and Services
AP Digital News (Internet and wireless news delivery)
AP Images (photo services)
AP Mobile (mobile applications)
APTN (AP Television News international television news service)
ENPS (electronic news production system)
Online Video Network (video content distribution)

COMPETITORS

Agence France-Presse	GlobeNewswire
Bloomberg L.P.	Marketwire
Business Wire	New York Times
Comtex News	PR Newswire
Corbis	Reuters
Dow Jones	TEGNA
E. W. Scripps	Tribune Media
Getty Images	UPI

HISTORICAL FINANCIALS
Company Type: Private

Income Statement				FYE: December 31
	REVENUE ($ mil.)	NET INCOME ($ mil.)	NET PROFIT MARGIN	EMPLOYEES
12/17	510	(73)	—	3,533
12/16	556	1	0.3%	—
12/15	568	183	32.3%	—
12/14	604	140	23.3%	—
Annual Growth	(5.5%)	—	—	—

2017 Year-End Financials
Return on assets: (-22.1%) Cash ($ mil.): 7
Return on equity: —
Current ratio: 0.50

THE BIG TEN CONFERENCE INC

EXECUTIVES

Comm, Jim Delany
SEC, Chad Hawley
Treas, Brad Traviolia
Administrative Assistant, Mary Jo O'Donoghue
Director of Information Techno, Brandon Winbush
Assistant Commissioner Communi, Jason Yellin
Controller, Julie Suderman
Assistant Director, Bryson Jones
Assistant Director, Ella Forrest
Human Resources Manager, Wendy Fallen
Information Technology Team ME, Mike McComiskey
Auditors: RSM US LLP CHICAGO IL

LOCATIONS

HQ: THE BIG TEN CONFERENCE INC
5440 PARK PL, ROSEMONT, IL 600183732
Phone: 847 696-1010
Web: WWW.BIGTEN.ORG

HISTORICAL FINANCIALS
Company Type: Private

Income Statement				FYE: June 30
	REVENUE ($ mil.)	NET INCOME ($ mil.)	NET PROFIT MARGIN	EMPLOYEES
06/16	483	(10)	—	25
06/15	448	12	2.8%	—
06/14	338	2	0.6%	—
06/13	318	5	1.9%	—
Annual Growth	14.9%	—	—	—

2016 Year-End Financials
Return on assets: (-8.6%) Cash ($ mil.): 28
Return on equity: (-17.6%)
Current ratio: 5.80

THE BLOOMBERG FAMILY FOUNDATION INC

EXECUTIVES

Prin, Steve Fadem
Associate, Matt Lipsky
Auditors: GELLER & COMPANY LLC NEW YORK

LOCATIONS

HQ: THE BLOOMBERG FAMILY FOUNDATION INC
909 3RD AVE, NEW YORK, NY 100224731
Phone: 212 205-0100
Web: WWW.BLOOMBERG.ORG

HISTORICAL FINANCIALS
Company Type: Private

Income Statement				FYE: December 31
	REVENUE ($ mil.)	NET INCOME ($ mil.)	NET PROFIT MARGIN	EMPLOYEES
12/15	1,194	736	61.7%	2
12/14	1,328	1,048	79.0%	—
12/13	809	538	66.5%	—
12/09	452	279	61.8%	—
Annual Growth	17.6%	17.5%	—	—

2015 Year-End Financials
Return on assets: 10.3% Cash ($ mil.): 73
Return on equity: 10.3%
Current ratio: —

THE BOLDT GROUP INC

EXECUTIVES

Pres, Oscar C Boldt
V Pres*, Thomas J Boldt
SEC*, Michelle M Gawinski
Project Financial Coordinator, Maria Drezek
Coo, Bob Dekoch
Director, Blaine Tuchscherer
Project Engineer, Brian Cutler
Project Manager, Chris Reitzner
Senior Designer, Eric Siebers

Area Manager, Gus Schultz
Project Manager, Jason Krueger
Auditors: SCHENCK SC APPLETON WISCONSI

LOCATIONS

HQ: THE BOLDT GROUP INC
  2525 N ROEMER RD, APPLETON, WI 549118623
Phone: 920 739-7800
Web: WWW.THEBOLDTCOMPANY.COM

HISTORICAL FINANCIALS

Company Type: Private

Income Statement			FYE: December 31	
	REVENUE ($ mil.)	NET INCOME ($ mil.)	NET PROFIT MARGIN	EMPLOYEES
12/17	989	0	—	1,500
12/16	1,022	17	1.7%	—
12/15	978	0	—	—
12/14	874	0	—	—
Annual Growth	4.2%		—	—

2017 Year-End Financials

Return on assets: —
Return on equity: —
Current ratio: 1.20
Cash ($ mil.): 31

THE BRANDT COMPANIES LLC

EXECUTIVES

MBR, Barry Moore
MBR*, Mark Zilbermann
MBR*, Mike Arthurs
Supervisor, Jennifer Groves
Business Manager, Kipp Webster
Safety Administrative Support, Megan Pulley
Staff Accountant, Sam Wolfe
Project Manager, Seth Lewis
Electrical Engineer, Aaron McConnell
Director Quality, Jerry Salter
Vice President of Mechanical O, Jimmy Hurley
Auditors: PAYNE & SMITH LLC DALLAS TX

LOCATIONS

HQ: THE BRANDT COMPANIES LLC
  1728 BRIERCROFT CT, CARROLLTON, TX 750066400
Phone: 972 241-9411
Web: WWW.BRANDT.US

HISTORICAL FINANCIALS

Company Type: Private

Income Statement			FYE: December 31	
	REVENUE ($ mil.)	NET INCOME ($ mil.)	NET PROFIT MARGIN	EMPLOYEES
12/17	497	14	3.0%	1,500
12/16	418	11	2.8%	—
12/15	398	12	3.2%	—
12/14	384	10	2.7%	—
Annual Growth	8.9%	11.7%	—	—

2017 Year-End Financials

Return on assets: 9.0%
Return on equity: 43.7%
Current ratio: 1.30
Cash ($ mil.): 4

THE BRIGHAM AND WOMEN'S HOSPITAL INC

EXECUTIVES

Pres, Elizabeth G Nabel
Immunologist, Annemieke De Jong
Chief Officer, Stanley W Ashley
Scientist, Ali Tavakkolizadeh
Staff, Deborah Dillon
Pathologist, Jeffrey Krane
Doctor, John Ready
Doctor, Marc Sabatine
Doctor, Michael Givertz
Executive Officer, Stuart Lipsitz
Chief Officer, Susan Rapple

LOCATIONS

HQ: THE BRIGHAM AND WOMEN'S HOSPITAL INC
  75 FRANCIS ST, BOSTON, MA 021156106
Phone: 617 732-5500
Web: WWW.BRIGHAMANDWOMENS.ORG

HISTORICAL FINANCIALS

Company Type: Private

Income Statement			FYE: September 30	
	REVENUE ($ mil.)	NET INCOME ($ mil.)	NET PROFIT MARGIN	EMPLOYEES
09/17	2,128	55	2.6%	8,376
09/16	1,938	94	4.9%	—
09/15	1,811	60	3.4%	—
09/14	1,797	151	8.4%	—
Annual Growth	5.8%	(28.3%)	—	—

2017 Year-End Financials

Return on assets: 1.9%
Return on equity: 7.9%
Current ratio: 1.30
Cash ($ mil.): 60

THE BROAD INSTITUTE INC

EXECUTIVES

Pres-Ceo-Dir, Eric Lander
Principal*, Derek Martyn
Exec V Pres-V Pres*, Alan Fein
Dir*, David Baltimore
Coo*, Samantha Singer
Cso*, Todd Golub
Cdo*, Justine Levin
Cco*, Clare Midgley
Cpo*, Andy Porter
Scientist, Ashlee M Earl
Scientist, Heng LI
Auditors: PRICEWATERHOUSECOOPERS LLP BO

LOCATIONS

HQ: THE BROAD INSTITUTE INC
  415 MAIN ST, CAMBRIDGE, MA 021421027
Phone: 617 714-7000
Web: WWW.BROADINSTITUTE.ORG

HISTORICAL FINANCIALS

Company Type: Private

Income Statement			FYE: June 30	
	REVENUE ($ mil.)	NET INCOME ($ mil.)	NET PROFIT MARGIN	EMPLOYEES
06/18	466	(18)	—	800
06/17	451	23	5.2%	—
06/16	377	(45)	—	—
06/15	355	37	10.6%	—
Annual Growth	9.5%			

2018 Year-End Financials

Return on assets: (-1.2%)
Return on equity: (-2.0%)
Current ratio: 1.90
Cash ($ mil.): 241

THE BROOKDALE HOSPITAL MEDICAL CENTER

LOCATIONS

HQ: THE BROOKDALE HOSPITAL MEDICAL CENTER
  1 BROOKDALE PLZ, BROOKLYN, NY 112123198
Phone: 718 240-5000

HISTORICAL FINANCIALS

Company Type: Private

Income Statement			FYE: December 31	
	REVENUE ($ mil.)	NET INCOME ($ mil.)	NET PROFIT MARGIN	EMPLOYEES
12/15	483	(24)	—	5
12/14	476	(18)	—	—
Annual Growth	1.5%	—	—	—

2015 Year-End Financials

Return on assets: (-12.8%)
Return on equity: —
Current ratio: 0.90
Cash ($ mil.): 13

THE CHARLES STARK DRAPER LABORATORY INC

The Charles Stark Draper Laboratory guides research into space under water and across continents. The not-for-profit corporation develops guidance navigation and control technologies for aircraft submarines missiles and spacecraft. It works with NASA the US Department of Defense and commercial businesses to develop technologies and fabricate prototypes. The organization also solves healthcare problems with its work in biomedical engineering. The lab boasts more than 850 engineers and scientists. Originally known as the Instrument Lab the laboratory was renamed in 1970 and became an independent institution three years later.

Operations
Draper Lab's innovations include a personal navigation system that allows soldiers to find their way in GPS-denied areas. It has also developed a micro-avionics system for a 20-gram nano air vehicle that's capable of flying in realistic wind conditions and equipped with a digital video recorder the size of a postage stamp.

The corporation boasts expertise in guidance navigation and control sytems; advanced algorithms and software; fault-tolerant computing; modeling and simulation; and microelectromechanical system (MEMS) and multichip module technology.

Geographic Reach
Draper Lab maintains operations in Cambridge Massachusetts; Houston; Huntsville Alabama; Tampa and St. Petersburg Florida; and Washington D.C.

Financial Performance
In fiscal 2013 Draper Lab made up for traction lost the previous year. Its revenue rose by 3% to $528 million in 2013 from 2012's $514 million. The company's revenues had decreased in 2012 by 3% due in part to a drop in subcontracts.

Primary funding sources include the US Navy the US Army other national security sponsors NASA and select non- Department of Defense sponsors.

Strategy
Fueled by the brain power and expertise of its hundreds of engineers Draper Lab aims to solve problems by designing developing and deploying solutions built using advanced technologies. Its primary areas of focus include space exploration security healthcare and energy.

Draper Lab completed the first missile flight of the MK6 MOD 1 boost guidance system for the Trident II D5 submarine-launched ballistic missile in 2012 with completely successful results. This flight was the culmination of 10 years of work by the laboratory in collaboration with the Navy Strategic Systems Program and a team of independent support contractors.

Another significant milestone was the deployment of the first close-in collection systems using its patented integrated ultra-high density (iUHD) packaging technology — the next generation of Draper Lab's vanishingly small systems (VSS) design techniques.

The lab's investments in biomedical and energy systems are paying dividends with a growing list of sponsors in each area. To this end Draper Lab is working with Shell Oil to design a backup system that will assist operators in getting an oil well under control in the event of a drilling accident. It's also partnering with the State of Rhode Island to prototype a clean energy research center in collaboration with Brown University and the University of Rhode Island.

Draper Lab continues to work alongside Progress Energy to improve the effectiveness of coal plant operation by improving combustion efficiency and monitoring critical equipment status to anticipate failures. Through a partnership with the Defense Advanced Research Projects Agency it's creating a versatile microfluidic platform that can incorporate up to 10 individually engineered microphysiological organ system modules in an interacting circuit.

Company Background
The organization was founded in 1932 by MIT professor Charles Stark Draper as a teaching lab.

EXECUTIVES
Vice President For Programs, Darryl Sargent

Vp Finance And Administration And Treasurer, Elizabeth Mora
President And Ceo, Kaigham (Ken) Gabriel
Vice President, Len Polizzotto
Vice President, Ted Rye
Vice President For Strategic Systems, Steve DiTullio
Chairman, Franklin C. (Frank) Miller
Auditors: MOODY FAMIGLIETTI & ANDRONICO

LOCATIONS
HQ: THE CHARLES STARK DRAPER LABORATORY INC
555 TECHNOLOGY SQ, CAMBRIDGE, MA 021393539
Phone: 617 258-1000
Web: WWW.DRAPER.COM

PRODUCTS/OPERATIONS

Selected Research Areas
Biomedical engineering
  Tissue engineering
  Sensor development
Space systems
  Military space systems
  Planetary exploration
  Scientific spacecraft
  Space transportation
Special operations
  Robotics
  Small low-power electronics
  Surveillance systems
Strategic systems
  Inertial guidance systems
Tactical systems
  Precision engagement systems
  Manned/unmanned systems
  Missile defense

COMPETITORS

Applied Research Associates	QinetiQ
Institute for Defense Analyses	Quantum Research

HISTORICAL FINANCIALS
Company Type: Private

Income Statement   FYE: July 31

	REVENUE ($ mil.)	NET INCOME ($ mil.)	NET PROFIT MARGIN	EMPLOYEES
07/16*	676	36	5.5%	1,134
06/14	522	28	5.4%	—
06/13	542	17	3.2%	—
06/12	514	(20)	—	—
Annual Growth	7.1%	—	—	—

*Fiscal year change

2016 Year-End Financials
Return on assets: 6.0%
Return on equity: 9.7%
Current ratio: 1.50
Cash ($ mil.): 51

THE CHARLOTTE-MECKLENBURG HOSPITAL AUTHORITY

TheÂ medical facilities under the watchful eye of theÂ Charlotte-Mecklenburg Hospital AuthorityÂ care for the injured and infirmed.Â As the largest health care system in the Carolinas the organizationÂ operating asÂ Carolinas HealthCare System (CHS)Â ownsÂ or managesÂ more thanÂ 30Â affiliated hospitals.Â It also operates long-term care facilities research centers rehabilitation facilitiesÂ surgery centersÂ home health agencies radiation therapy facilities and other health care operations.Â Collectively CHSÂ facilities have more than 6400 beds and affiliated physician practices employ more than 1700 doctors. The network's flagship facility is the 875-bedÂ Carolinas Medical Center in Charlotte North Carolina.

EXECUTIVES
Operating Room Dir, Ashley Sterchi
Director Of Pharmacy, Chris Barringer
Assistant Vice President Of Human Resources, Nehemie Owen
Auditors: KPMG LLP CHARLOTTE NORTH CAR

LOCATIONS
HQ: THE CHARLOTTE-MECKLENBURG HOSPITAL AUTHORITY
1000 BLYTHE BLVD, CHARLOTTE, NC 282035812
Phone: 704 355-2000
Web: WWW.ATRIUMHEALTH.ORG

PRODUCTS/OPERATIONS

2010 Revenue

	% of total
Tertiary & acute care services	72
Physicians' services	16
Post-acute care services	3
Specialty services	2
Other services & non-operating activities	7
Total	**100**

Selected Hospitals and Health Care Pavilions
AnMed Health Medical Center
AnMed Health Rehabilitation Hospital
AnMed Health Women's and Children's Hospital
Anson Community Hospital
Bon Secours/St. Francis Hospital
Cannon Memorial Hospital
Carolinas Medical Center
Carolinas Medical Center - Kannapolis (health care pavilion)
Carolinas Medical Center - Lincoln
Carolinas Medical Center - Mercy
Carolinas Medical Center - NorthEast
Carolinas Medical Center - Pineville
Carolinas Medical Center - Steele Creek (health care pavilion)
Carolinas Medical Center - Union
Carolinas Medical Center - University
Carolinas Medical Center - Waxhaw (health care pavilion)
Carolinas Rehabilitation
Carolinas Rehabilitation - Mount Holly
Cleveland Regional Medical Center
CMC - Randolph
Columbus Regional Healthcare System
Crawley Memorial Hospital
Grace Hospital
Kings Mountain Hospital
Levine Children's Hospital
MedWest - Harris
MedWest - Haywood
MedWest - Swain
Roper Hospital
Roper St. Francis - Mount Pleasant Hospital
Scotland Memorial Hospital
Stanly Regional Medical Center
St. Luke's Hospital
Valdese Hospital
Wallace Thomson Hospital
Wilkes Regional Medical Center

COMPETITORS

Alamance Regional Medical Center	Haywood Regional High Point Regional
CaroMont	Health System
Community Health Systems	McLeod Health Mission Hospitals
Cone Health	Morehead Memorial
Conway Medical Center	Hospital
Cumberland County Hospital System	New Hanover Regional Medical Center
Davis Regional Medical Center	Novant Health Palmetto Health
Duke University Health System	Presbyterian Healthcare
FirstHealth of the Carolinas	Rex Healthcare Soliant Health
Georgetown Hospital System	Tenet Healthcare UNC Hospitals
Grand Strand Regional Medical Center	Upstate Affiliate Vidant Health
HCA	WakeMed

HISTORICAL FINANCIALS

Company Type: Private

Income Statement
FYE: December 31

	REVENUE ($ mil.)	NET INCOME ($ mil.)	NET PROFIT MARGIN	EMPLOYEES
12/18	6,228	(69)	—	62,000
12/17	5,991	829	13.9%	
12/16	5,676	493	8.7%	
12/15	5,478	(247)	—	
Annual Growth	4.4%	—	—	—

2018 Year-End Financials

Return on assets: (-0.7%) Cash ($ mil.): 82
Return on equity: (-1.4%)
Current ratio: 0.80

THE CHEROKEE NATION

EXECUTIVES

Chief, Chad Smith
Human Resources, Loretta McNac
Accounting Manager, Larry T Smith
Manager, Tina Gonzalez
Information Specialist, Jeff Carroll
Law Specialist, Kristen T Mankiller
Project Coordinator, Ruth Hummingbird
Customer Representativ, Angel Galvan
Reporter, Jami Custer
Director, June Butler
Reading Specialist, Kim Livingston

LOCATIONS

HQ: THE CHEROKEE NATION
17675 S MUSKOGEE AVE, TAHLEQUAH, OK
744645492
Phone: 918 453-5000

HISTORICAL FINANCIALS

Company Type: Private

Income Statement
FYE: September 30

	REVENUE ($ mil.)	NET INCOME ($ mil.)	NET PROFIT MARGIN	EMPLOYEES
09/16	541	1	0.4%	5,500
09/15	511	(15)	—	
09/05	226	15	6.7%	
09/04	203	14	6.9%	
Annual Growth	8.5%	(15.3%)	—	—

2016 Year-End Financials

Return on assets: 0.1% Cash ($ mil.): 313
Return on equity: 0.1%
Current ratio: —

THE CHILDREN'S HOSPITAL CORPORATION

The Children's Hospital Corporation dba Boston Children's Hospital is a 400-bed hospital that offers acute health care and specialty services for children from birth through age 21. The medical center is Harvard Medical School's main teaching hospital for children's health care and it is the world's largest pediatric research center. Its John F. Enders Pediatric Research facility provides research for the treatment of childhood diseases. Specialty services are offered in the fields of cardiovascular surgery digestive care neurology oncology ophthalmology orthopedics autism spectrum disorder blood diseases and fetal care. The not-for-profit hospital was founded in 1869.

Operations

Boston Children's Hospital handles about 25000 inpatient visits per year as well as 27000 surgeries and more than 200000 radiological exams. Its 200+ specialized clinical programs handle about 560000 appointments annually. The hospital is considered a safety-net hospital and as such is one of the largest providers of medical care to low-income children in the state. About 30% of the hospital's patients are either uninsured or have health care coverage through public assistance.

In addition to its educational and research partnerships with Harvard the medical center collaborates with other universities as well as drug makers medical equipment firms and research institutes. Altogether it has some 1100 scientists at its research centers including the Enders Pediatric Research Laboratories and the Karp Family Research Laboratories. Children's Hospital Boston receives up to some $225 million in research funding per year.

Along with the main hospital the system operates a handful of primary and specialty care centers throughout the Boston area. It also operates a cancer clinic within the main campus through a partnership with the Dana Farber Cancer Institute.

In 2017 Boston Children's Hospital was named the country's best pediatric hospital by U.S. News & World Report for the fifth year in a row.

Geographic Reach

Boston Children's Hospital has satellite locations and affiliates throughout Massachusetts. In addition to its main campus in Boston it has satellites in Lexington North Dartmouth Peabody and Waltham; doctors' offices in Brockton Milford Norwood and Weymouth; and affiliates in Beverly Fall River Milford New Bedford South Weymouth Wareham and Winchester.

Strategy

Due to increasing economic troubles and health reform measures in the US Boston Children's Hospital has been working to cut costs. Despite the cost-control efforts the main campus is undergoing expansion renovation and modernization efforts as part of a 10-year expansion plan.

EXECUTIVES

Ceo, James Mandell
Coo, Sandra L. Fenwick, age 68
Cfo, Doug Vanderslice
Cio, Daniel Nigrin
Svp Patient Care Operations, Eileen Sporing
Surgeon-in-chief And Trustee, James Kasser
Trustee, Paul R. Hickey
Executive Director Satellite Clinical Operations, Julee Bolg
President Children's Hospital Trust, Lynn Susman
Svp And Chief Marketing And Communications Officer, Margaret Coughlin
Chief Investment Officer, Phil Rotner
Executive Director Satellite Administrative Operations, Jane Venti
Executive Vice President Of, Kevin Churchwell
Vice President For Research Chief Scientific Off, Bruce Zetter
Medical Director, Sharon Levy
Director Of Pharmacy, Crystal Tom
Vice President, Donna Casey
Executive Vice President, Andrea Pettinato
Medical Director, James Wall
Director Of Medical Records, Mary Radley
Vice President Research Administration, August Cervini
Vice President, Henry Tomasuolo
Senior Vice President Quality, Katherine Jenkins
Icu Intensitvist Vice President Of Cardiology, Patricia Hickey
Senior Vice President Network Development And Strategic Partnerships, Warring Wendy
Vice President Corporate, Carola Cadley
Clinical Director, Leslie Lehmann
Vice President Finance, Sophia G Holder
Vice President, Michael Gillespie
Senior Vice President And General Counsel, Michele Garvin
Vice President Research, Gus Cervini
Senior Vice President International Services, Cynthia Haines
Senior Vice President, Lisa Hogarty
Vice President Major Partnerships And Mergers, Susan Alesina
Medical Records Director, Mark Quinter
Vice President Development, Sophia Monaghan
Vice President Business Operations, Courtney Cannon
Vice President Corporate Development And Special Events, Michael Bornhost
Vice President, Mary Poyner Reed
Chair, Stephen R. Karp
Director Finance Corporate Service And Assistant Treasurer, Bruce Balter
Medical Secretary, Stephanie Ferrer

LOCATIONS

HQ: THE CHILDREN'S HOSPITAL CORPORATION
300 LONGWOOD AVE, BOSTON, MA 021155737
Phone: 617 355-6000
Web: WWW.CHILDRENSHOSPITAL.ORG

PRODUCTS/OPERATIONS

Selected Services
Major centers
  Brain Center
  Cancer and Blood Diseases Center
  Heart Center
  Orthopedic Center
  Transplant Center
Other Services
  Airway breathing and lungs
  Allergies and asthma
  Anatomy and function
  Bone joint and muscle
  Brain and nervous system
  Cancer and blood disorders
  Common childhood health topics and conditions
  Craniofacial anomalies
  Diet and nutrition

Digestive metabolic and renal disorders
Ears nose and throat
Emergency medicine and trauma
Eyes and vision
Genetic disorders and birth defects
Heart blood and circulation
International patient care
Medical tests
Newborns
Psychiatric (mental) conditions
Reproductive and urinary conditions
Skin and vascular
Viruses and infections

COMPETITORS

Baystate Medical Center
Beth Israel Deaconess Medical Center
Boston Medical Center
Cambridge Health Alliance
Cape Cod Hospital
Children's Hospital of Philadelphia
Nemours Foundation
Newton-Wellesley Hospital
Northeast Health System
Partners HealthCare
Shriners Hospitals For Children
Steward Health Care
Sturdy Memorial

HISTORICAL FINANCIALS

Company Type: Private

Income Statement — FYE: September 30

	REVENUE ($ mil.)	NET INCOME ($ mil.)	NET PROFIT MARGIN	EMPLOYEES
09/14	1,514	111	7.3%	8,000
09/09*	1,348	94	7.0%	—
06/05	4	0	13.0%	—
Annual Growth	89.2%	77.5%	—	—

*Fiscal year change

2014 Year-End Financials

Return on assets: 2.5%   Cash ($ mil.): —
Return on equity: 3.6%
Current ratio: 0.30

THE CHILDREN'S HOSPITAL OF ALABAMA

EXECUTIVES

Ceo, William Michael Warren Jr
Exec V Pres-Coo*, Thomas G Shufflebarger
Exec V Pres*, Mike McDevitt
Facilities Manager, David Cantrell
Operating Room Director, Blanche Lowery
Chief Officer, Coke Matthews
Supervisor Food, Dorothy Turner
Senior Software, Eric Brown
Department Director, Greg Lockridge
Neonatal Care Director, Jill Smith
Recruiter, Laura L Gosney
Auditors: WARREN AVERETT LLC BIRMINGHA

LOCATIONS

HQ: THE CHILDREN'S HOSPITAL OF ALABAMA
1600 7TH AVE S, BIRMINGHAM, AL 352331711
Phone: 205 939-9100
Web: WWW.CHILDRENSAL.ORG

HISTORICAL FINANCIALS

Company Type: Private

Income Statement — FYE: December 31

	REVENUE ($ mil.)	NET INCOME ($ mil.)	NET PROFIT MARGIN	EMPLOYEES
12/18	733	17	2.4%	3,329
12/17	736	113	15.4%	—
12/16	713	86	12.1%	—
12/15	670	(8)	—	—
Annual Growth	3.0%	—	—	—

2018 Year-End Financials

Return on assets: 1.2%   Cash ($ mil.): 138
Return on equity: 1.5%
Current ratio: 8.80

THE CHILDRENS HOSPITAL LOS ANGELES

Childrens Hospital Los Angeles (CHLA) is dedicated to treating the youngest critical care patients in the region. The about 570-bed hospital specializes in treating seriously ill and injured children from its neonatal intensive care unit to its pediatric organ transplant center. CHLA's pediatric specialists also provide care at its ambulatory care center in Arcadia and through about 40 off-site practice sites. The hospital's pediatric specialties include cancer kidney failure and cystic fibrosis care. CHLA serves more than 107000 children every year. It is one of only 12 children's hospitals in the nation (and the only one in California) ranked in all 10 pediatric specialties by U.S. News & World Report .

Operations
The CHLA medical staff includes about 600 physicians most of which are members of the CHLA Medical Group. Its emergency department treats some 71000 patients and the hospital sees more than 343000 outpatients annually. Nearly 50% of its patients are under the age of four. CHLA is also the only freestanding level I Pediatric Trauma Center in LA County approved by the Committee on Trauma of the American College of Surgeons and among only 5% of US hospitals to be designated as a Magnet Hospital by the American Nurses Credentialing Center.
It is also a teaching hospital through its affiliation with the Keck School of Medicine of the University of Southern California and is home to the Saban Research Institute which conducts biomedical research into pediatric diseases. CHLA's training programs include 575 medical students 85 full-time residents three chief residents and 98 fellows.

Financial Performance
Revenue decreased 7% to $803 million in 2014 due to a decline in net patient service revenue. Also that year the company reported a net loss of $30 million due to the decline in revenue and higher operating expenses.

Strategy
CHLA is expanding its facilities to keep up with demand. In 2015 it opened the doors of a new outpatient center in Encino.

Company Background
Although it sometimes operates as Children's Hospital Los Angeles the absent apostrophe in the legal Childrens Hospital of Los Angeles name is no accident. The intentional spelling honors the original incorporation documents filed in 1901 when the institution was founded as Childrens Hospital Society of Los Angeles.

EXECUTIVES

Assistant Vice President, Christian Nelson
Vice President Information Technology Operations, Dave Abbott
Vice President. Foundation, Anna Weiser
Vice President Of Research Operations, Jodi Ogden
Senior Vice President, Lara M Khouri
Senior Vice President Technology, Paul Viviano
Senior Vice President, Mamoon Syed
Auditors: DELOITTE & TOUCHE LLP LOS ANG

LOCATIONS

HQ: THE CHILDRENS HOSPITAL LOS ANGELES
4650 W SUNSET BLVD, LOS ANGELES, CA 900276062
Phone: 323 660-2450
Web: WWW.CHLA.ORG

COMPETITORS

Cedars-Sinai Medical Center
Children's Hopsital of Chicago
Children's Hospital & Research Center at Oakland
Children's Hospital Boston
Children's Hospital of Orange County
Children's Hospital of Philadelphia
Children's National Medical Center
Cincinnati Children's Hospital
Cook Children's Health Care System
Dignity Health
Good Samaritan Hospital (Los Angeles)
Hollywood Presbyterian Medical Center
Nationwide Children's Hospital
Shriners Hospitals For Children

HISTORICAL FINANCIALS

Company Type: Private

Income Statement — FYE: June 30

	REVENUE ($ mil.)	NET INCOME ($ mil.)	NET PROFIT MARGIN	EMPLOYEES
06/18	1,393	247	17.8%	3,000
06/17	1,035	(14)	—	—
06/15	891	27	3.0%	—
06/14	823	(46)	—	—
Annual Growth	14.1%	—	—	—

2018 Year-End Financials

Return on assets: 11.7%   Cash ($ mil.): 105
Return on equity: 18.5%
Current ratio: 2.00

THE CHRIST HOSPITAL

Perched on the hilltop of Mt. Auburn The Christ Hospital oversees the health of ailing residents throughout Greater Cincinnati. Along with the flagship 528-bed hospital the organization operates about 100 outpatient and physician practice locations throughout the area. The Christ Hospital offers specialized care in a variety of fields including cardiac care cancer treatment kidney transplantation spine treatment and orthopedics. The not-for-profit hospital also provides an internal medicine residency program a family medicine residency program and a school of nursing. The Christ Hospital conducts research through its Lindner Clinical Trial Center.

Operations

The Christ Hospital is a general medical and surgical facility with 24977 admissions a year. It performed 7320 annual inpatient and 17373 outpatient surgeries and its emergency room had 52066 visits.

Physicians at the center have participated in more than 1000 clinical research trials in obesity diabetes adult stem cell protocols and congestive heart failure among a range of other therapeutic specialties.

The hospital works with the Ohio Heart & Vascular Center to provide comprehensive heart care to Cincinnati and the surrounding region. As part of the affiliation The Christ Hospital owns some assets related to the Ohio Heart & Vascular Center and employs its physicians and other staff. The agreement allows the two to make use of each others resources and to better serve heart patients in rural areas.

Strategy

In 2015 The Christ Hospital completed the expansion of its main campus at Mt. Auburn in a major $265 million initiative that included a new orthopedic and spine center with connectors to its existing buildings a parking garage and a materials management building.

That year the hospital opened its Montgomery Outpatient Center in Ohio and a new primary care office in Kenwood. It also announced plans to build a comprehensive medical center in the fast growing Butler County community of Liberty Township.

Company Background

The hospital expanded its outpatient capabilities in 2012 by opening its newly constructed The Christ Hospital Outpatient Center in Green Township and by adding a new center in Fort Wright Kentucky. The Green Township center is home to physician practices in cardiology OB-GYN internal and family medicine. It also offers physical and occupational therapy laboratory services and diagnostic testing services including digital X-ray ultrasound echocardiogram and vascular screening. The Fort Wright center offers cardiovascular care and screening services family medicine diagnostic imaging (X-ray screening mammography and general ultrasound) and wound healing obstetrics and gynecology and lab services.

Along with expanding via new construction The Christ Hospital grows its outpatient locations by acquiring local physician practices in a range of specialties. The system was particularly focused on increasing its orthopedic and urogynecological holdings during 2010 while acquisitions in 2011 and 2012 include a breast surgery practice a family medicine center a hematology-oncology group and an internal medicine practice.

The Christ Hospital was founded in 1889. At one time it was a part of UC Health a health care organization based in Ohio until the two ended their affiliation following a years-long court battle. It began operating independently again in 2008.

EXECUTIVES

President Ceo, Susan Croushore
Vp And Chief Nursing Officer, Deborah (Debbie) Hayes
Vp And Chief Medical Officer, Berc Gawne
Vp And Cfo, Chris Bergman
Cio, Alex Vaillancourt
President Of The Christ College Of Nursing, Nathan Long
President Of The Christ Hospital Foundation, Richard F. Kammerer
Vice President Patient Services, Susan Wietholter

LOCATIONS

HQ: THE CHRIST HOSPITAL
2139 AUBURN AVE, CINCINNATI, OH 452192989
Phone: 513 585-2000
Web: WWW.THECHRISTHOSPITAL.COM

PRODUCTS/OPERATIONS

Selected Services

Cancer Services
Comprehensive Medicine
Heart & Vascular
Orthopaedics & Sports Medicine
Primary Care
Spine
Women's Health

COMPETITORS

Bethesda North	Premier Health
Cincinnati Children's	Partners
Hospital	St. Elizabeth
Deaconess Associations	Healthcare
Kettering Health	TriHealth
Network	UC Health

HISTORICAL FINANCIALS

Company Type: Private

Income Statement				FYE: June 30
	REVENUE ($ mil.)	NET INCOME ($ mil.)	NET PROFIT MARGIN	EMPLOYEES
06/17	929	14	1.5%	4,000
06/16	681	90	13.2%	—
06/15	647	89	13.9%	—
06/14	0	0	—	—
Annual Growth	—	—	—	—

2017 Year-End Financials

Return on assets: 1.2%   Cash ($ mil.): 46
Return on equity: 2.6%
Current ratio: 1.90

THE CITY OF SEATTLE-CITY LIGHT DEPARTMENT

City of Seattle - City Light Department (Seattle City Light) keeps guitars humming and coffee grinders running in the Seattle metropolitan area. The US's 10th largest municipally owned power company Seattle City Light transmits and distributes electricity to almost 1 million residential commercial industrial and government customers and owns hydroelectric power plants with more than 1800 MW of generation capacity. The utility also purchases power from the Bonneville Power Administration and other generators and it sells power to wholesale customers.

Operations

The company owns and operates generating transmission and distribution facilities and supplies electricity to 408000 customer meters in Seattle and certain surrounding communities. It also supplies electrical energy to other City agencies at rates prescribed by City ordinances.

Geographic Reach

The Seattle City Light service area includes all of the City of Seattle portions of the cities of Burien Tukwila SeaTac Shoreline Lake Forest Park and Renton as well as parts of unincorporated King County.

Financial Performance

Seattle City Light reported a revenue increase of 5% (to $842.2) in 2013 primarily due to increased retail power revenues stemming from a 4% rate increase and a 1.2% Bonneville Power Administration pass-through rate adjustment.

It net income increased that year due to higher retail power sales rate stabilization account unearned revenue transferred-in power related revenues and capital contributions. These were partially offset by higher expenses for generation customer service administrative and general taxes depreciation interest and lower investment earnings.

In 2013 Seattle City Light's operating cash inflow decreased to $229.7 (from $243.5 million in 2012) was due to higher tax paid and increased cash paid to a supplier.

Strategy

The company's long term objective is to continue to secure reliable low-cost and environmentally-sensitive power for its customers. To lower costs the utility is pushing its customers to conserve by taking green energy options such as installing more energy-efficient appliances and by buying renewable energy credits (allowing customers to pay for slightly higher costs of integrating renewable energy into the region's power grid).

Seattle City Light's six-year strategic plan adopted in 2012 calls for an annual rate increase of 4.7% to pay for expanding Seattle City Light's infrastructure and services including building its first electric substation for 30 years.

In 2013 the company added two new service request types to the 'Find It Fix It' smartphone app enabling Smartphone to report illegal dumping and streetlight outages in addition to its existing features for reporting abandoned vehicles graffiti potholes and parking enforcement issues.

That year Seattle City Light and the Seattle Aquarium announced the start of construction for the largest solar array at any aquarium on the West Coast as part of the utility's Community Solar and Green Up programs. The $330000 system will cover a large portion of the south side of the Seattle Aquarium's roof. Most of its 247 solar panels will produce electricity on behalf of City Light customers who want to buy solar power through the utility's Community Solar program. The rest of the panels are being installed as a demonstration project through the utility's voluntary Green Up renewable energy program with the electricity produced helping to power the Aquarium's operations.

Company Background

Evolving from several neighborhood electric companies that began serving Seattle in 1886 Seattle City Light was created in 1910 to power the city's streetlights. In 2005 the electric utility became the first in the US to become greenhouse gas neutral in its power generation.

EXECUTIVES

Superintendent, Jorge Carrasco
President City University Of Seattle, Richard Carter
Chief Technical Officer, Michael Mattmiller
Auditors: BAKER TILLY VIRCHOW KRAUZE LLP

LOCATIONS

HQ: THE CITY OF SEATTLE-CITY LIGHT DEPARTMENT
700 5TH AVE STE 3200, SEATTLE, WA 981045065
Phone: 206 684-3200

PRODUCTS/OPERATIONS

2013 Sales

	% of total
Non-residential	63
Residential	37
Total	**100**

COMPETITORS

Avista	PacifiCorp
Cascade Natural Gas	Portland General
IDACORP	Electric
NV Energy	Puget Energy
NW Natural	Xcel Energy

HISTORICAL FINANCIALS

Company Type: Private

Income Statement — FYE: December 31

	REVENUE ($ mil.)	NET INCOME ($ mil.)	NET PROFIT MARGIN	EMPLOYEES
12/18	991	162	16.4%	1,600
12/17	989	120	12.2%	—
12/16	903	85	9.4%	—
12/09	723	34	4.7%	—
Annual Growth	**3.6%**	**18.9%**	**—**	**—**

2018 Year-End Financials

Return on assets: 3.3%   Cash ($ mil.): 135
Return on equity: 10.8%
Current ratio: 1.20

THE CLEAR CREEK INDEPENDENT SCHOOL DISTRICT

EXECUTIVES

Supt, Greg Smith
Payroll Staff, Lynn Sonora
Accounting Staff, Amanda Anderson
Accounting Staff, Brandi Sonora
Vice-President Engineering, Lauren M Tragni
Coordinator, Felicia Andrews
Director of Risk Management, Alice Benzaia
Production, Chris Stout
Coordinator, Jill Cook
Payroll Staff, Kelly Kemp
Assistant Director, Eva Decardenas
Auditors: NULL-LAIRSON PC TEXAS CITY

LOCATIONS

HQ: THE CLEAR CREEK INDEPENDENT SCHOOL DISTRICT
2425 E MAIN ST, LEAGUE CITY, TX 775732743
Phone: 281 284-0000
Web: WWW.CCISD.NET

HISTORICAL FINANCIALS

Company Type: Private

Income Statement — FYE: August 31

	REVENUE ($ mil.)	NET INCOME ($ mil.)	NET PROFIT MARGIN	EMPLOYEES
08/18	459	125	27.3%	3,250
08/16	411	(103)	—	—
Annual Growth	**5.7%**	**—**	**—**	**—**

2018 Year-End Financials

Return on assets: 10.0%   Cash ($ mil.): 8
Return on equity: —
Current ratio: —

THE CLEVELAND CLINIC FOUNDATION

The not-for-profit Cleveland Clinic Foundation operates about 20 hospitals in Ohio Florida Abu Dhabi Toronto and soon in London. Combined the foundation's hospitals have nearly 6000 beds. Its flagship location is its namesake Cleveland Clinic an academic medical center in Cleveland Ohio. The campus specializes in cardiac care digestive disease treatment and urological and kidney care along with education and research opportunities. It has an international care center children's hospital and an outpatient center; it also contains research and educational institutes covering clinical drug research ophthalmic studies and cancer research as well as physician and scientist training programs.

Operations

The Cleveland Clinic Foundation operates more than 180 outpatient facilities in northern Ohio. These include outpatient family health centers ambulatory surgery centers physician offices specialized cancer centers and wellness centers. The system has more than 100 medical specialties and subspecialties.

The foundation operates the Lerner College of Medicine and the Lerner Research Institute through a partnership with Case Western Reserve University and it has continuing education nursing and residency programs. It also operates Cleveland Clinic Innovations a unit that oversees collaborative research and technology commercialization programs with partners including MedStar Health and the University of Notre Dame. Cleveland Clinic educates some 2000 residents and fellows and receives some $300 million in research funding (from grants contracts and federal support) each year.

Altogether the medical centers known as the Cleveland Clinic Health System include some 5400 beds and employ about 4000 full-time physicians. The group handles almost 240000 hospital admissions and around 8 million outpatient visits each year. In 2018 it had more than 220000 surgical cases.

Geographic Reach

In addition to its primary campus Cleveland Clinic Foundation operates regional hospitals and numerous family and specialty health centers in northeastern Ohio. It operates a handful of facilities in Florida and several brain clinics in Nevada.

Internationally Cleveland Clinic Foundation operates a health and wellness center in Canada and manages health centers in the United Arab Emirates.

Sales and Marketing

Cleveland Clinic Foundation receives about 55% of its net patient service revenue from managed care and commercial insurance reimbursements. Medicare reimbursements account for around 35% of net patient revenue with the remainder coming from self-pay and Medicaid customers.

Financial Performance

In 2018 Cleveland Clinic Foundation's total unrestricted revenue rose 6% to $8.9 billion. Net patient service revenue increased 3% to $8.0 billion while other revenue declined 1% to $895.8 million.

A 19% decline in operating income due to higher costs for providing care and falling reimbursement rates plus nearly $200 million in investment losses led to a sharp drop in excess revenue over expenses that year. That figure fell from $1.2 billion to $103.9 million.

The foundation ended 2018 with $444.8 million in net cash some $200000 more than it had at the end of 2017. Operating activities provided $745.5 million and financing activities provided another $134.2 million while investing activities used $671.2 million.

Strategy

Cleveland Clinic Foundation has been hailed by many as a model for delivering high-quality care at lower costs. Cleveland Clinic's cost-cutting innovations include paying doctors a salary rather than by procedure (the group practice model) and interactive supply closets that perform their own inventory and summon robotic refill carts from the warehouse. However care costs continue to rise and the company's operating income took a hit in 2018. To combat those expenses the system is focused on maximizing efficiency at its newer facilities. It is establishing a Center for the Study of Healthcare Delivery to help look for ways to ensure care is coordinated yet not redundant further cutting costs.

The foundation also improves its service offerings through facility and program expansion efforts as well as partnerships with other regional providers. In 2017 it expanded its sports medicine and rehabilitation operations by joining forces with Toronto-based Sports Medicine Specialists.

National and global expansion efforts are a big part of the organization's growth strategy. It hopes to double the number of patients it serves by 2024; telehealth and population health will be primary drivers of that growth.

Finally the system is investing in security measures to protect employees and patients.

Mergers and Acquisitions

In early 2019 Cleveland Clinic expanded its operations in the Sunshine State when it acquired Martin Health System and its three hospitals (with more than 520 beds) in Southeast Florida. It also acquired Indian River Medical Center which has more than 330 beds and is located on Florida's Treasure Coast. The system plans to invest millions in the newly added operations over the next few years.

Company Background

Cleveland Clinic Foundation traces its roots to 1921 when a group of Cleveland doctors teamed up to improve medical care and education. Its main campus has conducted breakthrough medical innovations through its history such as the first face transplant in 2008 and it is regularly named to the US News & World Report's list of America's Best Hospitals.

EXECUTIVES

Cio, C. Martin Harris
Chairman And Ceo, Delos M. (Toby) Cosgrove
Chairman Division Of Regional Medical Practice, David L. Bronson
Cfo And Treasurer, Steven C. Glass
Ceo Cleveland Clinic Abu Dhabi, A. Marc Harrison
Chief Medical Operations Officer, Robert Wyllie
Chief Of Operations, William (Bill) Peacock
Interim Ceo Sheikh Khalifa Medical City, Ben Frank
Interim Executive Chief Nursing Officer, K. Kelly Hancock
Chair Department Of Palm Ccm, Herbert Wiedemann
Vice President, Sanford Timen
Medical Director, Kevin Hopkins
Medical Director, Vladimir Burdjalov

Director Of Health Information, Bryan Holtz
Vice President Of Medical Operations, William Riebel
Vice President Of Operations, Kris Bennett
Medical Director, Annmarie Kozlowski
Vice President, Toribio Flores
Medical Director, Damon Kralovic
Medical Director, Michael Machuzak
Assistant Vice President Operations, Janet Gulley
Medical Director, John Donohue
Associate Medical Director, Faith Factora
Medical Director, Purva Grover
Vice President Oncology Services West, Susan Dunson
Pharmacy Manager Transitions Of Care, Erick Sokn
Vice President Market Leader, Grace Jen
Medical Director, Akhil Bindra
Medical Director Of Cardiac Rehabilitation, Rocco Michael
Chairman, Robert E. (Bob) Rich
Vice Chairman, Joseph M. (Joe) Scaminace
Secretary, Lynn Meyers
Medical Secretary, Judith Burdett
Secretary, Danielle Riedel
Secretary, Jennifer Gaizutis
Secretary, Marcie Chonko
Board Member, Donna Munic-Miller
Secretary, Christine Hughes
Unit Secretary, Karen Ginley
Medical Secretary, Heather Karn
Secretary, Caroline Walters
Secretary, Nancy Toll
Secretary, Joye Grebb
Department Secretary, Chris Morchak
Secretary, Marianne Simon
Medical Secretary, Linda Rosa
Auditors: ERNST & YOUNG LLP CLEVELAND

LOCATIONS

HQ: THE CLEVELAND CLINIC FOUNDATION
9500 EUCLID AVE, CLEVELAND, OH 441950002
Phone: 216 636-8335
Web: WWW.MY.CLEVELANDCLINIC.ORG

Selected Facilities

Ashtabula County Medical Center (Ashtabula Ohio; management contract)
The Cleveland Clinic (Cleveland Ohio)
  Cleveland Clinic Children's Hospital
  Cleveland Clinic International Center
Cleveland Clinic Canada (Toronto)
Cleveland Clinic Children's Hospital for Rehabilitation (Shaker Campus in Cleveland Ohio)
Cleveland Clinic Family Health Centers (multiple locations in northeast Ohio)
Cleveland Clinic Florida (Weston Florida)
Cleveland Clinic Florida (West Palm Beach Florida)
Cleveland Clinic Lou Ruvo Center for Brain Health (Elko Nevada)
Cleveland Clinic Lou Ruvo Center for Brain Health (Las Vegas Nevada)
Cleveland Clinic Lou Ruvo Center for Brain Health (Reno Nevada)
Euclid Hospital (Euclid Ohio)
Fairview Hospital (Cleveland Ohio)
Hillcrest Hospital (Mayfield Heights Ohio)
Lakewood Hospital (Lakewood Ohio)
Lutheran Hospital (Cleveland Ohio)
Marymount Hospital (Garfield Heights Ohio)
Medina Hospital (Medina Ohio)
Richard E. Jacobs Health Center (Avon Ohio)
South Pointe Hospital (Warrensville Heights Ohio)

Selected Institutes

Cleveland Clinic Institutes
  Anesthesiology and Pain Management
  Bariatric and Metabolic
  Cancer Center/Taussig Cancer Institute
  Cleveland Clinic Children's and Pediatric
  Dermatology and Plastic Surgery
  Digestive Disease and Surgery
  Emergency Services
  Endocrinology and Metabolism
  Genomics
  Head and Neck

  Heart and Vascular
  Imaging
  Medicine
  Neurological
  Nursing
  Orthopaedic and Rheumatologic
  Pathology and Laboratory Medicine
  Respiratory
  Urology and Kidney
  Wellness
Special Expertise Institutes
  Arts and Medicine
  Body Donation
  Patient Experience
  Philanthropy
  Professional Staff Affairs
  Quality and Patient Safety
  Research

PRODUCTS/OPERATIONS

2018 Sales

	$ mil.	% of total
Net patient service revenue		
Self-pay	4,465	50
Managed care & commercial	2,871	32
Medicare	649	7
Medicaid	45	1
Other	895	10
Total	**8,927**	**100**

COMPETITORS

Akron Children's Hospital
Catholic Health Initiatives
Deaconess Associations
Kettering Health Network
Lake Health
Mayo Clinic
Memorial Sloan-Kettering
MetroHealth System
OhioHealth
Parma Community General Hospital
Premier Health Partners
Robinson Memorial Hospital
Shriners Hospitals For Children
Summa Health System
University Hospitals Health System

HISTORICAL FINANCIALS

Company Type: Private

Income Statement			FYE: December 31	
	REVENUE ($ mil.)	NET INCOME ($ mil.)	NET PROFIT MARGIN	EMPLOYEES
12/18	8,927	176	2.0%	44,000
12/17	8,407	1,150	13.7%	—
12/16	8,037	513	6.4%	—
12/14	4,290	405	9.4%	—
Annual Growth	20.1%	(18.8%)	—	—

2018 Year-End Financials

Return on assets: 1.1%   Cash ($ mil.): 444
Return on equity: 1.9%
Current ratio: 1.00

THE CLEVELAND ELECTRIC ILLUMINATING COMPANY

The Cleveland Electric Illuminating Company (CEI) has a glowing reputation. The utility commonly referred to as The Illuminating Company distributes electricity to a base population of about 1.8 million inhabitants in a 1600 sq. ml. area of northeastern Ohio. CEI has 33210 milesÂ of distribution lines. In 2010 the utility met 4420 MW

of hourly maximum generatingÂ demand from interests in fossil-fueled and nuclear power plants (which are operated by fellow FirstEnergy subsidiaries). It also engages in wholesale energy transactions with other power companies. CEI isÂ also aÂ competitive retail electric service providerÂ in Ohio alongside sister companies Ohio Edison and Toledo Edison.

EXECUTIVES

Pres, John E Skory
Exec V Pres-Cfo, Mark T Clark
V Pres-Contrl, Harvey L Wagner
Exec V Pres-Gen Cnsl, L L Vespoli
V Pres-Treas, J F Pearson
Auditors: PRICEWATERHOUSECOOPERS LLP CL

LOCATIONS

HQ: THE CLEVELAND ELECTRIC ILLUMINATING COMPANY
76 S MAIN ST, AKRON, OH 443081812
Phone: 800 589-3101
Web: WWW.FIRSTENERGYCORP.COM

COMPETITORS

Columbia Gas of Ohio
DPL
Dominion East Ohio
Duke Energy Ohio
Ohio Power
Vectren Energy
Delivery of Ohio

HISTORICAL FINANCIALS

Company Type: Private

Income Statement			FYE: December 31	
	REVENUE ($ mil.)	NET INCOME ($ mil.)	NET PROFIT MARGIN	EMPLOYEES
12/16	928	37	4.0%	897
12/10	1,221	73	6.0%	—
12/09	1,676	(10)	—	—
12/08	1,815	284	15.7%	—
Annual Growth	(8.0%)	(22.4%)	—	—

THE COMMUNITY HOSPITAL GROUP INC

JFK Medical Center plays a central role in health care in central New Jersey. The medical center is an acute care facility with someÂ 500 beds and 950 physicians providing emergency surgicalÂ trauma and other inpatient services. The hospital includes theÂ JFK New Jersey Neuroscience Institute which treats stroke and other neurological conditions and the JFK Johnson Rehabilitation Institute which treatsÂ traumatic injuries. JFK Medical CenterÂ also offersÂ diagnosticÂ imaging cancerÂ care senior and hospice care and family practice services. It is also a teaching hospital affiliated withÂ several area universities. The hospital is part of the JFK Health System.

Strategy

To expand its capacity for emergency services JFK Medical CenterÂ launched construction ofÂ a new ER pavilion in 2013. The project includes the addition of a three-story structure above the existing ER facilities. To keep pace with cutting-edge medical technologies the hospitalÂ has also made recentÂ investmentsÂ in upgrades to its diagnosticÂ imaging cardiacÂ catheterization and wound healing equipment.

EXECUTIVES

Director Of Radiology, Srikanth Jaikumar
Medical Records Director, Nawal Haque
Medical Director Vice President, Sara Cuccurullo
Auditors: BAKER TILLY

LOCATIONS

HQ: THE COMMUNITY HOSPITAL GROUP INC
98 JAMES ST STE 400, EDISON, NJ 088203902
Phone: 732 321-7000
Web: WWW.JFKMC.ORG

PRODUCTS/OPERATIONS

Selected Centers and Affiliates

Adult Medical Day Program
Haven Hospice
JFK at Home
JFK Dental Clinic
JFK Family Medicine Center
JFK Hartwyck Nursing Convalescent and Rehabilitation
  Centers
JFK Johnson Rehabilitation Institute (JRI)
JFK Mediplex Surgery Center
JFK New Jersey Neuroscience Institute
JFK Medical Center Muhlenberg Campus/JFK-
  Muhlenberg Snyder Schools
Whispering Knoll Assisted Living

COMPETITORS

Ball Memorial Hospital	Newton Medical Center
Bergen Regional	Princeton HealthCare
Medical	Robert Wood Johnson
Capital Health System	University Hospital
CentraState Healthcare	Saint Peter's
System	University Hospital
Henry County Memorial	St. Joseph's
Hospital	Healthcare System
Monmouth Medical	
Center	

HISTORICAL FINANCIALS

Company Type: Private

Income Statement				FYE: December 31
	REVENUE ($ mil.)	NET INCOME ($ mil.)	NET PROFIT MARGIN	EMPLOYEES
12/17	551	(13)	—	3,000
12/16	532	28	5.3%	—
12/14	467	(3)	—	—
12/10	427	(17)	—	—
Annual Growth	3.7%	—	—	—

2017 Year-End Financials

Return on assets: (-4.9%)
Return on equity: (-46.5%)
Current ratio: 1.40
Cash ($ mil.): 39

THE CONLAN COMPANY

EXECUTIVES

Ceo, Gary D Condron
Pres*, Kevin Turpin
V Pres*, Tom Lutz
V Pres*, Ryan Triesenberg
Cfo*, Bill Hayne
Exec V Pres*, David Staley
Exec V Pres*, Stuart Price
Sr V Pres*, Scott Austin
V Pres*, Charles King
V Pres*, Ronnie Cupp
Interiors Administrative Assis, Kim London
Auditors: SMITH ADCOCK & COMPANY LLP A

LOCATIONS

HQ: THE CONLAN COMPANY
1800 PARKWAY PL SE # 1010, MARIETTA, GA
300678293
Phone: 770 423-8000
Web: WWW.CONLANCOMPANY.COM

HISTORICAL FINANCIALS

Company Type: Private

Income Statement				FYE: December 31
	REVENUE ($ mil.)	NET INCOME ($ mil.)	NET PROFIT MARGIN	EMPLOYEES
12/18	953	40	4.2%	391
12/17	930	40	4.3%	—
12/16	772	41	5.3%	—
12/15	589	13	2.3%	—
Annual Growth	17.3%	42.9%	—	—

2018 Year-End Financials

Return on assets: 16.3%
Return on equity: 90.9%
Current ratio: 1.20
Cash ($ mil.): 93

THE COOPER HEALTH SYSTEM

The Cooper Health System keeps folks along the Delaware River shoreline feeling fine. The not-for-profit organization includes clinics and hospitals located throughout southern New Jersey and the Delaware Valley including the 600-bed Cooper University Hospital and The Children's Regional Hospital. Cooper University Hospital is a teaching campus for the University of Medicine and Dentistry of New Jersey providing training for medical students nurses residents fellows and health professionals. Its more than 700 physicians operate in about 80 specialties. Founded in 1887 the health care system provides trauma cancer cardiology neuroscience psychiatric and orthopedic specialty centers.

Operations

Cooper Health System is home to the area's Level I Southern New Jersey Regional Trauma Center; the Cooper Cancer Institute the Cooper Heart Institute the Cooper Bone & Joint Institute the Cooper Neurosciences Institute and critical care medicine. Carrying the Level 1 moniker means that Cooper Health System will be the referral of hospital of choice for patients' with massive injuries in the service area.

In 2013 Cooper Health System had 26600 hospital admissions and 81000 emergency department visits.

Geographic Reach

The Cooper Health System operates clinics hospitals and home health services in New Jersey Pennsylvania and Delaware. Cooper University Hospital serves as Southern New Jersey's major tertiary-care referral hospital for specialized services.

Sales and Marketing

HMO payments accounted for 34% of Cooper's net patient revenue in 2013 while commercial payments accounted for 27%.

Financial Performance

The system's revenue increased 6% to $874 million in 2013 as net patient service earnings rose. Net income rose 57% to $90 million on increased investment returns and contributions for capital acquisitions.

Cash flow from operations declined 26% to $47 million that year due to changes in prepaid expenses and a decline in accrued payable and accrued expenses.

Strategy

As demand for health care services has grown in the areas in which Cooper Health System serves Cooper University Hospital itself has also been forced to expand. Additions include all private rooms more operating suites intensive care and laboratory units and a new larger lobby area. Cooper Health System also built a new emergency department.

In 2014 the system's university health care division established a partnership with Kennedy Health System to expand cardiac services in Gloucester County. The partners opened a Cardiac Catheterization Laboratory at Kennedy University Hospital that year.

Mergers and Acquisitions

Cooper University Health Care acquired a 20% interest in AmeriHealth New Jersey in 2014. Cooper and AmeriHealth plan to work together to develop co-branded health products.

EXECUTIVES

President And Ceo Cooper University Health Care, Adrienne Kirby
Evp Government Relations And Public Policy, Gary S. Young
President Ceo And Director, John P. Sheridan
Svp Operations, Maureen P. Barnes
Sevp And General Counsel, Gary J. Lesneski
Sevp And Cfo, Douglas E. Shirley
Chief Of Staff To The President; Ceo Cooper University Hospital, Louis S. Bezich
Svp Patient Care Services And Chief Nursing Officer, Dianne Charsha
Interim Chief Medical Officer; Chair Of The Radiology Department, Raymond L. Baraldi
Director Of Pharmacy, Jaqueline Sutton
Vp Quality, Adrienne Elberfeld
Assistant Vice President Regulatory Accreditation And Patient Safety, Danielle Majuri
Clinical Director, Jeanne Greer
Vice President, Beth Green
Assistant Vice President Of Operations, Patricia Shucoski
Medical Director, Magdy Takla
Medical Director, Helen Haupt
Associate Vice President Applications, Dustin Hufford
Senior Vice President Of Finance, Kenneth M Wright
Chairman, George E. Norcross, age 63
Vice Chairman, Joan S. Davis
Unit Secretary, Narcissis Gooden
Auditors: ERNST & YOUNG LLP ISELIN NJ

LOCATIONS

HQ: THE COOPER HEALTH SYSTEM
1 COOPER PLZ, CAMDEN, NJ 081031461
Phone: 856 342-2000
Web: WWW.COOPERHEALTH.ORG

PRODUCTS/OPERATIONS

2013 Net Patient Revenue

	%of total
HMO	34
Commercial	27
Medicare	19
Blue cross	13
Self-pay	3
Medicaid	4
Total	**100**

Selected Services

Adult Health Institute
Bariatric and Metabolic Surgery Center
Joint Replacement and Reconstruction Program

Manual Physical Therapy Program
Musculoskeletal Ultrasound
Neuromuscular Program
Orthopaedic Trauma Program
Otology/Neurotology
Pituitary Tumor and Neuroendocrine Program
Podiatry
Pulmonary Medicine
Rhinology / ENT Allergy / Skull-Base Surgery
Spine Center
Sports Medicine
Urogynecology
Urology
Women's Heart Program

COMPETITORS

Abington Memorial Hospital
Albert Einstein Healthcare Network
Aria Health
AtlantiCare
Capital Health System
Children's Hospital of Philadelphia
Crozer-Keystone Health System
Inspira Health Network
Lourdes Health
Mercy Health System
North Philadelphia Health System
Princeton HealthCare
Shore Memorial Hospital
Universal Health Services
University of Pennsylvania Health System
Virtua Health

HISTORICAL FINANCIALS

Company Type: Private

Income Statement				FYE: December 31
	REVENUE ($ mil.)	NET INCOME ($ mil.)	NET PROFIT MARGIN	EMPLOYEES
12/18	1,292	54	4.2%	4,900
12/17	1,197	33	2.8%	—
12/16	1,168	82	7.1%	—
12/15	1,055	64	6.1%	—
Annual Growth	7.0%	(5.3%)	—	—

2018 Year-End Financials

Return on assets: 4.0% Cash ($ mil.): 285
Return on equity: 7.1%
Current ratio: 2.60

THE DAVID AND LUCILE PACKARD FOUNDATION

One of the wealthiest philanthropic organizations in the US The David and Lucile Packard Foundation primarily provides grants to not-for-profit entities. The foundation focuses onÂ operating in three areas: conservation and science; children families and communities; and population. The David and Lucile Packard Foundation boasts approximately $4.6 billion in assets. In 2009Â the organizationÂ committed $100 millionÂ for the expansion of the Lucile Packard Children's Hospital at Stanford.Â The late David Packard (co-founder of Hewlett-Packard) and his wife the late Lucile Salter Packard created the foundation in 1964. Their children run the organization.

EXECUTIVES

Managing Director Of Marketable Securities, Kimberly Sargent
Auditors: PRICEWATERHOUSECOOPERS LLP

LOCATIONS

HQ: THE DAVID AND LUCILE PACKARD FOUNDATION
300 2ND ST, LOS ALTOS, CA 940223694
Phone: 650 917-7167
Web: WWW.PACKARD.ORG

HISTORICAL FINANCIALS

Company Type: Private

Income Statement				FYE: December 31
	REVENUE ($ mil.)	NET INCOME ($ mil.)	NET PROFIT MARGIN	EMPLOYEES
12/10	701	412	58.8%	85
12/09	398	74	18.8%	—
12/06	809	587	72.6%	—
12/05	0	0	69.6%	—
Annual Growth	302.5%	289.2%	—	—

2010 Year-End Financials

Return on assets: 6.7% Cash ($ mil.): 213
Return on equity: 6.8%
Current ratio: 2.00

THE DCH HEALTH CARE AUTHORITY

The DCH Healthcare Authority is concerned with the Druid City's health. The company which does business as DCH Health System provides health services to residents of Tuscaloosa and several other communities in Western Alabama. Its flagship facility is the 580-bed DCH Regional Medical Center a full-service teaching hospital located near the University of Alabama campus. DCH Health System also includes the Northport Pickens County and Fayette medical centers which together house 320 acute-care beds. The hospitals offer a full range of inpatient and outpatient services including primary diagnostic emergency surgical rehabilitative and home health care.

Operations

Several of the system's hospitals operate specialty centers. For instance DCH Regional has cancer and cardiology clinics while the Northport Medical Center has specialty rehabilitation and mental health departments. In addition Fayette Medical Center houses a 120-bed nursing home.

The DCH Health System which serves more than a quarter of a million people is community-owned and is governed by a board appointed by various city and county authorities as well as the hospitals' medical staff.

Strategy

As part of the system's plan to grow the next generation of health care providers it partners with the University of Alabama's College of Community Health Sciences and with Capstone College of Nursing. DCH Health System also expands as needed to keep up with the community. In 2014 it announced the construction of a $12 million 75-bed nursing and rehab hospital near Northport Medical Center.

Company Background

The "DCH" in the organization's name stands for Druid City Hospital the name of the system's first hospital which opened in 1923. Druid City is a nickname for Tuscaloosa.

EXECUTIVES

President And Ceo, Bryan N. Kindred
Cfo, John Winfrey

Administrator Dch Regional Medical Center, Bill Cassels
Administrator Pickens County Medical Center, Wayne McElroy
Administrator Northport Medical Center, Luke Standeffer
Administrator Fayette Medical Center, Barry S. Cochran
Executive Vice President Of Information Technology, Robin Holmes
Director Of Nursing, Jutta Beams
Pharmacy Manager And Hematology Oncology Specialist, Hind Hamid
Medical Director, Peter G Casten
Physical Therapy Assistants, Dana Taylor
Vice President Development, Molly Baldwin
Vp Patient Care Services, Lorraine Yehlen
Chairman, Samuel F. Clabaugh
Auditors: MORRISON & SMITH LLP TUSCALO

LOCATIONS

HQ: THE DCH HEALTH CARE AUTHORITY
809 UNIVERSITY BLVD E, TUSCALOOSA, AL 354012029
Phone: 205 759-7111
Web: WWW.DCHSYSTEM.COM

PRODUCTS/OPERATIONS

Selected Alabama Facilities
DCH Regional Medical Center (Tuscaloosa)
Fayette Medical Center (Fayette)
Northport Medical Center (Northport)
Pickens County Medical Center (Carrollton)

COMPETITORS

Baptist Health (AL)
Children's Health System
East Alabama Medical Center
Gadsden Regional Medical Center
Health Care Authority of the City of Huntsville
Jackson Hospital & Clinic of Alabama
University of South Alabama Health System

HISTORICAL FINANCIALS

Company Type: Private

Income Statement				FYE: September 30
	REVENUE ($ mil.)	NET INCOME ($ mil.)	NET PROFIT MARGIN	EMPLOYEES
09/18	520	6	1.3%	4,683
09/17	516	8	1.7%	—
09/16	531	23	4.5%	—
09/13	463	16	3.6%	—
Annual Growth	2.4%	(16.1%)	—	—

2018 Year-End Financials

Return on assets: 1.1% Cash ($ mil.): 72
Return on equity: 1.6%
Current ratio: 1.90

THE DELONG CO INC

EXECUTIVES

Pres-Ceo, David Delong
Treas*, William C Delong
SEC*, Charles R Delong
Chief Technology Officer, Brandon Bickham
Executive Officer, Cherie Schutt
Project Coordinator, John Elvekrog
Executive Officer, Cathy Chrislaw
Supervisor, Jessica Denison
Merchandizer, Laurie Harp
Vice-President, Bo Delong

Administrative Assistant, Felicia Kitzman
Auditors: CLIFTONLARSONALLEN LLP DIXON

LOCATIONS

HQ: THE DELONG CO INC
  214 ALLEN ST, CLINTON, WI 535259496
Phone: 800 356-0784

HISTORICAL FINANCIALS
Company Type: Private

Income Statement				FYE: September 30
	REVENUE ($ mil.)	NET INCOME ($ mil.)	NET PROFIT MARGIN	EMPLOYEES
09/16*	1,029	4	0.4%	350
12/15	1,029	4	0.4%	—
09/14	1,306	19	1.5%	—
09/13	1,326	25	1.9%	—
Annual Growth	(8.1%)	(45.9%)	—	—

*Fiscal year change

2016 Year-End Financials

Return on assets: 1.5%   Cash ($ mil.): 1
Return on equity: 2.7%
Current ratio: 2.40

THE DETROIT INSTITUTE OF ARTS

EXECUTIVES

Dir-Pres-Ceo, Graham W J Beal
Chm*, Eugene A Gargaro Jr
Coo*, Nettie Seabrooks
Internal Medicine Practitioner, Lisa Lorenzo
Vice-President, H W Burdett

LOCATIONS

HQ: THE DETROIT INSTITUTE OF ARTS
  5200 WOODWARD AVE, DETROIT, MI 482024094
Phone: 313 833-7900
Web: WWW.DIA.ORG

HISTORICAL FINANCIALS
Company Type: Private

Income Statement				FYE: June 30
	REVENUE ($ mil.)	NET INCOME ($ mil.)	NET PROFIT MARGIN	EMPLOYEES
06/15	606	28	4.7%	350
06/14	52	13	26.0%	—
06/09	47	0	—	—
06/08	58	(8)	—	—
Annual Growth	39.7%	—	—	—

2015 Year-End Financials

Return on assets: 8.4%   Cash ($ mil.): 49
Return on equity: 11.8%
Current ratio: —

THE DREES COMPANY

The Drees Company is a big homebuilder in Cincinnati and one of the nation's top private builders. Drees targets first-time and move-up buyers with homes that are priced from about $100000 to more than $1 million. Drees also builds condominiums townhomes and patio homes. Its homes portfolio ranges from its former Zaring Premier Homes luxury division to the company's more financially accessible and modest Marquis Homes division. Drees is active in Florida Indiana Kentucky Maryland North Carolina Ohio Tennessee Texas Virginia and Washington DC. The family-owned firm was founded in 1928.

Operations

In addition to home building architecture energy efficiency upgrades and design services Drees also provides new construction financing solutions through its subsidiary and mortgage lending business First Equity Mortgage which has closed more than $1 billion in loans.

Geographic Reach

Headquartered in Fort Mitchell Kentucky Drees operates across nearly 10 states in cities including Cincinnati and Cleveland Ohio; Indianapolis; Nashville; Raleigh North Carolina; Jacksonville Florida; Austin Houston and Dallas Texas; and the Greater Washington DC area.

Sales and Marketing

In recent years Drees has concentrated on the fast-growing "move up" segment market targeting home buyers looking to upgrade into larger houses.

In 2012 Drees converted its longtime Zaring Premier Homes luxury brand name to its flagship Drees Homes brand. While the move required re-branding in the greater Cincinnati area Drees is banking on its brand reputation and recognition. It also allowed the residential homebuilder to consolidate its advertising sales and marketing efforts.

Financial Performance

While full details of the private company could not be found Drees' CEO David Drees announced in July 2013 that he expected the company to reach $629 million in revenue by April 1 2014.

Looking further back Drees had revenues as high as $1.2 billion in 2006 which slid dramatically following the financial crisis to $490 million in revenue in 2010. To its benefit Texas markets — specifically Austin and Dallas — remained active throughout the recession. Drees was also helped by entering the recession with a relatively low debt load of $364 million. By March 2013 Drees had sold land to generate cash flow and reduced its debt to $125 million.

Strategy

Ranked among the top 25 largest national homebuilders by BUILDER Magazine Drees has been steadily expanding over the past few years to capitalize on an improving housing market.

In recent years Drees has concentrated on the fast-growing and lucrative "move up" segment of the homebuyer's market targeting home owners that are looking to upgrade to larger houses with higher-end amenities. In late 2014 the company landed a $100 million contract to build 237 homes in three Cincinnati-based residential communities with the average house priced between $307000 and $360000. In September 2014 the company entered its first ever foray into the Houston Texas market with plans to price its houses there for more than $300000 — prime pricing to lure these "move up" buyers.

Company Background

A family-operated enterprise since its founding by immigrant Theodore Drees in 1928 the company is run by the third generation of the Drees family.

EXECUTIVES

Chb-Ceo, Ralph Drees
Pres-Coo, David Drees
V Pres-Sec-Treas, Lawrence Herbst
Market Manager, Mike Tvinnereim
Architecture Specialist, Saavan Patel
Auditors: DELOITTE & TOUCHE LLP CINCINN

LOCATIONS

HQ: THE DREES COMPANY
  515 S CAPITAL OF TEXAS HWY, WEST LAKE HILLS, TX 787464314
Phone: 859 578-4200
Web: WWW.DREESHOMES.COM

Selected Locations

Florida
  Jacksonville
Indiana
  Indianapolis
Kentucky
  Fort Mitchell
Maryland
  Frederick
North Carolina
  Raleigh
Ohio
  Cincinnati
  Cleveland
  Dayton
Tennessee
  Nashville
Texas
  Austin
  Dallas
Washington DC

COMPETITORS

D.R. Horton   Lennar
Fischer Homes   M/I Homes
KB Home   PulteGroup

HISTORICAL FINANCIALS
Company Type: Private

Income Statement				FYE: March 31
	REVENUE ($ mil.)	NET INCOME ($ mil.)	NET PROFIT MARGIN	EMPLOYEES
03/16	722	31	4.3%	549
03/15	669	36	5.4%	—
03/14	683	35	5.3%	—
03/13	584	19	3.3%	—
Annual Growth	7.3%	17.6%	—	—

2016 Year-End Financials

Return on assets: 6.5%   Cash ($ mil.): 10
Return on equity: 14.1%
Current ratio: 1.90

THE EMPIRE DISTRICT ELECTRIC COMPANY

Empire District Electric (EDE) light ups the middle of the US. The utility transmits and distributes electricity to a population base of more than 450000 (about 217000 customers in southwestern Missouri and adjacent areas of Arkansas Kansas and Oklahoma. It also supplies water to three Missouri towns and natural gas throughout most of the state. EDE's interests in fossil-fueled and hydroelectric power plants give it a generating capacity of 1377 MW; it also wholesales power. The company also provides fiber-optic services. In early 2017 the company was bought by an Algonquin Power & Utilities unit in a C$3.2 billion (US$2.3 billion) deal.

Operations

EDE operates its businesses in three segments: electric gas and other. The electric segment serves an area of 10000 sq. ml. located principally in southwestern Missouri and also includes smaller areas in southeastern Kansas northeastern Oklahoma and northwestern Arkansas. It also provides water service to three towns in Missouri.

Coal-fired generating units 1 and 2 at the Iatan Plant are jointly-owned by KCP&L (a subsidiary of Great Plains Energy) Missouri Joint Municipal Electric Utility Commission Kansas Electric Power Cooperative and EDE with EDE's share of ownership being 12% in each plant. The Plum Point Energy Station is a 670-MW coal-fired generating facility near Osceola Arkansas of which EDE owns 50 MW of capacity.

EDE's natural gas operations distribute natural gas through The Empire District Gas Company. Its principal gas utility properties consist of about 87 miles of transmission mains and approximately 1160 miles of distribution mains.

EDE's other segment consists of its fiber optics business (which it also uses in its own utility operations).

In 2013 the company generated about 90% of its revenue from its electric segment.

Geographic Reach
The company serves customers in Arkansas Kansas Missouri and Oklahoma.

Sales and Marketing
EDE supplies retail electric service to 119 incorporated communities (and to various unincorporated areas) and wholesale service to four municipally owned distribution systems. The largest urban area it serves is the city of Joplin Missouri and its immediate vicinity with a population of 160000. Its three largest classes of customers are residential commercial and industrial which provided 43% 30% and 15% respectively of its electric operating revenues in 2013. The company derived about 90% of its retail electric revenues from Missouri.

Its gas operations serve 44000 customers in northwest north central and west central Missouri. It provides natural gas distribution to 48 communities and 377 transportation customers. The largest urban area it serves is the city of Sedalia with a population of more than 20000. Residential and commercial provided 63% and 27% respectively of its gas operating revenues in 2013.

EDE also has 118 fiber customers.

Financial Performance
The company's revenues increased by 7% in 2013 due to improved revenues across all of its segments. Electric sales increased due to higher electric rates a growth in customers and colder weather (which increased demand). However commercial sales decreased due to a net unbilled sales adjustment recorded in 2012; Industrial sales decreased due to operating reductions by several large industrial customers; and it wholesale sales decreased due to the closure of a large dairy facility in Monett Missouri.

EDE's gas retail sales and revenues increased due to the colder weather; and other revenues also increased due to a growth in Southwest Power Pool transmission revenues in 2013.

The company's net income increased by 14% in 2013 primarily due to higher revenues and as well as an increased allowance for equity funds used during construction.

EDE has seen growth in revenues since 2009 however it decreased in 2012 due to lower demand as a result of milder winter temperatures that year. The company has seen a healthy growth in cash flow from operations since 2009.

Strategy
The company has been boosting its generating capacity including through its partial ownership in the Plum Point Energy Station in Arkansas and through several wind farm contracts. Total property additions for the three years ending in 2013

totaled $398 million and retirements during the same period totaled $39 million.

Seeking to boost its revenues to cover maintenance and expansion costs in 2013 EDE filed for rate increases for its Arkansas and Missouri electric customers.

In 2013 the company filed an Integrated Resource Plan with the Missouri Public Service Commission to introduce additional demand-side management programs to help its customers use energy more efficiently.

Company Background
In May 2011 EDE's power system suffered extensive damage as as a result of the major tornado that tore through Joplin Missouri. Initial damage reports from the Joplin tornado included the loss of 130 transmission poles.

Mild weather and the global recession suppressed demand and revenues in 2009 but lower gas and power costs helped EDE post an increase in operating income for that year. Cooler-than-normal winter weather and warmer-than-usual summer weather and a rate increase helped to boost power usage and lifted the company's revenues in 2010. A shrinking gas customer base due to depressed economic conditions led to lower gas revenues that year. Lower expenses allowed EDE to report an overall improved net income position in 2010.

EXECUTIVES

President Ceo And Director, Bradley P. Beecher, $532,500 total compensation

Vp And Coo Gas, Ronald F. Gatz, $262,500 total compensation

Vp And Coo Electric, Kelly S. Walters, $312,500 total compensation

Vp Finance And Cfo, Laurie A. Delano, $295,000 total compensation

Vp Energy Supply And Delivery Operations, Blake A. Mertens, $240,000 total compensation

Vice President General Services, Tony Stark

Chairman, D. Randy Laney

Treasurer, Mark Timpe

LOCATIONS

HQ: THE EMPIRE DISTRICT ELECTRIC COMPANY
602 S JOPLIN AVE, JOPLIN, MO 648012337
Phone: 417 625-5100
Web: WWW.EMPIREDISTRICT.COM

PRODUCTS/OPERATIONS

Selected Subsidiaries
EDE Holdings Inc. (nonregulated operations)
Empire District Industries Inc. (fiber-optic services)
The Empire District Gas Company

COMPETITORS

AEP	Great Plains Energy
Ameren	OGE Energy
Associated Electric	Southern Union
Berkshire Hathaway	Spire
Energy	Westar Energy
Charter Communications	Western Farmers
Entergy	Electric
Grand River Dam	Xcel Energy
Authority	

HISTORICAL FINANCIALS
Company Type: Private

Income Statement				FYE: December 31
	REVENUE ($ mil.)	NET INCOME ($ mil.)	NET PROFIT MARGIN	EMPLOYEES
12/17	584	36	6.3%	749
12/16	568	64	11.3%	—
12/15	605	56	9.3%	—
12/14	652	67	10.3%	—
Annual Growth	**(3.6%)**	**(18.2%)**	**—**	**—**

2017 Year-End Financials

Return on assets: 1.5%	Cash ($ mil.): 5
Return on equity: 4.4%	
Current ratio: 1.20	

THE EVANGELICAL LUTHERAN GOOD SAMARITAN SOCIETY

The Evangelical Lutheran Good Samaritan Society strives to be a good neighbor to all particularly to the elderly people in need of housing and health care. The not-for-profit organization owns or leases some 200 senior living facilities including nursing homes assisted living facilities and affordable housing projects for seniors. Through its facilities it also provides home health care services outpatient rehabilitation adult day care and a variety of other services such as specialized units for people with Alzheimer's disease and related dementias. Good Samaritan Society merged with hospital system Sanford Health in early 2019.

EXECUTIVES

Pres, Randy Bury
V Pres-Cfo, Raye Nae Nylander
Prin, Diane M Cummins
Security Staff, Cindy Nielsen
Coordinator, Amy Smith
Coordinator, Michelle Erpenbach
Coordinator, Tanya Hickman
Corporate Compliance Officer, Blair Jackson
Administrator, Lisa Meyer
Business Office Manager, Tammie Bankhead
Human Resources Manager, Alan Hieb
Auditors: CLIFTON LARSON ALLEN LLP MINN

LOCATIONS

HQ: THE EVANGELICAL LUTHERAN GOOD SAMARITAN SOCIETY
4800 W 57TH ST, SIOUX FALLS, SD 571082239
Phone: 866 928-1635
Web: WWW.GOOD-SAM.COM

COMPETITORS

BPM Senior Living	Genesis Healthcare
Brookdale Senior	Golden Horizons
Living	Kindred Healthcare
Enlivant	RehabCare
Extendicare	Select Medical
Five Star Senior	Sunrise Senior Living
Living	

HISTORICAL FINANCIALS

Company Type: Private

Income Statement				FYE: December 31
	REVENUE ($ mil.)	NET INCOME ($ mil.)	NET PROFIT MARGIN	EMPLOYEES
12/15	1,011	(33)	—	24,000
12/13	979	0	0.0%	—
12/07	841	17	2.1%	—
12/06	836	44	5.3%	—
Annual Growth	2.1%	—	—	—

2015 Year-End Financials

Return on assets: (-1.9%)   Cash ($ mil.): 17
Return on equity: (-4.5%)
Current ratio: 2.30

THE FINISH LINE INC

The Finish Line sells performance and casual footwear and apparel through some 900 Finish Line stores and branded shops inside Macy's department stores across the US. Its core Finish Line stores are bigger than those of competitors and offer a wider array of clothing accessories and other merchandise including jackets backpacks sunglasses and watches. Finish Line offers big brand names (such as adidas NIKE and Timberland) and also markets its own private-label line of T-shirts socks and other basics. The company also sells athletic shoes and apparel online. It is a subsidiary of European sports retailer JD Sports.

Change in Company Type

In mid-2018 European sports retailer JD Sports paid some $558 million for Finish Line. It was purchased based on the strength of its US-based store network and its expertise in digital/online sales among other reasons.

Operations

Finish Line's namesake stores average some 5600 sq. ft. Footwear accounts for most of sales with apparel and accessories bringing in the rest. The company relies heavily on NIKE products which account for well over half of total sales.

Geographic Reach

Indianapolis-based Finish Line has stores across the US. Its largest markets are Texas Florida California Illinois Pennsylvania and Ohio.

Sales and Marketing

Nearly all of Finish Line's merchandise is shipped directly from suppliers to its distribution center in Indianapolis Indiana where the company processes and ships the merchandise by contract and common carriers to its stores/shops or directly to customers.

Financial Performance

In the five years before its acquisition Finish Line saw revenue rise nearly 15%. Net income however dropped 80% between fiscal 2014 and fiscal 2018.

In fiscal 2018 (ended February) — the last year its revenue was publicly reported — the company had sales of $1.8 billion flat from the prior year. Comparable-store sales for the standalone locations fell 4% which was offset by an additional week in the fiscal year and a rise in comparable-store sales for the Macy's department store locations.

Net income that year rebounded to $14.4 million from a loss of $18.2 million in fiscal 2017. The results were boosted by an income tax benefit related to the US Tax Act (compared to an expense in prior years) and a smaller loss from discontinued operations.

Cash at the end of fiscal 2018 was $93.4 million an increase of $2.5 million from the prior year. Cash from operations contributed $77.7 million to the coffers while investing activities used $52 million mainly for capital expenditures. Financing activities used another $23.3 million for dividends to stockholders primarily.

Strategy

Finish Line has been closing stores amid a decline in mall foot traffic and general retail industry woes. In 2019 the company had about 530 standalone stores compared to some 575 two years earlier; UK-based parent JD Sports has indicated it will continue closing underperforming locations. That said the European retailer plans to use the Finish Line store network as a foundation and a complement to its own network of stores planned for the US. Five JD stores have opened in the US four of which were Finish Line conversions.

As its brick-and-mortar operation continues to be streamlined Finish Line is focusing more on its e-commerce and mobile businesses. The company is investing in its online channel with design and content upgrades mobile and tablet applications and an expanded presence on social media and platform enhancements. Indeed the company considers its online sites (finishline.com and run.com) to be its most visible stores. As of 2019 online contributes more than 20% of revenue.

Leveraging its parent's strengths Finish Line has also embarked on a number of initiatives to improve its visual merchandising standards including the installation of new fixtures across some 70 locations.

Company Background

In 1976 boyhood friends Alan Cohen (a lawyer) and David Klapper (a retailer) founded Athletic Enterprises the Indiana franchisee for The Athlete's Foot. By 1981 they had all The Athlete's Foot stores that the state's big malls could hold — about a dozen. To expand beyond those confines the pair teamed up with Dave Fagin and Larry Sablosky and formed The Finish Line.

EXECUTIVES

Vice President And Corporate Controller, Beau J Swenson

Evp And Cfo, Edward W. (Ed) Wilhelm, age 61, $530,000 total compensation

Evp And President Running Specialty Group, Bill Kirkendall, age 65, $355,385 total compensation

Evp And Coo, Melissa Greenwell, age 52

Ceo, Samuel M. (Sam) Sato, age 55, $635,000 total compensation

Evp And Chief Omnichannel Officer, Imran Jooma, age 47, $31,673 total compensation

Vice President Of Operations, Jeff Morrell

Vice President Of Application Development, Jeff Kish

Vice President Information Technology, Awilda Hernandez

Vice President Of Customer Experience, Mark Roper

Vice President Of Human Resources And Payroll, Cindy Cook

Vice President Of Sales, Teresa Harkness

Vice President Inventory Management, Todd Kuebel

Vice President Store Operations And Trai, Greg Davis

Evp Of Chief Information And Technology Officer, Albert Sutera

Senior Vice President Planning And Allocation, Brad Eckhart

Senior Vice President Legal And Human Resources And General Counsel And Corporate Secretary, Chris Eck

Executive Vice President Chief Information And Technology Officer, AJ Sutera

Senior Vice President Real Estate And Store Development, Chad Edmundson

Chairman, Glenn S. Lyon, age 69

Board Member, Richard Crystal

Board Member, Torrence Boone

Board Member, Catherine Langham

Member Board Of Directors, Dolores Kunda

Board Member, Stephen Goldsmith

Board Member, Alyssa Jackson

LOCATIONS

HQ: THE FINISH LINE INC
3308 N MITTHOEFER RD, INDIANAPOLIS, IN 462352332
Phone: 317 899-1022
Web: WWW.FINISHLINE.COM

PRODUCTS/OPERATIONS

Selected Brands

adidas
Asics
Brooks
Lacoste
Mizuno
New Balance
NIKE
Pastry
Puma
Reebok
Saucony
The North Face
Timberland
Under Armour

Selected Products

Accessories
  Athletic equipment
  Athletic socks
  Backpacks
  Gym bags
  Headbands and sweatbands
  Shoe care
  Shoe insoles and liners
  Shoe laces
  Sunglasses
  Watches
Fan
  High school
  MLB
  NBA
  NCAA
  NFL
  Kids
  Shoes
  Clothing
Men's
  Caps
  Hats
  Jackets
  Jerseys
  Pants
  Shoes
  Shorts
  Socks
  Sweatshirts/fleece
  Tanks
  T-shirts
  Workout clothing
Women's
  Caps
  Hats
  Jackets
  Jerseys
  Pants
  Shoes
  Shorts
  Socks
  Sweatshirts/fleece
  Tanks
  T-shirts
  Team clothing
  Workout clothing

COMPETITORS

Academy Sports	Patagonia Inc.
DSW	REI
Dick's Sporting Goods	Rack Room Shoes
Foot Locker	Sears
Genesco	Sports Authority
Hat World	Target Corporation
Hibbett Sports	Wal-Mart
Kmart	Zappos.com
Modell's	shoebuy.com

HISTORICAL FINANCIALS

Company Type: Private

Income Statement
FYE: March 3

	REVENUE ($ mil.)	NET INCOME ($ mil.)	NET PROFIT MARGIN	EMPLOYEES
03/18*	1,838	14	0.8%	12,700
02/17	1,844	(18)	—	—
02/16	1,888	21	1.2%	—
02/15	1,820	79	4.4%	—
Annual Growth	0.3%	(43.5%)	—	—

*Fiscal year change

2018 Year-End Financials

Return on assets: 2.1%   Cash ($ mil.): 93
Return on equity: 3.2%
Current ratio: 2.70

THE FIRST DISTRICT ASSOCIATION

EXECUTIVES

Ceo, Clinton Fall
SEC*, Kevin Schueler
Controller, Tom Middendorf

LOCATIONS

HQ: THE FIRST DISTRICT ASSOCIATION
101 S SWIFT AVE, LITCHFIELD, MN 553552800
Phone: 320 693-3236
Web: WWW.FIRSTDISTRICT.COM

HISTORICAL FINANCIALS

Company Type: Private

Income Statement
FYE: September 30

	REVENUE ($ mil.)	NET INCOME ($ mil.)	NET PROFIT MARGIN	EMPLOYEES
09/18	556	14	2.6%	150
09/17	609	19	3.2%	—
09/16	553	19	3.5%	—
09/15	615	13	2.2%	—
Annual Growth	(3.3%)	2.2%	—	—

THE FORD FOUNDATION

As one of the nation's largest philanthropic organizations the Ford Foundation can afford to be generous. The foundation offers grants to individuals and institutions worldwide that work to meet its goals of strengthening democratic values reducing poverty and injustice promoting international cooperation and advancing human achieve-ment. The Ford Foundation's charitable giving has run the gamut from A (Association for Asian Studies) to Z (Zanzibar International Film Festival). The foundation has an endowment of about $10 billion. Established in 1936 by Edsel Ford whose father founded the Ford Motor Company the foundation no longer owns stock in the automaker or has ties to the founding family.

Operations

The foundation which is governed by an international board of trustees makes grants in all 50 US states and supports programs in more than 50 countries.

It boasts about 10 regional offices in Latin America Africa the Middle East and Asia.

Geographic Reach

Based in New York the Ford Foundation is a grantmaking foundation that primarily serves the US but also global programs.

Strategy

The Ford Foundation's programs address several social justice issues including democratic and accountable government freedom of expression access to education economic fairness and opportunity sexuality and reproductive rights sustainable development social justice metropolitan opportunity and human rights.

A small portion of its endowment is set aside for social investing. The foundation's funds typically finance critical projects set new business models and develop sustainable organizations. By investing $1 million or more in initiatives the Ford Foundation's investment strategy aims to make a noteworthy impact and encourage other investors to also fund projects.

EXECUTIVES

Secretary, Karen Mcburnie

LOCATIONS

HQ: THE FORD FOUNDATION
320 E 43RD ST FL 4, NEW YORK, NY 100174890
Phone: 212 573-5370
Web: WWW.FORDFOUND.ORG

PRODUCTS/OPERATIONS

Selected Core Issues

Democratic and accountable government
Economic fairness
Education opportunity and scholarship
Freedom of expression
Human rights
Metropolitan opportunity
Sexuality and reproductive health rights
Social justice philanthropy
Sustainable development

HISTORICAL FINANCIALS

Company Type: Private

Income Statement
FYE: December 31

	ASSETS ($ mil.)	NET INCOME ($ mil.)	INCOME AS % OF ASSETS	EMPLOYEES
12/15	12,114	(270)	—	556
12/14*	12,400	(7)	—	—
09/11	10,344	(5)	—	—
09/09	10,234	0	—	—
Annual Growth	2.8%	—	—	—

*Fiscal year change

2015 Year-End Financials

Return on assets: (-2.2%)   Sales ($ mil): 486
Return on equity: (-2.3%)

THE FRESH MARKET INC

When it comes to food fresh is best. The Fresh Market operates about 160 full-service upscale specialty grocery stores in some 25 US states from Florida to New York. As the name suggests the chain specializes in perishable goods including fruits and vegetables meat and seafood. The stores average 20500 sq. ft. about a third to half the size of a conventional supermarket. Founded by husband-and-wife team Ray and Beverly Berry who opened their first store in 1982 The Fresh Market was acquired by Apollo Global Management in mid-2016.

Strategy

The Fresh Market is revamping its strategy in the face of intense competition from other grocery chains which have expanded their specialty grocery selection.

In 2018 the company closed 15 stores and canceled new store openings as it struggled against a rise in grocery competition. It closed stores in Georgia Illinois Indiana Kentucky North Carolina New Hampshire Tennessee Virginia and Wisconsin.

The Fresh Market is refocusing on improving its existing operations. To better compete the company has increased its premium offerings such as USDA prime steaks and imported pastas and boosted its value promotions such as meal kits. The Fresh Market enlarged its beverage section in 2019 adding 300 new beverages to its shelves including cold brews energy drinks adaptogenics and kombuchas. It also began offering grocery delivery through Instacart following a successful pilot program.

EXECUTIVES

President And Ceo, Richard A. (Rick) Anicetti, age 62
Svp Merchandising And Marketing, Marc Jones, age 47, $285,697 total compensation
Svp And General Counsel, Scott Duggan, age 53, $254,510 total compensation
Evp And Cfo, Jeffrey (Jeff) Ackerman, age 55, $407,231 total compensation
Svp Real Estate And Development, Randy Young, age 61, $279,971 total compensation
Vice President Finance, Jeffrey B Short
Chairman, Ray Berry, age 78
Auditors: ERNST & YOUNG LLP CHARLOTTE

LOCATIONS

HQ: THE FRESH MARKET INC
628 GREEN VALLEY RD # 500, GREENSBORO, NC 274087791
Phone: 336 272-1338
Web: WWW.THEFRESHMARKET.COM

2016 Stores

	No.
Florida	45
North Carolina	22
Virginia	16
Georgia	15
Illinois	9
Tennessee	9
South Carolina	9
Alabama	6
Indiana	5
Louisiana	5
New York	5
Ohio	5
Pennsylvania	5
Maryland	4
Connecticut	3
Kentucky	3
New Jersey	3
Arkansas	2
Wisconsin	2
Delaware	1
Massachusetts	1

		1
Mississippi		1
New Hampshire		1
Oklahoma		1
Total		**178**

COMPETITORS

Earth Fare	Trader Joe's
Food Lion	Wal-Mart
Kroger	Wegmans
Publix	Weis Markets
Safeway	Whole Foods
Sprouts	Winn-Dixie
Target Corporation	

HISTORICAL FINANCIALS
Company Type: Private

Income Statement   FYE: January 31

	REVENUE ($ mil.)	NET INCOME ($ mil.)	NET PROFIT MARGIN	EMPLOYEES
01/16	1,857	65	3.5%	12,600
01/15	1,753	63	3.6%	—
01/14	1,511	50	3.4%	—
01/13	1,329	64	4.8%	—
Annual Growth	**11.8%**	**0.7%**		

2016 Year-End Financials

Return on assets: 11.3%   Cash ($ mil.): 60
Return on equity: 18.0%
Current ratio: 1.10

THE GEISINGER CLINIC

EXECUTIVES

Ceo, Glenn D Steele Jr
Sr V Pres-Treas, Frank J Trembulak
Vice-President Information Ser, David Macko
Emergency Room Directo, John Skiendzielewski

LOCATIONS

HQ: THE GEISINGER CLINIC
   100 N ACADEMY AVE, DANVILLE, PA 178229800
Phone: 570 271-6211
Web: WWW.GEISINGER.ORG

HISTORICAL FINANCIALS
Company Type: Private

Income Statement   FYE: June 30

	REVENUE ($ mil.)	NET INCOME ($ mil.)	NET PROFIT MARGIN	EMPLOYEES
06/15	991	(12)	—	12,000
06/14	849	(3)	—	—
06/10	572	(3)	—	—
06/09	504	(22)	—	—
Annual Growth	**11.9%**	—	—	—

2015 Year-End Financials

Return on assets: (-3.8%)   Cash ($ mil.): 23
Return on equity: (-19.1%)
Current ratio: —

THE GEORGE WASHINGTON UNIVERSITY

The George Washington University's name is just one more reminder of the regard the nation holds for its first president. The private coeducational university's more than 26000 students are scattered across its primary campus at Foggy Bottom as well as its campuses in Mount Vernon and Ashburn Virginia. With 1250 non-medical and 1200 medical faculty staff the school's student-teacher ratio is about 15:1. Its academic programs spread across 10 schools run the gamut from business to law to medicine. Notable alumni include former First Lady Jacqueline Kennedy Onassis actor Alec Baldwin and former US Secretary of State Colin Powell.

Operations

George Washington University the largest institution of higher education in the District of Columbia has students enrolled in a range of disciplines from forensic science and creative writing to international affairs and computer engineering as well as medicine public health the law and public policy.

Geographic Reach

The George Washington University's more than 26000 students from all 50 US states the District of Columbia and more than 130 other countries.

Strategy

George Washington University outlined its Vision 2021 strategy in 2018. The institute will invest $243 million to create 12 cross-disciplinary institutes to undertake research in new fields to solve significant societal problems hire 50-100 new faculty members improve the infrastructure that supports the new areas of research. The funding for the scheme will come from recommendations from the university's Innovation Task Force new funds from the academic budget school-based contributions philanthropy and sponsored research.

Company Background

Chartered by the US Congress in 1821 as The Columbian College in the District of Columbia the university adopted its present name in 1904.

EXECUTIVES

President, Steven Knapp
Evp And Treasurer, Louis H. Katz
Deputy Evp And Treasurer, Ann McCorvey
Dean Law School, Blake D. Morant
Dean Columbian College Of Arts And Sciences, Ben Vinson
Dean School Of Engineering And Applied Science, David S. Dolling
Dean College Of Professional Studies, Ali Eskandarian
Dean Graduate School Of Education And Human Development, Michael J. Feuer
Dean School Of Nursing, Pamela R. Jeffries
Dean Milken Institute School Of Public Health, Lynn R. Goldman
Vp Health Affairs And Dean School Of Medicine And Health Sciences, Jeffrey S. Akman
President, Thomas J. LeBlanc
Evp Academic Affairs And Provost, Forrest Maltzman
Dean Elliott School Of International Affairs, Reuben E. Brigety
Dean Of Libraries And Academic Innovation, Geneva Henry

Assistant Vice President Information Security And Compliance Services, Dennis Devlin
Senior Vice President, John Och
Director Of Admissions, Joke Ogundiran
Executive Vice President Academic Affairs, Donald Lehman
Vice President, Emily Reisch
Associate Vice President For Communications, Sarah Baldassaro
Assistant Vice President Academic Life, Natalie Fleischman
Assistant Vice President, Sharon Sullivan
Evp And Cfo, Mark Diaz
Vice President For Development And Alumni Relations, Donna Arbide
Avp University Programs, Katie Turcotte
Vice President, Jamie Meltzer
Assistant Vice President For Corporate And Industry Research, Thomas Russo
Vice President, Penelope Lantz
Chairman, Nelson A. Carbonell
Treasurer, Nicole Beyer
Secretary Faculty Support, Green Jacob L
Auditors: PRICEWATERHOUSECOOPERS LLP MC

LOCATIONS

HQ: THE GEORGE WASHINGTON UNIVERSITY
   1918 F ST NW, WASHINGTON, DC 200520042
Phone: 202 994-6600
Web: WWW.GWU.EDU

PRODUCTS/OPERATIONS

Selected Schools
College of Professional Studies
Columbian College of Arts and Sciences
Elliott School of International Affairs
George Washington School of Business
George Washington University Law School
Graduate School of Education and Human Development
Graduate School of Political Management
School of Engineering and Applied Science
School of Media and Public Affairs
School of Medicine and Health Sciences
School of Public Health and Health Services

HISTORICAL FINANCIALS
Company Type: Private

Income Statement   FYE: June 30

	REVENUE ($ mil.)	NET INCOME ($ mil.)	NET PROFIT MARGIN	EMPLOYEES
06/13	1,177	59	5.0%	5,000
06/06	921	146	15.9%	—
06/05	832	115	13.8%	—
Annual Growth	**4.4%**	**(7.9%)**	—	—

2013 Year-End Financials

Return on assets: 1.7%   Cash ($ mil.): 224
Return on equity: 3.1%
Current ratio: —

THE GEORGE WASHINGTON UNIVERSITY HOSPITAL

LOCATIONS

HQ: THE GEORGE WASHINGTON UNIVERSITY HOSPITAL
900 23RD ST NW, WASHINGTON, DC 200372342
Phone: 202 715-4000
Web: WWW.GWHOSPITAL.COM

HISTORICAL FINANCIALS

Company Type: Private

Income Statement				FYE: December 31
	REVENUE ($ mil.)	NET INCOME ($ mil.)	NET PROFIT MARGIN	EMPLOYEES
12/15	505	48	9.6%	2,300
12/14	450	33	7.4%	—
Annual Growth	12.0%	46.4%	—	—

THE GEORGETOWN UNIVERSITY

Georgetown University is the oldest Catholic university in the US. The institution's 17400 undergraduate and graduate students are instructed by more than 2340 faculty members (representing both full- and part-time) in nine schools ranging from the university's renowned Law Center to the Edmund A. Walsh School of Foreign Service and the Georgetown School of Medicine. The system has a student-teacher ratio of about 10:1. The university is also home to the Georgetown University Medical Center and has forged numerous ties with its neighboring institutions in the Washington DC community.

Operations

The Georgetown University Medical Center provides a variety of medical services to area residents in addition to serving as a teaching and research facility for the university. The medical center has several specialty medicine and research programs through a partnership with MedStar's Georgetown University Hospital including Huntington disease care and brain development studies. Georgetown's research institutes are working to discover new medical treatments including potential breast cancer therapies. The university receives some $179 million in research funding each year.

Geographic Reach

Georgetown University's main campus (54 buildings including the medical center) is located on about 100 acres on the banks of the Potomac in Washington DC. It also has locations in downtown Washington DC and in Arlington Virginia.

Internationally Georgetown University operates a School of Foreign Service campus in Qatar. The university also has study abroad programs in Argentina Turkey China Chile Italy and England and a nursing study program with the Australian Catholic University.

Financial Performance

Georgetown University reported about $1.12 billion in revenues in fiscal 2014 virtually flat with the previous year. Its earnings come from student tuition and fees grants and contracts auxiliary activities and other sources. In fiscal 2015 undergraduate tuition was $46200 per student (up from $44280 in fiscal 2014 and $42360 in fiscal 2013).

Strategy

Georgetown University expands and upgrades its facilities periodically to keep pace with modern technologies and appeal to a variety of students.

To expand its outreach programs Georgetown University built a new location for its School of Continuing Studies in downtown Washington DC. The new campus located near the Law Center opened in late 2013 and extends the reach of the university's presence downtown as it works to expand beyond its historical campus. It also officially launched its McCourt School of Public Policy in 2013.

It also launches new degree programs such as the MIDP (master's of international development policy) and the Master of Science in Global Health.

Company Background

In 2010 Georgetown University received its largest philanthropic gift ever when it was granted a nearly $90 million endowment to support medical research at the university's medical center from a charitable trust established by the will of the late Harry Toulmin in 1965.

Georgetown University was founded in 1789 by John Carroll the nation's first Catholic bishop. At the time of its founding Georgetown University's historic campus was located in Georgetown Maryland; the location is now part of the Washington DC metropolitan area. Among Georgetown University's alumni are President Bill Clinton basketball great Patrick Ewing and former US Surgeon General Antonia Novello.

EXECUTIVES

Associate Vice President Administrative Services, Lennie Carter
Senior Vice President Chief Financial Officer And, Christopher Augostini
Associate Vice President Risk Management, Joseph A Yohe
Vice President Institutional Diversity And Equity, Rosemary Kilkenny
Associate Vice President Alumni Relations, William Reynolds
Associate Vice President And Dean Of Students, Mitchell Bailin
Assistant Vice President, Regina Bleck
Associate Vice President Campaign Operations, Stephanie Jacobson-Landon
Vice President Corporate Engagement, Ellen Carberry
Vice President For Global Engagement, Tom Banchoff
Associate Vice President Advancement Services, Jo Grainger
Vice President Of Member Service, Laura Krivacek
Assistant Vice President For Student Health, Vince WinklerPrins
Assistant Vice President For Emergency Management, Tonya Coultas
Vice President Of Marketing And Communications Student Government Association Mba Class Of 2018, Mercedes Castro
Assistant Vice President, Lamarr Billups
Vice President, Sandra Horvathpeterson
Medical Director, Michelle Roett
Director Of Admissions, Monica Gray
Vice President Diversity Equity And Inclusion Evening Student Government Association Manager Business Analysis Candidate 2018, Zoya Awan
Vice President Of Social, Christine Hwang
Secretary Of The University, Edward Quinn
Auditors: PRICEWATERHOUSECOOPERS LLP MC

LOCATIONS

HQ: THE GEORGETOWN UNIVERSITY
37TH & O ST NW, WASHINGTON, DC 200570001
Phone: 202 687-0100
Web: WWW.GEORGETOWN.EDU

PRODUCTS/OPERATIONS

Selected Schools
Edmund A. Walsh School of Foreign Service
Georgetown College
Graduate School of Arts and Sciences
Law Center
McCourt School of Public Policy
Robert E. McDonough School of Business
School of Medicine
School of Nursing and Health Studies
School for Summer and Continuing Education

HISTORICAL FINANCIALS

Company Type: Private

Income Statement				FYE: June 30
	REVENUE ($ mil.)	NET INCOME ($ mil.)	NET PROFIT MARGIN	EMPLOYEES
06/18	1,249	130	10.4%	9,700
06/17	1,203	185	15.4%	—
06/13	1,120	188	16.8%	—
06/12	1,038	(88)	—	—
Annual Growth	3.1%	—	—	—

2018 Year-End Financials

Return on assets: 4.0%   Cash ($ mil.): 122
Return on equity: 7.2%
Current ratio: —

THE GOLUB CORPORATION

Supermarket operator The Golub Corporation offers tasty come-ons such as table-ready meals gift certificates automatic discount cards and a hotline where cooks answer food-related queries. Golub operates about 135 Price Chopper supermarkets and market 32 stores in six states in the northeastern US (New York is its largest market.) About 80 of the locations have in-store pharmacies and some New York stores provide shopping and delivery service through the Shops4U program. The founding Golub family runs the company and owns about 45% of the regional grocery chain; employees own slightly more than 45%.

Geographic Reach

Golub's Price Chopper chain is active in six US states. New York accounts for more than 60% of its locations while Massachusetts and Vermont each contribute more than 10%. It also has locations in Connecticut Pennsylvania and New Hampshire.

Sales and Marketing

The company sells its products in its stores and online.

Financial Performance

While privately-held Golub doesn't publish sales results for its Price Chopper chain its supermarkets ring up an estimated $3.5 billion in annual revenues.

Strategy

Golub continues to invest in its future through new locations improved products and services customer engagement and health and wellness initiatives environmental sustainability activities progressive technology digital marketing e-commerce and social networking.

In 2015 Price Chopper Supermarkets launched a specialty pharmacy program with Aureus Health Services a specialty pharmacy and health management company.

In 2014 the company announced plans to rebrand about 135 Price Chopper supermarkets under a new banner Market 32. The conversions will take place over the next several years. More than half of the conversions will be completed within five years representing a $300 million investment. The renamed stores will will include expanded food service options an enhanced product mix and an emphasis on customer service. The new name references 1932 the year the company was founded.

In late 2013 Golub invested some $10 million to relaunch a Latham New York store as Market Bistro by Price Chopper. The 87000-square-foot revamped location features a New York-style deli pizza counter cooking classes and indoor and outdoor patios.

Company Background

Like many other retailers the company is experimenting with new formats. In May 2012 it opened its first small-format store known as Price Chopper Limited. The 19000-square-foot store (about a third of the size of a typical Price Chopper supermarket) is located in a residential neighborhood in downtown Saratoga Springs New York. The "Limited" store offers an edited selection of Price Chopper's most popular products a bakery full-service meat deli and seafood departments and a cafe with eat-in or take-out meals.

In fall 2011 Price Chopper launched a new online ordering and home delivery program called Price Chopper Shops4U . The service charges a service fee of $10 with an additional $6 fee for delivery. Customers can either pick up their orders at the store or have them delivered.

Brothers Bill and Ben Golub founded the company in 1932.

EXECUTIVES

President And Ceo, Jerel T. (Jerry) Golub
Vp Public Relations And Consumer Services, Mona J. Golub
Svp Administration, David Golub
Vp Produce & Floral Merchandising, Rick Reed
Vice President Human Resources Operations, Shelley Florence
Vice President, Shawn Gonzalez
Vice President Marketing Analytics, Glen Bradley
Vice President Talent Management, Paul Rollins
Vice President Merchandising Group, Scott Evans
Senior Vice President Sales And Merchandising, Jerry Golub
Pharmd, Alisha Roberts
Vice President Risk Management, Anne Davis
Vice President Engineering And Construction, Ryan Hill
Vice President Supply Chain, Bernie Socha
Chairman And Ceo, Neil M. Golub

LOCATIONS

HQ: THE GOLUB CORPORATION
461 NOTT ST, SCHENECTADY, NY 123081812
Phone: 518 355-5000
Web: WWW.PRIMEBUSINESSDINING.COM

2013 Stores

	No.
New York	81
Massachusetts	16
Vermont	15
Connecticut	8
Pennsylvania	8
New Hampshire	4
Total	**132**

COMPETITORS

7-Eleven	Gerrity's
A&P	Hannaford Bros.
ALDI	Shaw's
BJ's Wholesale Club	Stewart's Shops
Big Y Foods	Stop & Shop
CVS	TOPS Markets
Costco Wholesale	Target Corporation
Cumberland Farms	Wal-Mart
DeMoulas Super Markets	Wegmans

HISTORICAL FINANCIALS

Company Type: Private

Income Statement   FYE: April 24

	REVENUE ($ mil.)	NET INCOME ($ mil.)	NET PROFIT MARGIN	EMPLOYEES
04/16	3,427	8	0.2%	19,500
04/15	3,476	21	0.6%	—
04/14	3,472	18	0.5%	—
Annual Growth	**(0.7%)**	**(32.3%)**	—	—

2016 Year-End Financials

Return on assets: 1.2%   Cash ($ mil.): 22
Return on equity: 13.3%
Current ratio: 0.70

THE HEALTH CARE AUTHORITY OF THE CITY OF HUNTSVILLE

Health Care Authority of the City of Huntsville ensures that residents get the medical attention they need. TheÂ volunteer board consists of nine members that governs the more than 880-bed Huntsville Hospital one of the largest medical centers in Alabama with a staff of more than 650 physicians as well as other medical facilities. Huntsville Hospital is also a teaching facility for the University of Alabama-Birmingham. The Health Care Authority of the City of Huntsville provides a list of nominees for board members to the City Council which decides who is appointed to the board.

EXECUTIVES

Eo, David Spillers
Cfo*, Kelly Towers
V Pres, Michael W Brown
Chief of Medicine, Richard Spera
Chief of Psychology/Psychiatry, Anupama Yedla
MD, Kevin S Ellis
Director of Pharmacy, Michael McDaniel
Auditors: WARREN AVERETT LLC HUNTSVILL

LOCATIONS

HQ: THE HEALTH CARE AUTHORITY OF THE CITY OF HUNTSVILLE
101 SIVLEY RD SW, HUNTSVILLE, AL 358014421
Phone: 256 265-1000
Web: WWW.HUNTSVILLEHOSPITAL.ORG

HISTORICAL FINANCIALS

Company Type: Private

Income Statement   FYE: June 30

	REVENUE ($ mil.)	NET INCOME ($ mil.)	NET PROFIT MARGIN	EMPLOYEES
06/18	1,524	53	3.5%	8,000
06/17	1,407	46	3.3%	—
06/07	591	49	8.3%	—
06/06	548	25	4.6%	—
Annual Growth	**8.9%**	**6.5%**	—	—

2018 Year-End Financials

Return on assets: 3.3%   Cash ($ mil.): 125
Return on equity: 4.8%
Current ratio: 1.50

THE HERTZ CORPORATION

EXECUTIVES

Pres-Ceo, Kathryn V Marinello
Non Exec Chb*, Henry R Keizer
Exec V Pres-Cfo, Jamere Jackson
Exec V Pres-Cmo, Jodi J Allen
Exec V Pres-Gen Counsel-Sec, M David Galainena
Sr V Pres-Cao, Richard E Esper
Evp Retail Oprs Officer, Paul E Stone
Evp-CIO, Opal G Perry
Evp-Chief Hr Officer, Murali Kuppuswamy
Director, Barry Beracha
Independent Lead Director, Linda Levinson
Auditors: PRICEWATERHOUSECOOPERS LLP FO

LOCATIONS

HQ: THE HERTZ CORPORATION
8501 WILLIAMS RD, ESTERO, FL 339283325
Phone: 239 301-7000
Web: WWW.HERTZ.COM

HISTORICAL FINANCIALS

Company Type: Private

Income Statement   FYE: December 31

	REVENUE ($ mil.)	NET INCOME ($ mil.)	NET PROFIT MARGIN	EMPLOYEES
12/17	8,803	332	3.8%	37,000
12/16	8,803	(488)	—	—
12/15	10,535	276	2.6%	—
Annual Growth	**(8.6%)**	**9.7%**	—	—

2017 Year-End Financials

Return on assets: 1.7%   Cash ($ mil.): 1,072
Return on equity: 21.8%
Current ratio: —

THE INCOME FUND OF AMERICA INC

EXECUTIVES

Chb, Janet McKinley
Pres, Darcy Kopcho
Treas, Dayna Yamabe
Sr V Pres, Stephen E Bepler
Sr V Pres, Abner K Goldstein
V Pres, John Smet
SEC, Patrick F Quan
Auditors: DELOITTE & TOUCHE LLP COSTA

LOCATIONS

HQ: THE INCOME FUND OF AMERICA INC
1 MARKET PLZ, SAN FRANCISCO, CA 941051101
Phone: 415 421-9360

HISTORICAL FINANCIALS

Company Type: Private

Income Statement   FYE: July 31

	REVENUE ($ mil.)	NET INCOME ($ mil.)	NET PROFIT MARGIN	EMPLOYEES
07/18	4,051	2,343	57.9%	7
07/16	3,577	6,660	186.2%	—
Annual Growth	6.4%	(40.7%)	—	—

2018 Year-End Financials

Return on assets: 2.1%   Cash ($ mil.): 89
Return on equity: 2.1%
Current ratio: —

THE INSTITUTE OF ELECTRICAL AND ELECTRONICS ENGINEERS INCORPORATED

A leading technology-related professional group The Institute of Electrical and Electronics Engineers (IEEE) has almost 430000 members including 100000-plus students in 160 countries. The IEEE provides technical and professional information to members on topics such as aerospace systems biomedical engineering computers consumer electronics electric power and telecommunications. It sponsors more than 1300 annual conferences and publishes a variety of technical literature including journals magazines and conference proceedings. The IEEE was formed in 1964 in a combination of the American Institute of Electrical Engineers (founded in 1884) and the Institute of Radio Engineers (founded in 1912).

Operations

Conferences and periodicals together contribute about three-fourths of IEEE's total revenue. The remaining revenue comes from memberships and public imperatives.

Geographic Reach

Nearly 50% of IEEE members live and practice their craft in the US. China India and the Pacific Rim countries account for nearly a fifth of its membership.

Financial Performance

IEEE's revenue rose some 2% in fiscal 2013 to $412.7 million from 2012's $405.3 million. Standard revenue — with an 8% increase — together with Periodicals' 4% boost in revenue contributed to the gains offset in part by other income. IEEE reported $55.1 million in profits in 2013 a $27 million increase thanks to higher sales offset by rising operating expenses across its business. The organization's cash flow in 2013 logged a $32 million bump from gains on the sale of investments.

Strategy

The institute caters to engineers who hail from a wide range of specialties — from aerospace and electronic systems to ultrasonics and frequency control — with nearly 40 different types of society memberships. The organization's membership grew despite the recent downturn in the global economy and continues to increase during the recovery. Among the IEEE more than one-fifth of its members are under the age of 30 and men outnumber women 9:1.

EXECUTIVES

Director, E. James (Jim) Prendergast
Managing Director Ieee-usa, Chris Brantley
Managing Director Educational Activities, Doug Gorham
Managing Director Member And Geographic Activities, Cecelia Jankowski
Cfo, Thomas Siegert
Managing Director Technical Activities, Mary Ward-Callan
President And Ceo, Howard E. Michel
Cio, Cherif Amirat
Managing Director Ieee-standards Association, Konstantinos Karachalios
Vice President Of Conferences, Eb Joffe
Vice President Executive Officer, Bruce Dsena
Vice President Ieee Pes Meetings, Tommy Mayne
Vice President, Forrest Sass
Vice President Executive Officer, Fjellstad Chris
Vice President, C Siegl
Vice President, Michael Edds
Vice President Finance And Administration, Madeleine Glick
Vice President, Robert Klein
Vice President Conferences, Geert De Veirman
Vice President Engineering Director Engi, Mark Aaldering
Vice President, Chuck Maccluer
Vice Chair, Davide Dardari
Treasurer, Hilton Lewis
Secretary, Fernando Guarin
Board Of Governors Member, Jill Gostin
Secretary, Walter Scudder
Auditors: GRANT THORNTON LLP ISELIN NE

LOCATIONS

HQ: THE INSTITUTE OF ELECTRICAL AND ELECTRONICS ENGINEERS INCORPORATED
445 HOES LN, PISCATAWAY, NJ 088544141
Phone: 212 419-7900
Web: WWW.IEEE.ORG

2013 Members

	% of total
US	47
India China & Pacific Rim	18
Canada	3
Other regions	32
Total	**100**

PRODUCTS/OPERATIONS

2013 Sales

	$ mil.	% of total
Periodicals	157	38
Conferences	153	37
Memberships & public imperatives	67	17
Standards	32	8
Other income	1	-
Total	**412**	**100**

Selected IEEE Societies

Aerospace and Electronic Systems
Antennas and Propagation
Broadcast Technology
Circuits and Systems
Communications
Computational Intelligence
Electromagnetic Compatibility
Geoscience and Remote Sensing

HISTORICAL FINANCIALS

Company Type: Private

Income Statement   FYE: December 31

	REVENUE ($ mil.)	NET INCOME ($ mil.)	NET PROFIT MARGIN	EMPLOYEES
12/17	494	34	6.9%	1,068
12/16	480	22	4.7%	—
12/09	338	18	5.5%	—
12/08	0	0	—	—
Annual Growth	—	—	—	—

2017 Year-End Financials

Return on assets: 5.2%   Cash ($ mil.): 79
Return on equity: 8.2%
Current ratio: 0.90

THE LANCASTER GENERAL HOSPITAL

Lancaster General Health (LG Health) is a 690-bed integrated health care delivery system serving residents of Lancaster County Pennsylvania and surrounding areas. Its flagship Lancaster General Hospital (LGH) - opened in 1893 - is known for its cardiology orthopedic and intensive care specialties. A separate Women & Babies hospital cares for those just making it into the world. The not-for-profit system also includes multiple outpatient clinics a rehab hospital home care services and a nursing center and health care college as well as a medical group of more than 300 physicians operating at more than 40 practices throughout the region.

Operations

Facilities in the LG Health system include the 533-bed flagship LGH the 98-bed Women & Babies Hospital the 59-bed Lancaster Rehabilitation Hospital and 14 outpatient centers. Specialty services include open-heart surgery obstetrics neurosurgery trauma care and behavioral health. The system also operates a number of outpatient programs such as a diabetes and nutritional Center and a sleep medicine center.

Every year LG Health sees some 972000 outpatients delivers some 4000 babies and performs around 38000 surgeries.

Geographic Reach

The system serves Pennsylvania's Lebanon Berks Dauphin York Chester and Lancaster counties.

Sales and Marketing

Commercial and HMO payments together account for about 40% of net patient revenues;

Medicare accounts for another 35% while Medicaid accounts for some 10%.

Financial Performance

LG Health's revenue rose 5% to $969 million in fiscal 2014 (ended June) on higher net patient revenue and medical services revenue. However net income fell 51% to $117 million as income from contributions and gifts declined; a change in pension liability also hurt the system's bottom line.

Cash flow from operations declined 43% to $43 million in fiscal 2014 as more cash was used in patient accounts receivable and changes were made in prepaid expenses assets and benefits.

Strategy

LG Health continues to make strategic investments to better serve its patients and the community. In 2013 the health system completed construction on the Ann B. Barshinger Cancer Center which opened its doors that year. Two years later it announced plans to expand LGH in a $60 million project that will add a new eight-story patient tower. With the addition of 60 new private rooms and the space for 80 more rooms as demand requires the hospital will have the room to convert its existing semi-private rooms to private rooms.

The system also partners with others in the community to improve patient care. In 2014 it formed an alliance with the University of Pennsylvania Health System to develop innovative care research and education programs.

EXECUTIVES

Senior Vice President Business Development, Susan Wynne
Medical Director Of The Blood Bank, Susan Bator
Svp And Cio, Gary Davidson
Evp Chief Population Health Officer; President Lg Health Innovation Solutions Inc., Marion A. McGowan
President And Ceo, Thomas E. (Tom) Beeman
Evp Chief Administrative And Legal Officer And Corporate Secretary, Robert P. Macina
Svp Post-acute Care, Geoffrey W. Eddowes
Evp And Cfo, Dennis R. Roemer
Svp Chief Physician Executive And Chief Medical Officer, Lee M. Duke
Svp Hospital Operations And Nurse Executive; President Lancaster General Hospital, Karen Flaherty-Oxler
Medical Director, Jeffrey Kirchner
Senior Vice President, Joseph Puskar
Medical Director, Kate Mullen
Vp Operations, Christopher Maley
Vice President General Manager, Norma Ferndinand
Vice President Legal Services, Margaret F Costella
Vice President Of Operations, Rich Paoletti
Vice President Of Customer Service, Carolyn Carlson
Medical Director, Lora Regan
Medical Director, John Eichenlaub
Vice President And Controller, Doug Rinehart
Director Of Nursing, Valerie Adams
Vice President Hospital Operations, Tammy Ober
Senior Vice President Hospital Operations, William Mccune
Vice President Operations Ph, Sean Reynolds
Director Of Nursing, Shirley Heisey
Medical Director Healthy Weight Management And Bariatric Surgery, Joseph R Mcphee
Chairman, C. Clair McCormick
Vice Chairman, Philip R. Wenger
Secretary, Susan Dickel
Board Member, Christine Vlassis
Secretary, Jennifer Edmonds
Electrophysiology Secretary, Beth A Bumgardner
Secretary, Pamela Miller
Pharmacy Secretary, Cindy Jenner
Secretary, Sheila Loreto

LOCATIONS

HQ: THE LANCASTER GENERAL HOSPITAL
555 N DUKE ST, LANCASTER, PA 176022207
Phone: 717 544-5511

PRODUCTS/OPERATIONS

2014 Sales

	$ mil.	% of total
Net patient services revenue less provision for bad debts	920	95
Medical services	10	4
Other revenue	35	1
Other	2	-
Total	**969**	**100**

Selected Specialties

Cardiology
Emergency medical
Intensive care
Neurology
Oncology
Radiology
Rehabilitation
Urology

COMPETITORS

Altoona Regional
Ascension Health
Catholic Health Initiatives
Evangelical Community Hospital
Hanover Healthcare
Holy Spirit
Lewistown Hospital
Main Line Health System
Memorial Hospital (PA)
PinnacleHealth System
Saint Vincent Health System
St. Luke's University Health Network
University of Pennsylvania Health System
WellSpan Health

HISTORICAL FINANCIALS

Company Type: Private

Income Statement

FYE: June 30

	REVENUE ($ mil.)	NET INCOME ($ mil.)	NET PROFIT MARGIN	EMPLOYEES
06/16	958	122	12.8%	7,000
06/15	920	110	12.1%	—
06/14	867	(13)	—	—
06/13	823	(15)	—	—
Annual Growth	5.2%	—	—	—

2016 Year-End Financials

Return on assets: 14.5%   Cash ($ mil.): 23
Return on equity: 28.6%
Current ratio: 2.50

THE LANE CONSTRUCTION CORPORATION

Lane likes people to be in the fast lane. For more than a century the heavy civil contractor and its affiliates have been widening paving and constructing lanes for highways bridges runways railroads dams and mass transit systems in the eastern and southern US. The group also produces bituminous and precast concrete and mines aggregates at plants and quarries in the northeastern mid-Atlantic and southern US. Additionally it sells and leases construction equipment. Founded in

1902 Lane Construction has offices in more than 20 states and is owned by descendants of Lane and employees.

Operations

Lane Construction specializes in heavy civil construction services and products in the transportation infrastructure and energy industries. During the past decade Lane Construction has participated in more than 70 design-building projects with a combined value of more than $4 billion.

Beyond its construction projects Lane operates divisions that manufacture bituminous and precast concrete with mine aggregates at 70 plants and 12 quarries throughout the U.S.

Lane's business divisions are spread across the US and include: Civil Wall Solutions Cold River Materials Prestress of the Carolinas Senate Asphalt Virginia Paving Company and Virginia Sign & Lighting Company.

Lane affiliates include New Hampshire-based Cold River Materials Senate Asphalt of Washington D.C. and Virginia Paving and Virginia Sign & Lighting Co. among about a half a dozen others. In 2013 its Rea Contracting division in the Carolinas changed its name to Lane Construction Corp.

Geographic Reach

Lane Construction has offices in more than 20 US states including Florida Illinois Maine North Carolina Pennsylvania Texas and Virginia. While most of Lane's projects take place along the East Coast it also operates in the South/Southwest and has international operations — under the Lane Worldwide Infrastructure Inc. name — in the Middle East.

Financial Performance

While full financials of the privately-held company were not available Lane Construction has posted annual revenues of more than $1 billion since 2010.

Strategy

The company continues to work for both public and private entities on a variety of high-value projects. In early 2015 the contractor was working on a joint-venture project with Skanska and Granite Construction Company on the $2.3 billion "I-4 Ultimate project" which involves design build finance operating and maintenance work on 21 miles of Interstate 4 from Orange County to Seminole County in Florida.

Also as of early 2015 Lane reported that it recently completed its $1.5-billion construction project on the I-495 Express Lanes in Virginia in one of the largest public-private joint ventures in the US. The same team also completed a $722 million expansion and improvement project on 29 miles of the I-95 Express (high occupancy toll road) lanes in Virginia. Both of these Virgina-based projects were completed ahead of schedule.

EXECUTIVES

Assistant Vice President Engineering, Tom Larson
Senior Vice President, Tim Reichwein
Vice President General Counsel, Seth T Firmender
Executive Vice President Human Resources And Organization, Adolfo Criscuolo
Auditors: KPMG LLP HARTFORD CT

LOCATIONS

HQ: THE LANE CONSTRUCTION CORPORATION
90 FIELDSTONE CT, CHESHIRE, CT 064101212
Phone: 203 235-3351
Web: WWW.LANECONSTRUCT.COM

PRODUCTS/OPERATIONS

Selected Projects
Airports
Bridges
Design-Build
Federal
Heavy Civil
Highways
Public Private Partnerships
Plants & Paving
Rail
Specialty Paving

Selected Divisions
Civil Wall Solutions
Cold River Materials Prestress of the Carolinas
Senate Asphalt
Sunquip
Sunrise Materials
Virginia Paving Company
Virginia Sun & Lighting Company
Wardwell
White Bros.

COMPETITORS

Angelo Iafrate	Sargent Corp
Austin Industries	Skanska USA Civil
Balfour Beatty Inc	The Middlesex
Bechtel	Corporation
Clark Enterprises	Turner Corporation
Granite Construction	Tutor-Saliba
J.F. White Contracting	Vecellio & Grogan
MBC Holding	Walsh Group
Peter Kiewit Sons'	

HISTORICAL FINANCIALS
Company Type: Private

Income Statement   FYE: December 31

	REVENUE ($ mil.)	NET INCOME ($ mil.)	NET PROFIT MARGIN	EMPLOYEES
12/18	847	76	9.0%	3,500
12/17	1,476	18	1.3%	—
12/16	1,196	39	3.3%	—
12/15	1,115	(16)	—	—
Annual Growth	(8.7%)	—	—	—

2018 Year-End Financials
Return on assets: 7.6%
Return on equity: 15.2%
Current ratio: 1.80
Cash ($ mil.): 136

THE MARY IMOGENE BASSETT HOSPITAL

EXECUTIVES

Pres-Ceo, Vance M Brown
Chm, Douglas Hastings
Exec V Pres-Coo, Bertine McKenna
V Pres-Cfo, Sue Andrews
Cco, Steven Heneghan
Evp-Chief Operating Officer, Ronette Wiley
Administrative Director, Scott Bonderoff
Vice-President, Scott Groom
Vascular Surgery, Shelby S Cooper
Rheumatology Specialist, David T Griger
Project Coordinator, Patricia Davis

LOCATIONS

HQ: THE MARY IMOGENE BASSETT HOSPITAL
  1 ATWELL RD, COOPERSTOWN, NY 133261394
Phone: 607 547-3456
Web: WWW.BASSETT.ORG

HISTORICAL FINANCIALS
Company Type: Private

Income Statement   FYE: December 31

	REVENUE ($ mil.)	NET INCOME ($ mil.)	NET PROFIT MARGIN	EMPLOYEES
12/17	547	4	0.8%	3,200
12/16	443	5	1.3%	—
12/15	412	(2)	—	—
12/14	486	18	3.7%	—
Annual Growth	4.0%	(39.0%)	—	—

2017 Year-End Financials
Return on assets: 1.0%
Return on equity: 1.5%
Current ratio: 0.70
Cash ($ mil.): 2

THE MASSACHUSETTS GENERAL HOSPITAL

The General Hospital Corporation is no soapy daytime drama. Doing business as Massachusetts General Hospital (or Mass General) the 200-year-old acute care facility is Harvard Medical School's original and largest teaching hospital. With some 1000 beds Mass General has its main campus in Boston and operates several health centers in surrounding communities. Its specialized medical departments include cancer cardiology and heart surgery; neurology and neurosurgery; and diabetes and endocrinology. As a leading research facility Mass General hosts a number of clinical drug and device trials and has an annual research budget of more than $850 million. The hospital is a founding member of the Partners HealthCare System (along with Brigham and Women's).

Operations

Founded in 1811 Mass General is the oldest and largest general hospital in New England as well as one of the oldest hospitals in the nation. It holds Level I certifications for adult and pediatric trauma and burn care making it a regional referral center for other area hospitals. The hospital also provides outpatient care through doctors' offices of the Mass General Physicians Organization.

Mass General Hospital for Children administers pediatric care services including primary care and rare disease treatment.

Additionally Mass General operates one of the largest hospital-based research networks in the nation consisting of more than 30 clinical departments and centers and conducting some 1200 clinical trials at any given time. With Harvard Mass General offers about 30 residency programs 145 fellowships and continuing medical education programs.

Each year the hospital has some 48000 inpatients more than 100000 emergency department visits and performs more than 42000 operations.

Geographic Reach Mass General's main hospital is located in downtown Boston. The medical center also operates clinics and community locations in Boston Charleston Chelsea Danvers Everett Foxborough Revere and Waltham.

EXECUTIVES

President And Trustee, Peter L. Slavin
Chief Radiation Oncology, Jay S. Loeffler
Chief Neurosurgery, Robert L. Martuza
Chief Orthopaedic Surgery, Harry E. Rubash
Director Cancer Center, Daniel A. Haber
Chief Of Pathology, David N. Louis
Chief Dermatology, David E. Fisher
Chief Molecular Biology, Robert E. Kingston
Chief Of Radiology, James Brink
Surgeon-in-chief And Chair Department Of Surgery, Keith D. Lillemoe
Chief Urology Service, Michael L. Blute
Physician-in-chief Department Of Medicine, Katrina A. Armstrong
Chief Department Of Emergency Medicine, David FM Brown
Chief Neurology Service, Merit Ester Cudkowicz
Chief Department Of Obstetrics And Gynecology, Jeffrey Lawrence (Jeff) Ecker
Chief Pediatric Surgery And Surgeon-in-chief Massgeneral Hospital For Children, Allan Moises Goldstein
Physician-in-chief Of Massgeneral Hospital For Children And Chief Of Partners Pediatrics, Ronald Ellis Kleinman
Chief Of Psychiatry, Jerrold Frank Rosenbaum
Chief Oral And Maxillofacial Surgery, Maria J. Troulis
Chief Of Anesthesia Critical Care And Pain Medicine, Jeanine P. Wiener-Kronish
Chief Physical Medicine And Rehabilitation, Ross D. Zafonte
Respiratory Therapy Director, Robert Kacmarek
Medical Director, Leonard Kaban
Director Of Him, Jackie Raymond
Medical Director, Mary Sabatini
Senior Vice President Human Resources, Jeff Davis
Clinical Director, David Ebb
Nursing Director, Hiyam Nadel
Vice President For Finance, Peter K Markell
Medical Director, David Berger
Pharmacist Manager, Jen Noce
Nursing Director, Christina Stone
Nursing Director, Lee Tata
Director Of Health, Goldberg Ross
Vice President National Sales, Mccauley Denise
Board Member, Daniel Rosenthal
Assistant Secretary, Joan Stoddard
Trustee, Cathy E. Minehan, age 71
Board Member, Antonia Stephen
Assistant Secretary, Mary Lalonde
Board Member, Frank Pedlow
Board Member, David Ryan
Board Member, Andrea Stidsen
Board Member, Cathleen Poliquin
Deputy Treasurer, Michael Manning

LOCATIONS

HQ: THE MASSACHUSETTS GENERAL HOSPITAL
  55 FRUIT ST, BOSTON, MA 021142696
Phone: 617 726-2000
Web: WWW.MGHBIOMED.COM

Selected Research Centers

AIDS

Cancer
Cardiovascular research
Computational and integrative biology
Cutaneous biology
Human genetics
Medical imaging
Neurodegenerative disorders
Photomedicine
Regenerative medicine
Reproductive biology
Systems biology
Transplantation biology

HISTORICAL FINANCIALS

Company Type: Private

Income Statement   FYE: September 30

	REVENUE ($ mil.)	NET INCOME ($ mil.)	NET PROFIT MARGIN	EMPLOYEES
09/15	2,452	211	8.6%	10,156
09/14	2,201	186	8.5%	—
09/13	2,274	148	6.5%	—
09/12	2,281	267	11.7%	—
Annual Growth	2.4%	(7.6%)	—	—

2015 Year-End Financials

Return on assets: 8.0%
Return on equity: 16.7%
Current ratio: 1.60

Cash ($ mil.): 99

THE MEDICAL CENTER OF CENTRAL GEORGIA INC

EXECUTIVES

Ceo, Ninfa M Saunders
Coo*, Mike Gilstrap
Sr V Pres-Cfo*, Virgil E Cooper Jr
Cfo*, Rhonda S Perry
SEC*, Kenneth B Banks
Chief of Medicine, Charles Buafo
Prin, David King

LOCATIONS

HQ: THE MEDICAL CENTER OF CENTRAL GEORGIA INC
777 HEMLOCK ST, MACON, GA 312012155
Phone: 478 633-1000
Web: WWW.NAVICENTHEALTH.ORG

HISTORICAL FINANCIALS

Company Type: Private

Income Statement   FYE: September 30

	REVENUE ($ mil.)	NET INCOME ($ mil.)	NET PROFIT MARGIN	EMPLOYEES
09/16	660	2	0.4%	3,750
09/15	717	93	13.0%	—
09/14	683	80	11.8%	—
09/09	656	10	1.7%	—
Annual Growth	0.1%	(18.3%)	—	—

2016 Year-End Financials

Return on assets: 0.2%
Return on equity: 0.3%
Current ratio: 14.00

Cash ($ mil.): 29

THE MEDICAL UNIVERSITY OF SOUTH CAROLINA

Established in 1824 the Medical University of South Carolina (MUSC) provides Charleston with a wide range of health-related services including medical care training and research. The 50-acre medical school has 1300 faculty members and trains about 2750 full- and part-time students and residents each year through its six schools which cover medical pharmacy nursing dental health professional and graduate training. The MUSC Health organization includes the MUSC Medical Center in Charleston which has some 700 beds and includes a children's hospital and a psychiatric institute as well as the University Medical Associates physician practice organization.

Operations

MUSC has extensive research facilities and programs in areas including bioengineering and translational sciences. The university also participates in drug discovery clinical trial research programs. Its technology transfer program allows small start-up companies to license or purchase research programs that are nearing commercial development stages.

Financial Performance

MUSC is primarily funded by grants and contracts (27% of revenue) and sales and services (also 27% in revenue). State and capital appropriations account for 15% of revenue while student tuition and fees account for 13%. In fiscal 2014 (ended June) the university reported a less-than 1% rise in total revenue to $642.4 million versus $640.7 million in 2013. The modest rise was attributed to an increase in tuition earnings but slightly offset by reductions in both grants/contracts and sales/services revenues.

Strategy

The MUSC strategic plan is focused around four major expansion initiatives: innovation and technology entrepreneurial activity cross-departmental collaboration and globalization. The innovation technology and entrepreneurial goals are centered around the MUSC medical and clinical research organizations which aim to increase external funding resources through grants collaborations and technology transfer agreements. Its collaboration initiative aims to increase inter-professional relationships across its patient care education and research divisions. The university has also been expanding its educational and research facilities.

The university has a total operating budget of some $1.1 billion.

Mergers and Acquisitions

In 2018 MUSC agreed to buy four hospitals in South Carolina from Community Health Systems for an undisclosed price. The purchase will more than double the beds in the university's portfolio. The hospitals including Springs Memorial in Lancaster will be the first ever acquired by MUSC.

Company Background

MUSC was created by an act of South Carolina's General Assembly in 1824. It is historically recognized as the first medical school in the South.

EXECUTIVES

Evp Finance And Operations, Lisa P. Montgomery
Dean College Of Medicine, Raymond N. DuBois
President, David Cole
Interim Vp Medical Affairs, Bruce Elliott

Vp Clinical Operations; Ceo And Executive Director Medical Center, Patrick J. Cawley
Cio, Michael J. Caputo
Unit Secretary, Deborah Davis-Kubofcik
Auditors: KPMG LLP GREENSBORO NC

LOCATIONS

HQ: THE MEDICAL UNIVERSITY OF SOUTH CAROLINA
171 ASHLEY AVE, CHARLESTON, SC 294258908
Phone: 843 792-2123
Web: WWW.MUSC.EDU

COMPETITORS

Beaufort Memorial
  Hospital
Carolinas Hospital
  System
Conway Medical Center
Duke University

Grand Strand Regional
  Medical Center
North Carolina State
  University
Roper St. Francis
  Healthcare

HISTORICAL FINANCIALS

Company Type: Private

Income Statement   FYE: June 30

	REVENUE ($ mil.)	NET INCOME ($ mil.)	NET PROFIT MARGIN	EMPLOYEES
06/18	992	4	0.4%	5,500
06/17	914	9	1.0%	—
06/13	780	26	3.3%	—
06/09	836	3	0.4%	—
Annual Growth	1.9%	1.8%	—	—

2018 Year-End Financials

Return on assets: 0.3%
Return on equity: 3.8%
Current ratio: 3.70

Cash ($ mil.): 322

THE MERCHANTS COMPANY

The Merchants Company which does business as Merchants Foodservice is a leading foodservice supplier that serves more than 6000 customers in 10 Southeastern states. From a handful of distribution warehouses in Alabama Georgia Mississippi and South Carolina the company supplies a wide range of food and non-food items to restaurants hospitals schools and other foodservice operations. The company was founded in 1904 as Fain Grocery Co. a wholesale grocery distributor and changed its name to Merchants Company in 1927. It began focusing on foodservice distribution in 1982 and was acquired by family owned holding company Tatum Development in 1988.

Operations

The company is one of 2600 food distribution companies in the US. The wholesale food distributor and restaurant supplier delivers an average of 8000 orders a week. Its 12000 foodservice items include frozen entrees fresh produce and meats.

Geographic Reach

Merchants Foodservice has four warehouse facilities in Mississippi Alabama Georgia and South Carolina.

Sales and Marketing

Merchants Foodservice serves more than 6000 customers. The company communicates with vendors customers and its sales force through Electronic Data Interchange and sells products via its sales force and online.

Strategy

The company grows through building and maintaining partnerships. Some of the company's strategic marketing partners are Advance Pierre ConAgra Inteplast Schreiber Simplot Tyson Nestle Dan's Prize Inc. Knouse Foods La Chiquita Tortilla MGF Bevolution Group National Checking Norpac Foods and Quality Bakeries.

It also grows via acquisitions.

Mergers and Acquisitions

In 2016 Merchants Foodservice acquired E.G. Forrest Co. a food distributor headquartered in Winston-Salem North Carolina.

The E.G. Forrest assets will improve the coverage and distribution area of Merchants Foodservice. The company planned to fold select E.G. Forrest assets into the new parent's distribution facility and warehouse in Newberry South Carolina.

Company Background

The company's Sunrise Fresh Produce subsidiary acquired a 47000-sq.-ft. produce distribution center in 2012 renaming it Sunrise Fresh Produce of Jacksonville Florida. The climate-controlled warehouse represents the subsidiary's second produce distribution center.

EXECUTIVES

Evp And Treasurer, Andrew B. (Andy) Mercier
Vp And Cfo, Jarrod Gray
Auditors: MCARTHUR THAMES SLAY AND DEW

LOCATIONS

HQ: THE MERCHANTS COMPANY
1100 EDWARDS ST, HATTIESBURG, MS 394015511
Phone: 601 353-2461
Web: WWW.MERCHANTSFOODSERVICE.COM

COMPETITORS

Ben E. Keith	Quirch Foods
Cheney Brothers	Reinhart FoodService
MAINES	Services Group of
McLane Foodservice	America
Meadowbrook Meat	Sysco
Company	US Foods

HISTORICAL FINANCIALS

Company Type: Private

Income Statement

FYE: September 30

	REVENUE ($ mil.)	NET INCOME ($ mil.)	NET PROFIT MARGIN	EMPLOYEES
09/11	489	2	0.5%	500
09/10	441	5	1.2%	—
09/08	294	1	0.4%	—
Annual Growth	18.5%	24.2%	—	—

2011 Year-End Financials

Return on assets: 2.3%
Return on equity: 11.0%
Current ratio: 1.90
Cash ($ mil.): —

THE METROHEALTH SYSTEM

Helping Cleveland's metropolitan citizens stay healthy (and healing them when they aren't) is what MetroHealth System is all about. At the center of the system is MetroHealth Medical Center a level I trauma center and acute care hospital that serves as a teaching affiliate for Case Western Reserve University. Services include oncology behavioral health vascular care orthopedics burn care and pediatrics. The system also operates outpatient clinics long-term care facilities a regional rehabilitation clinic a heart and vascular center two skilled nursing centers an outpatient center and a medical helicopter program. MetroHealth is owned by Ohio's Cuyahoga County.

Operations

More than 550 primary care and specialty care physicians and more than 1700 registered nurses practice within MetroHealth. On an annual basis MetroHealth Medical Center provides care to more than 28000 inpatients and delivers 2900 newborns. More than 950000 visits are recorded in the medical center's outpatient centers along with 17500 surgical cases and 100000 emergency room visits.

The system affiliates with Akron Children's Hospital to expand access to pediatric care throughout the region. Through the partnership Akron Children's provides specialty care at MetroHealth's main campus in the areas of pediatric cardiology gastroenterology cancer and blood disorders and critical care. The MetroHealth affiliation is Akron Children's fourth location in Cuyahoga County.

Geographic Reach

MetroHealth is one of the largest most comprehensive health care providers in Northeast Ohio serving the medical needs of the Greater Cleveland area through more than 15 locations.

Strategy

As emergency rooms continue to burst at the seams more hospitals are finding ways to divert non-emergency patients to more appropriate care settings. MetroHealth has done that with its MetroExpressCare unit for residents who need to see a doctor and would probably otherwise end up at the emergency room. The family medicine physicians who see patients at MetroExpressCare are also available to establish longer-term relationships with patients coming to MetroHealth for the first time. If the physician determines that it's a more serious problem the patient can be referred to MetroHealth's emergency department.

Having options such as MetroExpressCare available is especially important to MetroHealth because it is its region's safety net hospital. As such it receives the lion's share of uninsured patients many of whom end up in the ER because ERs are required to see all patients regardless of their ability to pay under the Emergency Medical Treatment and Active Labor Act. Being able to provide a less expensive option to those patients decreases MetroHealth's bad debt (or unpaid patient bills) and helps reduce crowding at its ER.

To serve non-ER patients Metrohealth opens a new clinic each year on average.

Mergers and Acquisitions

In 2018 MetroHealth agreed to buy Recovery Resources a not-for-profit organization that provides behavioral health and addiction services. MetroHealth will work with Recovery Resources to offer mental illness and addiction care the latter of which is very much in the nation's consciousness. In fact opioid addiction is one of MetroHealth's key areas of focus for the future. The deal will also expand MetroHealth's operations into Cuyahoga County. The purchase price was not disclosed.

Company Background

MetroHealth has been serving the medical needs of the Greater Cleveland community since 1837. It has been a major affiliate of Case Western Reserve University since 1914.

EXECUTIVES

Coo, Daniel K. Lewis
President And Ceo, Akram Boutros
Vp Marketing And Communications, Elizabeth Heller Allen, age 65
Chief Patient Experience Officer, Sara Laskey
Chief Nursing Officer, Mavis Bechtle
Chief Medical Officer And Chief Quality Officer, Alfred F. Connors
Cfo, Craig Richmond
Vp And Associate Cio, Donald Reichert
President Medical Staff, Sherrie Dixon-Williams
Medical Director, Annette Kyprianou
Medical Director, Carolyn Dziwis
Medical Director, Michael Infeld
Nursing Director, Alice Liskay
Vice President, Geoff Himes
Executive Vice President Chief Clinical Officer, Bernard Boulanger
Pharmacy Manager, Barb Isabella
Vice Chairman, J. B. Silvers
Chairman, Thomas M. McDonald
Secretary, Emigda Gabriel
Secretary Organizational Development, Tina Erickson
Medical Secretary, Pamela Mckenna
Auditors: RSM US LLP CLEVELAND OHIO

LOCATIONS

HQ: THE METROHEALTH SYSTEM
2500 METROHEALTH DR, CLEVELAND, OH 441091900
Phone: 216 398-6000
Web: WWW.METROHEALTH.ORG

Selected Locations

J. Glen Smith Health Center (In partnership with the City of Cleveland Cleveland)
MetroHealth Asia Town Health Center (Cleveland)
MetroHealth Beachwood Health Center (Beachwood Ohio)
MetroHealth Broadway Health Center (Cleveland)
MetroHealth Brooklyn Health Center (Cleveland)
MetroHealth Buckeye Health Center (Cleveland)
MetroHealth Center for Sleep Medicine South Campus (Independence Ohio)
MetroHealth Center for Sleep Medicine West Campus (Westlake Ohio)
MetroHealth Lakewood Health Center (Lakewood)
MetroHealth Lee-Harvard Health Center (Cleveland)
MetroHealth Medical Center Main Campus (Cleveland)
MetroHealth Old Brooklyn Campus (Cleveland)
MetroHealth Pepper Pike Health Center (Pepper Pike Ohio)
MetroHealth Premier Health Center (Westlake Ohio)
MetroHealth Rehabilitation Institute of Ohio (Cleveland)
MetroHealth Strongsville Health Center (Strongsville Ohio)
MetroHealth West 150th Health and Surgery Center (Cleveland)
MetroHealth Westlake Health Center (Westlake)
MetroHealth West Park Health Center (Cleveland)
The Elisabeth Severance Prentiss Center for Skilled Nursing Care at MetroHealth (Cleveland)
Thomas F. McCafferty Health Center (In partnership with the City of Cleveland Cleveland)

PRODUCTS/OPERATIONS

MetroHealth System Departments and Services

Aamoth Family Pediatric Wellness Center
Adolescent Clinic (Teen Health)
Advanced Gynecology (Center for Advanced Gynecology)
Advantage (MetroHealth Advantage)
Allergy & Immunology Clinic
Allergy Services (Department of Ear Nose & Throat)
Amigas Unidas Program
Anesthesiology
Art Therapy
Arthritis Center (Rheumatology)
Audiology
Bariatric Surgery (Weight Loss Surgery Program)
Behavioral Health (Child and Teen Mental Health Services)
Birth Control Procedures
Birthing Services

Bone Health and Surgery (Orthopaedics)
BREAST Program (Community Breast Cancer Outreach)
Burn Care Center
Cancer Care Center
Cardiology Cardiovascular (Heart & Vascular Center)
Center for Advanced Gynecology
Center for Behavioral Health (Child and Teen Mental
 Health Services)
Centers for Community Health
Center for Sleep Medicine
Cerebrovascular
Childbirth Education
Child Life and Education
Children's Health (Pediatrics)
Children's Health Specialties
Closing the Gap (MetroHealth Buckeye Health Center)
Comprehensive Care Program (Services for Children
 with Special Needs)
Concussion Clinic
Cosmetic Dermatology
Dentistry and Oral Health
Dermatology
Diabetes Self-Management Program
Digital Mammogram
Ear Nose and Throat (ENT/Otolaryngology)
Emergency Medicine/Emergency Department
Endocrinology
Endoscopy Suite (Gastroenterology)
ExpressCare (MetroExpressCare)
Family Medicine Clinic at MetroHealth Medical Center
Fertility Services
Freedom From Smoking
Gastroenterology and Endoscopy Suite
Genetics Clinic
Geriatrics (Senior Health & Wellness Center)
Gynecology
Gynecology Advanced (Center for Advanced Gynecology)
Gynecologic Oncology
Hand Center
Heart & Vascular Center
Hematology and Oncology (Cancer Care Center)
High-Risk Pregnancy Services
Hospital Medicine
Immunology (Allergy & Immunology Clinic)
Infectious Disease
Infertility Clinic
Infusion Therapy (Allergy & Immunology Clinic)
Internal Medicine Clinic at MetroHealth Medical Center
Internal Medicine and Pediatrics (Med-PEDS)
Kids' Health (Pediatrics
Kids' Korner Free Daycare Service at MetroHealth
 Medical Center
Latina Clinic: English | En espóol
LGBT Pride Clinic (At Thomas F. McCafferty Health
 Center Health Center)
Life Flight (Metro Life Flight)
Long-Term/Skilled Nursing Care
Maternal-Fetal Medicine (High-Risk Pregnancy Services)
Medicine (Department of Medicine)
Mental Health (Psychiatry)
Metro Life Flight
MetroHealth Advantage
MetroExpressCare
MetroHealth Rehabilitation Institute of Ohio
MetroHealth Select Health Plan
MetroHealth Simulation Center
Mi MetroHealth Mi Comunidad
MyChart
Neonatology Neonatal Intensive Care Unit (NICU)
Nephrology
Neurology
Neurosciences
Northeast Ohio Chapter of the National Spinal Cord
 Injury Association (NSCIA)
Northeast Ohio Regional Spinal Cord Injury System
 (NORSCIS)
Nose Ear and Throat (ENT Otolaryngology)
Nursing
Nutrition
Obstetrics
Obstetrics and Gynecology
Occupational Medicine
Oncology (Cancer Care Center)
Opthalmologic (Eye) Surgery
Oral Health (Dentistry)
Oral and Maxillofacial Surgery
Orthopaedics
Osteopathic Medicine
Otolaryngology (Ear Nose and Throat)
Pain Management
Palliative Care

Pastoral Care
Pathology
Pediatrics
Permanent Birth Control Procedures
Pharmacy
Pregnancy Resources
Pride Clinic (At Thomas F. McCafferty Health Center
 Health Center)
Psychiatry (Behavioral/Mental Health)
Pulmonary and Critical Care
Quality Indicators
Radiology
Rehab Rehabilitation Services (MetroHealth
 Rehabilitation Institute of Ohio)
Reiki
Reproductive Endocrinology and Infertility Clinic
Rheumatology (Arthritis Center)

Select Health Plan
Senior Health and Wellness Center
Simulation Center
Skeletal (Orthopaedics)
Skilled Nursing/Long-Term Care
Sleep Medicine Sleep Studies
Spanish-language Information
Special Needs Services for Children (Comprehensive
 Care)
Spine Center
Stroke Stroke & Cerebrovascular Center
Surgery
Throat (Otolaryngology ENT)
Teen Health
Trauma Burns and Critical Care
Travel Clinic
Urgent Care (MetroExpressCare
Urology
Vascular Health and Surgery (Heart & Vascular Center
Weight Loss Surgery Program (Bariatric Surgery)
X-ray (Radiology)

COMPETITORS

AdCare	Lake Health
Catholic Health	OhioHealth
Initiatives	Premier Health
Cincinnati Children's	Partners
Hospital	Robinson Memorial
Community Health	Hospital
Systems	The Cleveland Clinic
Kettering Health	University Hospitals
Network	Health System

HISTORICAL FINANCIALS
Company Type: Private

Income Statement   FYE: December 31

	REVENUE ($ mil.)	NET INCOME ($ mil.)	NET PROFIT MARGIN	EMPLOYEES
12/15	888	37	4.2%	6,000
12/13	813	41	5.1%	—
Annual Growth	4.5%	(5.4%)	—	—

2015 Year-End Financials
Return on assets: 3.6%   Cash ($ mil.): 4
Return on equity: 20.0%
Current ratio: 1.10

THE MIDDLE TENNESSEE ELECTRIC MEMBERSHIP CORPORATION

Middle Tennessee Electric Membership Corporation's service territory is smack dab in the middle of Tennessee. The utility cooperative distributes electricity to 190750 residential and business cus-tomers (member/owners) in four counties (Cannon Rutherford Williamson and Wilson) via more than 10470 miles of power lines connected to 34 electric distribution substations. Middle Tennessee Electric purchases its power supply from the Tennessee Valley Authority. The corporation is Tennessee's largest electric cooperative and the sixth largest in the US.

Geographic Reach
The cooperative serves customers in Cannon Rutherford Williamson and Wilson counties. According to a US Census report three of Tennessee's five fastest growing counties (Rutherford Williamson and Wilson) are in Middle Tennessee Electric's service area which also includes three of Tennessee's top five fastest-growing cities — LaVergne Smyrna and Franklin.

Strategy
To harness green energy as a way to limit fossil fuel power sources and reduce carbon emissions the utility cooperative is installing solar panels for customers. In 2012 the company completed a 850-panel solar field next to the City of Franklin's water plant. That year Middle Tennessee Electric had 70 solar projects operating across its service area and 30 more in the planning stages.

Company Background
Middle Tennessee Electric was formed in 1936 as part of a national rural electrification push.

EXECUTIVES

Vice President Of Information Systems, John Florida
Vice President Communications And Member Services, Robert White
Board Of Directors, Jim Mills
Vice Chairman, Will Jordan
Secretary Treasurer And Director, Mike Woods
Auditors: WINNETT ASSOCIATES PLLC SHELB

LOCATIONS

HQ: THE MIDDLE TENNESSEE ELECTRIC MEMBERSHIP CORPORATION
555 NEW SALEM HWY, MURFREESBORO, TN 371293390
Phone: 615 890-9762
Web: WWW.MTEMC.COM

HISTORICAL FINANCIALS
Company Type: Private

Income Statement   FYE: June 30

	REVENUE ($ mil.)	NET INCOME ($ mil.)	NET PROFIT MARGIN	EMPLOYEES
06/16	542	10	1.9%	410
06/13	524	27	5.3%	—
06/12	510	19	3.8%	—
06/11	1,841	0	—	—
Annual Growth	—	781.4%	—	—

2016 Year-End Financials
Return on assets: 1.7%   Cash ($ mil.): 74
Return on equity: 2.5%
Current ratio: 2.20

THE MITRE CORPORATION

Politicians try to engineer a better government but MITRE governs the country's best engineering. A private not-for-profit organization MITRE Corporation provides consulting engineering and technical research services primarily for agencies of the federal government. It employs more than 7000 scientists engineers and other specialists who work at primary research facilities in Massachusetts and Virginia. It also manages serveral federally funded research and development centers serving organizations such as the Department of Defense the Federal Aviation Administration the Internal Revenue Service and the Department of Veterans Affairs. MITRE was founded in 1958 by former MIT researchers.

Operations
MITRE also supports the Department of Homeland Security (DHS) and the Administrative Office of the US Courts. For the DHS MITRE provides systems engineering practices and acquisition expertise while it helps the US Courts with state-of-the-art technology to benefit the federal judicial system. The company has also assisted the Intelligence Community in safeguarding classified information.

Geographic Reach
In addition to primary research facilities in Bedford Massachusetts and McLean Virginia MITRE has international operations in Belgium Germany Japan the Netherlands South Korea Taiwan and the UK.

Strategy
The company is focusing on supporting the Department of Defense's operations and improving acquisition outcomes preserving an information advantage and addressing the government's enterprise IT consolidation. For the Intelligence Community it has been focusing on helping thwart cyber attacks to the nation's critical infrastructures.

EXECUTIVES

Svp Programs And Technology Center For Connected Government, Richard J. Byrne
President And Ceo, Jason F. Providakes
Vp And Director Center For Enterprise Modernization, James E. (Jim) Cook
Vp And Cio, Joel Jacobs
Svp And Coo, Peter Sherlock
Vp And Cto, Jay Schnitzer
Vp And Director Centers For Medicare & Medicaid Services (cms) Alliance To Modernize Healthcare, Patricia C. Steinbrech
Vp Joint And Services Portfolio National Security Engineering Center, Gregory K (Greg) Crawford
Vp Public Sector Programs Center For Programs And Technology, John M. Kreger
Vp Joint And Services Programs Center For Programs And Technology, Eileen M. Boettcher
Vp Intelligence Programs Center Programs And Technology, Kerry Buckley
Svp And General Manager Mitre National Security Sector, William LaPlante
Vp Air Force Portfolio National Security Engineering Center, Sarah MacConduibh
Vp And Cfo, Jean C. Milbrandt
Vp Air Force Programs Center For Programs And Technology, Douglas Robbins
Vp Intelligence Portfolios Mitre National Security Sector, Lori M. Scherer
Vp And Director Center For Enterprise Modernization Veterans Affairs Portfolio, Jacklyn Mitchell Wynn
Vice President Information Technology, Dwayne Allain
Vice President, Kathy Saunders
Vice President And Director Center For Cem Fet Ffrdc, Beth Meinert
Department Head Agile And Adaptive Software Engineering, Carole Mahoney
Department Head, David Hodulich
Department Head, Thomas Wilk
Vice Chairman, Donald M. Kerr
Chairman, John J. Hamre
Assistant Treasurer, Julie Trudeau

LOCATIONS
HQ: THE MITRE CORPORATION
202 BURLINGTON RD, BEDFORD, MA 017301420
Phone: 781 271-2000
Web: WWW.MITRE.ORG

COMPETITORS

Altarum	SITA
Battelle Memorial	SRI International
Berkeley Lab	Sandia National
ComGlobal Systems	Laboratories
EDSI	SwRI
General Atomics	The Scripps Research
Institute for Defense	Institute
Analyses	Wyle Information
Leidos	Systems
QinetiQ	

HISTORICAL FINANCIALS
Company Type: Private

Income Statement   FYE: October 5

	REVENUE ($ mil.)	NET INCOME ($ mil.)	NET PROFIT MARGIN	EMPLOYEES
10/08	1,234	22	1.8%	7,000
10/07	1,113	23	2.1%	—
Annual Growth	10.9%	(4.6%)	—	—

2008 Year-End Financials
Return on assets: —   Cash ($ mil.): 36
Return on equity: 1.8%
Current ratio: 0.80

THE MOSES H CONE MEMORIAL HOSPITAL

EXECUTIVES
Ceo, Terry Akin
Exec V Pres-Cfo, Jeff Jones
Coo, Judy Schanel
Trustee, William V Nutt
Chief of Medicine, Vanessa Haygood
Director, Edee Merritt
Director, Sheryl Booth
Information Specialist, Dana Dark
Vice President of Information, Frank V Aluisio
Accountant Wide, Frank Kauder
Assistant Director, Terry Lynn
Auditors: DELOITTE & TOUCHE LLP RALEIG

LOCATIONS
HQ: THE MOSES H CONE MEMORIAL HOSPITAL
1200 N ELM ST, GREENSBORO, NC 274011020
Phone: 336 832-7000

HISTORICAL FINANCIALS
Company Type: Private

Income Statement   FYE: September 30

	REVENUE ($ mil.)	NET INCOME ($ mil.)	NET PROFIT MARGIN	EMPLOYEES
09/18	2,001	88	4.4%	12,000
09/17	1,836	142	7.7%	—
09/16	1,678	49	3.0%	—
09/15	1,545	(27)	—	—
Annual Growth	9.0%	—	—	—

2018 Year-End Financials
Return on assets: 3.1%   Cash ($ mil.): 62
Return on equity: 5.1%
Current ratio: 0.90

THE NATURE CONSERVANCY

The Nature Conservancy is a nonprofit dedicated to preserving the diversity of Earth's wildlife by saving some 120 million acres of land 5000 miles of rivers and 100 marine areas in every US state and more than 35 countries worldwide. The organization boasts more than 1 million members. The Nature Conservancy originally carried out its mission by simply buying land but it has evolved to incorporate other methods to further its goals. In addition to land acquisition the organization partners with government corporate and private entities to reduce harmful use of natural areas to create conservation-friendly public policy and to increase conservation funding. The Nature Conservancy was founded in 1951.

Geographic Reach
Based in Arlington Virginia The Nature Conservancy operates in more than 35 countries worldwide and in all 50 US states. The organization works in Africa the Asia-Pacific region the Caribbean Europe and the Americas.

Financial Performance
The Nature Conservancy has posted two years of increased support and revenue after a dropoff in 2012. In 2014 it marshaled revenue of $1.1 billion up 17% from 2013. Dues and contributions were 28% higher in 2014 rising to $560 million. Investmetn income more than doubled to $235 million in 2014. The nonprofit had 24% less in land sales and gifts in 2014. Program efficiency remained strong at 73%.

Dues and Contributions from individuals represent about 50% The Nature Conservancy's total support and revenue. Land sales and gifts contribute nearly 12%.

Strategy
In 2014 The Nature Conservancy completed a five-year plan that put it on financially stable and sustainable ground. To expand its impact it launched NatureVest to source low-cost 'impact capital.' Such a project in Kenya its Livestock to Markets program helps communities get a better price for their cattle while managing grazing lands that also support wildlife.

The nonprofit uses about 75% of its funds on projects. Most of its donations come from individual contributors. The Nature Conservancy also makes money from the sale and lease of lands. The group is unapologetic about its pragmatic science-based approach to conservation. It has angered fellow environmentalists in the past because of its willingness to partner with governments and businesses as well as to just pay people to leave land alone. However the Nature Conservancy says its non-confrontational approach that is rooted in science has actually enabled its success.

In early 2014 The Nature Conservancy purchased nearly 120000 acres of forest rivers and wildlife habitat in the Lower Blackfoot River watershed of Montana for $85 million.

EXECUTIVES

Coo, Lois E. Quam, age 58
President And Ceo, Mark R. Tercek
Evp, Peter Wheeler
Cfo And Chief Administrative Officer, Stephen
  (Steve) Howell
Chief External Affairs Officer, Glenn T. Prickett
**Regional Managing Director Latin America
  Conservation Region,** Joseph (Joe) Keenan
Regional Managing Director Africa, David Banks
Regional Managing Director Asia Pacific, Charles
  E. Bedford
Director California, Mark Burget
Evp Global Conservation Initiatives, William (Bill)
  Ginn
Senior Science Advisor, Peter Kareiva
Chief Conservation Officer, Brian McPeek
Chief External Affairs Officer, Glenn Pricket
Global Managing Director Lands, Justin Adams
Chief Development Officer, Jim Asp
Global Managing Director Water, Giulio Boccaletti
Global Managing Director Oceans, Maria
  Damanaki
Global Managing Director Cities, Pascal
  Mittermaier
**Regional Managing Director Latin American
  Region,** Aurelio Ramos
Managing Director Public Policy, Lynn Scarlett
Acting Chief Scientist, Heather Tallis
**Chief Of Staff And Acting Chief Marketing
  Officer,** Janine M. Wilkin
Vice President, Laurel Mayer
Marketing And Government Relations, Shannon
  Crownover
Director Of Government Relations, April Donnelly
Vice President, Joe Keenan
Director Of Government Relations, Susan
  Donovan
Vice Chairman, James E. (Jim) Rogers
Chairman, Thomas J. Tierney
Board Director, Teresa Beck
Board Member, John Randall
Auditors: PRICEWATERHOUSECOOPERS LLP MC

LOCATIONS

HQ: THE NATURE CONSERVANCY
  4245 FAIRFAX DR STE 100, ARLINGTON, VA
  222031650
Phone: 703 841-5300
Web: WWW.NATURE.ORG

Selected Areas of Operation

Africa

Australia
Asia & the Pacific Islands
Caribbean
Central America
Europe
North America
South America

PRODUCTS/OPERATIONS

2014 Support & Revenue

	$ mil.	% of total
Dues & contributions	560	50
Investment income	235	22
Land sales & gifts		**138.5**
12		
Government grants	120	11
1Other income	59	5
Total	**1,114**	**100**

2014 Dues & Contributions

	%
Individuals	37
Foundations	28
Bequests	23
Other organizations	6
Corporations	6

Total	**100**

HISTORICAL FINANCIALS

Company Type: Private

Income Statement				FYE: June 30
	REVENUE ($ mil.)	NET INCOME ($ mil.)	NET PROFIT MARGIN	EMPLOYEES
06/17	1,143	306	26.8%	3,400
06/16	803	(8)	—	—
06/14	949	201	21.2%	—
06/13	859	106	12.4%	—
Annual Growth	7.4%	30.1%	—	—

2017 Year-End Financials

Return on assets: 4.4%
Return on equity: 4.9%
Current ratio: —

Cash ($ mil.): 55

THE NEBRASKA MEDICAL CENTER

Cornhuskers take note: If health care is what you seek The Nebraska Medical Center aims to please. The not-for-profit health system provides tertiary care at two campuses in Omaha University Hospital and Clarkson Hospital that collectively house about 680 licensed beds. The medical center the largest health care facility in Nebraska is the primary teaching facility of the University of Nebraska Medical Center (UNMC). It also serves as a designated trauma facility for eastern Nebraska and western Iowa and provides highly specialized care including organ transplantation. Its Clarkson West Medical Center campus houses outpatient surgery facilities an emergency room and doctors' offices.

Operations
The system has more than 1000 physicians. In 2013 it had some 51000 emergency department visits more than 24500 inpatient admissions and about 428000 outpatient visits.

In addition to University Hospital and Clarkson Hospital Nebraska Medical Center operates a network of 40 specialty and primary care clinics in and around Omaha. The health system's Centers of Excellence include its Cancer Center Heart Center Neurological Sciences Transplant Center and Women's Health.

Geographic Reach
In addition to serving the residents of Omaha the Nebraska Medical Center serves as a designated trauma facility for patients in eastern Nebraska and western Iowa.

Strategy
Like most other health care providers the Nebraska Medical Center is looking for ways to cut costs in the face of decreasing reimbursements from federal payers (such as Medicare and Medicaid) and as pressure from health care reform mounts and hospitals are required to implement expensive digital record-keeping and physician order entry systems. One way that Nebraska Medical Center has sought to reduce its expenses it by signing up with companies such as Medassets to receive sourcing and group purchasing (GPO) medical device and clinical consulting services for items used most by its physicians and for its pharmacy services.

The medical center and its sponsoring university are looking to expand its medical facilities to keep pace with a growing and aging population. UNMC is developing a new cancer center at the medical center's Omaha campus. Plans include three facilities - a multidisciplinary outpatient clinic a 98-lab research tower and a hospital tower with 108 beds dedicated to oncology patients. The project (estimated to cost $370 million) is expected to create 1200 new jobs by 2020 and pump $100 million annually into Nebraska's economy.

The system is also working with UNMC to add a new outpatient center to the university's midtown campus. The Lauritzen Outpatient Center will feature 10 operating rooms including four dedicated to opthalmic surgical procedures.

EXECUTIVES

Respiratory Therapy Director, Marlon Mcgough
Medical Director, Ron Kirschner
Auditors: KPMG LLP OMAHA NE

LOCATIONS

HQ: THE NEBRASKA MEDICAL CENTER
  987400 NEBRASKA MED CTR, OMAHA, NE
  681980001
Phone: 402 552-2000

PRODUCTS/OPERATIONS

Selected Services
Cancer Center
General Health Services
Heart and Vascular Services
Neurological Sciences
Transplantation

COMPETITORS

BryanLGH Medical Center
CHI Health
Children's Hospital & Medical Center
Fremont Area Medical Center
Madonna Rehabilitation Hospital
Methodist Health System
Saint Elizabeth Regional Medical Center

HISTORICAL FINANCIALS

Company Type: Private

Income Statement				FYE: June 30
	REVENUE ($ mil.)	NET INCOME ($ mil.)	NET PROFIT MARGIN	EMPLOYEES
06/17	1,389	74	5.4%	4,100
06/16	1,119	60	5.4%	—
Annual Growth	24.1%	22.1%	—	—

2017 Year-End Financials

Return on assets: 5.2%
Return on equity: 9.0%
Current ratio: 2.40

Cash ($ mil.): 67

THE NEW JERSEY TRANSIT CORPORATION

Government-owned New Jersey Transit (NJ TRANSIT) provides bus rail and light rail passenger transportation services. Its systems connect major points in New Jersey and provide links to the neighboring New York City and Philadelphia metropolitan areas. Overall the NJ TRANSIT service area spans about 5325 sq. miles. One of the largest transportation companies of its kind in the US NJ TRANSIT operates a fleet of more than 2000 buses 710 commuter trains and 45 light rail vehicles. Collectively the agency's passengers make more than 220 million trips a year. NJ TRANSIT oversees public transportation programs for the elderly people with disabilities and people in rural areas.

Financial Performance
From 2013 to 2014 the company's revenues increased 4% but it experienced a drop in net income due to the significance of Superstorm Sandy and other costs and operating expenses.

Strategy
NJ TRANSIT purchased 53 buses and seven sedans for its paratransit fleet in 2014. The new vehicles were distributed to contractors operating in 18 New Jersey counties.

Company Background
NJ TRANSIT was founded in 1979 by the New Jersey legislature.

EXECUTIVES

Executive Director, Veronique (Ronnie) Hakim
Vice President Of Diversity, Leo Sanders
Vice President, Leotis Sanders
Vice Chairman, Bruce Meisel
Chairman, Jamie Fox
Auditors: ERNST & YOUNG LLP ISELI NJ

LOCATIONS

HQ: THE NEW JERSEY TRANSIT CORPORATION
1 PENN PLZ E, NEWARK, NJ 071052245
Phone: 973 491-7000
Web: WWW.NJTRANSIT.COM

COMPETITORS

Port Imperial Ferry
Corp.

HISTORICAL FINANCIALS
Company Type: Private

Income Statement   FYE: June 30

	REVENUE ($ mil.)	NET INCOME ($ mil.)	NET PROFIT MARGIN	EMPLOYEES
06/18	1,056	(67)	—	1,000
06/04	583	256	44.0%	—
06/03	569	482	84.7%	—
06/02	542	357	65.8%	—
Annual Growth	4.2%	—	—	—

2018 Year-End Financials

Return on assets: (-0.9%)   Cash ($ mil.): 80
Return on equity: (-1.9%)
Current ratio: 0.90

THE NEW YORK AND PRESBYTERIAN HOSPITAL

The New York and Presbyterian Hospital is a learned institution: The not-for-profit hospital is affiliated with both the Columbia University College of Physicians & Surgeons and the Weill Cornell Medical College of Cornell University. Known as NewYork-Presbyterian Hospital the organization includes two major medical centers Columbia University Medical Center and Weill Cornell Medical Center which conduct educational and research programs in partnership with the universities. The two facilities combined have about 2600 beds and offer specialized programs for burns digestive diseases pediatrics women's health and other conditions. NewYork-Presbyterian Hospital is part of the NewYork-Presbyterian Healthcare System.

Operations
Altogether the NewYork-Presbyterian Hospital campuses handle some 2 million patient visits each year (both on an inpatient and outpatient basis) including inpatient admissions and more than 310000 emergency room visits and about 15000 births. The facilities employ a total of more than 6500 physicians including residents and fellows. NewYork-Presbyterian Hospital provides more than $108 million in charity and community care services each year.

Geographic Reach
In addition to its flagship campuses NewYork-Presbyterian/Columbia and NewYork-Presbyterian/Weill Cornell NewYork-Presbyterian Hospital operates two small community hospitals in Manhattan — the Allen Hospital and the Lower Manhattan Hospital — and an inpatient mental health facility (the Westchester Division). The broader NewYork-Presbyterian Healthcare System operates facilities in other areas of New York as well as in New Jersey and Connecticut. The NewYork-Presbyterian Hospital/Columbia campus houses the Morgan Stanley Children's Hospital as well as other specialist units.

Sales and Marketing
Medicare and Medicaid recipients account for more than 60% of NewYork-Presbyterian Hospital's patients. Commercial managed care organizations and insurance firms as well as self-pay customers account for the rest.

Financial Performance
NewYork-Presbyterian Hospital's revenue in fiscal 2015 totaled $4.8 billion.

Strategy
As the health care landscape has become increasingly complex and competitive especially with changing regulations and the push to provide more integrated patient care NewYork-Presbyterian Hospital has made some major organizational changes. Chief among its goals is to provide a patient-centered model of care creating a system that can easily be accessed by its patient consumers. It recently established its Community and Population Health division which includes community programs and initiatives ambulatory care network sites and the management of its new Accountable Care Organization.

It has also expanded beyond its former base of Manhattan in order to provide a regional system of care. For example the system took ownership of former affiliate Brooklyn Methodist in early 2017 with the intention of investing in the hospital's development; the move falls in line with its strategy of providing integrated care for communities particularly in light of a number of recent hospital failures in the borough.

Mergers and Acquisitions
New York Methodist Hospital (now NewYork-Presbyterian Brooklyn Methodist Hospital) was added to the organization in early 2017. Brooklyn Methodist will gain funds for a new $400 million ambulatory care building as part of the new relationship.

Company Background
NewYork-Presbyterian Hospital was formed through the 1998 merger of the New York Hospital (founded in 1771) and the Presbyterian Hospital (founded in 1868). New York Hospital was known for advancing care in areas including women's health and surgery while the Presbyterian Hospital was known for its pediatric division and its cancer center.

EXECUTIVES

Vice President, Valerie Punnett
Svp Cfo And Treasurer, Phyllis R. Lantos
President And Ceo, Steven J. (Steve) Corwin
Svp And Chief Nursing Officer, Wilhelmina Manzano
Evp And Coo, Laura L. Forese
Svp And Chief Medical Officer, Richard S. Liebowitz
Cio, William Lee
Evp Chief Legal Officer And General Counsel, Maxine Frank
Finance Vice President, Ana Arroyo
Vice President Facilities Management, Joseph Lorino
Information Security Vice President, Howard Goldman
Vice President Compensation Benefits And Hris, Mary Falkowitz
Senior Vice President And Chief, Karen S Westervelt
Operations Vice President, Elizabeth Vega
Vice President Human Resources, Lorraine Orlando
Vice President Finance, William Farrell
Finance Vice President, Salvatore Logiudice
Senior Vice President And Chief Quality, Henry Ting
Vice President Of Human Resources, April Rodgers
Vice President Public Affairs, Karen Sodomick
Clinical Director, Gina A Rivera
Vice President Finance, Lugeion Y Carter
Vice President, Tanya Clark
Vice President Branding And Stakeholder Relations, Catherine Ryan
Vice President And Chief Administrative Officer, Kim Roldan-sanchez
Vp Operations And Engagement, Keren Rozenfeld
Vice Chairman, Frank A. Bennack, age 86
President Ceo And Trustee, Herbert Pardes, age 85
Medical Secretary, Matthew Swader
Treasurer, Karen Turi
Assistant Treasurer, Sedare Coradine
Surgical Secretary, Eileen Chavez

LOCATIONS

HQ: THE NEW YORK AND PRESBYTERIAN HOSPITAL
525 E 68TH ST, NEW YORK, NY 100654870
Phone: 212 746-5454

PRODUCTS/OPERATIONS

2016 Patient Mix

	% of total
Medicare Managed	9
Medicare FFS	22
Medicaid Managed	23
Medicaid FFS	7
Managed Care and Other	37
Self-Pay	1
Workers Comp	1
Total	**100**

Selected Services

Cancer
Children's Health
Digestive
Geriatrics
Heart
Mens Health
Neuroscience
Orthopedic
Psychiatry
Rehabilitation Medicine
Transplant
Vascular
Womens Health

COMPETITORS

Ascension Health	MediSys Health Network
Beth Israel Medical Center	Memorial Sloan-Kettering
Bronx-Lebanon Hospital	Montefiore Medical
Catholic Healthcare System	New York City Health and Hospitals
Continuum Health Partners	Northwell Health
Lenox Hill Hospital	Winthrop-University Hospital
Lutheran HealthCare	Yale New Haven Health System
Maimonides Medical Center	

HISTORICAL FINANCIALS

Company Type: Private

Income Statement · FYE: December 31

	REVENUE ($ mil.)	NET INCOME ($ mil.)	NET PROFIT MARGIN	EMPLOYEES
12/18	8,483	526	6.2%	23,709
12/17	5,616	762	13.6%	—
12/16	4,935	496	10.1%	—
12/14	4,206	197	4.7%	—
Annual Growth	19.2%	27.8%		

2018 Year-End Financials

Return on assets: 3.7%
Return on equity: 6.3%
Current ratio: 2.50
Cash ($ mil.): 590

THE NEWTRON GROUP L L C

Some contractors bomb but The Newtron Group keeps on ticking. Through subsidiaries The Newtron Group offers a variety of industrial electrical and other specialty construction and contracting services nationwide. Services include instrumentation and control systems installation and maintenance; fiber optic installation and testing; industrial pipe and panel fabrication; aviation services; and electrical heat tracing. Newtron serves clients in such industries as refining power generation mining petrochemical and gas transmission. Subsidiaries include electrical contractor Triad Electric & Controls fiber optics firm Com-Net Services and NGI National Constructors. Founded in 1973 The Newtron Group serves the US from offices in California Louisiana Mississippi and Texas.

Operations

The Newtron Group held around a dozen subsidiary companies as of early 2016 with five under the Newtron brand including Newtron Beaumont which constructs and maintains electrical and instrumentation systems; Newtron Mechanical which deals with mechanical systems; Newtron Electrical Services which works with electrical meters breaker box replacement parking lot light and other electrical systems.

Other subsidiaries include: NGI National Constructors which constructs union projects; Triad Electric & Controls an open-shop contractor for electrical and instrumentation projects; and Executive Aviation Inc. a full-service Fixed Base Operator (FBO).

Geographic Reach

The Baton Rouge-based Newtron Group works on projects across the contiguous US from offices in California and on the coasts of Louisiana Mississippi and Texas.

Sales and Marketing

The group serves primarily the refining petrochemical power generation pulp and paper mining and metals and gas transmission industries (as of early 2016).

Strategy

Focusing on six core industries The Newtron Group and its subsidiaries continued in 2016 to work on projects ranging from small-capital projects and maintenance contracts up to multi-million dollar grassroots projects.

EXECUTIVES

Vp Marketing, Duff Schempf
President, Glen Redd
Auditors: HANNIS T BOURGEOIS LLP BATON

LOCATIONS

HQ: THE NEWTRON GROUP L L C
8183 W EL CAJON DR, BATON ROUGE, LA 708158093
Phone: 225 927-8921
Web: WWW.THENEWTRONGROUP.COM

PRODUCTS/OPERATIONS

Selected Subsidiaries

Com-Net Services Inc. (fiber optics)
Executive Aviation Inc. (hangar space fuel supplies)
Newtron Inc. (electrical and instrumentation)
Newtron Heat Trace (industrial heat tracing)
Newtron Mechanical (industrial mechanics)
Triad Electric and Controls Inc. (electrical and instrumentation)
Triad Control Systems Inc. (control panel fabrication)

Selected Industries

Cement
Electronics
Food processing
Gas transmission
Metals and mining
Petrochemical
Pharmaceuticals
Power generation
Pulp and paper
Refining
Semiconductors
Waste treatment

COMPETITORS

EMCOR	Jelec
Fisk Electric	MMR Group
Industrial Specialty Contractors	Motor City Electric
	Pike Corporation

HISTORICAL FINANCIALS

Company Type: Private

Income Statement · FYE: June 30

	REVENUE ($ mil.)	NET INCOME ($ mil.)	NET PROFIT MARGIN	EMPLOYEES
06/18	489	0	—	3,500
06/17	450	0	—	—
06/16	436	0	—	—
06/15	430	0	—	—
Annual Growth	4.4%	—	—	—

2018 Year-End Financials

Return on assets: —
Return on equity: —
Current ratio: 1.80
Cash ($ mil.): 20

THE NORTH CAROLINA MUTUAL WHOLESALE DRUG COMPANY

EXECUTIVES

Ceo, David S Moody
Pres*, Thomas P Davis
SEC*, Michael C Broome
V Pres*, Hal Harrison
Director of Purchasing, James Kellermann
Rx Buyer, John Hall
Contracts, Kevin Cross
Chief Financial Officer, Mike Broome
Accounts Payable, Tammy Roycroft
Auditors: THOMAS KNIGHT TRENT KING AN

LOCATIONS

HQ: THE NORTH CAROLINA MUTUAL WHOLESALE DRUG COMPANY
816 ELLIS RD, DURHAM, NC 277036019
Phone: 919 596-2151
Web: WWW.MUTUALDRUG.COM

HISTORICAL FINANCIALS

Company Type: Private

Income Statement · FYE: March 31

	REVENUE ($ mil.)	NET INCOME ($ mil.)	NET PROFIT MARGIN	EMPLOYEES
03/10	1,035	0	0.0%	160
03/09	1,024	0	0.1%	—
03/08	1,007	1	0.2%	—
Annual Growth	1.4%	(64.1%)	—	—

2010 Year-End Financials

Return on assets: 0.2%
Return on equity: 0.8%
Current ratio: 1.20
Cash ($ mil.): 53

THE OHIO STATE UNIVERSITY WEXNER MEDICAL CENTER

EXECUTIVES

Pres, Michael V Drake
Technical Specialist, Cindy Beery
Information Technology/Interne, Maria Gomez
Manager, Marisha Goldsmith
Information Technology Interne, Bill Speer
Office Coordinator, Laura Lucas
Senior Information Technology, Nancy Hannum
Hungerfoodhealth Program Manag, Amy Alwood
Neuroradiology Specialist, Andrew J Kalnin
Professor, Cheryl Carmin
Project Manager, Chris Heckler

LOCATIONS

HQ: THE OHIO STATE UNIVERSITY WEXNER MEDICAL CENTER
410 W 10TH AVE, COLUMBUS, OH 432101240
Phone: 614 293-8000

HISTORICAL FINANCIALS

Company Type: Private

Income Statement				FYE: June 30
	REVENUE ($ mil.)	NET INCOME ($ mil.)	NET PROFIT MARGIN	EMPLOYEES
06/18	3,106	137	4.4%	35,000
06/16	2,628	126	4.8%	—
Annual Growth	8.7%	4.4%	—	—

2018 Year-End Financials

Return on assets: 4.1%   Cash ($ mil.): 732
Return on equity: 23.0%
Current ratio: 3.80

THE ORANGE COUNTY PUBLIC SCHOOL DISTRICT

EXECUTIVES

Supt, Barbara Jenkins
Coordinator, David Garver
Executive of Information Techn, Giovanna Bravo
Coordinator, Jody Bernier
Information Technology Sap Dev, Gilberto Delgado
Teacher, Grayson Parks
Data Processing Exec, James Leslie
Engineer II, Jose Felix
Engineer, Rob Carlisi
Information Technology Manager, Robert Jones
Social Studies, Sandra Sanders
Auditors: CHERRY BEKAERT LLP ORLANDO

LOCATIONS

HQ: THE ORANGE COUNTY PUBLIC SCHOOL DISTRICT
445 W AMELIA ST, ORLANDO, FL 328011128
Phone: 407 317-3200
Web: WWW.CFLACADEMY.ORG

HISTORICAL FINANCIALS

Company Type: Private

Income Statement				FYE: June 30
	REVENUE ($ mil.)	NET INCOME ($ mil.)	NET PROFIT MARGIN	EMPLOYEES
06/18	2,506	107	4.3%	77
06/17	2,341	(25)	—	—
06/16	2,263	145	6.4%	—
Annual Growth	5.2%	(14.1%)	—	—

2018 Year-End Financials

Return on assets: 1.6%   Cash ($ mil.): 624
Return on equity: 2.6%
Current ratio: —

THE PARSONS CORPORATION

Industrial construction giant Parsons provides engineering construction and other services for corporate institutional and government projects worldwide. The company designs and builds structures such as power plants and dams; provides environmental remediation services including hazardous materials cleanup; and adds improvements to airports rail systems bridges and highways. Parsons has constructed over 10000 miles of roadways worked on more than 4500 bridges assisted on 400 airport projects and destroyed 5100 tons of chemical weapons agents. The employee-owned group was founded in 1944.

Operations

The international engineering firm competes in several major industries and in every major region of the world. Parsons has more than 13000 employees who are involved in over 2200 projects across 50 US states and 25 countries.

Its Infrastructure business is one of the world's largest transportation planning engineering and construction firms with a portfolio that includes rail & transit road & highway bridge & tunnel and aviation projects.

The Federal segment serves the defense environmental intelligence and security markets. It offers systems engineering intelligence services IT facility management and environmental/energy solutions to US government agencies worldwide. The segment has provided staff for space exploration US homeland security cybersecurity and ordinance cleanup.

The Industrial business designs and delivers solutions for complex projects involving water quality and infrastructure as well as industrial environmental and energy needs. It handles everything from vehicle inspection to high-rise construction to energy efficiency advisement.

Geographic Reach

Pasadena California-based Parsons USA has operations in more than 30 states including Alaska and Hawaii as well as the District of Columbia. Overseas Parsons has offices in 25 countries throughout the Middle East Africa Europe and Asia.

Sales and Marketing

Its client roster includes companies from the communications environmental facilities government services and transportation sectors. Some current and past notable clients include Pacific Gas & Electric South Oil Company of Iraq Chevron the City of Seattle Honeywell the US Navy the US Department of Defense and the US Federal Aviation Authority.

Financial Performance

While full financials of the private-held company are not available the company provides high-level information.

In 2017 Parsons generated $3.0 billion in revenue an almost identical amount as the prior year. Its revenue backlog grew marginally and was at $6.8 billion at the end of 2017. Net operating income increased 8% to $156 million slightly above its five-year average.

Strategy

Parsons has been expanding its service offerings on its own and through acquisitions to grow business in recent years. In 2017 the company acquired Williams Electric Company which provides energy infrastructure solutions to the US Government. In early 2018 Parson was selected to provide engineering support for a new bridge connecting Windsor Canada and Detroit Michigan and was also chosen for a design-build contract for Newark (NJ) Airport's Terminal One.

In 2017 Parsons and partner Tekfen Engineering were awarded a contract to build the world's largest suspension bridge (2023 meters) in Turkey. It is a six-year $2.8 billion project with an expected opening date sometime in 2023.

Mergers and Acquisitions

In 2019 Parsons Corporation agreed to acquire QRC from private equity firm DC Capital Partners for $215 million to expand its offerings in the radio frequency environment and signals intelligence market.

Parsons purchased Williams Electric Company in 2017. The firm provides control system integration electrical and general contracting and energy infrastructure solutions to the US Government.

In 2015 the company acquired T.J. Cross Engineers Inc. a private engineering and consulting business specializing in oil and gas to expand Parson's oil and gas expertise and strengthen its energy and chemicals project portfolio.

In April 2014 Parsons acquired Virginia-based Secure Mission Solutions a provider of critical asset protection and cyber security services to the national security and defense communities from the private equity firm Riordan Lewis & Haden Equity Partners. The purchase was consistent with Parson's goal of expanding its national security and defense business. Earlier in April the company purchased Delcan an international engineering planning and management and technology firm serving the transportation market.

EXECUTIVES

Vice Chairman And Managing Director Saudi Arabian Parsons Ltd; Country Manager Saudi Arabia, James R. (Jim) Shappell
Chairman And Ceo, Charles L. (Chuck) Harrington
Group Executive Operations And Risk, Thomas L. (Tom) Roell
President Transportation Group, Todd K. Wager
President Emea, Garold B. (Gary) Adams
President Water And Infrastructure, Anthony F. (Tony) Leketa
Evp Cfo And Treasurer, George L. Ball
President Middle East And North Africa, Jeffrey F. Squires
Evp And Global Business Development Manager Commercial Technology, Brent F. Harvey
Vp And Defense & Security Sector Manager, Kurt H Tripp
Svp And National Security & Defense Division Manager, Biff Lyons
President Government Services Group, Mary Ann Hopkins
Vice President And Regional Manager, David A Brown
Vice President, Robert Mannebach
Senior Vice President, Dean Radeloff
Senior Vice President And General Counsel, Clyde Ellis
Vice President Investor Relations, Spille Joins
Board Member, Curtis Bower
Auditors: PRICEWATERHOUSECOOPERS LLP LO

LOCATIONS

HQ: THE PARSONS CORPORATION
5875 TRINITY PKWY STE 300, CENTREVILLE, VA 201201971
Phone: 703 988-8500
Web: WWW.PARSONS.COM

PRODUCTS/OPERATIONS

Selected Markets and Services
Parsons Commercial Technology
   Advanced manufacturing
   Commercial facilities
   Data management services

Educational facilities
Entertainment
Health care
Industrial environmental remediation
Life sciences
Mission critical facilities
Telecommunications
Vehicle inspection and compliance
Wireless telecommunications systems
Parsons Infrastructure and Technology
Community relations
Construction
Construction management
Design
Engineering
Estimating
Operations
Operator training
Procurement
Program management
Start-up and operations
Parsons Transportation
Aviation
Bridges
Highways
Railroads
Revenue collection and management systems
Systems engineering
Transportation consumer services
Transportation planning
Tunneling
Urban Transit
Parsons Water and Infrastructure
Biosolids management
Combined sewer overflows
Construction/Construction management
Desalination and membrane technology
Design-build
Emergency response support
Environmental planning and restoration
Master planning
Ocean outfalls
Operations and maintenance
Storm water management
Utility tunneling
Wastewater collection systems
Wastewater treatment
Water resources
Water supply and pipelines

COMPETITORS

ABB	Kaiser Group
AECOM	Layne Christensen
ARCADIS	Lend Lease
Bechtel	Louis Berger
Black & Veatch	M. A. Mortenson
Bouygues	Michael Baker
Day & Zimmermann	Mott MacDonald
Fluor	Paragon Project
Gilbane	Resources
Granite Construction	Pernix Group
HOCHTIEF	Peter Kiewit Sons'
Halliburton	RBF Consulting
Hill International	RailWorks
Hyundai Engineering	TIC Holdings
and Construction	Turner Corporation
Jacobs Engineering	Tutor-Saliba
KBR	Vecellio & Grogan
KBR Building Group	

HISTORICAL FINANCIALS

Company Type: Private

Income Statement   FYE: December 31

	REVENUE ($ mil.)	NET INCOME ($ mil.)	NET PROFIT MARGIN	EMPLOYEES
12/18	3,560	239	6.7%	15,633
12/15	846	28	3.4%	—
Annual Growth	61.4%	102.7%	—	—

2018 Year-End Financials

Return on assets: 9.2%   Cash ($ mil.): 280
Return on equity: —
Current ratio: 1.50

THE PENNSYLVANIA HOSPITAL OF THE UNIVERSITY OF PENNSYLVANIA HEALTH SYSTEM

Early to bed early to rise may have made Ben Franklin healthy wealthy and wise. But for those not so healthy he (along with Dr. Thomas Bond) found it wise to establish Pennsylvania Hospital the nation's first such medical institution. The hospital is now a part of the University of Pennsylvania Health System (UPHS) and offers a comprehensive range of medical surgical and diagnostic services to the Philadelphia County area. Housing some 520 beds Pennsylvania Hospital offers specialized care in areas such as orthopedics vascular surgery neurosurgery and obstetrics; it is also a leading teaching hospital and a center for clinical research.

Operations

Pennsylvania Hospital has an average of about 29000 inpatient admissions per year including 5200 births as well as 115000 outpatient and emergency care visits. The medical center has more than 800 physicians on its medical staff. In addition to its extensive medical care services the company conducts medical training programs through its relationship with the University of Pennsylvania School of Medicine. Medical and clinical research programs are conducted with the school and with other research entities including government agencies. The hospital also collaborates with other UPHS entities including the Penn Presbyterian Medical Center and the Hospital of the University of Pennsylvania. The medical center also provides educational services across academic programs inlcuding Clinical Psychology Internship Program Medicine OB/GYN Pathology Radiology Sports Medicine Fellowship Surgery and Vascular Surgery Fellowship.

Financial Performance

For the fiscal year 2014 (ended June 30) Pennsylvania Hospital's revenues increased by 8.4% with a 9% increase in net patient service revenues 94% of total revenues); offset by a 1% decline in other revenues.

The company's net loss for the year decreased by 38% due to higher revenues and a decline in employee benefits paid.

Strategy

To improve the quality of care in the region UPHS is expanding specialist programs at its facilities.

In 2014 Pennsylvania Hospital opened its new Well Mother & Baby Unit which will represent Philadelphia's first all-private maternity suite unit. The new unit is part of Pennsylvania Hospital's $61 million long-range facility master plan and expands the company's offerings by providing private rooms to all of their maternity patients along with an array of obstetrical services from conception to discharge from the hospital following childbirth.

In 2013 UPHS expanded the orthopedic surgery program at Pennsylvania Hospital. The medical center is also enhancing services in fields including stroke care and women's health.

Company Background

The hospital was founded in 1751 by Benjamin Franklin and Dr. Thomas Bond to care for the sick-poor and insane of Philadelphia.

EXECUTIVES

Vice President, Kevin Guynn
Clinical Director, Dan Wilson
Medical Director, Charles Orellana
Medical Records Director, Scott Gilyard
Chair Department Of Neurology, Francisco Gonzalez-scarano
Vice President Operations, Susan Small
Medical Director Department Of Emergency Medicine, Kathleen Nasci
Vice President, Arthur Bartolozzi
Clinical Performance Vice President, John M Bruza
Vice President For Government Relations, Mary R Young
Auditors: LB PRICEWATERHOUSECOOPERS LLP

LOCATIONS

HQ: THE PENNSYLVANIA HOSPITAL OF THE UNIVERSITY OF PENNSYLVANIA HEALTH SYSTEM 800 SPRUCE ST, PHILADELPHIA, PA 191076130
Phone: 215 829-3000
Web: WWW.PENNMEDICINE.ORG

PRODUCTS/OPERATIONS

Selected Centers
ALS Center
Birthing Suite
Center for Bloodless Medicine and Surgery
Crisis Response Center
CyberKnife
Diabetes Education Center
Joan Karnell Cancer Center
Pain Management Center
Parkinson's Disease and Movement Disorders Center
Penn Comprehensive Neurosciences Center
Penn Orthopaedic Institute
Penn Center for Voice
Sports Medicine and Rehabilitation Center
Sleep Disorders Center
Vascular Center
Women's Imaging Center

Selected Services
Behavioral health
Heart and vascular
Neonatology
Neurosurgery
Obstetrics (including high-risk maternal and fetal services)
Orthopedics
Otorhinolaryngology (ENT)
Urology
Vascular medicine/surgery

COMPETITORS

Abington Memorial Hospital
Albert Einstein Healthcare Network
Aria Health
Bryn Mawr Hospital
Children's Hospital of Philadelphia
Crozer-Keystone Health System
Fox Chase Cancer Center
Jefferson Health
North Philadelphia Health System
TUHS
The Magee Memorial Hospital for Convalescents

HISTORICAL FINANCIALS

Company Type: Private

Income Statement

FYE: June 30

	REVENUE ($ mil.)	NET INCOME ($ mil.)	NET PROFIT MARGIN	EMPLOYEES
06/15	579	21	3.7%	2,200
06/14	534	(2)	—	—
06/10	485	27	5.7%	—
06/09	453	0	—	—
Annual Growth	4.2%	—	—	—

2015 Year-End Financials

Return on assets: 3.2%
Return on equity: 4.8%
Current ratio: 0.40

Cash ($ mil.): —

THE PENNSYLVANIA STATE UNIVERSITY

The Pennsylvania State University system is one of the largest state university systems in the US. Penn State has an enrollment of 100000 students; 15000 of them are graduate students. It offers 275 undergraduate and 200 graduate programs at about 25 campuses. The school's oldest and largest campus with about half of the system's undergraduate students is at University Park in central Pennsylvania. Other sites include the Penn State College of Medicine in Hershey Pennsylvania and the Dickinson School of Law in Carlisle Pennsylvania. Penn State contributes about $11.6 billion to the state's economy.

Financial Performance

Penn State had an annual operating budget in 2019-20 of $6.8 billion and an annual endowment of more than $2.5 billion. Its annual research funding is roughly $927 million of which $562 million comes from federal sources.

Strategy

Penn State is focused on fundraising and driving economic growth in the state through new programs tied to the university.

In 2019 the university's fundraising campaign A Greater Penn State for 21st Century Excellence surpassed its goal raising about $372 million in private donations. It marked the third consecutive year that the school raised more than $300 million in new commitments. Overall the campaign has raised about $1 billion toward its goal of $1.6 billion in 2021.

Through its Invent Penn State program the university has opened 21 innovation hubs across Pennsylvania that are designed to foster entrepreneurial and small business development.

Company Background

Chartered in 1855 to apply scientific principles to farming Penn State has conferred almost 800000 degrees since its founding.

The university's storied football program was hit in 2012 with a four year postseason ban the significant reduction of scholarships the vacating of 112 wins and a $60 million fine all stemming from the school's handling of the child molestation scandal involving former coach Jerry Sandusky. However in 2015 the NCAA reversed its decision on the vacating of wins restoring the late head coach Joe Paterno as the winningest coach in major college football history.

EXECUTIVES

Vice President For Student Affairs, Damon Sims
Svp Finance And Business And Treasurer, David J. Gray
Dean University Libraries And Scholarly Communications, Barbara I. Dewey
Dean Undergraduate Education, Robert N. Pangborn
Dean College Of Medicine, A. Craig Hillemeier
Dean College Of Arts And Architecture, Barbara O. Korner
Dean College Of Earth And Mineral Sciences, William E. Easterling
Dean College Of Education, David H. Monk
Dean College Of Health And Human Development, Ann C. (Nan) Crouter
Dean College Of The Liberal Arts, Susan Welch
Dean College Of Nursing, Paula Milone-Nuzzo
Dean Schreyer Honors College, Christian M. M. Brady
President, Eric J. Barron, age 68
Dean Smeal College Of Business, Charles H. Whiteman
Evp And Provost, Nicholas P. Jones
Chief Investment Officer, John Pomeroy
Dean Graduate School, Regina Vasilatos-Younken
Dean College Of Agricultural Sciences, Richard Roush
Dean College Of Communications, Marie Hardin
Dean College Of Engineering, Amr S. Elnashai
Vice President For Commonwealth Campuses, Madlyn Hanes
Department Head Learning And Performance Systems, Roy Clariana
Student Affairs Vice President Financial Officer, Rachael Diamond
Department Head, Mark Morrisson
Senior Vice President For Development And Alumni Relations, Tresa Ciprich
Vice President, Victor Sparrow
Vice President, Sandy Rothrock
Department Head Recreation Park And Tourism Management, Peter Newman
Assistant Vice President For Research And Industrial Partnerships, James Delattre
Vice President Development And Alumni Relations, Orrin Bundy
Department Head And Professor, Karen Thole
Chair Department Of Ophthlmlgy, David Quillen
Department Head, David Stensrud
Associate Vice President, Rachel Pell
Vice President, Katie Bridgens
Vice Chairman, Ira M. Lubert, age 69
Chairman, Keith E. Masser
Board Member, Jim Kustenbauter
Secretary, Hakan Can
Club Secretary, Jessica Baker
Board Member, Wilden Nuss
Board Member, Christine Igoe
Secretary, Bob Corman
Secretary Bookkeeper, Missie Estep
Board Member, Robert Martin
Board Member, Vickie Cunningham
Board Member, Ken Fohringer
Advisory Board Member, Tara Iona
Secretary [printing Services, Pamela Bechtel
Secretary [pulmonary Medicine, Joann Tucker
Auditors: DELOITTE & TOUCHE LLP PHILADE

LOCATIONS

HQ: THE PENNSYLVANIA STATE UNIVERSITY
201 OLD MAIN, UNIVERSITY PARK, PA 168021503
Phone: 814 865-4700

PRODUCTS/OPERATIONS

Selected Colleges

College of Agricultural Sciences
College of Arts and Architecture
Smeal College of Business
College of Communications
College of Earth and Mineral Sciences
College of Education
College of Engineering
College of Health and Human Development
College of Information Sciences and Technology
School of International Affairs
School of Law
College of the Liberal Arts
College of Medicine
School of Nursing
Eberly College of Science
Graduate School
Schreyer Honors College

Selected Campuses

Penn State Abington Penn State Altoona
Penn State Beaver
Penn State Berks
Penn State Brandywine
Penn State DuBois
Penn State Erie The Behrend College
Penn State Fayette The Eberly Campus
Penn State Greater Allegheny
Penn State Harrisburg
Penn State Hazleton
Penn State Lehigh Valley
Penn State Mont Alto
Penn State New Kensington
Penn State Schuylkill
Penn State Shenango
Penn State Wilkes-Barre
Penn State Worthington Scranton
Penn State York

HISTORICAL FINANCIALS

Company Type: Private

Income Statement

FYE: June 30

	REVENUE ($ mil.)	NET INCOME ($ mil.)	NET PROFIT MARGIN	EMPLOYEES
06/18	6,363	1,081	17.0%	44,000
06/17	6,059	635	10.5%	—
06/16	5,764	233	4.0%	—
06/15	5,293	289	5.5%	—
Annual Growth	6.3%	55.1%	—	—

2018 Year-End Financials

Return on assets: 7.2%
Return on equity: 10.9%
Current ratio: 2.80

Cash ($ mil.): 2,089

THE PEPPER COMPANIES INC

EXECUTIVES

Pres-Ceo, J Stanley Pepper
SEC, Richard S Pepper
Exec V Pres-Gen Counsel, Thomas M O'Leary
Exec V Pres, Christopher R Averill
Member, Thomas Hayward
Auditors: DELOITTE & TOUCHE LLP CHICAGO

LOCATIONS

HQ: THE PEPPER COMPANIES INC
643 N ORLEANS ST, CHICAGO, IL 606543608
Phone: 312 266-4703
Web: WWW.THOMASDHAYWARD.COM

HISTORICAL FINANCIALS
Company Type: Private

Income Statement   FYE: September 30

	REVENUE ($ mil.)	NET INCOME ($ mil.)	NET PROFIT MARGIN	EMPLOYEES
09/17	1,119	22	2.0%	1,100
09/16	1,179	21	1.8%	—
09/11	1,177	10	0.9%	—
09/10	911	7	0.9%	—
Annual Growth	3.0%	15.8%	—	—

2017 Year-End Financials
Return on assets: 5.9%
Return on equity: 20.9%
Current ratio: 1.20
Cash ($ mil.): 41

THE PEW CHARITABLE TRUSTS

Green is the grease The Pew Charitable Trusts uses to help not-for-profits run smoothly. Among the nation's largest private foundations it was established in 1948 in memory of Sun Oil founder Joseph Pew and his wife Mary by four of their children. Seven trusts were created between 1948 and 1979 to promote public health and welfare and to strengthen communities. With more than $5 billion in assets it distributes more than $100 million in grants annually to charitable organizations in culture education environment health and human services public policy and religion. The Pew Trusts has strong ties to Philadelphia and allocates a portion of its grants to programs in that area.

Operations
The non-profit organization also operates through the Pew Center on the States; the Pew Environment Group; the Pew Health Group; and the Pew Research Center. The organization became an independent public charity in 2004.

Geographic Reach
Pew has primary offices in Philadelphia and Washington DC.

Strategy
The Pew Charitable Trusts focuses its efforts on improving public policy informing the public of the latest topics and stimulating civic life mostly in the Philadelphia area. To that end in 2013 Pew announced it will provide almost $8.5 million over the next three years to 46 Philadelphia-area organizations serving some of the area's most disadvantaged children and their families. The aim is to improve the lives of poor children by offering support to instill social and learning skills thereby overcoming obstacles to academic success.

The non-profit organization has a broad reach beyond Philadelphia. Indeed its activities range from evaluating children's dental health policies across the 50 US states to investigating the impact of industrial-scale chicken farming on the nation's land and waterways. The Pew Environment Group is active in protecting boreal forest in Canada and the oceans' shark population through the establishment of shark sanctuaries.

EXECUTIVES

Senior Vice President Communications, Melissa Skolfield
Senior Vice President General Counsel And Corporate Secretary, James McMillan
Vice President Human Resources, Elaine Bowman
Auditors: GRANT THORNTON LLP PHILADELPH

LOCATIONS
HQ: THE PEW CHARITABLE TRUSTS
2005 MARKET ST FL 28, PHILADELPHIA, PA 191037019
Phone: 215 575-9050
Web: WWW.PEWTRUSTS.ORG

PRODUCTS/OPERATIONS

Selected Program Areas
Arts and Culture
Children and Youth
Computers and the Internet
Sentencing and Corrections
Education
Elections
Environment
Family Financial Security
Government Performance
Health
Hispanics in America
Media and Journalism
National Civic Initiatives
Philadelphia Area
Public Opinion
Religion and Public Life
Science
State Policy and Performance

HISTORICAL FINANCIALS
Company Type: Private

Income Statement   FYE: June 30

	REVENUE ($ mil.)	NET INCOME ($ mil.)	NET PROFIT MARGIN	EMPLOYEES
06/17	708	407	57.6%	1,100
06/16	397	77	19.5%	—
Annual Growth	78.4%	426.3%	—	—

2017 Year-End Financials
Return on assets: 6.2%
Return on equity: 6.5%
Current ratio: —
Cash ($ mil.): 10

THE PRESIDENT AND FELLOWS OF HARVARD COLLEGE

Auditors: PRICEWATERHOUSECOOPERS LLP B

LOCATIONS
HQ: THE PRESIDENT AND FELLOWS OF HARVARD COLLEGE
600 ATLANTIC AVE, BOSTON, MA 022102211
Phone: 617 495-1502
Web: WWW.WEBMEDIAUNIVERSITY.COM

HISTORICAL FINANCIALS
Company Type: Private

Income Statement   FYE: June 30

	REVENUE ($ mil.)	NET INCOME ($ mil.)	NET PROFIT MARGIN	EMPLOYEES
06/14	4,408	4,607	104.5%	11,500
06/13	4,214	1,056	25.1%	—
06/12	4,037	(1,446)	—	—
06/09	0	0	—	—
Annual Growth	—	—	—	—

2014 Year-End Financials
Return on assets: 7.2%
Return on equity: 104.5%
Current ratio: —
Cash ($ mil.): 87

THE PRIDDY FOUNDATION

EXECUTIVES
President, David Wolverton
Director, Debbie White

LOCATIONS
HQ: THE PRIDDY FOUNDATION
807 8TH ST STE 1010, WICHITA FALLS, TX 763013310
Phone: 940 723-8720
Web: WWW.PRIDDYFDN.ORG

HISTORICAL FINANCIALS
Company Type: Private

Income Statement   FYE: December 31

	REVENUE ($ mil.)	NET INCOME ($ mil.)	NET PROFIT MARGIN	EMPLOYEES
12/13	8,791	3	0.0%	4
12/12	3	(4)	—	—
12/10	32	27	86.7%	—
12/09	0	0	—	—
Annual Growth	—	—	—	—

2013 Year-End Financials
Return on assets: 2.5%
Return on equity: 2.5%
Current ratio: —
Cash ($ mil.): 14

THE QUEEN'S HEALTH SYSTEMS

EXECUTIVES
Pres-Ceo, Gary A Okamoto
Ceo, Arthur A Ushijima
Exec V Pres, Tracy Woo
Asst Treas, Kanoe Margol
Pres, William G Obana
V Pres, Mark Yamakawa
V Pres, Eric K Martinson
V Pres, Janice Kalanihuia
CIO, Harold Moscho
Coo, Jason C Chang
Senior Corporate Communication, Makana McClellan
Auditors: ERNST & YOUNG US LLP SAN DIEG

LOCATIONS
HQ: THE QUEEN'S HEALTH SYSTEMS
1301 PUNCHBOWL ST, HONOLULU, HI 968132402
Phone: 808 691-5900
Web: WWW.QUEENS.ORG

HISTORICAL FINANCIALS

Company Type: Private

Income Statement

FYE: June 30

	REVENUE ($ mil.)	NET INCOME ($ mil.)	NET PROFIT MARGIN	EMPLOYEES
06/17	1,279	173	13.6%	4,500
06/15	118	7	6.0%	—
06/11	24	3	14.2%	—
06/10	25	5	22.4%	—
Annual Growth	75.2%	63.1%	—	—

2017 Year-End Financials

Return on assets: 6.9%
Return on equity: 11.3%
Current ratio: 4.90

Cash ($ mil.): 80

HISTORICAL FINANCIALS

Company Type: Private

Income Statement

FYE: June 30

	REVENUE ($ mil.)	NET INCOME ($ mil.)	NET PROFIT MARGIN	EMPLOYEES
06/18	3,833	(197)	—	12,980
06/17	3,728	77	2.1%	—
06/16	3,451	72	2.1%	—
06/10	2,261	337	14.9%	—
Annual Growth	6.8%	—	—	—

2018 Year-End Financials

Return on assets: (-2.6%)
Return on equity: (-11.9%)
Current ratio: 1.50

Cash ($ mil.): 133

THE REGENTS OF THE UNIVERSITY OF COLORADO

The University of Colorado System spans four campuses and some 60000 students. The Boulder campus home to about 30000 students provides more than 2500 courses in 150-plus fields through nine colleges and schools. The University of Colorado at Denver has an enrollment of more than 14000 and has 120 study programs at a dozen schools and its nearby Anschutz Medical Campus serves more than 500000 patients annually. The smallest campus University of Colorado at Colorado Springs has six colleges with about 10000 students and offers nearly 60 undergraduate graduate uate and doctoral degree programs. The system which began in Boulder as the University of Colorado in 1876 boasts more than 4000 faculty members.

EXECUTIVES

Managing Director Center For Science And Technology Policy Research, Bobbie Klein
Assistant Vice President Risk Management, Terry Lee
Vice President Of Programming, Crystal Watson
Vice President Of Administration, David Jacobson
Board Member, Ally Ostrowski
Board Of Regents Member, Peter Steinhauer
Treasurer, David Lee
Board Member System Staff Council, Nicole Combs
Board Member, Walt Pounds
Auditors: CLIFTONLARSONALLEN LLP GREENW

LOCATIONS

HQ: THE REGENTS OF THE UNIVERSITY OF COLORADO
3100 MARINE ST STE 48157, BOULDER, CO 803031058
Phone: 303 735-6624

PRODUCTS/OPERATIONS

Selected Campuses
University
University of Colorado - Colorado Springs
University
University of Colorado Anschutz Medical Campus

THE RESEARCH FOUNDATION FOR THE STATE UNIVERSITY OF NEW YORK

The Research Foundation of State University of New York (The Research Foundation) collects and administers research and education grants from state and federal governments corporations and foundations on behalf of the 24-campus State University of New York known as SUNY. The foundation has formed several affiliated divisions — including Long Island High Technology Incubator and NanoTech Resources — to operate research facilities encourage scientific collaboration and otherwise facilitate research for the university. It facilitates research for studies such as engineering and nanotechnology; physical sciences and medicine; life sciences and medicine; social sciences; and computer and information sciences.

Operations

The foundation manages SUNY's research portfolio. Research Foundation administrators help SUNY faculty students and staff through every step of the research grant process allowing them to focus on their work and ensuring compliance with university grant sponsor and government requirements.

The Research Foundation protects SUNY's intellectual property (SUNY ranks among the nation's top faculty to commercialize their inventions for the public good).

The organization makes strategic investments to maximize the collective impact of SUNY research to drive investment and job growth. SUNY's Networks of Excellence assemble scientists and scholars from all campuses to collaborate on research projects in areas ranging from advanced manufacturing and energy to health and the humanities.

The Research Foundation is an integral partner in the execution and administration of the START-UP NY initiative to transform SUNY campuses and university communities across the state into tax-free communities for new and expanding businesses.

The organization funds its operations primarily from recoveries of indirect costs provided from grants and contracts.

Geographic Reach

The Research Foundation comprises a central office and operating units at 31 campus locations across New York State.

Financial Performance

The Research Foundation reported $1 billion in revenues in 2014 compared to $1.07 billion in 2013. The primary reason for the decline was due to decreased sales from federal grants and contracts private grants and contracts and investment income.

Investment income/loss included dividends and interest realized and unrealized gains and losses and equity adjustments from the foundation's investment in the Brookhaven Science Associates partnership.

The organization's net income decreased by $30 million in 2014 due to lower revenues and increased other program expenses.

Net cash provided by the operating activities increased by $127.7 million due to changes in interest payments on capital debts and other payments.

Strategy

In 2014 Iliad Neurosciences a company focused on the development of innovative approaches to diagnosing and treating Autism Spectrum Disorders entered into an Exclusive License Agreement with The Research Foundation for The State University of New York. Under this deal Iliad will provide a new biomarker to identify an abnormality in folate transport to the brain associated with susceptibility to Autism Spectrum Disorders. . The identification of this defect could lead to a targeted therapy that may improve the transport of folate to the brain in children and to the fetus in pregnant women who test positive for the folate receptor autoantibody.

Company Background

The Research Foundation was established in 1951 just three years after SUNY itself.

EXECUTIVES

Office Of The Vice President For Research, Edward Zablocki
Associate Vice President For Sponsored Programs Human Resources, Christy Spadaro
Associate Vice President For Research Administration, Joseph Barabino
Vice President And Chief Of Suny Police Security And Safety Management, Tom Louis
Assistant Vice President For Benefits And Leave Administration, Katie Tynan
Associate Vice President For Marketing And Media Outreach, Kristin Haacker
Assistant Vice President Metrology, Steve Novak
Assistant Vice President Special Events And Programs, Laura Wheeler
Assistant Vice President For Student Affairs And Student Recruitment And Public Outreach, Diana Dumesnil
Senior Vice President, Ronald Goldblatt
Assistant Vice President Business Development And Economic Outreach, Joseph Alteri
Vice President, Patricia Bucklin
Auditors: KPMG LLP BOSTON MA

LOCATIONS

HQ: THE RESEARCH FOUNDATION FOR THE STATE UNIVERSITY OF NEW YORK
35 STATE ST, ALBANY, NY 122072826
Phone: 518 434-7000

PRODUCTS/OPERATIONS

2014 Revenues

	% of total
Federal grants & contracts	50
Private grants & contracts	23
State grants & contracts	17
Investments	2
Inventions & licenses	2
Local grants & contracts	2
Investment income	0
Gifts capital gifts & grants	0
Other	4
Total	**100**

HISTORICAL FINANCIALS

Company Type: Private

Income Statement				FYE: June 30
	REVENUE ($ mil.)	NET INCOME ($ mil.)	NET PROFIT MARGIN	EMPLOYEES
06/13	1,079	42	3.9%	16,330
06/12	1,114	12	1.2%	—
06/09	985	(71)	—	—
Annual Growth	2.3%	—	—	—

2013 Year-End Financials

Return on assets: 7.2%
Return on equity: —
Current ratio: 1.30
Cash ($ mil.): —

THE RUDOLPH/LIBBE COMPANIES INC

The corporate model of a conglomerate composed of independent unrelated businesses is not for The Rudolph/Libbe Companies. The group of companies can build or oversee real estate projects (general contractor Rudolph/Libbe Inc.); perform mechanical electrical and structural work (GEM Industrial); and then represent those properties in the market (RLWest Properties). Operating in the Ohio/Michigan corridor the group provides site selection design/build and construction management. Its portfolio includes industrial retail municipal residential educational health care and mixed-use projects. Fritz and Phil Rudolph and their cousin Allan Libbe founded flagship subsidiary Rudolph/Libbe Inc. in 1955.

EXECUTIVES

Vice President Mechanical, Scott Kepp
Auditors: REHMANN ROBSON TOLEDO OH

LOCATIONS

HQ: THE RUDOLPH/LIBBE COMPANIES INC
6494 LATCHA RD, WALBRIDGE, OH 434659788
Phone: 419 241-5000
Web: WWW.RLGBUILDS.COM

COMPETITORS

Albert M. Higley	Messer Construction
Atlas Industrial	Ruhlin
Holdings	Skanska USA Building
Danis	

HISTORICAL FINANCIALS

Company Type: Private

Income Statement				FYE: December 31
	REVENUE ($ mil.)	NET INCOME ($ mil.)	NET PROFIT MARGIN	EMPLOYEES
12/18	573	16	2.8%	600
12/17	567	20	3.5%	—
12/16	502	23	4.8%	—
12/15	425	16	3.8%	—
Annual Growth	10.5%	(0.2%)	—	—

2018 Year-End Financials

Return on assets: 7.4%
Return on equity: 25.9%
Current ratio: 1.30
Cash ($ mil.): 16

THE SAINT CLOUD HOSPITAL

EXECUTIVES

Pres, Craig Broman
Cfo*, Greg Klugherz
Coordinator, Kevin Mentzer
Chief of Medicine, Richard Jolkovsky
Chief of Medicine, Peter Charvat
Administrative Assistant, Lisa Villarreal
Psychiatrist, Gavin P Meany
Board Member, Betsy Horsch
Analyst, Chris Stavros
Chief of Internal Medicine, Joe Mercuri
Research, Kim Hintermeister
Auditors: MCGLADREY LLP MINNEAPOLIS MN

LOCATIONS

HQ: THE SAINT CLOUD HOSPITAL
1406 6TH AVE N, SAINT CLOUD, MN 563031901
Phone: 320 251-2700
Web: WWW.CENTRACARE.COM

HISTORICAL FINANCIALS

Company Type: Private

Income Statement				FYE: June 30
	REVENUE ($ mil.)	NET INCOME ($ mil.)	NET PROFIT MARGIN	EMPLOYEES
06/18	864	39	4.5%	4,957
06/16	756	3	0.5%	—
06/15	767	170	22.2%	—
06/14	754	72	9.6%	—
Annual Growth	3.5%	(14.3%)	—	—

2018 Year-End Financials

Return on assets: 3.2%
Return on equity: 5.3%
Current ratio: 1.90
Cash ($ mil.): 33

THE SALVATION ARMY

EXECUTIVES

Pres-Trus, William A Bamford III
President-Trustee*, William A Bamfordiii
V Pre-Trustee*, Kenneth O Johnson Jr
Chb-Trustee*, David E Jeffrey
Treasurer-Trustee*, Donald W Lance
Secretary*, Michael J Southwick
Fist Asst Treas-Trustee*, D Sue Foley
Second Asst Treas*, Thomas O Henson
Asst SEC-Legal*, Richard D Allen
Asst Sec-Property*, Jorge E Diaz
Second Asst Sec-Property*, Adolph M Orlando
Auditors: GRANT THORNTON LLP NEW YORK

LOCATIONS

HQ: THE SALVATION ARMY
440 W NYACK RD OFC, WEST NYACK, NY 109941739
Phone: 845 620-7200

HISTORICAL FINANCIALS

Company Type: Private

Income Statement				FYE: September 30
	REVENUE ($ mil.)	NET INCOME ($ mil.)	NET PROFIT MARGIN	EMPLOYEES
09/16	859	(224)	—	10,447
09/12	1,034	207	20.0%	—
09/09	782	(96)	—	—
09/08	288	(463)	—	—
Annual Growth	14.6%	—	—	—

2016 Year-End Financials

Return on assets: (-5.4%)
Return on equity: (-9.7%)
Current ratio: 0.30
Cash ($ mil.): 122

THE SALVATION ARMY

EXECUTIVES

Chb, David Jeffrey
Pres*, Donald Bell
Treas*, James Seiler
Assis Treas*, Stephen Ellis
SEC*, Ward Matthews
V Pres*, Ralph Bukiewicz
MBR*, Susan Bukiewicz
MBR*, William Mockabee
Cfo*, Alberto Flores
Senior Manager, Colonel B Bailey
Member, Melanie M Brackett

LOCATIONS

HQ: THE SALVATION ARMY
1424 NORTHEAST EXPY NE, BROOKHAVEN, GA 303292088
Phone: 404 728-1300
Web: WWW.SALVATIONARMYUSA.ORG

HISTORICAL FINANCIALS

Company Type: Private

Income Statement				FYE: September 30
	REVENUE ($ mil.)	NET INCOME ($ mil.)	NET PROFIT MARGIN	EMPLOYEES
09/09	830	(220)	—	16,168
09/08	533	(336)	—	—
09/07	1,185	318	26.9%	—
Annual Growth	(16.3%)	—	—	—

Return on assets: (-6.7%)   Cash ($ mil.): 89
Return on equity: (-8.6%)
Current ratio: 1.30

THE SCHOOL BOARD OF MIAMI-DADE COUNTY

EXECUTIVES

Chb, Perla Tabares Hantman
Staff, Martin A Berkowitz
Administrative Assistant, Ana Herrera
Senior Programmer Analyst, Fred Young
Administrative Director, Tabitha Fazzino
Assistant, Juan Campbell
Auditors: MCGLADREY LLP MIAMI FLORIDA

LOCATIONS

HQ: THE SCHOOL BOARD OF MIAMI-DADE COUNTY
1450 NE 2ND AVE, MIAMI, FL 331321308
Phone: 305 995-1000
Web: WWW.YOURCHOICEMIAMI.ORG

HISTORICAL FINANCIALS
Company Type: Private

Income Statement   FYE: June 30

	REVENUE ($ mil.)	NET INCOME ($ mil.)	NET PROFIT MARGIN	EMPLOYEES
06/18	3,868	(46)	—	9
06/17	3,728	448	12.0%	—
06/16	3,631	136	3.8%	—
06/13	3,302	(127)	—	—
Annual Growth	3.2%	—	—	—

2018 Year-End Financials
Return on assets: (-0.7%)   Cash ($ mil.): 403
Return on equity: (-81.4%)
Current ratio: 1.70

THE SCHOOL BOARD OF SEMINOLE COUNTY FLORIDA

EXECUTIVES

Chm, Amy Lockhart
Poc*, Todd Seis
Prin*, Tina Calderone
Prin*, Karen Almond
Prin*, Abby Sanchez
Prin, Walt Griffin
Teacher, Dunlap Nancy
Teacher, Slaughter Patria
Teacher, Cost Lisa
Secretary, Debbie Parks
Social Studies, Kirby Kristen

LOCATIONS

HQ: THE SCHOOL BOARD OF SEMINOLE COUNTY
FLORIDA
400 E LAKE MARY BLVD, SANFORD, FL 327737125
Phone: 407 320-0050
Web: WWW.SCPS.K12.FL.US

HISTORICAL FINANCIALS
Company Type: Private

Income Statement   FYE: June 30

	REVENUE ($ mil.)	NET INCOME ($ mil.)	NET PROFIT MARGIN	EMPLOYEES
06/13	514	(3)	—	7,805
06/12	504	(15)	—	—
06/11	569	3	0.6%	—
Annual Growth	(5.0%)	—	—	—

2013 Year-End Financials
Return on assets: (-0.4%)   Cash ($ mil.): 5
Return on equity: (-0.7%)
Current ratio: —

THE SCHOOL DISTRICT OF COLLIER COUNTY FL

EXECUTIVES

Supt, Kamela Patton
Dir*, Nancy Sirko
Coordinator, Cedar Kraus
Payroll Staff, Beatrice Hernandez
Information Specialist, Becker Steven
Teacher, Brandon Heimberger
Teacher, Dana Henry
Coordinator, Evelyn Rivera
Coordinator, Sandra Stockdale
Teacher, Ted Borduas
Technology Specialist, Sheri Wiseman
Auditors: CHERRY BEKAERT & HOLLAND LL

LOCATIONS

HQ: THE SCHOOL DISTRICT OF COLLIER COUNTY FL
5775 OSCEOLA TRL, NAPLES, FL 341090919
Phone: 239 377-0001
Web: WWW.COLLIERSCHOOLS.COM

HISTORICAL FINANCIALS
Company Type: Private

Income Statement   FYE: June 30

	REVENUE ($ mil.)	NET INCOME ($ mil.)	NET PROFIT MARGIN	EMPLOYEES
06/11	533	13	2.5%	6,000
06/09	549	(13)	—	—
06/08	612	(7)	—	—
06/06	464	34	7.5%	—
Annual Growth	2.8%	(17.5%)	—	—

2011 Year-End Financials
Return on assets: 0.9%   Cash ($ mil.): 340
Return on equity: 1.5%
Current ratio: —

THE SCHOOL DISTRICT OF OSCEOLA COUNTY FL

EXECUTIVES

Supt, Melba Luciano
Cbfo*, Bill Collins
Principal, George Sullivan
Coordinator, Jean Riggs
Public Information Director, Dana Lee Schafer
Accounting Staff, Pam Fordham
Management Info Dir, Robert Curran Sr
Senior Buyer, Megan Pearison
Executive Director, Janice Franceschi
Editor, Laura Elam
Tech Prep Coordinator, Melanie Stefanowicz
Auditors: MOORE STEPHENS LOVELACE PA

LOCATIONS

HQ: THE SCHOOL DISTRICT OF OSCEOLA COUNTY
FL
817 BILL BECK BLVD, KISSIMMEE, FL 347444492
Phone: 407 870-4600
Web: WWW.FOURCORNERSCHARTER.ORG

HISTORICAL FINANCIALS
Company Type: Private

Income Statement   FYE: June 30

	REVENUE ($ mil.)	NET INCOME ($ mil.)	NET PROFIT MARGIN	EMPLOYEES
06/18	695	13	2.0%	6,250
06/17	638	117	18.4%	—
06/16	601	37	6.2%	—
06/15	545	6	1.3%	—
Annual Growth	8.5%	25.6%	—	—

2018 Year-End Financials
Return on assets: 1.1%   Cash ($ mil.): 132
Return on equity: 2.4%
Current ratio: —

THE SCHOOL DISTRICT OF PHILADELPHIA

EXECUTIVES

Spdt, William Hite Jr
Cfo*, Matthew E Stanski
Food Director, Wayne T Grasela
Teacher, Abram Taber
Computer Specialist, Danielle Schultz
Webmaster, Ezra Miller
Teacher, Julia Smith
Director, Majeedah Scott
Personnel Assistant, Michelle Stokes
Health, Brandon Coleman
Health Coordinator, Paula Miller
Auditors: CHRISTY BRADY CPA PHILADELPH

LOCATIONS

HQ: THE SCHOOL DISTRICT OF PHILADELPHIA
440 N BROAD ST, PHILADELPHIA, PA 191304090
Phone: 215 400-4000
Web: WWW.PHILASD.ORG

HISTORICAL FINANCIALS
Company Type: Private

Income Statement
FYE: June 30

	REVENUE ($ mil.)	NET INCOME ($ mil.)	NET PROFIT MARGIN	EMPLOYEES
06/18	3,473	210	6.1%	21,065
06/17	3,250	220	6.8%	—
06/16	3,064	23	0.8%	—
06/11	2,930	(259)	—	—
Annual Growth	2.5%	—	—	—

2018 Year-End Financials
Return on assets: 5.7% Cash ($ mil.): 190
Return on equity: —
Current ratio: —

THE SCHOOL DISTRICT OF WEST PALM BEACH COUNTY

EXECUTIVES

Coordinator, Elizabeth Parsley
Human Resources, Dionne Jelks
Administrative Secretary, Michelle Martin
Manager, Nancy Reese
Coordinator, Karensa Wright
Staff, Linda Esta
Assistant General Counsel, Bruce Harris
Coordinator, Noemi Moreno
Coordinator, Allyson Greene-Campbell
Technician, Edith Brown
Reading Teacher, Amy McGregor
Auditors: RSM US LLP WEST PALM BEACH F

LOCATIONS

HQ: THE SCHOOL DISTRICT OF WEST PALM BEACH COUNTY
3300 FOREST HILL BLVD, WEST PALM BEACH, FL 334065813
Phone: 561 434-8747
Web: WWW.PALMBEACHSCHOOLS.ORG

HISTORICAL FINANCIALS
Company Type: Private

Income Statement
FYE: June 30

	REVENUE ($ mil.)	NET INCOME ($ mil.)	NET PROFIT MARGIN	EMPLOYEES
06/18	2,307	136	5.9%	29,656
06/17	2,146	78	3.7%	—
06/16	1,986	64	3.2%	—
06/15	1,903	(61)	—	—
Annual Growth	6.6%	—	—	—

2018 Year-End Financials
Return on assets: 2.8% Cash ($ mil.): 959
Return on equity: 9.2%
Current ratio: —

THE SCOULAR COMPANY

The Scoular Company doesn't move food from farm to table but it does handle a good portion of the trip. The company buys sells stores handles and transports agricultural products (mainly grains) worldwide. It gets the mainstays of farming — corn millet sorghum soybeans and wheat — where they need to go. The company transports these products via rail truck barge and seagoing container vessels. Scoular's other divisions offer fishmeal products for farm-animal pet and aquaculture feeds; ingredients for food manufacturers; and renewable fuels as well as a host of risk management logistics and product-related services. It has customers worldwide.

Operations
Through more than 100 independent business units Scoular operates a grain marketing network that handles more than 100 products and some 1 billion bushels of grain annually. Ocean freight is transported via its TSC Container Freight business.

In addition to buying selling handling and transporting grain and other products the company offers risk management services and product-related services such as cleaning bagging sorting packaging and certifying.

Geographic Reach
Omaha-based Scoular and its affiliates have operations in about 20 US states and three Canadian provinces as well as in Mexico Argentina Paraguay Uruguay China and Singapore. The company has about two dozen offices and some 80 storage handling and processing facilities.

It serves markets in some 50 countries.

Sales and Marketing
Scoular serves local regional national and international customers in the food feed and renewable fuel markets.

Financial Performance
As a non-public company Scoular doesn't publicly release full financials. It reported 2018 revenue however of $4.4 billion.

Strategy
Scoular has built itself out piece by piece scouring the landscape for businesses that fit into its portfolio through acquisition or partnership. In 2018 Scoular invested in Ohio-based Rogers Grain to jointly grow the companies' specialty corn and soybean business.

Mergers and Acquisitions
In mid-2018 Scoular acquired the assets of Colorado-based Farmers Grain (dba Kontny Grain). The deal adds 1.7 million bushels of storage capacity.

Company Background
George Scoular founded the George Scoular Grain & Lumber Company in Nebraska in 1892. It was family-owned until 1967 when it was sold to a group of grain industry executives. It grew through acquisitions and partnerships over the following decades.

EXECUTIVES

Vice President, Randall Foster
Senior Vice President Of Asset Resources, John Heck
Chairman And President, David M. Faith
Svp And Division General Manager, Todd McQueen
Svp And Division General Manager, John Messerich
Cfo, Richard A. (Rick) Cogdill
Ceo, Paul T. Maass
Cio, Jeff Schreiner
Svp And Division General Manager, Bob Ludington
Vice President Finance And Tre, Roger L Barber
Vice President Finance, Omer Sagheer
Senior Vice President And General Counsel, Megan Belcher
Vp Commodity Risk Management, Ed Prosser
Auditors: KPMG LLP OMAHA NEBRASKA

LOCATIONS

HQ: THE SCOULAR COMPANY
2027 DODGE ST STE 200, OMAHA, NE 681021229
Phone: 402 342-3500
Web: WWW.SCOULAR.COM

COMPETITORS

ADM	Excel Maritime Carriers
Andersons	
Bartlett and Company	Louis Dreyfus Group
Bunge Limited	Syntroleum
CHS	TBS International
Cargill	TORM
DeBruce Grain	

HISTORICAL FINANCIALS
Company Type: Private

Income Statement
FYE: May 31

	REVENUE ($ mil.)	NET INCOME ($ mil.)	NET PROFIT MARGIN	EMPLOYEES
05/18	4,486	22	0.5%	801
05/17	4,366	25	0.6%	—
05/16	4,667	(10)	—	—
05/15	234	14	6.0%	—
Annual Growth	167.3%	17.1%	—	—

2018 Year-End Financials
Return on assets: 2.6% Cash ($ mil.): 37
Return on equity: 7.3%
Current ratio: 1.40

THE SIMONS FOUNDATION INC

EXECUTIVES

Pres, Marilyn Simons
V Pres*, Mark Silver
Chb*, James H Simons
Cfo*, Marlow Kee
Coo*, Euan Robertson
Information Technology Manager, Chris Fleisch
Vice-President Administration, Marion Greenup
Director, Apoorva Mandavilli
Accounting Manager, Lawrence Bianco
Program Manager, Elizabeth Roy
Accountant, Jan Fernandez

LOCATIONS

HQ: THE SIMONS FOUNDATION INC
160 5TH AVE FL 7, NEW YORK, NY 100107037
Phone: 646 654-0066
Web: WWW.SIMONSFOUNDATION.ORG

HISTORICAL FINANCIALS

Company Type: Private

Income Statement
FYE: December 31

	ASSETS ($ mil.)	NET INCOME ($ mil.)	INCOME AS % OF ASSETS	EMPLOYEES
12/17	3,297	236	7.2%	350
12/16	3,027	(39)	—	—
12/15	2,632	(211)	—	—
12/14	2,358	(92)	—	—
Annual Growth	11.8%	—	—	—

2017 Year-End Financials

Return on assets: 7.2%
Return on equity: 9.3%
Sales ($ mil): 645

THE SOMMERS COMPANY

EXECUTIVES

Pres, Jimmy F Sommers
SEC-Treas, Sarah W Sommers
V Pres, Wynelle Sommers
Coo, Randy Sommers
Cntrl, Michael Dionne
Controller, Mike Dionne
Auditors: TJS DEEMER DANA LLP SAVANNAH

LOCATIONS

HQ: THE SOMMERS COMPANY
1000 SOMMERS BLVD, RICHMOND HILL, GA
313248817
Phone: 800 654-6466
Web: WWW.SOMMERSOIL.COM

HISTORICAL FINANCIALS

Company Type: Private

Income Statement
FYE: June 30

	REVENUE ($ mil.)	NET INCOME ($ mil.)	NET PROFIT MARGIN	EMPLOYEES
06/18	454	1	0.3%	30
06/16	296	1	0.4%	—
06/15	426	1	0.3%	—
06/14	587	1	0.2%	—
Annual Growth	(6.2%)	(0.7%)	—	—

2018 Year-End Financials

Return on assets: 3.8%
Return on equity: 7.5%
Current ratio: 1.40
Cash ($ mil.): 5

THE SOUTHEASTERN CONFERENCE

EXECUTIVES

Commissioner, Greg Sankey
Commissioner*, Michael Flive
Commissioner*, Mark Womack
Associate Media Relations Dire, Tammy Wilson
Director Ticket Operations, John Gibson

Auditors: BARFIELD MURPHY SHANK & SMITH

LOCATIONS

HQ: THE SOUTHEASTERN CONFERENCE
2201 RICHARD ARRINGTN JR, BIRMINGHAM, AL
352031103
Phone: 205 949-8960
Web: WWW.SECSPORTS.COM

HISTORICAL FINANCIALS

Company Type: Private

Income Statement
FYE: August 31

	REVENUE ($ mil.)	NET INCOME ($ mil.)	NET PROFIT MARGIN	EMPLOYEES
08/16	639	17	2.7%	30
08/15	527	17	3.3%	—
08/14	325	2	0.7%	—
08/13	314	(3)	—	—
Annual Growth	26.7%	—	—	—

2016 Year-End Financials

Return on assets: 20.5%
Return on equity: 20.5%
Current ratio: —
Cash ($ mil.): 26

THE STELLAR COMPANIES INC

EXECUTIVES

Ceo, Mike Santarone
Pres-Coo*, Brian Kappele
V Pres Fin*, Clint Pyle
Cfo*, Scott V Witt
Project Coordinator, Daniel Weibelt
Project Manager Software Solut, Christine Shelley
Civil Engineer, Ron Fournier
Auditors: RSM US LLP JACKSONVILLE FLOR

LOCATIONS

HQ: THE STELLAR COMPANIES INC
2900 HARTLEY RD, JACKSONVILLE, FL 322578221
Phone: 904 899-9393
Web: WWW.STELLAR.NET

HISTORICAL FINANCIALS

Company Type: Private

Income Statement
FYE: September 30

	REVENUE ($ mil.)	NET INCOME ($ mil.)	NET PROFIT MARGIN	EMPLOYEES
09/17	508	7	1.6%	600
09/16	285	6	2.3%	—
09/15	336	2	0.9%	—
09/14	341	0	0.1%	—
Annual Growth	14.3%	212.5%	—	—

2017 Year-End Financials

Return on assets: 5.7%
Return on equity: 74.4%
Current ratio: 1.00
Cash ($ mil.): 16

THE SUNDT COMPANIES INC

Sundt has put its stamp on the Southwest. Through Sundt Construction and other subsidiaries The Sundt Companies offers preconstruction construction management general contracting and design/build services for commercial government and industrial clients. Projects include commercial buildings military bases light rails airports and schools. It builds mostly in Arizona Nevada California New Mexico and Texas. Sundt has overseen some notable projects including the development of the top-secret town of Los Alamos New Mexico (where the first atomic bomb was built) and the relocation of the London Bridge to Arizona. Sundt Companies was formed in 1998 as a holding company for various company interests.

Operations

The Sundt Companies performs its work through various divisions: Industrial; concrete; building; heavy civil; and federal. The building division is divided into geographic regions: California; Southwest; and Texas; as well as a Federal Division.

Strategy

Like its peers Sundt is dealing with the lingering effects of the construction downturn that greatly impacted the Southwest. (The company lost more than $750 million in government projects due to state budget constraints.) Indeed Sundt anticipates that it may be 2015 before it sees a strong economy for construction. In the meantime the firm has relied on a healthy backlog of projects and diversification efforts to sustain its business. To that end it entered new geographic markets in 2012 including New Mexico where it is building new dorms at New Mexico State University. It also recently began construction of new schools in El Paso Texas its first in the city. The firm formed a new Criminal Justice Specialization group in 2012 to win courthouse and detention facility work.

Sundt also has focused on making investments in improving technology used in the preconstruction and construction process. It also grew its self-perform work capabilities when it acquired Foley Masonry and Tile Inc. in 2010. Also that year Sundt opened a new office in San Antonio as part of the company's growth plan. The company expanded once again in 2011. It opened new offices to support projects in New Mexico North Carolina and Texas.

EXECUTIVES

Pres-Ceo, Mike Hoover
Svp/Cfo*, Kevin M Burnett
Sr V Pres-Gen Counsel*, Ronald Stuff
Executive Vice President Chief, Raymond C Bargull
Auditors: MAYER HOFFMAN & MCCANN

LOCATIONS

HQ: THE SUNDT COMPANIES INC
2015 W RIVER RD STE 101, TUCSON, AZ 857041676
Phone: 520 750-4600
Web: WWW.SUNDT.COM

PRODUCTS/OPERATIONS

Selected Projects

Aviation
Commercial buildings
Concrete construction
Courthouses
Federal government

Hospitality
Hospitals & health care
Infrastructure & site development
Juvenile detention facilities
K-12 schools
Mining
Mission critical/Data center
Municipal buildings
Parking structures
Power plants & alternative energy
Prisons
Research & development facilities
Residential
Retail
Roads & bridges
Student housing & dormitories
Universities & community colleges
Water & wastewater treatment

Selected Services

Build-to-suit
Construction manager at risk (CMAR)
Construction/program manager
Design-bid-build/general contractor (DBB)
Preconstruction
Self-perform contracting

COMPETITORS

Austin Industries	McCarthy Building
CORE Construction	Meadow Valley
Charles Pankow	O'Neil Industries
Builders	Peter Kiewit Sons'
DPR Construction	Swinerton
Granite Construction	Tutor Perini
Hunt Construction	Weitz
Kitchell	

HISTORICAL FINANCIALS

Company Type: Private

Income Statement				FYE: September 30
	REVENUE ($ mil.)	NET INCOME ($ mil.)	NET PROFIT MARGIN	EMPLOYEES
09/18	1,432	0	—	1,800
09/17	1,134	0	—	—
09/16*	813	0	—	—
06/16	0	0	—	—
Annual Growth	—	—	—	—

*Fiscal year change

2018 Year-End Financials

Return on assets: —
Return on equity: —
Current ratio: 1.30

Cash ($ mil.): 82

THE TOLEDO HOSPITAL

One of the region's largest acute-care facilities The Toledo Hospital provides medical care to the residents of northwestern Ohio and southeastern Michigan. Boasting nearly 800 beds the facility offers several specialties and services including the Jobst Vascular Center which provides cardiac and vascular services in conjunction with The University of Michigan. The Toledo Hospital which shares a medical complex with the Toledo Children's Hospital also operates trauma emergency outpatient arthritis sleep disorder and women's health centers. The Toledo Hospital is a member of Toledo-based ProMedica Health System a mission-based not-for-profit healthcare organization formed in 1986.

EXECUTIVES

Nursing Director, Deana Sievert
Senior Vice President Academic Affairs, Robert Fredrick

LOCATIONS

HQ: THE TOLEDO HOSPITAL
2142 N COVE BLVD, TOLEDO, OH 436063896
Phone: 419 291-4000

PRODUCTS/OPERATIONS

Selected Services

Arthritis and Osteoporosis Center
Bariatric Surgery
Behavioral Health and Psychiatric Services
Breast Care Center
Cancer Care
Critical Care
Diabetes
Dialysis
Emergency Services
Endoscopy Services
Fertility Services
Heart Care
Hemophilia Outpatient Clinic
Hyperbaric Medicine
Laboratory Services
Lactation Services
Maternal - Fetal Medicine
Mom & Me Boutique
Neurology
Neurophysiology
OccuHealth
Orthopaedics
Outpatient Surgery
Palliative Care
Radiology / Imaging Services
Rehabilitation Services
Respiratory Care
Sleep Medicine
Surgical Services
Trauma Services
Urology /
Vascular Services
Women's Services

COMPETITORS

Firelands Regional Health System	Tenet Healthcare
Mercy Health Partners Toledo	Trinity Health (Novi) University of Michigan Health System
Sylvania Franciscan Health	

HISTORICAL FINANCIALS

Company Type: Private

Income Statement				FYE: December 31
	REVENUE ($ mil.)	NET INCOME ($ mil.)	NET PROFIT MARGIN	EMPLOYEES
12/17	854	(115)	—	5,586
12/14	745	20	2.8%	—
12/09	635	19	3.0%	—
12/08	548	33	6.1%	—
Annual Growth	5.0%	—	—	—

2017 Year-End Financials

Return on assets: (-8.1%)
Return on equity: (-35.3%)
Current ratio: 0.30

Cash ($ mil.): 83

THE TRUSTEES OF PRINCETON UNIVERSITY

This prince's kingdom is covered with ivy. As one of the eight elite Ivy League schools in the Northeastern US Princeton is a research university that offers students degrees across 34 departments and 47 interdisciplinary certificate programs. It boasts more than 8000 students (5300 undergraduate and 2700 graduate students). The highly selective school which enjoys an undergraduate student-faculty ratio of 6:1 admits about 8% of its total applicants. Nobel Prize winners associated with Princeton include Woodrow Wilson writer Toni Morrison and physicist Richard Feynman. One of the nation's wealthiest universities Princeton has an endowment of more than $16 billion.

Operations

The Princeton campus comprises six residential colleges that are organized by grade level (freshmen sophomores juniors and seniors).

The university which is supported by 1140 faculty members that include visitors and part-time appointments operates three schools: the School of Architecture School of Engineering and Applied Science and the Woodrow Wilson School of Public and International Affairs. Princeton also has a large research base with some $200 million in funding per year primarily from federal grants. Its plasma physics research laboratory has a sizable research contract with the federal government.

Geographic Reach

Located in Princeton New Jersey Princeton's campus includes some 180 buildings that cover about 500 acres.

Sales and Marketing

Princeton sources its students from more than 98 countries. International graduate students hail primarily from Canada China India Germany and Korea. Some 60% of the university's undergraduate students receive financial aid. The average undergraduate financial aid reward for the Class of 2016 is $39700.

Financial Performance

For an Ivy League university with a top reputation in the US and internationally Princeton has not suffered as a result of turbulent economic conditions as much as some of its lower-ranked peers.

Company Background

Founded in 1746 as the College of New Jersey Princeton is the fourth-oldest college in the nation. In 1756 the college was moved to Nassau Hall which served as the temporary capitol of the US in 1783 and is still part of the Princeton campus.

EXECUTIVES

Vp Finance And Treasurer, Carolyn N. Ainslie
President, Christopher L. Eisgruber
Dean Admission, Janet L. Rapelye
Dean Undergraduate Students, Kathleen Deignan
President Princeton University Investment Co., Andrew K. Golden
Dean Religious Life And The Chapel, Alison L. Boden
Dean Wilson School Of Public And International Affairs, Cecilia E. Rouse
Vp Information Technology And Cio, Jay Dominick
Dean School Of Engineering And Applied Science, H. Vincent Poor
Provost, David S. Lee
Dean Of The Faculty, Deborah A. Prentice
Dean Graduate School, Sanjeev R. Kulkarni
Dean Of The College, Jill S. Dolan
Dean Research, Pablo G. Debenedetti
Dean School Of Architecture, Monica Ponce de Leon
Evp, Treby Williams
Program Assistant Vice President For Pppl, Janice Huang
Payroll Manager Payroll Office Of The Vice President For Finance And Treasurer, Lora J Benson
Executive Assistant Office Of The Vice President For Development, Deborah A Small
Vice President, David McComas
Assistant Vice President For Strategic Donor Engagement, Tim McGowan
Avp Human Capital Management Systems, Elaine Cha

LOCATIONS

HQ: THE TRUSTEES OF PRINCETON UNIVERSITY
1 NASSAU HALL, PRINCETON, NJ 085442001
Phone: 609 258-3000
Web: WWW.ETCWEB.PRINCETON.EDU

PRODUCTS/OPERATIONS

Select Councils Institutes and Centers
Bendheim Center for Finance
Center for Migration and Development
Center for the Study of Religion
Council of the Humanities
Council on Science and Technology
Davis Center for Historical Studies
James Madison Program in American Ideals and Institutions
Lewis-Sigler Institute for Integrative Genomics
Liechtenstein Institute on Self-Determination
Princeton Environmental Institute (PEI)
Princeton Institute for International and Regional Studies (PIIRS)
Princeton Institute for the Science and Technology of Materials (PRISM)
Princeton Writing Program
Program of Freshman Seminars in the Residential Colleges
Program in Law and Public Affairs
Program in Neuroscience
University Center for Human Values

COMPETITORS

Brown University	Harvard University
Columbia University	Penn
Cornell University	Rutgers University
Dartmouth	Yale University

HISTORICAL FINANCIALS

Company Type: Private

Income Statement				FYE: June 30
	REVENUE ($ mil.)	NET INCOME ($ mil.)	NET PROFIT MARGIN	EMPLOYEES
06/18	2,012	2,582	128.3%	6,000
06/17	1,813	2,096	115.6%	
06/16	1,687	(628)	—	
06/15	1,621	1,827	112.8%	
Annual Growth	7.5%	12.2%	—	—

2018 Year-End Financials

Return on assets: 8.2%   Cash ($ mil.): 23
Return on equity: 9.4%
Current ratio: —

THE TURNER CORPORATION

The Turner Corporation a subsidiary of German construction giant HOCHTIEF is the leading general building and construction management firm in the US (as ranked by Engineering News-Record) ahead of rivals Bechtel and Fluor. The firm operates primarily through subsidiary Turner Construction and has worked on notable projects such as Madison Square Garden the UN headquarters Yankee Stadium the Taipei 101 Tower and the 68000-seat open-air stadium for the San Francisco 49ers. Known for its large projects also offers services for midsized and smaller projects and provides interior construction and renovation services.

Operations

Turner works on more than 1500 projects in a year totaling $8 billion in volume. The group has divisions dedicated to serving the aviation health care biotechnology public assembly sports education justice and industrial sectors. Its homeland security group was established in order handle a growing demand for security systems and protection. The unit installed detection equipment in some 450 airports throughout the US. Turner Corporation also has an arm specializing in green building with a focus on Leadership in Energy and Environmental Design (LEED) -certified projects. Turner Green Building has more than 400 LEED projects and green projects either completed or in progress.

Turner Corporation has subsidiaries providing auxiliary operations. Turner's risk management department offers contract review project safety and claims handling. Turner Logistics handles procurement and supply chain management for projects and Turner Facilities Management Solutions offers ongoing operations services. Also the Turner School of Construction Management provides training for local subcontractors.

Geographic Reach

Dallas-based Turner Corporation boasts a network of offices across the US (with most in California and Ohio) and Canada (Vancouver and Toronto) with an global presence in 20 countries in Europe Africa East Asia India Latin America and the Caribbean.

Sales and Marketing

Turner works on variety of projects from several sectors. It's known for its work in the categories of healthcare education offices commercial properties cultural facilities sports facilities and hotels. The company is also a leader in the green building category.

Strategy

With the construction market rebounding from the economic downturn Turner is looking to high-growth markets in the US and overseas. As of early 2015 it was working on more than 1900 projects 80% of which were Education Commercial or Interior project-related. Some of these projects included the 17000 sq. ft- interior remodel for Salesforce's Vancouver office; the 325000 sq. ft- construction of the LEED-Certified RAND Corporation Headquarters in Santa Monica California; and the 25000-seat Charlotte Coliseum event arena for the City of Charlotte North Carolina.

The company has also been making moves to expand its business abroad in recent years. In 2012 for example Turner partnered with one of India's largest real estate developers Sahara Prime City Ltd. to form Sahara Turner which would lead the development and construction of multiple townships across the country with an approximate value of $2.5 billion by 2017. It also purchased a majority stake in Clark Builders Canada to capitalize on the country's growing construction market.

Turner often partners with fellow US-based HOCHTIEF subsidiary Flatiron which specializes in civil engineering. Examples of the teamwork are the expansions of airports in San Diego and Sacramento.

HISTORY

At the turn of the century an engineer and devout Quaker named Henry Chandlee Turner was convinced that a new type of steel-reinforced concrete (called the Ransome system) would change the construction industry. With this conviction and with the help of his partner D. H. Dixon Turner bought the rights to the technology for $25000 and in 1902 founded Turner Construction Company.

One of the company's early projects was building the stairways for New York's first subway stations. As the Ransome method proved to be successful Turner's reputation grew. Defense contracts during WWI raised Turner's take to $35 million in 1918.

Before the Depression Turner was building high-rises hotels and stadiums. During the economic crash that started in 1929 the company survived by building retail stores churches and public buildings a strategy it would employ successfully in later recessions.

Henry Turner retired in 1941. His brother Archer Turner managed the company during most of the war effort. As WWII raged more than 80% of the company's work was defense-related. Projects included building and managing a submarine base in Oak Ridge Tennessee during the development of the atomic bomb.

In 1947 Henry C. Turner Jr. the founder's son became president and within four years he had led the company to more than $100 million in sales. By the time he stepped down as chairman in 1970 the firm had built skyscrapers futuristic airports and such landmarks as Madison Square Garden and the United Nations Secretariat and Plaza in New York City. Turner went public in 1969.

Howard S. Turner (the final family member to head the business) led the company during the 1970s. The company extended its global presence opening offices in more countries including Iran Pakistan and the United Arab Emirates. Turner also developed construction management services.

In 1984 The Turner Corporation was formed as a holding company for the construction company and the subsidiaries created or acquired as a result of diversification. Property development was one of these activities but by 1987 Turner had begun to dispose of its real estate holdings. It did not move quickly enough however and when the real estate market crashed Turner was caught with a large portfolio.

As commercial projects slowed Turner sought work in more sectors including public works and amusement projects (aquariums arenas hospitals and universities). By 1994 these areas accounted for 70% of business. In 1993 as the building slump continued Turner began a cost-cutting plan which included laying off workers and closing offices. That year the company set up an $8.5 million restructuring reserve and as the real estate market eased into recovery Turner sold more of its real estate holdings.

In 1996 Turner won a contract to build a 10000-seat arena in Salt Lake City to be used for the 2002 Winter Olympics. In 1997 Turner contracted to renovate 811 schools and build two campuses in California's San Fernando Valley and in 1998 it was chosen to manage the construction of the Kansas City Motor Speedway.

Profits were recovering quickly. Nonetheless in 1999 the company agreed to be acquired by German construction giant HOCHTIEF in a $370 million deal that ended Turner's joint venture with Switzerland's Karl Steiner. The company also relocated its corporate headquarters to Dallas that year to take advantage of the construction boom in the US Southwest.

In 2000 Turner created three new business groups to serve the aviation pharmaceutical and sports sectors. By the next year Turner's sports group was working on 17 projects. In 2001 the company was a member of the construction team that responded to the September 11 devastation at Ground Zero in New York City.

The next year the company celebrated its 100th anniversary with an exhibit at the National Building Museum in Washington DC; the exhibit featured drawings and photos of some of Turner's notable projects during the past century. In 2003 Turner Construction acquired the assets of Tompkins Builders the third-largest construction company in the Washington DC area from former rival J.A. Jones Construction Co.

Turner Construction which celebrated its 100th anniversary in 2002 has ranked among the leading general builders in the US since WWI. For 80 of the 100 years the group had a Turner among its senior executives. Howard S. Turner was the last member of the family to serve in the company's senior ranks. The company's appointment of Peter Davoren in 2003 as president of Turner Construction reflected the rise of a new generation of leaders for the unit. Davoren was additionally appointed chairman and CEO in 2007.

Turner Construction announced in 2008 that it had signed the contract on its 15000th major project.

EXECUTIVES

Pres-Chb-Ceo, Peter J Davoren
Sr V Pres-Cfo & Treas, Karen Gould
V Pres-Finance & Asst Treas, Don Oshiro
Attrny, Richard L Smith Jr
Svp, Turner, Thomas B Gerlach Jr
Project Engineer, Bernardo Lomeli
Project Engineer, Blake Redmond
Office Manager, Lori Jackson
Senior Project Manager, Michael Weatherwax
Procurement Agent, Paul Dempsey
Information Manager, Shawn Daly
Auditors: DELOITTE & TOUCHE LLP DALLAS

LOCATIONS

HQ: THE TURNER CORPORATION
   375 HUDSON ST RM 700, NEW YORK, NY 100143667
Phone: 212 229-6000
Web: WWW.TURNERCONSTRUCTION.COM

PRODUCTS/OPERATIONS

Selected Related Companies
E. E. Cruz (infrastructure)
Flatiron Construction Corp. (transportation
   construction civil engineering)
Clark Builders (51% Canada)

Selected Markets Served
Aviation
Commercial
Cultural and entertainment
Data center
Education
Government
Green building
Health care
Infrastructure
Industrial
Interiors
Pharmaceutical
Public Assembly
Religious
Research and development
Residential/hotel
Sports

Selected Services
Building information modeling
Building maintenance
Construction management
Design-build
Design-build/finance
Facilities management
General construction

Lean construction
Logistics
Medical planning and procurement
Preconstruction consulting
Program management
Project management

COMPETITORS

Balfour Beatty	Hunt Construction
Construction	Imperial Construction
Bechtel	Group
Clark Construction	Jacobs Engineering
Group	Parsons Corporation
Fluor	Peter Kiewit Sons'
Gilbane Building	Skanska
Company	Structure Tone

HISTORICAL FINANCIALS
Company Type: Private

Income Statement   FYE: December 31

	REVENUE ($ mil.)	NET INCOME ($ mil.)	NET PROFIT MARGIN	EMPLOYEES
12/15	10,523	107	1.0%	5,000
12/14	10,560	95	0.9%	—
12/13	9,522	80	0.8%	—
12/12	8,575	74	0.9%	—
Annual Growth	7.1%	12.9%	—	—

2015 Year-End Financials

Return on assets: 2.9%   Cash ($ mil.): 880
Return on equity: 16.5%
Current ratio: 1.00

THE UNITED ILLUMINATING COMPANY

EXECUTIVES

Pres-Ceo, James P Torgerson
Chb*, Nathaniel D Woodson
Pres-Coo*, Anthony J Vallillo
V Pres-Finance-Cfo*, Richard Nicholas
Vp-Info Tech/CIO*, W Marie Zanavich
Vp-Controller*, Steven P Favuzza
Coordinator, Tammie Jones
Supervisor, Frankie Nieves
Coordinator, Paul Aiken
Executive Officer, Robert Pellegrini
Billing Supervisor, Adriene Britton

LOCATIONS

HQ: THE UNITED ILLUMINATING COMPANY
   157 CHURCH ST FL 16, NEW HAVEN, CT 065102103
Phone: 203 499-2000

HISTORICAL FINANCIALS
Company Type: Private

Income Statement   FYE: December 31

	REVENUE ($ mil.)	NET INCOME ($ mil.)	NET PROFIT MARGIN	EMPLOYEES
12/17	921	105	11.4%	920
12/16*	866	84	9.7%	—
06/00	344	34	10.0%	—
Annual Growth	5.6%	6.4%	—	—

*Fiscal year change

THE UNITY HOSPITAL OF ROCHESTER

EXECUTIVES

President, Timothy McCormick
Health Care Director, Kathy Bello

LOCATIONS

HQ: THE UNITY HOSPITAL OF ROCHESTER
   89 GENESEE ST, ROCHESTER, NY 146113201
Phone: 585 723-7000
Web: WWW.ROCHESTERREGIONAL.ORG

HISTORICAL FINANCIALS
Company Type: Private

Income Statement   FYE: December 31

	REVENUE ($ mil.)	NET INCOME ($ mil.)	NET PROFIT MARGIN	EMPLOYEES
12/18	498	18	3.7%	3,000
12/15	433	(24)	—	—
12/14	435	0	0.1%	—
12/12	398	8	2.1%	—
Annual Growth	3.8%	14.0%	—	—

2018 Year-End Financials

Return on assets: 4.4%   Cash ($ mil.): 61
Return on equity: 89.7%
Current ratio: 2.10

THE UNIVERSITY OF CHICAGO MEDICAL CENTER

It may have received its official dedication on Halloween but The University of Chicago Medical Center (UCMC) works hard to make visiting the hospital a little less spooky. UCMC is a complex of facilities located on The University of Chicago campus that include the acute care Bernard A. Mitchell Hospital the Comer Children's Hospital a women's health and maternity facility and an outpatient care center. Established in 1927 (and dedicated on Halloween of that year) the complex includes the affiliated University of Chicago Pritzker School of Medicine and forms the clinical arm of The University of Chicago Division of Biological Sciences. UCMC houses about 550 beds.

Operations

Its Bernard A. Mitchell Hospital includes helicopter transportation operations emergency level-one pediatric trauma services and regional burn and peri-natal units. The roughly 155-bed Comer Children's Hospital offers disease care education and research as well as expanded newborn intensive care services.

UCMC sees some 23000 inpatients and 75000 emergency room visits per year. The hospital is one of the largest providers of uncompensated care in Illinois providing millions of dollars in charity care every year.

As part of the university's Biological Sciences division UCMC operates medical research centers focused on cancer immunology diabetes cardiology and neurology. The cancer center is especially intent on discovering improved treatment and prevention measures using gene and protein-based treatments. The Gwen and Jules Knapp Center for Biomedical Discovery works on discovery programs for a variety of medical conditions including diabetes cancer and pediatrics.

Geographic Reach
UCMC is located in Hyde Park on the south side of Chicago. Its main medical campus includes the Center for Care and Discovery Comer Children's Hospital Bernard A. Mitchell Hospital Chicago Lying-in Hospital and Duchossois Center for Advanced Medicine. UCMC also manages a network of area physicians and specialty clinics located in Chicago and its suburbs as well as in northwestern Indiana.

Strategy
UCMC is widening its service offerings through facility construction efforts. It completed a 1.2 million sq. ft. medical research and patient-centered care hospital pavilion on its main campus (named the Center for Care and Discovery) in 2012; the new facility opened its doors to 145 patients the following year.

Mergers and Acquisitions
In 2016 UCMC merged with community hospital system Ingalls Health which is now part of the UChicago Medicine brand. The combination of the health care partners allows the group to provide care across a full spectrum from routine visits to complicated treatments for life-threatening issues.

Company Background
First Lady Michelle Obama served as VP for community and external affairs at UCMC; she resigned from her post in early 2009 when she made the move to the White House.

EXECUTIVES

President, Sharon O'Keefe
Evp Medical Affairs; Dean Division Of The Biological Sciences And Pritzker School Of Medicine, Kenneth S. Polonsky
Vp Legal And Government Affairs And General Counsel, Susan S. Sher
Coo And Associate Dean, Carolyn S. Wilson
Cfo, James M. Watson
Medical Director, Sanghyun Paik
Vice President Revenue Cycle, Charlie Brown
Medical Director, Howard Halpern
Vp And Cio, Heather Nelson
Health Care Director, Rosalyn Johnson
Associate Vice President Individual Giving, Karen Paciero
Vice President Operational Excellence, Greg Horner
Vice Chairman, Craig J. Duchossois
Vice Chairman, James S. (Jim) Frank
Chairman, Emily Nicklin
Auditors: PRICEWATERHOUSECOOPERS LLP WA

LOCATIONS
HQ: THE UNIVERSITY OF CHICAGO MEDICAL CENTER
5841 S MARYLAND AVE, CHICAGO, IL 606371443
Phone: 773 702-1000
Web: WWW.UCHICAGOMEDICINE.ORG

PRODUCTS/OPERATIONS

Selected Services

Cancer

Endocrinology

Gastroenterology

Geriatrics

Heart
Kidney disease
Neurosciences
Orthopaedics

Respiratory disease
Surgery
Transplantation
Women's services

Selected Facilities
Bernard A. Mitchell Hospital
Center for Care and Discovery
Chicago Lying-in Hospital (Maternity and Women's Hospital)
Comer Children's Hospital
Duchossois Center for Advanced Medicine (outpatient care and diagnostics)
Gwen and Jules Knapp Center for Biomedical Discovery
LaRabida Children's Hospital (affiliated facility)
Mercy Hospital (affiliated facility)
University of Chicago Pritzker School of Medicine
Weiss Memorial Hospital (affiliated facility)

COMPETITORS
Advocate Health Care
Alexian Brothers Health System
Covenant Ministries
Elmhurst Memorial Healthcare
Loyola University Health System
Mercy Hospital and Medical Center
NorthShore University HealthSystem
Northwest Community Healthcare
Northwestern Memorial HealthCare
Rush System for Health
Silver Cross Hospital
Sinai Health System
St. Bernard Hospital and Health Care Center

HISTORICAL FINANCIALS
Company Type: Private

Income Statement   FYE: June 30

	REVENUE ($ mil.)	NET INCOME ($ mil.)	NET PROFIT MARGIN	EMPLOYEES
06/18	2,212	49	2.2%	5,000
06/15	1,610	148	9.2%	—
06/14	1,495	114	7.7%	—
06/09	1,294	(190)	—	—
Annual Growth	6.1%	—	—	—

2018 Year-End Financials
Return on assets: 1.4%   Cash ($ mil.): 211
Return on equity: 2.7%
Current ratio: 1.30

THE UNIVERSITY OF IOWA

EXECUTIVES

V Pres, Marty Scholtz
Assistant Professor, Michael Eberlein
Assistant Professor, Adam Ward
Oral and Maxillofacial Surgeon, Emma Cole
Oral and Maxillofacial Surgeon, Grace Chabal
Scientist, Youhua Tang
Assistant Professor, Megan Gilster
Project Coordinator, Nick Benson
Executive Officer, Nitin Karandikar
Assistant Professor, Phuong Nguyen
Facilities Specialist, Quintin Garner

LOCATIONS
HQ: THE UNIVERSITY OF IOWA
2660 UCC, IOWA CITY, IA 52242
Phone: 319 335-2119
Web: WWW.UIOWA.EDU

HISTORICAL FINANCIALS
Company Type: Private

Income Statement   FYE: June 30

	REVENUE ($ mil.)	NET INCOME ($ mil.)	NET PROFIT MARGIN	EMPLOYEES
06/18	3,176	588	18.5%	10
06/17	2,950	144	4.9%	—
Annual Growth	7.7%	308.5%	—	—

2018 Year-End Financials
Return on assets: 8.6%   Cash ($ mil.): 145
Return on equity: 13.6%
Current ratio: 1.10

THE UNIVERSITY OF IOWA

The University of Iowa Hawkeyes see clearly from their perch as the state's largest university. Founded in 1847 the University of Iowa has some 30500 students (and a student-faculty ratio of about 15:1) at its Iowa City campus. It is home to nearly a dozen colleges spanning more than 100 areas of study including distinguished programs in audiology printmaking speech pathology nursing service administration and creative writing. Its Writers' Workshop was the nation's first creative writing advanced degree program. It also includes programs in law engineering teaching and medicine as well as the affiliated University of Iowa Hospitals and Clinics health care organization.

EXECUTIVES

President, J. Bruce Harreld, age 69
Svp And University Treasurer, Douglas K. True
Dean College Of Law, Gail B. Agrawal
Cio, Steve R. Fleagle
Dean Graduate College, John C. Keller
Dean College Of Dentistry, David C. Johnsen
Evp And Provost, P. Barry Butler
Dean College Of Public Health, Susan J. Curry
Dean College Of Liberal Arts And Sciences, Chaden Djalali
Dean Tippie College Of Business, Sarah Fisher Gardial
Dean College Of Engineering, Alec B. Scranton
Dean Carver College Of Medicine, Debra Schwinn
Dean College Of Nursing, Rita A. Frantz
Dean College Of Pharmacy, Donald E. Letendre
Dean University College, Beth F. Ingram
Vice President Of Marketing And Public Relations, James Oconnor
Associate Vice President Donor Relations, Erin Lewis
Assistant Vice President And Executive Director, Marie Kerbeshian
Assistant Vice President For Economic Development, David Conrad
Vice President, Gina Guerrieri
Executive Vice President Gamma Iota Sigma, Patrick Ergastolo
Vice President Information Solutions, Danielle Martinez
Senior Business Intelligence Developer, Siva Krishna
President Board Of Regents, Bruce L. Rastetter, age 62
President Pro Tem Board Of Regents, Katie S. Mulholland
Secretary, Kathy Bell

Secretary Transplant, Catherine A Chapman
Secretary Ii, Laura Gusomano
Secretary Iii Orthopaedic Surgery, Janelle L
 Schark
Secretary Iii Educational Services, Stacy L
 Steffens
Secretary Iii To The Dental Registrar, Shannon
 Knipfer
Auditors: MARY MOSIMAN CPA DES MOINES

LOCATIONS

HQ: THE UNIVERSITY OF IOWA
 5W JEFFERSON ST # 101, IOWA CITY, IA 52242
Phone: 319 335-3500
Web: WWW.UIHEALTHCARE.ORG

PRODUCTS/OPERATIONS

Selected Colleges
College of Dentistry
College of Education
College of Engineering
College of Law
College of Liberal Arts and Sciences
College of Nursing
College of Pharmacy
College of Public Health
Graduate College
Henry B. Tippie College of Business
Roy J. and Lucille A. Carver College of Medicine

HISTORICAL FINANCIALS

Company Type: Private

Income Statement | | | | FYE: June 30

	REVENUE ($ mil.)	NET INCOME ($ mil.)	NET PROFIT MARGIN	EMPLOYEES
06/16	2,859	253	8.9%	17,000
06/11	2,067	253	12.3%	—
06/08	1,684	150	8.9%	—
06/06	1,556	(237)	—	—
Annual Growth	6.3%	—	—	—

2016 Year-End Financials
Return on assets: 4.0%
Return on equity: 6.3%   Cash ($ mil.): 144
Current ratio: 1.20

THE UNIVERSITY OF KANSAS HOSPITAL

EXECUTIVES

Ceo, Bob Page
Prin, Angela Cook
Pediatric Urologist, J Pat Murphy
Chief of Medicine, Bart McCann
Principal, Linsey Gregory
Internal Medicine Practitioner, Ahmad Tarakji
Neurology Specialist, Bhavana Patel
Internal Medicine Practitioner, Calvin Madrigal
Internal Medicine Practitioner, Donald Campbell Jr
Anesthesiologist, Nicholas Kaup
Anesthesiologist, Nicolas Patonai

LOCATIONS

HQ: THE UNIVERSITY OF KANSAS HOSPITAL
 4000 CAMBRIDGE ST, KANSAS CITY, KS 661608501
Phone: 913 588-5000

HISTORICAL FINANCIALS

Company Type: Private

Income Statement | | | | FYE: June 30

	REVENUE ($ mil.)	NET INCOME ($ mil.)	NET PROFIT MARGIN	EMPLOYEES
06/15	1,362	156	11.5%	40
06/02	321	6	2.0%	—
Annual Growth	11.8%	28.1%	—	—

2015 Year-End Financials
Return on assets: 9.4%   Cash ($ mil.): 140
Return on equity: 17.3%
Current ratio: 2.00

THE UNIVERSITY OF NORTH CAROLINA

Tar heels can sink their feet into academia and athletics at The University of North Carolina. The system of 17 universities including the flagship University of North Carolina at Chapel Hill campus counts more than 220000 undergraduate and graduate students across its campuses. It offers degrees in more than 200 disciplines. The university system chartered in 1789 is home to medical schools a teaching hospital law schools a veterinary school at NC State a school of pharmacy nursing programs schools of education schools of engineering and a school for the arts. In addition the system also operates the NC School of Science and Mathematics a public residential high school for gifted students.

Operations
The university system comprises 17 public institutions that grant baccalaureate degrees. It also operates a public residential high school for gifted students under the name NC School of Science and Mathematics.

Each year the university graduates more than 30000 students.

Geographic Reach
The University of North Carolina system serves students worldwide. Of its enrollment the system attracts far more in-state students than out-of-state students.

Financial Performance
Revenue for fiscal 2014 was $1.9 billion.

Strategy
To extend its reach The University of North Carolina partners with half a dozen affiliates. They include UNC Center for Public Television The North Carolina Arboretum The North Carolina State Approving Agency The North Carolina Center for International Understanding The North Carolina State Education Assistance Authority and The University of North Carolina Press.

In 2013 the system adopted a five-year strategic plan entitled "Our Time Our Future." The plan's goals were designed to set priorities allocate resources plan programs and refine academic missions.

EXECUTIVES

Assistant Vice President Campus Safety And
 Emergency Operations, Brent Herron
Assistant Vice President, Tracey Ford
Vice President Of State Government Relations,
 Drew Moretz
Medical Director, Melissa Miller
Vice President, Bobbi Owen
Senior Vice President External Affairs, Kevin
 Howell
Vice President, Timothy A Minor
Interim Department Chair And Director Of
 Graduate Studies And Admissions Department
 Of Exercise And Sport Science, Ed Shields
Associate Vice President For Legal Affairs, Brooks
 Skinner
Vice President Government Relations, Elizabeth
 Morra
Assistant Vice President Of Development And Gift
 Planning, Stephen Watt
Senior Vice President Finance, Mark Miller
Senior Vice President Of Operations, Janet Hadar
Treasurer, Gail Mazzocco
Board Member, Channing Der
Vice Chair, Tim Ives

LOCATIONS

HQ: THE UNIVERSITY OF NORTH CAROLINA
 910 RALEIGH RD, CHAPEL HILL, NC 275143916
Phone: 919 962-2211
Web: WWW.NORTHCAROLINA.EDU

PRODUCTS/OPERATIONS

Selected Institutions
Appalachian State University
East Carolina University
Elizabeth City State University
Fayetteville State University
NC A&T State University
North Carolina Central University
NC State University
UNC Asheville
UNC Chapel Hill
UNC Charlotte
UNC Greensboro
UNC Pembroke
UNC Wilmington
UNC School of the Arts
Western Carolina University
Winston-Salem State University
NC School of Science and Mathematics

HISTORICAL FINANCIALS

Company Type: Private

Income Statement | | | | FYE: June 30

	REVENUE ($ mil.)	NET INCOME ($ mil.)	NET PROFIT MARGIN	EMPLOYEES
06/13	1,838	267	14.6%	55,000
06/12	0	(0)	—	—
06/06	30	(9)	—	—
Annual Growth	79.3%	—	—	—

2013 Year-End Financials
Return on assets: 3.3%   Cash ($ mil.): 520
Return on equity: 5.9%
Current ratio: 5.00

THE UNIVERSITY OF TEXAS HEALTH SCIENCE CENTER AT HOUSTON

EXECUTIVES

Pres, Larrty R Kaiser
Pres*, James T Willerson
Exec Pres-Coo-Fin*, Kevin Dillion
Sr Asst V Pres-Fin*, Michael Tramonte
M.D., Pres*, Giuseppe N Colasurdo

Sr V Pres*, Kevin Dillon
V Pres*, George M Stancel
Prin*, Roberta B Ness
V Pres-Co-Chief Legal Officer*, Daniel J Reat
V Pres-Co-Chief Legal Officer*, Melissa K Pifko
Assistant Professor, Danielle Garsin

LOCATIONS

HQ: THE UNIVERSITY OF TEXAS HEALTH SCIENCE
CENTER AT HOUSTON
7000 FANNIN ST STE 700A, HOUSTON, TX
770303814
Phone: 713 500-4472
Web: WWW.UTHEALTHSERVICES.COM

HISTORICAL FINANCIALS

Company Type: Private

Income Statement   FYE: August 31

	REVENUE ($ mil.)	NET INCOME ($ mil.)	NET PROFIT MARGIN	EMPLOYEES
08/08	529	1	0.2%	5,600
08/05	455	(146)	—	—
08/03	411	73	17.7%	—
Annual Growth	5.2%	(56.0%)	—	—

2008 Year-End Financials

Return on assets: 0.1%   Cash ($ mil.): 64
Return on equity: 0.1%
Current ratio: 1.50

THE UNIVERSITY OF TEXAS HEALTH SCIENCE CENTER AT SAN ANTONIO

EXECUTIVES

Pres, William L Henrich
Exec V Pres*, Steven A Wartman
Sr V Pres*, Michael E Black
Prin*, Mary G Delay
Endocrinology, Chris Mc Daniel
Thoracic Surgeon, Sreenath V Reddy
Assistant Professor, Jason Morrow
Project Coordinator, Sharon Bressette
Assistant Professor, Beth Thai
Assistant Professor, Sandeep Patel
Assistant Professor, Cristina Boccalandro

LOCATIONS

HQ: THE UNIVERSITY OF TEXAS HEALTH SCIENCE
CENTER AT SAN ANTONIO
7703 FLOYD CURL DR, SAN ANTONIO, TX 782293901
Phone: 210 567-7000
Web: WWW.UTHSCSA.EDU

HISTORICAL FINANCIALS

Company Type: Private

Income Statement   FYE: August 31

	REVENUE ($ mil.)	NET INCOME ($ mil.)	NET PROFIT MARGIN	EMPLOYEES
08/11	767	62	8.2%	6,000
08/05	289	56	19.6%	—
08/04	289	56	19.6%	—
Annual Growth	15.0%	1.5%	—	—

2011 Year-End Financials

Return on assets: 4.3%   Cash ($ mil.): 99
Return on equity: 4.9%
Current ratio: 1.60

THE UNIVERSITY OF TOLEDO

One of Ohio's 14 state universities The University of Toledo (UT) is the third-largest by operating budget. It enrolls about 23000 students and offers more than 350 programs of study including master's degree and doctoral programs in more than 60 instructional departments. The university has a student-to-faculty ratio of 19:1. Its 14 colleges focus on subjects ranging from visual and performing arts to business and innovation as well as education engineering law medicine nursing pharmacy languages and human services. The school also operates the University of Toledo Medical Center.

Operations
The University of Toledo Medical Center affiliated with UT is a teaching hospital has three hospitals located on the UT Health Science Campus with a total of 320 beds in all three hospitals combined (the UT Medical Center a Rehabilitation Hospital and the Kobacker Center).

The UT Medical Center features a Level I trauma center and extensive medical training programs on UT's Health Science Campus. It provides treatments for strokes and cancer that are unique within the state. Other specialties include kidney transplants and cardiology.

Geographic Reach
UT students come from 45 US states and about 80 international countries. The school has an extensive distance learning program. In addition to the main campus in Toledo UT operates several satellite centers in Toledo (including the Health Science Campus the Scott Park Campus and the Center for the Visual Arts facility) and the Lake Erie Research and Education Center in Oregon Ohio.

Strategy
UT is working to enhance resources to better serve students as well as patients of its medical center. In addition to infrastructure and building projects UT is focused on recruiting and retaining quality faculty members and enhancing the quality and ranking of its academic programs. The university is also enhancing research and technology resources including collaborations with other schools and organizations.

Company Background
UT and the Medical University of Ohio merged in 2006. UT is accredited by the Higher Learning Commission of the North Central Association of Colleges and Schools.

UT was established in 1872 and became a member of the state university system in 1967.

EXECUTIVES

Interim Svp Finance And Administration, Lawrence (Larry) Kelley
Interim Dean Scott Honors College, Kelly Moore
Dean College Of Pharmacy And Pharmaceutical Sciences, Johnnie L. Early
President, Sharon L. Gaber
Dean College Of Engineering, Nagi Naganathan
Evp; Ceo Ut Medical Center, David R. Morlock

Interim Provost And Evp Academic Affairs, John A. Barrett
Evp; Dean College Of Medicine And Life Sciences, Christopher J. Cooper
Vice Provost; Executive Dean College Of Applied Science And Technology, Todd A. Rickel
Dean College Of Health Sciences, Christopher D. Ingersoll
Dean College Of Languages Literature And Social Sciences, Jamie Barlowe
Dean College Of Natural Sciences And Mathematics, Karen S. Bjorkman
Dean College Of Communication And The Arts, Debra A. Davis
Interim Dean College Of Social Justice And Human Service, Thomas G. (Tom) Gutteridge
Dean College Of Business And Innovation, Gary S. Insch
Dean College Of Graduate Studies, Patricia R. Komuniecki
Dean College Of Adult And Lifelong Learning, Dennis S. Lettman
Vp Cio And Cto, William McCreary
Interim Dean Herb College Of Education, Virginia Keil
Dean College Of Law, D. Benjamin Barros
Interim Dean College Of Nursing, Kelly Phillips
Interim Dean Youcollege, Julie Fischer-Kinney
Associate Vice President For Finance, Bryan Dadey
Nursing Director, Andrew Fox
Associate Vice President, Jovita Williams
Nursing Director, Mo Smith
Vice President Student Affairs, David Meabon
Interim Vice President For Student Affairs, Phillip Cockrell
Interim Vice President For Enrollment Management, Stephanie Sanders
Assistant Vice President Enrollment Services And Financial Aid, Steve Schissler
Associate Vice President For Development, Barbara Tartaglia Poure
Vice President Student Body, Cameron Forsythe
Chairman, Sharon S. Speyer
Vice Chairman, Steven M. Cavanaugh
Secretary, Susan Rouppas
Secretary Ii, Patricia Baldwin
Secretary, Elaine Coopshaw
Ward Secretary, Pamela Thayer
Ward Secretary, Wendy Frick
Secretary 2 Radiation Safety, Deborah Frye
Secretary 1 Neurology, Mildred Wegener
Secretary 2 Medicine, Michelle McKenzie
Secretary 2 Medicine, Lisa Johnston
Secretary 1 College Of Nursing, Roni Hoskins
Board Member, Matthew Miller
Secretary Communication, Patricia Damschroder
Secretary, Nora Longsworth
Secretary 2 5ab Medical Surgery, Maura Luettke
Treasurer, Anne Riley
Secretary, Gregory Gilchrist
Secretary 1 Pediatrics, Michele Agocs
Secretary, Traci Mcdaniel
Secretary, Amada Esquivel
Secretary 2 Psychiatry, Jacquelyn Mcbee
Secretary, Lois Patek
Secretary I, Tamara Golkiewicz
Secretary 1 College Of Nursing, Margaret Desmond
Department Secretary, Bonnie Edmonds
Secretary, Kayla Wiemers
Secretary Ii, Laurie Flowers
Secretary, Tana Felkey
Ward Secretary, James Zeller
Secretary 2, Connie Butler
Secretary 1, Lilla Horton
Secretary General Inquiries, Jessica Bergman
Secretary, Kishore Mukherjee
Secretary, Lauri Vanwormer
Auditors: CLIFTONLARSONALLEN LLP TOLEDO

HISTORICAL FINANCIALS

Company Type: Private

Income Statement				FYE: June 30
	REVENUE ($ mil.)	NET INCOME ($ mil.)	NET PROFIT MARGIN	EMPLOYEES
06/18	716	55	7.8%	7,000
06/17	728	(62)	—	—
Annual Growth	(1.6%)	—	—	—

2018 Year-End Financials

Return on assets: 4.7%
Return on equity: 176.9%
Current ratio: 1.20
Cash ($ mil.): 40

THE UNIVERSITY OF UTAH

The University of Utah (U of U) has offered instruction since long before the Beehive State was a state. Founded in 1850 as the University of Deseret the "U of U" has a total enrollment of more than 31800 undergraduate and graduate students with a student-to-faculty ratio of some 14:1. It offers more than 70 undergraduate majors and some 90 graduate-level fields of study at about 20 colleges and schools; its business science humanities and engineering departments are the university's largest. It also offers medical nursing and pharmacy programs as well as health and social science research programs. U of U confers more than 8000 baccalaureate masters and doctoral degrees annually.

Operations

The university includes an academic health system University Health Care (UHC) which includes the U of U School of Medicine and the University of Utah Hospitals & Clinics. With a total enrollment of some 2000 students UHC trains about 600 health care professionals annually through residency fellowship and internship programs. U of U also includes institutes that conduct research programs in a variety of fields — including health energy information technology and engineering — as well as technology commercialization projects.

Geographic Reach

U of U has a main campus located on 1500 acres. The campus includes academic residency research and medical facilities.U of U's students hail from 23 Utah counties all 50 US states and 92 countries.

Financial Performance

U of U keeps a steady growth pace including a growth in revenue to from $3.5 billion in 2015 to $3.8 billion in 2016. The growth came from increases in student tuition revenue (increased enrollment and higher tuition rates)and higher grants and contracts sales and service and patient service revenue.

U of U's net operating loss was $204.9 million in 2016 (compared to a loss of $243.5 million in 2015) as a growth in revenues outpaced higher expenses including higher compensation and benefits and component unit and supply costs.

Strategy

A number of research programs at U of U are focused on bringing development-stage discoveries into the commercial realm. The university has an impressive track record for the creation of start-up companies and it is looking to advance its capabilities in this field. Other growth areas for the U of U include expanding its campus facilities and increasing the quality of care at its health care centers.

EXECUTIVES

Associate Vice President, Joan Gines
Svp Academic Affairs, David W. Pershing
Svp Health Sciences And Dean School Of Medicine And Ceo University Health Care, Vivian S. Lee
Svp Academic Affairs, Ruth V. Watkins
Cio, Steve Hess
Senior Chief Administrative Officer And Cfo, John E. Nixon
Vice President, Andrew Burkhardt
Vice President Government And Regulatory Affairs, Laura Nelson
Student Body Vice President, Madison Black
Vice President Human Resources, Wayne Imbrescia
Vice President Of Information Security, David Glod
Assistant Vice President Aux Services, Norman Chambers
Bs Pharmd, David Stenehjem
Vice President, David Warren
Assistant Vice President Student Development, Kari Ellingson
Ustar Professor And Department Chair, Gianluca Lazzi
Program Assistant Office Of The Vice President For Research, Mandi Peterson
Vice President, Kay Harward
Interim Associate Vice President For Equity And Diversity, Kathryn Stockton
Assistant Vice President, Gordon Wilson
Department Chair Humanities College Of Dean, Fernando Rubio
Department Chair Humanities College Of Dean, Ed Rubin
Panhellenic Vice President Of Judicial And Risk Reduction, Ginny Mitchell
Membership Vice President, Wendy Warner
Associate Vice President Of Academic Affairs, Martha Bradley
Pharmacy Manager, Jay Lewandowski
Medical Director, Feras Bader
Vice Presidential Fellow, Barbara Duffey
Vice Presidential Fellow, Ishion Hutchinson
Vice President, Scammon Debra
Chief Sales Officer, Matt Gregory
Pharmd, Patricia Jeppson
Medical Director Molecular Oncology, Larissa Furtado
Office Assistant For Vp Of Institutional Advancement, James Gessel
Svp Of Academic Affairs, Dan Reed
Associate Vice President Academic Administration, Cypers Breanna
Pharmacy Manager Inpatient Operations, Russell Findlay
Chair, Michele Mattsson
Vice Chair, Phillip W. Clinger
Treasurer, Johanna Watzinter
Medical Secretary, Tracey Mcgee
Clinical Secretary, Mary Looser
Medical Secretary, Ashley Adams
Medical Secretary, Elizabeth Royall
Secretary, Ivie Blussette Sofia
Medical Secretary, Chani Brown
Medical Secretary, Laura Fait
Secretary, Roche Mike
Auditors: OFFICE OF THE UTAH STATE AUDIT

PRODUCTS/OPERATIONS

2015 Sales

	$ mil.	% of total
Patient services net	1,816	53
Sales and services	740	21
Grants and contracts	362	10
Tuition and fees net	304	9
Auxiliary and other	237	7
Total	**3,460**	**100**

Selected Colleges

College of Architecture and Planning
College of Education
College of Engineering
College of Fine Arts
College of Health
College of Humanities
College of Law
College of Mines and Earth Sciences
College of Nursing
College of Pharmacy
College of Science
College of Social and Behavioral Sciences
College of Social Work
David Eccles School of Business
Graduate School
Honors College
School of Medicine

HISTORICAL FINANCIALS

Company Type: Private

Income Statement				FYE: June 30
	REVENUE ($ mil.)	NET INCOME ($ mil.)	NET PROFIT MARGIN	EMPLOYEES
06/13*	2,907	186	6.4%	18,000
12/08	0	0	—	—
06/08	22	(10)	—	—
Annual Growth	164.4%	—	—	—

*Fiscal year change

2013 Year-End Financials

Return on assets: 3.7%
Return on equity: 4.8%
Current ratio: 3.60
Cash ($ mil.): 486

THE UNIVERSITY OF VERMONT HEALTH NETWORK INC

EXECUTIVES

Ceo, John Brumsted
Coordinator, Linnea Oosterman
Staff, Lynz Parker
Coordinator, Mercy Gingras
Director Human Resources Total, Thomas Kess
Director of Accreditation, Carol Muzzy
Supervisor, Brian Douglas
Call Center Representative, Deborah Bryan
Information Analyst, Katelyn Muir
Director of Supply Chain Servi, Ken Jensen
Physician Assistant, Lauren Macnee
Auditors: PRICEWATERHOUSECOOPERS LLP BO

LOCATIONS

HQ: THE UNIVERSITY OF VERMONT HEALTH
NETWORK INC
462 SHELBURNE RD, BURLINGTON, VT 054016947
Phone: 844 886-4325
Web: WWW.UVMHEALTH.ORG

HISTORICAL FINANCIALS

Company Type: Private

Income Statement				FYE: September 30
	REVENUE ($ mil.)	NET INCOME ($ mil.)	NET PROFIT MARGIN	EMPLOYEES
09/18	2,169	129	6.0%	1,300
09/17	1,933	161	8.4%	—
09/16	1,748	92	5.3%	—
Annual Growth	11.4%	18.3%	—	—

2018 Year-End Financials

Return on assets: 5.5%   Cash ($ mil.): 246
Return on equity: 10.0%
Current ratio: 2.20

THE UNIVERSITY OF VERMONT MEDICAL CENTER INC

The University Of Vermont Medical Center (formerly Fletcher Allen Health Care) provides medical care in the Green Mountain State. The company operates an academic medical center in alliance with the University of Vermont. The not-for-profit health system serves residents of Vermont and northern New York through three primary hospital campuses and more than 130 outpatient clinics patient care sites and outreach programs. Its acute care medical centers have a combined 560-bed capacity and a medical staff of some 800 health care providers representing medical specializations including emergency/trauma care pediatrics and women's health. The health care system is a subsidiary of Fletcher Allen Partners.

Operations

The health system receives some 60000 emergency visits each year and its hospitals handle more than 50000 inpatient and outpatient visits per year as well as 2000 births.

Working with the University of Vermont's College of Medicine and College of Nursing and Health Sciences The University Of Vermont Medical Center helps connect bedside experience with medical research to improve overall quality of care. It also provides hands-on educational services for medical and nursing students as well as professionals undergoing specialty training.

Geographic Reach

The University Of Vermont Medical Center serves 160000 people who live in Vermont's Chittenden and Grand Isle counties.

Financial Performance

The company's revenues accounted for 68% of Fletcher Allen Partners' total revenues in 2014.

Strategy

In order to provide a cohesive health network in the region the health system is working to create an integrated care network in its service territory. It is also working to build out its IT and data management capabilities

The University of Vermont Medical Center also has affiliations with other area providers to increase referrals and cooperative care including Alice Hyde Medical Center Canton-Potsdam Hospital Moses Ludington Hospital Central Vermont Medical Center Champlain Valley Physicians Hospital and the Elizabethtown Community Hospital. It seeks to form new partnerships with additional facilities.

In 2015 the company changed its name from Fletcher Allen Health Care to The University of Vermont Medical Center as part of a branding strategy approved by the Fletcher Allen Partners and University of Vermont boards.

Company Background

The hospital system was created through the 1995 merger of the Fanny Allen Hospital (which opened in 1894) the Medical Center Hospital of Vermont (or Mary Fletcher Hospital founded in 1876) and the University Health Center (formed in 1971). The hospitals are now known as Fanny Allen Campus Medical Center Campus and UHC Campus.

Fletcher Allen Health Care completed the implementation of an electronic health records (EHR) system that connects patient records at all of its facilities in 2010.

EXECUTIVES

Medical Director, Terry Rabinowitz
Svp And Cio, Charles (Chuck) Podesta
President And Ceo, John R. Brumsted
Svp And Cfo, Roger Deshaies
President Faculty Practice, Paul Taheri
Vp Marketing And Communications, Teresa Murphy
Svp Coo And Chief Nursing Officer, Sandra L. Felis
Chief Medical Officer, Stephen Leffler
Interim President Uvm Medical Group Fletcher Allen, Howard Schapiro
Chief Medical Information Officer, Adam P. Buckley
Ceo Inter-lakes Health, Chip Holmes
Medical Director, Jeffrey Rimmer
Assistant Vice President Support Services And Radiation Oncology, Brian Irwin
Medical Director, Kennith Sartorelli
Medical Director, Janusz Kikut
Vice President Hospital Services, Dawn Lebaron
Vice President Information Systems And Supply Chain Services, Charles Miceli
Director Of Radiology, Paula Gonyea
Pharmacy Manager, Lisa Jackman
Network Senior Vice President External Relations, Theresa Alberghini Dipalma
Chairman, John Powell
Unit Secretary, Shirley Beecher
Unit Secretary, Carla Levesque
Secretary, Micheline Lafontaine
Auditors: PRICEWATERHOUSECOOPERS LLP BO

LOCATIONS

HQ: THE UNIVERSITY OF VERMONT MEDICAL
CENTER INC
111 COLCHESTER AVE, BURLINGTON, VT 054011473
Phone: 802 847-0000
Web: WWW.UVMHEALTH.ORG

PRODUCTS/OPERATIONS

Selected Services
Cancer Care
Heart & Vascular
Orthopedics
Primary Care
Urgent Care
Women's Health

COMPETITORS

Albany Medical Center	Rutland Regional
Ellis Hospital	Medical Center
New England Alliance for Health	Southwestern Vermont Health Care
NewYork-Presbyterian Healthcare	Springfield Hospital St. Peter's Health
Northwell Health	Partners

HISTORICAL FINANCIALS

Company Type: Private

Income Statement				FYE: September 30
	REVENUE ($ mil.)	NET INCOME ($ mil.)	NET PROFIT MARGIN	EMPLOYEES
09/18	1,363	68	5.1%	7,000
09/17	1,246	129	10.4%	—
09/16	1,181	85	7.2%	—
Annual Growth	7.4%	(10.0%)	—	—

2018 Year-End Financials

Return on assets: 4.1%   Cash ($ mil.): 144
Return on equity: 7.1%
Current ratio: 2.00

THE VALLEY HOSPITAL INC

The Valley Hospital is second to none when it comes to its Same-Day Service program. More than one-third of the company's annual patients experience its longstanding continuum of one-day service; fully half the surgeries performed are same-day. The not-for-profit hospital is a 450-bed facility providing general and emergency services to residents of New Jersey's Bergen County. The hospital belongs to the Valley Health System which also includes subsidiaries Valley Home Care and Valley Health Medical Group and is an affiliate member of NewYork-Presbyterian Healthcare. The Valley Hospital New Jersey's second busiest has more than 800 physicians on its medical staff.

Operations

The Valley Hospital is well known for its cardiology cancer maternity and neonatal care programs (including its neonatal ICU). Its key services also include emergency care orthopedics and neurosciences. The hospital's emergency department treated more than 75000 patients in 2013. That year the hospital also admitted more than 49240 patients and the delivered almost 3200 babies.

The Valley Hospital's cardiac service includes a full range of diagnostic and interventional cardiac treatment services including cardiac surgery coronary angioplasty and electrophysiology studies. The hospital is also known for its work in lung cancer diagnosis and treatment radiation oncology (including tomotherapy) chemotherapy and infusion GYN oncology prostate cancer care and other clinical and support services.

Geographic Reach

The hospital serves more than 440000 people in 32 towns in Bergen County and surrounding communities.

Strategy

The medical system is looking to improve its facilities and technology in order to keep up with demand. The Valley Hospital is the first and only hospital in northern New Jersey to offer brain and spinal surgery with a state-of-the-art O-armÂ®

surgical imaging system purchased through a $1 million grant from The Bolger Foundation.

In 2012 The Valley Hospital Valley became the first hospital in northern New Jersey to offer the latest breast imaging technology — 3D breast to-mosynthesis.

That year it also enhanced its capacity to perform minimally invasive surgery with the acquisition of the robotic da VinciÂ® Surgical System funded by a $1.6 million donation from The Bolger Foundation.

In 2012 the hospital opened a new Women's and Children's Resource Center to coordinate wide range of services for women and their families.

EXECUTIVES

Director Of Pharmacy, Ron Krych

LOCATIONS

HQ: THE VALLEY HOSPITAL INC
223 N VAN DIEN AVE, RIDGEWOOD, NJ 074502736
Phone: 201 447-8000
Web: WWW.VALLEYHEALTHCAREERS.COM

PRODUCTS/OPERATIONS

Selected Services
Adoption Screening and Evaluation Program
Ambulatory Infusion Center
Anticoagulation Management Service
Autism Services
Auxiliary
Barrett's Esophagus Center
Bariatric Surgery
Bereavement Services
Biplane
Bladder Cancer Care
Breast Center
Cancer Care
Capsule Endoscopy
Cardiac MRI
Cardiac Rehabilitation
Cardiac Surgery
Cardiology
Center for Childbirth
Kireker Center for Child Development
Center for Metabolic and Weight Loss Surgery
Center for Family Education
Center for Women's Heart Health
Center for Youth Fitness
Clinical Trials Oncology
Clinical Trials Cardiology
Colonoscopy
Community Resources
Complementary Medicine
Concussion Management Program
Continence Services
Cosmetic Laser Treatment
Critical Care
Diabetes Support Services
Diagnostic Imaging
Doula Program
Emergency Services
Emergency Services Pediatric
Employee Recognition
Endoscopic Ultrasound
Epilepsy Monitoring Program Adult
Epilepsy Center Pediatric
ERCP
Esophagogastroduodenoscopy (EGD)
Extended Care

COMPETITORS

Bergen Regional Medical
Englewood Hospital and Medical Center
Hackensack Meridian Health
Hackensack University Medical Center
Jersey City Medical Center
Newton Medical Center
Raritan Bay Medical Center
Robert Wood Johnson University Hospital at Rahway

HISTORICAL FINANCIALS

Company Type: Private

Income Statement — FYE: December 31

	REVENUE ($ mil.)	NET INCOME ($ mil.)	NET PROFIT MARGIN	EMPLOYEES
12/17	657	80	12.2%	2,900
12/16	638	73	11.6%	—
12/15	621	83	13.4%	—
12/14	605	56	9.3%	—
Annual Growth	2.8%	12.6%	—	—

2017 Year-End Financials

Return on assets: 7.4%   Cash ($ mil.): 4
Return on equity: 8.5%
Current ratio: 1.00

THE VANDERBILT UNIVERSITY

The house that Cornelius built Vanderbilt University was founded in 1873 with a $1 million grant from industrialist Cornelius Vanderbilt. Since then the university's endowment has grown to $4.1 billion making the Nashville school a haven for its roughly 12600 students and more than 4200 full-time faculty members. Boasting a 7:1 student-faculty ratio Vanderbilt offers undergraduate and graduate programs in areas such as education and human development divinity engineering and the arts and sciences. The university operates 10 schools and colleges. Vanderbilt's Owen Graduate School of Management and its medical school regularly rank near the top in national surveys.

Operations
A major research university Vanderbilt receives millions of dollars each year in research funding from a variety of sources.

Vanderbilt is closely affiliated with the comprehensive Vanderbilt University Medical Center (VUMC) which conducts clinical trials and trains medical students. It's home to an acute care hospital a children's hospital and several clinics as well as the university's medical school research facilities and nursing programs. In 2016 Vanderbilt and VUMC officially split severing financial and legal ties (but not their ongoing affiliations).

Financial Performance
Vanderbilt University's revenue increased 3% to $1.3 billion in fiscal 2017 (ended June). Tuition and education fees less student financial aid contributed 21% of that revenue while grants and contracts contributed 18%. The Department of Health and Human Services (primarily the National Institutes of Health) was the largest source of government grants and contracts.

The school's expenses totaled $1.2 billion that year. Salaries wages and benefits as well as supplies and services made up the bulk of those expenses.

Strategy
Vanderbilt works to retain and recruit world-class faculty expand its hospitals and clinics and enhance its athletic facilities. For example it opened a new engineering and science building in 2016.

In 2016 Vanderbilt separated from its medical center (which restructured as the not-for-profit Vanderbilt University Medical Center or VUMC). The move allowed VUMC to be financially independent while still collaborating with the university for research and education.

Company Background
During its first 40 years of existence Vanderbilt was under the auspices of the Methodist Episcopal Church South. The Vanderbilt Board of Trust severed its ties with the church in 1914 after a dispute with the bishops over who would appoint university trustees.

EXECUTIVES

Chancellor, Nicholas S. Zeppos
Vice Chancellor Health Affairs And Dean School Of Medicine, Jeffrey R. Balser
Dean Of The Blair School Of Music, Mark Wait
Dean Peabody College, Camilla Benbow
Associate Provost And Dean Of Students, Mark Bandas
Dean Of The School Of Divinity, Emilie M. Townes
Vice Chancellor Finance And Cfo, Brett Sweet
Dean Of The Law School, Chris Guthrie
Vice Chancellor For Information Technology, John M. Lutz
Dean Of The School Of Engineering, Philippe Fauchet
Vice Chancellor General Counsel And Secretary, Audrey J. Anderson
Provost And Vice Chancellor For Academic Affairs, Susan Wente
Vice Chancellor For Administration, Eric Kopstain
Vice Provost For Enrollment And Dean Of Admissions, Douglas L. Christiansen
Interim Dean Of Libraries, Joseph D. Combs
Dean Of The Owen Graduate School Of Management, M. Eric Johnson
Dean Of The School Of Nursing, Linda Norman
Vice President Finance, Elisabeth Hudson
Department Chairperson Professor, John York
Medical Director Vanderbilt Health, Mary Shepherd
Vice President For Diversity And Inclusion Atandt, Belinda Grant-anderson
Senior Vice President Human Resources Global Operations Hewlett Packard Company, Mike Dallas
Vice Chairman, Jackson W. Moore, age 70
Chairman, Mark F. Dalton, age 68
Vice Chairman, John Winkelried
Auditors: PRICEWATERHOUSECOOPERS LLP NE

LOCATIONS

HQ: THE VANDERBILT UNIVERSITY
2301 VANDERBILT PL, NASHVILLE, TN 372350002
Phone: 615 322-7311

PRODUCTS/OPERATIONS

Selected Schools and Colleges
Blair School of Music
College of Arts and Science
Divinity School
Graduate School
Law School
Owen Graduate School of Management
Peabody College of Education and Human Development
School of Engineering
School of Medicine
School of Nursing

HISTORICAL FINANCIALS

Company Type: Private

Income Statement   FYE: June 30

	REVENUE ($ mil.)	NET INCOME ($ mil.)	NET PROFIT MARGIN	EMPLOYEES
06/18	1,366	511	37.4%	21,000
06/17	1,311	374	28.6%	—
06/16	1,270	(569)	—	—
06/15	4,121	131	3.2%	—
Annual Growth	(30.8%)	57.3%	—	—

2018 Year-End Financials

Return on assets: 7.1%   Cash ($ mil.): 602
Return on equity: 8.1%
Current ratio: —

THE WALSH GROUP LTD

Operating through subsidiaries Walsh Construction Walsh Canada and Archer Western Contractors The Walsh Group provides design/build general contracting and construction services for industrial public and commercial projects. The family-owned company offers complete project management services from demolition and planning to general contracting and finance. The company is involved in the construction of highways water treatment facilities airports hotels convention centers correctional facilities and commercial industrial and residential buildings. Walsh operates out of roughly 20 offices in North America. The company was founded in 1898 by Matthew Myles Walsh.

Strategy

Walsh's geographic diversity and its wide range of project experience has helped it remain successful in recessions and in good times. Federal contracts have helped Walsh survive during times when private-sector building and construction were down.

Company Background

In 2012 Walsh Group acquired California-based R&L Brosamer which specializes in heavy highway and other transportation projects. R&L Brosamer often works on projects for Bay Area Rapid Transit California Department of Transportation and Los Angeles World Airports. The deal helped Walsh strengthen its presence in California and bordering states including Nevada and Arizona.

In 2011 Walsh was awarded its first overseas embassy project a $200 million contract to build the New American Embassy at Oslo Norway.

EXECUTIVES

Co-chairman And Ceo, Matthew M. (Matt) Walsh
President Building Division, Michael Whelan
President Heavy Civil Division, Don Gillis
Cfo, Tim Gerken
Vp Heavy/civil Division, Daniel Walsh
Vp Corporate Equipment, Michael Gibbons
Vp Building Division, Matthew Walsh
President Walsh Construction, Sean Walsh
Vice President, Kevin Swain
Co-chairman, Daniel J. Walsh
Auditors: WOLF & COMPANY LLP OAKBROOK T

LOCATIONS

HQ: THE WALSH GROUP LTD
929 W ADAMS ST, CHICAGO, IL 606073021
Phone: 312 563-5400
Web: WWW.WALSHGROUP.COM

PRODUCTS/OPERATIONS

Projects

Airports
Athletic facilities
Bridges
Conference centers
Correctional facilities
Data centers
Educational facilities
Entertainment
Government
Health care
High rise residential
Highways and bridges
Hotels
Interiors
Laboratories
Parking garages
Renovations
Retail centers
Senior housing
Treatment plants
Warehouse and distribution

COMPETITORS

Bechtel	James McHugh
Black & Veatch	Lane Construction
Brasfield & Gorrie	MWH Global
C. G. Schmidt	McCarthy Building
Flatiron Construction	Peter Kiewit Sons'
Fluor	Skanska
Granite Construction	TIC Holdings
Hunt Companies	Turner Corporation
Hunt Construction	Vecellio & Grogan
Jacobs Engineering	

HISTORICAL FINANCIALS

Company Type: Private

Income Statement   FYE: December 31

	REVENUE ($ mil.)	NET INCOME ($ mil.)	NET PROFIT MARGIN	EMPLOYEES
12/10	3,462	186	5.4%	5,000
12/09	3,316	191	5.8%	—
12/08	3,534	203	5.8%	—
Annual Growth	(1.0%)	(4.4%)	—	—

2010 Year-End Financials

Return on assets: 11.9%   Cash ($ mil.): 656
Return on equity: 27.9%
Current ratio: 1.80

THE WASHINGTON UNIVERSITY

Washington University also known as Washington University in St. Louis (WUSTL) is the gateway to higher education for more than 13000 students. Founded in 1853 the independent university offers 90 bachelor's master's and doctoral degrees and has about 3400 faculty members. It offers approximately 1500 courses in fields such as arts and sciences business design and visual arts engineering law medicine and social work. WUSTL which has multiple campuses in and near the city of St. Louis also offers associate degree and continuing education programs. The affiliated Washington University Medical Center is an acute-care hospital that also provides educational training and research services.

Operations

The Medical Campus conducts extensive collaborative studies between students faculty and hospital staff as well as external institutions. Areas of research include genome sequencing of cancer patients and children's developmental studies. The 2000-acre Tyson Research Center outside the city is a biological field station that conducts environmental studies and research activities including renewable energy and sustainability programs some of which is coordinated with outside groups.

The university has an 8:1 student-to-faculty ratio. Its libraries contain more than 3.6 million books journals and other print materials and have access to more than 65000 electronic journals and a half million e-books.

In the academic year ending spring 2015 annual undergraduate educational costs totaled $45700.

Geographic Reach

In addition to the main 170-acre Danforth Campus in St. Louis WUSTL's facilities include the nearby 165-acre Medical Campus (housing the School of Medicine and the hospital facilities). Other operations include three smaller satellite academic campuses and music research and art centers in the greater St. Louis area.

Financial Performance

In fiscal 2015 revenue increased 9% to $2.7 billion on higher tuition and fees endowment spending distribution gifts and patient services. However a decline in non-operating revenue such as investment returns led to a 71% drop in net income which fell to $270 million.

Cash flow from operations spiked 522% to $104 million as less cash was used in net gains on investments.

Strategy

WUSTL has made efforts to extend its collaborations with third parties which can help bring in academic and research funds. In addition the university has worked to attract more government research grants in recent years. It is also upgrading some classroom and student facilities as well as hiring more experienced teachers and medical staff members to maintain its tuition auxiliary enterprise (lodging and vending) health services and research income expectations.

EXECUTIVES

Executive Vice Chancellor Administration, Henry S. Webber
Executive Vice Chancellor Alumni And Development Programs, David T. Blasingame
Executive Vice Chancellor And General Counsel, Michael R. Cannon
Chancellor, Mark S. Wrighton, age 70
Vice Chancellor Finance And Cfo, Barbara A. Feiner
Executive Vice Chancellor Medical Affairs And Dean School Of Medicine, Larry J. Shapiro
Dean Olin Business School, Mahendra R. Gupta
Dean Sam Fox School Of Design And Visual Arts, Carmon Colangelo
Dean George Warren Brown School Of Social Work, Edward F. Lawlor
Dean School Of Law, Kent D. Syverud
Provost And Executive Vice Chancellor Academic Affairs, H. Holden Thorp, age 55
Dean School Of Engineering And Applied Science, Ralph S. Quatrano
Dean Faculty Of Arts And Sciences, Barbara A. Schaal
Dean College Of Arts And Sciences, Jennifer R. Smith
Dean Graduate School Of Arts And Sciences, Richard J. Smith
Cio, Michael P. (Mike) Caputo
Vice Chairman, John F. McDonnell, age 80
Chairman, David W. Kemper, age 68

Vice Chairman, Craig D. Schnuck, age 70
Chairman, Stephen F. Brauer, age 74
Auditors: PRICEWATERHOUSECOOPERS LLP L

LOCATIONS

HQ: THE WASHINGTON UNIVERSITY
1 BROOKINGS DR, SAINT LOUIS, MO 631304899
Phone: 314 935-8566
Web: WWW.WUSTL.EDU

PRODUCTS/OPERATIONS

2015 Sales

	$ mil.	% of total
Patient service	985	36
Grants	368	14
Tuition & fees	356	13
Endowment spending distribution	266	10
Gifts	186	7
Educational	162	6
Others	382	14
Total	**2,707**	**100**

Selected Schools and Colleges

College of Arts & Sciences
 Graduate School of Arts & Sciences
 University College and Summer School (Arts & Sciences)
George Warren Brown School of Social Work
Sam Fox School of Design & Visual Arts
School of Engineering & Applied Science
School of Law
School of Medicine
Olin Business School

COMPETITORS

Bucknell University	Southeast Missouri
Missouri State	State University
University	University of Missouri
Saint Louis University	

HISTORICAL FINANCIALS

Company Type: Private

Income Statement
FYE: June 30

	REVENUE ($ mil.)	NET INCOME ($ mil.)	NET PROFIT MARGIN	EMPLOYEES
06/18	3,543	1,011	28.6%	9,600
06/17	3,068	737	24.0%	—
06/16	2,876	(303)	—	—
06/15	2,707	270	10.0%	—
Annual Growth	**9.4%**	**55.3%**	**—**	**—**

2018 Year-End Financials

Return on assets: 7.6%   Cash ($ mil.): 366
Return on equity: 9.6%
Current ratio: —

THE WHITING-TURNER CONTRACTING COMPANY

Whiting-Turner Contracting provides construction management general contracting and design/build services primarily for large commercial institutional and infrastructure projects conducted across the US. A key player in retail construction the employee-owned company also undertakes such projects as biotech cleanrooms theme parks historical restorations senior living residences educational facilities stadiums and corporate headquarters. Clients past and present include the US military AT&T General Motors and Texas A&M University. Whiting-Turner Contracting operates from more than 30 offices across the US.

Geographic Reach

The Baltimore-based company has offices in Arizona California Colorado Connecticut Delaware Florida Georgia Maryland Massachusetts Missouri Nevada New Jersey New York North Carolina Ohio Pennsylvania Texas Virginia and Washington DC.

Sales and Marketing

The contractor works on projects across a wide range of industries related to arts and entertainment education federal and military healthcare industrial office retail multi-family residential sports and fitness transportation and utilities among other fields.

Strategy

Whiting-Turner prefers to grow organically instead of making acquisitions. It has been steadily expanding by opening new offices in places such as California Texas and Virginia. The company in 2016 continued to rank among the Engineering News Record (ENR) top domestic general building contractors in the nation.

Some of the firm's recently awarded projects (as of mid-2016) include the Tropicana Pedestrian Bridge the Jacksonville Lung Bio Facility the Westowne Elementary School the Lexington Market the Costco Meat Production Plant the Sentara Norfolk General Hospital and the CoolSprings Galleria among others.

Whiting-Turner Contracting's past projects include the Joseph B. Whitehead Building at Emory University Vanderbilt Hall at Yale University projects at Universal Studios theme park and a vaccine facility at Chesapeake Biological Laboratories. Projects in the firm's hometown of Baltimore have included the city's convention center and the football stadium for the Baltimore Ravens. More recent projects include the Horseshoe Casino Cleveland University of Maryland Baltimore County (UMBC) Performing Arts & Humanities Naval Facilities Engineering Command (NAVFAC) Jacksonville Sentara Princess Anne Hospital Norwalk Community College Texas A&M University at Galveston Mary Moody Northen Student Center renovation Opry Mills the College of Business & Economics Vinson Hall Parking Garage a Coastal Studies Institute facility a Blue Diamond Growers building and a USPS Call Center.

Company Background

G.W.C. Whiting and LeBaron Turner classmates at MIT founded the company in 1909 to build sewer lines.

EXECUTIVES

Vp Richmond, Dani Niccolucci
Svp Allentown, Jack DaSilva
Division Vp Fort Lauderdale, Robert (Rob) Mitchell
Division Vp Delaware And Maryland, James (Jim) Martini
Svp District Of Columbia, Richard L. Vogel
Division Vp Pleasanton, Troy Caldwell
Svp Irvine, Len Cannatelli
Svp Baltimore, Gino J. Gemignani
Division Vp Dallas, Espen S. Brooks
Vp Bridgewater, Chris Martinson
Svp Atlanta, Keith Douglas
Vp, Daniel (Dan) Bauer
Vp Boston, Kevin Shields
Regional Manager Las Vegas, Paul Schmitt
Division Vp Chantilly, Kempton C. Haile
Vp Tampa, Brent A. Voyles
Vp Denver, Mark Faul
Vp San Diego, Steven Likins
Vp Orlando, Robert Minutoli
Division Vp Raleigh, Chris Carlson
Vp White Plains, David Brickley
Vp San Antonio, Daryl Steinbeck
Vp Norfolk, John Berotti
Senior Project Manager Sacramento, Jack Stackalis
Vp Cleveland, Jeff Maeder
Regional Manager Kansas City, Adam Eshelbrenner
Regional Manager Charlotte, Chris Woods
Regional Manager Houston, Michael Browning
President And Ceo, Timothy J. Regan, age 63
Vice President Worldwide Operations, Robert Ryan
Executive Vice President, Frank Palmer
Vice President, Vince Masciantonio
Vice President Mechanical Electrical Services, David Reitmeyer
Vice President Mission Critical Mechanical Electrical Services, Greg Botteon
Vice President Ashe Chc, Bob Moore
Vice President Finance And Operations, Nick Weiss
Leed Ap Banking Division C Vice President, Patricia Carper
Vice President, Karen Evans
Vice President, Irene Knott
Vice President, David McGinnis
Vice President, Damon Ellis
Vice President, Bruce Delawder
Vice President, Sam Abutaleb
Division Vice President, David Mallik
Vice President San Diego, Miguel Huerta
Vice President San Diego, Steve Likins
Vice President Information Technology, Joseph Dittmer
Division Vice President, Brian Ott
Vice President, Bill Wahl
Vice President, Jeffrey Baxter
Vice President, Craig Rayner
Vice President, Charles Konkolics
Vice President, Andrew Linden
Vice President, Maynard Grizzard
Vice President, Terry Powell
Senior Vice President, Stephen Lambertson
Senior Vice President, Ron Eisenberg
Vice President, Bill Whiting
Vice President, Thomas Monticup
Vice President, Pete Valianatos
Vice Chairman, Nick Bloch

LOCATIONS

HQ: THE WHITING-TURNER CONTRACTING COMPANY
300 E JOPPA RD STE 800, BALTIMORE, MD 212863047
Phone: 410 821-1100
Web: WWW.WHITING-TURNER.COM

Selected Locations

Maryland - Baltimore (Headquarters)
 California
California - Los Angeles
 California
 California
California - San Diego
Colorado -
Connecticut - New Haven
 Delaware -
District of Columbia
Florida - Ft. Lauderdale
 Florida -
 Florida -
 Georgia -
 Maryland -
 Massachuse
Missouri - Kansas City
Nevada - Las Vegas
 New Jersey
New York - White Plains
 North Caro
 North Caro
 Ohio - Cle
 Pennsylvan
 Texas - Da
 Texas - Ho
Texas - San Antonio

Virginia -
Virginia -
Virginia -

PRODUCTS/OPERATIONS

Selected Services
Construction management
  Agency
  At-risk
Design/build
General contracting
Preconstruction

Selected Markets
Biotechnology and pharmaceutical
Cleanroom and high-technology
Education
Entertainment
Federal/military
Food/beverage distribution
Health care
Historical restoration
Industrial and manufacturing
Interiors
Life sciences
Lodging and hospitality
Mission critical facilities
Mixed use
Offices and headquarters
Parking garages
Restaurants
Retail
Senior living
Sports
Sustainable
Technology
  Microelectronics
  Nano
Theme parks
Utilities
Warehouse and distribution

COMPETITORS

Barton Malow	J.E. Dunn Construction
Bechtel	Group
Choate Construction	Jacobs Engineering
Clark Construction	Kitchell
Group	McCarthy Building
DPR Construction	Peter Kiewit Sons'
Fisher Development	Skanska
Fluor	Suffolk Construction
Gilbane	Swinerton
Hensel Phelps	Turner Corporation
Construction	Tutor Perini
Hoffman Corporation	Weitz

HISTORICAL FINANCIALS

Company Type: Private

Income Statement				FYE: December 31
	REVENUE ($ mil.)	NET INCOME ($ mil.)	NET PROFIT MARGIN	EMPLOYEES
12/16	5,522	90	1.6%	4,043
12/15	5,729	80	1.4%	—
12/14	6,347	75	1.2%	—
Annual Growth	(6.7%)	9.8%	—	—

2016 Year-End Financials
Return on assets: 3.6%   Cash ($ mil.): 26
Return on equity: 11.4%
Current ratio: 1.40

THE WILLS GROUP INC

The Wills Group willingly delivers petroleum products and related products and services to its customer base in southern Maryland and adjacent areas. The family-owned company operates four business subsidiaries: Dash-In Convenience Stores (with 35 locations including 18 franchises); DMO (provider of propane heating oil and HVAC equipment); and Southern Maryland Oil (SMO) and SMO Motor Fuels (distribution of diesel gasoline and kerosene products). More than 90% of SMO's gasoline products are Shell-branded fuels. The Wills Group supplies more than 300 dealer-operated gas stations in Delaware southern Maryland and Washington DC.

Operations
The Wills Group divides its business into four operations: Dash-In Convenience Stores (serving the Maryland; Delaware; and Tidewater Virgina regions); DMO (propane heating oil and HVAC equipment maker); and Southern Maryland Oil (SMO) and SMO Motor Fuels (distribution of diesel gasoline and kerosene products).

Company Background
The company was founded in 1926 by Jim Wills and Harold Swann. In 1942 The Wills Group was the first principal fuel supplier to the newly built Patuxent Naval Air Station. In 1972 the company developed the first branded self-service station in Maryland. In 2012 Lock Wills was serving as the president of The Wills Group.

EXECUTIVES

Vice President, Joseph M Wills
Executive Vice President, Mark Oliver
Auditors: RSM US LLP

LOCATIONS

HQ: THE WILLS GROUP INC
6355 CRAIN HWY, LA PLATA, MD 206464267
Phone: 301 932-3600
Web: WWW.WILLSGROUP.COM

COMPETITORS

Dixie Gas & Oil	Weis Markets
Petroleum Marketers	Woodfin Oil
Quarles Petroleum	

HISTORICAL FINANCIALS

Company Type: Private

Income Statement				FYE: September 30
	REVENUE ($ mil.)	NET INCOME ($ mil.)	NET PROFIT MARGIN	EMPLOYEES
09/18	1,035	66	6.4%	450
09/17	654	27	4.3%	—
Annual Growth	58.1%	137.1%	—	—

2018 Year-End Financials
Return on assets: 14.2%   Cash ($ mil.): 27
Return on equity: 29.4%
Current ratio: 0.80

THEDACARE, INC.

ThedaCare is a community health system that provides a wide range of health services to residents of nine central Wisconsin counties. It consists of five hospitals including Appleton Medical Center Theda Clark Medical Center New London Family Medical Center Shawano Medical Center and Riverside Medical Center in Waupaca; more than 20 physician locations; and community health and wellness programs. The hospitals provide primary and acute care and offer many specialized diagnostic and medical services including behavioral health care and women's and children's services. ThedaCare also operates long-term care and assisted living facilities and provides occupational health and emergency transport services.

Operations
The health system operates five hospitals and 22 physician locations and manages 150000 patients per year.

Geographic Reach
ThedaCare serves patients in more than nine counties in Eastern Wisconsin.

Strategy
ThedaCare is expanding its facilities to keep pace with demand.

In 2013 it began construction on the ThedaCare Medical Center-Shawano which is being built to replace the 82-year-old Shawano Medical Center. The less-than-$50 million project is expected to open in 2015.

In 2012 the company opened a new outpatient unit (featuring five private rooms) at the New London Family Medical Center (renamed ThedaCare Medical Center-New London as part of a rebranding push in 2013).

Expanding its insurance options in 2013 ThedaCare joined Anthem Blue Cross and Blue Shield's Blue Priority Network. Blue Priority is Anthem Blue Cross and Blue Shield's Accountable Care Organization network offering in eastern Wisconsin and was launched in 2012.

EXECUTIVES

Cio, Keith Livingston
Chief Medical Officer, Dean Gruner, age 64
Senior Medical Officer, Greg Long
Vp Spine And Orthopedic Business, Mary Downs
Cfo, Tim Olson
Coo, Maryjeanne Schaffmeyer
Coo And Chief Nursing Executive, Laura Reed
Operating Room Dir, Heather Habeck
Chair, John Davis
Secretary, Lynn Gosse
Auditors: WIPFLI LLP MILWAUKEE WISCONS

LOCATIONS

HQ: THEDACARE, INC.
122 E COLLEGE AVE STE 2A, APPLETON, WI 549115741
Phone: 920 735-5560

PRODUCTS/OPERATIONS

Selected Facilities and Programs
Appleton Medical Center
The Heritage Community (senior living)
ThedaCare Medical Center-New London
Peabody Manor (senior living)
Riverside Medical Center
Shawano Medical Center
Theda Clark Medical Center
ThedaCare at Home
ThedaCare at Work (occupational health services)
ThedaCare Behavioral Health
ThedaCare Physicians

COMPETITORS

Aspirus
Beaver Dam Community Hospitals
Beloit Health System
Benedictine Health System
Children's Hospital and Health System
Columbia St. Mary's
Dean Health Systems Inc.
Howard Young Health Care
Luther Midelfort
Marian Health System
Marshfield Clinic Health System
Sacred Heart Hospital
Tomah Memorial Hospital
UW Medical Foundation
University of Wisconsin Hospital and Clinics

HISTORICAL FINANCIALS

Company Type: Private

Income Statement

FYE: December 31

	REVENUE ($ mil.)	NET INCOME ($ mil.)	NET PROFIT MARGIN	EMPLOYEES
12/18	995	(1)	—	7,000
12/17	909	88	9.7%	—
12/14	809	76	9.4%	—
12/13	720	129	18.0%	—
Annual Growth	**6.7%**	—	—	—

2018 Year-End Financials

Return on assets: (-0.1%)   Cash ($ mil.): 111
Return on equity: (-0.2%)
Current ratio: 5.40

THOMAS JEFFERSON UNIVERSITY

Thomas Jefferson University named after a founding father of diverse interests is itself diversifying the world of medical training. Its Sidney Kimmel Medical College (formerly Jefferson Medical College) boasts departments in surgery and specialized areas including obstetrics neurology and psychiatry. The Graduate Studies department offers programs in public health and biomedical studies. The College of Health Professions has programs in nursing pharmacy bioscience technologies and counseling. Founded as Jefferson Medical College in 1824 it has granted more than 30000 medical degrees. In mid-2017 the school merged with Philadelphia University a design-focused liberal arts school.

Operations

Thomas Jefferson University has six schools: Jefferson College of Biomedical Sciences; Sidney Kimmel Medical College; Jefferson College of Health Professions; Jefferson College of Nursing; Jefferson College of Pharmacy; and Jefferson College of Population Health. It also operates six academic centers: the Clinical Skills & Simulation Center; the Interprofessional Education Center; the Career Development Center; the Center for Teaching & Learning; the Sidney Kimmel Cancer Center; and the Institute of Emerging Health Professions. Plans are in place to establish the Philadelphia University Honors Institute and the Philadelphia University Design Institute. It also offers several continuing education programs.

The combined university serves some 7500 students.

The university's medical school tests or treats 46000 inpatients and more than 1 million outpatients each year.

Geographic Reach

Thomas Jefferson University has campuses in the Center City and East Falls areas of Philadelphia.

Strategy

In 2015 Thomas Jefferson University merged with Abington Health a Philadelphia health care organization with two hospitals and several clinics. The merger gave Abington access to the university's educational and training facilities and expands the university's reach to the Philadelphia suburbs. In 2016 the organization's medical operations combined forces with Aria Health which now operates as Aria — Jefferson Health.

When the school completed its merger with Philadelphia University in 2017 the enlarged university retained the Thomas Jefferson University moniker.

Seeking to increase its brand recognition Thomas Jefferson University has paid almost $4 million to put its name on the transit station at its campus. The station previously the Market East Station will be the Jefferson Station for five years. The university has an option to renew for a total of nine years.

EXECUTIVES

Vp Finance And Cfo, Richard J. Schmid
President, Stephen K. Klasko
Cio, Doug Herrick
Dean Jefferson Medical College, Richard J. Tykocinski
Dean Graduate School Of Biomedical Sciences, Gerald B. Grunwald
Dean School Of Health Professions, Janice Burke
Dean School Of Nursing, Beth A. Swan
Dean School Of Pharmacy, Rebecca S. Finley
Dean School Of Population Health, David Nash
Dean Students And Admissions, Clara A. Callahan
Evp Chief Operating Officer, Larry Merlis
Chairman, Richard C. Gozon, age 81
Auditors: PRICEWATERHOUSECOOPERS LLP PH

LOCATIONS

HQ: THOMAS JEFFERSON UNIVERSITY
1020 WALNUT ST STE 1, PHILADELPHIA, PA 191075567
Phone: 215 955-6000

PRODUCTS/OPERATIONS

Selected Research Centers and Institutes
Center for Translational Medicine
Daniel Baugh Institute
Delaware Health Science Alliance
Farber Institute for Neuroscience
Jefferson Coordinating Center for Clinical Research
Jefferson Vaccine Center
Kimmel Cancer Center

Selected Colleges and Schools
Sidney Kimmel Medical College
Jefferson Graduate School of Biomedical Sciences
Jefferson School of Health Professions
Jefferson School of Nursing
Jefferson School of Pharmacy
Jefferson School of Population Health

HISTORICAL FINANCIALS

Company Type: Private

Income Statement

FYE: June 30

	REVENUE ($ mil.)	NET INCOME ($ mil.)	NET PROFIT MARGIN	EMPLOYEES
06/17	3,951	700	17.7%	10,625
06/16	136	8	6.5%	—
Annual Growth	**2788.6%**	**7723.4%**	—	—

2017 Year-End Financials

Return on assets: 12.0%   Cash ($ mil.): 259
Return on equity: 23.1%
Current ratio: 3.20

THOMAS JEFFERSON UNIVERSITY HOSPITALS, INC.

Named after the "Man of the People" Thomas Jefferson University Hospitals (dba Jefferson Health) serves the people of the Keystone State with a medical staff of more than 1200 and some 1550 beds. The system provides acute tertiary and specialty medical care from a dozen hospitals nearly 20 outpatient centers and about 10 urgent care centers. The hospital also administers cardiac care at the Jefferson Heart Institute which provides everything from minimally invasive surgical procedures to heart transplants. Additionally Jefferson Health operates as the teaching hospital for Thomas Jefferson University.

Operations

As part of its operations Jefferson Health offers several premier programs to its patients as well as 35 different specialties. The system performed Delaware Valley's first liver transplant and designated a kidney transplant center for live and deceased donor transplants. In addition to transplantation it provides surgical services heart and vascular digestive diseases and bones and joints in addition to its Kimmel Cancer Canter and Jefferson Hospital for Neuroscience. In 2014 the health system logged more than 470000 outpatient visits 45000 admissions and about 115000 emergency room visits.

Geographic Reach

Through a handful of locations Jefferson Health provides health care services to the residents of Philadelphia and the Delaware Valley. It shares a 13-acre campus with Thomas Jefferson University.

Strategy

In October 2017 Jefferson Health merged with New Jersey-based Kennedy Health which operated three hospitals. The transaction followed closely on the heels of Jefferson's mergers with Aria Health and Abington Health.

In 2015 Jefferson Health added a new feature to its telemedicine program JeffConnect called On-Demand Virtual Care which allows patients to connect with an emergency medicine physician via computers and mobile devices.

That year the Philadelphia 76ers partnered with the Rothman Institute and Jefferson Health. The Rothman Institute will provide the Official Orthopedics & Urgent Care of the Philadelphia 76ers as well as the Official Team Physicians; Jefferson Health became an official hospital of the Philadelphia 76ers.

In 2014 the system opened the Jefferson Angioplasty Center the outpatient practice for Jefferson's interventional cardiologists. It is co-located with the Vascular Center allowing for streamlined consultations and convenience as the two specialties often see the same patients.

That year it also introduced genomic analyses of breast cancer in-house using the Prosigna Breast Cancer Prognostic Gene Signature Assay significantly reducing turn-around time for test results and allowing patients to begin effective treatment sooner.

Company Background

Thomas Jefferson University Hospital was founded in 1825.

EXECUTIVES

Blood Bank Director, Jay Herman
Vice President Clinical Resource Management, Patrice Miller
Vice President Hospital Administration, Richard Webster
Vice President Finance, Elizabeth Smith
Pharmacy Manager, Robert Mcnutt
Managing Director Geriatric Medicine, Lilia Lakhtman
Director Of Clinical Services Administrator Musculoskeletal Service Line, Kristen Vogl
Senior Vice President Clinical Service, Rebecca Oshea
Secretary, Gerri Anderson

LOCATIONS

HQ: THOMAS JEFFERSON UNIVERSITY HOSPITALS, INC.
   111 S 11TH ST, PHILADELPHIA, PA 191074824
Phone: 215 955-5806

PRODUCTS/OPERATIONS

Selected Services

Cancer
Diabetes & Endocrinology
Ear Nose & Throat
Gastroenterology
Geriatrics
Gynecology
Nephrology
Orthopedics
Pulmonology
Rehabilitation
Urology

Selected University Locations

Jefferson at the Navy Yard
Jefferson Medical College
Jefferson College of Graduate Studies
Jefferson Radiology
Jefferson School of Health Professions
Jefferson School of Nursing
Jefferson School of Pharmacy
Jefferson School of Population Health
Jefferson Voorhees

COMPETITORS

Albert Einstein Healthcare Network
Bryn Mawr Hospital
Community Health Systems
Doylestown Hospital
Mercy Health System
North Philadelphia Health System
Our Lady of Lourdes Medical Center
Pennsylvania Hospital
TUHS
Universal Health Services
University of Pennsylvania Health System

HISTORICAL FINANCIALS

Company Type: Private

Income Statement				FYE: June 30
	REVENUE ($ mil.)	NET INCOME ($ mil.)	NET PROFIT MARGIN	EMPLOYEES
06/16	1,495	76	5.1%	4,701
06/15	1,456	42	2.9%	—
06/14	1,510	51	3.4%	—
06/10	1,250	49	4.0%	—
Annual Growth	3.0%	7.7%	—	—

2016 Year-End Financials

Return on assets: 4.4%   Cash ($ mil.): 57
Return on equity: 8.7%
Current ratio: 3.20

THOMPSON CREEK METALS COMPANY USA

EXECUTIVES

Pres-Ceo, Jacques Perron
Chb*, Kevin Loughrey
V Pres*, Robert Dorfler
Cfo*, Pamela L Saxton
Accounting Staff, Jamie Patterson
Coordinator, Raymond Gelinas
Manager, Mark Piper
Director, Robert Clifford
Auditors: KPMG LLP DENVER COLORADO

LOCATIONS

HQ: THOMPSON CREEK METALS COMPANY USA
   26 W DRY CREEK CIR # 225, LITTLETON, CO
   801208064
Phone: 303 761-8801

HISTORICAL FINANCIALS

Company Type: Private

Income Statement				FYE: December 31
	REVENUE ($ mil.)	NET INCOME ($ mil.)	NET PROFIT MARGIN	EMPLOYEES
12/14	806	(124)	—	1,700
12/13	434	(215)	—	—
12/12	401	(546)	—	—
Annual Growth	41.8%	—	—	—

2014 Year-End Financials

Return on assets: (-4.4%)   Cash ($ mil.): 265
Return on equity: (-14.0%)
Current ratio: 2.50

THRUWAY AUTHORITY OF NEW YORK STATE

Leaving Manhattan or Brooklyn to shuffle off to Buffalo? The New York State Thruway Authority oversees a 641-mile toll road system and a 524-mile canal system. The authority's toll road system known as the Governor Thomas E. Dewey Thruway is the largest in the US. It crosses the state from New York City to Buffalo and more than 80% of the population of New York State lives along the corridor formed by the Thruway's 426-mile main line. Other arms of the Thruway connect with toll roads and other highways in neighboring states. TheÂ New York State Canal Corporation oversees the state's canal system of five lakes andÂ four canalsÂ which connect bodies of water such as the Hudson River withÂ Lake Champlain.

EXECUTIVES

Xec Dir, Thomas Madison
Exec Dir*, Michael R Fleischer
Cfo*, John Bryan
Executive Director*, Bill Finch
Manager, James Benoit
Information Specialist, Shawn Mancini
Information Specialist, James Fogarty
Assistant, James Chicoine

Legal Staff, Marcy Dikeman
Buyer, Amy Bartczak
Software Engineer, Gene Greger
Auditors: TOSKI & CO CPAS PC WILLI

LOCATIONS

HQ: THRUWAY AUTHORITY OF NEW YORK STATE
   200 SOUTHERN BLVD, ALBANY, NY 122092018
Phone: 518 436-2700
Web: WWW.THRUWAY.NY.GOV

HISTORICAL FINANCIALS

Company Type: Private

Income Statement				FYE: December 31
	REVENUE ($ mil.)	NET INCOME ($ mil.)	NET PROFIT MARGIN	EMPLOYEES
12/10	674	(127)	—	2,840
12/09	640	(129)	—	—
12/08	598	(129)	—	—
Annual Growth	6.1%	—	—	—

2010 Year-End Financials

Return on assets: (-2.3%)   Cash ($ mil.): 203
Return on equity: (-6.1%)
Current ratio: 0.80

TMH PHYSICIAN ORGANIZATION

EXECUTIVES

V Pres-Ceo, John Lyle
Dir-Treas, Mike Giblin
Treas, Edward L Tyrrell
SEC, Marc L Boom
Manager, Ganesh Kalambur
Coordinator, Jennifer Hamilton
Information Specialist, Thomas Daubner
Vice-President, Liisa Ortegon
Vice-President, Hackett Carole
Manager, Jill Roach
Consultant, Jose Solis

LOCATIONS

HQ: TMH PHYSICIAN ORGANIZATION
   6565 FANNIN ST STE D200, HOUSTON, TX
   770302703
Phone: 713 441-4182
Web: WWW.HOUSTONMETHODIST.ORG

HISTORICAL FINANCIALS

Company Type: Private

Income Statement				FYE: December 31
	REVENUE ($ mil.)	NET INCOME ($ mil.)	NET PROFIT MARGIN	EMPLOYEES
12/17	532	(0)	—	11
12/15	413	0	0.2%	—
12/14	360	1	0.5%	—
Annual Growth	13.9%	—	—	—

2017 Year-End Financials

Return on assets: (-0.5%)   Cash ($ mil.): —
Return on equity: —
Current ratio: 0.50

TOLEDO PUBLIC SCHOOLS

EXECUTIVES

Pres, Bob Vasquez
V Pres*, Chris Varwig
Chb*, Cecelia Adams
Supt*, Romules Durant
Board of Directors*, Lisa Sobecki
Prin*, Polly Taylor-Gerken
Accounting Staff, Bodi S Sharon
Accounting Staff, Gloria Eckhart
Accounting Staff, Joan Jockett
Coordinator, Paula Martin
Acting Director, Teresa Quinn
Auditors: MARY TAYLOR CPA TOLEDO OH

LOCATIONS

HQ: TOLEDO PUBLIC SCHOOLS
   1609 N SUMMIT ST, TOLEDO, OH 436041806
Phone: 419 729-8200
Web: WWW.TPS.ORG

HISTORICAL FINANCIALS

Company Type: Private

Income Statement				FYE: June 30
	REVENUE ($ mil.)	NET INCOME ($ mil.)	NET PROFIT MARGIN	EMPLOYEES
06/18	466	15	3.4%	3,600
06/17	454	7	1.7%	—
06/16	441	13	3.2%	—
Annual Growth	2.8%	7.1%	—	—

2018 Year-End Financials

Return on assets: 1.5%   Cash ($ mil.): 185
Return on equity: 7.6%
Current ratio: —

TOM LANGE COMPANY, INC.

Tom Lange Company wants you to eat your veggies.Â One of the largest purchasers and distributors of fresh fruits and vegetables in theÂ US Tom LangeÂ supplies its comestibles to clientsÂ in the retail wholesale andÂ food service trades.Â The company also provides third party logistics services specializing in truckload freight movement. The company was founded in 1960 as a three-man operation in St. Louis Missouri Tom Lange has grown toÂ encompass 35 offices in the US and Canada. Produce subsidiaries include Seven Seas M&M Marketing and Seven Seas Fruit.

EXECUTIVES

Vice President Imports, Bill Weyland
Auditors: KERBER ECK & BRAECKEL LLP S

LOCATIONS

HQ: TOM LANGE COMPANY, INC.
   755 APPLE ORCHARD RD, SPRINGFIELD, IL
   627035914
Phone: 217 786-3300
Web: WWW.TOMLANGE.COM

HISTORICAL FINANCIALS

Company Type: Private

Income Statement				FYE: August 31
	REVENUE ($ mil.)	NET INCOME ($ mil.)	NET PROFIT MARGIN	EMPLOYEES
08/17	471	7	1.6%	110
08/16	466	2	0.6%	—
08/15	441	1	0.2%	—
08/14	447	(19)	—	—
Annual Growth	1.7%	—	—	—

2017 Year-End Financials

Return on assets: 9.4%   Cash ($ mil.): 15
Return on equity: 23.7%
Current ratio: 1.70

TRAMMO, INC.

Stockpiles of fertilizers liquefied petroleum gas (LPG) and petrochemicals are the "ammo" which international trader Trammo (formerly Transammonia) uses in its battle with competitors. The company trades distributes and transports these commodities around the world. Trammo's fertilizer business includes ammonia phosphates and urea. Its Sea-3 subsidiary imports and distributes propane to residential commercial and industrial customers in the northeastern US and Florida. The Trammochem unit trades in petrochemicals specializing in aromatics and olefins. Its Trammo Gas trades LPG and propane as well as ethane butane and natural gas in the US.

Operations

The company operates three divisions: Chemicals Commodities and Gas. The Chemicals Division's annual sales volumes is about 5.6 million metric tons. It key products include aromatics olefins and oxygenates. The Commodities Division accounts for two thirds of the Trammo's sales volumes and more than half of its revenues; it's worldwide traded volume is 29.2 million metric tons a year. The Gas Division's business areas include LPG business Trammo Gas and Petrochemicals Ltd and Sea-3 Inc. Trammo's international traded ammonia volume is 3 million metric tons annually.

Sea-3 is the largest importer and distributor of liquefied propane in the Northeastern US. It also supplies propane to the western and central portions of Florida. It moves 200000 metric tons of product per year.

Trammochem merchandises and trades in petrochemicals around the world.

Trammo Gas markets and trades LPG (primarily propane) in the US. Trammo Gas International Inc. operates two gas carriers which transport LPG worldwide for third parties.

Geographic Reach

Trammo has expanded its reach into the global market establishing merchandising and trading offices in Singapore China and the United Arab Emirates. Those offices complement its other global operations in Africa Asia Europe the Middle East and North and South America (Argentina Brazil and Chile). It has major representative offices in Beijing Cairo Dubai and Shanghai.

Its Fertilizers and Commodities Division's regional hubs are in Zurich Tampa Dubai Shanghai and Singapore; the Ammonia Division has hubs in Tampa and Dubai. The Chemicals Division maintains regional hubs in Zurich Dubai Shanghai and Singapore; while the Gas Division maintains hubs in Houston Tampa and Newington (New Hampshire).

Trammo has about 30 offices worldwide.

Sales and Marketing

To bridge the gap between the production locations and consumers sites Trammo owns and operates a fleet of railcars dedicated to transporting of molten sulfur in across the US. The Commodities Division about 650 railcars to ship dry and liquid fertilizers sulfur sulfuric acid and ammonia.

Strategy

In late 2016 it was reported that Trammo would exit the petrochemicals trading market following a reorganization.

In 2015 the company's Ammonia Division and Fertilizers and Commodities Division merged into a new division — Commodities. The merger allows Trammo to increase operational synergies use its global infrastructure to provide a larger portfolio of products and to more clearly present itself as a single company with different products.

Trammo opened offices in Ivory Coast and Dar Es Salaam in 2014 to strengthens its presence in the emerging African market.

Company Background

In 2013 Transammonia changed its name to Trammo to more accurately represent the broad spectrum of products and services it provides.

In 2010 the company's bulk carriers division entered the commodity shipping business. TA Bulk Carriers operates a fleet of 15 to 20 vessels which trade worldwide but focus on the handysize market (25000-35000 metric tons deadweight) in the Atlantic basin. In 2010 it transported about 2.9 million metric tons of cargo primarily fertilizers and grains.

Ronald Stanton founded the company in 1965 as an international ammonia trader. It branched into fertilizer merchandising and trading in 1967 LPG trading in 1978 and petrochemicals trading in 1987.

EXECUTIVES

Evp Coo And Cfo, Edward G. Weiner
Ceo Chemicals Division, Ashok Kishore
President Ceo Director And Ceo Commodities Division, Brent Hart
Svp Global Risk Management, Oliver K. Stanton
Senior Vice President, Dudley Cox
Senior Vice President Chief Accounting Officer, Robert Lovett
Vice President Of Human Resources, Pat Berry
Assistant Vice President, Donald Madden
Assistant Vice President, Jorge Melazzini
Vice President General Manager Europe, Mario Bassoni
Senior Vice President Member Of Senior Management, Santiago Orol
Auditors: RSM US LLP

LOCATIONS

HQ: TRAMMO, INC.
   667 MADISON AVE FL 4, NEW YORK, NY 100658029
Phone: 212 223-3200

PRODUCTS/OPERATIONS

Major SubsidiariesSea-3 (liquefied propane)Trammo Gas (LPG)Trammo Gas International Inc. (LPG transportation for third parties.Trammo Petroleum (crude oil and oil products)Trammochem (petrochemicals)Fertilizers and CommoditiesNitrogen BasedAnhydrous Ammo

COMPETITORS

BASF SE	HELM
CF Industries	Koch Industries Inc.
Cargill	Magellan Midstream
ConAgra	Yara

HISTORICAL FINANCIALS

Company Type: Private

Income Statement				FYE: December 31
	REVENUE ($ mil.)	NET INCOME ($ mil.)	NET PROFIT MARGIN	EMPLOYEES
12/18	3,212	(12)	—	250
12/16	6,453	(229)	—	—
12/14	11,266	31	0.3%	—
Annual Growth	(26.9%)	—	—	—

2018 Year-End Financials

Return on assets: (-2.0%)
Return on equity: (-9.7%)
Current ratio: 1.20
Cash ($ mil.): 96

TRI STAR ENERGY, LLC

EXECUTIVES

Mng MBR, John B Jewell III
Director of Operations, Rick Hamilton
Manager, Randy Alexander
Facilities Vice-President, Charlton Bell
Vice-President, Liane Taylor
R Credit Manager, Belinda Hilliard
Manager, Jack Cooper
District Manager, Keith Middleton
Database Analyst, Mark Roark
Vice President of Commercial F, Rob Jewell
Environmental Compliance Manag, Steve Biles
Auditors: LATTIMORE BLACK MORGAAN & CA

LOCATIONS

HQ: TRI STAR ENERGY, LLC
 1740 ED TEMPLE BLVD, NASHVILLE, TN 372081850
Phone: 615 313-3600
Web: WWW.TRISTARTN.COM

HISTORICAL FINANCIALS

Company Type: Private

Income Statement				FYE: December 31
	REVENUE ($ mil.)	NET INCOME ($ mil.)	NET PROFIT MARGIN	EMPLOYEES
12/11	730	3	0.5%	500
12/10	635	4	0.7%	—
12/09	547	0	0.0%	—
Annual Growth	15.5%	399.7%	—	—

2011 Year-End Financials

Return on assets: 3.1%
Return on equity: 7.4%
Current ratio: 0.70
Cash ($ mil.): —

TRIBOROUGH BRIDGE & TUNNEL AUTHORITY

EXECUTIVES

V Pres-Pres, Michael C Ascher
Offc Mgr, Choling Blakey
Contrl, Jim Elkin
Engineer, Teresa Ceragioli

LOCATIONS

HQ: TRIBOROUGH BRIDGE & TUNNEL AUTHORITY ROBERT MOSES BLDG RANDAL, NEW YORK, NY 10035
Phone: 212 360-3000

HISTORICAL FINANCIALS

Company Type: Private

Income Statement				FYE: December 31
	REVENUE ($ mil.)	NET INCOME ($ mil.)	NET PROFIT MARGIN	EMPLOYEES
12/18	1,999	453	22.7%	1,500
12/17	1,931	282	14.6%	—
12/16	1,895	202	10.7%	—
12/15	1,843	165	9.0%	—
Annual Growth	2.8%	39.9%	—	—

2018 Year-End Financials

Return on assets: 5.6%
Return on equity: —
Current ratio: 0.90
Cash ($ mil.): 10

TRINITY HEALTH

EXECUTIVES

Ceo, John M Kutch
Chm*, Patrick Holien
Cfo*, Dennis Empey
SEC-Treas*, Karen Krebsbach
Svp-Cso*, Sheri Shapiro
Personnel Executive, Renae Lenertz
Vice-President Legal, Karen Haroutunian
Vice-President Finance, Lannie Checketts
Human Resources, Courtney Arrington
Administrative Assistant, Diane Shaw
Coordinator, Dorian Moore
Auditors: CLIFTONLARSONALLEN LLP MINNEA

LOCATIONS

HQ: TRINITY HEALTH
 1 BURDICK EXPY W, MINOT, ND 587014406
Phone: 701 857-5260

HISTORICAL FINANCIALS

Company Type: Private

Income Statement				FYE: June 30
	REVENUE ($ mil.)	NET INCOME ($ mil.)	NET PROFIT MARGIN	EMPLOYEES
06/18	463	27	6.0%	2,600
06/17	445	15	3.5%	—
06/16	455	17	3.8%	—
06/15	430	16	3.9%	—
Annual Growth	2.4%	18.5%	—	—

2018 Year-End Financials

Return on assets: 3.8%
Return on equity: 12.5%
Current ratio: 2.50
Cash ($ mil.): 44

TRINITY HEALTH CORPORATION

EXECUTIVES

Pres-Ceo, Michael Slubowski
Sr V Pres-Cmo, Donald Bignotti
Sr V Pres-Chief Investment Off, James Bosscher
Sr V Pres, Paul F Conlon
Sr V Pres, Louis J Fierens II
Sr V Pres, Rebecca Havlisch
Sr V Pres-Chief Nursing Care, G Landstrom
Sr V Pres-Chief Info Officer, Marcus B Shipley
SEC, Paul G Neumann
Coo, Benjamin Carter
Chief Expi Officer, Cassandra Willis-Abner
Auditors: DELOITTE & TOUCHE LLP DETROIT

LOCATIONS

HQ: TRINITY HEALTH CORPORATION
 20555 VICTOR PKWY, LIVONIA, MI 481527031
Phone: 734 343-1000
Web: WWW.TRINITY-HEALTH.ORG

COMPETITORS

Advocate Health Care	Odyssey HealthCare
Amedisys	OhioHealth
Ascension Health	Resurrection Health
Beaumont Health System	Care
Community Health	St. Luke's Health
Systems	System
HCA	Tenet Healthcare
Health Management	Universal Health
Associates	Services
HealthSouth	University of Chicago
Henry Ford Health	Medical Center
System	VITAS Healthcare
Hospice of Michigan	Vanguard Health
Johns Hopkins Medicine	Systems
Kindred Healthcare	Wheaton Franciscan
Mayo Clinic	Services
MedStar Health	
Memorial Hospital	
& Health System	

HISTORICAL FINANCIALS

Company Type: Private

Income Statement				FYE: June 30
	REVENUE ($ mil.)	NET INCOME ($ mil.)	NET PROFIT MARGIN	EMPLOYEES
06/18	18,345	1,358	7.4%	51,100
06/15	1,375	19	1.4%	—
Annual Growth	137.1%	314.2%	—	—

2018 Year-End Financials

Return on assets: 5.2%
Return on equity: 10.2%
Current ratio: 1.90
Cash ($ mil.): 971

TRINITY HEALTH-MICHIGAN

EXECUTIVES

Ceo, Rebekah Smith
Cfo*, Mike Gusho
Director of Geriatric Programs, Mary Jo West
Coordinator, Catherine Popour
Coordinator, Jan Hansen
Coordinator, Karen Dalton
Coordinator, Kim Graham
Event Coordinator, Keri Larsen
Regional Director of Reimburse, Cheri Minock
Sleep Lab Manager, Rosemary Bruno
Director of Cyber Security, Shaun Swenson

LOCATIONS

HQ: TRINITY HEALTH-MICHIGAN
20555 VICTOR PKWY, LIVONIA, MI 481527031
Phone: 810 985-1500
Web: WWW.TRINITY-HEALTH.ORG

HISTORICAL FINANCIALS

Company Type: Private

Income Statement — FYE: June 30

	REVENUE ($ mil.)	NET INCOME ($ mil.)	NET PROFIT MARGIN	EMPLOYEES
06/18	3,595	303	8.4%	1,500
06/14	2,474	102	4.2%	—
06/13	2,475	138	5.6%	—
06/09	2,096	60	2.9%	—
Annual Growth	6.2%	19.6%	—	—

TRUMAN ARNOLD COMPANIES

TAC (previously Truman Arnold Companies) is one of the largest independent fuel wholesalers and aviation service providers in the US. Its energy business markets and sells more than 1.5 billion gallons of fuel to customers in industries like energy retail trucking utilities mining and construction. The company supplies refined products like gasoline diesel biodiesel ethanol renewable fuels and Diesel Exhaust Fluid (a non-hazardous product). TAC also serves the aviation industry by selling aviation fuel and providing Fixed Base Operations (aircraft fueling hangar space and transport) through some 15 locations in the US. Providing private charter flights and aircraft maintenance services is a small part of the company's business.

Operations

TAC operates through three major businesses ? TACenergy TAC Air (including Keystone Aviation) and TAC Investments.

Based in Dallas Texas TACenergy sells an annual fuel volume of more than 1.5 billion gallons through a vast terminal supply network. This segment also provides a 24/7 logistics call center a bulk trading desk and a real-time inventory intelligence service (matching inventory supply with trading prices) that helps minimize fuel costs for customers. A fleet upgrading program helps customers shift their fleet to biofuel-compatible engines that meet local state and federal regulations.

TAC Air is the company's aviation division which sells competitively priced aviation fuel and provides Fixed Base Operation services including ground handling aircraft fueling hangar space aircraft maintenance cargo handling and de-icing. Through Keystone Aviation this division also provides private charter flights aircraft management aircraft maintenance and a brokerage service.

The third segment TAC Investments manages the company's capital by investing in a wide pool of assets.

Sales and Marketing

TAC provides fuel and aviation services across the US through its major business lines.

Based in Dallas Texas TACenergy sells branded retail fuel to a range of customers including convenience stores supermarkets government agencies and industrial companies. The company has a vast terminal supply network with outlets across the continent plus a 24/7 logistical call center.

TAC Air has around 15 service centers in some ten US states.

Mergers and Acquisitions

TAC strengthened its energy business in 2018. Targeting an expansion into the US Southwest TACenergy acquired petroleum commodity supply and logistics firm Desert Fuels. The terms of the sale between the two privately held companies were not disclosed.

Company Background

Truman Arnold Companies was founded in 1964 as a Texas-based Conoco Distributor. It once operated a chain of 125 Road Runner convenience stores in eight states before selling this network to Total Petroleum in 1989. It revived the brand in 2003. The company presently focuses on fuel marketing and providing aviation services doing business under the TAC business name.

EXECUTIVES

General Counsel And Senior Vice President, James H Day
President And Coo, Gregory A. (Greg) Arnold
Svp And Cfo, Steve McMillen
Vp And Cio, Michael Davis
Vice President Marketing, Tad Perryman
Chairman And Ceo, Truman Arnold
Auditors: THOMAS & THOMAS LLP TEXARKANA

LOCATIONS

HQ: TRUMAN ARNOLD COMPANIES
701 S ROBISON RD, TEXARKANA, TX 755016747
Phone: 903 794-3835
Web: WWW.THEARNOLDCOS.COM

COMPETITORS

Atlantic Aviation	Sun Coast Resources
Million Air	
Petroleum Traders Corporation	

HISTORICAL FINANCIALS

Company Type: Private

Income Statement — FYE: September 30

	REVENUE ($ mil.)	NET INCOME ($ mil.)	NET PROFIT MARGIN	EMPLOYEES
09/18	3,174	18	0.6%	550
09/17	2,119	18	0.9%	—
09/16	1,525	18	1.2%	—
09/15	1,595	17	1.1%	—
Annual Growth	25.8%	1.2%	—	—

2018 Year-End Financials

Return on assets: 5.2%
Return on equity: 14.2%
Current ratio: 1.30
Cash ($ mil.): 2

TRUMAN MEDICAL CENTER, INCORPORATED

Truman Medical Center (TMC) provides primary and mental health care at two not-for-profit hospitals in the Kansas City (Missouri) area with a combined total of about 540 beds. Its Hospital Hill runs one of the busiest emergency rooms in Kansas City and is known for treatments related to asthma diabetes obstetrics ophthalmology weight management and women's health. TMC Lakewood is a leading academic medical center providing a range of health care services to the greater Kansas City metropolitan area including uninsured patients.

Operations

The hospital system has a combined capacity of more than 540 beds including 353 acute-care beds and 188 long-term-care beds. With a medical staff of more than 500 TMC admits more than 22000 patients and handles more than 322000 medical outpatient visits and more than 226000 mental health visits annually. It also treats more than 101000 emergency room patients every year.

Truman Medical Center Hospital Hill provides an array of acute care and outpatient services. In addition to Emergency Medicine and Trauma TMC Hospital Hill is also noted for treatments of asthma and diabetes and for providing obstetrics ophthalmology weight management and women's health programs.

TMC Lakewood is home to the University of Missouri Kansas City School of Medicine Community and Family Medicine Residency program.

Truman Medical Centers Behavioral Health is a leader in the treatment of mental health and substance abuse treatment. It serves more than 17000 patients a year and provides a comprehensive array of mental health and substance abuse treatment to persons living in the Kansas City Missouri metropolitan area.

Sales and Marketing

Medicare and Medicaid combined account for around half of TMC's net patient revenues; self-pay accounts represent about 35%.

Financial Performance

In fiscal 2014 (ended June) net revenues totaled $422 million.

Strategy

The system expands health care offerings by opening new care centers or by adding on to its existing ones. For example during 2014 it opened The Richard and Annette Bloch Cancer Center. It also opened Fairmount Family Medical Care in Western Independence Missouri a community that hadn't had a comprehensive health care facility since 2007.

It has also recently added a wound care center to its Hospital Hill campus.

Due to state and federal regulations TMC shut down the behavioral health emergency department at Hospital Hill in 2015. Going forward it will either treat incoming patients with acute mental health crises at its 47-bed standard emergency department or send them to another psychiatric facility.

EXECUTIVES

Cfo, Allen (Al) Johnson
Evp Clinical Coordination, Mark S. McPhee
Chief Medical Officer, Mark T. Steele
Coo Behavioral Health, Marsha L. Morgan
Svp Strategy Business Development And Performance Integration; Cio, Mitzi Cardenas
Corporate Quality Medical Director, Shauna R. Roberts

Coo, Lynette Wheeler
President And Ceo, Charles W. (Charlie) Shields
Vp Professional Health Services, Lynda Donegan
Executive Director Tmc Charitable Foundation, Karlyn Wilkins
Chief Nursing Officer, Amy Peters
Director Of Physical Therapy, Joel Hennenfent
Director Of Pharmacy, Erin Pender
First Vice President, Jerre Wiggans
Vice President Audit And Compliance, Barbara Zubeck
Auditors: BKD LLP KANSAS CITY MO

LOCATIONS

HQ: TRUMAN MEDICAL CENTER, INCORPORATED
2301 HOLMES ST, KANSAS CITY, MO 641082677
Phone: 816 404-1000
Web: WWW.TRUMED.ORG

PRODUCTS/OPERATIONS

Truman Medical Center Hospital Hill
Asthma Center
The Birthplace
Cardiovascular Center
Chiropractic Services KC CORE
Dental Maxillofacial Surgery
Diabetes Center
Emergency Care
Eye Clinic
Eye Foundation
GI Gastrointestinal
Hospital Hill Medical Pavilion
Infectious Disease Clinic
Oncology
Orthopaedics
Pulmonary Fibrosis
Radiology Services
Rehabilitation Services
Sickle Cell Disease Center
Sleep Center
Trauma Services
TruMed Clinic
Weight Management
Women's Care Breast Center
Women's Health Services
TMC Lakewood
Family Medicine Center
Lakewood Family Birthplace
Chiropractic Services
Counseling Services Lakewood
Dental Services
Dental Services Elks Mobile
GI Gastrointestinal
Emergency Medicine
Eye Care Center
Lakewood Medical Pavilion
Longterm Care Center
Medical Detox
Orthopaedic Services
Outpatient Surgery Center
Podiatry
Rehabilitation Services
Sports Medicine
Women's Health Services

COMPETITORS

Ascension Health	Shawnee Mission
Children's Mercy	Medical Center
Hospital	University of Kansas
CoxHealth	Medical Center
Saint Luke's Health	Via Christi Health
System	System

HISTORICAL FINANCIALS
Company Type: Private

Income Statement   FYE: June 30

	REVENUE ($ mil.)	NET INCOME ($ mil.)	NET PROFIT MARGIN	EMPLOYEES
06/18	562	22	4.0%	3,000
06/14	418	(78)	—	—
06/13	493	(4)	—	—
06/10	439	5	1.2%	—
Annual Growth	3.1%	20.3%	—	—

2018 Year-End Financials
Return on assets: 5.9%   Cash ($ mil.): 10
Return on equity: 23.1%
Current ratio: 1.40

TRUSTEES OF BOSTON COLLEGE

Students at Boston College (BC) get both academic excellence and the Red Sox. Located six miles from downtown Boston the university enrolls 14100 full- and part-time students (about a third of whom are graduate students) from every state in the US and 80 other countries. It has a student-teacher ratio of 13:1. BC offers degrees in more than 50 fields of study through its schools and colleges on four campuses. The university also has more than 20 research centers including the Institute for Scientific Research and the Center for International Higher Education. BC is one of the oldest Jesuit Catholic universities in the nation and has the largest Jesuit community in the world.

Operations
About 70% of its undergraduate student body are self-identified as Roman Catholic.

The university is home to more than 20 centers and institutes designated for research and teaching. Research opportunities including participation in faculty research projects exist for both undergraduate and graduate students. It also houses 8 libraries with 2.9 million volumes.

The cost of tuition stood a $46670 for 2014-15.

Geographic Reach
The university has campuses in Brighton Chestnut Hill Dover and Newton Massachusetts. It also operates a campus in Dublin Ireland.

Financial Performance
BC has enjoyed steady growth from voluntary giving by its alumni. Its endowment has grown to $2.2 billion placing it among the top 40 in the US. In 2014 it reported an operating budget of $917 million. Its revenues of $702.7 million were 5% up on the previous year due to growth in tuition and fees as well as auxiliary enterprises.

Strategy
BC's strategic plan includes adding 100 new faculty positions expanding research by faculty and graduate students increasing student financial aid to more than $128 million annually and extending undergraduate opportunities in international study internships and student formation. In 2013 it announced plans to build a $90 million residence hall near its Chestnut Hill campus.

Company Background
The university was founded by Jesuits in 1863. During its first seven decades BC was an exclusively undergraduate institution that served sons of the Irish working class. Its liberal arts emphasis was on the Greek and Latin classics English and

modern languages and philosophy and religion. Development into the college it is today did not begin until the 1920s when the Graduate School of Arts and Sciences the Law School and the Evening College (known today as the James A. Woods S.J. College of Advancing Studies) were inaugurated. All classes became co-educational in the 1970s and today BC has a fairly equal split among male and female students.

EXECUTIVES

Vice President Human Resources, Leo Sullivan
President, William P. Leahy
Chancellor, J. Donald Monan
Dean Carroll School Of Management, Andrew C. Boynton
Dean School Of Social Work, Alberto Godenzi
Evp, Patrick J. Keating
Associate Vp Applications And Systems Services, Michael Bourque
Financial Vp And Treasurer, John D. Burke
Provost And Dean Of Faculties, David Quigley
Dean Of Students, Tom Mogan
Dean School Of Theology And Ministry, Mark Massa
Dean Connell School Of Nursing, Susan Gennaro
Dean Lynch School Of Education, Maureen E. Kenny
Dean Law School, Vincent Rougeau
Interim Dean Morrissey College Of Arts And Sciences, Gregory Kalscheur
Dean Woods College Of Advancing Studies, James Burns
Vice President Information Technology, Mark Ben
Vice President, John Westman
Vice President Governmental And Community Affairs, Thomas Keady
Vice President For Student Affairs, Barbara Jones
Associate Vice President Human Resources, Robert Lewis
Associate Vice President For Student Affairs, George Arey
Vice President University Mission And, Joseph Appleyard
Assistant Vice President, Steven Sass
Associate Vice President Alumni Relations, Joy Moore
Vice President, Madeleine G Moore
Office Of The Executive Vice President, Jeanne Marquardt
Administrative Assistant Office Of The Senior Vice President, Tracy Karachi
Vice President Assistant To President, Mary Lou Delong
Vice President For Research, Thomas Chiles
Department Chair, Richard Tresch
Vice President, Pat Ryan
Associate Vice President For Operations And Planning, Brenda Ricard
Media Chair And Vice President, Luiza Justus
Associate Vice President, Thomas Mogan
Senior Vice President, John Gallant
Chairman, John F. Fish
Vice Chairman, Peter K. Markell, age 63
Secretary, Gloria Rufo
Investment Officer Office Of The Associate Treasurer, Travis Looker
Assistant Treasurer, Mark Conner
Board Member, Barbara Hebard
Secretary Campus School, Susan O'donnell
Treasurer, Michael Mckie
Auditors: PRICEWATERHOUSECOOPERS LLP BO

LOCATIONS

HQ: TRUSTEES OF BOSTON COLLEGE
140 COMMONWEALTH AVE, CHESTNUT HILL, MA 024673800
Phone: 617 552-8000
Web: WWW.BC.EDU

PRODUCTS/OPERATIONS

Selected Colleges and Schools
Carolyn A. and Peter S. Lynch School of Education
College of Arts and Sciences
Graduate School of Arts and Sciences
Graduate School of Social Work
James A. Woods S.J. College of Advancing Studies
School of Law
School of Theology and Ministry
Wallace E. Carroll School of Management
William F. Connell School of Nursing

HISTORICAL FINANCIALS

Company Type: Private

Income Statement				FYE: May 31
	REVENUE ($ mil.)	NET INCOME ($ mil.)	NET PROFIT MARGIN	EMPLOYEES
05/18	835	169	20.2%	2,493
05/17	798	279	34.9%	—
05/14	702	221	31.5%	—
05/13	671	270	40.3%	—
Annual Growth	4.5%	(9.0%)	—	—

2018 Year-End Financials
Return on assets: 3.5%   Cash ($ mil.): 9
Return on equity: 4.9%
Current ratio: —

TRUSTEES OF DARTMOUTH COLLEGE

Part of the esteemed Ivy League Dartmouth CollegeÂ is a private four-year liberal arts college with an enrollment ofÂ more thanÂ 6000 students.Â TheÂ universityÂ has an undergraduate college (offering about 40 programs)Â and graduate schools of business engineering and medicine plus graduate programs in the arts and sciences. Its student-teacher ratio is about 6:1. It is also home to a number of centers and institutes including Children's Hospital at Dartmouth; Dartmouth Center on Addiction Recovery andÂ Education; and Center for Digital Strategies. Notable alumni include Daniel Webster Robert Frost Theodore "Dr. Seuss" Geisel and Nelson Rockefeller.

Operations
Dartmouth is located on a 270-acre campus located in Hanover New Hampshire.Â It also conducts study-abroad programs in about 20 countries. Through its collective institutes and graduate schools the college conducts a number of research programs in areas including security capitalism energy and infectious disease. Altogether it has about 50 research-focused groups centers and institutes and attracts more than $200 million in sponsored research funding per year.

Financial Performance
For fiscal year 2011 Dartmouth reported revenues of some $763 million. Operating expenses for fiscal 2011 were some $738 million. Dartmouth has an endowment of some $3.5 billion.

Company Background
Dartmouth is the nation's ninth oldest college founded in 1769 by Reverend Eleazar Wheelock a Congregational minister from Connecticut. Land forÂ its campus in Hanover New Hampshire was conveyed by a charter from King George III; it was the last institution of higher education established in the US under colonial rule.

EXECUTIVES

Pres, Philip J Hanlon
Assistant Professor, John D Trout
Assistant Director, Karl Von Dubuche
Assistant Professor, Kelsey Wheeler
Assistant Professor, Linda M Hoover
Assistant Professor, Michael E Cox
Assistant Professor, Beverly J Entwisle
Assistant Professor, Marc L Bertrand
Assistant Professor, Richard F Hobbs
Assistant Professor, William B Gunn
Assistant Professor, Ralph D Beasley
Auditors: PRICEWATERHOUSECOOPERS LLP B

LOCATIONS

HQ: TRUSTEES OF DARTMOUTH COLLEGE
20 LEBANON ST, HANOVER, NH 037553564
Phone: 603 646-1110
Web: WWW.DARTMOUTH.EDU

PRODUCTS/OPERATIONS

Selected Divisions
Admissions and Financial Aid
Advancement Office
Campus Planning and Facilities
Dean of the College
Faculty of the Arts & Sciences
Finance and Administration
Geisel School of Medicine
President's Office
Provost's Office
Thayer School of Engineering
The Trustees of Dartmouth College
Tuck School of Business

HISTORICAL FINANCIALS

Company Type: Private

Income Statement				FYE: June 30
	REVENUE ($ mil.)	NET INCOME ($ mil.)	NET PROFIT MARGIN	EMPLOYEES
06/17	1,369	691	50.5%	5,000
06/16	859	(301)	—	—
06/15	876	236	27.0%	—
06/14	866	680	78.5%	—
Annual Growth	16.5%	0.5%	—	—

2017 Year-End Financials
Return on assets: 8.8%   Cash ($ mil.): 176
Return on equity: 12.1%
Current ratio: —

TRUSTEES OF INDIANA UNIVERSITY

Indiana University has been schooling Hoosiers (and others) since 1820. With a population of some 115000 students from all 50 states and more than 130 countries the university offers more than 1000 associate baccalaureate master's professional and doctoral degree programs at eight campuses: flagship institution IU-Bloomington; regional campuses in Fort Wayne Gary Kokomo New Albany Richmond and South Bend; and an urban campus in Indianapolis that is operated with Purdue University. The university has about 20000 faculty and professional and support staff. It has 200 research centers and institutes and offers courses in more than 70 languages.

Operations
The university offers more than 200 undergraduate majors and more than 300 graduate pro-

grams; it also boasts more than 300 study-abroad programs. It has a student-teacher ratio of about 17:1.

Indiana University has more than 306000 total living alumni including nearly 248000 Indiana residents. For the academic year 2014-15 the university charged undergraduate tuition and fees of $10388 for residents and $33240 for non-residents. It awarded $1.1 billion in financial aid that year.

Indiana University-Purdue University Indianapolis (IUPUI) is considered an "up and coming" university by U.S. News and World Report . With nearly 20 schools and degrees granted in more than 200 programs IUPUI enrolls more than 30000 students from both the Indiana University and Purdue University systems.

The IPFW Office of Research Engagement and Sponsored Programs supports research business efforts and establishes partnerships with area public and private organizations.

Geographic Reach
The university has major campuses in Bloomington and Indianapolis and regional campuses in Gary Kokomo New Albany Richmond and South Bend. It enrolls more than 50% of the students from the St. Joseph County area.

Financial Performance
Indiana University's revenues grew 1% in fiscal year 2015 to $2.2 billion. The largest single source of operating revenues for the university is student tuition and fees (accounting for 55% of total revenues). That year a 4% increase in student fees helped to offset a 40% decline in sales and services of educational units.

Net income fell 31% to $138 million in 2015 as interest earnings declined. Operating cash outflow remained flat at $534 million largely due to higher payments to employees.

Strategy
Indiana University is dedicated to keeping tuition increases as low as possible and providing extensive financial aid for qualified students. It also aims to educate its students on managing and reducing their student loan debt.

The university plans to expand and renovate its School of Public and Environmental Affairs building; the project will cost some $12 million and is expected to be complete in early 2017. In mid-2015 a new hall housing the Lilly Family School of Philanthropy was opened on the IUPUI campus. Also that year Indiana University completed the construction of a $53 million building for the new School of Global and International Studies.

The university will also continue to expand its Global Gateway Network. It officially opened offices in China and India in 2014; other target markets include the Middle East Europe Latin America and Africa.

Company Background
An 1820 statute created the Indiana Seminary the predecessor to Indiana University. In 1828 the legislature changed the name of the institution to Indiana College and in 1838 it established Indiana University.

EXECUTIVES

President, Michael A. McRobbie
Chancellor Iu Southeast, Sandra R. Patterson-Randles
Chancellor Iu South Bend, Una Mae Reck
Evp And Chancellor Iu-purdue University Indianapolis, Charles R. Bantz
Provost And Evp, Lauren Robel
Interim Vp Cfo And Treasurer, MaryFrances McCourt
Evp University Regional Affairs Planning And Policy, John S. Applegate

LOCATIONS

HQ: TRUSTEES OF INDIANA UNIVERSITY
BRYAN HALL 107 S IND AVE ST BRYAN HA, BLOOMINGTON, IN 47405
Phone: 812 855-4848
Web: WWW.INDIANA.EDU

PRODUCTS/OPERATIONS

2015 Sales

	$ mil.	% of total
Student fees	1,118	51
Auxiliary enterprises	318	14
Federal grants & contracts	293	13
Non-government grants & contracts	136	6
Sales and services of educational units	39	2
State & local grants & contracts	21	1
Other revenue	279	13
Total	2,207	100

HISTORICAL FINANCIALS

Company Type: Private

Income Statement   FYE: June 30

	REVENUE ($ mil.)	NET INCOME ($ mil.)	NET PROFIT MARGIN	EMPLOYEES
06/16	2,256	105	4.7%	16,000
06/15	2,207	138	6.3%	—
06/14	2,195	201	9.2%	—
06/13	2,146	189	8.8%	—
Annual Growth	1.7%	(17.7%)	—	—

2016 Year-End Financials

Return on assets: 2.0%
Return on equity: 2.8%
Current ratio: 1.60
Cash ($ mil.): 345

TRUSTEES OF THE ESTATE OF BERNICE PAUAHI BISHOP

Kamehameha Schools provides an education fit for a king ... or queen. The private charitable trust was founded and endowed by Princess Bernice Pauahi Bishop great granddaughter and last royal descendant of Kamehameha the Great. One of the largest independent schools in the US Kamehameha educates more than 5000 elementary middle school and high school students many of whom board at one of its three Hawaii campuses. In addition it operates some 30 preschools with a total enrollment of about 1500. Kamehameha Schools is also the largest private property owner in the state of Hawaii and uses the proceeds from its real estate operations to support its schools.

EXECUTIVES

Vice President Strategic Planning And Implementation, Christopher Pating
Vice President Human Resources, Winona White
Legal Secretary, Sharen Cordeiro
Auditors: PRICEWATERHOUSECOOPERS LLP WA

LOCATIONS

HQ: TRUSTEES OF THE ESTATE OF BERNICE PAUAHI BISHOP
567 S KING ST STE 200, HONOLULU, HI 968133079
Phone: 808 523-6200
Web: WWW.KSBE.EDU

COMPETITORS

Edison Learning   Learning Care Group

HISTORICAL FINANCIALS

Company Type: Private

Income Statement   FYE: June 30

	REVENUE ($ mil.)	NET INCOME ($ mil.)	NET PROFIT MARGIN	EMPLOYEES
06/15	767	333	43.5%	1,500
06/14	915	482	52.7%	—
06/13	519	109	21.1%	—
06/10	333	(21)	—	—
Annual Growth	18.1%			

2015 Year-End Financials

Return on assets: 3.7%
Return on equity: 4.0%
Current ratio: 0.60
Cash ($ mil.): 18

TRUSTEES OF TUFTS COLLEGE

Tufts University wants to light up the minds of New England scholars. The school offers undergraduate and graduate degrees in areas such as education engineering psychology art English music and medicine. The university enrolls some 11000 students and has 1300 faculty members and it offers classes in 70 fields at three campuses in Massachusetts (Boston Medford/Somerville and Grafton). It also has an international campus in Talloires France.Â Tufts University'sÂ Fletcher School of Law and Diplomacy is the oldest continuous international relations graduate program in the country. The school is also home to New England's only Veterinary School.

Operations
Tufts University has a number of research programs at all three campuses including clinical studies in medical dental veterinaryÂ and nutritional fields. It also has research programs in areas such as biology engineering and technology many of which are funded through grants and fellowship funds.

Financial Performance
Tufts University has an endowment of about $1.1 billion.

Strategy
Tufts University is working to expand the resourcesÂ its School of Medicine. In 2012 it moved to add a new medical research lab to study serious infectious diseases (such as tuberculosis)Â within the Biomedical Research and Public Health Building. It also expanded the Cummings School of Veterinary Medicine by adding a new clinic for the care and study ofÂ pets withÂ obesity problems. The university also expands by adding new degree programs such as a doctorate in mamalian genetics in 2011.

Company Background
Tufts was founded in 1852 through a land donation by Boston-area businessman Charles Tufts to the Universalist Church. The school adopted its motto Pax et Lux (Peace and Light) in 1857.

EXECUTIVES

Interim Assistant To David Kahle Vice President For Information Technology And Cio, Lucy Nunn
Vice President For Human Resources, Julien Carter
Auditors: PRICEWATERHOUSECOOPERS LLP BO

LOCATIONS

HQ: TRUSTEES OF TUFTS COLLEGE
169 HOLLAND ST STE 318, SOMERVILLE, MA 021442401
Phone: 617 628-5000
Web: WWW.TUFTS.EDU

PRODUCTS/OPERATIONS

Schools & Colleges
Cummings School of Veterinary Science
Graduate School of Arts & Sciences
The Fletcher School
Friedman School of Nutrition Science and Policy
Sackler School of Graduate Biomedical Sciences
School of Arts & Sciences
School of Dental Medicine
School of Engineering
School of Medicine
Tisch College of Citizenship and Public Service

HISTORICAL FINANCIALS
Company Type: Private

Income Statement · FYE: June 30

	REVENUE ($ mil.)	NET INCOME ($ mil.)	NET PROFIT MARGIN	EMPLOYEES
06/15	914	(25)	—	4,100
06/14	965	68	7.1%	—
06/13	768	127	16.6%	—
06/12	769	(100)	—	—
Annual Growth	5.9%	—	—	—

2015 Year-End Financials
Return on assets: (-0.8%)   Cash ($ mil.): 37
Return on equity: (-1.1%)
Current ratio: 0.20

TRUVEN HOLDING CORP.

EXECUTIVES

Pres- Ceo, Mike Boswood
Exec V Pres, Phil Buckingham
Exec V Pres, Jon Newpol
Coo, Roy Martin
Gen Counsel, Andra Heller
Manager, Christine Stefano
Senior Manager, Debbie Peebles
Vice President of Information, Edward Driscoll
Vice President Provider Consul, Sally Akers
Senior Business Analyst, Keith Severance
Auditors: PRICEWATERHOUSECOOPERS LLP NE

LOCATIONS

HQ: TRUVEN HOLDING CORP.
100 PHOENIX DR STE 100 # 100, ANN ARBOR, MI 481082600
Phone: 734 913-3000

HISTORICAL FINANCIALS
Company Type: Private

Income Statement · FYE: December 31

	REVENUE ($ mil.)	NET INCOME ($ mil.)	NET PROFIT MARGIN	EMPLOYEES
12/15	610	(75)	—	2,110
12/14	544	(37)	—	—
12/13	492	(344)	—	—
12/12	241	(54)	—	—
Annual Growth	36.2%	—	—	—

2015 Year-End Financials
Return on assets: (-6.4%)   Cash ($ mil.): 14
Return on equity: —
Current ratio: 0.80

TUCSON MEDICAL CENTER

EXECUTIVES

Pres-Ceo, Judith F Rich
V Pres*, Linda Wojtowicz
Chief Medical Offc, Palmer Evans
Clinical Supervisor, Christina Gonzalez
Lab Director, Jan Silva
Internist, Jeffrey Robertson
Registered Nurse, Joan Eustace
Director Perioperative, Karen Benedict
Director, Kevin Goeta-Kreisler
Manager, Kristen Moorehead
Adminstrative Associate, Leanna Dominguez

LOCATIONS

HQ: TUCSON MEDICAL CENTER
5301 E GRANT RD, TUCSON, AZ 857122874
Phone: 520 327-5461
Web: WWW.TMCAZ.COM

HISTORICAL FINANCIALS
Company Type: Private

Income Statement · FYE: December 31

	REVENUE ($ mil.)	NET INCOME ($ mil.)	NET PROFIT MARGIN	EMPLOYEES
12/17	559	19	3.4%	2,800
12/14	449	12	2.8%	—
12/13	462	16	3.5%	—
Annual Growth	4.9%	4.5%	—	—

2017 Year-End Financials
Return on assets: 4.1%   Cash ($ mil.): 29
Return on equity: 7.8%
Current ratio: 0.70

TUDOR INVESTMENT CORPORATION

EXECUTIVES

Managing Director And Associate General Counsel, Steve Waldman
Vice President Investor Relations, Susan Briggs
Vice President, Miriam Roiter
Vice President, Alberto Antonini
Secretary, Stephen Waldman
Auditors: ERNST & YOUNG LLP NEW YORK N

LOCATIONS

HQ: TUDOR INVESTMENT CORPORATION
200 ELM ST STE 200 # 200, STAMFORD, CT 069023826
Phone: 203 863-6700

COMPETITORS

Actua	Kleiner Perkins
Draper Fisher	Menlo Ventures
Jurvetson	NEA
EnTrust Capital	US Venture Partners
Hummer Winblad	Wexford Capital

HISTORICAL FINANCIALS
Company Type: Private

Income Statement · FYE: December 31

	ASSETS ($ mil.)	NET INCOME ($ mil.)	INCOME AS % OF ASSETS	EMPLOYEES
12/15	831	222	26.7%	291
12/14	819	(80)	—	—
12/13	905	486	53.7%	—
12/11	624	187	30.0%	—
Annual Growth	7.4%	4.4%	—	—

2015 Year-End Financials
Return on assets: 26.7%   Sales ($ mil): 784
Return on equity: 47.5%

TUFTS MEDICAL CENTER, INC.

EXECUTIVES

Int Pres-Ceo, Michael Wagner
Chb*, Malcolm L Sherman
Pres*, Deeb Salem
Cmo*, Saul N Weingart
Professor of Medicine, John Wong
Mgr, Kathyrn Huber
Senior Vice President CIO, Bill Shickolovich
Director, Brian Cohen
Director, Chenchen Wang
Trauma Program Manager, Cheryl Webber
Neonatologist, Dorothy Beazley
Auditors: DELOITTE & TOUCHE LLP BOSTON

LOCATIONS

HQ: TUFTS MEDICAL CENTER, INC.
  800 WASHINGTON ST, BOSTON, MA 021111552
Phone: 617 636-2254
Web: WWW.TUFTSMEDICALCENTER.ORG

HISTORICAL FINANCIALS
Company Type: Private

Income Statement				FYE: September 30
	REVENUE ($ mil.)	NET INCOME ($ mil.)	NET PROFIT MARGIN	EMPLOYEES
09/18	1,121	44	4.0%	3,800
09/17	681	12	1.8%	—
09/16	646	14	2.3%	—
09/15	595	(18)	—	—
Annual Growth 23.5%		—	—	—

2018 Year-End Financials

Return on assets: 4.8%   Cash ($ mil.): 72
Return on equity: 18.0%
Current ratio: 1.30

TURNER CONSTRUCTION COMPANY INC

Turner Construction has been the mastermind for scores of head-turning projects for more than a century. The company that built Madison Square Garden has ranked among the leading general builders in the US since the early 1900s. Turner provides construction and project management services for commercial and multifamily buildings airports and stadiums as well as correctional educational entertainment and manufacturing facilities. The company is also a leader in sustainable or green building practices. Founded in 1902 by Henry Turner the company is the main operating unit of The Turner Corporation which is a subsidiary of German construction group HOCHTIEF.

Operations

Turner Construction works on some 1500 projects each year. For decades Turner has kept tabs on construction prices with its quarterly Building Cost Index which forecasts construction costs by considering labor rates productivity and material prices.

The index is used by federal and state governments to track building costs and pricing trends.

As part of HOCHTIEF's Americas division Turner works alongside other contractors in the

US and Canada such as Flatiron its subsidiary E.E. Cruz and Clark Builders. The Americas division generates about 55% of HOCHTIEF's total revenue.

Geographic Reach

Headquartered in New York Turner Construction has offices across North America and has worked in more than 60 countries. It has operations in Latin America and the Caribbean India Europe and Central Asia Southeast Asia and the Middle East.

Sales and Marketing

Turner Construction works on projects in industries including aviation transportation commercial entertainment government green building manufacturing pharmaceutical research & development retail and sports.

Strategy

Turner Construction's ties to HOCHTIEF have helped strengthen the company's services and extend its international reach. Turner often teams with sister company Flatiron to complete projects. By collaborating and marketing their services jointly the two companies combine strengths in refurbishment and construction services.

Some of Turner's more recent projects include The Spiral?a tapered tower with an exterior ribbon of grass and trees which ascends its entire height; the Leadership in Energy and Environmental Design (LEED)-certified Audi Field soccer stadium in Washington DC; and a 12-story hospital tower for MetroHealth in Cleveland Ohio.

Turner has also worked to meet growing demand for green and sustainable construction. More than 630 of HOCHTIEF's American projects have received LEED or other green building certifications. A few of its green projects include the Seattle office of Perkins+Will the Yale University Health Services Center and RAND corporate headquarters.

As the residential markets slowed in past years Turner pivoted toward securing commercial projects in the public healthcare and science and technology sectors. Sports projects also provided the company with a solid pipeline; the company's dedicated sports division had completed more than $5 billion in work since 2000.

Company Background

Notable projects in Turner Construction's history include the World War II Memorial in Washington DC the John F. Kennedy Memorial Library in Boston and the Rock and Roll Hall of Fame. Turner also built the new Yankee Stadium in New York. The company reached a milestone in 2008 by inking its 15000th major contract.

EXECUTIVES

President, Peter J. Davoren
Vp, Stephen W. Fort
Evp (new York New Jersey Maryland Pennsylvania Connecticut And New England), Pasquale A. (Pat) Di Filippo
Svp, Michael J. (Mike) Kuntz
Svp, Mark A. Boyle
Evp (ohio Nashville Huntsville Atlanta Florida And The Carolinas), Richard P. Homan
Svp Turner Industrial Group And Chairman The Lathrop Company, Thomas J. (Tom) Manahan
Svp; President And Ceo Turner International, Abrar Sheriff
Svp And Cfo, Karen O. Gould
Svp (mid-atlantic And Southeast), Tom Reilly
President The Lathrop Company, Steve Johnson
Vice President, Neil D Jensen
Vice President, Phillip Parker
Senior Vice President, Christa Andresky
Vice President, Christoph Verbeek
Vp And Operations Manager Of Central Texas, Jeremiah Hudson

Vice President And General Manager, Tom Stachowiak
Vice President And Financial Manager, Sarah Garner
Vice President And Construction Executive, Bob Grace
Vp And Operations Manager Of Connecticut, Tom Dutchyshyn
Vice President, Dave Welber
Executive Vice President Operational Services, David Benton
Vice President, Stephen J Spaulding
Vice President, Carlo A Disilvestro
Vice President And Construction Executive Middle Atlantic, Derek Brown
Vice President, Peter S Ramstedt
Vice President, Davey Mass
Vp Of Special Projects Division Of Dallas, Nick Barker
Vice President, Douglas W Cooper
Vice President, Charles Egbert
Vice President, Maureen Kirkpatrick
Vice President, Filippo Restivo
Auditors: DELOITTE & TOUCHE LLP DALLAS

LOCATIONS

HQ: TURNER CONSTRUCTION COMPANY INC
  375 HUDSON ST FL 6, NEW YORK, NY 100143667
Phone: 212 229-6000
Web: WWW.TURNERCONSTRUCTION.COM

PRODUCTS/OPERATIONS

Selected Services

Turner Engineering Group
Design+Build
Turner Logistics: Procurement Services
Medical Planning and Procurement
Building Information Modeling (BIM)
Lean Construction

COMPETITORS

Bechtel	Hunt Construction
C. G. Schmidt	Jacobs Engineering
Catamount Constructors	PCL Employees Holdings
Dimeo Construction	Parsons Corporation
DooleyMack	Peter Kiewit Sons'
English Construction Company	Shook National Skanska USA Building
F.A. Wilhelm	Structure Tone
Fluor	Tully Construction
Gilbane Building Company	Tutor Perini
Hensel Phelps Construction	Winter Construction

HISTORICAL FINANCIALS
Company Type: Private

Income Statement				FYE: December 31
	REVENUE ($ mil.)	NET INCOME ($ mil.)	NET PROFIT MARGIN	EMPLOYEES
12/14	10,516	96	0.9%	5,000
12/13	9,488	76	0.8%	—
12/12	8,552	70	0.8%	—
Annual Growth 10.9%		17.2%	—	—

2014 Year-End Financials

Return on assets: 2.8%   Cash ($ mil.): 188
Return on equity: 14.1%
Current ratio: 1.10

TURTLE & HUGHES, INC

Turtle & Hughes' longevity has demonstrated that slow and steady really does win the race when it comes to distributing electrical and industrial equipment. The company's exhaustive lineup is sold through three subsidiaries: Turtle & Hughes Integrated Supply Turtle Data (wire cable and power protection devices) and Turtle Ebay Store. Its customers include industrial and construction companies electrical contractors telecommunications servers utilities and various government agencies. Family-owned the company is led by its fourth generation Jayne Millard its third female CEO. One-third of Turtle & Hughes is employee-owned.

Operations
Turtle & Hughes provides electrical products such as alarms signals and annunciators; anchors and plugs; automation products; ballasts; batteries and flashlights; boxes and covers; breakers bus ducts panels and switchgears; programmable controls; time clocks; transformers; wires cables and cords; wiring accessories and devices; and others.

The company also offers industrial products such as adhesives/tapes and compounds brushes/brooms carbide tools cutting tools fasteners lubricating devices material handling products power transmissions precision tools soldering equipment solenoid valves struts/channels tooling accessories and other products.

Geographic Reach
Turtle & Hughes operates through 17 branches across the US.

Sales and Marketing
Turtle & Hughes' customers include industrial firms construction companies electrical contractors telecommunications servers utilities and various government agencies and municipalities.

Company Background
Turtle & Hughes was founded in 1923 as an electrical supply house.

EXECUTIVES

Svp, Jack Sinagra
Ceo, Jayne Millard
Manager Corporate Operations, Chuck Noll
Evp; Branch Manager Bridgewater Distribution Center And Plainfield Branch, Rick Reffler
Executive Vice President Build A Brain Trust, Randy Roessle
President, Michael DeVoney
Chief Financial Officer, Chris Rausch
Vice President, Peter Landers
National Accounts Manager, Blake Varbero
National Sales Manager, Melissa Hartpence
Vice President Sales, Tony Ventola
Executive Vice President, Randall Roessle
Vice President Sales, Anthony Ventola
Senior Vice President, Al Fernandes
Vice President, William Wresch
Vice President Sales, Ken Pileggi
Vice President And General Manager, Jeff Stroin
Chairman, Suzanne Turtle Millard
Auditors: EISNERAMPER LLP ISELIN NEW J

LOCATIONS

HQ: TURTLE & HUGHES, INC
1900 LOWER RD, LINDEN, NJ 070366586
Phone: 732 574-3600
Web: WWW.TURTLE.COM

PRODUCTS/OPERATIONS

Selected Products
Datacom categories
Anchors and fasteners
Burial products/innerduct
Cabinets and enclosures
Cable management
Cable tray/ladder rack
Category rated and coax cable
Connectivity
Fiber-optic cable
Hand tools
Outside plant
Power protection
Raceway and duct systems
Safety
Security fencing
Splices connectors and lugs
Tools testers and safety
Electrical categories
Alarms annunciators and signals
Anchors and plugs
Automation products
Ballasts and transformers
Batteries and flashlights
Box enclosures
Breakers panels and switchgears
Cable trays and struts
Conduit fittings
Cord connectors
Dimming controls
Electrical tools
Emergency lighting
Enclosures
Fans
Fluorescent lighting
Fuse holders and terminal blocks
Generators
Groundings
Heat shrink
Heating
High-bay lighting
Incandescent lighting
Lamps
Limit temp. and proximity switch
Lugs and terminals
Metering equipment
Motor control
Motors AC and DC drivers
Outdoor lighting
Pole line products
Programmable controls
Relays
Strut/channel
Test equipment
Time clocks
Transformers
Wire cable and cord
Wiring accessories
Wiring devices
Industrial categories
Adhesives and tapes
Brushes and brooms
Carbide tools
Cutting fluid/lubricant
Cutting tools
Fasteners
Hand tools
Hoist chain and accessories
Industrial abrasives
Janitorial paper supplies
Ladders
Locks
Lubricating devices
Material handling
MRO supplies
Paint/markets
Pipe hangers
Pipe valves and fittings
Pneumatics
Pneumatic tools
Power tools
Safety equipment
Saw blades
Shim/shim stock
Solenoid valves
Strut/channel
Tooling accessories

COMPETITORS

C. R. Laurence	MSC Industrial Direct
Consolidated	Prime Advantage
Electrical	Rexel Inc.
Dillon Supply	Sonepar USA
Graybar Electric	Steiner Electric
Indoff	W.W. Grainger
Interline Brands	WESCO International
Kennametal	

HISTORICAL FINANCIALS
Company Type: Private

Income Statement   FYE: September 30

	REVENUE ($ mil.)	NET INCOME ($ mil.)	NET PROFIT MARGIN	EMPLOYEES
09/18	754	20	2.7%	900
09/17	671	18	2.7%	—
09/16	628	16	2.6%	—
09/15	590	17	3.0%	—
Annual Growth	8.5%	5.0%	—	—

2018 Year-End Financials
Return on assets: 7.9%   Cash ($ mil.): 10
Return on equity: 16.6%
Current ratio: 2.00

U.S. PIPELINE, INC.

EXECUTIVES

Prin, Kelly Osborn
Chb*, Greg Curran
Treas*, Imran Dossani
Cfo*, Bret Roper
Accounting Staff, Fernando Gonzalez
Vice President, Dan Holmes
Project Engineer, Aaron Rattray
Secretary, Beverly Doecke
Office Manager, Len Mutchler
Payroll Administrator, Lisa Hill
Vice President, Lowell Brien
Auditors: LAPORTE APAC HOUSTON TEXAS

LOCATIONS

HQ: U.S. PIPELINE, INC.
8100 WASHINGTON AVE # 200, HOUSTON, TX 770071085
Phone: 281 531-6100
Web: WWW.USPIPELINE.COM

HISTORICAL FINANCIALS
Company Type: Private

Income Statement   FYE: December 31

	REVENUE ($ mil.)	NET INCOME ($ mil.)	NET PROFIT MARGIN	EMPLOYEES
12/17	501	11	2.3%	1,500
12/16	72	0	0.6%	—
12/15	367	52	14.3%	—
12/14	557	0	—	—
Annual Growth	(3.5%)	—	—	—

2017 Year-End Financials
Return on assets: 10.1%   Cash ($ mil.): 15
Return on equity: 14.7%
Current ratio: 3.10

U.S. VENTURE, INC.

Privately held U.S. Venture Inc. is a North American leader in the distribution of fuel and transportation products. U.S. Oil its largest division transports more than 2 billion gallons of fuel annually via pipelines rail light oil-barges and trucks. The division maintains around 7 million BOE in storage capacity and has access to 330 terminals. Through U.S. AutoForce the company is also a top distributor of tires and car parts to independent tire retailers auto repair shops and dealerships. The company's Lubricants division maintains a competitive business as well set up to blend and market chemical products to automotive industrial and metalworking industries. Through the GAIN Clean Fuel brand U.S. Venture also sells clean biofuels.

Operations

U.S. Venture has four business divisions.

U.S. Oil its largest business is a leading distributor of branded and unbranded refined products in the US and Canada. It transports some 2 billion gallons of energy products annually. U.S. Oil also engages in energy trading.

Tires car parts and lubricants are distributed through the U.S. AutoForce division another industry leader. Its portfolio includes 30 tire brands 15 lubricant brands and many branded car parts (mostly brakes chassis repair equipment and exhausts).

U.S. Lubricants blends and distributes lubricants under its THRIVE brand for automotive industrial and metalworking needs. It also provides support services like mobile filtration systems oil analysis lab services and fluids storage and handling systems.

U.S. Venture is also developing and building alternative fuel transportation networks and filling stations in the US. Headed by the U.S. GAIN division the company supplies compressed natural gas (CNG) and renewable natural gas (RNG) to more than 50 fueling stations.

Geographic Reach

Headquartered in Appleton Wisconsin U.S. Venture operates throughout North America. U.S. Oil handles fuel supply in the Midwest with about 20 terminals a barge and some 330 third-party terminal partners. The company has a concentration of fuel tires car parts and convenience store services in the Midwest.

Sales and Marketing

U.S. Ventures is a leading distributor of fuels car parts and lubricants in North America.

The U.S. Oil division distributes products from nine major oil brands including BP Shell Exxon and Phillips 66. It offers flexible pricing fixed-fuel contracts and commodity trading. Traded products include gasoline ethanol biodiesel jet and marine fuels propane and butane. In the Midwest the company also owns the Express chain of convenience stores. U.S. Oil serves nearly 40 million Americans daily.

U.S. AutoForce offers 30 tire brands including Michelin Bridgestone Dunlop and Firestone. It has an equally extensive inventory of car parts and lubricants. It. The service centers strategically placed across North America serve the agricultural construction forestry and mining industries.

Strategy

U.S. Venture wants to become the dominant petroleum products marketer and wholesale distributor of automotive parts and tires in North America. Its operating model focuses on expanding the brand portfolio beyond oil distribution to incorporate automotive services and clean energy distribution within its model.

U.S. Venture has expanded its product lines and market reach through joint ventures (2017 partnership with Harrigan Industrial Technologies Inc.) and acquisitions (2018 purchase of Tire's Warehouse Inc). These efforts have expanded its revenue stream and cushioned it from fluctuations in its oil business.

However U.S. Venture's expansion of services may come at a cost. For instance in September 2017 a federal court in Chicago found that the U.S. Oil division of U.S. Venture infringed upon patents held by Sunoco Partners related to a system for blending butane into gasoline at the point of distribution. Legal proceedings are a drain on resources and negatively impact a company's brand image.

Competition is also heating up in the tire distribution industry. In 2018 Michelin North America Inc. and Sumitomo Corporation of Americas formed a new joint venture to strengthen their distribution system. This was followed by TireHub a joint distribution system of Goodyear Tire & Rubber Co. and Bridgestone Americas Inc. U.S. Venture may find it difficult to expand beyond its home turf of the Midwest in such a crowded field.

Mergers and Acquisitions

In June 2018 U.S. AutoForce acquired California based Tire's Warehouse Inc for an undisclosed price. U.S. Autoforce retained the Tire's Warehouse name company structure employees and ways of business but expects the acquisition to gain market share in California and Arizona. Tire's Warehouse was established in 1969 by the Helmle family and remained family-owned before the acquisition.

Company Background

U.S. Oil was established in 1951 as Schmidt Oil by the sons of local fuel distributor Albert Schmidt. The company changed its name to U.S. Venture in 2010 to reflect the company's increasingly diverse portfolio of entrepreneurial businesses. It has remained family-owned since its inception and today it is one of the largest privately held companies in Wisconsin.

EXECUTIVES

President And Ceo, John Schmidt
Vp Marketing And Strategy, Jeff Van Brunt
Vp Business Development U.s. Oil, Mike Koel
Vice President Treasurer Assistant Secretary, Lori Karls
Vp Of Sales And Operations, Kevin Olson
Senior Vice President Merchandise Planning And Allocation, Mark Duenig
Treasurer, Martin Tomczyk
Secretary And Treasurer, Ray Schmidt
Treasurer, Judy Engen-pazdera
Auditors: DELOITTE & TOUCHE LLP MILWAU

LOCATIONS

HQ: U.S. VENTURE, INC.
425 BETTER WAY, APPLETON, WI 549156192
Phone: 920 739-6101
Web: WWW.USOIL.COM

PRODUCTS/OPERATIONS

Selected Operations

U.S. AutoForce (exhaust pipe manufacturing and autoparts distribution)
U.S. Lubricants (motor oil and related products)
U.S. Oil (gasoline fuel oil and natural gas)
U.S Gain (compressed natural gas)

COMPETITORS

American Tire Distributors	Petroleum Traders Corporation
Guttman Oil	

HISTORICAL FINANCIALS

Company Type: Private

Income Statement

FYE: July 31

	REVENUE ($ mil.)	NET INCOME ($ mil.)	NET PROFIT MARGIN	EMPLOYEES
07/15	8,076	173	2.1%	1,182
07/14	9,088	49	0.5%	—
07/13	7,346	47	0.6%	—
Annual Growth	4.9%	91.7%	—	—

2015 Year-End Financials

Return on assets: 16.9%   Cash ($ mil.): 13
Return on equity: 53.2%
Current ratio: 1.70

UAW RETIREE MEDICAL BENEFITS TRUST

EXECUTIVES

Head of Trustees, Robert Naftaly
Prin*, Rober Naftaly
Senior Manager Human Resources, Karen Blair
Director Communications, Matthew Wood
Carrier Coordinator, Lisa Mosner
Manager, Evelyn White-Bruton
Strategy Consultant, Vince Ferri
Senior Accountant, Amy Hawkins
Senior Managing Director, Benjamin Cotton
Controller, Garon Meikle
Tax Compliance Manager, Laura Howard
Auditors: DELOITTE TAX LLP DETROIT MI

LOCATIONS

HQ: UAW RETIREE MEDICAL BENEFITS TRUST
200 WALKER ST STE 400, DETROIT, MI 482074229
Phone: 313 324-5900

HISTORICAL FINANCIALS

Company Type: Private

Income Statement

FYE: December 31

	ASSETS ($ mil.)	NET INCOME ($ mil.)	INCOME AS % OF ASSETS	EMPLOYEES
12/17	63,225	88	0.1%	94
12/16	58,966	(1,839)	—	—
Annual Growth	7.2%	—	—	—

2017 Year-End Financials

Return on assets: 0.1%   Sales ($ mil): 4,291
Return on equity: 0.1%

UC HEALTH, LLC.

UC Health is Cincinnati's scholarly health care provider. The medical provider is a partnership between the University of Cincinnati the 480-bed University of Cincinnati Medical Center and the University of Cincinnati Physicians organization. Additionally UC Health is home to the 160-bed West Chester Hospital (a full-service community hospital) the Drake Center long-term acute care (rehabilitation) hospital the UC Health Surgical Hospital and the Lindner Center of HOPE (mental health services). Specialized services include cancer cardiovascular neuroscience and metabolic disease treatment. The not-for-profit UC Health was formed in 1994.

Operations

After a major reorganization in 2010 the surviving UC Health organizationÂ core operations areÂ comprisedÂ of UniversityÂ Medical CenterÂ West Chester Medical Center and itsÂ primary and specialty careÂ centers.Â Through its affiliation with the University of Cincinnati the medical organization conducts educational and research programs.

Strategy

UC Health is working to expand its network through acquisitions. For instance it added a new women's health practice to its provider network in 2012 to widen its specialty service offerings.

UC Health acquired full control of the Drake Center from former partner (and former network member) Jewish Hospital in 2011. It also added the Lindner Center of HOPE to its network that year.

Company Background

Formerly known as The Health Alliance of Greater CincinnatiÂ the company changed its name to UC HealthÂ in 2010 after a number of its hospital members left the system and the University of Cincinnati took control of the remaining operations. Rumors of dissolution had swirled around theÂ organization since its members began jumping ship starting in 2007.

Four of the organization's foundingÂ hospitals ultimatelyÂ left the system: The 175-bed Fort Hamilton Hospital (now part of Kettering Health Network) and the 210-bedÂ Jewish Hospital (now part of Catholic Healthcare Partners) departedÂ in 2010. Two otherÂ hospitals (St. Luke's and Christ Hospital)Â broke off from the alliance after a long legal struggleÂ in 2007.

EXECUTIVES

Senior Vice President And Chief Human Resources Officer, Bob Griffith
Evp And Cfo, Rick Hinds
President And Ceo, Richard P. Lofgren
Chief Physicians Services, Myles Pensak
Coo, Peter N. Gilbert
President Uc Health Foundation, Chris Smith
Vice President Chief Marketing Officer, Anthony Condia
Senior Vice President And Cio, Jay Brown
Director Of Nursing, Salyer Heidi
Senior Vice President And Chief Human Resources Officer, Clarence Pauley
Vice President Audit And Compliance, Alton Knight
Senior Vice President Strategic Planning And Business Development, Gayla Harvey
Vice President Information Systems And Technology, Mark Carey
Senior Vice President And General Counsel, Charles Pangburn
Vice President Care Coordination, Andrew Cusher
Vice President Corporate Finance, Charity Fannin
Senior Vice President, Kyle Taylor
Chair Department Of Radiation Oncology, William Barrett
Medical Records Director, Frances Matre
Director Of Nursing Services, Ertel Todd
Vice President Government Relations, Candace Sabers
Vice President Operations, Ronald Rohlfing
Secretary Administrative, Pamela Becker
Medical Secretary, Amanda Morgan
Medical Secretary, Billie Sword
Auditors: DELOITTE TAX LLP CINCINNATI

LOCATIONS

HQ: UC HEALTH, LLC.
  3200 BURNET AVE, CINCINNATI, OH 452293019
Phone: 513 585-6000

PRODUCTS/OPERATIONS

Selected Ohio Facilities
Drake Center (Cincinnati)
Linder Center of HOPE (Mason)
UC Health Surgical Hospital (West Chester)
University of Cincinnati Physicians (Cincinnati)
University of Cincinnati Medical Center (Cincinnati)
West Chester Hospital (West Chester)

COMPETITORS

Catholic Health Initiatives
Cincinnati Children's Hospital
Kettering Health Network
Mercy Hospital Springfield
Premier Health Partners
St. Elizabeth Healthcare
The Christ Hospital Corporation
TriHealth

HISTORICAL FINANCIALS

Company Type: Private

Income Statement   FYE: June 30

	REVENUE ($ mil.)	NET INCOME ($ mil.)	NET PROFIT MARGIN	EMPLOYEES
06/18	1,661	40	2.5%	10,000
06/17	1,586	73	4.7%	—
06/10	138	(81)	—	—
06/09	102	0	—	—
Annual Growth	36.3%	—	—	—

2018 Year-End Financials
Return on assets: 2.5%   Cash ($ mil.): 76
Return on equity: 4.9%
Current ratio: 4.70

UCLA MEDICAL CENTER

EXECUTIVES

Pres, David Feinberg
Exec V Pres, Patricia Kapur
Internal Medicine Practitioner, Vicki Tran
Internist, Forster Chhean
Internist, Omar Kattan
Internal Medicine, Alexandra Drakaki
Hospitalist, Anne Belzowski
Pulmonologist, Colleen Channick
Associate Program Director, Daniel Lee
Director, Edward Hui
Orthopedic Surgeon, Edward McPherson

LOCATIONS

HQ: UCLA MEDICAL CENTER
  1250 16TH ST, SANTA MONICA, CA 904041249
Phone: 310 319-3816
Web: WWW.UCHEALTH.COM

HISTORICAL FINANCIALS

Company Type: Private

Income Statement   FYE: June 30

	REVENUE ($ mil.)	NET INCOME ($ mil.)	NET PROFIT MARGIN	EMPLOYEES
06/16	513	18	3.6%	1
06/15	479	44	9.3%	—
Annual Growth	7.3%	(58.1%)	—	—

2016 Year-End Financials
Return on assets: 2.2%   Cash ($ mil.): 15
Return on equity: 3.5%
Current ratio: 1.60

UFCW & EMPLOYERS TRUST LLC

Auditors: HEMMING MORSE CPA'S AND CONSUL

LOCATIONS

HQ: UFCW & EMPLOYERS TRUST LLC
  1000 BURNETT AVE STE 200, CONCORD, CA 945202058
Phone: 925 609-9068
Web: WWW.UFCWTRUST.COM

HISTORICAL FINANCIALS

Company Type: Private

Income Statement   FYE: December 31

	REVENUE ($ mil.)	NET INCOME ($ mil.)	NET PROFIT MARGIN	EMPLOYEES
12/14	553	33	6.0%	4
12/13	544	16	3.0%	—
Annual Growth	1.7%	107.2%	—	—

2014 Year-End Financials
Return on assets: 14.2%   Cash ($ mil.): 81
Return on equity: 26.2%
Current ratio: 40.60

UGI UTILITIES, INC.

EXECUTIVES

Chairman And Ceo, Lon R Greenberg

LOCATIONS

HQ: UGI UTILITIES, INC.
  1 UGI DR, DENVER, PA 175179039
Phone: 800 276-2722
Web: WWW.UGI.COM

HISTORICAL FINANCIALS

Company Type: Private

Income Statement   FYE: September 30

	REVENUE ($ mil.)	NET INCOME ($ mil.)	NET PROFIT MARGIN	EMPLOYEES
09/18	1,092	148	13.6%	1,520
09/17	887	116	13.1%	—
Annual Growth	23.1%	28.3%	—	—

2018 Year-End Financials
Return on assets: 4.6%   Cash ($ mil.): 10
Return on equity: 13.6%
Current ratio: 0.50

UMASS MEMORIAL COMMUNITY MEDICAL GROUP, INC.

Auditors: PRICEWATERHOUSECOOPERS LLP B

LOCATIONS

HQ: UMASS MEMORIAL COMMUNITY MEDICAL GROUP, INC.
121 LINCOLN ST, WORCESTER, MA 016052429
Phone: 508 757-7745
Web: WWW.COSMETICSURGICENTER.COM

HISTORICAL FINANCIALS

Company Type: Private

Income Statement   FYE: September 30

	REVENUE ($ mil.)	NET INCOME ($ mil.)	NET PROFIT MARGIN	EMPLOYEES
09/15	468	7	1.6%	3
09/11	451	8	1.9%	—
09/09	400	7	1.8%	—
09/08	360	1	0.4%	—
Annual Growth	3.8%	25.5%	—	—

2015 Year-End Financials

Return on assets: 3.8%   Cash ($ mil.): 18
Return on equity: 9.2%
Current ratio: 1.60

UMASS MEMORIAL HEALTH CARE INC AND AFFILIATES GROUP RETURN

Auditors: FEELEY & DRISCOLL PC BOSTON

LOCATIONS

HQ: UMASS MEMORIAL HEALTH CARE INC AND AFFILIATES GROUP RETURN
306 BELMONT ST 120, WORCESTER, MA 016041004
Phone: 508 334-5106
Web: WWW.UMMHC.ORG

HISTORICAL FINANCIALS

Company Type: Private

Income Statement   FYE: September 30

	REVENUE ($ mil.)	NET INCOME ($ mil.)	NET PROFIT MARGIN	EMPLOYEES
09/13	2,613	51	2.0%	500
09/10	2,594	65	2.5%	—
Annual Growth	0.2%	(7.7%)	—	—

2013 Year-End Financials

Return on assets: 2.4%   Cash ($ mil.): 156
Return on equity: 5.8%
Current ratio: 0.80

UMASS MEMORIAL HEALTH CARE, INC.

EXECUTIVES

Pres, Peter H Levine
V Pres-Cfo*, Todd Keating
Vice-President, Robert Feldmann
Nurse, Rosemary Cerqueira
Project Manager, Thomas Harrop
Chief of Medicine, Stephen Tosi
Physician Assistant, Donna Hayden
Director, William Garrison
Senior Vice-President, Dana Swenson
Compliance Staff, Barbara T Beausoleil
Emergency Medicine Specialist, Michael C Butler

LOCATIONS

HQ: UMASS MEMORIAL HEALTH CARE, INC.
365 PLANTATION ST STE 300, WORCESTER, MA 016052397
Phone: 508 334-1000
Web: WWW.UMASSMEMORIALHEALTHCARE.ORG

HISTORICAL FINANCIALS

Company Type: Private

Income Statement   FYE: September 30

	REVENUE ($ mil.)	NET INCOME ($ mil.)	NET PROFIT MARGIN	EMPLOYEES
09/18	2,496	25	1.0%	10,000
09/17	2,447	145	6.0%	—
09/16	2,373	(21)	—	—
09/15	2,241	(7)	—	—
Annual Growth	3.7%	—	—	—

2018 Year-End Financials

Return on assets: 1.0%   Cash ($ mil.): 218
Return on equity: 2.5%
Current ratio: 1.40

UMASS MEMORIAL MEDICAL CENTER, INC.

EXECUTIVES

Ceo, John Obrien
Exec V Pres, Wendy Waring
Sr V Pres, Gary Lapidas
Treas, Todd Keating
Pres, Eric Dickson M D
Chief of Medicine, Robert Finberg
Vice-President Business Develo, Willis Chandler
Executive of Information Techn, Denise Skrocki
Plastic Surgeon, Douglas M Rothkopf
Doctor, William Corbett
Doctor of Medicine, Dionyssios Robotis
Auditors: PRICEWATERHOUSECOOPERS LLP BO

LOCATIONS

HQ: UMASS MEMORIAL MEDICAL CENTER, INC.
1 BIOTECH 365 PLNTN ST, WORCESTER, MA 01605
Phone: 508 334-1000
Web: WWW.UMASSMEMORIALHEALTHCARE.ORG

HISTORICAL FINANCIALS

Company Type: Private

Income Statement   FYE: September 30

	REVENUE ($ mil.)	NET INCOME ($ mil.)	NET PROFIT MARGIN	EMPLOYEES
09/18	1,712	87	5.1%	55
09/17	1,668	(62)	—	—
09/16	1,621	(130)	—	—
09/15	1,508	(10)	—	—
Annual Growth	4.3%			

2018 Year-End Financials

Return on assets: 7.2%   Cash ($ mil.): 103
Return on equity: 49.2%
Current ratio: 1.20

UMASS MEMORIAL MEDICAL CENTER, INC.

EXECUTIVES

Doctor, Kirk Johnson
Internal Medicine Practitioner, Timothy P Fitzgibbons
Administrative Assistant, Carolyn Granger
MD, Frederic Baker
Clinical Engineering Manager, Joseph Williams
Chair Department of Obstetrics, Julia Johnson
Nurse Practitioner, Robin Mason
Office Manager, Sandra Buxton
Physician Pediatrics, Michael Hirsh
Doctor of Medicine, Nicholas Smyrnios
Registered Nurse, Angela Halloran
Auditors: PRICEWATERHOUSECOOPERS LLP BO

LOCATIONS

HQ: UMASS MEMORIAL MEDICAL CENTER, INC.
55 LAKE AVE N, WORCESTER, MA 016550002
Phone: 508 334-1000

HISTORICAL FINANCIALS

Company Type: Private

Income Statement   FYE: September 30

	REVENUE ($ mil.)	NET INCOME ($ mil.)	NET PROFIT MARGIN	EMPLOYEES
09/16	1,621	(130)	—	29
09/15	1,332	60	4.5%	—
09/14	1,258	19	1.6%	—
09/13	1,183	68	5.8%	—
Annual Growth	11.1%	—	—	—

2016 Year-End Financials

Return on assets: (-10.4%)   Cash ($ mil.): 124
Return on equity: (-83.3%)
Current ratio: 1.20

UNIFIED SCHOOL DISTRICT 259

EXECUTIVES

Supt, John Allison
Treas-Dir*, Linda Jones
Cfo*, Jim Freeman
Facilities, Debbie Kandt
Seventh Grade Science Teacher, Isabel Canizares
Office Technician, Mary Halley
Educator, Michele Steinbacher
Esl Teacher, Rhonda Shook
Payroll Supervisor, Sharon Hoyme
Risk Coordinator, Weston Schartz
Auditors: ALLEN GIBBS & HOULIK LC W

LOCATIONS

HQ: UNIFIED SCHOOL DISTRICT 259
903 S EDGEMOOR ST, WICHITA, KS 672183337
Phone: 316 973-4000
Web: WWW.USD259.ORG

HISTORICAL FINANCIALS
Company Type: Private

Income Statement   FYE: June 30

	REVENUE ($ mil.)	NET INCOME ($ mil.)	NET PROFIT MARGIN	EMPLOYEES
06/18	668	119	17.8%	5,406
06/17	632	15	2.4%	—
06/16	622	(31)	—	—
06/15	626	(55)	—	—
Annual Growth	2.2%	—	—	—

UNION BANK AND TRUST COMPANY

Union Bank & Trust a subsidiary of financial services holding company Farmers & Merchants Investment operates more than 35 branches throughout Nebraska and in Kansas. As Nebraska's third-largest privately-owned bank it offers traditional deposit and trust services as well as insurance equipment finance and investment management services. Consumer loans account for the largest portion of the bank's portfolio followed by commercial real estate and farmland loans. Union Bank also originates business loans and residential mortgages. Affiliate company Union Investment Advisors manages the Stratus family of mutual funds. Another Farmers & Merchants unit Nelnet Capital offers brokerage services.

Operations
Union Bank has grown to become one of Nebraska's largest privately-owned banks. As of mid-2013 it boasted bank assets of $2.6 billion and trust assets of $11.8 billion.

Aside from its branches in Nebraska and Kansas Union Bank offers banking products and services through its online mobile and electronic banking services.

Geographic Reach
Union Bank operates mostly in Nebraska but also in Kansas.

Sales and Marketing
The bank primarily serves customers in Lincoln and Omaha as well as the Kansas City metropolitan area.

Strategy
Union Bank continues to expand its footprint in existing markets. The financial institution will have added three new Nebraska branches to its portfolio by 2014.

Company Background
The bank was originally founded in 1917 as Farmer's State Bank. It took on the Union Bank name in 1935 and became Union Bank & Trust in 1959.

EXECUTIVES

Vice President, Tom Marchael
Vice President Small Business Banking, Stephanie Dinger
Vice President And Business Development Officer, Michael G Kulas
Vice President Financial Reporting And Controller, Kimberly Keller
Executive Vice President And Commercial Banking Group Executive, David V Ring
Vice President, Raymond Grace
Vice President And Trust Services Advisor, Douglas J Koenig
Assistant Vice President, Nick Nash

LOCATIONS

HQ: UNION BANK AND TRUST COMPANY
3643 S 48TH ST, LINCOLN, NE 685064390
Phone: 402 323-1235
Web: WWW.UBT.COM

PRODUCTS/OPERATIONS

Selected Services
Business banking
Investment & retirement
Personal banking
Wealth management

Selected Affiliates
InfoVisa
Nelnet Capital LLC
Nelnet Inc.
Union Agency Inc.
Union Equipment Finance LLC
Union Investment Advisors
Union Title Company LLC
Zelle

COMPETITORS

Bank of America	Great Western Bancorp
Bank of the West	JPMorgan Chase
Citigroup	Pinnacle Bancorp
First National of Nebraska	U.S. Bancorp
	Wells Fargo

HISTORICAL FINANCIALS
Company Type: Private

Income Statement   FYE: December 31

	ASSETS ($ mil.)	NET INCOME ($ mil.)	INCOME AS % OF ASSETS	EMPLOYEES
12/17	3,836	45	1.2%	800
12/16	3,595	40	1.1%	—
12/15	3,351	32	1.0%	—
12/14	3,040	29	1.0%	—
Annual Growth	8.1%	15.8%	—	—

2017 Year-End Financials
Return on assets: 1.2%   Sales ($ mil): 214
Return on equity: 11.7%

UNION HOSPITAL, INC.

Union Hospital is the flagship facility of the Union Hospital Health Group a health care system that serves communities in western Indiana and eastern Illinois. The not-for-profit hospital has about 320 beds boasts an equal number of physicians and provides general medical and surgical care as well as specialty services in areas such as women's health newborn intensive care unit (Level II) cancer cardiovascular disease and sports medicine. It also offers occupational health and physical rehabilitation as well as medical training programs. Other facilities that comprise the Union system include Union Hospital Clinton physician practices specialty clinics and a home health agency.

Operations
Besides the main Union Hospital which averages some 17000 patient admissions each year the hospital operates Union Hospital Clinton specialty clinics a home health agency and physician practices.

Geographic Reach
The teaching hospital serves patients in west-central Indiana and eastern Illinois.

Strategy
Union Hospital's main campus underwent a nearly $180 million expansion project in recent years. The patient tower provides for private rooms instead of six- to eight-bed wards.

As part of a strategic focus to extend the reach of its operations Union Hospital partners with AP&S Clinic a multi -specialty physician group practice to expand the two entities' services. Operating as Union Health System the collaboration looks to increase coordination of care between physician specialists.

In 2015 Union Hospital partnered with the Ob Hospitalist Group to provide around-the-clock physician care for expectant mothers.

Company Background
Union Hospital's roots go back to 1892.

EXECUTIVES

Vice President Human Resources And Talent Management, Cheryl Stearley
Medical Director, Grace Walker
Director Of Medical Records, Pamala Alexander
Medical Director, Richard Butler
Vice President Of Information Technology, Yevette Cress

LOCATIONS

HQ: UNION HOSPITAL, INC.
1606 N 7TH ST, TERRE HAUTE, IN 478042780
Phone: 812 238-7000
Web: WWW.MYUNIONHEALTH.ORG

PRODUCTS/OPERATIONS

Selected Services

Acupuncture
Advanced Medical Technology
Asthma
Behavioral Healthcare
Breast Care
Cancer Care Services
Cardiovascular Testing
Clara Fairbanks Center for Women
Clay City Center for Family Medicine
Cork Medical Center
Family Medicine Center

Infections

Joint Replacement Center
Landsbaum Center
Lugar Center for Rural Health
Medical Rehabilitation Center
Neonatal Intensive Care Unit (NICU)
Pediatrics
Pulmonary and Lung Health

Wound Healing Center
Union Hospital Terre Haute
Union Hospital Clinton
Union Hospital Foundation

COMPETITORS

Ascension Health	IU Health Bloomington
Carle Hospital	Hospital
Franciscan Alliance	Kosciusko Community
HCA	Hospital
IU Health	

HISTORICAL FINANCIALS

Company Type: Private

Income Statement				FYE: December 31
	REVENUE ($ mil.)	NET INCOME ($ mil.)	NET PROFIT MARGIN	EMPLOYEES
12/17	465	17	3.7%	2,700
12/16	416	(11)	—	—
12/15	384	6	1.8%	—
12/14	127	3	2.7%	—
Annual Growth	53.8%	71.8%	—	—

2017 Year-End Financials

Return on assets: 3.7%   Cash ($ mil.): 48
Return on equity: 11.9%
Current ratio: 0.40

UNIPRO FOODSERVICE, INC

UniPro Foodservice knows there's strength in numbers. As the largest US food service cooperative its members include more than 650 independent member companies that provide food and food-related products to more than 800000 food service customers including health care and educational institutions military installations and restaurants. UniPro provides training collective purchasing and marketing materials to all distributors. Its products — which include dry groceries and frozen and refrigerated foods — are sold under the brand names CODE ComSource Nifda and Nugget. Suppliers include Kraft Foods Reynolds Food Packaging Solo Cup Tyson Foods and Unilever Foodsolutions.

Operations

The cooperative's Multi-Unit Group (MUG) formed in 1985 to service multi-unit food service operators include some of the largest member distributors in the UniPro network. MUG members are like a one-stop shop for multi-unit operators offering fresh produce paper products and small wares from a single source in an effort to improve efficiency.

Geographic Reach

The Atlanta-based cooperative operates through more than 900 distribution centers across the US. Beyond the US it has distribution operations in Canada Mexico the Bahamas Australia Costa Rica Guam and Japan.

Sales and Marketing

Progressive Group Alliance a business unit distributes and supplies partners with sales marketing and advice to customers. Brands include Alliance Pro (non-food) Coral Princess (seafood) Gour-Mates (condiments) Harvest Gold (cheese butter and dairy-related products) and Premium Recipe (prepared entrees salsas and sauces).

Financial Performance

While privately-owned Unipro Foodservice doesn't report its financial results collectively the cooperatives ring up an estimated $64 billion in sales annually.

Strategy

To enhance its members' competitiveness at home and abroad in 2013 UniPro formed a strategic alliance with Technomic a leading research and consulting firm to the food service industry. As part of the partnership UnPro joined the steering committee of Technomic's Foodservice Category Management Institute.

EXECUTIVES

Vice President Of Finance, Dan Wolfram
Department Vice President Of Accounting Services, Martin Miller
Departmental Vice President Financial Services, Sharon Nesset
Regional Vice President, Gary Butler
Department Vice President Beef And Pork, Phillip Wilson
Executive Vice President Of Procurement, David Huch
Vice President Saels West, Scott Strull
Regional Vice President Of Sales, Bob Bossong
Senior Vice President Sales East, Keith Durnell
Departmental Vice President Vendor Engagement, Dave Devlin
Regional Vice President, Ed Delaney
Department Vice President Of National Brands, Diane Grimsley
Vice President Business Analysis, Van Perry
Regional Vice President Sales, Wayne Harrison
Regional Vice President, Matthew Milcoff
Departmental Vice President, Bob Salo
Departmental Vice President Frozen Fruits And Vegetables Imports, Beverly Deschon
Auditors: HA&W LLP ATLANTA GEORGIA

LOCATIONS

HQ: UNIPRO FOODSERVICE, INC
  2500 CUMBRLD PKWY SE 60, ATLANTA, GA 30339
Phone: 770 952-0871
Web: WWW.UNIPROFOODSERVICE.COM

PRODUCTS/OPERATIONS

Selected Suppliers

Cargill Foodservice
Durable Packaging International
Handgards Inc.
Kraft Foods
Reynolds Foodservice Packaging
Solo Cup Company
Unilever Foodsolutions

COMPETITORS

Ben E. Keith	Meadowbrook Meat
Foodbuy	Company
Golden State Foods	Services Group of
Keystone Foods	America
MAINES	Sysco
Martin-Brower	US Foods
McLane Foodservice	

HISTORICAL FINANCIALS

Company Type: Private

Income Statement				FYE: December 31
	REVENUE ($ mil.)	NET INCOME ($ mil.)	NET PROFIT MARGIN	EMPLOYEES
12/12	987	(0)	—	140
12/11	881	0	—	—
12/10	657	0	—	—
Annual Growth	22.5%	—	—	—

2012 Year-End Financials

Return on assets: (-0.2%)   Cash ($ mil.): 6
Return on equity: (-3.5%)
Current ratio: 1.00

UNITED CONCORDIA LIFE AND HEALTH INSURANCE COMPANY

EXECUTIVES

Ceo, Frederick Merkel
Fo, Daniel Wright
EC, Edward Bittner
Supervisor, Brenda Godusky

LOCATIONS

HQ: UNITED CONCORDIA LIFE AND HEALTH INSURANCE COMPANY
  4401 DEER PATH RD, HARRISBURG, PA 171103983
Phone: 717 260-7081
Web: WWW.UNITEDCONCORDIA.COM

HISTORICAL FINANCIALS

Company Type: Private

Income Statement				FYE: December 31
	REVENUE ($ mil.)	NET INCOME ($ mil.)	NET PROFIT MARGIN	EMPLOYEES
12/15	680	34	5.1%	1
12/14	731	57	7.9%	—
Annual Growth	(6.9%)	(39.8%)	—	—

2015 Year-End Financials

Return on assets: 10.3%   Cash ($ mil.): 54
Return on equity: 14.3%
Current ratio: 1.10

UNITED COOPERATIVE

EXECUTIVES

Ceo, David Cramer
Cfo*, Damian Girten
Chm*, Howard Bohl
SEC*, Robin Craker
Manager, Greg Thomson
Director Juneau, David Bischoff
Manager, Greg Adkins
Vice-President, Alan Jentz

LOCATIONS

HQ: UNITED COOPERATIVE
  N7160 RACEWAY RD, BEAVER DAM, WI 539169315
Phone: 920 887-1756
Web: WWW.UNITEDCOOPERATIVE.COM

HISTORICAL FINANCIALS
Company Type: Private

Income Statement   FYE: December 31

	REVENUE ($ mil.)	NET INCOME ($ mil.)	NET PROFIT MARGIN	EMPLOYEES
12/17	644	49	7.7%	358
12/16	630	41	6.6%	—
12/15	579	41	7.1%	—
12/14	577	57	10.0%	—
Annual Growth	3.7%	(4.7%)	—	—

2017 Year-End Financials
Return on assets: 8.0%   Cash ($ mil.): 22
Return on equity: 12.1%
Current ratio: 2.20

UNITED DAIRYMEN OF ARIZONA

Its name says it all: United Dairymen of Arizona (UDA) is a group of Arizona-based dairy farmers united together to stabilize and strengthen the market for milk products. Supplied by some 90-member producers the cooperative's plant has the capacity to process 10 million pounds of milk per day about 90% of the milk in the state. Products include sweet cream and butter fluid and condensed skim milk and non-fat dry milk among others. Customers include onsite cheese maker Schreiber Foods fluid milk processors and supermarket chains throughout The Grand Canyon State. UDA also makes dried lactose powder for food manufacturers. Started in 1960 the co-op was formed through a merger of two dairy associations.

EXECUTIVES

Vice President Of Engineering Projects, James Hrusovszky
Vice President Of Business Relations And Development Special Projects, Jimco Hrusovszky
Vice President Of Government Relations, Mike Billotte
Auditors: HERBEIN & COMPANY INC READI

LOCATIONS

HQ: UNITED DAIRYMEN OF ARIZONA
2008 S HARDY DR, TEMPE, AZ 852821211
Phone: 480 966-7211
Web: WWW.UDA.COOP

PRODUCTS/OPERATIONS

Selected Products and Services

Products
Dried
Dry milk blends
Kosher powder
Lactose powder
Milk protein concentrate
Nonfat dry milk
Fluid
Butter
Cream
Condensed skim milk
Skim milk
Services
Emergency repair
Installation
Preventative maintenance
Transportation
Supplies

Chemical
Equipment
Pharmaceutical

COMPETITORS

Associated Milk Producers	Main Street Ingredients
Dairy Farmers of America	Nestlé
Dairy Manufacturers	Shamrock Foods
Dean Foods	Smucker
Goya	Tate & Lyle Ingredients
Land O'Lakes	

HISTORICAL FINANCIALS
Company Type: Private

Income Statement   FYE: September 30

	REVENUE ($ mil.)	NET INCOME ($ mil.)	NET PROFIT MARGIN	EMPLOYEES
09/11	825	21	2.6%	190
09/10	612	12	2.0%	—
09/09	812	2	0.3%	—
Annual Growth	0.8%	203.7%	—	—

2011 Year-End Financials
Return on assets: 16.2%   Cash ($ mil.): 30
Return on equity: 32.4%
Current ratio: 1.40

UNITED FOOD AND COMMERCIAL WORKERS UNIONS AND FOOD EMPLOYERS BEN FUND

EXECUTIVES

Prin, Richard Klontz
Auditors: HEMMING MORSE CPA'S AND CONSUL

LOCATIONS

HQ: UNITED FOOD AND COMMERCIAL WORKERS UNIONS AND FOOD EMPLOYERS BEN FUND
6425 KATELLA AVE, CYPRESS, CA 906305246
Phone: 714 220-2297
Web: WWW.SCUFCWFUNDS.COM

HISTORICAL FINANCIALS
Company Type: Private

Income Statement   FYE: March 31

	REVENUE ($ mil.)	NET INCOME ($ mil.)	NET PROFIT MARGIN	EMPLOYEES
03/18	581	(13)	—	25
03/17	593	3	0.5%	—
03/12	512	(34)	—	—
03/11	460	(74)	—	—
Annual Growth	3.4%	—	—	—

2018 Year-End Financials
Return on assets: (-4.2%)   Cash ($ mil.): 45
Return on equity: (-7.0%)
Current ratio: 161.40

UNITED HEALTH SERVICES HOSPITAL, INC.

United Health Services Hospitals (UHS Hospitals) can service injuries from a slip in the snow or a slipped discÂ to health that's just plain slipping.Â The organizationÂ operates Binghamton General Hospital (about 200 beds) Wilson Medical Center (someÂ 280 beds) and a group of primary and specialty careÂ clinics inÂ upstate New York. Specialty services includeÂ cardiology dialysis neurology rehabilitation pediatricsÂ and psychiatry. The Wilson Medical Center serves as a teaching hospital offering residency and fellowship programs.Â UHS Hospitals is a subsidiary of United Health Services which operates a network of affiliated hospitalsÂ clinicsÂ long-term care centers and home health agencies in the region.

Geographic Reach
Binghamton General is located in Binghamton New York while Wilson Medical Center is located in Johnson City New York both within the boundaries of Broome County.Â UHSÂ HospitalsÂ also operates primary and specialty careÂ clinicsÂ in Broome Chenango Delaware and Tioga counties in upstate New York.

Strategy
United Health Services Hospitals is investing in equipment upgrades and facility improvementsÂ at Binghamton General to help the facility remain at the forefront of medical technology and services. Wilson Medical CenterÂ whichÂ acts as a regional referral centerÂ in areasÂ including emergency medicine newborn care neurology and heart surgery has also been the subject of enhancement measures. The hospital recently completed construction of the new Decker Center for Advanced Medical Treatment which offers high-tech diagnostic and acute care services.

EXECUTIVES

Pres, Atthew J Salanger
Sr V Pres, Robert Gomulka
Exec V Pres, Rajesh Dave
Dir, Halsey Bagg
Exe SEC, Brandi Phelan
Director, Gail Thalacker
Executive Director, Cory Jacobs
Qa Qc Manager, Kathleen Wold
Nurse Practitioner, Scott Rosman
Administrator, Ann Autio
Manager Financial Planning, Christian Burdick
Auditors: FUST CHARLES CHAMBERS LLP SYR

LOCATIONS

HQ: UNITED HEALTH SERVICES HOSPITAL, INC.
10-42 MITCHELL AVE, BINGHAMTON, NY 139031617
Phone: 607 762-2200
Web: WWW.TRUSTEDHEALTHSTATS.COM

COMPETITORS

Albany Medical Center	SUNY Upstate Medical University
Guthrie Healthcare	St. Joseph's Hospital Health Center
Kaleida Health	
Lifetime Health	
Oneida Healthcare Center	

HISTORICAL FINANCIALS

Company Type: Private

Income Statement				FYE: December 31
	REVENUE ($ mil.)	NET INCOME ($ mil.)	NET PROFIT MARGIN	EMPLOYEES
12/18	685	(0)	—	5,000
12/16	611	21	3.4%	—
12/15	575	13	2.3%	—
12/14	523	(23)	—	—
Annual Growth	**7.0%**	—	—	—

2018 Year-End Financials

Return on assets: —
Return on equity: (-0.1%)
Current ratio: 1.70

Cash ($ mil.): 32

UNITED INDEPENDENT SCHOOL DISTRICT

EXECUTIVES

Supt, Roberto J Santos
V Pres*, Juan Roberto Ramirez
EC*, Ricardo Rodriguez
Network Manager, Cesar Tamez
Tech Prep Coordinator, Alicia Carrillo
Computer Technician, Gabriel Ramirez
Coordinator, Maria Dominguez
Coordinator, Mary Lopez
Coordinator, Veronica Slaughter
Coordinator, Melinda Davila
Human Resources, Patty Gonzalez
Auditors: PATTILLO BROWN & HILL LLP BR

LOCATIONS

HQ: UNITED INDEPENDENT SCHOOL DISTRICT
201 LINDENWOOD DR, LAREDO, TX 780452429
Phone: 956 473-6201
Web: WWW.UISD.NET

HISTORICAL FINANCIALS

Company Type: Private

Income Statement				FYE: August 31
	REVENUE ($ mil.)	NET INCOME ($ mil.)	NET PROFIT MARGIN	EMPLOYEES
08/18	485	(69)	—	6,900
08/17	429	16	3.9%	—
08/16	464	(66)	—	—
08/15	444	64	14.5%	—
Annual Growth	**3.0%**	—	—	—

2018 Year-End Financials

Return on assets: (-9.0%)
Return on equity: —
Current ratio: —

Cash ($ mil.): 109

UNITED SPACE ALLIANCE, LLC

United Space Alliance (USA) is a space-race heavyweight; the Houston-based prime contractor has run NASA's 173000 pound Shuttles — Discovery Atlantis and Endeavour. USA a joint venture between Lockheed Martin and Boeing was formed in response to NASA's move to consolidate multiple Space Shuttle contracts under a single entity. It is now wrapping up those contracts. USA has supported mission operations astronaut and flight controller training flight software development Shuttle payload integration and vehicle processing launch and recovery. It also has led training and planning for the International Space Station. USA served the Johnson and Kennedy Space Centers and Marshall Space Flight Center.

Operations

The company has consolidated more than 30 heritage contracts which supported the Space Shuttle Program (including the Space Flight Operations contract the Space Program Operations Contract and the Integrated Mission Operations Contract).

Geographic Reach

Based in Houston the company has another location in Titusville Florida.

Strategy

The company served as NASA's primary partner in human space operations for the management of the Space Shuttle fleet and worked together for 55 Space Shuttle missions and more than 35 International Space Station increments.

In 2014 the company had no active contracts and will not pursue future contracts. The company is currently operating in an administrative capacity to close-out its managed government contracts (a process that will take a further about 5-7 years).

Company Background

In 2012 NASA awarded a one-year extension of the Integrated Mission Operations Contract to USA to continue providing mission and flight crew operations support for the International Space Station and Exploration Programs. The deal includes a further option for 2014. Throughout 2012 and 2013 however USA laid off waves of workers that resided in its former Space Shuttle program.

The launch of space shuttle Atlantis in July 2011 marked the end of NASA's 30-year Space Shuttle program. The shuttles have transported astronauts launched recovered and repaired satellites as well as driven new research and built and stocked the International Space Station with parts and provisions.

The joint venture was formed in 1996.

EXECUTIVES

Evp And Coo, Daniel C. (Dan) Brandenstein
President Chief Executive Officer, Virginia A. (Ginger) Barnes
Vp Huntsville Operations, Kimberly B. (Kim) Doering
Vp Launch And Recovery; Site Executive Florida, Mark Nappi
Cio, Toni Russell
Auditors: PRICEWATERHOUSECOOPERS LLP HO

LOCATIONS

HQ: UNITED SPACE ALLIANCE, LLC
3700 BAY AREA BLVD # 100, HOUSTON, TX 770582783
Phone: 281 282-2592
Web: WWW.EXPORTTEXAS.COM

PRODUCTS/OPERATIONS

Selected Capabilities

Flight software
Ground operations and processing
GSA (General Services Administration) services
Integrated logistics
Integration and program management
Mission operations
Safety

COMPETITORS

Airbus Group	Meggitt-USA
Arianespace	Northrop Grumman
Astrotech	Raytheon
BAE SYSTEMS	SGT
Honeywell Aerospace	Thales Aerospace

HISTORICAL FINANCIALS

Company Type: Private

Income Statement				FYE: December 31
	REVENUE ($ mil.)	NET INCOME ($ mil.)	NET PROFIT MARGIN	EMPLOYEES
12/07	1,859	168	9.0%	8,000
12/06	1,920	146	7.6%	—
Annual Growth	**(3.2%)**	**14.8%**	—	—

2007 Year-End Financials

Return on assets: 60.5%
Return on equity: —
Current ratio: 1.00

Cash ($ mil.): 57

UNITED STATES FUND FOR UNICEF

The US Fund for UNICEF is one of about 40 committees in America that raises money for The United Nations Children's Fund (better known as UNICEF a not-for-profit organization that works for the human rights protection and development of children worldwide through education advocacy and fundraising. Among its dedicated programs are the five-year $100 million fundraising campaign for HIV/AIDS prevention and a campaign to protect mothers and newborns from tetanus. The US Fund for UNICEF derives revenue from public support — through its signature Trick-or-Treat for UNICEF program gifts corporate grants and the sale of greeting cards and educational materials. The organization was founded in 1947.

Geographic Reach

The US Fund for UNICEF operates a handful of regional offices in Atlanta Boston Chicago Houston Los Angeles and San Francisco.

Financial Performance

The organization's revenue increased by 1% in 2012 versus 2011 to more than $500 million. The US Fund attributed the gain to an increase in public support including major gifts Internet donations and gifts in kind. The increase in giving was partially offset by a decline in investment returns. Net income rose 7% over the same period despite an increase in expenses tied to program and support services.

Strategy

The US Fund for UNICEF is rallying around its "Believe in Zero" campaign which aims to reduce the number of preventable deaths of children under five years of age to zero. The number of under-five child deaths has dropped more than 40 percent since 1990 to 19000.

EXECUTIVES

Managing Director Planned Giving, Karen Metzger
Vice President And Manager Of Prod. Services, Han Zhang
Board Of Directors, Lorraine Nelson
Auditors: KPMG LLP NEW YORK NY

LOCATIONS

HQ: UNITED STATES FUND FOR UNICEF
125 MAIDEN LN FL 11, NEW YORK, NY 100384999
Phone: 800 367-5437
Web: WWW.UNICEFUSA.ORG

HISTORICAL FINANCIALS

Company Type: Private

Income Statement				FYE: June 30
	REVENUE ($ mil.)	NET INCOME ($ mil.)	NET PROFIT MARGIN	EMPLOYEES
06/18	567	19	3.4%	230
06/16	568	7	1.2%	—
06/15	500	(29)	—	—
06/14	606	67	11.2%	—
Annual Growth	(1.7%)	(27.0%)	—	—

2018 Year-End Financials

Return on assets: 7.8%   Cash ($ mil.): 77
Return on equity: 14.6%
Current ratio: 1.80

UNITED STEEL PAPER AND FORESTRY RUBBER MANUFACTURING ENERGY ALLIED

Auditors: SCHNEIDER DOWNS & CO INC PITT

LOCATIONS

HQ: UNITED STEEL PAPER AND FORESTRY RUBBER MANUFACTURING ENERGY ALLIED
5 GATEWAY CTR, PITTSBURGH, PA 15222
Phone: 412 562-2400
Web: WWW.USW.ORG

HISTORICAL FINANCIALS

Company Type: Private

Income Statement				FYE: December 31
	REVENUE ($ mil.)	NET INCOME ($ mil.)	NET PROFIT MARGIN	EMPLOYEES
12/17	520	148	28.5%	12
12/13	489	83	17.0%	—
12/09	386	(28)	—	—
Annual Growth	3.8%	—	—	—

2017 Year-End Financials

Return on assets: 16.0%   Cash ($ mil.): 181
Return on equity: 36.5%
Current ratio: 3.90

UNIVERSITIES OF LOUISIANA SYSTEM

EXECUTIVES

President, Randy Moffett
Exec Dir, Caprice Leyoub
Pres, John Crain

LOCATIONS

HQ: UNIVERSITIES OF LOUISIANA SYSTEM
1201 N 3RD ST STE 7300, BATON ROUGE, LA 708025243
Phone: 225 342-6950
Web: WWW.ULSYSTEM.EDU

HISTORICAL FINANCIALS

Company Type: Private

Income Statement				FYE: June 30
	REVENUE ($ mil.)	NET INCOME ($ mil.)	NET PROFIT MARGIN	EMPLOYEES
06/18	930	101	10.9%	4,500
06/17	906	23	2.6%	—
06/16	845	25	3.0%	—
Annual Growth	4.9%	101.4%	—	—

2018 Year-End Financials

Return on assets: 3.6%   Cash ($ mil.): 269
Return on equity: —
Current ratio: 2.40

UNIVERSITY COMMUNITY HOSPITAL, INC.

University Community Health (doing business as Florida Hospital Tampa Bay Division) is a 1000-bed regional health care system with four locations spanning the Hillsborough Pinellas and Pasco counties of Florida. It oversees a network of eight hospitals in Florida's Tampa Bay area. Its four general hospitals — three located in Tampa and one in nearby Tarpon Springs — collectively house some 860 beds and provide emergency surgical and acute medical care as well as provide outpatient services. The system also includes a specialty heart hospital a women's hospital and a long-term acute care hospital. Florida Hospital Tampa Bay Division is part of the Adventist Health System.

Strategy

As part of the Adventist Health System's network the system has access to a broader statewide network of physicians and specialists as well as enhanced administrative and technological services organization.

In 2012 Florida Hospital Tampa Bay Division opened Florida Hospital Wesley Chapel and began work on three major construction projects including a new full-service Emergency Department (ED) expanding The Women's Center and exterior and interior upgrades to the main hospital which should add a total of 54000 sq. ft. to the scope of Florida Hospital Tampa.

Company Background

Its original name of University Community Health (UCH) reflected its proximity to the Univer-

---

sity of South Florida. UCH teamed up with Adventist Health in 2007 to build Wesley Chapel Medical Center. Buoyed by the success of the venture in 2010 UCH and Adventist Health reached an accord and UCH became a member of Adventist Health.

EXECUTIVES

Medical Director, Kurt Stonesifer

LOCATIONS

HQ: UNIVERSITY COMMUNITY HOSPITAL, INC.
3100 E FLETCHER AVE, TAMPA, FL 336134613
Phone: 813 971-6000
Web: WWW.ADVENTHEALTH.COM

PRODUCTS/OPERATIONS

Selected Centers

Diabetes and Endocrinology Institute
Don Lau Family Center for Cancer Care
Florida Hospital Pepin Heart Institute
Occupational Health Service
Orthopedic Care Center
Pediatric Care Center
Sleep Center
The Women's Center
Wound Healing Institute

Selected Hospitals

Florida Hospital at Connerton
Florida Hospital Carrollwood
Florida Hospital North Pinellas
Florida Hospital Pepin Heart Institute
Florida Hospital Tampa
Florida Hospital Wesley Chapel
Florida Hospital Zephyrhills
Long Term Acute Care

COMPETITORS

All Children's Hospital	Lakeland Regional Medical Center
BayCare Health System	Northside Hospital and Heart Institute
Bayfront Health	
HCA	Tampa General Hospital

HISTORICAL FINANCIALS

Company Type: Private

Income Statement				FYE: December 31
	REVENUE ($ mil.)	NET INCOME ($ mil.)	NET PROFIT MARGIN	EMPLOYEES
12/17	688	66	9.6%	8,000
12/16	483	39	8.2%	—
12/15	460	38	8.4%	—
12/14	381	24	6.5%	—
Annual Growth	21.7%	38.9%	—	—

2017 Year-End Financials

Return on assets: 6.4%   Cash ($ mil.): 258
Return on equity: 9.2%
Current ratio: 9.50

UNIVERSITY HEALTH CARE INC

University Health Care wants to giveÂ patients a passport to good health. The companyÂ which does business as Passport Health Plan provides managed MedicaidÂ insurance services to about 150000 members throughoutÂ 16 counties in Kentucky. Offerings include HMO Medicare Advantage and children's health plans. University Health Care was founded in 1997 by a group of affiliated providersÂ including theÂ University of

Louisville Medical Center Jewish Hospital and St. Mary's HealthCare and the Louisville/Jefferson County Primary Care Association. The health plan has an administration partnershipÂ withÂ the AmeriHealth Mercy organizationÂ a Medicaid managed careÂ joint venture between Ameri-Health and Mercy Health System.

EXECUTIVES

Vice President Of Public Affairs, Jill Bell
Vice President And Chief Compliance Officer,
 David Henley
Vice President And Chief Of Staff, Joanne McFall
Auditors: MOUNTJOY CHILTON MEDLEY LLP L

LOCATIONS

HQ: UNIVERSITY HEALTH CARE INC
 5100 CMMERCE CROSSINGS DR, LOUISVILLE, KY
 402292128
Phone: 502 585-7900
Web: WWW.PASSPORTHEALTHPLAN.COM

COMPETITORS

AMERIGROUP	Health Net
Aetna	HealthSpring
Anthem Health Plans of	Humana
Kentucky	Kaiser Foundation
Bluegrass Family	Health Plan
Health	UnitedHealth Group
CIGNA	

HISTORICAL FINANCIALS

Company Type: Private

Income Statement   FYE: December 31

	REVENUE ($ mil.)	NET INCOME ($ mil.)	NET PROFIT MARGIN	EMPLOYEES
12/14	1,299	114	8.8%	165
12/00	330	3	1.2%	—
12/99	284	5	2.0%	—
12/98	809	0	—	—
Annual Growth	3.0%	—	—	—

2014 Year-End Financials

Return on assets: 31.8%   Cash ($ mil.): 140
Return on equity: 52.2%
Current ratio: —

UNIVERSITY HOSPITALS HEALTH SYSTEM, INC.

University Hospitals Health System (UHHS) is on a mission to teach research and administer good health throughout northeastern Ohio. Its flagship facility University Hospitals of Cleveland (UHC) which operates as University Hospitals Case Medical Center (UHCMC) is a more than 1000-bed tertiary care center serving Cleveland and other parts of northeastern Ohio. The teaching hospital which is affiliated with Case Western Reserve University is also home to Rainbow Babies & Children's Hospital Seidman Cancer Center and MacDonald Women's Hospital. the not-for-profit UHHS is also home to community hospitals out-patient health and surgery centers mental health facilities and senior care centers.

Operations

UHHS' eight community hospitals some of which are operated through affiliation agreements provide a full range of specialty and general acute care from anesthesia to vascular surgery. Along with those the system operates urgent care and neighborhood medical centers throughout the region. The UH Extended Care Campus includes a specialty hospital outpatient rehabilitation and extended care facility. UHHS also operates home health occupational health wellness and managed care (health plan) divisions. The UHHS facilities have a total of some 1800 beds.

Altogether the network's facilities handle some 65000 inpatient visits per year as well as 5.8 million outpatient procedures and 206000 emergency room visits. It delivered more than 5200 babies and conducted more than 60000 surgeries in 2013.

In addition to conducting education and training programs for Case Western Reserve University School of Medicine students UHHS partners with the university to operate the Center for Clinical Research and Technology. The center is the largest biomedical research facility in Ohio and focuses on translational research which connects laboratory research to clinical bedside care.

UHHS' physician network consists of 1700 physicians and 3000 affiliated members. The system provided $270 million for community benefit and provided $253 million for research in 2013.

The hospital system is affiliated with three Cleveland-area health care providers: St. John Medical Center UH Rehabilitation Hospital (a joint venture with Center Healthcare) and Southwest General.

Geographic Reach

UHHS operates about 30 health centers and outpatient office buildings as well as more than 100 physician practice locations across the northeastern Ohio region. It serves 16 counties.

Financial Performance

UHHS' revenues increased by 4% to $2.3 billion in 2013 due to higher patient service revenues.

Operating income increased by 21% $78.6 million that year due to a change in fair value of derivative instruments and a growth in investment income partially offset by higher operating expenses.

UHHS' operating cash flow decreased by $143 million in 2013 due a change in beneficial interest in foundation and perpetual trusts pension liability adjustments and a change in operating assets and liabilities.

Strategy

The medical system is expanding by installing smaller regional and community hospitals and additional specialty care units within its larger facilities including a neonatal intensive care unit emergency care center and a cancer care center within UH Case Medical.

To strengthen its clinical capabilities it also expanded its established areas of excellence and developed new areas to improve access it has forged new hospital partnerships. To enhance care in the communities served by its new partners UHHS has opened satellites of some of its centers of excellence initially for cancer care cardiac care pediatrics and women's health. Pursuant to the growth strategy it has added two community hospitals that are now UHHS' largest: 387-bed UH Elyria Medical Center (formerly EMH Healthcare) and 332-bed UH Parma Medical Center (formerly The Parma Community General Hospital).

The company also plans to break ground on a $28 million state-of-the-art outpatient health center and freestanding emergency department in Broadview Heights with a projected completion date in late 2016. In 2013 University Hospitals Seidman Cancer Center expanded to Parma Community General Hospital providing integrated cancer care to residents in Parma and surrounding communities.

To expand in another neighboring community the system launched renovation of an office building that became the UH Solon Health Center in 2013. It also opened a new outpatient center the UH Aurora Health Center in 2012.

UHHS is also in the process of implementing an electronic health records (EHR) system across its facilities. The EHR system could make the network eligible for certain government incentives if they meet government guidelines for "meaningful use."

On the research front in 2014 UHHS Case Medical Center conducted a Phase 3 clinical trial to evaluate the safety and effectiveness of an investigational medicine called LMTX in people with a type of dementia known as behavioral-variant Frontotemporal Dementia (previously known as Pick's Disease).

Company Background

UHHS completed construction of the UH Ahuja Medical Center a new community hospital in 2011.

The company was founded in 1866.

EXECUTIVES

Vice President, Elizabeth Novak
Auditors: ERNST & YOUNG US LLP PITTSB

LOCATIONS

HQ: UNIVERSITY HOSPITALS HEALTH SYSTEM, INC.
 3605 WARRENSVILLE CTR RD, SHAKER HEIGHTS,
 OH 441225203
Phone: 216 767-8900

PRODUCTS/OPERATIONS

Selected Facilities
Main Campuses
 Case Medical Center
 MacDonald Women's Hospital
 Rainbow Babies & Children's Hospital
 Seidman Cancer Center
Community Hospitals
 Ahuja Medical Center
 Bedford Medical Center (UH Regional Hospitals)
 Conneaut Medical Center
 Elyria Medical Center
 Geauga Medical Center
 Geneva Medical Center
 Parma Medical Center
 Richmond Medical Center (UH Regional Hospitals)

COMPETITORS

Akron Children's Hospital	Parma Community General Hospital
Akron General Health System	Robinson Memorial Hospital
Lake Health	Summa Health System
Mercy Medical Center (OH)	The Cleveland Clinic
MetroHealth System	Trinity Health System

HISTORICAL FINANCIALS

Company Type: Private

Income Statement   FYE: December 31

	REVENUE ($ mil.)	NET INCOME ($ mil.)	NET PROFIT MARGIN	EMPLOYEES
12/17	580	33	5.7%	30,099
12/12	2,266	54	2.4%	—
12/09	1,938	110	5.7%	—
12/08	1,800	(153)	—	—
Annual Growth	(11.8%)	—	—	—

2017 Year-End Financials

Return on assets: 0.8%   Cash ($ mil.): 184
Return on equity: 1.6%
Current ratio: 0.20

UNIVERSITY MEDICAL CENTER INC

EXECUTIVES

Ceo, James Taylor
Pres*, Ken Marshall
Sr V Pres*, Mark Pfeifer
Cfo-Sr V Pres*, Robert P Barbier
SEC*, Amber Denham
Prin*, Mary Jane Adams
Assistant Professor of Radiolo, Peter Hentzen
Assistant Professor of Radiolo, Richard Goldwin
Assistant Professor of Radiolo, Barbara Pawley
Director of Oncology, Den Ellen Coldiron
Director, Hiram C Polk

LOCATIONS

HQ: UNIVERSITY MEDICAL CENTER INC
530 S JACKSON ST, LOUISVILLE, KY 402021675
Phone: 502 562-3000
Web: WWW.UOFLHOSPITAL.ORG

HISTORICAL FINANCIALS
Company Type: Private

| Income Statement | | | FYE: June 30 | |
	REVENUE ($ mil.)	NET INCOME ($ mil.)	NET PROFIT MARGIN	EMPLOYEES
06/18	487	(72)	—	2,000
06/16	501	35	7.1%	—
06/15	484	53	11.1%	—
Annual Growth	0.2%	—	—	—

2018 Year-End Financials
Return on assets: (-16.1%)   Cash ($ mil.): 80
Return on equity: (-35.5%)
Current ratio: 0.80

UNIVERSITY MEDICAL CENTER OF SOUTHERN NEVADA

For those who want to learn while they heal the ill University Medical Center of Southern Nevada (UMC)— an affiliate of the University of Nevada School of Medicine might just be the place. The medical center includes a teaching hospital and a network of community and urgent care health centers. Among its specialized services are cancer treatment heart care pediatrics and rehabilitation. It also offers birthing wound and burn care neurological disorder Level II Pediatric Trauma Lions Burn Care Center and Level 1 trauma centers. UMC serves southern Nevada along with parts of Arizona California and Utah.

Operations
UMC is also home to Children's Hospital of Nevada. Services at University Medical Center of Southern Nevada are comprehensive and include everything from ambulatory surgery to a birthing center cancer care infection prevention and organ donation.

The hospital operates 10 Quick Care urgent care locations around Las Vegas. Quick Cares provide primary and urgent care which means they accept minor injuries such as fractures and flus and pri-

mary care for patients who don't necessarily need to be seen right away and can make an appointment.

UMC offers residency programs in a whole slew of specialties including dental (pediatric and adult) emergency medicine family medicine internal medicine OB-GYN psychiatry surgery and trauma surgery and ophthalmology.

For doctors who have put medical school behind them UMC provides a range of Continuing Education Courses to keep them up to date on the latest procedures and technology.

More than 6500 patients are treated at UMC's emergency room per month and more than 600 children are treated per week. UMC's lab processes 4 million test results annually using the latest in technology and automation for the greatest accuracy and increased patient outcomes.

Sales and Marketing
Medicare accounted for 20% of the Center's 2014 revenues; Medicaid and self pay 50%; and commercial HMO and PPO 20%.

Financial Performance
UMC's revenues decreased by 20% in 2014 due to a decline in net patient revenues and other operating revenues.

It reported a net loss of $56 million in 2014 due to a decline in revenues and an increase in purchase services expenses as the result of consulting services received for operational improvements.

UMC reported cash outflow of $42 million in 2014 over cash inflow of 2013.

Company Background
The medical center opened its doors in 1931 with 20 beds.

EXECUTIVES

Radiology Director, Christopher Jones

LOCATIONS

HQ: UNIVERSITY MEDICAL CENTER OF SOUTHERN NEVADA
1800 W CHARLESTON BLVD, LAS VEGAS, NV 891022329
Phone: 702 383-2000
Web: WWW.UMCSN.COM

PRODUCTS/OPERATIONS

Selected Services
Bariatric Medicine
Birthing Center
Center for Transplantation
Emergency Services
Family Resource Center
Heart Center
HIV Wellness Center
Imaging Se
Infection Prevention
Interpretive Services
Lab Services
Lions Wound and Burn Care Center
Oncology Care Center
Outpatient Physical Therapy
Robotics
Surgical Services
Trauma Center

COMPETITORS

Desert Springs Hospital	Sunrise Hospital and Medical Center
Dignity Health	Valley Hospital
Summerlin Hospital	

HISTORICAL FINANCIALS
Company Type: Private

| Income Statement | | | FYE: June 30 | |
	REVENUE ($ mil.)	NET INCOME ($ mil.)	NET PROFIT MARGIN	EMPLOYEES
06/15	530	49	9.3%	3,700
06/03	412	20	5.0%	—
06/02	0	0	—	—
Annual Growth	—	—	—	—

2015 Year-End Financials
Return on assets: 13.1%   Cash ($ mil.): 83
Return on equity: —
Current ratio: 2.40

UNIVERSITY OF ALABAMA

EXECUTIVES

Exec Dir, Kevin Stevens
Accounting Staff, Lisa H McKinney
Accounting Staff, Tina Dorroh
Assistant Professor, Jane Rasco
Assistant To President, Charles Hilburn
Staff, June Vance
Staff, Paul A Leblanc
Staff, Sunee Lavender
Staff, Michael Steinberg
Staff, Paula House
Staff, Natalie Champion
Auditors: PRICEWATERHOUSECOOPERS LLP BI

LOCATIONS

HQ: UNIVERSITY OF ALABAMA
301 ROSE ADMIN BLDG, TUSCALOOSA, AL 354870001
Phone: 205 348-7840
Web: WWW.UA.EDU

HISTORICAL FINANCIALS
Company Type: Private

| Income Statement | | | FYE: September 30 | |
	REVENUE ($ mil.)	NET INCOME ($ mil.)	NET PROFIT MARGIN	EMPLOYEES
09/18	875	188	21.6%	3,950
09/17	833	224	26.9%	—
Annual Growth	5.0%	(15.8%)	—	—

2018 Year-End Financials
Return on assets: 4.1%   Cash ($ mil.): 71
Return on equity: 9.0%
Current ratio: 1.00

UNIVERSITY OF ALABAMA HEALTH SERVICES FOUNDATION, P.C.

EXECUTIVES

Ceo, Will Ferniany
Pres*, Anton Bueschen
V Pres*, Reed F Jones
Cfo*, Michael Heckman
Pres*, Dr Jim Bonner
Exec V Pres*, Patricia Pritchett
Exec Admin, Melanie Brewer
Project Coordinator, Niki Woodall
Controller, Stephanie McClinton
Director, Chuck Patrick
Professor, Holly Richter
Auditors: PRICEWATERHOUSECOOPERS LLP BI

LOCATIONS

HQ: UNIVERSITY OF ALABAMA HEALTH SERVICES
FOUNDATION, P.C.
500 22ND ST S STE 100, BIRMINGHAM, AL
352333110
Phone: 205 731-9600
Web: WWW.ALABAMAORGANCENTER.ORG

HISTORICAL FINANCIALS
Company Type: Private

Income Statement
FYE: September 30

	REVENUE ($ mil.)	NET INCOME ($ mil.)	NET PROFIT MARGIN	EMPLOYEES
09/18	668	12	1.9%	3,205
09/15	561	1	0.2%	—
09/14	26	0	1.6%	—
09/13	520	10	1.9%	—
Annual Growth	5.1%	4.9%	—	—

2018 Year-End Financials
Return on assets: 1.4%   Cash ($ mil.): 12
Return on equity: 3.1%
Current ratio: 0.90

UNIVERSITY OF ARKANSAS SYSTEM

Calling "Wooo Pig Sooie" at anyone in The University of Arkansas System (UA) is not an insult. The system encompasses more than a dozen schools institutes and campuses throughout the state including five universities a college of medicine a math and science high school and the Clinton School of Public Service started in 2004 by former president Bill Clinton and offering the only Master of Public Service degree in the country. UA which has an enrollment of more than 60000 hails the razorback or hog as its mascot. "Wooo Pig Sooie" or "hog calling" is the school's cheer at sporting events. Its student-teacher ratio is 19:1; it has about 17000 employees.

EXECUTIVES

Vice President For University Relations, Melissa Rust
Vice President For Academic Affairs, Michael Moore
Associate Vice President For Finance, Rita Fleming
Vice President Community Service, Robyn Jilg
Executive Vice President Student Alumni Board, Emma Buckner
Assistant Secretary, Kelly Eichler
Auditors: ROGER A NORMAN JD CPA CFE

LOCATIONS

HQ: UNIVERSITY OF ARKANSAS SYSTEM
2404 N UNIVERSITY AVE, LITTLE ROCK, AR
722073608
Phone: 501 686-2500
Web: WWW.UASYS.EDU

PRODUCTS/OPERATIONS

Selected Campuses
Arkansas Archeological Survey
Arkansas School for Mathematics Sciences and the Arts (high school)
Clinton School of Public Service
Cossatot Community College of the University of Arkansas
Criminal Justice Institute
Division of Agriculture
Phillips Community College of the University of Arkansas
University of Arkansas Community College at Morrilton
University of Arkansas Fayetteville
University of Arkansas at Fort Smith
University of Arkansas at Little Rock
University of Arkansas for Medical Sciences
University of Arkansas at Monticello
University of Arkansas at Pine Bluff
Winthrop Rockefeller Institute

HISTORICAL FINANCIALS
Company Type: Private

Income Statement
FYE: June 30

	REVENUE ($ mil.)	NET INCOME ($ mil.)	NET PROFIT MARGIN	EMPLOYEES
06/18	2,402	139	5.8%	14,025
06/17	2,297	88	3.9%	—
06/16	2,172	64	3.0%	—
06/15	1,970	30	1.6%	—
Annual Growth	6.8%	65.6%	—	—

2018 Year-End Financials
Return on assets: 3.0%   Cash ($ mil.): 426
Return on equity: 5.6%
Current ratio: 3.40

UNIVERSITY OF CALIFORNIA, DAVIS

If you want to grow grapes and make wine in Napa Valley or Sonoma County you might want to swing by the University of California Davis (UC Davis) first. The school one of 10 University of California campuses offers a wide variety of agricultural programs; its Viticulture and Enology department provides professional education for aspiring winemakers. Located between Sacramento and San Francisco UC Davis also has colleges and professional schools in biology engineering education law business medicine and veterinary medicine and it is recognized for its research programs.

UC Davis enrolls more than 37400 including more than 6700 graduate students and it has a student-faculty ratio of 19:1.

Operations
UC Davis comprises four colleges: Agricultural and Environmental Sciences; Biological Sciences; Engineering; and Letters and Science. It also operates six professional schools: Education; Law; Management; Medicine; Veterinary Medicine; and the Betty Irene Moore School of Nursing. It also includes a 620-bed acute care teaching hospital in Sacramento (UC Davis Health) and the UC Davis Veterinary Medicine Teaching Research Center in Tulane.

Geographic Reach
Spanning 5300 acres UC Davis was for many years the largest campus in the UC system but the newer University of California Merced campus (completed in 2005) has surpassed it with more than 7000 acres. UC Davis has satellite campuses in San Ramon and Sacramento as well as related educational facilities elsewhere in California and in Nevada.

Financial Performance
UC Davis had a budget of $4.3 billion in 2015-16 of which about 41% was designated to come from the medical center and 13% each from grants and contracts and from auxiliary sales and service fees.

Strategy
Deep state budget cuts have impacted the entire UC system. As a result UC Davis and its sister institutions have had to launch some cost-reduction efforts including the consolidation of certain administrative functions. Also with public funding in tight supply the university increasingly is looking to private funding sources to expand educational opportunities.

Company Background
The school was originally known as the University Farm School and accepted its first students at its new campus in the town of Davisville (later changed to Davis) in 1909. The California Legislature in 1905 authorized the establishment of a state agricultural college; the school that became UC Davis was administratively tied to UC Berkeley for decades before gaining its status as an independent university in 1959.

EXECUTIVES

Vice Provost Of Information And Educational Technology And Cio, Viji Murali
Ceo Uc Davis Medical Center, Ann Madden Rice
Chancellor, Linda P.B. Katehi
Executive Vice Chancellor And Provost, Ralph J. Hexter
Vice Chancellor For Finance Operations And Administration And Cfo, Dave Lawlor

LOCATIONS

HQ: UNIVERSITY OF CALIFORNIA, DAVIS
1 SHIELDS AVE, DAVIS, CA 956168500
Phone: 530 752-1011
Web: WWW.UCDAVIS.EDU

HISTORICAL FINANCIALS
Company Type: Private

Income Statement
FYE: June 30

	REVENUE ($ mil.)	NET INCOME ($ mil.)	NET PROFIT MARGIN	EMPLOYEES
06/11*	2,697	360	13.4%	17,741
12/08	0	0	9.6%	—
06/08	14	0	6.1%	—
Annual Growth	474.6%	644.1%	—	—
*Fiscal year change

UNIVERSITY OF CHICAGO

LOCATIONS

HQ: UNIVERSITY OF CHICAGO
   1414 E 59TH ST, CHICAGO, IL 606372916
Phone: 773 753-2270
Web: WWW.UCHICAGO.EDU

HISTORICAL FINANCIALS

Company Type: Private

Income Statement				FYE: June 30
	REVENUE ($ mil.)	NET INCOME ($ mil.)	NET PROFIT MARGIN	EMPLOYEES
06/13	3,091	182	5.9%	2
06/11	3,056	1,052	34.4%	—
Annual Growth	0.6%	(58.4%)	—	—

2013 Year-End Financials

Return on assets: 1.9%   Cash ($ mil.): 45
Return on equity: 2.9%
Current ratio: 0.20

UNIVERSITY OF CINCINNATI

The University of Cincinnati (UC) is a research institution offering undergraduate graduate and professional education from its seven campuses in Ohio. The university enrolls more than 44000 students and has more than a dozen colleges. Academic offerings include business law medicine applied science pharmacy and music. The institution offers about 70 doctoral programs and roughly 240 other degree programs. UC was founded in 1819 and became a state university in 1977; the school has an endowment of close to $1 billion. Notable alumni include former US president William Howard Taft and architect Michael Graves.

Operations

The university has a combined faculty and staff of almost 10000. The school's staff and students engage in experimentation that spans the gamut from basic clinical and translational research to creative works and performance.The largest employer in the region UC has an annual economic impact of about $4 billion.

Financial Performance

UC and its research affiliates generate about $430 million a year in research funding.

Company Background

UC traces its history all the way back to 1819 when Cincinnati College and the Medical College of Ohio were chartered. In 1870 the city established the University of Cincinnati which later absorbed Cincinnati College and the Medical College of Ohio. In 1906 UC created the first cooperative education program in the world. In 1977 UC joined the University System of Ohio. Today UC is classified as a research university (meaning it has "Very High Research Activity") by the Carnegie Commission and is ranked as one of America's top 25 public research universities by the National Science Foundation.

EXECUTIVES

President, Santa J. Ono
Svp Academic Affairs And Provost, Beverly Davenport
Svp Administration And Finance And Cfo, Robert F. (Bob) Ambach
Vp Information Technology And Cio, Nelson C. Vincent
Vpres Community Affairs Uc Hea, John Tew
Executive Vice President, Ryan M Hays
Vice President Fin Services Controller, Carol Metzger
Department Head, Amy Lind
Associate Vice President For Research And Advanced Studies, Judith Trent
Senior Vice President Finance, Kathleen Qualls
Edd Assistant Vice President Division Of Student Affairs, Nicole Mayo
Provost And Executive Vice President Academic Affairs, Kristi A Nelson
Associate Vice President, Mary McGrew
Assistant Vice President, Karen Losekamp
Vice President Of Finance, Patrick Kowalski
Senior Vice President And Provost Medical Center, Don Harrison
Assistant Vice President Housing Food And Retail Services, Todd Duncan
Vice President For Governmenta, Greg Vehr
Assistant Vice President Business Core Systems, Robin Pittman
Associate Vice President And Chief Human Resource Officer, Tamie Grunow
Associate Vice President Dorot, Dorothy Air
Assistant Vice President And Chief Risk Officer, Anita Ingram
Internal Vice President, Adam Kluesener
Associate Medical Director, Arden Wander
Assistant Vice President For Research Strategic Initiatives, Phil Taylor
Senior Vice President Of Advancement And Campaign Director, Donna Gastevich
University Of Cincinnati 18 Vice President, Lonna Sedam
Associate Vice President For Human Resources, Linda Bledsoe
Medical Director, Jon Divine
Vice President Of Professional Activities, Devin Lally
Assistant Vice President, Karen Goodwin
Vice President, Carrie White
Assistant Vice President For Student Affairs And Dean Of Students, Juan Guardia
Vice President For Safety And Reform, Robin Engel
Vice President Marketing And Communications, Chris Ralston
Department Head, Steve Carlton
Vice President Of Ambulatory Service, Rosemary Keiser
Chairperson Board Of Trustees, Thomas H. (Tom) Humes
Vice Chair Board Of Trustees, Robert E. Richardson
Treasurer, Gary Hunt
Secretary, Mary Brunner
Treasurer Office Accounts Payable, Amber Simkins
Ward Secretary, Elizabeth Davis
Medical Secretary, Darlene Pabst
Assistant Treasurer, Susan Albonetti
Assistant Treasurer, Sheri Williams
Treasurer, Benita Webster
Board Member, Jennifer Heisey
Secretary, Robin Lee
Board Member, Debbie Zorn
Treasurer, Amanda Mare
Auditors: BKD LLP CINCINNATI OHIO

LOCATIONS

HQ: UNIVERSITY OF CINCINNATI
   2600 CLIFTON AVE, CINCINNATI, OH 452202872
Phone: 513 556-6000
Web: WWW.UC.EDU

PRODUCTS/OPERATIONS

Selected Colleges & Schools
Clermont College (regional campus)
College-Conservatory of Music
College of Allied Health Sciences
College of Applied Science
College of Business
College of Design Architecture Art & Planning
College of Education Criminal Justice and Human Services
College of Engineering
College of Law
College of Medicine
College of Nursing
James L. Winkle College of Pharmacy
McMicken College of Arts & Sciences
Raymond Walters College (regional campus)
School of Social Work

HISTORICAL FINANCIALS

Company Type: Private

Income Statement				FYE: June 30
	REVENUE ($ mil.)	NET INCOME ($ mil.)	NET PROFIT MARGIN	EMPLOYEES
06/11	1,198	48	4.1%	14,600
06/07	594	112	18.9%	—
06/06	557	20	3.6%	—
Annual Growth	16.6%	19.2%	—	—

2011 Year-End Financials

Return on assets: 1.1%   Cash ($ mil.): 83
Return on equity: 1.5%
Current ratio: —

UNIVERSITY OF CINCINNATI MEDICAL CENTER, LLC

EXECUTIVES

Ceo, Bryan Gibler
Chief of Ob/Gyn, Arthur T Evans II
Director Records, Charlesetta Mc Cray
Assistant Professor, Sangita Kapur
Professor, Edward Silberstein
Internal Medicine Practitioner, Mark Andolina
Emergency Medicine Specialist, Matthew K Riddle
Anesthesiologist, Matthew Wallace
Diagnostic Radiologist, Raj Patel
Hematologist, Zartash Gul
Coordinator, Travis Doty

LOCATIONS

HQ: UNIVERSITY OF CINCINNATI MEDICAL CENTER, LLC
   234 GOODMAN ST, CINCINNATI, OH 452192364
Phone: 513 584-1000

HISTORICAL FINANCIALS

Company Type: Private

Income Statement

FYE: June 30

	REVENUE ($ mil.)	NET INCOME ($ mil.)	NET PROFIT MARGIN	EMPLOYEES
06/16	913	57	6.3%	5,000
06/15	873	64	7.4%	—
06/10	633	28	4.6%	—
06/09	562	20	3.6%	—
Annual Growth	7.2%	16.0%	—	—

2016 Year-End Financials

Return on assets: 9.2%   Cash ($ mil.): 2
Return on equity: 9.8%
Current ratio: 18.50

UNIVERSITY OF COLORADO

EXECUTIVES

Exec Dir, Hollie Stevenson
Sys Dir, Andreas Hoenger
Senior Research Associate, Robin Corley
Project Manager, Michael Gilbert
Senior Program Manager, Hailee Koehler

LOCATIONS

HQ: UNIVERSITY OF COLORADO
535 16TH ST STE 300, DENVER, CO 802024238
Phone: 303 831-6192

HISTORICAL FINANCIALS

Company Type: Private

Income Statement

FYE: June 30

	REVENUE ($ mil.)	NET INCOME ($ mil.)	NET PROFIT MARGIN	EMPLOYEES
06/13	2,774	308	11.1%	1
06/12	2,641	141	5.4%	—
Annual Growth	5.1%	118.3%	—	—

2013 Year-End Financials

Return on assets: 4.7%   Cash ($ mil.): 102
Return on equity: 7.6%
Current ratio: 1.30

UNIVERSITY OF COLORADO HEALTH

EXECUTIVES

General Counsel, Emily Weber
Internal Medicine Practitioner, Darlene B Tad-Y
Coordinator, Carrie Macdonald
Coordinator, Jessica Berry
Coordinator, Meredith Snyder
Internist, Ahmed Hassanin
Internist, Alexis Leal
Social Worker Clinical Lcsw CM, Allyson Drago
Administrative Assistant III, Amanda Whiting
Cardiovascular Disease, Amy Barley

Building Manager, Angela Janacek

LOCATIONS

HQ: UNIVERSITY OF COLORADO HEALTH
12401 E 17TH AVE STE F485, AURORA, CO
800452603
Phone: 720 848-1031

HISTORICAL FINANCIALS

Company Type: Private

Income Statement

FYE: June 30

	REVENUE ($ mil.)	NET INCOME ($ mil.)	NET PROFIT MARGIN	EMPLOYEES
06/18	4,341	747	17.2%	7,593
06/17	3,668	750	20.5%	—
Annual Growth	18.4%	(0.5%)	—	—

2018 Year-End Financials

Return on assets: 10.3%   Cash ($ mil.): 330
Return on equity: 16.8%
Current ratio: 1.20

UNIVERSITY OF COLORADO HOSPITAL AUTHORITY

University of Colorado Hospital Authority doing business as UCHealth operates the University of Colorado Hospital (UCH) in Aurora Colorado. The facility is a teaching institution for — you guessed it — the University of Colorado. UCH is a 400-bed community hospital that includes a number of specialty care facilities including centers specializing in oncology respiratory care and endocrinology. The facility also conducts medical training and research programs in partnership with the University of Colorado's Denver School of Medicine. In addition UCHealth operates 10 primary care clinics in the Denver metropolitan area.

Operations

UCH is located on the University of Colorado's Anschutz Medical Campus along with other health care providers and the University of Colorado's primary medical school campus in Aurora Colorado. Its Anschutz Inpatient Pavilion includes ICU operating imaging pharmacy and other care facilities. It also includes the Anschutz Cancer Pavilion which not only offers cancer treatment but also conducts research; Rocky Mountain Lions Eye Institute for ophthalmic care; and a rehabilitation department offering addiction treatment services.

While UCH's operations are closely tied to the University of Colorado UCH is governed by the UCH Authority a separate legal entity.

Strategy

UCHealth has upgraded its facilities in recent years to provide state-of-the art medical care and educational and research resources. Among its recent projects has been a $20 million renovation and expansion of the Anschutz Cancer Pavilion the addition of a brain tumor treatment lab to the Anschutz Outpatient Pavilion and the construction of a new 12-story emergency department tower.

In 2015 the authority broke ground on another project — the construction of a new $12.3 million emergency center at its Harmony Campus in Fort Collins Colorado. It also acquired a majority stake in a dozen freestanding emergency rooms in Colorado that are operated by Adeptus Health. The

facilities (plus two more under construction) operated under the First Choice banner but were rebranded as UCHealth ER.

EXECUTIVES

Vp Clinical Affairs, Gregory V. (Greg) Stiegmann
Vp Ambulatory Services, Suzanne Sullivan
President And Ceo, John P. Harney
President Medical Staff, Robert McIntyre
Vp Patient Services And Chief Nursing Officer, Carolyn Sanders
Vp Finance And Cfo, Barbara Carveth
Coo, Tom Gronow
Executive Director Center For Dependency Addiction And Rehabilitation, Steven Millette
Executive Director Cardiac And Vascular Center, Lorna Prutzman
Executive Director Neurosciences/spine And Rehabilitation Medicine, Kimberly Meyers
President And Ceo University Of Colorado Hospital, Will Cook
Chief Information Officer, Steve Hess
Vice President Of Education, Lauren Carter

LOCATIONS

HQ: UNIVERSITY OF COLORADO HOSPITAL
AUTHORITY
4200 E 9TH AVE, DENVER, CO 802203706
Phone: 720 848-0000

COMPETITORS

Banner Health	Memorial Health System
Catholic Health	(Colorado)
Initiatives	Poudre Valley Health
Centura Health	System
Denver Health and	Sisters of Charity of
Hospital Authority	Leavenworth
Exempla Healthcare	Valley View Hospital
HealthONE	

HISTORICAL FINANCIALS

Company Type: Private

Income Statement

FYE: June 30

	REVENUE ($ mil.)	NET INCOME ($ mil.)	NET PROFIT MARGIN	EMPLOYEES
06/10	795	151	19.1%	4,200
06/09	1	0	—	—
06/05	464	1	0.2%	—
Annual Growth	11.4%	169.7%	—	—

2010 Year-End Financials

Return on assets: 12.0%   Cash ($ mil.): 22
Return on equity: 24.3%
Current ratio: 1.30

UNIVERSITY OF DELAWARE

Delaware brings up images of many things our first president that famous river and now the private University of Delaware (UD). The school's flagship campus in Newark has an enrollment of roughly 17000 undergraduate and close to 4000 graduate students. The school also has four auxiliary campuses around the state. UD offers almost 150 undergraduate degrees about 120 master's programs and more than 50 doctoral programs as well as associate's and dual graduate programs through seven academic schools. Among its instructors are well-known authors scientists artists and Nobel Laureates.

Operations

UD is a Land Grant Sea Grant and Space Grant institution meaning the school is eligible for government grants in each of these areas. The Carnegie Foundation for the Advancement of Teaching also classifies UD as a research university with very high research activity — a designation given to less than 3% of US colleges and universities. UD ranks among the nation's top 100 universities in federal research and development support for science and engineering. The university even has its own 146-foot research vessel (named the Hugh R. Sharp) for undersea exploration.

The school has a student-teacher ratio of about 15:1. It has roughly 1130 faculty members nearly 80% of which are tenured. Almost 90% have doctorate or terminal professional degrees in their field. (A terminal degree is also referred to as a Ph.D and refers to the fact that no higher degree can be obtained on that track.)

UD's 2012-13 tuition and fees were $11682 (in-state) and $28772 (out-of-state).

Geographic Reach

The university has campuses in Dover Georgetown Lewes Newark and Wilmington.

Financial Performance

The school reported a 5% increase in revenues in 2012 as the result of an increase in tuition and fees contributions and sales and services of auxiliary enterprises.

However UD's net income dropped by 118% in 2012 over 2011 due to higher expenses and a larger net realized and unrealized loss and an increase in a post-retirement benefit obligation.

In 2012 the university was supported by $1.21 billion endowment.

Company Background

UD got its start in 1743 as a private academy and was chartered by the state of Delaware in 1833. In athletics the school began NCAA Division I competition for men in 1973 and for women in 1982. US Vice President Joe Biden and his wife Jill are both UD graduates.

EXECUTIVES

Vice President And General Counsel, Lawrence White
Vice President, Colby Banbury
Vice President For Human Resources, Wayne Guthrie
Vice President, Branndon Chen
Vice President, Lily Guastella
Vice President Communications And Marketing, Glenn Carter
Vice President And University Secretary, Jeffrey Garland
Treasurer, Monica Mooney
Secretary, Maria Van Venrooy
Secretary, Erin Hogan
Treasurer, Sydney Anunda
Secretary, Chase Thompson
Secretary, Anna Mcgough
Secretary, Eric Nahe
Auditors: KPMG LLP PHILADELPHIA PA

LOCATIONS

HQ: UNIVERSITY OF DELAWARE
220 HULLIHEN HALL, NEWARK, DE 197160099
Phone: 302 831-2107
Web: WWW.UDEL.EDU

PRODUCTS/OPERATIONS

Selected Schools and Colleges
Agriculture and Natural Resources
Arts and Sciences
Business and Economics
Earth Ocean and Environment
Education and Human Development
Engineering
Health Sciences

---

25 Most Popular Majors (2011)
Biological Sciences
Nursing
Finance
Psychology
Elementary Teacher Education
Exercise Science
Mechanical Engineering
Accounting
English
Chemical Engineering
Criminal Justice
Political Science
Civil Engineering
Marketing
Hotel Restaurant & Institutional Management
History
Human Services
Communication Interest
International Relations
Fashion Merchandising
Business Administration
Dietetics
Communication
Management
Pre-Veterinary Medicine & Animal Biosciences

HISTORICAL FINANCIALS

Company Type: Private

Income Statement				FYE: June 30
	REVENUE ($ mil.)	NET INCOME ($ mil.)	NET PROFIT MARGIN	EMPLOYEES
06/18	1,023	139	13.7%	3,600
06/17	992	159	16.1%	—
Annual Growth	3.2%	(12.6%)		

2018 Year-End Financials

Return on assets: 3.5% Cash ($ mil.): 85
Return on equity: 5.6%
Current ratio: —

UNIVERSITY OF FLORIDA

Founded in 1853 the University of Florida (UF) is the state's oldest university and one of the largest in the country with nearly 50000 students and some 5100 faculty and library staff members. UF is a major land-grant research university encompassing 2000 acres in Gainesville Florida. The university's 16 colleges offer more than 100 undergraduate majors and about 200 graduate programs including education law medicine psychology and philosophy. It is also a member of the Association of American Universities a confederation of the top research universities in North America. A founding member of the Southeastern Conference UF's athletic teams (the Florida Gators) are typically ranked nationally.

Operations

UF is active in research and operates more than 200 research institutes and centers including the Nanoscale Research Facility the Pathogens Research Facility and the Biomedical Sciences Building. It has research collaborations with the likes of Scripps Florida Moffitt Cancer Center and Burnham Institute for Medical Research. Altogether UF receives about $650 million in research grants annually.

UF also has extensive health education programs including nursing and pharmacy colleges. Its medical school conducts teaching and residency programs at several Shands hospitals.

Strategy

Like many public universities in the US UF is facing decreased funding from government agencies due to economic conditions. UF has also seen enrollment decreases in recent years but has keep tuition rates and fees low to attract and retain students.

To meet the needs of its large and diverse student population UF is conducting a number of expansion and renovation projects on its more than 900 buildings.

To combat budget shortfalls due to funding and economic conditions UF is also pursuing new research partnerships that will provide funding from commercial and institutional sources. The university is pursuing other revenue generation initiatives to become more financially independent.

Company Background

UF's alumni include Robert Cade the inventor of Gatorade; best-selling mystery novelist Michael Connelly; actress Faye Dunaway; and former US Senator and Florida Governor Bob Graham. Other UF alumni include two Nobel Prize winners and three NASA astronauts.

EXECUTIVES

Vp And Cfo, Michael V. (Mike) McKee
Associate Provost Academic Affairs, Joseph (Joe) Glover
Dean Of Students, Jen Day Shaw
Dean Warrington College Of Business Administration, John Kraft
Vp And Cio, Elias G. Eldayrie
Svp Health Affairs; President Uf Health, David S. Guzick
Dean College Of Journalism And Communications, Diane H. McFarlin
Dean College Of Public Health And Health Professions, Michael G. Perri
Dean College Of Medicine, Michael Good
Dean College Of Education, Glenn E. Good
Dean College Of Arts, Lucinda Lavelli
Dean University Libraries, Judith C. Russell
Dean College Of Design Construction And Planning, Christopher Silver
Svp And Coo, Charles E. Lane
President, W. Kent Fuchs
Dean College Of Engineering, Cammy Abernathy
Dean College Of Health And Human Performance, Michael Reid
Interim Dean College Of Liberal Arts And Sciences, David E. Richardson
Interim Dean College Of Dentistry, Boyd Robinson
Dean College Of Nursing, Anna McDaniel
Dean College Of Pharmacy, Julie A. Johnson
Dean College Of Veterinary Medicine, James Lloyd
Dean College Of Agricultural And Life Sciences, Elaine Turner
Dean Ifas Extension, Nick Place
Dean Ifas Research, Jacqueline Burns
Dean Graduate School, Henry T. Frierson
Vice President Technology, Lin Ai
Assistant Vice President, Mary Kay
Vice President, Greg Allen
Vice President Information Technology, Marjorie Chow
Assistant Vice President, Lisette Pellot
Senior Advisor To The Vp For Student Affairs, Jaquie Resnick
Vp Government And Community Relations, Mark Kaplan
Chairman, Steven M. Scott
Auditors: SHERRILL F NORMAN CPA TALLA

LOCATIONS

HQ: UNIVERSITY OF FLORIDA
300 SW 13TH ST, GAINESVILLE, FL 326110001
Phone: 352 392-3261
Web: WWW.UFLIB.UFL.EDU

PRODUCTS/OPERATIONS

Selected Colleges
College of Agricultural and Life Sciences
College of Dentistry
College of Design Construction and Planning
College of Education
College of Engineering
College of Health and Human Performance
College of Journalism and Communications
College of Liberal Arts and Sciences
College of Medicine
College of Nursing
College of Pharmacy
College of Public Health and Health Professions
College of the Arts
College of Veterinary Medicine
Levin College of Law
Warrington College of Business Administration

HISTORICAL FINANCIALS

Company Type: Private

Income Statement   FYE: June 30

	REVENUE ($ mil.)	NET INCOME ($ mil.)	NET PROFIT MARGIN	EMPLOYEES
06/17	1,897	62	3.3%	5,106
06/15	1,735	261	15.1%	—
06/12	3,939	64	1.6%	—
06/09	3,846	(343)	—	—
Annual Growth	(8.5%)	—	—	—

2017 Year-End Financials
Return on assets: 1.6%   Cash ($ mil.): 6
Return on equity: 2.6%
Current ratio: 3.80

UNIVERSITY OF GEORGIA

Located in the quintessential college town of Athens The University of Georgia (UGA) offers a wide range of degree programs to nearly 35000 students. Forest resources veterinary medicine and law are a few of the school's academic programs.Â UGA which also runsÂ 170-plus study-abroad and exchange programsÂ administers the prestigious Peabody Awards which honors media achievementsÂ and boasts one of the nation's largest map collections. Famous alumni include former US Senator Phil Gramm TV journalist Deborah Norville and former PBS president Pat Mitchell. The University of Georgia was chartered by the State of Georgia in 1785 and graduated its first class in 1804.

Operations
As part of its business UGA offers nearly two dozen bachelor's degrees in about 140 fields and roughly 35 master's degrees inÂ nearly 140 fields. Its doctorate or professional degrees cover a broad spectrum of disciplines such as law pharmacyÂ veterinary medicine and 90 other areas. The university has a student-teacher ratio of about 12:1.

Sales and Marketing
The university sources 80% of its students from the Peach State. Since 1851 25 Georgia governors have graduated from UGA. The institution also boasts nine Pulitzer Prize recipients 17 presidents or provosts of US colleges and universities and four members of the National Academy of Sciences.

Strategy
Despite its annual endowment of more than $50 million UGA has loggedÂ decreases in state appropriations in recent years due to overall declines in Georgia's budget. The result spurred UGA to cut its budget increaseÂ undergraduate tuition fees institute a "Special Institutional" mandatory fee of $200 per semester reduce employer health insurance contributions and increase energy conservation measures. Going forward UGA has also not ruled out the possibility of hiking tuition further citing that an increase ofÂ up toÂ 30% would help to replace all of the state fundingÂ the universityÂ has lost due toÂ the recession.

EXECUTIVES

Vice President Information Technology, Timothy M Chester
Franklin Professor Of History And History Department Chair, John Morrow
Auditors: GREG S GRIFFIN ATLANTA GEOR

LOCATIONS

HQ: UNIVERSITY OF GEORGIA
  424 E BROAD ST, ATHENS, GA 306021535
Phone: 706 542-2786
Web: WWW.UGA.EDU

PRODUCTS/OPERATIONS

Selected Schools and Colleges
Agricultural and Environmental Sciences
Arts and Sciences Business
Ecology
Education
Environment and Design
Family and Consumer Sciences
Forest Resources
Graduate School
Journalism and Mass Communication
Law
Pharmacy
Public Health
Public and International Affairs
Social Work
Veterinary Medicine
The GHSU/UGA Medical Partnership
Engineering

HISTORICAL FINANCIALS

Company Type: Private

Income Statement   FYE: June 30

	REVENUE ($ mil.)	NET INCOME ($ mil.)	NET PROFIT MARGIN	EMPLOYEES
06/18	997	111	11.2%	17,800
06/17	975	142	14.6%	—
06/12	776	72	9.3%	—
06/11	691	(12)	—	—
Annual Growth	5.4%	—	—	—

2018 Year-End Financials
Return on assets: 4.1%   Cash ($ mil.): 235
Return on equity: 22.4%
Current ratio: 2.80

UNIVERSITY OF HAWAI'I OF MANOA

EXECUTIVES

Dir, Terence Wesley-Smith
Chm, David Hanlon

Assistant Professor, Matthew Cain
Graduate Assistant, Daniel Dores
Research Assistant, Julio Rivera
Admin Officer, Chris T Kaukali
Instructor, Donna Deluz
Physician, Greg Sakamoto
Physician, Jason Kaneshige
Research Assistant, Jean Fantle
Professor, Robert Nichols

LOCATIONS

HQ: UNIVERSITY OF HAWAI'I OF MANOA
  2500 CAMPUS RD, HONOLULU, HI 968222217
Phone: 808 956-7700
Web: WWW.SOEST.HAWAII.EDU

HISTORICAL FINANCIALS

Company Type: Private

Income Statement   FYE: June 30

	REVENUE ($ mil.)	NET INCOME ($ mil.)	NET PROFIT MARGIN	EMPLOYEES
06/18	772	51	6.7%	8
06/11	871	139	16.0%	—
Annual Growth	(1.7%)	(13.2%)	—	—

2018 Year-End Financials
Return on assets: 1.2%   Cash ($ mil.): 122
Return on equity: —
Current ratio: 2.10

UNIVERSITY OF HAWAII SYSTEMS

With a reach that extends across half a dozen islands the University of Hawai'i System consists of three university campuses seven community college campuses and several job training and research centers. The public higher education system has an enrollment of more than 60000 students about 85% of which are Hawaii residents. It offers more than 600 different doctorate graduate undergraduate and associate degrees as well as professional certificates in more than 200 fields of study. The University of Hawai'i was founded in 1907 as the College of Agriculture and Mechanic Arts in Honolulu incidentally while Hawaii was still a US territory.

EXECUTIVES

Vice President, Bryan Tanaka
Vice President Korean Student Association Uhm Active Member Accounting Club Shidler College Of Business, Timothy Ahn
It Specialist Office Of The Vice President For Community Colleges, Gordon Furuto
Department Chair, Fletcher Marty
Secretary To The Chancellor, Cynthia Vinluan
Auditors: ACCUITY LLP HONOLULU HAWAII

LOCATIONS

HQ: UNIVERSITY OF HAWAII SYSTEMS
  2444 DOLE ST STE 105, HONOLULU, HI 968222388
Phone: 808 956-8111

Selected Campuses
Manoa
Hilo
West O'ahu
Hawai'i
Honolulu
Kapi'olani
Kaua'i

Leeward
Maui
Windward

HISTORICAL FINANCIALS
Company Type: Private

Income Statement
FYE: June 30

	REVENUE ($ mil.)	NET INCOME ($ mil.)	NET PROFIT MARGIN	EMPLOYEES
06/18	772	51	6.7%	12,000
06/17	771	33	4.3%	—
06/16	799	(116)	—	—
06/06	0	0	—	—
Annual Growth	—	—	—	—

2018 Year-End Financials
Return on assets: 1.2%   Cash ($ mil.): 122
Return on equity: —
Current ratio: 2.10

UNIVERSITY OF HOUSTON SYSTEM

The University of Houston System can't do much about the heat or humidity but it can provide higher education in Houston. The university system serves more than 65000 students at four Houston-area universities. Flagship institution the University of Houston was founded in 1927 and offers about 300 bachelor's master's and doctoral degree programs; it also conducts a number of research programs. Also under the system's umbrella are the University of Houston-Clear Lake the University of Houston-Downtown the University of Houston-Victoria as well as a handful of learning centers in the area. The system was established in 1977.

EXECUTIVES

President University Houston - Clear Lake, William A. Staples
Associate Vice Chancellor For Central Computing And Telecommunication Services, Dennis Fouty
President University Houston - Downtown, William V. (Bill) Flores
Executive Vice Chancellor For Administration And Finance, Carl P. Carlucci, age 70
Chancellor; President University Of Houston, Renu Khator
President University Houston - Victoria, Philip Castille
Chairman, Jarvis V. Hollingsworth

LOCATIONS

HQ: UNIVERSITY OF HOUSTON SYSTEM
4302 UNIVERSITY DR, HOUSTON, TX 772042011
Phone: 713 743-0945
Web: WWW.UHSYSTEM.EDU

PRODUCTS/OPERATIONS

Selected Colleges and Schools
University of Houston
  C.T. Bauer College of Business
  College of Education
  College of Liberal Arts and Social Sciences
  College of Natural Sciences and Mathematics
  College of Optometry
  College of Pharmacy
  College of Technology
  Conrad N. Hilton College of Hotel and Restaurant Management

Cullen College of Engineering
Gerald D. Hines College of Architecture
Graduate College of Social Work
Honors College
Law Center
University of Houston-Clear Lake
  School of Business
  School of Education
  School of Human Sciences and Humanities
  School of Science and Computer Engineering
University of Houston-Downtown
  College of Business
  College of Humanities and Social Sciences
  College of Public Service
  College of Sciences and Technology
University of Houston-Victoria
  School of Arts and Sciences
  School of Business Administration
  School of Education and Human Development
  School of Nursing

HISTORICAL FINANCIALS
Company Type: Private

Income Statement
FYE: August 31

	REVENUE ($ mil.)	NET INCOME ($ mil.)	NET PROFIT MARGIN	EMPLOYEES
08/15	605	41	6.9%	12,608
08/14	742	46	6.2%	—
08/13	1	81	6095.0%	—
08/12	688	132	19.3%	—
Annual Growth	(4.2%)	(31.9%)	—	—

UNIVERSITY OF IOWA HOSPITALS AND CLINICS

EXECUTIVES

Ceo, Kenneth P Kates
Ceo, Gordon Williams
Pres, Sally Mason
V Pres, Jean Robillard
Prin, Ann Williamson
Coo, Sabi Singh
Family Practitioner, Shalina Shaik
Coordinator, Kathy Moser
Pediatrician, Catherina Pinnaro
Diagnostic Radiologist, John D Newell
Internal Medicine Practitioner, Aubrey C Chan

LOCATIONS

HQ: UNIVERSITY OF IOWA HOSPITALS AND CLINICS
200 HAWKINS DR, IOWA CITY, IA 522421009
Phone: 319 356-1616

HISTORICAL FINANCIALS
Company Type: Private

Income Statement
FYE: June 30

	REVENUE ($ mil.)	NET INCOME ($ mil.)	NET PROFIT MARGIN	EMPLOYEES
06/18	1,666	296	17.8%	7,638
06/17	1,502	47	3.2%	—
06/16	1,395	117	8.4%	—
06/15	1,248	90	7.2%	—
Annual Growth	10.1%	48.6%	—	—

2018 Year-End Financials
Return on assets: 13.1%   Cash ($ mil.): 20
Return on equity: 19.3%
Current ratio: 1.60

UNIVERSITY OF LOUISVILLE

Living up to its mandate to be a leading metropolitan research university the University of Louisville (U of L) has hit a few out of the park. The U of L completed the first self-contained artificial heart implant and the first successful hand transplant at its University of Louisville Hospital.Â The health care focused university offers associate baccalaureate master's professional and doctorate degrees in some 170 fields of study including medicine dentistry nursing and public health as well asÂ arts and sciences education business law music social work and engineering.Â ItÂ has more than 22000 students enrolled inÂ about a dozenÂ colleges and schools on three campuses.

Geographic Reach
U of L's main campus the 290-acre Belknap Campus houses seven of the university's 12 colleges and schoolsÂ and is located three miles from downtown Louisville. The U of L Health Sciences Center (housing the health-related schools) is located in downtown Louisville while the Shelby Campus is in eastern Jefferson County.

Strategy
Despite its focus on health care pressures on the health care industry (including the high cost of running a full-service hospital) promptedÂ the school to explore a possible merger of the U of L Hospital with two other state health care providers Saint Joseph Health Care and Jewish HospitalÂ & St. Mary's HealthCare (JHSMH) in 2010. However U of L was ultimately left out of the deal (completed in 2012) after Kentucky's governor voiced concerns over the potential loss of control over the U of L Hospital which operates as a regional safety net medical care provider.

Company Background
The origins of the University of Louisville date back to 1798 with a meeting to establish Jefferson Seminary which didn't open its doors until 1813 and closed 16 years later. Subsequent incarnations eventually led to the creation of the University of Louisville in 1846.

Notable alumni include author Sue Grafton US Senator Christopher Dodd and William Akers inventor of the SPF sun protection rating system.

EXECUTIVES

Vice President Business Affairs, Larry Owsley
Executive Vice President And Provost, Shirley Willihnganz
Executive Vice President Health Affairs, Larry Cook
Medical Director, Christine Cook
Second Vice President, Joy Hart
Assistant Vice President For Finance, R Jason Tomlinson
Assistant Vice President For Business Affairs, Terri Rutledge
Vice President For Community E, Daniel Hall
Clinic Director General Pediatrics, Michael Howard
Senior Vice President For Administration, Jennifer Bobo

Senior Vice President For Administration, Anita Block

Vice President Of Recruitment, Angelo Ciliberti

Assistant Vice President For Health Affairs, Peter Diakov

Associate Vice President Business Services, Mark Watkins

Assistant Vice President For Development, Karen Kayser

Vice President Finance, Lisa Ward

Associate Vice President For Facilities Planning And Management, Nancy Tierney

Vice President Of Career Services, Holly Symonds Clark

Second Vice President, Steven Kniffley

Secretary Treasurer, William Armstrong

Secretary Ii, Deedra Ferguson

Secretary Of Faculty Senat, Gretchen Henry

Professor And Senior Vice Chairman, Roland Valdes

Auditors: BKD LLP LOUISVILLE KENTUCKY

LOCATIONS

HQ: UNIVERSITY OF LOUISVILLE
2301 S 3RD ST, LOUISVILLE, KY 402922001
Phone: 502 852-5555

PRODUCTS/OPERATIONS

Selected Colleges and Schools
Arts & Sciences
Brandeis School of Law
Business
Dentistry
Education & Human Development
Kent School of Social Work
Medicine
Music
Nursing
Public Health & Information Sciences
School of Interdisciplinary and Graduate Studies
Speed School of Engineering

HISTORICAL FINANCIALS

Company Type: Private

Income Statement   FYE: June 30

	REVENUE ($ mil.)	NET INCOME ($ mil.)	NET PROFIT MARGIN	EMPLOYEES
06/18	717	3	0.4%	6,275
06/12	559	(36)	—	—
06/11	591	32	5.4%	—
Annual Growth	2.8%	(28.5%)	—	—

2018 Year-End Financials
Return on assets: 0.2%   Cash ($ mil.): 80
Return on equity: 0.4%
Current ratio: 1.10

UNIVERSITY OF MAINE SYSTEM

University of Maine System is composed of seven public universities throughout Maine serving some 40000 students. It also operates eight regional outreach centers as well as distance education programs. The University of Maine System offers nearly 600 majors minors and concentrations; its flagship campus in Orono (UMaine) offers nearly 90 bachelor's degree programs more than 60 master's degree programs and about two dozen doctoral programs. UMaine was established in 1862 as the Maine College of Agriculture and Mechanic Arts; it adopted its current name in 1897.

The University of Maine System was created in 1968 by the state legislature.

Financial Performance

In 2014 (ended June) the University of Maine System saw a $2 million increase in revenue vs. 2013. Net student fees remained at 36% of total revenue. Although money from tuition and fees dropped by $1 million residence and dining fees increased by $2 million. State appropriations the second biggest source of revenue remained at 29% of the total.

Strategy

The system acted to expand in Portland Maine and to maintain the number of campuses at the University of Southern Maine. It moved forward to on an opportunity to develop a professional and graduate center in Portland. The closing of campuses at USM had been proposed to save money but the system defended their value and kept them open.

EXECUTIVES

Chancellor, James H Page

Account Executive, Monique St Pierre

Accounting Staff, Brenda Goodridge

Coordinator, Glenon Friedmann

Executive of Information Techn, Rick Thibeault

Staff, Steve Booth

Assistant Professor, Robert Heiser

Coordinator, Deirdre F Boylan

Assistant Professor, Kreg Ettenger

Assistant Professor, Jason Read

Coordinator, Jose Cordero

Auditors: BERRY DUNN MCNEIL & PARKER LL

LOCATIONS

HQ: UNIVERSITY OF MAINE SYSTEM
5703 ALUMNI HALL STE 101, ORONO, ME 044695703
Phone: 207 973-3300
Web: WWW.UMIT.MAINE.EDU

PRODUCTS/OPERATIONS

System Universities
University of Maine
University of Maine at Augusta
University of Maine at Farmington
University of Maine at Fort Kent
University of Maine at Machias
University of Maine at Presque Isle
University of Southern Maine Maine Law School

HISTORICAL FINANCIALS

Company Type: Private

Income Statement   FYE: June 30

	REVENUE ($ mil.)	NET INCOME ($ mil.)	NET PROFIT MARGIN	EMPLOYEES
06/18	458	15	3.5%	3,000
06/17	448	20	4.6%	—
06/13	460	27	6.1%	—
06/12	476	37	8.0%	—
Annual Growth	(0.7%)	(13.6%)	—	—

2018 Year-End Financials
Return on assets: 1.3%   Cash ($ mil.): 1
Return on equity: 1.9%
Current ratio: 4.50

UNIVERSITY OF MARYLAND MEDICAL SYSTEM CORPORATION

The 12 academic specialty and community hospitals of the University of Maryland Medical System (UMMS) dot the map of the state's eastern half on both sides of Chesapeake Bay. UMMS one of the largest employers in the Baltimore area has more than 2300 acute care beds and attends to such specialties as trauma care coma emergence kidney transplants orthopedic rehabilitation stroke intervention and pediatric care. University of Maryland Medical Center the system's teaching hub is one of the oldest academic hospitals in the US. In addition to its hospitals UMMS also includes community clinics to address mental health rehabilitation and primary care. The system was established in 1984.

Operations

UMMC's members hospitals include the University of Maryland Medical Center Baltimore Washington Medical Center Chester River Health System Civista Health System Kernan Orthopaedics and Rehabilitation Maryland General Hospital Mt. Washington Pediatric Hospital Shore Health System University of Maryland St. Joseph Medical Center and Upper Chesapeake Health.

University of Maryland Medical Center which houses about 800 beds is staffed entirely by physicians who double as faculty members at the University of Maryland School of Medicine (SOM) the system's longtime partner. The hospital contains additional specialty facilities dedicated to such areas as pediatrics cancer treatment cardiac disease diabetes organ transplants Parkinson's disease and shock trauma. The shock trauma center was the first of its kind in the world when it was founded in 1968.

Aside from its integral partnership with SOM UMMS has in recent years been bolstering its network of member hospitals to reach new markets in Maryland. Having been affilated with Upper Chesapeake Health (UCH) UMMS merged the systems in 2013. UCH owns a pair of hospitals in northeastern Maryland an underserved corner of the state that UMMS hadn't yet entered.

Financial Performance

UMMS's revenue in fiscal 2012 was $2.8 billion.

Company Background

The system's flagship hospital began on its present site in 1823 as Baltimore Infirmary. It later was known for many years as University Hospital until Maryland's legislature changed it from a state-run single-building facility to a private not-for-profit medical system in 1984. In short order UMMS began expanding mainly by adding existing hospitals.

EXECUTIVES

President And Ceo University Of Maryland Medical Center, Jeffrey A. Rivest

Ceo Chester River Health System, James E. Ross

Senior Vice President Chief Information Officer, Jon P. Burns

President And Ceo Maryland General Health Systems And Hospita, Sylvia Smith Johnson

President And Ceo, Karen E. Olscamp, age 59

Evp And Cfo, Henry J. Franey

Medical Director, Melissa Frisch

Senior Vice President Finance, Hank Franey

Vice President, Mia Zorzi

Vice President Financial, Prasanna Nair

Senior Vice President, Alicia Cunningham
Vice President, Kristin Jones Bryce
Vice President Information Technology, Lisa Vuolo
Director, Stephen A. Burch, age 69

LOCATIONS

HQ: UNIVERSITY OF MARYLAND MEDICAL SYSTEM
  CORPORATION
  250 W PRATT ST, BALTIMORE, MD 212012423
Phone: 410 328-8667
Web: WWW.UMMS.ORG

PRODUCTS/OPERATIONS

Selected Facilities and Affiliates
Baltimore Washington Medical Center
Chester River Health System
Civista Medical Center
Kernan Orthopaedics and Rehabilitation
Maryland General Hospital
Mt. Washington Pediatric Hospital
Shore Health System
  Dorchester General Hospital
  The Memorial Hospital at Easton
University of Maryland Medical Center
  Marlene and Stewart Greenebaum Cancer Center
  R Adams Cowley Shock Trauma Center
  University of Maryland Hospital for Children
University of Maryland St. Joseph Medical Center
University Specialty Hospital
Upper Chesapeake Health
  Harford Memorial Hospital
  Upper Chesapeake Medical Center

COMPETITORS

Adventist HealthCare	Franklin Square
Anne Arundel Medical	Hospital Center
Center	GBMC
Ascension Health	Johns Hopkins Health
Bon Secours Health	System
Catholic Health	LifeBridge Health
Initiatives	MedStar Health
Dimensions Healthcare	

HISTORICAL FINANCIALS
Company Type: Private

Income Statement				FYE: June 30
	REVENUE ($ mil.)	NET INCOME ($ mil.)	NET PROFIT MARGIN	EMPLOYEES
06/16	1,358	(29)	—	12,000
06/15	1,413	13	0.9%	—
06/14	1,824	17	1.0%	—
06/12	2,504	(17)	—	—
Annual Growth	(14.2%)	—	—	—

2016 Year-End Financials
Return on assets: (-1.0%)   Cash ($ mil.): 383
Return on equity: (-2.3%)
Current ratio: 1.00

UNIVERSITY OF MARYLAND, COLLEGE PARK

EXECUTIVES

Pres, Wallace Loh
Acting Chief Diversity Officer, Cynthia Edmunds
Administrative Assistant, Dee Allen
Accounting Staff, Showerman Stacey
Dean, Gregory Bullock

Accounting Staff, Janet Dudley-Eshbach
Manager, Jennifer Shannon
Scientist, Michael Osterman
Coordinator, Sheila Goebel
Coordinator, Omar Siddique
Law Specialist, Rebecca Hunsaker

LOCATIONS

HQ: UNIVERSITY OF MARYLAND, COLLEGE PARK
  PATUXENT BLDG 010, COLLEGE PARK, MD
  207420001
Phone: 301 405-1000

HISTORICAL FINANCIALS
Company Type: Private

Income Statement				FYE: June 30
	REVENUE ($ mil.)	NET INCOME ($ mil.)	NET PROFIT MARGIN	EMPLOYEES
06/18	1,369	100	7.3%	5,163
06/17	15	1	12.6%	—
Annual Growth	8577.7%	4931.4%	—	—

2018 Year-End Financials
Return on assets: 3.2%   Cash ($ mil.): 663
Return on equity: 5.0%
Current ratio: 2.90

UNIVERSITY OF MASSACHUSETTS

The University of Massachusetts (UMass) has been expanding across the commonwealth since its founding in 1863. About 72000 students are enrolled in UMass programs that range from art to journalism to engineering. The university's flagship campus in Amherst (with a student-teacher ratio of 18:1) offers its 22000 undergrad students degrees in more than 90 areas and its 6400 graduate students master's degrees in nearly 70 areas and doctorates in 50 areas. Its University of Massachusetts Medical School in Worcester has an affiliated teaching hospital and students studying medicine nursing and biomedical sciences. Other UMass campuses can be found in Boston Dartmouth and Lowell.

Operations
UMass Amherst is part of the Five Colleges consortium a partnership with other area universities including Amherst Hampshire Mount Holyoke and Smith colleges through which students at member institutions attend classes and benefit from being able to share resources at all of the schools.

The system's Boston and Dartmouth campuses are renowned for their academic programs. Boston is known as a research university with more than 90% of its faculty holding the highest degree available in their field. Dartmouth is credited with giving its students a "personalized' education that includes internships undergraduate research opportunities and service learning experiences.

Geographic Reach
While UMass serves students from all 50 US states and 100 other countries 80% of incoming freshmen are from the Commonwealth.

Financial Performance
Operating revenue increased at UMass 3% to $2.2 billion in fiscal 2014 due to increases in tuition and fees. Along with grants and contracts auxiliary services and services provided at the Worcester Medical School tuition and fees are the most significant sources of operating revenues.

UMass' endowment reached $758 million in 2014 when the fund grew by 14%. The endowment is being used for projects such as the Charles J. Hoff Scholarship. Created by former UMass trustee and alumnus Charles J. Hoff and his wife Josephine Hoff the scholarship is expected to provide financial support to more than 2500 students by 2017.

Strategy
UMass uses its funds to upgrade and expand it facilities. In 2014 it announced plans to build an academic center and home for administrative offices in downtown Boston. It also opened its first satellite center in Springfield which offers 40 courses in manufacturing cybersecurity IT and casino management based on area business needs. The center works with local community colleges to develop programs that allow students to transition from associate to bachelor degrees.

The university's Boston campus also received a new Integrated Sciences Complex completed in late 2014 and the General Academic Building slated for 2015.

Company Background
Notable UMass alumni include entertainer Bill Cosby singer Natalie Cole and former General Electric CEO Jack Welch.

EXECUTIVES

President, Robert L. Caret, age 71
Evp And Coo, James R. Julian
Svp Administration And Finance, Christine Wilda
Chancellor University Of Massachusetts Boston, J. Keith Motley
Chancellor University Of Massachusetts Amherst, Kumble R. (Swamy) Subbaswamy
Chancellor University Of Massachusetts Worcester, Michael F. Collins
Chancellor University Of Massachusetts Dartmouth, Divina Grossman
Vp And Cio, Robert Solis
Ceo Umass Online, John Cunningham
Chancellor Umass Lowell, Jacquie Moloney
Vice Chairman, Ruben J. King-Shaw, age 58
Vice Chairman, Maria D. Furman
Chairman, Victor Woolridge
Auditors: GRANT THORNTON LLP BOSTON M

LOCATIONS

HQ: UNIVERSITY OF MASSACHUSETTS
  1 BEACON ST, BOSTON, MA 021083107
Phone: 617 287-7000
Web: WWW.MASSACHUSETTS.EDU

PRODUCTS/OPERATIONS

Selected Colleges and Schools
College of Engineering
College of Humanities and Fine Arts
College of Natural Sciences and Mathematics
College of Social and Behavioral Sciences
Commonwealth College
Graduate School
School of Education
School of Management
School of Nursing
School of Public Health and Health Sciences

HISTORICAL FINANCIALS
Company Type: Private

Income Statement				FYE: June 30
	REVENUE ($ mil.)	NET INCOME ($ mil.)	NET PROFIT MARGIN	EMPLOYEES
06/18	2,468	77	3.1%	13,196
06/17	2,442	325	13.3%	—
06/16	2,403	129	5.4%	—
06/12	2,055	255	12.4%	—
Annual Growth	3.1%	(18.0%)	—	—

2018 Year-End Financials

Return on assets: 1.0%　　　Cash ($ mil.): 103
Return on equity: 3.2%
Current ratio: 1.00

UNIVERSITY OF MINNESOTA PHYSICIANS

EXECUTIVES

Ceo, Bobbi Daniels
Coo*, Mary Johnson
V Pres*, Barbara Gold
Cao*, Rachel Croson
Senior Project Manager, Brent Krzmarzick
Assistant Professor, Ila Harris
Health Professional, Alison Williams
Director, Sarah Byard
Coordinator, Anne Jedlicki
Patient Coordinator, Gwen Samuels
Breast Cancer Program Coordina, Susan Varco
Auditors: KPMG LLP MINNEAPOLIS MN

LOCATIONS

HQ: UNIVERSITY OF MINNESOTA PHYSICIANS
720 WASHINGTON AVE SE # 200, MINNEAPOLIS, MN
554142924
Phone: 612 884-0600
Web: WWW.UMPHYSICIANS.ORG

HISTORICAL FINANCIALS

Company Type: Private

Income Statement				FYE: June 30
	REVENUE ($ mil.)	NET INCOME ($ mil.)	NET PROFIT MARGIN	EMPLOYEES
06/15	482	10	2.2%	200
06/14	490	23	4.8%	—
06/13	452	12	2.8%	—
06/12	415	5	1.3%	—
Annual Growth	5.1%	24.7%	—	—

2015 Year-End Financials

Return on assets: 5.9%　　　Cash ($ mil.): 95
Return on equity: 9.1%
Current ratio: 2.10

UNIVERSITY OF MISSISSIPPI

They call her "Ole Miss" and she really is old: The University of Mississippi was chartered in 1844 as the first public university in the state and opened in 1848. Starting with 80 students the school's enrollment has grown to more than 23000 with most students attending the main Oxford campus. Ole Miss has additional campuses in Southaven (Desoto County) and Tupelo and it operates the University of Mississippi Medical Center in Jackson. The school is home to more than 30 research centers that specialize in business engineering law and other disciplines. Its academic institutes in-

clude the Croft Institute for International Studies and the William Winter Institute for Racial Reconciliation.

Operations

The Medical Center campus includes Mississippi's only children's hospital a women and infants' hospital and a critical care hospital. It is also home to the state's only Level 1 trauma center Level 4 neonatal intensive care nursery and organ transplant programs. Enrollment has grown at the university by some 59% since 2004 (when the school enrolled 14497 students).

Ole Miss has an endowment of approximately $462 million.

Geographic Reach

Minorities make up almost a fourth of Ole Miss students and more than 60% of all students at the university come from within the state. The student-faculty ratio is 19:1.

EXECUTIVES

Vice President For Instruction, Fowler Staines
Department Chair Mathematics, Mike Clement
Secretary To The Dean Of Stu Services, Matt Mclaughlin
Secretary, Frances E Clarkson
Workforce Secretary, Andrew Mark Abernathy
Secretary To The Dean Of Stu Services, Whitney Mckeon

LOCATIONS

HQ: UNIVERSITY OF MISSISSIPPI
113 FALKNER, UNIVERSITY, MS 386779704
Phone: 662 915-6538
Web: WWW.OLEMISS.EDU

PRODUCTS/OPERATIONS

Selected Colleges and Schools

Colleges
The College of Liberal Arts
The Residential College
The Sally McDonnell Barksdale Honors College
The University of Mississippi
Booneville (branch)
Grenada (branch)
Southaven Campus
Tupelo Campus
The University of Mississippi Graduate School
The University of Mississippi Medical Center
Schools
Meek School of Journalism and News Media
Patterson School of Accountancy
School of Applied Science
School of Business Administration
School of Education
School of Engineering
School of Law
School of Nursing (at The University of Mississippi Medical Center)
School of Pharmacy

Selected Research Centers

Center for Advanced Infrastructure Technology
Center for Applied Electromagnetic Systems Research
Center for Archaeological Research
Center for Community Earthquake Preparedness
Center for Educational Research and Evaluation
Center for Excellence in Literacy Instruction
Center for Excellence in Teaching and Learning
Center for Health Behavior Research
Center for Intelligence and Security Studies
Center for Manufacturing Excellence
Center for Marine Resources and Environmental Technology
Center for Mathematics and Science Education
Center for Pharmaceutical Marketing and Management
Center for Population Studies
Center for Speech and Hearing Research
Center for the Study of Southern Culture
Center for Water and Wetland Resources
Center for Wirelress Communications
INDO-US Joint Center for Research in Indian Systems of Medicine
Jamie Whitten National Center for Physical Acoustics

Magazine Innovation Center
National Center for Computational Hydroscience and Engineering
National Center for Justice and the Rule of Law
National Center for Natural Products Research
National Center for Remote Sensing Air and Space Law
National Sea Grant Law Center
Overby Center for Southern Journalism and Politics
Public Policy Research Center
Sarah Isom Center for Women's Studies
Sino-U.S. Traditional Chinese Medicines Research Center
University of Mississippi Geoinformatics Center

HISTORICAL FINANCIALS

Company Type: Private

Income Statement				FYE: December 31
	REVENUE ($ mil.)	NET INCOME ($ mil.)	NET PROFIT MARGIN	EMPLOYEES
12/17*	455	84	18.6%	8,700
06/17	681	15	2.3%	—
06/16	436	90	20.7%	—
06/15	401	101	25.4%	—
Annual Growth	4.4%	(5.9%)		

*Fiscal year change

2017 Year-End Financials

Return on assets: 5.0%　　　Cash ($ mil.): 80
Return on equity: 8.5%
Current ratio: 2.50

UNIVERSITY OF MISSISSIPPI MEDICAL CENTER

EXECUTIVES

Dir, Daniel W Jones
Administrative Assistant III, Linda Buckley

LOCATIONS

HQ: UNIVERSITY OF MISSISSIPPI MEDICAL CENTER
2500 N STATE ST, JACKSON, MS 392164500
Phone: 601 984-5670
Web: WWW.UMC.EDU

HISTORICAL FINANCIALS

Company Type: Private

Income Statement				FYE: June 30
	REVENUE ($ mil.)	NET INCOME ($ mil.)	NET PROFIT MARGIN	EMPLOYEES
06/14	1,042	30	2.9%	20
06/13	940	23	2.5%	—
Annual Growth	10.9%	29.9%		

2014 Year-End Financials

Return on assets: 8.9%　　　Cash ($ mil.): 176
Return on equity: 2.9%
Current ratio: 2.20

UNIVERSITY OF MISSOURI HEALTH CARE

EXECUTIVES

Ceo-Pres, Mitch Wasden
Dir of Treas, Ann Toellner
Cfo, Kevin Necas
Clinic Coordinator, Andrea Beneke
Purchasing Director, Carol Clark
Programmer Analyst, Cathy Schafer
Rheumatology Specialist, Chokkalingam Siva
Doctor, Debra Howenstine
Director, Keri Simon
Staff, Rhonda Cuddy
Project Manager, Cecilia Molina-Clark
Auditors: KPMG LLP

LOCATIONS

HQ: UNIVERSITY OF MISSOURI HEALTH CARE
1 HOSPITAL DR, COLUMBIA, MO 652015276
Phone: 573 882-4141

HISTORICAL FINANCIALS
Company Type: Private

Income Statement — FYE: June 30

	REVENUE ($ mil.)	NET INCOME ($ mil.)	NET PROFIT MARGIN	EMPLOYEES
06/16	749	62	8.4%	5,000
06/15	696	64	9.3%	—
06/08	0	0	1.0%	—
Annual Growth	140.0%	212.1%	—	—

2016 Year-End Financials
Return on assets: 5.9%
Return on equity: 10.0%
Current ratio: 1.40
Cash ($ mil.): 27

UNIVERSITY OF MISSOURI SYSTEM

Education isn't just for show in the Show Me State. The University of Missouri (UM) founded in 1839 educates about 76000 students at four campuses and through a statewide extension program; about a quarter of students are in graduate or professional programs. The university's campuses include flagship UM-Columbia (home to roughly 33000 students some 20 schools and colleges and the University of Missouri Health Sciences Center) UM-Kansas City UM-St. Louis and the Missouri University of Science and Technology. Nicknamed "Mizzou" the University of Missouri System has close to 6000 faculty members and a student-teacher enrollment of about 11:1.

Operations
In addition to its university campuses the University of Missouri System operates the University of Missouri Health System which encompasses University Hospital and Clinics Women's and Children's Hospital Ellis Fischel Cancer Center Rusk Rehabilitation Center Missouri Psychiatric Institute Missouri Orthopaedic Institute and University Physicians. Its hospitals and clinics provide high-risk obstetrics orthopedic surgery neurosciences and cardiovascular care among other services. It also has the region's only Level I Trauma Center.

Geographic Reach
The University of Missouri's four campuses are located in Columbia Kansas City Rolla and St. Louis. The system has an exchange program with South Africa through which UM students study at the University of the Western Cape in Bellville (Cape Town) South Africa and vice versa.

Financial Performance
The University of Missouri System had revenue of $3.1 billion in fiscal 2016. About one-third of that revenue came from net patient medical services; another 20% came from net tuition and fees. Its total operating expenses for that year totaled $2.8 billion. The system's endowment topped $1 billion for the first time in late 2017.

Strategy
The University of Missouri System has been strategically focused on five key priorities: attracting and retaining the best faculty and staff with competitive salaries benefits and workplace programs; expanding its online education offerings to improve students' success and bring in additional revenue; operating with efficiency and effectiveness; expanding research and economic development in the region; and improving communications with the community. However in early 2018 the system warned that growing state budget cuts could hamper its ability to improve student services and that layoffs program cuts and tuition hikes may be necessary.

EXECUTIVES

Chancellor University Of Missouri-kansas City, Leo E. Morton, age 74
Chancellor University Of Missouri-st. Louis, Thomas F. (Tom) George
Chancellor Missouri University Of Science And Technology, Cheryl B. Schrader
Vp Information Technology, Gary K. Allen
Evp Academic Affairs And Interim Chancellor University Of Missouri-columbia, Henry C. (Hank) Foley
Vp Finance And Cfo, Brian D. Burnett
Chief Investment Officer, Thomas Richards
Interim President, Mike Middleton
Medical Director, Johnathan Lauriello
Pharmacy Manager, Patrick Ege
Vice President Managed Care, Mike Larson
Education Technologist Vice President Undergraduate Studies, Faydre Paulus
Vice President Marketing, Brett Hayes
Vp, Anne Tenkhoff
Chairman, Donald L. Cupps
Vice Chairman, Pamela Q. Henrickson
Secretary To The Board, Cindy Harmon
Secretary To The Board, Kathleen Miller
Secretary, Lynda Larocque
Secretary Senior Mechanical And Aerosp, Cynthia Irsik
Secretary, Lila O'riley
Secretary, Tina Brownsberger
Secretary, Annette Valentine
Secretary, Diane Temmen
Secretary Henry County, Verlinda Talley
Secretary, Edythe Weber
Auditors: BKD LLP KANSAS CITY MISSOUR

LOCATIONS

HQ: UNIVERSITY OF MISSOURI SYSTEM
321 UNIVERSITY HALL, COLUMBIA, MO 652113020
Phone: 573 882-2712
Web: WWW.MURR.MISSOURI.EDU

PRODUCTS/OPERATIONS

Selected Campuses
University of Missouri-Columbia
University of Missouri Health System (Columbia)
UM-Kansas City
UM-St. Louis
Missouri University of Science and Technology (Rolla)

Selected Colleges and Schools
College of Agriculture Food and Natural Resources
School of Natural Resources
College of Arts and Sciences
School of Music
College of Education
School of Information Science and Learning Technologies
College of Engineering
College of Human Environmental Sciences
School of Social Work
College of Veterinary Medicine
Graduate School
Harry S Truman School of Public Affairs
School of Health Professions
School of Journalism
School of Law
School of Medicine
Sinclair College of Nursing
Trulaske College of Business
School of Accountancy

HISTORICAL FINANCIALS
Company Type: Private

Income Statement — FYE: June 30

	REVENUE ($ mil.)	NET INCOME ($ mil.)	NET PROFIT MARGIN	EMPLOYEES
06/18	2,851	267	9.4%	30,282
06/16	2,702	108	4.0%	—
06/13	2,404	221	9.2%	—
Annual Growth	3.5%	3.8%	—	—

2018 Year-End Financials
Return on assets: 3.1%
Return on equity: 5.5%
Current ratio: 1.30
Cash ($ mil.): 360

UNIVERSITY OF NEW MEXICO

With more than 36630 students The University of New Mexico (UNM) based in Albuquerque is most renowned for its schools of medicine law and education. Students also attend one of the school's four branches located around the northern part of the state at Gallup Los Alamos Rio Rancho Taos and Valencia. Through its schools and colleges the university offers 96 bachelor's degrees 71 master's degrees 37 doctorate degrees as well as professional practice programs in law medicine and pharmacy. Its annual budget tops $2 billion. UNM employs more than 22000 people across the state.

Operations
The university also serves non-traditional students through its Evening and Weekend Degree Program which offers some 1000 classes each semester that contribute to about 40 different degree programs. About 12000 working students attend UNM at night each semester.

Most of its students come from in-state and continue to live in New Mexico after graduation.

In conjunction with the university's health sciences medical nursing and pharmacy school programs the university operates the UNM Health Sciences Center. It's the state's largest integrated health care treatment research and education facility. The teaching hospital operates a trauma center and specialized care units for oncology and pediatrics.

Geographic Reach
UNM's main campus is located in Albuquerque. Satellite campuses are in Gallup Los Alamos Rio Rancho Taos and Valencia. Only Los Alamos and

Santa Fe offer graduate and upper division programs. The university hosts some 1500 international students and scholars.

Financial Performance

The majority of UNM's revenues (more than 60%) come from clinical operations and patient services from the UNM hospitals. Grants and contracts make up 18% while tuition and fees only account for 9% of the university's revenues.

In 2016 the university's revenues declined by $30 million to $1.56 billion due to lower other patient-related serivces and lower sales and serivces.

Operating expenses grew by about $112 million to $2.2 billion due to higher instruction research and public service costs and a rise in clinical operation expenses.

Company Background

UNM was founded in 1889.

EXECUTIVES

Dean School Of Engineering, Joseph L. Cecchi
Dean School Of Medicine, Paul B. Roth
Dean College Of University Libraries And Learning Sciences, Richard W. Clement
President, Robert G. Frank
Provost And Evp Academic Affairs, Chaouki T. Abdallah
Interim Dean Anderson School Of Management, Craig G. White
Dean College Of Arts And Sciences, Mark Peceny
Dean College Of Fine Arts, Kymberly Pinder
Dean Graduate Studies, Julie Coonrod
Dean Honors College, Catherine Krause
Dean College Of Nursing, Nancy Ridenour
Dean College Of Pharmacy, Lynda S. Welage
Dean School Of Architecture And Planning, Geraldine Forbes Isais
Dean School Of Law, David J. Herring
Dean School Of Public Administration, Mario Rivera
Dean College Of Education, S. Hector Ochoa
Financial Officer, Nicole Dopson
Cio, Gil Gonzales
President Board Of Regents, Jack L. Fortner
Auditors: MOSS ADAMS LLP ALBUQUERQUE N

LOCATIONS

HQ: UNIVERSITY OF NEW MEXICO
1800 ROMA BLVD NE, ALBUQUERQUE, NM 871310001
Phone: 505 277-0732
Web: WWW.UNM.EDU

PRODUCTS/OPERATIONS

2013 Sales

	% of sales
Clinical operations	42
Grants & contracts	21
Sales & services	16
Tuition & fees	10
Patients services	8
Other	3
Total	**100**

Schools and Colleges

Schools and Colleges
Anderson School of Management
College of Arts & Sciences
College of Education
College of Fine Arts
College of University Libraries & Learning Sciences
Honors College
School of Architecture & Planning
School of Engineering
School of Law
School of Public Administration
University College

HISTORICAL FINANCIALS

Company Type: Private

Income Statement   FYE: June 30

	REVENUE ($ mil.)	NET INCOME ($ mil.)	NET PROFIT MARGIN	EMPLOYEES
06/18	1,826	(181)	—	18,362
06/17	1,807	11	0.6%	—
06/16	1,893	6	0.3%	—
06/14	1,325	55	4.2%	—
Annual Growth	**8.3%**	—	—	—

2018 Year-End Financials

Return on assets: (-5.2%)   Cash ($ mil.): 375
Return on equity: (-43.1%)
Current ratio: 2.90

UNIVERSITY OF NORTH CAROLINA AT CHAPEL HILL

The University of North Carolina at Chapel Hill (UNC-Chapel Hill) has the education market cornered. One of the three original points making up North Carolina's Research Triangle (along with Duke University and North Carolina State University) Carolina is the flagship campus of the University of North Carolina (UNC) system. The institution is consistently among the top-ranked research schools in the US. It enrolls some 29000 students and offers more than 250 undergraduate graduate and professional programs including law and medicine. It has 3200 full-time faculty members.

Operations

The university includes 15 schools and colleges as well as an adult learning center for continuing education programs. Its degree offerings include more than 100 master's degrees and about 70 doctorate programs.

UNC-Chapel Hill conducts extensive research programs in a variety of fields at its five health science schools (medicine dentistry pharmacy nursing and public health) its patient care facilities (operated through the University of North Carolina Hospitals affiliate) and its scientific teaching divisions (at the College of Arts and Sciences). The university attracted some $770 million in research grants and contracts during 2012. Funding sources include the National Institutes of Health. Research funding at UNC-Chapel Hill makes up more than half of awards for the entire UNC system.

Geographic Reach

UNC-Chapel Hill is located on a 730-acre campus that holds about 300 buildings. The university attracts students from all 50 US states and more than 145 international countries. It also has study abroad opportunities.

Financial Performance

UNC-Chapel Hill reported $2.5 billion in total revenues in 2012. Operating revenues make up the majority of earnings ($1.7 billion) from activities including student tuition fees federal grants and contracts and patient services. Non-operating revenues include state appropriations non-capital grants and gifts and investment income. Operating expenses ran at about $2.4 billion for 2012 and the university had a budget for fiscal 2013 of some $2.5 billion.

Strategy

To expand its international education opportunities in 2013 UNC-Chapel Hill formed a dual-degree partnership with Tsinghua University in China. The partnership offers business administration executive master's degrees.

Company Background

Chartered in 1789 Carolina is the oldest public university in the US. Notable alumni include author Thomas Wolfe and President James K. Polk as well as athlete Michael Jordan and journalist Charles Kuralt.

EXECUTIVES

Vice Department Chair Pharmacology, Robert Nicholas
Vice President Of Finance And Administration, Betty M Whichard
Auditors: BETH A WOOD CPA

LOCATIONS

HQ: UNIVERSITY OF NORTH CAROLINA AT CHAPEL HILL
104 AIRPORT DR, CHAPEL HILL, NC 275995023
Phone: 919 962-1370
Web: WWW.UNC.EDU

PRODUCTS/OPERATIONS

Selected Schools Colleges and Centers

College of Arts and Sciences
Eshelman School of Pharmacy
Friday Center for Continuing Education
General College
Gillings School of Global Public Health
Graduate School
Kenan-Flagler Business School
School of Dentistry
School of Education
School of Government
School of Information and Library Science
School of Journalism and Mass Communication
School of Law
School of Medicine
School of Nursing
School of Social Work

Selected Academic Departments

African and AfroAmerican Studies
Air Force ROTC
Anthropology
Army ROTC
Art
Biology
Chemistry
Classics
Communication Studies
Dramatic Art
Economics
English and Comparative Literature
Exercise and Sport Science
Geography
History
Marine Sciences
Music
Nutrition
Pharmacology
Philosophy
Political Science
Psychology
Religious Studies
Sociology
Surgery

Company Type: Private

Income Statement · FYE: June 30

	REVENUE ($ mil.)	NET INCOME ($ mil.)	NET PROFIT MARGIN	EMPLOYEES
06/17	1,773	95	5.4%	12,204
06/11	1,704	391	23.0%	—
06/08	281	149	53.1%	—
06/05	3	2	57.7%	—
Annual Growth	66.3%	36.4%	—	—

2017 Year-End Financials

Return on assets: 3.8% Cash ($ mil.): 155
Return on equity: 6.8%
Current ratio: 2.10

UNIVERSITY OF NORTH CAROLINA HOSPITALS

University of North Carolina Hospitals (UNCH) is at the heart of the UNC Health Care System (UNC HCS). The medical center provides acute care to the Tar Heel State through North Carolina Memorial Hospital North Carolina Children's Hospital North Carolina Neurosciences Hospital and North Carolina Women's Hospital. Combined the facilities have more than 800 beds. Specialties include cancer treatment at the North Carolina Cancer Hospital organ transplantation cardiac care orthopedics wound management and rehabilitation. Not-for-profit UNC HCS is owned by the state of North Carolina and is affiliated with the UNC-Chapel Hill School of Medicine.

Operations

UNCH operates under the umbrella of UNC HCS.

UNC HCS already extends beyond Chapel Hill and into the greater Triangle area through its network of primary care and specialty physician practices located in Orange Wake Durham Chatham and Lee counties. The system treats some 800000 people at UNC HCS practices and clinics annually.

UNCH handles more than 37000 patients each year and delivers 3500 babies annually.

North Carolina Children's offers 150 inpatient beds and a comprehensive children's outpatient center. Every year provides specialty care to more than 70000 children from all 100 North Carolina counties. The North Carolina Cancer Hospital is the clinical home of the UNC Lineberger Comprehensive Cancer Center. The state's only public cancer hospital the North Carolina Cancer Hospital treats patients from every county in North Carolina with more than 135000 patient visits a year.

Geographic Reach

UNCH not only serves patients from all North Carolina counties with about a third coming from the Research Triangle area it also serves patients from neighboring states.

Strategy

Being one of the primary health care providers in the area UNC HCS is nearly always expanding its services and service areas either through acquisitions or new construction.

In 2015 UNCH filed a petition with state regulators seeking the ability to add 42 acute-care beds at its Chapel Hill campus. If approved UNC estimates it will cost the hospital $17 million and would be completed by mid-2018.

UNC HCS planned to open a new 86-bed acute-care hospital in Hillsborough in 2015 as part of an effort to reduce pressure on its Chapel Hill campus. The construction of the hospital will cost about $200 million. The new facility will offer an emergency department outpatient surgery and a range of inpatient services to our patients in Alamance and Western Orange counties.

Dedicated cancer care and cancer research is another area in which UNC HCS is expanding. It opened a North Carolina Cancer Hospital at Rex Hospital in 2014.

The system is also building an Imaging Research Building expected to open in 2013 to house the Biomedical Research Imaging Center and serve as a state resource for handling the acquisition processing analysis storage and retrieval of scientific images.

In 2013 UNC HCS established the first stage of its Hillsborough campus with the opening of a 60000-square-foot medical office building. The building includes hospital services such as imaging laboratory pharmacy and medical and surgical oncology.

Company Background

In 2011 the hospital opened a new wing of the Newborn Critical Care Unit in the North Carolina Children's Hospital that houses 10 new patient beds bringing the number of beds in the unit to 58.

UNCH was founded in 1952 under the name North Carolina Memorial Hospital. In 1989 the North Carolina General Assembly created UNCH.

EXECUTIVES

Pres, Gary Park
Exec V Pres, Brian P Goldstein
Svp and Cfo, Chris Ellington
Sr V Pres, Mary Beck
V Pres, Amy Bragg
Otolaryngology, Jill A Alexander Ritch
Accounting Staff, Mike Sumner
Coordinator, Samara Robinson
Staff, David Reed
Staff, Douglas Robinson
Coordinator, Margaret Brooks
Auditors: BETH A WOOD CPA RALEIGH NC

LOCATIONS

HQ: UNIVERSITY OF NORTH CAROLINA HOSPITALS
101 MANNING DR BLDG 2, CHAPEL HILL, NC 275144423
Phone: 919 966-5111

PRODUCTS/OPERATIONS

Selected Facilities
North Carolina Cancer Hospital (Chapel Hill)
  UNC Lineberger Comprehensive Cancer Center
North Carolina Children's Hospital (Chapel Hill)
North Carolina Memorial Hospital (Chapel Hill)
North Carolina Neurosciences Hospital (Chapel Hill)
North Carolina Women's Hospital (Chapel Hill)

COMPETITORS

Alamance Regional Medical Center	Grady Health System
Carolinas HealthCare System	High Point Regional Health System
Cone Health	Morehead Memorial Hospital
Cumberland County Hospital System	New Hanover Regional Medical Center
Danville Regional Medical Center	Rowan Regional Medical Center
Duke University Health System	Vidant Health
Emory Healthcare	WakeMed

Company Type: Private

Income Statement · FYE: June 30

	REVENUE ($ mil.)	NET INCOME ($ mil.)	NET PROFIT MARGIN	EMPLOYEES
06/18	1,892	88	4.7%	6,000
06/16	1,551	87	5.6%	—
06/15	1,385	110	8.0%	—
06/07	787	182	23.2%	—
Annual Growth	8.3%	(6.4%)	—	—

2018 Year-End Financials

Return on assets: 3.4% Cash ($ mil.): 49
Return on equity: —
Current ratio: 1.70

UNIVERSITY OF NORTH TEXAS SYSTEM

EXECUTIVES

Mgr, Cynthia Doll
Chief Human Capital Officer, Barbara Abercrombie
Content Management, Erika Vance
Chancellor, Lesa Roe
Interim Assistant Director, Renee McBride
Vice Chancellor, Gary Rahlfs
Auditors: GRANT THORNTON LLP DALLAS TE

LOCATIONS

HQ: UNIVERSITY OF NORTH TEXAS SYSTEM
1302 TEASLEY LN, DENTON, TX 762057946
Phone: 940 565-2281
Web: WWW.UNTHSC.EDU

HISTORICAL FINANCIALS
Company Type: Private

Income Statement · FYE: August 31

	REVENUE ($ mil.)	NET INCOME ($ mil.)	NET PROFIT MARGIN	EMPLOYEES
08/18	654	79	12.2%	525
08/17	619	82	13.4%	—
08/16	631	47	7.5%	—
08/09	463	47	10.2%	—
Annual Growth	3.9%	5.9%	—	—

2018 Year-End Financials

Return on assets: 3.5% Cash ($ mil.): 204
Return on equity: 9.9%
Current ratio: 1.50

UNIVERSITY OF OREGON

This school's got all its ducks in a row. As one of the largest schools in the state the University of Oregon (UO) has an enrollment of more than 23600 students and some 1500 faculty members. It offers its students eight different schools and colleges plus a graduate college with fields of study range from the arts and journalism to business and law. Part of the Oregon University System UO also offers development services an honors program research institutes and continuing education courses. The school's athletic department organizes more than 15 sports activities including lacrosse and football; the teams are called The Ducks.

Operations

UO has a student-to-teacher ratio of 17:1 and an average class size of 20. Course offerings range across lecture discussion seminar activity laboratory independent study and independent research formats and UO has a total of about 300 academic programs and 25 research centers and institutes. The university's most popular majors for undergraduates include accounting architecture art biology business administration chemistry education economics English environmental science human physiology journalism political science public relations and sociology. Its freshman retention success rate is more than 85%.

Geographic Reach

UO is located on a 295-acre campus in Eugene Oregon that includes about 80 buildings. It also has a satellite campus in Portland. Students come to UO from all 50 US states (plus Washington DC and two US territories) as well as 95 foreign countries. More than half of students are Oregon residents. A number of students also participate in more than 200 study abroad and internship programs in 90 international locations.

Financial Performance

UO reported an 3% increase in revenues in 2016 to $692.7 million due to increased earnings from net student tuition and fees state and local grants and contracts net auxiliary enterprise sales and other operating revenue sources. However the university also reported a decline in its net position from $888.6 million in 2015 to $840.4 million in 2016 due to higher operating expenses and interest expenses as well as a decline in restricted and unrestricted assets.

Company Background

The Oregon State Legislature created the university in 1872 and students first enrolled in 1876.

EXECUTIVES

Dean School Of Music And Dance, Brad Foley
Interim President, Scott Coltrane
Svp And Provost, Frances Bronet
Vp Finance And Administration, Jamie Moffitt
Vice Provost Information Services And Cio, Melissa Woo
Dean College Of Arts And Sciences, W. Andrew Marcus
Dean Lundquist College Of Business, Cornelis A. (Kees) de Kluyver
Dean College Of Education, Randy Kamphaus
Dean School Of Law, Michael Moffitt
Dean Clark Honors College, Terry Hunt
Interim Dean School Of Journalism And Communication, Julianne Newton
Acting Dean School Of Architecture And Allied Arts, Brook Muller
Dean Graduate School, Scott Pratt
Vice President Finance, Frances Dyke
Vice President University Communications, Kyle Henley
Associate Vice President For State And Community Affairs, Hans Bernard
Associate Vice President And Chief Of Staff, Melanie Muenzer
Vice President Worldwide Operations, Gene Evans
Associate Vice President, Kris Winter
Chairman, Charles M. (Chuck) Lillis
Vice Chairman, Ginevra Ralph
Board Member, Carl Hostica
Auditors: MOSS ADAMS LLP PORTLAND OREG

LOCATIONS

HQ: UNIVERSITY OF OREGON
 1585 E 13TH AVE, EUGENE, OR 974031657
Phone: 541 346-1000
Web: WWW.UOREGON.EDU

PRODUCTS/OPERATIONS

Colleges and Schools
Charles H. Lundquist College of Business
College of Arts and Sciences
College of Education
Graduate School
Robert D. Clark Honors College
School of Architecture and Allied Arts
School of Journalism and Communication
School of Law
School of Music and Dance

HISTORICAL FINANCIALS
Company Type: Private

Income Statement   FYE: June 30

	REVENUE ($ mil.)	NET INCOME ($ mil.)	NET PROFIT MARGIN	EMPLOYEES
06/18	740	(8)	—	7,971
06/17	713	31	4.5%	—
06/16	692	(48)	—	—
Annual Growth	3.4%	—	—	—

2018 Year-End Financials
Return on assets: (-0.4%)   Cash ($ mil.): 192
Return on equity: (-1.0%)
Current ratio: 1.40

UNIVERSITY OF PENNSYLVANIA

EXECUTIVES

Pres, Amy Gutmann
Market Researcher, Market Rese, Jane Anderson
Coordinator, Karen Stevenson
College and Career Programs Co, Laurie Engleman
Lsoca Coordinator, Mark Bardsley
University Recruiting Coordina, Marlene Williams
Administrative Coordinator, Patricia Kozak
Computer Analyst, Dan Bachovin Sr
Director Vpul Technology Servi, Mary Spada
Information Specialist, Caroline Elizabeth
Financial Support Spec, Janice Brown
Auditors: PRICEWATERHOUSECOOPERS LLP PH

LOCATIONS

HQ: UNIVERSITY OF PENNSYLVANIA
 3451 WALNUT ST RM 100, PHILADELPHIA, PA 191046243
Phone: 215 898-5000
Web: WWW.UPENN.EDU

HISTORICAL FINANCIALS
Company Type: Private

Income Statement   FYE: June 30

	REVENUE ($ mil.)	NET INCOME ($ mil.)	NET PROFIT MARGIN	EMPLOYEES
06/18	10,093	2,326	23.0%	70
06/16	8,576	1,021	11.9%	—
06/15	0	0	—	—
Annual Growth	—	—	—	—

2018 Year-End Financials
Return on assets: 8.8%   Cash ($ mil.): 1,431
Return on equity: 12.5%
Current ratio: —

UNIVERSITY OF PITTSBURGH

The University of Pittsburgh (Pitt for short) operates its flagship campus in the Oakland neighborhood of Pittsburgh. More than 35000 graduate and undergraduate students attend the main campus as well as four regional campuses. Pitt Panthers pursue degrees in about 400 disciplines including arts and sciences business law medicine and engineering. The school has a student-teacher ratio of 14:1. Pitt is also affiliated with the UPMC health system which operates about 20 hospitals numerous clinics and an insurance company. Pitt was founded in 1787 making it one of the oldest universities in the US.

Operations

Pitt is considered a leading US public research university and as such spends more than $700 million annually on research projects. Pitt is recognized for its work in about a dozen disciplines including computer modeling philosophy the humanities international studies aging neuroscience bioengineering commercial innovation education national preparedness drug discovery translational medicine and nanoscience. It was at Pitt that Jonas Salk developed the polio vaccine at what is now known as Salk Hall.

Notable Pitt alumni include Academy Award winner Gene Kelly Nobel Peace Prize winner Wangari Maathai Pulitzer Prize winner Michael Chabon and US Senator Orrin Hatch.

Geographic Reach

In addition to the main campus in Pittsburgh which houses 17 schools colleges and a center for social and urban research Pitt has regional campus locations in Bradford Greensburg Johnstown and Titusville.

Financial Performance

Pitt reported revenues of some $2 billion in 2014. Most of the university's revenues come from grants and contracts followed by student tuition and feescommonwealth appropriation endowment distributions and other sources of income.

Strategy

In addition to providing high quality education programs for its students Pitt works to engage in research scholarly and artistic projects that advance global learning. It also works to collaborate with government agencies and businesses to advance science medicine and technology seeking active partners as well as funding provider to further its programs.

EXECUTIVES

Department Chair Associate Professor, Mervat Abdelhak
Legal Secretary, Mary Kaye Bucher
Managing Director Vice Dean, Ann Thompson
Division Secretary, Dawn Beam
Id Secretary, Susan Sawyers
Resident Assistant Brackenridge Hall Service Chair Epsilon Sigma Alpha, Maria Dechant
Treasurer, Ning Gao
Auditors: KPMG LLP PITTSBURGH PENNSYLV

LOCATIONS

HQ: UNIVERSITY OF PITTSBURGH
4200 5TH AVE, PITTSBURGH, PA 152600001
Phone: 412 624-4141
Web: WWW.MEDSCHOOL.PITT.EDU

PRODUCTS/OPERATIONS

Selected Schools and Colleges
The John A. Swanson School of Engineering
The Joseph M. Katz Graduate School of Business
    College of Business Administration
Kenneth P. Dietrich School of Arts and Sciences
    College of General Studies
School of Dental Medicine
School of Education
School of Health and Rehabilitation Sciences
School of Information Sciences
School of Law
School of Medicine
School of Nursing
School of Pharmacy
School of Public and International Affairs
School of Public Health
School of Social Work
University Center for International Studies
University Honors College

HISTORICAL FINANCIALS

Company Type: Private

Income Statement				FYE: June 30
	REVENUE ($ mil.)	NET INCOME ($ mil.)	NET PROFIT MARGIN	EMPLOYEES
06/18	2,276	381	16.8%	9,607
06/17	2,169	487	22.5%	—
06/16	2,106	(212)	—	—
06/15	2,060	27	1.3%	—
Annual Growth	3.4%	141.5%	—	—

2018 Year-End Financials

Return on assets: 5.5%   Cash ($ mil.): 45
Return on equity: 7.5%
Current ratio: —

UNIVERSITY OF SOUTH ALABAMA

When you go by the moniker USA and the campus beauty queen wins the Miss USA title year after year (the Pi Kappa Phi Miss USA pageant that is) you're standing on hallowed ground. In this case it's the ground of the University of South Alabama situated on the upper Gulf Coast. The school's crown jewel is its College of Medicine and other facilities including USA Medical Center USA Knollwood Hospital and USA Children's and Women's Hospital. USA also offers degrees in Health Arts and Sciences Business Education Engineering Nursing Computer and Information Sciences Continuing Education and Special Programs and the Graduate School. More than 14880 students call the USA home.

Operations

USA offers 41 different bachelor programs 31 masters programs and 10 doctoral programs.

Financial Performance

The school reported an 8% increase in revenues in 2012 thanks to higher tuition and fee rates and an increase in student enrollment and credit hours taken and a rise in net patient service revenues (29% of total 2012 revenues). Other operating revenues also increased in 2012 thanks to higher rev-

enues from the Electronic Health Records Incentive Program.

USA reported net income in 2012 of $38 million (versus a net loss in 2011) due to decline in operating loss and an increase in non-operating revenues (primarily from higher investment returns and state appropriations).

The university saw an increase in revenues between 2010 and 2012 largely due to organic growth.

Strategy

USA is pushing to expand and strengthen its development program and increase student enrollment. In 2013 the school received a gift of $250000 from alumni Dr. and Mrs. Steven H. Stokes to start a new Center for Environmental Resiliency.

Company Background

Founded in 1963 USA has graduated more than 75000 students including 18200 teachers and school administrators (including 85% of Mobile's public school teachers).

EXECUTIVES

Assoc Vice President University Comp Services, Chris Cannon
Associate Vice President Academic Affair, Keith Harrison
Interim Associate Vice President For Academic Affairs, Julio Turrens
Department Head, Bob Shipp
Vice President Student Affairs, John Smith
Vice President, Sandra Corry
Secretary Of Asce Student Chapter Vice President, Brittany Mcmillan
Swe Vice President, Samantha Hamilton
Alapsa Program Chair Department Of Political Science And Criminal Justice University Of South, Jaclyn Bunch
Assistant Vice President Facilities Management, Moon Randy
Secretary, Marcina Lang
Secretary, Karen Barrick
Secretary, Lisa Callaghan
Secretary, Arneda Wilson
Secretary, Sharon Evans
Secretary Iv, Ayesha Kanwal
Secretary, Lord Shari
Secretary Iv, Rebecca Scarborough
Secretary V, Lanier Sharon
Auditors: KPMG LLP JACKSON MS

LOCATIONS

HQ: UNIVERSITY OF SOUTH ALABAMA
307 N UNIVERSITY BLVD # 380, MOBILE, AL 366083074
Phone: 251 460-6101
Web: WWW.SOUTHALABAMA.EDU

PRODUCTS/OPERATIONS

USA Colleges and Schools
Arts and Sciences
Auburn University School of Pharmacy at USA
Computing
Continuing Education and Special Programs
Education
Engineering
Mitchell College of Business
Medicine
Nursing
Pat Capps Covey College of Allied Health Professions

HISTORICAL FINANCIALS

Company Type: Private

Income Statement				FYE: September 30
	REVENUE ($ mil.)	NET INCOME ($ mil.)	NET PROFIT MARGIN	EMPLOYEES
09/18	653	(0)	—	5,403
09/17	662	47	7.2%	—
09/16	624	25	4.1%	—
09/15	556	9	1.7%	—
Annual Growth	5.5%	—	—	—

2018 Year-End Financials

Return on assets: (-0.1%)   Cash ($ mil.): 79
Return on equity: (-2.1%)
Current ratio: 1.20

UNIVERSITY OF SOUTH FLORIDA

The University of South Florida (USF) is bullishly educational. The school has nearly 50000 students at three campuses in Tampa St. Petersburg and Sarasota/Manatee. It offers some 180 undergraduate graduate specialty and doctoral degree programs through more than a dozen colleges including Arts and Sciences Business Education Engineering Marine Science Pharmacy and Public Health. USF also offers graduate certificates continuing education courses and teacher certifications and it is a major research institution among US universities. USF was founded in 1956; its mascot is the bull.

Operations

The university has more than 1700 teaching faculty members and maintains a 23:1 student-to-faculty ratio. USF's core offerings include an extensive health sciences program including medical nursing pharmacy and public health colleges grouped under the USF Health banner. The health organization also includes patient care facilities such as family care practices emergency clinics and Alzheimer's centers.

USF Health also hosts medical research programs in areas such as neurological conditions cardiovascular care pediatrics infectious disease and biotechnology. The university also has research programs in a range of science engineering and arts fields such as veteran reintegration and photovoltaic energy technologies. Altogether USF's research programs were granted more than $485 million in awards and contracts during fiscal 2016.

Extracurricular activities include 17 men's and women's varsity teams that participate in the American Athletics Conference at the NCAA level.

Geographic Reach

USF's international students (about 7% of the total student population) come from all 50 US states and more than 150 countries. USF also supports study abroad programs. The university's campuses in Florida encompass some 1600 acres. The main Tampa campus includes the USF Health facilities and health-related schools

Financial Performance

USF has a budget of some $1.6 billion annually as well as an annual economic impact of some $4.4 billion. The university has an endowment of some $417 million.

EXECUTIVES

President And Corporate Secretary, Judy L. Genshaft

Evp And Provost, Ralph Wilcox

Coo, John W. Long

Svp Research Innovation And Economic Development And President Usf Research Foundation, Paul R. Sanberg

Vp Information Technology And Cio, Sidney Fernandes

Vp Business And Finance And Cfo, Nick Trivunovich

Interim Vice President Student Affairs, Kofi Glover

Vice Provost Student Success, Paul J Dosal

Assistant Vice President For Research, Valerie McDevitt

Faap Florida Morsani College Of Medicine Executive And Medical Director, Joseph Puccio

Usf System Vice President, Roger Brindley

Vice President Research, Scott Mann

Vice President Research And Development, Don Clark

Vice President, Ricci Allen

Clinical Director, Henry Rodriguez

Medical Director Clinic Service, Arthur Andrews

Chair Department Of Mathematics And Statistics, Leslaw Skrzypek

Vice President Acad Affairs Stpetersburg, Melanie Marquez

Assistant Vice President For Donor Services, Tracy Muir

Associate Vp Information Technology, George Ellis

Vice President Research, Concetta M Carr

Vice President Acad Affairs St.petersburg, Helen D Levine

Sa Assistant Vice President Dean Of Students, Judy L Polk

Vice President, Chelsea Russell

Chair Department Of Surgery, Andrew M Smith

Events Vice President, Anna McGranaghan

Pharmacy Manager, Xilma Lemois

Senior Vice President For Strategic Development, Edmund Funai

Vice President, Andrew Miles

Vice President, Oscar Ayala-Gonzalez

Vice President Of The New Music Consortium, Lindsey Jones

Medical Director, Karen Bruder

Vice President, Audrey Richter

Assistant Vice President Human Resources And Risk Management, Martinez-kidde Edith

Interfraternity Council Vice President Of Administration, Mathew Bernstein

Vice President, Enzo Ferrara

Associate Vice President, Julie Gillespie

Svp Business And Financial Strategy, David Lechner

Vice President For Membership Finance, Lauren Baak

Medical Director And Professor, James Brownlee

Assistant Vice President, Terrie Daniel

Vice President, Nils Corrales

Vice President For Administrative Services, Calvin Williams

Vice President, Marilyn Washington

Vice President Harborside Activities Board Co President Vice President, Kelli Carmack

Executive Vice President American Academy Of Allergy Asthma And Immunology, Thomas Casale

Associate Vice President Chief Communications Officer Uf Health Communications, Melanie Ross

Chair, Harold W. Mullis

Vice Chair, Brian D. Lamb

Senior Secretary, Fran Schoel

Secretary, Pubudu Kaluarachchi

Senior Secretary, Kasch Laura

Secretary, Deborah Robinson

Auditors: DAVID W MARTIN CPA TALLAHASS

LOCATIONS

HQ: UNIVERSITY OF SOUTH FLORIDA
  4202 E FOWLER AVE, TAMPA, FL 336208000
Phone: 813 974-2011
Web: WWW.USF.EDU

PRODUCTS/OPERATIONS

2013 Revenue

	% of total
Contracts & grants	26
Student financial aid	26
Tuition	16
General revenue	14
Auxiliary enterprises	11
Intercollegiate athletics	3
Lottery	2
Concessions & fees	2
Total	**100**

Selected Colleges

The Arts
Arts & Sciences
Behavioral & Community Sciences
Business
Education
Engineering
Global Sustainability
Honors College
Marine Science
Medicine
Nursing
Pharmacy
Public Health
University College (graduate school)

COMPETITORS

Florida Atlantic University
Florida International University
Florida State University
University of Central Florida
University of Florida
University of Miami
University of North Florida

HISTORICAL FINANCIALS

Company Type: Private

Income Statement   FYE: June 30

	REVENUE ($ mil.)	NET INCOME ($ mil.)	NET PROFIT MARGIN	EMPLOYEES
06/18	871	36	4.1%	16,165
06/09	892	42	4.7%	—
06/07	533	148	27.8%	—
06/06	0	0	—	—
Annual Growth	—	—	—	—

2018 Year-End Financials

Return on assets: 1.7%   Cash ($ mil.): 68
Return on equity: 4.0%
Current ratio: 4.50

UNIVERSITY OF TENNESSEE

Whether you want to learn the art of aviation or get ready for a career in public service the University of Tennessee System (UT) is here to help. The 200-year-old school provides undergraduate graduate and professional academic programs to about 50000 students; programs include business engineering law pharmacy medicine and veterinary medicine. It has a student-teacher ratio of about 16:1. Campuses include the flagship Knoxville location as well as the Health Science Center at Memphis the Space Institute at Tullahoma the statewide Institute for Public Service and the Institute of Agriculture. Other UT System campuses are located in Chattanooga and Martin. UT was founded in 1794 as Blount College.

Financial Performance

UT's funding comes from gifts grants and contracts (about 30%) state appropriations (roughly 28%) tuition and fees (20%) and a handful of auxiliary enterprises and independent operations (the remainder).

Company Background

Notable alumni include former Senate Majority Leader Howard Baker Nobel Prize-winning economist James Buchanan and author Cormac McCarthy.

EXECUTIVES

Assistant Vice President, Chuck Shoopman

LOCATIONS

HQ: UNIVERSITY OF TENNESSEE
  1331 CIRCLE PARK DR, KNOXVILLE, TN 379163801
Phone: 865 974-2303
Web: WWW.UTK.EDU

PRODUCTS/OPERATIONS

Selected Colleges Schools and Institutes

College of Agricultural Sciences and Natural Resources
College of Allied Health Sciences
College of Architecture and Design
College of Arts and Sciences
College of Business Administration
College of Communication and Information
College of Dentistry
College of Education Health and Human Sciences
College of Engineering
College of Graduate Health Sciences
College of Health Science Engineering
College of Law
College of Medicine
College of Nursing
College of Pharmacy
College of Social Work
College of Veterinary Medicine
Graduate School of Medicine
School of Art
School of Music
Space Institute

HISTORICAL FINANCIALS

Company Type: Private

Income Statement   FYE: June 30

	REVENUE ($ mil.)	NET INCOME ($ mil.)	NET PROFIT MARGIN	EMPLOYEES
06/12	1,092	60	5.5%	12,000
06/11*	1,034	296	28.7%	—
12/08	1	0	—	—
Annual Growth	847.7%	—	—	—

*Fiscal year change

2012 Year-End Financials

Return on assets: 1.6%   Cash ($ mil.): 357
Return on equity: 2.3%
Current ratio: 1.50

UNIVERSITY OF UTAH HEALTH HOSPITALS AND CLINICS

Whether you've broken your leg on the ski slopes or need the latest treatment for a neurological condition the University of Utah Hospitals & Clinics is here for you. Part of the University of Utah Health Care system the medical services provider operates an acute and critical care hospital that has some 550 beds as well as a network of community clinics that provide primary health care pharmacy and eye care among other services. The University Hospital provides care in areas including surgery emergency care cardiology radiology and organ transplant services; it also houses centers for medical education training and research.

Operations

Also part of the Hospitals & Clinics system the Huntsman Cancer Institute home to the system's cancer inpatient and outpatient services and the University Orthopaedic Center which offers physical therapy and orthopedic surgery. The University Neuropsychiatric Institute provides inpatient and outpatient behavioral health care.

Strategy

As part of its plan to expand and prepare for the future University of Utah Hospitals & Clinics completed a new $24 million building at the school's College of Nursing in 2012.

EXECUTIVES

Ceo, David Entwistle
Cfo, Gordon Crabtree
Executive Director Service Line Administration Facilities And Support Services, Dan K. Lundergan
Executive Director Huntsman Cancer Hospital, Ray Lynch
Executive Director University Neuropsychiatric Institute, Ross Van Vranken
Executive Director Ambulatory Services Community Clinics And The John A. Moran Eye Center, Wayne Imbrescia
Executive Director University Of Utah Orthopaedic Center, Bart Adams
Cio, Jim Turnbull
Director Of Health Information, Connie Tohara
Medical Director Emergency Service Memorial Hospital Of Sweetwater County, Christian Theodosis
Technology Corporate Ambassador Office Of Vice President For Research, Andrew Buffmire
Vice President Uhsc Services, Kathleen Carlson
Medical Director, Martin Caravati
Associate Vice President Financial And Accounting Services, Jeffrey West
Medical Secretary, Sanders Nathan
Medical Secretary, Chelsey Olsen

LOCATIONS

HQ: UNIVERSITY OF UTAH HEALTH HOSPITALS AND CLINICS
50 N MEDICAL DR, SALT LAKE CITY, UT 841320001
Phone: 801 581-2121

COMPETITORS

CHRISTUS Health
Intermountain Health Care
LifePoint Health
Ogden Regional Medical Center
St. Mark's

HISTORICAL FINANCIALS
Company Type: Private

Income Statement

FYE: June 30

	REVENUE ($ mil.)	NET INCOME ($ mil.)	NET PROFIT MARGIN	EMPLOYEES
06/14	1,282	20	1.6%	4,200
06/06	0	(0)	—	—
06/05	0	(0)	—	—
Annual Growth	126.0%	—	—	—

2014 Year-End Financials

Return on assets: 2.0%
Return on equity: 4.5%
Current ratio: 2.30

Cash ($ mil.): 179

UNIVERSITY OF VERMONT & STATE AGRICULTURAL COLLEGE

The University of Vermont (UVM) boasts scenic views and comprehensive secondary education. the university offers more than 100 majors through its seven undergraduate colleges as well 46 master's programs and 21 doctoral programs at its Graduate College and College of Medicine. UVM has an enrollment of more than 12820 students including undergraduate graduate medical and continuing education program participants. The university also conducts research programs in areas including translational science cancer care and transportation. UVM a public land grant university has more than 1360 faculty members.

Operations

UVM comes from Universitas Veridis Montis which is Latin for "University of the Green Mountains." Its campus consists of more than a dozen dining facilities — including a pair of convenience stores and Cyber Cafe — and nearly 40 residence halls for on-campus students. Off-campus UVM offers a research park four research farms nine natural areas (including the summit of Mount Mansfield) and the Rubenstein Ecosystem Science Laboratory in the Leahy ECHO Center for Lake Champlain.

Geographic Reach

The UVM campus which spans 460 acres in Burlington Vermont enrolls students from nearly all US states. The university also provides education to some 350 international students from more than 50 countries.

Financial Performance

As a public land grant university UVM draws a portion of its budget from the state of Vermont. Other sources of income include student tuition and fees charitable gifts and returns on investment funds. The university's office of technology commercialization brings in some income by licensing out research discoveries to spinoff entities.

Strategy

To attract and retain a quality student population UVM regularly conducts construction and renovation efforts on its campus facilities in areas ranging from academics and recreation to research and athletics.

Furthermore UVM seeks to provide more flexible education options for students including expanding its onlinep rograms.

Company Background

UVM is the fifth oldest university in the New England area after Harvard Yale Dartmouth and Brown. It's the first institution of higher education to declare public support for the freedom of religion and the first university to admit women and African-Americans into Phi Beta Kappa honor society.

Notable alumni include education philosopher John Dewey and film producer Jon Kilik.

Ira Allen founded the university in 1791 the same year that Vermont became the 14th state. Located in between the Adirondack and Green mountain ranges UVM's motto is the Latin phrase Universitas Viridis Montis or University of the Green Mountains.

EXECUTIVES

Vice President, Lee Stewart
Senior Vice President, David Rosowsky
Interim Vice President Of Development And Director Of Principal Gifts, Kathleen Kelleher
Vice President, Margaret Battey
Vice President, Francine Bazluke
Vice President Research Admin Office, Eric Clark
Vice President, Ted Winfield
Department Chair, Dale Goldhaber
Vice President, Blaise Sullivan
Vice President, Carol Phillips
Vice President For Executive Operations, Bethany Wolfe
Associate Vice President, Robert Corran
Provost And Senior Vice President, John Hughes
Vice President, Willi Coleman
Vice President Enrollment Management, Christopher Lucier
Director Of Admissions, Sarah Smith
Assistant Vice President For University Operations, Jon Crystal
Senior Vice President, Catherine Symans
Vice President Alumni Relations, Alan Ryea
Sga Vice President, Tyler Davis
Vice President Preconstruction Services, John Stetson
Department Chair (interim), Kyle Ikeda
Vice President Student Government Association, Jason Maulucci
Vice President, Frances Carr
Vp Finance And Administration, Stephanie Woods
Assistant Vice President For Development And Gift Planning, Amy Palmer-ellis
Vice Chair, Karmen Swim
Board Member, Jeanne Goldhaber
Sga Treasurer, Jacquelyn Langham
Secretary, Richard Wolfson
Technical Secretary, Rachel Berube
Secretary Cardiovascular Group, Pam Burton
Sga Treasurer, Jamie Lapierre
Treasurer, Jesse Cases-villablanca
Auditors: KPMG LLP COLCHESTER VERMONT

LOCATIONS

HQ: UNIVERSITY OF VERMONT & STATE AGRICULTURAL COLLEGE
85 S PROSPECT ST WTRMN, BURLINGTON, VT 054050001
Phone: 802 656-3131
Web: WWW.UVM.EDU

PRODUCTS/OPERATIONS

Selected Colleges and Schools

College of Agriculture and Life Sciences
College of Arts and Sciences
College of Education and Social Services
College of Engineering and Mathematical Sciences
College of Medicine
College of Nursing and Health Sciences
Continuing Education
Graduate College
Honors College

Rubenstein School of Environment and Natural Resources
School of Business Administration

HISTORICAL FINANCIALS

Company Type: Private

Income Statement				FYE: June 30
	REVENUE ($ mil.)	NET INCOME ($ mil.)	NET PROFIT MARGIN	EMPLOYEES
06/17	613	34	5.6%	3,710
06/14	545	27	5.1%	—
06/13	557	19	3.4%	—
06/12	525	(30)	—	—
Annual Growth	3.1%	—	—	—

2017 Year-End Financials

Return on assets: 2.3%   Cash ($ mil.): 151
Return on equity: 6.3%
Current ratio: 2.10

UNIVERSITY OF WASHINGTON INC

The University of Washington (UW) is Husky indeed with an annual enrollment of more than 54000 students. Founded in 1861 as the Territorial University of Washington UW (pronounced "U-dub" by those on campus) has smaller branches in Tacoma and Bothell in addition to its main campus in downtown Seattle. The university whose mascot is a Husky offers more than 600 undergraduate graduate and professional degree programs through 16 colleges and schools. It also operates four hospitals: University of Washington Medical Center Harborview Medical Center Northwest Hospital and Valley Medical Center.

Operations

With more than 300 programs University of Washington confers some 12000 bachelor's master's doctoral and professional degrees each year. Its graduates include about 135 Fulbright and 35 Rhodes scholars. The school's top five bachelor degree fields include biology psychology political science economics and communications.

Research is a cornerstone of the university which has nearly 300 specialized research centers. The school's annual sponsored grant and contract research funding exceeds $1.6 billion. Some 300 new companies have emerged based on UW research advances.

Financial Performance

In fiscal 2017 (ended June) operating revenue for University of Washington totaled $5.8 billion. Patient service revenues account for the largest amount of funds received (38%) followed by federal grants and contracts (about 21%).

Operating expenses totaled $5.7 billion that year. Salaries accounted for nearly half of those expenses.

EXECUTIVES

Dean School Of Medicine, Paul G. Ramsey
Svp Finance And Facilities, V'Ella Warren
Chancellor Bothell Campus, Bjong Wolf Yeigh
Dean School Of Law, Kellye Testy
Dean Libraries, Lizabeth A. (Betsy) Wilson
Interim Chancellor Tacoma Campus, Kenyon S. Chan
Dean School Of Public Health, Howard Frumkin
President, Ana Mari Cauce
Dean Undergraduate Academic Affairs, Ed Taylor

Vp Information Technology And Cio, Kelli Trosvig
Dean College Of Arts And Sciences, Robert Stacey
Interim Dean College Of Built Environments, John Schaufelberger
Dean School Of Dentistry, Joel H. Berg
Dean College Of Education, Tom Stritikus
Dean College Of Engineering, Michael B. Bragg
Dean College Of The Environment, Lisa Graumlich
Dean Evans School Of Public Affairs, Sandra Archibald
Dean Foster School Of Business, James Jiambalvo
Dean Graduate School, Dave Eaton
Dean Information School, Harry Bruce
Dean School Of Nursing, Azita Emami
Dean School Of Pharmacy, Thomas Baillie
Dean School Of Social Work, Edwina (Eddie) Uehara
Associate Vice President, Lee Heck
Associate Vice President Financial Management, Susan Camber
Medical Director, Jean Haulman
Senior Vice President Ecommerce Mobile D, Brian Jones
Vp Of Marketing, Jennifer Wong
Extension Lecturer Vice President For Continuing Ed, Barbara Bell
Vice President For Student Life, Denzil Suite
Assistant Vice President For Student Life And, Pam Schreiber
Director Of Government Relations, Ian Goodhew
Medical Director, Rob Sweet
Associate Vice President For Information Management, Aaron Powell
Associate Vice President College Access, Patricia Loera
Executive Vice President, Jeffrey Scott
Assistant Vice President, Joanna Glicker
Director Of Admissions, Erin Town
Vice President, Lou Cariello
Medical Director, Matthew Grierson
Vice President External Affairs, Brian Taubeneck
Vice President, Ross Heath
Associate Vice President, Barbara Wingerson
Medical Director Uw Center For Pain Relief, Brett Stacey
Executive Vice President Provost, Gerald Balsasty
Vice President, Sean Campbell
Vice Chairman, William S. (Bill) Ayer
Chairman, Orin C. Smith
Secretary Senior, Gregory Daigle
Board Member, Melissa Cunningham
Msim Advisory Board Member, Cheryl Scott
Secretary Senior, Victoria Parker
Secretary, Brianna Watts
Board Of Directors, Craig Mauer
Board Member, Dan Brettler
Assistant Secretary, Louise Hine
Auditors: KPMG LLP SEATTLE WASHINGTON

LOCATIONS

HQ: UNIVERSITY OF WASHINGTON INC
4311 11TH AVE NE STE 600, SEATTLE, WA 981056369
Phone: 206 543-2100

PRODUCTS/OPERATIONS

Selected Colleges and Schools

College of Arts and Sciences
College of Built Environments
College of Education
College of Engineering
College of the Environment
Evans School of Public Affairs
The Graduate School
Information School
Michael G. Foster School of Business
School of Dentistry
School of Law
School of Medicine
School of Nursing

School of Pharmacy
School of Public Health
School of Social Work

HISTORICAL FINANCIALS

Company Type: Private

Income Statement				FYE: June 30
	REVENUE ($ mil.)	NET INCOME ($ mil.)	NET PROFIT MARGIN	EMPLOYEES
06/18	5,171	490	9.5%	27,228
06/17	4,893	363	7.4%	—
Annual Growth	5.7%	35.1%	—	—

2018 Year-End Financials

Return on assets: 4.0%   Cash ($ mil.): 144
Return on equity: 9.6%
Current ratio: 1.20

UNIVERSITY OF WISCONSIN MEDICAL FOUNDATION, INC.

UW Medical Foundation provides administrative services to faculty physicians at the University of Wisconsin School of Medicine and Public Health. The foundation a not-for-profit entity is a physician practice organization that works in cooperation with the UW Hospital and Clinics and other medical offices and clinics throughout the Badger State. The foundation coordinates clinical sites and provides technical and professional staffing services as well as administrative support for legal marketing information technology and logistics functions.

Operations

UW Medical Foundation provides support services for more than 1200 member doctors located at about 45 physician practices and 60 clinical outreach locations. It also helps clinical practices with quality initiatives. The foundation provides some $200 million in charity care each year. Its community activities include sponsoring health outreach events and donating safety products to low-income families.

Physicians in the organization provide services across a number of medical specialties including oncology gastroenterology women's health kidney care orthopedics respiratory therapy and urology.

Company Background

The organization has expanded over time: UW Medical Foundation merged with Physicians Plus Medical Group in 1998 and with the University Community Clinics in 2003.

EXECUTIVES

Ceo, Alan Kaplan
Chb, Robert Golden
Coo*, Robert Flannery
Sam Poc, Sarah Meyer
Information Specialist, Debra Hopke
Information Specialist, Jamie Buchanan
Hipaa Privacy Officer, Amanda Reese
Clinical Assistant Professiona, Deborah Raehl
Manager, Bonita Klein
Auditors: MCGLADREY LLP PALOS HILLS IL

LOCATIONS

HQ: UNIVERSITY OF WISCONSIN MEDICAL
  FOUNDATION, INC.
  7974 UW HEALTH CT, MIDDLETON, WI 535625531
Phone: 608 821-4223
Web: WWW.UWMF.WISC.EDU

COMPETITORS

Ascension Health	Marian Health System
Beaver Dam Community	Meriter Health
Hospitals	Services
Beloit Health System	ProHealth Care
Catholic Health	SSM Health Care
Initiatives	Stoughton Hospital
Dean Health Systems	ThedaCare Inc.
Inc.	Tomah Memorial
Hospital Sisters	Hospital
Health System	

HISTORICAL FINANCIALS

Company Type: Private

Income Statement   FYE: June 30

	REVENUE ($ mil.)	NET INCOME ($ mil.)	NET PROFIT MARGIN	EMPLOYEES
06/18	784	40	5.2%	3,200
06/15	766	26	3.4%	—
06/14	724	33	4.6%	—
06/13	0	22	—	—
Annual Growth	—	12.8%	—	—

2018 Year-End Financials

Return on assets: 7.2%   Cash ($ mil.): 124
Return on equity: 11.8%
Current ratio: 1.40

UNIVERSITY OF WISCONSIN SYSTEM

Unfortunately there is no School of Cheese in the University of Wisconsin System (UW System) but across its vast operations there are 13 four-year universities 13 two-year UW Colleges campuses and a statewide extension program that has offices in every Wisconsin county. The UW System is one of the largest public university systems in the US with more than 180000 students and 40000 faculty and staff members. Its top school is UW at Madison which offers more than 400 undergraduate majors master's degree programs and doctoral programs to some 43000 students. The system's other major campus is UW at Milwaukee with about 28000 students. The UW System has a student-teacher ratio of 17:1.

Operations

Combined the UW System's students have access to more than 250 undergraduate degree programs approximately 225 master's programs and 125 doctoral programs. More than 36000 degrees are conferred annually.

Geographic Reach

One of the nation's largest public universities the UW system boasts offices or campuses in every county in Wisconsin.

Sales and Marketing

About 85% of the system's students come from Wisconsin.

Financial Performance

UW System reported a 5% increase in overall revenues to $4.7 billion in fiscal 2013. Gifts grants and contracts was the system's largest source of revenue that year ($1.6 billion or more than a third

of total revenue); this channel grew 5% during the year. Tuition and fees (which increased 6% in 2013) and state appropriations (which grew 6%) are among the other primary sources of funds followed by sales and services of auxiliary enterprises.

Strategy

UW System operates with seven core strategies in mind: preparing students to thrive in the global society creating a stronger workforce building a stronger business environment building stronger communities growing its financial and human resources advancing its operational excellence and increasing collaborations between campuses and with other organizations.

As an increasing number of its students are working adults or students with nontraditional schedules the university has developed online accelerated and collaborative degree programs tailored to specific industries and emerging workforce needs.

Facing slow enrollment which has fallen some 32% since 2010 UW System in 2017 announced a plan to merge its 13 two-year schools with its four-year campuses. Under the plan the two-year schools will become branches of the four-year schools. The move is intended to help keep the two-year schools alive by making them more attractive to students: Associate degrees will be granted by the four-year colleges (and will therefore carry more clout) and transferring to one of the main campuses to pursue a bachelor's degree will also be easier.

EXECUTIVES

Vp Finance, Deborah A. (Debbie) Durcan
Chancellor Madison Campus, Rebecca M. Blank
President, Kevin P. Reilly
Interim Director Information Services, Lori Docken
Chancellor Eau Claire Campus, Gilles Bousquet
Chancellor Green Bay Campus, Thomas Harden
Chancellor La Crosse Campus, Joe Gow
Chancellor Milwaukee Campus, Michael Lovell
Chancellor Oshkosh Campus, Richard Wells
Chancellor Parkside Campus, Deborah (Debbie) Ford
Chancellor Platteville Campus, Dennis Shields
Chancellor River Falls Campus, Dean Van Galen
Chancellor Stevens Point Campus, Bernie Patterson
Chancellor Stout Campus, Charles W. Sorensen
Chancellor Superior Campus, Renée Wachter
Chancellor Whitewater Campus, Richard J. Telfer
Associate Vice President Economic Development, David Brukardt
Vice President, Larry Rubin
Vice President Academic Student Affairs, James Henderson
Associate Vice President For Learning And Information Technology Services, Steven Hopper
Vice Provost For Libraries, Lisa Carter
Regent President, Brent Smith
Regent Vp, Michael Falbo
Treasurer, Kelly Wilfert

LOCATIONS

HQ: UNIVERSITY OF WISCONSIN SYSTEM
  1220 LINDEN DR, MADISON, WI 537061525
Phone: 608 262-2321
Web: WWW.WISCONSIN.EDU

PRODUCTS/OPERATIONS

Selected Four-Year Campuses
UW-Eau Claire
UW-Green Bay
UW-La Crosse
UW-Madison
UW-Milwaukee
UW-Oshkosh
UW-Parkside
UW-Platteville
UW-River Falls
UW-Stevens Point
UW-Stout
UW-Superior
UW-Whitewater

Selected Two-Year Colleges
UW-Baraboo/Sauk County
UW-Barron County
UW-Fond du Lac
UW-Fox Valley
UW-Manitowoc
UW-Marathon County
UW-Marinette
UW-Marshfield/Wood County
UW-Richland
UW-Rock County
UW-Sheboygan
UW-Washington County
UW-Waukesha

HISTORICAL FINANCIALS

Company Type: Private

Income Statement   FYE: June 30

	REVENUE ($ mil.)	NET INCOME ($ mil.)	NET PROFIT MARGIN	EMPLOYEES
06/18	3,613	203	5.6%	3,190
06/17	3,702	(20)	—	—
Annual Growth	(2.4%)	—	—	—

2018 Year-End Financials

Return on assets: 2.2%   Cash ($ mil.): 1,868
Return on equity: 3.7%
Current ratio: 4.00

UNIVERSITY SYSTEM OF MARYLAND

The University System of Maryland (USM) operates one of the largest public university systems in the country serving more than 175000 students through a dozen institutions including Towson University University of Maryland University College and Bowie State University. Its flagship university in College Park boasts about 40000 students and some of the country's top-ranked education programs. The University of Maryland is also known for its successful athletic teams (named the Terrapins) which compete in the Big Ten Conference. The system also operates the University of Maryland Center for Environmental Science. Maryland established its university system in 1988.

Operations

USM has approximately 1000 buildings including 20 libraries. The university offers more than 1000 bachelor's master's doctoral and professional academic programs. Its colleges and schools include the A. James Clark School of Engineering College of Agriculture and Natural Resources School of Music and School of Public Policy among others.

Financial Performance

In fiscal 2017 (ended June) USM had operating revenue of $3.5 billion a 4% increase over the prior year. Some 38% of that revenue came from tuition and fees less scholarship allowances. However with operating expenses totaling $4.9 billion that year the system had an operating loss of $1.4 billion. This was an increase from the prior year's operating loss of $1.3 billion.

Strategy

USM has been implementing a strategy which focuses on the following goals: helping Maryland achieve 55% college degree completion by citizens aged 25 and up making Maryland more competitive by facilitating the creation of new companies and establishing five research centers of excellence redesigning courses to enhance student experiences operating in a fiscally efficient matter and achieving and sustaining national eminence through quality programs people and facilities. Its current 10-year strategic plan which runs through 2020 was established to help address such issues as the national drop in college completion growing demand for higher education and the growing role of technology in the world.

In 2017 the system launched University of Maryland Capital Region Health which provides primary and specialty health care to Prince George's County and the surrounding area. The organization was established when the University of Maryland Medical System combined forces with Dimensions Healthcare System. As part of that move UM Capital Region Health took over the Laurel Regional Hospital and the ailing Prince George's Hospital Center (which will be closed and replaced with a new medical center set to open in 2021).

Company Background

Notable University of Maryland alumni include Muppet creator Jim Henson news anchor Connie Chung Seinfeld creator Larry David and football legend Norman "Boomer" Esiason.

EXECUTIVES

Vice Chancellor Administration And Finance, Joseph F. Vivona
President University Of Maryland Baltimore County, Freeman A. Hrabowski
Associate Vice Chancellor And Cio, Donald Z. Spicer
Vice Chancellor Communications, Anne Moultrie
President Salisbury University, Janet Dudley-Eshbach
President University Of Maryland Center For Environmental Science, Donald F. (Don) Boesch
Vice Chancellor For Advancement, Leonard R. Raley
President University Of Maryland College Park, Wallace D. Loh
President University Of Maryland Baltimore, Jay A. Perman
President University Of Baltimore, Kurt L. Schmoke
President Bowie State University, Mickey L. Burnim
President Frostburg State University, Jonathan C. Gibralter
Chancellor, William E. Kirwan
Senior Vice Chancellor For Academic Affairs, Joann Boughman
President University Of Maryland Eastern Shore, Juliette B. Bell
President Coppin State University, Mortimer H. Neufville
Interim President Towson University, Timothy J.L. Chandler
President University Of Maryland University College, Javier Miyares
Executive Director Universities At Shady Grove, Stewart Edelstein
Executive Director University System Of Maryland At Hagerstown, Mark Halsey
Clinical Social Worker Vpsa Uhc Mental Health Sum, Jennifer Sherman
Fire Safety Manager Vpaa Environmental Safety, Luisa Ferreira
Information Technology Support Assistant Svpaap Nyumburu, Aaron Mcgrew
Vice President Of Finance And Chief Officer, Pamela Purcell

Business Manager Vpur Development, Ruth Hakulin
Collections Specialist Vpaa Compt Bursars Office, William Damiano
Chaplain Vpsa Chapel, Eli Backman
Manager Vpaa Environmental Safety, Steven Hand
Information Technology Program Analyst Vpsa Dining Services, Luisa Egan
Grounds Supervisor Vpsa Ds Maintenance, Jason Millar
Interior Designer Vpaa Fm Facilities Planning, Zoe Kyriacos
Postal Service Proc Vpaa Business Service Mail Services, Erik Krug
Mt Mlt Trd Chief Ii Vpsa Res Facilities Comm Maintenance, Joseph Sherman
Food Service Manager Vpsa Ds Bakery, Jeffrey Russo
Housekeeper Lead Vpsa Res Facilities North Campus, Maria Villegas
Motor Equipment Operations Ii Vpsa Transportation Services, Ian Bholai
Assistant Vice President Administration Program Manag, Katrina December
Vice President Quality And Patient Safet, Mary Jozwik
Vice President Chief Nurse Executive, Colleen Roach
Vice President Technology Tig Global, Matt Heller
Vice President Of Board Relations, Tom Gilbert
Chairman Board Of Regents, James L. Shea
Vice Chair Board Of Regents, Barry P. Gossett
Auditors: SB & COMPANY LLP HUNT VALLEY

LOCATIONS

HQ: UNIVERSITY SYSTEM OF MARYLAND
3300 METZEROTT RD, ADELPHI, MD 207831600
Phone: 301 445-2740
Web: WWW.UMUC.EDU

Selected Institutions

Bowie State University
Coppin State University
Frostburg State University
Salisbury University
Towson University
University of Baltimore
University of Maryland Baltimore
University of Maryland Baltimore County
University of Maryland College Park
University of Maryland Eastern Shore
University of Maryland University College
University of Maryland Center for Environmental Science

Selected Schools and Colleges

College of Agriculture and Natural Resources
School of Architecture Planning and Preservation
College of Arts and Humanities
College of Behavioral and Social Sciences
Robert H. Smith School of Business
College of Chemical and Life Sciences
College of Computer Mathematical and Physical Sciences
College of Education
A. James Clark School of Engineering
The Graduate School
Philip Merrill College of Journalism
College of Information Studies
School of Public Health
School of Public Policy
Office of Undergraduate Studies

HISTORICAL FINANCIALS

Company Type: Private

Income Statement				FYE: June 30
	REVENUE ($ mil.)	NET INCOME ($ mil.)	NET PROFIT MARGIN	EMPLOYEES
06/18	3,601	338	9.4%	28,000
06/17	3,515	355	10.1%	—
06/16	3,386	516	15.3%	—
Annual Growth	3.1%	(19.1%)	—	—

2018 Year-End Financials
Return on assets: 3.4%   Cash ($ mil.): 2,333
Return on equity: 5.2%
Current ratio: 3.50

UNIVERSITY SYSTEM OF NEW HAMPSHIRE

The University of New Hampshire (UNH) is a liberal arts college that serves about 12600 undergraduate and more than 2200 graduate students. The institution offers more than 100 majors and academic programs of study at nine colleges and schools. The student-faculty ratio is 20:1. UNH is the flagship institution of the University System of New Hampshire. In 2007 the university graduated its first international class in Seoul under a program run by its Whittemore School of Business and Economics. Founded in 1866 as the New Hampshire College of Agriculture and the Mechanic Arts UNH is a designated land-grant sea-grant and space-grant chartered school.

Operations

UNH's most popular bachelor's programs include business administration undeclared liberal arts psychology English and communication followed by mechanical engineering biology biomedical science civil engineering and political science.

The University System of New Hampshire includes Keene State College Plymouth State University and Granite State College in addition to UNH.

Geographic Reach

In addition to its main campus in Durham UNH has a campus in Manchester and its School of Law is in Concord. Almost 60% of the school's student body comes from within state with a concentration of others coming from the northeastern region of the US. UNH is developing new academic programs expanding its online courses and opportunities and creating new international initiatives for faculty and students in Costa Rica Chile Ghana India South Korea and China.

Strategy

UNH is engaged in a strategic plan to support its growth through 2020. Its plan for creating a learning-centered environment includes such initiatives as establishing a New Venture Fund to promote collaborative research and teaching opportunities; developing new programs to support independent research and scholarship; commercializing UNH's intellectual capital; and promoting diversity and inclusiveness as well as international opportunities. It also includes making major capital investments in technology to build a high-capacity cyber-infrastructure and a learning portal to promote interdisciplinary collaboration; renovating restoring and adding on to facilities; and constructing a new center for the arts.

EXECUTIVES

Chancellor, Todd Leach
Pres*, Melinda Treadwell
Vice Chancellor*, Catherine Provelcher
General Counsel*, Ron Rodgers
Pres*, James W Dean Jr
Assistant Professor, Lin Guo
Coordinator, Steve Wright
Assistant Professor, Weiwei MO
Assistant To President, Cheri O'Neil
Coordinator, Cynthia Nizzari-Mcclain
Manager, Scott Kimball
Auditors: KPMG LLP BOSTON MA

LOCATIONS

HQ: UNIVERSITY SYSTEM OF NEW HAMPSHIRE
5 CHENELL DR STE 301, CONCORD, NH 033018522
Phone: 603 862-1800
Web: WWW.KEENE.EDU

PRODUCTS/OPERATIONS

Selected Colleges and Schools
College of Engineering and Physical Sciences
College of Health and Human Services
College of Liberal Arts
College of Life Sciences and Agriculture
The Graduate School
Thompson School of Applied Science
University of New Hampshire at Manchester
University of New Hampshire School of Law
Whittemore School of Business and Economics
Special Academic Opportunities
Graduate Research Conference
Hamel Center for Undergraduate Reasearch
Honors program
International research opportunities program
Student internships
Study abroad
Undergraduate research opportunities program

HISTORICAL FINANCIALS

Company Type: Private

Income Statement   FYE: June 30

	REVENUE ($ mil.)	NET INCOME ($ mil.)	NET PROFIT MARGIN	EMPLOYEES
06/16	692	(9)	—	16,000
06/15	680	32	4.7%	—
06/14	0	128	—	—
06/13	800	111	14.0%	—
Annual Growth	(4.7%)	—	—	—

2016 Year-End Financials

Return on assets: (-0.4%)   Cash ($ mil.): 69
Return on equity: (-0.7%)
Current ratio: 1.90

UPMC

For University of Pittsburgh students and area residents medical care is spelled UPMC. University of Pittsburgh Medical Center (UPMC) is a leading not-for-profit health care delivery system in western Pennsylvania. The organization operates about 40 hospitals including campuses in the Pittsburgh area regional and community hospitals and specialty facilities such as Children's Hospital of Pittsburgh and the Magee-Womens Hospital. Altogether UPMC has more than 8500 inpatient beds. In addition the system provides care through hundreds of physician practices outpatient clinics cancer treatment facilities and rehab centers; it also offers health insurance home health care and long-term care through about 15 senior living facilities.

Operations

UPMC is organized into three primary operating divisions: Health Services Insurance Services and UPMC Enterprises.

The Health Services unit includes tertiary community and regional hospitals; specialty services such as women's health and behavioral health; in-home care and senior living; contract services including pharmacy and laboratories; and the system's 4900 physicians and their practices. The division also includes the system's supporting foundations and its captive insurance programs as well as the international services arm which exports the system's expertise abroad. Health Services brings in some 55% of UPMC's total revenue.

Insurance Services offers health insurance to employers and employees workers' compensation and disability services and behavioral health coverage to Medical Assistance beneficiaries. The division's health plans include UPMC for You UPMC Health Plan UPMC Health Network and UPMC for Life; altogether it serves some 3.5 million members. The division brings in more than 45% of total revenue.

UPMC Enterprises seeks commercialization opportunities and partnerships to generate new revenue streams. Its results are categorized as investing and financing activity rather than straight revenue.

As an academic medical center affiliated with the University of Pittsburgh's Schools of Health Sciences UPMC Jameson also focuses on medical research in a wide range of areas including the fields of regenerative medicine and biosecurity some of which is funded by the National Institutes of Health. The system is also renowned for its organ transplantation programs as well as for its cancer care psychiatric pediatric and women's health services. In addition UPMC Jameson is a forerunner in the health care information technology field.

Geographic Reach

UPMC's primary operating territory is the Pittsburgh area and western and central Pennsylvania. Outside the US UPMC Jameson operates health care facilities in Ireland Italy Quatar Cyprus and the UK. It also provides management and consulting services in other international countries to improve global health care partly through partnerships with health equipment and technology firms.

Sales and Marketing

The majority of UPMC's hospital services are rendered to patients under Medicare Highmark Blue Cross Blue Shield (a major area insurer) and medical assistance programs. Its patient service revenue comes from Medicare accounts which contribute about 50% of all patient revenue each year. Medicaid brings in more than 15% of revenue while UPMC Insurance Services commercial accounts bring in another 15%. Highmark BCBS accounts for more than 5% and the remaining 15% comes from other sources.

Financial Performance

UPMC's operating revenue increased 14% to $18.8 billion in 2018 due to increased net patient service revenue and insurance enrollment revenue. Health Services revenue increased thanks to hospital affiliations and payer rate increases while Insurance Services revenue rose due to membership growth. However operating expenses totaled $18.6 billion and the system lost $366.8 million from investing and financing activities. All told UPMC lost a net $290.3 million that year.

The system ended 2018 with $277.3 million in net cash about half of what it had at the end of 2017. Operating activities contributed $749.9 million while investing activities used $798.6 million and financing activities used $203.6 million.

Strategy

The UPMC network of facilities has grown over the years through acquisitions partnerships and the construction of new facilities. For example in March 2019 the system broke ground on a new vision and rehabilitation tower at UPMC Mercy as part of its $2 billion investment in specialty care.

The system has also advanced its technology systems to control costs and increase efficiencies. It spent more than $170 million in tech initiatives in 2018 including moving to a more secure data center expanding its telemedicine capabilities and installing biometric fingerprint scanners for patient security.

Mergers and Acquisitions

In early 2019 Somerset Hospital in Somerset Pennsylvania became an affiliate of UPMC. The hospital is now operating as UPMC Somerset. UPMC plans to invest at least $45 million in the facility over a 10-year period.

In 2017 UPMC acquired central Pennsylvania-based Pinnacle Health System (now UPMC Pinnacle). The purchase added two hospitals to the system's network and allowed UPMC to sell health insurance beyond its core market in western Pennsylvania.

Company Background

UPMC traces its roots to 1893 when Louise Lyle the wife of a Presbyterian minister founded its predecessor. The hospital was incorporated as Presbyterian Hospital of Pittsburgh two years later. In 1930 the hospital joined forces with the University of Pittsburgh and broke ground on a new location which opened its doors in 1938.

EXECUTIVES

President And Ceo, Jeffrey A. Romoff
Svp And Chief Human Resources And Administrative Services Officer, Gregory Peaslee
Evp And Cfo, Robert A. DeMichiei
Evp President Insurance Services Division And President And Ceo Upmc Health Plan, Diane P. Holder
Evp; President Hospital And Community Services Division, Elizabeth B. Concordia
President Magee Women's Hospital, Leslie C. Davis
Evp And Chief Legal Officer, W. Thomas (Tom) McGough
Evp And President International Commercial Services Division And President Upmc Cancercenter, Charles E. (Chuck) Bogosta
Svp And Chief Of Staff Office Of The President, David M. Farner
Evp Treasurer And President Upmc Enterprises, C. Talbot Heppenstall
Evp And Chief Medical Officer; President Physician Services Division, Marshall W. Webster
Evp Chief Medical And Scientific Officer And President Health Services Division, Steven D. Shapiro
Vice President Information Security And Privacy; Associate General Counsel, John Houston
Vice President Talent Acquisition Human Resources Innovation, Matt Rimer
Vice President Enterprise Technology Infrastructure, Iftekhar Kazi
Senior Vice President And Chro, John Galley
Vice President International Technology, Deb Salava
Medical Director Him, Adele Towers
Clinical Director, Debra Frank
Clinical Director, Cliff Cohen
Executive Vice President Treasurer And President Upmc Enterprises, C Talbot Heppenstall
Executive Vice President Upmc Enterprises Technology Development, Mark Stabingas
Vice President International Clinical Operations And Quality, Cheryl Brill
Clinical Director, Angela Scolieri
Vice President Of Medical Affairs, Gregory Beard
Cno Vice President Patient Care Services, Sandy Rader
Vice President Strategic Planning, David Russell
Director Of Pharmacy, Jennifer Belavic
Medical Director, Syed Hyder
Clinical Director, Susan Killmeyer
Medical Director Corporate Care Management, Roy Jacobson
Senior Staff Associate To The Senior Vice President And Chief Of Staff, Virginia L Brown
Senior Vice President Global Oncology Services, Elizabeth Wild
Senior Vice President Chief Risk Compliance And Ethics Officer, Kc Turan
Associate Medical Director, Richard Ambrosino

Vice President Government Programs Chief
 Engineer Ne Pa, Brendan Harris
Assistant Treasurer, Linda Zang
Medical Secretary, Fay Reed
Secretary, Aleesa Foltz
Vice Chair Clinical Services, Dwight Heron
Auditors: ERNST & YOUNG LLP

LOCATIONS

HQ: UPMC
 200 LOTHROP ST, PITTSBURGH, PA 152132536
Phone: 412 647-8762
Web: WWW.UPMC.COM

Selected Pennsylvania Facilities
Children's Hospital of Pittsburgh of UPMC
Magee-Womens Hospital of UPMC (Pittsburgh)
UPMC Bedford Memorial (Everett)
UPMC East (Pittsburgh)
UPMC Hamlot (Erie)
UPMC Horizon (Greenville and Shenango Valley)
UPMC McKeesport (McKeesport)
UPMC Mercy (Pittsburgh)
UPMC Montefiore (Pittsburgh)
UPMC Northwest (Seneca and Oil City)
UPMC Passavant (McCandless and Cranberry)
UPMC Presbyterian (Pittsburgh)
UPMC Shadyside (Pittsburgh)
UPMC St. Margaret (Pittsburgh)
UPMC Western Psychiatric Institute and Clinic
 (Pittsburgh)

PRODUCTS/OPERATIONS

2018 Sales

	$ mil.	% of total
Net patient services	8,823	47
Insurance enrollment	8,492	45
Other	1,462	8
Total	**18,777**	**100**

2018 Sales by Segment

	$ mil.	% of total
Health Services	11,881	57
Insurance Services	9,005	43
Adjustments	(2109)	-
Total	**18,777**	**100**

Selected Services
Behavioral and Mental Health Services
Cancer
COPD and Emphysema Center
Dermatology
Diabetes and Endocrinology
Ear Nose and Throat
Emergency Medicine
Family/Primary Care Medicine
Gastroenterology
Geriatrics
Heart and Vascular
Imaging Services
Kidney Disease
Liver
Neurology
Ophthalmology
Pain Medicine
Pathology
Pediatrics
Pulmonology and Respiratory
Rehabilitation
Rheumatology
Sports Medicine
Stroke Care
Thyroid
Urology
Women's Health
Wound Healing Services

COMPETITORS

AmeriHealth Mercy Health Plan
 Butler Health System
 Capital BlueCross
 Conemaugh Health System
 Excela Health
 Geisinger Health System
 HealthAmerica
 Heritage Valley Health
 Highmark
 Independence Blue Cross
 Jefferson Regional Medical Center of Pennsylvania
 Ohio Valley General
 St. Clair Health
 Universal Health Services
 West Penn Allegheny Health System

HISTORICAL FINANCIALS
Company Type: Private

Income Statement — FYE: June 30

	REVENUE ($ mil.)	NET INCOME ($ mil.)	NET PROFIT MARGIN	EMPLOYEES
06/15	614	326	53.1%	80,000
06/13*	10,188	441	4.3%	—
12/11	4,758	(2)	—	—
Annual Growth	(49.4%)	—	—	—

*Fiscal year change

2015 Year-End Financials
Return on assets: 5.7%　　Cash ($ mil.): 80
Return on equity: 25.7%
Current ratio: —

UPMC PINNACLE HOSPITALS

EXECUTIVES

Pres, Michael Young
Manager, Carole Velkoff
Analyst, Sherry Stoner
Pres Cumberland Region, Louis Baverso
Physician Assistant, Amy Nissley
Registered Nurse, Hannah Schutt
Physical Therapist, Joanne Basom
Center Coordinator, Marci Osborne
Other Other, Neil Freireich
Physician Assistant, Tammy Murphy
Information, Brian Leedy
Auditors: PARENTEBEARD LLC YORK PA

LOCATIONS

HQ: UPMC PINNACLE HOSPITALS
 409 S 2ND ST STE 1C, HARRISBURG, PA 171041612
Phone: 717 782-5678
Web: WWW.PINNACLEHEALTH.ORG

HISTORICAL FINANCIALS
Company Type: Private

Income Statement — FYE: June 30

	REVENUE ($ mil.)	NET INCOME ($ mil.)	NET PROFIT MARGIN	EMPLOYEES
06/10	559	14	2.5%	4,500
06/09	538	0	—	—
06/08	513	(14)	—	—
06/06	482	26	5.6%	—
Annual Growth	3.8%	(15.1%)	—	—

2010 Year-End Financials
Return on assets: 2.2%　　Cash ($ mil.): —
Return on equity: 7.3%
Current ratio: 0.20

UPMC PRESBYTERIAN SHADYSIDE

EXECUTIVES

Pres, John Innocenti
Cfo, Eileen Simmons
Nurse Practitioner, Kristen Baileys
Nurse Practitioner, Kristin Ermine-Baer
Director of Operations, Melanie Houston
Nurse Practitioner, Patti Gigliotti
Nurse Practitioner, Timothy Coleman
Manager, Vicki Bedel
Member, William S Dietrich II
Managing Partner, William Pietragallo II
Member, John Pelusi Jr
Auditors: ERNST & YOUNG LLP PITTSBURGH

LOCATIONS

HQ: UPMC PRESBYTERIAN SHADYSIDE
 200 LOTHROP ST MH-N739, PITTSBURGH, PA
 152132536
Phone: 412 647-2345
Web: WWW.UPMC.COM

HISTORICAL FINANCIALS
Company Type: Private

Income Statement — FYE: June 30

	REVENUE ($ mil.)	NET INCOME ($ mil.)	NET PROFIT MARGIN	EMPLOYEES
06/10	8,046	276	3.4%	8,200
06/09	1,723	83	4.8%	—
06/06	1,627	0	—	—
Annual Growth	49.1%	—	—	—

2010 Year-End Financials
Return on assets: 3.5%　　Cash ($ mil.): 158
Return on equity: 9.1%
Current ratio: 0.80

UPPER MISSOURI G & T ELECTRIC CO-OPERATIVE INC

EXECUTIVES

President, Roger Sorenson
Ice Pres, Allen Thiessen
Controller, Della Pewonka
Compliance Manager, Rick Engstrom
General Manager, Claire Vigesaa
Auditors: BRENNER AVERETT & CO PC SIDNE

LOCATIONS

HQ: UPPER MISSOURI G & T ELECTRIC CO-OPERATIVE INC
111 2ND AVE SW, SIDNEY, MT 592704017
Phone: 406 433-4100
Web: WWW.UPPERMO.COM

HISTORICAL FINANCIALS

Company Type: Private

Income Statement				FYE: December 31
	REVENUE ($ mil.)	NET INCOME ($ mil.)	NET PROFIT MARGIN	EMPLOYEES
12/18	548	78	14.2%	2
12/17	531	0	—	—
12/16	486	0	—	—
12/14	319	0	—	—
Annual Growth	14.5%			

2018 Year-End Financials

Return on assets: 27.5%
Return on equity: 34.7%
Current ratio: 1.00
Cash ($ mil.): 1

URM STORES, INC.

URM Stores is a leading wholesale food distribution cooperative serving more than 160 grocery stores in the Northwest. Its member-owner stores operate under a variety of banners including Family Foods Harvest Foods Super 1 Foods Trading Co. Stores and Yoke's Fresh Market. It also owns the Rosauers Supermarkets chain. In addition to grocery stores URM supplies 1500-plus restaurants hotels and convenience stores; it also offers such services as merchandising store development consulting and technology purchasing. The cooperative was founded in 1921 as United Retail Merchants. The business is privately owned by its members.

Operations

The company's Spokane Washington-based Peirone Produce distributionÂ subsidiaryÂ supplies fresh produce including organic produce as well as specialty items source from Arizona California Florida Mexico and Texas. In addition to groceries and produce URM Stores sells insurance to its members and food service customersÂ through URM Insurance Agency. Insurance products include business insurance for stores and personal lines of coverage for owns and their employees.

Geographic Reach

Regional wholesaler URM Stores supplies stores and other customers in much of eastern Washington northern Idaho Oregon and Montana.

Financial Performance

URM Stores rings up sales of about $775Â million employs more than 2700 people and has assets exceeding $100 million.

Strategy

In 2010 the company moved itsÂ Spokane Washington-based Peirone Produce distributionÂ subsidiaryÂ into a larger facility boasting 70000 sq. ft. of warehouse space and 7000 sq. ft. of office space. It is equipped with about 15 docks for loading outgoing trucks and another dozen docks for unloading incoming trucks. The facility is more than twice the size of Peirone's previous building which had nearly 10 docks total. Because of the larger space and greater number of docks Peirone Produce said it has been ableÂ to improve its productivity.

EXECUTIVES

Vice President Of Information Technology, Rich Stuber
Auditors: BDO USA LLP SPOKANE WA

LOCATIONS

HQ: URM STORES, INC.
7511 N FREYA ST, SPOKANE, WA 992178043
Phone: 509 467-2620
Web: WWW.URMSTORES.COM

PRODUCTS/OPERATIONS

Selected Banners
CenterPlace Market
Family Foods
Harvest Foods
Trading Co. Stores
Rosauers Supermarkets
Super 1 Foods
Yoke's Fresh Market

COMPETITORS

AMCON Distributing	McLane
Albertsons	SUPERVALU
Associated Food	Safeway
C&S Wholesale	Sysco
Core-Mark	US Foods
Farner-Bocken	Wal-Mart
Fred Meyer Stores	

HISTORICAL FINANCIALS

Company Type: Private

Income Statement				FYE: August 2
	REVENUE ($ mil.)	NET INCOME ($ mil.)	NET PROFIT MARGIN	EMPLOYEES
08/08*	932	8	0.9%	2,100
07/07	859	7	0.8%	—
07/06	799	4	0.6%	—
Annual Growth	8.0%	41.0%	—	—

*Fiscal year change

2008 Year-End Financials

Return on assets: 3.8%
Return on equity: 11.0%
Current ratio: 1.20
Cash ($ mil.): 2

USS-POSCO INDUSTRIES, A CALIFORNIA JOINT VENTURE

US and Korean steel manufacturing interests come together in the form of USS-POSCO Industries (UPI) a 50/50 joint venture between United States Steel (US Steel) and POSCO. The company operates a steel plant (formerly owned by US Steel) in Pittsburg Northern California. It manufactures flat-rolled steel sheets in various forms: cold-rolled steel galvanized steel and tinplate. In addition USS-POSCO churns out iron oxide which is used to make hard and soft ferrites. UPI sells its products to more than 150 customers in more than dozen states throughout the western US. End products include office furniture computer cabinets metal studs cans culverts and metal building materials.

Operations

UPI's main product lines include cold rolled sheet galvanized sheet hot rolled pickled and oiled sheet and tin plate. It has the capacity to produce about 1.5 million tons of product per year.

Geographic Reach

The company markets its products primarily in the western US.

Sales and Marketing

UPI ships steel products to more than 150 customers across North America. The company sells its products to a wide range of manufacturers whose end products include automotive parts computer cabinets culverts food packaging metal buildings metal studs and office furniture. About 1/3 of UPI's product line is tinplate for the canning industry.

Strategy

Its Korean co-owner supplied high quality raw materials for use at the plant. In order to stay competitive in the face of cheaper steel imports UPI jettisoned non-core product lines to focus on steel sheet and tin. However strong competition and poor market prices forced the company in 2011 to introduce furloughs at the plant and enforce temporary shutdowns of the facility.

Company Background

The company rebounded from a major fire in 2001. In 2010 UPI invested heavily in remediation measures to clean up soil and groundwater impacted by its plant activities.

US Steel teamed up with POSCO (then Pohang Iron & Steel Company) in 1986 as part of a major reorganization of the aging Pittsburg plant which first opened in 1910.

EXECUTIVES

Mgr, Michael Piekut
V Pres, Admin & Finance, Sungwon Shin
Partner, United States Steel Corporatio
Cntrl, Y S Kim
Staff, Jennifer Manto
Staff, David Martin
Law Specialist, Brandy Evans
Customer Representativ, Jacquie Davenport
Customer Manager, Maecy Jelly
Technology Coordinator, Young Sohn
Manager of Labor Relations, Denise Floyd
Auditors: KPMG LLP SACRAMENTO CALIFOR

LOCATIONS

HQ: USS-POSCO INDUSTRIES, A CALIFORNIA JOINT VENTURE
900 LOVERIDGE RD, PITTSBURG, CA 945652808
Phone: 800 877-7672
Web: WWW.USSPOSCO.COM

PRODUCTS/OPERATIONS

Selected Steel Products
Cold Rolled Annealed
Hot Dipped Galvanized
Hot Rolled Pickled and Oiled
Tinplate

COMPETITORS

AK Steel Holding Corporation	Gerdau Ameristeel
ArcelorMittal USA	Nucor
BlueScope Steel	Steel Dynamics

Company Type: Private

Income Statement				FYE: December 31
	REVENUE ($ mil.)	NET INCOME ($ mil.)	NET PROFIT MARGIN	EMPLOYEES
12/15	648	(4)	—	759
12/08	1,198	11	1.0%	—
12/07	998	(40)	—	—
12/06	1,034	14	1.4%	—
Annual Growth	(5.1%)	—	—	—

2015 Year-End Financials

Return on assets: (-1.5%)   Cash ($ mil.): —
Return on equity: —
Current ratio: 0.90

UTAH STATE UNIVERSITY

Utah State University (USU) has more than 40 academic departments at colleges of agriculture arts business education and human services engineering science natural resources and humanities and social sciences. It offers about 170 bachelor's degree programs and more than 140 graduate degree programs. Biology elementary education mechanical and aerospace engineering and business administration are among the university's most popular majors. About 29000 students attend its main campus in northern Utah its three branch campuses or extension facilities located across the state. USU was established in 1888 as an agricultural college.

Operations

USU has a student-to-faculty ratio of 18:1. Alumni of the university include Greg Carr founder of the Greg C. Carr Foundation and Charlie Denson former president of NIKE.

Geographic Reach

USU students hail from all 50 US states and some 80 international countries. The university's students have the opportunity to study abroad through partnerships with 140 other institutions located around the world. USU's main campuses or branch offices in Utah are located in Brigham City Logan San Juan Tooele and Uintah Basin.

Financial Performance

Revenues increased at USU by 4% to some $340 million due to increased income from tuition and fees higher enrollment and increased state appropriations. The gain was offset by decreases in gifts grants and contracts. Net income fell 41% to $68 million due to higher operating expenses from salary benefit and other costs.

Strategy

To expand its facilities and meet growing student needs USU is adding a new school of business building and a new athletics center to its main campus. The university recently completed construction of a new $47 million agricultural building on the main campus as well as a new administration building on the USU Eastern campus. In addition USU is building a new distance education building on its Logan campus.

To further expand resources for students USU began offering a Master of Business Administration (MBA) program at the Brigham Young University's Idaho campus in 2013.

EXECUTIVES

Vice President University Advancement, Fross Peterson
Department Head, Kim Lewis
Vice President For Business And Finance, David Cowley
Vice President University Advancement, Ross Peterson
Regional Vice President, Melanie Rodraguez
Secretary, Vanessa Chambers
Auditors: OFFICE OF THE STATE AUDITOR S

LOCATIONS

HQ: UTAH STATE UNIVERSITY
  1000 OLD MAIN HL, LOGAN, UT 843221000
Phone: 435 797-1000
Web: WWW.UTAHSTATEAGGIES.COM

HISTORICAL FINANCIALS

Company Type: Private

Income Statement				FYE: June 30
	REVENUE ($ mil.)	NET INCOME ($ mil.)	NET PROFIT MARGIN	EMPLOYEES
06/18	461	39	8.7%	6,000
06/17	435	59	13.7%	—
06/16	401	88	22.2%	—
06/15	382	55	14.4%	—
Annual Growth	6.4%	(10.1%)	—	—

2018 Year-End Financials

Return on assets: 2.3%   Cash ($ mil.): 41
Return on equity: 3.1%
Current ratio: 1.40

UTI, (U.S.) HOLDINGS, INC.

EXECUTIVES

Pres-Ceo, Christopher Dale
Treas*, Clinton Smith
Vice Pres*, Mary Anne Henry
Asst Treas*, Matthew Tachouet
Asst SEC*, Kristen Galbreath
Acct, Lorraine Disarlo
Acct Mgr, Patrick Billera
Cash Mgr, Mark Burrow
Director of Information Techno, Craig Jarrett
Vice-President, Tom Riester
Manager, Jay Newey
Auditors: DELOITTE & TOUCHE LLP LOS AN

LOCATIONS

HQ: UTI, (U.S.) HOLDINGS, INC.
  400 SW 6TH AVE STE 906, PORTLAND, OR 972041634
Phone: 503 953-1300

HISTORICAL FINANCIALS

Company Type: Private

Income Statement				FYE: January 31
	REVENUE ($ mil.)	NET INCOME ($ mil.)	NET PROFIT MARGIN	EMPLOYEES
01/10	3,567	45	1.3%	5,981
01/08	534	12	2.3%	—
Annual Growth	158.3%	91.3%	—	—

2010 Year-End Financials

Return on assets: 20.5%   Cash ($ mil.): 350
Return on equity: 1.3%
Current ratio: 1.20

VAL VERDE UNIFIED SCH DIS

EXECUTIVES

Pres, Shelly Yarbrough
V Pres*, Wraymond Sawyerr
Prin*, Michael M Vargas
J.D., Prin*, Fredy De Leon
Special Education Teacher, Alejandra Alas
Bb Coach, Brandon Baker
School, Fernando Betanzos
Chemistry Teacher, Jake Ray
Teacher, Laura Ivory
Teacher, Lori Reynolds
Teacher, Michelle Gates

LOCATIONS

HQ: VAL VERDE UNIFIED SCH DIS
  975 MORGAN ST, PERRIS, CA 925713103
Phone: 951 940-6100
Web: WWW.VALVERDE.EDU

HISTORICAL FINANCIALS

Company Type: Private

Income Statement				FYE: June 30
	REVENUE ($ mil.)	NET INCOME ($ mil.)	NET PROFIT MARGIN	EMPLOYEES
06/18	529	30	5.8%	1,500
06/17	479	38	8.1%	—
06/16	458	(12)	—	—
06/11	362	(0)	—	—
Annual Growth	5.6%	—	—	—

VALLEY CHILDREN'S HEALTHCARE

EXECUTIVES

Ceo, Todd Suntrapak
V Pres*, William Chaltraw
Supervisor, Suzie Burt
Director of Strategic Planning, Brian Sabbatini
Public Relations Manager, Zara Arboleda
Manager Information Technology, Chadd Milks
Supervisor of Molecular Pathol, Keith Zucker
Director of Information Securi, Joe Egan
Director, Rod Benedict
Director, Tim Curley
Director, Elsa Ozuna-Richards

LOCATIONS

HQ: VALLEY CHILDREN'S HEALTHCARE
  9300 VALLEY CHILDRENS PL, MADERA, CA 936368761
Phone: 559 353-3000
Web: WWW.VALLEYCHILDRENS.ORG

HISTORICAL FINANCIALS
Company Type: Private

Income Statement				FYE: September 30
	REVENUE ($ mil.)	NET INCOME ($ mil.)	NET PROFIT MARGIN	EMPLOYEES
09/18	698	122	17.6%	2,800
09/17	604	121	20.1%	—
09/16	601	83	13.9%	—
09/15	11	3	26.6%	—
Annual Growth	293.4%	242.5%	—	—

2018 Year-End Financials
Return on assets: 7.4% Cash ($ mil.): 41
Return on equity: 10.5%
Current ratio: 1.40

VALLEY CHILDREN'S HOSPITAL

EXECUTIVES

Pres- Ceo, Todd Sunterapak
Cfo*, Michele Waldrin
Coo*, Jessie Hudgins
Executive*, Stephanie Scott
Prin*, Gordon Alexander
Human Resources, Heather San Julian
Pediatrician, Paul Lebby
Pediatrician, Paul Lilles
Administrative Assistant, Barbara Parker
Vice President Chief Nursing O, Beverly Hugh-Pugh
Senior Chief Nursing Officer, Beverly H Pugh

LOCATIONS

HQ: VALLEY CHILDREN'S HOSPITAL
9300 VALLEY CHILDRENS PL, MADERA, CA
936368762
Phone: 559 353-3000
Web: WWW.VALLEYCHILDRENS.ORG

HISTORICAL FINANCIALS
Company Type: Private

Income Statement				FYE: September 30
	REVENUE ($ mil.)	NET INCOME ($ mil.)	NET PROFIT MARGIN	EMPLOYEES
09/15	575	24	4.3%	1,800
09/13*	542	103	19.0%	—
06/05	457	(24)	—	—
09/02	219	0	0.3%	—
Annual Growth	7.7%	33.9%	—	—

*Fiscal year change

2015 Year-End Financials
Return on assets: 2.3% Cash ($ mil.): 8
Return on equity: 3.0%
Current ratio: 2.30

VALLEY HEALTH SYSTEM GROUP RETURN

EXECUTIVES

Ex Dir, Kevin Callanan
Urology Specialist, John Warner
Auditors: VALLEY HEALTH SYSTEM WINCHEST

LOCATIONS

HQ: VALLEY HEALTH SYSTEM GROUP RETURN
220 CAMPUS BLVD STE 310, WINCHESTER, VA
226012889
Phone: 540 536-4302
Web: WWW.VALLEYHEALTH.COM

HISTORICAL FINANCIALS
Company Type: Private

Income Statement				FYE: December 31
	REVENUE ($ mil.)	NET INCOME ($ mil.)	NET PROFIT MARGIN	EMPLOYEES
12/17	904	32	3.6%	7
12/13	625	22	3.7%	—
12/12	628	46	7.4%	—
12/09	538	45	8.5%	—
Annual Growth	6.7%	(4.2%)	—	—

2017 Year-End Financials
Return on assets: 2.3% Cash ($ mil.): 65
Return on equity: 3.9%
Current ratio: 0.40

VALUE DRUG COMPANY

Value Drug Company sees a great deal of value in keeping independent pharmacies competitive. The company is a purchasing cooperative of hundreds of independent drugstores that provides wholesale pharmaceutical distribution services to its members primarily in the central Pennsylvania area. Its products include pharmaceuticals and non-prescription medications hospital and convalescent equipment health and beauty aids nutritional supplies and other health care-related products. The company works with some of the world's largest pharmaceutical makers. Value Drug was founded in 1934 and incorporated in 1936. The company is led by president Greg Drew a former Rite-Aid executive.

Operations

The company's private-label line includes nearly 1000 over-the-counter products. Value Drug participates in such retail initiatives as the federal 340B Drug Discount Program an adult immunization tracking program and competitive generic sourcing program OptiSource.

Geographic Reach

Value Drug is located in Pennsylvania and serves a market area covering 15 states.

EXECUTIVES

National Account Manager, Ellen Breitenbach
Vice President Of Operations, J Bover
Auditors: HILL BARTH & KING LLC WEXFOR

LOCATIONS

HQ: VALUE DRUG COMPANY
195 THEATER DR, DUNCANSVILLE, PA 166357144
Phone: 814 944-9316
Web: WWW.VALUEDRUGCO.COM

COMPETITORS

AmerisourceBergen	Kinray
Cardinal Health	McKesson
H. D. Smith Wholesale Drug	Quality King

HISTORICAL FINANCIALS
Company Type: Private

Income Statement				FYE: December 31
	REVENUE ($ mil.)	NET INCOME ($ mil.)	NET PROFIT MARGIN	EMPLOYEES
12/18	1,034	(0)	—	200
12/17	842	0	0.1%	—
12/16	816	0	0.0%	—
12/15	779	3	0.4%	—
Annual Growth	9.9%	—	—	—

2018 Year-End Financials
Return on assets: (-0.1%) Cash ($ mil.): 10
Return on equity: (-0.3%)
Current ratio: 1.40

VAN ATLAS LINES INC

The main subsidiary of Atlas World Group moving company Atlas Van Lines provides transportation of household goods throughout the US and between the US and Canada. The company is one of the largest movers in the US. Atlas Van Lines also offers specialized transportation services for such cargo as trade show materials fine art electronics pianos store fixtures and even individual cars and motorcycles. It operates through a network of some 500Å agents in the US and about 150 in Canada — independent companies that use the Atlas brand in assigned geographic territories and cooperate on interstate moves. Atlas Van Lines was formed in 1948 by a group of 33 small moving companies.

EXECUTIVES

Vice President Customer Services, Mark Spiehler
Vp Agency Development, Steve Hermann

LOCATIONS

HQ: VAN ATLAS LINES INC
1212 SAINT GEORGE RD, EVANSVILLE, IN
477112364
Phone: 812 424-4326
Web: WWW.ATLAS2290.COM

COMPETITORS

AMERCO	Penske Truck Leasing
Bekins	SIRVA
Graebel	United Van Lines

HISTORICAL FINANCIALS
Company Type: Private

Income Statement				FYE: December 31
	REVENUE ($ mil.)	NET INCOME ($ mil.)	NET PROFIT MARGIN	EMPLOYEES
12/08	696	19	2.8%	606
12/06	58	2	4.3%	—
12/05	59	3	6.5%	—
Annual Growth	127.4%	71.0%	—	—

VANDERBILT UNIVERSITY MEDICAL CENTER

The Vanderbilt University Medical Center (VUMC) is one of the top health care organizations in the US with its network of hospitals outpatient centers clinics and specialty institutes. Its medical education programs train hundreds of doctors and nurses each year and the center's Vanderbilt Clinics receive more than 1.5 million annual patient visits. Its Vanderbilt University Hospitals together with the clinics and specialty facilities have more than 1000 beds. VUMC boasts a children's hospital a psychiatric hospital a transplant center and a rehabilitation hospital as well as a biomedical research center and the Vanderbilt-Ingram Cancer Center a National Cancer Institute-designated facility.

Change in Company Type

In mid 2016 Vanderbilt University and VUMC officially split severing their financial and legal ties. The change allows VUMC more financial independence but the two institutions will still partner to provide research and education. VUMC will be reconfigured as a not-for-profit academic medical center; it will retain its current name.

Operations

VUMC includes a level I trauma center and a level IV neonatal intensive care unit (NICU). It also operates a regional burn center and comprehensive regional transplant program. Its nationally designated cancer center has multiple locations. In addition to some 630 beds at the main Vanderbilt University Hospital the medical center campus includes the 270-bed Children's Hospital at Vanderbilt the 90-bed Vanderbilt Psychiatric Hospital and the 90-bed Vanderbilt Stallworth Rehabilitation Hospital. Altogether VUMC's facilities handle some 50000 patient discharges 60000 emergency room visits and 35000 surgeries each year.

Since its establishment in 1875 the Vanderbilt University Medical Center has earned a reputation as a leader in patient care medical education and biomedical research. Its medical and nursing schools train more than 1800 students and its residencies and fellowships groom some 1400 students. Support for VUMC research funding has grown over the last decade with grants from all sources exceeding $570 million in fiscal 2012.

Geographic Reach

VUMC's hospitals affiliates physician practices and clinics cover more than 70 counties in Tennessee and Kentucky.

Strategy

VUMC launched its Vanderbilt Health Affiliated Network (VHAN) in 2013. The network aims to create one of the largest clinically integrated health care networks in the region. VHAN is used as an alternative health plan by Vanderbilt employees; the unit has also received a grant to study chronic disease management practices. Other patient and student service efforts in 2012 and 2013 included enhancing mobile and online applications and learning portals.

EXECUTIVES

Associate Vice Chancellor For Research, Jeffrey R. Balser
Deputy Ceo And Chief Health System Officer, C. Wright Pinson
Executive Vice President, Fletcher Lance
Vice Chair, Victoria Burrus
Auditors: ERNST & YOUNG LLP NASHVILLE

LOCATIONS

HQ: VANDERBILT UNIVERSITY MEDICAL CENTER 1211 MEDICAL CENTER DR, NASHVILLE, TN 372320004
Phone: 615 322-5000
Web: WWW.VANDERBILTHEALTH.COM

PRODUCTS/OPERATIONS

Selected Facilities

Annette and Irwin Eskind Biomedical Library
Bill Wilkerson Center for Otolaryngology and Communication Sciences
Comprehensive Spine Center
Dayani Center for Health and Wellness
Monroe Carell Jr. Children's Hospital at Vanderbilt
Orthopaedic Institute
School of Medicine
School of Nursing
Sports Medicine Center
Stallworth Rehabilitation Hospital
Transplant Center
Vanderbilt Center for Better Health
The Vanderbilt Clinic
Vanderbilt Heart and Vascular Institute
Vanderbilt Psychiatric Hospital
Vanderbilt University Hospital
Vanderbilt-Ingram Cancer Center

COMPETITORS

American HealthChoice
Ascension Health
Blount Memorial Hospital
Catholic Health Initiatives
Community Health Systems
Covenant Health
Duke University Health System
Emory Healthcare
Erlanger Health System
HCA
LifePoint Health
Mountain States Health
Tennova Healthcare

HISTORICAL FINANCIALS

Company Type: Private

Income Statement				FYE: June 30
	REVENUE ($ mil.)	NET INCOME ($ mil.)	NET PROFIT MARGIN	EMPLOYEES
06/18	4,086	98	2.4%	19,000
06/17	3,894	264	6.8%	—
Annual Growth	4.9%	(62.8%)	—	—

2018 Year-End Financials

Return on assets: 3.1%   Cash ($ mil.): 500
Return on equity: 10.6%
Current ratio: 2.20

VANGUARD CHARITABLE ENDOWMENT PROGRAM

EXECUTIVES

Pres, Benjamin R Pierce
Chief Dev't Officer, David S Ryder
Cfo, Kevin Cavanaugh
Cfo, Mark Froehlich
Marketing Manager, James R Barnes
Director, Joseph Klein
Specialized Grants Team Leader, Amanda Welsh
Project Manager, Sean Gordon
Internal Sales Consultant, Courtney Long
Senior Philanthropic, Jodi Rosen
Director of Finance, Mary Emery
Auditors: PRICEWATERHOUSECOOPERS LLP PH

LOCATIONS

HQ: VANGUARD CHARITABLE ENDOWMENT PROGRAM
100 VANGUARD BLVD G19, MALVERN, PA 193552331
Phone: 888 383-4483
Web: WWW.VANGUARDCHARITABLE.ORG

HISTORICAL FINANCIALS

Company Type: Private

Income Statement				FYE: June 30
	REVENUE ($ mil.)	NET INCOME ($ mil.)	NET PROFIT MARGIN	EMPLOYEES
06/13	1,117	608	54.4%	22
06/12	908	424	46.7%	—
06/11	890	402	45.2%	—
06/10	490	15	3.2%	—
Annual Growth	31.6%	239.7%	—	—

2013 Year-End Financials

Return on assets: 16.8%   Cash ($ mil.): 14
Return on equity: 16.9%
Current ratio: —

VARIETY CHILDREN'S HOSPITAL

Miami Children's Hospital (MCH) a not-for-profit medical center boasts some 290 beds and offers more than 40 different health care specialties and sub-specialties represented by more than 650 physicians and more than 130 pediatric sub-specialists. Some specialties include pediatric emergency care cancer treatment orthopedics and rehabilitation services. The hospital's neonatal unit treats newborns referred from other hospitals. Miami Children's Hospital operates the region's only free-standing pediatric trauma center. The MCH Research Institute conducts more than 210 clinical research studies in 26 sub-specialties.

Operations

The health system also operates mobile health units that provide preventive care to uninsured children throughout its service area. The units provide immunizations tuberculosis tests and hearing and vision screenings among other services.

In 2012 the hospital had 11550 inpatient admissions 91901 emergency room visits and 14360 surgical cases. Its neonatology division admits more than 600 newborns each year virtually all of them referred from general acute-care hospitals because they are in need of an advanced level of tertiary care.

In 2012 Radiology performed a total of 129794 Diagnostic x-rays MRI's CT Scans and ultrasounds at the main campus. The LifeFlight Critical Care Transport Team transported 2480 patients by air and ground to Miami Children's Hospital in 2012.

Geographic Reach

MCH caters to young Florida residents and their families as well as those in South America and Europe through its Dan Marino Outpatient Center which assists children with special needs and provides neurological and development services for special needs children. Its six outpatient centers are based in Doral Miami Lakes Palmetto Bay Weston West Kendall and West Palm Beach.

Sales and Marketing

MCH markets its products and services through radio and television advertising

Financial Performance

Net patient revenues accounted for about 90% MCH's revenues in 2012.

Strategy

The hospital is at the tail end of a multiyear nearly $70 million project to install an electronic medical record system at the medical center. The first phase of the project which wrapped up in 2012 included new prescribing methods and lab test protocols. It will also engender better communication between hospital staff. The entire system should be installed by 2015.

In 2013 it also launched a smartphone app for Apple iOS devices that uses Wi-Fi triangulation technology to offer patients the convenience of an on-campus indoor GPS-like way-finding system along with other service enhancements.

Expanding its physical infrastructure in 2014 FIU Health broke ground on a 36000-sq.-ft. ambulatory care center on FIU's Modesto A. Maidique Campus in west Miami-Dade County. In partnership with MCH the campus will house the first dedicated pediatric ambulatory surgical center in South Florida.

As part of an expansion project aimed at meeting the growing needs of the community that year MCH also opened 20 new exam rooms in the Emergency Department.

In 2013 the Florida legislature approved HB 1159 a bill that amends a law to make it possible for MCH to build a 10-bed unit to provide obstetrical services for healthy mothers expecting babies pre-diagnosed with congenital conditions requiring clinical intervention immediately after birth.

In 2012 MCH completed a six-story Advanced Pediatric Care Pavilion and the 21000-sq.-ft. Miami Children's Hospital Midtown Outpatient Center. It also opened Miami Children's Hospital Nicklaus Outpatient Center.

On the media front in 2014 MCH launched the MCH Television Network an in-house television network providing patients and families a customized resource for news research and entertainment that specifically caters to MCH patients and their families. It also revamped its in-house radio station that year.

Company Background

Variety Children's Hospital opened in 1950 and became Miami Children's Hospital in 1986.

The hospital first opened its doors in the 1940s as Miami Tent #33 of Variety Clubs International.

EXECUTIVES

Ceo, Narendra M Kini
V Pres, Mario Murgado
SEC, Keith Ward
Treas, Tim M Birkenstock
Sr V Pres, Timothy Birkenstock
Sr V Pres, Jacqueline L Gonzalez
Sr V Pres, Edward Martinez
SEC, Jefry M Biehler
Mgr, Alfredo Guevara
Immunologist, Susan V Benenati
Chief of Icu/Ccu, Andre Rasznski

LOCATIONS

HQ: VARIETY CHILDREN'S HOSPITAL
3100 SW 62ND AVE, MIAMI, FL 331553009
Phone: 305 666-6511
Web: WWW.NICKLAUSCHILDRENS.ORG

PRODUCTS/OPERATIONS

Selected Services

Cardiology and Cardiovascular Surgery
Children's Medical Services Primary Care Program
Clinical Research
Dermatology Early Steps Southernmost Coast
Endocrinology & Diabetes
Gastroenterology
Hematology & Oncology

MCH Pediatric Care Center
Neuroscience Center
Neurosurgery
Ophthalmology
Orthopaedics
Otolaryngology Outpatient Centers
Pediatric Advanced Comprehensive Care Team
Pediatric Critical Care Medicine
Pediatric Hospital Medicine Team Pediatric Medicine
Pediatric Surgery & Anesthesiology
Psychiatry & Psychology
Pulmonology
Radiology
Rehabilitation Services
Rheumatology
Urology

Selected Locations

Miami Children's Hospital Dan Marino Center
Miami Children's Hospital Doral Center
Miami Children's Hospital Miami Lakes Rehabilitation Center
Miami Children's Hospital Nicklaus Care Center
Miami Children's Hospital Palmetto Bay Center
Miami Children's Hospital West Kendall Center

COMPETITORS

Adventist Health System Sunbelt Healthcare
All Children's Hospital
Baptist Health South Florida
Children's Hospital of Philadelphia
HCA
Jackson Health System
Mount Sinai Medical Center of Florida
NCH Healthcare
Shriners Hospitals For Children
South Broward Hospital District
South Miami Hospital
UF&Shands
University of Miami
University of Miami Hospital

HISTORICAL FINANCIALS

Company Type: Private

Income Statement

	REVENUE ($ mil.)	NET INCOME ($ mil.)	NET PROFIT MARGIN	EMPLOYEES
12/18	655	(23)	—	3,700
12/17	674	60	9.0%	—
12/16	625	71	11.5%	—
12/14	618	77	12.5%	—
Annual Growth	1.5%	—	—	—

FYE: December 31

2018 Year-End Financials

Return on assets: (-1.9%)   Cash ($ mil.): 22
Return on equity: (-3.2%)
Current ratio: 1.40

VASSAR BROTHERS HOSPITAL

EXECUTIVES

Pres-Ceo, Daniel Aronzon
Cco, Janeth Ready
Admin SEC, Pat Keener
Director of Pharmacy, Bill Silta
Doctor, Manuel M Liu
Cardiology, Ronald J Tatelbaum

LOCATIONS

HQ: VASSAR BROTHERS HOSPITAL
45 READE PL, POUGHKEEPSIE, NY 126013990
Phone: 845 454-8500
Web: WWW.HEALTHQUEST.ORG

HISTORICAL FINANCIALS

Company Type: Private

Income Statement

	REVENUE ($ mil.)	NET INCOME ($ mil.)	NET PROFIT MARGIN	EMPLOYEES
12/14	459	20	4.6%	1,500
12/11	390	(12)	—	—
12/07	317	10	3.3%	—
Annual Growth	5.4%	10.5%	—	—

FYE: December 31

2014 Year-End Financials

Return on assets: 4.1%   Cash ($ mil.): 24
Return on equity: 8.4%
Current ratio: 4.00

VCU HEALTH SYSTEM AUTHORITY

EXECUTIVES

Ceo, John Duval
Pres, Michael RAO
Cfo-Evp, Dominic J Puleo
Coo, Deborah Davis
Administrative Secretary, Beverly Yazzie
Electrical Engineer, Dion Wright
Vice President Human Resources, Maria Curran
Clinical Coordinator, Regina Smithey
Supervisor, Alice Fowler
Physician, Andy Pinson
Rn, Ashley Martin
Auditors: ERNST & YOUNG LLP RICHMOND

LOCATIONS

HQ: VCU HEALTH SYSTEM AUTHORITY
1250 E MARSHALL ST, RICHMOND, VA 232985051
Phone: 804 828-9000

HISTORICAL FINANCIALS

Company Type: Private

Income Statement

	REVENUE ($ mil.)	NET INCOME ($ mil.)	NET PROFIT MARGIN	EMPLOYEES
06/18	3,399	162	4.8%	7,399
06/17	3,014	309	10.3%	—
06/05	899	47	5.3%	—
06/04	899	47	5.3%	—
Annual Growth	10.0%	9.1%	—	—

FYE: June 30

2018 Year-End Financials

Return on assets: 4.5%   Cash ($ mil.): 395
Return on equity: 6.7%
Current ratio: 2.30

VICTORY INTERNATIONAL GROUP, LLC

EXECUTIVES

Pres, Jiansheng Fan
Vice President, Amanda Meng

LOCATIONS

HQ: VICTORY INTERNATIONAL GROUP, LLC
14748 PIPELINE AVE STE B, CHINO HILLS, CA
917096024
Phone: 949 407-5888
Web: WWW.VICTORYINTLGROUP.COM

HISTORICAL FINANCIALS

Company Type: Private

Income Statement				FYE: December 31
	REVENUE ($ mil.)	NET INCOME ($ mil.)	NET PROFIT MARGIN	EMPLOYEES
12/15	873	42	4.8%	25
12/07	87	1	1.4%	—
Annual Growth	33.2%	55.5%	—	—

2015 Year-End Financials

Return on assets: 7.3%
Return on equity: 13.2%
Current ratio: 1.80

Cash ($ mil.): 40

VIRGINIA COLLEGE BUILDING AUTHORITY

EXECUTIVES

Prin, Robert F McDonnell

LOCATIONS

HQ: VIRGINIA COLLEGE BUILDING AUTHORITY
101 N 14TH ST FL 3, RICHMOND, VA 232193665
Phone: 804 225-2142
Web: WWW.VIRGINIA.GOV

HISTORICAL FINANCIALS

Company Type: Private

Income Statement				FYE: June 30
	ASSETS ($ mil.)	NET INCOME ($ mil.)	INCOME AS % OF ASSETS	EMPLOYEES
06/18	2,141	(145)	—	2
06/17	1,754	(98)	—	—
06/16	2,199	(327)	—	—
Annual Growth	(1.3%)	—	—	—

2018 Year-End Financials

Return on assets:
Return on equity: —

Sales ($ mil) 504

VIRGINIA COMMONWEALTH UNIVERSITY

Virginia Commonwealth University (VCU) serves the common interests of its more than 30000 enrolled students. The university offers more than 200 certificate undergraduate graduate and doctoral programs through its 15 schools. Spread across two campuses in Richmond: Monroe Park and Medical College of Virginia (MCV) which includes the Schools of Allied Health Dentistry Medicine Nursing Pharmacy and Public Health. Specialty facilities include the VCU Medical Center and a branch campus of the School of the Arts in Qatar. Founded in 1917 as the Richmond School of Social Work and Public Health in 1968 the school merged with the Medical College of Virginia to form VCU.

EXECUTIVES

Assistant Vice President For Human Resources, Cindy Andrews
Associate Vice President Facilities Management, Brian Ohlinger
Director Provost And Vice President Academic Affairs, Jamie Stillman
Associate Vice President, David Sarrett
Provost And Senior Vice President Academic Affairs, Gail Hackett
Associate Vice President Of Patient Care Services, Shirley Gibson
Assistant Vice President Academic Affairs, Alison Jones
First National Vice President The U. S. Complete, Art Mourino
Vice President Third, Matthew Balazik
Vice President, Bobby Krzyzanowski
Vice Chair, Van Tassell

LOCATIONS

HQ: VIRGINIA COMMONWEALTH UNIVERSITY
912 W FRANKLIN ST, RICHMOND, VA 232849040
Phone: 804 828-0100
Web: WWW.VCU.EDU

HISTORICAL FINANCIALS

Company Type: Private

Income Statement				FYE: June 30
	REVENUE ($ mil.)	NET INCOME ($ mil.)	NET PROFIT MARGIN	EMPLOYEES
06/18	763	12	1.7%	11,000
06/17	760	84	11.1%	—
06/16	737	37	5.1%	—
06/11	2,319	328	14.2%	—
Annual Growth	(14.7%)	(37.1%)	—	—

2018 Year-End Financials

Return on assets: 0.7%
Return on equity: 1.8%
Current ratio: 1.80

Cash ($ mil.): 65

VIRGINIA DEPARTMENT OF TRANSPORTATION

EXECUTIVES

Commissioner, C Kilpatrick
Commissioner*, Charles A Kilpatrick
Assistant Secretary*, Amy Wight
Acting Deputy SEC*, John W Lawson
Payroll Staff, Carol Clatterbaugh
Accounting Staff, Lu Lutero
Business Analyst, Liliya Fedzhora

LOCATIONS

HQ: VIRGINIA DEPARTMENT OF TRANSPORTATION
1401 E BROAD ST, RICHMOND, VA 232192052
Phone: 804 786-2701
Web: WWW.VIRGINIADOT.ORG

HISTORICAL FINANCIALS

Company Type: Private

Income Statement				FYE: June 30
	REVENUE ($ mil.)	NET INCOME ($ mil.)	NET PROFIT MARGIN	EMPLOYEES
06/10	3,240	473	14.6%	10,737
06/06	3,047	410	13.5%	—
06/05	0	0	—	—
06/04	2,857	56	2.0%	—
Annual Growth	2.1%	42.7%	—	—

2010 Year-End Financials

Return on assets: 2.3%
Return on equity: 2.7%
Current ratio: —

Cash ($ mil.): 2,013

VIRGINIA HOSPITAL CENTER ARLINGTON HEALTH SYSTEM

Virginia Hospital Center-Arlington Health Systems is a general medical-surgical facility providing health care services to residents of northern Virginia. The hospital has about 350 beds and boasts all-private rooms. The acute medical center includes emergency cardiology neurology orthopedics respiratory urology cancer care and women's health divisions as well as radiology and diagnostic imaging facilities. In addition Virginia Hospital Center provides outpatient rehabilitation services and runs an urgent care clinic that furnishes primary care for minor emergencies. The hospital is a teaching facility for the Georgetown University School of Medicine.

Financial Performance

In 2012 the company's revenue increased by 6% on the strength of an increase in patient services and other operating revenue. Those two categories account for 97% of the system's revenue. Net income seemed to increase nearly 400% but it was due to a change in market value of investments.

Strategy

The company needs access to deeper pockets to sustain its long term viability. As part of Virginia Hospital Center's strategy of searching for a larger system to acquire it the hospital has partnered with a division of Sentara Healthcare to create a new home-care business in the Washington suburbs. Sentara Enterprises owns 51% of the Northern Virginia Home Care joint venture and is contributing its technology and expertise. Virginia Hospital Center owns the remaining 49% and contributed office space for the startup. The agreement gives Sentara a northern beachhead for its home care service network.

Company Background

The hospital first opened its doors in 1944.

EXECUTIVES

Ceo, James Cole
V Pres*, Michael Malone
Chb*, John R Garrett
Coo*, Carl B Bahnlein
Cmo*, Jeffrey Dilisi
Acting Director, Jay Aceto
Accountant, Yoko Ota
Director, Farrukh Haqqani
Registered Nurse, Laura Gibson
Registered Nurse, Cathy Bowie
Vice President, David Crutchfield
Auditors: DIXON HUGHES GOODMAN LLP ROCK

LOCATIONS

HQ: VIRGINIA HOSPITAL CENTER ARLINGTON
HEALTH SYSTEM
1701 N GEORGE MASON DR, ARLINGTON, VA
222053610
Phone: 703 558-5668
Web: WWW.VIRGINIAHOSPITALCENTER.COM

PRODUCTS/OPERATIONS

2012 Sales

	% of total
HMO/PPO	53
Medicare	33
Medicaid	5
Other commercial payors	3
Other	6
Total	**100**

Selected Facilities and Services33

Acute Stroke
Arlington Free Clinic
Breast Health
Clinical Research
Colorectal Surgery
Emergency Med
Gastroenterology
General Surgery
Heart Services
Intensive Care
Laboratory Services
Neuroscience
Oncology
Ophthalmology
Orthopedic Surgery
Palliative Care
Pediatrics
Pelvic Floor Disorders
Physical Speech and Occupational Therapy
Primary Care
Psychiatry and Addiction
Pulmonary Special Procedures
Radiology and Medical Imaging
Sleep Lab and Sleep Medicine
Surgical Oncology
Urogynecology and Pelvic Surgery
Urology
Virginia Hospital Center Urgent Care
Weight Management Medicine and Surgery
Women & Infant Health
Wound Healing and Hyperbaric Center

COMPETITORS

Bon Secours Health
Carilion Clinic
Fauquier Hospital
HCA
Inova
Johns Hopkins Health System
Johns Hopkins Medicine
Martha Jefferson Hospital
MedStar Health
Novant Health
Prince William Health System
Sentara Northern Virginia Medical Center
University of Virginia Medical Center

HISTORICAL FINANCIALS
Company Type: Private

Income Statement — FYE: December 31

	REVENUE ($ mil.)	NET INCOME ($ mil.)	NET PROFIT MARGIN	EMPLOYEES
12/17	524	54	10.4%	2,000
12/10*	0	(0)	—	—
10/09	0	(0)	—	—
Annual Growth	190.3%	—	—	—

*Fiscal year change

2017 Year-End Financials

Return on assets: 4.6%　　　Cash ($ mil.): 14
Return on equity: 5.5%
Current ratio: 0.50

VIRGINIA HOSPITAL CENTER ARLINGTON HEALTH SYSTEM

Auditors: DIXON HUGHES GOODMAN LLP ROCK

LOCATIONS

HQ: VIRGINIA HOSPITAL CENTER ARLINGTON
HEALTH SYSTEM
1701 N GEORGE MASON DR, ARLINGTON, VA
222053610
Phone: 703 558-5000
Web: WWW.VIRGINIAHOSPITALCENTER.COM

HISTORICAL FINANCIALS
Company Type: Private

Income Statement — FYE: December 31

	REVENUE ($ mil.)	NET INCOME ($ mil.)	NET PROFIT MARGIN	EMPLOYEES
12/14	477	63	13.4%	11
12/09	322	27	8.5%	—
Annual Growth	8.1%	18.3%	—	—

2014 Year-End Financials

Return on assets: 6.4%　　　Cash ($ mil.): 20
Return on equity: 7.9%
Current ratio: 0.40

VIRGINIA HOUSING DEVELOPMENT AUTHORITY

Though Virginia is famous for its Civil War-era plantations these historic estates represent a lifestyle out of reach for most. For Virginians seeking a more modest homestead there's the Virginia Housing Development Authority (VHDA). The not-for-profit quasi-government agency founded by the Virginia General Assembly in 1972 provides developers of rentalÂ propertiesÂ and low- to moderate-income borrowers with low interest rate loans to renovate or purchase houses and apartments across the state. Its loan products are offered by more than 140 authorized lenders throughout Virginia. The VHDA is self-supporting issuing bonds to raise capital.

EXECUTIVES

Executive Director, Susan F. Dewey
Managing Director Rental Housing, Arthur N. (Art) Bowen
Managing Director Community Outreach, J. Michael Hawkins
Managing Director Executive Services, Llewellyn C. Anderson
Managing Director Homeownership, Janet Wiglesworth
Managing Director Internal Audit And Risk Management, Julie Camus
Managing Director Finance, Pat Carey
Acting Managing Director Information Technology Services, J. Kyle Howard
Vice President Of Operation, Jackie Gibbs
Vice President Of Operation, Sherry Estridge
Executive Vice President Claims And Customer Service Operations, Dyson Darrell
Chairman, Timothy M. Chapman
Vice Chairman, Sarah B. Stedfast
Treasurer, Gary Murray
Auditors: KPMG LLP RICHMOND VIRGINIA

LOCATIONS

HQ: VIRGINIA HOUSING DEVELOPMENT AUTHORITY
601 S BELVIDERE ST, RICHMOND, VA 232206504
Phone: 804 780-0789
Web: WWW.VHDA.COM

HISTORICAL FINANCIALS
Company Type: Private

Income Statement — FYE: June 30

	ASSETS ($ mil.)	NET INCOME ($ mil.)	INCOME AS % OF ASSETS	EMPLOYEES
06/18	7,292	132	1.8%	300
06/16	8,024	171	2.1%	—
06/15	8,070	176	2.2%	—
06/14	8,014	132	1.7%	—
Annual Growth	(2.3%)	(0.1%)	—	—

2018 Year-End Financials

Return on assets: 1.8%　　　Sales ($ mil): 505
Return on equity: 4.0%

VIRGINIA INTERNATIONAL TERMINALS, LLC

Virginia International Terminals (VIT) operates marine terminals and an inland port on behalf of the Virginia Port Authority (VPA) a state agency. Established in 1982Å VIT's marine terminals handle containerships and other vessels in Newport News Norfolk and Portsmouth. The terminals are linked by rail to the Virginia Inland Port in Front Royal which serves as an intermodal container transfer facility conveying cargo from ships to trucks and vice versa. CenterPoint Properties investment firm The Carlyle GroupÅ andÅ terminal operator Carrix Inc. bid to create a public-private partnership with VIT.Å TheÅ Transportation SecretaryÅ dismissed the bids in late 2010Å after cargo activity started improving.

EXECUTIVES

Ceo, Joseph P Ruddy
Pres, Joseph Dorto
Dir, Regina P Brayboy
V Pres, Wilson S Goode
Dir, Franklin P Earley
SEC-Treas, William M Grace
Coo, Shawn Tiddettes
Corporate Counsel, John M Ryan
Customer Representativ, Becky Coore
Customer Representativ, Patty Marlow
Coordinator, Shirby Dunton
Auditors: PBMARES LLP HARRISONBURG VI

LOCATIONS

HQ: VIRGINIA INTERNATIONAL TERMINALS, LLC
601 WORLD TRADE CTR, NORFOLK, VA 23510
Phone: 757 440-7120
Web: WWW.PORTOFVIRGINIA.COM

COMPETITORS

Georgia Ports Authority	Port Authority of New York and New Jersey
North Carolina State Ports Authority	South Carolina Ports

HISTORICAL FINANCIALS

Company Type: Private

Income Statement				FYE: June 30
	REVENUE ($ mil.)	NET INCOME ($ mil.)	NET PROFIT MARGIN	EMPLOYEES
06/18	521	16	3.1%	400
06/17	478	(7)	—	—
06/10	203	2	1.1%	—
06/08	254	(6)	—	—
Annual Growth	7.4%	—	—	—

2018 Year-End Financials
Return on assets: 8.6%   Cash ($ mil.): 19
Return on equity: 12.1%
Current ratio: 3.80

VIRGINIA MASON MEDICAL CENTER

EXECUTIVES

Pres, James Young
V Pres*, James Orlikoff
Treas*, Robert Lemon
SEC*, Dorothy Mann
Chb-Ceo*, Gary S Kaplan
Sr V Pres-Cio-Cfo*, Suzanne Anderson
Pres*, Carolyn Corvi
Physical Therapist, Johannes Van Buuren
Health Professional, Megan Stewart
Hematology, Andrew D Jacobs
Health Professional, Carol Ekbom
Auditors: KPMG LLP SEATTLE WA

LOCATIONS

HQ: VIRGINIA MASON MEDICAL CENTER
1100 9TH AVE, SEATTLE, WA 981012756
Phone: 206 223-6600
Web: WWW.VIRGINIAMASON.ORG

HISTORICAL FINANCIALS

Company Type: Private

Income Statement				FYE: December 31
	REVENUE ($ mil.)	NET INCOME ($ mil.)	NET PROFIT MARGIN	EMPLOYEES
12/18	1,101	(16)	—	5,000
12/17	1,025	33	3.2%	
Annual Growth	7.4%	—	—	—

2018 Year-End Financials
Return on assets: (-1.5%)   Cash ($ mil.): 61
Return on equity: (-3.5%)
Current ratio: 1.60

VIRGINIA POLYTECHNIC INSTITUTE & STATE UNIVERSITY

Virginia Polytechnic Institute and State University more commonly known as Virginia Tech is the state's largest university enrolling more than 32000 students. The university offers more than 200 undergraduate graduate and professional degree programs through eight academic colleges. It has a student-teacher ratio of 16 to 1. The school's most popular majors include agriculture business biology animal sciences and engineering. Virginia Tech which was formed in 1872 serves the surrounding community through outreach and education programs.

Operations

Virginia charges $13230 tuition and fees for in-state undergraduates and $31014 tuition and fees for out-of-state undergraduates.

Virginia Tech manages a research portfolio of nearly $500 million. Research is focused on new developments in agriculture biotechnology energy management (including fuel-cell technology and power electronics) information and communication technology transportation and other fields.

Geographic Reach

Virginia Tech has more than 210 campus buildings a 2600-acre main campus in Blacksburg off-campus educational facilities in Alexandria Arlington Falls Church Leesburg Manassas and Middleburg and a study-abroad site in Switzerland. It has about 10 research institutes.

Financial Performance

Virginia Tech's operating revenue increased 1% to $1.03 billion in fiscal 2017 (ended June). The increase was primarily due to a 3% increase in student tuition and fees revenue — thanks to a growing student body as well an increase in tuition and fee rates — but was partially offset by a 4% decrease in grants and contracts.

Operating expenses totaled $1.4 billion in 2017 a 4% increase from 2016. The university ended the year with $151.4 million in cash and cash equivalents some $112.7 million less than it had at the end of the prior year.

The Virginia Tech Foundation manages the school's endowment which topped $1 billion for the first time in 2018.

Strategy

Virginia Tech's strategic plan focuses on four broad areas: experiential learning diversity and inclusion cross-sector partnerships and philanthropy. Its initiatives in these areas are part of its goal of becoming one of the top 100 universities in the world. Towards those ends the university has introduced new multidisciplinary undergraduate courses and has increased the percentage of incoming students from underrepresented or underserved groups.

It also continues to improve and expand its campuses with renovations to academic buildings sports facilities and residence halls.

The university will acquire the Virginia Tech Carilion School of Medicine (VTCSOM) in mid-2018. VTCSOM was established from a 10-year private-public partnership with Carilion Clinic.

Company Background

Virginia Tech was founded as a land-grant college in 1872.

EXECUTIVES

Svp And Provost, Mark G. McNamee
Vp Finance And Cfo, M. Dwight Shelton
Vp And Dean Graduate Education, Karen P. DePauw
Ceo Virginia Tech Foundation, John E. Dooley
Dean Pamplin College Of Business, Robert T. Sumichrast
Dean Virginia-maryland College Of Veterinary Medicine, Cyril Clarke
President, Timothy D. (Tim) Sands
Vp Information Technology And Cio, Scott F. Midkiff
Dean College Of Agriculture And Life Sciences, Alan Grant
Dean College Of Architecture And Urban Studies, A. Jack Davis
Dean College Of Engineering, Richard Benson
Dean College Of Liberal Arts And Human Sciences, Elizabeth Spiller
Dean College Of Natural Resources And Environment, Paul M. Winistorfer
Dean College Of Science, Lay Nam Chang
Dean University Libraries, Tyler O. Walters
Department Chair, Dave Gerrard
Vice Chair For Education, John Ferrara
Board Member, Patrick Lowther
Treasurer, Candice Kortegast
Secretary External Affairs Athletics, Jean Ann Bailey
Auditors: COMMONWEALTH OF VIRGINIA AUDIT

LOCATIONS

HQ: VIRGINIA POLYTECHNIC INSTITUTE & STATE UNIVERSITY
300 TURNER ST NW STE 4200, BLACKSBURG, VA 240616100
Phone: 540 231-6000

PRODUCTS/OPERATIONS

Selected Colleges
College of Agriculture and Life Sciences
College Architecture and Urban Studies
College of Engineering
College of Liberal Arts and Human Sciences
College of Natural Resources and Environment
College of Science
Pamplin College of Business
Virginia-Maryland Regional College of Veterinary Medicine

HISTORICAL FINANCIALS

Company Type: Private

Income Statement				FYE: June 30
	REVENUE ($ mil.)	NET INCOME ($ mil.)	NET PROFIT MARGIN	EMPLOYEES
06/18	1,279	181	14.2%	6,866
06/17	1,031	64	6.2%	—
06/16	1,020	121	11.9%	—
06/15	1,129	114	10.2%	—
Annual Growth	4.2%	16.6%	—	—

2018 Year-End Financials

Return on assets: 4.0%   Cash ($ mil.): 191
Return on equity: 7.1%
Current ratio: 1.30

VIRGINIA PREMIER HEALTH PLAN, INC.

EXECUTIVES

Ceo, Linda Hines
Controller, Angel Moyer
Manager Clinical Applications, Brian Requejo
Manager, Preston St John
Transportation Manager, Randy Ledien
Facp Chief Officer, John Johnson
Certified Assistant, Khalefia Dungee
Administrator II Isom, Tony Gentry
Director of Government Relatio, Blair Hedgepeth
Sr Manager, Doris Mosocco
General Accounting Manager, Elsie Handy
Auditors: KPMG LLP MC LEAN VA

LOCATIONS

HQ: VIRGINIA PREMIER HEALTH PLAN, INC.
600 E BROAD ST STE 400, RICHMOND, VA 232191800
Phone: 804 819-5164
Web: WWW.VIRGINIAPREMIER.COM

HISTORICAL FINANCIALS

Company Type: Private

Income Statement				FYE: June 30
	REVENUE ($ mil.)	NET INCOME ($ mil.)	NET PROFIT MARGIN	EMPLOYEES
06/18	1,372	(14)	—	165
06/15	969	(0)	—	—
06/14*	749	14	1.9%	—
12/03	207	3	1.9%	—
Annual Growth	14.5%			

*Fiscal year change

2018 Year-End Financials

Return on assets: (-3.6%)   Cash ($ mil.): 31
Return on equity: (-10.1%)
Current ratio: 1.10

VIRGINIA WEST UNIVERSITY HOSPITALS INC

West Virginia University Hospitals (WVUH) has West Virginians covered. The health care system's 530-bed main campus includes the Ruby Memorial Hospital the WVU Children's Hospital and the behavioral health Chestnut Ridge Center as well as outpatient care centers.Â Other services include centers for eye and dental care cancer treatment and family medicine. WVUH's facilities serve as the primary teaching locations for the West Virginia University's health professions schools. Cheat Lake Physicians is the physicians group associated with the health system. WVUH is a member of the West Virginia United Health System.

Strategy

To increase its capacity for patient services WVUH launched a $230 million project to build a new tower addition at its main Ruby MemorialÂ Hospital facility in 2012. The project will add about 115 general inpatient beds.

WVUH is also working to expand its community outreach capabilities and lower the cost of inpatient care through technology initiatives. The health system is adding a number of tele-health services including psychiatry and stroke programs that allow patients to communicate with doctors via video conferencing systems. These services especially help residents living in rural settings.

EXECUTIVES

Secretary, Star Hammond

LOCATIONS

HQ: VIRGINIA WEST UNIVERSITY HOSPITALS INC
1 MEDICAL CENTER DR, MORGANTOWN, WV 265061200
Phone: 304 598-4000
Web: WWW.WVUCANCER.ORG

COMPETITORS

CAMC Health
HCA
West Penn Allegheny Health System

HISTORICAL FINANCIALS

Company Type: Private

Income Statement				FYE: December 31
	REVENUE ($ mil.)	NET INCOME ($ mil.)	NET PROFIT MARGIN	EMPLOYEES
12/18	1,193	(39)	—	6,267
12/12	1,386	96	6.9%	—
12/06	0	0	—	—
Annual Growth	—	—	—	—

2018 Year-End Financials

Return on assets: (-2.3%)   Cash ($ mil.): 21
Return on equity: (-5.4%)
Current ratio: 2.50

VIRTU FINANCIAL LLC

Auditors: DELOITTE & TOUCHE LLP NEW YOR

LOCATIONS

HQ: VIRTU FINANCIAL LLC
1 LIBERTY PLZ, NEW YORK, NY 100061404
Phone: 212 418-0100
Web: WWW.VIRTU.COM

HISTORICAL FINANCIALS

Company Type: Private

Income Statement				FYE: December 31
	ASSETS ($ mil.)	NET INCOME ($ mil.)	INCOME AS % OF ASSETS	EMPLOYEES
12/14	3,324	190	5.7%	18
12/13	3,963	182	4.6%	—
Annual Growth	(16.1%)	4.3%	—	—

2014 Year-End Financials

Return on assets: 5.7%   Sales ($ mil): 723
Return on equity: 89.5%

VIRTUA-WEST JERSEY HEALTH SYSTEM, INC.

EXECUTIVES

Pres-Ceo, Richard Miller
Chm*, Dennis Flanagan
Cfo*, Robert Segin
Treas*, David Kindlick
SEC*, Edward Cloues
Coordinator, Monica Fiorini
Staff, Beverly Crawford
Coordinator, Leha Anderson
Coordinator, Joanne Sebastiano
Vice President Finance, Jennifer L Romond
Government Business Process Co, Constance Lippincott

LOCATIONS

HQ: VIRTUA-WEST JERSEY HEALTH SYSTEM, INC.
1000 ATLANTIC AVE, CAMDEN, NJ 081041132
Phone: 856 246-3000
Web: WWW.VIRTUA.ORG

HISTORICAL FINANCIALS

Company Type: Private

Income Statement — FYE: December 31

	REVENUE ($ mil.)	NET INCOME ($ mil.)	NET PROFIT MARGIN	EMPLOYEES
12/17	919	207	22.6%	4,100
12/04	399	29	7.4%	—
12/03	354	6	1.8%	—
12/02	346	7	2.2%	—
Annual Growth	6.7%	24.6%	—	—

2017 Year-End Financials

Return on assets: 9.7%   Cash ($ mil.): 68
Return on equity: 16.1%
Current ratio: 0.20

VISITING NURSE SERVICE OF NEW YORK HOME CARE II

Auditors: KPMG LLP ALBANY NY

LOCATIONS

HQ: VISITING NURSE SERVICE OF NEW YORK HOME CARE II
5 PENN PLZ FL 12, NEW YORK, NY 100011824
Phone: 212 609-5716
Web: WWW.VNSNY.ORG

HISTORICAL FINANCIALS

Company Type: Private

Income Statement — FYE: December 31

	REVENUE ($ mil.)	NET INCOME ($ mil.)	NET PROFIT MARGIN	EMPLOYEES
12/14	462	(78)	—	7
12/13	617	(36)	—	—
12/09	602	1	0.2%	—
Annual Growth	(5.1%)	—	—	—

2014 Year-End Financials

Return on assets: (-95.3%)   Cash ($ mil.): 1
Return on equity: —
Current ratio: —

VITALANT

Vitalant (formerly Blood Systems) collects blood and provides blood products and services to more than 1000 hospitals in about 40 states. One of the largest US not-for-profit blood service companies Vitalant operates about 125 donation centers and conducts 30000 mobile blood drives each year. The company's BioCare division distributes plasma derivative products used in medical procedures while Vitalant Research Institute conducts blood-related research studies. Vitalant also provides blood donor testing services through its Creative Testing Solutions (CTS) venture (owned with American Red Cross and OneBlood).

Strategy

Vitalant widens its geographic reach by acquiring smaller donation center networks and by entering new hospital and group purchasing organization (GPO) service contracts in strategic markets. It has doubled the size of its network and extended its operations across most of the US over the past decade.

The company is expanding in transfusion medicine by conducting research into cellular therapy molecular biology immunology virus discovery and donor epidemiology through its Vitalant Research Institute. One division of the institute is working to develop novel transfusion methodologies and therapeutics; another unit works to reduce transfusion-transmitted diseases. Vitalant is also growing the range of biological products and specialty medications (for bleeding disorders) offered through its BioCare division.

The company changed its name from Blood Systems to Vitalant in 2018 to unify its operating divisions (10 blood-center brands research institute and specialty laboratory) under one brand. Former blood-center brands now operating as Vitalant include BloodSource LifeShare LifeSource United Blood Services and Blood Centers of the Pacific.

Company Background

The company which was founded in 1943 as the Salt River Valley Blood Bank is governed by a voluntary board of directors consisting of community and medical industry leaders.

Acquisitions of blood bank chains have included BloodSource and Lifeblood (both completed in 2015).

In 2018 Blood Systems changed its name to Vitalant and rebranded all of its blood center brands under the Vitalant name.

EXECUTIVES

Evp And General Counsel, Scott M. Nelson
Executive Vice President Chief Financial Officer, Susan L. Barnes
Evp And Chief Quality Officer, Mary Beth Bassett
Evp Business Services, Patrick Holt
President Chief Executive Officer, Daniel Connor
Executive Vice President Chief Medical & Scientific Officer, Ralph R. Vassallo
Medical Director, Hany Kamel
Auditors: GRANT THORNTON LLP PHOENIX A

LOCATIONS

HQ: VITALANT
6210 E OAK ST, SCOTTSDALE, AZ 852571101
Phone: 602 414-3819
Web: WWW.VITALANT.ORG

PRODUCTS/OPERATIONS

2013 Sales

	$ mil.	% of total
Blood component service fees	323	44
Laboratory testing services	208	28
Sales of pharmaceutical products	174	23
Other services & income	37	5
Total	**743**	**100**

Selected Services

Blood Centers
  Blood Components
  Component Therapy
  Commonly Ordered Derivatives
  Modified Blood Components
Laboratory Services
  Donor Counseling
  Histocompatibility Laboratory (HLA)
  Immunohematology Reference Laboratory (IRL)
Special Collections
  Directed Donation
  Perioperative Blood Salvage
  Pre-operative Autologous Donation (PAD)
  Stem Cell Processing
  Therapeutic (Clinical) Apheresis
Transfusion Medicine
  Blood Management Services
  Compatibility Services

COMPETITORS

CSL	New York Blood Center
Daxor	Puget Sound Blood
FFF Enterprises	Center
Grifols Inc.	Red Cross
HemaCare	SeraCare Life Sciences

HISTORICAL FINANCIALS

Company Type: Private

Income Statement — FYE: December 31

	REVENUE ($ mil.)	NET INCOME ($ mil.)	NET PROFIT MARGIN	EMPLOYEES
12/16	1,129	1	0.1%	5,000
12/15	966	2	0.3%	—
12/14	0	(62)	—	—
12/13	743	65	8.8%	—
Annual Growth	15.0%	(71.6%)	—	—

2016 Year-End Financials

Return on assets: 0.2%   Cash ($ mil.): 49
Return on equity: 0.4%
Current ratio: 2.60

VIZIO, INC.

VIZIO has done for HDTVs what Dell did for PCs: sell them for less. Best known for its sticker-friendly flat panel and plasma LCD HDTVs VIZIO also makes and sells Blue-Ray players sound bars and speakers headphones Internet routers PCs and other consumer electronics through retailers and wholesalers across North America. Sourcing its products from China and Taiwan VIZIO sells many of its low-priced electronics through top discount chains including Amazon Best Buy BJ's Wholesale Costco Wholesale Sam's Club Target and Walmart. Thanks to its low prices VIZIO ranked as the #1 sound bar seller and the #2 Smart HDTV seller in the US market by unit sales in 2014. The proposed acquisition of Vizio by Chinese tech company LeEco was called off in 2017.

Change in Company Type

LeEco halted its proposed acquisition of VIZIO in April 2017 in the face of regulatory opposition in China. The companies however agreed to partner. LeEco's apps will be included on some VIZIO products and LeEco will sell VIZIO products in China.

Geographic Reach

Irvine California-based VIZIO sells its products across North America.

Sales and Marketing

Sourcing its products from China and Taiwan VIZIO sells many of its low-priced electronics through top discount retailers and wholesalers including Amazon Best Buy BJ's Wholesale Costco Wholesale Sam's Club Target and Walmart.

Strategy

VIZIO settled an action by the US Federal Trace Commission by paying a $2.2 million fine in 2017. The government had charged VIZIO with keeing tabs of the viewing habits of owners of some of its TVs without permission. The settlement required VIZIO to disclose its data collection policies and obtain consent.

Keeping low-prices in mind VIZIO continues to innovate with its core HDTV product line. In December 2015 it introduced its D-Series Collection of Smart TV and 4K Ultra HD ranging in price from $149.99 for the 24" LED TV to $1299.99 for the 70" Full-Array LED Smart TV. In 2014 it launched its new E-Series Full-Array LED backlit HDTV collection as well as its 120-inch Reference Series Ultra HD Smart TV and sub-$1000 pricing on its 50-inch P-Series Ultra HD Smart TV at the Consumer Electronics Show in January.

Still with the market for flat TVs maturing VIZIO has been working to become a more diversified consumer electronics brand. In April 2015 after ranking the #1 unit seller of sound bars in the US for 2014 VIZIO released its 40" 5.1 Sound Bar System to complement screen sizes from 32" and up. The company has also been introducing its products beyond the US market introducing its HDTV and audio products to the Canadian market in late 2014 and to the Mexican market in August 2015. In 2013 in a bid to enter the booming market for smartphones VIZIO began testing an Android-powered smartphone that had been released in China.

Company Background
The company was founded by William Wang in 2002 and initially sold its TVs at membership retailers such as Costco Wholesale BJ's Wholesale Club and Sam's Club. It then extended its reach to discount retailers Wal-Mart and Sears.

The TV maker entered the market for smart TVs which are integrated with i nternet functionality when it shipped its first model during the second half of 2011.

VIZIO entered the PC market in mid-2012 with a new line of laptops and desktops starting at about $890. By combining its entertainment knowhow with the power of the latest Intel Core processors VIZIO hopes to set a new standard for the Windows experience. The line consists of the VIZIO Thin + Light Notebook and All-in-One PC.

EXECUTIVES

Vice President Operations, Rob L Brinkman
Ceo, William Wang
Cfo, Kurt Binder
Senior Vice President Information Technology Lead, Nancy Chow
Vice President Engineering, Marcus Apitz
Vice President Of Support, Scott Patten
Vice President Direct Sales, Michelle Nguyen
Vice President Sales, Hernandez Paul
Chief Sales Officer, Randy Waynick
Senior Vice President, Francis Ahn
National Account Manager, Erin Thompson
National Account Manager, Brandon McTeer

LOCATIONS

HQ: VIZIO, INC.
39 TESLA, IRVINE, CA 926184603
Phone: 949 428-2525
Web: WWW.VIZIO.COM

PRODUCTS/OPERATIONS

Selected Products
Cables and other accessories
Blue-ray disc players
HDTVs
HD home theater systems
Headphones
Internet routers
Personal computers
Tablet computers
Smartphones
Speakers

COMPETITORS

Acer	LG Electronics
Bose	Lenovo
Dell	Panasonic Corp
Funai Electric	Philips Electronics
Harman International	Pioneer Corporation
Hewlett-Packard	Samsung Electronics
Limited	Sony
Koss	Westinghouse

HISTORICAL FINANCIALS
Company Type: Private

Income Statement   FYE: December 31

	REVENUE ($ mil.)	NET INCOME ($ mil.)	NET PROFIT MARGIN	EMPLOYEES
12/08	2,006	10	0.5%	225
12/07	1,929	7	0.4%	—
12/06	671	1	0.2%	—
12/04	46	0	1.0%	—
Annual Growth	155.8%	115.7%		

2008 Year-End Financials

Return on assets: 3.2%   Cash ($ mil.): 42
Return on equity: 0.5%
Current ratio: 0.90

VNS CHOICE

EXECUTIVES

Prin, Mark Flannery
Auditors: KPMG LLP HARTFORD CT

LOCATIONS

HQ: VNS CHOICE
1250 BROADWAY, NEW YORK, NY 100013701
Phone: 212 609-7235
Web: WWW.VNSNYCHOICE.ORG

HISTORICAL FINANCIALS
Company Type: Private

Income Statement   FYE: December 31

	REVENUE ($ mil.)	NET INCOME ($ mil.)	NET PROFIT MARGIN	EMPLOYEES
12/14	1,388	(72)	—	651
12/13	1,299	(90)	—	—
12/09	419	4	1.0%	—
Annual Growth	27.0%			

2014 Year-End Financials

Return on assets: (-18.9%)   Cash ($ mil.): 1
Return on equity: —
Current ratio: —

W.S. BADCOCK CORPORATION

W.S. Badcock furnishes homes down in Dixie and beyond. As one of the largest privately-owned furniture retailers in the US the company sells furnitureÂ for every room in the house. It sells its furniture and accessoriesÂ through more than 300 stores that operate under the banner namesÂ Bad-cock Home Furnishing Centers and Badcock &more.Â Aside from its e-commerce site Badcock's stores networkÂ extends to nearly 10 southeastern states. Stores also carry appliances lawn equipment electronics mattresses rugs bedding lighting wall art and other decorative accessories. The company was founded by Henry S. Badcock in 1904 as a general mercantile store. Today it is in its fourth generation of family management.

Geographic Reach
Headquartered in Mulberry Florida with more than 1200 corporate employees W.S. Badcock operates primarily in the southeastern US. Its operations span the states of Georgia Alabama Mississippi Tennessee and the Carolinas expanding into Virginia West Virginia and Kentucky.

Strategy
Through the company's dealer business model more than 80% of Badcock's stores are individually owned. As part of the model the company does not require a franchise fee but instead consigns merchandise to the dealers. As opposed to the typical franchise systemÂ startup this consignment method aims to allow for a quicker startup along with the benefits of business ownership.

Already established in half a dozen states BadcockÂ has beenÂ expanding its store network in Virginia Kentucky and West Virginia. Despite a slowdown in its expansion plans amid the recession and downturn in furniture retailing the company aims to grow its stores network againÂ throughout the Southeast.

EXECUTIVES

Vice President And Controller, Greg Reeves
Senior Vice President Credit Services And Ar Management, Dave Gonyea
Vice President Of Operations, Derrick Taylor
Vice President, Nancy Young
Vp Marketing, Barb Scherer
Auditors: KPMG LLP TAMPA FL

LOCATIONS

HQ: W.S. BADCOCK CORPORATION
205 NW 2ND ST, MULBERRY, FL 338602405
Phone: 863 425-4921
Web: WWW.BADCOCK.COM

PRODUCTS/OPERATIONS

Selected Products

Accessories

Appliances

Electronics

Furniture

Mattresses

COMPETITORS

Aaron's Inc.	Ethan Allen
Ashley Furniture	Havertys
Baer's Furniture	Klaussner Furniture
Bassett Furniture	La-Z-Boy
City Furniture	Rooms To Go
El Dorado Furniture	Sealy

HISTORICAL FINANCIALS

Company Type: Private

Income Statement

FYE: June 30

	REVENUE ($ mil.)	NET INCOME ($ mil.)	NET PROFIT MARGIN	EMPLOYEES
06/18	802	33	4.2%	1,500
06/17	692	27	3.9%	—
06/16	681	25	3.8%	—
06/15	600	19	3.3%	—
Annual Growth	10.1%	19.5%	—	—

2018 Year-End Financials

Return on assets: 4.4%   Cash ($ mil.): 3
Return on equity: 10.0%
Current ratio: 4.70

WABASH VALLEY POWER ASSOCIATION INC

EXECUTIVES

Exec Dir-Ceo, Rick Coons
Cfo*, Jeffrey A Conrad
V Pres*, Katherine A Joyce
V Pres*, Curtis E Taylor
V Pres*, M Keith Thompson
Vice-President Business Develo, Greg Wagoner
Regional Economic, Diane Reinhart
Financial Analyst, Jeanette Surratt
Administrative Assistant, Stephanie Sohn
Controller, Theresay Young
Accounting, Denise Sewell
Auditors: DELOITTE & TOUCHE LLP INDIANA

LOCATIONS

HQ: WABASH VALLEY POWER ASSOCIATION INC
6702 INTECH BLVD, INDIANAPOLIS, IN 462782008
Phone: 317 481-2800
Web: WWW.WVPA.COM

HISTORICAL FINANCIALS

Company Type: Private

Income Statement

FYE: December 31

	REVENUE ($ mil.)	NET INCOME ($ mil.)	NET PROFIT MARGIN	EMPLOYEES
12/18	654	24	3.7%	65
12/17	702	19	2.7%	—
12/16	707	21	3.0%	—
12/15	740	18	2.4%	—
Annual Growth	(4.0%)	10.1%	—	—

2018 Year-End Financials

Return on assets: 2.0%   Cash ($ mil.): 84
Return on equity: 10.8%
Current ratio: 3.10

WAKE COUNTY PUBLIC SCHOOL SYSTEM

LOCATIONS

HQ: WAKE COUNTY PUBLIC SCHOOL SYSTEM
5625 DILLARD DR, CARY, NC 275189226
Phone: 919 431-7343
Web: WWW.WCPSS.NET

HISTORICAL FINANCIALS

Company Type: Private

Income Statement

FYE: June 30

	REVENUE ($ mil.)	NET INCOME ($ mil.)	NET PROFIT MARGIN	EMPLOYEES
06/10	1,224	13	1.1%	17,000
06/09	1,425	(7)	—	—
06/08	1,374	(1)	—	—
Annual Growth	(5.6%)	—	—	—

2010 Year-End Financials

Return on assets: 0.5%   Cash ($ mil.): 91
Return on equity: 0.5%
Current ratio: 1.40

WAKEFERN FOOD CORP.

Grocery stores getting supplies from this co-op may be on the "Rite" track. Wakefern Food is the largest member-owned wholesale distribution cooperative in the US supplying groceries and other merchandise to more than 250 supermarkets under the ShopRite and The Fresh Grocer banners in New Jersey New York Connecticut Delaware Maryland Pennsylvania and Virginia. It also operates more than 50 PriceRite stores in these states plus Rhode Island and Massachusetts. Beyond supplying its member-owned stores Wakerfern distributes products to other supermarkets across the northeastern US and Bermuda. Founded by seven grocers in 1946 the coop now boasts 50 members 70000-plus employees and over $15 billion in annual sales.

Operations

Wakefern Food supplies retail and wholesale members mostly in the Northeast US. PriceRite a subsidiary of Wakefern Food and its nearly 50 supermarkets offer over 500 grocery items at discounted prices such as fresh fruits and vegetables breads prepackaged meat and seafood kosher products and national brands. Stores average about 35000 square feet in size which are smaller than traditional supermarkets. While the vast majority of ShopRite brand stores are member owned subsidiary ShopRite Supermarkets Inc operates nearly 35 company-owned stores.

Sales and Marketing

The coop added its 50th member The Fresh Grocer in July 2013. Outside of its members the company also supplies grocery stores like Saker ShopRite (New Jersey) Village Super Market (New Jersey and Pennsylvania) and Inserra Supermarkets (New York and New Jersey).

Financial Performance

Wakern Food's revenues have been rising over the past several years thanks to new member additions and their store openings.

The company's retail sales rose 4% to a record $14.7 billion in fiscal 2014 (ended September 27) thanks to the addition of six new ShopRite stores five new PriceRite discount supermarkets and six new The Fresh Grocer stores over the course of the year. The company also continued to expand its ShopRite from Home services store reach which would be provided from a total of 214 of its stores.

Strategy

Like other grocery wholesalers Wakefern Food's success depends on its ability to distribute goods at the lowest possible cost to its customers meaning the company focuses on keeping expenses low and improving efficiencies throughout its supply operation. But as a member-owned cooperative the company differs from other wholesalers such as Nash-Finch in that its primary focus is on its member stores. Wakefern Food also has the added responsibility of promoting its ShopRite retail chain and helping its member retailers expand the chain's footprint.

The ShopRite chain boasts a loyal following in its core markets but the supermarkets have been feeling the pinch from rivals in the price-competitive grocery business. The company is especially feeling pressure from non-supermarket chains such as Wal-Mart CVS Health and Wawa. To help boost customer loyalty Wakefern has turned to new technology in the form of mobile applications (developed in partnership with technology firm MyWebGrocer) for the Apple iPhone that allow users to get alerts about weekly store specials in their area. The company also rolled out an online pharmacy where customers can place orders through the Internet.

Company Background

Wakefern Food announced in 2012 it was supplying New York-based Food Bazaar stores which had supermarkets in New York New Jersey and Connecticut. Wakefern will supply ShopRite private label brands along with non-private labels such as dairy frozen food grocery nonfoods and specialty products.

HISTORY

Wakefern Food was founded in 1946 by seven New York- and New Jersey-based grocers: Louis Weiss Sam and Al Aidekman Abe Kesselman Dave Fern Sam Garb and Albert Goldberg. The company got its name by taking the first letters of the last names of five of the original founders (Weiss Sam and Al Aidekman Kesselman and Fern). Like many cooperatives the association sought to lower costs by increasing its buying power as a group.

They each put in $1000 and began operating a 5000-sq.-ft. warehouse often putting in double time to keep both their stores and the warehouse running. The shopkeepers' collective buying power proved valuable enabling the grocers to stock many items at the same prices as their larger competitors.

In 1951 Wakefern members began pooling their resources to buy advertising space. A common store name — ShopRite — was chosen and each week co-op members met to decide which items would be sale priced. Within a year membership had grown to over 50. Expansion became a priority and in the mid-1950s co-op members united in small groups to take over failed supermarkets. One such group called the Supermarkets Operating Co. (SOC) was formed in 1956. Within 10 years it had acquired a number of failed stores remodeled them and given them the ShopRite name.

During the late 1950s sales at ShopRite stores slumped after Wakefern decided to buck the supermarket trend of offering trading stamps (which could then be exchanged for gifts) figuring that offering the stamps would ultimately lead to higher food prices. The move initially drove away customers but Wakefern cut grocery prices across the board and sales returned. The company did embrace another supermarket trend: stocking stores with nonfood items.

The co-op was severely shaken in 1966 when SOC merged with General Supermarkets a similar small group within Wakefern becoming Supermarkets General Corp. (SGC). SGC was a powerful entity with 71 supermarkets 10 drugstores six gas stations a wholesale bakery and a discount department store. Many Wakefern members opposed the merger and attempted to block the action with a court order. By 1968 SGC had beefed up its operations to include department store chains as well as its grocery stores. In a move that threatened to break Wakefern SGC broke away from the co-op and its stores were renamed Pathmark.

Wakefern not only weathered the storm it grew under the direction of chairman and CEO Thomas Infusino elected shortly after the split. The co-op focused on asserting its position as a seller of low-priced products. Wakefern developed private-label brands including the ShopRite brand. In the 1980s members began operating larger stores and adding more nonfood items to the ShopRite product mix. With its number of superstores on the rise and facing increased competition from club stores in 1992 Wakefern opened a centralized nonfood distribution center in New Jersey.

In 1995 30-year Wakefern veteran Dean Janeway was elected president of the co-op. The company debuted its ShopRite MasterCard co-branded with New Jersey's Valley National Bank in 1996. The following year the co-op purchased two of its customers' stores in Pennsylvania then threatened to close them when contract talks with the local union deteriorated. In 1998 Wakefern settled the dispute then sold the stores.

The company partnered with Internet bidding site Priceline in 1999 offering customers an opportunity to bid on groceries and then pick them up at ShopRite stores. Big V Wakefern's biggest customer filed for Chapter 11 bankruptcy protection in 2000 and said it was ending its distribution agreement with the co-op. In July 2002 however Wakefern's ShopRite Supermarkets subsidiary acquired all of Big V's assets for approximately $185 million in cash and assumed liabilities.

Infusino retired in May 2005 after 35 years with Wakefern Food. He was succeeded by former vice chairman Joseph Colalillo. The cooperative added to its footprint in 2007 when it acquired about 10 underperforming retail locations from Stop & Shop. The stores located mostly in South Jersey were rebranded under the ShopRite banner.

EXECUTIVES

Vice President Pharmacy, Jeffrey Mondelli
Vice President Quality Assurance Food Safety, Michael Ambrosio
Vice President Of Administration, Shawn Ravitz
Assistant Vice President Of Marketing, Maria Fiore
Vice President, Michael Rosenberg
Auditors: KPMG LLP SHORT HILLS NJ

LOCATIONS

HQ: WAKEFERN FOOD CORP.
  5000 RIVERSIDE DR, KEASBEY, NJ 088321209
Phone: 908 527-3300
Web: WWW.WAKEFERN.SHOPRITE.COM

PRODUCTS/OPERATIONS

2012 Corporate Stores

	No.
PriceRite	48
ShopRite	40
Total	**88**

COMPETITORS

A&P	IGA
Acme Markets	Krasdale Foods
Bozzuto's	SUPERVALU
C&S Wholesale	Stop & Shop
CVS	Wal-Mart
Hannaford Bros.	Wawa Inc.

HISTORICAL FINANCIALS

Company Type: Private

Income Statement | | | | FYE: September 27

	REVENUE ($ mil.)	NET INCOME ($ mil.)	NET PROFIT MARGIN	EMPLOYEES
09/14	11,871	5	0.0%	3,500
09/13	11,455	0	0.0%	—
09/12	11,010	5	0.0%	—
Annual Growth	**3.8%**	**(0.0%)**	**—**	**—**

2014 Year-End Financials

Return on assets: 0.3%   Cash ($ mil.): 128
Return on equity: 2.7%
Current ratio: 0.80

WALSH CONSTRUCTION COMPANY

EXECUTIVES

Chb-Ceo, Matthew M Walsh
Pres*, Daniel J Walsh
Dir Bus Dev, Patrick M Donley
V Pres, Hilda Rodriguez
Auditors: WOLF & COMPANY LLP OAKBROOK

LOCATIONS

HQ: WALSH CONSTRUCTION COMPANY
  929 W ADAMS ST, CHICAGO, IL 606073021
Phone: 312 563-5400
Web: WWW.WALSHGROUP.COM

HISTORICAL FINANCIALS

Company Type: Private

Income Statement | | | | FYE: December 31

	REVENUE ($ mil.)	NET INCOME ($ mil.)	NET PROFIT MARGIN	EMPLOYEES
12/10	1,627	35	2.2%	3,000
12/09	1,711	56	3.3%	—
12/08	1,847	68	3.7%	—
Annual Growth	**(6.2%)**	**(27.7%)**	**—**	**—**

2010 Year-End Financials

Return on assets: 4.7%   Cash ($ mil.): 281
Return on equity: 14.1%
Current ratio: 1.50

WALTON CONSTRUCTION - A CORE COMPANY, LLC

EXECUTIVES

Mng MBR, James K Jacobs
Director, Joshua Bentley
Executive Vice President, Brad Roberts
Senior Superintendent, Bob Sharp

LOCATIONS

HQ: WALTON CONSTRUCTION - A CORE COMPANY, LLC
  2 COMMERCE CT, NEW ORLEANS, LA 701233225
Phone: 504 733-2212
Web: WWW.WALTONCORE.COM

HISTORICAL FINANCIALS

Company Type: Private

Income Statement | | | | FYE: December 31

	REVENUE ($ mil.)	NET INCOME ($ mil.)	NET PROFIT MARGIN	EMPLOYEES
12/08	695	0	—	700
12/07	626	0	—	—
12/06	0	0	—	—
12/05	0	0	—	—
Annual Growth	**—**	**—**	**—**	**—**

2008 Year-End Financials

Return on assets: 15.8%   Cash ($ mil.): 4
Return on equity: —
Current ratio: 1.20

WALTON FAMILY FOUNDATION INC

EXECUTIVES

Exec Dir, Buddy Philpot
Officer, Jessica Young
Coordinator, Karis Butler
Operations Manager, Liz Heimbach
Director, Bob Smith
Computer Support Technician, Josh Senty
Senior Staff Accountant, Leah Myers
Senior Program Officer, Cathy N Lund
As Communications Director, Daphne Moore
Manager of Grants Administrati, Donna Osborn
Training Manager, Janet Post

LOCATIONS

HQ: WALTON FAMILY FOUNDATION INC
  125 W CENTRAL AVE RM 218, BENTONVILLE, AR 727125248
Phone: 479 273-5605
Web: WWW.WALTONFAMILYFOUNDATION.ORG

HISTORICAL FINANCIALS

Company Type: Private

Income Statement | | | | FYE: December 31

	REVENUE ($ mil.)	NET INCOME ($ mil.)	NET PROFIT MARGIN	EMPLOYEES
12/09	740	368	49.8%	7
12/08	421	244	58.0%	—
12/00	244	190	78.0%	—
Annual Growth	**13.1%**	**7.6%**	**—**	**—**

2009 Year-End Financials
Return on assets: 20.2%   Cash ($ mil.): 24
Return on equity: 20.2%
Current ratio: —

WARREN DISTRIBUTION, INC.

EXECUTIVES

Chb-Ceo, Robert N Schlott
Pres*, Charles P Downey
SEC*, Abraham N Schlott
Treas*, Donald H Nonnenkamp
Information Technology Manager, Geoff Beaune
Customer Representativ, Maggie Jelinek
Customer Manager, Mari Santa
Senior Cost Accountant, Terri Bricker
Auditors: BKD LLP OMAHA NEBRASKA

LOCATIONS

HQ: WARREN DISTRIBUTION, INC.
  950 S 10TH ST STE 300, OMAHA, NE 681083296
Phone: 402 341-9397
Web: WWW.WARRENDISTRIBUTION.COM

HISTORICAL FINANCIALS

Company Type: Private

Income Statement

	REVENUE ($ mil.)	NET INCOME ($ mil.)	NET PROFIT MARGIN	EMPLOYEES
02/14	450	8	1.9%	600
02/13	485	10	2.1%	—
02/12	470	5	1.1%	—
Annual Growth	(2.1%)	25.3%	—	—

FYE: February 22

2014 Year-End Financials

Return on assets: 4.3%   Cash ($ mil.): 1
Return on equity: 11.5%
Current ratio: 2.00

WASHINGTON HOSPITAL CENTER CORPORATION

Washington Hospital Center (doing business as MedStar Washington Hospital Center) may be the official hospital of the Washington Redskins but you don't have to be a professional football player to make use of the facility's services. The hospital at the heart of the MedStar Health system serves some 500000 patients living in and around the nation's capital each year. Washington Hospital Center has 912 beds and includes specialized care centers for cancer cardiovascular conditions and stroke. Other offerings include organ transplantation a regional burn treatment center and emergency air transportation. MedStar Washington also conducts clinical research and offers educational residency and fellowship programs.

Operations

MedStar Washington has about 1350 doctors and dentists on staff; many of whom are involved in Washington Hospital Center's 520 clinical re-search studies. The hospital is affiliated with the medical schools of The George Washington University Georgetown University Johns Hopkins and several other regional educational institutions. Its Cardiac Ventricular Assist Device program is accredited by The Joint Commission.

The hospital is also home to MedSTAR one of the country's top shock-trauma and medevac programs and also operates the region's only adult burn center.

MedStar Washington has some 390000 outpatient and 37000 inpatient visits each year. It also provides care for some 3500 births and some 87000 emergency department visits.

Company Background

Washington Hospital Center was created through the merger of three regional hospitals: Emergency Garfield and Episcopal Eye Ear and Throat. The actual idea of the Hospital Center was conceived in 1943 but it took nearly 15 years for funding planning and construction to be completed.

EXECUTIVES

Vp Professional Services, Cathie Monge
President, John Sullivan
Coo, Robert S. Ross
Cfo, William Gayne
Vice President Medical Staff Development, Anthony Watkins
Vice President Quality Safety Risk And R, Karen Jerome
Senior Vice President Administrative Services, James Hiltzer
Assistant Secretary And Assistant Treasu, Rafael Convit

LOCATIONS

HQ: WASHINGTON HOSPITAL CENTER CORPORATION
  110 IRVING ST NW, WASHINGTON, DC 200103017
Phone: 855 546-1686
Web: WWW.MEDSTARWASHINGTON.ORG

COMPETITORS

Adventist HealthCare	HSC Pediatric Center
Bon Secours Health	Inova
Children's National	Mary Washington
Medical Center	Healthcare
Dimensions Healthcare	Sibley Memorial
Doctors Community	Hospital
Hospital	Suburban Hospital

HISTORICAL FINANCIALS

Company Type: Private

Income Statement

	REVENUE ($ mil.)	NET INCOME ($ mil.)	NET PROFIT MARGIN	EMPLOYEES
06/16	1,166	36	3.1%	5,637
06/15	1,121	23	2.1%	—
06/14	1,107	22	2.1%	—
06/08	1,028	14	1.4%	—
Annual Growth	1.6%	12.3%	—	—

FYE: June 30

2016 Year-End Financials

Return on assets: 6.6%   Cash ($ mil.): —
Return on equity: 10.6%
Current ratio: 1.20

WASHINGTON SUBURBAN SANITARY COMMISSION (INC)

Used water in clean water out is the job description of the Washington Suburban Sanitary Commission (WSSC). The utility provides water and wastewater services in Maryland's Montgomery and Prince George's counties just outside the nation's capital. WSSC serves 460000 customers representing 1.8 million residents in an area of about 1000 square miles. The agency draws water from the Potomac and Patuxtent rivers and maintains three reservoirs. The commission also operates two water filtration plants six wastewater treatment plants and some 11000 miles of sewer and water main lines including a network of nearly 5600 miles of fresh water pipeline and over 5400 miles of sewer pipeline.

Operations

WSSC's three reservoirs (Triadelphia Rocky Gorge and Little Seneca) along with Jennings Randolph Reservoir which it shares with Fairfax Water and the Washington Aqueduct have a total holding capacity of 27 billion gallons. Its two water filtration plants (Patuxent and Potomac) produce nearly 170 million gallons of drinking water daily. The commission handles some 72 million gallons of wastewater daily through its six treatment plants (Damascus Hyattstown Parkway Piscataway Seneca and Western Branch).

Financial Performance

The company reported operating revenue of about $698 million in fiscal 2014 (ended June) up about 2% from the prior year. The growth was powered by an increase in water and sewer billing rates.

WSSC's proposed budgets for 2014 and 2015 were $1.5 billion and $1.3 billion respectively.

Company Background

WSSC was established in 1918.

EXECUTIVES

Chief Engineer, Gary Gumm
General Manager, Jerry N. Johnson
Cfo, Yvette Downs
Cio, Mujib Lodhi
Vpn Technician, Chandra Vavilala
Chairman, Omar M. Boulware
Vice Chairman, Adrienne A. Mandel
Auditors: BCA WATSON RICE LLP WASHINGTO

LOCATIONS

HQ: WASHINGTON SUBURBAN SANITARY COMMISSION (INC)
  14501 SWEITZER LN, LAUREL, MD 207075901
Phone: 301 206-8000
Web: WWW.WSSCWATER.COM

HISTORICAL FINANCIALS

Company Type: Private

Income Statement

	REVENUE ($ mil.)	NET INCOME ($ mil.)	NET PROFIT MARGIN	EMPLOYEES
06/18	725	119	16.5%	2,000
06/17	725	179	24.7%	—
06/16	649	214	33.0%	—
06/15	645	192	29.9%	—
Annual Growth	4.0%	(14.7%)	—	—

FYE: June 30

Return on assets: 1.4%   Cash ($ mil.): 120
Return on equity: 2.5%
Current ratio: 0.80

WASHINGTON TOWNSHIP HEALTHCARE DISTRICT

EXECUTIVES

Ceo, Nancy Farber
Treas*, Cathy Messman
Orthopedist, James M Hartford
Director, Bruce Nixon
Purchasing Director, Paulo Cruz
Engineer, Greg Worth
Information Specialist, David Garcia
Manager, Raju Thiara
Accounting Director, Dave Tapia
Vice-President Human Resources, Barbara McCullough
Radiologist, Bruce Lin
Auditors: PRICEWATERHOUSECOOPERS LLP SA

LOCATIONS

HQ: WASHINGTON TOWNSHIP HEALTHCARE DISTRICT
2000 MOWRY AVE, FREMONT, CA 945381716
Phone: 510 797-3342
Web: WWW.WHHS.COM

HISTORICAL FINANCIALS

Company Type: Private

Income Statement				FYE: June 30
	REVENUE ($ mil.)	NET INCOME ($ mil.)	NET PROFIT MARGIN	EMPLOYEES
06/18	526	27	5.3%	1,600
06/17	507	18	3.6%	—
Annual Growth	3.8%	50.6%	—	—

2018 Year-End Financials

Return on assets: 2.3%   Cash ($ mil.): 34
Return on equity: 7.9%
Current ratio: 1.40

WASHOE COUNTY SCHOOL DISTRICT

EXECUTIVES

Spdt, Traci Davis
Payroll Staff, Barbara Hawkins
Coordinator, Diana Cox
Coordinator, Josephine J Johnson
Coordinator, Lynette Larson
Coordinator, Marianne Campbell
Coordinator, Mary Green
Information Specialist, Kelli Pennington
Staff, Mariah Evans
Coordinator, Trudy Nunn

School Nurse, Erin Dehahn

LOCATIONS

HQ: WASHOE COUNTY SCHOOL DISTRICT
425 E 9TH ST, RENO, NV 895122800
Phone: 775 348-0200
Web: WWW.WASHOESCHOOLS.NET

HISTORICAL FINANCIALS

Company Type: Private

Income Statement				FYE: June 30
	REVENUE ($ mil.)	NET INCOME ($ mil.)	NET PROFIT MARGIN	EMPLOYEES
06/18	683	190	27.8%	7,000
06/17	640	57	8.9%	—
06/08	578	38	6.7%	—
06/06	479	67	14.1%	—
Annual Growth	3.0%	9.0%	—	—

WAUKESHA MEMORIAL HOSPITAL, INC.

Waukesha Memorial Hospital is a 300-bed teaching hospital that provides health care services for Wisconsin's Milwaukee Waukesha and DaneÂ counties. With aboutÂ 670 physicians representing several specialties and 2700 employees the hospitalÂ operates centers for excellence focused on cardiology oncology neurology women's health and orthopedics as well as emergency neonatal and family practice services.Â Additionally Waukesha Memorial HospitalÂ conducts a physician residency program.Â Established in 1914Â theÂ medical facilityÂ is a subsidiary of not-for-profit ProHealth Care aÂ medical networkÂ that servesÂ southeastern Wisconsin with acute care and specialty health services.

Operations

ProHealth Care runs Waukesha Memorial Hospital alongside its other critical-care hospital Oconomowoc Memorial Hospital. As part of its operations the hospitalÂ boasts aÂ neuroscience center orthopedic center regional cancer center regional heartÂ and vascular center and a women's center. Its newborn intensive care unitÂ and its emergency department which averages more than 39000 visitsÂ are bothÂ Level III.

Geographic Reach

Despite its name Waukesha Memorial Hospital serves the residents of Milwaukee and Dane counties along with Waukesha County.

EXECUTIVES

Vpma, James Gardner
Vice President Of Revenue Cycle, Curtis Glaunert
Rph, Christine Koehler
Auditors: PLANTE & MORAN PLLC GRAND RA

LOCATIONS

HQ: WAUKESHA MEMORIAL HOSPITAL, INC.
725 AMERICAN AVE, WAUKESHA, WI 531885099
Phone: 262 928-1000
Web: WWW.PROHEALTHCARE.ORG

PRODUCTS/OPERATIONS

Selected Services

Birthing
    Blood / Ly
Bones Joints & Muscles
Brain & Nerves
Cancer
Cancer Second Opinion
Children's Health
CyberKnife
Diabetes
Diagnostic Services
Digestive
Ear Nose & Throat
Emergency Services/Urgent Care
Eyes & Vision
General Surgery
Genetics
Heart & Vascular
Infections
Integrative Medicine
Kidneys & Urinary System
    Lungs / Br
Men's Health
Mental Health
Nutrition
Orthopedic
Pain
Rehabilitation Services
Senior's Health
Sleep
Stroke
Wellness & Lifestyle
Women's Health

COMPETITORS

Children's Hospital and Health System
    Columbia St. Mary's
    Froedtert Hospital
    Hospital Sisters Health System
    Ministry Health Care
    SwedishAmerican Health System
    University of Wisconsin Hospital and Clinics

HISTORICAL FINANCIALS

Company Type: Private

Income Statement				FYE: September 30
	REVENUE ($ mil.)	NET INCOME ($ mil.)	NET PROFIT MARGIN	EMPLOYEES
09/18	520	27	5.3%	2,071
09/17	470	59	12.6%	—
09/16	457	37	8.3%	—
09/15	460	29	6.3%	—
Annual Growth	4.2%	(2.0%)	—	—

2018 Year-End Financials

Return on assets: 5.3%   Cash ($ mil.): 4
Return on equity: 18.1%
Current ratio: 1.50

WAYNE STATE UNIVERSITY

Wayne State University is a public university with an annual enrollment of more than 27000 students and a student-to-teacher ratio of 16:1. It offers more than 350 bachelor's master's and doctoral degree programs as well as certificate specialist and professional programs through about a dozen colleges and schools. Located in midtown Detroit WSU traces its heritage back to 1868 with the founding of the Detroit Medical College now part of its School of Medicine. Prominent alumni include US Congressman John Conyers radio DJ Casey Kasem and actor Tom Sizemore.

Geographic Reach

WSU's 200-acre campus includes about 100 academic research and residential buildings. The university also has six satellite campuses around Detroit and five extension centers offering educational programs across southeastern Michigan.

It has affiliations with more than 100 institutions globally and offers study abroad programs in 20 countries.

The school hosts students from every US state and 70 countries.

Financial Performance

Operating revenue grew from $863 million in 2015 to $876 million in 2016 thanks to higher net student tuition and fees (31% of overall revenue) and higher non-operating revenue (including $39 million in capital gifts for the construction of a new business school).

Expenses dropped from $857 million in 2015 to $846 million in 2016 primarily due a reduction in academic staffing headcount.

Strategy

WSU is a partner in the University Research Corridor with the University of Michigan and Michigan State University. This program generates 95% of research in the state of Michigan.

It is also engaged in new construction. It is building a $50 million business school (the Mike Ilitch School of Business due to open in 2018) and WSU also plans to expand and improve its student housing facilities.

EXECUTIVES

Cio And Associate Vp Computing And Information Technology, Joseph F. Sawasky
President, M. Roy Wilson
Svp Academic Affairs And Provost, Margaret E. Winters
Cfo, Rick Nork
Vice President Research, Hilary Ratner
Associate Department Chair, Kendra L Schwartz
Assistant Vice President For Research Compliance, Phil Cunningham
Math Department Chair, Hengguang Li
Department Chair, Eva Powers
Assistant Vice President, Mark Byrd
Vice President Human Resources And Information Technology, Adrienne Mitchell
Vice President For Economic Development, Ned Staebler
Vice President, Romain Ducasse
Chair, Gary S. Pollard
Vice Chair, Paul E. Massaron
Secretary Iii, Lenora Paul
Board Of Governors Member, Lois Avery
Medical Secretary, Myra Meredith
Secretary, Gwendolyn Cotton
Auditors: PLANTE & MORAN PLLC CLINTON

LOCATIONS

HQ: WAYNE STATE UNIVERSITY
656 W KIRBY ST, DETROIT, MI 482023622
Phone: 313 577-2230
Web: WWW.WAYNE.EDU

PRODUCTS/OPERATIONS

Selected Colleges and Schools
College of Education
College of Engineering
College of Fine Performing and Communication Arts
College of Liberal Arts and Sciences
College of Nursing
Eugene Applebaum College of Pharmacy and Health Sciences
Irvin D. Reid Honors College
Law School
School of Business Administration
School of Library and Information Science
School of Medicine
School of Social Work
The Graduate School

HISTORICAL FINANCIALS
Company Type: Private

Income Statement　　　　　　　　　　FYE: September 30

	REVENUE ($ mil.)	NET INCOME ($ mil.)	NET PROFIT MARGIN	EMPLOYEES
09/17	640	46	7.2%	8,500
09/11	520	(15)	—	—
09/05	445	37	8.4%	—
09/04	418	(3)	—	—
Annual Growth	3.3%	—	—	—

2017 Year-End Financials

Return on assets: 3.2%　　　　Cash ($ mil.): 355
Return on equity: 7.0%
Current ratio: 1.90

WEEKS MARINE, INC.

Weeks Marine doesn't drag its feet when it comes to dredging. The company is one of the largest providers of dredging services in the Gulf of Mexico where a majority of all US dredging occurs. (Dredging involves the moving of sand and sediment to maintain and often deepen navigation channels at shipping ports.) One of Weeks Marine's main clients is the US Army Corps of Engineers for whom it has done dredging work on many projects. The family-owned company also performs construction and demolition of bridges piers jetties pipelines and offshore platforms throughout North and South America. It is also one of the largest stevedoring (cargo handling) companies on the US's East Coast.

Operations

Weeks Marine is a top-100 marine and tunneling contractor. As part of its business the firm owns and operates a diversified fleet of dredging and support equipment capable of performing complex and demanding dredging projects.

Additional activities include heavy lifting and salvage shoreline restoration and tugboat and towing services as well as the charter and rental of floating equipment such as barges cranes and tugboats. Subsidiary Healy Tibbitts Builders operates in Hawaii.

Weeks Marine has served the Canadian market since 2001 when it acquired Ontario-based heavy civil marine contractor and tunneling company McNally Construction which retained its identity. The company also bought Pennsylvania-based American Atlantic Company which was merged into its existing marine construction operations.

Weeks Marine serves its clients through five operating Divisions namely Construction Dredging Marine Services Healy Tibbitts Builders and McNally.

The Construction Division engineers and constructs marine facilities and structures. It does self-perform the construction of large complex coastal and near shore marine projects.

The Dredging division of Weeks Marine is a highly specialized marine contractor that owns operates and maintains a diverse and extensive fleet of dredging and support equipment.

The Marine Services division provides one-stop waterborne services.

Subsidiary McNally International is a heavy-construction company that specializes in tunnel and marine construction.

Healy Tibbitts Builders specializes in marine construction pile driving and deep-shoring systems. Healy's areas of expertise include the con-

struction of piers and wharves submarine pipelines and cables offshore structures dredging pile driving marine heavy lifts bulk stevedoring and marine transportation.

Geographic Reach

New Jersey-based Weeks Marine has regional offices in Louisiana Texas Virginia Hawaii and in Ontario and Quebec Canada. The seagoing firm has completed projects throughout North and South America the Caribbean and the Pacific Rim.

Sales and Marketing

Projects typically include marine structures oil and gas terminals piers and wharfs and pipelines and outfalls.

The company serves a range of markets including Marine Infrastructure Energy Transportation Environmental Chartering Heavy Lift and Salvage Stevedoring and Towing.

Strategy

The firm's projects have included Mobile Harbor HSC Mid Bay FDR Drive Rehabilitation and NWS Earle.

Company Background

Weeks Marine was founded in 1919 as the Weeks Stevedoring Company.

EXECUTIVES

President, Richard S. Weeks
Senior Vice President Dredging Division Manager, Stephen Chatry
Vice President, Eric Ellefsen

LOCATIONS

HQ: WEEKS MARINE, INC.
4 COMMERCE DR FL 2, CRANFORD, NJ 070163520
Phone: 908 272-4010
Web: WWW.WEEKSMARINE.COM

Selected Offices & Marine Yards
Aiea HI
Bourg LA
Camden NJ
Covington LA
Cranford NJ
Houma LA
Houston TX
Jersey City NJ
Portsmouth VA

PRODUCTS/OPERATIONS

Project Categories
Flood control
Harbor improvement
Navigation
Shore protection
Specialty
Reclamation

Selected Operations
Construction
Dredging
Equipment charter and rental
Heavy lift and salvage
Marine transportation
Stevedoring

COMPETITORS

Cianbro	Orion Group Holdings
Great Lakes Dredge & Dock	SSA Marine
Kajima USA	Willbros
Oceaneering International	

HISTORICAL FINANCIALS

Company Type: Private

Income Statement				FYE: December 31
	REVENUE ($ mil.)	NET INCOME ($ mil.)	NET PROFIT MARGIN	EMPLOYEES
12/10	536	100	18.7%	1,500
12/08	439	61	14.0%	—
12/07	472	53	11.3%	—
Annual Growth	4.3%	23.7%	—	—

2010 Year-End Financials

Return on assets: 25.8% Cash ($ mil.): 27
Return on equity: 33.7%
Current ratio: 4.50

WELCH FOODS INC., A COOPERATIVE

Welch Foods has a taste for the grape. An operating subsidiary of the National Grape Cooperative (owned by some 900 farmers) Welch produces the Welch's brand grape and white grape juices and jellies. Its beverage line includes refrigerated and sparkling juices and cocktails frozen and shelf-stable concentrates and single-serve drinks. Welch supplies fresh grapes and snacks as well as preserved offerings (jellies jams and spreads). The co-op licenses the Welch's name to other manufactures of frozen fruit confections dried fruit and carbonated beverages among many. Its products are purchased by grocery retailers and food service operators in the US and some 50 other countries.

Geographic Reach

Massachusetts-based Welch Foods has vineyards in four regions across the US where the climate is optimal: the Finger Lakes Region of New York; the shore of Lake Erie in New York Pennsylvania and Ohio; the shore of Lake Michigan in southwestern Michigan; and the Yakima Valley in Washington State.

It sells its products in the US and some 50 other countries.

Strategy

As grape juice consumption in the US falls Welch Foods is focused on expanding its product line. In 2019 it partnered with Cornell University and the New York Wine & Grape Foundation to develop technology to neutralize the smell and taste of Concord grape juice; the neutralized juice could then be used as a base wine or blender. It had already introduced a Niagara grape juice product to serve that purpose the prior year. Also in 2018 the company launched limited-release energy drinks made with Welch's juice and began offering frozen avocado chunks.

Welch Foods is also targeting more men in its advertising as studies show Generation X men are more loyal to juice than the average buyer. The company's advertising strategy in 2018 included spots during NFL games and on the Howard Stern radio show.

Company Background

In 1869 Dr. Thomas Bramwell Welch pasteurized Concord grape juice to create a non-alcoholic alternative to wine for his church. The beverage was a hit at the World's Fair in Chicago in 1893 and by 1923 Concord grape jelly was introduced.

The farmers who grew grapes for Welch's took ownership of the company and began operating it as a co-op in 1952.

EXECUTIVES

President And Ceo, Bradley C. Irwin, age 60
Vice President Information Technology, Phyllis Gutz
Chairman Of The Board, Joseph C. Falcone

LOCATIONS

HQ: WELCH FOODS INC., A COOPERATIVE
300 BAKER AVE STE 101, CONCORD, MA 017422131
Phone: 978 371-1000
Web: WWW.WELCHS.COM

PRODUCTS/OPERATIONS

Selected Brands and Products

BAMA
  Jams jellies and preserves
  Peanut butter
Welch
  Bottled and canned juices
  Dried fruit
  Fresh table grapes
  Frozen juices
  Fruit juice bars
  Jams jellies and preserves
  Pourable concentrated juices
  Refrigerated juices
  Single-serve juices

COMPETITORS

Chiquita Brands	Old Orchard
Citrus World	Silver Springs
Coca-Cola	Smucker
Coloma Frozen Foods	Snapple
Dole Food	South Beach Beverage
Fresh Del Monte Produce	Stapleton-Spence Packing
Great Western Juice	Sun-Maid
Lion Raisins	Sunny Delight
Monster Beverage	Sunview Vineyards
Mott's	Tree Top
Naked Juice	Tropicana
National Raisin	Unilever NV
Ocean Spray	Wet Planet Beverages
Odwalla	

HISTORICAL FINANCIALS

Company Type: Private

Income Statement				FYE: August 31
	REVENUE ($ mil.)	NET INCOME ($ mil.)	NET PROFIT MARGIN	EMPLOYEES
08/16	600	83	14.0%	1,000
08/15	609	81	13.3%	—
08/14	609	76	12.6%	—
08/13	608	65	10.7%	—
Annual Growth	(0.5%)	8.8%	—	—

2016 Year-End Financials

Return on assets: 20.6% Cash ($ mil.): 7
Return on equity: 233.2%
Current ratio: 1.40

WELLMONT HEALTH SYSTEM

At Wellmont Health System wellness is paramount. Wellmont Health System provides general and advanced medical-surgical care to residents of northeastern Tennessee and southwestern Virginia. The health system consists of about a dozen owned and affiliated hospitals that collectively have more than 1000 licensed beds. One of its facilities is a rehabilitation hospital operated in partnership with HealthSouth. The system's Holston Valley Medical Center features a level I trauma center and a level III neonatal intensive care unit (NICU). Wellmont also operates numerous ancillary facilities including an assisted living center a mental health clinic home health care and hospice agencies and outpatient centers.

Operations

Today Wellmont is one of the region's largest employers with a staff of more than 6500 medical professionals. Nearly 600 physicians deliver care at Wellmont's facilities that include eight hospitals in Tennessee and Virginia. Other facilities include an outpatient surgery center a child development center a cancer center urgent care centers and a health network of physicians that include occupational health providers. The hospital also offers urgent care transportation with its Wellmont One Air Transport.

Wellmont is the only health system in Tennessee to offer two major trauma centers (at Holston Valley Medical Center in Kingsport and Bristol Regional Medical Center in Bristol).

Sales and Marketing

Medicare payments accounted for nearly 85% of Wellmont's net patient revenue in fiscal 2013 (ended June); Medicaid and TennCare (Tennessee's state Medicaid program) each accounted for nearly 10%.

Financial Performance

Revenue increased 1% to $798 million in fiscal 2013 (ended June) on higher net patient revenue. However patient volumes were mixed: Some categories declined while others increased. For example emergency department visits dropped 7% as more patients chose to visit the system's more affordable urgent care centers.

Net income rose significantly that year increasing 79% to $47 million. This was due to a change in net unrealized gains on investments and a change in the funded status of benefit plans. Cash flow from operations fell 5% to $74 million.

Strategy

Wellmont has expanded by opening new outpatient facilities including a new physical therapy clinic in 2013 and by acquiring existing medical facilities. For example in 2015 it agreed to buy out Adventist Health in their partnership owning Takoma Regional Hospital in Tennessee. The system also expands its service territory by partnering with other area care providers.

In 2014 the company migrated to a new electronic medical records (EMR) system replacing its four existing EHR platforms.

Mergers and Acquisitions

In 2015 Wellmont announced plans to merge with a neighboring health system Mountain States Health Alliance. By combining operations the two systems hope to better provide care for communities in northeast Tennessee as well as Virginia Kentucky and North Carolina. The states of Tennessee and Virginia have to approve the transaction.

Company Background

Founded in 1996 Wellmont has grown over the years primarily through acquisitions including Lee Regional Medical Center Mountain View Regional Medical Center and Takoma Regional Hospital (through a partnership with Adventist Health).

EXECUTIVES

President And Ceo Wellmont Medical Associates, David L. Brash
President And Ceo, Bart Hove
President Bristol Regional Medical Center, Greg Neal
Svp Legal Affairs, Gary Miller

Svp System Advancement And President Wellmont Foundation, Todd Norris
Chief Executive Medical Officer Wellmont Medical Associates, Stephen Combs
President Holston Valley Medical Center, Tim Attebery
Evp And Coo, Eric Deaton
President Of Hawkins County Memorial Hospital And Hancock County Hospital, Rebecca Beck
President Mountain View Regional Medical Center And Lonesome Pine Hospital, Dale Clark
Interim Cio, Martha O. Chill
Vice President Director Of Project Management Office, Kim Whiteaker
Chairman, Roger Leonard
Vice Chairman, Julie Bennett

LOCATIONS

HQ: WELLMONT HEALTH SYSTEM
1905 AMERICAN WAY, KINGSPORT, TN 376605882
Phone: 423 230-8200
Web: WWW.BALLADHEALTH.ORG

PRODUCTS/OPERATIONS

Selected Facilities

Bristol Regional Medical Center (Bristol Tennessee)
Hancock County Hospital (Sneedville Tennessee)
Hawkins County Memorial Hospital (Rogersville Tennessee)
HealthSouth Rehabilitation Hospital of Kingsport (HealthSouth partnership; Kingsport Tennessee)
Holston Valley Medical Center (Kingsport Tennessee)
Lee Regional Medical Center (Pennington Gap Virginia)
Lonesome Pine Hospital (Big Stone Gap Virginia)
Mountain View Regional Medical Center (Norton Virginia)
Takoma Regional Hospital (Greeneville Tennessee)

Selected Services

Cancer Care
Children
Diabetes
Emergency and Trauma
Family Medicine
Hearing Services
Heart Care
Home Care
Hospice
Hospitalists
Marsh Regional Blood Center
Neurology
Occupational Medicine
Orthopedics
Palliative Care
Psychiatry
Radiology
Rehabilitation and Therapy
Sleep Medicine
Stroke Care
Surgical Services
Weight Loss
Women's Health

COMPETITORS

Ascension Health
Baptist Memorial Health Care
Community Health Systems
Cookeville Regional Medical Center
Kindred Healthcare
LifePoint Health
Mountain States Health
Tenet Healthcare

HISTORICAL FINANCIALS

Company Type: Private

Income Statement				FYE: June 30
	REVENUE ($ mil.)	NET INCOME ($ mil.)	NET PROFIT MARGIN	EMPLOYEES
06/17	908	53	5.9%	6,114
06/10	622	33	5.5%	—
06/09	2	0	—	—
Annual Growth	104.4%	—	—	—

WELLS REAL ESTATE INVESTMENT TRUST II

Auditors: DELOITTE & TOUCHE LLP ATLANT

LOCATIONS

HQ: WELLS REAL ESTATE INVESTMENT TRUST II
1 GLENLAKE PKWY STE 1200, ATLANTA, GA 303287267
Phone: 404 465-2200
Web: WWW.WELLSREITII.COM

HISTORICAL FINANCIALS

Company Type: Private

Income Statement				FYE: December 31
	REVENUE ($ mil.)	NET INCOME ($ mil.)	NET PROFIT MARGIN	EMPLOYEES
12/12	576	48	8.3%	9
12/11	613	56	9.2%	—
Annual Growth	(5.9%)	(15.2%)	—	—

2012 Year-End Financials

Return on assets: —
Return on equity: 8.3%
Current ratio: 0.10
Cash ($ mil.): —

WESLEY MEDICAL CENTER, LLC

EXECUTIVES

Ceo, Hugh Tappan
Prin*, Carl Fitch
Chief Operating Officer*, Bill Voloch
Cfo*, Matt Leary
Office Manager, Dale Graham
Coordinator, Diana Lippoldt
Training and Direc, Sharon Bowles
Director, David Miller
Human Resources Director, Nikki Freeman
Director of Pharmacy, Jack Bond
Coordinator, Stacey Wright

LOCATIONS

HQ: WESLEY MEDICAL CENTER, LLC
550 N HILLSIDE ST, WICHITA, KS 672144976
Phone: 316 962-2000
Web: WWW.WESLEYMC.COM

2017 Year-End Financials

Return on assets: 4.5%
Return on equity: 8.8%
Current ratio: 1.60
Cash ($ mil.): 60

HISTORICAL FINANCIALS

Company Type: Private

Income Statement				FYE: December 31
	REVENUE ($ mil.)	NET INCOME ($ mil.)	NET PROFIT MARGIN	EMPLOYEES
12/17	608	80	13.3%	40
12/16	555	56	10.3%	—
12/15	545	60	11.1%	—
12/14	520	88	17.0%	—
Annual Growth	5.3%	(3.0%)	—	—

WEST CONTRA COSTA UNIFIED SCHOOL DISTRICT

EXECUTIVES

Pres, Charles T Ramsey
Ceo*, Raul Ramirez
Supt*, Matthew Duffy
Assistant Superintendent, Alan Del Simone
Occupational Specia, Kasey Dutra
Occupational Specia, Kendall Becker
Teacher, Edward Dunn
Accounting Staff, Megan Falk
Information Specialist, Coleen Denny
Occupational Specia, Trisha Cuskaden
Education Specialist, Ayisha Benham
Auditors: CROWE HORWATH LLP SACRAMENTO

LOCATIONS

HQ: WEST CONTRA COSTA UNIFIED SCHOOL DISTRICT
1108 BISSELL AVE, RICHMOND, CA 948013135
Phone: 510 231-1100
Web: WWW.WCCUSD.NET

HISTORICAL FINANCIALS

Company Type: Private

Income Statement				FYE: June 30
	REVENUE ($ mil.)	NET INCOME ($ mil.)	NET PROFIT MARGIN	EMPLOYEES
06/18	481	97	20.2%	3,800
06/17	451	(55)	—	—
06/16	457	83	18.2%	—
06/02	291	46	15.9%	—
Annual Growth	3.2%	4.7%	—	—

WEST PENN POWER COMPANY

LOCATIONS

HQ: WEST PENN POWER COMPANY
76 S MAIN ST BSMT, AKRON, OH 443081817
Phone: 800 686-0021
Web: WWW.FIRSTENERGYCORP.COM

HISTORICAL FINANCIALS
Company Type: Private

Income Statement				FYE: December 31
	REVENUE ($ mil.)	NET INCOME ($ mil.)	NET PROFIT MARGIN	EMPLOYEES
12/17	1,009	110	11.0%	11
12/16	1,020	116	11.4%	—
Annual Growth	(1.1%)	(5.0%)	—	—

WEST VIRGINIA UNITED HEALTH SYSTEM, INC.

West Virginia United Health System (WVUHS) helps residents in the Mountain State stay on top of their health.Â The systemÂ operates United Hospital Center (in Clarksburg) as well asÂ hospitals inÂ the West Virginia University Hospitals (WVUH) system including City Hospital (Martinsburg) Jefferson Memorial Hospital (Ranson) and WVUH's home hospital in Morgantown.Â In addition WVUHS operates WVUH's Cheat Lake physicians ambulatory center as well as a network of about a dozen primary care clinics located throughout central and northern West Virginia. Combined the system's hospitals and clinics have more than 1000 beds and treat approximately 1.4 million patients annually.

EXECUTIVES

Associate Vice President Investments, Jennifer Cunanan
Auditors: BAKER TILLY VIRCHOW KRAUSE LL

LOCATIONS

HQ: WEST VIRGINIA UNITED HEALTH SYSTEM, INC.
1 MEDICAL CENTER DR, MORGANTOWN, WV 265061200
Phone: 304 598-4000
Web: WWW.WVUMEDICINE.ORG

PRODUCTS/OPERATIONS

Selected facilities
Barbour Country Family Medicine
Bridgeport Physicians Care
Chestnut Ridge Center
City Hospital
Doddridge Family Medicine
Elk Memorial Clinic
Harrisville Medical Center
Jefferson Memorial Hospital
Lumberport Family Medicine
Oakland Family Medicine Center
Pennsboro Medical Center
Pinewood Medical Center
Shinnston Healthcare Clinic
United Hospital Center
United Summit Center
WVU Hospitals

COMPETITORS

CAMC Health
HCA
West Penn Allegheny Health System

HISTORICAL FINANCIALS
Company Type: Private

Income Statement				FYE: December 31
	REVENUE ($ mil.)	NET INCOME ($ mil.)	NET PROFIT MARGIN	EMPLOYEES
12/17	2,172	132	6.1%	7,000
12/16	1,877	103	5.5%	—
12/15	1,651	23	1.5%	—
12/14	9	(0)	—	—
Annual Growth	507.8%	—	—	—

2017 Year-End Financials
Return on assets: 4.7%
Return on equity: 9.9%
Current ratio: 1.80
Cash ($ mil.): 121

WEST VIRGINIA UNIVERSITY

West Virginia University (WVU) is the intellectual home of more than 29000 Mountaineers (the school's mascot) and the state's preeminent institution of higher learning. WVU offers more than 180 bachelor's master's doctoral and professional degree programs through some 15 colleges and schools. The university's clinical psychology and forestry programs have been recognized nationally and it boasts 100% post-graduate job placement for its nursing pharmacy and mining engineering majors. WVU also runs a two-year residential school Potomac State College in Keyser West Virginia.

Operations
Its 1099 acres campus university offers a joint petroleum and natural gas engineering major. It also operates eight experimental farms and four forests throughout the state in addition to WVU Jackson's Mill State 4-H Camp and Lifelong Learning Center near Weston. Some 93% of its full-time faculty have earned doctorates or first-professional degrees in their disciplines. More than 800 students traveled to another country for study abroad courses in the 2011-12 academic year. Undergraduate tuition and fees for the 2012-13 year was reported as $9808.

WVU is an independent operating unit of the West Virginia Higher Education Fund.

Geographic Reach
The university's main campus is in Morgantown. It also has divisional campuses in Charleston Keyser Martinsburg and Montgomery.

Financial Performance
The university reported a 4% increase in revenues in 2012 due to a growth in capital grants and gifts revenue tuition and fees as well as revenues from auxiliary enterprise gifts and other sources. Capital grants and gifts increased by $55.9 million thanks to a donation of a master license agreement from Siemens PLM for educational software. Tuition and fees increased by $19.9 million in 2012 thanks to a fee rate hike and an increase in non-resident student enrollment. Auxiliary revenues grew by $12.2 million due to an increase in revenues from room and dining services auxiliary fees and athletics revenues. Organic growth has lifted the company's revenues since 2009.

Net income increased by 51% in 2012 due to a growth in other net non-operating revenues of $3.2 million as a result of a settlement agreement

---

in the amount of $7.2 million partially offset by operating revenues.

Strategy
In addition to WVU's campus-based activities the university is focusing on expanding its online and distance learning options to increase educational access and research activities.

Company Background
WVU was founded in 1867 as a public land-grant institution. It one of only 11 schools in the US that are land-grant doctoral research universities with a comprehensive medical school.

EXECUTIVES

Vp, David Fryson
Assistant Vice President Retention Program, Candace Tackett
Vice President, Ghazala Khokar
Secretary, Lisa Berry
Vice Chairman, Nancy Bremar
Auditors: CLIFTONLARSONALLEN LLP PLYMOU

LOCATIONS

HQ: WEST VIRGINIA UNIVERSITY
103 STEWART HL, MORGANTOWN, WV 26506
Phone: 304 293-2545

PRODUCTS/OPERATIONS

Selected Colleges and Schools
Benjamin M. Statler College of Engineering and Mineral Resources
College of Business and Economics
College of Creative Arts
College of Education and Human Services
College of Law
College of Physical Activity and Sport Sciences
Davis College of Agriculture Natural Resources and Design
Eberly College of Arts and Sciences
Perley Isaac Reed School of Journalism
Potomac State College of WVU
School of Dentistry
School of Medicine
School of Nursing
School of Pharmacy
School of Public Health
WVU Institute of Technology

HISTORICAL FINANCIALS
Company Type: Private

Income Statement				FYE: June 30
	REVENUE ($ mil.)	NET INCOME ($ mil.)	NET PROFIT MARGIN	EMPLOYEES
06/18	808	41	5.1%	6,245
06/17	783	8	1.1%	—
Annual Growth	3.2%	390.3%	—	—

2018 Year-End Financials
Return on assets: 1.8%
Return on equity: 3.9%
Current ratio: 1.40
Cash ($ mil.): 85

WESTAT, INC.

Survey the market research business and you'll find Westat among the leaders of the pack. A statistical survey organization the company provides research and consulting services including study design and analysis data collection program evaluation and communications campaign development. It has technical expertise in survey and analytical methods computer systems technology biomedical science and clinical trials. Westat serves US state and local government clients in addition to businesses and foundations. It has offices in five US states as well as international locations around the world. The company was founded in 1963 and is employee-owned.

Geographic Reach

Westat has nine regional offices in the US along with offices in five countries overseas.

Strategy

In 2014 Westat and the Pew Research Center partnered with SurveyMonkey to explore methods and tools that can be used with new technologies to provide useful data in an era when contacting survey respondents and gaining cooperation is more difficult that ever.

Mergers and Acquisitions

In 2015 the company acquired Edvance Reseach an education research and technical assistance organization. That same year Westat also acquired Fenestra an information technology solutions company. The acquisitions enhanced Westat's research capabilities.

EXECUTIVES

Cto, James E. Smith
Vp Planning And Finance, Patricia Espey-English
Vice President, Boni Fash
Vice President, Laurie May
Vice President, David Cantor
Vice President, Steve Durako
Vice President, Mark Freedman
Senior Vice President, Renee Slobasky
Vice President Of Information Systems, Greg Binzer
Senior Vice President Of Mis, Wajhiuddin Khawaja
Senior Vice President Administration, Martha Palan
Vice President, Doreen Deleonardis
Vice President, Kerry Levin
Vice President, Sue Connor
Vice President, Don Vicars
Vice President, David Morganstein
Senior Vice President Human Resources, Joseph Hunt
Vice President, Jim Greenlees
Vice President, Pat Ward
Vice President, Andrea Sedlak
Vice President, David Maklan
Vice President, Sherman Edwards
Vice President Human Resources, Louis Intili
Vice President, Fran Bents
Medical Secretary, Linda Sprouse
Auditors: RUBINO & COMPANY BETHESDA MD

LOCATIONS

HQ: WESTAT, INC.
1600 RESEARCH BLVD, ROCKVILLE, MD 208503129
Phone: 301 251-1500
Web: WWW.WESTAT.COM

PRODUCTS/OPERATIONS

Selected Operations and Services
Program areas
 Alcohol tobacco and other drug studies
 Consulting services and marketing research
 Customer satisfaction
 Education
 Employment and training
 Energy
 Environmental protection
 Health and medical studies
 Housing
 Military human resources
 Organizational and personnel studies
 Science and technology
 Social services and community development
 Transportation
Research services
 Clinical trials management
 Conference planning and support
 Data analysis and reporting
 Data preparation and processing

Focus groups
Program evaluation
Qualitative studies
Statistical sample design
Study design
Survey Services
 Data collection from institutions and businesses
 Data preparation and processing
 Design
 In-field measurement and biospecimen collection
 Interviewing
 Mail surveys
 On-site data collection coordination
 Telephone surveys
 Web-based surveys

COMPETITORS

Gallup	Nielsen
GfK	ORC International
Harris Interactive	QinetiQ
IMS Health	SDI Health
Ipsos	Social & Scientific
J.D. Power	Systems
Kantar Group	Walker Information
Maritz Research	

HISTORICAL FINANCIALS
Company Type: Private

Income Statement				FYE: December 31
	REVENUE ($ mil.)	NET INCOME ($ mil.)	NET PROFIT MARGIN	EMPLOYEES
12/16	510	23	4.7%	2,000
12/15	509	20	4.0%	—
12/14	517	22	4.3%	—
12/13	582	23	4.1%	—
Annual Growth	(4.3%)	0.2%	—	—

2016 Year-End Financials
Return on assets: 7.3%   Cash ($ mil.): 22
Return on equity: 10.6%
Current ratio: 2.70

WESTCHESTER COUNTY HEALTH CARE CORPORATION

EXECUTIVES

Ceo-Pres, Michael D Israel
Sr V Pres, Anthony Mahler
Cfo, Gary Brudnicki
Executive Vice President, Julie Switzer
Sr V Pres, John Morgan
Public Relations Director, David Billig
Director of Telecommunications, Carl Pugni
Director, Mary Delaney
Senior Vice-President, John Moustakakis
Information Specialist, Michelle Weinraub
Information Specialist, Omar Ziyadeh
Auditors: GRANT THORNTON NEW YORK NY

LOCATIONS

HQ: WESTCHESTER COUNTY HEALTH CARE CORPORATION
100 WOODS RD, VALHALLA, NY 105951530
Phone: 914 493-7000
Web: WWW.WESTCHESTERMEDICALCENTER.COM

HISTORICAL FINANCIALS
Company Type: Private

Income Statement				FYE: December 31
	REVENUE ($ mil.)	NET INCOME ($ mil.)	NET PROFIT MARGIN	EMPLOYEES
12/18	1,641	(10)	—	12,000
12/16	2,008	45	2.3%	—
12/15	1,069	33	3.1%	—
12/13	918	6	0.7%	—
Annual Growth	12.3%	—	—	—

2018 Year-End Financials
Return on assets: (-0.7%)   Cash ($ mil.): 112
Return on equity: —
Current ratio: 1.50

WESTERN CONNECTICUT HEALTH NETWORK FOUNDATION, INC.

EXECUTIVES

Chairman, Anthony Rizzo Jr
Vice Chairman, Deborah L Seidel
Treasurer, Steven Rosenberg

LOCATIONS

HQ: WESTERN CONNECTICUT HEALTH NETWORK FOUNDATION, INC.
24 HOSPITAL AVE FL 6, DANBURY, CT 068106099
Phone: 203 797-7000

HISTORICAL FINANCIALS
Company Type: Private

Income Statement				FYE: September 30
	REVENUE ($ mil.)	NET INCOME ($ mil.)	NET PROFIT MARGIN	EMPLOYEES
09/12	502	53	10.6%	6
09/09	5	(2)	—	—
09/08	12	5	47.0%	—
09/01	0	0	—	—
Annual Growth	—	—	—	—

2012 Year-End Financials
Return on assets: 6.5%   Cash ($ mil.): 54
Return on equity: 12.0%
Current ratio: 7.60

WESTERN CONNECTICUT HEALTH NETWORK, INC.

Nuvance Health is a not-for-profit health system serving New York's Hudson Valley and western Connecticut. The system has about a half-dozen hospitals including Connecticut's Danbury Hospital and New Milford Hospital and New York's Northern Dutchess Hospital and Putnam Hospital Center. It also includes a network of primary care and specialty practices. Altogether the system has more than 2600 aligned physicians. Nuvance Health was established through the 2019 merger of Western Connecticut Health Network and New York-based Health Quest.

EXECUTIVES

Pres, John M Murphy
Pres*, Frank J Kelly
SEC-Treas*, Arthur N Tedesco
Sr V Pres*, Steven H Rosenberg
SEC*, Donna Kaplanis
Auditors: ERNST & YOUNG LLP HARTFORD C

LOCATIONS

HQ: WESTERN CONNECTICUT HEALTH NETWORK, INC.
24 HOSPITAL AVE, DANBURY, CT 068106099
Phone: 203 739-7000
Web: WWW.WESTERNCONNECTICUTHEALTHNETWORK.ORG

COMPETITORS

Connecticut Children's Medical Center
Griffin Health
Hospital of Central Connecticut
MidHudson Regional Hospital
St. Vincent's Health Services
Stamford Health
Waterbury Hospital
Yale New Haven Health System
Yale-New Haven Hospital Saint Raphael Campus

HISTORICAL FINANCIALS

Company Type: Private

Income Statement   FYE: September 30

	REVENUE ($ mil.)	NET INCOME ($ mil.)	NET PROFIT MARGIN	EMPLOYEES
09/18	1,195	57	4.8%	3,000
09/16	1	(3)	—	—
09/15	23	12	52.4%	—
09/10	624	48	7.8%	—
Annual Growth	8.4%	2.1%	—	—

2018 Year-End Financials

Return on assets: 3.6%   Cash ($ mil.): 103
Return on equity: 6.1%
Current ratio: 1.80

WESTERN FARMERS ELECTRIC COOPERATIVE

Power also comes sweeping down the plain in Oklahoma thanks to the Western Farmers Electric Cooperative. Led by its coal- and natural gas-fueled generating plants — three in Anadarko one in Mooreland and one in Hugo (all in Oklahoma) — the generation and transmission co-op produces more than 1845 MW of capacity. It pipes power over 3700 miles of transmission lines to two-thirds of rural Oklahoma and parts of New Mexico. It also operates 264 substations and 59 switch stations. Western Farmers Electric Cooperative which is owned by its member distribution cooperatives supplies 22 distribution co-ops and Altus Air Force base which serve a total of a half million members.

Operations

The company maintains a well-balanced and diversified portfolio of generation resources reflecting a mix of technologies and fuel types. In 2013 coal represented 33% of Western Farmers Electric Cooperative's energy production with natural gas at 12 percent. Power generated from wind resources represents about 14% of the coop's energy mix hydro 7%. Economy purchases energy imbalance purchases and contract power (primarily natural gas) made up the balance.

Geographic Reach

Western Farmers Electric Cooperative's members consist of 22 distribution cooperatives (serving customers in Kansas Oklahoma New Mexico and Texas) and the Altus Air Force Base in Oklahoma.

Financial Performance

In 2013 the company's revenues increased by 15% to $525.3 million due to a 7.7% energy sales increase. (Its average MWh sales growth rate of 5.5% over the past three year is above the national average). Western Farmers Electric Cooperative also gets a small amount of off-system sales from three of its four New Mexico members. Power sales increased $64 million in 2013 due to higher MWh sales a slight increase in wholesale power rates and a 40% rise in natural gas prices.

Western Farmers Electric Cooperative's net income increased by 61% in 2013 due to higher sales and an increase in noninterest income.

That year the company's operating cash inflow increased to $53.3 million (compared to $21.2 million in 2012) primarily due to higher net income and increased coal and oil inventory.

Strategy

Western Farmers Electric Cooperative has diversified its fuel mix to meet green energy regulations and boasts one of the state's largest renewable energy portfolios. The diversity in generation mix helps reduce exposure to changing market conditions helping to keep rates competitive.

In 2013 the company signed a purchase with Apex Clean Energy through its subsidiary Balko Wind LLC for 100 MW of wind energy from the Balko Wind Project. With this agreement Apex has sold all the capacity of 300 MW project which will produce enough electricity to power over 110000 U.S. homes. This new site represents the fifth Oklahoma wind farm development that is a part of an ongoing commitment to diversify Western Farmers Electric Cooperative's portfolio of generation sources.

That year it also entered into a purchase and sale agreement with community-wind developer National Renewable Solutions to acquire the development assets for the Broadview Wind Projects in New Mexico. The two projects with a combined 19.8 MW capacity will each sell power over the next 20 years to Western Farmers Electric Cooperative. This wind farm site is in the service territory of Western Farmers Electric Cooperative member Farmers' Electric Cooperative.

In 2012 the company teamed up with Enel Green Power which that year began operating the 150-MW Rocky Ridge Wind Project in Kiowa and Washita counties Oklahoma. The energy generated by the wind farm will be bought by Western Farmers Electric Cooperative.

In 2012 Calpine Corporation agreed to supply Western Farmers Electric Cooperative with electric generation capacity and power (up to 280 MW) from Calpine's gas-fired Oneta Energy Center from June 2014 through 2035.

Company Background

Growing its geographic coverage in late 2010 Western Farmers Electric Cooperative added four New Mexico-based cooperatives (Farmers' Central Valley Lea County and Roosevelt County with a total of 400 MW of load) to its membership.

Responding to a growing demand for power in 2009 the power co-op completed an expansion project at its gas-fueled Anadarko plant adding some 145 MW of power generating capacity.

Western Farmers Electric Cooperative was organized in 1941 by western Oklahoma rural electric distribution cooperatives in order to secure power generation and distribution at an affordable rate. The co-op began generating power in 1950.

EXECUTIVES

Secretary Transmission Services, Kelli Keeling
Secretary, Shelly Trammell
Secretary T And D Engineering, Shelli Pearson
Secretary, White Susie
Auditors: KPMG LLP OKLAHOMA CITY OK

LOCATIONS

HQ: WESTERN FARMERS ELECTRIC COOPERATIVE
701 NE 7TH ST, ANADARKO, OK 730052297
Phone: 405 247-3351
Web: WWW.WFEC.COM

COMPETITORS

Empire District   OGE Energy
Electric   ONEOK
Entergy   PG&E Corporation
Grand River Dam
Authority

HISTORICAL FINANCIALS

Company Type: Private

Income Statement   FYE: December 31

	REVENUE ($ mil.)	NET INCOME ($ mil.)	NET PROFIT MARGIN	EMPLOYEES
12/18	715	14	2.0%	378
12/17	686	13	2.0%	—
12/16	655	24	3.7%	—
12/15	671	31	4.6%	—
Annual Growth	2.2%	(22.8%)	—	—

2018 Year-End Financials

Return on assets: 1.0%   Cash ($ mil.): 14
Return on equity: 3.9%
Current ratio: 1.10

WESTERN OREGON UNIVERSITY

EXECUTIVES

Pres, Mark D Weiss
Project Coordinator, Angela Christensen
Staff, Heitho Reuter
Coordinator, Philip Reid
Assistant Professor, Lauren Roscoe
Education Specialist, Michael Baltzley
Coordinator, Emily Lafon
Associate Professor, Becka Morgan
Assistant Professor, Erin Barnes
Project Coordinator, Gina Herrera
Project Coordinator, Ruth McDonald

LOCATIONS

HQ: WESTERN OREGON UNIVERSITY
345 MONMOUTH AVE N, MONMOUTH, OR 973611329
Phone: 503 838-8000
Web: WWW.WOU.EDU

HISTORICAL FINANCIALS
Company Type: Private

Income Statement
FYE: June 30

	REVENUE ($ mil.)	NET INCOME ($ mil.)	NET PROFIT MARGIN	EMPLOYEES
06/08	1,251	80	6.4%	706
06/06*	0	(0)	—	
12/05	1	0	30.1%	
06/04	1	0	22.9%	
Annual Growth	483.6%	324.8%	—	—

*Fiscal year change

2008 Year-End Financials
Return on assets: —
Return on equity: 6.4%
Current ratio: 0.70
Cash ($ mil.): 355

WESTMORELAND REGIONAL HOSPITAL

EXECUTIVES

Ceo, David Gallatin
Sr V Pres-Cfo*, Jeffrey T Curry
V Pres*, Sharon P Smith
SEC*, Dirk Kalp
Treas*, Thomas L Sochacki
Ceo*, Robert J Rogalski
Occupational Specia, Joni Beckman
Coordinator, Karen Edmunds
Administrative Assistant, Maureen Crevak
Coordinator, Rich Laurenti
Coordinator, Roz Colarusso

LOCATIONS

HQ: WESTMORELAND REGIONAL HOSPITAL
532 W PITTSBURGH ST, GREENSBURG, PA
156012282
Phone: 724 832-4000
Web: WWW.EXCELAHEALTH.ORG

HISTORICAL FINANCIALS
Company Type: Private

Income Statement
FYE: June 30

	REVENUE ($ mil.)	NET INCOME ($ mil.)	NET PROFIT MARGIN	EMPLOYEES
06/18	571	36	6.4%	2,000
06/16	248	15	6.3%	
06/15	245	24	9.8%	
06/14	12	8	64.1%	
Annual Growth	159.4%	45.7%	—	—

2018 Year-End Financials
Return on assets: 5.2%
Return on equity: 9.9%
Current ratio: 1.60
Cash ($ mil.): 39

WGL HOLDINGS, INC.

WGL Holdings owners of the regulated Washington Gas Light Company sells natural gas to more than 1 million customers in the District of Columbia Maryland and Virginia. It has about 600 miles of transmission mains more than 13000 miles of distribution mains and some 12500 miles of distribution lines. The company's unregulated segment also provides energy marketing clean-energy products and services and midstream asset management. In July 2018 WGL Holdings was bought by Canada-based AltaGas for $6.4 billion deal.

Operations
WGL Holdings has four segments: Regulated Utility Retail Energy-Marketing Commercial Energy Systems and Midstream Energy Services.

Regulated Utility (more than 50% of revenue) consists of Washington Gas (regulated gas distribution/transportation services) and Hampshire Gas (regulated interstate natural gas storage services).

The Retail Energy-Marketing (some 40%) competes with regulated utilities and unregulated third-party marketers to sell natural gas and electricity to some 210000 customers in Maryland Virginia Delaware Pennsylvania and DC.

Commercial Energy Systems sells products like solar PV systems combined heat and power plants and natural gas fuel cells; it also provides installation services for technological upgrades. It generates 340000 megawatt hours of clean energy a year.

Midstream Energy Services manages natural gas storage and transportation assets.

Geographic Reach
WGL Holdings primarily operates in Washington DC Maryland and Virginia. It also serves customers across the US through its non-utility segments. Washington Gas has peak shaving facilities in Springfield Virginia (Ravensworth Plant) and Rockville Maryland (Rockville Plant).

Sales and Marketing
WGL sells and delivers natural gas and/or electricity directly to residential commercial and industrial customers. Washington Gas has some 1.2 million customers in the District of Columbia Maryland and Virginia while its Energy Services business count some 210000 retail customers in the same area.

Financial Performance
WGL has not been a growing company lately. In the last five years company revenue fell from $2.7 billion in 2014 to $2.3 billion in 2018. In 2018 (ended September 30) revenue fell less than a percentage point to $2.34 billion (compared to $2.35 billion in 2017). The fall came due to lower sales volumes in the retail energy (non-utility) business.

Net income slashed from $192 million in 2017 to $49 million in 2018 mostly due to a YOY $364 million increase in operation and maintenance costs related to the merger with AltaGas as well as a YOY $114 million increase in the utility cost of gas. Lower realized margins in the regulated utility segment further reduced its coffers.

Cash holdings at the company shot up from only $8 billion at the end of 2017 to $122 million at 2018 end. Operations provided $322 million and a further $715 million came in from financial activities which was offset by $923 million going into investments.

Company Background
WGL was established in the year 2000 as a Virginia corporation. On January 25 2017 WGL entered into an Agreement and Plan of Merger (Merger Agreement) to combine with AltaGas Ltd. a Canadian Corporation (AltaGas). On July 6 2018 the merger was consummated between AltaGas WGL and Wrangler Inc. (Merger Sub) a newly formed indirect wholly owned subsidiary of AltaGas.

EXECUTIVES

President And Coo Wgl Holdings Inc. And Washington Gas Light Company, Adrian P. Chapman, $551,000 total compensation
Svp And Cfo Wgl Holdings And Washington Gas Light Company, Vincent L. Ammann, $460,000 total compensation
Chairman And Ceo Wgl Holdings And Washington Gas Light Company, Terry D. McCallister, $824,000 total compensation
Vp Strategy Business Development And Non-utility Operations, Gautam Chandra, $420,000 total compensation
Svp General Counsel And Corporate Secretary, Leslie Thornton, $380,000 total compensation
Executive Vice President Business Development Of The Bank, Nigeria Poole

LOCATIONS

HQ: WGL HOLDINGS, INC.
1000 MAINE AVE SW, WASHINGTON, DC 200243494
Phone: 703 750-2000
Web: WWW.WGLHOLDINGS.COM

PRODUCTS/OPERATIONS

2018 Sales

	$ mil.	% of total
Retail energy marketing	1,009	42
Utility	1,248	53
Commercial energy services	79	3
Midstream energy services	40	2
Eliminations	(36.4)	-
Total	**2,341**	**100**

2018 Sales

	$ mil.	% of total
Non-utility	1,112	47
Utility	1,229	53
Total	**2,341**	**100**

Selected Subsidiaries
Hampshire Gas Company (underground natural gas storage)
Wrangler SPE LLC
Washington Gas Light Company (natural gas utility)
Washington Gas Resources Corp. (nonregulated business holding company)
Washington Gas Energy Services Inc. (retail energy services)
Washington Gas Energy Systems Inc. (commercial energy systems and HVAC services)

COMPETITORS

Appalachian Power	Northern Virginia
Comfort Systems USA	Electric Cooperative
Commerce Energy Group	Pepco Holdings
Constellation Energy Group	RGC Resources
Dominion Energy	Rappahannock Electric Cooperative
FirstEnergy	

HISTORICAL FINANCIALS
Company Type: Private

Income Statement
FYE: September 30

	REVENUE ($ mil.)	NET INCOME ($ mil.)	NET PROFIT MARGIN	EMPLOYEES
09/18	2,341	21	0.9%	1,586
09/17	2,354	177	7.6%	—
09/16	2,349	168	7.2%	—
09/15	2,659	132	5.0%	—
Annual Growth	(4.2%)	(45.8%)	—	—

2018 Year-End Financials
Return on assets: 0.3%
Return on equity: 1.2%
Current ratio: 0.60
Cash ($ mil.): 57

WHEATON FRANCISCAN SERVICES, INC.

Wheaton Franciscan Services Inc. (WFSI) is the not-for-profit parent company for more than 100 health care housing and social service organizations in Colorado Illinois Iowa and Wisconsin. Also known as Wheaton Franciscan Healthcare WFSI operates about 15 hospitals including Affinity Health System Rush Oak Park Hospital and United Hospital System with more than 1600 beds total. WFSI also includes long-term care centers home health agencies and physician offices. Its Franciscan Ministries division provides affordable housing units including assisted-living facilities and low-income dwellings. The health system is sponsored by The Franciscan Sisters Daughters of the Sacred Hearts of Jesus and Mary.

Operations
Many of WFSI's hospitals are operated in partnership with other area providers. For instance the Affinity Health System in Wisconsin is jointly sponsored by Wheaton Franciscan Sisters and Ministry Health Care while the Rush Oak Park Hospital in Illinois is operated through a partnership between WFSI and the Rush System for Health.

The health system partners with the YMCA of Milwaukee to try to address chronic health concerns of area residents. The two organizations converted a local YMCA campus into the YMCA Healthy Lifestyle Village. The center offers health screenings health education outpatient therapy and fitness services. WFSI and the YMCA have more Healthy Lifestyle Village campuses planned for other locations within their service areas.

The organization had a total of 1656 beds and 2620 housing units at the end of 2014.

In fiscal 2013 WSFI delivered more than 8000 babies and had more than 330000 emergency department visits. It reported more than 1580000 outpatient visits and some 64000 hospital admissions. It employs more than 500 physicians and has some 2000 affiliated physicians.

Geographic Reach
WFSI operates in Wisconsin Iowa Colorado and Illinois.

Financial Performance
The not-for-profit system's revenues were flat in fiscal 2014 at $1.8 billion. Net income totaled $184 million.

Strategy
To increase the scope of specialty health care services it can provide to the community WFSI recruits new physicians and specialists to the Wheaton Franciscan Medical Group. The system also works to improve communication among its physicians and facilities by adding electronic health record (EHR) systems.

In 2013 the system opened a new 80000-sq.-ft. outpatient center specializing in neurology services.

Company Background
The Franciscan Sisters Daughters of the Sacred Hearts of Jesus and Mary (also known as the Wheaton Franciscan Sisters) founded WSFI in 1983 as a holding company for their ministry operations. The health system traces its roots back to the founding of the St. Mary's Hospital in Racine Wisconsin in 1882.

EXECUTIVES

Pres-Ceo, John D Oliverio
Chm, Joseph Lewis
V Chm, Michael Mack
SEC, Michael Murry
Treas, Robert Walker
Epic Certified Manager, Jeff Brodzeller
Manager, Denise Nitsch
Director of Language, Ibzan Monteagudo
Director Retirement Plans, Karen Hanley
Senior Accountant, Michael Koser
Manager, Cherie Finnie
Auditors: KPMG LLP CHICAGO IL

LOCATIONS

HQ: WHEATON FRANCISCAN SERVICES, INC.
400 W RIVER WOODS PKWY, GLENDALE, WI 532121060
Phone: 414 465-3000

PRODUCTS/OPERATIONS

Selected Operations
Franciscan Ministries Inc. (housing in Colorado Illinois Iowa and Wisconsin)
Illinois
  Marianjoy Rehabilitation Hospital (Wheaton)
  Rush Oak Park Hospital (affiliate Oak Park)
Iowa (Wheaton Franciscan Healthcare of Iowa)
  Covenant Medical Center (Waterloo)
  Mercy Hospital (Oelwein)
  Sartori Memorial Hospital (Cedar Falls)
Wisconsin
  Affinity Health System (partnership with Minstry Health Care)
  Calumet Medical Center (Chilton)
  Mercy Medical Center (Oshkosh)
  St. Elizabeth Hospital (Appleton)
  Wheaton Franciscan Healthcare of Southeast Wisconsin
  All Saints Hospital (two campuses in Racine)
  Elmbrook Memorial Hospital (Brookfield)
  Franklin Hospital (Franklin)
  St. Francis Hospital (Milwaukee)
  St. Joseph Hospital (Milwaukee)
  Wisconsin Heart Hospital (Wauwatosa)
  United Hospital System Inc. (affiliated system)
  Kenosha Medical Center (Kenosha)
  St. Catherine's Medical Center (Pleasant Prairie)

COMPETITORS

Advocate Health Care	KishHealth
Alden Management Services	Loyola University Health System
Children's Hospital and Health System	Ministry Health Care
	Morris Hospital
Columbia St. Mary's	NorthShore University HealthSystem
Elmhurst Memorial Healthcare	OSF Healthcare System
FHN	ProHealth Care
Froedtert Hospital	Rockford Health System
Hospital Sisters Health System	SwedishAmerican Health System

HISTORICAL FINANCIALS
Company Type: Private

Income Statement
FYE: June 30

	REVENUE ($ mil.)	NET INCOME ($ mil.)	NET PROFIT MARGIN	EMPLOYEES
06/15	1,809	18	1.0%	18,000
06/14	1,754	128	7.3%	—
06/13	1,763	177	10.1%	—
06/12	1,723	(112)	—	—
Annual Growth	1.6%			

2015 Year-End Financials
Return on assets: 0.8%   Cash ($ mil.): 81
Return on equity: 1.6%
Current ratio: 1.30

WHEELING-NISSHIN, INC.

Wheeling-Nisshin aÂ subsidiary of Nisshin Steel produces a variety of hot-dip coated steels such as stainless steel. The company's output includes 400000 tons produced at its aluminizing and galvanizing line facility and 300000 tons produced at its continuous galvanizing line facility. Both of the facilities are located at the company's headquarters site inÂ West Virginia. Its primary customers are in the automotive appliance and construction industries. Wheeling-Nisshin was founded in 1986. It had been a joint venture between Nisshin and US steel producer Wheeling Pitt (now operating as Severstal Wheeling)Â until the Japanese steel company bought out its partner in early 2008.

EXECUTIVES

Vice President Of Finance, Jay Mclaughlin
Vp Sales, Ricky Onishi
Vice President Commercial, William Reder
Auditors: ERNST & YOUNG LLP

LOCATIONS

HQ: WHEELING-NISSHIN, INC.
400 PENN ST, FOLLANSBEE, WV 260371412
Phone: 304 527-2800
Web: WWW.WHEELING-NISSHIN.COM

COMPETITORS

Dofasco	United States Steel
ThyssenKrupp Stainless	

HISTORICAL FINANCIALS
Company Type: Private

Income Statement
FYE: December 31

	REVENUE ($ mil.)	NET INCOME ($ mil.)	NET PROFIT MARGIN	EMPLOYEES
12/14	483	5	1.2%	175
12/13	391	2	0.7%	—
Annual Growth	23.5%	100.5%	—	—

2014 Year-End Financials
Return on assets: 3.8%   Cash ($ mil.): 40
Return on equity: 5.1%
Current ratio: 4.50

WHITE PLAINS HOSPITAL MEDICAL CENTER

EXECUTIVES

Pres-Ceo, Jon B Schandler
Chb, Paul Weissman
Pres, Susan Fox
Exec V Pres-Coo, Edward F Leonard
V Pres-Fin-Cfo, John Schiurba
Chief Operating Officer, Jeffrey Tiesi
Information Specialist, Gary Soso
Information Specialist, Allison Schurko
Information Specialist, Anna Perselis

Information Specialist, Carmita Pacheco
Information Specialist, Celia Caceres

LOCATIONS

HQ: WHITE PLAINS HOSPITAL MEDICAL CENTER
41 E POST RD, WHITE PLAINS, NY 106014607
Phone: 914 681-0600

HISTORICAL FINANCIALS

Company Type: Private

Income Statement				FYE: December 31
	REVENUE ($ mil.)	NET INCOME ($ mil.)	NET PROFIT MARGIN	EMPLOYEES
12/17	620	40	6.5%	2,000
12/16	460	23	5.1%	—
12/15	389	23	6.1%	—
12/14	353	8	2.3%	—
Annual Growth	20.7%	70.9%	—	—

2017 Year-End Financials

Return on assets: 5.9%   Cash ($ mil.): 45
Return on equity: 10.1%
Current ratio: 1.00

WHITEWAVE FOODS COMPANY

WhiteWave Foods rides a wave of dietary changes as consumers seek alternatives to conventional foods. The company is best known for its refrigerated Silk soymilk in the US and Alpro brand soy products in Europe. WhiteWave also produces organic dairy products under the Horizon Organic label and dairy related foods including International Delight coffee creamers and LAND O'LAKES-branded creamers and dairy dessert toppings (licensed from dairy co-op Land O'Lakes). WhiteWave products are sold through natural food and grocery stores as well as mass merchandisers and restaurants and food service businesses in the US and Canada and parts of Europe. WhiteWave has been part of French dairy giant Danone since 2017.

Operations

WhiteWave's plant-based food and drinks include Silk (milk from soy almonds cashews and coconuts as well as dairy-free yogurt); So Delicious Dairy Free (drinks creamers ice-cream shredded cheese); Alpro (dairy alternatives); and Vega (plant-based sports nutrition).

Other brands include Horizon (organic milk-based products); International Delight (sweet drinks and iced coffee); Half & Half (creamer); Earthbound Farm (salads frozen and dried fruit and fresh fruit and vegetables).

Geographic Reach

WhiteWave is headquartered in Denver Colorado.

Financial Performance

WhiteWave has maintained healthy if not entirely organic revenue gains for the past ten years.

EXECUTIVES

Chairman And Ceo, Gregg L. Engles, $1,120,000 total compensation
President Americas Fresh Foods, Kevin C. Yost, $550,000 total compensation
President Americas Foods & Beverages, Blaine E. McPeak, $650,000 total compensation
Evp And General Counsel, Roger E. Theodoredis

Evp Human Resources, Thomas N. Zanetich, $445,000 total compensation
Evp Strategy And Corporate Development, Edward F. Fugger, $362,000 total compensation
President Europe Foods And Beverages, Bernard P. J. Deryckere, $504,076 total compensation
Evp And Cfo, Greg S. Christenson
Senior Vice President, Tommy Zanetich
Vice President Engineering And Extraction, Rick Wietharn
Auditors: DELOITTE & TOUCHE LLP DENVER

LOCATIONS

HQ: WHITEWAVE FOODS COMPANY
12002 AIRPORT WAY, BROOMFIELD, CO 800212546
Phone: 303 635-4500
Web: WWW.WHITEWAVE.COM

2016 Sales

	% of total
North America	86
Europe	14
Total	100

PRODUCTS/OPERATIONS

Selected Products and Brands

Europe
Plant-based foods and beverages (Alpro Provamel)
Almond
Hazelnut
Oat
Rice
Soy
North America
Coffee creamers and beverages (Land O Lakes International Delight)
Flavored coffee creamers
Half & Half
Iced coffee
Unflavored coffee creamers
Plant-based foods and beverages (Silk)
Almond
Coconut
Soy
Premium dairy (Horizon Organic)
Organic milk
Other organic dairy
Other premium milk

COMPETITORS

Aurora Organic Dairy	Lifeway Foods
Eden Foods	Nestlé
Galaxy Nutritional Foods	Odwalla
HP Hood	Old Home Foods
Hain Celestial	Organic Valley
Kraft Heinz	Rockview Dairies
	Springfield Creamery

HISTORICAL FINANCIALS

Company Type: Private

Income Statement				FYE: December 31
	REVENUE ($ mil.)	NET INCOME ($ mil.)	NET PROFIT MARGIN	EMPLOYEES
12/15	3,866	168	4.4%	5,800
12/14	3,436	140	4.1%	—
12/13	2,542	99	3.9%	—
Annual Growth	23.3%	30.4%	—	—

2015 Year-End Financials

Return on assets: 4.0%   Cash ($ mil.): 38
Return on equity: 13.9%
Current ratio: 1.00

WHOLE FOODS MARKET, INC.

Whole Foods Market is the world's largest natural foods grocery chain. Founded in 1980 it pioneered the supermarket concept in natural and organic foods retailing. The company operates some 500 stores throughout the US Canada and the UK and focuses on organic perishable and prepared products. It sells private-label items through its 365 Organic Everyday Value and Allegro Coffee lines among others and offers a variety of non-GMO vegan and gluten-free foods. Whole Foods was acquired by Amazon.com for $13.7 billion in 2017.

HISTORY

With a $10000 loan from his father John Mackey started SaferWay Natural Foods in Austin Texas in 1978. Despite struggling Mackey dreamed of opening a larger supermarket-sized natural foods store. Two years later SaferWay merged with Clarksville Natural Grocery and Whole Foods Market was born. Led by Mackey that year it opened an 11000-sq.-ft. supermarket in the counterculture hotbed of Austin. The store was an instant success and a second store was added 18 months later in suburban Austin.

The company slowly expanded in Texas opening or buying stores in Houston in 1984 and Dallas in 1986. Whole Foods expanded into Louisiana in 1988 with the purchase of like-named Whole Food Co. a single New Orleans store owned by Peter Roy (who served as the company's president from 1993 to 1998). Sticking to university towns Whole Foods added another store in California the next year and acquired Wellspring Grocery (two stores North Carolina) in 1991. In 1992 it debuted its first private-label products under the Whole Foods name. Seeking capital to expand even more the company raised $23 million by going public in early 1992 with 12 stores.

Every competitor in the fragmented health foods industry became a potential acquisition and the chain began growing rapidly. In 1992 Whole Foods bought the six-store Bread & Circus chain in New England. The next year it added Mrs. Gooch's Natural Foods Markets (seven stores in the Los Angeles area). Its biggest acquisition came in 1996 when it bought Fresh Fields the second-largest US natural foods chain (22 stores on the East Coast and in Chicago). Although the purchase hurt profits in 1996 sales surpassed $1 billion for the first time in fiscal 1997 as Whole Foods neared 70 stores. In 1997 it introduced the less-expensive 365 private label and acquired the Granary Market (Monterey California) and Bread of Life (two stores South Florida) natural foods supermarkets.

Capitalizing on the growing popularity of nutraceuticals (natural supplements with benefits similar to pharmaceuticals) the company paid $146 million in 1997 for Amrion a maker of nutraceuticals and other nutritional supplements (merged with subsidiary WholePeople.com in 2000). It capped the year by buying coffee roaster Allegro Coffee. (Both companies are based in Boulder Colorado home of its former main rival the smaller Wild Oats.) Also in 1997 Whole Foods acquired the six-store Merchant of Vino natural foods and wine shop chain to foster the development of its wine departments.

In 1998 Whole Foods opened its first store in Boulder — a 39000-sq.-ft. superstore with amenities such as a juice bar and a prepared foods section. At year's end Roy resigned as president and was replaced by Chris Hitt. In 1999 Whole Foods bought four-store Boston-area chain Nature's Heartland.

In 2000 Whole Foods merged its online operations (wholefoods.com) with its direct marketing and nutritional supplement unit (Amrion) to form Wholepeople.com. Later that year the company merged Wholepeople.com with lifestyle marketing firm Gaiam; Whole Foods received a minority stake in Gaiam and started selling food online through Gaiam.com.

Hitt resigned in mid-2001 and Mackey took over his duties. Later that year Whole Foods acquired the three upscale Harry's Farmers Market stores in Atlanta; the sale did not include the Harry's In A Hurry stores which later shut down.

In 2002 Whole Foods crossed the border into Canada. Its first foreign store opened in downtown Toronto that May.

Mackey was named Entrepreneur of the Year in 2003 by consulting firm Ernst & Young. That year Whole Foods acquired Select Fish a Seattle-based seafood processor and distributor and opened a seafood distribution facility in Atlanta.

In 2004 Whole Foods opened a 59000-sq.-ft. store in the new Time Warner Center in Manhattan. The new store which includes a 248-seat cafe sushi bar wine shop and gourmet bakery is the largest supermarket in New York City. That year the company acquired the UK organic-food retailer Fresh & Wild for $38 million.

To support its rapid growth in 2004 Whole Foods Market expanded its number of operating regions from eight to 10 by separating the Southwest region into the Southwest and Rocky Mountain regions and the Northern Pacific region into the Northern California and Pacific Northwest region. The company announced the opening of its first Gluten-Free Bakehouse a dedicated gluten-free baking facility located outside Raleigh North Carolina. Overall the company opened 12 new stores in 2004.

In January 2005 Whole Foods launched the Animal Compassion Foundation an independent non-profit organization dedicated to the compassionate treatment of livestock. The company moved that month to its new corporate headquarters across the street from its old location in downtown Austin. Its new flagship store opened its doors in March at the same location. In October Whole Foods increased its number of operating regions from 10 to 11 by separating the North Atlantic region into the North Atlantic and Tri-State regions. Overall in fiscal 2005 the company opened a dozen new stores including its first in Nebraska and Ohio. In 2006 the company acquired a store in Portland Maine and converted it to the Whole Foods Market banner.

In August 2007 Whole Foods acquired its main competitor — Boulder Colorado-based Wild Oats Markets — in a deal valued at about $565 million (plus $106 million in debt). In early October the company sold 35 Henry's Farmers Market and Sun Harvest stores to a subsidiary of Los Angeles-based Smart & Final for about $166 million. The stores in California and Texas were acquired with Wild Oats.

The company launched a bi-monthly magazine called Whole Foods Market Magazine at its midwestern stores in 2008. On the heels of its disappointing third-quarter results in August 2008 shares of the company's stock fell to a six-year low and Whole Foods suspended its dividend. Blaming the poor economy the company announced the layoffs of some 50 employees at its Austin headquarters in August 2008. Overall in fiscal 2008 the company introduced about 300 new private-label items.

For the first time in its 29-year history Whole Foods reported negative same-store sales in the quarter ended December 2008 as traffic in its stores fell.

In March 2009 the company reached a settlement in its long-running dispute with the FTC over its acquisition of Wild Oats in 2007. Whole Foods agreed to sell 32 stores including 19 Wild Oats locations that had already been closed. In exchange the FTC dropped its crusade to undo the merger. In December 2009 John Elstrott was named chairman of Whole Foods Market after Mackey voluntarily relinquished the chairmanship which he had held since 1980. In May 2010 Walter Robb formerly co-president of the company was promoted to co-CEO of Whole Foods a title he now shares with Mackey.

EXECUTIVES

Ceo, John P. Mackey, $1 total compensation
President Northeast Region, A. C. Gallo, $501,110 total compensation
President Florida Region, Juan Nuñez
Chairman Whole Kids Foundation And Whole Cities Foundation, Walter E. Robb, $501,110 total compensation
Evp Operations U.s. And Whole Foods 365, David Lannon, $501,110 total compensation
Vp Purchasing Midwest Division, Jeff Turnas
Evp Operations, Christina Minardi
President Southern Pacific Region, Patrick Bradley
President Mid-atlantic Region, Scott Allshouse
President Rocky Mountain Region, Bill Jordan
President Midwest Region, Michael Bashaw
President North Atlantic Region, Laura Derba
Evp And Cio, Jason Buechel, $501,110 total compensation
President South Region, Omar Gaye
President Northern California Region, Rob Twyman
Evp Operations U.s. And The U.k., Kenneth (Ken) Meyer, $486,510 total compensation
Evp Growth And Business Development, James (Jim) Sud, $486,510 total compensation
Evp And Cfo, Keith Manbeck
President Pacific Northwest Region, Angela Lorenzen
Global Vp Marketing, Sonya Gafsi Oblisk
President Northeast Region, Nicole Wescoe
Global Vice President, Lee Matecko
Executive Vice President Operations, Kenny Meyer
Vice President And Marketing Manager, Desa Abbamondi
Vice President Vendor Manager, Ray Hudson
Vice President Administration, John Agnew
Senior Vice President Technology Manager, Pedro Adame
Global Vice President Commmunications, Brooke Buchanan
Vice President And Loan Officer And Branch Manager, Francisco Ibarra
Assistant Vice President And Mortgage Market Manager, Craig Moore
Assistant Vice President Product Manager Marketing, Merijoy Rucker
Regional Vice President, Scott Saulsberry
Regional Vice President, Tim Gates
Regional Vice President, Steve Epidendio
Vice President Digital Marketing Crm Loyalty And Ecommerce, Ryan Linders
Chairman, John B. Elstrott
Auditors: ERNST & YOUNG LLP AUSTIN TEX

LOCATIONS

HQ: WHOLE FOODS MARKET, INC.
  550 BOWIE ST, AUSTIN, TX 787034644
Phone: 512 477-4455
Web: WWW.WHOLEFOODSMARKET.COM

PRODUCTS/OPERATIONS

Selected Product Categories

Bakery
Body care
Educational products
Floral
Grocery
Household products
Meat and poultry
Nutritional supplements
Pet products
Prepared foods
Produce
Seafood
Specialty (beer wine cheese)
Textiles

COMPETITORS

ALDI	Natural Grocers by
Albertsons	Vitamin Cottage
Costco Wholesale	Publix
Fiesta Mart	Safeway
GNC	Sprouts
H-E-B	Tesco
Kroger	Trader Joe's
Loblaw	Wal-Mart

HISTORICAL FINANCIALS

Company Type: Private

Income Statement				FYE: September 24
	REVENUE ($ mil.)	NET INCOME ($ mil.)	NET PROFIT MARGIN	EMPLOYEES
09/17	16,030	245	1.5%	89,000
09/16	15,724	507	3.2%	—
09/15	15,389	536	3.5%	—
09/14	14,194	579	4.1%	—
Annual Growth	4.1%	(24.9%)	—	—

2017 Year-End Financials

Return on assets: 3.7%   Cash ($ mil.): 322
Return on equity: 7.1%
Current ratio: 1.60

WILBUR-ELLIS HOLDINGS II, INC.

"Seed 'em weed 'em and feed 'em" could be the motto of San Francisco's Wilbur-Ellis Co. (aka WECO). Through its agribusiness division WECO sells fertilizer herbicides insecticides seed and farm machinery in North America. The Connell Bros. unit exports and distributes food ingredients and specialty chemicals throughout the Pacific Rim. Its feed division serves international customers in the livestock pet food and aquaculture industries. Additionally WECO provides consulting pesticide application and other agriculture-related services. Beyond North America WECO has operations in about 15 countries in the Asia/Pacific Region. WECO was founded in 1921 by Brayton Wilbur Sr. and Floyd Ellis.

Operations

WECO's Agribusiness division is one of the top marketers and distributors of agricultural products in the US with sales of $2 billion. Connell Bros. is the largest marketer and distributor of specialty chemicals and ingredients with about three dozen offices across the Asia/Pacific region and annual sales of about $815 million. The $500-million-in-sales Feed division supplies value-added feed ingredients and markets for customers' by-products.

Geographic Reach

The San Francisco-based company has agribusiness operations in the West Southwest and Midwest regions on the US. Connell Bros. has offices in 17 countries across the Asia/Pacific Region including Australia China and Vietnam. The Feed unit has operations in North America and in Australia and New Zealand.

Sales and Marketing

WECO's ProMarket business serves such markets as nurseries greenhouses forests and golf courses and sporting facilities. The Connel Bros. division sells ingredients and specialty chemicals to the coatings food personal care plastics paper construction and other industries.

Financial Performance

WECO's annual sales continue to exceed $3 billion.

Strategy

WECO employs a strategy of acquiring successful businesses and integrating them into its existing operations. Geography is no barrier when it comes to buying companies: The group has acquired operations in such faraway places as Malaysia Taiwan the Philippines China Australia and New Zealand. WECO continues to expand both through acquisitions and organically across its three divisions.

Mergers and Acquisitions

The company continued its acquisitive streak in 2014 and 2015. In early 2014 it acquired one of its alliance partners New Horizons Ag Service an agricultural retail business in Elgin North Dakota. New Horizons became part of Wilbur-Ellis Midwest. The company also acquired Accu-Rate Services a full-service agricultural retailer in Sedgwick Kansas and Advanced Ag located in Creston Iowa. Other agribusinesses added in 2014 included retail facility Poynter's Ag Supply (North Dakota) and feed provider Allied Premium Protein.

Also that year WECO's Connell Brothers unit purchased Enzyme Solutions of Melbourne Australia extending its capabilities in enzymes. Furthering its Asia/Pacific business it acquired Bioworld Fine Chemical (Shanghai) which distributes upscale botanical oils and plant extracts.

Agribusiness purchases in 2015 include The Seed House a Nebraska-based professional seed company; Lacey's Farmacy a South Dakota-based agriculture retail outfit and Aero Spray Services an aerial spraying and fire-fighting firm also based in South Dakota.

EXECUTIVES

Vp Treasurer And Cfo, James D. Crawford
President Agribusiness Division, Daniel R. (Dan) Vradenburg
President And Ceo, John P. Thacher
Vp South Central Operations, Steven J. Dietze
Vp Western Operations, Scott Hushbeck
President Feed Division, Rob Fullerton
President Wilbur-ellis Japan, Iguchi Shinichi
President Connell Brothers, Azita Owlia
Vice President Finance, Steve Flowers
Chairman, Herbert B. Tully
Auditors: PRICEWATERHOUSECOOPERS

LOCATIONS

HQ: WILBUR-ELLIS HOLDINGS II, INC.
345 CALIFORNIA ST FL 27, SAN FRANCISCO, CA 941042644
Phone: 415 772-4000
Web: WWW.WILBURELLIS.COM

PRODUCTS/OPERATIONS

Selected Products and Services
Agribusiness Division
  Agricultural chemicals
  Fertilizers
  Fungicides
  Herbicides
  Insecticides
  Machinery
  Pesticides
  Seed protectants
  Seed treatments
  Sprayers
  Supply-chain management
Connell Bros. Division
  Industrial chemicals
Feed Division
  Aquaculture products
  Feed ingredients
  Food oils
  Forage products
  Pet food
Professional Products
  Forestry
  Fungicides
  Herbicides
  Golf
  Fungicides
  Landscape
  Fungicides
  Nursery/Greenhouse
  Fungicides
  Vegetation Management
  Selective and nonselective growth regulators

COMPETITORS

ADM	DuPont Agriculture
AGRI Industries	Frontier Agriculture
Ag Processing Inc.	GROWMARK
Andersons	Goulding Chemicals
BASF SE	Ingredion
Bayer CropScience	JR Simplot
CF Industries	Land O'Lakes Purina
CHS	Feed
Cargill	Southern States
Dow AgroSciences	

HISTORICAL FINANCIALS
Company Type: Private

Income Statement FYE: December 31

	REVENUE ($ mil.)	NET INCOME ($ mil.)	NET PROFIT MARGIN	EMPLOYEES
12/11	2,812	0	—	4,600
12/10	2,342	0	—	—
12/09	0	0	—	—
12/00	1,100	0	—	—
Annual Growth	8.9%	—	—	—

WILLIAM BEAUMONT HOSPITAL

EXECUTIVES

Ceo-Pres, Gene Michalski
Pres, Brian Connolly
SEC, Gale R Colwell
Treas, Barbara Mahone
Chief Med, Ananias Diokno
Chm, Stephen R Howard
V Chm, Mark Shaevsky
Sr V Pres, Margaret Casey
Fo/Exe V Pres, John Keuten
Director, Hadley Mack French
Director, Martha James Quay

LOCATIONS

HQ: WILLIAM BEAUMONT HOSPITAL
3601 W 13 MILE RD, ROYAL OAK, MI 480736712
Phone: 248 898-5000
Web: WWW.BEAUMONT.ORG

HISTORICAL FINANCIALS
Company Type: Private

Income Statement FYE: December 31

	REVENUE ($ mil.)	NET INCOME ($ mil.)	NET PROFIT MARGIN	EMPLOYEES
12/17	1,473	71	4.9%	18,050
12/16	1,396	118	8.5%	—
12/15	1,300	142	10.9%	—
12/14	1,235	127	10.3%	—
Annual Growth	6.0%	(17.5%)	—	—

2017 Year-End Financials

Return on assets: 3.8%   Cash ($ mil.): 175
Return on equity: 3.9%
Current ratio: 12.30

WILLIS-KNIGHTON MEDICAL CENTER

EXECUTIVES

Pres, James K Elrod
Exec V Pres*, Robert Huie
V Pres*, Nila Willhoite
Doctor, Alan J Sorkey
Oncology, Anil Veluvolu
Blood Bank Director, April Johnson
Network Coordinator, Cody Adams
Patient Access Manager, Daniel Nickerson
Revenue Management, Debbie Miller
Director of Nursing, Debbie Olds
Analyst, Eric Cochran
Auditors: COLE EVANS & PETERSON SHREVEP

LOCATIONS

HQ: WILLIS-KNIGHTON MEDICAL CENTER
2600 GREENWOOD RD, SHREVEPORT, LA 711033908
Phone: 318 212-4000
Web: WWW.WKHS.COM

HISTORICAL FINANCIALS
Company Type: Private

Income Statement FYE: September 30

	REVENUE ($ mil.)	NET INCOME ($ mil.)	NET PROFIT MARGIN	EMPLOYEES
09/18	1,130	105	9.4%	3,089
09/15	1,019	97	9.6%	—
Annual Growth	3.5%	2.8%	—	—

2018 Year-End Financials

Return on assets: 8.0%   Cash ($ mil.): 60
Return on equity: 9.8%
Current ratio: 5.20

WILMINGTON TRUST COMPANY

EXECUTIVES

Executive Vice President, Mark A Graham
Chief Executive Officer, Robert Harra
Group Vice President, Richard Marsh
Vice President, Charles Gummey
Vice President, Peter Finkel
Assistant Vice President, Donald Haverstick
Vice President, Steven Cimalore
Vice President Global Capital Markets, Vito Iacovazzi
Vice President Private Banking, Heather Ford
Vice President Business Application Support Manager, Gary Powers
Vice President, Jared Grunig
Vice President Global Capital Markets, Nicholas Adams
Vice President, Mary Avery
Vice President, Margaret Pulgini
Vice President, Sergio Godinho
Vice President, Jennifer Matz
Training Manager Vice President, Lynn Dibonaventura
Vice President, Charles Hicks
Assistant Vice President, Steve Barone
Vice President, Lisa Fricke
Vice President Wilmington Trust Fsb, Josh Stump
Vice President, Wendy White
Vice President, Janice Cirillo
Vice President, George Chen
Vice President Of Marketing And Communications, Jim Klabe
Vice President Risk Management, Myfanwy Bonilla
Vice President Of Data Center, Ed Olkowski
Vice President Marketing, Sherry Costanzo
Senior Vice President Administration, John N Beeson
Vice President Corporate Client Services, Christie Longo
Vice President Client Development, Rob Barnett
Vice President, Jeanette Madaya
Vice President, Kevin Bruggeman
Vice President, Nadine Black
Vice President Risk Manager, Holly Stiefel
Assistant Vice President, Laura Barone
Senior Vice President Secretary, Michael Digregorio
Assistant Vice President, Deanne M Welsh
Vice President, Arlene Moyer
Vice President, Karen Touchstone
Assistant Vice President, Liz Hudgens
Vice President, Virginia Machamer
Vice President Network And Desktop Computing, Rob Averbach
Vice President, Robert Quinn
Vice President, Jane Snyder
Assistant Vice President, Greg Cherewko
Vice President And Portfolio Manager, Luke Betterly
Vice President, Joe Fahey
Senior Vice President, James Riley
Vice President Wealth Advisory Senior Private Client Fiduciary Advisor, Latonya Hubbard
Vice President, Steven Kochie
Vice President, Thomas Herring
Vice President And Senior Private Client Fiduciary Advisor, Cindy White
Vice President Esop Services, Kristy Britsch
Assistant Vice President, Ryan Thompson
Vice President, Jason Johnson
Executive Vice President, Bill Farrell
Vice President And Senior Client Development Officer For Wtris, Robert Barnett
Vice President, Chris Slaybaugh

Assistant Vice President, Thomas Kalafut
Vice President Wealth Advisory Services, Blair Talty
Assistant Vice President Of Lending, Mary Fisher
Group Vice President, Tom Pierce
Vice President, Clay Weisenberg
Assistant Vice President Loan Agency Group, Jennifer Anderson
Vice President Software Development Investment Management, John Driban
Vice President Equity Management, Mark Horst
Vice President And Portfolio Manager, Dan Rambert
Vice President Corporate Capital Markets, Aaron Soper
Assistant Vice President, Michael Moorehead
Assistant Vice President, Barry Butina
Vice President, Robert Reynolds
Assistant Vice President, Bonnie Metcalfe
Vice President, Joe Garniewski
Vice President, Robert Collins
Assistant Vice President Global Capital Markets, Clarice Wright
Vice President Institutional Relationship Manager, Jeffrey Petroske
Assistant Vice President, Melissa Jalace-vasold
Vice President Senior Private Client Advisor, Sandra Besso Plowinske
Vice President, Ann Harris-johnson
Vice President, Christopher Guardino
Vice President, Josh James
Assistant Vice President, Joann Petry
Avp, Lisa Lewis
Assistant Vice President, Carleen Terranova
Vice President Wealth Advisory Services, Paul Bartkowski
Assistant Vice President Commercial Real Estate, Rachel Skrabak
Vice President Channel Management, John J Hurley
Assistant Vice President, Greg Golden
Assistant Vice President, Melissa Marion
Vice President, Karen Bonn
Vp Senior Private Client Investment Advisor, Jim Mcdonald
Vice President And Senior Private Client Investment Advisor, Sue Schnaars
Vice President Private Banking, Julia Odonnell
Assistant Vice President, Brenda Parker
Vice President, Al Miller
Vice President, Barbara Obrien
Vice President, Charlie Buehler
Vice President And Senior Investment Advisor, Andrew Cloud
Assistant Vice President, Andrea Rybczynski
Vice President, Joseph Odonnell
Vice President, Renee Buchner
Assistant Vice President, Nancy Hagner
Assistant Vice President, Catherine Chandler
Vice President, Kyle Barry
Assistant Vice President, Maureen Auld
Vice President, Denise Sbraccia
Assistant Vice President, Sophie Pendolino
Assistant Vice President, Christopher Hickok
Assistant Vice President, Ruth Ann Mcmillen
Assistant Vice President, Jose Paredes
Vice President, Howard Gordon
Vice President, David Bagley
Vice President Private Client Advisor, Ed Barone
Vice President, Jeffrey Ritchie
Vice President, Kaye Crouch
Assistant Vice President, Kevin Ebert
Vice President, Nickole Garrison
Vice President Senior Private Banker, Nicholas Macechko
Assistant Vice President, Russell Whitley
Assistant Vice President, Matthew Lyndaker
Vice President And Investment Advisor, Darren Jordan
Vice President, Erin Miller

Vice President, William Gering
Vice President, Joseph Baker
Vice President, Stephen Seivold
Vice President, Theresa Drew
Assistant Vice President, Tammy Krawczyk
Vice President, Todd Bemiller
Vice President, Brooks Von Arx Jr
Vice President And Team Leader, Donald Hargadon
Vice President, Mindy Jones
Vice President, Patrick Wood
Vice President, Donna Oleary
Assistant Vice President, James Wisniewski
Vice President, Michael Edgington
Assistant Vice President, Susan Laratonda
Group Vice President Family Wealth, Anna Smith
Vice President Mortgage Backed Securities Trader And Analyst, Eric Smookler
Vice President, Glenn Klinger
Assistant Vice President, David Mcguire
Assistant Vice President, Stevie C Blackston
Vice President Administrative, Meghan Ashue
Vice President, Debra Berry
Vice President, Anne Stclair
Vice President, James Maloney
Vice President, Chris Sponenberg
Secretary Iii, Susan Alban
Board Member, Belinda Cunningham

LOCATIONS

HQ: WILMINGTON TRUST COMPANY
1100 N MARKET ST, WILMINGTON, DE 198900001
Phone: 302 651-1000

HISTORICAL FINANCIALS

Company Type: Private

Income Statement				FYE: December 31
	ASSETS ($ mil.)	NET INCOME ($ mil.)	INCOME AS % OF ASSETS	EMPLOYEES
12/17	4,960	30	0.6%	518
12/16	3,685	17	0.5%	—
12/15	1,928	36	1.9%	—
Annual Growth	60.4%	(9.0%)	—	—

2017 Year-End Financials

Return on assets: 0.6%   Sales ($ mil.): 234
Return on equity: 5.7%

WINCHESTER MEDICAL CENTER

EXECUTIVES

Prin, Mark H Merrill
Ceo*, Philips Grady
V Pres*, Thurman Suanne
V Pres*, Nicolas C Restrepo
Chief Staff, Gregory G Stanford
Senior Director, Bonnie Pitt
Director of Risk Management, Carla Dallman
Pathologist, Catherine Mathieu
Manager, Jim Miller
Doctor, Randolph Renzi
Physical Therapist, Robert Diaz

LOCATIONS

HQ: WINCHESTER MEDICAL CENTER
1840 AMHERST ST, WINCHESTER, VA 226012808
Phone: 540 536-8000
Web: WWW.VALLEYHEALTHLINK.COM

HISTORICAL FINANCIALS

Company Type: Private

Income Statement

FYE: September 30

	REVENUE ($ mil.)	NET INCOME ($ mil.)	NET PROFIT MARGIN	EMPLOYEES
09/14*	470	28	6.0%	2,500
12/08	410	9	2.3%	—
Annual Growth	2.3%	19.9%	—	—

*Fiscal year change

2014 Year-End Financials

Return on assets: 3.0% Cash ($ mil.): 22
Return on equity: 5.2%
Current ratio: 16.20

WINCHESTER MEDICAL CENTER AUXILIARY, INC.

Winchester Medical Center is the flagship facility of Valley Health System a not-for-profit health care organization serving the residents of Virginia's Shenandoah Valley. The full-service general hospital which has more than 400 inpatient beds serves as a regional referral center for the system's smaller community hospitals. It provides medical services across a number of specialties (including neuroscience heart disease and cancer) and offers surgical diagnostic and rehabilitative care. The hospital's campus also features outpatient diagnostic and surgical facilities an adult psychiatric facility and doctors' offices. Winchester Medical Center opened its doors in 1903.

EXECUTIVES

Secretary, Susie Bell
Auditors: ARNETT & FOSTER PLLC CHA

LOCATIONS

HQ: WINCHESTER MEDICAL CENTER AUXILIARY, INC.
  1840 AMHERST ST, WINCHESTER, VA 226012808
Phone: 540 536-8000
Web: WWW.VALLEYHEALTHLINK.COM

COMPETITORS

Ascension Health
 Carilion Clinic
 Fauquier Hospital
 Georgetown University Hospital
 HCA
 Inova
 Johns Hopkins Health System
 Loudoun Healthcare
 Martha Jefferson Hospital
 MedStar Health
 Novant Health
 Prince William Health System
 Rockingham Memorial Hospital
 Sentara Northern Virginia Medical Center

HISTORICAL FINANCIALS

Company Type: Private

Income Statement

FYE: December 31

	REVENUE ($ mil.)	NET INCOME ($ mil.)	NET PROFIT MARGIN	EMPLOYEES
12/07	453	48	10.8%	2,046
12/06	413	61	14.9%	—
12/05	382	55	14.6%	—
Annual Growth	8.9%	(6.6%)	—	—

2007 Year-End Financials

Return on assets: 6.9% Cash ($ mil.): 18
Return on equity: 10.8%
Current ratio: 4.80

WINCO HOLDINGS, INC.

EXECUTIVES

Pres-Ceo, Steven Goddard
Vp-Cfo-Sec-treas, David Butler
Vp-Coo, Richard Charrier
Chb, Gary R Piva
Vice-President Engineering, Dick Vanderlinden
Business Analyst, Dustin Earl
Director of Information Techno, Hank Fitchett
Engineer, Matthew Sabin
Director of Information Techno, Gary Mountain
Vice-President, Robert Rhodes
Administrative Assistant, Steven Peele
Auditors: KPMG LLP BOISE ID

LOCATIONS

HQ: WINCO HOLDINGS, INC.
  650 N ARMSTRONG PL, BOISE, ID 837040825
Phone: 208 377-0110
Web: WWW.WINCOFOODS.COM

HISTORICAL FINANCIALS

Company Type: Private

Income Statement

FYE: March 28

	REVENUE ($ mil.)	NET INCOME ($ mil.)	NET PROFIT MARGIN	EMPLOYEES
03/09	4,104	225	5.5%	14,000
03/08	3,515	132	3.8%	—
03/07	2,976	106	3.6%	—
Annual Growth	17.4%	45.5%	—	—

2009 Year-End Financials

Return on assets: 15.2% Cash ($ mil.): 146
Return on equity: 24.4%
Current ratio: 1.30

WINDSTREAM EAGLE HOLDINGS, LLC

EXECUTIVES

Ceo-Pres, Tony Thomas
Cfo, Bob Gunderman
Ezec V Pres-CHR, John Fletcher
Cmo, Joe Harding
Exec V Pres-Enterprises Sales, Jeff Howe
Pres-Consumer, Sarah Day
Pres-Wholesale, Mike Shippey
Exec V Pres-Access, John Dobbins
Exec V Pres, Engr, Jeff Small
Auditors: ERNST & YOUNG LLP ATLANTA GE

LOCATIONS

HQ: WINDSTREAM EAGLE HOLDINGS, LLC
  1170 PEACHTREE ST NE # 900, ATLANTA, GA
  303097649
Phone: 404 815-0770

HISTORICAL FINANCIALS

Company Type: Private

Income Statement

FYE: December 31

	REVENUE ($ mil.)	NET INCOME ($ mil.)	NET PROFIT MARGIN	EMPLOYEES
12/16	959	7	0.8%	60
12/15	1,097	(43)	—	—
12/14	1,176	(72)	—	—
Annual Growth	(9.7%)		—	—

2016 Year-End Financials

Return on assets: 1.2% Cash ($ mil.): 51
Return on equity: 38.0%
Current ratio: 1.00

WINSTON-SALEM/FORSYTH COUNTY SCHOOLS

EXECUTIVES

Supr, Donald L Martin
Supr*, Beverly Emory
Coordinator, Ana Ortiz
Coordinator, Eva Phillips
Information Specialist, Amanda Carol
Coordinator, Debbie Herrin
Superintendent, Ron Rash

LOCATIONS

HQ: WINSTON-SALEM/FORSYTH COUNTY SCHOOLS
  475 CORPORATE SQUARE DR, WINSTON SALEM, NC
  271059100
Phone: 336 748-4000
Web: WWW.WSFCS.K12.NC.US

HISTORICAL FINANCIALS

Company Type: Private

Income Statement

FYE: June 30

	REVENUE ($ mil.)	NET INCOME ($ mil.)	NET PROFIT MARGIN	EMPLOYEES
06/08	484	0	0.1%	6,841
06/07	451	0	—	—
06/06	145	28	19.9%	—
Annual Growth	82.6%	(88.6%)	—	—

2008 Year-End Financials

Return on assets: 0.1% Cash ($ mil.): 12
Return on equity: 0.1%
Current ratio: 1.10

WIPRO, LLC

EXECUTIVES

Ceo, Abidali Neemuchwala
Pres*, Mallathur Balasubramanian
SEC*, Mitchell Mackler
Cfo-Treas*, Ashish Chawla
Project Manager, Aravinth Thatchanamoorth

Information Technology Departm, Fernando Cardoza
Senior Hardware Analyst, Mark Hutchins
Vice President (Corporate Hum, Pratik S Kumar
Auditors: FOR DELOITTE HASKINS & SELLS L

LOCATIONS

HQ: WIPRO, LLC
  2 TOWER CENTER BLVD # 2200, EAST BRUNSWICK, NJ 088161100
Phone: 732 509-1664
Web: WWW.WIPRO.COM

HISTORICAL FINANCIALS

Company Type: Private

Income Statement				FYE: March 31
	REVENUE ($ mil.)	NET INCOME ($ mil.)	NET PROFIT MARGIN	EMPLOYEES
03/18	585	(45)	—	800
03/13	120	(17)	—	—
Annual Growth	37.1%	—	—	—

2018 Year-End Financials

Return on assets: (-4.8%)   Cash ($ mil.): 22
Return on equity: (-20.4%)
Current ratio: 0.70

WITHLACOOCHEE RIVER ELECTRIC COOPERATIVE INC

Withlacoochee River Electric Cooperative keeps the power flowing to theÂ residences and businesses ofÂ more thanÂ 200360 member-owners in five counties along the central Florida Gulf Coast. The power distribution utility which was originally set up in 1941 receives wholesale generation and transmission services from the Seminole Electric Cooperative. Withlacoochee River Electric a non-profit organization returns any funds remaining at the end of each year to its membership. The cooperative has returned more than $190 million to its member-owners.

EXECUTIVES

District Secretary, Kira Bassett
Auditors: PURVIS GRAY & COMPANY LLP DAD

LOCATIONS

HQ: WITHLACOOCHEE RIVER ELECTRIC COOPERATIVE INC
  14651 21ST ST, DADE CITY, FL 335232920
Phone: 352 567-5133
Web: WWW.WREC.NET

HISTORICAL FINANCIALS

Company Type: Private

Income Statement				FYE: December 31
	REVENUE ($ mil.)	NET INCOME ($ mil.)	NET PROFIT MARGIN	EMPLOYEES
12/16	458	26	5.8%	458
12/15	474	24	5.1%	—
12/14	459	28	6.2%	—
12/13	433	16	3.8%	—
Annual Growth	1.9%	16.6%	—	—

2016 Year-End Financials

Return on assets: 2.6%   Cash ($ mil.): 154
Return on equity: 5.3%
Current ratio: 0.60

WOLVERINE POWER SUPPLY COOPERATIVE, INC.

Named after a voracious carnivore Wolverine Power Supply Cooperative makes sure that that voracious consumer of electricity — the American public — gets the power its needs. The non-profit company is an electric generation and transmission utility that provides services to five member distribution cooperatives in Michigan. Wolverine Power Supply Cooperative monitors and operates 1600 miles of bulk transmission lines and owns five power plants that generate 200 megawatts of capacity. It also maintains about 130 distribution substations and 36 transmission stations as well as purchases power (including windpower energy)Â from other utilities and marketers to distribute to its customers.

EXECUTIVES

Vice President Generation, Dan Decoeur
Vice President General Counsel, Joseph Baumann
Auditors: PLANTE & MORAN PLLC CHICAGO

LOCATIONS

HQ: WOLVERINE POWER SUPPLY COOPERATIVE, INC.
  10125 W WATERGATE RD, CADILLAC, MI 496018458
Phone: 231 775-5700
Web: WWW.WOLVERINEPOWERCOOPERATIVE.COM

COMPETITORS

ITC Holdings Corp.	Midland Cogeneration Venture
Lansing Board of Water and Light	

HISTORICAL FINANCIALS

Company Type: Private

Income Statement				FYE: December 31
	REVENUE ($ mil.)	NET INCOME ($ mil.)	NET PROFIT MARGIN	EMPLOYEES
12/18	476	19	4.2%	110
12/17	433	18	4.3%	—
12/16	431	27	6.3%	—
12/15	389	23	6.0%	—
Annual Growth	7.0%	(5.4%)	—	—

2018 Year-End Financials

Return on assets: 2.5%   Cash ($ mil.): 6
Return on equity: 9.3%
Current ratio: 0.90

WOMEN & INFANTS HOSPITAL OF RHODE ISLAND

EXECUTIVES

Ceo, Dennis D Keefe
Exec V Pres*, Patricia R Recupero
Chief of Pathology & Laborator*, C James Sung
Compliance Staff, Ralph Handlesman
Chief of Medicine, Carol Mnning
Coordinator, Bernice Dimauro
Executive Vice President, Mark Marcantano
Access, Carmena Bishop
Safety Director, David Schnell
Doctor, James Fanale
Cnm, Janet E Singer
Auditors: PRICEWATERHOUSECOOPERS LLP BO

LOCATIONS

HQ: WOMEN & INFANTS HOSPITAL OF RHODE ISLAND
  101 DUDLEY ST, PROVIDENCE, RI 029052499
Phone: 401 274-1100
Web: WWW.WOMENANDINFANTS.ORG

HISTORICAL FINANCIALS

Company Type: Private

Income Statement				FYE: September 30
	REVENUE ($ mil.)	NET INCOME ($ mil.)	NET PROFIT MARGIN	EMPLOYEES
09/16	504	35	7.0%	2,800
09/15	428	3	0.8%	—
09/14	438	19	4.5%	—
09/13	411	14	3.6%	—
Annual Growth	7.0%	33.5%	—	—

2016 Year-End Financials

Return on assets: 7.3%   Cash ($ mil.): 66
Return on equity: 11.0%
Current ratio: 2.70

WORLD WIDE TECHNOLOGY HOLDING CO., LLC

EXECUTIVES

Ceo, James P Kavanaugh
Chb*, David Steward
Cfo*, Tom Strunk
Director, Holly Kriegesmann
Project Coordinator, Jennifer Barrett
Business Manager, Nicole Reichert
Project Manager, Vidhya Borade
Specialist, Jennifer Geisler
Client Director, Scott Wilson
Human Resources Manager, Paul Koetting
Project Manager, Mike Brown
Auditors: ERNST & YOUNG LLP ST LOUIS

LOCATIONS

HQ: WORLD WIDE TECHNOLOGY HOLDING CO., LLC
1 WORLD WIDE WAY, SAINT LOUIS, MO 631463002
Phone: 314 919-1400
Web: WWW.2.WWT.COM

HISTORICAL FINANCIALS

Company Type: Private

Income Statement | | | | FYE: December 31
	REVENUE ($ mil.)	**NET INCOME** ($ mil.)	**NET PROFIT MARGIN**	**EMPLOYEES**
12/14	6,702	88	1.3%	1,052
12/13	6,392	77	1.2%	—
12/12	5,041	68	1.3%	—
Annual Growth	15.3%	14.2%	—	—

2014 Year-End Financials

Return on assets: 6.4%   Cash ($ mil.): 109
Return on equity: 38.0%
Current ratio: 1.20

WORLD WIDE TECHNOLOGY, LLC

World Wide Technology (WWT) has a broad view of its business. The company primarily provides such IT services as network design and installation systems and application integration and procurement. It also offers a range of Web-based products and services including e-commerce systems development order tracking and catalog management. WWT serves businesses in the automotive retail and telecommunications industries as well as government agencies. Top clients have included Dell the State of Missouri and the State of Alaska. WWT was founded in 1990.

Geographic Reach

WWT has more than 25 facilities throughout the world and about 2 million-sq.-ft of warehouse and distribution space in the US. It also has three distribution outlets in Brazil Mexico and Singapore as well as facilities in London; Amsterdam; Hong Kong; and Chengdu China.

Mergers and Acquisitions

In 2015 WWT purchased St. Louis-based software development firm Asynchrony. The strategic acquisition will allow WWT to deliver complete custom user-facing software and the systems and infrastructure that support it.

EXECUTIVES

Ceo, James P. (Jim) Kavanaugh
President Commercial Sales, Mark J. Catalano
Cfo, Thomas W. (Tom) Strunk
Vp Corporate Properties, Dan B. Svoboda
President, Joseph G. (Joe) Koenig
Vp Professional Services, Matt Horner
Vp Supply Chain Operations, Kurt Grimminger
Vp Global Supply Chain, Mark Franke
Vice President Of Information Technology, Mike P. Taylor
Vice President Sales Operations, Tim Loughman
Vice President Engineering And Innovation, Christopher Black
Vice President Professional Services, Tom Gain
Vice President Of Sales, John Lynch
Vice President Of Federal Sales, Bill Mckeon
Vice President Global Accounts, Leo Makhlin
Vice President Head Of Asia Pacific, Nilesh Mistry
Senior Vice President, Kraig Ecker

Vice President, Jeree Hanavec
Chairman, David L. Steward

LOCATIONS

HQ: WORLD WIDE TECHNOLOGY, LLC
1 WORLD WIDE WAY, SAINT LOUIS, MO 631463002
Phone: 314 569-7000

PRODUCTS/OPERATIONS

Selected Services
IT Products and Solutions
  Facilities Infrastructure
  Integration and Staging
  Leasing
  Managed Services
  Order Management and Reporting

                                     Pre-Sales Support

  Value Added Reseller
Professional Services
  Configuration
  Implementation
  Planning and Design
  Training
Supply Chain Services
  Business Process Outsourcing
  Logistics/Warehousing
  Material Planning and Scheduling
  Outsourced Procurement
  Supplier Management

COMPETITORS

Accenture	HP Enterprise Services
Black Box	IBM Global Services
Computer Sciences	PC Mall
Corp.	Rose International
DataSpan	Unisys
Dynamics Research	WebLinc
En Pointe	

HISTORICAL FINANCIALS

Company Type: Private

Income Statement | | | | FYE: December 31
	REVENUE ($ mil.)	**NET INCOME** ($ mil.)	**NET PROFIT MARGIN**	**EMPLOYEES**
12/15	5,927	95	1.6%	1,052
12/14	5,057	95	1.9%	—
12/13	4,545	77	1.7%	—
12/12	3,396	57	1.7%	—
Annual Growth	20.4%	18.3%	—	—

2015 Year-End Financials

Return on assets: 5.7%   Cash ($ mil.): 46
Return on equity: 18.8%
Current ratio: 1.40

WORLEY & OBETZ, INC.

Auditors: HOROVITZ RUDOY & ROTEMAN LLC

LOCATIONS

HQ: WORLEY & OBETZ, INC.
85 WHITE OAK RD, MANHEIM, PA 175458550
Phone: 717 665-6891
Web: WWW.WORLEYOBETZ.COM

HISTORICAL FINANCIALS

Company Type: Private

Income Statement | | | | FYE: August 31
	REVENUE ($ mil.)	**NET INCOME** ($ mil.)	**NET PROFIT MARGIN**	**EMPLOYEES**
08/17	677	2	0.4%	68
08/16	584	1	0.3%	—
08/15	520	2	0.4%	—
08/14	466	1	0.4%	—
Annual Growth	13.2%	14.0%	—	—

2017 Year-End Financials

Return on assets: 3.0%   Cash ($ mil.): —
Return on equity: 16.3%
Current ratio: 1.50

WTG GAS PROCESSING, L.P.

EXECUTIVES

Gen Ptnr, Ealmoor GP
Gen Ptnr, James L Davis
Controller, Barbara Geffken
Sales and Marketing Staff, Boris Buschkowiak

LOCATIONS

HQ: WTG GAS PROCESSING, L.P.
211 N COLORADO ST, MIDLAND, TX 797014607
Phone: 432 682-4349
Web: WWW.WTGGASPROCESSING.COM

HISTORICAL FINANCIALS

Company Type: Private

Income Statement | | | | FYE: December 31
	REVENUE ($ mil.)	**NET INCOME** ($ mil.)	**NET PROFIT MARGIN**	**EMPLOYEES**
12/07	588	85	14.5%	25
12/06	498	64	13.0%	—
12/05	484	69	14.4%	—
12/04	342	39	11.5%	—
Annual Growth	19.7%	29.2%	—	—

2007 Year-End Financials

Return on assets: 29.8%   Cash ($ mil.): 45
Return on equity: 37.2%
Current ratio: 2.90

YAKIMA VALLEY MEMORIAL HOSPITAL ASSOCIATION INC

Whether you're a major yakker or quiet as a mouse Yakima Valley Memorial Hospital serves the health care needs of patients of all types. The health provider's acute-care hospital skilled-nursing facilities and outpatient specialty treatment facilities serve patients in and around Yakima in Washington State. The hospital has about 225 beds and provides a variety of services such as heart care orthopedics pediatrics cancer treatment women's health and mental health care. It also offers sleep and wound care and provides home health and hospice services. The organization is a not-for-profit group governed by a board of directors.

Operations
Yakima Valley Memorial Hospital sees about 15000 inpatients each year as well as 77000 emergency room visits and 3100 births. It serves a total of more than 130000 patient per year.

The organization provides a full range of inpatient and outpatient services that include critical care surgery diagnostics cancer care heart care orthopedics a family birthplace a neonatal intensive care unit pediatrics physical therapy and psychiatric care. Its Children's Village provides care for kids with special health or development needs. Other specialty units include the Garden Village skilled nursing center and the Cottage in the Meadow hospice facility. The organization also runs a community education program and a maternal health preventative care program.

Among its staff are 330 physicians representing 35 medical specialties.

Geographic Reach
In addition to its main 26-acre campus in Yakima Washington the organization has 15 locations throughout Yakima County.

Financial Performance
During 2012 the hospital provided $73.7 million in Community Benefits (22% more than in 2011). Included in this number was more than $33 million to cover a shortfall from Medicare funding. Net patient revenue in 2012 was $286 million.

Strategy
Yakima Valley Memorial Hospital is upgrading its infrastructure and its technologies to better serve area residents. In 2013 for instance it added digital breast screening systems to its mammography center and in 2012 the facility invested $1.3 million to replace aging beds.

In 2013 the hospital announced that it was looking for a partner to help it with several challenges including Medicare reimbursement cuts state Medicaid funding woes and the high costs of health information technology. The three prospective groups (which submitted proposals) included Virginia Mason Medical Center in Seattle; Seattle-based Swedish Health Services and Renton-based Providence Health & Services; and Vancouver (Washington)-based PeaceHealth and the University of Washington Medicine Medicine in Seattle.

Company Background
Yakima Valley Memorial Hospital was founded in 1950.

EXECUTIVES

Vice President, Jim Aberle
Ceo, Russ Myers
Senior Vice President, Mely Davenport
Medical Records Director, Jamie Beaman
Vice President, Gail Weaver
Vice President, Melhorn Timothy
Chairman, James Berg
Vice Chairman, Scott Wagner
Auditors: MOSS-ADAMS LLP YAKIMA WASHIN

LOCATIONS

HQ: YAKIMA VALLEY MEMORIAL HOSPITAL ASSOCIATION INC
2811 TIETON DR, YAKIMA, WA 989023761
Phone: 509 249-5129
Web: WWW.YAKIMAMEMORIAL.ORG

PRODUCTS/OPERATIONS

Selected Services and Locations

16th Avenue Pavilion
Apple Valley Family Medicine
Cardiac Rehabilitation and Wellness Center
Cascade Surgical Partners
Children's Village
Family Medicine of Yakima
Garden Village
Home Health and Hospice
Memorial Cornerstone Medicine
Memorial Hospitalist Program
Memorial's Valley Imaging
North Star Lodge Cancer Center
'Ohana Mammography Center
Pacific Crest Family Medicine
Selah Family Medicine
Sleep Center at Memorial
Surgi-Center at Memorial
The Springs Rehabilitation and Occupational Medicine
Water's Edge Pain Relief Institute
Yakima Gastroenterology Associates
Yakima Internal Medicine
Yakima Neurosurgery Associates
Yakima Plastic Surgery Associates
Yakima Vascular Associates

COMPETITORS

Adventist Health System West
Catholic Health Initiatives
Franciscan Health System
HCA
Harrison Medical Center
MultiCare Health System

Overlake Hospital
PeaceHealth
Providence Health & Services-Washington
Providence St. Joseph Health
Swedish Health Services
Watson Institute

HISTORICAL FINANCIALS

Company Type: Private

Income Statement   FYE: December 31

	REVENUE ($ mil.)	NET INCOME ($ mil.)	NET PROFIT MARGIN	EMPLOYEES
12/18	470	(12)		1,150
12/17	457	0	0.1%	—
12/16*	424	83	19.6%	—
10/12	309	(6)	—	—
Annual Growth	7.2%	—	—	—

*Fiscal year change

2018 Year-End Financials

Return on assets: (-3.5%)   Cash ($ mil.): 28
Return on equity: (-5.8%)
Current ratio: 1.20

YALE UNIVERSITY

What do former President George W. Bush and actress Meryl Streep have in common? They are Yalies. Yale University is one of the nation's most prestigious private liberal arts institutions as well as one of its oldest (founded in 1701). Yale comprises an undergraduate college a graduate school and more than a dozen professional schools. Programs of study include architecture law medicine and drama. Its 12 residential colleges (a system borrowed from Oxford) serve as dormitory dining hall and social center. The school has around 12000 students and nearly 4000 faculty members.

Operations
Yale's graduate students of which there are more than 6500 outnumber its more than 5300 undergrads. Undergraduate tuition runs at around $42000 per year plus $13000 in room and board. Graduate tuition is about $35000 per year. The university has some 4000 faculty members.

The university has extensive research programs affiliated with its graduate school and its graduate-level professional schools which cover architecture art divinity drama engineering and applied science forestry and environmental studies law management medicine music nursing and public health.

Yale also operates the Yale University Press which publishes works of academics and professionals including e-books and traditional books. It published 475 titles during 2012 and has produced about 9000 titles in total.

Geographic Reach
Yale's facilities cover a total of 1100 acres including a 340-acre central campus with 260 buildings in New Haven Connecticut; a 140-acre West Campus on the edge of New Haven; and 600 acres of athletic fields and natural preserve areas outside of town. Yale's students come from all 50 US states and about 110 foreign countries.

Financial Performance
Sales for Yale have grown over the last five years and the university showed a 1% increase in revenues to more than $2.8 billion in 2012 due to higher student income grants and contracts (for research and training programs) medical service revenues and other income sources. Endowment income and grants and contracts are the largest source of revenue.

Yale's annual operating budget is about $2.7 billion.

Yale's roughly $19 billion endowment ranks as one of the largest in the US. Yale's Endowment grew about 9% in 2010 producing a gain of $1.4 billion.

Company Background
Yale was founded in 1701 through the vision of a group of colonial clergymen who began planning for a university in the 1640s. It was named Yale College in 1718 after a Welsh merchant Elihu Yale who made a sizable donation to the institution.

EXECUTIVES

Chair Department Of Physics, Paul Tipton
Medical Director, Karen Santucci
Vice Chairman, John Geibel
Assistant Secretary, ERIN JOHNSON
Auditors: PRICEWATERHOUSECOOPERS LLP HA

LOCATIONS

HQ: YALE UNIVERSITY
105 WALL ST, NEW HAVEN, CT 065118917
Phone: 203 432-2550

PRODUCTS/OPERATIONS

Colleges and Schools
Graduate School of Arts and Sciences
Professional schools
  School of Architecture
  School of Art
  Divinity School
  School of Drama
  School of Engineering & Applied Science
  School of Forestry & Environmental Studies
  Law School
  School of Management
  School of Medicine
  School of Music
  School of Nursing
  School of Public Health
  Institute of Sacred Music
Yale College (undergraduate studies)
Residential Colleges
Berkeley College
Branford College
Calhoun College
Davenport College

Ezra Stiles College
Jonathan Edwards College
Morse College
Pierson College
Saybrook College
Silliman College
Timothy Dwight College
Trumbull College

HISTORICAL FINANCIALS
Company Type: Private

Income Statement				FYE: June 30
	REVENUE ($ mil.)	NET INCOME ($ mil.)	NET PROFIT MARGIN	EMPLOYEES
06/18	3,848	3,270	85.0%	11,000
06/17	3,647	2,447	67.1%	—
06/16	3,449	(846)		—
06/13	2,936	1,965	66.9%	—
Annual Growth	5.6%	10.7%	—	—

2018 Year-End Financials
Return on assets: 7.8%
Return on equity: 10.1%
Current ratio: —
Cash ($ mil.): 587

YALE-NEW HAVEN HOSPITAL, INC.

Yale-New Haven supports its community and the brainiacs at Yale. Yale-New Haven Hospital (YNHH) is the flagship member of the Yale New Haven Health System. It provides tertiary care in more than 100 medical specialties to residents of southwestern Connecticut. The not-for-profit hospital has more than 1500 beds on two campuses. Its main location includes the Yale-New Haven Children's Hospital and the Yale-New Haven Psychiatric Hospital. Smilow Cancer Hospital with 170 beds is also part of the hospital complex. YNHH provides cardiac and cancer care performs organ transplants and offers a variety of outpatient clinics. The medical center serves as the primary teaching hospital for Yale University's medical school.

Operations
YNHH handles some 80000 inpatient admissions each year including more than 5000 births. It also has more than 150000 emergency room and urgent care encounters. The hospital's campuses employ some 4250 medical staffers.

A key component of the main hospital facility is the Smilow Cancer Hospital which conducts cancer care and research in partnership with Yale University's Cancer Center.

Financial Performance
YNHH's patient services contribute the bulk of the hospital's total operating revenue. In fiscal 2016 (ended September) operating revenue increased 5% to $2.7 billion as patient volume rose. However operating expenses also increased that year; supplies and other expenses rose to $1.3 billion (versus $1.2 billion in fiscal 2015). Total operating expenses in 2016 reached $2.6 billion. All told the hospital's excess of revenue over expenses increased 50% to $158.5 million.

Strategy
Despite facing challenges including state budget cuts YNHH has been working on the integration of its second campus Saint Raphael. The hospital has also invested some $100 million towards capital improvements at the campus. The combined organization allows YNHH to increase coordination of care and reduce redundancies for area communities.

EXECUTIVES

Evp Coo And Trustee, Marna P. Borgstrom
Svp Patient Services And Chief Nursing Officer, Patricia Sue Fitzsimons
Svp Operations; Executive Director Women's And Children's Services, Cynthia N. Sparer
President And Trustee, Richard D'Aquila
Svp Patient Safety And Quality And Chief Medical Officer, Thomas J. Balcezak
Svp Operations; Executive Director Smilow Cancer Hospital, Abe Lopman
Evp And Cfo Yale New Haven Health System And Cfo Yale New Haven Hospital (ynhh), Vincent Tammaro
Vice President Executive Director Cardiovascular Services, Keith Churchwell
Medical Director, Robert Ostroff
Vice Chairman, Julia M. McNamara, age 77
Chair, Mary C. Farrell, age 69
Secretary Administrative Assistant, Adria Coleman
Secretary, Stephanie Pane
Secretary, Sheryl Raffile
Medical Secretary, Jenifer Yoston

LOCATIONS
HQ: YALE-NEW HAVEN HOSPITAL, INC.
20 YORK ST, NEW HAVEN, CT 065103220
Phone: 203 688-4242
Web: WWW.YNHH.ORG

PRODUCTS/OPERATIONS

Selected Services
Ambulatory (outpatient) services
Bariatric surgery
Blood draw stations
Dental center
Diabetes and endocrinology
Diagnostic radiology
Ear nose and throat
Emergency services
Endocrine surgery
Gastroenterology
Geriatrics
Kidney disease
Maternity
Psychiatry
Pulmonology
Urology

COMPETITORS

Bristol Hospital	St. Vincent's Health
Connecticut Children's	Services
Medical Center	Waterbury Hospital
Griffin Hospital	Western Connecticut
Hartford Health Care	Health Network
New Milford Hospital	

HISTORICAL FINANCIALS
Company Type: Private

Income Statement				FYE: September 30
	REVENUE ($ mil.)	NET INCOME ($ mil.)	NET PROFIT MARGIN	EMPLOYEES
09/15	2,388	107	4.5%	22,000
09/14	2,360	120	5.1%	—
09/13	2,360	120	5.1%	—
09/09	1,237	52	4.3%	—
Annual Growth	11.6%	12.5%	—	—

2015 Year-End Financials
Return on assets: 3.6%
Return on equity: 9.8%
Current ratio: 3.40
Cash ($ mil.): 101

YATES GROUP, INC.

E-Z Mart Stores aims to make filling gas tanks and stomachs EZR for small-town America. The regional convenience store chain operates about 295 stores across four neighboring states including Arkansas Louisiana Oklahoma and Texas. Rather than build its own stores the company usually expands through acquisitions. In addition to the standard hot dogs sodas coffee and cigarettes most E-Z Mart locations also offer Shell Conoco Phillips 66 or CITGO gasoline. E-Z Mart was founded in 1970 by Jim Yates in Nashville Arkansas. Yates died in 1998 when the plane he was piloting crashed leaving his daughter Sonja Hubbard at the company's helm as CEO.

Geographic Reach
Ranked #35 on Convenience Store News ' "Top 100 Convenience Stores Report" E-Z Mart is a regional c-store chain that primarily serves Texas and Arkansas as well as Oklahoma and Louisiana.

Sales and Marketing
Aiming to offer the chain's customers access to updated fuel prices a list of locations and in-store promotions among other items E-Z Mart partnered with OpenStore by GasBuddy to roll out a new E-Z Mart website and mobile app. The fully integrated mobile app enables consumers to send feedback from their mobile phones and receive time-sensitive electronic mobile coupons.

Strategy
While E-Z Mart has trimmed its store count during the past decade or so including exiting markets such as Missouri it continues to make strategic acquisitions. Like other convenience store operators seeking to boost in-store sales E-Z Mart is expanding its food and beverage offering adding fresh-brewed iced tea to all of its stores and installing freezers. Outside the company has a deal with Redbox to place its movie rental kiosks outside of E-Z Mart stores.

EXECUTIVES

Vice President, Lifford Luthringer
Auditors: BKD LLP PORT SMITH ARKANSAS

LOCATIONS
HQ: YATES GROUP, INC.
2015 GALLERIA OAKS DR, TEXARKANA, TX 755034618
Phone: 903 832-6502
Web: WWW.EZMART.COM

2014 Stores

	No.
Texas	96
Arkansas	95
Oklahoma	80
Louisiana	18
Total	**289**

COMPETITORS

7-Eleven	Love's Country Stores
Allsup's	QuikTrip
Brookshire Grocery	Racetrac Petroleum
Chevron	Susser Holdings
Exxon Mobil	Valero Energy
Krause Gentle	

HISTORICAL FINANCIALS

Company Type: Private

Income Statement				FYE: December 31
	REVENUE ($ mil.)	NET INCOME ($ mil.)	NET PROFIT MARGIN	EMPLOYEES
12/16	786	16	2.1%	2,100
12/15	827	16	2.0%	—
12/14	1,026	19	1.9%	—
12/13	1,003	15	1.5%	—
Annual Growth	(7.8%)		3.2%	

2016 Year-End Financials

Return on assets: 7.9%   Cash ($ mil.): 7
Return on equity: 12.6%
Current ratio: 1.30

YORK HOSPITAL

York Hospital operating as WellSpan York Hospital takes its name from the community whose health it seeks to preserve. Part of WellSpan Health the medical center has about 570 beds and serves residents of York and surrounding area of south-central Pennsylvania. It is a regional leader in cardiovascular and orthopedic care and has programs in other specialty areas including oncology behavioral health and geriatrics. Additionally WellSpan York Hospital operates a Level 1 trauma center offers outpatient surgery emergency home health and diagnostic imaging services. It is also has teaching and research programs. The hospital was founded in 1880.

Operations

WellSpan York Hospital has been recognized as a top 100 US hospital by US News for more than five years in a row. It is also recognized for its cardiovascular and orthopedic programs. The center employs about 700 doctors.

The hospital's education programs include five allied health schools and seven residency programs. Affiliated organizations include the medical schools of Drexel University Pennsylvania State University and University of Maryland.

Strategy

WellSpan York Hospital is working to improve its specialist programs to meet the growing medical needs of area residents. In 2011 for instance it collaborated with technology firm Cerner and pharmaceuticals firm Hospira to form an infusion management program for its intensive care unit; the program aims to reduce infusion-related errors. In addition it launched a urinary catheter removal protocol to reduce infection rates and it implemented an aortic valve replacement program (making it one of three facilities in Pennsylvania to offer the open-heart surgery alternative).

EXECUTIVES

Vice President Of Sales, Richard Brown
Vice President, Peter Hartmann
Senior Vice President, Michael Oconnor
Pharmacy Manager, Courtney Rodgers
Medical Director, Creston Tate
Managing Director General Surgeon, Matthew Souder
Pharmacist Manager, Tony Bixler
Vice President, John Holmes
Senior Vice President And General Counsel, Glen Moffett
Senior Vice President, Charles Chodroff
Vice President Neurosciences, Lori Clark

Vice President Treasury Management Services, Richard Harley
Pharmacy Manager, Leslie Appleby
Medical Director Neurosciences, Todd Barron
Vice President Of Medical Affairs Wellspan Gettysburg Hospital, Charles Marley
Vice President Operations Chief Officer, Vicky Diamond
Vice President Planning, William Lafferty
Pharmacist Manager, Kim Oconnor

LOCATIONS

HQ: YORK HOSPITAL
1001 S GEORGE ST, YORK, PA 174033645
Phone: 717 851-2345
Web: WWW.WELLSPANMEDICALEDUCATION.ORG

COMPETITORS

Ascension Health
Catholic Health Initiatives
Geisinger Health System
Guthrie Healthcare
Hanover Healthcare
Hershey Medical Center
Holy Spirit
Lancaster General
Memorial Hospital (PA)
PinnacleHealth System

HISTORICAL FINANCIALS

Company Type: Private

Income Statement				FYE: June 30
	REVENUE ($ mil.)	NET INCOME ($ mil.)	NET PROFIT MARGIN	EMPLOYEES
06/18	1,063	181	17.0%	6,200
06/16	990	17	1.8%	—
06/15	925	82	9.0%	—
06/14	853	136	16.0%	—
Annual Growth	5.7%		7.3%	

2018 Year-End Financials

Return on assets: 10.6%   Cash ($ mil.): 16
Return on equity: 15.0%
Current ratio: 2.60

YSLETA INDEPENDENT SCHOOL DISTRICT

EXECUTIVES

Supt, Xavier Delatorre
Controller*, Mary Haynie
Staff, Shannon Carroll
Designer, Liliana Sepulveda
Superintendent, De La Torre
Special Education Coordinator, Leslie Armbruster
3rd Grade Teacher, Teresa Burton
Assistant, Claudia Poblano
Secretary, Elizabeth Dimmitt
Girls Athletic Director, Eric Frontz
Secretary, Marina Gonzalez
Auditors: WHITLEY PENN LLP HOUSTON TEX

LOCATIONS

HQ: YSLETA INDEPENDENT SCHOOL DISTRICT
9600 SIMS DR, EL PASO, TX 799257225
Phone: 915 434-0240
Web: WWW.YISD.NET

HISTORICAL FINANCIALS

Company Type: Private

Income Statement				FYE: June 30
	REVENUE ($ mil.)	NET INCOME ($ mil.)	NET PROFIT MARGIN	EMPLOYEES
06/18	488	(164)	—	7,155
06/17	471	150	32.0%	—
06/16	462	257	55.6%	—
06/15	449	(3)	—	—
Annual Growth	2.8%		—	

2018 Year-End Financials

Return on assets: (-15.6%)   Cash ($ mil.): 339
Return on equity: —
Current ratio: —

YUMA REGIONAL MEDICAL CENTER INC

Yuma Regional Medical Center (YRMC) is an acute care hospital that provides medical services for Yuma Arizona and its surrounding communities. The not-for-profit hospital which has more than 400 beds and 400 doctors provides general medical surgical and emergency services. YRMC also operates about 30 additional facilities around Yuma including a rehabilitation hospital laboratories a wound care clinic primary care clinics and diagnostic imaging centers.

Operations

YRMC offers a free program called Silver Care in which patients who are 55 and older are encouraged to live active and healthy lives by being offered a number of benefits such as discounts at local stores specially reduced rates on selected lab tests including cholesterol and blood glucose screenings. Additionally Silver Care members are eligible for free membership in the Fit for Life cardiac wellness program.

The hospital's medical personnel have completed advanced procedures such as a transcatheter aortic valve replacement and a one-level cervical disc replacement using Mobi-C technology.

Strategy

Being a regional hospital YRMC works hard to recruit physicians who might otherwise be drawn to larger teaching hospitals with more advanced technological equipment and complex patient cases. In order to lure in such specialists the hospital offers extended medical education career weekends and a number of specialized centers in which physicians can perform procedures solely in their specialty such as a neonatal ICU and a pediatric sub-specialty unit.

The system has grown by adding new specialty clinics to its network. For example its newest clinic is the YRMC Plastic and Reconstructive Surgery center. It expanded and renovated its emergency department (adding two heliports) in 2017.

EXECUTIVES

Medical Director Of Pathology, Victor Alvarez
Vp Information Technology And Cio, Gene Shaw
Interim President And Ceo, Camie Overton
Vp Patient Care Services And Chief Nursing Officer, Deb Carver
Cfo, David Willie
Interim Vp Medical Affairs And Chief Medical Officer, Robert Cannell

Medical Director, Ismael Guerrero
Director Of Pharmacy, Zulma Rodriguez
Physical Therapy Director, Jennifer Breen
Vice President Of Operations, Trudie Milner
Vice President Treasurer And Assistant Secretary,
  Michelle Martinez
Radiology Director, Savita Samaroo
Vice President, Sugata Das
Anesthesia Secretary, Sandy Hovanec

LOCATIONS

HQ: YUMA REGIONAL MEDICAL CENTER INC
  2400 S AVENUE A, YUMA, AZ 853647170
Phone: 928 344-2000
Web: WWW.YUMAREGIONAL.ORG

PRODUCTS/OPERATIONS

Selected Services

Children
Cancer Care
Children's Rehabilitative Services
Critical Care
Diabetes Education
Diagnostic Imaging
Emergency Department
First Health Medical Supply
Gastroenterology
Heart
Hospitalist Program
Lab
Medical Staff Services
Nursing Units
Outpatient Surgical Center
Pharmacy
Spiritual Care and Patient Advocacy
Surgical Services
Weight Loss
Women's Services
Wound Care Center

COMPETITORS

Banner Health	Northern Arizona
Community Health	Healthcare
Systems	Phoenix Children's
Dignity Health	Hospital
HCA	Providence St. Joseph
John C. Lincoln Health	Health
Network	Scottsdale Healthcare

HISTORICAL FINANCIALS
Company Type: Private

Income Statement				FYE: September 30
	REVENUE ($ mil.)	NET INCOME ($ mil.)	NET PROFIT MARGIN	EMPLOYEES
09/18	483	66	13.7%	2,400
09/17	442	50	11.5%	—
09/16	410	37	9.2%	—
09/15	371	(8)	—	—
Annual Growth	9.2%	—	—	—

ZEN-NOH GRAIN CORPORATION

EXECUTIVES

Ceo, John D Williams
Exec V Pres*, Shin Inoue
Sr. V Pres*, Charles E Colbert
Ctlr*, Robin Gerarve
Dir*, Hiroyuki Kawasaki
Dir*, Yoshihiro Sugiyama

Dir*, Yoshinori Ohara
Executive Vice-President, Osamu Yako
Executive Vice-President, Tomoaki Miyamoto
Purchasing Manager, David Falgout
Vice President Secretary and C, Frank Beguiristain

LOCATIONS

HQ: ZEN-NOH GRAIN CORPORATION
  1127 HWY 190 E SERVICE RD, COVINGTON, LA
  704334929
Phone: 985 867-3500
Web: WWW.CGB.COM

HISTORICAL FINANCIALS
Company Type: Private

Income Statement				FYE: May 31
	REVENUE ($ mil.)	NET INCOME ($ mil.)	NET PROFIT MARGIN	EMPLOYEES
05/18	6,971	101	1.5%	188
05/17	7,047	67	1.0%	—
05/16	5,722	37	0.7%	—
05/15	6,000	86	1.4%	—
Annual Growth	5.1%	5.7%	—	—

2018 Year-End Financials

Return on assets: 4.4%   Cash ($ mil.): 43
Return on equity: 18.2%
Current ratio: 1.10

ZYDUS PHARMACEUTICALS USA INC

EXECUTIVES

Ceo, Joseph D Renner
Cfo*, Ravi Yadavar
Pres*, Michael Keenley
Senior Manager, Freddy Rosado
Corporate Account Manager, Jodi Weber
Senior Director, Kevin Green
Director of Offer Develpment, Maria Falcone

LOCATIONS

HQ: ZYDUS PHARMACEUTICALS USA INC
  73 ROUTE 31 N, PENNINGTON, NJ 085343601
Phone: 609 730-1900
Web: WWW.ZYDUSUSA.COM

HISTORICAL FINANCIALS
Company Type: Private

Income Statement				FYE: December 31
	REVENUE ($ mil.)	NET INCOME ($ mil.)	NET PROFIT MARGIN	EMPLOYEES
12/14	466	5	1.3%	31
12/13	315	5	1.6%	—
12/12	277	3	1.2%	—
12/11	252	8	3.5%	—
Annual Growth	22.7%	(11.8%)	—	—

2014 Year-End Financials

Return on assets: 2.7%   Cash ($ mil.): 7
Return on equity: 78.8%
Current ratio: 1.40

Hoover's Handbook of

Private Companies

Index of Executives

Index of Executives

A

A, Wright Nathan 610
Aaldering, Mark 572
Aaron, Carol 410
Aaron, Todd 528
Aaronson, Diane 300
Aase, Rune 196
Aass, Luke 14
Abbamondi, Desa 669
Abbeele, Annick D. Van den 172
Abberton, James 382
Abbott, Mary J 265
Abbott, Greg 526
Abbott, Dave 559
Abdallah, Chaouki T. 634
Abdel-Kerim, Ahmed 41
Abdelhafiz, Gada M 229
Abdelhak, Mervat 636
Abdo, Marcus 316
Abdraboh, Seif 164
Abduljalil, Hala 517
Abdullah, Sakinah 494
Abe, Karrie 535
Abel, Scott 300
Abelsen, James N 496
Abelson, David J. 406
Abercrombie, Les 210
Abercrombie, Barbara 635
Aberle, Jim 675
Abernathy, Gill 253
Abernathy, Cammy 627
Abernathy, Andrew Mark 632
Abhyankar, Vivek 325
Ables, Dorothy M. 509
Aboody, Linda 325
Abraham, Karen 90
Abraham, Laurence J 206
Abraham, John 276
Abraham, Christine 280
Abrahamson, Tom 283
Abramowitz, Bernard H 369
Abrams, Dave 86
Abrams, Robin 230
Abrams, Paul 254
Abreau, Yolanda 368
Abutaleb, Sam 601
Aceituno, Walter 286
Acereda, Alberto 191
Aceto, Jay 651
Acevedo, Ellen 2
Acevedo, Debby 457
Achat, Catherine 161
Ackerman, John 171
Ackerman, Jeffrey (Jeff) 568
Acklin, Mark 404
Ackroyd, Jim 4
Acosta, Philip A 499
Acosta-Trant, Ivette 65
Acres, Harold R 163
Acton, Bryan 91
Adam, Bradley J 506
Adame, Theresa 22
Adame, Pedro 669
Adames, Ivan 175
Adams, J Phillip 10
Adams, John V 22
Adams, James R. 82
Adams, Cathy 144
Adams, Kevin D 156
Adams, Marsha 179
Adams, Scott 212
Adams, David 256
Adams, William 264
Adams, Gregory A. 271
Adams, Joe M 274
Adams, H E 279
Adams, H E 280
Adams, Martin L. 299
Adams, Andy 329
Adams, Joseph (Joe) 355
Adams, Walter 361
Adams, Erin 371

Adams, Todd 389
Adams, Kendra 425
Adams, Melody 448
Adams, Mary 454
Adams, Michele 511
Adams, Valerie 573
Adams, Justin 579
Adams, Garold B. (Gary) 582
Adams, Ashley 597
Adams, Cecelia 605
Adams, Mary Jane 623
Adams, Bart 639
Adams, Cody 670
Adams, Nicholas 671
Adamson, Nancy 61
Adcock, Richard 515
Addison, Paul 394
Addoh, Carla 508
Adebo, Olo 174
Adelman, Fredie 497
Aden, Chandler 274
Adepeder, Suzanne 175
Ades, Susan 497
Adesnik, Ryan 290
Adkins, Chuck 255
Adkins, Greg 618
Adler, Don 300
Adler, Robert 304
Adler, Michael M. 351
Adome, Amy 489
Adorjan, J. Joe 465
Adsuar, Natalie 285
Afable, Richard 517
Agee, Nancy Howell 112
Aggarwal, Prateek 230
Aggus, Gary L. 239
Agnes, Pierre 93
Agnew, John 669
Agnos, Alexandra 482
Agocs, Michele 596
Agrawal, Gail B. 594
Agugliaro, Aubrey 103
Aguilar, Ashley 107
Aguilar, Jesse 276
Aguilar, Shannon 356
Aguilar, Gayla 378
Aguilar, Leslie 477
Aguirre, Adriana 499
Aharony, Nadav 314
Ahern, Paula 197
Ahern, Michael 198
Ahern, F. Gregory 202
Ahern, Gregory 202
Ahlgrimm, Marijo 34
Ahmar, Wasim 6
Ahmed, Waseem 171
Ahmed, Riffat K 236
Ahn, Jean 72
Ahn, Henry 480
Ahn, Timothy 628
Ahn, Francis 655
Aho, Dustin 6
Aho, Todd R 236
Ahrens, Chris 140
Ahrens, Jere M 196
Ahrens, Charles E. 470
Ahuja, Kishore 376
Ahuja, Rohit 448
Ahuja, Naresh 504
Ai, Lin 627
Aiken, Jefferson K. (Jeff) 289
Aiken, Paul 593
Aikens, Jason 248
Aikens-allen, Karla 432
Aimee, Heeter 610
Aing, Melissa 324
Ainslie, Carolyn N. 591
Air, Dorothy 625
Aird, Dan 512
Aishman, Lisa 255
Ajmani, Deep 389
Akalaeva, Nailya 459
Akamatsu, Yayoi 375
Akers, David (Dave) 104

Akers, Harlan 469
Akers, Sally 611
Akey, Douglas 333
Akin, Rich 461
Akin, Terry 578
Akins, Nicholas K 32
Akman, Jeffrey S. 569
Akpik, Debbie 43
Akpoguma, Andrea 76
Akroush, Ghada 276
Al-Ghanoudi, Ashirf 218
Alack, Marisa M 284
Alaimo, Chris 309
Alaniz, Carol 486
alarcon, Alessandro De 128
Alarcon, Mari 183
Alas, Alejandra 646
Alba, Alex 536
Alban, Susan 671
Alberici, John S 18
Alberici, John S 19
Albert, Justin 453
Albert, Elizabeth 517
Alberto, Carl 520
Alberts, Jim 274
Albertson, Paul 365
Albonetti, Susan 625
Albrecht, Raymond P 340
Albright, Dave 379
Albright, Linda 451
Albright, Steven 526
Alcock, Charles R. 497
Alday, Joseph 459
Aldersley, Stephen 456
Alderson, Tony 119
Alderson, Philip O. 465
Aldred, Linda 548
Aldrich, Sister Barbara 523
Aldridge, Bryan 56
Aleksic, Aleksandar 7
Ales, Donna 284
Alesina, Susan 558
Aletta, Joseph 180
Alex, Bodney 415
Alexaitis, Irene 489
Alexander, Nick 5
Alexander, Jackie 27
Alexander, Craig 170
Alexander, Allen 174
Alexander, Gaylord 236
Alexander, Lisa 291
Alexander, Sherrie 334
Alexander, James 346
Alexander, Jim 411
Alexander, Kelly 508
Alexander, Randy 606
Alexander, Pamala 617
Alexander, Gordon 647
Alexiou, Joy 472
Alford, William C. 87
Alford, Katherine 480
Alford, Barbara 541
Alford, Bobby 548
Alfred, Richard L. 486
Alger, Robert 285
Algoe, Eric 551
Alhadeff, Kathie 418
Ali, Syed A 64
Ali, Syed Arbab 236
Alicandri, John 246
Alicea, Maria 97
Alicea, Marisa 175
Alicea, Jaime 539
Aligheri, Tim 262
Alkire, Michael 428
Allain, Dwayne 578
Allam, Anthony 68
Alldian, David P 90
Allen, Michael D. 13
Allen, Amy 45
Allen, Les 82
Allen, Susan 126
Allen, Jeff 151
Allen, Jennifer 162

Allen, James 202
Allen, Herbert 204
Allen, Robert 256
Allen, Daniel P 258
Allen, Stephen P 279
Allen, Clay M 284
Allen, Jon 328
Allen, Steve 359
Allen, David J. 374
Allen, Erin 387
Allen, Mark 422
Allen, Traci 423
Allen, Trina 445
Allen, Kim 490
Allen, Gloria 530
Allen, Cindy 541
Allen, Jodi J 571
Allen, Elizabeth Heller 576
Allen, Richard D 587
Allen, Greg 627
Allen, Dee 631
Allen, Gary K. 633
Allen, Ricci 638
Allison, Les 225
Allison, David 302
Allison, Stephen 308
Allison, William 360
Allison, Julie 361
Allison, John 617
Allman, Dora 56
Allocca, Lori 502
Allred, Justin 58
Allshouse, Scott 669
Almaraz, Frank 164
Almon, Lorie E. 486
Almond, Karen 588
Alonzo, Leonicio 59
Alpay, John M 110
Alperstein, Janet 370
Alsip, Bryan 82
Alspaw, Mark 308
Alston, Debra 325
Alstrom, Eric 173
Altaras, June 537
Altenborf, Mike 182
Altendorf, Michael J. (Mike) 182
Alter, Tom 415
Alteri, Joseph 586
Altieri, Len 420
Altschuler, Glenn C. 159
Aluisio, Frank V 578
Alvarado, Paulina 161
Alvarado, Angelita 250
Alvarado, Douglas 404
Alvarez, Carolina 299
Alvarez, Sorita 325
Alvarez, Terry 518
Alvarez, Victor 677
alver, 159
Alvey, Jack 251
Alvey, Jennifer 252
Alviani, Joseph D 407
Alwood, Amy 581
Alyea, Ryan 119
Alzamora, Esteban 404
Amadou, Teddy 242
Amadu, Sule 193
Amanullah, Aman 19
Amaro, Denise 244
Amato, David 140
Amato, Gavin 453
Ambach, Robert F. (Bob) 625
Ambrose, Sherie 182
Ambrose, Kelly 298
Ambrosino, Richard 643
Ambrosio, Michael 657
Ambrowiak, Alice 453
Ameismeier, Donna 459
Amend, Matt 25
Amend, Chris 199
America, James 146
Americas, Levi Strauss 293
Amerine, Teri 462
Amerson, Leon T. (Timmy) 11

Index of Executives

Ames, Richard 196
Amirat, Cherif 572
Ammann, Vincent L. 666
Amoruso, Robert C 519
Amos, Sister Helen 332
Amos, Gregg 491
Amoussou, Ben 422
Amparan, Oscar L. 550
Amrik, Nicole 19
Amsell, David 459
An, Weizhe 336
Ana, Coleen Santa 484
Analdo, Stephen F 411
Anand, Manish 230
Anand, Lawrence 230
Anastasi, Michelle 407
Ancell, Murray T. 386
Andel, Steve Van 29
Andel, Stephen Van 500
Anders, Bob 270
Anders, Marjorie 335
Andersen, Paul 246
Anderskow, Jerry 14
Anderson, Warren 38
Anderson, Erik 49
Anderson, Eric 49
Anderson, Colleen 59
Anderson, Michael 64
Anderson, Thomas R 78
Anderson, Doug 85
Anderson, Lois 97
Anderson, Lois 110
Anderson, Markham J J 121
Anderson, David 128
Anderson, Sharon 132
Anderson, Staci 153
Anderson, Tricia 184
Anderson, C. Colt 206
Anderson, Barbara 207
Anderson, Rebecca 212
Anderson, Janet 215
Anderson, Anjanette 220
Anderson, Lcpl 244
Anderson, Cevin 247
Anderson, Don 250
Anderson, Larry 255
Anderson, A. Scott 256
Anderson, Kenneth W 258
Anderson, Ronnie K 281
Anderson, Carl A. 282
Anderson, Steven 285
Anderson, Allyson 288
Anderson, Gregory A 310
Anderson, Traci K. 321
Anderson, Angela 362
Anderson, Jill 367
Anderson, Terry Sam 382
Anderson, Shelly 407
Anderson, Jim 415
Anderson, Richard 415
Anderson, Joe Dean 419
Anderson, Carole 433
Anderson, Cheryl 451
Anderson, Richard A 466
Anderson, Terry D 467
Anderson, Misty 471
Anderson, Richard A 513
Anderson, Julie 515
Anderson, Charles K 522
Anderson, Geri 525
Anderson, Gregory 546
Anderson, Sophie 549
Anderson, Stephanie J 552
Anderson, Amanda 561
Anderson, Audrey J. 599
Anderson, Gerri 604
Anderson, Eric 610
Anderson, Jane 636
Anderson, Llewellyn C. 651
Anderson, Suzanne 652
Anderson, Leha 653
Anderson, Jennifer 671
Andersson, Roland 405
Andes, John 511

Andolina, Mark 625
Andrabi, Imran A 330
Andrade, Mauro 196
Andre-Brunet, Marc 282
Andresen, Andy 215
Andresen, Elena 399
Andreski, Lynne 513
Andresky, Christa 612
Andrew, Briggs 112
Andrews, Briggs 112
Andrews, Nancy C. 187
Andrews, Stephanie 252
Andrews, Haven 315
Andrews, Bill 369
Andrews, Susan Mc 451
Andrews, Wayne (Keith) 452
Andrews, Josh 552
Andrews, Felicia 561
Andrews, Sue 574
Andrews, Teresa 610
Andrews, Arthur 638
Andrews, Cindy 650
Andreyka, Timothy 16
Andrichik, Kenneth 202
Andro, Ronald 23
Anello, Neil 255
Anfinnsen, Tor Martin 197
Angelico, Michael D 97
Angelle, Bryant 142
Angle, Greg 300
Angley, James 369
Angulo, Carlos 265
Angulo, Christine Stiltner 501
Angus, Jeff 189
Anicetti, Richard A. (Rick) 568
Ankrum, Bob 333
Annecharico, Mary Alice 236
Annunziato, Frank 546
Anschutz, J Barron 117
Anson, Betty 515
Anspach, Angela 117
Antes, John 344
Anthony, Donna 254
Anthony, Tim 360
Anthony, Jim 405
Anthony, David 456
Antis, Connie 518
Anton, Daniela 43
Anton, John J 124
Anton, Michael E 124
Antonelli, Cecille 526
Antoniello, Angela 383
Antonini, Alberto 611
Antonino, John 180
Antonucci, Toni 444
Anunda, Sydney 627
Aoun, Joseph E. 383
Ao'brien, Kathryn 175
Apitz, Marcus 655
Aplington, David 513
Appel, Jeff 43
Appel, Ron 43
Apperson, Kevin 315
Appia, Janey 354
Applbaum, Hilda L 31
Appleby, Leslie 677
Applefeld, Jack 478
Applegate, John S. 609
Appleyard, Joseph 608
Appold, Stacy R 161
Appolonia, John 14
Appolonia, Jack 14
Aquino, Michelle 37
Aquino, Osvaldo 369
Arabie, Cheryl 467
Aragon, Manuela 537
Aragon, Patrick 546
Araki, Gavin 399
Aran, Pete 464
Arand, Donna 276
Aranda, Marc 212
Arbide, Donna 569
Arboleda, Zara 646
Arbuckle, Barry 298

Arcand, Alfred 111
Arcaro, Katri 202
Arcaro, John 610
Archer, Brandi 8
Archer, Donna 274
Archibald, Sandra 640
Archie, Thomas 14
Ardalkar, Prashant 286
Arellano, Richard 410
Arendt, Brian 317
Arevalo, Ruth M 431
Arey, George 608
Argue, David 231
Arii, Carrie 437
Arikat, Yazeed 519
Arimanithaya, Sreehanth Krishnan 154
Arkof, Anna 259
Arm, Amy Steele 125
Armater, Ann 233
Armato, Carl S. 390
Armato, Carl 428
Armbruster, Leslie 677
Arment, Daniel J. (Dan) 97
Armentrout, Tracy A 391
Armfield, Jeff 501
Armini, Michael 383
Armour, Meri 335
Arms, William C 515
Armstrong, Jason 61
Armstrong, Scott A. 172
Armstrong, Wayne 186
Armstrong, Kevin R 252
Armstrong, Greg L 422
Armstrong, Mary 487
Armstrong, Katrina A. 574
Armstrong, William 630
Arndt, Gerald 225
Arner, Steve 112
Arneson, Georgene 429
Arneson, Craig 431
Arnn, Roger 199
Arnold, Steve 50
Arnold, Jeff 83
Arnold, Bradley 126
Arnold, Jason 134
Arnold, Craig 190
Arnold, Kay K 196
Arnold, Sandra 206
Arnold, David 258
Arnold, Doug 452
Arnold, Gregory A. (Greg) 607
Arnold, Truman 607
Arnow, Bruce 290
Arntzen, Corry 511
Aronne, Brian 246
Aronov, Tina 108
Aronzon, Daniel 649
Arous, Gérard Ben 370
Arrington, Pat 261
Arrington, Courtney 606
Arroyo, Ana 580
Arsenault, Julie 454
Arthur, Randal 36
Arthur, Kory 293
Arthurs, Mike 556
Artman, Michael 327
Arts, Sander 53
Arvin, Ann Margaret 290
Arwari, Andy 113
Ascher, Michael C 606
Ashby, Valerie S. 187
Ashby, Michael 484
Ashenfelter, Lacey 359
Ashley, Dennis 33
Ashley, Marion 161
Ashley, Stanley W 556
Ashlyn, Sowell 269
Ashmeade-Brown, Jamila 21
Ashtary, Mishel 34
Ashton, Melinda 230
Ashue, Meghan 671
Asmus, Sharon 460
Asp, Jim 579
Asrat, Mack 494

Assaf, Michal 229
Assaf, Ronald G. 390
Assef, Eduardo 136
Astor, Frank 357
Ata, Sana 284
Atcherman, S Jeffrey 334
Atchley, Kecia 431
Athavale, Atul 230
Atherton, Andrea 425
Atkins, Patricia J 489
Atkinson, Mike 6
Atkinson, Corrinne 231
Atmore, Gillian 362
Attanasio, John B. 505
Attaway, David 51
Attaway, John A. 435
Attebery, Tim 662
Attrill, Ed 180
Atwood, Paul 220
Atwood, Anita 245
Atwood, Denver 506
Au, Mei 375
Aubin, Michael D. 63
Aucoin, Gary 197
Audiffred, Doug 318
Audiffred, J Douglas 319
Auger, Stephen 204
Augostini, Christopher 570
Augsburger, Tod 293
Augustine, Lesley 453
Augustino, Philip 194
Aul, Christopher 168
Auld, Maureen 671
Aultmon, Gisela 409
Aurand, Martin 114
Aurilio, Lisa 131
Ausenhus, Dennis 247
Ausere, Michael J 198
Aust, Dee 402
Austen, Karla 355
Austin, Danielle 58
Austin, Scott 343
Austin, Joe 417
Austin, Joe 417
Austin, Jennifer 476
Austin, Pam 511
Austin, Scott 563
Autio, Ann 619
Averbach, Rob 671
Averett, J W 506
Averette, Joseph W 458
Averill, Chris 412
Averill, Chris 412
Averill, Christopher R 584
Avery, Emily 122
Avery, Jeffrey 195
Avery, Jonathan 288
Avery, Sonja 302
Avery, Thomas 517
Avery, Lois 660
Avery, Mary 671
Avetikov, Albert 459
Avila, Luisa 107
Aviles, Alan D. 365
Avis, Nancy 377
Awan, Zoya 570
Awells, Rebecca 175
Axelrod, Susan F. 202
Axenson, Tanya 24
Axtell, Tom 432
Axtman, Renee 29
Ayala-Gonzalez, Oscar 638
Ayar, Alper 496
Ayer, William S. (Bill) 640
Ayers, Joshua 280
Ayers, Lori 349
Ayers, Mark 361
Aylor, James H. 442
Ayscue, Charles F 344
Azam, Asif 287
Azar, Mario 86
Azar, Gordon 386
Azar, Robert B 389
Azarela, Michael (Mike) 531

Index of Executives

Index of Executives

Index of Executives

Index of Executives

Index of Executives

Brown, Marcus V 196
Brown, Deirdre A 203
Brown, Marilyn 209
Brown, Tom 212
Brown, Eric 225
Brown, Jim 228
Brown, Janet 237
Brown, Amy 255
Brown, Jeff 255
Brown, Michael 268
Brown, James D 280
Brown, George J. 288
Brown, Cathy A 296
Brown, Kevin 299
Brown, Diona 323
Brown, Kim 327
Brown, Dan 358
Brown, Luke 359
Brown, Leonard 361
Brown, Michael 373
Brown, Jane 383
Brown, Kathleen 396
Brown, Bartholomew 396
Brown, Kevin 418
Brown, Geoff 418
Brown, Janine 418
Brown, Dr Kenneth 429
Brown, Brian 440
Brown, Dan 444
Brown, Carole 445
Brown, Drew 478
Brown, Robin B. 479
Brown, Cassie 480
Brown, Nancy 482
Brown, Venessa 486
Brown, W 501
Brown, Daniel A. 551
Brown, Eric 559
Brown, Michael W 571
Brown, Vance M 574
Brown, David FM 574
Brown, David A 582
Brown, Edith 589
Brown, Charlie 594
Brown, Chani 597
Brown, Derek 612
Brown, Jay 615
Brown, Janice 636
Brown, Virginia L 643
Brown, Mike 673
Brown, Richard 677
Browne, Mark 162
Browne, Paul 236
Browne, Janelle 551
Brownell, Kelly D. 187
Brownell, Mark 395
Brownie, Susan 488
Browning, Deborah 128
Browning, Chris 128
Browning, Chris 351
Browning, Allan 361
Browning, Debbie 424
Browning, Michael 601
Brownlee, James 638
Brownsberger, Tina 633
Broyles, Rob 204
Broyles, Andy 480
Bruce, Timothy 98
Bruce, Carrie 442
Bruce, Anne 493
Bruce, Harry 640
Bruchman, Robert 30
Bruck, Lori A 546
Bruckner, Brian M 102
Bruckner, Chris B 102
Bruder, Eric 610
Bruder, Karen 638
Brudnicki, Gary 664
Brueck, Margaret 486
Bruggeman, Kevin 671
Bruhn, Michelle 471
Brukardt, David 641
Brumagim, Jeannie 429
Brumberg, Leonard 98

Brumfield, Chris N 200
Brumley, Susan 175
Brumley, Blake 549
Brumm, Jennifer L 316
Brummit, John 247
Brummitt, Charles 55
Brumsted, John 597
Brumsted, John R. 598
Brundige, Cynthia 513
Bruner, Robert F. 442
Brunk, Debbie 186
Brunner, Mary 625
Bruno, John P 519
Bruno, Rosemary 607
Brunt, Jeff Van 614
Bruun, Ed 508
Bruxvoort, Keith 530
Bruza, John M 583
Bryan, Joe 162
Bryan, Lawana 383
Bryan, Deborah 597
Bryan, John 604
Bryant, Phil 263
Bryant, Mary 263
Bryant, Kevin E 274
Bryant, Bret 281
Bryant, Jay 312
Bryant, Dawn 379
Bryar, Alex 300
Bryce, Kristin Jones 631
Bryke, Christine 79
Brysch, Paul 502
Brzoskowski, Ryszard 544
Buafo, Charles 575
Bubnov, Sergey 458
Buchanan, Jason 98
Buchanan, Kenneth (Ken) 171
Buchanan, Maxine 174
Buchanan, Jennifer 204
Buchanan, Kathryn 334
Buchanan, Stephen G. (Steve) 460
Buchanan, Jamie 640
Buchanan, Brooke 669
Buchbinder, David K 129
Buchenau, Blaine 207
Bucher, Charles 159
Bucher, Al 197
Bucher, Mary Kaye 636
Buchholtz, Chris 447
Buchholz, Thomas 479
Buchner, Renee 671
Buck, Haydee 183
Buck, Catherine (Cathy) 211
Buck, Sean 261
Buck, Tiffany 547
Buckalew, Steve 223
Bucker, Robert 505
Buckingham, Rob 381
Buckingham, Phil 611
Buckley, David P 43
Buckley, Morgan 155
Buckley, John L. 423
Buckley, Gerard J. 456
Buckley, Erin 482
Buckley, Guy G. 509
Buckley, Kerry 578
Buckley, Adam P. 598
Buckley, Linda 632
Bucklin, Patricia 586
Buckner, Alma 8
Buckner, Emma 624
Buechel, Jason 669
Buehler, Ralf 193
Buehler, Charlie 671
Buenaseda, Jude 370
Buergel, Erich 326
Bueschen, Anton 624
Buescher, John 318
Bufferd, Allan S 79
Bufferd, Allan 314
Buffington, Heidi 465
Buffmire, Andrew 639
Bugher, Mark D. 309
Bugher, Daniel 505

Buhr, Steve 78
Bui-Thompson, Nancy 462
Buijs, Peter 158
Buit, Tim 365
Bujold-Lee, Sue 8
Bukiewicz, Ralph 587
Bukiewicz, Susan 587
Bulawa, Bryan F 340
Bull, Harry 126
Bull, Mick 457
Bullard, Coby 104
Bullington, Amy 105
Bullion, Diana 431
Bullock, Diana 193
Bullock, Timothy 302
Bullock, Gregory 631
Bulpitt, Amy 516
Bumgardner, Beth A 573
Bunch, Lonnie G. 497
Bunch, Jaclyn 637
Bunder, Lawrence 370
Bundy, Michael 109
Bundy, Orrin 584
Bunker, Mike 112
Bunnell, Ronald R. (Ron) 61
Bunnell, Craig A. 172
Bunsness, Joe 98
Bunting, Glenn 43
Bunton, Kris 549
Bunyard, Steve 395
Buonanno, Bernie 2
Buongiorno, Michael 305
Buono, Tim 475
Buonpastore, Andy 370
Burba, Deron 497
Burbach, Nicole 250
Burback, Katie 15
Burbage, Lois 201
Burby, Chris 529
Burch, Eric 251
Burch, Stephen A. 631
Burchart, Nathalie De Vos 85
Burchett, Ronald 419
Burdett, Judith 562
Burdett, H W 565
Burdick, Christian 619
Burdjalov, Vladimir 561
Burdolski, Jane 491
Burelli, Laura 395
Burfitt, Gregory H 117
Burge, Patty 45
Burgess, Conal 405
Burgess, Patrice 463
Burget, Mark 579
Burgos, Sonia 203
Burington, Judy 51
Burkard, Joe 283
Burke, Ed 14
Burke, Michael W 19
Burke, Ryan 137
Burke, Edmund F 178
Burke, Timothy J. (Tim) 396
Burke, John 440
Burke, Gerald 442
Burke, Thomas M. 464
Burke, James F. 478
Burke, James F 479
Burke, Alan 514
Burke, Janice 603
Burke, John D. 608
Burkel, Terri 417
Burkett, Steven 228
Burkett, Lynn 441
Burkhardt, Steve 5
Burkhardt, Andrew 597
Burkhart, James R. 203
Burkhart, Craig 524
Burkholder, Michael 412
Burlage, David P. 143
Burls, Chris 354
Burmaster, Brad 297
Burmester, Mark A 362
Burnell, Jody 402
Burnett, Bonnie 21

Burnett, Janice 94
Burnett, Archie 96
Burnett, Don 160
Burnett, Walter 174
Burnett, Mark 337
Burnett, Kevin M 532
Burnett, Kevin M 590
Burnett, Brian D. 633
Burnette, Don 160
Burnette, Peg 179
Burney, Pete 261
Burnfield, Richard G. 503
Burnich, Jeffrey 535
Burnim, Mickey L. 642
Burnosky, James 369
Burns, Glenn 59
Burns, Steve 245
Burns, Mandy 333
Burns, Patricia 344
Burns, Joseph E 462
Burns, Sister Miriam 514
Burns, Ryan 543
Burns, James 608
Burns, Jacqueline 627
Burns, Jon P. 630
Burnstein, Mark I 236
Burpee, Steve 457
Burrell, Carol 383
Burrell, Cheryl 526
Burrescia, Dominic 453
Burrin, Stephen E 553
Burris, Brian 281
Burriss, Steve 448
Burriss, Steve 448
Burroughs, Clint 106
Burroughs, Lisa 481
Burrow, Mark 646
Burrus, Victoria 648
Burry, Todd 176
Burson, Michael L 135
Burt, Linda K 362
Burt, Suzie 646
Burton, Steven L 105
Burton, Marianne 129
Burton, Christa 276
Burton, Mary 331
Burton, Mary 444
Burton, Carol 476
Burton, Pam 639
Burton, Teresa 677
Bury, Randy 566
Busacca, Brian 263
Busam, James 217
Busch, Todd 166
Busch, Jonathan 442
Buschkowiak, Boris 674
Bush, Frederick S Steve 22
Bush, Emily 56
Bush, Vicki 289
Bush, Stephen 478
Bush, William L 509
Bussel, Marina 405
Bussells, Walter 264
Bussy, Jean-Franois 153
Buster, Bob 161
Butina, Barry 671
Butler, Charl L. 11
Butler, Paul Edd 83
Butler, Rich 132
Butler, Steve 183
Butler, Annmarie 259
Butler, Alice 332
Butler, Mike 431
Butler, Michael 431
Butler, Linda 448
Butler, Linda 448
Butler, Timothy 453
Butler, June 558
Butler, P. Barry 594
Butler, Connie 596
Butler, Michael C 616
Butler, Richard 617
Butler, Gary 618
Butler, Karis 657

Index of Executives

Index of Executives

Index of Executives

Index of Executives

Index of Executives

Curphy, Rona 61
Currall, Steven 505
Curran, Michael J. 321
Curran, Greg 613
Curran, Maria 649
Currie, Dean W. 107
Currie, John 361
Currier, Rand 220
Curry, Robert 137
Curry, Robert 137
Curry, Denise 153
Curry, Wanda C 196
Curry, Randal 212
Curry, Maridee 320
Curry, Mike Mc 328
Curry, Kevin 439
Curry, John 443
Curry, Susan J. 594
Curry, Jeffrey T 666
Curry-Briggs, Doreen 40
Curti, Joseph Tate 193
Curtis, Michael 312
Curtis, Lynda D. 365
Curtis, Lucy 418
Curtis, Yvonne 425
Curto, Chris 239
Curtwright, Lois 128
Cury, Jason 307
Cusher, Andrew 615
Cushing, Robert 17
Cushman, Audrey 315
Cuskaden, Trisha 662
Custer, Jami 558
Cutchins, Alexis G 194
Cutler, Juanita 116
Cutler, Brian 555
Cutliff, Scott 439
Cutter, Brian 157
Cutter, David 475
Czajkowski, Andrew 241
Czarnetzki, Theresa 216
Czebotar, Jerry A 358
Czumak, Michael 325

D

D, Pedro Cazabon M 394
D, Eric Dickson M 616
Dabbs, Lorrie 246
Dachenbach, Angie 247
Dadey, Bryan 596
Daeihagh, Pirouz 377
Dahl, Roslyn 18
Dahlberg, Edwin 522
Dahlstrom, Richard (Rick) 320
Dai, Hai-Lung 546
Daigle, Gregory 640
Daik, Sam 543
Dailey, Mike 385
Dailey, John 480
Dailey, John R. (Jack) 497
Dajany, Adam 28
Dake, Gary C 529
Dake, William P 529
Dalal, Kosha 202
Dale, Nancy 300
Dale, Ken 555
Dale, Christopher 646
Daleo, Robert D. (Bob) 206
Dallala, Daniel 114
Dallas, Mike 599
Dallman, Carla 671
Dalrymple, Cara 160
Dalsky, David 116
Dalton, Willam S 226
Dalton, William 227
Dalton, Chuck 386
Dalton, James T. 444
Dalton, Jay 539
Dalton, Mark F. 599
Dalton, Karen 607
Daly, Ronald E. 2

Daly, Marilyn 27
Daly, Kevin 96
Daly, Eric 246
Daly, Ashley 327
Daly, Patricia 330
Daly, Shawn 593
Damanaki, Maria 579
Dameron, Jeffrey C 124
Dames, Peter 485
Damiano, William 642
Damico, Anthony 489
Dammon, Robert M. 114
Damon, Lisa J. 486
Damore, Joseph 344
Damschroder, Patricia 596
Dan, Jackson 383
Dana, Ashley 165
Dandorph, Michael J 459
Danes, Mike 50
Daney, Jennifer M 48
Dangelo, Kathryn 546
Dani, Shaila 370
Daniel, Karen L. 85
Daniel, Becky 551
Daniel, Chris Mc 596
Daniel, Terrie 638
Daniels, Stephen 127
Daniels, Andria 161
Daniels, Ronald J. (Ron) 268
Daniels, Jacqueline R. 390
Daniels, Vince 487
Daniels, Mark 511
Daniels, Bobbi 632
Danielson, Sandra 357
Dankner, Wayne 405
Danon, Saar 298
Dantas, Bruno 51
Daprile, Joseph R 193
Daprile, Jospeh R 372
Darby, Paul 208
Darcy, Mike 154
Dardari, Davide 572
Darger, Ford STANFORD 375
Darji, Rajesh 452
Dark, Dana 578
Darr, Alex 444
Darrell, Dyson 651
Darrow, Bruce 351
Darrow, Rebecca 511
Dart, Richard C. 179
Das, Sugata 678
Dasgupta, Satarupa 371
DaSilva, Jack 601
Daskalos, Paul 469
Dasossa, Mag 176
Datema, Scott 87
Daubner, Thomas 604
Dauer, Jennifer 128
Daugherty, Michael 553
Daugiala, Alfredas 496
Dauphine, Jon 2
Daurio, Nancy 304
Dauterive, F Ralph 394
Dave, Naimesh 140
Dave, Rajesh 619
Davenport, DeWitt 109
Davenport, John 303
Davenport, Charles 408
Davenport, Beverly 625
Davenport, Jacquie 645
Davenport, Mely 675
Davert, Marshall 356
Davich, Joe 176
David, Mark 126
David, Prabu 340
David, Steven 371
David, Evan 407
Davidoff, Ravin 95
Davidson, Julie 184
Davidson, Robert G 332
Davidson, Candi 477
Davidson, Jay 506
Davidson, Martin D 506
Davidson, Brian 523

Davidson, Gary 573
Davies, Neal 333
Davila, Diana 245
Davila, Rosa 344
Davila, Melinda 620
Davilla, Nancy 486
Davis, Yolanda 9
Davis, James C. (Jim) 24
Davis, Chris 64
Davis, Mary 77
Davis, Joan 89
Davis, Jason 105
Davis, Benjamin 113
Davis, Pamela Bowles 116
Davis, Carolyn 131
Davis, Scott 134
Davis, Ellen F. 187
Davis, Adora 188
Davis, Pamela 191
Davis, Brian 192
Davis, Matt 205
Davis, Gary 206
Davis, Becky 209
Davis, Chris 235
Davis, Ken 248
Davis, Shirley 250
Davis, Auston 302
Davis, Leslie C 303
Davis, Kenneth L 351
Davis, Jed 361
Davis, Latia 370
Davis, Richard E. 389
Davis, Mark 395
Davis, Tim 417
Davis, Belinda 420
Davis, Debbie 451
Davis, Cory 453
Davis, Paul 475
Davis, Crystal 482
Davis, Jonathan S. 484
Davis, Jodi 535
Davis, Myra 548
Davis, Shawn 548
Davis, Muzzet 551
Davis, Dawn 554
Davis, Joan S. 563
Davis, Greg 567
Davis, Anne 571
Davis, Patricia 574
Davis, Jeff 574
Davis, Thomas P 581
Davis, Debra A. 596
Davis, John 602
Davis, Michael 607
Davis, Elizabeth 625
Davis, Tyler 639
Davis, Leslie C. 643
Davis, Deborah 649
Davis, A. Jack 652
Davis, Traci 659
Davis, James L 674
Davis-Kubofcik, Deborah 575
Davison, J Scott 396
Davoren, Peter J 593
Davoren, Peter J. 612
Davy, Alan 443
Dawes, Christopher 290
Dawes, Christopher 302
Dawley, Mary 54
Dawoodbhai, Moiz 55
Day, Timothy 80
Day, Terri 277
Day, Debbie 352
Day, Lynn Carmen 451
Day, James H 607
Day, Sarah 672
Dayal, Gaurov 512
Days, Karen 359
DC, Sister Bernice Coreil 47
DC, Sister Maureen McGuire 47
DDS, Will Daniels 77
DDS, L Kenneth Heuler 129
DDS, Edwin Zechman 131
DDS, Phillip Wenk 177

De, Monica 102
Dean, DOT 28
Dean, Edward 58
Dean, James D 85
Dean, Jerry 168
Dean, Lloyd H. 181
Dean, Doug 193
Dean, Gregory 202
Dean, Pam 377
Dean, Lesley 396
Dean, Antoinette 465
Dean, Susanne 532
Dean, Christina 610
Dearborn, Grant 232
Dearth, Randall S. (Randy) 106
Deaton, John 160
Deaton, Eric 662
Deb, Stone 111
Debenedetti, Pablo G. 591
Debertin, Jay 133
Debra, Scammon 597
Debrecht, Ken 18
Debruin, Christopher 531
Decardenas, Eva 561
Decastro, Victoria 128
December, Katrina 642
Dechant, Maria 636
Dechiro, Carlo V 509
Decicco, Dawn 453
Decker, Andrea 330
Decoeur, Dan 673
Dee, Tim 404
Deering, Michael 299
Defenbaugh, Raymond E 82
DeFord, Drexel 528
Degoede, Arthur 168
DeGrand, Robert 211
Dehahn, Erin 659
Deibert, Karen 399
Deignan, Kathleen 591
Deis, Colin 496
Dejarme, Lindy 70
Dekay, Donald F 257
Dekay, Barry 362
Dekeyser, Paul 356
Dekoch, Bob 555
DeKosky, Steven T. (Steve) 442
Delacour, Alia 481
Delagardelle, Pam 258
Delancey, Virginia 389
Delaney, Thomas A. (Tom) 370
Delaney, Michelle Anne 497
Delaney, Ed 618
Delaney, Mary 664
Delano, Laurie A. 566
Delanois, Gary 1
Delany, Jim 555
Delatorre, Xavier 677
Delattre, James 584
Delauder, Brad 161
Delawder, Bruce 601
Delay, Mary G 596
Delellis, Ronald A 448
Deleon, Marcos 269
Deleon, Leo 484
Deleonardis, Doreen 664
Delessio, Linda 215
Delgadillo, Joe 387
Delgado, Gilberto 582
Dellaselva, Chris 138
Dellinger, Lisa 312
Deloach, Darlene 508
Delombarde, Joey 235
Delone, Carrie L 213
Delong, David 564
Delong, William C 564
Delong, Charles R 564
Delong, Bo 564
Delong, Mary Lou 608
Delotta, Debbie 500
Delozier, Sharon 449
Delpropoto, Zachary 236
Delrosso, Irene 409

Index of Executives

Deluca, Vince 297
Deluke, Linda 482
Deluz, Donna 628
Delvecchio, Steve 2
Demahy, Anita 481
Demarie, John 70
Dematas, Teri 252
Demay, David 274
Demello, Daphne 417
DeMichiei, Robert A. 643
Deming, Peggy 82
Demirovski, Fluturi 445
Demme, Kendra 101
Demoleas, John P 527
Demourkas, Cat 472
Dempsey, Paul 593
Demski, Renee 269
Den, Sara 465
Denault, Leo P 196
denBoer, Marten 175
Denges, Jim 530
Dengg, Robb 256
Denham, Amber 623
DeNichilo, Nicholas 303
Deninger, Matthew 315
Denise, Mccauley 574
Denison, Jessica 564
Denizli, Alexandra 459
Denk, Peter 452
Denningham, Wayne A. 20
Dennis, Lakisha 137
Dennis, Patrick 261
Dennis, Everette E. 388
Dennis, Tyler 415
Dennis, Monica 420
Dennison, Kay 40
Denny, Coleen 662
Denoble, Ubavka 405
Densham, Edward 469
Denton, Kelly 264
Denty, Kimberly 187
Deo, Rajat 244
Deoliveira, Jessica 370
Deon, Pasquale T. (Pat) 503
Depaolo, Joseph J 493
Depaolo, Mary-beth 496
DePauw, Karen P. 652
DePell, Fred (Fred) 387
DePiano, Frank 389
Der, Channing 595
Derba, Laura 669
Derby, Cindy 513
Derita, Nancy 516
Derosa, Peter 138
Derr, David 411
Derrick, Brian 19
Derrick, Brian 326
DeRue, Scott 444
Derwinski, Janet 404
Deryckere, Bernard P. J. 668
Derzypolski, Stephanie 541
Desai, Anup 349
Desarno, Fred 294
Deschon, Beverly 618
Desfosses, Kristina 287
Deshaies, Roger 598
Deshazo, Nina 130
Deshong, Leanne 117
Deshpande, Jayant K. 45
Desimas, Danny 274
Desisto, Donna 473
Deskins, Juanita 419
Desmarais, Brian 525
Desmond, Neil 390
Desmond, Margaret 596
Desormeaux, Joseph 215
Despeaux, Kimberly H 196
Deste, Dario 202
DeStefano, Joanne M. 159
Destler, William W. (Bill) 456
Dete, Brendan 5
Detmer, Don 442
Deuschle, James R. (Jim) 449
Dev, Raj 547

Devaney, Jack 74
Devens, Michael 185
Devine, David 360
Devivo, Zita 366
Devlin, Dennis 569
Devlin, Dave 618
Devoe, Michael 52
Devoe, Ellen 96
Devoney, William 191
DeVoney, Michael 613
Devooght, Shawn 233
Devore, Susan 428
DeVos, Doug 29
Devos, Mr Doug L 500
Dewald, Julius 388
Dewerff, Mike 258
Dewey, Barbara I. 584
Dewey, Susan F. 651
Dews, Maria 58
Dhanapal, Kishore 286
Dhanda, Anuj 20
Diakov, Peter 630
Dials, Kelly 359
Dialto, Margaret 527
Diamond, Gene 207
Diamond, Mark C 236
Diamond, Margae 477
Diamond, Lester 514
Diamond, Rachael 584
Diamond, Vicky 677
Diamond-wells, Tammy R 45
Dian, Ali 493
Diao, Charles 154
Diasio, Anthony 325
Diaz, Raymond 336
Diaz, Jesse 417
Diaz, Jose Antonio 525
Diaz, Mark 569
Diaz, Jorge E 587
Diaz, Robert 671
Diaz-infante, Alfred 468
Dibattista, Vincent 229
Dibonaventura, Lynn 671
Dibrell, Henry 274
Dicesare, Thor 119
Diciurcio, John 202
Dickel, Susan 573
Dickens, Dave 108
Dickenson, James 264
Dickerson, John C. 301
Dickerson, Staci 489
Dickey, Elbert 92
Dickherber, Alice 465
Dickman, Susan F 265
Dickman, Paul 417
Dickson, Tom 61
Dickson, Kevin 199
Didawick, Kathy 89
Diddee, Anu 284
Didden, Andrew 202
Diebolt, Dennis 444
Dieckmann, Anita 235
Diederich, Tom 417
Diefenderfer, Joe 181
Diehl, Valerie 117
Diehm, Russell C 95
Diemer, John W 453
Diennen, Rob 491
Diesel, R Wayne 526
Dietrich, Lavonne 169
Dietrich, Bob 384
Dietrich, Katherine 523
Dietrich, William S 644
Dietsche, Jim 76
Dietsche, Jim 76
Dietz, Robert J 212
Dietze, Steven J. 670
Diganci, Todd T. 202
Diggins, Terry 231
Dighe, Prafad 519
Digregorio, Michael 671
Dijk, Carol Van 341
Dikeman, Marcy 604
Dilan, Jose 369

Diliberto, Matthew J 441
Dilisi, Jeffrey 651
Dilka, Krystal 525
Dill, Richard 143
Dill, Julie 549
Dillard, Monica 551
Diller, Lisa R. 172
Dillion, Kevin 595
Dillon, Daniel 44
Dillon, Tim 246
Dillon, Danel 319
Dillon, Deborah 556
Dillon, Kevin 596
DiLorenzo, Dennis 370
Dilts, Sandra 500
Dimarco, Tony 116
Dimarco, Dana 409
Dimas, Michelle 138
Dimauro, Bernice 673
Dimitian, Diana 293
Dimmick, Ruth 21
Dimmick, Scott W 284
Dimmitt, Elizabeth 677
Dimond, Bob 20
DiNapoli, Mark L. 531
DiNapoli, Michael (Mike) 531
DiNapoli, Mike 531
Dinger, Stephanie 617
Diniz, Cem 395
Dinnie, Holly 72
Dinsmore, Richard 202
Diokno, Ananias 670
Dionne, Michael 590
Dionne, Mike 590
Dipalma, Theresa Alberghini 598
Dipaolo, Joseph A 12
Dipaolo, Michael 495
DiPrima, Natasha 389
DiPrisco, Dan 548
Director, Goodin 61
Dirmyer, Richard 456
Dirscherl, Dan 246
Disarlo, Lorraine 646
Dishaw, Michael 68
Dishaw, Michael F 68
Dishman, Pam 177
Dishman, Roy 445
Disilvestro, Carlo A 612
Disney, David L 261
Dispensa, James V 92
Dittemore, Karen 234
Dittmar, Brian 297
Dittmer, Joseph 601
DiTullio, Steve 557
Diven, Cathy 70
Divine, Jon 625
Diwa, Portia 535
Dixon, Emily E 81
Dixon, Cora 168
Dixon, Anastasia 188
Dixon, Jonathan 203
Dixon, April 225
Dixon, Yolanda 401
Dixon-Williams, Sherrie 576
Djalali, Chaden 594
DMD, Steven Kramm 282
Do, Orlando Chapa 157
Doan, Peter 55
Dobbelaere, Jeff 306
Dobbelaere, Arthur G 341
Dobbins, John 672
Dobelbower, Peter 242
Dobre, Mircea 453
Dobrinski, Everett M. 143
Docken, Lori 641
Dockins, Cynthia 550
Docobo, Angel 349
Dodd, Susan 467
Dodds, Vince 331
Dodge, Richard E. 389
Dodi, Joe 232
DOE, Cindy 240
Doebler, Carl 230
Doecke, Beverly 613

Doering, Richard 242
Doering, Lina 259
Doering, Kimberly B. (Kim) 620
Doerr, David M. 13
Doerr, David 13
Doerr, Andrea 422
Doerrer, Ann 378
Doherty, Chris 200
Doherty, Thomas 304
Doherty, Paul 491
Dohman, Pammie 472
Dohzen, Shirley 553
Doig, Russ 213
Dokich, Sretenka 438
Dolan, Kelly 22
Dolan, Cole B 316
Dolan, Jill S. 591
Dolan-wilson, Allison 314
Dolen, Jim 185
Doligale, Anne 493
Doliner, Susan 306
Doliner, Peggy 306
Doll, Cynthia 635
Dollaghan, Jim 184
Dolling, David S. 569
Dombchewsky, Orest 51
DomBourian, Melkon 127
Domersant, Rachmani 205
Dominguez, Oscar 499
Dominguez, Leanna 611
Dominguez, Maria 620
Dominick, Jay 591
Donado, Yvette 191
Donaghue, Jason M 516
Donahoe, Tim 319
Donahoo, Mark 185
Donahue, Michael 190
Donald, Bruce Mc 97
Donaldson, David 163
Donaldson, Amy 247
Donavan, James 341
Donder, Daniel J 342
Donegan, Mark 428
Donegan, Lynda 608
Donelan, Cindy 131
Dong, Vicky 57
Donley, Jeffrey 115
Donley, Michael B. 553
Donley, Patrick M 657
Donnell, Cathy Mc 129
Donnell, Steve 199
Donnellan, Kevin 2
Donnelly, Mel 270
Donnelly, Thomas 333
Donnelly, April 579
Donner, Lee 296
Dono, Robert 452
Donohue, Sean P. 171
Donohue, John 562
Donovan, Paul 79
Donovan, Thomas C. (Tom) 404
Donovan, Mike 480
Donovan, R. Nowell 549
Donovan, Susan 579
Dooher, Peter 485
Dooley, Meta 150
Dooley, Bill 155
Dooley, John E. 652
Doordan, Martin L 40
Dopson, Nicole 634
Doram, Keith R 6
Dorchester, Wendy 298
Dorcheus, Shane 20
Doren, Craig 51
Dores, Daniel 628
Dorfler, Robert 604
Dori, Holnagel 242
Dormo, Cindy 131
Dorph, Martin S. 370
Dorris, Keith 453
Dorroh, Tina 623
Dortch, Thomas W 219
Dorto, Joseph 652
Dosal, Paul J 638

Index of Executives

Doshi, Pranav S 236
Dosi, Abhishek 535
Doss, David 432
Dossani, Imran 613
Dostal, Drew 61
Dotson, Tony 228
Dotson, Sonya 429
Doty, David D 104
Doty, David 104
Doty, Rob 251
Doty, Larry 421
Doty, William S 505
Doty, Travis 625
Doucette, Elmer 190
Doucette, Elmer 190
Doucette, Jami 428
Doucette, Mike J 450
Doudna, Dave 146
Dougherty, Robert A. 14
Dougherty, James 58
Dougherty, Kirsten 291
Douglas, Matthew 375
Douglas, Dan 384
Douglas, Laurie Z. 435
Douglas, Brian 597
Douglas, Keith 601
Douglass, Stephen B 108
Douglass, Travis L 232
Doukas, Peter 546
Doull, Jim 85
Dour, Joanne 518
Douthard, Ross 408
Dove, Reid 1
Dover, Steve 193
Dow, Melinda 535
Dowd, Lacey 539
Dowling, Joseph L. 102
Dowling, Dennis 382
Downer, Michael J 33
Downey, William B 450
Downey, William 451
Downey, Frank 453
Downey, Charles P 658
Downie, Sara 467
Downing, Denise 122
Downing, Mark A. 446
Downing, Helen Dean 474
Downs, Mary 602
Downs, Yvette 658
Doyal, Brian S. 453
Doyle, Larry 11
Doyle, John D 47
Doyle, Jim 142
Doyle, Johnna 148
Doyle, James 175
Doyle, John 190
Doyle, Brian 334
Doyle, John 416
Doyle, Terry A 461
Doyle, Mary E 479
Dozier, Michael 284
Dozier, Luann 552
Dozono, Elisa 399
Dragas, Helen E. 442
Drago, William 220
Drago, Allyson 626
Drakaki, Alexandra 615
Drake, Kelrick 371
Drake, Daniel 421
Drake, Michael V 581
Draper, Derrick 86
Drass, M. Joy 321
Draxler, Deb 49
Dreal, John Van 467
Drebin, Jeffrey A. 325
Drees, Ralph 565
Drees, David 565
Drefs, Cheryl 525
Drell, Persis S. 290
Drengler, Kathy 49
Dressel, Bruce 51
Drew, Swazenne 7
Drew, Joel 110
Drew, Alton 199

Drew, Theresa 671
Drewes, Kevin 359
Dreyfus, Andrew 89
Drezek, Maria 555
Driban, John 671
Driggers, Jason 428
Drillings, Robert M 369
Driscoll, Stephen 2
Driscoll, Paul 202
Driscoll, Jeff 375
Driscoll, Brian J. 499
Driscoll, Edward 611
Driver, Darienne 342
Driver, Jeff 524
Drolet, Patricia 382
Drone, Nicole 227
Drop, Jeffrey S. 150
Drossaert, Wim 356
Drouse, Lisa 155
Drumm, Ann 314
Drummond, Danielle 284
Drummond, Donna 382
Drusin, Lewis 368
Dsena, Bruce 572
Dsylva, Brenda 137
Dua, Naveen 174
Duban, Heike 150
Dube, Joyce 467
Dubes, Christopher 93
Dubin, James M 225
Dublin, Ardenia 19
Dubois, Erin 222
DuBois, Raymond N. 575
Dubose, Cory 55
Dubose, Jack 163
Dubuche, Karl Von 609
Ducasse, Romain 660
Duce, Ronald C 279
Ducey, Leslie 474
Ducher, Daniel 358
Duchossois, Craig J. 594
Duchow, Tim 453
Duckworth, Jana 491
Dudish, Sherry 226
Dudley, Warren 327
Dudley, Michael M. 484
Dudley, Jenny 548
Dudley-Eshbach, Janet 631
Dudley-Eshbach, Janet 642
Duenig, Mark 614
Duerk, Jeffrey 116
Duff, Michael 290
Duff, John 291
Duffey, Barbara 597
Dufford, Shawn 465
Duffy, Stephen W 282
Duffy, Brian J. 496
Duffy, Matthew 662
Dufour, Pierre 14
Dufour, Victoria 516
Dufour, Jannette 552
Dugan, Edna 159
Dugent, Paul 197
Duggan, Scott 568
Duhamel, Mary 482
Duke, Steven 92
Duke, Tom 555
Duke, Lee M. 573
Dulak, Catherine 103
Dulmaine, Jean 279
Dumesnil, Diana 586
Dumont, Stephanie 202
Dunaway, Mike 316
Dunbar, Kent 157
Dunbar, Kent 157
Duncan, Jim 84
Duncan, Gary 205
Duncan, Ronald 213
Duncan, Andy 356
Duncan, Jonathan 358
Duncan, Traci 383
Duncan, Janelle 431
Duncan, Amy 477
Duncan, Todd 625

Dungee, Khalefia 653
Dunham, Kara 121
Dunkelman, David 26
Dunkle, Jason 184
Dunlap, David L. 111
Dunlap, Edward B. 119
Dunlap, Timothy M. 119
Dunlap, Patrick 119
Dunlap, Ray 443
Dunn, Allison 143
Dunn, Jim 171
Dunn, Cindy 220
Dunn, Amy 225
Dunn, Terry 261
Dunn, William H 261
Dunn, Steve 261
Dunn, William H. (Bill) 261
Dunn, Bob 261
Dunn, Stephen D. (Steve) 261
Dunn, Greg 308
Dunn, James 314
Dunn, Steve 351
Dunn, Gregory W. (Greg) 443
Dunn, Donna 478
Dunn, Randy J 504
Dunn, Edward 662
Dunn-Krause, Debbie 301
Dunne, Thomas 206
Dunne, Liz 410
Dunnie, Tookie 15
Dunson, Susan 562
Dunton, Shirby 652
Duplessis, Chad 106
Dupont, Michael R 363
Dupont, Christine 536
Dupuy, Sheila 287
Durako, Steve 664
Duran, Susan 449
Duran, Alejandro 530
Durand, Bob 50
Durand, Pierre 300
Durant, Romules 605
Durcan, Deborah A. (Debbie) 641
Durgin, Linda 311
Durham, Pamala 160
Durkovic, Svelana 409
Durnell, Shawn 108
Durnell, Keith 618
Durr, Paul 489
Durr, Kristi 514
Dusang, Nina 122
Dutcher, Phillip C 357
Dutcher, Phillip 357
Dutchyshyn, Tom 612
Dutra, Kasey 662
Dutt, Asha 129
Dutta, Soumitra 159
Dutton, Jim 82
Dutton, John 536
Duty, Earnie 280
Duva, Judith 401
Duval, Melany 172
Duval, John 649
Dvm, Prem Paul 103
Dworkin, Darren 118
Dworkin, Aaron 444
Dwyer, Jay 76
Dwyer, Michael 410
Dwyer, Shannon 431
Dwyer, Shannon 517
Dych, Jennifer 25
Dyck, Earl 14
Dye, Kathleen 5
Dye, Justin 20
Dyer, Emily 363
Dyer, Adam 422
Dyke, William R. (Bill) Van 85
Dyke, David 103
Dyke, Frances 636
Dykes, Menia 93
Dykes, Bradford W. 252
Dykes, Melissa 264
Dykes, Mary H. 417
Dynes, David 200

Dzierzbinski, Danusia 257
Dziuk, David A 233
Dziwis, Carolyn 576
D'Angelo, John 254
D'Aniello, Gianluca 555
D'Aquila, Richard 676
D'Arienzo, Annette Marino 90
D'Ascoli, Fred 364
D'Aveni, Richard 173
D- az, Eduardo 497

E

E, Thomas Kevin 356
Eade-Viele, Carol 22
Eadie, Cynthia M 183
Eager, Pamela 114
Eames, Frederick 18
Eames, Andy 511
Earl, Nancy 489
Earl, Ashlee M 556
Earl, Dustin 672
Earle, Cletis 272
Earley, Franklin P 652
Early, Charles 360
Early, Betsy 484
Early, Johnnie L. 596
Earnhart, Michele 153
Easley, Matthew 51
Easley, Stephen T 274
Eason, David 469
Easterlin, Edward 147
Easterlin, Edward E. 396
Easterling, William E. 584
Eaton, Carrie 259
Eaton, Dave 640
Ebb, David 574
Ebel, Gregory L. (Greg) 509
Eberhart, Dan 442
Eberlein, Michael 594
Ebert, Deborah 298
Ebert, Kevin 671
Ebken, Stephanie 128
Ebye, Amanya 257
Echavarria, Vivian 16
Echiverri, Henry C 192
Echols, Lee 386
Echols, Edwin 547
Eck, Stefan 239
Eck, Chris 567
Eckel, Robert A. (Bob) 248
Ecker, Jeffrey Lawrence (Jeff) 574
Ecker, Kraig 674
Eckert, Matthew 55
Eckert, Bob 251
Eckert, Liz 409
Eckhart, Brad 567
Eckhart, Gloria 605
Eddinger, Ronnie 95
Eddins, Brad 549
Eddowes, Geoffrey W. 573
Edds, Michael 572
Eddy, Lee A 45
Eddy, Janet 94
Edeker, Randy 247
Edelstein, Martin P 382
Edelstein, Stewart 642
Edema, Douglas 508
Edgar, Robin 329
Edge, Jillian 302
Edgell, Garland 361
Edgell, Eleonore 444
Edgerton, Ivis 358
Edgett, Paul W. 150
Edgington, Michael 671
Edith, Martinez-kidde 638
Edler, Marie 475
Edminster, Susan 11
Edmonds, Jennifer 573
Edmonds, Bonnie 596
Edmunds, Cynthia 631
Edmunds, Karen 666

Index of Executives

Edmundson, Chad 567
Edney, Jerry 50
Edson, Pam 359
Edwards, Steven L. 85
Edwards, Steven J 86
Edwards, Steve 86
Edwards, Steve L 104
Edwards, Mary 112
Edwards, Michael 116
Edwards, Thomas K 135
Edwards, Bill 260
Edwards, Katherine 269
Edwards, Gordon 288
Edwards, Steven D. (Steve) 291
Edwards, Dean 293
Edwards, Marcie L. 299
Edwards, Brady 301
Edwards, Gordon T. 309
Edwards, Janet 405
Edwards, Pearse 424
Edwards, Gerry 446
Edwards, Jennifer 451
Edwards, Rebecca 456
Edwards, Clarence 481
Edwards, Teresa L. (Terrie) 484
Edwards, Sherman 664
Effron, Seth 229
Egan, Karen 190
Egan, Luisa 642
Egan, Joe 646
Egbert, Charles 612
Ege, Fred 364
Ege, Patrick 633
Eggers, Drew 387
Egidi, Kenneth 412
Ehlers, Mary 55
Ehlert, Kimberly 463
Ehlert, Angela 511
Ehlinger, Jon D 185
Ehrler, Richard 403
Ehrlich, Robert 313
Ehrlich, Beth 400
Ehrman, Larry 302
Eichelberger, Mitch 126
Eichenlaub, John 573
Eichfeld, William 504
Eichler, Kelly 624
Eide, Kjell 196
Eifler, Robert W 376
Eiland, Mattie 505
Eiler, Justin 447
Eisenberg, Burton 242
Eisenberg, Debra 382
Eisenberg, Ron 601
Eisenbrandt, Peter 303
Eisenkraft, James 351
Eisentrout, Craig 81
Eisgruber, Christopher L. 591
Ekbom, Carol 652
Elachi, Charles 107
Elam, Laura 588
Elamine, A K 502
Elbaum, Richard 118
Elberfeld, Adrienne 563
Eldayrie, Elias G. 627
Elder, Larry 83
Elder, Krystle 116
Elderkin, Greg 510
Elebash, Joe 306
Elgohary, Nivin 143
Elia, Maryellen 240
Elias, Jack A. 101
Elices, Simone 549
Elisabeth, Ricci 407
Elizabeth, Caroline 636
Eljaiek, Lester 484
Elkin, Neil 444
Elkin, Jim 606
Elkins, Carla 471
Elkinson, Ken 357
Ellard, Beth 2
Ellefsen, Eric 660
Ellehuus, Christoffer 117
Ellen, Hanson 230

Ellen, Maclauglin 407
Ellenbecker, Brian 453
Eller, Jeff 6
Ellerbrook, Niel C 505
Ellingson, Kari 597
Ellington, Chris 635
Elliot, Cynthia 454
Elliot, Charles 536
Elliott, Wayne 83
Elliott, Tj 191
Elliott, Carla 253
Elliott, Brett 347
Elliott, Steven 542
Elliott, Bruce 575
Ellis, Justin 61
Ellis, Beverly 108
Ellis, Richard 132
Ellis, David 162
Ellis, John W 213
Ellis, Colleen 251
Ellis, Karen 330
Ellis, David 337
Ellis, Sabrina 370
Ellis, Bret 382
Ellis, Mark 428
Ellis, CynthiaLynn 444
Ellis, Kevin S 571
Ellis, Clyde 582
Ellis, Stephen 587
Ellis, Damon 601
Ellis, George 638
Ellison, Edward 271
Ellison, Seth M. 293
Elmasri, Fakhir F 285
Elnashai, Amr S. 584
Elrich, Marc 161
Elrod, David 185
Elrod, James K 670
Elsbrock, Natalie 128
Else, Ryan 26
Elson, Clifford 355
Elster, Nanette 301
Elstrott, John B. 669
Elswick, Shannon 400
Elvekrog, John 564
Ely, Lisa 469
Emami, Azita 640
Emans, Jedd 35
Embry, Kevin 161
Emerson, Rob 508
Emery, Andrea 512
Emery, Mary 648
Eminovic, Sead 257
Emison, Kevin 222
Emler, Jessica 180
Emmans, John 108
Emmons, Christopher W. 306
Emmons, Michael 508
Emory, Beverly 672
Empey, Dennis 606
Emrich, Richard 389
Enderson, Taryl 343
Eng, Phil 336
Engel, Robert B. 143
Engel, Robin 625
Engelhardt, Brent 457
Engelman, Dan 72
Engen-pazdera, Judy 614
Enger, Mark 399
England, Todd D. 104
England, Corey D. 104
England, Chad 104
England, Josh 104
England, Zach 104
England, Dustin 104
England, Daniel E. (Dan) 104
England, Dean D. 104
Engleman, Laurie 636
Englett, Richard M 545
Engles, Gregg L. 668
English, Francine 242
Engstrom, Rick 644
Ennerfelt, P Goeran 293
Ennerfelt, Goeran P 293

Ennis, Elizabeth 64
Ennis, Daniel G. 268
Enomoto, Hideto 375
Enos, Deborah C. 407
Entwisle, Beverly J 609
Entwistle, David 524
Entwistle, David 639
Epidendio, Steve 669
Eppich, Timothy 116
Epps, JoAnne A. 546
Epstein, Norman P 531
Erb, Jane 389
Erb, Jane 407
Erber, Ralph 175
Erdman, Leonard 101
Erekson, O. Homer 549
Ergastolo, Patrick 594
Erickson, Scott 26
Erickson, Lynn 55
Erickson, Zachary 107
Erickson, Elizabeth 138
Erickson, Sue 332
Erickson, Tina 576
Ericson, Brent 223
Erik, Shank 407
Erika, Hofmann 407
Ermine-Baer, Kristin 644
Ernest, William 404
Ernie, Barry 505
Erpenbach, Michelle 566
Erpenbeck, Donald A 356
Ervin, Juanita D 93
Erwin, Duane 49
Erwin, Duane L. 49
Erwin, Steven 103
Erwin, Michael A 176
Erwin, Terry 308
Escamilla, Edward 164
Escarrer, Gabriel 179
Escasa-Haigh, Jo Ann 431
Escasa-Halgh, Jo Ann 517
Esch, Cort 212
Esch, Alyson 422
Eschenauer, Robert 517
Escover, Norman 356
Escudero, Jaime 412
Escuyer, Vincent 233
Esfahani, Sam 432
Eshelbrenner, Adam 601
Eshghi, Fleur 206
Eskandarian, Ali 569
Eslick, Rob 247
Esparza, Mary Lou L 102
Esparza, Ryan 262
Esper, Richard E 571
Espey-English, Patricia 664
Espinosa, Carlos 60
Espinoza, Aurora 408
Espinoza, Jose 499
Espinoza, Edna 537
Esposito, Frank 266
Esposito, Michael 525
Espy, Kevan 144
Esquibel, Emillo 476
Esquith, Stephen L. (Steve) 339
Esquivel, Amada 596
Esrael, Craig 432
Esrig, Cynthia 248
Essenberg, Janice 76
Essig, Marshall 143
Esta, Linda 589
Estabrook, Madeleine 383
Estby, Becky 145
Esteban, A. Gabriel 175
Estep, Missie 584
Esterman, Michelle 29
Estes, Rob W. 197
Estes, David 308
Estes, Melinda L. 466
Esther, Chet 224
Estridge, Sherry 651
Etchemendy, John W. 290
Etchemendy, Kathi 467
Etheridge, Don 358

Etienne, Carissa 404
Etten, Peter Van 187
Ettenger, Kreg 630
Etter, Carl J. 479
Etti-williams, Jimmy 549
Ettl, Robert A 229
Etzell, Joan 535
Eubanks, Clifford 196
Eugster, Cris 164
Eustace, Joan 611
Evans, Sean 32
Evans, Doug 126
Evans, Jeremy 174
Evans, Crystal 194
Evans, Dave 214
Evans, Robert 242
Evans, Jeremy S 282
Evans, Stephen R. T. 321
Evans, Donnie W 409
Evans, Steve 415
Evans, Malik 454
Evans, Peggy 484
Evans, Scott 489
Evans, Russ 500
Evans, Kimberly 532
Evans, Scott 571
Evans, Karen 601
Evans, Palmer 611
Evans, Arthur T 625
Evans, Gene 636
Evans, Sharon 637
Evans, Brandy 645
Evans, Mariah 659
Evanson, Paul J 347
Evanson, Douglas (Doug) 470
Everett, Greg 333
Everette, James 70
Everhart, Martin 454
Evers, Peter 155
Evert, Nancy 445
Evey, Lee 548
Evitts, Aaron 126
Ewert, Brian H 310
Ewert, Phil 469
Ewing, Justin 20
Ewing, Marilyn E 253
Eyeington, Thomas 499
Eynon, Eric 449
Eyre, Brandon 55
ez, 669
Ezer, Dorit Ben 129

F

F, Yvonne 102
Fabis, Joe 240
Fache, Jameson Smith 117
Fache, Adrienne Palmer 318
Factor, Saul 260
Factora, Faith 562
Fadem, Steve 555
Fagan, Cathlyn 382
Fagan, Charles 432
Fagan, Mary 438
Fagan, Tiffani 464
Fagan, Shiraz M. 479
Fagen, Richard E. (Rich) 107
Fagin, Michelle 122
Fagnani, Jennifer 182
Fahey, Lisbeth 127
Fahey, Walter J. 304
Fahey, Joe 671
Fahim, Shafei 55
Fahner, Dawn 337
Fails, Ashley 313
Fain, Jonathan D. 544
Fair, Sonia 22
Fairbanks, Donald 344
Fairchild, Larry 200
Faison, Lauren 541
Fait, Laura 597
Faith, David M. 589

Index of Executives

Falaguerra, Robert J. (Bob) 464
Falb, Derek J 134
Falbo, Michael 641
Falci, Mark 453
Falcone, Joseph C 358
Falcone, Joseph C. 661
Falcone, Maria 678
Fale, Mr Robert 11
Falgout, David 678
Falk, Linda 76
Falk, Samantha 524
Falk, Megan 662
Falkner, Keon 64
Falkowitz, Mary 580
Fall, Clinton 568
Fallen, Wendy 555
Fallon, Jeanne M. 109
Fallon, David J. 140
Falstad, Daniel T 196
Famuyiwa, Oluyemisi O 242
Fan, Jiansheng 650
Fanale, James 111
Fanale, James 673
Fanchar, Brent 471
Fanelli, Denise 253
Fang, Bin 227
Fannin, Charity 615
Fanning, Thomas A 506
Fansler, Janet 284
Fantle, Jean 628
Fantorno, Carla 540
Fanucchi, Margaret A 472
Farber, Nancy 659
Farbes, Hubert A. 179
Farden, John 474
Fare, Brenda 177
Farkas, Chris 240
Farland, Bill 147
Farland, Kenn Mc 343
Farley, Lucille 31
Farley, Joseph M 110
Farley, Leigh 333
Farmer, Paul J 167
Farmer, Dennis 223
Farner, David M. 643
Farney, Cheryl 333
Farnum, Marissa 191
Farnum, Allan 252
Farr, Rich 104
Farr, David 529
Farr, Paul A 540
Farrell, Mary A 217
Farrell, Edward 306
Farrell, William 580
Farrell, Bill 671
Farrell, Mary C. 676
Farren, John 554
Farrier, Joe 361
Farrimond, Katherine 378
Farrington, Shannon 428
Farris, Bain 465
Farris, Bain J 465
Farris, Bain J 518
Fash, Boni 664
Fasino, Jeffrey 149
Fateh, Kiran 215
Fauchet, Philippe 599
Faul, Mark 601
Faulds, Jason 476
Faulkner, Archimedes 333
Favarelli, Andrea 75
Favuzza, Steven P 593
Fazzino, Tabitha 588
Fearon, Richard 190
Fecker, Alicia 425
Feczko, Peter J 236
Federenko, Garvin 16
Fedyszyn, Karen 4
Fedzhora, Liliya 650
Feely, Terri 253
Feeney, Paul M. 78
Fees, Nick 475
Fehnel, Stephen H 441
Feidner, Susan 129

Fein, Alan 556
Feinberg, David A. 172
Feinberg, David T. 213
Feinberg, David 615
Feiner, Barbara A. 600
Feistauer, Marcelo 14
Feld, John 480
Feldman, Dorothy 382
Feldmann, Robert 616
Feliciano, Stephanie 552
Felis, Sandra L. 598
Felix, Ruth 437
Felix, Jorge 459
Felix, Jose 582
Felkey, Tana 596
Felkner, Joseph (Joe) 232
Fellinger, Robert E. (Bob) 198
Fellows, Steven 472
Felton, Alison 46
Felton, Tom 318
Felts, Marcia 505
Fender, Brooke 329
Fenley, Michelle 333
Fenn, Scott 64
Fenner, Simon 302
Fenwick, Sandra L. 558
Fenzel, Paul 261
Feragne, Mark A 24
Ferbet, Charlie 308
Ferch, Wayne 6
Ferdschneider, Marcy 370
Ferencz, Steven M. 119
Feret, Peter 480
Ferguson, Stewart 16
Ferguson, Gary 132
Ferguson, Brent 260
Ferguson, Joel I. 340
Ferguson, Amy 481
Ferguson, Jeff 508
Ferguson, John R. 551
Ferguson, Deedra 630
Ferlita, Christine 476
Fernandes, Al 613
Fernandes, Sidney 638
Fernandez, Mary 298
Fernandez, Aurelio M. 500
Fernandez, Jan 589
Ferndinand, Norma 573
Ferniany, Will 624
Ferracone, Robin A. 187
Ferranti, Richard M. 449
Ferrar, Stephen 240
Ferrara, Enzo 638
Ferrara, John 652
Ferrari, Mauro 334
Ferree, John N. 478
Ferreira, Luisa 642
Ferrell, Ashley 56
Ferrell, Tyler 102
Ferrell, Ronnie 201
Ferrell, Woody 281
Ferrer, Stephanie 558
Ferreri, Anthony C 527
Ferrero, Adam 546
Ferretti, Gerald 116
Ferretti, Nicole 442
Ferri, Vince 614
Ferriman, Robert 453
Ferris, Cindi 554
Ferrise, Sam 140
Ferrufino, Jimena 125
Ferry, Thomas 22
Fesko, Frankie 150
Fesko, Frankie L 354
Feuer, Michael J 569
Feuring, Joerge 239
Feus, Andrea 341
Fichtel, Howard 359
Fiddler, Lori 441
Fiedler, Uwe 405
Fiedorek, R. Mark 509
Field, Sam 447
Fields, Karin 199

Fields, Sherry 264
Fields, Diana 276
Fields, Dana 428
Fiene, Bryan 453
Fierens, Louis J 606
Fierke, Carol A. 444
Fifer, Joseph J 509
Fighs, Charles 499
Figueroa, Juan 552
Filetti, Robert 453
Filipov, Douglas 113
Filippo, Pasquale A. (Pat) Di 612
Filtz, Joe 119
Finberg, Robert 616
Finch, Bob 277
Finch, Kathleen 480
Finch, Bill 604
Finchem, Timothy W. (Tim) 415
Findlay, Russell 597
Findley, Mary 171
Fine, Kim 17
Fine, Peter S. 61
Fine, Michael H 451
Finholt, Thomas A. 444
Finis, Mario 356
Fink, Michael 472
Fink, Robert 552
Finkel, Peter 671
Finkelstein, Andy 232
Finkelstein, David 513
Finley, Wayne 161
Finley, Lowell 233
Finley, Marcy 453
Finley, Rebecca S. 603
Finn, William A. 501
Finnie, Cherie 667
Fioravanti, Mark 460
Fiore, Maria 657
Fiorelli, Bill 125
Fiori, Debra 406
Fiorini, Monica 653
Firdaus, Dave 90
Fireman, Cassie 308
Firestone, Robert 484
Firmender, Seth T 573
Firmery, Steve 78
Firmin, Lynne 552
Firpo, Jan 456
Fischer, Michael R. (Mike) 59
Fischer, Steven 79
Fischer, Alex 359
Fischer, Susan 372
Fischer, Jennifer 402
Fischer-Kinney, Julie 596
Fish, Mark 355
Fish, Kathleen 355
Fish, John F. 531
Fish, John F. 610
Fisher, Phoebe 22
Fisher, Tiffanie 98
Fisher, Robby 102
Fisher, Michael 128
Fisher, Scott 197
Fisher, Alexandra 206
Fisher, Seth 215
Fisher, Ruth 236
Fisher, Sherri R 242
Fisher, Donald 302
Fisher, Morris 306
Fisher, Kyle 390
Fisher, Michelle 418
Fisher, James 456
Fisher, Steve 484
Fisher, Scott W. 541
Fisher, Rand 553
Fisher, David E. 574
Fisher, Ben 610
Fisher, Mary 671
Fishman, Matthew E. 27
Fishman, Robert E 356
Fishman, Robert 444
Fitch, Karl 407
Fitch, Carl 662
Fitchett, Hank 672

Fitzgerald, Timothy 214
Fitzgerald, Timothy 215
Fitzgerald, Anne 407
Fitzgerald, Kevin 472
Fitzgerald-mays, Linda 75
Fitzgibbons, Carol A 253
Fitzgibbons, Carol 253
Fitzgibbons, Michael A 397
Fitzgibbons, Timothy P 616
Fitzpatrick, David 12
Fitzpatrick, Sean 523
Fitzsimmons, Bill 156
Fitzsimmons, William 156
Fitzsimmons, Rhiannon 268
Fitzsimons, Patricia Sue 676
Flaherty, Joe 220
Flaherty, Maureen 325
Flaherty, Eileen 407
Flaherty-Oxler, Karen 573
Flakes-Cuffee, Alicia 74
Flaks, Jeffrey A 229
Flanagan, Dennis 653
Flanders, Sam 74
Flanigan, John 9
Flannery, Rhonda 291
Flannery, Robert 640
Flannery, Mark 655
Flareau, Bruce 70
Flattery, Bill 112
Flattery, William J 112
Flaugh, Jenny 311
Flavin, Karen 22
Flaws, Brandan 235
Fleagle, Steve R. 594
Fleisch, Chris 589
Fleischer, Michael R 604
Fleischman, Natalie 569
Fleites, Fernando 94
Fleming, Gerald 120
Fleming, Nancy 173
Fleming, Stan 356
Fleming, Lee Ann 400
Fleming, Dave 532
Fleming, Scott 544
Fleming, John 551
Fleming, Rhonda 552
Fleming, Rita 624
Flescher, Mark 525
Fletcher, Neil 284
Fletcher, Andrea 306
Fletcher, Gary 522
Fletcher, John 672
Fleuriet, Cathy 552
Fleury, Gustave 370
Fleury, Alison J 490
Flewelling, Linda 155
Flinois, Xavier 405
Flitman, David E 347
Flive, Michael 590
Flood, Donna L. 97
Flood, Michael 416
Flood, Rory 428
Flood-Shaffer, Kellie 541
Florence, Jared 175
Florence, Shelley 571
Florentine, Mary 384
Flores, Debbie 61
Flores, Mary 102
Flores, Jeanne 118
Flores, Noel 183
Flores, Doug 293
Flores, Hector 456
Flores, Dr Steven 457
Flores, Debra A. 484
Flores, Eloisa 486
Flores, Toribio 562
Flores, Alberto 587
Flores, William V. (Bill) 629
Florida, John 577
Florio, Carlo V. di 202
Floris, Karla 265
Flowers, Toni 112
Flowers, Randy 136
Flowers, Edtra 175

Index of Executives

Flowers, Carolyn 354
Flowers, Laurie 596
Flowers, Steve 670
Floyd, P 112
Floyd, Jay 501
Floyd, Gary 541
Floyd, Denise 645
Flury, Elizabeth 130
Fly, Daniel 354
Flynn, Barbara 6
Flynn, Lynn 74
Flynn, Lauren 123
Flynn, Rick 213
Flynn, Jennifer 215
Flynn, Michael J 236
Flynn, Colleen 329
Foad, Jon 458
Fobbs, Shari 45
Fogarty, John 79
Fogarty, Kevin M 282
Fogarty, James 604
Fogel, Richard 47
Fohringer, Ken 584
Fojtasek, Georgia 235
Foley, Patrick M 396
Foley, Anne 486
Foley, D Sue 587
Foley, Henry C. (Hank) 633
Foley, Brad 636
Folgado, Nicolas 125
Folger, Karen 452
Folger, Sherrie 511
Foli, Elsie 302
Folkins, Brad 450
Folks, Jacqueline 115
Folks, John 387
Follis, Bob 233
Follmer, Cathy 329
Folse, William 467
Foltz, Aleesa 644
Folz, Gregory 176
Fontaine, Keith 229
Fontaine, Dorrie K. 442
Fontem, Franklin 383
Foo, Chok-Pin 307
Foote, Warren 407
Fopma, Rick 277
Foran, Robert E. (Bob) 336
Forbes, Kelli 7
Forbes, Jeff S 196
Ford, Kale 120
Ford, Mike 185
Ford, Gary 334
Ford, Tim 379
Ford, Dorvetta 448
Ford, Tracey 595
Ford, Deborah (Debbie) 641
Ford, Heather 671
Forde, Terry 7
Forde, Wayne 116
Fordham, Yolanda 371
Fordham, Pam 588
Foreman, Jeff 260
Foreman, Jennifer 351
Foreman, Ken 443
Forese, Laura L. 580
Forger, James (Jim) 339
Foris, Nico 225
Formella, Nancy 79
Fornberg, Anders 104
Forney, Stephen 163
Forrest, Dawn 138
Forrest, Beth 147
Forrest, Stephen 444
Forrest, Ella 555
Forster, Eric James 444
Forster, Ann 483
Forsythe, Cameron 596
Fort, Bob 484
Fort, Stephen W. 612
Forthman, Michael A 213
Fortner, Jack L. 634
Fortunas, Paula 541
Fortwangler, Robert 106

Foshee, Kevin 31
Fossett, Sheryl 312
Foster, Delecia 12
Foster, Chris 105
Foster, Chris 117
Foster, Andrew 139
Foster, Scott 160
Foster, David 190
Foster, Michael 237
Foster, Paul D. 262
Foster, Janet 293
Foster, Andy 306
Foster, Richard 347
Foster, Pamela 478
Foster, Robert F 499
Foster, Randall 589
Foti, Joe 309
Foulke, Elvia 137
Fountain, JoAnn 256
Fournier, Dave 391
Fournier, Michele 405
Fournier, Ron 590
Fouty, Dennis 629
Fowler, Charles D. (Chuck) 116
Fowler, W Randall 196
Fowler, Bob 197
Fowler, W Randall 340
Fowler, James C 391
Fowler, Jim 391
Fowler, Maggie 512
Fowler, John C 552
Fowler, Mike 610
Fowler, Alice 649
Fox, Hannah 56
Fox, Gregory C. 91
Fox, Leana 94
Fox, John T 194
Fox, Rebecca 274
Fox, Robin 300
Fox, Tricia 518
Fox, Jamie 580
Fox, Andrew 596
Fox, Susan 667
Fox-andrews, Dana 215
Frable, Anna 391
Fraczkowski, Kurt 149
Fragale, Michael 160
Fragnoli, Stephen 149
Frahm, Eric 339
Frain, Diane 244
Fraley, Alton 274
Fralick, Julie 536
Frampton, Marcus 16
Frampton, John 547
Franceschi, Janice 588
Francia, Chris 148
Francis, Beth 64
Francis, Maxine James 101
Francis, Charles P. 181
Francis, Charlie 181
Francis, Robert 286
Francis, Evette 348
Francis, Michael 511
Francois, Holly 308
Franczek, Carol 386
Franey, Henry J. 630
Franey, Hank 630
Frank, Aaron 70
Frank, Edward H. (Ed) 114
Frank, Isabelle 206
Frank, Norm 223
Frank, Ben 561
Frank, Maxine 580
Frank, James S. (Jim) 594
Frank, Robert G. 634
Frank, Debra 643
Frank-lightfoot, Lorraine 353
Franke, Paul 16
Franke, Charlene 444
Franke, Mark 674
Frankel, Bonnie 174
Franklin, Carol 245
Franklin, William H. 262
Franklin, Tamara 480

Frantz, T K 110
Frantz, Rita A. 594
Fraser, Carol 298
Fraser, John M 362
Fraser, Gertrude 442
Frasier, Timothy (Tim) 452
Fratantoni, Karen 130
Fratini, Adrienne M 308
Frawley, Owen 282
Frazer, Beverly 225
Frazier, Seth 236
Frazier, Bryan 532
Fredell, Thomas 333
Frederick, Lori 333
Frederick, Jeff 447
Fredericks, Raymond 266
Fredrick, Robert 591
Freed, Todd 261
Freed, Dean 326
Freedman, Barry 19
Freedman, Stephen 206
Freedman, Mark 664
Freeman, Joshua 117
Freeman, Richard 190
Freeman, Dennis M. 314
Freeman, Charles 319
Freeman, Amy 332
Freeman, Marcus 378
Freeman, Todd 391
Freeman, Richard 489
Freeman, Jim 617
Freeman, Nikki 662
Freemon, Mildred 552
Freer, Rudell S 299
Frei, Theresa 535
Freiburg, Debbie 130
Freidenfelds, Lauris 459
Freireich, Neil 644
Freisleben, Ron 453
Freitag, Kristine 524
French, Susan 97
French, Robert W 202
French, Constance 399
French, Amber 444
French, Hadley Mack 670
Frescura, Louis 285
Freshour, Kimberly 486
Fretwell, Roger 210
Freund, Lothar P 282
Frey, Daniel 157
Frey, Michelle 336
Frey, James 336
Frey, R 463
Frey, Pamela 519
Frick, Wendy 596
Fricke, Lisa 671
Fricker, Michael 220
Friday, Gary 305
Friebis, Dawn 359
Fried, Arthur 527
Friedel, Bobby 508
Friedell, Andrew 315
Friedman, Wayne 487
Friedman, Paula J. 512
Friedman, Michael 525
Friedmann, Paul 72
Friedmann, Glenon 630
Friend, Gwyn 175
Frierson, Henry T. 627
Fries, Rick 23
Fries, James 173
Fries, Robert 477
Friesen, Carol 401
Frint, Yhonis 481
Frisbee, Kimberly 45
Frisch, Scott 2
Frisch, Steven M. 17
Frisch, Stephen 17
Frisch, Hans 75
Frisch, Benjamin 75
Frisch, Mark 75
Frisch, Ann 365
Frisch, Melissa 630
Fritz, James S. 64

Fritz, Susan M. 92
Frizzell, Benjamin 524
Frock, Charles T 349
Froehlich, Patti 209
Froehlich, Mark 648
Fromille, Carla 228
Frontczak, Deborah 116
Frontz, Eric 677
Frost, David 305
Fruhling, Julian L 479
Frumkin, Howard 640
Fry, Patrick E 536
Frye, John 150
Frye, Deborah 596
Fryson, David 663
Fryz, Mike 74
Fuchs, Mary Ann 187
Fuchs, W. Kent 627
Fuerstenberg, Jeffrey 302
Fugger, Edward F. 668
Fuhrman, Stephen E 122
Fujii, Hideaki 34
Fulkerson, William J. 187
Fulkerson, Perry 204
Fulkerson, Rick 212
Fuller, Scott 181
Fuller, Jim 353
Fullerton, Rob 670
Fulton, Mark 306
Fulton, Cedrick 336
Fulton, Matthew 371
Fultz, Kelli 5
Funai, Edmund 638
Funderburk, William W. 299
Fung, Vincent 536
Funk, Dan 50
Funk, Robert A. 198
Funk, Justin 506
Funkhouser, Cameron K. 202
Funston, Linda 475
Funston, Karen 525
Furman, Maria D. 631
Furnish, Kyle 215
Furnstahl, Lawrence J. 399
Furtado, Larissa 597
Furuto, Gordon 628
Fusco, Art 120
Fuson, Micah 168
Futhey, Tracy 186
Fybel, Gary G. 479

G

Gabel, Timothy J. (Tim) 447
Gaber, Sharon L. 596
Gabilondo, Natalia F 329
Gabriel, Kaigham (Ken) 557
Gabriel, Emigda 576
Gabrys, Gerard T. 224
Gacke, Brad 462
Gadberry, Kirk 376
Gaddis, Byron J. 428
Gaden, Nancy 95
Gadis, David L 174
Gadow, Julie 537
Gadzinski, Norman 356
Gaeta, Mary 97
Gaffney, Marie 418
Gagua, Irina 218
Gai, Michael 85
Gain, Tom 674
Gaines, Zach 412
Gainsburg, Daniel 248
Gaither, J. Michael (Mike) 35
Gaither, Chris 450
Gaizutis, Jennifer 562
Galainena, M David 571
Galarza, Adrian 114
Galarza, Maria 383
Galarza, Charles 453
Galbraith, John F 117
Galbraith, Katie 187

Index of Executives

Index of Executives

Giuffra, Robert 31
Given, Barbara 508
Givertz, Michael 556
Glade, Doug 169
Gladys, Taylor 116
Glanvill, Derek W. 318
Glaros, Dean 268
Glasel, Dan 180
Glaser, Garry 152
Glaser, William D 279
Glasgow, Diane 163
Glass, Cynthia 463
Glass, Gene 549
Glass, Steven C. 561
Glasscock, Melbern G 547
Glasser, Ted 64
Glassman, Jerry 332
Glaunert, Curtis 659
Glavey, Patrick 355
Glazier, Paula 19
Glazier, Steve 400
Gleason, Hugh 197
GLEASON, SUSAN 236
Glenn, Richard K. 43
Glenn, Nicholls 116
Glenn, Ellie 513
Glenney, Chris 133
Glick, Jason 181
Glick, Madeleine 572
Glicker, Joanna 640
Glied, Sherry A. 370
Glimcher, Laurie H. 172
Glimcher, Paul 370
Global, Akal 15
Glod, Dan 415
Glod, David 597
Gloor, Wendy 410
Gloria, Doriane 364
Glover, Connie 56
Glover, Joseph (Joe) 627
Glover, Kofi 638
Gluck, Jason 229
Goar, Michael 343
Goble, Jonathan 252
Goddard, Steven 672
Godenzi, Alberto 608
Godfrey, Todd 203
Godina, Susie 499
Godinez, Alberto 7
Godinho, Sergio 671
Godusky, Brenda 618
Godwin, John T. 119
Goebel, Sheila 631
Goedecke, Nancy Collat 316
Goedecke, Glenn 316
Goel, Vishal 505
Goelzer, Angela 202
Goenn, Elizabeth 550
Goeppinger, Kathleen H 340
Goeta-Kreisler, Kevin 611
Goetz-Krummel, Melissa 270
Goff, Mike 86
Goffnett, Carol 49
Goffney, Dr Latonya 21
Goh, Eng Lim 494
Goicouria, Luis 415
Golanowski, Marie 55
Golato, Andrea 551
Golba, Curtis 260
Golbus, Joseph 386
Gold, Jeffrey P. 92
Gold, Gary 164
Gold, Barbara 632
Goldberg, Jonathan 27
Goldberg, Carla 38
Goldberg, Michael 204
Goldberg, Richard 321
Goldberg, Mark A. 405
Goldberg, Neil 440
Goldberg, Michael 440
Goldberg, Steven 440
Goldblatt, Ronald 586
Golden, Becky S 279
Golden, John 527

Golden, Andrew K. 591
Golden, Robert 640
Golden, Greg 671
Goldfarb, Timothy M. 489
Goldgeier, Eileen 102
Goldhaber, Dale 639
Goldhaber, Jeanne 639
Goldhahn, Laura 77
Goldin, Derek 390
Goldman, Marc 208
Goldman, Michael N. 375
Goldman, Lynn R. 569
Goldman, Howard 580
Goldring, Steven 368
Goldsberry, Brian 220
Goldschmidt, Lawrence E 225
Goldschmidt, Nancy 399
Goldsmith, David L. 267
Goldsmith, Leo L 370
Goldsmith, Stephen 567
Goldsmith, Marisha 581
Goldstein, Adam 126
Goldstein, Lewis 158
Goldstein, Mary 290
Goldstein, Lisa A 368
Goldstein, Abner K 572
Goldstein, Allan Moises 574
Goldstein, Brian P 635
Goldstine, Abner 31
Goldszer, Robert C. 351
Goldwin, Richard 623
Golkiewicz, Tamara 596
Gollert, Barb 293
Golub, Todd 556
Golub, Jerel T. (Jerry) 571
Golub, Mona J. 571
Golub, David 571
Golub, Jerry 571
Golub, Neil M. 571
Golz, Judy Briscoe 153
Gomes, Maria 299
Gomez, Rick 183
Gomez, Jim Gaton 351
Gomez, Julie 445
Gomez, Maria 581
Gomulka, Robert 619
Gonick, Lev S. 44
Gonick, Lev 116
Gonick, Denise V. 355
Gonyea, Paula 598
Gonyea, Dave 655
Gonzales, Darolyn 286
Gonzales, Erika 537
Gonzales, Gil 634
Gonzalez, Arthur A. 179
Gonzalez, Angel 205
Gonzalez, Andres 211
Gonzalez, Jorge 312
Gonzalez, Zocima 351
Gonzalez, Catalina 390
Gonzalez, Eva 507
Gonzalez, Tina 558
Gonzalez, Shawn 571
Gonzalez, Christina 611
Gonzalez, Fernando 613
Gonzalez, Patty 620
Gonzalez, Jacqueline L 649
Gonzalez, Marina 677
Gonzalez-Flores, Elizabeth 409
Gonzalez-scarano, Francisco 583
Goocher, Robert 505
Good, Sue 131
Good, Michael P 360
Good, Tina 526
Good, Michael 627
Good, Glenn E. 627
Goode, Jeff 124
Goode, Wilson S 652
Gooden, Narcissis 563
Gooderham, JP 552
Goodfellow, Kathy 220
Goodhall, Gary 247
Goodhew, Ian 640
Goodman, Lindsay 206

Goodman, Gary J 479
Goodman, Wayne H. 553
Goodnow, John 77
Goodridge, Brenda 630
Goodrum, Ryan 552
Goodwin, Jean 333
Goodwin, Linda 395
Goodwin, Deanna 543
Goodwin, Karen 625
Goold, Alex 28
Goolsby, Steven 115
Goorevich, Charlie 487
Gopffarth, Lance 194
Gopinath, Brijesh 286
Gorder, Christopher D. Van 479
Gordin, Peggy 513
Gordon, Crystal L 13
Gordon, Jeffrey 17
Gordon, Robert A. (Bob) 20
Gordon, Scott R. 45
Gordon, Dan 85
Gordon, Ora 118
Gordon, Thomas D 118
Gordon, Pam 135
Gordon, Eric 141
Gordon, Vivian 237
Gordon, Bernard 284
Gordon, Andrew 370
Gordon, Sean 648
Gordon, Howard 671
Gore, Steve 423
Goree, Dr T Lamar 105
Gorham, Doug 572
Gorin, Joanna 191
Gorman, Eric 119
Gorman, Kathleen E. Chavanu 130
Gorman, Kathleen Chavanu 130
Gorman, Donna 298
Gorman, Paul A 317
Gorman, Luke 551
Gormley, Alice 309
Gorney, David J. 553
Gorrie, Thomas M. 187
Gorski, Bill 537
Gorsky, Alex 391
Gosian, Jonathan 220
Gosney, Laura L 559
Goss, Jeanne 254
Gossard, Cheryl 270
Gosse, Lynn 602
Gossett, Paul 20
Gossett, Barry P. 642
Gostin, Jill 572
Gothard, Joe 250
Gottardy, Brian G 378
Gottlieb, Jonathan E. 252
Gottlieb, Robert 407
Gough, Jim 59
Gough, Fredric 383
Gough, Michael W 389
Gould, Cristie 12
Gould, R Marcia 31
Gould, Rod 138
Gould, Karen 593
Gould, Karen O. 612
Goulding, Philip L 347
Gourdine, Jerome 392
Gourio, Francois 96
Gourley, Fletcher 426
Gouveia, Jeffrey 531
Gove, Matt 418
Govil, Anita 19
Gow, Joe 641
Goyanes, Everardo 422
Goyette, Karen 229
Gozon, Richard C. 603
Gozzarino, Katie 517
GP, Ealmoor 674
Grab, Edward L 230
Graber, Tim 343
Grabusic, Cynthia 546
Grace, Bob 612
Grace, Raymond 617
Grace, William M 652

Gracias, Antonio 547
Graczewski, Cheryl 34
Graddy, Steven 210
Graddy, Gwendolyn 236
Grady, Christopher 51
Grady, Max 276
Grady, Jason 383
Grady, James 514
Grady, Philips 671
Graebner, Clark 333
Graf, Jane 331
Graff, Jeffrey 6
Graff, Michael J. (Mike) 14
Graff, Ed 38
Graff, K E 200
Grafman, Laura R. 478
Gragg, Jodi 352
Graham, Jeffrey J. 5
Graham, Louis 66
Graham, John C 219
Graham, Eugene W 219
Graham, Matthew X 219
Graham, Patrick T 219
Graham, Dionne 230
Graham, Ed 338
Graham, Randolph 358
Graham, Paul 373
Graham, Franklin 469
Graham, Melissa 492
Graham, Peter 508
Graham, Kim 607
Graham, Dale 662
Graham, Mark A 671
Grainger, Jo 570
Grajeda, Jessica 407
Graley, David 105
Gram, Dwight 449
Grambart, Sean 113
Grambo, Francis 228
Granado, Alejandro 136
Granath, Herbert A 206
Granato, Jerome 150
Granberry, Debbie 154
Grandia, Larry D 428
Granger, Jason 189
Granger, Harvey 503
Granger, Carolyn 616
Gransbery, Wayne 529
Grant, Belinda 6
Grant, Thomas 7
Grant, Susan 75
Grant, Diana 161
Grant, Jack 265
Grant, Duane 498
Grant, Alan 652
Grant-anderson, Belinda 599
Grasela, Wayne T 588
Grassinger, Maxine 491
Graugnard, Milton 105
Graugnard, Milton 106
Graumlich, Lisa 640
Graves, Gerry 6
Graves, Marti 244
Graves, Mayra 431
Gravilla, Katie 456
Gravino, Ronald 363
Gray, Linsey 38
Gray, David L. 64
Gray, Larry W. 64
Gray, Darcey 188
Gray, Thomas L 274
Gray, Jake 316
Gray, Nancy 333
Gray, Brent 419
Gray, John 497
Gray, Tracey 530
Gray, Monica 570
Gray, Jarrod 576
Gray, David J. 584
Graybeal, R Steven 312
Grebb, Joye 562
Grebe, Charles 228
Greck, Sonya B 343
Greco, Suzanne 183

Index of Executives

Greco, Donna 219
Greek, Matt 69
Greelish, James 115
Green, Dee 6
Green, Jon 30
Green, Ronnie 92
Green, Teresa 117
Green, Greg 135
Green, Thomas B 140
Green, Ann 147
Green, Mike 161
Green, Judy 161
Green, David 242
Green, Steve 242
Green, Mart 242
Green, Lance 284
Green, Marie 356
Green, Allyson 370
Green, James 375
Green, Wendy 392
Green, Crickett 442
Green, Jane 448
Green, Gene E 502
Green, Teressia 508
Green, Beth 563
Green, Mary 659
Green, Kevin 678
Greenberg, Richard 19
Greenberg, Lawrence 553
Greenberg, Lon R 615
Greene, A. Hugh 63
Greene, Tim 109
Greene, John 157
Greene, John 157
Greene, Michael 175
Greene, Sonja 182
Greene, Matt 190
Greene, Graham F 284
Greene, Charles J 356
Greene, Toni 476
Greene, Queen 477
Greene, Hugh 503
Greene-Campbell, Allyson 589
Greener, Fred 83
Greener, Fred L 83
Greenfield, Karen 429
Greenglass, Alan S 132
Greengold, Alexander 324
Greenlees, Jim 664
Greenstreet, Michelle M 511
Greensweig, Gary 472
Greenup, Marion 589
Greenwald, Vicki 112
Greenwald, Judy 541
Greenwell, Melissa 567
Greer, Emily S 34
Greer, Jon 343
Greer, Jeanne 563
Greg, Perticone 268
Greger, Gene 604
Gregory, Sean J. 410
Gregory, Christy 478
Gregory, Robert 505
Gregory, Linsey 595
Gregory, Matt 597
Greig, Jeffrey 186
Greiner, James (Jim) 13
Grenon, Yves 405
Greubel, Scott 185
Grewal, Harjinder 70
Grewcock, Bruce E 279
Grewcock, Bruce 279
Grewcock, Bruce E. 414
Grewe, Jerry 443
GREWE, MELISSA 471
Gribbin, Mary 370
Gridley, Maryanne 184
Grier, Rosa 546
Grierson, Matthew 640
Griessenauer, Christoph 215
Griffeth, Jack T 383
Griffin, Michael 6
Griffin, Donnie 86
Griffin, James D. 172

Griffin, Caroline 184
Griffin, Anthony H 199
Griffin, Mike 235
Griffin, April 240
Griffin, Justin 260
Griffin, Charles 274
Griffin, Marcus 430
Griffin, B R 430
Griffin, Doug 456
Griffin, Noelle 468
Griffin, Alison 505
Griffin, Walt 588
Griffis, Mark 1
Griffith, Donna H 311
Griffith, J. Brian 337
Griffith, John 383
Griffith, Bob 615
Griger, David T 574
Grigg, Richard R 37
Grigg, William 210
Griggs, Karessa 551
Grigsby, Todd 105
Grigsby, Lane 105
Grigsby, Todd 106
Grigsby, L Lane 106
Grillo, Loraine 366
Grillo, Anthony 514
Grima, Edward 74
Grimes, Robert R. 206
Grimes, Cynda 551
Grimet, Howard 274
Grimm, Susan 116
Grimm, Carol 301
Grimm, Douglas 334
Grimminger, Kurt 674
Grimshaw, Matt 150
Grimsley, Diane 618
Grinthal, Karen 480
Grisez, Todd 131
Grisham, Dorothy 150
Grizzard, Maynard 601
Grodowski, Jenie 527
Groff, Stacey 247
Groh, Paul 351
Groll, Jeanine 103
Groneman, Joseph L 174
Gronow, Tom 626
Groom, Scott 574
Grosby, Karen 389
Gross, Kevin 12
Gross, Arthur 17
Gross, Anne 172
Gross, Roy 333
Gross, Daniel L. (Dan) 489
Grosser, Joy M. 258
Grossman, Rick 181
Grossman, Robert I. 370
Grossman, Divina 631
Grosvenor, Mark 375
Grottenthaler, Bob 68
Grotzinger, John P. 107
Grove, Gerri 89
Grove, Scott 96
Grover, Purva 562
Groves, S Van 279
Groves, Ned 325
Groves, Allen 442
Groves, Jennifer 556
Gruener, Gregory 39
Gruenthal, Michael 17
Grugan, Anne 19
Grune, Robert B. (Rob) 166
Gruner, Dean 602
Grunig, Jared 671
Grunow, Tamie 625
Gruntz, Cory 196
Grunwald, Gerald B. 603
Grussendorf, Christi 16
Grynspan, Devora 389
Gryzbek, Thomas 207
Guadagnoli, Donald A. 109
Gualdoni, Donald 35
Guardia, Juan 625
Guardino, Christopher 671

Guarin, Fernando 572
Guarino, Mary 193
Guarisco, Pete 209
Guarneschelli, Philip 420
Guastella, Lily 627
Guatam, Anjali 114
Gubler, Blaise 529
Guenthner, Steven 27
Guerci, Alan 515
Guerra, Homero 31
Guerra, Joe 242
Guerra, Dylan 505
Guerrero, Ismael 678
Guerrieri, Gina 594
Guevara, Alfredo 649
Guge, Brett 107
Guglielmo, Michael 546
Guiley, Thomas E 184
Guinee, Arnaud 140
Guire, Peter Mc 465
Gul, Zartash 625
Gulley, Janet 562
Gumbs, Milton A 100
Gumeringer, Bert 548
Gumm, Gary 658
Gummey, Charles 671
Gunderman, Bob 672
Gundersen, Curtis 184
Gunn, Deborah 164
Gunn, William B 609
Gunter, Jim 82
Gunter, Marcus 331
Guo, Lin 642
Gupta, Amit 70
Gupta, Pranjal 269
Gupta, Sunny 446
Gupta, Vinayak 547
Gupta, Mahendra R. 600
Gupton, Donna 2
Gurin, Patricia B 34
Gurk, Kevin Mc 76
Gurley, Tony 162
Gurri, Mia 253
Gurtman, Jeff 159
Gusho, Mike 607
Gusomano, Laura 595
Guss, Fred 392
Gust, Don 283
Gustafson, John 32
Gustafson, Lynn 96
Gustas, Lisa 120
Gutch, Matthew 529
Gutgesell, Emily 250
Guth, Amy 188
Guthrie, Linda 389
Guthrie, Kevin 389
Guthrie, Chris 599
Guthrie, Wayne 627
Gutierrez, Brian G. 549
Gutman, Luisa 243
Gutmann, Amy 636
Gutnick, Michael P. 325
Gutteridge, Thomas G. (Tom) 596
Gutz, Phyllis 661
Guy, Barbara 502
Guy, Kimberly 519
Guynn, Kevin 583
Guyon, Robert E. (Bob) 528
Guzick, David S. 489
Guzick, David S. 627
Guzik, Bill 4
Guzman, Manuel 32
Guzman, Melissa 253
Guzman-Petter, Teresa 472
Gwin, Andrew 47
Gwinn, Nancy E. 497
Gyurci, John 333
Gyurisin, Margie 531

H

Ha, Bao 456

Haacker, Kristin 586
Haagenson, Deb 150
Haake, Anne 456
Haas, Mark P. 339
Haas, Nancy 360
Haas, Gerard 502
Haas-Kogan, Daphne 172
Habeck, Heather 602
Haber, Daniel A. 574
Haberman, Shelley 11
Haberman, Bruce 506
Habib, Hadi 210
Habib, Reza 504
Habingreither, Robert 551
Haby, Jeff 470
Hachey, Barbara 261
Hachey, Barb 261
Hackenberg, Kim 214
Hacker, Harold 240
Hackerman, Nancy 494
Hackett, Steven G. (Steve) 428
Hackett, Sylvia 448
Hackett, Sylvia 448
Hackett, Gail 650
Hackman, Mark 351
Hackney, Carol 446
Hadar, Janet 595
Haddad, Gabriel G. 438
Haddad, Ghassan 501
Haddox, Matthew 266
Hadjiliadis, Dennis 244
Hadley, David 254
Hadley, Lester 356
Haefner, Jeremy A. 456
Hafer, Greg 461
Hagan, Nicole 51
Hagan, Diane 258
Hagans, Robert R. 2
Hagel, Shawn R. 428
Hagen, Kelly 30
Hagen, Bruce 395
Hagens, William 505
Hager, Dan 58
Hagerman, Yvonne 137
Hagey, Michelle 419
Haggen, Brad 227
Hagler, Mendel 365
Hagner, Nancy 671
Hagy, Michelle 419
Hahl, Barbara 351
Hahn, William C. 172
Hahn, Brian F 546
Haidar, Wael 94
Haile, Elizabeth 592
Haile, Kempton C. 601
Hailey, Robert 157
Haines, Paul 318
Haines, Mike 347
Haines, Cynthia 558
Hair, Ken 246
Haire, Gary 204
Haire, Stephen I 349
Hajny, Mark 536
Hakanson, David 465
Hake, James 379
Hakim, Veronique 336
Hakim, Veronique (Ronnie) 580
Hakulin, Ruth 642
Halamka, John D. 79
Haldeman, Greg 185
Halderen, Tracy Van 511
Hale, Kenneston 196
Hale, Robert T. (Rob) 220
Hale, Philip 301
Hale, Kathleen 306
Hale, Daniel G 329
Hale, David F. 438
Hale, Mark S. 480
Hale, Jordan 526
Hale, Blake 542
Haley, Tim M 233
Haley, Michael 252
Halkos, Elizabeth 435
Hall, Richard 16

Index of Executives

Index of Executives

Index of Executives

Index of Executives

Index of Executives

Jacobs, Richard F. 45
Jacobs, Michael 116
Jacobs, Richard B. 118
Jacobs, Rick 118
Jacobs, Brian 130
Jacobs, Jill 137
Jacobs, Ronald D 242
Jacobs, John 260
Jacobs, John 261
Jacobs, Stefanie 325
Jacobs, Caroline 365
Jacobs, Louis H 418
Jacobs, Joel 578
Jacobs, Cory 619
Jacobs, Andrew D 652
Jacobs, James K 657
Jacobson, Carlton 6
Jacobson, Sandy 150
Jacobson, Catherine A. 211
Jacobson, David 586
Jacobson, Roy 643
Jacobson-Landon, Stephanie 570
Jacques, Carolyn 120
Jacques, Dale 453
Jacquez, Erica 300
Jacquinot, Bob 260
Jacquinot, Robert 261
Jadlowski, Mary 168
Jaegers, Christine 214
Jafa, Krishna 424
Jafarnia, Korsh 334
Jaffe, Ian 187
Jaffe, Seth R. 293
Jaffe, Harry J 386
Jagger, Hal 492
Jaggers, Richard 59
Jahanian, Farnam 114
Jahn, Jill 25
Jahn, Timothy 64
Jahn, Barb 465
Jahn, Barb 477
Jahn, Barb 518
Jahnsson, Olli 422
Jaikumar, Srikanth 563
Jain, Renu 22
Jain, Abhi Shek 85
Jain, Sahil 114
Jain, Alok 286
Jain, Manisha 296
Jain, Anshu 344
Jain, Sujit 452
Jaiswal, Jyoti 127
Jakosky, Donn 403
Jalace-vasold, Melissa 671
Jalona, Sanjay 286
James, Carl G 74
James, Marianne F. 128
James, David 143
James, Eric 177
James, Fred 190
James, Jeff 204
James, William T 206
James, W Thomas 206
James, Carl G 206
James, Autumn 395
James, Jan 425
James, Rank 455
James, Drew 512
James, Laura 522
James, Anthony 532
James, Josh 671
James-Francis, Ma 377
Jamieson, Dick 116
Jamieson, T J 263
Jamieson, Lee 263
Jamrozek, Jim 376
Janacek, Angela 626
Janell, Joseph E 97
Janesz, Brandon 449
Janis, Robert (Bob) 174
Janise, Carlton 105
Janish, Thomas 40
Janisko, Jenny 45
Janitzky, Amanda 456

Janke, Harry 6
Janki, Daniel 215
Jankos, Dianna 346
Jankowski, Gary 310
Jankowski, Cecelia 572
Jannasch, Charlyn 409
Janney, Michelle 252
Janney, Karen 537
Jansen, Robert 180
Jantzen, Daniel 173
Jara, Armando 534
Jaramillo, Richard 313
Jaramillo, Gilbert 385
Jarell, Tim 144
Jarman, Samuel Y 28
Jaro, Vic 498
Jarrett, Dr Ehren 456
Jarrett, Craig 646
Jarvis, Candice 370
Jarvis, Erin 439
Jarvis, Kevin 501
Jarzabek, Gerald 453
Jaskunas, Jeremy W 332
Jaspers, Allen 253
Jastrow, Bill 251
Jaurequi, Pat 471
Javallana, Maria 548
Javorka, Tony 151
Jawad, Muhammad 400
JD, Howard R Grant 284
Jedlicki, Anne 632
Jeffcoat, Sally 463
Jeffers, Linda 153
Jeffers, Lewis 426
Jefferson, Timothy 219
Jeffrey, Hanks 160
Jeffrey, David E 587
Jeffrey, David 587
Jeffries, Alex 554
Jeffries, Pamela R. 569
Jeffs, Mike 153
Jelenchick, Erin 453
Jelinek, Maggie 658
Jelks, Dionne 589
Jelle, Lorraine 84
Jelly, Maecy 645
Jen, Grace 562
Jenkins, Jo Ann C. 2
Jenkins, Gina 177
Jenkins, Ladenea 270
Jenkins, Kerri 379
Jenkins, Flo 403
Jenkins, Lori 417
Jenkins, Margaret L. 430
Jenkins, Alitha 431
Jenkins, Buddy 436
Jenkins, Matt 447
Jenkins, A. Dale 448
Jenkins, Barbara M 476
Jenkins, Malinda 506
Jenkins, Jeff 535
Jenkins, Katherine 558
Jenkins, Barbara 582
Jenks, Maria 274
Jenner, Cindy 573
Jenness, Calvin E. 87
Jennifer, Faase 477
Jennings, Sarah 2
Jennings, Gary 50
Jennings, William M 97
Jennings, Stacy 256
Jennings, Denyse 323
Jennings, Stephen 438
Jenrette, John 118
Jensen, Linda A 198
Jensen, Bevan 256
Jensen, Karen 400
Jensen, Jennifer 493
Jensen, Ken 597
Jensen, Espen 610
Jensen, Neil D 612
Jenson, Susy 173
Jent, Dave 610
Jentz, Alan 618

Jeppesen, Poul 496
Jeppson, Patricia 597
Jepson, Brian D. 395
Jepson, Brian D 395
Jerabek, Judy 317
Jernigan, Donald 6
Jernigan, Jeff 58
Jerome, Brian S 282
Jerome, Karen 658
Jerosch-herold, Michael 407
Jerpe, David 411
Jerry, Estimable 407
Jervis, Olivia 525
Jesel, Eugene 469
Jesiolowski, Craig A. 528
Jesko, Danielle 144
Jessee, William 465
Jesus, Carmencita De 298
Jesus, Angelo D 532
Jesus, Joe De 546
Jett, Betsy 364
Jetter, Frederick 453
Jetty, Sathish 5
Jewell, Meg 430
Jewell, John B 606
Jewell, Rob 606
Jhaveri, Vishu 90
Jiambalvo, James 640
Jiang, Tina 290
Jiang, Shibo 364
Jiang, Joseph 502
Jick, Daniel 79
Jiga, Anthony 370
Jilg, Robyn 624
Jimenez, Laura 164
Jimenez, Ed 489
Jimenez, Carmen 530
Jimerson, Rori 55
Jin, Yadong 49
Jindal, Meenu 430
Jingnan, Liu 187
Jinks, Mark 137
Jivanov, Iasmina 287
Jiwani, Zahra 266
Joachim, Steven A. (Steve) 202
Jobalia, Amul 472
Jobe, Meredith 6
Jockett, Joan 605
Joergenrud, Odd 452
Joeris, Gary 266
Joffe, Eb 572
Joffrion, Barry 421
Johanneman, Ben 318
Johansen, Jakob V 194
John, Beulah 392
John, Kreidler 450
John, Preston St 653
Johnk, Kellee 471
Johnnie, Mark 59
Johns, Bobbie 188
Johnsen, Tim 254
Johnsen, Nola 465
Johnsen, David C. 594
Johnsgaard, Dag 196
Johnson, Marta 31
Johnson, Charlotte 45
Johnson, Nicole Conley 56
Johnson, George 56
Johnson, George 56
Johnson, Antonia Axson 57
Johnson, Dennis 64
Johnson, John H 86
Johnson, Gerald D. (Jerry) 87
Johnson, Dannis 91
Johnson, Bobby 96
Johnson, Peter S 101
Johnson, Paul 102
Johnson, Pete 108
Johnson, Bret 111
Johnson, Tod S. 114
Johnson, Kelly M. 127
Johnson, John 134
Johnson, Charles 137

Johnson, Larue 148
Johnson, Kathryn 150
Johnson, J D 162
Johnson, Bruce E. 172
Johnson, Stacey 174
Johnson, H Keith 180
Johnson, Deborah C 190
Johnson, David 193
Johnson, Jt 197
Johnson, Steven P. 232
Johnson, Don 237
Johnson, Patsy 244
Johnson, Kimberly 244
Johnson, Michelle R 250
Johnson, Mark 258
Johnson, Donna 260
Johnson, Patrice 270
Johnson, Neil 280
Johnson, Antonia Axson 293
Johnson, Carrie 302
Johnson, Colleen 313
Johnson, Kimiko 320
Johnson, Oliver M. 321
Johnson, Mark 329
Johnson, Rodney D. 333
Johnson, Cato 335
Johnson, Barbara 338
Johnson, Karen D 340
Johnson, Bernadeia 343
Johnson, Karen 355
Johnson, David D 358
Johnson, Ryan 379
Johnson, Tracy 383
Johnson, Hattie 388
Johnson, Tony 395
Johnson, Pamela 402
Johnson, Andrew 425
Johnson, Joey 428
Johnson, J Keith 429
Johnson, Sandra 456
Johnson, Dale 462
Johnson, Jani L. 466
Johnson, Lisa 466
Johnson, Jani L 467
Johnson, Ken 478
Johnson, Robert C 479
Johnson, Carol 481
Johnson, Kirk 497
Johnson, Bryan 523
Johnson, Sara 531
Johnson, Frank 532
Johnson, Raymond 546
Johnson, Mark L. 549
Johnson, Willie 551
Johnson, Maurice 552
Johnson, Brian 552
Johnson, Ray F 553
Johnson, Rosalyn 594
Johnson, M. Eric 599
Johnson, Allen (Al) 607
Johnson, Steve 612
Johnson, Kirk 616
Johnson, Julia 616
Johnson, Julie A. 627
Johnson, Sylvia Smith 630
Johnson, Mary 632
Johnson, John 653
Johnson, Jerry N. 658
Johnson, Josephine J 659
Johnson, April 670
Johnson, Jason 671
JOHNSON, ERIN 675
Johnston, Mark 14
Johnston, Adriane 32
Johnston, Greg 64
Johnston, Kenneth 66
Johnston, Craig 201
Johnston, Christine 285
Johnston, Jeffrey 331
Johnston, Diann 346
Johnston, Andy 487
Johnston, James W. 499
Johnston, Lisa 596
Joins, Spille 582

Index of Executives

Jokerst, Russell 520
Jolkovsky, Richard 587
Jolley, Burke 270
Jonas, Richard 130
Jones, Don 6
Jones, Greg 9
Jones, Douglas L. (Doug) 14
Jones, Ross 14
Jones, Sandra S 19
Jones, Lynwood A 22
Jones, Gala 46
Jones, Doug 59
Jones, Theresa 60
Jones, C. Todd 64
Jones, Stephen 66
Jones, Lakeisha 105
Jones, Michael 109
Jones, Christopher 116
Jones, Melody L 117
Jones, Michael 129
Jones, Bruce 142
Jones, Anthony 150
Jones, Timothy P 155
Jones, Ross 157
Jones, Vernon 161
Jones, Amy 168
Jones, Scott 186
Jones, Dan 206
Jones, Chris 209
Jones, Jim 221
Jones, Theresa 223
Jones, Kearline 232
Jones, Jeff 233
Jones, Stephanie 235
Jones, Sheri 256
Jones, Brian 258
Jones, Mark A 265
Jones, Evan C 284
Jones, David 290
Jones, Charles E 336
Jones, Barbara 337
Jones, Gordon L 344
Jones, Suzanne 375
Jones, Mark A. 400
Jones, Jeff C 403
Jones, Jacqueline 409
Jones, Charles E 411
Jones, Janel 412
Jones, Misty 417
Jones, Randall T. (Todd) 435
Jones, Larry 435
Jones, Marna 448
Jones, Dylan P. 480
Jones, Harold 517
Jones, Mike 522
Jones, Sterling 525
Jones, Barbara 526
Jones, Lisa 546
Jones, Elizabeth 551
Jones, Bryson 555
Jones, Marc 568
Jones, Jeff 578
Jones, Robert 582
Jones, Nicholas P. 584
Jones, Tammie 593
Jones, Barbara 608
Jones, Linda 617
Jones, Christopher 623
Jones, Reed F 624
Jones, Daniel W 632
Jones, Lindsey 638
Jones, Brian 640
Jones, Alison 650
Jones, Mindy 671
Jong, Annemieke De 556
Jooma, Imran 567
Joplin, Joe 382
Jorandby, Kendra 309
Jordahl, Mark S. 26
Jordan, James 46
Jordan, Steve 120
Jordan, George 120
Jordan, Patrick 173
Jordan, Denisha 188

Jordan, Arthur 189
Jordan, Javoris 280
Jordan, Marie K. (Kim) 289
Jordan, Tom 370
Jordan, Will 577
Jordan, David 610
Jordan, Bill 669
Jordan, Darren 671
Jordon, Stacy 481
Jorgensen, Helge 173
Jorgensen, Jeff 247
Jorgensen, Mary 298
Joseph, Cathy 212
Joseph, Simone 325
Joseph, Dennis 405
Joshi, Amit 433
Joslin, Tim A. 153
Joslin, Tim 153
Joslin, Tim A 210
Joslyn, Scott 298
Jovanovic, Veka 75
Joyce, Katherine A 656
Joyner, Matt 540
Jozwik, Mary 642
Jr, Hugh Inman 5
Jr, Leroy J Stromberg 19
Jr, Richard Kruse 22
Jr, Walter Sullivan 24
Jr, Paul G Haaga 30
Jr, Paul G Haaga 31
Jr, Donald M Clements 32
Jr, Rick Shadyac 34
Jr, Richard K Trowbridge 37
Jr, John A Miller 38
Jr, James F McEncaney 40
Jr, William J Ferguson 58
Jr, J James Pearce 81
Jr, John F George 85
Jr, Joseph Sarpy 85
Jr, Andrew Hove 103
Jr, Floyd Eharlow 105
Jr, Jack E Counts 108
Jr, George Robert Vaughan 112
Jr, Arthur C Evans 150
Jr, Robert Rosene 157
Jr, Robert B Rosene 157
Jr, John Kennedy 162
Jr, Joseph P Santucci 165
Jr, John C Fryer 188
Jr, Theo Bunting 196
Jr, Herbert H Huddleston 201
Jr, Glenn D Steele 214
Jr, Albert Bothe 214
Jr, Glenn D Steele 214
Jr, Glenn D Steele 215
Jr, Robert Hill 240
Jr, Ewing Werlein 245
Jr, Ernest J Novak 265
Jr, Howard L Barton 279
Jr, Stephen Paul Carter 279
Jr, Carlos Cole 280
Jr, Jerry Lamon Falwell 295
Jr, Martin Salinas 297
Jr, Robert L Lord 310
Jr, Charles A Collat 316
Jr, John M Starcher 329
Jr, Thomas M Dono 334
Jr, Norris L Hodgins 349
Jr, David D Desper 349
Jr, Robert Blount 387
Jr, Theodore T Myre 389
Jr, Charles E Jones 394
Jr, Ronald J Nicolas 403
Jr, Richard C Owens 408
Jr, Michael Perrone 423
Jr, Glenn Steel 428
Jr, Donald Anderson 431
Jr, Robert Allen 439
Jr, Thomas J McCraken 445
Jr, Walter W Austin 450
Jr, William Delong 466
Jr, J Harry Haslam 474
Jr, Jerome A Benkert 505
Jr, Phillip D Joseph 511

Jr, Lawrence C Franklin 526
Jr, John B King 526
Jr, Elmo M Cavin 552
Jr, William Michael Warren 559
Jr, Eugene A Gargaro 565
Jr, Glenn D Steele 569
Jr, Virgil E Cooper 575
Jr, Kenneth O Johnson 587
Jr, William Hite 588
Jr, Richard L Smith 593
Jr, Thomas B Gerlach 593
Jr, Donald Campbell 595
Jr, James W Dean 642
Jr, John Pelusi 644
Jr, Anthony Rizzo 664
Jr, Brooks Von Arx 671
Ju, Jennifer 534
Juarez, Alfonso 250
Juday, Mark 27
Judge, Kenan 247
Judge, Daniel P 268
Juett, Phillip 333
Julian, Steve 484
Julian, James R. 631
Julian, Heather San 647
Julie, Campbell 137
Julie, Norton 383
Julien, Robert 274
Jun, Albert 268
Junck, Mary E. 555
Junco, Kirk 285
Jung, Yoosung 248
Jung, Holger R 282
Junglas, Steve 222
Junk, Luke 453
Juntti, Debbie 308
Jupe, Joel — 164
Jurczyk, Andrew D. 486
Jurgens, Michael 247
Jusino, Arnaldo 86
Jusko, James 553
Jussame, Raymond 340
Justice, Peggy Rasnick 419
Justice, Lorraine 456
Justus, Luiza 608
Jyothinagaram, Sathya 61

K

K, Sandvik Helvi 356
Kaaihue, Herb 112
Kaare, Rae 49
Kaban, Leonard 574
Kabat, Amanda 7
Kabay, Laura 110
Kabrick, Elizabeth 516
Kacavas, John 173
Kacmarek, Robert 574
Kaelin, Michael H. (Mike) 447
Kaestner, Angie 465
Kafer, Ann 223
Kafer, Tim 306
Kahanek, Jacob 196
Kahanek, Sheila 532
Kahanek, Debra 548
Kahl, Cathy 313
Kahlich, Randy 432
Kahn, Brad 14
Kail, Marilyn 114
Kaiser, Nicole 174
Kaiser, Michael 193
Kaiser, Laura S. 256
Kaiser, Cindy 266
Kaiser, Daphne 282
Kaiser, Larry R. 546
Kaiser, Ken 546
Kaiser, Larrty R 595
Kaji, Lucy 198
Kakkis, Jane 323
Kakuda, Kevin 150
Kalafatis, Lara 116
Kalafut, Thomas 671

Kalambur, Ganesh 604
Kalanihuia, Janice 585
Kale, Kimberly 180
Kaliappan, Eswaramoorthy 445
Kalinoski, Joe 97
Kalinowski, Tracy 500
Kalish, Carol 473
Kalkwarf, Lane 200
Kallenbach, Charles 234
Kalnin, Andrew J 581
Kalp, Dirk 666
Kalsbeck, Brad Van 281
Kalsbeek, David 175
Kalscheur, Gregory 608
Kaluarachchi, Pubudu 638
Kam, Keith 534
Kamano, Michel 422
Kamara, Ernest T 383
Kamath, Vijita 444
Kamel, Hany 654
Kamell, Ralph 300
Kamerling, Allison 258
Kamlani, Kunal S 443
Kammerer, Richard F. 560
Kammerman, Susan 405
Kamphaus, Randy 636
Kanaan, Matthew 187
Kandt, Debbie 617
Kane, Patrick 109
Kane, Jenny 193
Kane, Maggie 255
Kane, Terri 256
Kane, Kenneth 299
Kane, Julie 391
Kane, Martha 407
Kane, Allen R. 497
Kaneb, Gary 363
Kaneshige, Jason 628
Kang, Hyun C 472
Kanis, Karla 405
Kansara, Dushyant 85
Kansky, Bill 178
Kant, Surya 542
Kantor, Hans 237
Kanwal, Ayesha 637
Kaplan, Paul 185
Kaplan, Matthew 343
Kaplan, Ross 399
Kaplan, Mark 627
Kaplan, Alan 640
Kaplan, Gary S 652
Kaplanis, Donna 665
Kaplon, Sari 346
Kapoor, Pragati 357
Kappele, Brian 590
Kapur, Patricia 615
Kapur, Sangita 625
Karachalios, Konstantinos 572
Karachi, Tracy 608
Karageorges, Carolyn 128
Karandikar, Nitin 594
Karavolos, Nick 381
Karcz, Adam 252
Karczewski, Alicia 477
Kareiva, Peter 579
Karl, Patricia 163
Karls, Lori 614
Karn, Heather 562
Karner, Sabine 136
Karo, Rachel 428
Karp, Harold M 543
Karp, Stephen R. 558
Karpiak, Stephen 371
Karr, Michael 403
Karrer, Joy 389
Kasargod, Sameer 321
Kaseman, Sheila 127
Kasey, Jay 351
Kaska, Tony 247
Kasman, Glenn 352
Kassem, Rona 332
Kasser, James 558
Kassir, Abdul 153
Kaszowski, Richard 394

Index of Executives

Katayama, James 248
Katehi, Linda P.B. 624
Kates, Kenneth P 629
Katsouleas, Thomas C. 442
Katsoyannis, George 459
Kattan, Omar 615
Katterheinrich, Lean 148
Katz, Jason 34
Katz, Ellen 81
Katz, Martin J. (Marty) 146
Katz, Maxine 365
Katz, Kevin 386
Katz, Erin 444
Katz, Kristine 524
Katz, Louis H. 569
Kauder, Frank 578
Kaufman, Dan 260
Kaufman, Dan 261
Kaufman, Charles 340
Kaufman, Richard 407
Kaufman, Irvin A 437
Kaufman, Irvin A. 438
Kaukali, Chris T 628
Kaul, Will 221
Kaup, Nicholas 595
Kaupa, Michael B. 406
Kausch, Thomas 456
Kavanaugh, John 154
Kavanaugh, James P 673
Kavanaugh, James P. (Jim) 674
Kavthekar, Suhas 502
Kawasaki, Hiroyuki 678
Kawata, Hiro 218
Kay, Mary 627
Kayatta, Dominic 304
Kays, Karmy 224
Kayser, Karen 630
Kazazian, Haig 268
Kazerounian, Reza 53
Kazi, Iftekhar 643
Kboudi, Caryn 154
Keables, Michael 146
Keach, Camillia 546
Keady, Thomas 608
Kealey, Katie 304
Kealy, Mary V 300
Kean, Steve 360
Keane, John B 32
Keane, Merry 410
Keane, Valerie 484
Keaney, Ellen 280
Kearline, Jones 232
Kearney, Rick 306
Kearns, Jim 28
Kearns, Richard 50
Kearns, Donald B 437
Kearns, Donald 438
Kearson, Margaretta 500
Keating, Mary J 198
Keating, Michael 333
Keating, Patrick J. 608
Keating, Todd 616
Keating, Todd 616
Keaveny, Mark 496
Keckeis, Thomas M. (Tom) 334
Kee, Marlow 589
Keefe, Dennis D 673
Keefer, Elizabeth 116
Keefer, Ben 425
Keegan, Michael 439
Keeler, Brian 161
Keeler, Tracy 246
Keeley, Brian E. 63
Keeley, John 96
Keeling, E F 399
Keeling, Kelli 665
Keen, Eric L 230
Keen, Eric L. 231
Keenan, Joseph (Joe) 579
Keenan, Joe 579
Keene, Mark 13
Keene, Kristi 387
Keener, Pat 649
Keenley, Michael 678

Keffer, Michelle 456
Kegley, Clark 479
Kehoe, Kendra 233
Keil, Michael 365
Keil, Richard 532
Keil, Virginia 596
Keilin, Eugene J. 304
Keiper, Joel 236
Keiser, Harold 196
Keiser, Rosemary 625
Keith, Elizabeth 181
Keithgiordano, Mary 489
Keivani, Beth 386
Keizer, Henry R 571
Kellar, Brian 61
Kelleher, Margaret Ann 349
Kelleher, Kathleen 639
Kellen, Vincent 175
Keller, Jonell 22
Keller, San 34
Keller, Kevin 231
Keller, John C. 594
Keller, Kimberly 617
Kellerhouse, James 17
Kellermann, Doug 249
Kellermann, James 581
Kelley, Bridgett 5
Kelley, Jennifer 12
Kelley, Laura 120
Kelley, Daniel T. (Dan) 143
Kelley, H. Lynn 291
Kelley, Brian 315
Kelley, Susan 423
Kelley, Laurie 431
Kelley, Mike 432
Kelley, Trenton L 547
Kelley, Lawrence (Larry) 596
Kelly, John J. 3
Kelly, Thomas B. (Tom) 9
Kelly, Gail 12
Kelly, William M 90
Kelly, Jhon 96
Kelly, Mike 120
Kelly, Karen 149
Kelly, Patty 250
Kelly, Patrick E. 282
Kelly, Thomas 301
Kelly, Julie 316
Kelly, Joseph J 331
Kelly, Paul 384
Kelly, Michael 416
Kelly, Jane 418
Kelly, Angela 426
Kelly, Michael J. (Mike) 432
Kelly, Carstens 477
Kelly, Alan 478
Kelly, Alan B 479
Kelly, Dennis 497
Kelly, Robin 519
Kelly, Carol 525
Kelly, Frank J 665
Kelseth, Carrie 362
Kelso, Brian 453
Kelvinton, William C 411
Kemick, Allura 484
Kemp, Nicole 332
Kemp, Matthew 336
Kemp, Chuck 425
Kemp, Anne 513
Kemp, Kelly 561
Kemper, David W. 600
Kemppel, Denali 43
Kenagy, John 288
Kendall, Randolph L. (Randy) 553
Kendra, Chris 239
Kendrick, David 122
Kendrick, Kenny 246
Kennamore, Jackie 105
Kennard, Corey 516
Kenneally, Anthony 220
Kennedy, Blake 5
Kennedy, Brad 9
Kennedy, Charles A. 114
Kennedy, Marie 182

Kennedy, Dannie 240
Kennedy, Bruce 334
Kennedy, Peter 386
Kennedy, Danny 449
Kennedy, Deborah 477
Kennedy, Steven L. 486
Kennedy, James 610
Kenner, Shane 222
Kenneth, Andrews 237
Kenney, George 546
Kenny, Maureen E. 608
Kent, Rodney D 257
Kent, Geoff 257
Kent, James L. (Jim) 319
Kent, Peter 415
Kenyon, Robert 52
Kenzie, Lesa Mc 465
Keough, Adam 117
Kepp, Scott 587
Keppel, Mary Ann 233
Kepple, Yann 233
Kerbeshian, Marie 594
Kerby, Michael 83
Kerger, Paula A. 432
Kerk, Julie 211
Kern, Howard P. 484
Kern, Howard 484
Kerndl, John 75
Keroack, Mark A. 72
Keroack, Mark A. 73
Kerouani, Farida 404
Kerr, Mary E. 116
Kerr, Robert 156
Kerr, Donald M. 578
Kersten, Rebecca 45
Kerstetter, Mitzie 214
Kerth, Rob 462
Kerwin, George 76
Kerwin, George 76
Kesler-Arnold, Kimberly 356
Kess, Thomas 597
Kessel, Donna Van 496
Kessler, Joe 151
Kessler, Andrea 252
Kester, Jenny 184
Ketola, Todd 68
Ketter, Andrew 453
Ketterling, Terry L 498
Kettler, Tamara 379
Keucher, Stephen 610
Keucher, Steve 610
Keuer, Steve 133
Keup, Gregory 41
Keuten, John 670
Kevin, Liney 416
Key, Daniel 143
Key, George 223
Key, Lester 278
Key, Charles 278
Khait-Palant, Olga V 433
Khaleghi, Trisha 489
Khalsa, Mehtab 15
Khamseh, Ladan 397
Khan, Nasir 89
Khan, Karen 114
Khan, Nazeer 189
Khan, Adil 215
Khan, S S 500
Khan, M Aness 519
Khatib, Riad 516
Khator, Renu 629
Khawaja, Wajhiuddin 664
Khazanchi, Shal 456
Khokar, Ghazala 663
Khom, Alexander 206
Khorasani, Mohammad 182
Khosla, Suresh 1
Khosla, Ashok K 1
Khosla, Leena 1
Khouri, Lara M 559
Khoury, Nabil 236
Khoury, Aldo 519
Khrimian, Tigran 202
Khurana, Sanjay 2

Kiamos, James 199
Kickbusch, Laura 119
Kieffer, Steve 74
Kieffer, Amy 225
Kiener, Mary 449
Kiesewetter, Scott 35
Kijewski, Peter 325
Kiksman, Allen 471
Kikuchi, Kent 230
Kikumoto, C. David 13
Kikut, Janusz 598
Kilborn, Jim 31
Kilbride, Marc 195
Kilduff, Jennifer 111
Kile, Pam K 140
Kiley, Ernie 10
Kiley, Tom 314
Kilkenny, Rosemary 570
Killeen, Steve 200
Killeen, Tom 333
Killmer, Jonathon 241
Killmeyer, Susan 643
Kilpatrick, Dona 34
Kilpatrick, C 650
Kilpatrick, Charles A 650
Kim, Joe 118
Kim, Ginny 118
Kim, Taeeuk 248
Kim, Changyoung 248
Kim, Chung 296
Kim, Phillip 305
Kim, Dong Eun 361
Kim, Bill 419
Kim, Robert 488
Kim, Helen 546
Kim, Y S 645
Kimball, Scott 642
Kimbell, Jimmy 38
Kimble, Sarah 308
Kimmel, Bradford 149
Kimmerle, David 184
Kimmerle, Sandra Sue 184
Kimmons, Herb 438
Kinaitis, Eric 554
Kinder, Richard D 360
Kindler, Mark 453
Kindlick, David 653
Kindred, Bryan N. 564
King, Jeff 96
King, Gena 133
King, Randy 142
King, Timothy 149
King, Letitia 160
King, Yolanda 160
King, Vanessa 168
King, Jerry 215
King, Victoria 220
King, Michele 303
King, Victoria 410
King, Andrea 415
King, Suzanne 453
King, Robert 453
King, Jared 466
King, Bernard F 467
King, Jeffrey 484
King, Kathleen 506
King, Kirk 551
King, Charles 563
King, David 575
King-Shaw, Ruben J. 631
Kingbury, Mike 210
Kingsley, Scott 505
Kingsmore, Stephen 438
Kingston, Robert E. 574
Kini, Narendra M 649
Kinman, Thomas 128
Kinman, Mary 551
Kinneer, Mike 148
Kinner, Scott 86
Kinney, Stephanie 128
Kinney, Anthony 425
Kinsey, Jon 193
Kinslow, Anthony D 116
Kintigh, Denise 467

Index of Executives

Index of Executives

Kummeth, Janet 211
Kumpula, Jim 537
Kunash, Amanda 22
Kunda, Dolores 567
Kunimoto, Yoshihiko 534
Kunisaki, Tom 488
Kuntz, Louann 17
Kuntz, Kevin 318
Kuntz, Michael J. (Mike) 612
Kunze, Shane 435
Kupka, Alyssa 175
Kuppuswamy, Murali 571
Kurdle, Florence B 40
Kurin, Richard 497
Kuritsky, Lloyd 489
Kurtz, Jeffrey 86
Kurtz, William 429
Kustenbauter, Jim 584
Kutateladze, Andrei 146
Kutch, John M 606
Kutina, Kenneth 116
Kuzas, Betsy 417
Kvasnikoff, Wayne 392
Kvistad, Gregg 146
Kwak, Jin 248
Kwasnica, Christina 181
Kwok, Daphne 2
Kwon, Kenneth 343
Kwong, Melsen 118
Kyprianou, Annette 576
Kyriacos, Zoe 642

L

L, Green Jacob 569
La, Paul De 404
LaBelle, James 479
Labonte, Chip 356
Labosky, Laura 138
Labrecque, Andre G 24
Labrecque, Christine 300
Lacey, Diane E. 365
Lachman, Barry 171
Lachman, Sandy 445
Lacombe, Philip 72
Ladd, Edward H. (Ted) 79
Ladd, Kevin 205
Ladd, Steven 223
Lafferty, William 677
Lafloure, Thomas 134
Lafon, Emily 665
Lafontaine, Micheline 598
Lage, Jose L. 505
Lager, Jeffrey T 31
Lagerlef, Brenda 422
Lago, Jim 190
Lagoy, Ned 166
Lague, Richard C 329
Lai, Julius 30
Laing, Sheila 247
Laird, William 301
Lake, Robert 180
Lake, Marcelino 249
Lakhtman, Lilia 604
Lakin, Kenneth S 95
Lakin, Peter D 95
Lakin, Edwin A 95
Lalas, Jose W 160
Lally, Thomas 475
Lally, Devin 625
Lalonde, Mary 574
Lalor, William 58
Lalor, William 58
Lamar, Jim 218
Lamarre, Anne 204
Lamas, Terry 102
Lamb, Jim 120
Lamb, Eric 185
Lamb, John 309
Lamb, Michael 376
Lamb, Mark 506
Lamb, Todd 526

Lamb, Jureen 541
Lamb, Brian D. 638
Lambert, Phil 488
Lambertson, Stephen 601
Lamble, Mark 246
Lambros, Cindy 122
Lamm, Kimberly 450
Lamoreaux, Brent 249
Lampe, Adam 319
Lampert, Steven 54
Lampman, Rusty 199
Lancaster, Rick 221
Lance, Phil 254
Lance, Donald W 587
Lance, Fletcher 648
Land, Jeff 181
Landa, Howard 535
Landaker, Larry 410
Lande, Ruth 325
Lander, Ryan 422
Lander, Eric 556
Landers, Lisa 27
Landers, Peter 613
Landes, Barbara L. 432
Landever, Alan 198
Landewee, Cassy 337
Landreth, Laura 554
Landrum, Marilyn 141
Landry, Doug 384
Landstrom, G 606
Lane, Danny 50
Lane, Conan 234
Lane, Becca 259
Lane, Linda 421
Lane, Colin 511
Lane, Charles E. 627
Lanese, Katherine 116
Laney, Mark 234
Laney, Mark 349
Laney, D. Randy 566
Lang, Marcina 637
Langberg, Michael L. 118
Langberg, Joanna 199
Lange, Julie 46
Lange, Donald H 134
Lange, Gerald 404
Langenderfer, Randy 548
Langenfeld, Jon A. 453
Langford, Barbara 28
Langford, Stephen 76
Langford, Mark D 279
Langhals, Ken 270
Langham, Catherine 567
Langham, Jacquelyn 639
Langlais, Tracy 110
Langley, W. John 315
Langley, John 315
Langlois, Jennifer 86
Langston, Scott 452
Langston, Mark 475
Lanier, Gina 55
Lannon, David 669
Lanoha, Richard A 279
Lansford, Gordon E. 260
Lansford, Gordon E. 261
Lansing, Linda 475
Lant, Stephen 121
Lantos, Phyllis 371
Lantos, Phyllis R. 580
Lantz, Penelope 569
Lantzy, Mark 252
Laperriere, Nick 475
Lapeyre, Elizabeth 393
Lapiana, John K. 497
Lapidas, Gary 616
Lapierre, Jamie 639
LaPlante, William 578
Lapointe, Margot 236
LaPorte, Todd 478
Laporte, Todd 479
Lappala, Kris 414
Laprade, Patricia 59
Laratonda, Susan 671
Laraway, Dennis L. 61

Laraway, Dennis 324
Lareau, Doug 491
Larger, Cary 127
Larkin, Frank 166
Larocque, Lynda 633
Larsen, Burke 173
Larsen, Shild 196
Larsen, Brian 316
Larsen, Daniel 478
Larsen, Matthew 497
Larsen, Keri 607
Larsh, Herbert 471
Larson, Steve 28
Larson, Les 41
Larson, Lawrence 102
Larson, John 213
Larson, Elwin 231
Larson, Earl 393
Larson, Warren 471
Larson, Todd 478
Larson, Tom 573
Larson, Mike 633
Larson, Lynette 659
Larsson, John 361
Lartigue, Donna 444
Lasaga, Manuel 65
Lash, Joan 276
Lashier, Mark E 126
Lashin, Joanne 482
Laskey, Sara 576
Lasko, Jonathan 156
Laskowski, Robert 132
Laskowski, Alicia 213
Lasky, Lawrence 357
Lassa, Bradley J 316
Lassiter, Wright L. 236
Laster, Annette 448
Latacki, Nancy 455
Lateef, Omar 459
Lathan, Grenita 245
Lathrop, Ann 165
Latsko, Felicia 127
Lattanzio, Nicole 522
Latushie, Dick 439
Lau, James 290
Lau, Paul 462
Laubach, Harold E. 389
Laubacher, Pat 554
Lauf, Michael K. (Mike) 109
Laufenberg, Wade 73
Laughridge, Alan 418
Laughton, Kim 477
Laur, James 118
Laura, Kasch 638
Laurenti, Rich 666
Laures, Karen 318
Lauria, Joe 356
Lauriello, Johnathan 633
Lauring, Josh 268
Laurito, James 121
Lavan, Maryanne R 206
Lavas, Helen 374
Laveck, Bill 512
Lavelli, Lucinda 627
Lavender, Sunee 623
Laver, Michael 370
Lavery, Michelle 471
Lavoie, Blair 356
Lavoie, Karen 407
Lawhon, Pres 452
Lawhorn, Wesley L 102
Lawhorn, Alex 453
Lawler, Nelda 197
Lawler, Michael A 234
Lawless, Stephen T 22
Lawlor, Dave 309
Lawlor, Edward F. 600
Lawlor, Dave 624
Lawonn, Ken 489
Lawonn, Ken 490
Lawrence, Terri 11
Lawrence, Ida 191
Lawrence, Bruce 254
Lawrence, Heather 298

Lawrence, Mike 312
Lawrence, Sandra A. J. 327
Lawrence, Elin 333
Lawrence, Edward P. 407
Lawrence, Joseph 428
Lawrence, Beth 480
Lawrence, William B. 505
Lawrence, Kenneth 546
Lawrence, Silvana 548
Lawson, Linda 50
Lawson, Ralph E. 63
Lawson, Ralph 65
Lawson, James W. (Jim) 67
Lawson, Ken 245
Lawson, Carmen 286
Lawson, Matt 318
Lawson, Matthew 319
Lawson, Michael 395
Lawson, Sherri 511
Lawson, John W 650
Lawton, Patrick S. (Pat) 453
Lawton, Michael 488
Lay, Jeri 256
Laychak, Heather 553
Layman, Mark 59
Layne, Christopher 354
Laytart, David 329
Layton, Robert 189
Layton, Mary Jo 266
Lazarus, Larry S. 61
Lazo, Marusya 424
Lazrus, Paula 517
Lazzi, Gianluca 597
Le, Hung 33
Le, Christian 152
Le, Andy 371
Le, Brian 441
Lea, Jenny 282
Leach, Mary Anne 127
Leach, Joy 305
Leach, Todd 642
Leahy, Mary 94
Leahy, Kevin 207
Leahy, William P. 608
Leal, Santiago 12
Leal, Alexis 626
LeaMond, Nancy A. 2
Leamy, Audrey 18
Leary, Alison 370
Leary, Angus 531
Leary, Matt 662
Leatherman, Jacob 52
Lebaron, Dawn 598
Lebby, Paul 647
Lebens, Michael C 546
Leber, Charlie 493
Leblanc, Deirdre 171
Leblanc, Stephen 173
Leblanc, Fernis 394
LeBlanc, Thomas J. 569
Leblanc, Paul A 623
LeBlanc-Burley, Jelynne 164
Lebowits, Michelle 265
Lechliter, Katarzyna M 40
Lechner, David E. 92
Lechner, David 638
Leckman, Linda C. 256
Leclair, Michael D 58
Lecorgne, R Paker 394
Ledbetter, David H. 213
Lederer, Bertram M. 544
Lederman, Mark 333
Lederman, Marvin 355
Ledford, Carolyn 337
Ledgister, Mahon 325
Ledien, Randy 653
Ledyard, Robin 151
Lee, Julie 2
Lee, James G. 7
Lee, Stephen 64
Lee, Terry G. 97
Lee, David L. 107
Lee, Ted 114
Lee, Judy 115

Index of Executives

Lee, Ronald 125
Lee, Ellen 150
Lee, Daniel 162
Lee, Chris 176
Lee, Eric 180
Lee, Yauk 182
Lee, Micheal 207
Lee, Ken 232
Lee, Do Hyun 248
Lee, G Scott 282
Lee, Hana 290
Lee, Mary 340
Lee, Angela Y 389
Lee, Thomas H. 407
Lee, Davis 419
Lee, Shiuh 444
Lee, Sandy 461
Lee, John 485
Lee, Thai 492
Lee, Felecia 549
Lee, William 580
Lee, Terry 586
Lee, David 586
Lee, David S. 591
Lee, Vivian S. 597
Lee, Gentry Patrick 610
Lee, Daniel 615
Lee, Robin 625
Lee-Vester, Kris 263
Leedy, Lori 531
Leedy, Brian 644
Leef, Serge 326
Leeming, Rosemary 214
Leenen, Renee 170
Lees, Richard A 393
Lefebvre, David 85
Leffler, Stephen 598
Lefko, Kim 4
Leganza, Nannette 213
Legg, Russell 55
Legoretta, Alfredo 308
Legrand, Jeff 204
Legro, Jeffrey 442
Lehman, Jeffrey S. 370
Lehman, Donald 569
Lehmann, Leslie 558
Lehmuth, Rich 417
Lehn, Chuck 61
Lehne, Kathy 532
Lehne, Kyle 532
Lehoux, Becky 163
Lehrer, Deborah 351
Leiber, Phil 299
Leiderman, Roni 390
Leifheit, Kurt 113
Leigh, Stacey 453
Leighty, Scott 329
Leikhim, William 322
Leist, Drew 59
Leith, Andrew 300
Leiting, Jim 82
Leitner, Lars 202
Leiva, Michele 185
Leketa, Anthony F. (Tony) 582
Lekkala, Maneesh 114
Lemay, Lori 503
Leming, Rudy 166
Lemire, Debbie 33
Lemmer, Teresa 445
Lemoine, Frederick 405
Lemois, Xilma 638
Lemon, Robert 652
Lemperle, John 18
Lempka, Joseph R 279
Lenahan, Kevin 12
Lenertz, Renae 606
Lennen, Anthony 151
Lennon, Kevin 358
Lenson, Celia 308
Lentell, Troy 554
Lenti-Ponsetto, Jean 175
Lentini, Matt 68
Lentz, Darrell 49
Lenzen, John 542

Leo, Christina 272
Leo, Koguan 492
Leon, Sonny 50
Leon, Andres De 378
Leon, Monica Ponce de 591
Leon, Fredy De 646
Leonard, Mark 74
Leonard, James C. 113
Leonard, Pat 364
Leonard, Margaret 369
Leonard, Jim 431
Leonard, Jim 462
Leonard, Judith E. 497
Leonard, Roger 662
Leonard, Edward F 667
Leonardi, Phil 382
Leone, Bob 255
Leone, Timothy 420
Leonhardt, Darrell T. 45
Leopold, Jay 185
Lepage, Mark A 310
Lepley, John 329
Lerner, J Scott 155
Leshan, Tim 383
Leskoski, Darren 31
Leslie, Paul 171
Leslie, Andy 361
Leslie, James 582
Lesneski, Gary J. 563
Lesperance, Thomas F 25
Lessler, Becky 383
Lester, William 103
Lester, Mark C. 551
Letendre, Donald E. 594
Letier, Scott 354
Letinsky, Daniel 433
Leto, Lara 240
Letson, Alicia 237
Lett, Rosalind K 194
Lett, Stan 242
Lettero, Tom 108
Lettman, Dennis S. 596
Leupold, Mary 230
Levar, Mary E 453
Levasseur, Rita 243
Levasseur, INA 312
Levesque, Carla 598
Levi, David F. 187
Levi, Donna 610
Levin, David 14
Levin, Jesse 117
Levin, Rosalyn 304
Levin, Roy 361
Levin, Barry F 494
Levin, Justine 556
Levin, Kerry 664
Levine, Jordan 32
Levine, Mel 299
Levine, Stephen 300
Levine, Robert 370
Levine, Peter H 616
Levine, Helen D 638
Levinson, Linda 571
Levit, Polina 191
Levy, Susan Nestor 47
Levy, Ofer 125
Levy, Michael 160
Levy, Ann 361
Levy, Lester A 361
Levy, Judd S 369
Levy, Sharon 558
Lewandowski, Joel 149
Lewandowski, Christopher 236
Lewandowski, Jay 597
Lewin, Cindy 2
Lewis, Michael 2
Lewis, Sherry 25
Lewis, Flint 32
Lewis, Derrick 34
Lewis, James R. (Jim) 85
Lewis, Lisa 164
Lewis, Eric 196
Lewis, David 198
Lewis, Curtis 219

Lewis, Jonathan 233
Lewis, Jake 250
Lewis, Tamara 256
Lewis, Melanie 319
Lewis, Tony 361
Lewis, John 363
Lewis, Dr Kirk 408
Lewis, Ky 489
Lewis, Kelli 518
Lewis, Seth 556
Lewis, Hilton 572
Lewis, Daniel K. 576
Lewis, Erin 594
Lewis, Robert 608
Lewis, Kim 646
Lewis, Joseph 667
Lewis, Lisa 671
Lewton, Zachary R 472
Leyoub, Caprice 621
Lhota, Joseph J. 336
LI, Jie 49
LI, WEI 49
Li, Ruohao 444
Li, Mehra 489
LI, Heng 556
Li, Hengguang 660
Liao, Frances 444
Liao, Edward 502
Liarikos, Angelo 366
Libertino, John 284
Licalzi, Maria 357
Lichtenwalner, Thomas P 466
Lichtenwalner, Rthomas P 513
Liddy, Casey 395
Liebowitz, Richard S. 580
Liede, Kathryn 314
Liedel, Christopher 497
Liekar, John 119
Lienhart, Ross 428
Liesegang, Skip 250
Lifka, David 159
Light, Darla 206
Light, Amber 469
Lightfoot, Jeremy 199
Lightfoot, Lance 548
Lightner, Margaret 75
Liguori, Kathryn 66
Liimatainen, Sherman 221
Likins, Steven 601
Likins, Steve 601
Lilek, Ronald 75
Liles, Don 311
Liles, Scott 477
Lillemoe, Keith D. 574
Lilles, Paul 647
Lillian, Robles 230
Lillis, Charles M. (Chuck) 636
Lim, Douglas 217
Lim, Jolene 402
Lim, Rina 404
Limehouse, Capers 112
Limjoco, Adrianne 453
Lin, Isaac 182
Lin, Wilson W. 374
Lin, Maria 388
Lin, Tian 395
Lin, Senshang 517
Lin, Kathryn 610
Lin, Bruce 659
Lincoln, Butch 43
Lincoln, David R 163
Lincoln, Bonni 264
Lincoln, Dood 356
Lind, Sharon 61
Lind, Amy 625
Linda, Doherty 407
Lindahl, Richard S 117
Lindahl, Lennart 501
Lindauer, Jeff 610
Lindberg, Chuck 200
Lindblom, Mike 531
Linde, Ronald K. 107
Lindell, James 356
Lindemann, Deven 333

Linden, Andrew 601
Linder, James 92
Linder, Charlie 282
Linders, Ryan 669
Lindholm, Wayne S. 238
Lindley, Melissa 138
Lindley, Randy 387
Lindsay, Mike 25
Lindsay, Jeff 253
Lindsay, Jeff 390
Lindsey, Mark 35
Lindsey, H. Eugene (Gene) 54
Lindsey, Steven L 510
Lindsey, Don 541
Lindstrom, Donnie 261
Line, Ann 49
Lineberger, Terry 453
Liner, Sallye A. 390
Lingerfeldt, Lezli 251
Lingerfelt, Lisa 185
Lingg, Danielle 162
Link, Denise W 141
Link, Dave 471
Linney, Brian 312
Linss, Roxanne 212
Linzer, Daniel I. 388
Lipani, Laura 333
Lipert, John 176
Lipner, Zachary 66
Lipomi, Jack 109
Lippard, Nicole 91
Lippincott, Constance 653
Lippman, Frederick 389
Lippoldt, Diana 662
Lipscomb, Jean 206
Lipsitz, Stuart 556
Lipsky, Matt 555
Lisa, Cost 588
Liscidini, Fabio 496
Lish, Ethan 202
Liskay, Alice 576
Lison, Karen 531
Listenbee, Rashaan 539
Listengart, Joseph 360
Lister, Noel 446
Liszt, Mark 286
Liszt, Max 286
Litavec, Viliam 206
Litchford, Susan 70
Litchy, William 318
Little, Steve 11
Little, George A 230
Little, George 230
Little, George A. 231
Little, Daniel 444
Littlefield, Mark D 200
Littlejohn, Bill 489
Litton, Wayne 106
Litwin, Jim 250
Liu, Anthony 129
Liu, Catherine 368
Liu, Guangliang 501
Liu, Manuel M 649
Lively, David 389
Livesay, Jackie J 160
Livingood, Jack 83
Livingston, Larry 35
Livingston, Randall S. (Randy) 290
Livingston, Lee 371
Livingston, Kim 558
Livingston, Keith 602
Lizhong, Yu 370
LLC, Wyoming Acquisition GP 441
LLC, SES Holdings 482
Lloyd, Tim 102
Lloyd, Kathy 160
Lloyd, John R 251
Lloyd, Lisa Kay 551
Lloyd, James 627
Lobaugh, Mike 227
Locke, Justin 164
Locke, Jay E 277
Lockhart, Marvin 189
Lockhart, Ann 393

Index of Executives

Index of Executives

Index of Executives

Index of Executives

Index of Executives

Mill, Jack De 437
Mill, Georgia 457
Millar, Jason 642
Millard, Robert B. 314
Millard, Jayne 613
Millard, Suzanne Turtle 613
Miller, Robert G. (Bob) 20
Miller, Sue 26
Miller, Mary 55
Miller, Amanda 58
Miller, Dale 58
Miller, Heather 94
Miller, Corie 94
Miller, Toni 95
Miller, James 101
Miller, Alex 128
Miller, Jonathan 153
Miller, David 175
Miller, Timothy (Tim) 182
Miller, Lynn 213
Miller, Lynn 214
Miller, Deborah 214
Miller, Clark 220
Miller, Dale 235
Miller, Edwin (Glen) 238
Miller, Deloris 242
Miller, Scott 245
Miller, Vickie 250
Miller, James 260
Miller, Diane 260
Miller, Victoria 301
Miller, Chris 309
Miller, Cathy 333
Miller, Allison 333
Miller, Rick 359
Miller, Glenn 371
Miller, Jeff 404
Miller, Patrick 429
Miller, Ronald 436
Miller, Tara 443
Miller, James 456
Miller, Alex 473
Miller, Janice 478
Miller, Tim 478
Miller, Jennifer 479
Miller, Peter C. 486
Miller, Scott 497
Miller, Rob 499
Miller, Barbara 502
Miller, Josh 510
Miller, Tim 514
Miller, Don 519
Miller, Jon 521
Miller, Adam 526
Miller, Kurt 540
Miller, Randy 552
Miller, Franklin C. (Frank) 557
Miller, Pamela 573
Miller, Ezra 588
Miller, Paula 588
Miller, Melissa 595
Miller, Mark 595
Miller, Matthew 596
Miller, Patrice 604
Miller, Martin 618
Miller, Kathleen 633
Miller, Richard 653
Miller, Gary 661
Miller, David 662
Miller, Debbie 670
Miller, Al 671
Miller, Erin 671
Miller, Jim 671
Millette, Steven 626
Milligan, Michael D 57
Millikan, J. Scott 84
Milliken, Bob 74
Millman, Bert 105
Mills, Curtis 112
Mills, Bryan A. 151
Mills, Chris 245
Mills, Sharrie 253
Mills, David C 254
Mills, Don 337

Mills, Angel 488
Mills, Ed 493
Mills, Jim 577
Millsap, Mark 247
Milne, Robb A 125
Milner, Trudie 678
Milone-Nuzzo, Paula 584
Milot, Marie-Claude 387
Milowski, Nicholas 206
Milstein, Maxine 230
Mims, Rod 51
Mims, Krystal 551
Minardi, Christina 669
Minarich, Jacob 362
Minehan, Cathy E. 574
Miner, Jim 342
Mines, Michael A. (Mick) 396
Minniti, John 2
Minock, Cheri 607
Minor, Richard 189
Minor, Vicki 268
Minor, Lloyd 290
Minor, Tony 465
Minor, Timothy A 595
Minter, Clarence 168
Minter, Gordon 245
Mintner, Christina 171
Mintz, Alan 300
Minutoli, Robert 601
Minzler, Dennis 359
Miracle, Dan 25
Miranda, Mark 94
Miritello, Suzanne 496
Misawa, Naoshi 376
Mishina, Craig 485
Mishra, Soumyadeep 286
Misita, Bill 416
Mislan, Tim 344
Misra, Sanjay 467
Mistry, Nilesh 674
Mitarotonda, Robert 503
Mitchell, Tony 32
Mitchell, Ken 83
Mitchell, Charles 86
Mitchell, Laura 135
Mitchell, Susan 192
Mitchell, Susan 192
Mitchell, Jennifer 202
Mitchell, J. Stuart 232
Mitchell, Jim 252
Mitchell, Matt 256
Mitchell, Michael R 295
Mitchell, John 447
Mitchell, Harmon 456
Mitchell, Herry 506
Mitchell, Jenny 515
Mitchell, Sharon 539
Mitchell, Howard 553
Mitchell, Ginny 597
Mitchell, Robert (Rob) 601
Mitchell, Adrienne 660
Mitrick, Joseph M. (Joe) 63
Mitschke, Gina 286
Mittal, Vijay 47
Mittermaier, Pascal 579
Mitzner, Jennifer 242
Mix, Heidi 455
Miyamoto, Michael 343
Miyamoto, Gene 523
Miyamoto, Tomoaki 678
Miyares, Javier 642
Mladenovic, Jeanette 399
Mnning, Carol 673
MO, Weiwei 642
Moalli, Pamela 303
Moberg, Kirk 113
Moccio, Cindy 274
Mock, Teresa A 329
Mockabee, William 587
Modawell, Debbie 46
Modde, Margaret Mary 163
Modell, Mitchell B. (Mitch) 237
Mody-Baily, Priti 82
Modzelewski, Sophia 175

Moe, Melinda 55
Moeller, Michael 166
Moen, Russ 198
Moerhing, Mike 310
Moffet, Brian L 494
Moffett, Debbie 153
Moffett, Randy 621
Moffett, Glen 677
Moffitt, John 337
Moffitt, Jamie 636
Moffitt, Michael 636
Mogan, Tom 608
Mogan, Thomas 608
Mogg, Denise 467
Mohan, Maya 286
Mohanty, Prasanna 118
Mohr, Todd M. 9
Mohr, David 484
Mohr, Mr Michael 500
Mohrman, Mike 458
Mohta, Namita 407
Moje, Elizabeth Birr 444
Molbert, Paul 284
Moldovan, Regina 505
Molesevich, Patrice 214
Molina, Luis 179
Molina, Sergio 306
Molina-Clark, Cecilia 633
Molina-frias, Maria Null 175
Molko, Cindy 467
Molle, Josephine 236
Mollet, Chris 192
Mollet, Chris 192
Molmen, David 29
Molnar, Cindy 119
Moloney, Jacquie 631
Monaghan, Meghan 389
Monaghan, Sophia 558
Monahan, Dennis 55
Monahan, Thomas L 117
Monahan, Mike Null 389
Monahan, Jay 415
Monan, J. Donald 608
Moncrief, Kit Tennison 549
Mondelli, Jeffrey 657
Mondragon, Brian 138
Mones, Ann 138
Monfeli, Mike 453
Monfre, Andy 55
Mong, Marla 155
Monge, Cathie 658
Monk, David H. 584
Monroe, Tim 276
Monroe, Rosemary 290
Monroe, Sheila 514
Monson, Dale D. 145
Montague, Jason 443
Montague, Jason 453
Montano, Chris 20
Monte, John 327
Monteagudo, Ibzan 667
Monteiro, Manuel 95
Montenegro, Sara 548
Montero, Alejandro 445
Montesino, Orlando C 453
Montgomery, Michael 5
Montgomery, Carol 175
Montgomery, Angel 239
Montgomery, Toni-Marie 388
Montgomery, Lisa P. 575
Monticup, Thomas 601
Montoya, Veronica 456
Mood, Shawn 117
Moody, Doug 149
Moody, Craig 396
Moody, David S 581
Mooers, Blaine 526
Moon, Kimberly 185
Moon, Don 295
Moon, Harry 390
Moon, Jenny 546
Moonesinghe, Dee 151
Mooney, John 161
Mooney, Randy 169

Mooney, Monica 627
Moore, Pennie 6
Moore, Bud 76
Moore, Rob 83
Moore, Cory 83
Moore, Andrew 114
Moore, Dana 127
Moore, Maricela S. 132
Moore, Stephen L 150
Moore, Dayna 184
Moore, Joseph 187
Moore, Michael 200
Moore, Kimberly 208
Moore, Matthew 243
Moore, Stephanie 248
Moore, James D. 254
Moore, Mikelle 256
Moore, Mary 270
Moore, William L 274
Moore, Morgan 277
Moore, Robert 312
Moore, Debra L 323
Moore, Amanda 328
Moore, David 337
Moore, Joe 387
Moore, Dana 420
Moore, Rachel 425
Moore, Kim 434
Moore, William M. 447
Moore, Edward 449
Moore, John 456
Moore, Lori 489
Moore, Jason 541
Moore, Gary 552
Moore, Barry 556
Moore, Kelly 596
Moore, Jackson W. 599
Moore, Bob 601
Moore, Dorian 606
Moore, Joy 608
Moore, Madeleine G 608
Moore, Michael 624
Moore, Daphne 657
Moore, Craig 669
Moorehead, Kimberly 2
Moorehead, Kristen 611
Moorehead, Michael 671
Moorhead, Keith 179
Moorman, Kathy 63
Moose, Savannah 315
Moose, Selina 356
Moots, Stephanie 57
Mora, Elizabeth 557
Morabito, Leonardo 414
Morack, Sarah J 222
Morais, Diane E 27
Morales, David 2
Morales, Ray 256
Morales, Jimmy 319
Morales, Jose 350
Morales, Ralph 461
Moran, Michael F. 73
Moran, Tim 150
Moran, Thomas 190
Moran, Veronica 368
Moran, John 387
Moran, James 465
Morant, Blake D. 569
Morar, August 370
Morchak, Chris 562
Morde, Vishal 66
More, Ed 125
Moreau, Gary 298
Moreland, Jeffrey 91
Moreno, Vanesa 204
Moreno, Imelda 482
Moreno, Noemi 589
Moretti, Marty 234
Moretti, Darlene 500
Moretz, Drew 595
Morgan, Ada 108
Morgan, Marissa 116
Morgan, Kenneth 153
Morgan, Mark 265

Index of Executives

Morgan, Amanda 319
Morgan, Bill 325
Morgan, Shana 331
Morgan, Crystal 334
Morgan, Dianna 400
Morgan, Vickie 408
Morgan, Rick 416
Morgan, Robert 416
Morgan, Henry 431
Morgan, Marsha L. 607
Morgan, Amanda 615
Morgan, John 664
Morgan, Becka 665
Morganstein, David 664
Morgante, Elizabeth 222
Morgante, Beth 489
Morgenstern, H Richard 329
Moriarty, Daniel 54
Moriarty, Brad 247
Moriguchi, Jaime 118
Morin, Jamie 553
Morissette, Daniel J. 181
Moritz, John 473
Mork, Lee 26
Morlacci, Laura 512
Morley, Jim 86
Morley, Debra 270
Morlock, David R. 596
Morningstar, Ashley 202
Morra, Elizabeth 595
Morray, Jeffrey P. 417
Morrell, Jeff 567
Morrelli, Keri 168
Morrill, Angela 425
Morris, Susan 20
Morris, Thomas 94
Morris, Kenneth 156
Morris, Kenneth C. 187
Morris, David 213
Morris, Patrick 283
Morris, Walker 349
Morris, Pamela 370
Morris, Christine 433
Morris, Sherrill 436
Morris, Tonia G 453
Morris, Patrick 458
Morrisett, J. Gregory 159
Morrison, Julia 22
Morrison, Allen 44
Morrison, Dean 119
Morrison, Dr Bob 212
Morrison, Trevor 370
Morrison, Marni 378
Morrison, Karen 395
Morrison, Tom 445
Morrison, Jeffrey 450
Morrissey, Deborah 407
Morrisson, Mark 584
Morrow, Sherry 18
Morrow, W. Robert 45
Morrow, W. Robert (Bob) 130
Morrow, Richard 154
Morrow, Kent 235
Morrow, Shawn 323
Morrow, Joseph 354
Morrow, Carol 370
Morrow, Kirk 461
Morrow, Jason 596
Morrow, John 628
Morse, Lara 66
Morse, Jim 68
Morse, Alan R 225
Morse, Edward J 349
Morsi, Deborah S. 54
Mortensen, Brian 471
Morton, Margaret 198
Morton, Michele 242
Morton, Kerry 395
Morton, Leo E. 633
Morway, Joe 487
Mory, Scott 114
Mosca, Andrew 250
Moscho, Harold 352
Moscho, Harold 585

Mosemann, Richard 312
Moser, Phillip G 15
Moser, Joseph D 40
Moser, Len 68
Moser, Kathy 629
Mosingo, Jerry L 543
Moskal, Joseph T 112
Moskowitz, Amy 161
Moskowitz, Samuel E. 321
Mosley, Christopher R 219
Mosley, Anthony 252
Mosner, Lisa 614
Mosocco, Doris 653
Mosquera, Juan-Miguel 459
Moss, Howard 118
Moss, Jackie 177
Moss, R. Lawrence 359
Moss, Chad 426
Moss, Amanda 507
Moss, Leah 549
Mossallam, Usamah 236
Mostaert, Christine 319
Motakef, Shahin 478
Mote, Gale 530
Motel, George 96
Motley, J. Keith 631
Mott, Joe 256
Motta, Edgar 179
Moulder, Bill 308
Moulton, Don 361
Moultrie, Anne 642
Mountain, Gary 672
Mountjoy, Ryan 5
Mourad, Waleed 228
Mourad, Bachar 543
Mourino, Art 650
Moustakakis, John 664
Mower, David 28
Mowery, Jamie 476
Mowreader, Jack 415
Moy, Ji W 366
Moye, Ginny 453
Moyer, Nancy 269
Moyer, Dale 475
Moyer, Angel 653
Moyer, Arlene 671
Mozrall, Jacqueline 456
MPA, Charity 12
Mucha, Bob 70
Mucha, John 236
Mudge, Rex 530
Mudler, Gordon A 329
Mueller, Christopher 86
Mueller, Ken 439
Mueller, Manfred 452
Mueller, John 508
Muenzer, Melanie 636
Mugg, Jason 2
Muhart, Matthew J. 500
Muhlfelder, Teddy 197
Muir, Katelyn 597
Muir, Tracy 638
Muirhead, David 227
Muke, Maureen 329
Mukherjee, Preetika 514
Mukherjee, Kishore 596
Mul, James J 227
Muldoon, Christine 274
Muldowney, David 284
Mulhern, Ben 343
Mulholland, Katie S. 594
Mullane, Marietta 493
Mulle, Mike 530
Mullen, Tom 116
Mullen, David 126
Mullen, Kay 306
Mullen, Thomas 329
Mullen, Thomas R 332
Mullen, Paddy C 364
Mullen, John R 364
Mullen, Kate 573
Mullendore, Scott 432
Muller, Frank 233

Muller, David 351
Muller, Garrick 513
Muller, Brook 636
Mullin, Shelly 352
Mullins, Debbie 150
Mullins, Dennis 252
Mullins, Karyn 262
Mullis, Michael 48
Mullis, Harold W. 638
Mulqueen, Tom 14
Mulroy, Kevin 109
Mumford, Mark D. 128
Mundie, Linda 167
Munic-Miller, Donna 562
Munkelt, Larry L 463
Munn, Rico 55
Munoz, Juan 376
Munoz, Rita 470
Munroe, Twuanna 480
Murali, Narayana S. 309
Murali, Viji 624
Murchy, Jodie 82
Murdoch, Brian 143
Murgado, Mario 649
Muri, Scott R 511
Murillo, Jorge 501
Murillo, Juan 508
Murino, John 19
Murphey, Mike 222
Murphy, Mary 7
Murphy, John 57
Murphy, Terry 70
Murphy, John E. 85
Murphy, Lisa 96
Murphy, Brian 102
Murphy, Edward 112
Murphy, Del 115
Murphy, Michael 134
Murphy, Connie 149
Murphy, Karen 214
Murphy, Michelle 220
Murphy, Dennis M. 252
Murphy, Rebecca S 276
Murphy, Erin 302
Murphy, Mike 306
Murphy, Donna 310
Murphy, Mary 332
Murphy, Amy 442
Murphy, John 448
Murphy, Tony 449
Murphy, Michael W. (Mike) 489
Murphy, Richard J 502
Murphy, Teresa 525
Murphy, Daniel 525
Murphy, Michael 538
Murphy, J Pat 595
Murphy, Teresa 598
Murphy, Tammy 644
Murphy, John M 665
Murray, Donald 164
Murray, Jonathan 199
Murray, Danny 266
Murray, Miriam 275
Murray, Gerry 425
Murray, Bruce H 509
Murray, William J. (Bill) 544
Murray, Bill 544
Murray, Gary 651
Murry, Dana 70
Murry, Johnnie 312
Murry, Michael 667
Mursuli, Vivian 547
Murtha, Joseph 373
Murtos, Kristen 386
Musacchia, Jacqueline 116
Muscarella, Linda 382
Musgrove, David 552
Musheno, Donise 219
Musk, Elon 547
Musselman, Kerri 94
Mustian, Morton 197
Mutcherson, James A 130
Mutchler, Len 613
Muthukrishnan, Prakash 435

Muzzy, Carol 597
Myers, Brock 23
Myers, Joseph 30
Myers, David 34
Myers, Isaac J. 64
Myers, Douglas T. 130
Myers, Todd 142
Myers, Ben 173
Myers, Clint 235
Myers, Becky 259
Myers, Ben 268
Myers, Dwayne 312
Myers, Zach 337
Myers, Seth 364
Myers, Fred 370
Myers, Douglas T. 417
Myers, Johnathon 491
Myers, Leah 657
Myers, Russ 675

N

Nabel, Elizabeth G. (Betsy) 407
Nabel, Elizabeth G 556
Naber, Mike 128
Nace, Jeffrey 252
Nachtigal, Amy 467
Nackers, Gary 182
Nadar, Shiv 230
Nadarajan, Gunalan 444
Nadeau, Kim 184
Nadel, Hiyam 574
Nader, Tony 253
Naftaly, Robert 614
Naftaly, Rober 614
Naganathan, Nagi 596
Nagesh, Reddivalen 235
Nagler, Harris M. 80
Nagowski, Michael 168
Nagpal, Pooja 211
Nagra, Erica 99
Nagy, Ryan 252
Nahata, Babu 163
Nahata, Leena 359
Nahe, Eric 627
Naidoo, Shirley 390
Naig, Kris 471
Nail, Steve 201
Naiman, Catherine 515
Nair, Prasanna 630
Naish, Rob 32
Naito, Hiroshi 34
Naja, Khaled 171
Najjar, Fred 181
Nakano, Tom 387
Naldi, Robert 304
Nama, Veeresh 236
Nance, Jim 160
Nancy, Taussig 474
Nancy, Dunlap 588
Nantz, Mark S. 94
Napier, Adam 425
Napoli, Cathleen 333
Napoli, John P. 486
Napper, Terry 171
Nappi, Ralph A. 382
Nappi, Mark 620
Naqvi, Syed 118
Narang, Steve 61
Narang, Vic 500
Naranjo, Carlos 525
Narasimhan, Ramesh 546
Narayanan, Ramanathan 10
Narla, Mohandas 364
Narmi, Charles 453
Narr, Bradly J 316
Nasci, Kathleen 583
Nash, David 603
Nash, Nick 617
Naspinski, Ed 542
Nassar, Daniel 6
Nastase, Mary 165

Index of Executives

Nastasi, Richard 31
Natale, Peter 337
Natarajan, Stephen 365
Nath, Pravene 524
Nathan, Jim 287
Nathan, Cornell 515
Nathan, Sanders 639
Nathenson, Michael (Mike) 88
Natoli, Joe 63
Natoli, Joseph 63
Nauert, Gary 185
Naugler, Scott 399
Nausedas, Darius 122
Navarra, Linda 110
Navert, Robin 463
Navran, Susan H. 90
Nay, Emma 249
Nayak, Vinayak 9
Nayak, Harsh 255
Nazarian, Marita Q 45
Nazarian, Jeanette 268
Ndiaye, Abdoulaye 422
Neal, Lavone 71
Neal, Mikele 190
Neal, Michael 274
Neal, Stephen C. 293
Neal, Shelly 335
Neal, Jake 549
Neal, Greg 661
Neaman, Mark R. 386
Nease, Andrea 459
Necas, Kevin 633
Nedbalek, Dwayne 543
Needham, Sabine 18
Needham, Judy 207
Needham, Clark 352
Needleman, Scott 249
Needles, Adam 14
Neeley, Paige 300
Neely, Tonya 93
Neely, Denise 99
Neely, Wayne 498
Neemuchwala, Abidali 672
Neff, Raymond 116
Neff, Cheryl 117
Negro, Jack 97
Neidenbach, Joseph J 523
Neil, Carl 201
Neilson, Duncan 288
Neilson, Eric G. 388
Neilson, Dutch 493
Nellis, Jake 261
Nelms, Charlie 610
Nelsen, Karen 252
Nelsen, Suzanne 505
Nelson, Baltazar-huntersville 35
Nelson, David 46
Nelson, Kimberly 54
Nelson, Shelby 61
Nelson, Dan 86
Nelson, Kristin 110
Nelson, Sheila 110
Nelson, Carrie 114
Nelson, Beth 140
Nelson, Karen 142
Nelson, David 148
Nelson, Mark W. 159
Nelson, Scott 191
Nelson, Glenn 192
Nelson, Deana L. 203
Nelson, Brent 220
Nelson, Rick 223
Nelson, Gregory V 245
Nelson, William 249
Nelson, Doug 273
Nelson, Connia 296
Nelson, Karen 304
Nelson, Susan K. 321
Nelson, Keith 323
Nelson, Krista 327
Nelson, Cynthia 330
Nelson, Carl 375
Nelson, Charlie 375
Nelson, Kristina 429

Nelson, Marie 432
Nelson, Brock 445
Nelson, Becky 471
Nelson, Elaine 550
Nelson, Christian 559
Nelson, Heather 594
Nelson, Laura 597
Nelson, Lorraine 621
Nelson, Kristi A 625
Nelson, Scott M. 654
Nemeth, Joseph 330
Nemshick, Scott 412
Nenzel, Andrea 410
Neri, Leticia 151
Nerino, Alfred 336
Nesbit, Dennis 445
Ness, Jon 282
Ness, Roberta B 596
Nesse, Robert 316
Nesselbush, Robert J 272
Nesselbush, Robert 455
Nesset, Sharon 618
Nester, Brian A. 289
Nesti, Sarah 384
Nestor, Kat 549
Neufeld, Kathy 340
Neufville, Mortimer H. 642
Neuhaus, Joan 21
Neuman, John 206
Neuman, Jennifer 370
Neumann, Neal 304
Neumann, Paul G 606
Neumeister, Irene 468
Nevers, Rick L. 49
Nevins, Janice 132
New, Wayne 161
Newallis, David 33
Newbrough, James P. 395
Newcomb, Mike 288
Newell, John D 629
Newey, Jay 646
Newman, Kurt 127
Newman, Kurt D. 130
Newman, Kurt 131
Newman, Mark F. 187
Newman, Bryan 523
Newman, Peter 584
Newman, Allison 610
Newmyer, Joyce 6
Newpol, Jon 611
Newsom, Terri T. 430
Newsom, Gavin 525
Newsome, Jana 377
Newton, Julianne 636
Neyland, Stephen J 340
Nezhat, Ceana 386
Ngeow, Susan 368
Ngt, Steve 392
Nguyen, Andy H 162
Nguyen, Phubinh 199
Nguyen, Lan Quoc 212
Nguyen, Steven 212
Nguyen, Chao 233
Nguyen, Derek 246
Nguyen, Mong Thi 530
Nguyen, Tricia 551
Nguyen, Phuong 594
Nguyen, Michelle 655
Niccolucci, Dani 601
Nichitean, Florin 184
Nicholas, Ken 4
Nicholas, Jack 125
Nicholas, Marc 235
Nicholas, Richard 593
Nicholas, Robert 634
Nichols, Wanda 122
Nichols, Gretchen 288
Nichols, Jimmy 315
Nichols, Amanda 319
Nichols, Lara 375
Nichols, Julie 477
Nichols, Brandie 548
Nichols, Robert 628
Nicholson, James B 429

Nicholson, James M 429
Nicholson, David A 429
Niciu, Carrie 529
Nickel, Jackie 3
Nickel, Daryl 43
Nickerson, Nate 314
Nickerson, Daniel 670
Nickless, David 166
Nicklin, Emily 594
Nickol, Thomas 282
Nicol, Ronald L 187
Nicolino, Lynda 299
Nicols, Maureen 300
Nicosia, Santo V 227
Nidiffer, Douglas 104
Niederberger, Mary 407
Niederhuber, John 253
Nields, Rosanne 463
Nielsen, Merilee 8
Nielsen, Paul D. 114
Nielsen, Cindy 566
Nielson, Sephen 481
Niemaseck, Ken 197
Niemi, Albert W. 505
Nienen, Marge 129
Nietfeld, Kathi 148
Nieves, Antonio De Jesus 79
Nieves, Frankie 593
Nigrin, Daniel 558
Nigro, Rich 453
Niles, Brenda 56
Niles, Amy 409
Nilsson, Gunilla 496
Nimbley, Thomas J 123
Nishizaki, Tsuyoshi 534
Nissen, James A 412
Nissley, Amy 644
Nitsch, Denise 667
Niven, Christine 333
Nix, D Mark 252
Nixon, John E. 597
Nixon, Bruce 659
Nizza, Arthur 258
Nizzari-Mcclain, Cynthia 642
Nober, Roger 91
Noble, Steve 141
Noble, David 219
Noble, Kim 502
Nobles, Anne 252
Nobles, Melissa 314
Noce, Jen 574
Noell, Samantha 371
Noetzel, Alex 549
Noga, James W. (Jim) 407
Nolan, Matthew 196
Nolan, Gary 282
Nolan, Carrie 308
Nolan, Kevin 392
Noland, William M 200
Noll, Chuck 613
Nolte, Jeremy 343
Nonaka, Susan 230
Nonnemaker, Jason 456
Nonnenkamp, Donald H 658
Nook, Greg 260
Nook, Gregory E. (Greg) 261
Norberg, Kim 41
Norby, Stephanie L. 497
Norcross, George E. 563
Nordin, Brandon 32
Noritz, Garey 359
Nork, Rick 660
Norkunas, Kathy 153
Norland, Jerry 20
Norling, Richard A 428
Norman, Linda 599
Norris, Michael 195
Norris, Julie 319
Norris, Todd 662
Northorp, Dale 6
Norton, Janet 64
Norton, Andrew J 211
Norton, Rick 223
Norton, Michael F 279

Norton, Melissa 306
Norton, Robert G. (Bob) 407
Norton, Margareta E 437
Norton, Margareta E. (Meg) 438
Noseworthy, John H 318
Noskin, Gary 388
Nosowitz, Barry 496
Nottage, Lavieria 423
Nourot, Mary 536
Novac, Tim 4
Novak, Matt 237
Novak, Kim 359
Novak, Steve 586
Novak, Elizabeth 622
Nowell, Ana 8
Nowiski, Dave 329
Nuest, Vaughn 610
Nugent, Cchea 505
Nunez, Sylvia 160
Nunez, Milton 296
Nunez, Jeanette 433
Nunez-Mejia, Bibi 409
Nunn, Lucy 611
Nunn, Trudy 659
Nurmi, Kelsey 116
Nurse, Paul 325
Nusbaum, Nancy 551
Nuss, Wilden 584
Nutt, Pam 235
Nutt, Raymond 443
Nutt, William V 578
Nye, Lara 256
Nyenhuis, Michael 37
Nykoluk, Tim 168
Nylander, Raye Nae 566
Nylen, Tim 152
Nyul, Renata 383

O

Oaconnor, Stephen 217
Oakes, John 201
Oakman, Scott 445
Oaks, Patrick 261
Oaks, Kenneth 278
Obana, William G 585
Ober, Tammy 573
Oberacker, Beth 306
Oberg, Chris 220
Obermeyer, Jaime 264
Obermiller, John 546
Oblisk, Sonya Gafsi 669
Obray, Bob 50
Obrien, Gary 442
Obrien, John 616
Obrien, Barbara 671
Obryan, Megan 141
Obryant, Sid 552
Och, John 569
Ochoa, Arthur 118
Ochoa, Andrew 302
Ochoa, S. Hector 634
Ochsner, Brian 78
Ochsner, Lisa Cloud 424
OConnell, Rick 462
Oconnor, Christopher J 502
Oconnor, Caitlin 526
Oconnor, James 594
Oconnor, Michael 677
Oconnor, Kim 677
Odegaard, Richard 223
Odell, Deborah 150
Odell, Robert 492
Oditt, Alex 252
Odonnell, Morgan 6
Odonnell, Julia 671
Odonnell, Joseph 671
Odrzywolski, Jason 125
Oechsner, Susan 250
Oehlert, Christine 157
Oehling, James P 411
Oestreich, Rebecca 511

Index of Executives

Oetgen, William J. 321
Offers, Nathan 552
Oftedal, Siv 196
Ogden, Jodi 559
Ogg, Tom 131
Oglesby, Charles M 135
Ogletree, Dan 419
Ogren, Dan 161
Ogundiran, Joke 569
Ohabor, Constantine 183
Ohara, Ruth 290
Ohara, Michele 407
Ohara, Yoshinori 678
Ohemeng-Dapaah, Michael 295
Ohk, Joohee 165
Ohlinger, Brian 650
Ohtake, Takashi 376
Okabe, David 230
Okafor, Kenosa 329
Okamoto, Gary A 585
Okolie, Patricia 242
Okpalla, Nneka 406
Okun, Robert B 225
Olaes, John 60
Olander, Kristen 126
Olander, Anastasia 420
Olberding, Elizabeth 522
Old, Tim 499
Oldenburg, Kim M 316
Oldham, Paul 545
Olds, Debbie 670
Oleary, Donna 671
Olejniczak, Dave 516
Olenick, Evelyn 417
Oles, Karen 335
Olion, Marion Gillis 168
Oliphant, Gerald 218
Oliva, Harvey 68
Olivares, Jacob 393
Olivares, Ana 420
Oliveira, Victor 109
Oliver, Kevin 143
Oliver, George 269
Oliver, George R 270
Oliver, Wes 453
Oliver, Mark 602
Oliveras, Noel 390
Oliverio, Dale 54
Oliverio, John D 667
Olivo, Rene 458
Olkowski, Ed 671
Oller, Robert S. 390
Oloughlin, Jane 70
Olscamp, Karen E. 630
Olsen, Morgan R. 44
Olsen, Neil 200
Olsen, Richelle 208
Olsen, Kathy 240
Olsen, Chelsey 639
Olson, Maribeth 26
Olson, Beth 30
Olson, Greg 284
Olson, Gerald 298
Olson, Kristin 318
Olson, David 354
Olson, Toni 434
Olson, Thomas 453
Olson, Matt 469
Olson, Carrie 476
Olson, Ryan 546
Olson, Tim 602
Olson, Kevin 614
Oltman, Renee 396
Omalley, William 384
Omalley, Kimberly 447
Omoto, Christiane 146
Oneal, Adreanne 251
Onell, Lia 330
Onishi, Ricky 667
Ono, Santa J. 625
Oosterman, Linnea 597
Opedal, Anders 196
Opembe, Patrick 117
Ophaug, Courtney 61

Opperman, Carl 78
Opstedahl, Deeanna 150
Oranje, Joop 282
Orchard, Arlen 462
Orellana, Charles 583
Orf, Mike 247
Orf, Harry 407
Ori, Indira 364
Oriol, Albert 438
Orisek, Philip 536
Orisio, Lori 554
Orlando, Lorraine 580
Orlando, Adolph M 587
Orlikoff, James 652
Ormond, Tommy 25
Ormuz, Tammy 551
Orndorf, Karen 15
Ornt, Daniel B. 456
Orol, Santiago 605
Orourke, Terry 117
Orozco, Ruben 472
Orr, Natassia 101
Orr, Mark 223
Orr, James 311
Orson, Marshall D 176
Ortega, Adela 51
Ortega, Rebecca 486
Ortegon, Liisa 604
Ortiz, Veronica 184
Ortiz, Christine 314
Ortiz, Claudia 404
Ortiz, Ana 672
Osborn, Richard S 270
Osborn, William A. 389
Osborn, Megan 465
Osborn, Kelly 613
Osborn, Donna 657
Osborne, Casey 417
Osborne, Robert D 459
Osborne, Marci 644
Oshea, Steven 11
Oshea, Rebecca 604
Oshiro, Don 593
Oskouie, Ali 336
Oskvig, O. H. (Dean) 85
Osorio, Maryluz 101
Osorio, Jonathan 392
Ostendorf, Todd 379
Oster, Mike 318
Osterday, Rick 11
Ostergard, Winston 165
Osterman, Michael 631
Ostermeier, Timothy 425
Ostrander, Noam 175
Ostroff, Robert 676
Ostrowski, Ally 586
Ostrowsky, Barry 66
Oswald, Kathy 236
Ota, Yoko 651
Otero, Tony 166
Otey, Brianne 141
Otey, Sarah 358
Otley, Brian 221
Ott, Dusty 83
Ott, Richard A 282
Ott, Brian 601
Ottera, Magne 196
Ottino, Julio M. 388
Ottman, Dan 305
Otto, Noreen 247
Ottolini, Mary 130
Ouchida, Michael 249
Ounesavath, John 210
Ousley, Peter 126
Outar, Gerald 360
Ovel, Jack 327
Overstreet, Kelly 120
Overton, Camie 677
Owen, Julie 66
Owen, Paul 196
Owen, Brad 202
Owen, Nehemie 557
Owen, Bobbi 595
Owens, Thomas A. 187

Owens, Fritz 392
Owens, Richard 408
Owens, Ben 514
Owings, Nancy 430
Owlia, Azita 670
Ownby, David H. 443
Owsley, Larry 629
Oxley, Scott 190
Oyler, Jason 375
Oyler, Clinton 445
Ozmen, Fatih 493
Ozmen, Eren 493
Ozuah, Philip O. 348
Ozuna-Richards, Elsa 646
O'Brien, Lindsay 37
O'Brien, Robert P. (Bob) 106
O'Brien, Charles T 197
O'Brien, Kristine 389
O'Brien, Gary 442
O'Bryan, Brent 26
O'Connor, Thomas (Tom) 26
O'Connor, Daniel 156
O'connor, James 236
O'Connor, Michael J. (Mike) 282
O'Connor, Gina 300
O'Connor, John 526
O'Connor, Patrick J. (Pat) 546
O'Dea, Edward 289
O'Donnell, Robert G 31
O'Donnell, Randall L. 327
O'Donnell, Patrick 531
O'donnell, Susan 608
O'Donoghue, Mary Jo 555
O'Flaherty, Lori L. 143
O'gara, Kevin 261
O'Hanley, Ronald P. (Ron) 79
O'hare, Dennis 26
O'Keefe, Barbara J. 388
O'Keefe, Daniel 501
O'Keefe, Sharon 594
O'Leary, Ray 195
O'Leary, Rand 410
O'Leary, Thomas M 584
O'mara, Shay 395
O'Meara, Patrick 610
O'Neil, Logan 340
O'Neil, Cheri 642
O'neill, William 236
O'Neill, Liz 293
O'Neill, John P. 428
O'Quinn, Marvin 181
O'Reilly, Charles 231
O'Reilly, Brian 416
O'riley, Lila 633
O'Rourke, Tracy 530
O'Rourke, Timothy C. 546
O'Shell, Michael 458
O'Sullivan, Paul 324
O'sullivan, Joe 361
OÂ'Brien, Martin 326
OÂ'Bryant, G. Mark 541
OÂ'Grady, Sean 386
OÂ'Malley, Edward 375

P

P. Kern Howard 484
Pabst, Darlene 625
Pace, Sonia 21
Pace, Gerald 342
Pace, Cathy 432
Pacey, David 273
Pacheco, Carmita 668
Pachman, Louis J 231
Paciero, Karen 594
Pack, Barry 399
Packard, John A 502
Packer, Roger J. 130
Packer, Steven J 152
Padilla, Jose 175
Paeth, Mary 507
Paez, Rene A 501

Pagano, Shelly 41
Page, Crystal 112
Page, Elaine 382
Page, Bob 595
Page, James H 630
Pagels, George A 467
Pagliazzo, Charlie 220
Pagura, Annie 337
Paich, Joyce 184
Paiewonsky, Steve 265
Paige, Lacie 489
Paik, Sanghyun 594
Painter, Patty 160
Pak, Chris 370
Pala, Amy 200
Palan, Martha 664
Palkoski, Linda 454
Palla, Wayne 169
Pallamary, Richard J 371
Palm, Richard 453
Palmberg, Rob 170
Palmberg, Kent 530
Palmer, Steve 57
Palmer, Mike 197
Palmer, Kelly 443
Palmer, Roberta Ruth 444
Palmer, Harvey 456
Palmer, Bart 480
Palmer, Edna 518
Palmer, Frank 601
Palmer-ellis, Amy 639
Palmerio, Anthony 371
Palmore, Kysten 209
Paluch, Heather 103
Palzkill, Leslie 216
Pan, Gordon G. 453
Pana, Camelia 450
Panaccio, Frank 405
Panchanathan, Sethuraman (Panch) 44
Pande, Sunil 286
Pane, Stephanie 676
Panettieri, Christopher 233
Pangborn, Robert N. 584
Pangburn, Charles 615
Pankratz, Barbara 417
Panzino, Jodi 155
Paoletti, Rich 573
Pape, Kathy 411
Papouras, Julia 131
Papp, Harry A. 90
Pappagallo, Michael 98
Pappas, Thomas 202
Pappas, Natalie 547
Parag, Prakash J 511
Paras, Heather 486
Parazynski, Gail M 548
Parchment, Nadia 287
Parden, Diana 235
Pardes, Herbert 580
Pardo, Emilio 2
Paredes, Jose 671
Parent, Bob 356
Paris, Nancy 259
Parish, Glenda 141
Parisi, Vince 148
Parisi, Rita 229
Parisi, Jennifer 287
Parisi, Janet 368
Park, Scott 140
Park, Hyun 347
Park, Jihye 363
Park, Gary 635
Parker, Zachary 11
Parker, Chris 62
Parker, Bobby 133
Parker, Chuck 197
Parker, Karen 209
Parker, Calvin 319
Parker, Beck 337
Parker, Terra 358
Parker, Scott 360
Parker, Jeff 374
Parker, Dorothy 407
Parker, Douglas 523

Index of Executives

Parker, Lynz 597
Parker, Phillip 612
Parker, Victoria 640
Parker, Barbara 647
Parker, Brenda 671
Parkinson, Robert L. 301
Parks, Jasmine 236
Parks, Phil 393
Parks, R M 436
Parks, Grayson 582
Parks, Debbie 588
Parlato, Tanya 272
Parnell, Winfred 171
Parnes, Marvin 444
Parolisi, John 59
Parr, Ixchel 54
Parris, Carla M 206
Parrish, David K. 87
Parrish, Harvey 201
Parrish, Mike 379
Parrish, Jim 390
Parrish, Chris 514
Parrott, Keith 64
Parrott, Mike 453
Parsley, Shawn D. 551
Parsley, Elizabeth 589
Parsons, Kristen 184
Parsons, Blake 513
Partridge, Ronald K. (Ron) 404
Pascale, John 57
Pascale, John 293
Pascuzzi, Shelley 369
Pasicznyk, John G 184
Paslawsky, William 466
Pasley, Debi 462
Pass, Chris 267
Pastore, Martin J 197
Patchett, Richard B 310
Pate, Tammy 75
Pate, David C. 521
Patek, Lois 596
Patel, Ketul J. 150
Patel, Amrish 195
Patel, Suresh C 236
Patel, Sidd 269
Patel, Samir 366
Patel, Saavan 565
Patel, Bhavana 595
Patel, Sandeep 596
Patel, Raj 625
Pathak, Sumit 322
Patin, Al 284
Pating, Christopher 610
Patino, Dan 195
Patkotak, Crawford 43
Patonai, Nicolas 595
Patria, Slaughter 588
Patric, Sharon 198
Patrick, Chad 344
Patrick, Barbara 610
Patrick, Chuck 624
Patricoff, Tracey C 501
Patruno, Joseph 289
Patry, Dean 40
Patry, Fernando 310
Pattee, Russell 428
Patten, Brad Van 259
Patten, Liz 592
Patten, Scott 655
Patterson, Pat 45
Patterson, Dean 116
Patterson, Linda 196
Patterson, Geoff 236
Patterson, Douglas E 279
Patterson, Douglas E 279
Patterson, Jason 436
Patterson, Jamie 604
Patterson, Bernie 641
Patterson-Randles, Sandra R. 609
Patton, Ross 105
Patton, Alex 265
Patton, Kamela 588
Pattterson, Jerry 344
Patz, Melanie 64

Paul, Stamy 14
Paul, Barbara 236
Paul, Janet 293
Paul, Chausse 306
Paul, Terre 368
Paul, Janelle 491
Paul, Valerie J. 497
Paul, Ann 515
Paul, Hernandez 655
Paul, Lenora 660
Pauley, Clarence 615
Paulikas, George 553
Paulk, Jennifer 117
Paulo, Donna Null 293
Paulos, William J 108
Paulsen, Amy 259
Paulson, Dana 286
Paulus, Ronald A 343
Paulus, Ronald A 344
Paulus, Faydre 633
Pauly, Greg 453
Pavelich, Gerald (Jerry) 66
Pavone, Alicia 409
Pawar, Manoj 150
Pawley, Patrick 321
Pawley, Barbara 623
Pawsat, Karen 334
Pax, Gina 549
Paxson, Christina H. 102
Paxson, Kara 277
Paxton, Ken 54
Paxton, Robert 309
Payne, Jim 29
Payne, Jon 50
Payne, Robert 83
Payne, Phyllis 469
Payne, Penelope (Nell) 497
Paz, Milton De La 171
Peacock, William (Bill) 561
Pearce, Zach 155
Pearce, Charles T 273
Pearce, David 471
Pearison, Megan 588
Pearlberg, Jay 236
Pearlman, Michael 96
Pearson, Jeffrey T 34
Pearson, Kermit 69
Pearson, Tamara 94
Pearson, Kathryn 241
Pearson, Kristian 266
Pearson, Ken 310
Pearson, James F 336
Pearson, James F 394
Pearson, James F 411
Pearson, Bruce 478
Pearson, J F 562
Pearson, Shelli 665
Peart, Vereena 331
Pearte, Camille 369
Pease, Alexander W. 499
Peaslee, Gregory 643
Pecenka, Michelle 551
Peceny, Mark 634
Peck, Lori 49
Peck, Cynthia 152
Peck, Kimberly 332
Peck, Jane 467
Peckham, Bob 375
Peckham, Michael P. (Mike) 438
Peckinpaugh, David 308
Pedersen, Joel 92
Pedersen, Jeff 453
Pederson, Judy 314
Pedlow, Bernadette 17
Pedlow, Frank 574
Pedonti, Patrick J 186
Peebles, Debbie 611
Peek, Audrey 34
Peel, Matthew 185
Peele, Steven 672
Peeples, Jon 416
Peery, Bryan 43
Peeters, Clare 57
Pefanis, Harry N 422

Peffer, Deb 444
Peggy, Sease 122
Pehrson, Timothy T. 256
Peigen, Seth 343
Pelayo, Arturo 515
Pelfrey, Harvey 394
Pelissero, John 301
Pelka, Deb 22
Pell, Rachel 584
Pellegrini, Frank 361
Pellegrini, Robert 593
Peller, Holger 425
Pellot, Lisette 627
Peltier, Wayne 69
Pelzel, Brent 340
Pemberton, Rick 157
Pempek, Kalynn 49
Pena, Yvette 2
Pena, Kelvin 366
Pena, Rodrigo F. Troni 499
Pender, Erin 608
Pendergast, Jim 2
Pendergast, Jim 115
Pendleton, Linda 151
Pendolino, Sophie 671
Peng, Shane 512
Penland, Cindy 255
Penn, Kevin 334
Penne, David 354
Pennella, William A. (Bill) 166
Pennes, David 509
Penney, Robert T. 119
Pennington, Bob 136
Pennington, Keith 337
Pennington, Chip 492
Pennington, Kelli 659
Pensak, Myles 615
Peoples, Rasheda 429
Peoples, Chanda 476
Pepe, Joseph 142
Pepitone, Andrea 425
Pepper, J David 412
Pepper, Dave 412
Pepper, J Stanley 584
Pepper, Richard S 584
Peppiatt-Combes, James 329
Peralta, Pennie 111
Perch, Jeanmarie 429
Perea, Jennifer Rosato 175
Pereira, Jose 136
Pereira, Alvaro 205
Perez, Marta 7
Perez, Marta Brito 7
Perez, Virginia 21
Perez, Jorge 65
Perez, Roberta 412
Perez, Dr Sylvester Syl 469
Perez, Olga 469
Periago, Mirta 404
Perille, Thomas 518
Perillo, Louis 266
Perkash, Om 1
Perkins, Jim 20
Perkins, Rhonda 131
Perkins, Paul 274
Perkovich, Brian 336
Perlewitz, Kathi 211
Perlman, Harvey S. 92
Perlman, Joel A. 348
Perman, Jay A. 642
Permet, Robert 234
Permut, Howard 335
Pernas, Rick 161
Perng, Danny 326
Perno, Joseph 269
Perren, Katharine 390
Perri, Linda 206
Perri, Michael G. 627
Perriere, Pierre La 217
Perrin, Mary 300
Perrins, Alexander 425
Perris, Chris 223
Perron, Jacques 604
Perrone, Michael 220

Perry, Doni 13
Perry, Karl E 60
Perry, Jason 76
Perry, Sabrina 80
Perry, Janet 153
Perry, J Thomas 177
Perry, James 180
Perry, Barbara 253
Perry, Tia 280
Perry, Glenn 326
Perry, Tom 415
Perry, Thomas 415
Perry, Thirsty 467
Perry, Carol 530
Perry, Dan 552
Perry, Opal G 571
Perry, Rhonda S 575
Perry, Van 618
Perryman, Tad 607
Persaud, Donna 171
Perselis, Anna 667
Pershing, David W. 597
Persico, Asid 266
Person, Peter 496
Pesci, Nello-John (NJ) 480
Pestello, Fred P. 465
Peter, John St 11
Peters, Heather 23
Peters, Theresa 75
Peters, Juergen 452
Peters, Dana 514
Peters, Alexandra 549
Peters, Amy 608
Peterschick, Shannon 511
Petersen, Andy Kramer 61
Petersen, Beth 212
Petersen, Katherine 259
Petersen, Jeffrey P 279
Petersen, Jeffrey P 280
Petersen, Richard W. (Rich) 305
Petersen, Gary 422
Peterson, Richard D 10
Peterson, Barbara 40
Peterson, Tina 61
Peterson, Jeannette 82
Peterson, Richard D 123
Peterson, Richard 123
Peterson, Terry 126
Peterson, Mark 220
Peterson, Tim 241
Peterson, Kenzie 249
Peterson, Ronald 268
Peterson, Erin 375
Peterson, Penelope L. 388
Peterson, Teresa 431
Peterson, James H 443
Peterson, Denise M. 464
Peterson, Ken 492
Peterson, Larry 503
Peterson, Randall 530
Peterson, Randy 530
Peterson, Glenn E 553
Peterson, Mandi 597
Peterson, Fross 646
Peterson, Ross 646
Petillo, Chris 382
Petrocelli, Danielle 365
Petrosino, John 151
Petroske, Jeffrey 671
Petrusky, Chuck 246
Petry, Joann 671
Petti, Filippo 382
Pettinato, Andrea 558
Pettit, Dirk 140
Pettus, John 157
Petty, Meredith L 175
Petty, Lora 328
Petty, Trent 541
Peuch, Olivier Le 108
Peverly, Francis 397
Pewonka, Della 644
Peyvan, Bianca 515
Pezzulo, Paolo 202
Pfeffer, George 185

Index of Executives

Index of Executives

Index of Executives

Index of Executives

Robitaille, Mark 311
Roble, Mark A. 453
Robledo, Grace 164
Robles, Monica 140
Robles, Norberto (Bert) 365
Robles, Wilma 390
Robles, Adriane 470
Robotis, Dionyssios 616
Roca, Silvia De La 8
Rocha, Carmen 333
Roche, Bob 119
Roche, Alexandra 129
Roche, Jamie 229
Roche, Brian 264
Roche, Lucy 474
Roche-Carter, Noreen 462
Rocheleau, John 76
Rocher, Leslie 74
Rochiell, Sievert Jules 384
Rock, Rex A. 43
Rock, Jessica J 188
Rockett, Stephanie 45
Rockey, Anne 191
Rockwood, John D. 321
Rocourt, Brittney 422
Roda, Ann 7
Roddick, Catherine 143
Rodell, Angela 16
Roden, George 347
Roderick, Ryan 446
Rodgers, Karri 479
Rodgers, April 580
Rodgers, Ron 642
Rodgers, Courtney 677
Rodis, John 464
Rodraguez, Melanie 646
Rodrigues, Karen 486
Rodriguez, Barbara 162
Rodriguez, Vicki 199
Rodriguez, Camille 207
Rodriguez, Rick 212
Rodriguez, Mandy 242
Rodriguez, Yolanda 245
Rodriguez, Manuel 245
Rodriguez, Daniel B. 388
Rodriguez, Leticia 403
Rodriguez, Suzanne 462
Rodriguez, Barbara 469
Rodriguez, Domingo C 501
Rodriguez, Sylvia 507
Rodriguez, Eddie 508
Rodriguez, Edwin 523
Rodriguez, Havidan 526
Rodriguez, Carlos 548
Rodriguez, Darlene 551
Rodriguez, Ricardo 620
Rodriguez, Henry 638
Rodriguez, Hilda 657
Rodriguez, Zulma 678
Roe, Deanna 115
Roe, Stacy 525
Roe, Lesa 635
Roebuck, Mark 506
Roeck, Seppe De 95
Roed, Andy 453
Roell, Thomas L. (Tom) 582
Roemer, Dennis 519
Roemer, Dennis R. 573
Roesch, Richard 453
Roeser, William 508
Roesle, Scott 85
Roessle, Randy 613
Roessle, Randall 613
Roett, Michelle 570
Rogalski, Robert J 666
Rogers, Carolyn 126
Rogers, Lana 142
Rogers, Harlan 158
Rogers, Woody 239
Rogers, Marchel 251
Rogers, John 354
Rogers, Cleveland 360
Rogers, Joseph 377
Rogers, Rich 430

Rogers, Richard 430
Rogers, Bobby 436
Rogers, James E. (Jim) 579
Roggie, Brent 358
Roheim, John 361
Rohit, Mehra 444
Rohlfing, Ronald 615
Rohman, Cindy 294
Rohmer, Cheryl 482
Rohr, James E. (Jim) 114
Rohrer, Martin 291
Roiter, Miriam 611
Rojas, Manuel F 79
Rojas, Reynaldo 166
Rojas, Saul 367
Rojek, Kenneth J 376
Rolando, Fredric V 357
Roldan-sanchez, Kim 580
Rolfe, Cynthia 89
Roller, Bill 251
Roller, Mark 396
Rollerson, Monica 19
Rollin, Wilber 385
Rollins, Barrett J. 172
Rollins, Greg 356
Rollins, Paul 571
Rollison, Marvin L 274
Romain, Peter 370
Roman, Nelson 206
Roman, Sheila 268
Roman, Anthony 332
Romano, Peter 97
Romanoff, Neil 118
Romanowski, Mike 143
Romer, Paul 370
Romero, Robert 253
Romero, Javier 299
Romero, Tifinni 488
Romick, Steven 118
Romine, Donnie 523
Romoff, Jeffrey A. 643
Romond, Jennifer L 653
Rondon, Manuel 202
Rood, Carol 148
Roodman, Richard D 433
Root, Carole 32
Root, George L 397
Roper, Margie 181
Roper, John 443
Roper, Mark 567
Roper, Bret 613
Rosa, Jessica 138
Rosa, Enrica De 245
Rosa, Linda 562
Rosado, Robert 525
Rosado, Freddy 678
Rosario, Elvis 25
Rosario, Angela 225
Rosbrough, Martha 202
Roscoe, Lauren 665
Rose, Matthew K. (Matt) 91
Rose, Douglas 128
Rose, Sheryl 150
Rose, Virginia 551
Rosen, Marc 293
Rosen, Dan 432
Rosen, Andrew 432
Rosen, Jimmy 610
Rosen, Jodi 648
Rosenbach, Lynn 61
Rosenbaum, Thomas F. 107
Rosenbaum, Jerrold Frank 574
Rosenberg, Stuart 79
Rosenberg, Stuart A 230
Rosenberg, Michael 241
Rosenberg, Andrew 444
Rosenberg, Michael 657
Rosenberg, Steven 664
Rosenberg, Steven H 665
Rosenberger, T 217
Rosenberger, Thomas 217
Rosenberger, Angie 247
Rosenblum, Don 390
Rosenhauer, Joan 117

Rosenthal, Robert 94
Rosenthal, Jean-Laurent 107
Rosenthal, Gary E 391
Rosenthal, Daniel 574
Rosero, Barbie 476
Rosier, W. Grady 319
Rosman, Scott 619
Rosner, Robert L 1
Rosowsky, David 639
Ross, Jeannette 21
Ross, David 64
Ross, Samuel L. 94
Ross, Joyce M. 150
Ross, Duncan 182
Ross, Ryan 252
Ross, James 263
Ross, Trisha 263
Ross, Duncan 369
Ross, Roxana 390
Ross, Jim 423
Ross, Stephen M. 444
Ross, Rebecca 453
Ross, Bernadette 453
Ross, Sylvia 470
Ross, Don 511
Ross, Robert 514
Ross, Goldberg 574
Ross, James E. 630
Ross, Melanie 638
Ross, Robert S. 658
Rosser, Carrene G 307
Rosser, Brian 450
Rossi, Christopher 130
Rossignoll, Tom 407
Rossini, Lynn 464
Rossman, Eric 56
Rossmann, Barbara W. 236
Rossmccalib, Laureen 221
Rossomanno, Jennifer 134
Rost, Fred 493
Rotch, James E 357
Rotenberg, Lesli 432
Roth, Kevin 41
Roth, Steve 43
Roth, Norman 97
Roth, Greg 133
Roth, Doug 182
Roth, Theodore D. (Ted) 438
Roth, Paul B. 634
Rothberger, Richard K. 479
Rothchild, Ellen 116
Rothkopf, Douglas M 616
Rothrock, Sandy 584
Rotner, Phil 558
Rotondi, Thomas 65
Roty, Christopher M. (Chris) 64
Rougeau, Vincent 608
Rounds, Bruce 25
Rounds, Mary D 105
Rountree, Gordon 284
Rouppas, Susan 596
Rouse, Matt 117
Rouse, Donald J 458
Rouse, Thomas B 458
Rouse, Cecilia E. 591
Roush, Richard 584
Rousseau, David 468
Roussos, Michael 141
Routly, Kathy 456
Roux, Roger G 437
Rowe, Steve 387
Rowe, Robert 610
Rowland, David J. 486
Rowly, Cade 532
Roy, Steve 1
Roy, Lynne 118
Roy, Elizabeth 589
Royall, Elizabeth 597
Roycroft, Tammy 581
Royer, Adam 228
Rozek, Charles 116
Rozelle, Matt 315
Rozenfeld, Jon 512
Rozenfeld, Keren 580

Rozwadowski, Jeanne 179
Rozzi, Ted 160
Rozzi, Carlo 451
Ruark, Joseph 150
Rubash, Harry E. 574
Rubenstein, David M. 187
Rubenstein, Ira 432
Rubin, David 162
Rubin, Allan 249
Rubin, Amir Dan 290
Rubin, Patricia Lee 370
Rubin, Ed 597
Rubin, Larry 641
Rubinstein, Pablo 364
Rubio, Fernando 597
Rucker, Craig 81
Rucker, Craig 218
Rucker, Rob 251
Rucker, Michael 475
Rucker, Merijoy 669
Rudd, Paul 199
Ruddy, Joseph P 652
Rude, Brian 170
Rudolph, Sandra 265
Rudolph, Lynn 453
Rudow, Dale 453
Rudy, John 9
Rudy, Viscomi 407
Rudy, Wendy 514
Rudzik, Robert J. 119
Rudzik, John 119
Rue, Lisa La 157
Rueber, Joel 49
Ruehl, Alison 512
Ruester, Robert 206
Rueter, Jens 190
Ruf, Dave 260
Ruff, Joan 2
Ruff, Patricia 211
Ruff, Heather 390
Ruffolo, Carmel 309
Rufino, Michael G. 202
Rufo, Gloria 608
Ruggeri, Nunzio 23
Ruggiero, Nick 137
Ruhbusch, Alayna M 316
Ruhnke, Atalie 259
Ruhnke, Brenda 379
Rui, Estrela 407
Ruiz, Amanda 160
Ruiz, Ashley A 198
Ruiz, Israel 314
Ruiz, Jose M 436
Ruiz, Aurelio 436
Ruiz, Bernardo 481
Ruiz, Rosa 537
Rule, Scott 541
Ruman, Deborah 298
Rumans, Mark C. 84
Rumer, Rich 546
Runcie, Robert W 101
Runck, Cathy 26
Rundall, Thomas 267
Runge, Marschall S. 444
Runion, Scott 530
Runyan, Kirsten 255
Runyon, Leah 135
Runyon, Mark 256
Ruocco, Jennifer 399
Rupe, Michael D 135
Rupert, Dennis 116
Rupert, Nora 476
Rush, Greg 405
Rush, William 445
Rushton, Dale 123
Rusnak, Gregory J. 430
Russ, Gary 476
Russel, Kimberly 103
Russell, John 26
Russell, Kevin 119
Russell, Gregg 203
Russell, Caroline 232
Russell, Jon 267
Russell, Bob 429

Index of Executives

Russell, Toni 620
Russell, Judith C. 627
Russell, Chelsea 638
Russell, David 643
Russo, Kristina 444
Russo, Ralph 496
Russo, Thomas 569
Russo, Jeffrey 642
Rust, Brian 8
Rust, Tami 286
Rust, Steven 340
Rust, Melissa 624
Ruth, John 74
Rutkowski, Claire 356
Rutland, James B 344
Rutledge, Terri 629
Rutter, Kenneth S. 69
Ruwe, Curtis 165
Ruwe, Steve 432
Ruzicka, Laura 511
Ryan, Cicely 20
Ryan, Kevin 205
Ryan, Barbara 233
Ryan, Philip J. 260
Ryan, Keith 282
Ryan, Michael 325
Ryan, Paula 407
Ryan, Jackie 417
Ryan, Clay 453
Ryan, Tim 462
Ryan, Mickey 476
Ryan, Doug O' 519
Ryan, David 574
Ryan, Catherine 580
Ryan, Robert 601
Ryan, Pat 608
Ryan, John 610
Ryan, John M 652
Rybczynski, Andrea 671
Rychlik, Wendell 319
Rycyna, Kevin 383
Rydell, David R 537
Ryder, John 31
Ryder, Mark 285
Ryder, Paige 313
Ryder, David S 648
Rye, Curtis 252
Rye, Ted 557
Ryea, Alan 639
Ryerson, Lisa M. 2
Ryge, Svend 535
Ryman, David 123
Ryn, Janice Van 168
Rynaski, Theresa 453
Ryner, Robert 476
Rynhart, Betsey 155
Ryno, Marrianne 247
Ryors, Alfred 610

S

Saari, Carolyn 301
Saarony, Gadi 405
Sabatine, Marc 556
Sabatini, Mary 574
Sabbatini, Brian 646
Sabella, Deborah 512
Sabella, Deb E 512
Saberi, Asif 275
Sabers, Candace 615
Sabin, Matthew 672
Sabutis, Mike 333
Sacco, Henry 100
Sacco, Barbara 284
Sacco, Frank V. 500
Saccone, Robert 486
Sacerio, Joan 488
Sachtleben, Michael C. 321
Sackett, John 7
Sackett, Neil 115
Sackett, Walter 277
Sada, Crystal 592

Sadau, Ernie W. 132
Sadler, Laurie 272
Sadofsky, Lynn 480
Sadosty, Annie 317
Sadovnik, Lev 493
Sadro, Cheryl A 323
Sadro, Cheryl 323
Sadvary, Thomas J. (Tom) 478
Saenz, Luis 526
Safady, Randolph W. 132
Saferian, Candee M 429
Saff, Eric 153
Saffer, Lori Polep 156
Safi, Arshad 531
Safyer, Steven M. 348
Sagen, James 189
Saggau, David 221
Sagheer, Omer 589
Saha, Samar 96
Saint-val, Serge 220
Sajed, Amer 66
Sajet, Kim 497
Sakamoto, Greg 628
Sakata, Mark 375
Sakil, Kim 546
Saladonis, Melissa 128
Salamorin, Emelyn 351
Salanger, Atthew J 619
Salava, Deb 643
Salchli, Karen 128
Sale, Paul 326
Salem, Charbel 280
Salem, Laura 343
Salem, Deeb 612
Saletnik, Laurie 269
Salgueiro, Sandro 314
Saligram, Ravi 263
Salinas, Theresa 469
Salins, Peter D 526
Salisbury, Barbara 129
Saller, Richard P. 290
Sallstrom, Jim 343
Salnas, Todd 472
Salo, Bob 618
Salomon, Robert 546
Saloner, Garth 290
Salsberry, David 541
Salsbury, Jill 402
Salter, Jerry 556
Salvador, Michael 356
Salvador, Allan 543
Salvati, Peter A. 185
Salvatore, David 526
Salvino, Sonia 116
Salyer, Kelly 160
Salzer, Steve 432
Samaroo, Savita 678
Sambasivan, Pallavi 370
Sambel, Andreas 452
Samet, Kenneth A. 321
Samii, Jason 65
Sammarco, Michael J 197
Sample, Mike 610
Samples, Dustin 22
Samples, Joe 470
Samples, Jim 480
Sampson, Shane 20
Sampson, Ley 141
Sampson, Luke 356
Sampson, Bryan 453
Sams, Pam King 130
Sams, Thomas 150
Samson, Ley 141
Samsonov, Anastasia 402
Samudio, Irma 489
Samuel, Noel N 249
Samuel, Noel 250
Samuels, Carol 116
Samuels, Mark 498
Samuels, Gwen 632
Samulewicz, Connie 304
Samz, Jeff 247
Sanberg, Paul R. 638
Sances, James 22

Sanchez, Nadia 137
Sanchez, Debra Tica 160
Sanchez, Christina 259
Sanchez, Maria 407
Sanchez, Michael 513
Sanchez, Abby 588
Sandberg, Susan 448
Sandberg, Debbie 536
Sandeen, Mark 10
Sandeno, Greg 145
Sander, Ed 420
Sanders, Joann 157
Sanders, Marshall 247
Sanders, Jeffrey D. (Jeff) 305
Sanders, Rachelle 348
Sanders, Brenda 361
Sanders, Leo 580
Sanders, Leotis 580
Sanders, Sandra 582
Sanders, Stephanie 596
Sanders, Carolyn 626
Sanderson, Travee 128
Sanderson, La Verne 184
Sanderson, Brad 239
Sandhu, Dalpinder 153
Sandler, Pamela 30
Sandler, Anthony 130
Sandlin, Keith 409
Sandoval, Stefano 262
Sandoval, Donald 464
Sands, Timothy D. (Tim) 652
Sandvik, Helvi 356
Sandy, Jody 247
Sanford, Kathleen D. 150
Sanford, Deborah 190
Sanford, Julie 476
Sanger, Steve 400
Sangster, Denise 92
Sankey, Greg 590
Sanman, Randall P 279
Santa, Mari 658
Santana, Angel 135
Santana, Carlos 482
Santarone, Mike 590
Santelises, Sonja B 60
Santillan, Alfredo A 227
Santilli, Ann Unkcd 299
Santoki, Tsutomu 534
Santoro, Sandy 500
Santos, Rebecca 223
Santos, Roberto J 620
Santucci, Karen 675
Saperstein, Arnold 365
Saperstein, Karen 481
Sapyta, Tim 113
Saradhi, Vijay 365
Saraei, Armin 363
Sargent, Jennifer 407
Sargent, Annie 408
Sargent, Darryl 557
Sargent, Kimberly 564
Sarhan, Monty 337
Sarid, Tamar 431
Sarkar, Avik 195
Sarkis, Hashim 314
Sarma, Karthik 293
Sarma, Sanjay 314
Sarno, Michael 384
Sarosdy, Randall 552
Saroyan, Rob 153
Sarratt, Karin 396
Sarrett, David 650
Sarsfield, Sally 57
Sartor-chicowski, Aline 259
Sartorelli, Kennith 598
Sartorio, James 496
Sasich, Keith N 279
Sass, Forrest 572
Sass, Steven 608
Sasser, Gary D 56
Sasser, Gary D. 56
Satele, Evelyn 298
Sato, Lisa 402
Sato, Beverly 485

Sato, Samuel M. (Sam) 567
Satre, Lindsey 182
Saucier, Grady 345
Sauer, Dave 69
Saul, J. Philip 359
Saulsberry, Scott 669
Saunders, Jim 360
Saunders, Jane 552
Saunders, Ninfa M 575
Saunders, Kathy 578
Savage, Kelly 29
Savell, Jason 349
Savoff, Mark T 196
Sawanoi, Makoto 248
Sawasky, Joseph F. 660
Sawicki, Joseph 162
Sawicki, Joseph D. (Joe) 326
Sawicki, Joe 326
Sawyer, David 160
Sawyer, Billy 219
Sawyer, Guy 453
Sawyerr, Wraymond 646
Sawyers, Susan 636
Saxton, Carol 353
Saxton, Ron 410
Saxton, Pamela L 604
Sayavedra, Laura 340
Saybe, Victoria 116
Sayiner, Necip 446
Sayles, Andy 436
Saylor, Jeb 456
Sayre, Donald L. 51
Sbarbaro, Cory 222
Sbraccia, Denise 671
Scaer, Robert 212
Scaggiante, Michele 364
Scaggs, Thomas 113
Scales, John 548
Scalzo, Helen 331
Scamihorn, Randy 144
Scaminace, Joseph M. (Joe) 562
Scanio, Kurt 138
Scanlan, John 141
Scanlon, Ryan 93
Scanlon, John P. 119
Scaradavou, Andromachi 364
Scarborough, Fred 45
Scarborough, Rebecca 637
Scarbrough, Brenda 372
Scarcinci, Susan 458
Scarlett, Dale 237
Scarlett, Lynn 579
Scarpa, Joseph 94
Schaal, Barbara A. 600
Schaber, Carolina 438
Schach, Eric J 505
Schacht, Jessica 488
Schaefer, Ronald 164
Schaefer, Chris 423
Schaeffer, Joel 175
Schaeffer, Aaron 278
Schaeffer, Tammi 306
Schafer, Dirk 260
Schafer, Dirk 261
Schafer, Scott 452
Schafer, Dana Lee 588
Schafer, Cathy 633
Schaffel, Mary 57
Schaffer, Chris 10
Schaffer, Barbara 175
Schaffmeyer, Maryjeanne 602
Schaffner, Fulton 265
Schager, Marty 9
Schandler, Jon B 667
Schanel, Judy 578
Schaper, Katie 18
Schapiro, Sara 432
Schapiro, Howard 598
Schapper, Brian 334
Scharbauer, Clarence 549
Scharf, Michael P. 116
Schark, Janelle L 595
Scharmann, Steve 182
Schartz, Weston 617

Index of Executives

Schau, Duane 610
Schaufelberger, John 640
Schechter, Chris 140
Scheessele, Marc 465
Schefer, Catherine 356
Scheib, Barbara 378
Scheines, Richard 114
Schek, Judy 202
Schell, Kenneth 489
Schemmel, Sarah 507
Schempf, Duff 581
Schendel, Jennifer 456
Schenk, John 266
Schenkel, Cari 254
Schenkel, Carolyn 330
Scheppke, James B 399
Scherba, Lena 517
Scherer, Chad 356
Scherer, Lori M. 578
Scherer, Barb 655
Scherler, Lynn 143
Scherman, Carol E. 93
Scherpbier, Harm 305
Scherrer, Philip 290
Schettler, David N 546
Scheuring, Steve 14
Schexnayder, Stephen 45
Schick, Mike 149
Schieck-Solomon, Ann 343
Schiegg, Brian 393
Schier, Joseph 359
Schiesl, Troy 76
Schiffner, Wayne 254
Schiller, Robert M. 80
Schiller, Mark 285
Schiller, Guy 405
Schiller, Lisa 448
Schiltz, Christine 60
Schimmelpfennig, Katie 521
Schimmoller, Kelly 270
Schinski, James E. (Jim) 540
Schissler, Steve 596
Schiurba, John 667
Schlaegel, Leslie 290
Schlaff, Raymond C 359
Schlapia, Jennifer 396
Schlappich, Julie 441
Schlechty, Rachael 276
Schlein, Michael 364
Schlemmer, David 500
Schleper, Denny 141
Schlichting, Nancy M. 236
Schlipmann, Adam 251
Schlissel, Mark S. 101
Schlissel, Mark S. 444
Schlott, Robert N 658
Schlott, Abraham N 658
Schlumberger, Allan 429
Schmauderer, Jennifer 251
Schmaus, Becky 101
Schmid, Lauren 113
Schmid, Larry 221
Schmid, Richard J. 603
Schmidl, Kurt 450
Schmidt, Diane Grob 32
Schmidt, Pamela 94
Schmidt, Brent 150
Schmidt, Beth 157
Schmidt, Barry 223
Schmidt, Martin A. 314
Schmidt, Todd 390
Schmidt, William 430
Schmidt, Laura A 480
Schmidt, John 614
Schmidt, Ray 614
Schmiedel, Rob 182
Schmitdgall, Beth 251
Schmitt, Peggy 379
Schmitt, Kay 445
Schmitt, Matthew H 453
Schmitt, Paul 601
Schmittlein, David C. 314
Schmitz, Bonnie R 11
Schmitz, Tara 11

Schmitz, John 482
Schmitz, John D 485
Schmoke, Kurt L. 642
Schmoll, David N. 423
Schmoll, Dave 423
Schnaars, Sue 671
Schnabel, Diane 535
Schneider, Pat 252
Schneider, Robert 276
Schneider, Mark K. 321
Schneider, Brett 375
Schneider, Angela 399
Schneider, Amy 462
Schneider, Jennifer S. 464
Schnell, David 673
Schnieders, James 86
Schnirring, Greg 160
Schnitzer, Jay 578
Schnuck, Craig D. 601
Schnuckle, Scott 233
Schock, Larry 141
Schodde, Joseph 246
Schoel, Fran 638
Schoenemann, Maureen 456
Schoenfelder, Kevin 208
Schoenherr, Melissa 406
Schoening, Lisa 519
Schoenwaelder, Thom 405
Schoepp, Jan Rune 197
Scholl, Barbara 110
Scholten, Danielle E 295
Scholtz, Jennifer 94
Scholtz, Marty 594
Schomber, Joe 134
Schonewolf, Lil 522
Schons, Jeri 471
Schooler, Richard D 210
Schooler, Rick 400
Schoolmaster, F. Andrew 549
Schopbach, Colin 333
Schorer, Emily 109
Schott, Stevan R. 106
Schowengerdt, Anna 474
Schrader, Michael 397
Schrader, Cheryl B. 633
Schramm, William 236
Schreiber, John R. 73
Schreiber, Bill 170
Schreiber, Michelle 236
Schreiber, Nicolette 433
Schreiber, Pam 640
Schreiner, Margaret 221
Schreiner, Jeff 589
Schroeder, Karl 20
Schroeder, Michael J. (Mike) 453
Schropp, Tobin A 279
Schrupp, Susan 150
Schueler, Kevin 568
Schuerman, Janice 337
Schuette, Stuart 35
Schuetze, Joergen 404
Schull, Janette 445
Schulman, Mona 403
Schulte, Ted 14
Schultheis, Wayne M 300
Schultz, Andrea 159
Schultz, Tatiana 300
Schultz, Joshua 405
Schultz, Clayton 459
Schultz, Gus 556
Schultz, Danielle 588
Schulz, Patricia 141
Schulz, Matthew 358
Schulz, Dawn 444
Schumacher, Matt 18
Schumacher, Michael 50
Schumacher, Larry 150
Schumacher, John 242
Schurko, Allison 667
Schurman, Kim 363
Schuster, Michael 361
Schuster, Doug 373
Schuster, Francis B. (Frank) 499
Schutt, Cherie 564

Schutt, Hannah 644
Schwab, Heidi 476
Schwab-Pomerantz, Carrie 477
Schwager, Charles 360
Schwaibold, Fred 418
Schwalm, Laura 212
Schwarctz, Laurie 182
Schwartz, Steven 96
Schwartz, Hollie 202
Schwartz, James K 391
Schwartz, Kendra L 660
Schwartzberg, Jennifer 57
Schwarz, Ronald F. 282
Schwarz, Ron 282
Schwarz, Amy 332
Schwarz, David 453
Schwarzbach, Fred 370
Schwedhelm, Kevin 21
Schwei, Russell P. (Russ) 453
Schwertner, Chris 508
Schwilke, Tom 20
Schwinn, Debra 594
Schwister, Jay 453
Schwoerke, Jacqueline 489
Sciame-Giesecke, Susan 610
Sciortino, Cathy L 160
Scirica, Anthony J. 546
Scoggin, Andrew (Andy) 20
Scolieri, Angela 643
Scoma, SophiaS 444
Sconzo, Guy M 246
Scorsone, Ada 117
Scotland, Michael 255
Scott, Rob 57
Scott, Sam 104
Scott, Pamela 141
Scott, Mychelle 151
Scott, Yvonne 165
Scott, Angela 204
Scott, Selwyn 220
Scott, Eric M 280
Scott, Joseph 371
Scott, Stacey 375
Scott, Cindy 406
Scott, Susan 418
Scott, Peter M. 447
Scott, Charlene 491
Scott, Majeedah 588
Scott, Steven M. 627
Scott, Jeffrey 640
Scott, Cheryl 640
Scott, Stephanie 647
Scranton, Alec B. 594
Scribner, Kent 206
Scudder, Daniel 22
Scudder, Walter 572
Scully, Jodi 510
Scungio, Dan 484
Scurfield, Keith 515
Sczudlo, Raymond S. 130
Sczygelski, Sidney 49
Seabrooks, Nettie 565
Seagren, John 16
Seaman, Chuck 247
Searle, Mark 44
Searles, Sean 356
Sears, Melissa 508
Seastrom, Dave 185
Seaton, Bree-Annette 160
Sebastiano, Joanne 653
Seck, Jason 86
Seckinger, Mark 395
Secor, Aleyne 375
Sedam, Lonna 625
Sedey, Ray 318
Sedey, Raymond J 319
Sedlak, Andrea 664
Sedmak, Thomas 74
Segal, David 27
Segal, Nancy 191
Segall, Peter 351
Segatto, James 199
Segin, Robert 653
Sehi, John 232

Sehring, Robert 401
Seianna, Apollonia 478
Seibert, William 191
Seidcheck, Thomas 453
Seidel, Laura 239
Seidel, Andrew 466
Seidel, Deborah L 664
Seidl, David 337
Seidler, Rick 258
Seidner, Erin 408
Seiler, James 587
Seinsheimer, Matthew 543
Seis, Todd 588
Seitz, Charles W 293
Seivold, Stephen 671
Sekerka, Robert 114
Self, Amy 506
Seligman, Heather L 383
Sellas, Susie 470
Sellers, Ronnie 200
Sellers, Angie 204
Sellers, Thomas 226
Selman, Thomas M. (Tom) 202
Selosse, Eric 326
Selva, Bert 492
Semanek, Jamie 77
Semeraro, Nicole 475
Semerdjian, Nancy 386
Semple, Heather 279
Senevy, Steven 207
Senisse, Alessandra 404
Senker, T. J. 321
Senty, Josh 657
Sepe, Billye 166
Sepulveda, Juan 432
Sepulveda, Liliana 677
Sequin, Donny 478
Serck-hanssen, Sverre 196
Sereda, Dexter 500
Serhal, Ed 553
Serkes, Jeffrey David 347
Seroka, Gene 424
Serota, Scott P. 89
Serpico, Donna 489
Serrato, Pedro 192
Serre, Nicholas 41
Seshadri, Sridhar 524
Sessions, Roy B. 80
Settle, Tom 247
Settle, Judy 389
Settle, Peggy 407
Settle, Diane 473
Severance, Matthew 111
Severance, Keith 611
Severiano, Gilda 206
Severson, Gerald 253
Sevier, John 56
Sevilla, Javier 202
Sewalls, Travis 465
Seward, Michelle 266
Seward, Robert 333
Sewell, Leigh 94
Sewell, Denise 656
Sexton, Kevin 242
Sexton, John 371
Sey, Jennifer (Jen) 293
Seybold, Henry 379
Sfamenos, Steve 85
Shabot, M. Michael 324
Shade, Elizabeth F 40
Shadle, Roger 531
Shadwick, Susan 325
Shaeffer, Carrie 68
Shaevsky, Mark 670
Shaffer, Stephen 22
Shaffer, Stephen 171
Shaffer, Shelly 247
Shaffer, Rachel 383
Shagimuratova, Elvira 408
Shah, Mahesh 503
Shah, Rashmi 503
Shah, Summit 503
Shahid, Mohammad 488
Shaik, Shalina 629

Index of Executives

Shaikh, Jalil 53
Shaker, Mark 338
Shalkham, Anna 294
Shammo, Brian 14
Shane, Tarah 273
Shane, Leslie 536
Shank, Diana 340
Shank, Theresa 362
Shanker, Nick 281
Shanks, Laura 113
Shanks, Scott 534
Shanmugam, Nataraj 182
Shannon, Jason 35
Shannon, Kelly 301
Shannon, Nicole 457
Shannon, Jetawn 476
Shannon, Jennifer 631
Shapiro, Steven 111
Shapiro, Karin 187
Shapiro, Donna 287
Shapiro, Louis 368
Shapiro, Robert S. (Bob) 382
Shapiro, Morton O. 388
Shapiro, Larry J. 600
Shapiro, Sheri 606
Shapiro, Steven D. 643
Shapleigh, Greg 97
Shappell, James R. (Jim) 582
Share, Christopher J. 130
Share, Douglas G. 130
Sharff, Rich 475
Shari, Lord 637
Sharifzadeh, Shahin 53
Sharkey, Allan 445
Sharma, Roger 137
Sharma, Amit 467
Sharon, Bodi S 605
Sharon, Lanier 637
Sharoni, Elan 375
Sharp, John F 85
Sharp, Joseph 144
Sharp, Mike 215
Sharp, Carissa 233
Sharp, Eddie 410
Sharp, Linda 412
Sharp, Lindsey 448
Sharp, Christopher (Topher) 524
Sharp, Bob 657
Shaulis, Charlie 32
Shaver, Bill 493
Shaw, Sean 46
Shaw, Tom 83
Shaw, Jennifer 93
Shaw, Chris 190
Shaw, Angela 199
Shaw, Chuck 476
Shaw, Keeasha 552
Shaw, Diane 606
Shaw, Jen Day 627
Shaw, Gene 677
Shaye, Gary 474
Shea, Dennis 175
Shea, Agnes A 337
Shea, Daniel 416
Shea, James L. 642
Sheckleford-lister, Peter 85
Sheedy, Linda L 391
Sheehan, John F. 14
Sheehan, Casey 199
Sheehan, Arlene 302
Sheehan, Timothy 555
Sheets, Anna 128
Sheets, Brian 235
Sheets, Roger 494
Sheffield, Tamara 256
Shehee, Virginia K 85
Shelby, Thomas S. 414
Shelby, Laura Wilson 486
Shell, Ellen 96
Shelley, Christine 590
Shellman, Carolyn E. 164
Shelly, Lisa 135
Shelton, Jean 121
Shelton, Anna 207

Shelton, Natalie 549
Shelton, M. Dwight 652
Shen, Sam 290
Shendell-Falik, Nancy 72
Shendell-Falik, Nancy 73
Shepard, Ken 297
Shepard, Alan G 388
Shepheard, Hillary 549
Shepherd, Richard 278
Shepherd, Mary 386
Shepherd, Glenn 481
Shepherd, Mary 599
Shepler, Mary 465
Sheppard, Linda 440
Sheppard, Dennis 511
Sheppard, William D 511
Sheppard, William 511
Shepro, William B 29
Sher, Susan S. 594
Sherer, Matt 541
Sheridan, Chris 116
Sheridan, James 335
Sheridan, Arthur 526
Sheridan, John P. 563
Sheriff, Abrar 612
Sherlock, Kevin 247
Sherlock, Peter 578
Sherman, Kim 360
Sherman, Harry 368
Sherman, Mark 479
Sherman, Malcolm L 612
Sherman, Jennifer 642
Sherman, Joseph 642
Shermer, Teresa 126
Sherpa, Chheki 190
Shervington, Allyson 351
Sherwin, R Lawrence 510
Shi, Patricia 364
Shi, Diana 475
Shickolovich, Bill 612
Shields, Richard 93
Shields, Christine 135
Shields, Robert 524
Shields, Ed 595
Shields, Kevin 601
Shields, Charles W. (Charlie) 608
Shields, Dennis 641
Shiels, Julie 358
Shiflett, Susan 150
Shih, Elizabeth 181
Shihara, Yoshito 534
Shiltz, LauraA 444
Shimberg, David A 428
Shin, Sungwon 645
Shinichi, Iguchi 670
Shinkle, Kevin 282
Shipek, Melanie 390
Shipley, Marcus B 606
Shipp, Vicki 465
Shipp, Bob 637
Shippey, Mike 672
Shirato, Masayoshi 34
Shirey, Richard T 229
Shirley, Dennis 316
Shirley, Jasmin 377
Shirley, Lee 546
Shirley, David W 552
Shirley, Douglas E. 563
Shirtcliff, Chris 72
Shisler, Jessica 175
Shively, Kari 356
Shmerling, James E. 127
Shoemaker, Jonathan 26
Shoemaker, Carey 369
Shomento, Stacy 84
Shomette, Tom 126
Shontere, Jim 492
Shook, Rhonda 617
Shoop, James 58
Shoopman, Chuck 638
Shor, David 389
Shore, Melissa 172
Short, Brian 119
Short, Steve 203

Short, Jason 539
Short, Jeffrey B 568
Shoulders, Patrick A. 610
Showman, Brian 306
Shows, W T 158
Shrair, David A 156
Shreiber, Kathleen 134
Shrewsbury, Amber 227
Shrum, Kayse 526
Shuck, Theresa 523
Shucoski, Patricia 563
Shufflebarger, Thomas G 559
Shuh, Monson 168
Shull, Thomas C. (Tom) 46
Shulman, Brett 455
Shultheis, Sherri 445
Shumann, C R 234
Shupe, Rachel 548
Si, Stephanie L 161
Siak, Stacey 149
Sibley, Karen 102
Sibley, Miriam 171
Sicola, Tom 319
Siddique, Omar 631
Siddiqui, Omer 174
Sideras, John F. 116
Sidhu, Libby 223
Sidrys, Paul 126
Siebenborn, Bill 169
Siebers, Eric 555
Siebert, April 179
Siegel, James 94
Siegel, Steven F 98
Siegel, Steven 98
Siegel, Richard 181
Siegel, Deana 540
Siegert, Thomas 572
Siegfried, Scott 466
Siegl, C 572
Sielak, George 43
Siemer, Julie 463
Siemon, George 158
Sierras, Jennifer 535
Sievers, Hans Christian 235
Sievers, Glen 412
Sievert, Deana 591
Siggeman, Carlee 456
Sigler, John J 459
Sigler, Russell 459
Sigler, Lee Lanning 459
Sigmon, William 58
Signorille, Mary 2
Sikand, Yash 393
Silberberg, Allison 137
Silberstein, Edward 625
Silfen, Lori 337
Silk, Robert 383
Sills, James 83
Silta, Bill 649
Silva, Joseph M 236
Silva, Jan 611
Silvagni, Anthony J. 390
Silver, Richard 478
Silver, Mark 589
Silver, Christopher 627
Silveria, Richard 95
Silverman, Jan 23
Silverman, Barry J. 390
Silverman, Daniel C 494
Silvers, J. B. 576
Silverstein, Marni 173
Silverstein, Douglas M. 386
Silvestri, Jennifer 546
Silvi, Marcus 392
Sim, Edward 63
Simerly, Rick 260
Simhon, Gail 304
Siminoff, Laura A. 546
Simio, Frank 206
Simkins, Amber 625
Simmelink, Scott 10
Simmons, Sharon 101
Simmons, Paul 116
Simmons, Jodi 256

Simmons, Leslie 295
Simmons, Tj 303
Simmons, Elizabeth H. 339
Simmons, Eileen 644
Simmons-Oliver, Cheryl 296
Simms, Susan 411
Simon, Sam 52
Simon, Mary 203
Simon, Brian 245
Simon, Debbie 258
Simon, Lou Anna K. 339
Simon, Don 382
Simon, Jolynn 486
Simon, Linda 518
Simon, Marianne 562
Simon, Keri 633
Simone, Alan Del 662
Simoneau, Ron 491
Simons, Marilyn 589
Simons, James H 589
Simpson, Joshua 35
Simpson, Jennie 187
Simpson, Jennifer 382
SIMS, SUZANNE 171
Sims, Dominique 505
Sims, Damon 584
Sinagra, Jack 613
Sinchak, David 610
Sinclair, Rebecca 35
Sinclair, Shannon 253
Sinclair, Julia 407
Sinewgz, Larry 96
Singer, Jolie 368
Singer, Samantha 556
Singer, Janet E 673
Singh, Sukhwinder 15
Singh, Gurbir 47
Singh, Rajinder 276
Singh, Ankush 286
Singh, Harmit J. 293
Singh, Harry 364
Singh, Vijayeta 383
Singh, Sabi 629
Singla, Anjali 17
Singleton, John Knox 253
Singleton, Kali 282
Singleton, Palmer C 354
Singleton, H. Wells 390
Singleton, Arnold R. 501
Sinner, Anna 205
Sinopoli, Angelo 430
Sipser, Michael 314
Siragusa, Paul 416
Sirianni, Frank 206
Sirko, Nancy 588
Sirleaf, James 307
Sirois, Bonnie 96
Sironen, Jason 529
Sirstins, Max 184
Sisisky, Richard L 503
Sisitsky, Todd B. 475
Sisney, Dan 532
Sisson, William G. 64
Sites, Larry 280
Sitherwood, Suzanne 510
Siu, Albert 248
Siu, Albert 351
Siva, Chokkalingam 633
Sizemore, Vicki 60
Sizemore, Stephen 162
Sizemore, Jay 228
Sizemore, Mark 431
Sjulin, Renee 103
Skabelund, Hoyt 61
Skaggs, Stephen A. (Steve) 53
Skarulis, Patricia C. 325
Skelsey, Maral 322
Skidmore, Timothy 133
Skiendzielewski, John 214
Skiendzielewski, John 569
Skinner, Jessica 227
Skinner, Claudia 519
Skinner, Stephen 531
Skinner, Brooks 595

Index of Executives

Sklenar, John 230
Skluth, Nancy 333
Skogsbergh, James H 7
Skogsbergh, James H 8
Skokan, Mike 247
Skolfield, Melissa 585
Skorkowsky, Patrick 140
Skoro, A T 280
Skorton, David J. 497
Skory, John E 562
Skrabak, Rachel 671
Skrivanos, Stephen F 85
Skrocki, Denise 616
Skrzypek, Leslaw 638
Slack, Karoliina 471
Slaff, Morgan 444
Slaton, Shawn 126
Slaughter, James G. 461
Slaughter, Veronica 620
Slavin, Peter L. 407
Slavin, Kevin 519
Slavin, Peter L. 574
Slaybaugh, Chris 671
Slenker, Kirk 493
Slifer, Celeste 24
Sloan, Gayle 467
Sloane, Scott 155
Slobasky, Renee 664
Slominski, Donald D. (Don) 320
Slomsky, David 531
Slubowski, Michael 606
Sluka, Joseph 445
Sluka, Joe 514
Sly, Patrick J. 465
Small, David R. 433
Small, J. Radford 547
Small, Susan 583
Small, Deborah A 591
Small, Jeff 672
Smalley, John 315
Smalls, Kandi 168
Smart, Denise T. 551
Smet, John H 31
Smet, John 572
Smiley, Alice 131
Smilo, Bettina 74
Smit, Rod 343
Smith, David 7
Smith, Mary Pat 24
Smith, Caitlyn 25
Smith, Lisa 26
Smith, Stephan 33
Smith, Rosi 45
Smith, Judy 49
Smith, David 50
Smith, Chip 51
Smith, Guy H 51
Smith, Ginny 51
Smith, Lamont 54
Smith, Jodi 56
Smith, Ryan 61
Smith, A 61
Smith, Andrew 74
Smith, Stuart 83
Smith, Taylor 93
Smith, Nate 93
Smith, Catherine 97
Smith, Jared M 101
Smith, Shane 102
Smith, Patricia 108
Smith, Charles 160
Smith, Rockwell E. (Rocky) 166
Smith, Rockwell 166
Smith, Richard P. (Rick) 169
Smith, Annette 170
Smith, Sean 173
Smith, Barbara A 173
Smith, Larry 173
Smith, Stephanie 175
Smith, Howard 194
Smith, Jim 195
Smith, Robert 201
Smith, Stephanie 203
Smith, Jane 205

Smith, Christina 212
Smith, Dolois 242
Smith, Lachlan 244
Smith, Brian 246
Smith, Doug 255
Smith, Eugene 261
Smith, Robert 276
Smith, Steven E 281
Smith, Randy Smith Randy 295
Smith, Quiara 302
Smith, Wes 316
Smith, Jeralyn Waller 318
Smith, Amy M 330
Smith, Allen 337
Smith, Alex 344
Smith, Diane R 349
Smith, Brian 351
Smith, David A. 356
Smith, Donald 356
Smith, P 356
Smith, Harold 358
Smith, Doug 363
Smith, Lawrence G. 382
Smith, Steve 383
Smith, Debra 384
Smith, Steven 386
Smith, Ryan 391
Smith, Jim 395
Smith, Kent 403
Smith, Hank 404
Smith, Rob 406
Smith, Allen L. 407
Smith, Van 421
Smith, Eddie 422
Smith, Carole 425
Smith, Suzanne 428
Smith, Michelle Taylor 430
Smith, Martha 430
Smith, Andrew O 433
Smith, Randy 443
Smith, David 450
Smith, Shawn B 453
Smith, Shawn 460
Smith, Linda 463
Smith, Jonathan 465
Smith, Sheryl 465
Smith, Meg 466
Smith, Cydni 467
Smith, Brenda 484
Smith, Tim 489
Smith, Andrea 505
Smith, Astria 505
Smith, Stephen 505
Smith, Kenneth A. (Ken) 510
Smith, Todd 535
Smith, Devonna 546
Smith, Dillon 549
Smith, Ray 549
Smith, Joanne 551
Smith, Elyse 554
Smith, Chad 558
Smith, Larry T 558
Smith, Jill 559
Smith, Greg 561
Smith, Amy 566
Smith, Julia 588
Smith, Mo 596
Smith, Jennifer R. 600
Smith, Richard J. 600
Smith, Elizabeth 604
Smith, Rebekah 607
Smith, Chris 615
Smith, John 637
Smith, Andrew M 638
Smith, Sarah 639
Smith, Orin C. 640
Smith, Brent 641
Smith, Clinton 646
Smith, Bob 657
Smith, James E. 664
Smith, Sharon P 666
Smith, Anna 671
Smith-Acuna, Shelly 146
Smith-Calascibetta, Patricia 7

Smith-Hill, Janet 390
Smithey, Regina 649
Smithwick, Michael 477
Smits, Robert 215
Smookler, Eric 671
Smoot, Steve 256
Smothers, Kevin 7
Smuland, Brad 333
Smullen, F W 117
Smylie, John 496
Smyrnios, Nicholas 616
Snarr, Jack 389
Snel, Michael 27
Snider, Diane 7
Snider, Eric 492
Snively, Melissa 240
Snoddy, Aimee 526
Snodgrass, Greg 552
Snow, Stuart 168
Snow, Kimberly 420
Snowden, Joseph I. 428
Snustad, John 30
Snyder, Chandra 38
Snyder, Barbara R. 116
Snyder, Kyle 213
Snyder, Kenneth 272
Snyder, Tammy 430
Snyder, Meredith 626
Snyder, Jane 671
Soab, Alan 281
Soares, Denise C. 365
Sobanet, Henry 148
Sobecki, Lisa 605
Sobson, Carol L 387
Socha, Bernie 571
Sochacki, Thomas L 666
Sock, Shannon 328
Sodano, Kerrie 14
Soderstrom, Gerry 479
Sodomick, Karen 580
Soete, Elizabeth 175
Soetenga, Deanne 453
Soffer, Patricia G 518
Sofia, Ivie Blussette 597
Soghier, Lamia 130
Sohn, Regina 405
Sohn, Young 405
Sohn, Stephanie 656
Soifer, B. Thomas 107
Soiffer, Robert J. 172
Soike, Dave 424
Sokn, Erick 562
Sokobin, Jonathan S. 202
Sokola, Thomas 213
Sokolov, Lisa 370
Solanski, David 234
Solazzo, Mark J. 382
Solberg, Jeff 223
Solberg, Jeffrey M 223
Soldo, Stephen 462
Soles, Darren 214
Solis, Raul 168
Solis, Jose 604
Solis, Robert 631
Solomon, Lesley 172
Solomon, Sarah 172
Solomon, Lisa 299
Somanchi, Subba 326
Somerhalder, John W. 146
Somerville, Susan 382
Sommer, Alan 4
Sommer, Harry 443
Sommers, John 4
Sommers, Jimmy F 590
Sommers, Sarah W 590
Sommers, Wynelle 590
Sommers, Randy 590
Sommerville, Gwen 308
Sonenreich, Steven D. 351
Song, Norman 86
Songer, Terri 45
Sonnier, Buford 105
Sonora, Lynn 561
Sonora, Brandi 561

Sonthalia, Ashok 286
Sontheimer, Dan 291
Sonty, S Sita 493
Sood, Rohit 405
Soper, Aaron 671
Sorber, William 78
Sordillo, Emilia 514
Sorensen, Donn 331
Sorensen, Jim 439
Sorensen, Charles W. 641
Sorenson, Meredith 116
Sorenson, Charles 249
Sorenson, Roger 644
Sori, Alfredo E 280
Sorice, Maria 94
Sorkey, Alan J 670
Soroka, Dina 369
Sorrell, Kellie 56
Sorrentino, Renee 407
Sorter, Michael 128
Sorto, Rafael 26
Sorvillo, Domenico 202
Sosebee, Lori 115
Sosebee, Tim 144
Sosebee, Tina 551
Soso, Gary 667
Sossi, Frank 154
Sotelo, Dan 303
Soterakis, Jack 515
Soto, Zoemy 55
Soto, Dannette 286
Sotos, Michelle 218
Souder, Matthew 677
Souders, Michael 297
Soukup, Beth 260
Soukup, Beth 261
South, John R 234
Southam, Arthur M. 132
Southard, Bill 347
Southern, Jenny 297
Southwick, Michael J 587
Souza, Clinton De 408
Sow, Christine 424
Sowa, Mark 270
Sowder, Dianna 75
Sowmarpet, Mandasmitha 330
Soy, Randall 443
Spada, Mary 636
Spadaro, Christy 586
Spahr, Dalena 536
Spain, Wayne 56
Spain-Remy, Claire 352
Spalding, William R 1
Spalding, Susan 171
Spangler, Tammy 340
Sparer, Cynthia N. 676
Spargo, Glenn 163
Sparke, Andrea 333
Sparkman, Julie 444
Sparks, David 143
Sparks, Lisa 252
Sparks, Danny 392
Sparks, Dennis 464
Sparrow, Victor 584
Spas, Paula 323
Spaugh, Gary 181
Spaulding, Stephen J 612
Spaziano, Greg 111
Spear, Lorna 511
Spearman, Terri 94
Spears, L Steven 331
Spears, David 340
Spector, Ruth 218
Speer, Samantha 114
Speer, Kevin P 235
Speer, Bill 581
Speidell, Paul 484
Speizer, Howard 447
Spellecy, Mike 308
Spence, Jenny 412
Spenceley, James 86
Spencer, John 28
Spencer, Jill 38
Spencer, Rhonda 67

Index of Executives

Index of Executives

Strangeway, Christine 519
Straub, Karl 262
Straub, Maximiliane 452
Strauss, Cindy 431
Strauss, Cindy 431
Strauss, Cindy 431
Strayer, Joe 260
Straz, David A. 203
Streck, Richard J 15
Stredit-Thomas, Sukari 246
Street, Doug 9
Street, Brad 20
Streeter, Bill 337
Streeter, Monica 459
Streeter, Debra 507
Streett, Sarah 290
Streif, Mary 465
Strength, Brent 261
Strey, Jean 161
Strickland, Robert 150
Stringer, Ruth M 161
Stritikus, Tom 640
Strobel, Marsha 205
Strobel, Victoria L 310
Stroh, Elizabeth 253
Strohaver, Deborah 235
Strohfus, Joseph 476
Strohl, Kingman 116
Stroin, Jeff 613
Stroker, Robert T. 546
Stromann, Nicholas 160
Stromberg, Leroy 18
Stromberg, Stephanie 256
Stromski, Christopher 520
Strong, Gary B 157
Strong, David W. 400
Stroud, Martin 444
Stroz, Edward M. 206
Strull, Scott 618
Strumwasser, Todd 181
Strunk, Tom 673
Strunk, Thomas W. (Tom) 674
Struth, Werner 452
Struthers, Darren 200
Strykowski, Jill 26
Stuart, Kelly 94
Stuart, Cindy 240
Stuart, Paul 304
Stuart, Tim 400
Stuart, Rob 432
Stubbs, Willie 196
Stubbs, Henry 430
Stuber, Rich 645
Stucky, Duane 504
Studer, Dianne 379
Studt, Amanda 206
Stueve, Jo 327
Stuff, Ronald 532
Stuff, Ronald 590
Stulken, Judy 11
Stull, Terrence L 417
Stump, Kate Lucas 278
Stump, Josh 671
Stumpf, Elizabeth 160
Stumpf, Patricia 486
Stumpf, Jeff 610
Stuopis, Cecilia 314
Sturgeon, Sara 610
Sturges, Anthony 55
Sturgess, David E 307
Sturtevant, John 326
Sturza, Scott G 236
Stutz, Byron 228
Stutzman, Paul 220
Styons, Connie 541
Stys, Richard 229
Su, John 309
Suanne, Thurman 671
Subbaswamy, Kumble R. (Swamy) 631
Sublette, Bill 476
Subzposh, Faiz 215
Sucher, Theresa 441
Suchy, Frederick J. 127
Sud, James (Jim) 669

Sudbury, Cathy 263
Suderman, Julie 555
Sudmyer, Nancy 539
Suffridge, Guy 461
Suggs, Carolyn 341
Sughrue, Timothy 445
Sugiyama, Deborah 383
Sugiyama, Yoshihiro 678
Suhl, Randy 547
Suit, John M 40
Suite, Denzil 640
Suiter, Paul A 236
Sukut, Paul 69
Sullivan, Wynn 6
Sullivan, John 32
Sullivan, Sean 64
Sullivan, Kevin M. 66
Sullivan, Tim 67
Sullivan, Joan 72
Sullivan, John 111
Sullivan, Devon 160
Sullivan, Caroline 162
Sullivan, Janelle 165
Sullivan, Jacqueline 171
Sullivan, Kevin 180
Sullivan, Kathleen 181
Sullivan, Paul 220
Sullivan, Chris 303
Sullivan, John 321
Sullivan, Robert A 330
Sullivan, Anne Marie 365
Sullivan, Brian 383
Sullivan, Margaret 389
Sullivan, Timothy F 412
Sullivan, Teresa A. 442
Sullivan, Sharon 569
Sullivan, George 588
Sullivan, Leo 608
Sullivan, Suzanne 626
Sullivan, Blaise 639
Sullivan, John 658
Sullivan-Marx, Eileen 370
Sult, John R 193
Sult, John R 506
Sumichrast, Robert T. 652
Summers, Curtis 45
Summers, Barbara (Barb) 151
Summers-brown, Shelly 62
Summit, Shah 503
Sumner, Tom 157
Sumner, Mike 635
Sumpter, Thomas 92
Sumpter, Nikki 541
Sumrall, Paul 93
Sun, Julie 402
Sun, John 453
Sundara, Ano 498
Sundharam, Mallik 384
Sung, Keehyuk 246
Sung, C James 673
Sunterapak, Todd 647
Suntrapak, Todd 646
Sunu, Virginia 453
Suresh, Subra 114
Suresh, Sailaja 392
Surratt, Jeanette 656
Surridge, Sally B 327
Susan, Schmidt 431
Susel, Allison 38
Susie, White 665
Susman, Lynn 558
Sutera, Albert 567
Sutera, AJ 567
Sutherland, Janet 274
Sutley, Nancy 299
Sutton, Dave 50
Sutton, Denise 315
Sutton, Ellen 387
Sutton, Deborah 416
Sutton, Robin 523
Sutton, Jaqueline 563
Suvalic, Adnan 257
Suzuki, Yoshihiro 24
Svihel, Alice 55

Svoboda, Dan B. 674
Svymbersky, Andy 74
Swaby, Jonathan 140
Swader, Matthew 580
Swain, John 173
Swain, Stacy 343
Swain, Jayme 432
Swain, Debra 476
Swain, Kevin 600
Swallow, Michael F 149
Swallow, Edward M. (Ed) 553
Swallow, Ed 553
Swan, Dennis 508
Swan, Beth A. 603
Swanberg, Dale 202
Swander, Robert 12
Swango, Gary 223
Swanholm, John 199
Swank, Colleen 30
Swann, Joan 46
Swanson, Paulyn 16
Swanson, Brian 58
Swanson, Scott J. 172
Swanson, Al 422
Swapp, Russell B. 486
Swart, Mackenzie 444
Swartz, Brian 417
Swayne, Tashaan 140
Swearingen, Stanley A. (Stan) 53
Swearingen, Fritz Null 215
Swecker, Ben 429
Sweeney, Alex 166
Sweeney, William 204
Sweeney, Tim 255
Sweeney, Chris 310
Sweeney, Karen 453
Sweeney, Nathan 537
Sweet, Stephen J. 73
Sweet, Brett 599
Sweet, Rob 640
Swenarton, Geri 454
Swenson, Douglas 174
Swenson, Jessica 299
Swenson, Beau J 567
Swenson, Shaun 607
Swenson, Dana 616
Swevish, Joseph 329
Swilley, Lori 226
Swim, Karmen 639
Swindle, J. Dean 150
Swinehart, Alice 333
Swinney, Brad 199
Swinton, Matt L 280
Swist, Kyle 220
Switzer, Julie 664
Sword, Billie 615
Swygert, Jenny 6
Swyres, Christine 329
Syamaprasad, Sindhu 66
Sydnor, Walker P. 120
Syed, Mamoon 559
Syler-Jones, Tracy 549
Sylvia-Reardon, Mary 407
Symans, Catherine 639
Symmonds, Joslyn 443
Symonds, Taft 422
Sytsma, Dan 297
Syverud, Kent D. 600
Szabad, David 369
Szablowski, Paul 551
Szarkowski, Amy 230
Szebenyi, Steven E. 232
Szilagyi, Paul 236
Szurkus, Dennis 484
Szymanski, Paul 255
Szymanski, Ken 287
Szymczak, Stephen J 281

T

Tabb, Kevin 79
Taber, Rodman 509

Taber, Abram 588
Tachouet, Matthew 646
Tackett, Candace 663
Tad-Y, Darlene B 626
Taffe, Pat 379
Tagg, Sherri 34
Taheri, Paul 598
Tahir, Sumbul 386
Takara, Kurt 326
Takeda, Becky 148
Takemoto, Sue 514
Taketa, Richard 242
Takla, Magdy 563
Talan, Melba 296
Talati, Rakesh 72
Talavera, Alvaro 244
Talbot, Angela 261
Talbott, Gregory 228
Talka, Michele 72
Tallent, William 528
Talley, Linda 130
Talley, Erik 325
Talley, Verlinda 633
Talley-Smith, Christy 93
Tallis, Heather 579
Talty, Blair 671
Tamaka, Hideo 33
Tamez, Cesar 620
Tammaro, Vincent 676
Tanaka, Bryan 628
Tanchoco, Silvino 325
Tande, Brett 472
Tandler, Jaclyn 524
Tandon, Manu 79
Tang, Kin 366
Tang, Youhua 594
Tanner, Edward 268
Tannert, Silvio 114
Tanzer, Kim 442
Tanzer, Tobi 445
Tapia, Dave 659
Taplin, Mary-Ellen 172
Taplin, Bill 356
Tapp, Tim 83
Tappan, Hugh 662
Tappert, Tod N. 430
Tarakji, Ahmad 595
Taraskavage, Joe 87
Tarasov, Aleksey 459
Tarling, Neil 197
Tarpey, John 59
Tartaglia, Michael 365
Tasker, Benjamin 193
Tasooji, Michael B. 93
Tassell, Van 650
Tata, Lee 574
Tate, Marian 55
Tate, Allyson 157
Tate, Mike 386
Tate, Creston 677
Tatelbaum, Ronald J 649
Tatelbaumm, Ron 233
Taton, Jacqueline 542
Taubeneck, Brian 640
Tauber, David W. 542
Tauber, Richard E. 542
Tauscher, Randall L 311
Tavaglinoe, John 161
Tavakkolizadeh, Ali 556
Tavares, Luis 229
Taylor, Robert 20
Taylor, Kari 77
Taylor, Mike 111
Taylor, Cyrus 116
Taylor, Seth 185
Taylor, Monica 210
Taylor, Jennifer 250
Taylor, Mark 300
Taylor, Dana 303
Taylor, Scott 333
Taylor, Denise 357
Taylor, Nikki 378
Taylor, Karen 382
Taylor, Michael 404

Index of Executives

Index of Executives

Index of Executives

Index of Executives

Waters, Glenn 70
Watkins, W Juan 85
Watkins, Thomas 179
Watkins, Jesse 193
Watkins, Ron 245
Watkins, Brad 549
Watkins, Ruth V. 597
Watkins, Mark 630
Watkins, Anthony 658
Watriss, Whitney 497
Watson, Glenn 66
Watson, Marsha 93
Watson, Nancy 114
Watson, Anne 209
Watson, James 286
Watson, Veronica 326
Watson, George E 354
Watson, Jackie 363
Watson, Christopher 389
Watson, Robin 421
Watson, Harry 463
Watson, Leslyn 472
Watson, Bud 478
Watson, Amy E. 510
Watson, Dean 541
Watson, Crystal 586
Watson, James M. 594
Watt, Stephen 595
Watters, Jim 247
Watters, James H. 456
Watts, Karen 171
Watts, Tom 273
Watts, Richard 411
Watts, Christella 514
Watts, Charles 537
Watts, Brianna 640
Watzinter, Johanna 597
Waugh, Scott 407
Waxman, Herbert S 19
Wayling, Brian 256
Waymack, Randy 376
Wayne, John C. 423
Waynick, Randy 655
Weathers, Will 201
Weathers, Melanie 204
Weatherwax, Michael 593
Weaver, Amy 38
Weaver, Ron 281
Weaver, Tyler 399
Weaver, Carl 405
Weaver, Jeremy 439
Weaver, Amanda 552
Weaver, Gail 675
Webb, Tammy 45
Webb, James 67
Webb, Jim 67
Webb, David 70
Webb, Donna 112
Webb, Patricia G. (Pat) 150
Webb, Aaron 193
Webb, Marie 193
Webb, Kim 282
Webb, Steven 372
Webb, Maryjo 489
Webber, Katey 146
Webber, Henry S. 600
Webber, Cheryl 612
Weber, Roger 14
Weber, Ron 14
Weber, Peter 102
Weber, Jeff 103
Weber, Robert 157
Weber, Amy 265
Weber, Jennifer 324
Weber, Jeff 336
Weber, Julie 354
Weber, Joyce 529
Weber, Emily 626
Weber, Edythe 633
Weber, Jodi 678
Webster, Keith 114
Webster, Kathleen 298
Webster, William M. 430
Webster, Kipp 556

Webster, Richard 604
Webster, Benita 625
Webster, Marshall W. 643
Weddington, Sharon 419
Weekley, Kathy 30
Weeks, Susan 549
Weeks, Richard S. 660
Wegelin, Mark 31
Wegener, Mildred 596
Weglarz, Brian 31
Wegman, Jim 28
Wegman, Jill 157
Wegner, James 387
Wehe, Brad 29
Wehring, Brad 469
Weibelt, Daniel 590
Weidner, Frank 432
Weigley, David E. 7
Weih, Lori 258
Weil, Robert J. 150
Weil, Robert J. 213
Weiland, Ed 471
Weiler, Nathan 49
Weill, Brendon 201
Weinberg, Meryl 365
Weiner, Jack 329
Weiner, Eli 392
Weiner, Edward G. 605
Weinfurter, Daniel 174
Weingart, Saul N 612
Weinick, Robin 447
Weinraub, Michelle 664
Weinstein, Michael Arthur 12
Weinstein, James 173
Weinstein, Nelson 293
Weinstein, Roslyn 365
Weintraub, Jonathan 161
Weir, Walter 92
Weir, Daniela 125
Weir, David 368
Weir, Bob 383
Weirick, Cecilia 209
Weisberg, James 194
Weisblatt, Rick 54
Weise, Lori 118
Weisenberg, Clay 671
Weisenfeld, Paul 447
Weiser, Anna 559
Weishan, Dennis 453
Weisickle, John 33
Weiss, John 351
Weiss, Gary E. 386
Weiss, Jeff 461
Weiss, Philippe 486
Weiss, Nick 601
Weiss, Mark D 665
Weissinger, Allison 177
Weissman, Mark 130
Weissman, Neil J. 321
Weissman, Seth R. 547
Weissman, Paul 667
Weissmann, Josh 592
Weitzner, John S 459
Welage, Lynda S. 634
Welber, Dave 612
Welborn, Jim 6
Welborn, Tom 344
Welborn, Thomas 345
Welborn, Ruth B. 551
Welch, Jim 70
Welch, Shelly 133
Welch, Kevin 260
Welch, Patrick J 270
Welch, Patrick 270
Welch, H Ray 330
Welch, Kevin 359
Welch, Kip 417
Welch, Susan 584
Weldon, Terry 198
Weldon, Aaron 203
Weldon, Dennis 326
Weldy, Dave 252
Welker, Kevin P 279
Welkie, Katherine A. (Katy) 256

Welkomer, Dalena 453
Wellendorf, Don 303
Weller, Matthew 273
Weller, Heiko 452
Wellins, Chris 306
Wells, Brooks 9
Wells, Tammy 45
Wells, Charles 268
Wells, John 351
Wells, Jill 516
Wells, Janet 519
Wells, Richard 641
Welsh, Charles 330
Welsh, Richard 382
Welsh, Peter 531
Welsh, Amanda 648
Welsh, Deanne M 671
Welu, Todd 165
Welz, Edward A. (Ed) 367
Wenaas, Jeffrey K. (Jeff) 238
Wendel, Jon S. 247
Wendelken, Roger 446
Wendt, Stephen C 184
Wendy, Warring 558
Weng, Kirsti 290
Wenger, Philip R. 573
Wente, Lisa 493
Wente, Tony 507
Wente, Susan 599
Wentworth, Kerry 389
Wentz, Deanna 22
Werft, Ronald C 472
Werkhoven, Jim 387
Werner, Todd S. 61
Wernette, Terry 163
Wernick, Mark 22
Wernick, Joel 417
Werrbach, John 22
Werth, Clinton 52
Werth, Dennis L. 374
Werthman, Ronald 268
Wertman, Jessica 400
Wescoe, David 350
Wescoe, Nicole 669
Wesley-Smith, Terence 628
Wesoff, Nancy 300
Wesolowski, Karen 153
Wessel, David 130
Wessler, Alan 337
West, Robert F. (Rob) 143
West, James 162
West, George 212
West, Sandy 277
West, Mary 329
West, David 340
West, Tom 390
West, James R 419
West, Mark D. 444
West, Jack 487
West, Karin 546
West, Mary Jo 607
West, Jeffrey 639
Westad, Erik 196
Westapher, Bernard 404
Westbrook, Bennett D. 460
Westcott, David 204
Westervelt, Karen S 580
Westlake, Wayne 356
Westle, Marc B 343
Westlund, Jessie 151
Westman, David 328
Westman, John 608
Weston, Ivy 138
Weston, Marc A 173
Weston, Andrew 491
Westrick, Karl J 307
Wetherell, Russell 277
Wettersten, Virginia 5
Wexner, Abigail S. 359
Weyland, Bill 605
Whalen, Chad 106
Whalen, Thomas V. 289
Whalen, Anna 299
Whaley, Alan 252

Whang, Kyujung 592
Wharton, Danny 115
Wheat, Mary 399
Wheeler, Penny Ann 26
Wheeler, Philip 331
Wheeler, Steven M. (Steve) 478
Wheeler, Peter 579
Wheeler, Laura 586
Wheeler, Lynette 608
Wheeler, Kelsey 609
Wheeler, Bradley C. (Brad) 610
Wheeler, Brad 610
Wheeler-Fair, Martha 342
Whelan, Kathleen 541
Whelan, Michael 600
Whelan, John 610
Whelton, Pamela Daley 502
Wherry, Robert 490
Whetstine, Michael J 279
Whetstone, Hal 180
Whetstone, Jim 310
Whichard, Betty M 634
Whiddon, Jeremiah 52
Whiddon, Georgia 552
Whiitely, B Glen 162
Whipple, John 431
Whipple, John 431
Whisperer, Shoe 108
White, Matthew 11
White, Thomas 14
White, Kim 45
White, Doug 45
White, Lisa 60
White, Rev. William W. 63
White, William W 65
White, Albert 122
White, Cooper 131
White, Inez 132
White, Joseph 135
White, Keith A. 140
White, Paul 140
White, Bonni L 174
White, Shannon 174
White, Tracy 174
White, Linda E 176
White, Kevin 187
White, Charles 204
White, Gregory 221
White, Joseph E 234
White, Bryan 249
White, Sandra 253
White, James 254
White, Joseph 300
White, Laura 314
White, David 327
White, Robert 370
White, Thomas D 391
White, Brad 395
White, Eric 399
White, Andy 444
White, Van Henri 454
White, Louise 489
White, Lori 505
White, Craig 544
White, Robert 577
White, Debbie 585
White, Winona 610
White, Carrie 625
White, Lawrence 627
White, Craig G. 634
White, Wendy 671
White, Cindy 671
White-Bruton, Evelyn 614
Whiteaker, Kim 662
Whitehead, H 130
Whitehead, David 229
Whitehouse, Donna 489
Whitehurst, Jim 487
Whitely, B Glen 162
Whiteman, Jeffrey S. (Jeff) 195
Whiteman, Charles H. 584
Whitener, Pam 300
Whiteside, Darwin 382
Whiteside, James 522

Index of Executives

Index of Executives

Wolt, Dave 487
Wolterman, Daniel J. 324
Wolverton, David 585
Womack, Patty 182
Womack, Robert R 467
Womack, Mark 590
Womble, Aaron 359
Womersley, Beth 13
Wong, Dhobie 6
Wong, Art 154
Wong, Lok 225
Wong, Stephen 290
Wong, Xx 377
Wong, John 612
Wong, Jennifer 640
Woo, Meredith J. E. 442
Woo, Tracy 585
Woo, Melissa 636
Wood, Dawn 60
Wood, Ronald 78
Wood, Erik 84
Wood, William 180
Wood, Kurt 185
Wood, Robert 202
Wood, Laura 268
Wood, Elizabeth 293
Wood, Jeff 412
Wood, Nancy 537
Wood, Matthew 614
Wood, Patrick 671
Woodall, Charles 291
Woodall, Niki 624
Woodard, Beth 426
Woodard, Elizabeth 426
Woodard, Eric 497
Woodcock, John 59
Woodcock, John 59
Woodie, Joe 318
Woodland, Luann 76
Woodring, Paula 469
Woodruff, David 314
Woods, Don 50
Woods, Douglas E. (Doug) 185
Woods, Mike 223
Woods, Brian T 387
Woods, Randall 404
Woods, Christopher 531
Woods, Mike 577
Woods, Chris 601
Woods, Stephanie 639
Woodson, Geraldine 60
Woodson, Nathaniel D 593
Woodward, David 204
Woodward, James L 332
Woody, Craig W. 146
Wool, Julius 365
Wooldridge, Matthew 155
Wooley, Mylowe 389
Woolfolk, James W 105
Woolridge, Diane 343
Woolridge, Victor 631
Woolsey, Christine 477
Woolston, Kristina 125
Wooten, Scott 63
Wooten, Karen 486
Worcester, Hilary 340
Wordell, Doug 511
Workman, Sue B. 116
Workman, Tamora 504
Worley, Allan 523
Wormley, Mike 277
Wornow, Scott M. 53
Worrell, Larry 83
Worth, Denny 223
Worth, Greg 659
Worthington, Bill 472
Wortman, William 108
Wozniak, Greg 522
Wrassman, Owen 453
Wray, Joyce 259
Wray, Christine R. 321
Wresch, William 613
Wright, Rodney L 12
Wright, Craig 46

Wright, Victoria 116
Wright, Joseph 130
Wright, Nancy 177
Wright, Jordan 182
Wright, Mary 222
Wright, John 238
Wright, Roxanne 253
Wright, Lori A 274
Wright, Jamal 280
Wright, David H. (Dave) 299
Wright, Jamie 303
Wright, Alex 319
Wright, Rachel 350
Wright, Dale 368
Wright, Eric 375
Wright, Nancy 383
Wright, Adam 385
Wright, Lori 403
Wright, Douglas 429
Wright, Robert S 472
Wright, Donna 477
Wright, Judy 504
Wright, Kenneth M 563
Wright, Karensa 589
Wright, Daniel 618
Wright, Steve 642
Wright, Dion 649
Wright, Stacey 662
Wright, Clarice 671
Wrighton, Mark S. 600
Wrona, Jennifer 477
Wroten, Paul 149
Wu, Michael 49
Wu, Tsung-Ching 53
Wu, Jiang 218
Wu, Wendy 472
Wu, Samuel 548
Wurman, Richard 220
Wurster, Sarah 431
Wutke, Steve 364
Wyatt, Christa 189
Wyatt, Mark 509
Wyborg, Brian 4
Wyffels, Chad 511
Wykoff, Phyllis 337
Wyles, Rick 357
Wyllie, Robert 561
Wyman, William 300
Wyman, Peter 393
Wynn, Karen 177
Wynn, Barry 501
Wynn, Jacklyn Mitchell 578
Wynne, Susan 573
Wyrsch, Martha B 549
Wyss, Andre 391

Y

Yacob, Desalegn 359
Yadavar, Ravi 678
Yaeger, Jackie 225
Yaggy, Lynne 291
Yako, Osamu 678
Yalamanchili, Lakshmi 496
Yaldo, Zaid 47
Yale, Neha 74
Yamabe, Dayna 572
Yamada, Maureen 551
Yamakawa, Mark 585
Yamatsuka, Jean 33
Yan, Lihua 49
Yang, Honggang 390
Yanik, Sahin 182
Yano, Nancy 242
Yap, Ronald 155
Yapp, Kelli 444
Yarbrough, Gerald 299
Yarbrough, Shelly 646
Yardley, William T 22
Yardley, Bill 22
Yardley, Scott 256
Yardley, William T. (Bill) 509

Yarobough, Martin 206
Yaryura, Ricardo 473
Yates, Richard 189
Yates, Vinson M. 395
Yaudes, Jason T. 35
Yazzie, Beverly 649
Yedla, Anupama 571
Yedvab, Lauren 374
Yehiely, Fruma 389
Yehlen, Lorraine 564
Yeigh, Bjong Wolf 640
Yellig, Laura 415
Yellin, Jason 555
Yennie, Heather 247
Yeo, Sally 246
Yeoman, Justin 356
Yepes, Maria 299
Yeskie, Andrew 313
Yin, Paul 49
Yin, Cynthia 290
Yocham, William 424
Yochum, Alice 114
Yocum, Deb 530
Yocum, Patricia R 537
Yoder, Ernest 47
Yoder, Lamont 61
Yoder, Katherine 171
Yoder, Cathy 519
Yoder, Kylie 610
Yohe, Joseph A 570
Yoldas, Erol 101
York, Johnny 96
York, John 599
Yoshioka, James 137
Yost, Kevin C. 668
Yoston, Jenifer 676
Yosu, Steve 214
Youatt, June 339
Youkey, Jerry R. 430
Young, Kevin 7
Young, Robert H. 14
Young, James N 27
Young, Lynn 114
Young, Christopher 140
Young, Mark 199
Young, Terrance 225
Young, Rebecca 227
Young, Tammy 233
Young, Zachary 274
Young, Carmen 338
Young, Joanna 339
Young, Sandra 344
Young, Dori 352
Young, Svetlana 402
Young, Bob 496
Young, Gary S. 563
Young, Randy 568
Young, Mary R 583
Young, Fred 588
Young, Michael 644
Young, James 652
Young, Nancy 655
Young, Theresay 656
Young, Jessica 657
Youngblood, Mike 319
Younger, Jon 537
Youngquist, Gene 82
Youngs, Michael 171
Yount, Dave 409
Youso, Steven R. 213
Youssef, Elie 122
Youssef, Matthew 335
Yu, Nancy 333
Yu, Chun-mei 507
Yuen, Shelten G 227
Yultyev, Aleksandr 218
Yunck, Kara 76
Yvonne, Luttschwager 529
Yzaguirre, Joe 153

Z

Zaas, David 187
Zabaneh, Samir 234
Zabicki, Katherina 407
Zablocki, Edward 586
Zacharias, Elizabeth 290
Zacharius, Sherrie 553
Zachary, Beth D. 6
Zachary, Jayton 302
Zachazewski, James 407
Zafonte, Ross D. 574
Zaharis, Chris 195
Zahka, Susan 220
Zahn, Chip 475
Zahrt, Deb 49
Zalewski, Mark 453
Zammer, William 109
Zamorski, Thomas 237
Zanavich, W Marie 593
Zanetich, Thomas N. 668
Zanetich, Tommy 668
Zang, Linda 644
Zanni, Dave 5
Zarcufsky, Shana 405
Zarian, Vladimir 137
Zarling, Kathy 467
Zarske, Samantha 285
Zarubi, Kathy 478
Zasaretti, Loletta 465
Zatina, Mary 75
Zauk, Adel M 519
Zauner, Alois 472
Zavaglia, Mary 453
Zavala, Donna 162
Zboray, Colleen 254
Zdunich, Amber 270
Zebroski, Robin 439
Zeevi, Gary 484
Zehm, Laura 152
Zeidel, Mark L. 79
Zeine, Elias 47
Zeithaml, Carl P. 442
Zell, Lisa 133
Zeller, Pat 469
Zeller, James 596
Zellman, David 524
Zendejas, Esperanza 102
Zender, Dale 410
Zeng, Qiang 543
Zeno, Zoraida 466
Zens, Scot 173
Zepeda, Carl 133
Zeppos, Nicholas S. 599
Zernicke, Paul 383
Zettel, John 57
Zetter, Bruce 558
Zevitas, Zachary 229
Zhang, Steve 49
Zhang, Cherry 93
Zhang, Haizheng 314
Zhang, Richard 314
Zhang, Luxi 610
Zhang, Han 621
Zhao, Susan X 472
Zheng, Baohua 475
Zhou, Ping 304
Zickefoose, John Z 160
Ziecheck, Hal 349
Ziegler, Richard A 37
Ziegler, Andy 476
Ziemianski, Karen 197
Zientara, David B 82
Zietlow, Donald P. (Don) 283
Zietlow, Steve 283
Ziffer, Jack A. 63
Zilbermann, Mark 556
Zimmaro, Lisa 546
Zimmer, Anthony 27
Zimmer, Tyler 215
Zimmer, Kris A. 512
Zimmerli, Bert 249
Zimmerli, Bert R. 256

Index of Executives

Zimmerman, Jennifer 81
Zimmerman, Christopher (Chris) 97
Zimmerman, Kate 306
Zimmerman, Christine 452
Zimmermann, Deirdre A. 439
Zingariello, Filippo 496
Zinger, INA 129
Zingman, Barry 348
Zink, Lauren 252
Zinkan, Rob 610
Zinkin, Peter 60
Zinn, Judy 101
Zinner, Michael J. 63
Zionts, Paul 175
Zipparro, Vincent 356
Zito-Volynets, Patricia 369
Ziyadeh, Omar 664
Zlaket, Mike 97
Zmich, Kenneth W. 119
Zmoyro, Larisa 304
Zohn, Patrick 141
Zoilo, John 131
Zolenas, Joseph 268
Zoller, Richard 334
Zollmann, Mary Ann 301
ZORN, ELIZABETH 418
Zorn, Debbie 625
Zorzi, Mia 630
Zubeck, Barbara 608
Zuber, Maria 314
Zuber, Steven 362
Zucal, Jim 384
Zucker, Keith 646
Zuhlke, Dan 256
Zuhlke, Eric 478
Zuk, Donna 75
Zukowski, Andrew 448
Zuniga, Aamsa 439
Zurack, Marlene 365
Zuraitis, Nancy 56
Zurek, Thomas M 396
Zussman, Corey 412
Zuziak, Jeffrey 496
Zvada, Robert 181
Zwiebel, Rob 453
Zyl, Adriaan Van 58